Stanley Gibbons SIMPLIFIED CATALOGUE

Stamps of the World

2004 Edition

IN COLOUR

An illustrated and priced four-volume guide to the postage stamps of the whole world, excluding changes of paper, perforation, shade and watermark

VOLUME 4

COUNTRIES S–Z

STANLEY GIBBONS LTD
London and Ringwood

By Appointment to
Her Majesty the Queen
Stanley Gibbons Limited
London
Philatelists

69th Edition

Published in Great Britain by
Stanley Gibbons Ltd
Publications Editorial, Sales Offices and Distribution Centre
Parkside, Christchurch Road,
Ringwood, Hampshire BH24 3SH
Telephone 01425 472363

ISBN: 085259-553-0

Published as Stanley Gibbons Simplified Stamp Catalogue from 1934 to 1970, renamed Stamps of the World in 1971, and produced in two (1982-88), three (1989-2001) or four (from 2002) volumes as Stanley Gibbons Simplified Catalogue of Stamps of the World.
This volume published November 2003

S.G. Item No. 2884 (04)

Printed in Great Britain by Unwin Brothers Ltd, Old Woking, Surrey

Stanley Gibbons
SIMPLIFIED CATALOGUE

Stamps of the World

This popular catalogue is a straightforward listing of the stamps that have been issued everywhere in the world since the very first–Great Britain's famous Penny Black in 1840.

This edition, in which both the text and the illustrations have been captured electronically, is arranged completely alphabetically in a four-volume format. Volume 1 (Countries A–D), Volume 2 (Countries E–J), Volume 3 (Countries K–R) and Volume 4 (Countries S–Z).

Readers are reminded that the Catalogue Supplements, published in each issue of **Gibbons Stamp Monthly**, can be used to update the listings in **Stamps of the World** as well as our 22-part standard catalogue. To make the supplement even more useful the Type numbers given to the illustrations are the same in the Stamps of the World as in the standard catalogues. The first Catalogue Supplement to this Volume appeared in the September 2003 issue of **Gibbons Stamp Monthly**.

Gibbons Stamp Monthly can be obtained through newsagents or on postal subscription from Stanley Gibbons Publications, Parkside, Christchurch Road, Ringwood, Hants BH24 3SH.

The catalogue has many important features:

- The vast majority of illustrations are now in full colour to aid stamp identification.
- All Commonwealth miniature sheets are now included.
- As an indication of current values virtually every stamp is priced. Thousands of alterations have been made since the last edition.
- By being set out on a simplified basis that excludes changes of paper, perforation, shade, watermark, gum or printer's and date imprints it is particularly easy to use. (For its exact scope see "Information for users" pages following.)
- The thousands of colour illustrations and helpful descriptions of stamp designs make it of maximum appeal to collectors with thematic interests.
- Its catalogue numbers are the world-recognised Stanley Gibbons numbers throughout.
- Helpful introductory notes for the collector are included, backed by much historical, geographical and currency information.
- A very detailed index gives instant location of countries in this volume, and a cross-reference to those included in the other volumes.

Over 16,790 stamps and miniature sheets and 2,675 new illustrations have been added to the listings in this volume. This year's four-volumes now contain over 406,730 stamps and 97,315 illustrations.

The listings in this edition are based on the standard catalogues: Part 1, Commonwealth & British Empire Stamps 1840–1952, Part 2 (Austria & Hungary) (6th edition), Part 3 (Balkans) (4th edition), Part 4 (Benelux) (5th edition), Part 5 (Czechoslovakia & Poland) (6th edition), Part 6 (France) (5th edition), Part 7 (Germany) (6th edition), Part 8 (Italy & Switzerland) (6th edition), Part 9 (Portugal & Spain) (4th edition), Part 10 (Russia) (5th edition), Part 11 (Scandinavia) (5th edition), Part 12 (Africa since Independence A-E) (2nd edition), Part 13 (Africa since Independence F-M) (1st edition), Part 14 (Africa since Independence N-Z) (1st edition), Part 15 (Central America) (2nd edition), Part 16 (Central Asia) (3rd edition), Part 17 (China) (6th edition), Part 18 (Japan & Korea) (4th edition), Part 19 (Middle East) (5th edition), Part 20 (South America) (3rd edition), Part 21 (South-East Asia) (3rd edition) and Part 22 (United States) (5th edition).

This edition includes major repricing for all Western Europe countries in addition to the changes for Benelux Part 4, Italy and Switzerland Part 8 and Czechoslovakia & Poland Part 5. Also, the United States of America and the United Nations New York Headquarters, together will all thematic Bird issues have been revised for this volume.

Acknowledgements

A wide-ranging revision of prices for Western European countries has been undertaken for this edition with the intention that the catalogue should be more accurate to reflect the market for foreign issues.

Many dealers in both Great Britain and overseas have participated in this scheme by supplying copies of their retail price lists on which the research has been based.

We would like to acknowledge the assistance of the following for this edition:

ALMAZ CO
of Brooklyn, U.S.A.

AMATEUR COLLECTOR LTD, THE
of London, England

E. ANGELOPOULOS
of Thessaloniki, Greece

AVION THEMATICS
of Nottingham, England

J BAREFOOT LTD
of York, England

BELGIAN PHILATELIC SPECIALISTS INC
of Larchmont, U.S.A.

Sir CHARLES BLOMEFIELD
of Chipping Camden, England

T. BRAY
of Shipley, West Yorks, England

CENTRAL PHILATELIQUE
of Brussels, Belgium

JEAN-PIERRE DELMONTE
of Paris, France

EUROPEAN & FOREIGN STAMPS
of Pontypridd, Wales

FILATELIA LLACH SL
of Barcelona, Spain

FILATELIA RIVA RENO
of Bologna, Italy

FILATELIA TORI
of Barcelona, Spain

FORMOSA STAMP COMPANY, THE
of Koahsiung, Taiwan

FORSTAMPS
of Battle, England

ANTHONY GRAINGER
of Leeds, England

HOLMGREN STAMPS
of Bollnas, Sweden

INDIGO
of Orewa, New Zealand

ALEC JACQUES
of Selby, England

M. JANKOWSKI
of Warsaw, Poland

D.J.M. KERR
of Earlston, England

H. M. NIELSEN
of Vejle, Denmark

LEO BARESCH LTD
of Hassocks, England

LORIEN STAMPS
of Chesterfield, England

MANDARIN TRADING CO
of Alhambra, U.S.A.

MICHAEL ROGERS INC
of Winter Park, U.S.A.

PHILATELIC SUPPLIES
of Letchworth, England

PHIL-INDEX
of Eastbourne, England

PHILTRADE A/S
of Copenhagen, Denmark

PITTERI SA
of Chiasso, Switzerland

KEVIN RIGLER
of Shifnal, England

ROLF GUMMESSON AB
of Stockholm, Sweden

R. D. TOLSON
of Undercliffe, England

JAY SMITH
of Snow Camp, U.S.A.

R. SCHNEIDER
of Belleville, U.S.A.

ROBSTINE STAMPS
of Hampshire, England

SOUTHERN MAIL
of Eastbourne, England

STAMP CENTER
of Reykjavik, Iceland

REX WHITE
of Winchester, England

Western European countries will now be repriced each year in Stamps of the World and where there is no up-to-date specialised foreign volume in a country these will be the new Stanley Gibbons prices.

It is hoped that this improved pricing scheme will be extended to other foreign countries and thematic issues as information is consolidated.

Information for users

Aim

The aim of this catalogue is to provide a straightforward illustrated and priced guide to the postage stamps of the whole world to help you to enjoy the greatest hobby of the present day.

Arrangement

The catalogue lists countries in alphabetical order and there is a complete index at the end of each volume. For ease of reference country names are also printed at the head of each page.

Within each country, postage stamps are listed first. They are followed by separate sections for such other categories as postage due stamps, parcel post stamps, express stamps, official stamps, etc.

All catalogue lists are set out according to dates of issue of the stamps, starting from the earliest and working through to the most recent.

Scope of the Catalogue

The *Simplified Catalogue of Stamps of the World* contains listings of postage stamps only. Apart from the ordinary definitive, commemorative and airmail stamps of each country – which appear first in each list – there are sections for the following where appropriate:

- postage due stamps
- parcel post stamps
- official stamps
- express and special delivery stamps
- charity and compulsory tax stamps
- newspaper and journal stamps
- printed matter stamps
- registration stamps
- acknowledgement of receipt stamps
- late fee and too late stamps
- military post stamps
- recorded message stamps
- personal delivery stamps

We receive numerous enquiries from collectors about other items which do not fall within the categories set out above and which consequently do not appear in the catalogue lists. It may be helpful, therefore, to summarise the other kinds of stamp that exist but which we deliberately exclude from this postage stamp catalogue.

We do *not* list the following:

Fiscal or revenue stamps: stamps used solely in collecting taxes or fees for non-postal purposes. Examples would be stamps which pay a tax on a receipt, represent the stamp duty on a contract or frank a customs document. Common inscriptions found include: Documentary, Proprietary, Inter. Revenue, Contract Note.

Local stamps: postage stamps whose validity and use are limited in area, say to a single town or city, though in some cases they provided, with official sanction, services in parts of countries not covered by the respective government.

Local carriage labels and Private local issues: many labels exist ostensibly to cover the cost of ferrying mail from one of Great Britain's offshore islands to the nearest mainland post office. They are not recognised as valid for national or international mail. Examples: Calf of Man, Davaar, Herm, Lundy, Pabay, Stroma. Items from some other places have only the status of tourist souvenir labels.

Telegraph stamps: stamps intended solely for the prepayment of telegraphic communication.

Bogus or "phantom" stamps: labels from mythical places or non-existent administrations. Examples in the classical period were Sedang, Counani, Clipperton Island and in modern times Thomond and Monte Bello Islands. Numerous labels have also appeared since the War from dissident groups as propaganda for their claims and without authority from the home governments. Common examples are labels for "Free Albania", "Free Rumania" and "Free Croatia" and numerous issues for Nagaland, Indonesia and the South Moluccas ("Republik Maluku Selatan").

Railway letter fee stamps: special stamps issued by railway companies for the conveyance of letters by rail. Example: Talyllyn Railway. Similar services are now offered by some bus companies and the labels they issue likewise do not qualify for inclusion in the catalogue.

Perfins ("perforated initials"): numerous postage stamps may be found with initial letters or designs punctured through them by tiny holes. These are applied by private and public concerns as a precaution against theft and do not qualify for separate mention.

Information for users

Labels: innumerable items exist resembling stamps but – as they do not prepay postage – they are classified as labels. The commonest categories are:

- propaganda and publicity labels: designed to further a cause or campaign;
- exhibition labels: particularly souvenirs from philatelic events;
- testing labels: stamp-size labels used in testing stamp-vending machines;
- Post Office training school stamps: British stamps overprinted with two thick vertical bars or SCHOOL SPECIMEN are produced by the Post Office for training purposes;
- seals and stickers: numerous charities produce stamp-like labels, particularly at Christmas and Easter, as a means of raising funds and these have no postal validity.

Cut-outs: items of postal stationary, such as envelopes, cards and wrappers, often have stamps impressed or imprinted on them. They may usually be cut out and affixed to envelopes, etc., for postal use if desired, but such items are not listed in this catalogue.

Collectors wanting further information about exact definitions are referred to *Philatelic Terms Illustrated,* published by Stanley Gibbons and containing many illustrations in colour.

There is also a priced listing of the postal fiscals of Great Britain in our *Commonwealth & British Empire Stamps 1840–1952* Catalogue and in Volume 1 of the *Great Britain Specialised* Catalogue (5th and later editions).

Catalogue Numbers

Stanley Gibbons catalogue numbers are recognised universally and any individual stamp can be identified by quoting the catalogue number (the one at the left of the column) prefixed by the name of the country and the letters "S.G.". Do not confuse the catalogue number with the type numbers which refer to illustrations.

Prices

Prices in the left-hand column are for unused stamps and those in the right-hand column for used. Prices are given in pence and pounds:

100 pence (p) 1 pound (£1).

Prices are shown as follows:

10 means 10p (10 pence);
1.50 means £1.50 (1 pound and 50 pence);
For £100 and above, prices are in whole pounds.

Our prices are for stamps in fine condition, and in issues where condition varies we may ask more for the superb and less for the sub-standard.

The minimum catalogue price quoted is 10p. For individual stamps prices between 10p and 45p are provided as a guide for catalogue users. The lowest price charged for individual stamps purchased from Stanley Gibbons is 50p.

The prices quoted are generally for the cheapest variety of stamps but it is worth noting that differences of watermark, perforation, or other details, outside the scope of this catalogue, may often increase the value of the stamp.

Prices quoted for mint issues are for single examples. Those in se-tenant pairs, strips, blocks or sheets may be worth more.

Where prices are not given in either column it is either because the stamps are not known to exist in that particular condition, or, more usually, because there is no reliable information as to value.

All prices are subject to change without prior notice and we give no guarantee to supply all stamps priced. Prices quoted for albums, publications, etc. advertised in this catalogue are also subject to change without prior notice.

Due to different production methods it is sometimes possible for new editions of Parts 2 to 22 to appear showing revised prices which are not included in that year's *Stamps of the World.*

Unused Stamps

In the case of stamps from *Great Britain* and the *Commonwealth,* prices for unused stamps of Queen Victoria to King George V are for lightly hinged examples; unused prices of King Edward VIII to Queen Elizabeth II issues are for unmounted mint. The prices of unused Foreign stamps are for lightly hinged examples for those issued before 1946, thereafter for examples unmounted mint.

Used Stamps

Prices for used stamps generally refer to fine postally used examples, though for certain issues they are for cancelled-to-order.

Information for users

Guarantee

All stamps supplied by us are guaranteed originals in the following terms:

If not as described, and returned by the purchaser, we undertake to refund the price paid to us in the original transaction. If any stamp is certified as genuine by the Expert Committee of the Royal Philatelic Society, London, or by B.P.A. Expertising Ltd., the purchaser shall not be entitled to make any claim against us for any error, omission or mistake in such certificate.

Consumers' statutory rights are not affected by the above guarantee.

Currency

At the beginning of each country brief details give the currencies in which the values of the stamps are expressed. The dates, where given, are those of the earliest stamp issues in the particular currency. Where the currency is obvious, e.g. where the colony has the same currency as the mother country, no details are given.

Illustrations

Illustrations of any surcharges and overprints which are shown and not described are actual size; stamp illustrations are reduced to $\frac{3}{4}$ linear, *unless otherwise stated.*

"Key-Types"

A number of standard designs occur so frequently in the stamps of the French, German, Portuguese and Spanish colonies that it would be a waste of space to repeat them. Instead these are all illustrated on page xiv together with the descriptive names and letters by which they are referred to in the lists.

Type Numbers

These are the bold figures found below each illustration. References to "Type **6**", for example, in the lists of a country should therefore be understood to refer to the illustration below which the number **"6"** appears. These type numbers are also given in the second column of figures alongside each list of stamps, thus indicating clearly the design of each stamp. In the case of Key-Types – see above – letters take the place of the type numbers.

Where an issue comprises stamps of similar design, represented in this catalogue by one illustration, the corresponding type numbers should be taken as indicating this general design.

Where there are blanks in the type number column it means that the type of the corresponding stamps is that shown by the last number above in the type column of the same issue.

A dash (–) in the type column means that no illustration of the stamp is shown.

Where type numbers refer to stamps of another country, e.g. where stamps of one country are overprinted for use in another, this is always made clear in the text.

Stamp Designs

Brief descriptions of the subjects of the stamp designs are given either below or beside the illustrations, at the foot of the list of the issue concerned, or in the actual lists. Where a particular subject, e.g. the portrait of a well-known monarch, recurs frequently the description is not repeated, nor are obvious designs described.

Generally, the unillustrated designs are in the same shape and size as the one illustrated, except where otherwise indicated.

Surcharges and Overprints

Surcharges and overprints are usually described in the headings to the issues concerned. Where the actual wording of a surcharge or overprint is given it is shown in bold type.

Some stamps are described as being "Surcharged in words", e.g. **TWO CENTS**, and others "Surcharged in figures and words", e.g. **20 CENTS**, although of course many surcharges are in foreign languages and combinations of words and figures are numerous. There are often bars, etc., obliterating old values or inscriptions but in general these are only mentioned where it is necessary to avoid confusion.

No attention is paid in this catalogue to colours of overprints and surcharges so that stamps with the same overprints in different colours are not listed separately.

Numbers in brackets after the descriptions of overprinted or surcharged stamps are the catalogue numbers of the unoverprinted stamps.

Note – the words "inscribed" or "inscription" always refer to wording incorporated in the design of a stamp and not surcharges or overprints.

Coloured Papers

Where stamps are printed on coloured paper the description is given as e.g. "4 c. black on blue" – a stamp printed in black on blue paper. No attention is paid in this catalogue to difference in the texture of paper, e.g. laid, wove.

Information for users

Watermarks

Stamps having different watermarks, but otherwise the same, are not listed separately. No reference is therefore made to watermarks in this volume.

Stamp Colours

Colour names are only required for the identification of stamps, therefore they have been made as simple as possible. Thus "scarlet", "vermilion", "carmine" are all usually called red. Qualifying colour names have been introduced only where necessary for the sake of clearness.

Where stamps are printed in two or more colours the central portion of the design is in the first colour given, unless otherwise stated.

Perforations

All stamps are perforated unless otherwise stated. No distinction is made between the various gauges of perforation but early stamp issues which exist both imperforate and perforated are usually listed separately.

Where a heading states "Imperf. or perf". or "Perf. or rouletted" this does not necessarily mean that all values of the issue are found in both conditions.

Dates of Issue

The date given at the head of each issue is that of the appearance of the earliest stamp in the series. As stamps of the same design or issue are usually grouped together a list of King George VI stamps, for example, headed "1938" may include stamps issued from 1938 to the end of the reign.

Se-tenant Pairs

Many modern issues are printed in sheets containing different designs or face values. Such pairs, blocks, strips or sheets are described as being "se-tenant" and they are outside the scope of this catalogue, although reference to them may occur in instances where they form a composite design.

Miniature Sheets

As an increasing number of stamps are now only found in miniature sheets, Stamps of the World will, in future, list these items. This edition lists all Commonwealth countries' miniature sheets, plus those of all non-Commonwealth countries which have appeared in the catalogue supplement during the past year. Earlier miniature sheets of non-Commonwealth countries will be listed in future editions.

"Appendix" Countries

We regret that, since 1968, it has been necessary to establish an Appendix (at the end of each country as appropriate) to which numerous stamps have had to be consigned. Several countries imagine that by issuing huge quantities of unnecessary stamps they will have a ready source of income from stamp collectors – and particularly from the less-experienced ones. Stanley Gibbons refuse to encourage this exploitation of the hobby and we do not stock the stamps concerned.

Two kinds of stamp are therefore given the briefest of mentions in the Appendix, purely for the sake of record. Administrations issuing stamps greatly in excess of true postal needs have the offending issues placed there. Likewise it contains stamps which have not fulfilled all the normal conditions for full catalogue listing.

These conditions are that the stamps must be issued by a legitimate postal authority, recognised by the government concerned, and are adhesives, valid for proper postal use in the class of service for which they are inscribed. Stamps, with the exception of such categories as postage dues and officials, must be available to the general public at face value with no artificial restrictions being imposed on their distribution.

The publishers of this catalogue have observed, with concern, the proliferation of 'artificial' stamp-issuing territories. On several occasions this has resulted in separately inscribed issues for various component parts of otherwise united states or territories.

Stanley Gibbons Publications have decided that where such circumstances occur, they will not, in the future, list these items in the SG catalogue without first satisfying themselves that the stamps represent a genuine political, historical or postal division within the country concerned. Any such issues which do not fulfil this stipulation will be recorded in the Catalogue Appendix only.

Stamps in the Appendix are kept under review in the light of any newly acquired information about them. If we are satisfied that a stamp qualifies for proper listing in the body of the catalogue it is moved there.

Information for users

"Undesirable Issues"

The rules governing many competitive exhibitions are set by the Federation Internationale de Philatelie and stipulate a downgrading of marks for stamps classed as "undesirable issues".

This catalogue can be taken as a guide to status. All stamps in the main listings and Addenda are acceptable. Stamps in the Appendix should not be entered for competition as these are the "undesirable issues".

Particular care is advised with Aden Protectorate States, Ajman, Bhutan, Chad, Fujeira, Khor Fakkan, Manama, Ras al Khaima, Sharjah, Umm al Qiwain and Yemen. Totally bogus stamps exist (as explained in Appendix notes) and these are to be avoided also for competition. As distinct from "undesirable stamps" certain categories are not covered in this catalogue purely by reason of its scope (see page viii). Consult the particular competition rules to see if such are admissable even though not listed by us.

Where to Look for More Detailed Listings

The present work deliberately omits details of paper, perforation, shade and watermark. But as you become more absorbed in stamp collecting and wish to get greater enjoyment from the hobby you may well want to study these matters.

All the information you require about any particular postage stamp will be found in the main Stanley Gibbons Catalogues.

Commonwealth countries before 1952 are covered by the Commonwealth & British Empire Stamps 1840–1952 published annually.

For foreign countries you can easily find which catalogue to consult by looking at the country headings in the present book.

To the right of each country name are code letters specifying which volume of our main catalogues contains that country's listing.

The code letters are as follows:

Pt. 2 Part 2

Pt. 3 Part 3 etc.

(See page xiii for complete list of Parts.)

So, for example, if you want to know more about Chinese stamps than is contained in the *Simplified Catalogue of Stamps of the World* the reference to

CHINA Pt. 17

guides you to the Gibbons Part 17 *(China)* Catalogue listing for the details you require.

New editions of Parts 2 to 22 appear at irregular intervals.

Correspondence

Whilst we welcome information and suggestions we must ask correspondents to include the cost of postage for the return of any stamps submitted plus registration where appropriate. Letters should be addressed to The Catalogue Editor at Ringwood.

Where information is solicited purely for the benefit of the enquirer we regret we cannot undertake to reply.

Identification of Stamps

We regret we do not give opinions as to the genuineness of stamps, nor do we identify stamps or number them by our Catalogue.

Users of this catalogue are referred to our companion booklet entitled *Stamp Collecting – How to Identify Stamps.* It explains how to look up stamps in this catalogue, contains a full checklist of stamp inscriptions and gives help in dealing with unfamiliar scripts.

Stanley Gibbons would like to complement your collection

At Stanley Gibbons we offer a range of services which are designed to complement your collection.

Our modern stamp shop, the largest in Europe, together with our rare stamp department has one of the most comprehensive stocks of Great Britain in the world, so whether you are a beginner or an experienced philatelist you are certain to find something to suit your special requirements.

Alternatively, through our Mail Order services you can control the growth of your collection from the comfort of your own home. Our Postal Sales Department regularly sends out mailings of Special Offers. We can also help with your wants list—so why not ask us for those elusive items?

Why not take advantage of the many services we have to offer? Visit our premises in the Strand or, for more information, write to the appropriate address on page x.

The Stanley Gibbons Group Addresses

Stanley Gibbons Limited,
Stanley Gibbons Auctions

339 Strand, London WC2R 0LX
Telephone 020 7836 8444, Fax 020 7836 7342,
E-mail: enquiries@stanleygibbons.co.uk
Internet: www.stanleygibbons.com for all departments.

Auction Room and Specialist Stamp Departments.
Open Monday–Friday 9.30 a.m. to 5 p.m.

Shop. Open Monday–Friday 9 a.m. to 5.30 p.m. and Saturday 9.30 a.m. to 5.30 p.m.

Fraser's
(a division of Stanley Gibbons Ltd)

399 Strand, London WC2R 0LX
Autographs, photographs, letters and documents

Telephone 020 7836 8444, Fax 020 7836 7342,
E-mail: info@frasersautographs.co.uk
Internet: www.frasersautographs.com

Monday–Friday 9 a.m. to 5.30 p.m. and Saturday 10 a.m. to 4 p.m.

Stanley Gibbons Publications

Parkside, Christchurch Road, Ringwood, Hants BH24 3SH.
Telephone 01425 472363 (24 hour answer phone service), Fax 01425 470247,
E-mail: info@stanleygibbons.co.uk

Publications Mail Order. FREEPHONE 0800 611622
Monday–Friday 8.30 a.m. to 5 p.m.

Stanley Gibbons Publications Overseas Representation

Stanley Gibbons Publications are represented overseas by the following sole distributors (*), distributors (**) or licensees (***).

Australia
Lighthouse Philatelic (Aust.) Pty. Ltd.*
Locked Bag 5900 Botany DC, New South Wales, 2019 Australia.

Stanley Gibbons (Australia) Pty. Ltd.***
Level 6, 36 Clarence Street, Sydney, New South Wales 2000, Australia.

Belgium and Luxembourg**
Davo c/o Philac, Rue du Midi 48, Bruxelles, 1000 Belgium.

Canada*
Lighthouse Publications (Canada) Ltd., 255 Duke Street, Montreal Quebec, Canada H3C 2M2.

Denmark**
Samlerforum/Davo, Ostergade 3, DK 7470 Karup, Denmark.

Finland**
Davo c/o Kapylan Merkkiky Pohjolankatu 1 00610 Helsinki, Finland.

France*
Davo France (Casteilla), 10, Rue Leon Foucault, 78184 St. Quentin Yvelines Cesex, France.

Hong Kong**
Po-on Stamp Service, GPO Box 2498, Hong Kong.

Israel**
Capital Stamps, P.O. Box 3769, Jerusalem 91036, Israel.

Italy*
Ernesto Marini Srl, Via Struppa 300, I-16165, Genova GE, Italy.

Japan**
Japan Philatelic Co. Ltd., P.O. Box 2, Suginami-Minami, Tokyo, Japan.

Netherlands*
Davo Publications, P.O. Box 411, 7400 AK Deventer, Netherlands.

New Zealand***
Mowbray Collectables.
P.O. Box 80, Wellington, New Zealand.

Norway**
Davo Norge A/S, P.O. Box 738 Sentrum, N-0105, Oslo, Norway.

Singapore**
Stamp Inc Collectibles Pte Ltd., 10 Ubi Cresent, #01-43 Ubi Tech Park, Singapore 408564.

Sweden*
Chr Winther Soerensen AB, Box 43, S-310 Knaered, Sweden.

Switzerland**
Phila Service, Burgstrasse 160, CH 4125, Riehen, Switzerland.

Abbreviations

Anniv.	denotes	Anniversary
Assn.	,,	Association
Bis.	,,	Bistre
Bl.	,,	Blue
Bldg.	,,	Building
Blk.	,,	Black
Br.	,,	British or Bridge
Brn.	,,	Brown
B.W.I.	,,	British West Indies
C.A.R.I.F.T.A.	,,	Caribbean Free Trade Area
Cent.	,,	Centenary
Chest.	,,	Chestnut
Choc.	,,	Chocolate
Clar.	,,	Claret
Coll.	,,	College
Commem.	,,	Commemoration
Conf.	,,	Conference
Diag.	,,	Diagonally
E.C.A.F.E.	,,	Economic Commission for Asia and Far East
Emer.	,,	Emerald
E.P.T. Conference	,,	European Postal and Telecommunications Conference
Exn.		Exhibition
F.A.O.	,,	Food and Agriculture Organization
Fig.	,,	Figure
G.A.T.T.	,,	General Agreement on Tariffs and Trade
G.B.	,,	Great Britain
Gen.	,,	General
Govt.	,,	Government
Grn.	,,	Green
Horiz.	,,	Horizontal
H.Q.	,,	Headquarters
Imperf.	,,	Imperforate
Inaug.	,,	Inauguration
Ind.	,,	Indigo
Inscr.	,,	Inscribed or inscription
Int.	,,	International
I.A.T.A.	,,	International Air Transport Association
I.C.A.O.	,,	International Civil Aviation Organization
I.C.Y.	,,	International Co-operation Year
I.G.Y.	,,	International Geophysical Year
I.L.O.	,,	International Labour Office (or later, Organization)
I.M.C.O.	,,	Inter-Governmental Maritime Consultative Organization
I.T.U.	,,	International Telecommunication Union
Is.	,,	Islands
Lav.	,,	Lavender
Mar.	,,	Maroon
mm.	,,	Millimetres
Mult.	,,	Multicoloured
Mve.	denotes	Mauve
Nat.	,,	National
N.A.T.O.	,,	North Atlantic Treaty Organization
O.D.E.C.A.	,,	Organization of Central American States
Ol.	,,	Olive
Optd.	,,	Overprinted
Orge. or oran.	,,	Orange
P.A.T.A.	,,	Pacific Area Travel Association
Perf.	,,	Perforated
Post.	,,	Postage
Pres.	,,	President
P.U.	,,	Postal Union
Pur.	,,	Purple
R.	,,	River
R.S.A.	,,	Republic of South Africa
Roul.	,,	Rouletted
Sep.	,,	Sepia
S.E.A.T.O.	,,	South East Asia Treaty Organization
Surch.	,,	Surcharged
T.	,,	Type
T.U.C.	,,	Trades Union Congress
Turq.	,,	Turquoise
Ultram.	,,	Ultramarine
U.N.E.S.C.O.	,,	United Nations Educational, Scientific Cultural Organization
U.N.I.C.E.F.	,,	United Nations Children's Fund
U.N.O.	,,	United Nations Organization
U.N.R.W.A.	,,	United Nations Relief and Works Agency for Palestine Refugees in the Near East
U.N.T.E.A.	,,	United Nations Temporary Executive Authority
U.N.R.R.A.	,,	United Nations Relief and Rehabilitation Administration
U.P.U.	,,	Universal Postal Union
Verm.	,,	Vermilion
Vert.	,,	Vertical
Vio.	,,	Violet
W.F.T.U.	,,	World Federation of Trade Unions
W.H.O.	,,	World Health Organization
Yell.	,,	Yellow

Arabic Numerals

As in the case of European figures, the details of the Arabic numerals vary in different stamp designs, but they should be readily recognised with the aid of this illustration:

٠	١	٢	٣	٤
0	1	2	3	4
٥	٦	٧	٨	٩
5	6	7	8	9

Stanley Gibbons Stamp Catalogue
Complete List of Parts

1 Commonwealth & British Empire Stamps 1840–1952 (Annual)

Foreign Countries

2 Austria & Hungary (6th edition, 2002)
Austria · U.N. (Vienna) · Hungary

3 Balkans (4th edition, 1998)
Albania · Bosnia & Herzegovina · Bulgaria · Croatia · Greece & Islands · Macedonia · Rumania · Slovenia · Yugoslavia

4 Benelux (5th edition, 2003)
Belgium & Colonies · Luxembourg · Netherlands & Colonies

5 Czechoslovakia & Poland (6th edition, 2002)
Czechoslovakia · Czech Republic · Slovakia · Poland

6 France (5th edition, 2001)
France · Colonies · Post Offices · Andorra · Monaco

7 Germany (6th edition, 2002)
Germany · States · Colonies · Post Offices

8 Italy & Switzerland (6th edition, 2003)
Italy & Colonies · Liechtenstein · San Marino · Switzerland · U.N. (Geneva) · Vatican City

9 Portugal & Spain (4th edition, 1996)
Andorra · Portugal & Colonies · Spain & Colonies

10 Russia (5th edition, 1999)
Russia · Armenia · Azerbaijan · Belarus · Estonia · Georgia · Kazakhstan · Kyrgyzstan · Latvia · Lithuania · Moldova · Tajikistan · Turkmenistan · Ukraine · Uzbekistan · Mongolia

11 Scandinavia (5th edition, 2001)
Aland Islands · Denmark · Faroe Islands · Finland · Greenland · Iceland · Norway · Sweden

12 Africa since Independence A-E (2nd edition, 1983)
Algeria · Angola · Benin · Burundi · Cameroun · Cape Verdi · Central African Republic · Chad · Comoro Islands · Congo · Djibouti · Equatorial Guinea · Ethiopia

13 Africa since Independence F-M (1st edition, 1981)
Gabon · Guinea · Guinea-Bissau · Ivory Coast · Liberia · Libya · Malagasy Republic · Mali · Mauritania · Morocco · Mozambique

14 Africa since Independence N-Z (1st edition, 1981)
Niger Republic · Rwanda · St. Thomas & Prince · Senegal · Somalia · Sudan · Togo · Tunisia · Upper Volta · Zaire

15 Central America (2nd edition, 1984)
Costa Rica · Cuba · Dominican Republic · El Salvador · Guatemala · Haiti · Honduras · Mexico · Nicaragua · Panama

16 Central Asia (3rd edition, 1992)
Afghanistan · Iran · Turkey

17 China (6th edition,1998)
China · Taiwan · Tibet · Foreign P.O.s · Hong Kong · Macao

18 Japan & Korea (4th edition, 1997)
Japan · Korean Empire · South Korea · North Korea

19 Middle East (5th edition, 1996)
Bahrain · Egypt · Iraq · Israel · Jordan · Kuwait · Lebanon · Oman · Qatar · Saudi Arabia · Syria · U.A.E. · Yemen

20 South America (3rd edition, 1989)
Argentina · Bolivia · Brazil · Chile · Colombia · Ecuador · Paraguay · Peru · Surinam · Uruguay · Venezuela

21 South-East Asia (3rd edition, 1995)
Bhutan · Burma · Indonesia · Kampuchea · Laos · Nepal · Philippines · Thailand · Vietnam

22 United States (5th edition, 2000)
U.S. & Possessions · Marshall Islands · Micronesia · Palau · U.N. (New York, Geneva, Vienna)

Thematic Catalogues

Stanley Gibbons Catalogues for use with **Stamps of the World.**
Collect Aircraft on Stamps (out of print)
Collect Birds on Stamps (5th edition, 2003)
Collect Chess on Stamps (2nd edition, 1999)
Collect Fish on Stamps (1st edition, 1999)
Collect Fungi on Stamps (2nd edition, 1997)
Collect Motor Vehicles on Stamps (in preparation)
Collect Railways on Stamps (3rd edition, 1999)
Collect Shells on Stamps (1st edition, 1995)
Collect Ships on Stamps (3rd edition, 2001)

Key-Types

(see note on page vii)

French Group

A. "Blanc."

B. "Mouchon."

C "Merson."

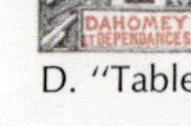

D. "Tablet."

E.

F.

G.

H.

"International Colonial Exhibition."

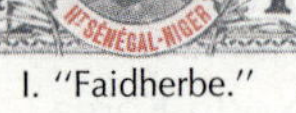

I. "Faidherbe."

J. "Palms."

K. "Balay."

L. "Natives."

M. "Figure."

German Group

N. "Yacht."

O. "Yacht."

Spanish Group

X. "Alfonso XII."

Y. "Baby."

Z. "Curly Head"

Portuguese Group

P. "Crown."

Q. "Embossed."

R. "Figures."

S. "Carlos."

T. "Manoel."

U. "Ceres."

V. "Newspaper."

W. "Due."

STANLEY GIBBONS SIMPLIFIED CATALOGUE OF STAMPS OF THE WORLD—VOLUME 4 COUNTRIES S–Z

SAAR Pt. 7

A German territory South-east of Luxembourg. Occupied by France under League of Nations control from 1920 to 1935. Following a plebiscite, Saar returned to Germany in 1935 from when German stamps were used until the French occupation in 1945, after which Nos. F1/13 of Germany followed by Nos. 203 etc of Saar were used. The territory was autonomous under French protection until it again returned to Germany at the end of 1956 following a national referendum. Issues from 1957 were authorised by the German Federal Republic pending the adoption of German currency on 6 July 1959, after which West German stamps were used.

1920–May 1921. 100 pfennig = 1 mark.
May 1921–March 1935. 100 centimes = 1 franc.
1935–47. 100 pfennig = 1 reichsmark.
1947. 100 pfennig = 1 Saarmark.
November 1947–July 1959. 100 centimes = 1 franc.
From 1959. 100 pfennig = 1 Deutsche mark.

LEAGUE OF NATIONS COMMISSION

1920. German stamps inscr "DEUTSCHES REICH" optd **Sarre** and bar.

1 **24** 2pf. grey . . . 90 3·50
2 c 2½pf. grey . . . 1·80 5·00
3 **10** 3pf. brown . . . 80 1·90
4 c 5pf. green . . . 15 25
5 **24** 7½pf. orange . . . 45 1·20
6 **10** 10pf. red . . . 35 60
7 **24** 15pf. violet . . . 35 60
8 **10** 20pf. blue . . . 35 60
9 25pf. black & red on yellow . . . 10·50 15·00
10 30pf. black & orange on buff . . . 21·00 30·00
11 **24** 35pf. brown . . . 45 60
12 **10** 40pf. black and red . . . 45 85
13 50pf. black & pur on cream . . . 70 85
14 60pf. purple . . . 70 95
15 75pf. black and green . . . 65 70
16 80pf. black and red on red . . . £225 £275
17ab **12** 1m. red . . . 23·00 32·00

1920. Bavarian stamps optd **Sarre** or **SARRE** (Nos. 30/1) and bars.

18 **15** 5pf. green . . . 90 1·90
19 10pf. red . . . 90 1·40
19a 15pf. red . . . 75 1·60
21 20pf. blue . . . 85 1·50
22 25pf. grey . . . 8·50 17·00
23 30pf. orange . . . 7·75 10·50
24 40pf. green . . . 8·50 15·00
25 50pf. brown . . . 1·30 1·70
26 60pf. green . . . 4·25 6·75
27 **16** 1m. brown . . . 24·00 28·00
28 2m. violet . . . 60·00 £130
29 3m. red . . . £100 £160
30 – 5m. blue (No. 192) . . . £650 £800
31 – 10m. green (No. 193) . . . £120 £275

1920. German stamps inscr "DEUTSCHES REICH" optd **SAARGEBIET**.

32 **10** 5pf. green . . . 30 40
33 5pf. brown . . . 35 40
34 10pf. red . . . 35 40
35 10pf. orange . . . 35 40
36 **24** 15pf. violet . . . 35 40
37 **10** 20pf. blue . . . 35 40
38 20pf. green . . . 35 45
39 30pf. black & orange on buff . . . 35 40
40 30pf. blue . . . 70 70
41 40pf. black and red . . . 30 40
42 40pf. red . . . 30 50
43 50pf. black & purple on buff 50 40
44 60pf. purple . . . 70 45
45 75pf. black and green . . . 90 45
46 **12** 1m.25 green . . . 2·10 1·30
47 1m.50 brown . . . 2·10 1·30
48 **13** 2m.50 purple . . . 7·00 12·00
49 **10** 4m. red and black . . . 12·00 21·00

1920. No. 45 of Saar surch **20** and No. 102 of Germany surch **SAARGEBIET**, arms and value.

50 **10** 20 on 75pf. black and green 55 1·10
51 **24** 5m. on 15pf. purple . . . 9·75 15·00
52 10m. on 15pf. purple . . . 9·75 17·00

9 Miner

11 Colliery Shafthead

12 Burbach Steelworks

1921.

53 – 5pf. violet and green . . . 35 40
54 **9** 10pf. orange and blue . . . 35 40
55 – 20pf. grey and green . . . 50 85
56 – 25pf. blue and brown . . . 50 75
57 – 30pf. brown and green . . . 50 70
58 – 40pf. red . . . 50 40
59 – 50pf. black and grey . . . 80 3·50
60 – 60pf. brown and red . . . 2·50 2·75
61 – 80pf. blue . . . 1·00 1·10
62 – 1m. black and red . . . 1·00 1·70
63 **11** 1m.25 green and brown . . . 1·40 2·00
64 – 2m. black and orange . . . 2·30 3·50
65 – 3m. sepia and brown . . . 5·50 8·50
66 – 5m. violet and yellow . . . 14·00 20·00
67 – 10m. brown and green . . . 14·00 22·00
68 **12** 25m. blue, black and red . . . 49·00 70·00

DESIGNS—As Type **11**. HORIZ: 5pf. Mill above Mettlach; 20pf. Pit head at Reden; 25pf. River traffic, Saarbrucken; 30pf. River Saar at Mettlach; 40pf. Slag-heap, Volklingen; 50pf. Signal gantry, Saarbrucken; 80pf. "Old Bridge", Saarbrucken; 1m. Wire-rope Railway; 2m. Town Hall, Saarbrucken; 3m. Pottery, Mettlach; 5m. St. Ludwig's Church; 10m. Chief Magistrate's and Saar Commissioner's Offices. VERT: 60pf. Gothic Chapel, Mettlach.

See also Nos. 84/97.

1921. Nos. 55/68 surch in French currency.

70 3c. on 20pf. grey and green . . . 35 45
71 5c. on 25pf. blue and brown . . . 35 40
72 10c. on 30pf. brown and green 35 40
73 15c. on 40pf. red . . . 35 40
74 20c. on 50pf. black and grey . . . 40 25
75 25c. on 60pf. brown and red . . . 50 25
76 30c. on 80pf. blue . . . 1·70 75
77 40c. on 1m. black and red . . . 2·10 50
78 50c. on 1m.25 green & brown 3·50 75
79 75c. on 2m. black and orange 5·00 1·30
80 1f. on 3m. black and brown . . . 5·00 2·20
81 2f. on 5m. violet and yellow . . . 14·00 5·50
82 3f. on 10m. brown and green 19·00 24·00
83 5f. on 25m. blue, black and red . . . 28·00 31·00

1922. Larger designs (except 5f.) and value in French currency.

84 3c. green (as No. 62) . . . 35 50
85 5c. black & orange (as No. 54) . . . 35 20
86 10c. green (as No. 61) . . . 35 20
87 15c. brown (as No. 62) . . . 80 20
98 15c. orange (as No. 62) . . . 3·50 40
88 20c. blue & yellow (as No. 64) . . . 2·30 25
100 25c. red and yellow (as No. 64) . . . 2·75 20
90 30c. red and yellow (as No. 58) . . . 1·90 1·10
91 40c. brown & yell (as No. 65) 80 75
92 50c. blue & yellow (as No. 56) . . . 80 20
101 75c. green & yellow (as No. 65) . . . 28·00 2·50
94 1f. brown (as No. 66) . . . 3·50 60
95 2f. violet (as No. 63) . . . 3·50 2·30
96 3f. green & orange (as No. 60) . . . 15·00 3·75
97 5f. brown & choc (as No. 68) 28·00 42·00

14 Madonna of Blieskastel

15 Army Medical Service

1925.

102 **14** 45c. purple . . . 3·50 3·25
103 10f. brown (31 × 36 mm) . . . 14·00 22·00

1926. Welfare Fund.

104 **15** 20c.+20c. green . . . 8·00 19·00
105 – 40c.+40c. brown . . . 8·00 19·00
106 – 50c.+50c. orange . . . 8·00 15·00
107 – 1f.50+1f.50 blue . . . 20·00 42·00

DESIGNS: 40c. Hospital work (nurse and patient); 50c. Child welfare (children at a spring); 1f.50, Maternity nursing service.

18 Tholey Abbey

1926.

108 – 10c. brown . . . 90 15
109 – 15c. green . . . 60 75
110 – 20c. brown . . . 60 15
111 **18** 25c. blue . . . 60 30
112 – 30c. green . . . 60 30
113 – 40c. brown . . . 60 30
114 **18** 50c. red . . . 60 15
114a – 60c. orange . . . 3·00 30
115 – 75c. purple . . . 60 15
116 – 80c. orange . . . 2·50 8·50
116a – 90c. red . . . 7·50 15·00
117 – 1f. violet . . . 1·80 30
118 – 1f.50 blue . . . 4·50 30
119 – 2f. red . . . 4·50 30
120 – 3f. green . . . 11·00 1·30
121 – 5f. brown . . . 11·00 7·00

DESIGNS—VERT: 10, 30c. Fountain, St. Johann, Saarbrucken. HORIZ: 15, 75c. Saar Valley near Gudingen; 20, 40, 90c. View from Saarlouis fortifications; 60, 80c., 1f. Colliery shafthead; 1f.50, 2, 3, 5f. Burbach Steelworks.

1927. Welfare Fund. Optd **1927–28.**

122 **15** 20c.+20c. green . . . 11·50 27·00
123 40c.+40c. brown . . . 11·50 27·00
124 50c.+50c. orange . . . 9·50 17·00
125 1f.50+1f.50 blue . . . 15·00 65·00

19 Breguet 14 Biplane over Saarbrucken

20 "The Blind Beggar" by Dyckmanns

1928. Air.

126 **19** 50c. red . . . 2·75 3·50
127 1f. violet . . . 3·00 4·25

1928. Christmas Charity.

128 **20** 40c.(+40c.) brown . . . 10·00 70·00
129 50c.(+50c.) purple . . . 10·00 70·00
130 1f.(+1f.) violet . . . 10·00 70·00
131 – 1f.50(+1f.50) blue . . . 10·00 70·00
132 – 2f.(+2f.) red . . . 14·00 £100
133 – 3f.(+3f.) green . . . 14·00 £150
134 – 10f.(+10f.) brown . . . £375 £3750

DESIGNS: 1f.50, 2, 3f. "Almsgiving" by Schiestl; 10f. "Charity" by Raphael (picture in circle).

1929. Christmas Charity. Paintings. As T **20**.

135 40c.(+15c.) green . . . 1·40 5·00
136 50c.(+20c.) red . . . 4·50 8·50
137 1f.(+50c.) purple . . . 4·50 10·50
138 1f.50(+75c.) blue . . . 4·50 10·50
139 2f.(+1f.) red . . . 4·50 10·50
140 3f.(+2f.) green . . . 7·50 25·00
141 10f.(+8f.) brown . . . 42·00 £150

DESIGNS: 40c. to 1f. "Orphaned" by H. Kaulbach; 1f.50, 2, 3f. "St. Ottilia" by M. Feuerstein; 10f. "The Little Madonna" by Ferruzzio.

1930. Nos. 114 and 116 surch.

141a **18** 40c. on 50c. red . . . 85 1·30
142 – 60c. on 80c. orange . . . 85 2·10

1931. Christmas Charity (1930 issue). Paintings. As T **20**.

143 40c.(+15c.) brown . . . 7·75 22·00
144 60c.(+20c.) orange . . . 7·75 22·00
145 1f.(+50c.) red . . . 7·75 42·00
146 1f.50(+75c.) blue . . . 11·00 42·00
147 2f.(+1f.) brown . . . 11·00 42·00
148 3f.(+2f.) green . . . 19·00 42·00
149 10f.(+10f.) brown . . . £100 £300

DESIGNS: 40, 60c., 1f.50, "The Safetyman" (miner and lamp) by F. Zolnhofer; 1, 2, 3f. "The Good Samaritan" by J. Heinemann; 10f. "At the Window" by F. G. Waldmuller.

1931. Christmas Charity. Paintings. As T **20**.

150 40c.(+15c.) brown . . . 11·50 24·00
151 60c.(+20c.) red . . . 11·50 24·00
152 1f.(+50c.) purple . . . 14·00 38·00
153 1f.50(+75c.) blue . . . 18·00 38·00
154 2f.(+1f.) red . . . 23·00 38·00
155 3f.(+2f.) green . . . 28·00 £110
156 5f.(+5f.) brown . . . 95·00 £300

DESIGNS: 40c. to 1f. "St. Martin" by F. Boehle; 1f.50, 2f. "Charity" by Ridgeway-Knight; 5f. "The Widow's Mite" by Dubufe.

29 Focke Wulf A-17 Mowe over Saarbrucken Airport

30 Kirkel Castle Ruins

1932. Air.

157 **29** 60c. red . . . 6·00 4·25
158 5f. brown . . . 38·00 85·00

1932. Christmas Charity.

159 **30** 40c.(+15c.) brown . . . 9·50 25·00
160 – 60c.(+20c.) red . . . 9·50 25·00
161 – 1f.(+50c.) purple . . . 13·50 42·00
162 – 1f.50(+75c.) blue . . . 19·00 50·00
163 – 2f.(+1f.) red . . . 19·00 60·00
164 – 3f.(+2f.) green . . . 60·00 £180
165 – 5f.(+5f.) brown . . . £120 £300

DESIGNS—VERT: 60c. Blieskastel Church; 1f. Ottweiler Church; 1f.50, St. Michael's Church, Saarbrucken; 2f. Cathedral and fountain, St. Wendel; 3f. St. John's Church, Saarbrucken. HORIZ: 5f. Kerpen Castle, Illingen.

32 Scene of the Disaster

33 "Love"

1933. Neunkirchen Explosion Disaster.

166 **32** 60c.(+60c.) orange . . . 13·50 23·00
167 3f.(+3f.) green . . . 38·00 80·00
168 5f.(+5f.) brown . . . 38·00 80·00

1934. Christmas Charity.

169 **33** 40c.(+15c.) brown . . . 5·00 17·00
170 – 60c.(+20c.) red . . . 5·00 17·00
171 – 1f.(+50c.) mauve . . . 7·50 19·00
172 – 1f.50(+75c.) blue . . . 13·50 35·00
173 – 2f.(+1f.) red . . . 10·50 35·00
174 – 3f.(+2f.) green . . . 13·50 35·00
175 – 5f.(+5f.) brown . . . 23·00 85·00

DESIGNS: 60c. "Solicitude". 1f. "Peace". 1f.50, "Consolation". 2f. "Welfare". 3f. "Truth". 5f. Countess Elizabeth von Nassau.

Nos. 169/74 show statues by C. L. Pozzi in church of St. Louis, Saarbrucken.

1934. Saar Plebiscite. Optd **VOLKSABSTIMMUNG 1935.** (a) Postage. On Nos. 108/15, 116a/21 and 103.

176 – 10c. brown . . . 45 55
177 – 15c. green . . . 45 55
178 – 20c. brown . . . 60 1·30
179 **18** 25c. blue . . . 60 1·30
180 – 30c. green . . . 45 40
181 – 40c. brown . . . 45 70
182 **18** 50c. red . . . 70 1·10
183 – 60c. orange . . . 45 55
184 – 75c. purple . . . 70 1·40
185 – 90c. red . . . 70 1·40
186 – 1f. violet . . . 80 1·40
187 – 1f.50 blue . . . 1·20 2·75
188 – 2f. red . . . 1·80 4·25
189 – 3f. green . . . 3·25 7·75
190 – 5f. brown . . . 18·00 28·00
191 **14** 10f. brown . . . 21·00 00

(b) Air. On Nos. 126/7 and 157/8.

192 **19** 50c. red . . . 4·25 7·00
193 **29** 60c. red . . . 3·25 2·75
194 **19** 1r. violet . . . 5·50 8·50
195 **29** 5f. brown . . . 6·50 8·50

1934. Christmas Charity. Nos. 169/75 optd **VOLKSABSTIMMUNG 1935.**

196 **33** 40c.(+15c.) brown . . . 3·50 17·00
197 – 60c.(+20c.) red . . . 3·50 17·00
198 – 1f.(+50c.) mauve . . . 9·50 28·00
199 – 1f.50(+75c.) blue . . . 7·50 28·00
200 – 2f.(+1f.) red . . . 9·00 42·00
201 – 3f.(+2f.) green . . . 8·75 35·00
202 – 5f.(+5f.) brown . . . 15·00 38·00

FRENCH OCCUPATION

36 Coal-miner 37 Loop of the Saar

1947. Inscr "SAAR".

203	36	2pf. grey	15	30
204		3pf. orange	15	35
205		6pf. green	15	25
206		8pf. red	15	25
207		10pf. mauve	15	25
208		12pf. green	15	30
209	–	15pf. brown	15	3·00
210	–	16pf. blue	15	30
211	–	20pf. red	15	30
212	–	24pf. brown	15	25
213	–	25pf. mauve	40	14·00
214	–	30pf. green	15	65
215	–	40pf. brown	15	65
216	–	45pf. red	30	12·50
217	–	50pf. violet	20	15·00
218	–	60pf. violet	20	16·00
219	–	75pf. blue	15	40
220	–	80pf. orange	15	40
221	–	84pf. brown	20	40
222	37	1m. green	20	40

DESIGNS—As T 36: 15pf. to 24pf. Steel workers; 25pf. to 50pf. Sugar beet harvesters; 60pf. to 80pf. Mettlach Abbey. As T 37—VERT: 84pf. Marshal Ney.

1947. As last surch in French currency.

223B	36	10c. on 2pf. grey	25	55
224B		60c. on 3pf. orange	25	85
225B		1f. on 10pf. mauve	25	50
226B		2f. on 12pf. green	25	1·20
227B	–	3f. on 15pf. brown	25	1·20
228B	–	4f. on 16pf. blue	25	5·50
229B	–	5f. on 20pf. red	25	85
230B	–	6f. on 24pf. brown	25	50
231B	–	9f. on 30pf. green	25	10·50
232B	–	10f. on 50pf. violet	40	12·00
233B	–	14f. on 60pf. violet	55	10·50
234B	–	20f. on 84pf. brown	85	7·00
235B	37	50f. on 1m. green	1·20	13·50

42 Clasped Hands 43 Builders

44 Saar Valley

1948. Inscr "SAARPOST".

236	42	10c. red (postage)	65	1·50
237		60c. blue	65	1·50
238		1f. black	30	30
239	–	2f. red	30	20
240	–	3f. brown	30	20
241	–	4f. red	30	20
242	–	5f. violet	30	20
243	–	6f. red	70	20
244	–	9f. blue	4·25	1·40
245	–	10f. blue	2·50	45
246	–	14f. purple	3·50	85
247	43	20f. red	6·25	75
248	–	50f. blue	14·00	2·30
249	44	25f. red (air)	7·00	2·75
250		50f. blue	2·75	1·70
251		200f. red	21·00	30·00

DESIGNS—As Type 42: 2, 3f. Man's head;. 4, 5f. Woman's head; 6, 9f. Miner's head. As Type 43: 10f. Blast furnace chimney; 14f. Foundry; 50f. Facade of Mettlach Abbey.

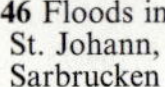

46 Floods in St. Johann, Saarbrucken 47 Map of Saarland

1948. Flood Disaster Relief Fund. Flood Scenes.

252	–	5f.+5f. green (postage)	4·50	35·00
253	46	6f.+4f. purple	4·50	28·00
254	–	12f.+8f. red	5·25	38·00
255	–	18f.+12f. blue	7·25	48·00
256	–	25f.+25f. brown (air)	29·00	£250

DESIGNS—VERT: 18f. Flooded street, Saarbrucken. HORIZ: 5f. Flooded industrial area; 12f. Landtag building, Saarbrucken; 25f. Floods at Ensdorf, Saarlouis.

1948. 1st Anniv of Constitution.

257	47	10f. red	1·70	1·90
258		25f. blue	2·40	6·25

48 Hikers and Ludweiler Hostel

1949. Youth Hostels Fund.

259	48	8f.+5f. brown	2·40	70·00
260	–	10f.+7f. green	3·25	70·00

DESIGN: 10f. Hikers and Weisskirchen hostel.

49 Chemical Research 50 Mare and Foal

1949. Saar University.

261	49	15f. red	3·75	35

1949. Horse Day.

262	50	15f.+5f. red	13·50	24·00
263	–	25f.+15f. blue	15·00	28·00

DESIGN: 25f. Two horses in steeple-chase.

51 Symbolic of Typography 52 Labourer and Foundry

1949.

264	–	10c. purple	30	1·60
265	–	60c. black	20	1·60
266	–	1f. red	1·20	20
267	–	3f. brown	8·50	30
268	–	5f. violet	2·75	20
269	–	6f. green	9·00	35
270	–	8f. green	80	35
271	51	10f. orange	5·00	20
272	–	12f. green	18·00	20
273	–	15f. red	8·50	20
274	–	18f. mauve	3·50	4·50
275	52	20f. grey	2·75	25
276	–	25f. blue	21·00	25
277	–	30f. red	18·00	40
278	–	45f. purple	5·50	40
279	–	60f. green	7·00	1·70
280	–	100f. brown	12·50	1·80

DESIGNS—As Type 51: 10c. Building trade; 60c. Beethoven; 1f. and 3f. Heavy industries; 5f. Slag heap; 6f. and 15f. Colliery; 8f. Posthorn and telephone; 12f. and 18f. Pottery. As Type 52—VERT: 25f. Blast furnace worker; 60f. Landsweiler; 100f. Wiebelskirchen. HORIZ: 30f. St. Arnual; 45f. "Giant's Boot", Rentrisch.

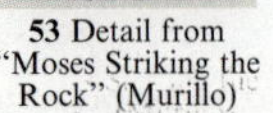

53 Detail from "Moses Striking the Rock" (Murillo) 54 A. Kolping

1949. National Relief Fund.

281	53	8f.+2f. blue	8·00	42·00
282	–	12f.+3f. green	10·00	48·00
283	–	15f.+5f. purple	14·00	85·00
284	–	25f.+10f. blue	20·00	£130
285	–	50f.+20f. brown	35·00	£250

DESIGNS: 12f. "Our Lord healing the Paralytic" (Murillo); 15f. "The Sick Child" (Metsu); 25f. "St. Thomas of Villanueva" (Murillo); 50f. "Madonna of Blieskastel".

1950. Honouring Adolf Kolping (miners' padre).

286	54	15f.+5f. red	23·00	60·00

55 P. Wust

1950. 10th Death Anniv of Peter Wust (philosopher).

287	55	15f. red	13·50	5·50

56 Mail Coach

1950. Stamp Day.

288	56	15f.+5f. brown and red	55·00	85·00

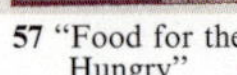

57 "Food for the Hungry" 58 St. Peter

1950. Red Cross Fund.

289	57	25f.+10f. lake and red	25·00	44·00

1950. Holy Year.

290	58	12f. green	3·75	8·50
291		15f. red	4·25	8·50
292		25f. blue	7·75	16·00

59 Town Hall, Ottweiler 61

1950. 400th Anniv of Ottweiler.

293	59	10f. brown	2·75	7·00

1950. Saar's Admission to Council of Europe.

294	61	25f. blue (postage)	34·00	7·75
295	–	200f. red (air)	£140	£225

DESIGN: 200f. As T 61 but with dove in flight over book.

62 St. Lutwinus enters Monastery

1950. National Relief Fund. Inscr "VOLKSHILFE".

296	62	8f.+2f. brown	5·25	14·50
297	–	12f.+3f. green	5·25	14·50
298	–	15f.+5f. brown	5·50	25·00
299	–	25f.+10f. blue	8·75	35·00
300	–	50f.+20f. purple	12·50	50·00

DESIGNS: 12f. Lutwinus builds Mettlach Abbey; 15f. Lutwinus as Abbot; 25f. Bishop Lutwinus confirming children at Rheims; 50f. Lutwinus helping needy.

63 Orphans 65 Allegory

64 Mail-carriers, 1760

1951. Red Cross Fund.

301	63	25f.+10f. green and red	18·00	39·00

1951. Stamp Day.

302	64	15f. purple	6·25	17·00

1951. Trade Fair.

303	65	15f. green	3·50	4·25

66 Flowers and Building 67 Calvin and Luther

1951. Horticultural Show, Bexbach.

304	66	15f. green	3·50	1·70

1951. 375th Anniv of Reformation in Saar.

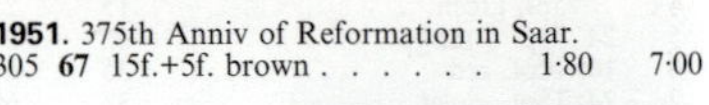

305	67	15f.+5f. brown	1·80	7·00

68 "The Good Mother" (Lepicie) 69 Mounted Postman

1951. National Relief Fund. Inscr "VOLKSHILFE 1951".

306	68	12f.+3f. green	4·25	18·00
307	–	15f.+5f. violet	4·25	18·00
308	–	18f.+7f. red	5·00	18·00
309	–	30f.+10f. blue	7·75	32·00
310	–	50f.+20f. brown	17·00	70·00

PAINTINGS: 18f. "Outside the Theatre" (Kampf); 18f. "Sisters of Charity" (Browne); 30f. "The Good Samaritan" (Bassano); 50f. "St. Martin and the Poor" (Van Dyck).

1952. Stamp Day.

311	69	30f.+10f. blue	9·00	27·00

70 Athlete bearing Olympic Flame 71 Globe and Emblem

1952. 15th Olympic Games, Helsinki. Inscr "OLYMPISCHE SPIELE 1952".

312	70	15f.+5f. green	4·25	10·50
313	–	30f.+5f. blue	4·50	12·50

DESIGN: 30f. Hand, laurels and globe.

1952. Saar Fair.

314	71	15f. red	2·40	1·20

72 Red Cross and Refugees 73 G.P.O., Saarbrucken

1952. Red Cross Week.

315	72	15f. red	1·70	1·20

1952. (A) Without inscr in or below design. (B) With inscr.
316 – 1f. green (B) 30 20
317 – 2f. violet 30 20
318 – 3f. red 30 20
319 **73** 5f. green (A) . . . . . . 5·50 20
320 5f. green (B) 30 20
321 – 6f. purple 40 20
322 – 10f. brown 55 20
323 **73** 12f. green (B) 40 20
324 – 15f. brown (A) . . . . . . 7·25 20
325 – 15f. brown (B) . . . . . . 2·75 15
326 – 15f. red (B) 20 15
327 – 18f. purple . . . . 3·25 3·50
329 – 30f. blue . . . . 1·00 60
334 – 500f. red . . . . 14·00 42·00
DESIGNS—HORIZ: 1, 15f. (3) Colliery shafthead; 2, 10f. Ludwigs High School, Saarbrucken; 3, 18f. Gersweiler Bridge; 6f. Mettlach Bridge; 30f. University Library, Saarbrucken. VERT: 500f. St. Ludwig's Church, Saarbrucken.

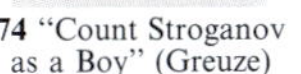
74 "Count Stroganov as a Boy" (Greuze) **75** Fair Symbol

1952. National Relief Fund. Paintings inscr "VOLKSHILFE 1952".
335 **74** 15f.+5f. brown . . . . . . 3·75 9·75
336 – 18f.+7f. red . . . . 5·00 12·50
337 – 30f.+10f. blue . . . . . . 5·50 14·00
PORTRAITS: 18f. "The Holy Shepherd" (Murillo); 30f. "Portrait of a Boy" (Kraus).

1953. Saar Fair.
338 **75** 15f. blue . . . . 2·20 1·40

76 Postilions **77** Henri Dunant

1953. Stamp Day.
339 **76** 15f. blue . . . . 3·50 12·50

1953. Red Cross Week and 125th Anniv of Birth of Dunant (founder).
340 **77** 15f.+5f. brown and red . . 1·90 5·50

78 "Painter's Young Son" (Rubens) **79** St. Benedict blessing St. Maurus

1953. National Relief Fund. Paintings inscr "VOLKSHILFE 1953".
341 – 15f.+5f. violet . . . . . . 1·80 5·00
342 – 18f.+7f. red . . . . 1·90 5·50
343 **78** 30f.+10f. green . . . . . 4·75 9·75
DESIGNS—VERT: 15f. "Clarice Strozzi" (Titian). HORIZ: 18f. "Painter's Children" (Rubens).

1953. Tholey Abbey Fund.
344 **79** 30f.+10f. black . . . . . 2·00 7·00

80 Saar Fair **82** Red Cross and Child

81 Postal Motor Coach

1954. Saar Fair.
345 **80** 15f. green . . . . 2·00 85

1954. Stamp Day.
346 **81** 15f. red . . . . 2·75 9·75

1954. Red Cross Week.
347 **82** 15f.+5f. brown . . . . . . 2·00 5·50

83 Madonna and Child (Holbein)

1954. Marian Year.
348 **83** 5f. red . . . . 75 1·40
349 – 10f. green . . . . 1·00 1·80
350 – 15f. blue . . . . 1·40 3·50
DESIGNS: 10f. "Sistine Madonna" (Raphael); 15f. "Madonna and Child with Pear" (Durer).

84 "Street Urchin with a Melon" (Murillo) **85** Cyclist and Flag

1954. National Relief Fund. Paintings inscr "VOLKSHILFE 1954".
351 **84** 5f.+3f. red . . . . 80 1·10
352 – 10f.+5f. green . . . . . . 80 1·30
353 – 15f.+7f. violet . . . . . . 1·00 1·80
DESIGNS: 10f. "Maria de Medici" (A. Bronzino); 15f. "Baron Emil von Maucler" (J. F. Dietrich).

1955. World Cross-Country Cycle Race.
354 **85** 15f. blue, red and black . . 35 70

86 Rotary Emblem and Industrial Plant

1955. 50th Anniv of Rotary International.
355 **86** 15f. brown 35 70

87 Exhibitors' Flags **88** Nurse and Baby

1955. Saar Fair.
356 **87** 15f. multicoloured 35 70

1955. Red Cross Week.
357 **88** 15f.+5f. black and red . . 40 1·10

89 Postman **91** "Mother" (Durer)

1955. Stamp Day.
358 **89** 15f. purple . . . . 65 1·70

1955. Referendum. Optd **VOLKSBEFRAGUNG 1955.**
359 15f. red (No. 326) 30 55
360 18f. purple (No. 327) 35 40
361 30f. blue (No. 329) 55 70

1955. National Relief Fund. Durer paintings inscr as in T **91**.
362 **91** 5f.+3f. green 50 70
363 – 10f.+5f. green . . . . . . 80 1·30
364 – 15f.+7f. bistre . . . . . . 1·00 1·70
PAINTINGS: 10f. "The Praying Hands"; 15f. "The Old Man from Antwerp".

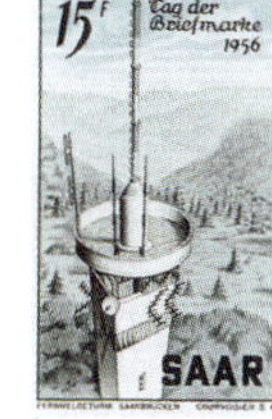
92 **93** Radio Tower

1956. Saar Fair.
365 **92** 15f. green and red 25 70

1956. Stamp Day.
366 **93** 15f. green and turquoise . . 30 70

94 Casualty Station **95**

1956. Red Cross Week.
367 **94** 15f.+5f. brown 30 70

1956. Olympic Games.
368 **95** 12f.+3f. blue and green . . 45 70
369 15f.+5f. brown & purple 45 70

96 Winterberg Memorial **97** "Portrait of Lucrezia Crivelli" (da Vinci)

1956. Winterberg Memorial Reconstruction Fund.
370 **96** 5f.+2f. green 25 30
371 12f.+3f. purple 30 40
372 15f.+5f. brown 30 55

1956. National Relief Fund. Inscr as in T **97**.
373 **97** 5f.+3f. blue 20 30
374 – 10f.+5f. red 25 40
375 – 15f.+7f. green 35 85
PAINTINGS: 10f. "Saskia" (Rembrandt); 15f. "Lady Playing Spinet" (Floris).

RETURN TO GERMANY

98 Arms of the Saar **99** President Heuse

1957. Return of the Saar to Germany.
376 **98** 15f. blue and red 25 30

1957. (a) Without "F" after figure of value.
377 **99** 1f. green 25 15
378 2f. violet 25 15
379 3f. brown 25 15
380 4f. mauve 35 70
381 5f. green 25 15
382 6f. red 25 40
383 10f. grey 25 30
384 12f. orange 25 15
385 15f. green 25 15
386 18f. red . . . . 80 2·10
387 25f. lilac 55 85
388 30f. purple 45 70
389 45f. green . . . . 1·20 2·75
390 50f. brown . . . . 1·20 1·30
391 60f. red . . . . 1·80 3·00
392 70f. orange . . . . 3·00 5·00
393 80f. green . . . . 95 2·75
394 90f. grey . . . . 3·00 5·50
395 100f. red (24 × 29½ mm) . . 2·50 8·00
396 200f. lilac (24 × 29½ mm) 6·25 22·00

(b) With "F" after figure of value.
406 **99** 1f. grey 25 15
407 3f. blue 25 15
408 5f. green 25 15
409 6f. brown 25 40
410 10f. violet 25 30
411 12f. orange 25 15
412 15f. green 45 15
413 18f. grey . . . . 1·90 5·00
414 20f. green . . . . 1·20 2·75
415 25f. brown 45 40
416 30f. mauve 90 40
417 35f. brown . . . . 2·20 3·50
418 45f. green . . . . 1·90 3·50
419 50f. brown . . . . 1·00 2·00
420 70f. green . . . . 4·75 5·00
421 80f. blue . . . . 2·30 5·00
422 90f. red . . . . 5·75 6·25
423 100f. orange (24 × 29½ mm) 4·50 7·00
424 200f. green (24 × 29½ mm) 9·00 24·00
425 300f. blue (24 × 29½ mm) 10·00 28·00

100 Iron Foundry **101** Arms of Merzig and St. Pierre Church

1957. Saar Fair.
397 **100** 15f. red and black 20 40

1957. Centenary of Merzig.
398 **101** 15f. blue 20 40

101a "Europa" Tree **101b** Young Miner

1957. Europa.
399 **101a** 20f. orange and yellow 45 1·00
400 35f. violet and pink . . . 80 1·30

1957. Humanitarian Relief Fund.
401 **101b** 6f.+4f. black & brown 20 30
402 – 12f.+6f. black & green 25 30
403 – 15f.+7f. black and red 35 40
404 – 30f.+10f. black & blue 45 70
DESIGNS: 12f. Miner drilling at coalface; 15f. Miner with coal-cutting machine; 30f. Operator at mine lift-shaft.

101c Carrier Pigeons **101d** Max and Moritz (cartoon characters)

1957. International Correspondence Week.
405 **101c** 15f. black and red . . . 25 40

1958. 150th Death Anniv of Wilhelm Busch (writer and illustrator).
426 **101d** 12f. green and black . . 25 30
427 – 15f. red and black . . . 30 40
DESIGN: 15f. Wilhelm Busch.

101e "Prevent Forest Fires"

101g "The Fox who stole the Goose"

101f Diesel and First Oil Engine

1958. Forest Fires Prevention Campaign.
428 **101e** 15f. black and red . . . 20 40

1958. Birth Centenary of Rudolf Diesel (engineer).
429 **101f** 12f. green 20 30

1958. Berlin Students' Fund.
430 **101g** 12f.+6f. red, black and green 25 30
431 – 15f.+7f. brown, green and red 25 40
DESIGN: 15f. "A Hunter from the Palatinate".

102 Saarbrucken Town Hall and Fair Emblem

103 Homburg

1958. Saar Fair.
432 **102** 15f. purple 20 30

1958. 400th Anniv of Homburg.
433 **103** 15f. green 20 30

103a Emblem

103b Schulze-Delitzsch

1958. 150th Anniv of German Gymnastics.
434 **103a** 12f. black, green and grey 20 30

1958. 150th Birth of Schulze-Delitzsch (pioneer of German Co-operative Movement).
435 **103b** 12f. green 20 30

103c "Europa"

103d Friedrich Raiffeisen (philanthropist)

1958. Europa.
436 **103c** 12f. blue and green . . . 60 85
437 – 30f. red and blue . . . . 80 1·40

1958. Humanitarian Relief and Welfare Funds.
438 **103d** 6f.+4f. brn, lt brn & chest 25 30
439 – 12f.+6f. red, yell & grn 25 30
440 – 15f.+7f. blue, grn & red 45 40
441 – 30f.+10f. yellow, grn & bl 50 70
DESIGNS—Inscr "WOHLFAHRTSMARKE": 12f. Dairymaid; 15f. Vine-dresser 30f. Farm labourer.

103e Fugger

104 Hands holding Crates

1959. 500th Birth Anniv of Jakob Fugger (merchant prince).
442 **103e** 15f. black and red . . . 20 30

1959. Saar Fair.
443 **104** 15f. red 20 30

105 Saarbrucken

105a Humboldt

1959. 50th Anniv of Greater Saarbrucken.
444 **105** 15f. blue 20 30

1959. Death Centenary of Alexander von Humboldt (naturalist).
445 **105a** 15f. blue 20 40

OFFICIAL STAMPS

1922. Nos. 84 to 94 optd **DIENSTMARKE**.
O 98 3c. green . . . . 1·50 24·00
O 99 5c. black and orange . . . 70 30
O100 10c. green 70 30
O101 15c. brown 70 30
O109 15c. orange . . . . 2·50 45
O102 20c. blue and yellow . . . 2·50 30
O111 25c. red and yellow . . . 3·50 40
O104 30c. red and yellow . . . 1·40 30
O105 40c. brown and yellow . . 1·80 30
O106 50c. blue and yellow . . . 1·80 30
O112 75c. green and yellow . . 12·00 2·10
O108a 1f. brown . . . . 7·00 2·10

1927. Nos. 108/15, 117 and 119 optd **DIENSTMARKE**.
O128 10c. brown . . . . 2·75 2·20
O129 15c. green . . . . 3·50 6·25
O130 20c. brown . . . . 00 1·40
O131 25c. blue . . . . 3·50 5·50
O122 30c. green . . . . 3·50 30
O133 40c. brown . . . . 6·00 30
O134 50c. red . . . . 10·00 30
O135 60c. orange . . . . 1·40 30
O136 75c. purple . . . . 6·00 70
O137 1f. violet . . . . 8·25 40
O138 2f. red . . . . 8·25 30

O 51 Arms

1949.
O264 **O 51** 10c. red . . . . 50 15·00
O265 30c. black . . . . . . 70 17·00
O266 1f. green 40 65
O267 2f. red . . . . 2·10 1·30
O268 5f. blue . . . . 2·10 65
O269 10f. black 90 65
O270 12f. mauve . . . . . . 9·00 10·50
O271 15f. blue 80 65
O272 20f. green . . . . . . 1·90 1·20
O273 30f. mauve . . . . . . 1·40 4·25
O274 50f. purple . . . . . . 1·40 3·50
O275 100f. brown . . . . . . 75·00 £325

SABAH Pt. 1

Formerly North Borneo, now part of Malaysia.

100 cents = 1 Malaysian dollar.

1964. Nos. 391/406 of North Borneo optd **SABAH**.
408 1c. green and red 10 10
409 4c. olive and orange 15 50
410 5c. sepia and violet 30 10
411 6c. black and turquoise . . . 70 10
412 10c. green and red . . . . . 1·00 10
413 12c. brown and myrtle . . . 15 10
414 20c. turquoise and blue . . . 3·50 10
415 25c. black and red 65 90
416 30c. sepia and olive 25 10
417 35c. slate and brown 30 20
418 50c. green and bistre 30 10
419 75c. blue and purple . . . . 3·25 65
420 $1 brown and green . . . . 6·00 65
421 $2 brown and slate . . . . . 12·00 2·00
422 $5 green and purple . . . . 12·00 12·00
423 $10 red and blue . . . . . . 13·00 26·00

138 "Vanda hookeriana"

1965. As No. 115/21 of Kedah, but with Arms of Sabah inset as T **138**.
424 **138** 1c. multicoloured . . . . 10 1·25
425 – 2c. multicoloured . . . . 10 1·25
426 – 5c. multicoloured 10 10
427 – 6c. multicoloured . . . . 30 1·25
428 – 10c. multicoloured 30 10
429 – 15c. multicoloured . . . . 2·00 10
430 – 20c. multicoloured . . . . 2·75 60
The higher values used in Sabah were Nos. 20/7 of Malaysia.

139 "Hebomoia glaucippe"

1971. Butterflies. As Nos. 124/30 of Kedah, but with Sabah Arms inset as T **139**.
432 – 1c. multicoloured . . . . 50 2·25
433 – 2c. multicoloured . . . . 60 2·25
434 – 5c. multicoloured 80 40
435 – 6c. multicoloured . . . . 1·00 1·75
436 **139** 10c. multicoloured 80 15
437 – 15c. multicoloured . . . . 1·00 10
438 – 20c. multicoloured . . . . 1·10 1·00
The higher values in use with this issue were Nos. 64/71 of Malaysia.

140 "Hibiscus rosa-sinensis"

141 Coffee

1979. As Nos. 135/41 of Kedah, but with Arms of Sabah as T **140**.
445 1c. "Rafflesia hasseltii" . . . 10 1·40
446 2c. "Pterocarpus indicus" . . 10 1·40
447 5c. "Lagerstroemia speciosa" 15 45
448 10c. "Durio zibethinus" . . . 30 10
449 15c. Type **140** 50 10
450 20c. "Rhododendron scortechinii" 30 10
451 25c. "Etlingera elatior" (inscr "Phaeomeria speciosa") . . 65 10
The higher values in use with this issue were Nos. 190/7 of Malaysia.

1986. As Nos. 152/8 of Kedah but with Arms of Sabah as in T **141**.
459 1c. Type **141** 10 10
460 2c. Coconuts 10 10
461 5c. Cocoa 10 10
462 10c. Black pepper 10 10
463 15c. Rubber 10 10
464 20c. Oil palm 10 10
465 30c. Rice 10 15

ST. CHRISTOPHER Pt. 1

One of the Leeward Is. Stamps superseded in 1890 by Leeward Islands general issue.

12 pence = 1 shilling.

1

1870.
11 **1** 1d. green . . . . 1·25 1·50
6 1d. mauve . . . . 65·00 7·00
13 1d. red . . . . 1·00 2·25
14 2d. brown . . . . £180 60·00
16 2d. blue . . . . 1·50 1·50
8 4d. blue . . . . £160 15·00
18 4d. grey . . . . 1·25 1·00
9 6d. green . . . . 55·00 5·00
19 6d. olive . . . . 80·00 £300
20 1s. mauve . . . . 90·00 65·00

1885. Surch in words.
23 **1** ½d. on half of 1d. red . . . . 24·00 40·00
26 1d. on ½d. green . . . . . . 32·00 42·00
28 1d. on 2½d. blue . . . . . . 60·00 60·00
24 1d. on 6d. green . . . . . . 19·00 29·00
22 4d. on 6d. green . . . . . . 65·00 50·00

1886. Surch in figures.
25 **1** 4d. on 6d. green . . . . . . 48·00 90·00

ST. HELENA Pt. 1

An island in the South Atlantic Ocean, west of Africa.

1856. 12 pence = 1 shilling;
20 shillings = 1 pound.
1971. 100 pence = 1 pound.

1

11

The early stamps of St. Helena, other than the 6d, were formed by printing the 6d., in various colours and surcharging it with new values in words or (in case of the 2½d.) in figures.

1856. Imperf.
4 **1** 1d. on 6d. red £120 £170
5 4d. on 6d. red £500 £250
1 6d. blue £500 £180

1861. Perf.
36 **1** ½d. on 6d. green . . . . . 1·75 2·00
37 1d. on 6d. red . . . . . . 3·50 3·00
39 2d. on 6d. yellow . . . . . 1·75 5·00
40 2½d. on 6d. blue . . . . . 2·25 5·00
42 3d. on 6d. purple . . . . . 3·75 4·00
14 4d. on 6d. red . . . . . . 90·00 48·00
43c 4d. on 6d. brown . . . . . 20·00 13·00
25 6d. blue . . . . £350 48·00
44 6d. grey . . . . 17·00 4·25
30 1s. on 6d. green . . . . . . 20·00 12·00
20 5s. on 6d. yellow . . . . . 45·00 60·00

1890.
46 **11** ½d. green . . . . 2·75 5·00
47 1d. red . . . . 14·00 1·00
48 1½d. brown and green . . . 4·50 7·00
49 2d. yellow . . . . 5·00 12·00
50 2½d. blue . . . . 11·00 12·00
51 5d. violet . . . . 11·00 27·00
52 10d. brown . . . . 23·00 60·00

12

13 Government House

14 The Wharf

1902. Inscr "POSTAGE POSTAGE".
53 **12** ½d. green . . . . 1·50 2·25
54 1d. red . . . . 5·50 70

1903.
55 **13** ½d. brown and green . . . . 2·00 3·25
56 **14** 1d. black and red . . . . . 1·50 35
57 **13** 2d. black and green . . . . 6·50 1·25
58 **14** 8d. black and brown . . . . 22·00 32·00
59 **13** 1s. brown and orange . . . 23·00 40·00
60 **14** 2s. black and violet . . . . 48·00 85·00

1908. Inscr "POSTAGE & REVENUE".
64 **12** 2½d. blue . . . . 1·50 1·50
66a 4d. black and red on yellow . . . . 3·00 16·00
67a 6d. purple . . . . 3·75 14·00
71 10s. green and red on green £180 £250

1912. As T **13/14** but with medallion of King George V.
72 **13** ½d. black and green . . . . 2·25 10·00
73 **14** 1d. black and red . . . . . 4·25 1·75
89 1d. green . . . . 1·75 27·00
74 1½d. black and orange . . . 3·50 5·50
90 1½d. red . . . . 10·00 27·00
75 **13** 2d. black and grey . . . . 4·25 1·75
76 **14** 2½d. black and blue . . . . 3·50 5·50
77 **13** 3d. black & purple on yellow . . . . 3·50 5·00
91 3d. blue . . . . 18·00 55·00
78 **14** 8d. black and purple . . . . 7·00 50·00
79 **13** 1s. black on green . . . . . 9·00 35·00
80 **14** 2s. black and blue on blue 40·00 80·00
81 3s. black and violet . . . . 55·00 £130

18

22 Badge of St. Helena

1912. Inscr "POSTAGE & REVENUE".
83 **18** 4d. black and red on yellow 11·00 23·00
84 6d. purple 4·00 5·00

1913. Inscr "POSTAGE POSTAGE".
85 **18** 4d. black and red on yellow 8·00 2·75
86 6d. purple 14·00 26·00

1916. Surch **WAR TAX ONE PENNY**.
87 1d.+1d. black and red (No. 73) 1·75 3·25

1919. Surch **WAR TAX 1d.**
88 1d.+1d. black and red (No. 73) 1·50 4·50

1922.
97 **22** ½d. grey and black 2·25 2·25
98 1d. grey and green 2·50 1·60
99 1½d. red 2·75 13·00
100 2d. grey and brown 3·75 2·00
101 3d. blue 2·00 4·00
92 4d. grey and black on yellow 11·00 6·00
103 5d. green and red on green 3·00 5·50
104 6d. grey and purple 4·50 8·00
105 8d. grey and violet 3·75 7·00
106 1s. grey and brown 6·50 9·00
107 1s.6d. grey & green on grn 15·00 45·00
108 2s. purple and blue on blue 17·00 40·00
109 2s.6d. grey & red on yellow 14·00 55·00
110 5s. grey and green on yellow 38·00 75·00
111 7s.6d. grey and orange 75·00 £120
112 10s. grey and green £110 £170
113 15s. grey and purple on blue £800 £1500
96 £1 grey and purple on red £350 £450

23 Lot and Lot's Wife

1934. Centenary of British Colonization.
114 **23** ½d. black and purple 1·00 80
115 – 1d. black and green 65 85
116 – 1½d. black and red 2·50 3·25
117 – 2d. black and orange 2·25 1·25
118 – 3d. black and blue 1·40 4·50
119 – 6d. black and blue 3·25 3·00
120 – 1s. black and brown 6·50 18·00
121 – 2s.6d. black and red 35·00 48·00
122 – 5s. black and brown 75·00 80·00
123 – 10s. black and purple £200 £250
DESIGNS—HORIZ: 1d. The "Plantation"; 1½d. Map of St. Helena; 2d. Quay, Jamestown; 3d. James Valley; 6d. Jamestown; 1s. Munden's Promontory; 5s. High Knoll; 10s. Badge of St. Helena. VERT: 2s.6d. St. Helena.

32a Windsor Castle

1935. Silver Jubilee.
124 **32a** 1½d. blue and red 75 5·50
125 2d. blue and grey 1·25 90
126 6d. green and blue 6·50 3·25
127 1s. grey and purple 10·00 13·00

32b King George VI and Queen Elizabeth

1937. Coronation.
128 **32b** 1d. green 40 35
129 2d. orange 55 35
130 3d. blue 80 40

33 Badge of St. Helena

1938.
131 **33** ½d. violet 10 65
132 1d. green 9·00 2·25
132a 1d. orange 20 30
149 1d. black and green 80 1·00
133 1½d. red 20 40
150 1½d. black and red 80 1·00
134 2d. orange 20 15
151 2d. black and red 80 1·40
135 3d. blue 80·00 18·00
135a 3d. grey 30 30
135b 4d. blue 2·00 80
136 6d. blue 2·00 80
136a 8d. green 3·25 90
137 1s. brown 1·00 30
138 2s.6d. purple 17·00 6·50
139 5s. brown 18·00 12·00
140 10s. purple 18·00 18·00

33a Houses of Parliament, London

1946. Victory.
141 **33a** 2d. orange 15 10
142 4d. blue 15 10

33b King George VI and Queen Elizabeth

33c King George VI and Queen Elizabeth

1948. Silver Wedding.
143 **33b** 3d. black 30 20
144 **33c** 10s. blue 23·00 28·00

33d Hermes, Globe and Forms of Transport

33e Hemispheres, Jet-powered Vickers Viking Airliner and Steamer

33f Hermes and Globe

33g U.P.U. Monument

1949. U.P.U.
145 **33d** 3d. red 25 50
146 **33e** 4d. blue 3·00 1·00
147 **33f** 6d. green 45 1·25
148 **33g** 1s. black 35 1·10

33h Queen Elizabeth II

34 Badge of St. Helena

1953. Coronation.
152 **33h** 3d. black and lilac 1·00 1·25

1953.
153 **34** ½d. black and green 30 30
154 – 1d. black and green 15 20
155 – 1½d. black and purple 2·50 1·00
156 – 2d. black and red 50 30
157 – 2½d. black and red 40 30
158 – 3d. black and brown 3·25 30
159 – 4d. black and blue 40 70
160 – 6d. black and violet 40 30
161 – 7d. black and grey 65 1·50
162 – 1s. black and red 40 50
163 – 2s.6d. black and violet 11·00 5·50
164 – 5s. black and sepia 14·00 7·00
165 – 10s. black and yellow 32·00 13·00
DESIGNS—HORIZ: 1d. Flax plantation; 2d. Lace-making; 2½d. Drying flax; 3d. St. Helena sand plover; 4d. Flagstaff and The Barn (hills); 6d. Donkeys carrying flax; 7d. Map; 1s. The Castle; 2s.6d. Cutting flax; 5s. Jamestown; 10s. Longwood House. VERT: 1½d. Heart-shaped Waterfall.

45 Stamp of 1856

47 East Indiaman "London" off James Bay

1956. Cent of First St. Helena Postage Stamp.
166 **45** 3d. blue and red 10 10
167 4d. blue and brown 10 20
168 6d. blue and purple 15 25

1959. Tercentenary of Settlement.
169 – 3d. black and red 10 15
170 **47** 6d. green and blue 40 75
171 – 1s. black and orange 40 75
DESIGNS—HORIZ: 3d. Arms of East India Company; 1s. Commemoration Stone.

1961. Tristan Relief Fund. Nos. 46 and 49/51 of Tristan da Cunha surch **ST. HELENA Tristan Relief** and premium.
172 2½c.+3d. black and red — £425
173 5c.+6d. black and blue — £450
174 7½c.+9d. black and red — £550
175 10c.+1s. black and brown — £650

50 St. Helena Butterflyfish

63 Queen Elizabeth II with Prince Andrew (after Cecil Beaton)

1961.
176 **50** 1d. multicoloured 40 20
177 – 1½d. multicoloured 50 20
178 – 2d. red and grey 15 20
179 – 3d. multicoloured 70 20
180 – 4½d. multicoloured 60 60
181 – 6d. red, sepia and olive 5·50 70
182 – 7d. brown, black and violet 35 70
183 – 10d. purple and blue 35 70
184 – 1s. yellow, green and brown 55 1·00
185 – 1s.6d. grey and blue 11·00 4·75
186 – 2s.6d. red, yellow & turq 2·50 2·50
187 – 5s. yellow, brown and green 12·00 4·00
188 – 10s. red, black and blue 13·00 10·00
189 **63** £1 brown and blue 12·00 14·00
DESIGNS—VERT (as Type **50**): 1½d. Yellow canary; 3d. Queen Elizabeth II; 4½d. Red-wood flower; 6d. Madagascar red fody; 1s. Gum-wood flower; 1s.6d. White tern; 5s. Night-blooming Cereus. HORIZ (as T **50**): 2d. Brittle starfish; 7d. Trumpetfish; 10d. Feather starfish; 2s.6d. Orange starfish; 10s. Deep-water bullseye.

63a Protein Foods

1963. Freedom from Hunger.
190 **63a** 1s.6d. blue 75 40

63b Red Cross Emblem

1963. Centenary of Red Cross.
191 **63b** 3d. red and black 40 25
192 1s.6d. red and blue 85 1·50

1965. First Local Post. Optd **FIRST LOCAL POST 4th JANUARY 1965**.
193 **50** 1d. multicoloured 10 20
194 – 3d. multicoloured (No. 179) 10 20
195 – 6d. red, sepia and olive (No. 181) 40 20
196 – 1s.6d. grey & blue (No. 185) 60 20

64a I.T.U. Emblem

1965. Centenary of I.T.U.
197 **64a** 3d. blue and brown 25 25
198 6d. purple and green 35 25

64b I.C.Y. Emblem

1965. Centenary of I.C.Y.
199 **64b** 1d. purple and turquoise 30 15
200 6d. green and lavender 30 15

64c Sir Winston Churchill and St. Paul's Cathedral in Wartime

1966. Churchill Commemoration.
201 **64c** 1d. blue 15 20
202 3d. green 25 20
203 6d. brown 40 25
204 1s.6d. violet 45 75

64d Footballer's Legs, Ball and Jules Rimet Cup

1966. World Cup Football Championship.
205 **64d** 3d. multicoloured 50 35
206 6d. multicoloured 75 35

64e W.H.O. Emblem

1966. Inauguration of W.H.O. Headquarters, Geneva.
207 **64e** 3d. black, green and blue 75 20
208 1s.6d. black, purple & ochre 2·25 1·00

64f "Education"

64g "Science"

64h "Culture"

1966. 20th Anniv of UNESCO.
209 **64f** 3d. multicoloured 75 20
210 **64g** 6d. yellow, violet and olive . . . . 1·25 50
211 **64h** 1s.6d. black, purple & orge . . . . 2·00 1·75

65 Badge of St. Helena

1967. New Constitution.
212 **65** 1s. multicoloured 10 10
213 2s.6d. multicoloured . . . 20 20

66 Fire of London

1967. 300th Anniv of Arrival of Settlers after Great Fire of London.
214 **66** 1d. red and black 15 10
215 – 3d. blue and black 20 10
216 – 6d. violet and black . . . 20 15
217 – 1s.6d. green and black . . 20 20
DESIGNS: 3d. East Indiaman "Charles"; 6d. Settlers landing at Jamestown; 1s.6d. Settlers clearing scrub.

70 Interlocking Maps of Tristan and St. Helena

1968. 30th Anniv of Tristan da Cunha as a Dependency of St. Helena.
218 **70** 4d. purple and brown . . . 10 10
219 – 8d. olive and brown . . . 10 30
220 **70** 1s.9d. blue and brown . . 10 40
221 – 2s.3d. blue and brown . . 15 40
DESIGNS: 8d. and 2s.3d. Interlocking maps of Tristan and St. Helena (different).

72 Queen Elizabeth and Sir Hudson Lowe

1968. 150th Anniv of Abolition of Slavery in St. Helena.
222 **72** 3d. multicoloured 10 15
223 9d. multicoloured 10 20
224 – 1s.6d. multicoloured . . . 15 30
225 – 2s.6d. multicoloured . . . 25 45
DESIGN: Nos. 224 and 225, Queen Elizabeth and Sir George Bingham.

74 Blue Gum Eucalyptus and Road Construction

1968. Multicoloured.
226 ½d. Type **74** 10 10
227 1d. Electricity development 10 10
228 1½d. Dental unit 15 10
229 2d. Pest control 15 10
230 3d. Flats in Jamestown . . . 30 10
231 4d. Livestock improvement 20 10
232 6d. Schools broadcasting . . 50 10
233 8d. Country Cottages . . . 30 10
234 10d. New school buildings . . 30 10
235 1s. Reafforestation 30 10
236 1s.6d. Heavy lift crane . . . 70 2·75
237 2s.6d. Lady Field Children's Home . . . . 70 3·25
238 5s. Agricultural training . . . 70 3·50
239 10s. New General Hospital 2·00 4·00
240 £1 Lifeboat "John Dutton" 6·00 15·00
PLANTS SHOWN: ½, 4d., 1s.6d. Blue gum eucalyptus; 1d., 6d., 2s.6d. Cabbage-tree; 1½d., 8d., 5s. St. Helena redwood; 2, 10d., 10s. Scrubweed; 3d., 1s., £1 Tree-fern.

89 Brig "Perseverance"

1969. Mail Communications. Multicoloured.
241 4d. Type **89** 20 20
242 8d. "Phoebe" (screw steamer) 25 40
243 1s.9d. "Llandovery Castle" (liner) 25 60
244 2s.3d. "Good Hope Castle" (cargo liner) 25 75

93 W.O. and Drummer of the 53rd Foot, 1815

1969. Military Uniforms. Multicoloured.
245 6d. Type **93** 15 25
246 8d. Officer and Surgeon, 20th Foot, 1816 . . . . . . 15 25
247 1s.8d. Drum Major, 66th Foot, 1816, and Royal Artillery Officer, 1920 . . . 20 45
248 2s.6d. Private, 91st Foot, and 2nd Corporal, Royal Sappers and Miners, 1832 20 55

97 Dickens, Mr. Pickwick and Job Trotter ("Pickwick Papers")

1970. Death Cent of Charles Dickens. Mult.
249 4d. Type **97** 40 15
250 8d. Mr. Bumble and Oliver ("Oliver Twist") 50 15
251 1s.6d. Sairey Gamp and Mark Tapley ("Martin Chuzzlewit") 60 20
252 2s.6d. Jo and Mr. Turveydrop ("Bleak House") 70 25
All designs include a portrait of Dickens as Type **97**.

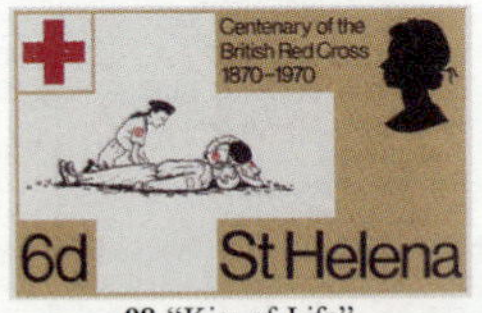

98 "Kiss of Life"

1970. Centenary of British Red Cross.
253 **98** 6d. bistre, red and black 15 15
254 – 9d. green, red and black 15 20
255 – 1s.9d. grey, red and black 20 30
256 – 2s.3d. lilac, red and black 20 45
DESIGNS: 9d. Nurse with girl in wheelchair; 1s.9d. Nurse bandaging child's knee; 2s.3d. Red Cross emblem.

99 Officer's Shako Plate (20th Foot)

1970. Military Equipment (1st issue). Mult.
257 4d. Type **99** 20 20
258 9d. Officer's breast plate (66th Foot) 25 30
259 1s.3d. Officer's Full Dress shako (91st Foot) 25 40
260 2s.11d. Ensign's shako (53rd Foot) 30 60
See also Nos. 281/4, 285/8 and 291/4.

100 Electricity Development

1971. Decimal Currency. Designs as Nos. 227/40, inscr as T **100**.
261 ½p. multicoloured 10 10
262 1p. multicoloured 10 10
263 1½p. multicoloured 10 10
264 2p. multicoloured . . . . . 1·75 1·00
265 2½p. multicoloured 10 10
266 3½p. multicoloured 30 10
267 4½p. multicoloured 10 10
268 5p. multicoloured 10 10
269 7½p. multicoloured 40 35
270 10p. multicoloured 30 35
271 12½p. muticoloured 30 50
272 25p. multicoloured . . . . . 60 1·25
273 50p. multicoloured . . . . . 1·00 2·00
273 50p. multicoloured . . . . . 1·00 2·00
274 £1 multicoloured . . . . . . 20·00 15·00

101 St. Helena holding the "True Cross" 102 Napoleon (after painting by J. L. David) and Tomb on St. Helena

1971. Easter.
275 **101** 2p. multicoloured 10 10
276 5p. multicoloured 10 15
277 7½p. multicoloured 15 20
278 12½p. multicoloured . . . 20 25

1971. 150th Death Anniv of Napoleon. Mult.
279 2p. Type **102** 20 50
280 34p. "Napoleon at St. Helena" (H. Delaroche) 45 1·00

1971. Military Equipment (2nd issue). As T **99**. Multicoloured.
281 1½p. Artillery Private's hanger 25 30
282 4p. Baker rifle and socket bayonet 30 60
283 6p. Infantry Officer's sword 30 80
284 22½p. Baker rifle and sword bayonet . . . . 55 1·25

1972. Military Equipment (3rd issue). As T **99**. Multicoloured.
285 2p. multicoloured 15 20
286 5p. lilac, blue and black . . . 15 40
287 7½p. multicoloured 20 50
288 12½p. sepia, brown and black 30 60
DESIGNS: 2p. Royal Sappers and Miners breast-plate, post 1823; 5p. Infantry sergeant's spontoon, c. 1830; 7½p. Royal Artillery officer's breast-plate, c. 1830; 12½p. English military pistol, c. 1800.

103 St. Helena Sand Plover and White Tern

1972. Royal Silver Wedding.
289 **103** 2p. green 20 40
290 16p. brown 30 85

1973. Military Equipment (4th issue). As T **99**. Multicoloured.
291 2p. Other Rank's shako, 53rd Foot, 1815 . . . . . . 30 55
292 5p. Band and Drums sword, 1830 . . . . 35 1·00
293 7½p. Royal Sappers and Miners Officer's hat, 1830 50 1·25
294 12½p. General's sword, 1831 60 1·50

103a Princess Anne and Captain Mark Phillips

1973. Royal Wedding. Multicoloured, background colours given.
295 **103a** 2p. blue 15 10
296 18p. green 25 20

104 "Westminster" and "Claudine" beached, 1849

1973. Tercentenary of East India Company Charter. Multicoloured.
297 1½p. Type **104** 30 45
298 4p. "True Briton", 1790 . . 40 70
299 6p. "General Goddard" in action, 1795 . . . . 40 70
300 22½p. "Kent" burning in the Bay of Biscay, 1825 . . . 85 2·25

105 U.P.U. Emblem and Ships

1974. Centenary of U.P.U. Multicoloured.
301 5p. Type **105** 20 25
302 25p. U.P.U. emblem and letters 40 55
MS303 89 × 84 mm. Nos. 301/2 75 1·50

106 Churchill in Sailor Suit and Blenheim Palace

1974. Birth Cent of Sir Winston Churchill.
304 **106** 5p. multicoloured 20 20
305 – 25p. black, pink and purple 30 60
MS306 108 × 93 mm. Nos. 304/5 75 2·00
DESIGN: 25p. Churchill and River Thames.

107 Capt. Cook and H.M.S. "Resolution" 108 "Mellissia begonifolia" (tree)

1975. Bicentenary of Capt. Cook's Return to St. Helena. Multicoloured.
307 5p. Type **107** 30 20
308 25p. Capt. Cook and Jamestown 40 40

1975. Centenary of Publication of "St. Helena" by J. C. Melliss. Multicoloured.
310 2p. Type **108** 15 30
311 5p. "Mellissius adumbratus" (beetle) 15 35
312 12p. St. Helena sand plover (bird) (horiz) 50 80
313 25p. Melliss's scorpionfish (horiz) . . . . 50 1·00

109 £1 Note

1976. First Issue of Currency Notes. Mult.
314 8p. Type **109** 30 30
315 33p. £5 Note 60 80

110 1d. Stamp of 1863

1976. Festival of Stamps, London.
316 **110** 5p. brown, black and pink 15 15
317 – 8p. black, green & lt green 20 30
318 – 25p. multicoloured . . . 35 45
DESIGNS—VERT: 8p. 1d. stamp of 1922. HORIZ: 25p. Mail carrier "Good Hope Castle".

111 "High Knoll, 1806" (Capt. Barnett)

1976. Aquatints and Lithographs of St. Helena. Multicoloured.
319B 1p. Type **111** 30 75
320A 3p. "The Friar Rock, 1815" (G. Bellasis) . . . . . . 40 1·25
321A 5p. "The Column Lot, 1815" (G. Bellasis) . . . 30 1·25
322A 6p. "Sandy Bay Valley, 1809" (H. Salt) . . . . . 30 1·25
323A 8p. "Scene from Castle Terrace, 1815" (G. Bellasis) . . . . . . 40 1·25
324A 9p. "The Briars, 1815" . . 40 1·25
325A 10p. "Plantation House, 1821" (J. Wathen) . . . 50 60
326A 15p. "Longwood House, 1821" (J. Wathen) . . . 45 55
327A 18p. "St. Paul's Church" (V. Brooks) . . . . . . 45 1·50
328A 26p. "St. James's Valley, 1815" (Capt. Hastings) 45 1·50
329A 40p. "St. Matthew's Church, 1860" (V. Brooks) . . . . . . 70 1·75
330A £1 "St. Helena, 1815" (G. Bellasis) . . . . . . 1·75 3·75
331B £2 "Sugar Loaf Hill, 1821" (J. Wathen) . . . . . . 2·75 5·00
Nos. 330A and 331B are larger, 47 × 34 mm.
The 1 and 10p. and the £2 come with or without date imprint.

112 Duke of Edinburgh paying Homage

1977. Silver Jubilee. Multicoloured.
332 8p. Royal Visit, 1947 . . . . 10 20
333 15p. Queen's sceptre with dove 20 25
334 26p. Type **112** 30 35

113 Halley's Comet (from Bayeux Tapestry)

1977. Tercentenary of Halley's Visit. Mult.
335 5p. Type **113** 35 25
336 8p. Late 17th-century sextant 50 25
337 27p. Halley and Halley's Mount, St. Helena . . . . 1·00 60

114 Sea Lion

1978. 25th Anniv of Coronation.
338 – 25p. agate, red and silver 30 50
339 – 25p. multicoloured . . . 30 50
340 **114** 25p. agate, red and silver 30 50
DESIGNS: No. 338, Black Dragon of Ulster; No. 339, Queen Elizabeth II.

115 Period Engraving of St. Helena

1978. Wreck of the "Witte Leeuw". Multicoloured.
341 3p. Type **115** 15 15
342 5p. Chinese porcelain 15 20
343 8p. Bronze cannon 20 30
344 9p. Chinese porcelain (different) 20 35
345 15p. Pewter mug and ceramic flasks 30 55
346 20p. Dutch East Indiaman 40 70

116 H.M.S. "Discovery" **117** Sir Rowland Hill

1979. Bicentenary of Captain Cook's Voyages, 1768–79. Multicoloured.
347 3p. Type **116** 15 15
348 8p. Cook's portable observatory 15 25
349 12p. "Pharnaceum acidum" (sketch by Joseph Banks) 20 35
350 25p. Flaxman/Wedgwood medallion of Capt. Cook 30 90

1979. Death Centenary of Sir Rowland Hill.
351 **117** 5p. multicoloured 10 15
352 – 8p. multicoloured 15 20
353 – 20p. multicoloured . . . 30 40
354 – 32p. black, magenta & mve 40 55
DESIGNS—HORIZ: 8p. 1965 1d. First Local Post stamp; 20p. 1863 1d. on 6d. surcharged stamp; 32p. 1902 1d. stamp.

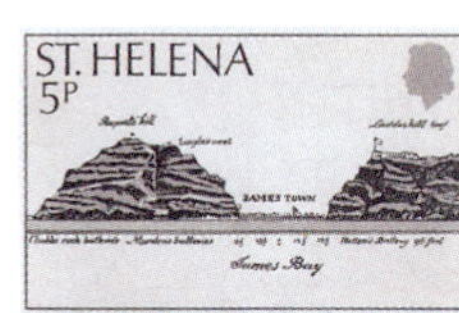

118 R. F. Seal's Chart of 1823 showing the Elevation of the Coastline

1979. 150th Anniv of Inclined Plane.
355 **118** 5p. black, grey and stone 15 15
356 – 8p. black, grey and stone 15 20
357 – 50p. multicoloured . . . 60 75
DESIGNS—HORIZ: 8p. The Inclined Plane in 1829; VERT: 50p. The Inclined Plane in 1979.

119 Napoleon's Tomb, 1848

1980. Centenary of Empress Eugenie's Visit.
358 **119** 5p. brown, pink and gold 10 20
359 – 8p. brown, stone and gold 15 25
360 – 62p. brown, flesh and gold 65 80
MS361 180 × 110 mm. Nos. 358/60 80 1·10
DESIGNS: 8p. Landing at St. Helena; 62p. The Empress at Napoleon's Tomb.

120 East Indiaman

1980. "London 1980" Int Stamp Exhibition. Mult.
362 5p. Type **120** 10 15
363 8p. "Dolphin" postal stone 10 15
364 47p. Postal stone outside Castle entrance, Jamestown 50 60
MS365 111 × 120 mm. Nos. 362/4 60 80

121 Queen Elizabeth the Queen Mother in 1974

1980. 80th Birthday of the Queen Mother.
366 **121** 24p. multicoloured . . . 35 50

122 The Briars, 1815

1980. 175th Anniv of Wellington's Visit. Multicoloured.
367 9p. Type **122** 15 15
368 30p. "Wellington" (Goya) (vert) 45 45

123 Redwood

1981. Endemic Plants. Multicoloured.
369 5p. Type **123** 15 20
370 8p. Old father live forever . . 15 20
371 15p. Gumwood 20 25
372 27p. Black cabbage 35 45

124 Detail from Reinel Portolan Chart, c. 1530

1981. Early Maps.
373 **124** 5p. multicoloured 15 15
374 – 8p. black, red and grey 15 20
375 – 20p. multicoloured . . . 30 35
376 – 30p. multicoloured . . . 35 50
MS377 114 × 83 mm.— 24p. black and grey 40 65
DESIGNS: 8p. John Thornton's Map of St. Helena, c. 1700; 20p. Map of St. Helena, 1815; 24p. Part of Gastaldi's map of Africa, 16th-century; 30p. Map of St. Helena, 1817.

125 Prince Charles as Royal Navy Commander **126** Atlantic Trumpet Triton

1981. Royal Wedding. Multicoloured.
378 14p. Wedding bouquet from St. Helena 15 20
379 29p. Type **125** 25 30
380 32p. Prince Charles and Lady Diana Spencer 30 35

1981. Sea Shells. Multicoloured.
381 7p. Type **126** 20 20
382 10p. St. Helena cowrie . . . 25 20
383 25p. Common purple janthina 35 40
384 53p. Rude pen shell . . . . 55 1·00

127 Traffic Duty

1981. 25th Anniv of Duke of Edinburgh Award Scheme. Multicoloured.
385 7p. Type **127** 10 10
386 11p. Signposting 15 15
387 25p. Animal care 30 30
388 50p. Duke of Edinburgh, in Guard's uniform, on horseback 60 60

128 "Sympetrum dilatatum" (dragonfly)

1981. Insects (1st series). Multicoloured.
389 7p. Type **128** 20 20
390 10p. "Aplothorax burchelli" (beetle) 20 20
391 25p. "Ampulex compressa" (wasp) 35 35
392 32p. "Labidura herculeana" (earwig) 35 35
See also Nos. 411/14.

129 Charles Darwin

1982. 150th Anniv of Charles Darwin's Voyage. Multicoloured.
393 7p. Type **129** 20 20
394 14p. Flagstaff Hill and Darwin's hammer 25 35
395 25p. Common pheasant ("Ring-necked Pheasant") and Chukar partridge . . . 50 70
396 29p. H.M.S. "Beagle" off St. Helena 60 80

130 Prince and Princess of Wales at Balmoral, Autumn, 1981 **132** Lord Baden-Powell

1982. 21st Birthday of Princess of Wales. Multicoloured.
397 7p. St. Helena coat of arms 10 15
398 11p. Type **130** 25 15
399 29p. Bride on Palace balcony 40 35
400 55p. Formal portrait . . . . 1·00 60

1982. Commonwealth Games, Brisbane. Nos. 326 and 328 optd **1st PARTICIPATION COMMONWEALTH GAMES 1982**.
401 15p. "Longwood House, 1821" (J. Wathen) 25 25
402 26p. "St. James's Valley, 1815" (Capt. Hastings) . . 45 45

1982. 75th Anniv of Boy Scout Movement.
403 **132** 3p. brown, grey and yellow 15 15
404 – 11p. brown, grey and green 20 25
405 – 29p. brown, grey & orange 30 60
406 – 59p. brown, grey and green . . . . 60 1·25

DESIGNS—HORIZ: 11p. Boy Scout (drawing by Lord Baden-Powell); 59p. Camping at Thompsons Wood. VERT: 29p. Canon Walcott.

133 King and Queen Rocks

134 "Trametes versicolor" ("Coriolus versicolor")

1982. Views of St. Helena by Roland Svensson. Multicoloured.
407 7p. Type **133** 15 20
408 11p. "Turk's Cap" 15 25
409 29p. Coastline from Jamestown (horiz) 35 65
410 59p. "Mundens Point" (horiz) 60 1·40

1983. Insects (2nd series). As T **128**. Mult.
411 11p. "Acherontia atropos" (hawk moth) 15 30
412 15p. "Helenasaldula aberrans" (shore-bug) 15 35
413 29p. "Anchastus compositarum" (click beetle) 25 55
414 59p. "Lamprochrus cossonoides" (weevil) 55 1·25

1983. Fungi. Multicoloured.
415 11p. Type **134** 20 25
416 15p. "Pluteus brunneisucus" 20 40
417 29p. "Polyporus induratus" (horiz) 30 60
418 59p. "Coprinus angulatus" 55 1·25

135 Java Sparrow

136 Birth of St. Helena

1983. Birds. Multicoloured.
419 7p. Type **135** 30 20
420 15p. Madagascar red fody 45 35
421 33p. Common waxbill 80 70
422 59p. Yellow canary 1·50 1·40

1983. Christmas. Life of St. Helena (1st series). Multicoloured.
423 10p. Type **136** 20 35
424 15p. St. Helena being taken to convent 20 35
See also Nos. 450/3 and 468/71.

137 1934 Centenary $\frac{1}{2}$d. Stamp

139 "St. Helena" (schooner)

138 Prince Andrew and H.M.S. "Invincible" (aircraft carrier)

1984. 150th Anniv of St. Helena as a British Colony. Multicoloured.
425 1p. Type **137** 10 20
426 3p. 1934 1d. stamp 10 20
427 6p. 1934 $1\frac{1}{2}$d. stamp 10 30
428 7p. 1934 2d. stamp 15 30
429 11p. 1934 3d. stamp 20 40
430 15p. 1934 6d. stamp 25 45
431 29p. 1934 1s. stamp 40 95
432 33p. 1934 5s. stamp 45 1·25
433 59p. 1934 10s. stamp 65 2·00
434 £1 1934 2s.6d. stamp 1·00 3·25
435 £2 St. Helena Coat of Arms 1·75 5·00

1984. Visit of Prince Andrew. Multicoloured.
436 11p. Type **138** 25 25
437 60p. Prince Andrew and H.M.S. "Herald" (survey ship) 75 1·40

1984. 250th Anniv of "Lloyd's List" (newspaper). Multicoloured.
438 10p. Type **139** 20 20
439 18p. Solomons Facade (local agent) 25 35
440 25p. Lloyd's Coffee House, London 30 55
441 50p. "Papanui" (freighter) 75 1·00

140 Twopenny Coin and Donkey

1984. New Coinage. Multicoloured.
442 10p. Type **140** 20 35
443 15p. Five pence coin and St. Helena sand plover 20 45
444 29p. Penny coin and yellow-finned tuna 30 75
445 50p. Ten pence coin and arum lily 40 1·25

141 Mrs. Rebecca Fuller (former Corps Secretary)

142 Queen Elizabeth the Queen Mother aged Two

1984. Centenary of Salvation Army on St. Helena. Multicoloured.
446 7p. Type **141** 15 35
447 11p. Meals-on-wheels service (horiz) 15 45
448 25p. Salvation Army Citadel, Jamestown (horiz) 20 80
449 60p. Salvation Army band at Jamestown Clock Tower 55 2·00

1984. Christmas. Life of St. Helena (2nd series). As T **136**. Multicoloured.
450 6p. St. Helena visits prisoners 15 20
451 10p. Betrothal of St. Helena 20 30
452 15p. Marriage of St. Helena to Constantius 25 40
453 33p. Birth of Constantine 50 70

1985. Life and Times of Queen Elizabeth the Queen Mother. Multicoloured.
454 11p. Type **142** 20 25
455 15p. At Ascot with the Queen 20 35
456 29p. Attending Gala Ballet at Covent Garden 40 65
457 55p. With Prince Henry at his christening 60 1·00
MS458 91 × 73 mm. 70p. The Queen Mother with Ford "V8 Pilot" 1·75 1·60

143 Axillary Cardinalfish

144 John J. Audubon

1985. Marine Life. Multicoloured.
459 7p. Type **143** 15 25
460 11p. Chub mackerel 15 30
461 15p. Skipjack tuna 20 40
462 33p. Yellow-finned tuna 35 75
463 50p. Stump 50 1·25

1985. Birth Bicentenary of John J. Audubon (ornithologist).
464 **144** 11p. black and brown 15 25
465 – 15p. multicoloured 30 35
466 – 25p. multicoloured 40 55
467 – 60p. multicoloured 65 1·40
DESIGN—HORIZ (from original Audubon paintings): 15p. Moorhen ("Common Gallinule); 25p. White-tailed tropic bird; 68p. Common noddy.

1985. Christmas. Life of St. Helena (3rd series). As T **136**. Multicoloured.
468 7p. St. Helena jouneys to the Holy Land 20 25
469 10p. Zambres slays the bull 20 30
470 15p. The bull restored to life: conversion of St. Helena 25 40
471 60p. Resurrection of the corpse: the True Cross identified 75 1·50

145 Church Provident Society for Women Banner

1986. Friendly Societies' Banners. Mult.
472 10p. Type **145** 15 25
473 11p. Working Men's Christian Association 15 25
474 25p. Church Benefit Society for Children 25 55
475 29p. Mechanics and Friendly Benefit Society 25 65
476 33p. Ancient Order of Foresters 30 70

145a Princess Elizabeth making 21st Birthday Broadcast, South Africa, 1947

146 Plaque at Site of Halley's Observatory on St. Helena

1986. 60th Birthday of Queen Elizabeth II. Mult.
477 10p. Type **145a** 15 20
478 15p. Silver Jubilee photograph, 1977 25 30
479 20p. Princess Elizabeth on board H.M.S. "Vanguard", 1947 30 35
480 50p. In the U.S.A., 1976 45 1·00
481 65p. At Crown Agents Head Office, London, 1983 50 1·10

1986. Appearance of Halley's Comet. Multicoloured.
482 9p. Type **146** 25 35
483 12p. Edmond Halley 30 35
484 20p. Halley's planisphere of the southern stars 55 70
485 65p. "Unity" on passage to St. Helena, 1676 1·75 2·50

146a Prince Andrew and Miss Sarah Ferguson

1986. Royal Wedding. Multicoloured.
486 10p. Type **146a** 20 25
487 40p. Prince Andrew with Governor J. Massingham on St. Helena 80 85

147 James Ross and H.M.S. "Erebus"

1986. Explorers.
488 **147** 1p. brown and pink 30 1·50
489 – 3p. deep blue and blue 30 1·50
490 – 5p. deep green and green 30 1·50
491 – 9p. brown and red 40 1·50
492 – 10p. deep brown and brown 40 1·50
493 – 12p. green and light green 50 1·50
494 – 15p. brown and pink 60 1·50
495 – 20p. blue and light blue 70 1·50
496 – 25p. sepia and pink 70 1·50
497 – 40p. deep green and green 80 1·75
498 – 60p. deep brown and brown 80 2·00
499 – £1 deep blue and blue 1·00 3·00
500 – £2 deep lilac and lilac 1·75 5·00
DESIGNS: 3p. Robert FitzRoy and H.M.S. "Beagle"; 5p. Adam Johann von Krusenstern and "Nadezhda"; 9p. William Bligh and H.M.S. "Resolution"; 10p. Otto von Kotzebue and "Rurik"; 12p. Philip Carteret and H.M.S. "Swallow"; 15p. Thomas Cavendish and "Desire"; 20p. Louis-Antoine de Bougainville and "La Boudeuse"; 25p. Fyedor Petrovich Litke and "Senyavin"; 40p. Louis Isidore Duperrey and "La Coquille"; 60p. John Byron and H.M.S. "Dolphin"; £1 James Cook and H.M.S. "Endeavour"; £2 Jules Dumont d'Urville and "L'Astrolabe".

148 Prince Edward and H.M.S. "Repulse" (battle cruiser), 1925

1987. Royal Visits to St. Helena. Multicoloured.
501 9p. Type **148** 70 70
502 13p. King George VI and H.M.S. "Vanguard" (battleship), 1947 95 1·00
503 38p. Prince Philip and Royal Yacht "Britannia", 1957 2·00 2·75
504 45p. Prince Andrew and H.M.S. "Herald" (survey ship), 1984 2·25 3·00

149 St. Helena Tea Plant

1987. Rare Plants (1st series). Multicoloured.
505 9p. Type **149** 65 55
506 13p. Baby's toes 80 75
507 38p. Salad plant 1·50 2·00
508 45p. Scrubwood 1·75 2·25
See also Nos. 531/4.

150 Lesser Rorqual

1987. Marine Mammals. Multicoloured.
509 9p. Type **150** 1·25 75
510 13p. Risso's dolphin 1·25 1·00
511 45p. Sperm whale 3·00 3·25
512 60p. Euphrosyne dolphin 3·25 3·75
MS513 102 × 72 mm. 75p. Humpback whale (48 × 31 mm) 6·50 7·00

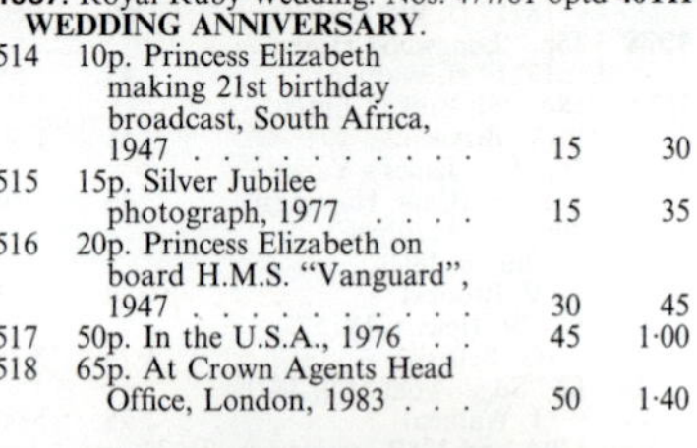

1987. Royal Ruby Wedding. Nos. 477/81 optd **40TH WEDDING ANNIVERSARY**.
514 10p. Princess Elizabeth making 21st birthday broadcast, South Africa, 1947 15 30
515 15p. Silver Jubilee photograph, 1977 15 35
516 20p. Princess Elizabeth on board H.M.S. "Vanguard", 1947 30 45
517 50p. In the U.S.A., 1976 45 1·00
518 65p. At Crown Agents Head Office, London, 1983 50 1·40

151 "Defence" and Dampier's Signature. 1691

1988. Bicentenary of Australian Settlement. Ships and Signatures. Multicoloured.
519 9p. Type **151** 1·50 90
520 13p. H.M.S. "Resolution" (Cook), 1775 2·00 2·00
521 45p. H.M.S. "Providence" (Bligh), 1792 3·25 4·00
522 60p. H.M.S. "Beagle" (Darwin), 1836 4·25 5·50

152 "The Holy Virgin with the Child"

152a Lloyds Underwriting Room, 1886

1988. Christmas. Religious Paintings. Mult.
523 5p. Type **152** 10 30
524 20p. "Madonna" 40 50

525 38p. "The Holy Family with St. John" . . . . 75 1·50
526 60p. "The Holy Virgin with the Child" . . . . 1·25 2·00

1988. 300th Anniv of Lloyd's of London.
527 **152a** 9p. deep brown and brown 25 30
528 – 20p. multicoloured . . . 1·00 60
529 – 45p. multicoloured . . . 1·60 1·40
530 – 60p. multicoloured . . . 1·75 1·60
DESIGNS—VERT: 60p. "Spangereid" (full-rigged ship) on fire, St. Helena, 1920. HORIZ: 20p. "Edinburgh Castle" (liner); 45p. "Bosun Bird" (freighter).

153 Ebony

154 Private, 53rd Foot

1989. Rare Plants (2nd series). Multicoloured.
531 9p. Type **153** 40 40
532 20p. St. Helena lobelia . . . 70 70
533 45p. Large bellflower . . . . 1·40 2·00
534 60p. She cabbage tree . . . . 1·60 2·50

1989. Military Uniforms of 1815. Multicoloured.
535 9p. Type **154** 65 90
536 13p. Officer, 53rd Foot . . . 75 1·00
537 20p. Royal Marine . . . . . 85 1·10
538 45p. Officer, 66th Foot . . . 1·40 1·90
539 60p. Private, 66th Foot . . . 1·60 2·25

1989. "Philexfrance 89" International Stamp Exhibition, Paris. Nos. 535/9 optd **PHILEXFRANCE 89** and emblem.
540 9p. Type **154** . . . . 80 1·10
541 13p. Officer, 53rd Foot . . . 90 1·25
542 20p. Royal Marine . . . . . 1·10 1·40
543 45p. Officer, 66th Foot . . . 1·50 2·00
544 60p. Private, 66th Foot . . . 1·60 2·25

156 Agricultural Studies

1989. New Prince Andrew Central School. Mult.
545 13p. Type **156** 60 55
546 20p. Geography lesson . . . 1·00 1·00
547 25p. Walkway and classroom block . . . . 1·10 1·10
548 60p. Aerial view of School 2·50 3·50

157 "The Madonna with the Pear" (Durer)

159 Sheep

158 Chevrolet "6" 30 cwt Lorry, 1930

1989. Christmas. Religious Paintings. Multicoloured.
549 10p. Type **157** 60 50
550 20p. "The Holy Family under the Appletree" (Rubens) 85 90
551 45p. "The Virgin in the Meadow" (Raphael) . . . 2·00 2·50
552 60p. "The Holy Family with St. John" (Raphael) . . . 2·50 3·50

1989. Early Vehicles. Multicoloured.
553 9p. Type **158** 85 80
554 20p. Austin "Seven", 1929 . . 1·50 1·50
555 45p. Morris "Cowley" 11.9h.p., 1929 . . . . . . 2·25 2·75
556 60p. Sunbeam 25h.p., 1932 2·75 3·75
MS557 93 × 74 mm. £1 Ford "Model A Fordor" . . . . 6·50 7·50

1990. Farm Animals. Multicoloured.
558 9p. Type **159** 50 60
559 13p. Pigs 60 75
560 45p. Cow and calf . . . . . 1·50 2·25
561 60p. Geese . . . . 2·00 3·25

160 1840 Twopence Blue

1990. "Stamp World London 90" International Stamp Exhibition, London.
562 **160** 13p. black and blue . . . 50 50
563 – 20p. multicoloured . . . 75 85
564 – 38p. multicoloured . . . 1·25 2·00
565 – 45p. multicoloured . . . 1·60 2·25
DESIGNS: 20p. 1840 Penny Black and 19th-century St. Helena postmark; 38p. Delivering mail to sub-post office; 45p. Mail van and Post Office, Jamestown.

161 Satellite Dish

161a Lady Elizabeth Bowes-Lyon, April, 1923

1990. Modern Telecommunications Links. Mult.
566 20p. Type **161** . . . . 75 1·10
567 20p. Digital telephone exchange . . . . 75 1·10
568 20p. Public card phone . . . 75 1·10
569 20p. Facsimile machine . . . 75 1·10

1990. 90th Birthday of Queen Elizabeth the Queen Mother.
570 **161a** 25p. multicoloured . . . 1·00 75
571 – £1 black and brown . . 2·75 3·75
DESIGN—29 × 37 mm: £1 Queen Elizabeth visiting communal kitchen, 1940.

162 "Dane" (mail ship), 1857

1990. Maiden Voyage of "St. Helena II". Multicoloured.
572 13p. Type **162** . . . . 1·25 85
573 20p. "St. Helena I" off-loading at St. Helena . . . 1·60 1·40
574 38p. Launch of "St. Helena II" . . . . 2·25 2·75
575 45p. The Duke of York launching "St. Helena II" 2·75 3·50
MS576 100 × 100 mm. £1 "St. Helena II" and outline map of St. Helena . . . . 8·50 9·00

163 Baptist Chapel, Sandy Bay

1990. Christmas. Local Churches. Multicoloured.
577 10p. Type **163** 30 30
578 13p. St. Martin in the Hills Church 35 35
579 20p. St. Helena and the Cross Church 55 65
580 38p. St. James Church . . . 1·00 2·00
581 45p. St. Paul's Cathedral . . 1·25 2·00

164 "Funeral Cortege, Jamestown Wharf" (detail V. Adam)

1990. 150th Anniv of Removal of Napoleon's Body.
582 **164** 13p. black, brown & green . . . . 1·00 80
583 – 20p. black, brown and blue . . . . 1·50 1·50
584 – 38p. black, brown & mauve . . . . 2·25 2·50
585 – 45p. multicoloured . . . 2·50 3·25
DESIGNS: 20p. "Coffin being conveyed to the 'Belle Poule' " (detail, V. Adam); 38p. "Transfer of the Coffin to the 'Normandie', Cherbourg" (detail, V. Adam); 45p. "Napoleon's Tomb, St. Helena" (T. Sutherland).

165 Officer, Leicestershire Regiment

165a Queen Elizabeth II

1991. Military Uniforms of 1897. Multicoloured.
586 13p. Type **165** . . . . 1·00 1·00
587 15p. Officer, York & Lancaster Regiment . . . 1·10 1·10
588 20p. Colour-sergeant, Leicestershire Regiment . . 1·40 1·40
589 38p. Bandsman, York and Lancaster Regiment . . . 2·25 2·75
590 45p. Lance-corporal, York and Lancaster Regiment 2·75 3·25

1991. 65th Birthday of Queen Elizabeth II and 70th Birthday of Prince Philip. Multicoloured.
591 25p. Type **165a** . . . . . . 80 1·25
592 25p. Prince Philip in naval uniform . . . . 80 1·25

166 "Madonna and Child" (T. Vecellio)

1991. Christmas. Religious Paintings. Multicoloured.
593 10p. Type **166** 70 55
594 13p. "The Holy Family" (A. Mengs) 80 65
595 20p. "Madonna and Child" (W. Dyce) . . . . 1·25 1·00
596 38p. "The Two Trinities" (B. Murillo) . . . . 2·00 2·50
597 45p. "The Virgin and Child" (G. Bellini) . . . . 2·25 3·00

167 Matchless (346cc) Motorcycle, 1947

1991. "Phila Nippon '91" International Stamp Exn, Tokyo. Motorcycles. Multicoloured.
598 13p. Type **167** . . . . 1·00 80
599 20p. Triumph "Tiger 100" (500cc), 1950 . . . . . 1·50 1·10
600 38p. Honda "CD" (175cc), 1967 . . . . 2·25 2·75
601 45p. Yamaha "DTE 400", 1976 . . . . 2·50 3·00
MS602 72 × 49 mm. 65p. Suzuki "RM" (250cc), 1984 . . . . . 7·50 9·00

168 "Eye of the Wind" (cadet brig) and Compass Rose

1992. 500th Anniv of Discovery of America by Columbus and Re-enactment Voyages. Multicoloured.
603 15p. Type **168** . . . . . . 1·25 90
604 25p. "Soren Larsen" (cadet brigantine) and map of Re-enactment Voyages . . . . 1·75 1·75
605 35p. "Santa Maria", "Nina" and "Pinta" . . . . 2·25 2·75
606 50p. Columbus and "Santa Maria" . . . . 2·50 3·50

168a Prince Andrew Central School

1992. 40th Anniv of Queen Elizabeth II's Accession. Multicoloured.
607 11p. Type **168a** 40 40
608 15p. Plantation House . . . 55 55
609 25p. Jamestown 85 95
610 35p. Three portraits of Queen Elizabeth . . . . 1·10 1·50
611 50p. Queen Elizabeth II . . . 1·40 1·90

169 H.M.S. "Ledbury" (minesweeper)

1992. 10th Anniv of Liberation of Falkland Islands. Ships. Multicoloured.
612 13p. Type **169** 80 80
613 20p. H.M.S. "Brecon" (minesweeper) . . . . . . 1·10 1·10
614 38p. "St. Helena I" (mail ship) off South Georgia . . 1·75 2·25
615 45p. Launch collecting first mail drop, 1982 . . . . . 2·25 3·00
MS616 116 × 116 mm. 13p.+3p. Type **169**; 20p.+4p. As No. 613; 38p.+8p. As No. 614; 45p.+9p. As No. 615 . . . . 5·50 5·50
The premium on No. **MS**616 were for the S.S.A.F.A.

170 Shepherds and Angel Gabriel

1992. Christmas. Children's Nativity Plays. Multicoloured.
617 13p. Type **170** . . . . 1·00 85
618 15p. Shepherds and Three Kings . . . . 1·10 95
619 20p. Mary and Joseph . . . 1·25 1·00
620 45p. Nativity scene . . . . . 2·50 3·75

171 Disc Jockey, Radio St. Helena (25th anniv)

172 Moses in the Bulrush

1992. Local Anniversaries. Multicoloured.
621 13p. Type **171** 75 70
622 20p. Scout parade (75th anniv of Scouting on St. Helena) . . . . 1·25 1·10
623 38p. H.M.S. "Providence" (sloop) and breadfruit (bicent of Capt. Bligh's visit) . . . . 2·25 3·00
624 45p. Governor Brooke and Plantation House (bicent) 2·25 3·00

1993. Flowers (1st series). Multicoloured.
625 9p. Type **172** 85 75
626 13p. Periwinkle . . . . . . 1·10 90
627 20p. Everlasting flower . . . 1·40 1·25
628 38p. Cigar plant . . . . . . 2·50 3·25
629 45p. "Lobelia erinus" . . . . 2·50 3·25
See also Nos. 676/80.

173 Adult St. Helena Sand Plover and Eggs

1993. Endangered Species. St. Helena Sand Plover ("Wirebird"). Multicoloured.
630 3p. Type **173** 60 60
631 5p. Male attending brooding female 60 60
632 12p. Adult with downy young 1·25 1·25

633 25p. Two birds in immature plumage . . . . 1·40 1·40
634 40p. Adult in flight . . . . . 1·50 1·75
635 60p. Young bird on rocks . . 1·75 2·50
Nos. 634/5 are without the W.W.F. emblem.

174 Yellow Canary ("Swainson's Canary")
176 Arum Lily

175 Football and Teddy Bear

1993. Birds. Multicoloured.
636 1p. Type **174** 30 80
637 3p. Rock partridge 40 80
638 11p. Feral rock pigeon . . . 55 70
639 12p. Common waxbill . . . 55 70
640 15p. Common mynah 60 75
641 18p. Java sparrow 65 75
642 25p. Red-billed tropic bird (horiz) 80 90
643 35p. Madeiran storm petrel (horiz) . . . . 1·10 1·25
644 75p. Madagascar red fody . . 2·00 3·00
645 £1 White tern ("Common fairy tern") (horiz) . . . 2·25 3·25
646 £2 Giant petrel (horiz) . . . 4·25 6·50
647 £5 St. Helena sand plover ("Wirebird") . . . . . . 10·00 12·00

1993. Christmas. Toys. Multicoloured.
648 12p. Type **175** 75 70
649 15p. Yacht and doll 80 75
650 18p. Palette and rocking horse 85 80
651 25p. Model airplane and kite 1·25 1·50
652 60p. Guitar and roller skates 2·25 3·50

1994. Flowers and Children's Art. Multicoloured.
653 12p. Type **176** 40 65
654 12p. "Arum Lily" (Delphia Mittens) 40 65
655 25p. Ebony . . . . 75 1·00
656 25p. "Ebony" (Jason Rogers) 75 1·00
657 35p. Shell ginger . . . . . 95 1·10
658 35p. "Shell Ginger" (Jeremy Moyce) . . . . 95 1·10

177 Abyssinian Guinea Pig

1994. "Hong Kong '94" International Stamp Exhibition. Pets. Multicoloured.
659 12p. Type **177** 70 70
660 25p. Common tabby cat . . 1·40 1·40
661 53p. Plain white and black rabbits . . . . 2·25 3·00
662 60p. Golden labrador . . . . 2·50 3·25

178 Springer's Blenny

1994. Fishes. Multicoloured.
663 12p. Type **178** 75 75
664 25p. St. Helena damselfish . . 1·50 1·50
665 53p. Melliss's scorpionfish . . 2·25 3·00
666 60p. St. Helena wrasse . . . 2·75 3·25

179 "Lampides boeticus"

1994. Butterflies. Multicoloured.
667 12p. Type **179** 75 75
668 25p. "Cynthia cardui" . . . 1·50 1·50
669 53p. "Hypolimnas bolina" . . 2·25 2·75
670 60p. "Danaus chrysippus" . . 2·75 3·25

180 "Silent Night!"

1994. Christmas. Carols. Multicoloured.
671 12p. Type **180** 55 45
672 15p. "While Shepherds watched their Flocks by Night" 60 50
673 25p. "Away in a Manger" . . 1·00 90
674 38p. "We Three Kings" . . . 1·50 2·00
675 60p. "Angels from the Realms of Glory" . . . . 2·25 3·50

1994. Flowers (2nd series). As T **172**. Multicoloured.
676 12p. Honeysuckle 35 35
677 15p. Gobblegheer 40 40
678 25p. African lily 70 80
679 38p. Prince of Wales feathers 1·00 1·60
680 60p. St. Johns lily . . . . . 1·75 3·00

181 Fire Engine

1995. Emergency Services. Multicoloured.
681 12p. Type **181** . . . . 1·25 75
682 25p. Lifeboat . . . . 1·40 90
683 53p. Police car . . . . . . 2·75 3·00
684 60p. Ambulance . . . . . . 3·00 3·50

182 Site Clearance

1995. Construction of Harpers Valley Earth Dam. Multicoloured.
685 25p. Type **182** . . . . . . 80 1·00
686 25p. Earthworks in progress 80 1·00
687 25p. Laying outlet pipes . . . 80 1·00
688 25p. Revetment block protection . . . . 80 1·00
689 25p. Completed dam . . . . 80 1·00
Nos. 685/9 were printed together, se-tenant, forming a composite design.

182a "Lady Denison Pender" (cable ship)

1995. 50th Anniv of End of Second World War. As T **161** of Ascension. Multicoloured.
690 5p. Type **182a** 70 80
691 5p. H.M.S. "Dragon" (cruiser) 70 80
692 12p. R.F.A. "Darkdale" (tanker) . . . . 1·00 1·25
693 12p. H.M.S. "Hermes" (aircraft carrier, launched 1919) . . . . 1·00 1·25
694 25p. Men of St. Helena Rifles 1·50 1·75
695 25p. Governor Major W. J. Bain Gray taking salute . . 1·50 1·75
696 53p. 6-inch coastal gun, Ladder Hill . . . . 2·00 2·25
697 53p. Flags signalling "VICTORY" . . . . 2·00 2·25
MS698 75 × 85 mm. £1 Reverse of 1939–45 War Medal (vert) . . 2·50 2·75
The two designs for each value were printed together, se-tenant, forming composite designs.

183 Blushing Snail

1995. Endemic Invertebrates. Multicoloured.
699 12p. Type **183** 80 80
700 25p. Golden sail spider . . . 1·50 1·50
701 53p. Spiky yellow woodlouse 2·25 3·00
702 60p. St. Helena shore crab . . 2·50 3·25
MS703 85 × 83 mm. £1 Giant earwig 4·50 6·00

184 Epidendrum ibaguense

1995. "Singapore '95" International Stamp Exhibition. Orchids. Sheet, 122 × 74 mm, containing T **184** and similar vert design. Multicoloured.
MS704 50p. Type **184**; 50p. "Vanda Miss Joaquim" . . . . 5·00 6·00

185 "Santa Claus outside Market" (Jason Alex Rogers)

1995. Christmas. Children's Paintings. Multicoloured.
705 12p. Type **185** 35 35
706 15p. "Santa Claus and band" (Che David Yon) 45 45
707 25p. "Santa Claus outside Community Centre" (Leon Williams) 70 75
708 38p. "Santa Claus in decorated street" (Stacey McDaniel) . . . . 1·00 1·25
709 60p. "Make a better World" (Kissha Karla Kacy Thomas) . . . . 1·75 3·25

186 "Walmer Castle", 1915

1996. Union Castle Mail Ships (1st series). Multicoloured.
710 12p. Type **186** 45 35
711 25p. "Llangibby Castle", 1934 . . . . 75 65
712 53p. "Stirling Castle", 1940 1·40 2·00
713 60p. "Pendennis Castle", 1965 . . . . 1·60 2·25
See also Nos. 757/60.

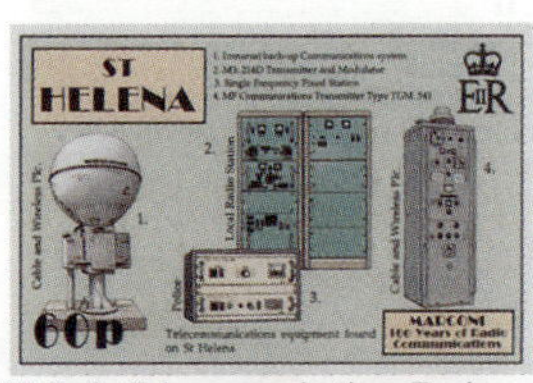

187 Early Telecommunications Equipment

1996. Centenary of Radio. Multicoloured.
714 60p. Type **187** . . . . 1·50 2·00
715 £1 Guglielmo Marconi and "Elettra" (yacht) . . . . . 2·25 3·25

1996. 70th Birthday of Queen Elizabeth II. As T **55** of Tokelau, each incorporating a different photograph of the Queen. Multicoloured.
716 15p. Jamestown 40 40
717 25p. Prince Andrew School . . 65 65
718 53p. Castle entrance . . . . 1·25 2·00
719 60p. Plantation House . . . 1·50 2·25
MS720 64 × 86 mm. £1.50 Queen Elizabeth II . . . . 3·25 4·50

188 Helicopter Mail to H.M.S. "Protector" (ice patrol ship), 1964

1996. "CAPEX '96" International Stamp Exhibition, Toronto. Mail Transport. Mult.
721 12p. Type **188** 50 45
722 25p. Postman on motor scooter, 1965 . . . . . . 75 65
723 53p. Loading mail plane, Wideawake Airfield, Ascension Island . . . . . 1·40 2·00
724 60p. "St. Helena II" (mail ship) unloading at St. Helena . . . . 1·50 2·25
MS725 98 × 73 mm. £1 L.M.S. No. 5624 "St. Helena" locomotive (43 × 27 mm) . . . . 2·75 3·75

189 "Mr. Porteous's House"

1996. Napoleonic Sites. Multicoloured.
726 12p. Type **189** 35 35
727 25p. "The Briars' Pavilion" . 65 65
728 53p. "Longwood House" . . 1·40 2·00
729 60p. "Napoleon's Tomb" . . 1·50 2·25

190 Frangipani and Sandy Bay from Diana's Peak
191 Black Cabbage Tree

1996. Christmas. Flowers and Views. Multicoloured.
730 12p. Type **190** 40 40
731 15p. Bougainvillaea and Upper Jamestown from Sampsons's Battery 50 50
732 25p. Jacaranda and Jacob's Ladder 75 75
733 £1 Pink periwinkle and Lot's Wife Ponds . . . . . . 2·75 4·50

1997. Endemic Plants from Diana's Peak National Park. Multicoloured.
734 25p. Type **191** . . . . . . 1·00 1·25
735 25p. Whitewood . . . . . . 1·00 1·25
736 25p. Tree fern . . . . 1·00 1·25
737 25p. Dwarf jellico . . . . . 1·00 1·25
738 25p. Lobelia . . . . 1·00 1·25
739 25p. Dogwood . . . . 1·00 1·25
Nos. 734/9 were printed together, se-tenant, with the backgrounds forming a composite design.

1997. "HONG KONG '97" International Stamp Exhibition. Sheet 130 × 90 mm, containing design as No. 644.
MS740 75p. Madagascar red fody 1·75 2·25

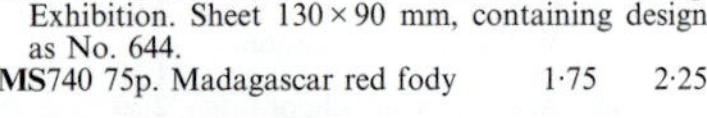

192 Joao da Nova's Lookout sighting St. Helena, 1502
192a Royal Family's Visit, 1947

1997. 500th Anniv of the Discovery of St. Helena (1st issue). Multicoloured.
741 20p. Type **192** 80 65
742 25p. Don Fernando Lopez (first inhabitant) and cockerel, 1515 . . . . . . 90 75
743 30p. Thomas Cavendish and "Desire", 1588 . . . . . 1·00 1·00
744 80p. "Royal Merchant" (English galleon), 1591 . . 2·50 3·50
See also Nos. 762/5, 786/9, 810/13, 828/31 and 857/60.

1997. Return of Hong Kong to China. Sheet 130 × 90 mm, containing design as No. 647, but changed face value and imprint date. W w **14** (sideways). P $14\frac{1}{2} \times 14$.
MS745 75p. St. Helena Sand Plover ("Wirebird") . . . . 1·75 2·25

1997. Golden Wedding of Queen Elizabeth and Prince Philip. Multicoloured.
746 10p. Type **192a** 60 75
747 10p. Wedding photograph of Princess Elizabeth and Prince Philip 60 75
748 15p. Princess Elizabeth and Prince Philip, 1947 . . . . 75 90
749 15p. Presenting bouquets, Royal Visit, 1947 . . . . . 75 90

260 New Parliament House from North

1999. Opening of New Parliament House. Mult.
1010 (22c.) Type **260** 30 20
1011 60c. North-east view 60 60
1012 $1 South-east view 90 1·00
1013 $2 West view 1·60 2·25

No. 1010 is inscribed "For Local Addresses Only".

The lion's head emblem on these stamps is printed in optically variable ink which changes colour when viewed from different angles.

261 Sir Stamford Raffles and Sir Frank Swettenham (British Governers) and Raffles Museum

1999. New Millennium (1st issue). 20th Century Singapore. Multicoloured.
1014 (22c.) Type **261** 30 35
1015 (22c.) Past and present schooling 30 35
1016 35c. Street scene, 1900, and Samsui woman 45 55
1017 35c. Parliament (Government) 45 55
1018 60c. British surrender, 1942, and Lord Mountbatten celebrating Japanese surrender, 1945 60 70
1019 60c. Soldiers firing missile and fighter aircraft 60 70
1020 70c. Singapore River, 1902, and modern forms of transportation 70 80
1021 70c. Festival scenes 70 80
1022 $1 Housing, past and present 95 1·10
1023 $1 Skyscrapers 95 1·10

Nos. 1014/15 are inscribed "for Local addresses only".

See also Nos. 1027/30.

262 Dragon

263 Information Technology Equipment

2000. Chinese New Year ("Year of the Dragon"). Multicoloured.
1024 (22c.) Type **262** 25 20
1025 $2 Dragon curled around spheres 1·75 2·25
MS1026 105 × 65 mm. $10 As No. 1025 8·00 9·50

No. 1024 is inscribed "FOR LOCAL ADDRESSES ONLY".

No. MS1026 was only sold in a decorative hongbao (envelope).

2000. New Millennium (2nd issue). Singapore in 2000. Multicoloured.
1027 (22c.) Type **263** 25 20
1028 60c. Symbols of Arts and Culture 60 60
1029 $1 Heritage artifacts 95 1·10
1030 $2 Modern global communications 1·60 2·25
MS1031 140 × 75 mm. 22c. As Type **263** and Nos. 1028/30 2·75 3·75

No. 1027 is inscribed "For local addresses only".

264 Post Office from across Singapore River, 1854

2000. Opening of Singapore Post Centre. Postal Landmarks. Multicoloured.
1032 (22c.) Type **264** 25 20
1033 60c. General Post Office, c. 1873 60 60
1034 $1 G.P.O. Fullerton Building, 1928 95 1·00
1035 $2 Singapore Post Centre, 2000 1·90 2·25
MS1036 110 × 94 mm. 22c. As Type **264** and Nos. 1033/5 2·75 3·50

No. 1032 is inscribed "FOR LOCAL ADDRESSES ONLY".

2000. "Bangkok 2000" International Stamp Exhibition. Sheet 123 × 75 mm. Multicoloured.
MS1037 22c. As Type **262**; $2 No. 1025 1·75 2·25

265 "yipee"

267 "Future Lifestyle" (Liu Jiang Wen)

266 Singapore River, 1920s

2000. Self-adhesive Greetings Stamps. Multicoloured.
1038 (22c.) Type **265** 35 50
1039 (22c.) "yeah" 35 50
1040 (22c.) "hurray" 35 50
1041 (22c.) "yes" 35 50
1042 (22c.) "happy" 35 50

Nos. 1038/42 are inscribed "For Local Addresses Only".

2000. "The Stamp Show 2000" International Stamp Exhibition, London. Sheet, 123 × 75 mm, containing Nos. 1024/5. Multicoloured.
MS1043 22c. As Type **262**; $2 No. 1025 1·90 2·40

2000. "naba 2000" National Stamp Exhibition, St. Gallen, Switzerland. Sheet, 123 × 75 mm, containing Nos. 1024/5. Multicoloured.
MS1044 22c. As Type **262**; $2 No. 1025 1·90 2·40

2000. "A Century on Singapore River". Showing scenes and common map section. Multicoloured.
1045 (22c.) Type **266** 35 40
1046 (22c.) South Boat Quay, 1930s 35 40
1047 (22c.) Social gathering, 1950s 35 40
1048 (22c.) Skyscrapers, 1980s 35 40
1049 (22c.) River Regatta, 1900s 35 40
1050 60c. Sampans at river mouth, 1990s 50 60
1051 60c. Stevedores, 1910s 50 60
1052 60c. Lighters, 1940s 50 60
1053 60c. Men at work on junk, 1960s 50 60
1054 60c. Unloading with crane, 1970s 50 60

Nos. 1045/9 are inscribed "For local addresses only".

Nos. 1045/54 were printed together, se-tenant, with the backgrounds forming a composite design.

2000. "Stampin' the Future" (children's stamp design competition). Multicoloured.
1055 (22c.) Type **267** 25 20
1056 60c. "Future Homes" (Shaun Yew Chuan Bin) 60 60
1057 $1 "Home Automation" (Gwendolyn Soh) 90 1·00
1058 $2 "Floating City" (Dawn Koh) 1·60 2·25
MS1059 125 × 80 mm. Nos. 1055/8 3·00 3·50

No. 1055 is inscribed "FOR LOCAL ADDRESSES ONLY".

268 Archer Fish

2000. Wetland Wildlife. Multicoloured.
1060 (22c.) Type **268** 35 30
1061 (22c.) Smooth otter and cubs 35 30
1062 $1 White-collared kingfisher ("Collared Kingfisher") 1·10 1·25
1063 $1 Orange fiddler crab 1·10 1·25
MS1064 294 × 210 mm. Nos. 1060/3, both perf and imperf in se-tenant blocks of 4 4·25 5·00

Nos. 1060/1 are inscribed "For Local Addresses Only".

Nos. 1060/3 were printed together, se-tenant, with the backgrounds forming composite designs.

269 High Jump and Swimming

2000. Olympic Games, Sydney. Designs showing a sport within the outline of another. Multicoloured.
1065 (22c.) Type **269** 25 20
1066 60c. Discus and badminton 60 60
1067 $1 Hurdles and football 90 1·00
1068 $2 Gymnastics and table tennis 1·75 2·25

No. 1065 is inscribed "For local addresses only".

270 Chinese New Year

2000. Festivals. Multicoloured. (a) Normal gum.
1069 (22c.) Type **270** 30 35
1070 (22c.) Hari Raya Aidilfitri 30 35
1071 (22c.) Deepavali 30 35
1072 (22c.) Christmas 30 35
1073 30c. Chinese New Year (different) (diamond, 36 × 23 mm) 40 45
1074 30c. Hari Raya Aidilfitri (different) (diamond, 36 × 23 mm) 40 45
1075 30c. Deepavali (different) (diamond, 36 × 23 mm) 40 45
1076 30c. Christmas (different) (diamond, 36 × 23 mm) 40 45

(b) Self-adhesive.
1077 (22c.) Type **270** 60 65
1078 (22c.) As No. 1070 60 65
1079 (22c.) As No. 1071 60 65
1080 (22c.) As No. 1072 60 65

Nos. 1069/72 and 1077/80 are inscribed "FOR LOCAL ADDRESSES ONLY".

2000. "Guangzhou 2000" International Stamp and Coin Exhibition, China. Sheet 123 × 75 mm. Multicoloured.
MS1081 (22c.) As Type **262**; $2 No. 1025 2·00 2·50

271 Snake

2001. Chinese New Year ("Year of the Snake"). Mult.
1082 (22c.) Type **271** 15 20
1083 $2 Two snakes 1·40 1·50

No. 1082 is inscribed "FOR LOCAL ADDRESSES ONLY".

2001. "Hong Kong 2001" Stamp Exhibition. Sheet 123 × 75 mm. Multicoloured.
MS1084 22c. As Type **271**; $2 No. 1083 1·60 1·75

272 Tan Tock Seng

273 People holding Hands ("Co-operation")

2001. Famous Citizens of Singapore. Multicoloured.
1085 $1 Type **272** 1·00 1·10
1086 $1 Eunos bin Abdullah 1·00 1·10
1087 $1 P. Govindasamy Pillai 1·00 1·10
1088 $1 Edwin John Tessensohn 1·00 1·10

2001. 25th Anniv of Commonwealth Day. Mult.
1089 (22c.) Type **273** 25 20
1090 60c. People using computers ("Education") 60 60
1091 $1 Sporting activities ("Sports") 90 1·00
1092 $2 Dancers and musicians ("Arts and Culture") 1·75 2·25

No. 1089 is inscribed "FOR LOCAL ADDRESSES ONLY".

274 Balloons

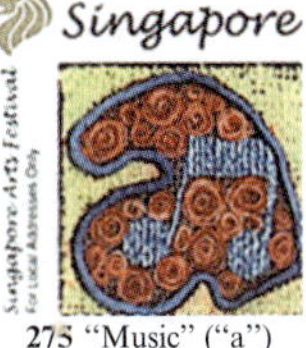

275 "Music" ("a")

2001. Self-adhesive Greetings Stamps. "Occasions". Multicoloured.
1093 (22c.) Type **274** 30 40
1094 (22c.) Stars 30 40
1095 (22c.) Tulips 30 40
1096 (22c.) Parcels 30 40
1097 (22c.) Musical instruments 30 40

Nos. 1093/7 are inscribed "FOR LOCAL ADDRESSES ONLY".

2001. Arts Festival. Multicoloured.
1098 (22c.) Type **275** 15 20
1099 60c. "Painting" ("r") 40 45
1100 $1 "Dance" ("t") 70 75
1101 $2 "Theatre" ("s") 1·40 1·50

No. 1098 is inscribed "For Local Addresses Only".

2001. "BELGICA 2001" International Stamp Exhibition, Brussels. Sheet 123 × 75 mm. Multicoloured.
MS1102 (22c) Type **271**; $2 No. 1083 2·00 2·50

276 Cockatiels

277

2001. "Singpex '01" National Stamp Exhibition. Pets. (a) Multicoloured.
1103 (22c.) Type **276** 15 20
1104 (22c.) Fish in tank 15 20
1105 (22c.) Tortoise 15 20
1106 (22c.) Ducklings 15 20
1107 (22c.) Cat looking at mouse (24 × 34 mm) 15 20
1108 (22c.) Dog looking at fish in bowl (24 × 34 mm) 15 20
1109 50c. West Highland white terrier and bird (24 × 41 mm) 35 40
1110 50c. Two cats (24 × 41 mm) 35 40
1111 $1 Green-winged macaw and Senegal parrot (24 × 41 mm) 70 75
1112 $1 Cat in basket and rabbit (24 × 41 mm) 70 75

(b) T **277** and similar multicoloured frame. Self-adhesive.
1113 (22c.) Type **277** (24 × 24 mm) 30 30
1114 (22c.) As Type **277**, but 24 × 34 mm 30 30

Nos. 1103/8 and 1113/14 are inscribed "For local addresses only".

Nos. 1103/12 were printed together, se-tenant, forming a composite picture of household pets.

2001. "Philanippon '01" International Stamp Exhibition, Tokyo. Sheet 123 × 75 mm. Multicoloured.
MS1115 (22c.) Type **271**; $2 No. 1083 2·00 2·50

278 Young Ah Meng

280 Moorish Idol

279 *Melastoma malabathricum*

2001. Orang Utan Conservation. Designs showing Ah Meng. Multicoloured. (a) Ordinary gum.
1116 (22c.) Type **278** 15 20
1117 60c. Ah Meng with mate 40 45
1118 $1 Ah Meng with offspring 70 75
1119 $1 Three generations of Ah Meng's family 70 75
MS1120 190 × 180 mm. Nos. 1116/19 (sold for $3.90) 2·75 3·00

(b) Self-adhesive.
1121 (22c.) Type **278** 30 30

Nos. 1116 and 1121 are inscribed "For Local Addresses Only".

No. **MS**1120 is in the shape of a seated orang utan.

2001. Singapore–Switzerland Joint Issue. Flowers. Multicoloured.
1122 (22c.) Type **279** 25 20
1123 60c. *Leontopodium alpinum* 60 60
1124 $1 *Saraca cauliflora* 90 1·00
1125 $2 *Gentiana clusii* 1·75 2·25
MS1126 98 × 68 mm. Nos. 1122/5 2·75 3·00

No. 1122 is inscribed "FOR LOCAL ADDRESSES ONLY".

2001. Tropical Marine Fish. Multicoloured. Size 26 × 19mm. (a) Ordinary gum.
1127 5c. Type **280** 10 10
1128 20c. Thread-finned butterflyfish 15 20
1129 (22c.) Copper-banded butterflyfish 15 20
1130 30c. Pearl-scaled butterflyfish 20 25

1131 40c. Melon butterflyfish ("Rainbow Butterflyfish") 30 35
1132 50c. Yellow-faced angelfish 35 40
1133 60c. Emperor angelfish . . . 40 45
1134 70c. Sail-finned tang 50 55
1135 80c. Palette surgeonfish ("Palette Tang") 55 60
MS1136 149 × 90 mm. Nos. 1127/35 2·75 3·25

(b) Size 29 × 24½ mm.

1137 $1 Blue turquoise 70 75
1138 $2 Brown discus . . . . . 1·40 1·50
1139 $5 Red alenguer . . . . . 3·50 3·75
1140 $10 Red turquoise . . . . . 7·00 7·25
MS1141 128 × 75 mm. Nos. 1137/40

(c) Self-adhesive.

1142 (22c.) As No. 1129 . . . . 15 20

Nos. 1129 and 1137 are inscribed "FOR LOCAL ADDRESSES ONLY".

Two types of 50c.:

I. Inscribed "xanthometopon" in error.

II. Correctly inscribed "xanthometapon".

281 Horse

2002. Chinese New Year ("Year of the Horse"). Multicoloured.

1143 (22c.) Type **281** 15 20
1144 (22c.) As Type 290 but horse embossed in silver 15 20
1145 $2 Two horses rearing . . . 1·40 1·50
1146 $2 As No. 1145, but horses embossed in gold . . . . . 1·40 1·50

Nos. 1143/4 are inscribed "FOR LOCAL ADDRESSES ONLY" and were sold for 22c. each.

282 Long-tailed Porcupine

2002. Natural History Drawings from The William Farquhar Collection (1st series). Animals, Reptiles, Fruits and Plants. Multicoloured. Ordinary or self-adhesive gum.

1147 (22c.) Type **282** 15 20
1148 (22c.) Tapir 15 20
1149 (22c.) "Landak Kelubu" . . 15 20
1150 (22c.) Slow loris 15 20
1151 (22c.) "Biawak Tanah" (lizard) 15 20
1152 (22c.) Flying fox 15 20
1153 (22c.) Small-clawed otter . . 15 20
1154 (22c.) "Biawak Pasir" (lizard) 15 20
1155 (22c.) "Tupai Kerawak" (mouse) (vert) 15 20
1156 (22c.) Mouse deer (vert) . . 15 20
1157 (22c.) "Buah rumenia" . . 15 20
1158 (22c.) "Manggis Hutan" . . 15 20
1159 (22c.) "Cempedak" . . . 15 20
1160 (22c.) "Bunga Dedap" . . . 15 20
1161 (22c.) "Jeringau" (vert) . . 15 20
1162 (22c.) "Rotang" (vert) . . 15 20
1163 (22c.) "Tuba" (vert) 15 20
1164 (22c.) "Tebu Gagak" (vert) 15 20
1165 (22c.) "Temu Kunci"(vert) 15 20
1166 (22c.) "Rambutan" (vert) . . 15 20

Nos. 1147/56 (animals and reptiles), 1157/66 (fruits and plants), and are inscribed "For Local Addresses Only". Each stamp was sold for 22c.

2002. Natural History Drawings from The William Farquhar Collection (2nd series). Birds and Fish. As T **282**. Multicoloured. Ordinary or self-adhesive gum.

1187 (22c.) "Burung Gaji-gaji" 15 20
1188 (22c.) "Kuau Cermin" . . . 15 20
1189 (22c.) "Ayam Kolam" . . . 15 20
1190 (22c.) "Kelengking" . . . 15 20
1191 (22c.) "Burung Kuang" . . 15 20
1192 (22c.) "Puhung" 15 20
1193 (22c.) "Burung Kunyit" (vert) 15 20
1194 (22c.) "Burung Pacap Sayat Biru" (vert) 15 20
1195 (22c.) "Burung Murai" (vert) 15 20
1196 (22c.) "Burung Berek-Berek" (vert) 15 20
1197 (22c.) "Ikan Tenggiri Papan" 15 20
1198 (22c.) "Ikan Kertang" . . . 15 20
1199 (22c.) "Ikan Kakatua" . . . 15 20
1200 (22c.) "Ikan Bambangan" 15 20
1201 (22c.) "Ikan Parang" . . . 15 20
1202 (22c.) "Ikan Buntal Pisang" 15 20
1203 (22c.) "Ikan Ketang" . . . 15 20
1204 (22c.) "Pari Hitam" . . . 15 20
1205 (22c.) "Telinga Gajah" . . . 15 20
1206 (22c.) "Ikan Babi" 15 20

Nos. 1187/96 (birds), 1197/206 (fish), and are inscribed "For Local Addresses Only". Each stamp was sold for 22c.

283 Lego Town

2002. Toys. Multicoloured.

1227 (22c.) Type **283** 15 20
1228 60c. Cowboy, Indian, soldier and robot 40 45
1229 70c. Dolls 45 50
1230 $1 Racing cars and bike . . 70 75

No. 1227 is inscribed "For local addresses only" and was sold for 22c.

284 Red-throated Sunbird

2002. Singapore – Malaysia Joint Issue. Birds. Multicoloured.

1231 (22c.) Type **284** 15 20
1232 60c. Asian fairy bluebird . . 40 45
1233 $1 Black-naped oriole . . . 70 75
1234 $2 White-bellied woodpecker 1·40 1·50
MS1235 135 × 94 mm Nos. 1231/4 2·60 2·75

2002. "Philakorea 2002" International Stamp Exhibition, Seoul.

MS1236 123 × 75 mm. Nos. 1143 and 1145 . . . . 1·50 1·60

285 Kolam (doorstep decoration), Deepavali

286 Kolam (doorstep decoration), Deepavali

2002. Festivals. Multicoloured. (a) T **285**. Ordinary or self-adhesive gum.

1237 (22c.) Type **285** 15 20
1238 (22c.) Ketupat (rice cake) wrapper, Hari Raya Aidilfitri 15 20
1239 (22c.) Snowflake in bauble, Christmas 15 20
1240 (22c.) Fish paper decoration, Chinese New Year . . . 15 20

(b) T **286**.

1245 50c. Type **286** 35 40
1246 50c. Ketupat (rice cake) wrapper, Hari Raya Aidilfitri 35 40
1246 50c. Snowflake in bauble, Christmas 35 40
1248 50c. Fish paper decoration, Chinese New Year . . . 35 40

Nos. 1237/44 are inscribed "For Local Addresses Only" and each stamp was sold for 22c.

The central designs on Nos. 1237/48 are foil holograms.

287 Flame of the Forest

289 Two Yachts

288 Esplanade, Performing Arts Centre, Marina Bay

2002. Heritage Trees Scheme. Multicoloured.

1249 (22c.) Type **287** 15 20
1250 60c. Rain Tree 40 45
1251 $1 Kapok Tree 70 75
1252 $1 Tembusu 70 75

No. 1249 also comes self-adhesive.

Nos. 1249 and 1253 are inscribed "FOR LOCAL ADDRESSES ONLY" and were sold for 22c.

2002. Esplanade, Theatres on the Bay. Esplanade from different angles. Multicoloured.

1254 (22c.) Type **288** 15 20
1255 60c. With brown background 40 45
1256 $1 Single shell of Esplanade 70 75
1257 $2 Aerial view of both shells 1·40 1·50
MS1258 104 × 80 mm. Nos. 1254/7 2·60 2·75

2002. Singapore-A Global City. (1st series). Leisure and Lifestyle. Multicoloured.

1259 $2 Type **289** . . . . 1·40 1·50
1260 $2 Conductor's hands and baton . . . . 1·40 1·50
MS1261 135 × 95 mm. Nos. 1259/60 2·75 3·00

290 Goat

2003. Chinese New Year ("Year of the Goat"). Multicoloured.

1262 (22c.) Type **290** 15 20
1263 $2 Goat butting tree . . . . 1·40 1·50

No. 1262 is inscribed "FOR LOCAL ADDRESSES ONLY" and was sold for 22c.

291 Empress Place Building as Government Offices

2003. Opening of Asian Civilizations Museum in Empress Place Building. Multicoloured.

1264 (22c.) Type **291** 15 20
1265 60c. Empress Place Building as Registrar's Office . . . 40 45
1266 $1 Empress Place Museum 70 75
1267 $2 Empress Place Building, as Asian Civilizations Museum . . . . 1·40 1·40

No. 1264 is inscribed "For local addresses only" and was sold for 22c.

292 Tarsier

2003. Creatures of the Night. Multicoloured.

1268 (22c.) Type **292** 15 20
1269 40c. Barn owl 30 35
1270 $1 Babirusa 70 75
1271 $2 Clouded leopard . . . . 1·40 1·50
MS1272 136 × 99 mm. Nos. 1268/71 2·50 2·75

No. 1268 is inscribed "FOR LOCAL ADDRESSES ONLY" and was sold for 22c.

293 Community Policewomen and Block of Flats

2003. Singapore Police Force. Multicoloured. No. 1273 is inscribed "For Local Addresses Only" and was sold at 22c.

1273 (22c.) Type **293** 15 20
1274 40c. Traffic policeman with motor-cycle 30 35
1275 £1 Maritime policeman and launch 70 75
1276 £2 Singapore police on U.N. peacekeeping duties . . . 1·40 1·50

POSTAGE DUE STAMPS

The postage due stamps of Malayan Postal Union were in use in Singapore from 1948 until replaced by the following issue.

D 1

D 2

1968.

D1 D 1 1c. green . . . . 60 2·00
D2 2c. red . . . . 1·40 2·50
D3 4c. orange . . . . 1·75 5·50
D4 8c. brown . . . . 1·00 2·00
D5 10c. mauve . . . . 1·00 90
D6 12c. violet . . . . 2·25 2·75
D7 20c. blue . . . . 2·00 3·50
D8 50c. green . . . . 10·00 5·50

1978.

D16a D 2 1c. green . . . . 15 4·00
D17a 4c. orange . . . . . . 20 5·50
D18a 10c. blue . . . . 50 1·75
D19a 20c. blue . . . . 65 2·25
D20a 50c. green . . . . . . 90 2·75

D 3

1989.

D21 D 3 1c. green . . . .
D22 4c. brown . . . .
D23 5c. mauve 20 50
D24 10c. red 20 40
D25 20c. blue 30 60
D26 50c. green . . . . 60 1·00
D27 $1 brown . . . . 3·00 4·00

SIRMOOR Pt. 1

A state of the Punjab, India. Now uses Indian stamps.

12 pies = 1 anna; 16 annas = 1 rupee.

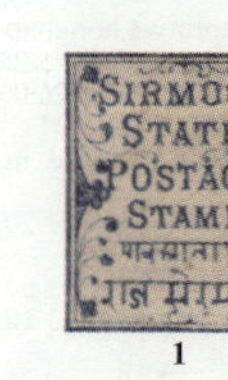

1

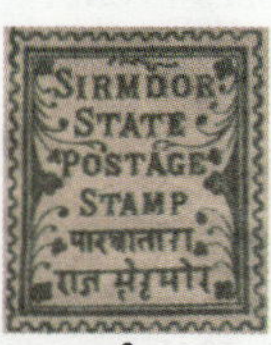

2

1876.

1 1 1pice green . . . . 11·00 £250
2 1pice blue . . . . 4·00 £150

1892.

3b 2 1pice green 70 75
4 1pice blue 80 80

3 Raja Shamsher Parkash

4

1885.

5a 3 3p. brown 30 35
6a 3p. orange 30 20
7c 6p. green 60 35
8d 1a. blue . . . . 50 1·75
9a 2a. red . . . . 3·50 3·00

1895.

22 4 3p. orange . . . 2·00 30
23 6p. green . . . 75 30
24 1a. blue . . . 3·25 1·25
25 2a. red . . . 1·75 1·00
26 3a. green . . . 17·00 30·00
27 4a. green . . . 9·00 16·00
28 8a. blue . . . 13·00 21·00
29 1r. red . . . 27·00 48·00

5 Raja Shamsher Parkash

1899.

30 5 3a. green . . . 2·00 21·00
31 4a. green . . . 2·75 15·00
32 8a. blue . . . 4·50 12·00
33 1r. red . . . 9·00 38·00

OFFICIAL STAMPS

1890. Optd **On S. S. S.**

60 3 3p. orange . . . 60 50
79 6p. green . . . 50 45
80 1a. blue . . . 35 50
63a 2a. red . . . 7·00 7·00

SLESVIG Pt. 11

Stamps issued during the plebiscite of 1920.

100 pfennig = 1 German mark.
100 ore = 1 Danish krone.

1 Arms

3 Rural View

1920.

1 1 2½pf. grey . . . 10 10
2 5pf. green . . . 10 10
3 7½pf. brown . . . 10 10
4 10pf. red . . . 10 10
5 15pf. purple . . . 10 10
6 20pf. blue . . . 10 10
7 25pf. orange . . . 25 60
8 35pf. brown . . . 1·10 1·50
9 40pf. violet . . . 25 95
10 75pf. green . . . 1·25 2·40
11 3 1m. brown . . . 95 3·00
12 2m. blue . . . 2·40 6·00
13 5m. green . . . 4·00 9·25
14 10m. red . . . 10·50 23·00

1920. Values in Danish currency and optd **1. ZONE.**

29 1 1ore grey . . . 20 35
30 5ore green . . . 20 25
31 7ore brown . . . 20 40
32 10ore red . . . 20 40
33 15ore purple . . . 20 40
34 20ore blue . . . 20 70
35 25ore orange . . . 30 3·25
36 35ore brown . . . 90 5·25
37 40ore violet . . . 75 1·40
38 75ore green . . . 50 3·50
39 3 1k. brown . . . 75 5·25
40 2k. blue . . . 1·60 26·00
41 5k. green . . . 2·75 32·00
42 10k. red . . . 8·50 60·00

OFFICIAL STAMPS

1920. Nos. 1/14 optd **C.I.S.** (= "Comission Interalliee Slesvig").

O15 1 2½pf. grey . . . 50·00 55·00
O16 5pf. green . . . 50·00 55·00
O17 7½pf. brown . . . 50·00 55·00
O18 10pf. red . . . 50·00 60·00
O19 15pf. red . . . 50·00 48·00
O20 20pf. blue . . . 50·00 48·00
O21 25pf. orange . . . 70·00 80·00
O22 35pf. brown . . . 70·00 80·00
O23 40pf. violet . . . 75·00 55·00
O24 75pf. green . . . 70·00 £150
O25 3 1m. brown . . . £110 £160
O26 2m. blue . . . £120 £180
O27 5m. green . . . £190 £300
O28 10m. red . . . £350 £450

SLOVAKIA Pt. 5

Formerly part of Hungary, Slovakia joined with Bohemia and Moravia in 1918 to form Czechoslovakia. From 1939 to 1945 they were separate states.

In 1993 the federation of Czechoslovakia was dissolved and Slovakia became an independent republic.

100 haleru = 1 koruna.

A. REPUBLIC OF SLOVAKIA

1939. Stamps of Czechoslovakia optd **Slovensky stat 1939.**

2 34 5h. blue . . . 45 80
3 10h. brown . . . 10 10
4 20h. red . . . 10 10
5 25h. green . . . 75 1·60
6 30h. purple . . . 10 10
7 59 40h. blue . . . 10 25
8 60a 50h. green . . . 10 10
9 66 50h. green . . . 10 10
10 60a 60h. violet . . . 10 10
11 60h. blue . . . 6·00 9·50
12 61 1k. purple . . . 10 10
13 – 1k.20 purple (No. 354) . . 20 30
14 64 1k.50 red . . . 20 30
15 – 1k.60 green (No. 355a) . . 1·40 2·40
16 – 2k. green (No. 356) . . . 1·40 2·40
17 – 2k.50 blue (No. 357) . . 30 45
18 – 3k. brown (No. 358) . . 30 60
19 – 3k.50 violet (No. 359) . . 14·00 23·00
20 65 4k. violet . . . 6·00 13·00
21 – 5k. green (No. 361) . . . 7·50 14·00
22 – 10k. blue (No. 362) . . . 60·00 80·00

4 Father Hlinka

7 Krivan

8 Chamois

9 Mgr. Tiso 10 Weaving

11 Sawyer

12 Presidential Palace, Bratislava

1939. As T **4**, but inscr "CESKO-SLOVENSKO SLOVENSKA POSTA", optd **SLOVENSKY STAT.**

23 4 50h. green . . . 1·00 60
24 1k. red . . . 1·00 60

1939. Perf or imperf (20, 30h.), perf (others).

25 4 5h. blue . . . 25 45
26 10h. green . . . 45 65
27a 20h. red . . . 30 65
28 30h. violet . . . 45 85
29 50h. green . . . 40 65
33 1k. red . . . 45 50
31 2k.50 blue . . . 45 30
35a 3k. sepia . . . 75 75
See also No. 81.

1939.

40 – 5h. green . . . 10 20
41 7 10h. brown . . . 10 15
42 – 20h. grey . . . 10 10
43 8 25h. brown . . . 40 20
44 – 30h. brown . . . 15 20
45 9 50h. green . . . 10 25
46 70h. brown . . . 30 10
47 10 2k. green . . . 2·25 45
48 11 4k. brown . . . 55 65
49 – 5k. red . . . 55 30
50 12 10k. blue . . . 55 60

DESIGNS—As Type **7**: 5h., Zelene Pleso; 20h. Kvety Satier (Edelweiss); 30h. Javorina. As Type **11**: 5k. Woman filling ewer at spring.

For 10 to 50h. values in larger size, see Nos. 125/9.

13 Rev. J. Murgas and Wireless Masts

1939. 10th Death Anniv of Rev. J. Murgas.

53 13 60h. violet . . . 10 20
52 1k.20 grey . . . 40 20

1939. Child Welfare. As No. 45 but larger (24 × 30 mm) and inscr "+2.50 DETOM".

54 2k.50+2k.50 blue . . . 1·90 2·25

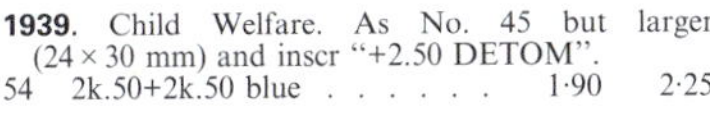

14 Heinkel He 111C over Lake Csorba

15 Heinkel He 116A over Tatra Mountains

16 Eagle and Aero A-204

1939. Air.

55 14 30h. violet . . . 20 30
56 50h. green . . . 20 30
57 1k. red . . . 25 30
58 15 2k. green . . . 40 45
59 3k. brown . . . 75 85
60 4k. blue . . . 1·40 1·75
62 16 5k. purple . . . 85 1·25
63 10k. grey . . . 1·10 1·50
64 20k. green . . . 1·40 1·90

17 Stiavnica Castle

18 S. M. Daxner and Bishop Moyses

1941.

65 17 1k.20 purple . . . 15 10
66 – 1k.50 red (Lietava) . . 15 10
67 – 1k.60 blue (Spissky Hrad) 20 10
68 – 2k. green (Bojnice) . . . 15 10

1941. 80th Anniv of Presentation of Slovak Memorandum to Emperor Francis Joseph.

69 18 50h. green . . . 70 1·10
70 1k. blue . . . 3·00 4·25
71 2k. black . . . 3·00 4·25

19 Wounded Soldier and Red Cross Orderly

1941. Red Cross Fund.

72 19 50h.+50h. green . . . 25 30
73 1k.+1k. purple . . . 30 40
74 2k.+1k. blue . . . 85 1·00

20 Mother and Child

21 Soldier with Hlinka Youth Member

1941. Child Welfare Fund.

75 20 50h.+50h. green . . . 45 60
76 1k.+1k. brown . . . 45 60
77 2k.+1k. violet . . . 45 60

1942. Hlinka Youth Fund.

78 21 70h.+1k. brown . . . 20 20
79 1k.30+1k. blue . . . 25 30
80 2k.+1k. red . . . 60 65

1942. Father Hlinka. As T **4** but inscr "SLOVENSKO" (without "POSTA").

81 1k.30 violet . . . 25 15

22 Boy Stamp Collector

23 Dove and St. Stephen's

1942. Philatelic Exhibition, Bratislava.

82 – 30h. green . . . 55 85
83 22 70h. red . . . 55 85

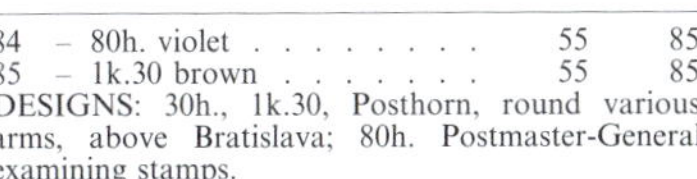

84 – 80h. violet . . . 55 85
85 – 1k.30 brown . . . 55 85

DESIGNS: 30h., 1k.30, Posthorn, round various arms, above Bratislava; 80h. Postmaster-General examining stamps.

1942. European Postal Congress.

86 23 70h. green . . . 60 60
87 1k.30 green . . . 60 90
88 2k. blue . . . 1·25 1·75

24 Inaugural Ceremony

25 L. Stur

1942. 15th Anniv of Foundation of National Literacy Society.

89 24 70h. black . . . 10 10
90 1k. red . . . 10 10
91 1k.30 blue . . . 10 10
92 2k. brown . . . 10 10
93 3k. green . . . 30 30
94 4k. violet . . . 30 30

1943.

95 25 80h. green . . . 10 10
96 – 1k. red . . . 10 15
97 – 1k.30 blue . . . 10 10

PORTRAITS: 1k. M. Razus; 1k.30, Father Hlinka.

27 National Costumes

30 Railway Tunnel

29 Infantry

1943. Winter Relief Fund.

98 27 50h.+50h. green . . . 10 25
99 – 70h.+1k. red . . . 10 25
100 – 80h.+2k. blue . . . 10 30

DESIGNS: 70h. Mother and child; 80h. Mother and two children.

1943. Fighting Forces.

106 29 70h.+2k. red . . . 30 60
107 – 1k.30+2k. blue . . . 45 85
108 – 2k.+2k. green . . . 35 70

DESIGNS—HORIZ: 2k. Artillery. VERT: 1k.30, Air Force.

1943. Opening of the Strazke–Presov Railway.

109 – 70h. purple . . . 35 45
110 – 80h. blue . . . 45 45
111 30 1k.30 black . . . 45 55
112 – 2k. brown . . . 60 75

DESIGNS—HORIZ: 70h. Route map and Presov Church; 2k. Railway viaduct. VERT: 80h. Steam locomotive.

32 "The Slovak Language is our Life"

33 National Museum

1943. Culture Fund.

113 32 30h.+1k. brown . . . 25 30
114 33 70h.+1k. green . . . 30 35
115 – 80h.+2k. blue . . . 25 30
116 – 1k.30+2k. brown . . . 25 30

DESIGNS—HORIZ: 80h. Matica Slovenska College. VERT: 1k.30, Agricultural student.

34 Prince Pribina Okolo

35 Footballer

1944. 5th Anniv of Declaration of Independence.

117 34 50h. green . . . 10 10
118 – 70h. mauve . . . 10 10
119 – 80h. brown . . . 10 10
120 – 1k.30 blue . . . 10 10
121 – 2k. blue . . . 10 30

122 – 3k. brown 25 30
123 – 5k. violet 45 45
124 – 10k. black . . . . 1·25 1·50
DESIGNS: 70h. Prince Mojmir; 80h. Prince Ratislav; 1k.30, King Svatopluk; 2k. Prince Kocel; 3k. Prince Mojmir II; 5k. Prince Svatopluk II; 10k. Prince Braslav.

1944. As 1939 issue but larger (18½ × 22½ mm).
125 **7** 10h. red 10 20
126 – 20h. blue 10 20
127 **8** 25h. purple 10 20
128 – 30h. purple 10 20
129 – 50h. green 10 20
DESIGN: 50h. Zelene Pleso (as No. 40).

1944. Sports.
130 **35** 70h.+70h. green 30 50
131 – 1k.+1k. violet 40 55
132 – 1k.30+1k.30 green 40 55
133 – 2k.+2k. brown 40 65
DESIGNS—VERT: 1k. Skiing; 1k.30, Diving. HORIZ: 2k. Running.

36 Symbolic of "Protection"

1944. Protection Series.
134 **36** 70h.+4k. blue 55 85
135 1k.30+4k. brown 55 85
136 2k. green 20 25
137 3k.80 purple 20 25

37 Children Playing
38 Mgr. Tiso

1944. Child Welfare.
138 **37** 2k.+4k. blue . . . . 1·50 1·90

1945.
139 **38** 1k. orange 75 40
140 1k.50 brown 20 15
141 2k. green 25 40
142 4k. red 75 60
143 5k. blue 75 40
144 10k. purple 55 30

B. SLOVAK REPUBLIC

39 State Arms
40 Ruzomberok

1993.
145 **39** 3k. multicoloured 35 30
146 8k. mult (26 × 40 mm) . . 3·75 3·75

1993.
146a – 50h. lilac and blue . . . 10 10
146b – 2k. pink, black and blue 20 10
146c – 3k. black, blue and red 30 10
146d – 4k. black, green and blue 30 10
146e – 4k. green, black and red 30 10
147 **40** 5k. blue and red 35 20
147a – 5k. black, yellow and blue 35 10
147b – 6k. blue, red and yellow 45 25
147c – 7k. black and pink . . . 45 25
147d – 8k. black, blue and red 65 25
147e – 9k. black, yellow and green 65 35
148 – 10k. lilac and orange . . 75 45
148a – 10k. black, blue and red 75 45
148b – 16k. black and blue . . . 1·25 50
149 – 20k. blue and ochre . . . 1·00 50
150 – 30k. black, blue and red 1·75 75
150a – 40k. ochre and black . . 1·10 65
151 – 50k. black, orange & bl 3·75 1·90
152 – 50k. black, blue and red 1·40 80
DESIGNS—VERT: 50h. Bardejov; 2k. Nitra; 4k. (146c) Nova Bana; 4k. (146d) Presov; 5k. Trnava; 6k. Arms of Senica; 7k. St Martin's Church, Martin; 9k. Zilina; 10k. Kosice; 10k. (148a) Kezmarok; 20k. Roznava Watchtower; 50k. (151) Bratislava; 50k. (152) Komarno. HORIZ: 3k. Banska Bystrica; 8k. Trencin; 16k. Levoca; 30k. Suden Castle; 40k. Piestany.

41 Pres. Michal Kovac
42 St. John and Charles Bridge, Prague

1993.
156 **41** 2k. black 10 10
157 3k. brown and mauve . . . 20 10

1993. 600th Death Anniv of St. John of Nepomuk (patron saint of Bohemia).
158 **42** 8k. multicoloured 65 35

43 Pedunculate Oak
44 Jan Levoslav Bella (composer)

1993. Trees. Multicoloured.
159 3k. Type **43** 20 10
160 4k. Hornbeam 30 20
161 10k. Scots pine 80 55

1993. Anniversaries.
162 **44** 5k. cream, brown and blue 35 25
163 – 8k. brown, sepia and red 65 35
164 – 20k. buff, blue and orange 1·50 75
DESIGNS: 5k. Type **44** (150th birth anniv); 8k. Alexander Dubcek (statesman) (1st death anniv); 20k. Jan Kollar (poet and scholar) (birth bicent).

45 "Woman with Jug" (Marian Cunderlik)

1993. Europa. Contemporary Art.
165 **45** 14k. multicoloured . . . . 6·00 4·00

46 Sun
47 Arms of Dubnica nad Vahom

1993. Anniversaries. Multicoloured.
166 2k. Type **46** (150th anniv of Slovakian written language) 20 10
167 8k. Sts. Cyril and Methodius (1130th anniv of arrival in Moravia) 65 35

1993.
168 **47** 1k. silver, black and blue 10 10

48 "The Big Pets" (Lane Smith)

1993. 14th Biennial Exhibition of Book Illustrations for Children, Bratislava.
169 **48** 5k. multicoloured 35 15

49 Canal Lock, Gabcikovo

1993. Rhine–Main–Danube Canal.
170 **49** 10k. multicoloured 90 35

50 Child's Face in Blood-drop
51 "Madonna and Child" (Jozef Klemens)

1993. Red Cross.
171 **50** 3k.+1k. red and blue . . . 30 30

1993. Christmas.
172 **51** 2k. multicoloured 10 10

53 "The Labourer's Spring" (Jozef Kostka)

1993. Art (1st series).
174 **53** 9k. multicoloured . . . . 3·00 1·90
See also Nos. 198/9, 227/8, 246/8, 271/3, 297, 300/1, 326/7, 351/2 and 374/6.

54 Ski Jumping
55 Family

1994. Winter Olympic Games, Lillehammer, Norway.
175 **54** 2k. black, mauve and blue 10 10

1994. International Year of the Family.
176 **55** 3k. multicoloured 20 15

56 Antoine de Saint-Exupery (writer and pilot) (50th death)
57 Jozef Murgas (radio-telegraphy pioneer)

1994. Anniversaries.
177 – 8k. red and blue 70 45
178 **56** 9k. multicoloured 70 45
DESIGNS: 8k. Janos Andras Segner (mathematician and physicist) (290th birth).

1994. Europa. Inventions.
179 **57** 28k. multicoloured . . . . 2·25 2·25

58 Cigarettes
59 Football Pitch as Tie

1994. World No Smoking Day.
180 **58** 3k. multicoloured 20 10

1994. World Cup Football Championship, U.S.A.
181 **59** 2k. multicoloured 10 10

60 Ancient Greek Runner passing Baton to Modern Athlete

1994. Centenary of International Olympic Committee.
182 **60** 3k. multicoloured 20 25

61 Golden Eagle
63 Rowing Boat with Stamp for Sail

62 Prince Svatopluk

1994. Birds. Multicoloured.
183 4k. Type **61** 35 50
184 5k. Peregrine falcon 55 30
185 7k. Eagle owl 60 45

1994. 1100th Death Anniv of Prince Svatopluk of Moravia.
186 **62** 12k. brown, buff and black 1·10 1·10

1994. 120th Anniv of Universal Postal Union.
187 **63** 8k. multicoloured 65 30

64 Generals Rudolf Viest and Jan Golian

1994. 50th Anniv of Slovak Uprising.
188 **64** 6k. blue, pink and yellow 35 30
189 – 8k. multicoloured 60 35
DESIGNS: 8k. French volunteers and their Memorial.

66 Medal (O. Spaniel) and Faculty Emblems
68 St. George's Church, Kostolany pod Tribecom

67 Tajar (winner of first race)

1994. 75th Anniv of Comenius University, Bratislava.
191 **66** 12k. gold, black and red 90 50

1994. 180th Anniv of Mojmirovce Horse Race.
192 **67** 2k. blue and yellow 10 10

1994.
193 **68** 20k. multicoloured . . . . 1·50 75

69 "Nativity" (early 19th-century glass painting)

1994. Christmas.
194 **69** 2k. multicoloured 10 10

70 Chattam Sofer, Rabbi of Bratislava

1994. Anniversaries. Multicoloured.
195 5k. Type **70** (165th death) . . 35 25
196 6k. Wolfgang Kempelen (conducted study into human speech) (190th death) 45 25
197 10k. Stefan Banic (inventor of parachute) (125th birth (1995)) 75 40

1994. Art (2nd series). As T **53**. Multicoloured.
198 7k. "Girls" (Janko Alexy) (horiz) 45 60
199 14k. "Bulls" (Vincent Hloznik) . . . . 1·25 1·25

71 Container Ship

1994. Ships. Multicoloured.
200 5k. Type **71** 45 25
201 8k. "Ryn" (freighter) 60 35
202 10k. Passenger liner 65 35

72 Samuel Jurkovic (founder)

73 "Ciminalis clusii"

1995. 150th Anniv of Landlords' Association.
203 **72** 9k. multicoloured 80 35

1995. European Nature Protection Year. Flowers. Multicoloured.
204 2k. Type **73** 20 10
205 3k. "Pulsatilla slavica" . . . 30 10
206 8k. "Onosma tornense" . . . 1·25 45

74 Theatre Masks

1995. 75th Anniv of Slovak National Theatre..
207 **74** 10k. pink, black and blue 75 35

75 Ice Hockey Equipment

1995. World Cup Ice Hockey Championship Group B Qualifying Round, Bratislava.
208 **75** 5k. yellow and blue 45 20

76 Bela Bartok (composer, 50th death)

1995. Anniversaries.
209 **76** 3k. yellow, blue and black 30 10
210 – 6k. multicoloured 45 30
DESIGN: 6k. Jan Bahyl (inventor, 80th death (1996)) and helicopter design.

77 Allegory of Freedom

1995. Europa. Peace and Freedom.
212 **77** 8k. multicoloured . . . . 60 1·10

78 Concentration Camp Victims

1995. 50th Anniv of Liberation of Concentration Camps.
213 **78** 12k. multicoloured 90 50

79 Scout

1995.
214 **79** 5k. multicoloured 35 25

80 Pope John Paul II, Map and Arms

82 Banska Stiavnica

1995. Papal Visit.
215 **80** 3k. red and pink 30 10

1995. U.N.E.S.C.O. World Heritage Sites. Multicoloured.
217 7k. Type **82** 45 25
218 10k. Spis Castle (horiz) . . . 75 30
219 15k. Vlkolinec (horiz) . . . . 1·10 50

83 Player

84 Sad Clown (Lorenzo Mattotti)

1995. Centenary of Volleyball.
220 **83** 9k. blue, black and yellow 75 45

1995. 15th Biennial Exhibition of Book Illustrations for Children, Bratislava. Multicoloured.
221 2k. Type **84** 15 10
222 3k. Thin and fat men with long noses (Dusan Kallay) 20 10

85 Tree, Arch and Association Emblem

1995. St. Adalbert Association.
223 **85** 4k. black, green and pink 35 10

86 Map of Czechoslovakia, Linden Leaves and National Colours

1995. 80th Anniv of Cleveland Agreement.
224 **86** 5k. yellow, blue and red . . 45 10

87 Allegory of Celebration and Peace

1995. 50th Anniv of United Nations Organization.
225 **87** 8k. multicoloured 75 75

88 Christmas Crib (Peter Palka)

1995. Christmas.
226 **88** 2k. multicoloured 15 10

1995. Art (3rd series). As T **53**. Multicoloured.
227 8k. "Hlohovec Nativity" . . 65 60
228 16k. "Two Women" (Mikulas Galanda) . . . . 1·40 1·25

89 Jozef Ciger-Hronsky (writer)

90 Alojz Szokol, Athens, 1896

1996. Anniversaries. Multicoloured.
229 3k. Type **89** (death centenary) 30 10
230 4k. Jozef Ludovit Holuby (botanist, 160th birth anniv) 30 10

1996. Centenary of Modern Olympic Games.
231 **90** 9k. multicoloured 75 35

91 Dousing Woman in Water

93 Izabela Textorisova (botanist)

1996. Easter.
232 **91** 2k. multicoloured 15 10

1996. Europa. Famous Women. Multicoloured.
234 8k. Type **93** 75 60
235 8k. Botanist holding thistle 75 60

96 Cyclist

97 Page and Mountains

1996. Round Slovakia Cycle Race.
238 **96** 3k. black, blue and red . . 20 10

1996. 150th Anniv of "Slovenske Pohl'ady" ("Slovak Perspectives" (review))
239 **97** 18k. black, red and blue 1·50 75

98 European Bison

99 Popradske

1996. Mammals. Multicoloured.
240 4k. Type **98** 35 10
241 4k. Mouflon ("Ovis musimon") 35 10
242 4k. Chamois ("Rupicapra rupicapra") 35 10

1996. Mountain Lakes. Multicoloured.
243 4k. Type **99** 30 10
244 8k. Skalnate 65 30
245 12k. Strbsky . . . . 1·10 45

1996. Art (4th series). As T **53**.
246 7k. multicoloured 60 60
247 10k. deep blue, lilac and blue 80 75
248 14k. multicoloured . . . . . 1·00 1·25
DESIGNS: 7k. "Queen Ntombi Twala" (Andy Warhol); 10k. "Suppressed Laughter" (Franz Messerschmidt); 14k. Baroque chair (Endre Nemes).

100 Horse Tram and Bratislava and Trnava Stations

101 Snow-covered Village, Kysuce

1996. Technological Monuments. Multicoloured.
249 4k. Type **100** 30 30
250 6k. Andrej Kvasz and his airplane 50 30

1996. Christmas.
251 **101** 2k. multicoloured 10 10

102 Unissued Stamp Design and Benka

1996. Stamp Day. 25th Death Anniv of Martin Benka (stamp designer).
252 **102** 3k. buff and blue 20 10

103 Michal Martikan

1996. Slovak Achievements at Olympic Games, Atlanta.
253 **103** 3k. brown and stone . . . 20 10

104 Bishop Stefan Moyses

105 Biathlon

1997. Birth Anniversaries of National Activists. Multicoloured.
254 3k. Type **104** (first chairman of Matican Slovenska, bicentenary) 20 10
255 4k. Svetozar Vajansky (writer, 150th) 30 10

1997. World Biathlon Championship, Osrblie.
256 **105** 6k. multicoloured 45 30

106 Collecting Dew

107 Church

1997. Folk Traditions.
257 **106** 3k. multicoloured 20 10

1997. 700th Anniv of Franciscan Church, Bratislava.
258 **107** 16k. black, orange and blue . . . . 1·10 60

108 Guglielmo Marconi and Radio Waves

1997. Centenary of Wireless Telegraphy.
259 **108** 10k. black, blue and yellow 75 45

109 Miraculous Rain of Hron

110 Domica Cave

1997. Europa. Tales and Legends.
260 **109** 9k. black, orange and blue 65 75

1997. Caves. Multicoloured.
261 6k. Type **110** 45 45
262 8k. Argonite Cave, Ochtinska 60 60

112 "Dance" (Martin Jonas)

1997. Naive Art Triennale.
264 **112** 3k. multicoloured 20 10

113 Woman

114 Cherubs blowing Horns (J. Kiselova-Sitekova)

1997. International Slovak Year.
265 **113** 9k. multicoloured 65 45

1997. 16th Biennial Exhibition of Book Illustrations for Children, Bratislava.
266 **114** 3k. multicoloured 20 10

115 Water Mill, Jelka

116 Flag, Arms and Linden Leaves

1997.
267 **115** 4k. multicoloured 25 10

1997. 5th Anniv of Constitution.
268 **116** 4k. multicoloured 25 10

117 Runners

119 Weeping Woman and Church

1997. 6th World Half-marathon Championship, Kosice.
269 **117** 9k. multicoloured 65 45

1997. Art (5th series). As T **53**.
271 9k. multicoloured 65 45
272 10k. multicoloured 75 60
273 12k. buff, black and red . . . 90 75
DESIGNS—VERT: 9k. "Self-portrait with Wife" (Jan Kupecky); 12k. "For Aim" (Koloman Sokol). HORIZ: 10k. "St. Lucy and St. Peter" (detail of Bojnice altarpiece, Nardo di Cione).

1997. 90th Anniv of Cernova Massacre.
274 **119** 4k. lilac and green 25 10

120 Nativity

121 Nepela

1997. Christmas.
275 **120** 3k. multicoloured 20 10

1997. Ondrej Nepela (figure skater).
276 **121** 5k. black, mauve and green 30 10

122 Risen Christ amongst Disciples

1997. Spiritual Regeneration.
277 **122** 4k. multicoloured 25 10

123 Burin as Posthorn

1997. Stamp Day.
278 **123** 4k. brown and blue . . . 25 10

124 Bratislava and Arms of District Towns

1998. 5th Anniv of Independence.
279 **124** 4k. multicoloured 25 10

125 Martin Razus

127 Banishing of Moraine

126 Ice Hockey

1998. Writers' Anniversaries. Multicoloured.
280 4k. Type **125** (110th birth anniv) 25 10
281 4k. Jozef Skultety and Slovak Cultural Society building (50th death anniv) 25 10
282 4k. Jan Smrek (birth centenary) 25 10

1998. Winter Olympic Games, Nagano, Japan.
283 **126** 19k. yellow, black and blue . . . . 1·25 90

1998. Folk Traditions.
284 **127** 3k. multicoloured 20 10

128 Budatin Castle

1998. Castles. Multicoloured.
285 6k. Type **128** 45 25
286 11k. Krasna Hoka castle . . 75 40

129 "Sending Down of the Holy Spirit" (Vincent Hloznik)

130 Tekov Wedding

1998. Spiritual Renewal.
288 **129** 4k. multicoloured 25 10

1998. Europa. National Festivals.
289 **130** 12k. multicoloured . . . 90 60

131 "Butterfly and Rainbow" (Livia Merenicova)

132 Viktor Kolibrik (revolutionary)

1998. Children's Centre.
290 **131** 3k. multicoloured 20 10

1998. 80th Anniv of Kragujevac Uprising.
291 **132** 3k. multicoloured 20 10

133 Rebels

1998. 150th Anniv of Slovak Insurrection.
292 **133** 4k. black, blue and red 25 10

134 Steam Locomotive

136 Stone and Butterfly

1998. 150th Anniv of Railway in Slovakia.
293 **134** 4k. black, red and blue 25 10
294 – 10k. black, yellow and blue 65 45
295 – 15k. black, yellow and brown . . . . 1·10 60
DESIGNS: 10k. Electric locomotive; 15k. Diesel locomotive.

1998. Art (6th series). As T **53**. Multicoloured.
297 18k. "Pieta" (sculpture in Basilica of Virgin Mary, Sastin) . . . . 1·25 75

1998. Anti-drugs Campaign.
298 **136** 3k. multicoloured 20 10

137 Sunflower

138 Adoration of the Magi

1998. 25th Anniv of Ekotopfilm.
299 **137** 4k. orange, yellow and blue 25 10

1998. Art (7th series). As T **53**. Multicoloured.
300 10k. "Countryside at Terchova" (Martin Benka) 75 60
301 12k. "Fishermen" (Ludovit Fulla) 95 60

1998. Christmas.
302 **138** 3k. multicoloured 20 10

139 Postman on Bicycle

1998. Stamp Day.
303 **139** 4k. multicoloured 25 10

140 Snowboarders

1999. 19th World University and Fourth EYOD Winter Games, Poprad-Tatry.
304 **140** 12k. black, blue and red 90 40

141 Matej Bel (historian, 250th death)

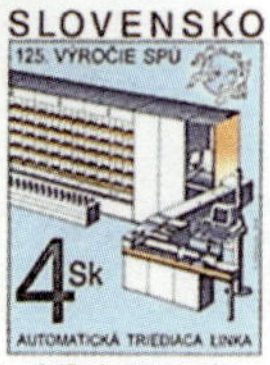

142 Automatic Sorting Machine

1999. Anniversaries.
305 **141** 3k. black, yellow and brown 25 10
306 – 4k. deep lilac, yellow and lilac 25 10
307 – 11k. purple, orange and blue 80 45
DESIGNS: 4k. Cardinal Juraj Haulik (130th death); 11k. Pavol Orszagh (pseudonym) Hviezdoslav (poet, 150th birth).

1999. 125th Anniv of Universal Postal Union.
308 **142** 4k. multicoloured 25 10

143 Cajkov

144 "Transfiguration"

1999. Women's Traditional Bonnets. Multicoloured.
309 4k. Type **143** 20 10
310 15k. Hel'pa . . . . 1·00 70
311 18k. Madunice . . . . . . 1·25 1·00

1999. Spiritual Renewal.
312 **144** 5k. multicoloured 35 10

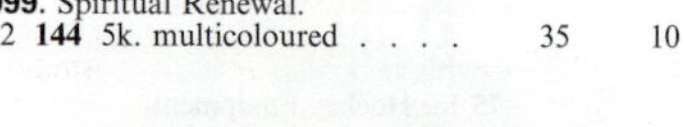

145 High Tatras National Park (right-hand detail)

1999. Europa. Parks and Gardens. Multicoloured.
313 9k. Type **145** . . . . . . 50 1·00
314 11k. High Tatras National Park (left-hand detail) . . 95 1·10
Nos. 313/14 were issued together, se-tenant, forming a composite design.

146 Face within Council Emblem

1999. 50th Anniv of Council of Europe.
315 **146** 16k. ultramarine, blue and yellow . . . . 1·50 1·50

147 Nightingale, Score and Violin Head

148 Hands of Three Generations

1999. 50th Anniv of Slovak Philharmonic Orchestra.
317 **147** 4k. multicoloured 25 10

1999. International Year of the Elderly.
318 **148** 5k. black, flesh and green 30 10

150 Zilina University, Open Book and Keyboard

151 Spotlights on Theatre Stage

1999. 125th Anniv of Universal Postal Union. Multicoloured.
320 12k. Type **150** 55 60
321 16k. Globe and Slovak postal emblem 65 75

1999. 50th Anniv of University of Fine Arts, Bratislava.
322 **151** 4k. black, blue and pink 25 10

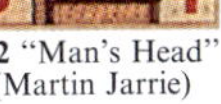
152 "Man's Head" (Martin Jarrie)

155 Children playing in Snow (Stanislav Sekeres)

153 Water Pillar Machine (J. K. Hell)

1999. 17th Biennial Exhibition of Book Illustrations for Children, Bratislava.
323 **152** 5k. multicoloured 30 10

1999. Technical Monuments.
324 **153** 7k. yellow and brown . . 45 10

1999. Art (8th series). As T **53**. Multicoloured.
326 13k. "Malatina" (Milos Alexander Bazovsky) (horiz) . . . . 1·10 1·00
327 14k. "Study of the Resting Blacksmith" (Dominik Skutecky) . . . . 1·10 1·10

1999. Christmas.
328 **155** 4k. multicoloured 25 10

156 Woman's Head

1999. 10th Anniv of Velvet Revolution.
329 **156** 5k. blue, red and black 40 20

157 18th-century Urn showing Visit to Sick Man

1999. Museum of Jewish Culture, Bratislava. Multicoloured.
330 12k. Type **157** . . . . 95 1·10
331 18k. 18th-century urn showing funeral procession 1·40 1·75

158 Albin Brunovsky (stamp designer) and "Czechoslovakia"

1999. Stamp Day.
332 **158** 5k. brown, stone and green 30 10

159 Dunajec Gap

160 Hana Melickova (actress)

2000. Valleys. Multicoloured.
333 10k. Type **159** . . . . 80 1·00
334 12k. Vah Gap . . . . 90 1·00

2000. Birth Anniversaries. Multicoloured.
335 4k. Type **160** (centenary) . . 25 10
336 5k. Stefan Anian Jedlik (scientist, bicentenary) . . 35 10

161 Christ's Head (detail of altar panel), St. Jacob's Church, Levoca

162 Globe as Basketball in Net

2000. Easter.
337 **161** 4k. brown 25 10

2000. Women's European Basketball Championship, Ruzomberok.
338 **162** 4k. multicoloured 25 10

163 Juraj Hronec and Stefan Schwarz (mathematicians)

2000. World Mathematics Year.
339 **163** 5k. multicoloured 30 10

164 Jan Holly (poet and priest)

165 "Building Europe"

2000.
340 **164** 5k.50 black, blue and red 30 10

2000. Europa.
341 **165** 12k. multicoloured . . . 1·00 50

166 "Animals from Rainbow" (Alexandra Baníkova)

167 Postman, Austria 1850 2k. Stamp

2000. United Nations Children's Fund.
342 **166** 5k.50 multicoloured . . . 35 10

2000. First Stamps Used in Slovakia.
343 **167** 10k. multicoloured . . . 75 60

168 Pres. Rudolf Schuster

169 Rifle Shooting

2000.
344 **168** 5k.50 brown 15 10

2000. Olympic Games, Sydney.
345 **169** 18k. multicoloured . . . 50 25

170 Emblem

2000. 25th Anniv of Organization for Security and Co-operation in Europe.
346 **170** 4k. black and blue . . . 10 10

171 Timber Bridge, Klukava

173 Mary and Jesus

2000.
347 **171** 6k. multicoloured 20 10

2000. Holy Year 2000. Christmas.
349 **173** 4k. multicoloured 10 10

174 Emblem

2000. Agreement between the Postal Administration of the Slovak Republic and the Sovereign Order of the Knights of St. John.
350 **174** 10k. multicoloured . . . 25 15

2000. Art (9th series). As T **53**. Multicoloured.
351 18k. Nativity (detail) (altar panel, Spisska-Stara Ves Church) 50 30
352 20k. "Descent from the Cross" (mural, Kocelovce Church) (horiz) 55 30

175 Apple on Newspaper

2000. Stamp Day.
353 **175** 5k.50 multicoloured . . . 15 10

176 Maria Theresa

2000. History of Postal Law.
354 **176** 20k. multicoloured . . . 55 30

177 Rococo Mantle Clock

178 Blaho

2001.
355 **177** 13k. multicoloured . . . 35 20

2001. Birth Centenary of Janko Blaho (opera singer).
356 **178** 5k.50 multicoloured . . . 15 10

179 Ice Skater

180 Male

2001. European Figure Skating Championships, Bratislava.
357 **179** 16k. multicoloured . . . 40 25

2001. Traditional Costumes of Detva. Multicoloured.
358 5k.50 Type **180** 15 10
359 6k. Woman in costume, Detva 15 10

181 Woman with Apple

2001. 50th Anniv of Central Control and Check Agricultural Institute, Bratislava.
360 **181** 12k. multicoloured . . . 30 20

182 1st-century Gate and Celtic Coins, Liptovska Mara, Havranok

2001. Archaeological Sites. Multicoloured.
361 12k. Type **182** 30 20
362 15k. 9th-century courtyard, jewellery and button, Ducove, Kostelec 40 25

183 Studenovodsky Waterfall

2001. Europa. Water Resources.
363 **183** 18k. multicoloured . . . 50 30

186 Guitar and Map of United States

2001. Dobro Resonator Guitar.
366 **186** 19k. multicoloured . . . 50 30

187 Man in Boat (Peter Uchnar) 190 Flowers

188 Face and Hand

2001. 18th Biennial Exhibition of Book Illustrations for Children, Bratislava.
367 **187** 7k. multicoloured 20 10

2001. Memorial Day for Victims of the Holocaust.
368 **188** 14k. multicoloured . . . 40 25

2001. Political Trials.
370 **190** 10k. multicoloured . . . 25 15

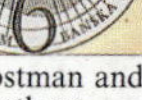

191 Postman and Posthorn 192 Nativity

2001. Opening of Slovak Postal Museum, Banska Bystrica.
371 **191** 6k. multicoloured 15 10

2001. Christmas.
372 **192** 5k.50 multicoloured . . . 15 10

193 Sturovo–Ostrihom Bridge

2001.
373 **193** 10k. multicoloured . . . 25 15

2001. Art (10th series). As T **53**.
374 16k. multicoloured 40 25
375 18k. green and brown 50 30
376 20k. multicoloured 55 30
DESIGNS: 16k. "Raftsman's Dream" (Imrich Weiner-Kral); 18k. "Light of the Soul" (Albin Brunovsky); 20k. "St. Michael the Archangel with the Group of Saints" (icon).

194 Juraj Papanek 196 Dogs pulling Sledge

195 Skiers

2002. Anniversaries. Multicoloured.
377 10k. Type **194** (historian, death bicentenary) 35 20
378 14k. Bjornstjerne Bjornson (writer and poet, 170th birth anniv) 45 30

2002. Winter Olympic Games, Salt Lake City, U.S.A.
379 **195** 18k. multicoloured . . . 60 35

2002. European Sled Dog Race Championship, Donovaly.
380 **196** 6k. multicoloured 20 10

197 Jesus and Flowers (Karol Ondreicka) 198 Martin Gymnasium and Open Book

2002. Easter.
381 **197** 5k.50 multicoloured . . . 20 10

2002. Educational Anniversaries. Multicoloured.
382 12k. Type **198** (140th anniv) 40 25
383 13k. Revuca Gymnasium (140th anniv) 45 30
384 15k. Klastor pod Znievom Gymnasium (133rd anniv) 50 30

199 "Clown with Trumpet" (Emil Bacík)

2002. Europa. Circus.
385 **199** 18k. multicoloured . . . 60 35

200 Beer Barrel and Kegs

2002. Industrial Technology. Multicoloured.
386 7k. Type **200** 25 15
387 9k. Wine press and grapes . . 30 20

201 Southern Festoon (*Zerynthia polyxena*)

2002. Endangered Species. Butterflies. Sheet 109 × 165 mm containing T **201** and similar horiz designs. Multicoloured.
MS388 10k. Type **201**; 16k. Peacock (*Inachis io*); 25k. Swallowtail (*Papilio machaon*) . . . . . . 1·75 1·75

202 Two Doves

2002. Greetings Stamp. "Congratulations".
389 **202** 6k. multicoloured 20 10

203 Player and Trophy

2002. Slovakia–Winners of World Ice Hockey Championship, Sweden.
390 **203** 10k. multicoloured . . . 35 20

204 Rudnay

2002. 171st Death Anniv of Alexander Rudnay (Archbishop of Esztergom). Sheet 81 × 108 mm.
MS391 204 17k. multicoloured 55 55

NEWSPAPER STAMPS

1939. Nos. of Czechoslovakia optd **1939 SLOVENSKY STAT.**
N25 2h. brown 20 30
N26 5h. blue 20 30
N27 7h. red 20 30
N28 9h. green 20 30
N29 10h. red 20 30
N30 12h. blue 20 30
N31 20h. green 40 60
N32 50h. brown . . . . 1·25 1·50
N33 1k. green . . . . 4·50 7·00

N 7 N 29 Printer's Type

1939. Imperf.
N40 **N 7** 2h. brown 10 10
N65 5h. blue 10 25
N42 7h. red 10 25
N43 9h. green 10 25
N66 10h. red 10 10
N45 12h. blue 70 75
N67 15h. purple 15 10
N68 20h. green 30 50
N69 25h. blue 30 50
N70 40h. red 30 50
N71 50h. brown 55 60
N72 1k. green 55 60
N73 2k. green . . . . 1·00 1·10

1943. Imperf.
N101 **N 29** 10h. green 10 10
N102 15h. brown 10 10
N103 20h. blue 10 10
N104 50h. red 10 10
N105 1k. green 25 30
N106 2k. blue 45 50

PERSONAL DELIVERY STAMPS

P 17

1940. Imperf.
P65 **P 17** 50h. blue . . . . 45 1·25
P66 50h. red . . . . 45 1·25

POSTAGE DUE STAMPS

D 13 D 24

1939.
D51 **D 13** 5h. blue 20 40
D52 10h. blue 20 35
D53 20h. blue 20 35
D54 30h. blue . . . . . . 1·00 1·40
D55 40h. blue 35 40
D56 50h. blue 35 60
D57 60h. blue 35 65
D58 1k. red 40 65
D59 2k. red . . . . 5·00 5·00
D60 5k. red . . . . 1·10 1·75
D61 10k. red . . . . . . 1·00 1·75
D62 20k. red . . . . . . 6·00 6·00

1942.
D 89 **D 24** 10h. brown 10 10
D 90 20h. brown 10 10
D 91 40h. brown 10 10
D 92 50h. brown 45 45
D 93 60h. brown 10 10
D 94 80h. brown 10 10
D 95 1k. red 10 10
D 96 1k.10 red 25 40
D 97 1k.30 red 20 10
D 98 1k.60 red 25 10
D 99 2k. red 30 10
D100 2k.60 red 60 60
D101 3k.50 red . . . . . 3·75 5·25
D102 5k. red . . . . . . 1·40 1·50
D103 10k. red . . . . . 1·75 2·00

SLOVENIA Pt. 3

Formerly part of Austria, in 1918 Slovenia was combined with other areas to form Yugoslavia. Separate stamps were issued during the Second World War whilst under Italian and German Occupation.

In 1991 Slovenia seceded and became an independent state.

1941. 100 paras = 1 dinar.
1991. 100 stotinas = 1 tolar.

ITALIAN OCCUPATION, 1941

1941. Nos. 330/1 and 414/26 of Yugoslavia optd **Co. Ci.**
1 **99** 25p. black 30 50
2 50p. orange 30 50
3 1d. green 30 50
4 1d.50 red 30 50
5 2d. red 30 50
6 3d. brown 30 50
7 4d. blue 30 50
8 5d. blue 30 50
9 5d.50 violet 30 50
10 6d. blue 50 50
11 8d. brown 50 75
12 **70** 10d. violet 35 75
13 **99** 12d. violet . . . . 1·00 75
14 **70** 15d. olive £100 £120
15 **99** 16d. purple . . . . 1·00 1·00
16 20d. blue . . . . 3·00 3·50
17 30d. pink . . . . 15·00 18·00

1941. Nos. 330 and 414/26 of Yugoslavia optd **R.Commissariato Civile Territori Sloveni occupati LUBIANA**, with four lines of dots at foot.
23 **99** 25p. black 30 50
24 50p. orange 30 50
25 1d. green 30 50
26 1d.50 red 30 50
27 2d. red 30 50
28 3d. brown 30 50
29 4d. blue 30 50
30 5d. blue 60 65
31 5d.50 violet 35 65
32 6d. blue 35 65
33 8d. brown 35 65
34 **70** 10d. violet . . . . 1·50 1·25
35 **99** 12d. violet 50 65
36 16d. purple . . . . 1·25 1·25
37 20d. blue . . . . 2·50 2·75
38 30d. pink . . . . 30·00 24·00

1941. Nos. 446/9 of Yugoslavia optd as Nos. 23/38 but with only three lines of dots at foot.
45 50p.+50p. on 5d. violet . . . 4·00 5·00
46 1d.+1d. on 10d. lake . . . . 4·00 5·00
47 1d.50+1d.50 on 20d. green . . 4·00 5·00
48 2d.+2d. on 30d. blue . . . . 4·00 5·00

1941. Air. Nos. 360/7 and 443/4 of Yugoslavia optd as Nos. 23/38, with three or four (No. 57) lines of dots at foot.
49 50p. brown . . . . 1·10 2·00
50 1d. green . . . . 1·10 2·00
51 2d. blue . . . . 1·25 2·00
52 2d.50 red . . . . 1·25 2·00
53 5d. violet . . . . 3·00 3·00
54 10d. lake . . . . 3·00 3·00
55 20d. green . . . . 14·00 15·00
56 30d. blue . . . . 30·00 30·00
57 40d. green . . . . 70·00 80·00
58 50d. blue . . . . 70·00 70·00

1941. Nos. 26 and 29 surch.
59 **99** 0d.50 on 1d.50 red 25 35
60 0d.50 on 1d.50 red £400 £650
61 1d. on 4d. blue 25 35

POSTAGE DUE STAMPS

1941. Postage Due stamps of Yugoslavia, Nos. D89/93 optd Co. Ci.
D18 **D 56** 50p. violet 35 50
D19 1d. mauve 35 50
D20 2d. blue 35 50
D21 5d. orange . . . . . . 4·00 3·75
D22 10d. brown . . . . . . 4·00 3·75

Optd as Nos. 23/38, but with four lines of dots at top.
D40 **D 56** 50p. violet 30 50
D41 1d. mauve 30 50
D42 2d. blue 60 75
D43 5d. orange . . . . . . 16·00 18·00
D44 10d. brown . . . . . . 7·00 8·00

Optd as Nos. D40/44, but with narrower lettering.
D62 **D 56** 50p. violet 65 90
D63 1d. mauve . . . . . . 1·00 1·50
D64 2d. blue . . . . 12·50 16·00

GERMAN OCCUPATION, 1943–45

(3) (4)

1944. Stamps of Italy optd with Types **3** or **4**. (a) On Postage stamps of 1929.
65 **4** 5c. brown . . . . 20 1·10
66 **3** 10c. brown . . . . 20 1·10
67 **4** 15c. green . . . . 20 1·10

No.	Type	Description	Mint	Used
68	3	20c. red	20	1·10
69	4	25c. green	20	1·10
70	3	30c. brown	20	1·10
71	4	35c. blue	35	1·10
72	3	50c. violet	35	1·75
73	4	75c. red	30	2·40
74	3	1l. violet	30	2·40
75	4	1l.25 blue	30	1·40
76	3	1l.75 orange	1·00	11·50
77	4	2l. red	30	2·50
78	3	10l. violet	5·50	35·00

Surch with new value.

No.	Type	Description	Mint	Used
79	–	2l.55 on 5c. brown	85	6·00
80	4	5l. on 25c. green	85	8·00
81		20l. on 20c. red	4·75	40·00
82	3	25l. on 2l. red	5·50	85·00
83	4	50l. on 1l.75 orange	15·00	£130

In No. 79 the overprint inscriptions are at each side of the eagle.

(b) On Air stamps, Nos. 270, etc.

No.	Type	Description	Mint	Used
84	4	25c. green	3·00	17·00
85	3	50c. brown	5·25	70·00
86	4	75c. brown	2·75	23·00
87	3	1l. violet	6·25	70·00
88	4	2l. blue	4·00	60·00
89	3	5l. green	4·00	70·00
90	4	10l. red	3·25	60·00

(c) On Air Express stamp.

No.	Type	Description	Mint	Used
E91	3	2l. black (No. E370)	6·25	60·00

(d) On Express Letter stamp.

No.	Type	Description	Mint	Used
E92	3	1l.25 green (No. E350)	2·00	10·00

1944. Red Cross. Express Letter stamps of Italy surch as Types **3** or **4** with a red cross and new value alongside.

No.	Type	Description	Mint	Used
102	E **132**	1l.25+50l. green	15·00	£325
103		2l.50+50l. orange	15·00	£325

1944. Homeless Relief Fund. Express Letter stamps of Italy surch as Types **3** and **4**, but in circular frame, and **BREZDOMCEM DEN OBDACHLOSEN** alongside with new value between.

No.	Type	Description	Mint	Used
104	E **132**	1l.25+50l. green	15·00	£325
105		2l.50+50l. orange	15·00	£325

1944. Air. Orphans' Fund. Air stamps of Italy Nos. 270, etc., surch as Types **3** and **4**, but in circular frame between **DEN WAISEN SIROTAM** and new value.

No.	Type	Description	Mint	Used
106	–	25c.+10l. green	8·00	£200
107	**110**	50c.+10l. brown	8·00	£200
108	–	75c.+20l. brown	8·00	£200
109	–	1l.+20l. violet	8·00	£200
110	**113**	2l.+20l. blue	8·00	£200
111	**110**	5l.+20l. green	8·00	£200

1944. Air. Winter Relief Fund. Air stamps of Italy Nos. 270, etc., surch as Types **3** and **4**, but between **ZIMSKA POMOC WINTERHILFE** and new value.

No.	Type	Description	Mint	Used
112	–	25c.+10l. green	8·00	£200
113	**110**	50c.+10l. brown	8·00	£200
114	–	75c.+20l. brown	8·00	£200
115	–	1l.+20l. violet	8·00	£200
116	**113**	2l.+20l. blue	8·00	£200
117	**110**	5l.+20l. green	8·00	£200

9 Railway Viaduct, Borovnice

10 Church in Novo Mesto

1945. Inscr "PROVINZ LAIBACH".

No.	Type	Description	Mint	Used
118	–	5c. brown	35	2·40
119	–	10c. orange	35	2·40
120	**9**	20c. brown	35	2·40
121	–	25c. green	35	2·40
122	**10**	50c. violet	35	2·40
123	–	75c. red	35	2·40
124	–	1l. green	35	2·40
125	–	1l.25 blue	35	5·25
126	–	1l.50 green	35	5·25
127	–	2l. blue	60	6·50
128	–	2l.50 brown	60	6·50
129	–	3l. mauve	95	12·00
130	–	5l. brown	1·25	12·00
131	–	10l. green	2·25	60·00
132	–	20l. blue	11·00	£160
133	–	30l. red	55·00	£700

DESIGNS—VERT: 5c. Stalagmites, Krizna Jama; 1l.25, Kocevje; 1l.50, Borovnice Falls; 3l. Castle, Zuzemberg; 30l. View and Tabor Church. HORIZ: 10c. Zirknitz Lake; 25c. Farm near Ljubljana; 75c. View from Ribnica; 1l. Old Castle, Ljubljana; 2l. Castle, Kostanjevica; 2l.50, Castle, Turjak; 5l. View on River Krka; 10l. Castle, Otocec; 20l. Farm at Dolenjskom.

POSTAGE DUE STAMPS

(D 5)

(D 6)

1944. Postage Due stamps of Italy, Nos. D395, etc., optd as Type D 5.

No.	Type	Description	Mint	Used
D93	D **141**	5c. brown	1·10	50·00
D94		10c. blue	1·10	50·00
D95		20c. red	35	1·40
D96		25c. green	35	1·40
D97		50c. violet	30	1·40
D98	D **142**	1l. orange	1·00	60·00
D99		2l. green	1·00	60·00

Surch as Type D **6**.

No.	Type	Description	Mint	Used
D100	D **141**	30c. on 50c. violet	50	1·40
D101		40c. on 5c. brown	50	1·40

INDEPENDENT STATE

11 Parliament Building

12 Arms

1991. Declaration of Independence.

No.	Type	Description	Mint	Used
134	**11**	5d. multicoloured	75	60

1991.

No.	Type	Description	Mint	Used
135	**12**	1t. multicoloured	10	10
136		4t. multicoloured	15	15
137		5t. multicoloured	20	15
138		11t. multicoloured	45	40

13 Ski Jumping

1992. Winter Olympic Games, Albertville. Multicoloured.

No.	Type	Description	Mint	Used
139		30t. Type **13**	90	90
140		50t. Slalom	1·60	1·60

14 Arms

15 Opera House

1992. Multicoloured, background colours given.

No.	Type	Description	Mint	Used
141	**14**	1t. brown	10	10
142		2t. purple	10	10
143		4t. green	15	15
144		5t. red	20	15
145		6t. yellow	30	20
146		11t. orange	35	25
147		15t. blue	40	30
148		20t. violet	65	50
149		50t. green	1·00	85
150		100t. grey	2·25	1·90

1992. Centenary of Ljubljana Opera House.

No.	Type	Description	Mint	Used
155	**15**	20t. multicoloured	60	60

16 Tartini and Violins

1992. 300th Birth Anniv of Giuseppe Tartini (violinist and composer).

No.	Type	Description	Mint	Used
156	**16**	27t. multicoloured	70	70

17 Map and Marko Anton Kappus preaching to Amerindians

18

1992. 500th Anniv of Discovery of America by Columbus. Multicoloured.

No.	Type	Description	Mint	Used
157		27t. Type **17**	1·00	1·00
158		47t. Map and "Santa Maria"	1·75	1·75

1992. Obligatory Tax. Red Cross.

No.	Type	Description	Mint	Used
159	**18**	3t. black, red and blue	50	40

19 Collapsible Chair by Niko Kralj and Map

1992. 17th World Industrial Design Congress, Ljubljana.

No.	Type	Description	Mint	Used
160	**19**	41t. multicoloured	85	65

20 Slomsek

1992. 130th Death Anniv of Anton Slomsek, Bishop of Maribor.

No.	Type	Description	Mint	Used
161	**20**	41t. multicoloured	20	20

21 Wreckage

22 Rescuing Mountaineer

1992. Obligatory Tax. Solidarity Week. Perf and imperf.

No.	Type	Description	Mint	Used
162	**21**	3t. brown, black and red	40	30

1992. 80th Anniv of Alpine Rescue Service.

No.	Type	Description	Mint	Used
164	**22**	41t. multicoloured	80	70

23 River Jousting

24 Linden Leaf and Flowers

1992. 900th Anniv of River Jousting in Ljubljana.

No.	Type	Description	Mint	Used
165	**23**	6t. multicoloured	20	20

1992. 1st Anniv of Independence.

No.	Type	Description	Mint	Used
166	**24**	41t. multicoloured	70	70

25 Leon Stukelj and Medals

1992. Olympic Games, Barcelona. Multicoloured.

No.	Type	Description	Mint	Used
167		40t. Type **25**	85	85
168		46t. Head of Apoxymenos repeated in three Slovene colours	1·25	1·25

26 Sheepdog

1992. "Psov '92" World Dog-training Championships, Ljubljana.

No.	Type	Description	Mint	Used
169	**26**	40t. multicoloured	80	80

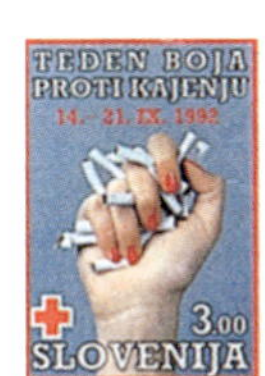

27 Hand crushing Cigarettes

28 Kogoj and scene from "Black Masks" (opera)

1992. Obligatory Tax. Red Cross. Anti-smoking Week.

No.	Type	Description	Mint	Used
170	**27**	3t. multicoloured	35	20

1992. Birth Centenary of Marij Kogoj (composer).

No.	Type	Description	Mint	Used
171	**28**	40t. multicoloured	75	75

29 Langus (self-portrait)

1992. Birth Bicentenary of Matevz Langus (painter).

No.	Type	Description	Mint	Used
172	**29**	40t. multicoloured	75	75

30 Nativity

1992. Christmas. Multicoloured.

No.	Type	Description	Mint	Used
173		6t. Type **30**	10	10
174		7t. Type **30**	15	15
175		41t. "Madonna and Child" (stained-glass window by V. Sorli-Puc in St. Mary's Church, Bovec) (vert)	85	75

31 Potocnik, View of Earth from Space and Satellite

1992. Birth Centenary of Herman Potocnik (space flight pioneer).

No.	Type	Description	Mint	Used
176	**31**	46t. multicoloured	85	85

32 Illustration from "Solzice"

1993. Birth Centenary of Prezihov Voranc (writer).

No.	Type	Description	Mint	Used
177	**32**	7t. multicoloured	15	15

33 "Underneath the Birches"

1993. 50th Death Anniv of Rihard Jakopic (painter).

No.	Type	Description	Mint	Used
178	**33**	44t. multicoloured	70	70

34 Bust of Stefan (J. Savinsek)

35 Honey-cake from Skofja Loka

1993. Death Centenary of Jozef Stefan (physicist).

No.	Type	Description	Mint	Used
179	**34**	51t. multicoloured	80	80

1993. Slovene Culture.
180 **35** 1t. brown, ochre & dp brn 10 10
181 – 2t. green and light green 10 10
182 – 5t. dp grey, grey & mauve 10 10
183 – 6t. lt green, green & yellow 10 10
184 – 7t. red, crimson and grey 10 10
185 – 8t. green, dp green & olive 10 10
186 – 9t. red, brown and grey 15 10
187 – 10t. brown and light brown 15 10
188 – 11t. green, lt green & yell 15 10
189 – 12t. red, orange and grey 15 10
189 a – 13t. green, black & dp grn 15 10
189 b – 14t. red, brown and grey 20 10
189 c – 15t. black, drab and red 10 10
189 d – 16t. brown, blue and orange 15 10
189 e – 17t. chocolate, yellow & brn 20 10
189 f – 18t. brown, black and blue 25 10
190 – 20t. green and grey . . . 35 25
191 – 44t. blue, dp blue & blk 50 35
192 – 50t. purple and mauve 65 45
193 – 55t. black, grey & orge 45 30
194 – 65t. ochre, brown & pink 55 35
195 – 70t. grey, brown and green 65 45
196 – 75t. green, blue and lilac 65 45
197 – 80t. multicoloured . . . 70 45
197 a – 90t. brown, red and grey 75 50
198 – 100t. brown, red & lt brn . . . . 1·00 85
198 a – 300t. chestnut and brown . . . . 2·75 1·90
198ab – 200t. purple, green and blue . . . . 1·40 1·40
198 b – 400t. red and brown . . 3·75 2·50
198 c – 500t. violet, orge & grey 3·25 3·25

DESIGNS: 2t. Reed pipes; 5t. Double hay-drying frame; 6t. Shepherd's hut, Velika Planina; 7t. Zither; 8t. Mill on the Mur; 9t. Sledge; 10t. Earthenware double-bass; 11t. Hay basket; 12t. Boy on horse (statuette), Ribnica; 13t. Wind-operated bird-scarer, Prlekija; 14t. Hen-shaped wine jug, Sentjernej; 15t. Blast furnace, Zelezniki; 16t. Windmill, Stari, Gori; 17t. Maize store, Ptujskopolje; 18t. Accordion, Kranjska Gora; 20t. Farmhouse, Prekmurje; 44t. House, Karst; 50t. Wind-propelled pump, Secovlje salt-pans; 55t. Easter eggs, Bela Krajina; 65t. Lamp, Trzic; 70t. Ski; 75t. Wrought iron window lattice; 80t. Palm Sunday bundle, Ljubljana; 90t. Apiary; 100t. Nut cake; 200t. Bootjack in shape of stag beetle; 300t. Straw sculpture; 400t. Wine press; 500t. Decorated table.

36 Mountains and Founder Members

1993. Centenary of Alpine Association.
199 **36** 7t. multicoloured 15 15

37 Cop's Route up Triglav

38 Chainbreaker (1919 stamp design)

1993. Birth Centenary of Joza Cop (climber and mountain rescuer).
200 **37** 44t. multicoloured 70 70

1993. 75th Anniv of Slovenian Postal Service.
201 **38** 7t. multicoloured 15 15

39 "St. Nicholas" (altar painting, Tintoretto)

40 "Table in Pompeii" (Marij Pregelj)

1993. 500th Anniv of College Chapter of Novo Mesto. Multicoloured.
202 7t. Type **39** 15 15
203 44t. Arms 65 65

1993. Europa. Contemporary Art. Multicoloured.
204 44t. Type **40** . . . . 1·00 60
205 159t. "Girl with Toy" (Gabrijel Stupica) . . . . 2·75 2·10

41 "Schwagerina carniolica"

42

1993. Fossils.
206 **41** 44t. multicoloured 65 65

1993. Obligatory Tax. Red Cross.
207 **42** 3t.50 black, red and blue 10 10

43 6th-century B.C. Vase

44 Red Cross Rescue Workers

1993. 1st Anniv of Admission to United Nations Organization.
208 **43** 62t. multicoloured 85 85

1993. Obligatory Tax. Solidarity Week.
209 **44** 3t.50 multicoloured 10 10

45 Basketball, Johann and Swimming

1993. Mediterranean Games, Roussillon (Languedoc).
210 **45** 36t. multicoloured 50 50

46 "Battle of Sisak" (Johann Valvasor)

1993. 400th Anniv of Battle of Sisak.
211 **46** 49t. multicoloured 65 65

47 "Monolistra spinosissima"

1993. Cave Fauna. Multicoloured.
212 7t. Type **47** 15 15
213 40t. "Aphaenopidius kamnikensis" (insect) . . . 50 50
214 55t. "Proteus anguinus" . . . 70 70
215 65t. "Zospeum spelaeum" (mollusc) 90 90

48 Horse and Diagram of Movements

49 Boy smoking and Emblem

1993. European Dressage Championships, Lipica.
216 **48** 65t. multicoloured 85 85

1993. Obligatory Tax. Red Cross. Anti-smoking Week.
217 **49** 4t.50 multicoloured 10 10

50 Valvasor Arms

1993. 300th Anniversaries.
218 **50** 9t. black, lilac and gold . . 15 15
219 – 65t. black, stone and gold 75 75

DESIGN: 9t. Type **50** (death anniv of Johann Valvasor (historian)); 65t. Arms of Academia Operosorum.

51 "Slovenian Family at Christmas Crib" (M. Gaspari)

1993. Christmas. Multicoloured.
220 9t. Type **51** 15 15
221 65t. Dr. Joze Pogacnik (archbishop) (after B. Jakac) and seal 75 75

52 Illustration from "The Vagabond"

53 Hearts

1994. 150th Anniversaries. Multicoloured.
222 8t. Type **52** (birth anniv of Josip Juncic (writer)) . . . 10 10
223 9t. Nightingale and bridge over river (birth anniv of Simon Gregorcic, poet) . . 15 15
224 55t. Book showing Slovenian vowels (birth anniv of Stanislav Skrabec, philologist) 80 80
225 65t. Cover of grammar book (death anniv of Jernei Kopitar, philologist) . . . 90 90

1994. Greetings Stamp.
226 **53** 9t. multicoloured 15 15

54 Cross-country Skiing

1994. Winter Olympic Games, Lillehammer, Norway. Multicoloured.
227 9t. Type **54** 15 15
228 65t. Slalom skiing 75 75

55 Ski Jumping

1994. 60th Anniv of Ski Jumping Championships, Planica.
229 **55** 70t. multicoloured 80 80

56 Town Names

1994. 850th Anniv of First Official Record of Ljubljana.
230 **56** 9t. multicoloured 15 15

57 Janez Puhar and Camera

1994. Europa. Discoveries and Inventions. Multicoloured.
231 70t. Type **57** (invention of glass-plate photography) 75 75
232 215t. Moon, natural logarithm diagram and Jurij Vega (mathematician) 2·50 2·50

58 Balloons

1994. Obligatory Tax. Red Cross.
233 **58** 4t.50 multicoloured 10 10

59 "Primula carniolica"

1994. Flowers. Multicoloured.
234 9t. Type **59** 10 10
235 44t. "Hladnikia pastinacifolia" 50 50
236 60t. "Daphne blagayana" . . 70 70
237 70t. "Campanula zoysii" . . 95 95

60 Red Cross Worker with Child

61 Inflating "Globe" Football

1994. Obligatory Tax. Solidarity Week.
238 **60** 4t.50 multicoloured 10 10

1994. World Cup Football Championship, U.S.A.
239 **61** 44t. multicoloured 50 50

62 Globes in Olympic Colours and Flags

63 Mt. Ojstrica

68 **3** 20c. red . . . . 20 1·10
69 **4** 25c. green . . . . 20 1·10
70 **3** 30c. brown . . . . 20 1·10
71 **4** 35c. blue . . . . 35 1·10
72 **3** 50c. violet . . . . 35 1·75
73 **4** 75c. red . . . . 30 2·40
74 **3** 1l. violet . . . . 30 2·40
75 **4** 1l.25 blue . . . . 30 1·40
76 **3** 1l.75 orange . . . . 1·00 11·50
77 **4** 2l. red . . . . 30 2·50
78 **3** 10l. violet . . . . 5·50 35·00

Surch with new value.
79 – 2l.55 on 5c. brown . . . . . 85 6·00
80 **4** 5l. on 25c. green . . . . . . 85 8·00
81 20l. on 20c. red . . . . . . 4·75 40·00
82 **3** 25l. on 2l. red . . . . . . 5·50 85·00
83 **4** 50l. on 1l.75 orange . . . . 15·00 £130

In No. 79 the overprint inscriptions are at each side of the eagle.

(b) On Air stamps, Nos. 270, etc.
84 **4** 25c. green . . . . 3·00 17·00
85 **3** 50c. brown . . . . 5·25 70·00
86 **4** 75c. brown . . . . 2·75 23·00
87 **3** 1l. violet . . . . 6·25 70·00
88 **4** 2l. blue . . . . 4·00 60·00
89 **3** 5l. green . . . . 4·00 70·00
90 **4** 10l. red . . . . 3·25 60·00

(c) On Air Express stamp.
E91 **3** 2l. black (No. E370) . . . . 6·25 60·00

(d) On Express Letter stamp.
E92 **3** 1l.25 green (No. E350) . . . 2·00 10·00

1944. Red Cross. Express Letter stamps of Italy surch as Types **3** or **4** with a red cross and new value alongside.
102 E **132** 1l.25+50l. green . . . . 15·00 £325
103 2l.50+50l. orange . . . 15·00 £325

1944. Homeless Relief Fund. Express Letter stamps of Italy surch as Types **3** and **4**, but in circular frame, and **BREZDOMCEM DEN OBDACHLOSEN** alongside with new value between.
104 E **132** 1l.25+50l. green . . . . 15·00 £325
105 2l.50+50l. orange . . . 15·00 £325

1944. Air. Orphans' Fund. Air stamps of Italy Nos. 270, etc., surch as Types **3** and **4**, but in circular frame between **DEN WAISEN SIROTAM** and new value.
106 – 25c.+10l. green . . . . . 8·00 £200
107 **110** 50c.+10l. brown . . . . . 8·00 £200
108 – 75c.+20l. brown . . . . . 8·00 £200
109 – 1l.+20l. violet . . . . . . 8·00 £200
110 **113** 2l.+20l. blue . . . . . . 8·00 £200
111 **110** 5l.+20l. green . . . . . . 8·00 £200

1944. Air. Winter Relief Fund. Air stamps of Italy Nos. 270, etc., surch as Types **3** and **4**, but between **ZIMSKA POMOC WINTERHILFE** and new value.
112 – 25c.+10l. green . . . . . 8·00 £200
113 **110** 50c.+10l. brown . . . . . 8·00 £200
114 – 75c.+20l. brown . . . . . 8·00 £200
115 – 1l.+20l. violet . . . . . . 8·00 £200
116 **113** 2l.+20l. blue . . . . . . 8·00 £200
117 **110** 5l.+20l. green . . . . . . 8·00 £200

9 Railway Viaduct, Borovnice **10** Church in Novo Mesto

1945. Inscr "PROVINZ LAIBACH".
118 – 5c. brown . . . . 35 2·40
119 – 10c. orange . . . . 35 2·40
120 **9** 20c. brown . . . . 35 2·40
121 – 25c. green . . . . 35 2·40
122 **10** 50c. violet . . . . 35 2·40
123 – 75c. red . . . . 35 2·40
124 – 1l. green . . . . 35 2·40
125 – 1l.25 blue . . . . 35 5·25
126 – 1l.50 green . . . . 35 5·25
127 – 2l. blue . . . . 60 6·50
128 – 2l.50 brown . . . . 60 6·50
129 – 3l. mauve . . . . 95 12·00
130 – 5l. brown . . . . 1·25 12·00
131 – 10l. green . . . . 2·25 60·00
132 – 20l. blue . . . . 11·00 £160
133 – 30l. red . . . . 55·00 £700

DESIGNS—VERT: 5c. Stalagmites, Krizna Jama; 1l.25, Kocevje; 1l.50, Borovnice Falls; 3l. Castle, Zuzemberg; 30l. View and Tabor Church. HORIZ: 10c. Zirknitz Lake; 25c. Farm near Ljubljana; 75c. View from Ribnica; 1l. Old Castle, Ljubljana; 2l. Castle, Kostanjevica; 2l.50, Castle, Turjak; 5l. View on River Krka; 10l. Castle, Otocec; 20l. Farm at Dolenjskom.

POSTAGE DUE STAMPS

(D 5) (D 6)

1944. Postage Due stamps of Italy, Nos. D395, etc., optd as Type D **5**.
D93 D **141** 5c. brown . . . . . 1·10 50·00
D94 10c. blue . . . . . 1·10 50·00
D95 20c. red . . . . . 35 1·40
D96 25c. green . . . . 35 1·40
D97 50c. violet . . . . . 30 1·40
D98 D **142** 1l. orange . . . . . 1·00 60·00
D99. 2l. green . . . . . 1·00 60·00

Surch as Type D **6**.
D100 D **141** 30c. on 50c. violet . . 50 1·40
D101 40c. on 5c. brown . . 50 1·40

INDEPENDENT STATE

11 Parliament Building **12** Arms

1991. Declaration of Independence.
134 **11** 5d. multicoloured 75 60

1991.
135 **12** 1t. multicoloured 10 10
136 4t. multicoloured 15 15
137 5t. multicoloured 20 15
138 11t. multicoloured 45 40

13 Ski Jumping

1992. Winter Olympic Games, Albertville. Multicoloured.
139 30t. Type **13** 90 90
140 50t. Slalom . . . . 1·60 1·60

14 Arms **15** Opera House

1992. Multicoloured, background colours given.
141 **14** 1t. brown 10 10
142 2t. purple 10 10
143 4t. green 15 15
144 5t. red 20 15
145 6t. yellow 30 20
146 11t. orange 35 25
147 15t. blue 40 30
148 20t. violet 65 50
149 50t. green . . . . 1·00 85
150 100t. grey . . . . 2·25 1·90

1992. Centenary of Ljubljana Opera House.
155 **15** 20t. multicoloured 60 60

16 Tartini and Violins

1992. 300th Birth Anniv of Giuseppe Tartini (violinist and composer).
156 **16** 27t. multicoloured 70 70

17 Map and Marko Anton Kappus preaching to Amerindians **18**

1992. 500th Anniv of Discovery of America by Columbus. Multicoloured.
157 27t. Type **17** . . . . 1·00 1·00
158 47t. Map and "Santa Maria" 1·75 1·75

1992. Obligatory Tax. Red Cross.
159 **18** 3t. black, red and blue . . 50 40

19 Collapsible Chair by Niko Kralj and Map

1992. 17th World Industrial Design Congress, Ljubljana.
160 **19** 41t. multicoloured 85 65

20 Slomsek

1992. 130th Death Anniv of Anton Slomsek, Bishop of Maribor.
161 **20** 41t. multicoloured 20 20

21 Wreckage **22** Rescuing Mountaineer

1992. Obligatory Tax. Solidarity Week. Perf and imperf.
162 **21** 3t. brown, black and red 40 30

1992. 80th Anniv of Alpine Rescue Service.
164 **22** 41t. multicoloured 80 70

23 River Jousting **24** Linden Leaf and Flowers

1992. 900th Anniv of River Jousting in Ljubljana.
165 **23** 6t. multicoloured 20 20

1992. 1st Anniv of Independence.
166 **24** 41t. multicoloured 70 70

25 Leon Stukelj and Medals

1992. Olympic Games, Barcelona. Multicoloured.
167 40t. Type **25** 85 85
168 46t. Head of Apoxymenos repeated in three Slovene colours . . . . 1·25 1·25

26 Sheepdog

1992. "Psov '92" World Dog-training Championships, Ljubljana.
169 **26** 40t. multicoloured 80 80

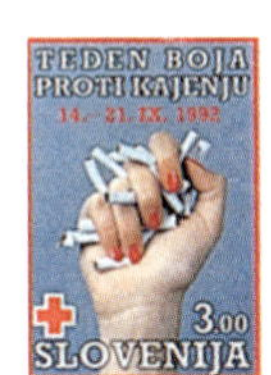

27 Hand crushing Cigarettes **28** Kogoj and scene from "Black Masks" (opera)

1992. Obligatory Tax. Red Cross. Anti-smoking Week.
170 **27** 3t. multicoloured 35 20

1992. Birth Centenary of Marij Kogoj (composer).
171 **28** 40t. multicoloured 75 75

29 Langus (self-portrait)

1992. Birth Bicentenary of Matevz Langus (painter).
172 **29** 40t. multicoloured 75 75

30 Nativity

1992. Christmas. Multicoloured.
173 6t. Type **30** 10 10
174 7t. Type **30** 15 15
175 41t. "Madonna and Child" (stained-glass window by V. Sorli-Puc in St. Mary's Church, Bovec) (vert) . . . 85 75

31 Potocnik, View of Earth from Space and Satellite

1992. Birth Centenary of Herman Potocnik (space flight pioneer).
176 **31** 46t. multicoloured 85 85

32 Illustration from "Solzice"

1993. Birth Centenary of Prezihov Voranc (writer).
177 **32** 7t. multicoloured 15 15

33 "Underneath the Birches"

1993. 50th Death Anniv of Rihard Jakopic (painter).
178 **33** 44t. multicoloured 70 70

34 Bust of Stefan (J. Savinsek) **35** Honey-cake from Skofja Loka

1993. Death Centenary of Jozef Stefan (physicist).
179 **34** 51t. multicoloured 80 80

1993. Slovene Culture.

180 **35** 1t. brown, ochre & dp brn 10 10
181 – 2t. green and light green 10 10
182 – 5t. dp grey, grey & mauve 10 10
183 – 6t. lt green, green & yellow 10 10
184 – 7t. red, crimson and grey 10 10
185 – 8t. green, dp green & olive 10 10
186 – 9t. red, brown and grey 15 10
187 – 10t. brown and light brown 15 10
188 – 11t. green, lt green & yell 15 10
189 – 12t. red, orange and grey 15 10
189 a – 13t. green, black & dp grn 15 10
189 b – 14t. red, brown and grey 20 10
189 c – 15t. black, drab and red 10 10
189 d – 16t. brown, blue and orange 15 10
189 e – 17t. chocolate, yellow & brn 20 10
189 f – 18t. brown, black and blue 25 10
190 – 20t. green and grey . . . 35 25
191 – 44t. blue, dp blue & blk 50 35
192 – 50t. purple and mauve 65 45
193 – 55t. black, grey & orge 45 30
194 – 65t. ochre, brown & pink 55 35
195 – 70t. grey, brown and green 65 45
196 – 75t. green, blue and lilac 65 45
197 – 80t. multicoloured . . . 70 45
197 a – 90t. brown, red and grey 75 50
198 – 100t. brown, red & lt brn . . . . 1·00 85
198 a – 300t. chestnut and brown . . . . 2·75 1·90
198ab – 200t. purple, green and blue . . . . 1·40 1·40
198 b – 400t. red and brown . . 3·75 2·50
198 c – 500t. violet, orge & grey 3·25 3·25

DESIGNS: 2t. Reed pipes; 5t. Double hay-drying frame; 6t. Shepherd's hut, Velika Planina; 7t. Zither; 8t. Mill on the Mur; 9t. Sledge; 10t. Earthenware double-bass; 11t. Hay basket; 12t. Boy on horse (statuette), Ribnica; 13t. Wind-operated bird-scarer, Prlekija; 14t. Hen-shaped wine jug, Sentjernej; 15t. Blast furnace, Zelezniki; 16t. Windmill, Stari, Gori; 17t. Maize store, Ptujskopolje; 18t. Accordion, Kranjska Gora; 20t. Farmhouse, Prekmurje; 44t. House, Karst; 50t. Wind-propelled pump, Secovlje salt-pans; 55t. Easter eggs, Bela Krajina; 65t. Lamp, Trzic; 70t. Ski; 75t. Wrought iron window lattice; 80t. Palm Sunday bundle, Ljubljana; 90t. Apiary; 100t. Nut cake; 200t. Bootjack in shape of stag beetle; 300t. Straw sculpture; 400t. Wine press; 500t. Decorated table.

36 Mountains and Founder Members

1993. Centenary of Alpine Association.

199 **36** 7t. multicoloured 15 15

37 Cop's Route up Triglav

38 Chainbreaker (1919 stamp design)

1993. Birth Centenary of Joza Cop (climber and mountain rescuer).

200 **37** 44t. multicoloured 70 70

1993. 75th Anniv of Slovenian Postal Service.

201 **38** 7t. multicoloured 15 15

39 "St. Nicholas" (altar painting, Tintoretto)

40 "Table in Pompeii" (Marij Pregelj)

1993. 500th Anniv of College Chapter of Novo Mesto. Multicoloured.

202 7t. Type **39** 15 15
203 44t. Arms 65 65

1993. Europa. Contemporary Art. Multicoloured.

204 44t. Type **40** . . . . 1·00 60
205 159t. "Girl with Toy" (Gabrijel Stupica) . . . . 2·75 2·10

41 "Schwagerina carniolica"

42

1993. Fossils.

206 **41** 44t. multicoloured 65 65

1993. Obligatory Tax. Red Cross.

207 **42** 3t.50 black, red and blue 10 10

43 6th-century B.C. Vase

44 Red Cross Rescue Workers

1993. 1st Anniv of Admission to United Nations Organization.

208 **43** 62t. multicoloured 85 85

1993. Obligatory Tax. Solidarity Week.

209 **44** 3t.50 multicoloured 10 10

45 Basketball, Johann and Swimming

1993. Mediterranean Games, Roussillon (Languedoc).

210 **45** 36t. multicoloured 50 50

46 "Battle of Sisak" (Johann Valvasor)

1993. 400th Anniv of Battle of Sisak.

211 **46** 49t. multicoloured 65 65

47 "Monolistra spinosissima"

1993. Cave Fauna. Multicoloured.

212 7t. Type **47** 15 15
213 40t. "Aphaenopidius kamnikensis" (insect) . . 50 50
214 55t. "Proteus anguinus" . . . 70 70
215 65t. "Zospeum spelaeum" (mollusc) 90 90

48 Horse and Diagram of Movements

49 Boy smoking and Emblem

1993. European Dressage Championships, Lipica.

216 **48** 65t. multicoloured 85 85

1993. Obligatory Tax. Red Cross. Anti-smoking Week.

217 **49** 4t.50 multicoloured 10 10

50 Valvasor Arms

1993. 300th Anniversaries.

218 **50** 9t. black, lilac and gold . . 15 15
219 – 65t. black, stone and gold 75 75

DESIGN: 9t. Type **50** (death anniv of Johann Valvasor (historian)); 65t. Arms of Academia Operosorum.

51 "Slovenian Family at Christmas Crib" (M. Gaspari)

1993. Christmas. Multicoloured.

220 9t. Type **51** 15 15
221 65t. Dr. Joze Pogacnik (archbishop) (after B. Jakac) and seal 75 75

52 Illustration from "The Vagabond"

53 Hearts

1994. 150th Anniversaries. Multicoloured.

222 8t. Type **52** (birth anniv of Josip Juncic (writer)) . . . 10 10
223 9t. Nightingale and bridge over river (birth anniv of Simon Gregorcic, poet) . . 15 15
224 55t. Book showing Slovenian vowels (birth anniv of Stanislav Skrabec, philologist) 80 80
225 65t. Cover of grammar book (death anniv of Jernei Kopitar, philologist) . . . 90 90

1994. Greetings Stamp.

226 **53** 9t. multicoloured 15 15

54 Cross-country Skiing

1994. Winter Olympic Games, Lillehammer, Norway. Multicoloured.

227 9t. Type **54** 15 15
228 65t. Slalom skiing 75 75

55 Ski Jumping

1994. 60th Anniv of Ski Jumping Championships, Planica.

229 **55** 70t. multicoloured 80 80

56 Town Names

1994. 850th Anniv of First Official Record of Ljubljana.

230 **56** 9t. multicoloured 15 15

57 Janez Puhar and Camera

1994. Europa. Discoveries and Inventions. Multicoloured.

231 70t. Type **57** (invention of glass-plate photography) 75 75
232 215t. Moon, natural logarithm diagram and Jurij Vega (mathematician) 2·50 2·50

58 Balloons

1994. Obligatory Tax. Red Cross.

233 **58** 4t.50 multicoloured 10 10

59 "Primula carniolica"

1994. Flowers. Multicoloured.

234 9t. Type **59** 10 10
235 44t. "Hladnikia pastinacifolia" 50 50
236 60t. "Daphne blagayana" . . 70 70
237 70t. "Campanula zoysii" . . 95 95

60 Red Cross Worker with Child

61 Inflating "Globe" Football

1994. Obligatory Tax. Solidarity Week.

238 **60** 4t.50 multicoloured 10 10

1994. World Cup Football Championship, U.S.A.

239 **61** 44t. multicoloured 50 50

62 Globes in Olympic Colours and Flags

63 Mt. Ojstrica

1994. Centenary of International Olympic Committee.
240 **62** 100t. multicoloured . . . . 1·25 1·25

1994.
241 **63** 12t. multicoloured 20 20

64 Maks Pletersnik (compiler) and University of Laibach Professors

1994. Centenary of First Slovenian–German Dictionary.
242 **64** 70t. multicoloured 85 85

65 Roman Infantry

1994. 1600th Anniv of Battle of Frigidus.
243 **65** 60t. red, black and grey . . 70 70

66 Post Office

1994. Centenary of Maribor Post Office.
244 **66** 70t. multicoloured 80 80

67 Series kkStB Steam Locomotive No. 5722

1994. Centenary of Ljubljana Railway.
245 **67** 70t. multicoloured . . . . 1·25 1·25

68 Orchestra Venue and Music

1994. Bicentenary of Ljubljana Philharmonic Society. Multicoloured.
246 12t. Type **68** 15 15
247 70t. Ludwig van Beethoven, Johannes Brahms, Antonin Dvorak and Joseph Haydn (composers) and Niccolo Paganini (violinist) 75 75

69 Christmas Tree, Window and Candles

70 "Madonna and Child" (statue, Loreto Basilica)

1994. Christmas and International Year of the Family.
248 **69** 12t. multicoloured 15 15
249 – 70t. cream, black and blue 75 75
DESIGN: 70t. "Children with Christmas Tree" (F. Kralj) and I.Y.F. emblem.

1994. 700th Anniv of Loreto.
250 **70** 70t. multicoloured 80 80

71 Ivan Hribar, Mihajlo Rostohar and Danilo Majaron (founders) and University

1994. 75th Anniv of Ljubljana University.
251 **71** 70t. multicoloured 80 80

72 Postal Emblem

73 Lili Novy (writer, 110th birth)

1995.
252 **72** 13t. multicoloured 15 15

1995. Anniversaries.
253 **73** 20t. red, black and grey . . 25 25
254 – 70t. yellow, black and gold 85 85
255 – 70t. multicoloured 85 85
DESIGNS—HORIZ: No. 253, Silhouettes of figures and signature of Anton Tomasz Linhart (dramatist, death bicentenary). VERT: No. 255, Detail of facade of Zadruzna Co-operative Bank, Ljubljana (110th birth anniv (1994) of Ivan Vurnik (architect)).

74 Cats and Hearts (Jure Kos)

75 Allegory

1995. Greetings Stamp.
256 **74** 20t. multicoloured 30 30

1995. 50th Anniv of End of Second World War.
257 **75** 13t. multicoloured 15 15

76 Skeleton and Woman

1995. Europa. Peace and Freedom. Multicoloured.
258 60t. Type **76** (50th anniv of liberation of concentration camps) 75 75
259 70t. Woman running free . . 1·00 1·00

77 "Karavankina schellwieni"

1995. Fossils.
260 **77** 70t. multicoloured 90 90

78 Alpine Iris, Triglav National Park and Alpine Poppy

1995. European Nature Conservation Year.
261 **78** 70t. multicoloured 80 80

79 Child painting Red Cross

80 First Aiders tending Casualty

1995. Obligatory Tax. Red Cross.
262 **79** 6t. multicoloured 10 10

1995. Obligatory Tax. Solidarity Week.
263 **80** 6t.50 multicoloured 10 10

81 Lesser Kestrel

1995. Birds. Multicoloured.
264 13t. Type **81** 25 25
265 60t. European roller 90 90
266 70t. Lesser grey shrike . . . 1·10 1·10
267 215t. Black-headed bunting 2·50 2·50

82 Radovljica

1995. 500th Anniv of Radovljica.
268 **82** 44t. multicoloured 60 60

83 Class KRB 37 Steam Locomotive "Podnart"

1995. 125th Anniv of Ljubljana–Jesenice Railway.
269 **83** 70t. black, red and yellow 1·10 1·10

84 Mountain and Presbytery

1995. Centenary of Jakob Aljaz Presbytery, Mount Triglav.
270 **84** 100t. blue, black and red 1·40 1·40

85 Scouts around Campfire

1995. Scouting.
271 **85** 70t. multicoloured 90 90

86 "Death of a Genius"

1995. Birth Centenary of France Kralz (artist). Multicoloured.
272 60t. Type **86** 75 75
273 70t. "Family of Horses" . . 85 85

87 Handshake, Anniversary Emblem and Different Nationalities

88 "Winter" (Marlenka Stupica)

1995. 50th Anniversaries of U.N.O. (274) and F.A.O. (275). Multicoloured.
274 70t. Type **87** 85 85
275 70t. Foodstuffs, anniversary emblem and different nationalities 85 85

1995. Christmas. Paintings. Multicoloured.
276 13t. Type **88** 20 20
277 70t. "Madonna and Child" (Leopold Layer) 80 80

89 Birds and Heart (Karmen Podgornik)

1996. Greetings Stamp.
278 **89** 13t. multicoloured 20 15

90 Swimming

1996. The European Pond Turtle. Multicoloured.
279 13t. Type **90** 25 25
280 50t. On bank 70 70
281 60t. In water 80 80
282 70t. Pair of turtles climbing up bank 95 95

91 Ptujsko Polje

1996. Masked Costumes. Multicoloured.
283 13t. Type **91** 20 20
284 70t. Dravsko Polje 80 80

92 Steam Locomotive "Aussee"

1996. 150th Anniv of Slovenian Railways.
285 **92** 70t. multicoloured . . . . 1·10 1·10

93 Fran Finzgar (writer)

1996. Birth Anniversaries. Multicoloured.
286 13t. Type **93** (125th anniv) 10 10
287 100t. Ita Rina (actress) (89th anniv) . . . . 1·25 1·25

94 Child feeding Birds and Children of different Nationalities

95 "Vase of Dahlias"

1996. 50th Anniv of U.N.I.C.E.F.
288 **94** 65t. multicoloured 70 70

1996. Europa. Famous Women. 70th Death Anniv of Ivana Koblica (painter). Multicoloured.
289 65t. "Children in the Grass" (detail) 75 75
290 75t. Type **95** 85 85

96 Pope John Paul II

97 Anniversary Emblem

1996. Papal Visit.
291 **96** 75t. multicoloured 85 85

1996. Obligatory Tax. 130th Anniv of Slovenian Red Cross.
293 **97** 7t. multicoloured 10 10

98 Clasped Hands

1996. Obligatory Tax. Solidarity Week.
294 **98** 7t. multicoloured 10 10

99 Gallenberg Castle

1996. 700th Anniv of Zagorje ob Savi.
295 **99** 24t. multicoloured 25 25

100 Cyclists

1996. World Youth Cycling Championships, Novo Mesto.
296 **100** 55t. multicoloured 55 55

101 Stars over Mountains

103 Rowing and Canoeing

1996. 5th Anniv of Independence.
297 **101** 75t. multicoloured 75 75

1996. Centenary of Modern Olympic Games and Olympic Games, Atlanta. Multicoloured.
299 75t. Type **103** 75 75
300 100t. High jumping and hurdling . . . . 1·00 1·00

104 Corner

106 Cave

105 "Moscon Family"

1996. Traditional Lace Designs from Idria.

301	**104**	1t. brown	10	10
302	–	1t. brown	10	10
303	–	2t. red	10	10
304	–	2t. red	10	10
305	–	5t. blue	10	10
306	–	5t. blue	10	10
307	–	10t. mauve	10	10
308	–	10t. mauve	10	10
309	–	12t. green	15	15
310	–	12t. green	15	15
311	–	13t. red	15	15
312	–	13t. red	15	15
313	–	20t. violet	15	15
314	–	20t. violet	15	15
315	–	44t. blue	30	30
316	–	44t. blue	30	30
317	–	50t. purple	50	50
318	–	50t. purple	50	50
325	–	100t. brown	70	70
326	–	100t. brown	70	70

DESIGNS: No. 302, Corner (different); 303, Rounded collar incorporating scrolls; 304, Pointed collar with scalloped edging; 305, Flowers and leaves forming circular design; 306, Framed rose; 307, Oval with flower in centre; 308, "Q"-shaped with trefoil in centre; 309, Flower; 310, Diamond with flower in centre; 311, Square enclosing diamonds containing "flowers"; 312, Square containing circular motifs; 313, Butterfly; 314, Diamond; 315, Square; 316, Circle; 317, Heart-shaped edging; 318, Ornate edging; 325, Leaf; 326, Insect.

1996. 130th Death Anniv of Jozef Tominc (painter).
331 **105** 65t. multicoloured 60 60

1996. U.N.E.S.C.O. World Heritage Sites. Skocjan Cave.
332 **106** 55t. multicoloured 50 50

107 Gimbals

1996. 250th Anniv of Novo Mesto School.
333 **107** 55t. multicoloured 50 50

108 Heart

109 Post Office Building, Ljubljana, and Doves carrying Letter

1996. Centenary of Modern Cardiology.
334 **108** 12t. red, brown and cream 15 15

1996. Centenary of Post and Telecommunications Office.
335 **109** 100t. multicoloured . . . 90 90

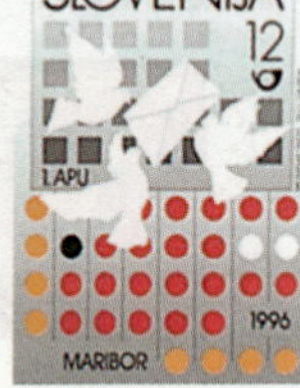

110 Doves carrying Letter and Stylized Letter Sorting

1996. Introduction of Automatic Letter Sorting.
336 **110** 12t. black, red and orange 15 15

111 Children and Christmas Tree on Sledge

1996. Christmas. Multicoloured.
337 12t. Type **111** 15 15
338 65t. "Adoration of the Wise Men" (Stefan Subic) . . . 55 55

112 Cupids

1997. Greeting Stamp.
339 **112** 15t. multicoloured 15 15

113 Mt. Sneznik

1997.
340 **113** 20t. multicoloured 15 15

114 "Ta Terjast"

1997. Masked Costumes. Multicoloured.
341 20r. Type **114** 15 15
342 80r. "Pust" 70 70

115 Marbled Trout

1997. Fishes. Multicoloured.
343 12t. Type **115** 10 10
344 13t. Streber 10 10
345 80t. Zahrte 70 70
346 90t. European mudminnow 75 75

116 The Golden Horns

1997. Europa. Tales and Legends.
348 **116** 80t. multicoloured 70 70

117 Wulfenite

1997. Minerals.
349 **117** 80t. multicoloured 70 70

118 Brick

1997. Red Cross.
350 **118** 7t. multicoloured 10 10

119 Matija Cop (scholar)

120 Cockerel and Fireman's Helmet

1997. Birth Anniversaries. Multicoloured.
351 13t. Type **119** (bicentenary) 10 10
352 24t. Ziga Zois (naturalist, 250th) 20 20
353 80t. Skof Baraga (missionary, bicentenary) 70 70

1997. Fire Service.
354 **120** 70t. multicoloured 60 60

121 Series SZ Steam Locomotive

1997. 140th Anniv of Ljubljana–Trieste Railway.
355 **121** 80t. black, yellow and red 70 70

122 Red Cross

124 Girl with Dog (Andrejka Cufer)

1997. Obligatory Tax. Solidarity Week.
356 **122** 7t. multicoloured 10 10

1997. Children's Week.
358 **124** 14t. multicoloured 10 10

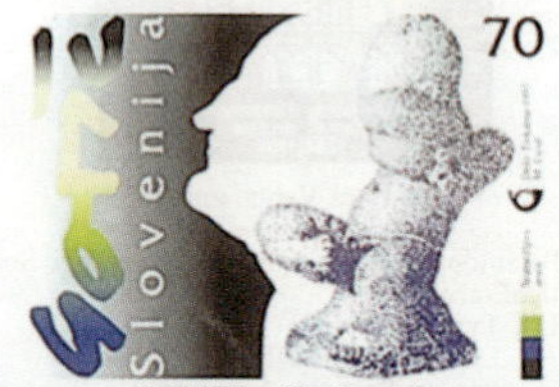

125 "The Shy Lover"

1997. Birth Centenary of France Gorse (sculptor). Multicoloured.
359 70t. Type **125** 50 50
360 80t. "The Farmer's Wife" . . 55 55

126 Judo Bout

127 Venezia Guilia and Istria 1945 Stamp, Anchor and Rose

1997. European Youth Judo Championships, Ljubljana.
361 **126** 90t. multicoloured 65 65

1997. 50th Anniv of Incorporation of Istria and Slovene Coast into Yugoslavia.
362 **127** 50t. multicoloured 40 40

128 Children watching Birds

1997. Christmas and New Year. Multicoloured.
363 14t. Type **128** 10 10
364 90t. Crib (Liza Hribar), Church of the Blessed Virgin, Krope 65 65

129 Globe, Golden Vixen and Skier

130 Dove, Envelope and Postal Centre

1997. World Cup Alpine Skiing Championships.
365 **129** 90t. multicoloured 65 65

1997. Inauguration of New Postal Centre, Ljubljana.
366 **130** 30t. multicoloured 20 20

131 Guests and Attendants

1998. Traditional Pine Brush Wedding. Mult.
367 20t. Type **131** 15 15
368 80t. Priest, accordionist and bride and groom 60 60
Nos. 367/8 were issued together, se-tenant, forming a composite design.

132 Figure Skating

1998. Winter Olympic Games, Nagano, Japan. Multicoloured.
369 70t. Type **132** 50 50
370 90t. Biathlon 65 65

133 Airplane, Air Traffic Controllers and Flight Paths

1998. 35th Anniv of Eurocontrol Convention (on regional aviation safety co-operation).
371 **133** 90t. multicoloured 65 65

134 Lakotnik eating Potato

1998. Cartoon Characters by Miki Muster. Multicoloured.
372 14t. Type **134** 10 10
373 105t. Trdonja (turtle) in sea 75 75
374 118t. Zvitorepec (fox) walking through meadow 85 85

135 Louis Adamic and Maps highlighting Birthplace and American Residence

1998. Birth Anniversaries. Multicoloured.
376 26t. Type **135** (writer, centenary) 20 20
377 90t. Altar figure from Zagreb Cathedral and fountain (300th anniv of Francesco Robba (sculptor)) 65 65

136 St. George's Festival

1997. Europa. National Festivals.
378 **136** 90t. multicoloured 65 65

137 Red Cross and Blood Drop

138 Red Cross

1998. Obligatory Tax. Red Cross.
379 **137** 7t. red and black 10 10

1998. Obligatory Tax. Solidarity Week. Each red and black.
380 7t. Type **138** 10 10
381 7t. Red cross (value at right) 10 10
Nos. 380/1 were issued together, se-tenant, forming a composite design.

139 Mt. Boc

1998.
382 **139** 14t. multicoloured 10 10

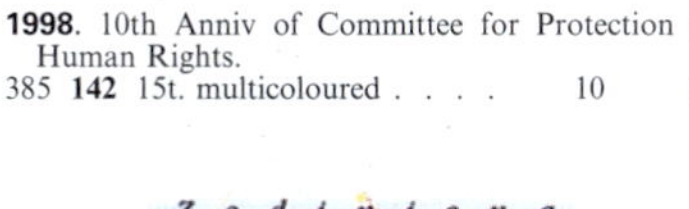

141 Series SZ 06-018 Steam Locomotive

142 Victory Sign

1998.
384 **141** 80t. multicoloured 60 60

1998. 10th Anniv of Committee for Protection of Human Rights.
385 **142** 15t. multicoloured 10 10

143 Map of Slovenia

1998. 150th Anniv of Movement for the Independence of Slovenia.
386 **143** 80t. multicoloured 60 60

144 St. Bernard of Clairvaux, Sticna Monastery Church and Foundation Document

1998. 900th Anniv of Cistercian Order and Centenary of Return of Cistercians to Sticna.
387 **144** 14t. multicoloured 10 10

145 Sound Waves and European Cuckoo

1998. 70th Anniv of Cuckoo Emblem of Radio Ljubljana.
388 **145** 50t. multicoloured 35 35

146 "The Banker" (watercolour and collage)

1998. Birth Centenary of August Cernigoj (artist). Multicoloured.
389 70t. Type **146** 50 50
390 80t. "El" (sculpture) 60 60

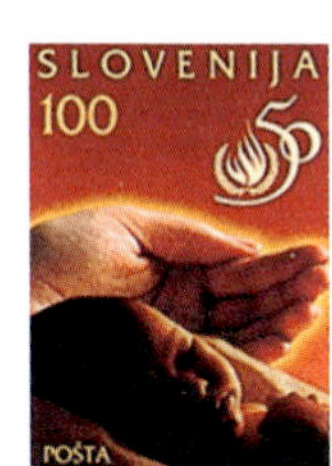

147 Hands cradling Sleeping Infant

1998. 50th Anniv of Universal Declaration of Human Rights.
391 **147** 100t. multicoloured . . . 70 70

148 Children with Candle (Marjanca Bozic)

1998. Christmas and New Year. Multicoloured.
392 15t. Type **148** 10 10
393 90t. "Adoration of the Wise Men" (fresco, St. Nicholas's Church, Mace) 60 60

150 Peter Kozler (cartographer)

1999. Anniversaries. Multicoloured.
395 14t. Type **150** (125th birth anniv) 10 10
396 15t. Bozidar Lavric (surgeon, birth centenary) 10 10
397 70t. General Rudolf Maister (125th birth anniv) 45 45
398 80t. France Preseren (writer, 150th death anniv) 50 50

151 White Horses, Planets and Hearts

1999. Greetings Stamp.
399 **151** 15t. multicoloured 10 10

152 Carnival Procession

1999. Skoromati Carnival. Multicoloured.
400 20t. Type **152** 15 15
401 80t. Horn-blower and procession 50 50
Nos. 400/1 were issued together, se-tenant, forming a composite design.

153 Mt. Golica

1999.
402 **153** 15t. multicoloured 10 10

154 1919 20v. and 1997 14t. Stamps

1999. 50th Anniv of Slovenian Philatelic Society.
403 **154** 16t. multicoloured 10 10

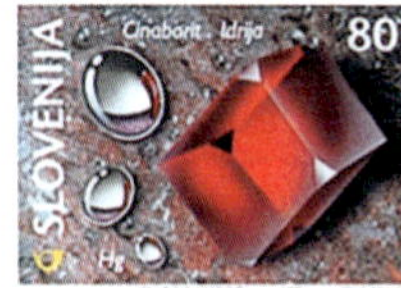

155 Cinnabarite

1999. Minerals.
404 **155** 80t. multicoloured 50 50

156 "Co-operation"

1999. 50th Anniv of Council of Europe.
405 **156** 80t. multicoloured 50 50

157 Triglav National Park

1999. Europa. Parks and Gardens.
406 **157** 90t. multicoloured 60 60

158 Figures with Raised Arms

159 Early Postman and Moon

1999. Obligatory Tax. Red Cross.
407 **158** 8t. black and red 10 10

1999. 125th Anniv of Universal Postal Union. Multicoloured.
408 30t. Type **159** 20 20
409 90t. Astronaut on moon, posthorn and Earth . . . 60 60

160 Slovenian Coldblood

1999. Horses. Multicoloured.
410 60t. Type **160** 45 45
411 70t. Ljutomer trotting horse 45 45
412 120t. Slovenian warmblood (show jumping) 80 80
413 350t. Lipizzaner . . . . . . 2·25 2·25

161 Dogs and Handlers

1999. World Rescue Dogs Championship.
415 **161** 80t. multicoloured 50 50

162 Children's Toys

1999. Year Multicoloured.
416 20t. Type **162** 15 15
417 70t. Forms of communication 45 45
418 80t. Symbols of science and culture 50 50
419 90t. Tree with symbols of education 60 60

163 "Self-portrait" and "Unravelling the Mysteries of Life"

1999. Birth Centenary of Bozidar Jakac (artist). Multicoloured.
420 70t. Type **163** 45 45
421 80t. "Self-portrait" and "Novo Mesto" 50 50

164 Terglou Locomotive

1999. 150th Anniv of Arrival of First Train in Ljubljana.
422 **164** 80t. multicoloured 50 50

165 Slomsek

166 Family watching Fireworks

1999. Beatification of Bishop Anton Martin Slomsk.
423 **165** 90t. multicoloured 60 60

1999. Obligatory Tax. Solidarity Week. As T **138**. Each orange, black and red.
424 9t. Red cross (value at left) 10 10
425 9t. Red cross (value at right) 10 10
Nos. 424/5 were issued together, se-tenant, each pair forming a composite design of a link in a chain.

1999. Christmas. Multicoloured.
426 17t. Type **166** 10 10
427 18t. Type **166** 10 10
428 80t. Letter "h" illuminated with Nativity scene (Kranj antiphonary) 45 45
429 90t. As No. 428 . . . . . . 50 50

167 Teddy Bear and Baby's Bottle

169 Sailing Ship and Tone Seliskar (writer)

168 Masqueraders

2000. Greetings Stamp.
430 **167** 34t. multicoloured 20 20

2000. Pustovi Carnival Masks. Multicoloured.
431 34t. Type **168** 20 20
432 80t. Four masqueraders . . . 45 45

2000. Birth Centenaries. Multicoloured.
433 64t. Type **169** 35 35
434 120t. Elvira Kralj (actress) and actors holding masks 65 65

170 Stage Coach

172 Muri the Tom Cat

171 Mt. Storzic

2000. 500th Anniv of Postal Service in Slovenia.
435 **170** 500t. multicoloured . . . 2·75 2·75

2000.
436 **171** 18t. multicoloured 10 10

2000. Characters from Children's Books. Multicoloured. Ordinary or self-adhesive gum.
437 20t. Type **172** 15 15
438 20t. Mojca Pokrajculja . . . 15 15
439 20t. Pedenjped 15 15

173 Swallows

2000. 55th Anniv of Return of Slovene Exiles.
443 **173** 25t. multicoloured 15 15

174 Trilobite

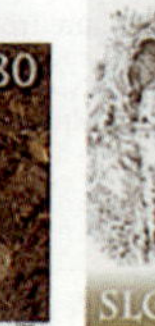

176 Predjama Castle

2000. Fossil and Mineral. Multicoloured.
444 80t. Type **174** 45 45
445 90t. Magnesium-tourmaliae 50 50

2000. Castles.
447 **176** 1t. brown and bistre . . . 10 10
448 – 1t. brown and bistre . . . 10 10
449 – 100t. deep brown and brown 55 55
450 – 100t. deep brown and brown 55 55
DESIGNS: No. 448, Velenje Castle; 449, Podsreda Castle; 450, Bled Castle.

177 Apple Blossom Weevil on Flower Bed

179 Red Cross

2000. The Apple. Multicoloured.
451 10t. Type **177** 10 10
452 10t. Apple blossom 10 10
453 10t. Apple 10 10

2000. No. 189e surch **19.00**.
454 19t. on 17t. choc, yell & brn 10 10

2000. Obligatory Tax. Red Cross Week.
455 **179** 10t. red and black 10 10

180 Globe and Radio Operator

2000. 3rd World Radiosport Team Championship and 50th Anniv of Amateur Radio in Slovenia.
456 **180** 20t. multicoloured 10 10

181 Chicken and Football

183 "Building Europe"

182 Racing Dinghies

2000. European Football Championship, Belgium and The Netherlands.
457 **181** 40t. multicoloured 20 20

2000. Olympic Games, Sydney. Multicoloured.
458 80t. Type **182** 45 45
459 90t. Sydney Opera House . . 50 50
Nos. 458/9 were issued together, se-tenant, forming a composite design.

2000. Europa.
460 **183** 90t. multicoloured 50 50

184 Flowers, Frog, Dragonfly and Plants within Life Ring

2000. World Environment Day.
461 **184** 90t. multicoloured 50 50

185 Lightning, Weather Vane and Carline Thistle

186 Cherry Blossom

2000. World Meteorological Day. 150th Anniv of Meteorological Observation in Slovenia.
462 **185** 150t. multicoloured . . . 75 75

2000. The Cherry. Multicoloured.
463 5t. Type **186** 10 10
464 5t. European cherry fruit fly 10 10
465 5t. Vigred sweet cherries . . 10 10

187 Ptuj Castle

188 Zelen Grape

2000. Castles and Manor Houses (1st series).
466 **187** A (18t.) brown and yellow 10 10
467 – A (18t.) brown and yellow 10 10
468 – B (19t.) brown and green 10 10
469 – B (19t.) brown and green 10 10
DESIGNS: No. 466, Type **187**; 467, Otocec Castle; 468, Zuzemberk Castle; 469, Turjak Castle.
See also Nos. 520/3.

2000. Wine Grapes. Multicoloured.
470 20t. Type **188** 10 10
471 40t. Ranfol 20 20
472 80t. Zametovka 45 45
473 130t. Rumeni plavec 70 70

189 "Self-portrait" and "Storm"

2000. Birth Centenary of Tone Kralj (artist). Multicoloured.
475 70t. Type **189** 40 40
476 80t. "Self-portrait" and "Judita" 45 45

190 Iztok Cop and Luka Spik (coxless pairs)

2000. Olympic Gold Medal Winners. Multicoloured.
477 21t. Type **190** 20 20
478 21t. Rajmond Debevec (rifle-shooting) 20 20

2000. Obligatory Tax. Solidarity Week. As T **138**. Each grey, black and red.
479 10t. Type **191** 10 10
480 10t. Red Cross (value at right) 10 10
Nos. 479/80 were issued together, se-tenant, forming a composite design.

191 Healthy and Damaged Environments

2000. New Millennium. "EXPO 2000" World's Fair, Hanover, Germany.
481 **191** 40t. multicoloured 20 20

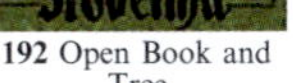

192 Open Book and Tree
194 Bucket (Dragotin Kette (poet))

193 Children

2000. 450th Anniv of First Printed Book in Slovenian Language.
482 **192** 50t. multicoloured 30 30

2000. Christmas. Multicoloured. Ordinary or self-adhesive gum.
483 B (21t.) Type **193** 10 10
484 90t. Baby Jesus 50 50

2001. Birth Anniversaries. Multicoloured.
487 A(24t.) Type **194** (125th anniv) 15 15
488 95t. Jar of flowers (Ivan Tavcar (politician and writer)) (150th anniv) . . . 50 50
489 107t. Cup of coffee (Ivan Cankar (writer)) (125th anniv) 60 60

195 Bride and Groom riding Bicycle

2001. Wedding Greetings Stamp.
490 **195** B (2t.) multicoloured . . 10 10

196 Colourful Headdresses

2001. Dobrepolje Folk Masks. Multicoloured.
491 50t. Type **196** 30 30
492 95t. Procession 50 50

197 Mt. Jalovec
198 Cowboy Pipec

2001.
493 **197** B (25t.) multicoloured . . 15 15

2001. Cowboy Pipec (cartoon character) by Bozo Kos. Multicoloured. Ordinary or self-adhesive gum.
494 B (25t.) Type **198** 15 15
495 B (25t.) Beetroot (Native American boy) 15 15

199 Fluorite

2001.
498 **199** 95t. multicoloured 55 55

200 Fossilized Starfish

2001.
499 **200** 107t. multicoloured . . . 65 65

201 Stars, Goddess Europa and Bull

2001. Europe Day (9 May).
500 **201** 221t. multicoloured . . . 1·25 1·25

202 Soca River and Bridge, Solkan

2001. Millenary of Solkan.
501 **202** 261t. multicoloured . . . 1·60 1·60

203 Dove with Lime Leaf

2001. 60th Anniv of Liberation Front.
502 **203** 24t. multicoloured 15 15

204 Red Cross

2001. Obligatory Tax. Red Cross Week.
503 **204** 12t. red and grey 10 10

205 Worker Bee gathering Nectar

2001. The Carniolan Honey Bee (*Apis mellifera carnica*). Sheet 113 × 80 mm containing T **205** and similar horiz designs. Multicoloured.
MS504 24t. Type **205**; 48t. Queen bee and drones; 95t. Queen, workers and drones on edge of honeycomb; 170t. Building and swarm . . . . 2·00 2·00

206 Flag

2001. 10th Anniv of Independence
505 **206** 100t. multicoloured . . . 60 60

207 Gospodicna Spring, Gorjanci

2001. Europa. Water Resources.
506 **207** 107t. multicoloured . . . 65 85

208 Tramcar No. 5

2001. Centenary of Introduction of Trams to Ljubljana.
507 **208** 113t. multicoloured . . . 70 70

209 Maxi-Ball and Ljubljana Skyline

2001. 6th World Maxi-Basketball Championship, Ljubljana.
508 **209** 261t. multicoloured . . . 1·60 1·60

210 American and Russian Flags behind Bridge, Ljubljana
211 Peach Blossom Dragon

2001. 1st Summit Meeting between Pres. George W. Bush of America and Pres. Vladimir Putin of Russian Federation, Brdo Castle, Kranj.
509 **210** 107t. multicoloured . . . 65 65
MS510 60 × 90 mm. No. 509 . . 65 65

2001. Peach Cultivation. Multicoloured.
511 50t. Type **211** 30 30
512 50t. Green peach aphid . . . 30 30
513 50t. Redhaven peach 30 30

212 "Mohorjev koledar" 1920 Calendar Cover

2001. 150th Anniv of "Mohorjeva Druzba" Publishing House.
514 **212** B (31t.) multicoloured . . 20 20

213 Logarithms, Building and Globe

2001. Centenary of Jurij Vega Grammar School, Idrija.
515 **213** A (26t.) multicoloured . . 15 15

214 Score and Blaz Arnic

2001. Composers. Multicoloured.
516 95t. Type **214** 55 55
517 107t. Lucijan Marija Skerjanc and score 65 65

215 Cat
216 Children encircling Globe

2001. World Animal Day (4th October).
518 **215** 107t. multicoloured . . . 65 65

2001. United Nations Year of Dialogue among Civilizations.
519 **216** 107t. multicoloured . . . 65 65

2001. Castles and Manor Houses (2nd series). As T **187**.
520 C (95t.) brown and vermilion 55 55
521 C (95t.) brown and red . . . 55 55
522 D (107t.) deep blue and blue 65 65
523 D (107t.) indigo and blue . . 65 65
DESIGNS: No. 520, Dobrovo Manor; 521, Brezice Castle; 522, Olimje Manor; 523, Murska Sobota Manor.

217 Handprints
218 Christmas Tree

2001. Obligatory Tax. Solidarity Week.
524 **217** 13t. multicoloured 10 10

2001. Christmas. Multicoloured. Ordinary or self-adhesive gum.
525 B (31t.) Type **218** 20 20
526 D (107t.) Nativity 65 65

SOLOMON ISLANDS Pt. 1

A group of islands in the west Pacific, east of New Guinea.

1907. 12 pence = 1 shilling;
20 shillings = 1 pound.
1966. 100 cents = $1 Australian.

1
2

1907.
1 **1** $\frac{1}{2}$d. blue . . . . 9·00 14·00
2 1d. red . . . . 23·00 25·00
3 2d. blue . . . . 29·00 30·00
4 2$\frac{1}{2}$d. yellow . . . . 32·00 42·00
5 5d. green . . . . 55·00 65·00
6 6d. brown . . . . 50·00 60·00
7 1s. purple . . . . 70·00 75·00

1908.

No.	Type	Description	Unused	Used
8	2	½d. green	1·50	1·00
9		1d. red	1·25	1·00
10		2d. grey	1·25	1·00
11		2½d. blue	3·75	2·00
11a		4d. red on yellow	3·25	11·00
12		5d. olive	9·00	7·00
13		6d. red	10·00	6·50
14		1s. black on green	8·50	7·00
15		2s. purple on blue	40·00	55·00
16		2s.6d. red on blue	48·00	70·00
17		5s. green on yellow	75·00	£100

3

5 Spears and Shield

1913. Inscr "POSTAGE POSTAGE".

No.	Type	Description	Unused	Used
18	3	½d. green	80	3·50
19		1d. red	1·00	14·00
42		1½d. red	2·25	60
20		3d. purple on yellow	80	4·00
21		11d. purple and red	3·00	12·00

1914. Inscr "POSTAGE REVENUE".

No.	Type	Description	Unused	Used
39	3	½d. green	30	3·50
24		1d. red	1·50	1·25
41		1d. violet	1·00	7·50
26		2d. grey	3·00	9·00
27		2½d. blue	2·00	5·00
28		3d. purple on yellow	20·00	85·00
44		3d. blue	70	4·50
29		4d. black and red on yellow	2·00	2·50
45a		4½d. brown	3·00	20·00
46		5d. purple and green	3·00	27·00
47		6d. purple	3·75	27·00
33		1s. black on green	4·75	7·00
34		2s. purple and blue on blue	7·00	10·00
35		2s.6d. black and red on blue	9·50	20·00
36		5s. green and red on yellow	28·00	48·00
37		10s. green and red on green	75·00	80·00
38		£1 purple and black on red	£225	£120

1935. Silver Jubilee. As T **32a** of St. Helena.

No.	Description	Unused	Used
53	1½d. blue and red	1·00	1·00
54	3d. brown and blue	3·00	6·00
55	6d. blue and green	9·00	12·00
56	1s. grey and purple	7·50	10·00

1937. Coronation. As T **32b** of St. Helena.

No.	Description	Unused	Used
57	1d. violet	30	70
58	1½d. red	30	60
59	3d. blue	50	50

1939. Portrait of King George VI.

No.	Type	Description	Unused	Used
60	5	½d. blue and green	15	1·00
61	–	1d. brown and violet	30	1·25
62	–	1½d. green and red	70	1·25
63a	–	2d. brown and black	30	1·50
64	–	2½d. mauve and olive	2·25	2·00
65	–	3d. black and blue	1·00	1·50
66	–	4½d. green and brown	4·00	13·00
67	–	6d. violet and purple	75	1·00
68	–	1s. green and black	1·25	1·00
69	–	2s. black and orange	6·50	5·50
70	–	2s.6d. black and violet	26·00	4·50
71	–	5s. green and red	32·00	10·00
72	–	10s. green and mauve	4·00	8·50

DESIGNS—VERT: 1d. Native constable and chief; 4½d., 10s. Native house, Reef Islands; 6d. Coconut plantation. HORIZ: 1½d. Artificial Island., Malaita; 2½d. Roviana canoe; 1s. Breadfruit; 5s. Malaita canoe. LARGER (35½ × 22 mm): 2d. Canoe house; 3d. Roviana canoes; 2s. Tinakula volcano; 2s.6d. Bismarck scrub fowl.

1946. Victory. As T **33a** of St. Helena.

No.	Description	Unused	Used
73	1½d. red	15	80
74	3d. blue	15	10

1949. Silver Wedding. As T **33b/c** of St. Helena.

No.	Description	Unused	Used
75	2d. grey	50	50
76	10s. mauve	10·00	8·00

1949. 75th Anniv of U.P.U. As T **33d/g** of St. Helena.

No.	Description	Unused	Used
77	2d. brown	50	1·00
78	3d. blue	2·25	1·25
79	5d. green	50	1·60
80	1s. black	50	1·25

1953. Coronation. As T **33h** of St. Helena.

No.	Description	Unused	Used
81	2d. black and grey	50	1·25

17 Ysabel Canoe

1956. Portrait of Queen Elizabeth II.

No.	Type	Description	Unused	Used
82	17	½d. orange and purple	15	50
83	–	1d. green & brn (as No. 65)	15	15
84	–	1½d. slate and red (No. 62)	15	80
105	–	2d. sepia and green (No. 63)	20	20
86	–	2½d. black and blue	60	50
106	–	3d. green and red (No. 71)	55	15
88	–	5d. black and blue	30	55
89	–	6d. black and green	50	25
90	–	8d. blue and black	25	15
108	–	9d. green and black	40	35
91	–	1s. slate and brown	50	50
109	–	1s.3d. black and blue	60	70
110	–	2s. black and red (No. 69)	1·00	5·50
93	–	2s.6d. green & pur (No. 66)	7·50	45
94	–	5s. brown	15·00	4·00
95	–	10s. sepia (No. 61)	20·00	5·00
96	–	£1 black and blue	30·00	35·00

DESIGNS—VERT: 2½d. Prow of Roviana canoe. 10s. Similar to No. 61, but constable in different uniform, without rifle; HORIZ: 5d., 1s.3d. Map; 6d. "Miena" (Schooner); 8d., 9d. Henderson Airfield, Guadalcanal; 1s. Chart showing voyage of H.M.S. "Swallow" in 1767; 5s. Mendana and "Todos los Santos"; £1 Arms of the Protectorate.

32 Great Frigate Bird

1961. New Constitution, 1960.

No.	Type	Description	Unused	Used
97	32	2d. black and turquoise	10	30
98		3d. black and red	10	10
99		9d. black and purple	15	30

1963. Freedom from Hunger. As T **63a** of St. Helena.

No.	Description	Unused	Used
100	1s.3d. blue	75	35

1963. Cent of Red Cross. As T **63b** of St. Helena.

No.	Description	Unused	Used
101	2d. red and black	25	20
102	9d. red and blue	50	90

33 Makira Food Bowl

1965. Central design in black; background colours given.

No.	Type	Description	Unused	Used
112	33	½d. blue and light blue	10	1·00
113	–	1d. orange and yellow	70	60
114	–	1½d. blue and green	35	50
115	–	2d. ultramarine and blue	60	75
116	–	2½d. brown and light brown	10	60
117	–	3d. green and light green	10	10
118	–	6d. mauve and orange	35	80
119	–	9d. green and yellow	40	15
120	–	1s. brown and mauve	1·00	15
121	–	1s.3d. red	4·00	2·25
122	–	2s. purple and lilac	8·00	2·75
123	–	2s.6d. brown and light brown	1·00	70
124	–	5s. blue and violet	12·00	4·00
125	–	10s. green and yellow	15·00	3·00
126	–	£1 violet and pink	11·00	4·00

DESIGNS: 1d. "Dendrobium veratrifolium" (orchid); 1½d. Chiragra spider conch; 2d. Blyth's hornbill ("Hornbill"); 2½d. Ysabel shield; 3d. Rennellese club; 6d. Moorish idol (fish); 9d. Lesser frigate bird ("Frigate Bird"); 1s. "Dendrobium macrophyllum" (orchid); 1s.3d. "Dendrobium spectabilis" (orchid); 2s. Sanford's sea eagle ("Sanford's Eagle"); 2s.6d. Malaita belt; 5s. "Ornithoptera victoreae" (butterfly); 10s. Ducorp's cockatoo ("White Cockatoo"); £1 Western canoe figurehead.

1965. Cent of I.T.U. As T **64a** of St. Helena.

No.	Description	Unused	Used
127	2d. red and turquoise	20	15
128	3d. turquoise and drab	20	15

1965. I.C.Y. As T **64b** of St. Helena.

No.	Description	Unused	Used
129	1d. purple and turquoise	10	10
130	2s.6d. green and lavender	45	20

1966. Churchill Commemoration. As T **64c** of St. Helena.

No.	Description	Unused	Used
131	2d. blue	15	10
132	9d. green	25	10
133	1s.3d. brown	35	10
134	2s.6d. violet	40	25

1966. Decimal Currency. Nos. 112/26 surch.

No.	Description	Unused	Used
135A	1c. on ½d.	10	10
136A	2c. on 1d.	10	10
137A	3c. on 1½d.	10	10
138A	4c. on 2d.	15	10
139A	5c. on 6d.	15	10
140B	6c. on 2½d.	15	10
141B	7c. on 3d.	15	10
142B	8c. on 9d.	15	10
143A	10c. on 1s.	30	10
144B	12c. on 1s.3d.	65	10
145A	13c. on 1s.3d.	2·50	15
146B	14c. on 3d.	40	10
147A	20c. on 2s.	2·50	25
148A	25c. on 2s.6d.	60	40
149B	35c. on 2d.	2·00	25
150A	50c. on 5s.	4·50	1·50
151A	$1 on 10s.	2·50	1·50
152A	$2 on £1	2·25	3·00

1966. World Cup Football Championship. As T **64d** of St. Helena.

No.	Description	Unused	Used
153	8c. multicoloured	15	15
154	35c. multicoloured	30	15

1966. Inauguration of W.H.O. Headquarters. Geneva. As T **64e** of St. Helena.

No.	Description	Unused	Used
155	3c. black, green and blue	20	10
156	50c. black, purple and ochre	60	20

1966. 20th Anniv of U.N.E.S.C.O. As T **64f/h** of St. Helena.

No.	Description	Unused	Used
157	3c. multicoloured	15	10
158	25c. yellow, violet and olive	30	15
159	$1 black, purple and orange	75	70

49 Henderson Field

1967. 25th Anniv of Guadalcanal Campaign (Pacific War). Multicoloured.

No.	Description	Unused	Used
160	8c. Type **49**	15	15
161	35c. Red Beach landings	15	15

51 Mendana's "Todos los Santos" off Point Cruz

1968. 400th Anniv of Discovery of the Solomon Is. Multicoloured.

No.	Description	Unused	Used
162	3c. Type **51**	20	10
163	8c. Arrival of missionaries	20	10
164	35c. Pacific Campaign, World War II	40	10
165	$1 Proclamation of the Protectorate	60	1·00

55 Vine Fishing

1968.

No.	Type	Description	Unused	Used
166	55	1c. blue, black and brown	10	10
167	–	2c. green, black and brown	10	10
168	–	3c. green, myrtle and black	10	10
169	–	4c. purple, black and brown	15	10
170	–	6c. multicoloured	30	10
171	–	8c. multicoloured	25	10
172	–	12c. ochre, red and black	65	40
173	–	14c. red, brown and black	2·25	3·50
174	–	15c. multicoloured	80	80
175	–	20c. blue, red and black	4·25	3·00
176	–	24c. red, black and yellow	2·00	3·25
177	–	35c. multicoloured	2·00	30
178	–	45c. multicoloured	1·50	30
179	–	$1 blue, green and black	2·50	1·50
180	–	$2 multicoloured	6·00	3·50

DESIGNS: 2c. Kite fishing; 3c. Platform fishing; 4c. Net fishing; 6c. Gold lip shell diving; 8c. Night fishing; 12c. Boat building; 14c. Cocoa; 15c. Road building; 20c. Geological survey; 24c. Hauling timber; 35c. Copra; 45c. Harvesting rice; $1 Honiara Port; $2 Internal air service.

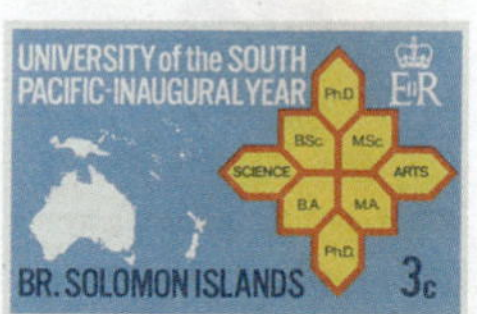

70 Map of Australasia and Diagram

1969. Inaugural Year of South Pacific University.

No.	Type	Description	Unused	Used
181	70	3c. multicoloured	10	10
182		12c. multicoloured	10	10
183		35c. multicoloured	15	10

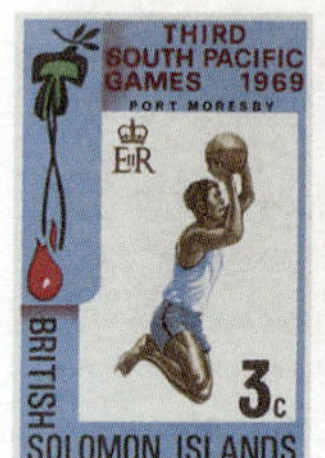

71 Basketball Player

75 South Sea Island with Star of Bethlehem

1969. 3rd South Pacific Games, Port Moresby. Multicoloured.

No.	Description	Unused	Used
184	3c. Type **71**	10	10
185	8c. Footballer	10	10
186	14c. Sprinter	10	10
187	45c. Rugby player	20	15
MS188	126×120 mm. Nos. 184/7	2·75	8·00

1969. Christmas.

No.	Type	Description	Unused	Used
189	75	8c. black, violet and green	10	10
190	–	35c. multicoloured	20	20

DESIGN; 35c. Southern Cross, "PAX" and frigate bird (stained glass window).

77 "Paid" Stamp, New South Wales 1896–1906 2d. Stamp and 1906–07 Tulagi Postmark

1970. New G.P.O., Honiara.

No.	Type	Description	Unused	Used
191	77	7c. mauve, blue and black	15	15
192	–	14c. green, blue and black	20	15
193	–	18c. multicoloured	20	15
194	–	23c. multicoloured	20	20

DESIGNS: 14c. 1906–07 2d. stamp and C. M. Woodford; 18c. 1910–14 5s. stamp and Tulagi postmark, 1913; 23c. New G.P.O., Honiara.

81 Coat of Arms

1970. New Constitution.

No.	Type	Description	Unused	Used
195	81	18c. multicoloured	15	10
196	–	35c. green, blue and ochre	35	20

DESIGN—HORIZ: 35c. Map.

83 British Red Cross H.Q., Honiara

1970. Centenary of British Red Cross.

No.	Type	Description	Unused	Used
197	83	3c. multicoloured	10	10
198	–	35c. blue, red and black	25	20

DESIGN—VERT: 35c. Wheelchair and map.

86 Reredos (Altar Screen)

1970. Christmas.

No.	Type	Description	Unused	Used
199	–	8c. ochre and violet	10	10
200	86	45c. chestnut, orange and brown	25	20

DESIGN—HORIZ: 8c. Carved angel.

87 La Perouse and "La Boussole"

1971. Ships and Navigators (1st series). Mult.

No.	Description	Unused	Used
201	3c. Type **87**	45	20
202	4c. Astrolabe and Polynesian reed map	45	20

203 12c. Abel Tasman and "Heemskerk" 60 30
204 35c. Te puki canoe, Santa Cruz 70 50
See also Nos. 215/18, 236/9, 254/7 and 272/5.

88 J. Atkin, Bishop Patteson and S. Taroaniara

1971. Death Cent of Bishop Patteson. Mult.
205 2c. Type **88** 10 10
206 4c. Last landing at Nukapu 10 10
207 14c. Memorial Cross and Nukapu (vert) 10 10
208 45c. Knotted leaf and canoe (vert) 20 10

89 Torch Emblem and Boxers

1971. South Pacific Games, Tahiti. Mult.
209 3c. Type **89** 10 10
210 8c. Emblem and footballers 10 15
211 12c. Emblem and runner . . 10 20
212 35c. Emblem and skin-diver 15 20

90 Melanesian Lectern

1971. Christmas. Multicoloured.
213 9c. Type **90** 10 10
214 45c. "United we Stand" (Margarita Bara) 20 20

1972. Ships and Navigators (2nd series). As T **87**. Multicoloured.
215 4c. Bougainville and "La Boudeuse" 30 10
216 9c. Horizontal planisphere and ivory backstaff 35 10
217 15c. Philip Carteret and H.M.S. "Swallow" 60 15
218 45c. Malaita canoe 70 90

91 "Cupha woodfordi"

1972. Multicoloured.
219 1c. Type **91** 15 50
220 2c. "Ornithoptera priamus" 25 50
221 3c. "Vindula sapor" 25 60
222 4c. "Papilio ulysses" 25 60
223 5c. Big-eyed trevally 25 30
224 8c. Australian bonito . . . 40 50
225 9c. Blue demoiselle 50 65
226 12c. "Costus speciosus" . . 1·25 90
227 15c. Clown anemonefish ("Orange anemone fish") 1·25 1·00
228 20c. "Spathoglottis plicata" 3·00 1·75
229 25c. "Ephemerantha comata" . . . . 3·00 1·50
230 35c. "Dendrobium cuthbertsonii" . . . . . 3·00 2·25
231 45c. "Heliconia salomonica" 2·50 3·00
232 $1 Dotty triggerfish . . . . 3·00 4·50
233 $2 "Ornithoptera alottei" 9·00 15·00
233a $5 Great frigate bird . . . . 14·00 16·00
The 2, 3, 4c. and $2 are butterflies; the 5, 8, 9, 15c. and $1 are fishes, and the 12, 20, 25, 35, 45c. are flowers.

1972. Royal Silver Wedding. As T **103** of St. Helena, but with Greetings and Message Drum in background.
234 8c. red 10 10
235 45c. green 20 20

1973. Ships and Navigators (3rd series). As T **87**. Multicoloured.
236 4c. D'Entrecasteaux and "La Recherche" 30 20
237 9c. Ship's hour-glass and chronometer 35 20
238 15c. Lt. Shortland and H.M.S. "Alexander" . . . 70 30
239 35c. Tomoko (war canoe) . . 75 1·10

93 Pan Pipes

1973. Musical Instruments. Multicoloured.
240 4c. Type **93** 10 10
241 9c. Castanets 10 10
242 15c. Bamboo flute 15 10
243 35c. Bauro gongs 20 25
244 45c. Bamboo band 20 30

1973. Royal Wedding. As T **74a** of Pitcairn Islands.
245 4c. blue 10 10
246 35c. blue 15 10

94 "Adoration of the Kings" (Jan Brueghel)

1973. Christmas. "Adoration of the Kings" by the artists listed. Multicoloured.
247 8c. Type **94** 10 10
248 22c. Pieter Brueghel (vert) . . 20 25
249 45c. Botticelli (48 × 35 mm) 50 50

95 Queen Elizabeth II and Map

1974. Royal Visit.
250 **95** 4c. multicoloured 25 10
251 9c. multicoloured 25 10
252 15c. multicoloured 30 20
253 35c. multicoloured . . . . 50 1·25

1974. Ships and Navigators (4th series). As T **87**. Multicoloured.
254 4c. Commissioner landing from S.S. "Titus" 20 10
255 9c. Radar scanner 20 10
256 15c. Natives being transported to a "Blackbirder" brig 25 15
257 45c. Lieut. John F. Kennedy's "P.T. 109" 1·00 90

96 "Postman"

1974. Centenary of U.P.U.
258 **96** 4c. green, dp green & black 10 10
259 – 9c. lt brown, brown & black 10 10
260 – 15c. mauve, purple & black 15 10
261 – 45c. blue, deep blue & black . . . . 35 1·40
DESIGNS (Origami figures)—HORIZ: 9c. Carrier-pigeon; 45c. Pegasus. VERT: 15c. St. Gabriel.

97 "New Constitution" Stamp of 1970

1974. New Constitution.
262 **97** 4c. multicoloured 10 10
263 – 9c. red, black and brown 10 10
264 – 15c. red, black and brown 15 10
265 **97** 35c. multicoloured 30 50
MS266 134 × 84 mm. Nos. 262/5 1·50 3·50
DESIGNS: 9 c, 15c. "New Constitution" stamp of 1961 (inscr "1960").

98 Mangrove Golden Whistler ("Golden Whislter")

1975. Birds. Multicoloured.
267 1c. Type **98** 45 85
268 2c. River kingfisher . . . . . 50 1·00
269 3c. Red-bibbed fruit dove ("Red-throated Fruit Dove") . . . . 55 1·00
270 4c. Red-backed button quail ("Button Quail") 55 85
271 $2 Duchess lorikeet . . . . . 8·00 10·50
See also Nos. 305/20.

1975. Ships and Navigators (5th series). As T **87**. Multicoloured.
272 4c. "Walande" (coaster) . . . 35 10
273 9c. "Melanesian" (coaster) . . 45 10
274 15c. "Marsina" (container ship) 60 15
275 45c. "Himalaya" (liner) . . . 1·10 1·50

99 800 Metres Race

1975. 5th South Pacific Games. Multicoloured.
276 4c. Type **99** 10 10
277 9c. Long jump 10 10
278 15c. Javelin-throwing 15 10
279 45c. Football 45 45
MS280 130 × 95 mm. Nos. 276/9 4·00 4·00

100 Nativity Scene and Candles

1975. Christmas. Multicoloured.
281 15c. Type **100** 15 10
282 35c. Shepherds, angels and candles 30 15
283 45c. The Magi and candles 40 40
MS284 140 × 130 mm. Nos. 281/3 4·00 5·00

1975. Nos. 267/70, 223/32, 271 and 233a with obliterating bar over "BRITISH". Mult.
285 1c. Type **98** 60 55
286 2c. River kingfisher . . . . 1·00 55
287 3c. Red-bibbed fruit dove . . 70 55
288 4c. Red-backed button quail 1·00 55
289 5c. Big-eyed trevally 50 55
290 8c. Australian bonito 50 60
291 9c. Blue demoiselle 50 60
292 12c. "Costus speciosus" . . . 1·50 1·00
293 15c. Clown anemonefish ("Orange anemone fish") 1·50 1·25
294 20c. "Spathoglottis plicata" 1·50 1·50
295 25c. "Ephemerantha comata" 1·50 1·75
296 35c. "Dendrobium cuthbertsonii" . . . . . . 1·50 1·25
297 45c. "Heliconia salomonica" 1·25 2·00
298 $1 Dotty triggerfish . . . . . 1·00 1·25
299 $2 Duchess lorikeet . . . . . 3·50 6·00
300 $5 Great frigate bird . . . . 3·25 8·00

102 Ceremonial Food-bowl

1975. Artefacts (1st series). Multicoloured.
301 4c. Type **102** 10 10
302 15c. Chieftains' money . . . 10 10
303 35c. Nguzu-nguzu (canoe protector spirit) (vert) . . . 25 20
304 45c. Nguzu-nguzu canoe prow 30 25
See also Nos. 337/40, 353/6 and 376/9.

103 Mangrove Golden Whistler

1976. Multicoloured.
305 1c. Type **103** 50 50
306 2c. River kingfisher . . . . 1·00 80
307 3c. Red-bibbed fruit dove . . 85 50
308 4c. Red-backed button quail 85 50
309 5c. Willie wagtail . . . . . . 1·00 80
310 6c. Golden cowrie 70 50
311 10c. Glory of the sea cone . . 70 60
312 12c. Rainbow lory . . . . . 1·00 80
313 15c. Chambered or pearly nautilus 65 40
314 20c. Venus comb murex . . . 1·00 45
315 25c. Commercial trochus . . . 70 50
316 35c. Blood-red volute 80 50
317 45c. Orange spider conch . . 80 60
318 $1 Trumpet triton . . . . . 1·00 1·75
319 $2 Duchess lorikeet . . . . . 2·50 3·50
320 $5 Great frigate bird . . . . 1·75 3·75

104 Coastwatchers, 1942

1976. Bicent of American Revolution. Mult.
321 6c. Type **104** 20 10
322 20c. "Amagiri" (Japanese destroyer) ramming U.S.S. "PT109" and Lt. J. F. Kennedy 45 30
323 35c. Henderson Airfield . . . 50 40
324 45c. Map of Guadalcanal . . 50 70
MS325 95 × 115 mm. Nos. 321/4 6·50 9·00

105 Alexander Graham Bell

107 The Communion Plate

106 B.A.C. One Eleven 200/400

1976. Centenary of Telephone.
326 **105** 6c. multicoloured 10 10
327 – 20c. multicoloured 15 10
328 – 35c. brown, orange and red 20 15
329 – 45c. multicoloured 25 35
DESIGNS: 20c. Radio telephone via satellite; 35c. Ericson's magneto telephone; 45c. Stick telephone and first telephone.

1976. 50th Anniv of First Flight to Solomon Is. Multicoloured.
330 6c. Type **106** 35 10
331 20c. Britten Norman Islander 65 15
332 35c. Douglas DC-3 . . . . . 90 20
333 45c. De Havilland D.H.50A Seaplane A8-1 . . . . . . 95 55

1977. Silver Jubilee. Multicoloured.
334 6c. Queen's visit, 1974 . . . 10 10
335 35c. Type **107** 15 20
336 45c. The Communion 25 45

108 Carving from New Georgia

110 The Shepherds

109 Spraying Roof and Mosquito

1977. Artefacts (2nd series). Carvings.
337 **108** 6c. multicoloured 10 10
338 – 20c. multicoloured 10 10
339 – 35c. black, grey and red 20 15
340 – 45c. multicoloured 25 30
DESIGNS: 20c. Sea adaro (spirit); 35c. Shark-headed man; 45c. Man from Ulawa or Malaita.

1977. Malaria Eradication. Multicoloured.
341 6c. Type **109** 10 10
342 20c. Taking blood samples 15 10
343 35c. Microscope and map . . 20 15
344 45c. Delivering drugs 30 40

1977. Christmas. Multicoloured.
345 6c. Type **110** 10 10
346 20c. Mary and Jesus in stable 10 10
347 35c. The Three Kings 20 15
348 45c. "The Flight into Egypt" 25 25

111 Feather Money

1977. Introduction of Solomon Islands Coins and Bank-notes. Multicoloured.
349 6c. Type **111** 10 10
350 6c. New currency coins . . . 10 10
351 45c. New currency notes . . 25 25
352 45c. Shell money 25 25

112 Figure from Shortland Island

113 Sanford's Sea Eagle

1977. Artefacts (3rd series).
353 **112** 6c. multicoloured 10 10
354 – 20c. multicoloured 10 10
355 – 35c. brown, black & orge 20 15
356 – 45c. multicoloured 25 30
DESIGNS: 20c. Ceremonial shield; 35c. Santa Cruz ritual figure; 45c. Decorative combs.

1978. 25th Anniv of Coronation. Multicoloured.
357 – 45c. black, red and silver 15 25
358 – 45c. multicoloured 15 25
359 **113** 45c. black, red and silver 15 25
DESIGNS: No. 357, King's Dragon; 358, Queen Elizabeth II.

114 National Flag

115 John

1978. Independence. Multicoloured.
360 6c. Type **114** 15 10
361 15c. Governor-General's flag 20 10
362 35c. The Cenotaph, Honiara 35 30
363 45c. National coat of arms 40 50

1978. 450th Death Anniv of Durer. Detail's from "Four Apostles". Multicoloured.
364 6c. Type **115** 10 10
365 20c. Peter 15 10
366 35c. Paul 20 15
367 45c. Mark 30 30

116 Firelighting

1978. 50th Anniv of Scouting in Solomon Islands. Multicoloured.
368 6c. Type **116** 15 10
369 20c. Camping 20 20
370 35c. Solomon Islands scouts 40 40
371 45c. Canoeing 50 70

117 H.M.S. "Discovery"

1979. Bicentenary of Captain Cook's Voyages, 1768–79.
372 **117** 8c. multicoloured 25 10
373 – 18c. multicoloured 25 15
374 – 35c. black, green and grey 30 25
375 – 45c. multicoloured 30 40
DESIGNS: 18c. Portrait of Captain Cook by Nathaniel Dance; 35c. Sextant; 45c. Flaxman/Wedgwood medallion of Captain Cook.

118 Fish Net Float

1979. Artefacts (4th series).
376 **118** 8c. multicoloured 10 10
377 – 20c. multicoloured 10 10
378 – 35c. black, grey and red 15 15
379 – 45c. black, brown & green 20 30
DESIGNS—VERT: 20c. Armband of shell money; 45c. Forehead ornament. HORIZ: 35c. Ceremonial food bowl.

119 Running

120 1908 6d. Stamp

1979. South Pacific Games, Fiji. Multicoloured.
380 8c. Type **119** 10 10
381 20c. Hurdling 10 10
382 35c. Football 15 15
383 45c. Swimming 25 35

1979. Death Centenary of Sir Rowland Hill.
384 **120** 8c. red and pink 10 10
385 – 20c. mauve & pale mauve 15 30
386 – 35c. multicoloured 25 45
MS387 121 × 121 mm. 45c. red, green and pink 45 65
DESIGNS: 20c. Great Britian 1856 6d.; 35c. 1978 45c. Independence commemorative.

121 Sea Snake

122 "Madonna and Child" (Morando)

1979. Reptiles. Multicoloured.
388A 1c. Type **121** . . . . . . 10 1·00
389A 3c. Red-banded tree snake 10 1·00
390A 4c. Whip snake . . . . . 10 1·00
391A 6c. Pacific boa . . . . . 10 1·00
392A 8c. Skink 10 80
393A 10c. Gecko 10 80
394Bw 12c. Monitor . . . . . . 30 1·00
395A 15c. Anglehead . . . . . 30 1·00
396A 20c. Giant toad 30 60
397Bw 25c. Marsh frog . . . . . 30 1·00
398A 30c. Horned frog . . . . 1·50 1·00
399A 35c. Tree frog . . . . . . 30 1·00
399cB 40c. Burrowing snake . . 45 1·75
400A 45c. Guppy's snake . . . 30 1·25
400cB 50c. Tree gecko . . . . . 50 1·25
401B $1 Large skink . . . . . 1·50 75
402A $2 Guppy's frog . . . . . 60 2·00
403A $5 Estuarine crocodile . . 1·00 2·25
403cB $10 Hawksbill turtle . . . 4·00 5·50

1979. International Year of the Child. "Madonna and Child" paintings by various artists. Mult.
404 4c. Type **122** 10 10
405 20c. Luini 15 15
406 35c. Bellini 20 15
407 50c. Raphael 30 70
MS408 92 × 133 mm. Nos. 404/7 1·00 1·50

123 H.M.S. "Curacoa" (frigate), 1839

1980. Ships and Crests (1st series). Mult.
409 8c. Type **123** 30 20
410 20c. H.M.S. "Herald" (survey ship), 1854 . . . . 45 40
411 35c. H.M.S. "Royalist" (screw corvette), 1889 . . . 65 80
412 45c. H.M.S. "Beagle" (survey schooner), 1878 . . . . . 70 1·75
See also Nos. 430/3.

124 "Solomon Fisher" (fishery training vessel)

1980. Fishing. Ancillary Craft. Multicoloured.
413 8c. Type **124** 15 10
414 20c. "Solomon Hunter" (fishery training vessel) . . 20 20
415 45c. "Ufi Na Tasi" (refrigerated fish transport) 35 40
416 80c. Research vessel . . . . 60 1·75

125 "Comliebank" (cargo-liner) and 1935 Tulagi Registered Letter Postmark

1980. "London 1980" International Stamp Exhibition. Mail-carrying Transport. Multicoloured.
417 45c. Type **125** 30 45
418 45c. Douglas C-47 Skytrain (U.S. Army Postal Service, 1943) 30 45
419 45c. B.A.C. One Eleven airliner and 1979 Honiara postmark 30 45
420 45c. "Corabank" (container ship) and 1979 Auki postmark 30 45

126 Queen Elizabeth the Queen Mother

1980. 80th Birthday of The Queen Mother.
421 **126** 45c. multicoloured 30 35

127 Angel with Trumpet

129 Francisco Antonio Maurelle

128 "Parthenos sylvia"

1980. Christmas. Multicoloured.
422 8c. Type **127** 10 10
423 20c. Angel with fiddle 10 10
424 45c. Angel with trumpet (different) 25 25
425 80c. Angel with lute 40 45

1980. Butterflies (1st series). Multicoloured.
426 8c. Type **128** 40 10
427 20c. "Delias schoenbergi" . . 55 20
428 45c. "Jamides cephion" . . . 90 40
429 80c. "Ornithoptera victoriae" 1·50 1·40
See also Nos. 456/9 and 610/13.

1981. Ships and Crests (2nd series). As T **123**. Multicoloured.
430 8c. H.M.S. "Mounts Bay" (frigate), 1959 . . . . . . 15 10
431 20c. H.M.S. "Charybdis" (frigate), 1970 . . . . . . 25 20
432 45c. H.M.S. "Hydra" (survey ship), 1972 . . . . . . 40 40
433 $1 Royal Yacht "Britannia", 1974 . . . . 1·00 1·75

1981. Bicentenary of Maurelle's Visit and Production of Bauche's Chart, 1791.
434 **129** 8c. black, brown and yellow 15 10
435 – 10c. black, red and yellow 20 10
436 – 45c. multicoloured 60 65
437 – $1 multicoloured . . . . 1·00 1·10
MS438 126 × 91 mm. 25c. × 4, each black, red and stone . . . . . 65 1·10
DESIGNS—HORIZ: 10c. Bellin's map of 1742 showing route of "La Princesa"; 45c. "La Princesa". VERT: $1 Spanish compass cards, 1745; **MS**438 "Chart of a part of the South Sea" (each stamp 44 × 28 mm).
The stamps in No. **MS**438 form a composite design.

130 Netball

131 Prince Charles as Colonel-in-Chief, Royal Regiment of Wales

1981. Mini South Pacific Games. Multicoloured.
439 8c. Type **130** 10 10
440 10c. Tennis 15 15
441 25c. Running 25 25
442 30c. Football 25 25
443 45c. Boxing 40 40
MS444 102 × 67 mm. $1 Stylised athletes 70 75

1981. Royal Wedding. Multicoloured.
445 8c. Wedding bouquet from Solomon Islands 10 10
446 45c. Type **131** 15 15
447 $1 Prince Charles and Lady Diana Spencer 45 70

132 "Music"

135 Pair of Sanford's Sea Eagles constructing Nest

133 Primitive Church

1981. 25th Anniv of Duke of Edinburgh Award Scheme. Multicoloured.
448 8c. Type **132** 10 10
449 25c. "Handicrafts" 10 10
450 45c. "Canoeing" 15 10
451 $1 Duke of Edinburgh . . . 35 60

1981. Christmas. Churches.
452 **133** 8c. black, buff and blue 10 10
453 – 10c. multicoloured 10 10
454 – 25c. black, buff and green 10 10
455 – $2 multicoloured . . . . 45 1·25
DESIGNS: 10c. St. Barnabas Anglican Cathedral, Honiara; 25c. Early church; $2 Holy Cross Cathedral, Honiara.

1982. Butterflies (2nd series). As T **128**. Mult.
456 10c. "Doleschallia bisaltide" 25 10
457 25c. "Papilio bridgei" 45 25
458 35c. "Taenaris phorcas" . . . 50 30
459 $1 "Graphium sarpedon" . . 1·10 1·50

1982. Cyclone Relief Fund. No. 447 surch **50 CENTS SURCHARGE CYCLONE RELIEF FUND 1982.**
460 $1+50c. Prince Charles and Lady Diana Spencer . . . 75 2·00

1982. Sanford's Sea Eagle. Multicoloured.
461 12c. Type **135** 35 60
462 12c. Egg and chick 35 60
463 12c. Hen feeding chicks . . . 35 60
464 12c. Fledgelings 35 60
465 12c. Young bird in flight . . . 35 60
466 12c. Pair of birds and village dwellings 35 60

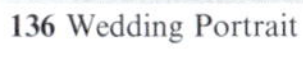

136 Wedding Portrait
137 Flags of Solomon Islands and United Kingdom

1982. 21st Birthday of Princess of Wales. Multicoloured.
467 12c. Solomon Islands coat of arms 10 10
468 40c. Lady Diana Spencer at Broadlands, May 1981 . . 40 25
469 50c. Type **136** 70 50
470 $1 Formal portrait . . . . . 1·50 1·75

1982. Royal Visit (Nos. 471/2) and Commonwealth Games, Brisbane (Nos. 473/4). Multicoloured.
471 12c. Type **137** 15 20
472 12c. Queen and Prince Philip 15 20
473 25c. Running 30 45
474 25c. Boxing 30 45
MS475 123 × 123 mm. Nos. 471/2 and $1 Royal Yacht "Britannia" 1·75 2·50
MS476 123 × 123 mm. Nos. 473/4 and $1 Royal Yacht "Britannia" 1·75 2·50

138 Boy Scouts

1982. 75th Anniv of Boy Scout Movement (Nos. 477, 479, 481, 483) and Centenary of Boys' Brigade (others). Multicoloured.
477 12c. Type **138** 10 15
478 12c. Boys' Brigade cadets . . . 10 15
479 25c. Lord Baden-Powell . . . 15 40
480 25c. Sir William Smith . . . 15 40
481 35c. Type **138** 15 50
482 35c. As No. 478 . . . . . . 15 50
483 50c. As No. 479 . . . . . . 20 1·10
484 50c. As No. 480 . . . . . . 20 1·10

139 Leatherback Turtle

1983. Turtles. Multicoloured.
485 18c. Type **139** 35 25
486 35c. Loggerhead turtle . . . 45 45
487 45c. Pacific ridley turtle . . . 50 60
488 50c. Green turtle 50 65

140 Black Olive, General Cone and Troschell's Murex

1983. Commonwealth Day. Shells. Mult.
489 12c. Type **140** 15 15
490 35c. Romu, Kurila, Kakadu and money belt 35 40
491 45c. Shells from "Bride-price" necklaces 50 60
492 50c. Commercial trochus polished and in its natural state 55 65

141 Montgolfier Balloon

1983. Bicentenary of Manned Flight. Mult.
493 30c. Type **141** 25 40
494 35c. R.A.A.F. Lockheed Hercules 30 45
495 40c. Wright Brothers' Type A 35 55
496 45c. Space shuttle "Columbia" 40 60
497 50c. Beech C55 Baron . . . 40 65

142 Weto Dancers

1983. Christmas. Multicoloured.
498 12c. Type **142** 10 10
499 15c. Custom wrestling . . . 10 20
500 18c. Girl dancers 15 20
501 20c. Devil dancers 15 20
502 25c. Bamboo band 20 35
503 35c. Gilbertese dancers . . . 25 45
504 40c. Pan pipers 25 55
505 45c. Girl dancers 30 65
506 50c. Cross surrounded by flowers 30 70
MS507 153 × 112 mm. Nos. 498/506 1·00 3·00
Stamps from No. **MS**507 are without the inscription, "Christmas 1983", on Nos. 498/506.

143 Earth Satellite Station

1983. World Communications Year. Mult.
508 12c. Type **143** 15 15
509 18c. Ham radio operator . . 15 20
510 25c. 1908 2½d. Canoe stamp 15 30
511 $1 1908 6d. Canoe stamp . . 40 3·00
MS512 131 × 103 mm. No. 511 1·40 2·25

144 "Calvatia gardneri"
146 "Olivebank" (barque), 1882

145 Cross surrounded by Flowers

1984. Fungi. Multicoloured.
513 6c. Type **144** 10 10
514 18c. "Marasmiellus inoderma" 20 25
515 35c. "Pycnoporus sanguineus" 35 45
516 $2 "Filoboletus manipularis" 2·25 3·25

1984. Visit of Pope John Paul II.
517 **145** 12c. multicoloured 20 15
518 50c. multicoloured . . . . 65 1·40

1984. 250th Anniv of "Lloyds List" (newspaper). Multicoloured.
519 12c. Type **146** 70 15
520 15c. "Tinhow" (freighter), 1906 . . . . 75 40
521 18c. "Oriana" (liner) at Point Cruz, Honiara 85 60
522 $1 "Silwyn Range" (container ship), Point Cruz, Honiara 1·40 3·25

1984. Universal Postal Union Congress, Hamburg. As No. **MS**512 but with changed sheet inscriptions and U.P.U. logo in margin. Multicoloured.
MS523 $1 1908 6d. Canoe stamp 1·60 1·60

147 Village Drums

1984. 20th Anniv of Asia-Pacific Broadcasting Union. Multicoloured.
524 12c. Type **147** 15 15
525 45c. Radio City, Guadalcanal 35 60
526 60c. S.I.B.C. studios, Honiara 50 80
527 $1 S.I.B.C. Broadcasting House . . . . 60 1·40

148 Solomon Islands Flag and Torch-bearer
149 Little Pied Cormorant

1984. Olympic Games, Los Angeles. Multicoloured.
528 12c. Type **148** 15 10
529 25c. Lawson Tama Stadium, Honiara (horiz) 15 10
530 50c. Honiara Community Centre (horiz) 20 25
531 95c. Alick Wickham inventing crawl stroke, Bronte Baths, New South Wales, 1898 (horiz) . . . . 8·00 11·00
532 $1 Olympic Stadium, Los Angeles (horiz) 30 75

1984. "Ausipex" International Stamp Exhibition, Melbourne. Birds. Multicoloured.
533 12c. Type **149** 50 50
534 18c. Pacific black duck ("Australian Grey Duck") 65 60
535 35c. Nankeen night heron . . 90 60
536 $1 Eastern broad-billed roller ("Dollar-bird") . . . . . 1·60 4·00
MS537 130 × 96 mm. Nos. 533/6 3·00 4·25

150 The Queen Mother with Princess Margaret at Badminton Horse Trials

1985. Life and Times of Queen Elizabeth the Queen Mother. Multicoloured.
538 12c. With Winston Churchill at Buckingham Palace, VE Day, 1945 . . . . 40 10
539 25c. Type **150** 30 30
540 35c. At St. Patrick's Day parade 30 35
541 $1 With Prince Henry at his christening (from photo by Lord Snowdon) 80 95
MS542 91 × 73 mm. $1.50 In a gondola, Venice, 1985 . . . . 1·10 1·50

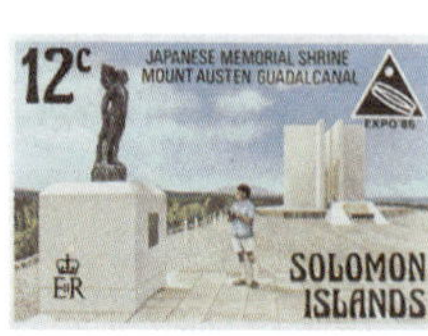

151 Japanese Memorial Shrine, Mount Austen, Guadalcanal

1985. "Expo '85" World Fair, Japan. Multicoloured.
543 12c. Type **151** 10 10
544 25c. Digital telephone exchange equipment . . . 20 30
545 45c. Fishing vessel "Soltai No. 7" 50 55
546 85c. Coastal village scene . . 60 1·40

152 Titiana Village

1985. Christmas. "Going Home for the Holiday". Multicoloured.
547 12c. Type **152** 10 10
548 25c. Sigana, Santa Isabel . . 25 30
549 35c. Artificial Island and Langa Lagoon 30 35

153 Girl Guide Activities

1985. 75th Anniv of Girl Guide Movement (12, 45c.) and International Youth Year (others). Mult.
550 12c. Type **153** 60 10
551 15c. Boys playing and child in wheelchair (Stop Polio) 65 40
552 25c. Runners and Solomon Island scenes 90 70
553 35c. Runners and Australian scenes ("Run Round Australia") . . . . 1·10 80
554 45c. Guide colour party and badges . . . . 1·25 90
MS555 100 × 75 mm. Nos. 552/3 1·00 1·00

154 Osprey
155 Water-powered Generator, Iriri

1985. Birth Bicentenary of John J. Audubon (ornithologist). Sheet 121 × 107 mm containing T 154 and similar vert design.
MS556 45c. black, gold and blue; 50c. (× 2) multicoloured . . . 3·25 4·00
DESIGNS: 45c. John J. Audubon.

1986. Village Hydro-electric Schemes. Sheet 109 × 135 mm. containing T **155** and similar vert design. Multicoloured.
MS557 30c. Type **155**; 60c. Domestic lighting 75 80

156 Building Red Cross Centre, Gizo
158 "Freedom" (winner, 1980)

157 U.S. Memorial Obelisks, Henderson Airfield, Guadalcanal

1986. Operation Raleigh (volunteer project). Multicoloured.
558 18c. Type **156** 80 20
559 30c. Exploring rainforest . . 1·50 45
560 60c. Observing Halley's Comet . . . . 2·25 1·40
561 $1 "Sir Walter Raleigh" (support ship) and "Zebu" (brigantine) . . . . . . 2·75 2·00

1986. 60th Birthday of Queen Elizabeth II. As T **145a** of St. Helena. Multicoloured.
562 5c. Princess Elizabeth and Duke of Edinburgh at Clydebank Town Hall, 1947 . . . . 10 10
563 18c. At St. Paul's Cathedral for Queen Mother's 80th birthday service, 1980 . . . 15 20
564 22c. With children, Solomon Islands, 1982 . . . . . . 20 25

565 55c. At Windsor Castle on her 50th birthday, 1976 . . 40 45
566 $2 At Crown Agents Head Office, London, 1983 . . . 1·40 1·50

1986. "Ameripex '86" International Stamp Exhibition, Chicago. International Peace Year. Sheet 100 × 75 mm containing T **157** and similar horiz design. Multicoloured.
MS567 55c. Type **157**; $1.65 Peace Corps emblem, President Kennedy and Statue of Liberty (25th anniv of Peace Corps) . . . . 1·10 1·25

1986. Royal Wedding. As T **146a** of St. Helena. Multicoloured.
568 55c. Prince Andrew and Miss Sarah Ferguson 40 55
569 60c. Prince Andrew at helm of yacht "Bluenose II" off Nova Scotia, 1985 . . . . 45 70

1986. America's Cup Yachting Championship (1987).
570 **158** 18c. multicoloured 20 45
571 – 30c. multicoloured . . . . 75 2·25
572 – $1 multicoloured . . . . 50 1·25
Nos. 570/2 were issued as a sheet of 50, each horizontal strip of 5 being separated by gutter margins. The sheet contains 20 different designs at 18c., 10 at 30c. and 20 at $1. Individual stamps depict yachts, charts, the America's Cup or the emblem of the Royal Perth Yacht Club.
See also No. **MS**575.

1986. Cyclone Relief Fund. No. 541 surch **+ 50c Cyclone Relief Fund 1986**.
573 $1+50c. Queen Mother with Prince Henry at his christening . . . . 75 1·25
MS574 100 × 75 mm. 55c.+25c. Type **157**; $1.65+75c. Peace Corps emblem, President Kennedy and Statue of Liberty (25th anniv of Peace Corps) . . . . 3·25 3·00
The surcharges on No. **MS**574 do not include "1986".

1987. America's Cup Yachting Championship ("nd issue). Sheet 111 × 75 mm, containing vert design as T **158**. Multicoloured.
MS575 $5 "Stars and Stripes" (1987 winner) . . . . 3·50 4·25

160 "Dendrophyllia gracilis"

1987. Corals. Multicoloured.
576 18c. Type **160** 20 15
577 45c. "Dendronephthya sp." . . 40 50
578 60c. "Clavularia sp." . . . . 55 1·40
579 $1.50 "Melithaea squamata" . 1·10 3·50

161 "Cassia fistula"

1987. Flowers. Multicoloured.
580 1c. Type **161** 10 70
581 5c. "Allamanda cathartica" . 20 80
582 10c. "Catharanthus roseus" . 30 80
583 18c. "Mimosa pudica" . . . 50 15
584 20c. "Hibiscus rosa-sinensis" . 50 15
585 22c. "Clerodendrum thomsonae" 50 15
586 25c. "Bauhinia variegata" . . 50 30
587 28c. "Gloriosa rothschildiana" 55 30
588 30c. "Heliconia solomonensis" 60 30
589 40c. "Episcia" hybrid 70 30
590 45c. "Bougainvillea" hybrid . 70 30
591 50c. "Alpinia purpurata" . . 70 30
592 55c. "Plumeria rubra" . . . 75 35
593 60c. "Acacia farnesiana" . . 85 60
594 $1 "Ipomea purpurea" . . . 2·00 80
595 $2 "Dianella ensifolia" . . . 3·00 4·50
596 $5 "Passiflora foetida" . . . 4·50 8·50
597 $10 "Hemigraphis sp" . . . 7·00 13·00

162 Mangrove Kingfisher on Branch

163 "Dendrobium conanthum"

1987. Mangrove Kingfisher. Multicoloured.
598 60c. Type **162** . . . . 2·40 3·00
599 60c. Kingfisher diving . . . . 2·40 3·00
600 60c. Entering water . . . . . 2·40 3·00
601 60c. Kingfisher with prey . . 2·40 3·00
Nos. 598/601 were printed together, se-tenant, forming a composite design.

1987. Christmas. Orchids (1st series). Mult.
602 18c. Type **163** 85 10
603 30c. "Spathoglottis plicata" . 1·50 20
604 55c. "Dendrobium gouldii" . 1·75 50
605 $1.50 "Dendrobium goldfinchii" . . . . 3·75 3·75
See also Nos. 640/3 and 748/51.

164 Telecommunications Control Room and Satellite

1987. Asia-Pacific Transport and Communications Decade. Multicoloured.
606 18c. Type **164** 20 15
607 30c. De Havilland Twin Otter 300 mail plane 45 20
608 60c. Guadalcanal road improvement project . . . 50 60
609 $2 Beech 80 Queen Air and Henderson Control Tower . 2·00 2·50

165 Pupa of "Ornithoptera victoriae"

166 Student and National Agriculture Training Institute

1987. Butterflies (3rd series). "Ornithoptera victoriae" (Queen Victoria's Birdwing). Mult.
610 45c. Type **165** . . . . 3·50 3·50
611 45c. Larva . . . . 3·50 3·50
612 45c. Female butterfly . . . . 3·50 3·50
613 45c. Male butterfly . . . . . 3·50 3·50

1988. 10th Anniv of International Fund for Agricultural Development. Multicoloured.
614 50c. Type **166** 40 55
615 50c. Students working in fields 40 55
616 $1 Transport by lorry . . . . 50 1·00
617 $1 Canoe transport . . . . . 50 1·00
Nos. 614/15 and 616/17 were printed together, se-tenant, each pair forming a composite design.

167 Building Fishing Boat

1988. "Expo '88" World Fair, Brisbane. Mult.
618 22c. Type **167** 20 15
619 80c. War canoe 50 45
620 $1.50 Traditional village . . . 95 85
MS621 130 × 53 mm. Nos. 618/20 . 1·50 1·40

168 "Todos los Santos" in Estrella Bay, 1568

1988. 10th Anniv of Independence. Mult.
622 22c. Type **168** 80 15
623 55c. Raising the Union Jack, 1893 . . . . 1·00 45
624 80c. High Court Building . . 1·25 1·10
625 $1 Dancers at traditional celebration . . . . 1·40 1·40

169 "Papuan Chief" (container ship)

1988. "Sydpex '88" National Stamp Exhibition, Sydney and Bicentenary of Australian Settlement. Multicoloured.
626 35c. Type **169** . . . . 1·00 25
627 60c. "Nimos" (container ship) 1·40 40
628 70c. "Malaita" (liner) . . . . 1·40 65
629 $1.30 "Makambo" (inter-island freighter) . . . . 1·75 1·50
MS630 140 × 76 mm. Nos. 626/9 . 2·50 2·00

170 Archery

171 "Bulbophyllum dennisii"

1988. Olympic Games, Seoul. Multicoloured.
631 22c. Type **170** 75 20
632 55c. Weightlifting 85 45
633 70c. Athletics . . . . 1·00 65
634 80c. Boxing . . . . 1·10 70
MS635 100 × 80 mm. $2 Olympic Stadium (horiz) . . . . 1·25 1·25

1988. 300th Anniv of Lloyd's of London. As T **152a** of St. Helena.
636 22c. black and brown 30 15
637 50c. multicoloured . . . . . 1·10 30
638 65c. multicoloured . . . . . 1·25 55
639 $2 multicoloured . . . . . . 2·75 1·75
DESIGNS—VERT: 22c. King George V and Queen Mary laying foundation stone of Leadenhall Street Building, 1925; $2 "Empress of China" (liner), 1911. HORIZ: 50c. "Forthbank" (container ship); 65c. Soltel satellite com-munications station.

1989. Orchids (2nd series). Multicoloured.
640 22c. Type **171** 75 20
641 35c. "Calanthe langei" . . . 90 35
642 55c. "Bulbophyllum blumei" 1·25 55
643 $2 "Grammatophyllum speciosum" . . . . 2·00 3·50

172 Red Cross Workers with Handicapped Children

1989. 125th Anniv of Int Red Cross. Mult.
644 35c. Type **172** 35 35
645 35c. Handicapped Children Centre minibus 35 35
646 $1.50 Blood donor . . . . . 1·25 1·25
647 $1.50 Balance test . . . . . 1·25 1·25
Nos. 644/5 and 646/7 were each printed together, se-tenant, each pair forming a composite design.

173 Varicose Nudibranch

1989. Nudibranchs (Sea Slugs). Multicoloured.
648 22c. Type **173** 80 20
649 70c. Bullock's nudibranch . . 2·00 1·50
650 80c. "Chromodoris leopardus" . . . . 2·00 1·60
651 $1.50 "Phidiana indica" . . . 2·50 3·50

1989. 20th Anniv of First Manned Landing on Moon. As T **50a** of St. Kitts. Multicoloured.
652 22c. "Apollo 16" descending by parachute 45 20
653 35c. Launch of "Apollo 16" (30 × 30 mm) 70 45
654 70c. "Apollo 16" emblem (30 × 30 mm) . . . . . . 1·25 1·75
655 80c. Ultra-violet colour photograph of Earth . . . 1·40 2·00
MS656 100 × 83 mm. $4 Moon's surface seen from Space . . . 3·00 3·00

174 Five Stones Catch

176 Man wearing Headband, Necklace and Sash

175 Fishermen and Butterfly

1989. "World Stamp Expo '89". International Stamp Exhibition, Washington. Children's Games. Multicoloured.
657 5c. Type **174** 15 40
658 67c. Blowing soap bubbles (horiz) . . . . 1·25 1·40
659 73c. Coconut shell game (horiz) . . . . 1·25 1·40
660 $1 Seed wind sound . . . . 1·75 2·00
MS661 72 × 72 mm. $3 Softball . 6·50 6·50

1989. Christmas. Multicoloured.
662 18c. Type **175** 40 10
663 25c. The Nativity 55 20
664 45c. Hospital ward at Christmas . . . . 1·00 30
665 $1.50 Village tug-of-war . . . 2·50 4·50

1990. Personal Ornaments. Multicoloured.
666 5c. Type **176** 30 75
667 12c. Pendant 40 30
668 18c. Man wearing medallion, nose ring and earrings . . 40 30
669 $2 Forehead ornament . . . 4·00 6·50

177 Spindle Cowrie or Tokio's Volva

1990. Cowrie Shells. Multicoloured.
670 4c. Type **177** 30 75
671 20c. All-red map cowrie . . . 75 30
672 35c. Sieve cowrie . . . . . . 1·00 35
673 50c. Umbilical ovula or little egg cowrie . . . . 1·40 1·60
674 $1 Valentine or prince cowrie 2·25 3·25

1990. 90th Birthday of Queen Elizabeth the Queen Mother. As T **161a** of St. Helena.
675 25c. multicoloured 75 25
676 $5 black and red . . . . . . 3·75 4·75
DESIGNS—21 × 36 mm: 25c. Queen Mother, 1987. 29 × 37 mm: $5 King George VI and Queen Elizabeth inspecting bomb damage to Buckingham Palace, 1940.

178 Postman with Mail Van

1990. 150th Anniv of the Penny Black. Mult.
677 35c. Type **178** . . . . 1·10 35
678 45c. General Post Office . . . 1·25 40
679 50c. 1907 ½d. stamp . . . . 1·40 1·50
680 55c. Child collecting stamps . 1·60 2·00
681 60c. Penny Black and Solomon Islands 1913 1d. stamp . . . . 1·75 3·00

179 Purple Swamphen

1990. "Birdpex '90" Stamp Exhibition, Christchurch, New Zealand. Multicoloured.
682 10c. Type **179** 65 70
683 25c. Mackinlay's cuckoo dove ("Rufous Brown Pheasant Dove") . . . . 1·00 50
684 30c. Superb fruit dove . . . 1·25 55
685 45c. Cardinal honeyeater . . 1·40 60
686 $2 Finsch's pygmy parrot ("Pigmy Parrot") . . . . . 2·25 4·25

180 "Cylas formicarius" (weevil)

182 Volleyball

181 Child drinking from Coconut

1991. Crop Pests. Multicoloured.

687	7c. Type **180**	55	40
688	25c. "Dacus cucurbitae" (fruit-fly)	85	30
689	40c. "Papuana uninodis" (beetle)	1·25	45
690	90c. "Pantorhytes biplagiastus" (weevil)	2·00	2·25
691	$1.50 "Scapanes australis" (beetle)	2·25	3·50

1991. 65th Birthday of Queen Elizabeth II and 70th Birthday of Prince Philip. As T **165a** of St. Helena. Multicoloured.

692	90c. Prince Philip in evening dress	1·00	1·25
693	$2 Queen Elizabeth II	2·40	3·00

1991. Health Campaign. Multicoloured.

694	5c. Type **181**	15	40
695	75c. Mother feeding child	1·10	1·10
696	80c. Breast feeding	1·25	1·40
697	90c. Local produce	1·40	1·60

1991. 9th South Pacific Games. Multicoloured.

698	25c. Type **182**	90	25
699	40c. Judo	1·25	55
700	65c. Squash	1·75	2·00
701	90c. Bowling	2·25	3·00
MS702	92 × 112 mm. $2 Games emblem	4·50	6·50

183 Preparing Food for Christmas

1991. Christmas. Multicoloured.

703	10c. Type **183**	30	10
704	25c. Christmas Day church service	60	15
705	65c. Christmas Day feast	1·50	85
706	$2 Cricket match	3·75	5·00
MS707	138 × 110 mm. Nos. 703/6	5·50	7·00

184 Yellow-finned Tuna

1991. "Phila Nippon '91" International Stamp Exhibition, Tokyo. Tuna Fishing. Mult.

708	5c. Type **184**	10	20
709	30c. Pole and line tuna fishing boat	60	25
710	80c. Pole and line fishing	1·50	1·75
711	$2 Processing "arabushi" (smoked tuna)	2·75	4·00
MS712	101 × 80 mm. 80c. Plate of "tori nanban" (25 × 42 mm); 80c. Bowl of "aka miso" (25 × 42 mm)	1·75	2·00

1992. 40th Anniv of Queen Elizabeth II's Accession. As T **122c** of Pitcairn Islands. Multicoloured.

713	5c. Aerial view of Honiara	25	50
714	20c. Sunset across lagoon	50	20
715	40c. Honiara harbour	75	40
716	60c. Three portraits of Queen Elizabeth	80	1·00
717	$5 Queen Elizabeth II	3·25	4·50

185 Mendana's Fleet in Thousand Ships Bay, 1568

1992. "Granada '92" International Stamp Exhibition, Spain. Mendana's Discovery of Solomon Islands. Multicoloured.

718	10c. Type **185**	50	30
719	65c. Map of voyage	1·00	60
720	80c. Alvaro Mendana de Niera	1·25	1·50
721	$1 Settlement at Graciosa Bay	1·60	2·00
722	$5 Mendana's fleet at sea	3·75	5·00

186 Sgt-major Jacob Vouza

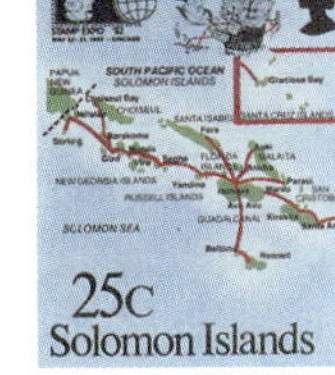

187 Solomon Airlines Domestic Routes

1992. Birth Centenary of Sgt-major Jacob Vouza (war hero). Multicoloured.

723	25c. Type **186**	50	30
724	70c. Vouza in U.S. Marine Corps battle dress	1·00	1·25
725	90c. Vouza in U.S. Marine Corps uniform	1·00	1·40
726	$2 Statue of Vouza	1·25	2·25
MS727	113 × 76 mm. $4 Sgt-major Vouza in ceremonial uniform	5·50	5·50

1992. 500th Anniv of Discovery of America by Columbus and "World Columbian Stamp Expo '92" Exhibition, Chicago. Multicoloured.

728	25c. Type **187**	60	20
729	80c. Solomon Airlines Boeing 737-400 "Guadalcanal"	1·40	1·25
730	$1.50 Solomon Airlines international routes	2·00	2·25
731	$5 Columbus and "Santa Maria"	4·75	6·00
MS732	120 × 94 mm. Nos. 728/31	8·00	9·00

188 Japanese Troops landing at Esperance

1992. 50th Anniv of Battle of Guadalcanal. Multicoloured.

733	30c. Type **188**	80	80
734	30c. American troops in landing craft	80	80
735	30c. H.M.A.S. "Hobart" (cruiser)	80	80
736	30c. U.S. Navy post office	80	80
737	30c. R.N.Z.A.F. Consolidated PBY-5A Catalina flying boat	80	80
738	80c. U.S. Marine Corps Grumman F4F Wildcat fighters	1·00	1·00
739	80c. Henderson Field	1·00	1·00
740	80c. U.S.S. "Quincy" (heavy cruiser)	1·00	1·00
741	80c. H.M.A.S. "Canberra" (heavy cruiser)	1·00	1·00
742	80c. U.S. Marine Corps landing craft	1·00	1·00
743	80c. "Ryujo" (Japanese aircraft carrier)	1·00	1·00
744	80c. Japanese Mitsubishi A6M Zero-Sen fighters	1·00	1·00
745	80c. Japanese Mitsubishi G4M "Betty" bombers	1·00	1·00
746	80c. Japanese destroyer	1·00	1·00
747	80c. "Chockai" (Japanese heavy cruiser)	1·00	1·00

189 "Dendrobium" hybrid

1992. Orchids (3rd series). Multicoloured.

748	15c. Type **189**	50	20
749	70c. "Vanda Amy Laycock"	1·00	90
750	95c. "Dendrobium mirbelianum"	1·25	1·25
751	$2.50 "Dendrobium macrophyllum"	2·00	3·50

190 Stalk-eyed Ghost Crab

1993. Crabs. Multicoloured.

752	5c. Type **190**	20	60
753	10c. Red-spotted crab	20	60
754	25c. Flat crab	25	60
755	30c. Land hermit crab	25	20
756	40c. Grapsid crab	25	30
757	45c. Red and white painted crab	25	30
758	55c. Swift-footed crab	30	30
759	60c. Spanner crab	30	30
760	70c. Red hermit crab	40	40
761	80c. Red-eyed crab	40	40
762	90c. Rathbun red crab	40	50
763	$1 Coconut crab	50	50
764	$1.10 Red-spotted white crab	50	60
765	$4 Ghost crab	1·75	3·00
766	$10 Mangrove fiddler crab	3·25	5·50

191 U.S. War Memorial, Skyline Ridge

1993. 50th Anniv of Second World War. Multicoloured.

767	30c. Type **191**	35	20
768	80c. National flags at half mast	1·00	1·10
769	95c. Major-general Alexander Vandegrift and map	1·10	1·25
770	$4 Aerial dogfight, U.S. carrier and Solomon Islands scouts	4·00	5·00

1993. 14th World Orchid Conference, Glasgow. As Nos. 748 and 751, but different face values, additionally inscr "World Orchid Conference". Multicoloured.

771	20c. Type **189**	40	25
772	$3 "Dendrobium macrophyllum"	2·00	2·75

1993. "Indopex '93" International Stamp Exhibition, Surabaya. As Nos. 749/50, but different face values, additionally inscr "Indopex '93" Exhibition". Multicoloured.

773	85c. "Vanda Amy Laycock"	90	1·00
774	$1.15 "Dendrobium mirbelianum"	1·00	1·25

192 U.S.S. "PT 109" being rammed by "Amagiri" (Japanese destroyer)

1993. 50th Anniv of Sinking of U.S.S. "PT 109" (motor torpedo-boat commanded by John F. Kennedy). Multicoloured.

775	30c. Type **192**	45	25
776	50c. Kennedy thanking islander	60	45
777	95c. Message in coconut shell and islanders in canoe	80	1·00
778	$1.10 Pres. Kennedy and medal	1·00	1·60
MS779	77 × 43 mm. $5 U.S.S. "PT 109"	4·75	6·00

1993. "Taipei '93" Asian International Stamp Exhibition Taiwan. No. **MS**732 optd "TAIPEI '93" and emblem on sheet margin.

MS780	120 × 94 mm. Nos. 728/31	4·50	6·00

193 Nicobar Pigeon

1993. Endangered Species. Nicobar Pigeon. Multicoloured.

781	30c. Type **193**	35	20
782	50c. Pigeon on ground	50	35
783	65c. Pair of pigeons perched on branches	60	50
784	70c. Pigeon on branch looking left	65	60
785	$1.10 Pigeon on branch looking right	1·00	1·25
786	$3 Pigeons in flight	2·25	3·25

194 Pair of Dachshunds

1994. "Hong Kong '94" Int Stamp Exn. Chinese New Year ("Year of the Dog"). Mult.

787	30c. Type **194**	50	30
788	80c. German shepherd dog	80	95
789	95c. Pair of Dobermann pinschers	90	1·25
790	$1.10 Australian cattle dog	1·00	1·50
MS791	70 × 55 mm. $4 Boxer	5·50	6·50

195 Striped Dolphin

1994. Dolphins. Multicoloured.

792	75c. Type **195**	70	65
793	85c. Risso's dolphin	80	80
794	$1.15 Common dolphin	1·10	1·40
795	$2.50 Spinner dolphin	2·25	3·25
796	$3 Bottlenose dolphin	2·50	3·50

196 "Vindula sapor"

1994. "Philakorea '94" International Stamp Exhibition, Seoul. Butterflies. Multicoloured.

797	70c. Type **196**	50	70
798	70c. "Papilio aegeus"	50	70
799	70c. "Graphium hicetaon"	50	70
800	70c. "Graphium mendana"	50	70
801	70c. Exhibition logo	50	70
802	70c. "Graphium meeki"	50	70
803	70c. "Danaus schenkii"	50	70
804	70c. "Papilio ptolychus"	50	70
805	70c. "Phaedyma fissizonata vella"	50	70

197 Girl in Brisbane writing letter to Family in Santa Isabel

1994. Int Year of the Family. Mult.

806	$1.10 Type **197**	80	1·25
807	$1.10 Boeing 737-400 leaving Brisbane	80	1·25
808	$1.10 Boeing 737-400 at Henderson Airfield and De Havilland D.H.C.6 Twin Otter leaving for Santa Isabel	80	1·25
809	$1.10 De Havilland D.H.C.6 Twin Otter at Fera Airfield, Santa Isabe	80	1·25
810	$1.10 Family reunited	80	1·25
MS811	160 × 75 mm. Nos. 806/10	3·50	5·00

198 Cook Island Volcano, 1967

1994. Volcanoes. Multicoloured.

812	30c. Type **198**	30	25
813	70c. Kavachi underwater eruption, 1977	50	90
814	80c. Kavachi volcano forming temporary island, 1978	60	1·00
815	90c. Tinakula volcanic island	80	1·40
MS816	130 × 60 mm. $2 Map of Solomon Islands volcanoes; $2 Diagram showing formation of volcanic islands	2·50	3·00

199 La Perouse with King Louis XVI and Map

1994. Loss of the La Perouse Expedition, Santa Cruz Islands, 1788. Multicoloured.
817 30c. Type **199** 40 20
818 80c. Map of Ile de La Perouse 80 80
819 95c. "L'Astrolabe" . . . . . 85 1·00
820 $1.10 "La Boussole" . . . . 1·00 1·25
821 $3 "L'Astrolabe" foundering on reef . . . . 2·00 3·75

200 Hermit Crab, Shells and Dancers

1995. Visit South Pacific Year. Multicoloured.
822 30c. Type **200** 20 20
823 50c. "Dendrobium rennellii" (orchid) and "Danaus plexippus" (butterfly) . . . 50 45
824 95c. Scuba diver and fish . . 60 1·10
825 $1.15 Grapsid crab, canoes, rusty Second World War gun and catamaran . . . . 65 1·25
MS826 98 × 81 mm. $4 Yellow-bibbed lory . . . . 4·75 5·50

201 Emblem and Bananas

1995. 50th Anniv of F.A.O. Fruits. Multicoloured.
827 70c. Type **201** 70 70
828 75c. Paw paws 70 70
829 95c. Pomelos . . . . 85 1·00
830 $2 Star fruits . . . . . . 2·00 3·25
MS831 90 × 75 mm. $3 Mangos . . 1·60 2·25

1995. 50th Anniv of End of Second World War. As T **182a** of St. Helena. Multicoloured.
832 95c. Vice-Admiral Nagumo and "Akagi" (Japanese aircraft carrier) . . . . . 1·00 1·00
833 $1 Rear-Admiral Fletcher and U.S.S. "Yorktown" (aircraft carrier) . . . . . 1·00 1·00
834 $2 Vice-Admiral Ghormley and U.S.S. "Wasp" (aircraft carrier) . . . . . 1·75 2·75
835 $3 Vice-Admiral Halsey and U.S.S. "Enterprise" (aircraft carrier) . . . . . 2·50 3·50
MS836 75 × 85 mm. $5 Reverse of 1939-45 War Medal (vert) . . 2·25 2·75

202 "Calanthe triplicata"

204 Marconi demonstrating Radio Transmitter, Salisbury Plain, 1896

203 Start of Canoe Race

1995. Orchids. Mutlicoloured.
837 45c. Type **202** . . . . . . 1·25 30
838 75c. "Dendrobium mohlianum" . . . . 1·50 1·10
839 85c. "Flickingeria comata" 1·50 1·50
840 $1.15 "Dendrobium spectabile" . . . . 2·00 2·50
MS841 75 × 90 mm. $4 "Coelogyne asperata" . . . . 2·75 4·00

No. **MS**841 includes the "Singapore '95" International Stamp Exhibition emblem on the sheet margin.

1995. Christmas. Local Festivities. Multicoloured.
842 90c. Type **203** 70 60
843 $1.05 Pan-pipe players and Christmas Tree . . . . . 70 1·00
844 $1.25 Picnic on the beach . . 80 1·10
845 $1.45 Church service and infant Jesus . . . . 1·00 1·60

1996. Centenary of Radio. Multicoloured.
846 $1.05 Type **204** 70 80
847 $1.20 Ship's radio room, 1900 80 1·00
848 $1.35 Wireless transmitter, Croydon Aerodrome, 1920 90 1·50
849 $1.45 Marconi in Japan, 1933 1·00 1·75

205 Palm Lorikeet

1996. Birds. Multicoloured.
850 75c. Type **205** 70 55
851 $1.05 Duchess lorikeet . . . 85 75
852 $1.20 Yellow-bibbed lory . . 90 1·00
853 $1.35 Cardinal lory . . . . . 1·25 1·75
854 $1.45 Meek's lorikeet . . . . 1·25 1·75
MS855 94 × 69 mm. $3 Rainbow lory ("Rainbow Lorikeet") . . 2·40 2·75

206 Dug-out Canoe on Beach and Canoe with Outboard Motor

1996. "CAPEX '96" International Stamp Exhibition, Toronto. Mail Transport. Multicoloured.
856 40c. Type **206** 35 20
857 90c. Postman with bicycle . . 1·00 80
858 $1.20 Post van . . . . 1·00 1·00
859 $1.45 "Tulagi Express" (cruise launch) . . . . . 1·50 2·25
MS860 88 × 73 mm. $4 "Tepuke" (traditional canoe) . . . . . . 1·90 2·75

207 Tokyo 1964 Poster

209 Sanford's Sea Eagle

208 Suiesi and Map of Makira Bay

1996. Centenary of Modern Olympic Games. Promotional Posters from Previous Games.
861 90c. Type **207** 50 40
862 $1.20 Los Angeles, 1932 . . . 60 70
863 $1.35 Paris, 1924 . . . . . . 65 85
864 $2.50 London, 1908 . . . . 1·10 2·25

1996. 150th Anniv of First Christian Mission. Multicoloured.
865 40c. Type **208** 30 20
866 65c. Surimahe and sketches of artefacts by Revd. L. Verguet 45 45
867 $1.35 Bishop Espalle and grave, Isabel . . . . . . 60 1·25
868 $1.45 John Claude Colin and Makira Mission . . . . . 65 1·40

1996. "Taipei '96" 10th Asian International Stamp Exhibition, Taiwan. Sheet 100 × 80 mm.
MS869 **209** $1.50, multicoloured 75 1·00

210 Children eating Fruit

1996. 50th Anniv of U.N.I.C.E.F. Multicoloured.
870 40c. Type **210** 25 20
871 $1.05 Children in canoes . . 50 50
872 $1.35 Doctor and child . . . 60 75
873 $2.50 Teacher and child . . . 1·00 2·50

1997. "HONG KONG '97" International Stamp Exhibition. Sheet 130 × 90 mm, containing design as No. 765. Multicoloured.
MS874 $4 Ghost crab . . . . . 1·75 2·25

1997. "Singpex '97" International Stamp Exhibition. No. 797 optd **SINGPEX '97 FEBRUARY 21–23 SINGAPORE** and logo within "perforation" frame across the entire sheetlet.
875 70c. Type **196** 55 70
876 70c. "Papilio aegeus" 55 70
877 70c. "Graphium hicetaon" . . 55 70
878 70c. "Graphium mendana" . . 55 70
879 70c. "Exhibition logo" . . . 55 70
880 70c. "Graphium meeki" . . . 55 70
881 70c. "Danaus schenkii" . . . 55 70
882 70c. "Papilio ptolychus" . . 55 70
883 70c. "Phaedyma fissizonata vella" 55 70

Individual stamps show parts of the overprint only.

211 Common Phalanger

1997. Common Phalanger ("Northern Common Cuscus"). Multicoloured.
884 15c. Type **211** 20 15
885 60c. Common phalanger eating fruit 30 30
886 $2.50 Common phalanger hanging on branch . . . . 85 1·40
887 $3 Two common phalangers 95 1·60

212 Whale and Calf

1997. "Pacific '97" International Stamp Exhibition, San Francisco. Sheet 96 × 74 mm, containnig T **212** and similar multicoloured design.
MS888 $2 Type **212**; $2 Whale breaking surface (horiz) . . . 2·00 2·50

1997. Golden Wedding of Queen Elizabeth and Prince Philip. As T **192a** of St. Helena. Multicoloured.
889 $3 Prince Philip playing polo 2·00 2·25
890 $3 Queen Elizabeth . . . . . 2·00 2·25
891 $3 Queen Elizabeth leading two horses . . . . 2·00 2·25
892 $3 Prince Philip . . . . . . 2·00 2·25
MS893 110 × 70 mm. $3 Queen Elizabeth and Prince Philip in landau (horiz) . . . . 1·40 1·75

Nos. 889/90 and 891/2 respectively were printed together, se-tenant, with the backgrounds forming composite designs.

213 Turtle laying Eggs

1997. 50th Anniv of the South Pacific Commission. Common Green Turtle. Multicoloured.
894 50c. Type **213** 30 20
895 90c. Young turtles heading towards sea 50 50
896 $1.50 Four turtles swimming under water . . . . . . 70 1·25
897 $2 Pair of turtles swimming 85 1·60

214 Oni Mako Player

1997. Christmas. Multicoloured.
898 $1.10 Type **214** 50 35
899 $1.40 Ysabel dancing women 60 70
900 $1.50 Pan pipers from Small Malaita 60 90
901 $1.70 Western bamboo band 75 1·50

215 Golden Whistler

216 Black Marlin

1997. "Bangkok '97" China Stamp Exhibition, Thailand. Christmas. Sheet 135 × 87 mm, containing T **215** and similar vert design. Multicoloured.
MS902 $1.50 Type **215**; $1.50 "Papilio aegeus" and "Graphium meeki" (butterflies) . . . . . . 2·50 2·75

1998. Billfishes. Multicoloured.
903 50c. Type **216** 60 20
904 $1.20 Shortbill swordfish . . 95 75
905 $1.40 Swordfish . . . . . . 1·10 1·10
906 $2 Indo-Pacific sailfish . . . 1·60 2·25

See also No. **MS**922.

1998. Diana, Princess of Wales Commemoration. As T **62a** of Tokelau. Multicoloured.
907 $2 Wearing pearl earrings . . 60 75
MS908 145 × 70 mm. $2.50 As No. 907; $2.50 Wearing white hat; $2.50 In evening dress; $2.50 Accepting flowers from children (sold at $10+50c. charity premium) . . . . 3·25 3·50

217 Water Melon Cultivation

1998. Technical Co-operation between Solomon Islands and Republic of China (Taiwan). Multicoloured.
909 50c. Type **217** 20 20
910 $1.50 Harvesting rice 55 95
MS911 105 × 60 mm. 80c. Growing cucumbers; $1.20 Inspecting tomato plants . . . . 75 1·00

218 War Dance

1998. Melanesian Trade and Culture Show. Multicoloured.
912 50c. Type **218** 40 55
913 50c. Islanders with bows and arrows 40 55
914 50c. Man on beach 40 55
915 $1.20 War dance (different) 50 65
916 $1.20 Warrior in mask . . . 50 65
917 $1.20 Woman wearing shell necklace and headband . . 50 65
918 $1.50 Dance with poles . . . 55 70
919 $1.50 Hunter with spear, shield and axe 55 70
920 $1.50 Man with nose and ear ornaments 55 70

219 New National Parliament Building

1998. 20th Anniv of Independence. Sheet 110 × 79 mm.
MS921 **219** $4 multicoloured . . 1·50 2·25

1998. "Singpex 98" International Stamp Exhibition and International Year of the Ocean. Sheet 90 × 60 mm, containing No. 906. Multicoloured.
MS922 $2 Indo-pacific sailfish . . 1·25 1·75

220 H.M.S. "Endeavour" (Cook), 1770

1999. "Australia '99" World Stamp Exhibition, Melbourne. Maritime History. Sheet, 96 × 55 mm, containing T **220** and similar horiz design. Multicoloured.
MS923 $10 Type **220**; $10 "Los Reyes" (Alvare Mendana) careened at Guadalcanal, 1568 . . 5·50 7·00

221 Beach

1999. "PhilexFrance '99" International Stamp Exhibition, Paris. Marine Life. Multicoloured.
924 $1 Type **221** 35 50
925 $1 Great frigate bird 35 50
926 $1 Coconut crab 35 50
927 $1 Green turtle 35 50
928 $1 Royal Spanish dancer nudibranch 35 50
929 $1 Sun noon and stars butterflyfish 35 50
930 $1 Striped sweetlips 35 50
931 $1 Saddle-back butterflyfish 35 50
932 $1 Cuttlefish 35 50
933 $1 Giant clam 35 50
934 $1 Lionfish 35 50
935 $1 Spiny lobster 35 50
Nos. 924/35 were printed together, se-tenant, with the backgrounds forming a composite design.

1999. 30th Anniv of First Manned Landing on Moon. As T **94a** of St. Kitts. Multicoloured.
936 50c. Lift-off 25 20
937 $1.50 Lunar module above Moon's surface 60 60
938 $2.50 Buzz Aldrin with American flag on Moon . . 90 1·40
939 $3.40 Command module splashdown . . . . . . 1·25 1·90
MS940 90 × 80 mm. $4 Earth as seen from Moon (circular, 40 mm diam) . . . . 1·40 1·75

1999. "Queen Elizabeth the Queen Mother's Century". As T **199** of St. Helena. Multicoloured (except $5).
941 $1 Inspecting bomb damage at Portsmouth, 1941 . . . 50 30
942 $1.50 At the Derby, 1983 . . 65 55
943 $2.30 Receiving birthday bouquets from children . . 80 1·10
944 $4.90 Inspecting Royal Army Medical Corps parade . . 1·50 2·50
MS945 145 × 70 mm. $5 Duchess of York, 1920s, and with King George VI and Prime Minister Winston Churchill, VE Day, 1945 (black) . . . . 1·75 2·50

1999. "China '99" International Stamp Exhibition, Beijing. No. 687 optd **SOLOMON ISLANDS: 21-30 AUGUST CHINA 1999.**
946 7c. Type **180** 30 30

223 Ferrari 212 E

1999. Birth Centenary of Enzo Ferrari (car designer) (1998). Racing Cars. Multicoloured.
947 $1 Type **223** 45 35
948 $1.50 250 TR 55 50
949 $3.30 250 LM . . . . 1·00 1·60
950 $4.20 612 CAN-AM . . . . 1·25 1·75

224 Bishop George Augustus Selwyn

1999. Christmas. 150th Anniv of Melanesian Mission. Multicoloured (except $3.30).
951 $1 Type **224** 40 60
952 $1 Bishop John Coleridge Patteson 40 60
953 $1.50 Stained glass windows 50 70
954 $1.50 "Southern Cross" (missionary ship) and religious symbols 50 70
955 $3.30 "150 YEARS MELANESIAN MISSION" (black) . . . . 75 1·25
Nos. 951/5 were printed together, se-tenant, with the $3.30 in the centre, throughout the sheet with the backgrounds forming a composite design.

225 National Flags at Half Mast

1999. Second World War Veterans' Millennium Visit. Multicoloured.
956 30c. Type **225** 15 25
957 30c. The Cenotaph, Honiara 15 25
958 30c. Solomon Peace Memorial Park 15 25
959 30c. U.S. War Memorial, Skyline Ridge 15 25
960 30c. "Ocean Pearl" (cruise ship) 15 25
It was originally intended to issue Nos. 956/60 as part of the 1992 50th Anniv of Battle of Guadalcanal set, Nos. 733/47. This strip of 5 designs was removed from the sheet and was not placed on sale until late 1999.

226 Munda Lighthouse and War Canoe

2000. New Millennium. Multicoloured.
961 $1 Type **226** 75 80
962 $4 Tulagi Lighthouse and launch . . . . 3·00 3·25
MS963 96 × 74 mm. Nos. 961/2 . . . 3·75 4·00

227 Islanders

2000. Commonwealth Youth Ministers' Meeting, Honiara. Sheet 130 × 90 mm.
MS964 **227** $6 multicoloured . . 4·50 4·75

2000. "EXPO 2000". International Stamp Exhibition, Anaheim, U.S.A. No. **MS**940 optd **"WORLD STAMP EXPO 2000 - USA VALUE $5.00"** on the sheet margin.
MS965 90 × 80 mm. $4 Earth as seen from Moon . . . . 1·40 1·60

228 Dragon

2000. Chinese New Year ("Year of the Dragon"). Multicoloured.
966 $1 Type **228** 35 30
967 $3.90 Dragon roaring . . . . 1·25 1·75
MS968 131 × 85 mm. Nos. 966/7 . . 1·60 2·00

229 Rennell Island from the Sea

2000. Declaration of East Rennell Island as World Heritage Site. Multicoloured.
969 50c. Type **229** 30 40
970 $3.40 Canoe on Lake Tegano 1·25 1·40
971 $4 Rennell shrikebill . . . . 1·75 2·00
972 $4.90 Endemic orchid . . . . 2·25 2·25

230 Woman running

2000. Olympic Games, Sydney. Multicoloured.
973 $1 Type **230** 50 30
974 $4.50 Man running . . . . . 2·00 2·50
MS975 105 × 90 mm. Nos. 973/4 . . 2·50 2·75

231 Yellow-throated White-Eye

2001. Birds. Multicoloured.
976 5c. Type **231** 10 10
977 20c. Purple swamphen . . . 10 10
978 50c. Blyth's hornbill 10 15
979 80c. Yellow-faced myna . . . 15 20
980 90c. Blue-faced parrot finch 15 20
981 $1 Greater crested tern ("Crested Tern") 15 20
982 $2 Rainbow lory ("Rainbow Lorikeet") 35 40
983 $3 Eclectus parrot 50 55
984 $4 Dwarf kingfisher 65 70
985 $10 Australian stone-curlew ("Beach Thick-knee") . . . 1·60 1·75
986 $20 Brahminy kite (46 × 37 mm) . . . . . . 3·25 3·50
987 $50 Superb fruit-dove (46 × 37 mm) . . . . . . 8·25 8·50

232 Snake and Exhibition Emblem

2001. "Hong Kong 2001" Stamp Exhibition.
988 **232** $1.70 multicoloured . . . 80 90
989 $2.30 multicoloured . . . 95 1·10
MS990 115 × 85 mm. $5 multicoloured (as No. 972) . . 1·75 2·00

233 Refugees

2001. 50th Anniv of U.N. High Commission for Refugees.
991 **233** 50c. blue and black . . . 10 10
992 – $1 red and black 15 20
993 – $1.90 green and black . . . 35 40
994 – $2.30 brown and black . . 40 45
DESIGNS: $1 Red Cross volunteers distributing medical aid; $1.90 Temporary tent accommodation; $2.30 Refugee family.

2001. Chinese New Year ("Year of the Snake"). Sheet, 140 × 75 mm, containing designs as Nos. 389/91 and 400, each 24½ × 35 mm and inscr "YEAR OF THE SNAKE 2001". Multicoloured.
MS995 $1 Red-banded tree snake; $1 Whip snake; $1 Pacific boa; $1 Guppy's snake 65 70

234 *Amphiprion chrysopterus* (fish)

2001. Reef Fish. Multicoloured.
996 70c. Type **234** 35 25
997 90c. *Amphiprion perideraion* 40 30
998 $1 *Premnas biaculeatus* . . . 45 30
999 $1.50 *Amphiprion melanopus* 65 50
1000 $2.10 *Amphiprion clarkii* . . 80 1·00
1001 $4.50 *Dascyllus trimaculatus* 1·50 2·00
MS1002 160 × 85 mm. Nos. 996/1001 3·75 4·00

235 Grey Cuscus on Branch

2002. Endangered Species. Grey Cuscus. Multicoloured.
1003 $1 Type **235** 45 25
1004 $1.70 Grey Cuscus on branch 70 55
1005 $2.30 Grey Cuscus in leaves 85 85
1006 $5 Grey Cuscus in leaves . . 1·75 2·00

2002. Golden Jubilee. As T **211** of St. Helena.
1007 $1 black, red and gold . . . 45 30
1008 $1.90 multicoloured 75 75
1009 $2.10 black, red and gold 80 85
1010 $2.30 multicoloured 85 90
MS1011 162 × 95 mm. Nos. 1002/5 and $10 multicoloured . . . . 5·50 6·00
DESIGNS—HORIZ (as Type **211** of St. Helena): $1 Princess Elizabeth with doll's pram, 1933; $1.90, Queen Elizabeth wearing sunglasses; $2.10, Queen Elizabeth in evening dress, 1955; $2.30, Queen Elizabeth in blue hat. VERT (38 × 51 mm): $10 Queen Elizabeth after Annigoni
Designs as nos. 1002/5 in No. **MS**1011 omit the gold frame around each stamp and the "Golden Jubilee 1952-2002" inscription.

236 Old School Building, Western Solomons

2002. Centenary of Methodist Mission. Multicoloured.
1012 $1 Type **236** 15 20
1013 $1.70 Mrs. Goldie in canoe 30 35
1014 $2.10 Tandanya (missionary schooner) 35 40
1015 $2.30 Revd J Goldie with local chiefs 40 45
MS1016 140 × 80 mm. $5 Revd. J. Goldie with Sam Aqarao (vert) 80 85

2002. "United We Stand". Support for Victims of 11 September 2001 Terrorist Attacks. As T **445** of St.Vincent. Multicoloured
1017 $2.10 US flag as Statue of Liberty and Solomon Islands flag 35 40

237 Signalman 1st Class Douglas Munro (USCG)

238 Horse's Head

2002. 60th Anniv of Battle of Guadalcanal. Medal Recipients. Each green and black.
1018 $1 Type **237** 15 20
1019 $1.90 Captain Joe Foss (USMC) 30 35
1020 $2.10 Platoon Sergeant Mitchell Paige (USMC) 35 40
1021 $2.30 Rear Admiral Norman Scott (USN) 40 45
MS1022 127 × 181 mm. Nos. 1018/19, but each with a face value of $5 . . . . 80 85

2002. Chinese New Year ("Year of the Horse"). Sheet, 140 × 80 mm, containing T **238** and similar design, each brown and green.
MS1023 Type **238**; $4 Horse (horiz) 1·25 1·40

239 Sieve Cowrie Shell

2002. "Philakorea 2002" International Stamp Exhibition, Seoul. Cowrie Shells. Multicoloured.
1024 $1 Type **239** 15 20
1025 $1 Kitten cowrie 15 20
1026 $1 Eroded cowrie and stolid cowrie 15 20
1027 $1.90 Tapering cowrie . . . 30 35
1028 $1.90 Tiger cowrie 30 35
1029 $1.90 Lynx cowrie 30 35
1030 $2.30 Map cowrie 40 45

1031 $2.30 Pacific deer cowrie . . 40 45
1032 $2.30 Tortoise cowrie . . . 40 45
MS1033 88 × 58 mm. $10 Golden cowrie . . . . 1·60 1·75

2002. Queen Elizabeth the Queen Mother Commemoration. As T **215** of St. Helena.
1034 $1 brown, gold and purple 15 20
1035 $2.30 multicoloured 40 45
MS1036 145 × 70 mm. $5 black and gold; $5 multicoloured . . . . 1·60 1·75
DESIGNS: $1 Duchess of York, 1930; $2.30, Queen Mother at Royal Caledonian School, Bushey; $5 (black and gold) Queen Mother in evening dress, 1954; $5 (multicoloured) Queen Mother at St. Paul's Cathedral, 1997. Designs in No. MS1036 omit the "1900–2002" inscription and the coloured frame.

240 "Christmas Night"

2002. Christmas. Religious Paintings. Mult.
1037 $1 Type **240** 15 20
1038 $2.10 "Madonna and Child" (Giovanni Bellini) 35 40
1039 $2.30 "Nativity" (Perugino) (horiz) 40 45
1040 $5 "Madonna and Child" (Simone Martini) 80 85

2003. World Aids Day. No. 872 surch **$1.35** and pink ribbon.
1041 $1.35+$3 Doctor and child 20 25

POSTAGE DUE STAMPS

D 1

1940.
D1 D 1 1d. green . . . . 6·50 7·00
D2 2d. red . . . . 7·00 7·00
D3 3d. brown . . . . 7·00 11·00
D4 4d. blue . . . . 11·00 11·00
D5 5d. olive . . . . 12·00 21·00
D6 6d. purple . . . . 12·00 15·00
D7 1s. violet . . . . 14·00 26·00
D8 1s.6d. green . . . . . . 28·00 48·00

SOMALIA Pt. 8; Pt. 14

A former Italian colony in East Africa on the Gulf of Aden, including Benadir (S. Somaliland), and Jubaland. Under British Administration 1943–50 (for stamps issued during this period see volume 1). Then under United Nations control with Italian Administration. Became independent on 1 July 1960. Following a revolution in October 1969, the country was designated "Somali Democratic Republic". See also Middle East Forces.

1903. 64 besa = 16 annas = 1 rupia.
1905. 100 centesimi = 1 lira.
1922. 100 besa = 1 rupia.
1926. 100 centesimi = 1 lira.
1950. 100 centesimi = 1 somalo.
1961. 100 cents = 1 Somali shilling.

1 African Elephant

2 Somali Lion

1903.
1 **1** 1b. brown . . . . 29·00 5·50
2 2b. green . . . . 1·00 3·00
3 **2** 1a. red . . . . 1·00 4·75
4 2a. brown . . . . 1·90 10·00
5 2½a. blue . . . . 1·00 10·00
6 5a. yellow . . . . 1·90 21·00
7 10a. lilac . . . . 1·90 21·00

1905. Surch with new value without bars at top.
10 **1** 2c. on 1b. brown . . . . . 6·50 11·00
11 5c. on 2b. green . . . . . 6·50 7·50
12 **2** 10c. on 1a. red . . . . . 6·50 7·50
13 15c. on 2a. brown . . . . . 6·50 7·50
8 15c. on 5a. yellow £2500 £600
13a 20c. on 2a. brown . . . . £300 7·50
14 25c. on 2½a. blue . . . . 11·00 7·50
9 40c. on 10a. lilac £600 £190
15 50c. on 5a. yellow . . . . . 19·00 19·00
16 1l. on 10a. lilac . . . . . . 19·00 26·00
For stamps with bars at top, see Nos. 68, etc.

1916. Nos. 15 and 16 re-surcharged and with bars cancelling original surcharge.
17 **2** 5c. on 50c. on 5a. yellow . . 31·00 30·00
18 20c. on 1l. on 10a. lilac . . . 5·50 21·00

1916. Red Cross stamps of Italy optd **SOMALIA**.
19 **53** 10c.+5c. red . . . . 8·00 21·00
20 **54** 15c.+5c. grey . . . . 25·00 26·00
21 20c.+5c. orange . . . . . 25·00 42·00
22 20 on 15c.+5c. grey . . . . 8·00 22·00

1922. Nos. 12, etc., again surch at top.
23 **1** 3b. on 5c. on 2b. green . . . 9·25 15·00
24 **2** 6b. on 10c. on 1a. red . . . 17·00 11·00
25 9b. on 15c. on 2a. brown . . 17·00 15·00
26 15b. on 25c. on 2½a. blue . . 19·00 11·00
27 30b. on 50c. on 5a. yellow . . 21·00 28·00
28 60b. on 1l. on 10a. lilac . . . 21·00 50·00

1922. Victory stamps of Italy surch **SOMALIA ITALIANA** and new value.
29 **62** 3b. on 5c. green . . . . . . 1·30 5·50
30 6b. on 10c. red . . . . . . 1·30 5·50
31 9b. on 15c. grey . . . . . . 1·30 7·50
32 15b. on 25c. blue . . . . . 1·30 7·50

1923. Nos. 11 to 16 re-surcharged with new values and bars (No. 33 is optd with bars only at bottom).
33 **1** bars on 2c. on 1b. brown . . 7·50 21·00
34 2 on 2c. on 1b. brown . . . 7·50 21·00
35 3 on 2c. on 1b. brown . . . 7·50 12·00
36 **2** 5b. on 50c. on 5a. yellow . . 7·50 10·00
37 **1** 6 on 5c. on 2b. green . . . . 13·00 10·00
38 **2** 18b. on 10c. on 1a. red . . . 13·00 10·00
39 20b. on 15c. on 2a. brown . . 13·50 10·00
40 25b. on 15c. on 2a. brown . . 16·00 10·00
41 30b. on 25c. on 2½a. blue . . 17·00 14·50
42 60b. on 1l. on 10a. lilac . . . 17·00 30·00
43 1r. on 1l. on 10a. lilac . . . 30·00 38·00

1923. Propaganda of Faith stamps of Italy surch **SOMALIA ITALIANA** and new value.
44 **66** 6b. on 20c. orange & green 4·50 20·00
45 13b. on 30c. orange and red 4·50 20·00
46 20b. on 50c. orange & violet 3·00 22·00
47 30b. on 1l. orange and blue 3·00 30·00

1923. Fascist March on Rome stamps of Italy surch **SOMALIA ITALIA** and new value.
48 **73** 3b. on 10c. green . . . . . 5·50 8·25
49 13b. on 30c. violet . . . . . 5·50 8·25
50 20b. on 50c. red . . . . . 5·50 9·25
51 **74** 30b. on 1l. blue . . . . . . 5·50 24·00
52 1r. on 2l. brown . . . . . 5·50 28·00
53 **75** 3l. on 5l. black and blue . . 5·50 40·00

1924. Manzoni stamps of Italy surch **SOMALIA ITALIANA** and new value.
54 **77** 6b. on 10c. black and purple 5·50 22·00
55 9b. on 15c. black and green 5·50 22·00
56 13b. on 30c. black . . . . . 5·50 22·00
57 20b. on 50c. black & brown 5·50 22·00
58 30b. on 1l. black and blue 45·00 £170
59 3r. on 5l. black and purple £450 £1500

1925. Holy Year stamps of Italy surch **SOMALIA ITALIANA** and new value.
60 – 6b.+3b. on 20c.+10c. brown and green . . . . 3·00 13·00
61 **81** 13b.+6b. on 30c.+15c. brown and chocolate . . 3·00 15·00
62 – 15b.+8b. on 50c.+25c. brown and violet . . . . 3·00 13·00
63 – 18b.+9b. on 60c.+30c. brown and red . . . . . 3·00 17·00
64 – 30b.+15b. on 1l.+50c. purple and blue . . . . 3·00 22·00
65 – 1r.+50b. on 5l.+2l.50 purple and red . . . . 3·00 34·00

1925. Royal Jubilee stamps of Italy optd **SOMALIA ITALIANA**.
66A **82** 60c. red . . . . 75 4·50
67B 1l. blue . . . . 1·50 6·75
67aA 1l.25 blue . . . . 35 11·00

1926. Nos. 10/13 and 13a/16 optd with bars at top.
68 **1** 2c. on 1b. brown . . . . . 21·00 30·00
69 5c. on 2b. green . . . . . 13·00 17·00
70 **2** 10c. on 1a. pink . . . . . 8·25 5·50
71 15c. on 2a. brown . . . . . 8·25 7·50
72 20c. on 2a. brown . . . . . 9·50 7·50
73 25c. on 2½a. blue . . . . . 9·25 11·00
74 50c. on 5a. yellow . . . . . 13·00 19·00
75 1l. on 10a. lilac . . . . . . 21·00 24·00

1926. St. Francis of Assisi stamps of Italy optd **SOMALIA ITALIANA** (76/8) or **Somalia** (79/80).
76 **83** 20c. green . . . . 1·70 7·75
77 40c. violet . . . . 1·70 7·75
78 60c. red . . . . 1·70 13·00
79 1l.25 blue . . . . 1·70 21·00
80 5l.+2l.50 green . . . . . . 4·75 40·00

21

24

1926. Italian Colonial Institute.
81 **21** 5c.+5c. brown . . . . . . 70 4·50
82 10c.+5c. olive . . . . . . 70 4·50
83 20c.+5c. green . . . . . . 70 4·50
84 40c.+5c. red . . . . 70 4·50
85 60c.+5c. orange . . . . . . 70 4·50
86 1l.+5c. blue . . . . 70 7·50

1926. Italian stamps optd **SOMALIA ITALIANA**.
87 **31** 2c. brown . . . . 1·90 3·50
88 **37** 5c. green . . . . 1·90 3·50
89 **92** 7½c. brown . . . . 17·00 30·00
90 **37** 10c. pink . . . . 1·30 40
91 **39** 20c. purple . . . . 1·30 1·50
92 **34** 25c. green and light green 1·30 1·20
92a **39** 30c. black . . . . 10·50 19·00
93 **91** 50c. grey and brown . . . 18·00 5·50
94 **92** 50c. mauve . . . . 26·00 32·00
95 **39** 60c. orange . . . . 3·00 5·25
96 **34** 75c. red and carmine . . . 90·00 19·00
97 1l. brown and green . . . 3·00 75
98 1l.25 blue & ultram . . . 7·50 1·90
99 **91** 1l.75 brown . . . . 60·00 13·00
100 **34** 2l. green and orange . . . 21·00 10·00
101 2l.50 green and orange . . 21·00 13·00
102 5l. blue and pink . . . . 55·00 28·00
103 10l. green and pink . . . 55·00 45·00

1927. 1st National Defence issue of Italy (lira colours changed) optd **SOMALIA ITALIANA**.
104 **89** 40c.+20c. black & brown 2·10 17·00
105 – 60c.+30c. brown and red 2·10 17·00
106 – 1l.25+60c. black & blue . . 2·10 35·00
107 – 5l.+2l.50 black & green . . 3·75 45·00

1927. Centenary of Volta Stamps of Italy (colours changed) optd **Somalia Italiana**.
108 **90** 20c. violet . . . . 4·75 21·00
109 50c. orange . . . . 7·50 13·00
110 1l.25 blue . . . . 10·00 30·00

1928. 45th Anniv of Italian–African Society.
111 **24** 20c.+5c. green . . . . . . 1·90 6·00
112 30c.+5c. red . . . . 1·90 6·00
113 50c.+10c. violet . . . . . 1·90 10·50
114 1l.25+20c. blue . . . . . 2·10 12·00

1929. 2nd National Defence issue of Italy (colours changed) optd **SOMALIA ITALIANA**.
115 **89** 30c.+10c. black and red . . 3·50 12·00
116 – 50c.+20c. grey and lilac . . 3·50 14·00
117 – 1l.25+50c. blue & brown 4·25 22·00
118 – 5l.+2l. black and green . . 4·25 40·00

1929. Montecassino Abbey stamps of Italy (colours changed) optd **Somalia Italiana** (10l.) or **SOMALIA ITALIANA** (others).
119 **104** 20c. green . . . . 4·25 10·00
120 – 25c. red . . . . 4·25 10·00
121 – 50c.+10c. red . . . . . . 4·25 11·00
122 – 75c.+15c. brown . . . . 4·50 11·00
123 **104** 1l.25+25c. purple . . . . 8·00 19·00
124 – 5l.+1l. blue . . . . . . 8·00 22·00
125 – 10l.+2l. brown . . . . . 8·00 30·00

1930. Royal Wedding stamps of Italy (colours changed) optd **SOMALIA ITALIANA**.
126 **109** 20c. green . . . . 1·20 3·50
127 50c.+10c. red . . . . . . 1·00 4·75
128 1l.25+25c. red . . . . . 1·00 10·50

1930. Ferrucci stamps of Italy (colours changed) optd **SOMALIA ITALIANA**.
129 **114** 20c. violet . . . . 1·90 2·00
130 – 25c. green (No. 283) . . 1·90 1·90
131 – 50c. black (No. 284) . . 1·90 3·75
132 – 1l.25 blue (No. 285) . . 1·90 7·50
133 – 5l.+2l. red (No. 286) . . 5·50 15·00

1930. 3rd National Defence issue of Italy (colours changed) optd **SOMALIA ITALIANA**.
134 **89** 30c.+10c. green & dp grn 15·00 19·00
135 – 50c.+10c. purple & green 15·00 22·00
136 – 1l.25+30c. brown and deep brown . . . . 15·00 35·00
137 – 5l.+1l.50 green and blue . . 48·00 75·00

29 Irrigation Canal

1930. 25th Anniv (1929) of Colonial Agricultural Institute.
138 **29** 50c.+20c. brown . . . . . 2·75 11·00
139 1l.25+20c. blue . . . . . 2·75 11·00
140 1l.75+20c. green . . . . . 2·75 13·50
141 2l.55+50c. violet . . . . . 3·75 22·00
142 5l.+1l. red . . . . 3·75 32·00

1930. Bimillenary of Virgil stamps of Italy (colours changed) optd **SOMALIA**.
143 15c. grey . . . . 1·00 4·50
144 20c. brown . . . . 1·00 2·20
145 25c. green . . . . 1·00 1·90
146 30c. brown . . . . 1·00 2·20
147 50c. purple . . . . 1·00 1·90
148 75c. red . . . . 1·00 3·50
149 1l.25 blue . . . . 1·00 4·50
150 5l.+1l.50 purple . . . . . . 3·50 24·00
151 10l.+2l.50 brown . . . . . . 3·50 38·00

1931. Stamps of Italy optd **SOMALIA ITALIANA**.
152 – 25c. green (No. 244) . . . 9·25 11·00
153 **103** 50c. violet . . . . 9·25 3·75

1931. St. Antony of Padua stamps of Italy optd **Somalia** (75c., 5l.) or **SOMALIA** (others).
154 **121** 20c. brown . . . . 1·50 9·25
155 – 25c. green . . . . 1·50 3·75
156 – 30c. brown . . . . 1·50 3·75
157 – 50c. purple . . . . 1·50 3·75
158 – 75c. grey . . . . 1·50 9·25
159 – 1l.25 blue . . . . 1·50 19·00
160 – 5l.+2l.50 brown . . . . . 4·25 42·00

32 Tower at Mnara-Ciromo

33 Hippopotamus

1932.
161a – 5c. brown . . . . 2·10 3·50
162a – 7½c. violet . . . . 11·00 8·00
163a – 10c. black . . . . 4·50 35
164 – 15c. green . . . . 1·50 95
165a **32** 20c. red £170 25
166a 25c. green . . . . 1·50 35
167a 30c. brown . . . . 15·00 1·00
168 – 35c. blue . . . . 2·75 4·50
169a – 50c. violet . . . . £250 4·50
170 – 75c. red . . . . 1·90 60
171 – 1l.25 blue . . . . 9·25 50
172 – 1l.75 red . . . . 4·50 60
173 – 2l. red . . . . 1·90 40
174 – 2l.55 blue . . . . 15·00 38·00
175a – 5l. red . . . . 7·25 2·30
176 **33** 10l. violet . . . . 19·00 11·00
177 – 20l. green . . . . 48·00 48·00
178 – 25l. blue . . . . 48·00 75·00
DESIGNS—HORIZ: 5, 7½, 10, 15c. Francesco Crispi Lighthouse, Cape Guardafui; 35, 50, 75c. Governor's Residence, Mogadishu; 25l. Lioness. VERT: 1l.25, 1l.75, 2l. Termitarium (ant-hill); 2l.55, 5l. Ostrich; 20l. Lesser kudu.

1934. Honouring the Duke of the Abruzzi. Stamps of 1932 (some colours changed) optd **ONORANZE AL DUCA DEGLI ABRUZZI**.
179 – 10c. brown . . . . 7·00 12·00
180 **32** 25c. green . . . . 6·75 12·00
181 – 50c. purple . . . . 4·50 12·00
182 – 1l.25 blue . . . . 4·50 12·00
183 – 5l. black . . . . 4·50 12·00
184 **33** 10l. red . . . . 6·75 19·00
185 – 20l. blue . . . . 6·50 19·00
186 – 25l. green . . . . 6·50 19·00

35 Woman and Child

37 King Victor Emmanuel III

36

1934. 2nd Int Colonial Exhibition, Naples.
187 **35** 5c. green & brown (postage) . . . . 3·50 10·50
188 10c. brown and black . . . 3·50 10·00
189 20c. red and blue . . . . . 3·50 8·25
190 50c. violet and brown . . . 3·50 8·25
191 60c. brown and slate . . . 3·50 11·00
192 1l.25 blue and green . . . 3·50 19·00
193 – 25c. blue and orange (air) 3·50 10·00
194 – 50c. green and blue . . . 3·50 8·25
195 – 75c. brown and orange . . 3·50 8·25
196 – 80c. brown and green . . . 3·50 10·00
197 – 1l. red and green . . . . . 3·50 11·00
198 – 2l. blue and brown . . . . 3·50 19·00
DESIGNS: 25c. to 75c. Caproni Ca 101 airplane over River Juba; 80c. to 2l. Cheetahs watching Caproni Ca 101 airplane.

1934. Air. Rome–Mogadishu Flight.
199 **36** 25c.+10c. green . . . . . . 3·50 5·50
200 50c.+10c. brown . . . . . 3·50 5·50
201 75c.+15c. red . . . . . . 3·50 5·50
202 80c.+15c. black . . . . . 3·50 5·50
203 1l.+20c. brown . . . . . . 3·50 5·50
204 2l.+20c. blue . . . . 3·50 5·50
205 3l.+25c. violet . . . . . . 18·00 48·00
206 5l.+25c. red . . . . 18·00 48·00

207 10l.+30c. purple . . . . . 18·00 48·00
208 25l.+2l. green . . . . . . 18·00 48·00

1934. King of Italy's Visit to Italian Somaliland.
209 **37** 5c.+5c. black . . . . . . 1·90 11·00
210 7½c.+7½c. purple . . . . 1·90 11·00
211 15c.+10c. green . . . . . 1·90 11·00
212 20c.+10c. red . . . . . . 1·90 11·00
213 25c.+10c. green . . . . . 1·90 11·00
214 30c.+10c. brown . . . . . 1·90 11·00
215 50c.+10c. violet . . . . . 1·90 11·00
216 75c.+15c. red . . . . . . 1·90 11·00
217 1l.25+15c. blue . . . . . 1·90 11·00
218 1l.75+25c. orange . . . . 1·90 11·00
219 2l.75+25c. blue . . . . . 12·50 38·00
220 5l.+1l. purple . . . . . . 12·50 38·00
221 10l.+1l.80 brown . . . . . 12·50 38·00
222 – 25l.+2l.75 sepia & brn . . £120 £190
DESIGN—36×44 mm: 25l. King Victor Emmanuel III on horseback.

38a Native Girl and Macchi Castoldi MC-94 Flying Boat

1936. Air.
223 – 25c. green . . . . 1·25 3·00
224 – 50c. brown 25 25
225 – 60c. orange . . . . 1·90 5·50
226 – 75c. brown . . . . 1·20 1·50
227 **38a** 1l. blue 25 25
228 – 1l.50 violet . . . . 1·20 75
229 – 2l. blue . . . . 4·25 1·20
230 **38a** 3l. red . . . . 13·00 5·00
231 – 5l. green . . . . 15·00 9·25
232 – 10l. red . . . . 19·00 15·00
DESIGNS: 25c., 1l.50, Banana trees; 50c., 2l. Native woman in cotton plantation; 60c., 5l. Orchard; 75c., 10l. Native women harvesting.

ITALIAN TRUST TERRITORY

40 Tower at Mnara-Ciromo

41 Ostrich

42 Governor's Residence, Mogadishu

43 River Scene

1950.
233 **40** 1c. black 10 10
234 **41** 5c. red 75 25
235 **42** 6c. violet 15 10
236 **40** 8c. green 15 10
237 **42** 10c. green 10 10
238 **41** 20c. green . . . . 1·25 20
239 **40** 35c. red 35 20
240 **42** 55c. blue 45 15
241 **41** 60c. violet . . . . 1·75 35
242 **40** 65c. brown 70 15
243 **42** 1s. orange 85 15

1950. Air.
244 **43** 30c. brown 30 30
245 45c. red 30 30
246 65c. violet 30 30
247 70c. blue 30 30
248 90c. brown 30 30
249 1s. purple 45 30
250 1s.35 violet 70 70
251 1s.50 green 85 50
252 3s. blue . . . . 7·00 2·25
253 5s. brown . . . . 8·00 3·00
254 10s. orange . . . . . . 9·50 2·25

44 Councillors

45 Symbol of Fair

1951. 1st Territorial Council.
255 **44** 20c. brown & grn (postage) 2·00 20
256 55c. violet and brown . . . 3·75 3·50
257 – 1s. blue and violet (air) . . 2·25 70
258 – 1s.50 brown and green . . . 3·75 2·75
DESIGN—VERT: 1s., 1s.50, Flags and Savoia Marchetti S.M.95C airliner over Mogadiscio.

1952. 1st Somali Fair, Mogadiscio.
259 **45** 25c. brown & red (postage) 1·75 1·75
260 55c. brown and blue . . . 1·75 1·75
261 – 1s.20 blue and bistre (air) 2·00 2·00
DESIGN: 1s.20, Palm tree, Douglas DC-4 airliner and minaret.

46 Mother and Baby

47 Somali and Entrance to Fair

1953. Anti-tuberculosis Campaign.
262 **46** 5c. brown & violet (postage) 10 10
263 25c. brown and red 15 10
264 50c. brown and blue . . . 70 70
265 1s.20 brown and green (air) 85 85

1953. 2nd Somali Fair, Mogadiscio.
266 **47** 25c. green & grey (postage) 20 20
267 60c. blue and grey 40 40
268 – 1s.20 red and pink (air) . . 40 40
269 – 1s.50 brown and buff . . . 40 40
DESIGN: 1s.20, 1s.50, Palm, airplane and entrance.

48 Stamps of 1903 and Map

1953. 50th Anniv of First Stamps of Italian Somaliland. (a) Postage.
270 **48** 25c. brown, red and lake 25 25
271 35c. brown, red and green 25 25
272 60c. brown, red and orange 25 25

(b) Air. Aeroplane on Map.
273 **48** 60c. brown, red & chestnut 45 45
274 1s. brown, red and black 45 45

49 Airplane and Constellations

1953. Air. 75th Anniv of U.P.U.
275 **49** 1s.20 red and buff 35 35
276 1s.50 brown and buff . . . 40 40
277 2s. green and blue 45 40

50 Somali Bush Country

51 Alexander Island and River Juba

1954. Leprosy Relief Convention.
278 **50** 25c. green & blue (postage) 30 30
279 60c. sepia and brown . . . 30 30
280 **51** 1s.20 brown & green (air) 40 40
281 2s. purple and red 55 65

52 Somali Flag

52a "Adenium somalense"

1954. Institution of Somali Flag.
282 **52** 25c. multicoloured (postage) 25 25
283 1s.20 multicoloured (air) 25 25

1955. Floral Designs.
284 **52a** 1c. red, black and blue 10 10
285 – 5c. mauve, green and blue 10 10
290c – 10c. yellow, green & lilac 10 10
290d – 15c. multicoloured . . . 20 20
290e – 25c. yellow, green & brn 15 10
290f – 50c. multicoloured . . . 30 30
288 – 60c. red, green and black 10 15
289 – 1s. yellow, green & purple 15 20
290 – 1s.20 yellow, green & brn 20 20
FLOWERS: 5c. Blood lily; 10c. "Grinum scabrum"; 15c. Baobab; 25c. "Poinciana elata"; 50c. Glory lily; 60c. "Calatropis procera"; 1s. Sea lily; 1s.20, "Sesamothamnus bussernus".

54 Oribi

54a Lesser Kudu

1955. Air. Antelopes. (a) As T **54**. Heads in black and orange.
291 **54** 35c. green 30 20
292 – 45c. violet . . . . 1·25 35
293 – 50c. violet 30 20
294 – 75c. red 65 25
295 – 1s.20 green 65 25
296 – 1s.50 blue 75 45
ANTELOPES: 45c. Salt's dik-dik; 50c. Speke's gazelle; 75c. Gerenuk; 1s.20, Soemmering's gazelle; 1s.50, Waterbuck.

(b) As T **54a**.
296a **54a** 3s. purple and brown . . 1·00 85
296b – 5s. yellow and black . . 1·00 85
DESIGN: 5s. Hunter's hartebeest.

55 Native Weaver

56 Voters and Map

1955. 3rd Somali Fair.
297 **55** 25c. brown (postage) 25 25
298 – 30c. green 25 25
299 – 45c. brown and orange (air) 25 25
300 – 1s.20 blue and pink 35 35
DESIGNS: 30c. Cattle fording river; 45c. Camels around well; 1s.20, Native woman at well.

1956. 1st Legislative Assembly.
301 **56** 5c. brown & green (postage) 10 10
302 10c. sepia and brown . . . 10 10
303 25c. brown and red 10 10
304 60c. brown and blue (air) 15 15
305 1s.20 brown and orange . . 20 20

57 Somali Arms

58 Falcheiro Barrage

1957. Inauguration of National Emblem. Arms in blue and brown.
306 **57** 5c. brown (postage) . . . 10 10
307 25c. red 15 15
308 60c. violet 15 15
309 45c. blue (air) 20 20
310 1s.20 green 25 25

1957. 4th Somali Fair.
311 **58** 5c. lilac & brown (postage) 10 10
312 – 10c. green and bistre . . . 10 10
313 – 25c. blue and red 15 15
314 – 60c. brown and blue (air) 25 25
315 – 1s.20 black and red 25 25
DESIGNS—HORIZ: 10c. Juba River bridge; 25c. Silos at Margherita; 60c. Irrigation canal. VERT: 1s.20, Oil well.

59 Somali Nurse with Baby

60 Track Running

1957. Tuberculosis Relief Campaign.
316 **59** 10c.+10c. brown and red (postage) 15 15
317 25c.+10c. brown & green 15 15
318 55c.+20c. brown and blue (air) 20 20
319 1s.20c.+20c. brown and violet 30 30

1958. Sports.
320 **60** 2c. lilac (postage) 10 10
321 – 4c. green (Football) 10 10
322 – 5c. red (Discus) 10 10
323 – 6c. black (Motor-cycling) 10 10
324 – 8c. blue (Fencing) 10 10
325 – 10c. orange (Archery) . . . 10 10
326 – 25c. green (Boxing) 10 10
327 – 60c. brown (Running) (air) 10 10
328 – 1s.20 blue (Cycling) . . . 15 15
329 – 1s.50 red (Basketball) . . . 20 15
The 4, 6, 10 and 25c. are horiz.

61 The Constitution and Assembly Building, Mogadishu

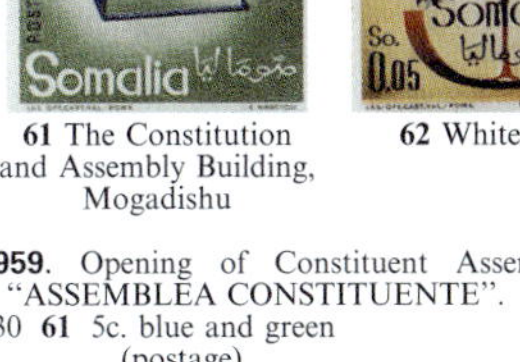

62 White Stork

1959. Opening of Constituent Assembly. Inscr "ASSEMBLEA CONSTITUENTE".
330 **61** 5c. blue and green (postage) 10 10
331 25c. blue and brown . . . 10 10
332 – 1s.20 blue and brown (air) 25 25
333 – 1s.50 blue and green . . . 25 25
DESIGNS—HORIZ: 1s.20, 1s.50, Police bugler.

1959. Somali Water Birds.
334 **62** 5c. black, red and yellow (postage) 20 10
335 – 10c. red, yellow and brown 20 10
336 – 15c. black and orange . . 20 10
337 – 25c. black, orange and red 20 10
338 – 1s.20 black, red and violet (air) . . . . 1·10 50
339 – 2s. red and blue . . . . . 1·10 50
BIRDS—VERT: 10c. Saddle-bill stork; 15c. Sacred ibis; 25c. Pink-backed pelicans. HORIZ: 1s.20, Marabou stork; 2s. Great egret.

63 Incense Tree

64 Institute Badge

1959. 5th Somali Fair.
340 **63** 20c. black & orge (postage) 10 10
341 – 60c. black, red and orange 20 20
342 – 1s.20 black and red (air) 25 25
343 – 2s. black, brown and blue 40 40
DESIGNS—VERT: 60c. Somali child with incense-burner. HORIZ: 1s.20, Ancient Egyptian transport of incense; 2s. Incense-burner and Mogadishu Harbour.

1960. Opening of University Institute of Somalia, Mogadishu.
344 **64** 5c. red and brown (postage) 10 10
345 – 50c. brown and blue . . . 10 10
346 – 80c. black and red 20 20
347 – 45c. brown, black and green (air) 20 20
348 – 1s.20 blue, black & lt blue 35 35
DESIGNS—HORIZ: 45c., 1s.20, Institute build-ings; 50c. Map of Africa. VERT: 80c. Institute emblem.

65 "The Horn of Africa"

1960. World Refugee Year.
349 **65** 10c. green, black and brown (postage) 10 10
350 – 60c. brown, ochre and black 10 10
351 – 80c. green, black and pink 10 10
352 – 1s.50 red, blue and green (air) 60 60
DESIGNS—HORIZ: 60c. Similar to Type **65**. VERT: 80c. Palm; 1s.50, White stork.

REPUBLIC

1960. Optd **Somaliland Independence 26 June 1960**.
353 10c. yellow, green and lilac (No. 290c) (postage) . . . 12·00 12·00
354 50c. black, orange and violet (No. 293) (air) . . . . . . 22·00 17·00
355 1s.20 blk, orge & turq (No. 295) . . . . 19·00 17·00
Nos. 353/5 were only issued in the former British protectorate, which united with Somalia when the latter became independent on 1 July 1960.

67 Gazelle and Map of Africa
68 Olympic Flame and Somali Flag

1960. Proclamation of Independence.
356 **67** 5c. brn, bl & lilac (postage) 20 20
357 – 25c. blue 35 35
358 – 1s. brown, red & green (air) 40 20
359 – 1s.80 blue and orange . . . 1·10 90
DESIGNS—VERT: 25c. U.N. Flag and Headquarters Building. HORIZ: 1s. Chamber of Deputies, Montecitorio Palace, Rome; 1s.80, Somali Flag.

1960. Olympic Games. Inscr "1960".
360 **68** 5c. blue and green (postage) 15 10
361 – 10c. blue and yellow . . . 15 10
362 – 45c. blue and lilac (air) . . 10 15
363 – 1s.80 blue and red . . . . 1·10 95
DESIGNS: 10c. Relay race; 45c. Runner breasting tape; 1s.80, Runner.

69 Child drawing Giraffe
70 Girl harvesting Papaws

1960. Child Welfare. Inscr "PRO INFANZIA".
364 **69** 10c. black, brown and green (postage) 10 10
365 – 15c. black, light green & red 15 15
366 – 25c. brown, black & yellow 30 30
367 – 3s. orange, black, blue and green (air) . . . . . . 1·60 1·10
ANIMALS: 15c. Common zebra; 25c. Black rhinoceros; 3s. Leopard.

1961. Multicoloured. Designs each show a girl harvesting.
368 5c. Type **70** 10 10
369 10c. Girl harvesting durra . . 10 10
370 20c. Cotton 15 15
371 25c. Sesame 15 15
372 40c. Sugar cane 20 20
373 50c. Bananas 35 35
374 75c. Groundnuts (horiz) . . . 55 55
375 80c. Grapefruit (horiz) . . . 1·10 1·10

71 "Amauris hyalites"
72 Shield, Bow and Arrow, Quiver and Dagger

1961. Air. Butterflies. Multicoloured.
376 60c. Type **71** 25 15
377 90c. "Euryphura chalcis" . . 30 20
378 1s. "Papilio lormieri" . . . 3·25 25
379 1s.80 "Druryia antimachus" 75 45
380 3s. "Danaus formosa" . . . 90 60
381 5s. "Papilio phorcas" . . . . 3·25 90
382 10s. "Charaxes cynthia" . . . 6·75 2·40

1961. 6th Somali Trade Fair.
383 **72** 25c. yellow, black and red (postage) 10 10
384 – 45c. yellow, black and green 20 20
385 – 1s. yellow, black & bl (air) 55 45
386 – 1s.80 brown, black & yell 1·10 65
DESIGNS—Handicrafts—VERT: 45c. "Tungi" wooden vase and pottery. HORIZ: 1s. National head-dress, support and comb; 1s.80, Statuettes of camel and man, and balancing novelty.

73 Girl embroidering
75 Auxiliaries tending Casualty

74 Mosquito

1962. Child Welfare. Tropical Fishes. Inscr "PRO INFANZIA". Multicoloured.
387 15c. Type **73** (postage) . . . 15 15
388 25c. Semicircle angelfish . . . 15 15
389 40c. Dragon wrasse 80 80
390 2s.70 Emperor snapper (air) 2·50 1·10

1962. Malaria Eradication. Inscr "MONDO UNITO CONTRO LA MALARIA".
391 **74** 10c. green and red (postage) 15 15
392 – 25c. brown and mauve . . 30 30
393 – 1s. brown and black (air) 55 20
394 – 1s.80 green and black . . . 1·10 90
DESIGNS—VERT: 25c. Insecticide sprayer; 1s., 1s.80, Campaign emblem and mosquitoes.

1963. Women's Auxiliary Forces Formation. Multicoloured.
395 5c. Policewoman (postage) . . 10 10
396 10c. Army auxiliary 20 20
397 25c. Policewomen with patrol car 35 35
398 75c. Type **75** 45 45
399 1s. Policewomen marching with flag (air) 55 35
400 1s.80 Army auxiliaries at attention with flag . . . . 1·40 80
The 5c., 10c. and 25c. are horiz.

76 Wooden Spoon and Fork

1963. Freedom from Hunger.
401 **76** 75c. brown & grn (postage) 45 45
402 – 1s. multicoloured (air) . . 1·10 65
DESIGN: 1s. Sower.

77 Pres. Osman and Arms
78 Open-air Theatre

1963. 3rd Anniv of Independence. Arms in blue and yellow.
403 **77** 25c. sepia & blue (postage) 30 15
404 1s. sepia and red (air) . . . 65 35
405 1s.80 sepia and green . . . 1·00 55

1963. 7th Somali Fair.
406 **78** 25c. green (postage) . . . 20 20
407 – 55c. red 65 45
408 – 1s.80 blue (air) . . . . . 1·40 90
DESIGNS: 55c. African Trade Building; 1s.80, Government Pavilion.

79 Credit Bank, Mogadishu

1964. 10th Anniv of Somali Credit Bank. Multicoloured.
409 60c. Type **79** (postage) . . . 45 20
410 1s. Map of Somalia and globe (air) 90 45
411 1s.80 Bank emblem . . . . 1·40 90

80 Running

1964. Olympic Games, Tokyo. Each sepia, brown and blue.
412 10c. Type **80** (postage) . . . 15 15
413 25c. High-jumping 20 20
414 90c. Diving (air) 55 45
415 1s.80 Footballer . . . . . 1·10 65

81 Douglas DC-3 Airliner

1964. Inauguration of Somali Airlines.
416 **81** 5c. blue and red (postage) 20 35
417 – 20c. blue and orange . . . 65 35
418 – 1s. ochre and green (air) 1·10 55
419 – 1s.80 blue and black . . . 2·25 1·60
DESIGNS: 20c. Passengers disembarking from DC-3; DC-3 in flight over: 1s. African elephants; 1s.80, Mogadishu.

82 Refugees
83 I.T.U. Emblem on Map of Africa

1964. Somali Refugees Fund.
420 **82** 25c.+10c. red and blue (postage) 55 20
421 – 75c.+20c. purple, black and red (air) 45 45
422 – 1s.80+50c. green, black and bistre . . . . 1·50 1·25
DESIGNS—HORIZ: 75c. Ruined houses. VERT: 1s.80, Soldier with child refugees.

1965. I.T.U. Centenary.
423 **83** 25c. blue & orange (postage) 45 10
424 1s. black and green (air) 85 55
425 1s.80 brown and mauve . . 1·60 1·10

84 Tanning

1965. Somali Industries.
426 **84** 10c. sepia and buff (postage) 15 15
427 – 25c. sepia and pink 20 15
428 – 35c. sepia and blue . . . 35 15
429 – 1s.50 sepia and green (air) 1·10 55
430 – 2s. sepia and mauve . . . 2·25 1·10
DESIGNS: 25c. Meat processing and canning; 35c. Fish processing and canning; 1s.50, Sugar—cutting cane and refining; 2s. Dairying—milking and bottling.

85 Hottentot Fig and Gazelle

1965. Somali Flora and Fauna. Multicoloured.
431 20c. Type **85** 10 10
432 60c. African tulips and giraffes 20 10
433 1s. White lotus and greater flamingoes 75 55
434 1s.30 Pervincia and ostriches 1·60 1·40
435 1s.80 Bignonia and common zebras . . . . 2·25 80

86 Narina's Trogon

1966. Somali Birds. Multicoloured.
436 25c. Type **86** 35 25
437 35c. Bateleur (vert) 50 25
438 50c. Ruppell's griffon . . . 65 55
439 1s.30 European roller . . . . 1·40 1·25
440 2s. Vulturine guineafowl (vert) . . . . 1·50 1·40

87 Globe and U.N. Emblem

1966. 21st Anniv of U.N.O. Multicoloured.
441 35c. Type **87** 35 15
442 1s. Map of Africa and U.N. emblem 45 20
443 1s.50 Map of Somalia and U.N. emblem 90 45

88 Woman sitting on Crocodile

1966. Somali Art. Showing Paintings from Garesa Museum, Mogadishu. Multicoloured.
444 25c. Type **88** 10 10
445 1s. Woman and warrior . . . 20 10
446 1s.50 Boy leading camel . . . 45 20
447 2s. Women pounding grain 90 55

89 U.N.E.S.C.O. Emblem and Palm
90 Oribi

1966. 20th Anniv of U.N.E.S.C.O.
448 **89** 35c. black, red and grey . . 10 10
449 1s. black, green and yellow 15 10
450 1s.80 black, blue and red 85 45

1967. Antelopes.
451 **90** 35c. ochre, black and blue 10 10
452 – 60c. brown, black & orange 15 15
453 – 1s. bistre, black and red . . 30 20
454 – 1s.80 ochre, black & green 1·10 60
ANTELOPES: 60c. Kirk's dik-dik; 1s. Gerenuk gazelle; 1s.80, Soemmering's gazelle.

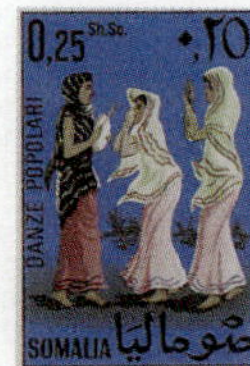

91 Somali Dancers
92 Badge and Scout Saluting

1967. "Popular Dances". Designs showing dancers.
455 **91** 25c. multicoloured 10 10
456 – 50c. multicoloured 10 10
457 – 1s.30 multicoloured 35 30
458 – 2s. multicoloured . . . . . 1·10 60

1967. World Scout Jamboree. Multicoloured.
459 35c. Type **92** 10 10
460 50c. Scouts and flags 15 10
461 1s. Camp scene 40 20
462 1s.80 Jamboree emblem . . . 1·00 65

93 Pres. Schermarche and King Faisal

1967. Visit of King Faisal of Saudi Arabia.
463 **93** 50c. black & blue (postage) 20 10
464 – 1s. multicoloured 45 35
465 – 1s.80 multicoloured (air) 90 55
DESIGNS: 1s. Somali and Saudi Arabian flags; 1s.80, Kaaba, Mecca and portraits as Type **93**.

94 Black-spotted Sweetlips

1967. Fishes. Multicoloured.
466 35c. Type **94** 10 10
467 50c. Blue-cheeked butterflyfish 20 10
468 1s. Catalufa 50 35
469 1s.80 Summana grouper 1·10 55

95 Inoculation **96** Somali Girl with Lemons

1968. 20th Anniv of W.H.O.
470 **95** 35c. multicoloured 10 10
471 – 1s. black, brown and green 20 20
472 – 1s.80 black brown & orge 90 55
DESIGNS: 1s. Chest examination; 1s.80, Heart examination.

1968. Agricultural Produce. Multicoloured.
473 5c. Type **96** 10 10
474 10c. Oranges 10 10
475 25c. Coconuts 10 10
476 35c. Papaws 15 10
477 40c. Mangoes 15 10
478 50c. Grapefruit 15 10
479 1s. Bananas 55 20
480 1s.30 Cotton bolls 85 45
Each design includes a Somali girl.

97 Waterbuck **98** Throwing the Javelin

1968. Somali Antelopes. Multicoloured.
481 1s.50 Type **97** 35 20
482 1s.80 Speke's gazelle 45 35
483 2s. Lesser kudu 60 35
484 5s. Hunter's hartebeest 1·40 80
485 10s. Dibatag gazelle 4·50 1·60

1968. Olympic Games, Mexico.
486 **98** 35c. black, brown & lemon 10 10
487 – 50c. black, brown and red 10 10
488 – 80c. black, brown & purple 20 20
489 – 1s.50 black, brown & green 1·40 65
DESIGNS: 50c. Running; 80c. Pole-vaulting; 1s.50, Basketball.

99 Great Egret **100** "Pounding Meal"

1968. Air. Birds. Multicoloured.
491 35c. Type **99** 25 25
492 1s. Carmine bee eater 70 70
493 1s.30 Yellow-bellied green pigeon 90 90
494 1s.80 Paradise whydah 2·75 2·75

1968. Somali Art.
495 **100** 25c. brown, black and lilac 15 10
496 – 35c. brown, black and red 15 10
497 – 2s.80 brown, black & grn 20 20
DESIGNS (wood-carvings): 35c. "Preparing food"; 2s.80, "Rug-making".

101 Cornflower **102** Workers at Anvil

1969. Flowers. Multicoloured.
498 40c. Type **101** 10 10
499 80c. Sunflower 20 15
500 1s. Oleander 55 30
501 1s.80 Chrysanthemum 1·40 85

1969. 50th Anniv of I.L.O. Multicoloured.
502 25c. Type **102** 10 10
503 1s. Ploughing with oxen 20 20
504 1s.80 Drawing water for irrigation 80 45

103 Gandhi, and Hands releasing Dove

1969. Birth Centenary of Mahatma Gandhi.
505 – 35c. purple 10 10
506 **103** 1s.50 orange 45 30
507 – 1s.80 brown 1·10 70
DESIGNS—VERT—(Size 25½ × 36 mm): 35c. Mahatma Gandhi; 1s.80, Gandhi seated.

SOMALI DEMOCRATIC REPUBLIC

An issue for the "Apollo 11" Moon Landing was prepared in 1970, but not issued.

104 "Charaxes varanes" **105** Lenin with Children

1970. Butterflies. Multicoloured.
508 25c. Type **104** 15 10
509 50c. "Cethosia lamarcki" 40 10
510 1s.50 "Troides aeacus" 55 45
511 2s. "Chrysiridia ripheus" 1·40 55

1970. Birth Centenary of Lenin.
512 **105** 25c. multicoloured 10 10
513 – 1s. multicoloured 20 15
514 – 1s.80 black, orange and brown 80 55
DESIGNS—VERT: 1s. Lenin making speech. HORIZ: 1s.80, Lenin at desk.

106 Dove feeding Young

1970. 10th Anniv of Independence.
515 25c. Type **106** 10 10
516 35c. Dagahtur Memorial 10 10
517 1s. Somali arms (vert) 35 20
518 2s.80 Camel and star (vert) 1·10 90

107 Tractor and Produce

1970. 1st Anniv of 21 October Revolution.
519 **107** 35c. multicoloured 10 10
520 – 40c. black and blue 10 10
521 – 1s. black and brown 35 20
522 – 1s.80 multicoloured 80 45
DESIGNS: 40c. Soldier and flag; 1s. Hand on open book; 1s.80, Emblems of Peace, Justice and Prosperity.

108 African within Snake's Coils

1971. Racial Equality Year.
523 **108** 1s.30 multicoloured 45 20
524 – 1s.80 black, red & brown 65 45
DESIGN: 1s.80, Human figures, chain and barbed wire.

109 I.T.U. Emblem

1971. World Telecommunications Day.
525 **109** 25c. black, ultram & bl 10 10
526 – 2s.80 black, blue & green 1·10 65
DESIGN: 2s.80, Global emblem.

110 Telecommunications Map

1971. Pan-African Telecommunications Network.
527 **110** 1s. green, black and blue 35 20
528 – 1s.50 black, green & yell 80 35
DESIGN: 1s.50, similar to Type **110** but with different network pattern.

111 White Rhinoceros

1971. Wild Animals.
529 **111** 35c. multicoloured 20 20
530 – 1s. multicoloured 35 35
531 – 1s.30 black, yellow and violet 90 90
532 – 1s.80 multicoloured 1·40 1·40
DESIGNS: 1s. Cheetahs; 1s.30, Common zebras; 1s.80, Lion attacking dromedary.

112 Ancient Desert City

1971. East and Central African Summit Conference, Mogadishu.
533 **112** 1s.30 brown, black & red 55 55
534 – 1s.50 multicoloured 95 95
DESIGN: 1s.50, Headquarters building, Mogadishu.

113 Memorial

1971. 2nd Anniv of Revolution.
535 **113** 10c. black, cobalt and blue 10 10
536 – 1s. multicoloured 30 30
537 – 1s.35 multicoloured 1·00 1·00
DESIGNS: 1s. Agricultural workers; 1s.35, Building workers.

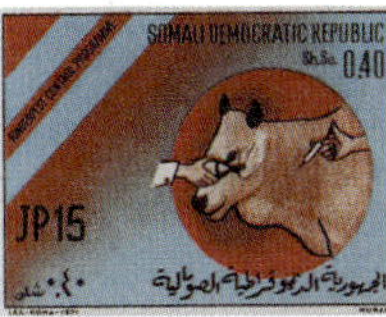

114 Inoculating Cattle

1971. Rinderpest Control Programme. Multicoloured.
538 40c. Type **114** 55 35
539 1s.80 Herdsmen with cattle 1·10 80

115 A.P.U. Emblem and Back of Airmail Envelope

1972. 10th Anniv of African Postal Union.
540 1s.50 A.P.U. emblem and dove with letter (postage) 80 55
541 1s.30 Type **115** (air) 90 65

116 Mother and Child

1972. 25th Anniv of U.N.I.C.E.F.
542 **116** 50c. black, brown and light brown 20 10
543 – 2s.80 multicoloured 1·40 1·00
DESIGNS—HORIZ: 2s.80, U.N.I.C.E.F. emblem and schoolchildren.

117 Dromedary

1972. Domestic Animals.
544 **117** 5c. multicoloured 10 10
545 – 10c. multicoloured 10 10
546 – 20c. multicoloured 10 10
547 – 40c. black, brown and red 20 20
548 – 1s.70 black, green & black 1·60 1·60
DESIGNS: 10c. Cattle on quayside; 20c. Bull; 40c. Black-headed sheep; 1s.70, Goat.

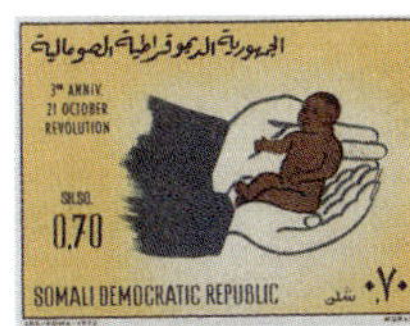

118 Child within Cupped Hands

1972. 3rd Anniv of 21 October Revolution. Multicoloured.
549 70c. Type **118** 20 10
550 1s. Parade of standards 30 15
551 1s.50 Youth Camps emblem 90 55

119 Folk Dancers

1973. Folk Dances. Multicoloured.
552 5c. Type **119** 10 10
553 40c. Pair of dancers (vert) 10 10
554 1s. Team of dancers (vert) 45 20
555 2s. Three dancers 1·00 55

120 Old Alphabet in Flames **121** Soldiers and Chains within O.A.U. Emblem

1973. Introduction of New Somali Script.
556 **120** 40c. multicoloured 10 10
557 – 1s. multicoloured 20 15
558 – 2s. black, stone and yellow 80 55
DESIGNS—HORIZ: 1s. Alphabet in sun's rays; 2s. Writing new script.

1974. 10th Anniv (1973) of Organization of African Unity. Multicoloured.
559 40c. Type **121** 20 10
560 2s. Spiral on map of Africa 90 65

122 Hurdling

1974. Sports.
561 **122** 50c. black, red and orange 15 10
562 – 1s. black, grey and green 35 20
563 – 1s.40 black, grey and olive 90 55
DESIGNS—HORIZ: 1s. Running. VERT: 1s.40, Basketball.

123 Somali Youth and Girl

1974. Guulwade Youth Movement. Multicoloured.
564 40c. Type **123** 10 10
565 2s. Guulwade members helping old woman . . . . 1·00 65

124 Map of League Members

1974. 30th Anniv (1975) of Arab League. Multicoloured.
566 1s.50 Type **124** 55 35
567 1s.70 Flags of Arab League countries 85 55

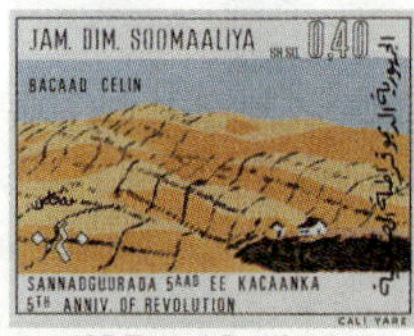

125 Desert Landscape

1975. 5th Anniv of 21 October Revolution. Multicoloured.
568 40c. Type **125** 20 15
569 2s. Somali villagers reading books (vert) 90 65

126 Doves

128

1975. Centenary of U.P.U. Multicoloured.
570 50c. Type **126** 30 10
571 3s. Mounted postman . . . . 2·00 1·00

1975. African Postal Union. As T **126**. Multicoloured.
572 1s. Maps of Africa (repetitive motif) 35 20
573 1s.50 Dove with letter . . . 1·00 65

1975. Traditional Costumes.
574 **128** 10c. multicoloured 10 10
575 – 40c. multicoloured 10 10
576 – 50c. multicoloured 15 10
577 – 1s. multicoloured 35 20
578 – 5s. multicoloured . . . . 2·10 85
579 – 10s. multicoloured . . . . 4·50 2·50
DESIGNS: 40c. to 10s. Various costumes.

129 Independence Square, Mogadishu

1976. Int Women's Year. Multicoloured.
580 50c. Type **129** 30 10
581 2s.30 I.W.Y. emblem (horiz) 1·40 1·00

130 Hassan Statue

1976. Sayed M. A. Hassan Commemoration. Mult.
582 50c. Type **130** 15 10
583 60c. Hassan directing warriors (vert) 20 10
584 1s.50 Hassan inspiring warriors (vert) 55 35
585 2s.30 Hassan leading attack 1·60 55

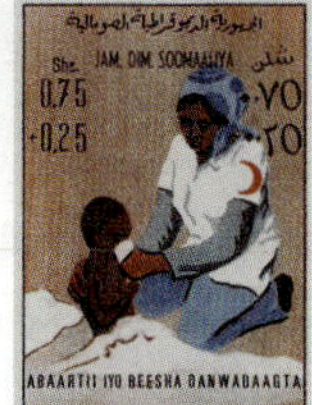

131 Nurse and Child

1976. Famine Relief. Multicoloured.
586 75c.+25c. Type **131** 45 45
587 80c.+20c. Devastated land (horiz) 45 45
588 2s.40+10c. Somali family with produce 80 80
589 2s.90+10c. Relief emblem and medical officer (horiz) . . . 1·60 1·60

132 Noted Graceful Cowrie

1976. Somali Sea Shells. Multicoloured.
590 50c. Type **132** 30 15
591 75c. "Charonia bardayi" . . 30 15
592 1s. Townsend's scallop . . . 50 25
593 2s. Ranzani's triton . . . . 1·25 60
594 2s.75 Clay cone . . . . . 1·50 95
595 2s.90 Old's conch . . . . . 2·25 95

133 Benin Head and Hunters

1977. Second World Black and African Festival of Arts and Cultures, Lagos, Nigeria. Multicoloured.
597 50c. Type **133** 20 15
598 75c. Handicrafts 35 30
599 2s. Dancers 85 65
600 2s.90 Musicians . . . . . . 1·60 1·10
The Benin Head appears on all designs.

134 Somali Flags

1977. 1st Anniv of Somali Socialist Revolutionary Party. Multicoloured.
601 75c. Type **134** 20 10
602 1s. Somali Arms (horiz) . . . 35 20
603 1s.50 Pres. Barre and globe (horiz) 55 35
604 2s. Arms over rising sun . . 85 45

135 Hunting Dog

1977. Protected Animals. Multicoloured.
605 50c. Type **135** 15 10
606 75c. Lesser bushbaby 20 10
607 1s. African ass 45 20
608 1s.50 Aardwolf 55 35
609 2s. Greater kudu . . . . . 1·10 55
610 3s. Giraffe . . . . 2·00 90

136 Leonardo da Vinci's Drawing of Helicopter

1977. 30th Anniv of I.C.A.O. Multicoloured.
612 1s. Type **136** 35 25
613 1s.50 Montgolfier Brothers' balloon 45 35
614 2s. Wright Flyer I 65 45
615 2s.90 Boeing 720B of Somali Airlines . . . . 1·40 65

137 Dome of the Rock

1978. Palestine Freedom-Fighters.
617 **137** 75c. black, green and pink 20 10
618 2s. black, red and blue . . 90 55

138 Stadium and Footballer

1978. World Cup Football Championship, Argentina. Multicoloured.
619 1s.50 Type **138** 45 35
620 4s.90 Stadium and goalkeeper 1·50 1·00
621 5s.50 Stadium and footballer (different) . . . . 2·00 1·40

139 "Acacia tortilis"

1978. Trees. Multicoloured.
623 40c. Type **139** 15 10
624 50c. "Ficus sycomorus" (vert) 30 20
625 75c. "Terminalia catapa" (vert) 45 35
626 2s.90 "Adansonia digitata" 1·40 65

140 "Hibiscus rosa-sinensis"

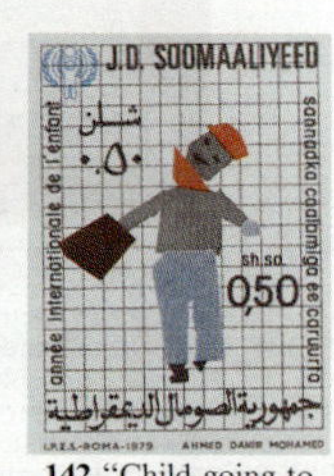

142 "Child going to School" (Ahmed Dahir Mohamed)

141 Fishing from Punt and Marbled Rabbitfish

1978. Flowers. Multicoloured.
627 50c. Type **140** 20 10
628 1s. "Cassia baccarinii" . . . 45 20
629 1s.50 "Kigelia somalensis" . . 80 45
630 2s.30 "Dichrostachys glomerata" . . . . 1·40 65

1979. Fishing. Multicoloured.
632 75c. Type **141** 25 10
633 80c. Fishing from felucca and black-spotted sweetlips . . 30 15
634 2s.30 Fishing fleet and leerfish . . . . 1·40 55
635 2s.50 Trawler and narrow-barred Spanish mackerel 1·90 85

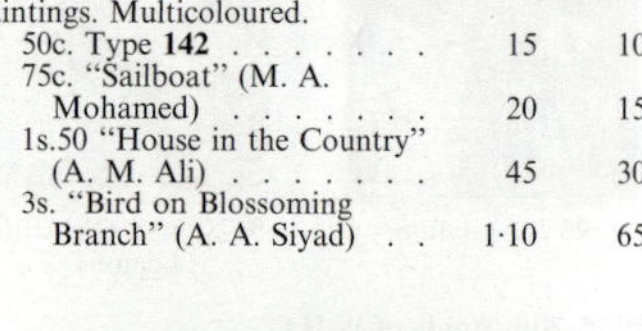

1979. International Year of the Child. Children's Paintings. Multicoloured.
636 50c. Type **142** 15 10
637 75c. "Sailboat" (M. A. Mohamed) 20 15
638 1s.50 "House in the Country" (A. M. Ali) 45 30
639 3s. "Bird on Blossoming Branch" (A. A. Siyad) . . 1·10 65

143 University Students and Open-air Class

1979. 10th Anniv of Revolution. Multicoloured.
641 20c. Type **143** 10 10
642 50c. Housing construction . . 10 10
643 75c. Children at play 20 10
644 1s. Health and agriculture . . 35 20
645 2s.40 Hydro-electric power 80 45
646 3s. Telecommunications . . . 1·25 65

144 Devecchi's Cave Barb

1979. Fish. Multicoloured.
647 50c. Type **144** 25 10
648 90c. Andruzzi's caveminnow 70 20
649 1s. Somali blind catfish . . . 90 35
650 2s.50 Tarabini's catfish . . . 1·50 65

145 Taleh Fortress

1980. 1st International Congress of Somali Studies.
652 **145** 2s.25 multicoloured . . . 85 45
653 3s.50 multicoloured . . . 1·10 65

146 Marka

1980. Landscapes (1st series). Multicoloured.
654 75c. Type **146** 20 10
655 1s. Gandershe 35 20
656 2s.30 Afgooye 85 35
657 3s.50 Mogadishu . . . . . . 1·10 65
See also Nos. 673/6.

147 Pygmy Puff-back Flycatcher

148 Parabolic Antenna and Shepherd

1980. Birds. Multicoloured.
658 1s. Type **147** 80 60
659 2s.25 Golden-winged grosbeak . . . . 2·00 1·40
660 5s. Red-crowned bush shrike 3·25 3·25

1981. World Telecommunications Day.
662 **148** 1s. multicoloured 40 20
663 – 3s. blue, black and red . . 1·00 55
664 – 4s.60 multicoloured . . . 1·40 90
DESIGNS: 3s., 4s.60, Ribbons forming caduceus, I.T.U. and W.H.O. emblems.

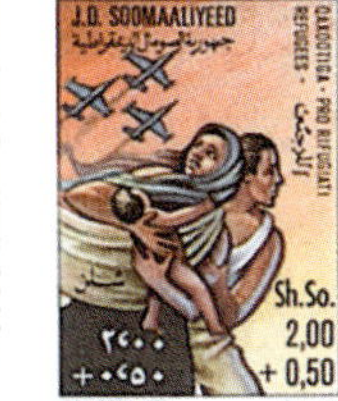

149 F.A.O. Emblem and Stylized Wheat

150 Refugee Family

1981. World Food Day. Multicoloured.
665 75c. Type **149** 20 15
666 3s.25 F.A.O. emblem on stylized field (horiz.) . . . . 1·10 55
667 5s.50 Type **149** . . . . . . 2·00 95

1981. Refugee Aid.
668 **150** 2s.+50c. multicoloured . . 70 45
669 6s.80+50c. multicoloured 2·50 1·25

151 Mosques, Mecca and Medina

153 Footballer

1981. 1500th Anniv of Hejira.
671 **151** 1s.50 multicoloured . . . 45 35
672 3s.80 multicoloured . . . 1·50 80

1982. Landscapes (2nd series). As T **146**. Multicoloured.
673 2s.25 Balcad 80 45
674 4s. Jowhar . . . . 1·40 90
675 5s.50 Golaleey . . . . 1·60 1·10
676 8s.30 Muqdisho . . . . . . 2·75 2·00

1982. World Cup Football Championship, Spain. Multicoloured.
677 1s. Type **153** 35 20
678 1s.50 Footballer running to right 80 45
679 3s.25 Footballer running to left . . . . 1·60 1·00

154 I.T.U. Emblem

1982. I.T.U. Delegates' Conference, Nairobi.
681 **154** 75c. multicoloured 20 15
682 3s.25 multicoloured . . . 1·10 65
683 5s.50 multicoloured . . . 2·00 1·10

155 "Bitis arietans somalica"

1982. Snakes. Multicoloured.
684 2s.80 Type **155** . . . . . . 1·10 45
685 3s.20 "Psammophis punctulatus trivirgatus" . . 1·60 65
686 4s.60 "Rhamphiophis oxyrhynchis rostratus" . . 2·25 1·10

156 Bacillus, Microscope and Dr. Robert Koch

1982. Centenary of Discovery of Tubercle Bacillus.
688 **156** 4s.60+60c. mult . . . . . 1·10 1·10
689 5s.80+60c. mult . . . . . 1·40 1·40

157 Somali Woman

158 W.C.Y. Emblem

1982.
690 **157** 1s. multicoloured 15 10
691 5s.20 multicoloured . . . 80 35
692 5s.80 multicoloured . . . 1·00 45
693 6s.40 multicoloured . . . 1·10 60
694 9s.40 multicoloured . . . 1·60 1·00
695 25s. multicoloured . . . 4·25 1·60

1983. World Communications Year.
696 **158** 5s.20 multicoloured . . . 45 35
697 6s.40 multicoloured . . . 85 40

159 View of Hamburg

1983. 2nd International Congress of Somali Studies, Hamburg. Multicoloured.
698 5s.20 Type **159** 85 65
699 6s.40 View of Hamburg (different) . . . . 1·25 1·00

160 Air Force Uniform

1983. Military Uniforms. Multicoloured.
700 3s.20 Type **160** . . . . . . 1·00 55
701 3s.20 Women's Auxiliary Corps . . . . 1·00 55
702 3s.20 Border Police . . . . . 1·00 55
703 3s.20 People's Militia . . . . 1·00 55
704 3s.20 Infantry . . . . 1·00 55
705 3s.20 Custodial Corps . . . 1·00 55
706 3s.20 Police Force . . . . . 1·00 55
707 3s.20 Navy . . . . 1·00 55

161 Barawe

1983. Landscapes. Multicoloured.
708 2s.80 Type **161** 55 35
709 3s.20 Bur Hakaba 65 45
710 5s.50 Baydhabo . . . . . . 1·00 60
711 8s.60 Dooy Nuunaay . . . . 1·60 1·10

162 "Volutocorbis rosavittoriae"

1984. Shells. Multicoloured.
712 2s.80 Type **162** 80 40
713 3s.20 Valdiva bonnet . . . . 1·25 50
714 5s.50 Glory of India cone . . 3·00 1·00

163 Running

165 Girl holding Spider Conch to Ear

164 North African Crested Porcupine

1984. Olympic Games, Los Angeles. Multicoloured.
716 1s.50 Type **163** 35 20
717 3s. Throwing the discus . . . 80 45
718 8s. High jumping . . . . . . 2·25 1·00

1984. Mammals. Multicoloured.
720 1s. Type **164** 20 20
721 1s.50 White-tailed mongoose 35 20
722 2s. Banded mongoose 55 35
723 4s. Ratel . . . . 1·10 65

1984. 36th International Fair, Riccione.
725 **165** 5s.20 multicoloured . . . 2·00 65
726 6s.40 multicoloured . . . 2·75 1·10

166 Emblem within Winged Horse

1985. 40th Anniv of International Civil Aviation Organization.
727 **166** 3s. multicoloured 65 35
728 6s.40 multicoloured . . . 1·10 80

167 Aquila

169 Woman and Posthorn

168 Ras Kiambone

1985. Constellations. Illustrations from "The Book of Stars" by Abd al-Rahman al-Sufi. Multicoloured.
730 4s.30 Type **167** 55 20
731 11s. Taurus . . . . 1·40 65
732 12s.50 Aries . . . . 1·60 80
733 13s. Orion . . . . 2·00 1·10

1985. Architecture (1st series). Multicoloured.
734 2s. Type **168** 20 20
735 6s.60 Hannassa 90 35
736 10s. Mnarani . . . . 1·10 65
737 18s.60 Ras Kiambone (different) . . . . 2·25 1·25
See also Nos. 758/61.

1985. "Italia '85" Stamp Exhibition, Rome.
738 **169** 2s. multicoloured 55 35
739 20s. multicoloured . . . . 2·75 1·40

170 Persian Leaf-nosed Bat

1985. Bats. Multicoloured.
741 2s.50 Type **170** 55 35
742 4s.50 Heart-nosed false vampire bat 85 55
743 16s. Wrinkle-lipped bat . . . 2·25 1·40
744 18s. Mozambique sheath-tailed bat . . . . 2·50 1·60

171 Kenyan and Somali Presidents, Solar System and Industry

1986. Trade Agreement with Kenya.
746 **171** 9s. multicoloured 65 45
747 14s.50 multicoloured . . . 1·60 65

172 Flower Arrangement

173 Seated Man holding Pottery Flask

1986. "Euroflora" International Flower Exhibition, Genoa. Multicoloured.
748 10s. Type **172** 65 55
749 15s. Flower arrangement (different) . . . . 1·60 1·10

1986. 3rd International Somali Studies Conference, Rome.
751 **173** 11s.35 multicoloured . . . 65 45
752 20s. multicoloured . . . . 1·60 90

174 Footballers

1986. World Cup Football Championship, Mexico. Footballing Scenes.
753 **174** 3s.60 multicoloured . . . 35 20
754 – 4s.80 multicoloured . . . 45 20
755 – 6s.80 multicoloured . . . 90 45
756 – 22s.60 multicoloured . . . 1·50 1·10

1986. Architecture (2nd series). As T **168**. Multicoloured.
758 10s. Bulaxaar ruins 55 30
759 15s. Saylac mosque 85 45
760 20s. Saylac mosque (different) 1·40 65
761 31s. Jasiiradaha Jawaay tomb 2·25 1·10

175 Rehabilitation Centre, Mogadishu

176 Runner

1987. Norwegian Red Cross in Somalia.
762 **175** 56s. multicoloured 2·75 2·25

1987. "Olymphilex '87" Olympic Stamps Exhibition, Rome. Multicoloured.
764 20s. Type **176** 85 55
765 40s. Javelin thrower 2·00 1·10

177 Modern and Shanty Towns

178 Western Indian Ocean 160,000,000 Years Ago

1987. International Year of Shelter for the Homeless.
767 **177** 53s. multicoloured 1·40 65
768 72s. multicoloured 2·00 1·10

1987. "Geosom 87" Geological Evolution of Western Indian Ocean Symposium. Multicoloured.
769 10s. Type **178** 20 10
770 20s. 60,000,000 years ago 55 20
771 40s. 15,000,000 years ago 90 45
772 50s. Today 1·60 90

179 Baby receiving Oral Vaccination (Italian inscr)

180 Somali Hare

1988. 40th Anniv of W.H.O.
774 **179** 50s. multicoloured 45 20
775 168s. multicoloured (English inscr) 1·75 90

1989. Animals. Multicoloured.
776 75s. Type **180** 45 20
777 198s. African buffalo 1·10 35
778 200s. Hamadryas baboon (horiz) 1·25 45
779 216s. Hippopotamus (horiz) 1·60 65

181 Water Lily and Boys playing Football

1989. 20th Anniv of 21 October Revolution. Multicoloured.
781 70s. Type **181** 35 20
782 100s. Boys playing on swing 45 20
783 150s. Girls on see-saw 90 35
784 300s. Girl skipping and boy rolling hoop 1·60 65

182 Dove and Broken Chain

183 Sun, Building and Scaffolding

1991. Liberation. (a) Type **182** (without opt).
785 **182** 150s. multicoloured 85 35
786 300s. multicoloured 1·60 80

(b) No. 785 additionally optd **"FREEDOM"**.
787 **182** 150s. multicoloured 3·00 2·75

1991. Reconstruction.
788 **183** 70s. multicoloured 35 20
789 100s. multicoloured 55 35
790 150s. multicoloured 80 45
791 300s. multicoloured 1·60 65

EXPRESS LETTER STAMPS

1923. Express Letter stamps of Italy surch **Somalia Italiana** and value.
E44 **E 12** 30b. on 60c. red 24·00 17·00
E45 **E 13** 60b. on 1l.20 blue & pink 35·00 34·00

E 17

1924.
E60 **E 17** 30b. brown and red 9·25 10·00
E61 60b. pink and blue 14·00 18·00
No. E61 is inscr "EXPRES".

1926. Nos. E60/1 surch.
E104 70c. on 30b. brown and red 10·00 13·00
E106 1l.25 on 30b. brown and red 12·00 9·25
E105 2l.50 on 60b. blue and pink 13·00 15·00

E 44 Grant's Gazelle

1950.
E255 **E 44** 40c. green 5·00 3·50
E256 80c. violet 8·00 6·00

E 54 "Gardenia lutea"

1955.
E291 **E 54** 50c. yellow, grn & lilac 40 85
E292 – 1s. red, green and blue 75 1·10
FLOWER: 1s. Coral tree.

E 61 Young Gazelles

1958. Air.
E330 **E 61** 1s.70 red and black 1·90 1·50

OFFICIAL STAMPS

1934. Air. Rome–Mogadishu Flight. As No. 208, but colour changed, optd **SERVIZIO DI STATO** and crown.
O209 **36** 25l.+2l. pink £1900 £2750

1934. Air. No. 193 optd **11 NOV. 1934-XIII SERVIZIO AEREO SPECIALE** and crown.
O210 25c. blue and orange £2000 £2500

PARCEL POST STAMPS

Nos. P23 to P122 are Parcel Post stamps of Italy optd or surch on each half of stamp.
Unused prices are for complete pairs, used prices for a half stamp.

1920. Optd **SOMALIA ITALIANA**.
P23 **P 53** 5c. brown 1·50 21·00
P24 10c. blue 2·20 15·00
P82 20c. black 34·00 24·00
P26 25c. red 5·50 28·00
P84 50c. orange 34·00 20·00
P28 1l. violet 24·00 24·00
P29 2l. green 34·00 38·00
P87 3l. yellow 10·00 24·00
P88 4l. grey 10·00 24·00
P89 10l. purple 19·00 32·00
P90 12l. brown 19·00 32·00
P91 15l. green 19·00 45·00
P92 20l. purple 19·00 45·00

1922. Optd **SOMALIA**.
P32 **P 53** 25c. red 38·00 12·50
P33 50c. orange 48·00 3·75
P34 1l. violet 48·00 4·50
P35 2l. green 60·00 5·75
P36 3l. yellow 75·00 10·50
P37 4l. grey 75·00 11·50

1923. Surch **SOMALIA ITALIANA** and value.
P44 **P 53** 3b. on 5c. brown 3·50 13·00
P45 5b. on 5c. brown 3·50 13·00
P46 10b. on 10c. blue 2·00 11·00
P47 25b. on 25c. red 3·00 19·00
P48 50b. on 50c. orange 3·25 28·00
P49 1r. on 1l. violet 3·50 28·00
P50 2r. on 2l. green 6·50 37·00
P51 3r. on 3l. yellow 9·00 37·00
P52 4r. on 4l. grey 14·00 37·00

1928. Optd **SOMALIA ITALIANA**.
P111 **P 92** 5c. brown 1·20 3·75
P112 10c. blue 1·50 3·75
P113 25c. red 30·00 13·00
P114 30c. blue 60 1·50
P115 50c. orange £12000 95·00
P116 60c. red 60 1·90
P127 1l. violet 32·00 3·25
P128 2l. green 32·00 3·25
P119 3l. yellow 1·90 6·75
P120 4l. black 1·90 6·75
P121 10l. mauve £300 £300
P122 20l. purple £300 £300

P 44

1950.
P255 **P 44** 1c. red 1·50 1·50
P256 3c. violet 1·50 1·50
P257 5c. purple 1·50 1·50
P258 10c. orange 1·50 1·50
P259 20c. brown 1·50 1·50
P260 50c. green 3·75 3·75
P261 1s. violet 15·00 15·00
P262 2s. brown 19·00 19·00
P263 3s. blue 30·00 30·00

POSTAGE DUE STAMPS

Nos. D17 to D199 are Postage Due stamps of Italy optd or surch.

1906. Optd **Somalia Italiana Meridionale**.
D17 **D 12** 5c. mauve and orange 6·25 22·00
D18 10c. mauve and orange 34·00 28·00
D19 20c. mauve and orange 24·00 36·00
D20 30c. mauve and orange 21·00 40·00
D21 40c. mauve and orange £170 40·00
D22 50c. mauve and orange 40·00 48·00
D23 60c. mauve and orange 38·00 48·00
D24 1l. mauve and blue £750 £190
D25 2l. mauve and blue £700 £190
D26 5l. mauve and blue £700 £225
D27 10l. mauve and blue £120 £190

1909. Optd **Somalia Italiana**.
D28 **D 12** 5c. mauve and orange 3·00 12·50
D29 10c. mauve and orange 3·00 12·50
D30 20c. mauve and orange 7·50 21·00
D31 30c. mauve and orange 22·00 21·00
D32 40c. mauve and orange 22·00 24·00
D33 50c. mauve and orange 22·00 40·00
D34 60c. mauve and orange 32·00 34·00
D35 1l. mauve and blue 85·00 40·00
D36 2l. mauve and blue £110 £100
D48 5l. mauve and blue £110 £120
D38 10l. mauve and blue 22·00 45·00

1923. Stamps without figures of value, surch **Somalia Italiana** and value in "besa" or "rupia" in figures and words.
D49 **D 12** 1b. orange 95 3·50
D50 2b. orange 95 3·50
D51 3b. orange 95 3·50
D52 5b. orange 1·90 3·50
D53 10b. orange 1·90 3·50
D54 20b. orange 1·90 3·50
D55 40b. orange 1·90 3·50
D56 1r. blue 3·00 19·00

1926. Optd **Somalia Italiana** and surch with figures only.
D76 5c. orange 15·00 17·00
D77 10c. orange 15·00 9·25
D78 20c. orange 15·00 17·00
D79 30c. orange 15·00 9·25
D80 40c. orange 15·00 9·25
D81 50c. orange 19·00 9·25
D82 60c. orange 19·00 9·25
D83 1l. blue 32·00 17·00
D84 2l. blue 45·00 17·00
D85 5l. blue 50·00 25·00
D86 10l. blue 48·00 32·00

1934. Optd **SOMALIA ITALIANA**.
D187 **D 141** 5c. brown 60 1·90
D188 10c. blue 60 1·90
D189 20c. red 2·20 3·75
D190 25c. green 2·20 3·75
D191 30c. red 5·50 6·75
D192 40c. brown 5·50 9·25
D193 50c. violet 11·00 2·75
D194 60c. blue 15·00 21·00
D195 **D 142** 1l. orange 17·00 7·50
D196 2l. green 32·00 21·00
D197 5l. violet 45·00 38·00
D198 10l. blue 45·00 40·00
D199 20l. red 40·00 48·00

D 44

1950.
D255 **D 44** 1c. violet 75 75
D256 2c. blue 75 75
D257 5c. green 75 75
D258 10c. purple 75 75
D259 40c. violet 4·50 4·50
D260 1s. brown 6·75 6·75

SOMALILAND PROTECTORATE

Pt. 1

A British protectorate in north-east Africa on the Gulf of Aden. Amalgamated with the Somalia Republic on 1 July 1960, whose stamps it now uses.

1903. 16 annas = 1 rupee.
1951. 100 cents = 1 shilling.

1903. Stamps of India (Queen Victoria) optd **BRITISH SOMALILAND**.
1 **23** ½a. green 2·75 4·00
2 – 1a. red 2·75 3·75
3 – 2a. lilac 2·25 1·50
4 – 2½a. blue 2·00 1·75
5 – 3a. orange 3·25 3·00
6 – 4a. green (No. 96) 3·50 2·75
7 – 6a. brown (No. 80) 4·75 4·50
8 – 8a. mauve 3·75 5·00
9 – 12a. purple on red 3·25 7·00
21 **37** 1r. green and red 3·25 11·00
11 **38** 2r. red and orange 26·00 42·00
12 3r. brown and green 22·00 48·00
13 5r. blue and violet 38·00 55·00

1903. Stamps of India of 1902 (King Edward VII) optd **BRITISH SOMALILAND**.
25 ½a. green (No. 122) 2·25 55
26 1a. red (No. 123) 1·25 30
27 2a. lilac 1·75 2·50
28 3a. orange 2·50 2·50
29 4a. olive 1·50 4·00
30 8a. mauve 1·75 2·25

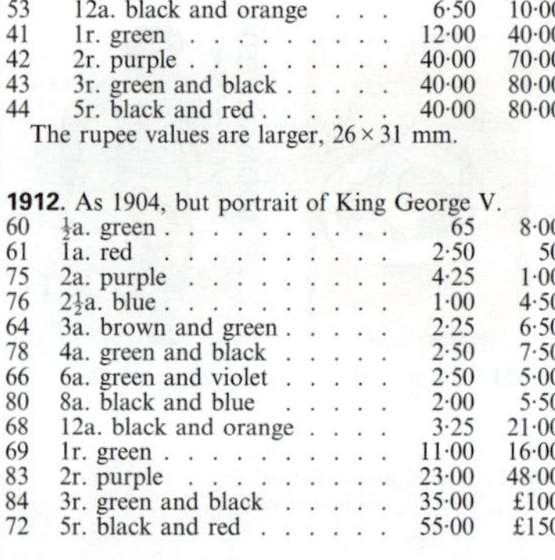

2

1904.
32 **2** ½a. green 1·50 4·25
33 1a. black and red 9·00 3·25
59 1a. red 2·50 2·00
34 2a. purple 1·75 2·25
35 2½a. blue 2·75 3·75
36 3a. brown and green 1·75 2·50
37 4a. green and black 1·75 4·75
38 6a. green and violet 4·25 17·00
39 8a. black and blue 3·50 5·50
53 12a. black and orange 6·50 10·00
41 1r. green 12·00 40·00
42 2r. purple 40·00 70·00
43 3r. green and black 40·00 80·00
44 5r. black and red 40·00 80·00
The rupee values are larger, 26×31 mm.

1912. As 1904, but portrait of King George V.
60 ½a. green 65 8·00
61 1a. red 2·50 50
75 2a. purple 4·25 1·00
76 2½a. blue 1·00 4·50
64 3a. brown and green 2·25 6·50
78 4a. green and black 2·50 7·50
66 6a. green and violet 2·50 5·00
80 8a. black and blue 2·00 5·50
68 12a. black and orange 3·25 21·00
69 1r. green 11·00 16·00
83 2r. purple 23·00 48·00
84 3r. green and black 35·00 £100
72 5r. black and red 55·00 £150

1935. Silver Jubilee. As T **32a** of St. Helena.
86 1a. blue and red 2·25 3·00
87 2a. blue and grey 2·75 2·75
88 3a. brown and blue 2·25 12·00
89 1r. grey and purple 7·00 12·00

1937. Coronation. As T **32b** of St. Helena.
90 1a. red 15 20
91 2a. grey 55 1·50
92 3a. blue 70 55

6 Berbera Blackhead Sheep

9 Berbera Blackhead Sheep

8 Somaliland Protectorate

1938. Portrait faces left.
93 **6** ½a. green 40 5·00
94 1a. red 40 1·50
95 2a. purple 1·75 1·75
96 3a. blue 8·00 10·00
97 – 4a. brown 4·50 8·00
98 – 6a. violet 7·00 12·00
99 – 8a. grey 1·50 12·00
100 – 12a. orange 6·50 15·00
101 **8** 1r. green 8·50 50·00
102 2r. purple 15·00 50·00

103		3r. blue	18·00	29·00
104		5r. black	20·00	29·00

DESIGN—As T 6: 4a. to 12a. Lesser kudu antelope.

1942. As Nos. 93/104 but with full-face portraits as in T **9**.

105	**9**	½a. green	20	30
106		1a. red	20	10
107		2a. purple	50	20
108		3a. blue	1·75	20
109	–	4a. brown	2·75	20
110	–	6a. violet	2·75	20
111	–	8a. grey	3·00	20
112	–	12a. orange	3·00	40
113	–	1r. green	1·25	50
114	–	2r. purple	1·25	4·00
115	–	3r. blue	2·25	7·50
116	–	5r. black	7·00	6·50

1946. Victory. As T **33a** of St. Helena.

117	1a. red	10	10
118	3a. blue	10	10

1949. Silver Wedding. As T **33b/c** of St. Helena.

119	1a. red	10	10
120	5r. black	3·50	3·25

1949. 75th Anniv of U.P.U. As T **33d/g** of St. Helena.

121	1a. on 10c. red	20	15
122	3a. on 30c. blue	1·00	75
123	6a. on 50c. purple	35	1·00
124	12a. on 1s. orange	35	50

1951. 1942 issue surch with figures and **Cents** or **Shillings**.

125	5c. on ½a. green	30	1·00
126	10c. on 2a. purple	30	4·00
127	15c. on 3a. blue	1·25	1·00
128	20c. on 4a. brown	1·75	20
129	30c. on 6a. violet	1·75	50
130	50c. on 8a. grey	2·00	20
131	70c. on 2a. orange	3·00	3·50
132	1s. on 1r. green	1·00	30
133	2s. on 2r. purple	4·75	12·00
134	2s. on 3r. blue	5·50	4·50
135	5s. on 5r. black	6·00	6·50

1953. Coronation. As T **33h** of St. Helena.

136	15c. black and green	30	20

12 Camel and Gurgi

13 Sentry, Somaliland Scouts

1953.

137	**12**	5c. black	15	50
138	**13**	10c. orange	2·00	60
139	**12**	15c. green	60	60
140		20c. red	60	40
141	**13**	30c. brown	2·00	40
142	–	35c. blue	4·50	1·75
143	–	50c. brown and red	4·50	55
144	–	1s. blue	50	30
145	–	1s.30 blue and black	9·00	3·25
146	–	2s. brown and violet	24·00	5·50
147	–	5s. brown and green	24·00	6·00
148	–	10s. brown and violet	16·00	16·00

DESIGNS—HORIZ: 35c., 2s. Somali pigeon; 50c., 5s. Martial eagle; 1s. Berbera blackhead sheep; 1s.30, Sheikh Isaaq's Tomb, Mait; 10s. Taleh Fort.

1957. Opening of Legislative Council. Optd **OPENING OF THE LEGISLATIVE COUNCIL 1957.**

149	**12**	20c. red	10	15
150	–	1s. blue (No. 144)	30	15

1960. Legislative Council's Unofficial Majority. Optd **LEGISLATIVE COUNCIL UNOFFICIAL MAJORITY, 1960.**

151	**12**	20c. red	10	15
152	–	1s.30 blue and black (No. 145)	1·25	15

OFFICIAL STAMPS

1903. Official stamps of India (Queen Victoria) (optd **O.H.M.S.**) further optd **BRITISH SOMALILAND.**

O1	**23**	½a. turquoise	6·50	48·00
O2	–	1a. red	15·00	8·00
O3	–	2a. lilac	8·00	48·00
O4	–	8a. mauve	10·00	£375
O5	**37**	1r. green and red	10·00	£550

1904. Stamps of 1904 optd **O.H.M.S.**

O10	**2**	½a. green	3·50	48·00
O11		1a. black and red	3·25	7·00
O12		2a. purple	£170	60·00
O13		8a. black and blue	60·00	£130
O15	–	1r. green (No. 41)	£160	£550

SORUTH Pt. 1

A state of India. In 1948 the Saurashtra Union was formed which included Jasdan, Morvi, Nawanagar and Wadhwan as well as Soruth. Now uses Indian stamps.

12 pies = 1 anna; 16 annas = 1 rupee.

JUNAGADH

1

2 (1a.)

1864. On paper of various colours. Imperf.

1	**1**	1a. black	£650	60·00

1867. (Nos. 11 and 13 are on paper of various colours). Imperf.

11	**2**	1a. black	70·00	8·00
13		1a. red	18·00	19·00
15		4a. black	£110	£180

6

7

1877. Imperf or perf.

40	**7**	3p. green	85	35
19	**6**	1a. green	40	15
41		1a. red	90	1·50
20	**7**	4a. red	1·40	75

1913. Surch in words in English and in native characters.

33	**6**	3p. on 1a. green	15	20
34	**7**	1a. on 4a. red	1·75	5·00

(14)

13 Nawab Mahabat Khan III

1923. Surch as T **14**.

43	**13**	3p. on 1a. red	3·75	7·00

1924. Imperf or perf.

44	**13**	3p. mauve	35	45
46b		1a. red	3·25	3·50

The 1a. is smaller.

15 Junagadh City

17 Nawab Mahabat Khan III

1929. Inscr "POSTAGE".

49	**15**	3p. black and green	80	10
50	–	½a. black and blue	5·00	10
51	**17**	1a. black and red	4·25	1·00
52	–	2a. black and orange	11·00	1·90
53	**15**	3a. black and red	4·25	8·00
54	–	4a. black and purple	13·00	22·00
55	–	8a. black and green	10·00	21·00
56	**17**	1r. black and blue	6·00	22·00

DESIGNS—HORIZ: ½a., 4a. Lion; 2a., 8a. Kathi horse.

1936. Inscr "POSTAGE AND REVENUE".

57	**17**	1a. black and red	5·50	1·00

OFFICIAL STAMPS

1929. Nos. 49/56 optd **SARKARI**.

O1a	**15**	3p. black and green	85	10
O2	–	½a. black and blue	2·25	10
O3a	**17**	1a. black and red	2·00	15
O4	–	2a. black and orange	2·50	90
O5	**15**	3a. black and red	75	30
O6	–	4a. black and purple	2·75	45
O7	–	8a. black and green	2·75	2·25
O8	**17**	1r. black and blue	2·50	17·00

1938. No. 57 optd **SARKARI**.

O13a	**17**	1a. black and red	11·00	1·50

UNITED STATE OF SAURASHTRA

1949. Surch **POSTAGE & REVENUE ONE ANNA.**

61	**15**	1a. on 3p. black and green	40·00	55·00
58	–	1a. on ½a. black & bl (No. 50)	9·50	4·75

1949. Surch **Postage & Revenue ONE ANNA.**

59	1a. on 2a. grey & yell (No. 52)	11·00	22·00

21

1949.

60	**21**	1s. purple	9·50	9·50

1948. Official stamps of 1929 surch **ONE ANNA**.

O14	1a. on 2a. grey and yellow	£7000	24·00
O15	1a. on 3a. black and red	£1900	55·00
O16	1a. on 4a. black and purple	£300	48·00
O17	1a. on 8a. black and green	£275	38·00
O19	1a. on 1r. black and blue	£550	40·00

1949. No. 59 optd **SARKARI**.

O22	1a. on 2a. grey and yellow	75·00	23·00

SOUTH AFRICA Pt.1

The Union of South Africa consisted of the Provinces of the Cape of Good Hope, Natal, the Orange Free State and the Transvaal. It became an independent republic outside the Commonwealth on 31 May 1961. Rejoined the Commonwealth on 1 June 1994.

1910. 12 pence = 1 shilling;
20 shillings = 1 pound.
1961. 100 cents = 1 rand.

1

2

1910.

2	**1**	2½d. blue	1·75	1·40

1913.

3	**2**	½d. green	1·25	30
4		1d. red	1·50	10
5		1½d. brown	80	10
6		2d. purple	1·75	10
7		2½d. blue	3·75	1·60
8		3d. black and red	9·50	30
9		3d. blue	3·50	1·75
10a		4d. orange and green	6·50	55
11		6d. black and violet	5·50	60
12		1s. orange	16·00	80
13		1s.3d. violet	13·00	7·00
14		2s.6d. purple and green	55·00	1·50
15		5s. purple and blue	£110	7·50
16		10s. blue and olive	£180	7·50
17		£1 green and red	£600	£350

5 De Havilland D.H.9 Biplane

1925. Air.

26	**5**	1d. red	3·75	9·50
27		3d. blue	7·00	9·50
28		6d. mauve	9·00	11·00
29		9d. green	23·00	50·00

NOTE—"Bilingual" in heading indicates that the stamps are inscribed alternately in English and Afrikaans throughout the sheet. Our prices for such issues are for mint bilingual pairs and used single stamps of either inscription.

6 Springbok

7 "Dromedaris" (Van Riebeeck's ship)

8 Orange Tree

10 "Hope"

11 Union Buildings, Pretoria

12 Groot Schuur

1926. Bilingual pairs ("SUIDAFRIKA" in one word on Afrikaans stamps). No. 33 is imperf.

42w	**6**	½d. black and green	2·75	10
31	**7**	1d. black and red	2·00	10
34	**11**	2d. grey and purple	11·00	60
44cw		2d. grey and lilac	16·00	20
44d		2d. blue and violet	£300	2·50
35	**12**	3d. black and red	15·00	60
45cw		3d. blue	6·00	10
33	**10**	4d. blue	1·75	1·25
46c	–	4d. brown	3·25	10
47	**8**	6d. green and orange	13·00	10
36	–	1s. brown and blue	29·00	1·00
49	–	2s.6d. green and brown	95·00	3·25
49b	–	2s.6d. blue and brown	25·00	20
38	–	5s. black and green	£225	35·00
39	–	10s. blue and brown	£150	10·00

DESIGNS—As Type **11**: 4d. (No. 118) A native kraal; 1s. Black and blue wildebeest; 2s.6d. Ox-wagon inspanned; 5s. Ox-wagon outspanned; 10s. Cape Town and Table Bay.

On No. 33 the English and Afrikaans inscriptions are on separate sheets and our prices are for a single stamp of either language.

For these designs with Afrikaans stamps inscr "SUID-AFRIKA", see Nos. 114 etc (issued 1933). For ½d., 1d., 2d., 3d. and 10s. in similar designs see Nos. 105/6, 107a, 116/17 and 64ba respectively.

17 De Havilland D.H.60 Cirrus Moth

18 Church of the Vow

1929. Air.

40	**17**	4d. green	5·50	2·50
41		1s. orange	16·00	13·00

1933. Voortrekker Memorial Fund. Inscr as in T **18**. Bilingual pairs.

50	**18**	½d.+½d. green	3·50	50
51	–	1d.+½d. black and pink	2·75	25
52	–	2d.+1d. green and purple	3·50	55
53	–	3d.+1½d. green and blue	5·50	70

DESIGNS: 1d. The "Great Trek" (C. Michell); 2d. Voortrekker man; 3d. Voortrekker woman.

22 Gold Mine

1933. As Nos. 42 etc but with Afrikaans stamps inscr "SUID-AFRIKA" (with hyphen) and new design. Bilingual pairs.

114	**6**	½d. grey and green	2·00	10
56	**7**	1d. grey and red	1·25	10
57	**22**	1½d. green and gold	3·00	10
58	**11**	2d. blue and violet	70·00	10
58a		2d. grey and purple	48·00	1·25
118	–	4d. brown	3·00	10
119a	**8**	6d. green and red	2·75	10
120	–	1s. brown and blue	10·00	10
121	–	2s.6d. green and brown	10·00	1·00
64b	–	5s. black and green	38·00	35

24

1935. Silver Jubilee. Bilingual pairs.

65	**24**	½d. black and green	2·25	10
66		1d. black and red	2·25	10
67		3d. blue	13·00	2·25
68		6d. green and orange	25·00	3·25

The positions of Afrikaans and English inscriptions are transposed on alternate stamps.

1936. Johannesburg International Philatelic Exhibition. Optd **JIPEX 1936**.

Un sheet / Us sheet
MS69 **6** ½d. grey and green (No. 114) 3·50 10·00
MS70 **7** 1d. grey and red (No. 56) 2·75 7·00
Issued each in miniature sheet of six stamps.

25 King George VI

1937. Coronation. Bilingual pairs.
71 **25** ½d. grey and green 70 10
72 1d. grey and red 70 10
73 1½d. orange and green . . . 70 10
74 3d. blue . . . . 1·50 10
75 1s. brown and blue . . . . 2·25 15

27 Wagon crossing Drakensberg

28 Signing of Dingaan-Retief Treaty

1938. Voortrekker Centenary Memorial Fund. Dated "1838 1938". Bilingual pairs.
76 – ½d.+½d. blue and green . . 11·00 30
77 **27** 1d.+1d. blue and red . . . 12·00 40
78 **28** 1½d.+1½d. brown and green 16·00 80
79 – 3d.+3d. blue . . . . 17·00 1·00
DESIGNS—As T **27**: ½d. Voortrekker ploughing. As T **28**: 3d. Voortrekker Monument.

31 Voortrekker Family

1938. Voortrekker Commem. Bilingual pairs.
80 – 1d. blue and red . . . . . 6·00 30
81 **31** 1½d. blue and brown . . . . 8·00 30
DESIGN: 1d. Wagon wheel.

22a Groot Schuur

23 Groot Constantia

1939. Bilingual pairs.
117 **22a** 3d. blue . . . . 2·50 10
64ca **23** 10s. blue and brown . . 42·00 30

32 Old Vicarage, Paarl, now a Museum

33 Symbol of the Reformation

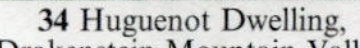
34 Huguenot Dwelling, Drakenstein Mountain Valley

34a Gold Mine

1939. 250th Anniv of Landing of Huguenots in South Africa. Bilingual pairs.
82 **32** ½d.+½d. brown and green . . 4·75 30
83 **33** 1d.+1d. green and red . . . 11·00 30
84 **34** 1½d.+1½d. green and purple 26·00 1·00

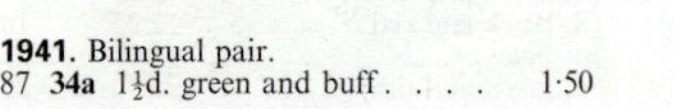
1941. Bilingual pair.
87 **34a** 1½d. green and buff . . . . 1·50 10

35 Infantry

38 Sailor, Destroyer and Lifebelts

39 Women's Auxiliary Services

1941. War Effort. Bilingual pairs except the 2d. and 1s. which are inscr in both languages on each stamp.
88 **35** ½d. green . . . . 1·50 10
89 – 1d. red . . . . 2·00 10
90 – 1½d. green . . . . 1·50 10
95 **38** 2d. violet 90 30
91 **39** 3d. blue . . . . 22·00 50
92 – 4d. brown . . . . 21·00 15
93 – 6d. orange . . . . 12·00 15
96 – 1s. brown . . . . 3·25 50
94a – 1s.3d. brown . . . . . . 4·00 20
DESIGNS—As Type **35**: 1d. Nurse and ambulance; 1½d. Airman; 1s.3d. Signaller. As Type **38**: 4d. Artillery; 6d. Welding. As Type **39**: 1s. Tank corps.

43 Infantry

54 Union Buildings, Pretoria

1942. War Effort. Reduced size. Bilingual except 4d. and 1s. which are inscr in both languages on each stamp.
97 **43** ½d. green . . . . 1·50 10
98a – 1d. red . . . . 1·00 10
99 – 1½d. brown 65 10
100 – 2d. violet 90 10
101 – 3d. blue . . . . 7·00 10
103 – 4d. green . . . . 18·00 10
102 – 6d. orange . . . . 2·00 10
104 – 1s. brown . . . . 15·00 10
DESIGNS—VERT: 1d. Nurse; 1½d. Airman; 2d. Sailor; 6d. Welder. HORIZ: 3d. Women's Auxillary Services; 6d. Heavy gun; 1s. Tanks.
Our unused prices for Nos. 97, 98, 101 and 103 are for units of three. The other stamps are in units of two.

1943. As 1926, but in single colours and with plain background to central oval. Bilingual pairs.
105 **6** ½d. green . . . . 2·00 20
106 **7** 1d. red . . . . 3·00 15

1945. Type **11** redrawn. Bilingual pairs.
107a **54** 2d. slate and violet . . . 3·00 15
116 2d. blue and purple . . . 2·25 10

55 "Victory"

58 King George VI

59 King George VI and Queen Elizabeth

1945. Victory. Bilingual pairs.
108 **55** 1d. brown and red 20 10
109 – 2d. blue and violet 20 10
110 – 3d. blue 20 10
DESIGNS: 2d. Man and oxen ploughing ("Peace"); 3d. Man and woman gazing at a star ("Hope").

1947. Royal Visit. Bilingual pairs.
111 **58** 1d. black and red 10 10
112 **59** 2d. violet 15 10
113 – 3d. blue 15 10
DESIGN—As Type **59**: 3d. Queen Elizabeth II when Princess and Princess Margaret.

61 Gold Mine

62 King George VI and Queen Elizabeth

1948. Bilingual.
124 **61** 1½d. green and buff . . . . 2·25 10
The price for No. 124 is for a unit of four stamps.

1948. Royal Silver Wedding. Bilingual pair.
125 **62** 3d. blue and silver 50 10

63 "Wanderer" (emigrant ship) entering Durban

64 Hermes

1949. Centenary of Arrival of British Settlers in Natal. Bilingual pair.
127 **63** 1½d. brown 70 10

1949. 75th Anniv of U.P.U. Bilingual pairs.
128 **64** ½d. green 50 10
129 1½d. red 50 10
130 3d. blue 60 10

65 Wagons approaching Bingham's Berg

68 Union Buildings, Pretoria

1949. Inauguration of Voortrekker Monument, Pretoria.
131 **65** 1d. mauve 10 10
132 – 1½d. green 10 10
133 – 3d. blue 15 15
DESIGNS: 1½d. Voortrekker Monument, Pretoria; 3d. Bible, candle and Voortrekkers.

1950. Bilingual pair.
134 **68** 2d. blue and violet 40 10

INSCRIPTIONS. In all later issues except Nos. 167 and 262/5, the stamps are inscribed in both Afrikaans and English. Our prices are for single examples, unused and used.

70 "Maria de la Quellerie" (D. Craey)

76 Queen Elizabeth II

1952. Tercentenary of Landing of Van Riebeeck. Dated "1652–1952".
136 – ½d. purple and sepia . . . 10 10
137 **70** 1d. green 10 10
138 – 2d. violet 50 10
139 – 4½d. blue 10 10
140 – 1s. brown 40 10
DESIGNS—HORIZ: ½d. Seal and monogram; 2d. Arrival of Van Riebeeck's ships; 1s. Landing at the Cape (D. Craey). VERT: 4½d. "Jan van Riebeeck" (D. Craey).

1952. South African Tercentenary Stamp Exn, Cape Town. No. 137 optd **SATISE** and No. 138 optd **SADIPU**.
141 **70** 1d. green . . . . 20 1·75
142 – 2d. violet . . . . 50 1·25

1953. Coronation.
143 **76** 2d. blue 30 10

77 1d. Cape Triangular Stamp

1953. Stamp Cent of Cape of Good Hope.
144 **77** 1d. sepia and red 10 10
145 – 4d. indigo and blue 50 20
DESIGN: 4d. as Type **77** but reproducing 4d. "Triangular".

79 Merino Ram

1953.
146 **79** 4½d. purple and yellow . . 20 10
147 – 1s.3d. brown . . . . . . 1·50 10
148 – 1s.6d. red and green . . . 80 55
DESIGNS: 1s.3d. Springbok; 1s.6d. Aloes.

82 Arms of Orange Free State and Scroll

1954. Centenary of Orange Free State.
149 **82** 2d. sepia and red 10 10
150 4½d. purple and grey . . . 20 50

83 Warthog

87 White Rhinoceros

1954. Wild Animals.
151 **83** ½d. turquoise 10 10
152 – 1d. lake 10 10
153 – 1½d. sepia 10 10
154 – 2d. plum 10 10
155 **87** 3d. brown and blue . . . . 1·00 10
156 – 4d. blue and green . . . . 1·00 10
157 – 4½d. indigo and blue . . . 60 1·00
158 – 6d. sepia and orange . . . 50 10
159 – 1s. brown and red . . . . 1·25 10
160 – 1s.3d. brown and green . . 2·25 10
161 – 1s.6d. brown and pink . . 1·75 60
162 – 2s.6d. sepia and green . . 3·50 20
163 – 5s. sepia and buff . . . . 8·00 1·60
164 – 10s. black and blue . . . . 13·00 4·50
DESIGNS—VERT (as Type **83**): 1d. Black wildebeest; 1½d. Leopard; 2d. Mountain zebra. (As Type **87**): 4d. African elephant; 4½d. Hippopotamus; 1s. Greater kudu; 1s.6d. Gemsbok; 2s.6d. Nyala; 5s. Giraffe; 10s. Sable antelope. HORIZ (as Type **87**): 6d. Lion; 1s.3d. Springbok.

97 President Kruger

99 A. Pretorius, Church of the Vow and Flag

1955. Centenary of Pretoria.
165 **97** 3d. green 10 10
166 – 6d. purple (Pres. M. Pretorius) 10 30

1955. Voortrekker Covenant Celebrations Pietermaritzburg. Bilingual pair.
167 **99** 2d. blue and red 45 10

100 Settlers' Block- wagon and House

1958. Centenary of Arrival of German Settlers in South Africa.
168 **100** 2d. brown and purple . . 10 10

101 Arms of the Academy

1959. 50th Anniv of South African Academy of Science and Art, Pretoria.
169 **101** 3d. blue and turquoise . . 10 10

103 Globe and Antarctic Scene

104 Union Flag

1959. South African National Antarctic Expedition.
178 **103** 3d. turquoise and orange . . 20 10

1960. 50th Anniv of Union of South Africa.
179 **104** 4d. orange and blue . . . 30 10
180 – 6d. red, brown and green 30 10
181 – 1s. blue and yellow . . . 30 10
182 – 1s.6d. black and blue . . 70 2·25
DESIGNS—VERT: 6d. Union arms. HORIZ: 1s. "Wheel of Progress"; 1s.6d. Union Festival emblem.
See also Nos. 190 and 192/3.

108 Steam Locomotives "Natal" (1860) and Class 25 (1950s)

1960. Centenary of South African Railways.
183 **108** 1s.3d. blue . . . . 1·10 30

109 Prime Ministers Botha, Smuts, Hertzog, Malan, Strijdom and Verwoerd

1960. Union Day.
184 **109** 3d. brown and light brown 15 10

1961. Types as before but new currency.
185 **83** ½c. turquoise 10 10
186 – 1c. lake (as No. 152) . . 10 10
187 – 1½c. sepia (as No. 153) . . 10 10
188 – 2c. plum (as No. 154) . . 10 65
189 **109** 2½c. brown 20 10
190 **104** 3½c. orange and blue . . 15 1·75
191 – 5c. sepia & orge (as No. 158) 20 10
192 – 7½c. red, brown and green (as No. 180) . . . . 20 2·25
193 – 10c. bl & yell (as No. 181) 40 50
194 – 12½c. brown and green (as No. 160) . . . . . . 1·00 1·25
195 – 20c. brown and pink (as No. 161) . . . . . . 2·25 2·75
196 – 50c. sepia and buff (as No. 163) . . . . . . 4·50 10·00
197 – 1r. black & blue (as No. 164) . . . . 14·00 24·00

110 African Pygmy Kingfisher

115 Burchell's Gonolek

1961. Republic Issue.
198 **110** ½c. blue, red and brown 10 10
199 – 1c. red and grey 10 10
200 – 1½c. lake and purple . . . 10 10
241 – 2c. blue and yellow . . . 20 10
230 – 2½c. violet and green . . . 10 10
243 **115** 3c. red and blue 30 10
288 – 4c. violet and green . . . 40 50
204 – 5c. yellow and turquoise 30 10
290 – 6c. brown and green . . . 70 30
205 – 7½c. brown and green . . 60 10
292 – 9c. red, yellow and green 1·25 30
233 – 10c. sepia and green . . . 40 10
247 – 12½c. red, yellow and green . . . . 1·00 40
248 – 15c. black, olive & orange 85 25
234 – 20c. turq, red & salmon 1·00 80
250 – 50c. black and blue . . . 1·50 40
251 – 1r. orange, green and blue 1·50 1·00
DESIGNS—VERT (as Type **110**): 1c. Kafferboom flower (As Type **115**): 2½, 4c. Groot Constantia; 5c. Baobab tree; 6, 7½c. Maize; 9, 12½c. Protea (flower); 10c. Cape Town Castle entrance; 15c. Industry; 20c. Secretary bird. HORIZ (as Type **110**): 1½c. Afrikander bull. (As Type **115**) 2c. Pouring gold; 50c. Cape Town harbour; 1r. Strelitzia (flower).
Most values exist in two forms showing differences in the size of the inscriptions and figures of value.
See also Nos. 276/7.

123 Bleriot XI Monoplane and Boeing 707 Airliner over Table Mountain

124 Folk-dancers

1962. 50th Anniv of First South African Aerial Post.
220 **123** 3c. blue and red 50 10

1962. 50th Anniv of Volkspele (folk-dancing) in South Africa.
221 **124** 2½c. red and brown . . . 15 10

125 "The Chapman" (emigrant ship)

1962. Unveiling of Precinct Stone, British Settlers Monument, Grahamstown.
222 **125** 2½c. green and purple . . 50 10
223 12½c. blue and brown . . 2·50 1·25

126 Red Disa (orchid), Castle Rock and Gardens

128 Centenary Emblem and Nurse

1963. 50th Anniv of Kirstenbosch Botanic Gardens, Cape Town.
224 **126** 2½c. multicoloured 20 10

1963. Cent of Red Cross. Inscr "1863–1963".
225 **128** 2½c. red, black and purple 20 10
226 – 12½c. red and blue . . . . 2·25 1·00
DESIGN—HORIZ: 12½c. Centenary emblem and globe.

130 Assembly Building, Umtata

145 "Springbok" Badge of Rugby Board

1963. First Meeting of Transkei Legislative Assembly.
237 **130** 2½c. sepia and green . . . 10 10

1964. 75th Anniv of South African Rugby Board.
252 **145** 2½c. brown and green . . 15 10
253 – 12½c. black and green . . 3·00 3·75
DESIGN—HORIZ: 12½c. Rugby footballer.

147 Calvin

148 Nurse's Lamp

1964. 400th Death Anniv of Calvin (Protestant reformer).
254 **147** 2½c. cerise, violet & brown 10 10

1964. 50th Anniv of South African Nursing Association.
255 **148** 2½c. blue and gold 10 10
257 – 12½c. blue and gold . . . 2·75 1·75
DESIGN—HORIZ: 12½c. Nurse holding lamp.

150 I.T.U. Emblem and Satellites

152 Pulpit in Groote Kerk, Cape Town

1965. Centenary of I.T.U.
258 **150** 2½c. orange and blue . . 25 10
259 – 12½c. purple and green . . 1·25 1·00
DESIGN: 12½c. I.T.U. emblem and symbols.

1965. Tercentenary of Nederduites Gereformeerde Kerk (Dutch Reformed Church) in South Africa.
260 **152** 2½c. brown and yellow . . 15 10
261 – 12½c. black, orange & blue 70 85
DESIGN—HORIZ: 12½c. Church emblem.

155 Bird in Flight

1965. 5th Anniv of Republic. Bilingual pairs.
262 – 1c. black, green and yellow 45 10
263 **155** 2½c. blue, indigo and green 85 10
264 – 3c. red, yellow and brown 3·00 10
265 – 7½c. blue, ultram & yell 3·75 20
DESIGNS—VERT: 1c. Diamond; 3c. Maize plants. HORIZ: 7½c. Mountain landscape.

158 Verwoerd and Union Buildings, Pretoria

161 "Martin Luther" (Cranach the Elder)

1966. Verwoerd Commemoration.
266 **158** 2½c. brown and turquoise 10 10
267 – 3c. brown and green . . . 10 10
268 – 12½c. brown and blue . . 60 60
DESIGNS: 3c. "Dr. H. F. Verwoerd" (I. Henkel); 12½c. Verwoerd and map of South Africa.

1967. 450th Anniv of Reformation.
269 **161** 2½c. black and red 10 10
270 – 12½c. black and orange . . 1·25 2·00
DESIGN: 12½c. Wittenberg Church door.

163 "Profile of Pres. Fouche" (I. Henkel)

165 Hertzog in 1902

1968. Inauguration of President Fouche.
271 **163** 2½c. brown 10 10
272 – 12½c. blue . . . . 60 1·00
DESIGN: 12½c. Portrait of Pres. Fouche.

1968. Inauguration of General Hertzog Monument, Bloemfontein.
273 **165** 2½c. black, brown & yellow 10 10
274 – 3c. multicoloured 15 10
275 – 12½c. black, red and orange . . . . 1·50 1·50
DESIGNS—HORIZ: 3c. Hertzog in 1924. VERT; 12½c. Hertzog Monument.

168 African Pygmy Kingfisher

170 Springbok and Olympic Torch

1969.
276 **168** ½c. blue, red and ochre . . 10 30
277 – 1c. red and brown 10 10
DESIGN—VERT: 1c. Kafferboom flower.

1969. South African Games, Bloemfontein.
278 **170** 2½c. black, red and green 15 10
279 12½c. black, red and brown . . . . 70 1·50

171 Professor Barnard and Groote Schuur Hospital

1969. World's First Heart Transplant and 47th South African Medical Association Congress.
280 **171** 2½c. purple and red . . . 15 10
281 – 12½c. red and blue . . . . 1·25 2·00
DESIGN: 12½c. Hands holding heart.

173 Mail Coach

1969. Centenary of First Stamps of the South African Republic (Transvaal).
297 **173** 2½c. yellow, blue & brown 15 10
298 – 12½c. green, gold & brown 2·75 3·50
DESIGN—VERT: 12½c. Transvaal stamp of 1869.

175 "Water 70" Emblem

177 "The Sower"

1970. Water 70 Campaign.
299 **175** 2½c. green, blue and brown 30 10
300 – 3c. blue and buff 30 20
DESIGN—HORIZ: 3c. Symbolic waves.

1970. 150th Anniv of Bible Society of South Africa.
301 **177** 2½c. multicoloured 15 10
302 – 12½c. gold, black and blue 1·50 2·00
DESIGN—HORIZ: 12½c. "Biblia" and open book.

178 J. G. Strijdom and Strijdom Tower

179 Map and Antarctic Landscape

1971. "Interstex" Stamp Exhibition, Cape Town.
303A **178** 5c. blue, black and yellow 20 10

1971. 10th Anniv of Antarctic Treaty.
304 **179** 12½c. black, blue and red 1·50 4·00

180 "Landing of British Settlers, 1820" (T. Baines)

1971. 10th Anniv of Republic of South Africa.

305	**180**	2c. flesh and red	15	20
306	–	4c. green and black	15	10

DESIGN—VERT: 4c. Presidents Steyn and Kruger and Treaty of Vereeniging Monument.

181 View of Dam

1972. Opening of Hendrik Verwoerd Dam. Multicoloured.

307		4c. Type **181**	20	10
308		5c. Aerial view of dam	25	10
309		10c. Dam and surrounding country (58×21 mm)	1·50	2·50

182 Sheep **183** Black and Siamese Cats

1972. Sheep and Wool Industry.

310	**182**	4c. multicoloured	30	10
311	–	15c. stone, dp blue & blue	2·25	20

DESIGN: 15c. Lamb.

1972. Centenary of Societies for the Prevention of Cruelty to Animals.

312	**183**	5c. multicoloured	1·25	10

184 Transport and Industry **185** University Coat of Arms

1973. 50th Anniv of ESCOM (Electricity Supply Commission). Multicoloured.

326		4c. Type **184**	20	10
327		5c. Pylon (21×28 mm)	30	10
328		15c. Cooling towers (21×28 mm)	3·00	3·50

1973. Centenary of University of South Africa.

329	**185**	4c. multicoloured	20	10
330	–	5c. multicoloured	30	15
331	–	15c. black and gold	3·00	3·50

DESIGNS—HORIZ (38×21 mm): 5c. University Complex, Pretoria. VERT (as Type **185**): 15c. Old University Building, Cape Town.

186 Rescuing Sailors

1973. Bicentenary of Rescue by Wolraad Woltemade.

332	**186**	4c. brown, green and black	20	10
333	–	5c. olive, green and black	40	10
334	–	15c. brown, green & black	5·00	6·50

DESIGNS: 5c. "De Jonge Thomas" foundering; 15c. "De Jonge Thomas" breaking up and sailors drowning.

187 C. J. Langenhoven

1973. Birth Cent of C. J. Langenhoven (politician and composer of national anthem).

335	**187**	4c. multicoloured	25	10
336	–	5c. multicoloured	35	10
337	–	15c. multicoloured	3·50	5·00

Nos. 336/7 are as Type **187** but with motifs rearranged. The 5c. is vert, 21×38 mm, and the 15c. is horiz, 38×21 mm.

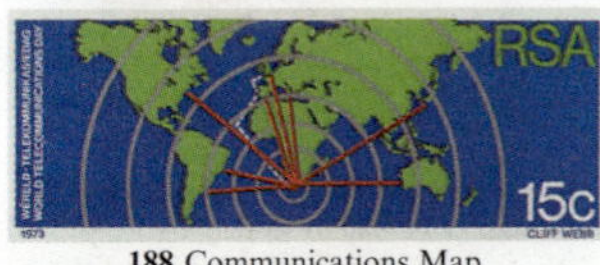

188 Communications Map

1973. World Communications Day.

338	**188**	15c. multicoloured	50	1·40

189 Restored Buildings **190** Burgerspond (obverse and reverse)

1974. Restoration of Tulbagh. Multicoloured.

340		4c. Type **189**	15	10
341		5c. Restored Church Street (58×21 mm)	40	90

1974. Centenary of Burgerspond (coin).

342	**190**	9c. brown, red and olive	60	1·00

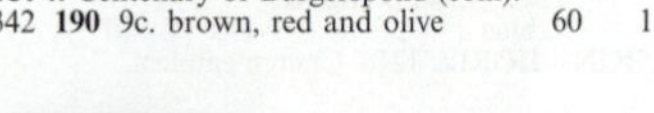

191 Dr. Malan **192** Congress Emblem

1974. Birth Centenary of Dr. D. F. Malan (Prime Minister).

343	**191**	4c. blue and light blue	20	10

1974. 15th World Sugar Congress, Durban.

344	**192**	15c. blue and silver	75	1·40

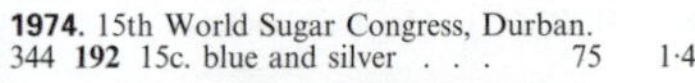

193 "50" and Radio Waves

1974. 50th Anniv of Broadcasting in South Africa.

345	**193**	4c. red and black	10	10

194 Monument Building

1974. Inauguration of British Settlers' Monument, Grahamstown.

346	**194**	5c. red and black	10	10

195 Stamps of the South African Provinces

1974. Centenary of Universal Postal Union.

347	**195**	15c. multicoloured	70	80

196 Iris **197** Bokmakierie Shrikes

1974. Multicoloured. (a) As Type **196**.

348	1c. Type **196**	10	10
349a	2c. Wild heath	10	10
350a	3c. Geranium	10	10
351a	4c. Arum lily	10	10
352	5c. Cape gannet (horiz)	20	10
353	6c. Galjoen (fish) (horiz)	1·00	10
354	7c. Bontrok seabream (horiz)	25	10
355	9c. Dusky batfish (horiz)	30	30
356	10c. Moorish idol (horiz)	30	10
357	14c. Roman seabream (horiz)	30	10
358	15c. Greater double-collared sunbird (horiz)	30	10
359	20c. Southern yellow-billed hornbill (horiz)	45	10
360	25c. Barberton daisy	45	10

(b) As Type **197**.

361	30c. Type **197**	7·00	70
362	50c. Stanley cranes	1·00	35
363	1r. Bateleurs	4·00	3·00

1974. Coil Stamps. As Nos. 348/9a, 352 and 356. Colours changed.

370a	**196**	1c. violet and pink	55	60
371	–	2c. green and yellow	80	60
372	–	5c. black and blue	1·75	80
373a	–	10c. violet and blue	4·00	5·25

198 Voortrekker Monument and Encampment

1974. 25th Anniv of Voortrekker Monument, Pretoria.

374	**198**	4c. multicoloured	20	30

199 SASOL Complex

1975. 25th Anniv of South African Coal, Oil and Gas Corporation Ltd (SASOL).

375	**199**	15c. multicoloured	75	1·50

200 President Diederichs **201** Jan Smuts

1975. Inauguration of State President.

376	**200**	4c. brown and gold	10	10
377		15c. blue and gold	50	1·25

1975. Smuts Commemoration.

378	**201**	4c. black and grey	10	10

202 "Dutch East Indiaman, Table Bay"

1975. Death Centenary of Thomas Baines (painter). Multicoloured.

379	5c. Type **202**	15	10
380	9c. "Cradock, 1848"	15	15
381	15c. "Thirsty Flat, 1848"	25	25
382	30c. "Pretoria, 1874"	40	1·50
MS383	120×95 mm. Nos. 379/82	1·25	3·75

203 Gideon Malherbe's House, Paarl

1975. Cent of Genootskap van Regte Afrikaners (Afrikaner Language Movement).

384	**203**	4c. multicoloured	10	10

204 "Automatic Sorting" **205** Title Page of "Die Afrikaanse Patriot"

1975. Postal Mechanization.

385	**204**	4c. multicoloured	10	10

1975. Inaug of Language Monument, Paarl.

386	**205**	4c. black, brown & orange	10	10
387	–	5c. multicoloured	10	10

DESIGN: 5c. "Afrikaanse Taalmonument".

206 Table Mountain

1975. Tourism. Multicoloured.

388	15c. Type **206**	2·00	3·00
389	15c. Johannesburg	2·00	3·00
390	15c. Cape vineyards	2·00	3·00
391	15c. Lions in Kruger National Park	2·00	3·00

207 Globe and Satellites

1975. Satellite Communication.

392	**207**	15c. multicoloured	30	30

208 Bowls **210** "Picnic under a Baobab Tree"

1976. Sporting Commemorations.

393	**208**	15c. black and green	20	75
394	–	15c. black and green	50	1·00
395	–	15c. black and green	20	60
396	–	15c. black and green	50	60
MS397		161×109 mm. Nos. 393/6	1·50	4·00

DESIGNS AND EVENTS: No. 393, Type **208** (World Bowls Championships, Johannesburg); 394, Batsman (Centenary of organized cricket in South Africa); 395, Polo player; 396, Gary Player (golfer).

1976. South Africa's Victory in World Bowls Championships. Optd **WERELDKAMPIOENE WORLD CHAMPIONS**.

398	**208**	15c. black and green	30	1·00

1976. Birth Cent of Erich Mayer (painter). Mult.

399	4c. Type **210**	15	10
400	10c. "Foot of the Blaawberg"	25	20
401	15c. "Harteespoort Dam"	30	90
402	20c. "Street scene, Doornfontein"	40	1·25
MS403	121×95 mm. Nos. 399/402	1·50	4·00

211 Cheetah

1976. World Environment Day. Multicoloured.

404	3c. Type **211**	15	10
405	10c. Black rhinoceros	40	30
406	15c. Blesbok	40	40
407	20c. Mountain zebra	45	75

212 "Emily Hobhouse" (H. Naude) **214** Family with Globe

213 "Donrobin Castle" (mail ship), 1876

1976. 50th Death Anniv of Emily Hobhouse (welfare worker).
408 **212** 4c. multicoloured 10 10

1976. Centenary of Ocean Mail Service.
409 **213** 10c. multicoloured . . . . 60 1·00

1976. Family Planning and Child Welfare.
410 **214** 4c. brown and orange . . 10 10

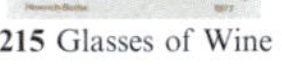

215 Glasses of Wine 216 Dr. Jacob du Toit

1977. International Wine Symposium, Cape Town.
411 **215** 15c. multicoloured . . . . 40 1·25

1977. Birth Centenary of J. D. du Toit (theologian and poet).
412 **216** 4c. multicoloured 10 10

217 Palace of Justice

1977. Centenary of Transvaal Supreme Court.
413 **217** 4c. brown 10 10

218 "Protea repens" 219 Gymnast

1977. Succulents. Multicoloured.
414 1c. Type **218** 10 10
431 1c. "Leucadendron argenteum" . . . . . . 35 1·00
415 2c. "P. punctata" 15 50
432 2c. "Mimetes cucullatus" . . 35 1·00
416 3c. "P. neriifolia" 10 10
417 4c. "P. longifolia" 10 10
418 5c. "P. cynaroides" 10 10
433 5c. "Serruria florida" . . . 35 1·00
419b 6c. "P. canaliculata" 30 80
420b 7c. "P. lorea" 20 80
421a 8c. "P. mundii" 15 10
422 9c. "P. roupelliae" 20 70
423 10c. "P. aristata" 30 10
434 10c. "Leucadendron sessile" 35 1·00
424 15c. "P. eximia" 25 10
425 20c. "P. magnifica" 30 10
426c 25c. "P. grandiceps" 40 75
427 30c. "P. amplexicaulis" . . 45 10
428a 50c. "Leucospermum cordifolium" 45 15
429a 1r. "Paranomus reflexus" 50 75
430a 2r. "Orothamnus zeyheri" 60 1·00

1977. 8th Congress of Int Assn of Physical Education and Sports for Girls and Women.
435 **219** 15c. black, red and yellow 30 30

220 Metrication Symbol on Globe

1977. Metrication.
436 **220** 15c. multicoloured 30 30

221 Atomic Diagram

1977. Uranium Development.
437 **221** 15c. multicoloured 40 30

222 National Flag 224 Dr. Andrew Murray

223 Walvis Bay, 1878

1977. 50th Anniv of National Flag.
438 **222** 5c. multicoloured 10 10

1977. Centenary of Annexation of Walvis Bay.
439 **223** 15c. multicoloured 60 60

1978. 150th Birth Anniv of Dr. Andrew Murray (church statesman).
440 **224** 4c. multicoloured 10 10

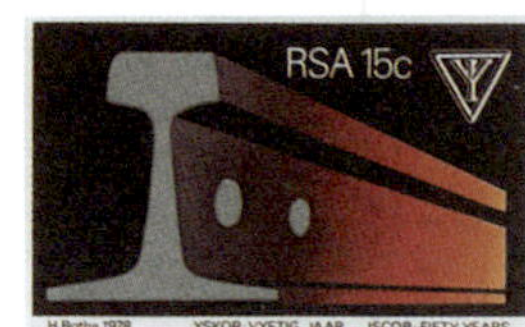

225 Steel Rail

1978. 50th Anniv of I.S.C.O.R. (South African Iron and Steel Industrial Corporation).
441 **225** 15c. multicoloured 30 30

226 Richards Bay

1978. Harbours. Multicoloured.
442 15c. Type **226** . . . . 50 1·00
443 15c. Saldanhabaai . . . . . 50 1·00

227 "Shepherd's Lonely Dwelling, Riversdale"

1978. 125th Birth Anniv of J. E. A. Volschenk (painter). Multicoloured.
444 10c. Type **227** 15 20
445 15c. "Clouds and Sunshine, Laneberg Range, Riversdale" 20 30
446 20c. "At the Foot of the Mountain" 30 75
447 25c. "Evening on the Veldt" 35 1·40
MS448 124 × 90 mm. Nos. 444/7 1·25 4·00

228 Pres. B. J. Vorster

1978. Inauguration of President Vorster.
449a **228** 4c. brown and gold . . . 10 10
450 15c. violet and gold . . 25 60

229 Golden Gate

1978. Tourism. Multicoloured.
451 10c. Type **229** 15 10
452 15c. Blyde River Canyon . . 25 35
453 20c. Amphitheatre, Drakensberg . . . . 40 1·10
454 25c. Cango Caves . . . . . 55 1·50

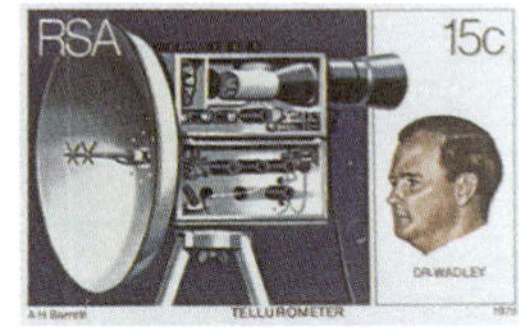

230 Dr. Wadley (inventor) and Tellurometer

1979. 25th Anniv of Tellurometer (radio distance measurer).
455 **230** 15c. multicoloured 20 20

231 1929 4d. Airmail Stamp

1979. 50th Anniv of Stamp Production in South Africa.
456 **231** 15c. green, cream and grey 30 20

232 "Save Fuel"

1979. Fuel Conservation.
457 **232** 4c. black and red 25 65
458 – 4c. black and red 25 65
No. 458 is as Type **232** but with face value and country initials in bottom left-hand corner, and Afrikaans inscription above English.

233 Isandlwana

1979. Centenary of Zulu War.
459 **233** 4c. black and red 20 10
460 – 15c. black and red 55 50
461 – 20c. black and red . . . . 70 1·00
MS462 125 × 90 mm. Nos. 459/61 2·25 3·50
DESIGNS: 15c. Ulundi; 20c. Rorke's Drift.

234 "Health Care"

1979. Health Year.
463 **234** 4c. multicoloured 10 10

235 Children looking at Candle

1979. 50th Anniv of Christmas Stamp Fund.
464 **235** 4c. multicoloured 10 10

236 University of Cape Town 237 "Gary Player"

1979. 50th Anniv of University of Cape Town.
465a **236** 4c. multicoloured 15 15

1979. "Rosafari 1979" World Rose Convention, Pretoria. Multicoloured.
466 4c. Type **237** 15 10
467 15c. "Prof. Chris Barnard" 30 40
468 20c. "Southern Sun" 40 60
469 25c. "Soaring Wings" 40 85
MS470 100 × 125 mm. Nos. 466/9 1·40 2·50

238 University of Stellenbosch

1979. 300th Anniv of Stellenbosch (oldest town in South Africa). Multicoloured.
471 4c. Type **238** 10 10
472 15c. Rhenish Church on the Braak 20 40

239 F.A.K. Emblem 240 "Still-life with Sweet Peas"

1979. 50th Anniv of F.A.K. (Federation of Afrikaans Cultural Societies).
473 **239** 4c. multicoloured 10 15

1980. Paintings by Pieter Wenning. Multicoloured.
474 5c. Type **240** 10 10
475 25c. "House in the Suburbs, Cape Town" (44½ × 37 mm) 40 60
MS476 94 × 121 mm. Nos. 474/5 1·00 1·60

241 "Cullinan II" 242 C. L. Leipoldt

1980. World Diamond Congresses, Johannesburg. Multicoloured.
477 15c. Type **241** 60 60
478 20c. "Cullinan I (Great Star of Africa)" 65 65

1980. Birth Centenary of C. L. Leipoldt (poet).
479 **242** 5c. multicoloured 10 10

243 University of Pretoria

1980. 50th Anniv of University of Pretoria.
480 **243** 5c. multicoloured 10 10

244 "Marine with Shipping" (Willem van de Velde)

1980. Paintings from South African National Gallery, Cape Town. Multicoloured.
481 5c. Type **244** 15 10
482 10c. "Firetail and his Trainer" (George Stubbs) 20 25
483 15c. "Lavinia" (Thomas Gainsborough) (vert) . . . 25 50
484 20c. "Classical Landscape" (Pieter Post) 30 80
MS485 126 × 90 mm. Nos. 481/4 1·00 1·75

245 Joubert, Kruger and M. Pretorius (Triumvirate Government)

1980. Centenary of Paardekraal Monument (cairn commemorating formation of Boer Triumvirate Government). Multicoloured.
486 5c. Type **245** 10 10
487 10c. Paardekraal Monument (vert) 20 65

246 Boers advancing up Amajuba Mountain

1981. Centenary of Battle of Amajuba. Mult.
488 5c. Type **246** 20 10
489 15c. British troops defending hill (horiz) 40 75

247 Ballet "Raka"

1981. Opening of State Theatre, Pretoria. Multicoloured.
490 20c. Type **247** 25 30
491 25c. Opera "Aida" 40 35
MS492 110 × 90 mm. Nos. 490/1 65 70

248 Former Presidents C. R. Swart, J. J. Fouche, N. Diederichs and B. J. Vorster

1981. 20th Anniv of Republic.
493 **248** 5c. black, green and brown 15 10
494 – 15c. multicoloured 30 30
DESIGN—28 × 22 mm: 15c. President Marais Viljoen.

249 Girl with Hearing Aid

250 Microscope

1981. Centenary of Institutes for Deaf and Blind, Worcester. Multicoloured.
495 5c. Type **249** 10 10
496 15c. Boy reading braille . . . 20 50

1981. 50th Anniv of National Cancer Association.
497 **250** 5c. multicoloured 10 10

251 "Calanthe natalensis"

252 Voortrekkers in Uniform

1981. 10th World Orchid Conference, Durban. Multicoloured.
498 5c. Type **251** 10 10
499 15c. "Eulophia speciosa" . . 20 35
500 20c. "Disperis fanniniae" . . 20 75
501 25c. "Disa uniflora" . . . . 25 1·10
MS502 120 × 91 mm. Nos. 498/501 2·25 2·00

1981. 50th Anniv of Voortrekker Movement (Afrikaans cultural youth organization).
503 **252** 5c. multicoloured 10 10

253 Lord Baden-Powell **254** Dr. Robert Koch

1982. 75th Anniv of Boy Scout Movement.
504 **253** 15c. multicoloured 30 30

1981. Cent of Discovery of Tubercle Bacillus.
505 **254** 20c. multicoloured 20 30

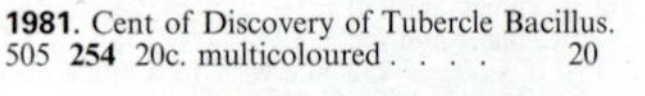

255 "Maria van Riejbeck" submarine

1982. 25th Anniv of Simonstown as South African Naval Base. Multicoloured.
506 8c. Type **255** 15 10
507 15c. Missile patrol vessel . . 20 30
508 20c. "Durban" (minesweeper) 25 60
509 25c. Harbour patrol boats . . 30 85
MS510 125 × 90 mm. Nos. 506/9 2·00 2·00

256 Old Provost, Grahamstown

257 Bradysaurus

1982. South African Architecture.
511 **256** 1c. brown 15 20
512b – 2c. green 10 20
513 – 3c. violet 30 30
514 – 4c. green 20 15
515 – 5c. red 30 30
515a – 5c. purple 10 10
516 – 6c. green 45 40
517 – 7c. green 30 75
518a – 8c. blue 40 10
519 – 9c. mauve 40 20
520 – 10c. red 40 55
520a – 10c. brown 35 10
520b – 11c. mauve 40 20
520c – 12c. blue 70 10
520d – 14c. brown . . . . . . 1·75 10
521 – 15c. blue 30 15
521a – 16c. red . . . . 1·00 1·00
522 – 20c. red 65 30
522a – 20c. black 80 10
523 – 25c. brown 50 50
524 – 30c. brown 50 30
525 – 50c. blue 50 30
526 – 1r. violet 50 15
527 – 2r. red 65 40

DESIGNS—(28 × 20 mm): 2c. Tuynhuys, Cape Town; 3c. Appelhof, Bloemfontein; 4c. Raadsaal, Pretoria; 5c. Cape Town Castle; 6c. Goewermentsgebou, Bloemfontein; 7c. Drostdy, Graaff-Reinet; 8c. Leeuwenhof, Cape Town; 9c. Libertas, Pretoria; 10c. City Hall, Pietermaritzburg; 11c. City Hall, Kimberley; 12c. City Hall, Port Elizabeth; 14c. City Hall, Johannesburg; 15c. Matjesfontein; 16c. City Hall, Durban; 20c. Post Office, Durban; 25c. Melrose House, Pretoria. (45 × 28 mm): 30c. Old Legislative Asembly Building, Pietermaritzburg; 50c. Raadsaal, Bloemfontein; 1r. Houses of Parliament, Cape Town; 2r. Uniegebou, Pretoria.

1982. Coil Stamps. As T **256**.
528 1c. brown 30 70
529 2c. green 30 75
530 5c. brown 30 75
531 10c. brown 30 80
DESIGNS: 1c. Drostdy, Swellendam; 2c. City Hall, East London; 5c. Head Post Office, Johannesburg; 10c. Morgenster, Somerset West.

1982. Karoo Fossils. Multicoloured.
532 8c. Type **257** 30 10
533 15c. Lystrosaurus 35 60
534 20c. Euparkeria 40 75
535 25c. Thrinaxodon 45 90
MS536 107 × 95 mm. Nos. 532/5 1·50 3·25

258 Gough Island Base

1983. Weather Stations. Multicoloured.
537 8c. Type **258** 20 10
538 20c. Marion Island base . . . 30 45
539 25c. Taking meteorological readings 30 50
540 40c. Launching weather balloon, Sanae 40 90

259 Class S2 Krupp Locomotive, 1952 **260** Rugby

1983. Steam Railway Locomotives. Multicoloured.
541 10c. Type **259** 35 10
542 20c. Class 16E Henschel express locomotive, 1935 60 70
543 25c. Class 6H locomotive, 1901 . . . . 70 80
544 40c. Class 15F locomotive, 1939 . . . . 85 1·50

1983. Sport in South Africa. Multicoloured.
545 10c. Type **260** 15 10
546 20c. Soccer (horiz) 20 30
547 25c. Yachting 25 40
548 40c. Horse-racing (horiz) . . 40 80

261 Plettenberg Bay

1983. Tourism Beaches. Multicoloured.
549 10c. Type **261** 10 10
550 20c. Durban 20 30
551 25c. West coast 20 35
552 40c. Clifton 35 65
MS553 128 × 90 mm. Nos. 549/52 1·75 2·50

262 Thomas Pringle **263** Manganese

1984. South African English Authors.
554 **262** 10c. brown, lt brn & grey 10 10
555 – 20c. brown, green and grey 20 40
556 – 25c. brown, pink and grey 20 50
557 – 40c. brown, lt brn & grey 35 85
DESIGNS: 20c. Pauline Smith; 25c. Olive Schreiner; 40c. Sir Percy Fitzpatrick.

1984. Strategic Minerals. Multicoloured.
558 11c. Type **263** 30 10
559 20c. Chromium 45 60
560 25c. Vanadium 50 80
561 30c. Titanium 60 90

264 Bloukrans River Bridge

1984. South African Bridges. Multicoloured.
562 11c. Type **264** 25 10
563 25c. Durban four-level interchange 40 60
564 30c. Mfolozi railway bridge 45 75
565 45c. Gouritz River bridge . . 55 1·40

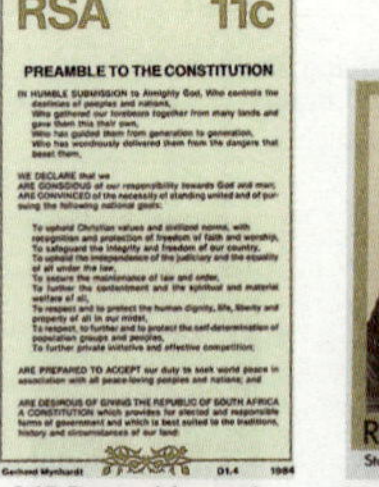

265 Preamble to the Constitution in Afrikaans **266** Pres. P. W. Botha

1984. New Constitution.
566 – 11c. stone, black and bistre . . . . 70 1·25
567 **265** 11c. stone, black and bistre . . . . 70 1·25
568 – 25c. stone, purple and bistre 45 50
569 – 30c. multicoloured 45 50
DESIGNS: No. 566, Preamble to the Constitution in English; 568, Last two lines of National Anthem; 569, South African coat of arms.

1984. Inauguration of President Botha.
570 **266** 11c. multicoloured 30 10
571 25c. multicoloured 55 40

267 Pro Patria Medal

268 "Reflections" (Frans Oerder)

1984. Military Decorations. Multicoloured.
572 11c. Type **267** 20 10
573 25c. De Wet decoration . . . 30 45
574 30c. John Chard decoration 30 65
575 45c. Honoris Crux (Diamond) decoration . . 35 1·10
MS576 71 × 116 mm. Nos. 572/5 1·50 3·00

1985. Paintings by Frans Oerder. Multicoloured.
577 11c. Type **268** 20 15
578 25c. "Ladies in a Garden" 25 35
579 30c. "Still-life with Lobster" 25 45
580 50c. "Still-life with Marigolds" 40 70
MS581 129 × 74 mm. Nos. 577/80 2·00 3·00

269 Cape Parliament Building **270** Freesia

1985. Centenary of Cape Parliament Building. Multicoloured.
582 12c. Type **269** 15 10
583 25c. Speaker's Chair 25 30
584 30c. "National Convention 1908–9" (Edward Roworth) 25 40
585 50c. Republic Parliamentary emblem . . . . 40 1·10

1985. Floral Emigrants. Multicoloured.
586 12c. Type **270** 15 10
587 25c. Nerine 25 30
588 30c. Ixia 25 45
589 50c. Gladiolus . . . . 40 1·25

271 Sugar Bowl

1985. Cape Silverware. Multicoloured.

590 12c. Type **271** 20 10
591 25c. Teapot 30 30
592 30c. Loving cup (vert) 30 45
593 50c. Coffee pot (vert) 45 1·50

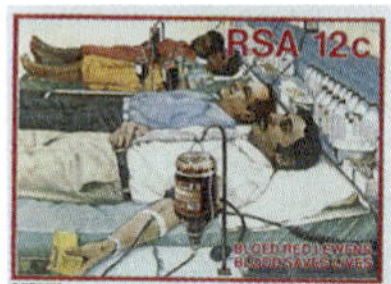

272 Blood Donor Session

1986. Blood Donor Campaign. Multicoloured.

594 12c. Type **272** 45 10
595 20c. Baby receiving blood transfusion 75 80
596 25c. Operation in progress 80 95
597 30c. Ambulanceman and accident victim 95 1·60

273 National Flag

1986. 25th Anniv of Republic of South Africa.

598 14c. Type **273** 75 1·00
599 14c. As Type **273**, but inscr "UNITY IS STRENGTH" 75 1·00

274 Drostdyhof, Graaff-Reinet

1986. Restoration of Historic Buildings. Multicoloured.

600 14c. Type **274** 30 10
601 20c. Pilgrim's Rest mining village 55 70
602 25c. Strapp's Store, Bethlehem 60 90
603 30c. Palmdene, Pietermaritzburg 75 1·40

275 Von Brandis Square, Johannesburg, c. 1900

1986. Centenary of Johannesburg. Multicoloured.

604 14c. Type **275** 35 10
605 20c. Gold mine (26 × 20 mm) 1·25 1·25
606 25c. Johannesburg skyline, 1986 1·00 1·60
607 30c. Gold bars (26 × 20 mm) 1·75 2·50

276 Gordon's Rock, Paarlberg

277 "Cicindela regalis"

1986. Rock Formations. Multicoloured.

608 14c. Type **276** 45 10
609 20c. The Column, Drakensberg 70 80
610 25c. Maltese Cross, Sederberge 75 1·00
611 30c. Bourke's Luck Potholes, Blyde River Gorge 85 1·50

1987. South African Beetles. Multicoloured.

612 14c. Type **277** 40 10
613 20c. "Trichostetha fascicularis" 55 60
614 25c. "Julodis viridipes" 65 90
615 30c. "Ceroplesis militaris" 75 1·75

278 Eland, Sebaaieni Cave

1987. Rock Paintings. Multicoloured.

616 16c. Type **278** 40 10
617 20c. Leaping lion, Clocolan 60 65
618 25c. Black wildebeest, uMhlwazini Valley 75 90
619 30c. Bushman dance, Floukraal 80 1·60

279 Oude Pastorie, Paarl

1987. 300th Anniv of Paarl. Multicoloured.

620 16c. Type **279** 20 10
621 20c. Grapevines 35 55
622 25c. Wagon-building 40 65
623 30c. KWV Cathedral Wine Cellar 45 1·25

1987. Natal Flood Relief Fund (1st issue). No. 521a surch.

624 16c.+10c. red (surch **VLOEDRAMP NATAL +10c**) 30 80
625 16c.+10c. (surch **NATAL FLOOD DISASTER +10c**) 30 80

See also Nos. 629/30 and 635/6.

281 "Belshazzar's Feast" (Rembrandt)

1987. The Bible Society of South Africa. Multicoloured.

626 16c. "The Bible" in 75 languages (54 × 34 mm) 30 10
627 30c. Type **281** 45 60
628 50c. "St. Matthew and the Angel" (Rembrandt) (vert) 75 1·40

1987. Natal Flood Relief Fund (2nd issue). No. 626 surch.

629 16c.+10c. multicoloured (surch as No. 625) 45 70
630 16c.+10c. multicoloured (surch as No. 624) 45 70

282 Bartolomeu Dias and Cape of Good Hope

1988. 500th Anniv of Discovery of Cape of Good Hope by Bartolomeu Dias. Multicoloured.

631 16c. Type **282** 60 10
632 30c. Kwaaihoek Monument 80 85
633 40c. Caravels 1·40 1·50
634 50c. Martellus map, c. 1489 1·75 2·25

1988. Natal Flood Relief Fund (3rd issue). No. 631 surch.

635 16c.+10c. multicoloured (surch as No. 624) 45 70
636 16c.+10c. multicoloured (surch as No. 625) 45 70

283 Huguenot Monument, Franschhoek

1988. 300th Anniv of Arrival of First French Huguenots at the Cape. Multicoloured.

637 16c. Type **283** 30 10
638 30c. Map of France showing Huguenot areas 85 80
639 40c. Title page of French/Dutch New Testament of 1672 85 1·25
640 50c. St. Bartholomew's Day Massacre, Paris, 1572 1·10 1·50

1988. National Flood Relief Fund Nos. 637/40 surch in English (**National Flood Disaster +10c**) (E) or in Afrikaans (**Nasionale Vloedramp +10c**) (A).

641 16c.+10c. multicoloured (E) 40 65
642 16c.+10c. multicoloured (A) 40 65
643 30c.+10c. multicoloured (A) 55 75
644 30c.+10c. multicoloured (E) 55 75
645 40c.+10c. multicoloured (A) 70 90
646 40c.+10c. multicoloured (E) 70 90
647 50c.+10c. multicoloured (E) 90 1·25
648 50c.+10c. multicoloured (A) 90 1·25

285 Pelican Point Lighthouse, Walvis Bay

1988. Lighthouses. Multicoloured.

649 16c. Type **285** 50 10
650 30c. Green Point, Cape Town 70 70
651 40c. Cape Agulhas 90 1·25
652 50c. Umhlanga Rocks, Durban 1·25 1·75
MS653 132 × 112 mm. Nos. 649/52 4·50 4·25

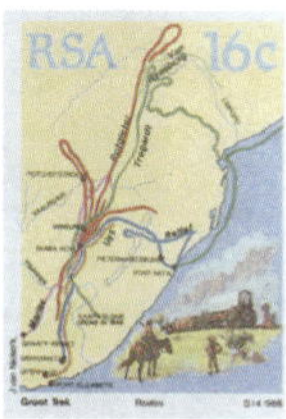

286 "Huernia zebrina"

287 Map of Great Trek Routes

1988. Succulents. Multicoloured.

654 1c. Type **286** 10 10
655 2c. "Euphorbia symmetrica" 10 10
656 5c. "Lithops dorotheae" 10 10
657 7c. "Gibbaeum nebrownii" 15 10
658 10c. "Didymaotus lapidiformis" 15 10
659 16c. "Vanheerdea divergens" 60 10
659a 18c. "Faucaria tigrina" 50 10
660 20c. "Conophytum mundum" 80 10
660a 21c. "Gasteria armstrongii" 40 10
661 25c. "Cheiridopsis peculiaris" 80 10
662 30c. "Tavaresia barklyi" 60 20
663 35c. "Dinteranthus wilmotianus" 1·00 20
664 40c. "Frithia pulchra" 1·00 25
665 50c. "Lapidaria margaretae" 1·00 25
666 90c. "Dioscorea elephantipes" 1·25 45
667 1r. "Trichocaulon cactiforme" 1·00 50
668 2r. "Crassula columnaris" 1·25 90
668a 5r. "Anacampseros albissima" 2·25 2·40

See also No. 778.

1988. Coil stamps. As T **286**. Multicoloured.

669 1c. "Adromischus marianiae" 1·00 1·50
670 2c. "Titanopsis calcarea" 50 60
671 5c. "Dactylopsis digitata" 50 60
672 10c. "Pleiospilos bolusii" 55 70

1988. 150th Anniv of Great Trek. Multicoloured.

673 16c. Type **287** 60 10
674 30c. "Exodus" (tapestry by W. Coetzer) (56 × 20 mm) 90 90
675 40c. "Crossing the Drakensberg" (tapestry by W. Coetzer) (77 × 20 mm) 1·10 1·10
676 50c. "After the Service, Church of the Vow" (J. H. Pierneef) (horiz) 1·40 1·75

288 Coelacanth

1989. 50th Anniv of Discovery of Coelacanth. Multicoloured.

677 16c. Type **288** 75 15
678 30c. Prof. J. L. B. Smith and Dr. M. Courtenay-Latimer examining Coelacanth 1·10 1·25
679 40c. J. L. B. Smith Institute of Ichthyology, Grahamstown 1·40 1·60
680 50c. Coelacanth and "GEO" midget submarine 1·50 2·25

289 Man-made Desert

1989. National Grazing Strategy. Multicoloured.

681 18c. Type **289** 40 15
682 30c. Formation of erosion gully 65 75
683 40c. Concrete barrage in gully 70 1·00
684 50c. Reclaimed veldt 80 1·40

290 South Africa v. France Match, 1980

1989. Cent of South African Rugby Board. Mult.

685 18c. Type **290** 80 15
686 30c. South Africa v. Australia, 1963 1·25 90
687 40c. South Africa v. New Zealand, 1937 1·40 1·50
688 50c. South Africa v. British Isles, 1896 1·40 2·00

291 "Composition in Blue"

292 Pres. F. W. de Klerk

1989. Paintings by Jacob Hendrik Pierneef. Multicoloured.

689 18c. Type **291** 45 15
690 30c. "Zanzibar" 70 60
691 40c. "The Bushveld" 90 1·10
692 50c. "Cape Homestead" 1·00 1·50
MS693 114 × 86 mm. Nos. 689/92 2·25 2·75

1989. Inaug of President F. W. de Klerk. Mult.

694 18c. Type **292** 50 15
695 45c. F. W. de Klerk (different) 75 1·40

293 Gas-drilling Rig, Mossel Bay

1989. Energy Sources. Multicoloured.

696 18c. Type **293** 40 10
697 30c. Coal to oil conversion plant 70 70
698 40c. Nuclear power station 80 85
699 50c. Thermal electric power station 90 1·25

294 Electric Goods Train and Map of Railway Routes

1990. Co-operation in Southern Africa. Mult.

700 18c. Cahora Bassa Hydro-electric Scheme, Mozambique, and map of transmission lines (68 × 26 mm) 70 25
701 30c. Type **294** 90 70
702 40c. Projected dam on upper Orange River, Lesotho, and map of Highlands Water Project (68 × 26 mm) 1·10 1·10
703 50c. Cow, syringe and outline map of Africa 1·40 1·25
MS704 136 × 78 mm. Nos. 700/3 3·25 2·75

295 Great Britain 1840 Penny Black
296 Green Turaco

1990. National Stamp Day. Multicoloured.
705 21c. Type **295** 40 50
706 21c. Cape of Good Hope 1853 4d. triangular pair . . 40 50
707 21c. Natal 1857 1s. 40 50
708 21c. Orange Free State 1868 1s. 40 50
709 21c. Transvaal 1869 1s. . . . 40 50

1990. Birds. Multicoloured.
710 21c. Type **296** 70 20
711 35c. Red-capped robin chat 90 80
712 40c. Rufous-naped bush lark 90 1·10
713 50c. Bokmakierie shrike . . . 1·25 1·50

297 Karoo Landscape near Britstown
298 Woltemade Cross for Bravery

1990. Tourism. Multicoloured.
714 50c. Type **297** . . . . 1·10 1·40
715 50c. Camps Bay, Cape of Good Hope . . . . 1·10 1·40
716 50c. Giraffes in Kruger National Park . . . . . . 1·10 1·40
717 50c. Boschendal Vineyard, Drakenstein Mts . . . . . 1·10 1·40

1990. National Orders. Multicoloured.
718 21c. Type **298** 50 60
719 21c. Order of the Southern Cross 50 60
720 21c. Order of the Star of South Africa 50 60
721 21c. Order for Meritorious Service 50 60
722 21c. Order of Good Hope . . 50 60
MS723 143 × 70 mm. Nos. 718/22 2·25 2·75

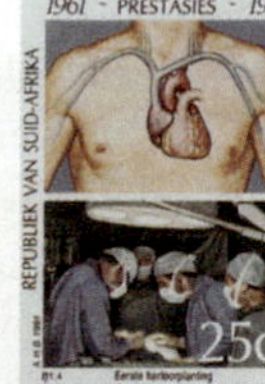

299 Boer Horses
300 Diagram of Human Heart and Transplant Operation

1991. Animal Breeding in South Africa. Mult.
724 21c. Type **299** 70 70
725 21c. Bonsmara bull 70 70
726 21c. Dorper sheep 70 70
727 21c. Ridgeback dogs 70 70
728 21c. Putterie racing pigeons 70 70

1991. 30th Anniv of Republic. Scientific and Technological Achievements. Multicoloured.
729 25c. Type **300** 20 10
730 40c. Matimba Power Station (horiz) 35 35
731 50c. Dolos design breakwater (horiz) 45 45
732 60c. Western Deep Levels gold mine 60 60

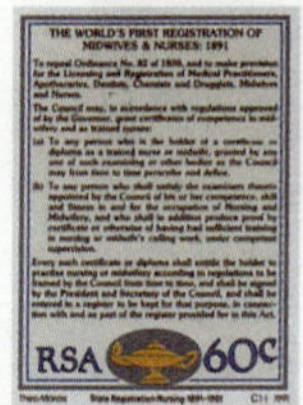

301 State Registration of Nurses Act, 1891
302 South Africa Post Office Ltd Emblem

1991. Centenary of State Registration for Nurses and Midwives.
733 **301** 60c. multicoloured 60 60

1991. Establishment of Post Office Ltd and Telekom Ltd. Multicoloured.
734 27c. Type **302** 50 50
735 27c. Telekom SA Ltd emblem 50 50

303 Sir Arnold Theiler (veterinarian)

1991. South African Scientists. Multicoloured.
736 27c. Type **303** 30 15
737 45c. Sir Basil Schonland (physicist) 60 60
738 65c. Dr. Robert Broom (palaeontologist) 80 90
739 85c. Dr. Alex du Toit (geologist) . . . . 1·00 1·75

304 "Agulhas" (Antarctic research ship)

1991. 30th Anniv of Antarctic Treaty. Mult.
740 27c. Type **304** . . . . 1·00 20
741 65c. Chart showing South African National Antarctic Expedition base . . . . . 1·50 80

305 Soil Conservation

1992. Environmental Conservation. Mult.
742 27c. Type **305** 50 15
743 65c. Water pollution . . . . 1·25 1·10
744 85c. Air pollution . . . . . 1·50 1·50

306 Dutch Fleet approaching Table Bay
307 Queen Anne Settee, c. 1750

1992. National Stamp Day. Cape of Good Hope Postal Stones. Multicoloured.
745 35c. Type **306** 60 60
746 35c. Landing for water and provisions 60 60
747 35c. Discovering a postal stone 60 60
748 35c. Leaving letters under a stone 60 60
749 35c. Reading letters 60 60

1992. Antique Cape Furniture. Multicoloured.
750 35c. Type **307** 50 50
751 35c. Stinkwood settee, c. 1800 50 50
752 35c. Canopy bed, c. 1800 (vert) 50 50
753 35c. 19th-century rocking cradle 50 50
754 35c. Water butt, c. 1800 (vert) 50 50
755 35c. Flemish style cabinet, c. 1700 (vert) . . . 50 50
756 35c. Armoire, c. 1780 (vert) 50 50
757 35c. Late 17th-century church chair (vert) 50 50
758 35c. Tub chair, c. 1770 (vert) 50 50
759 35c. Bible desk, c. 1750 (vert) 50 50

308 Grand Prix Motor Racing
309 "Women's Monument" (Van Wouw)

1992. Sports. Multicoloured.
760 35c. Type **308** 25 25
761 35c. Football 25 25
762 55c. Total Paris–Cape Motor Rally 35 35
763 70c. Athletics 50 50
764 90c. Rugby 65 65
765 1r.05 Cricket . . . . 1·00 1·00
MS766 167 × 69 mm. Nos. 760/5 3·25 3·00

1992. 130th Birth Anniv of Anton van Wouw (sculptor). Multicoloured.
767 35c. Type **309** 40 20
768 70c. "Sekupu Player" 80 60
769 90c. "The Hunter" . . . . . 1·00 80
770 1r.05 "Postman Lehman" . . 1·10 1·00
MS771 96 × 149 mm. Nos. 767/70 2·75 2·40

310 Walvis Bay Harbour
311 Bristol "Boxkite", 1907

1993. South African Harbours. Multicoloured.
772 35c. Type **310** 35 20
773 55c. East London 45 35
774 70c. Port Elizabeth 70 50
775 90c. Cape Town 90 75
776 1r.05 Durban 95 95
MS777 147 × 112 mm. Nos. 772/6 2·75 2·50

1993. Succulents. As T **286**, but inscr "Standardised mail" in English and Afrikaans.
778 (–) "Stapelia grandiflora" . . 60 10
No. 778 was sold at 45c.

1993. Aviation in South Africa. Multicoloured.
779 45c. Type **311** 65 60
780 45c. Voisin "Boxkite", 1909 65 60
781 45c. Bleriot XI, 1911 . . . . 65 60
782 45c. Paterson No. 2 biplane, 1913 . . . . 65 60
783 45c. Henri Farman H.F.27, 1915 . . . . 65 60
784 45c. Royal Aircraft Factory B.E.2.E, 1918 . . . . . . 65 60
785 45c. Vickers Vimy "Silver Queen II", 1920 . . . . . 65 60
786 45c. Royal Aircraft Factory S.E.5.A, 1921 . . . . . . 65 60
787 45c. Avro 504k, 1921 . . . . 65 60
788 45c. Armstrong Whitworth Atalanta, 1930 . . . . . 65 60
789 45c. De Havilland D.H.66 Hercules, 1931 . . . . . 65 60
790 45c. Westland Wapiti, 1931 65 60
791 45c. Junkers F-13, 1932 . . . 65 60
792 45c. Handley Page H.P.42, 1933 . . . . 65 60
793 45c. Junkers Ju 52/3m, 1934 65 60
794 45c. Junkers Ju 86, 1936 . . 65 60
795 45c. Hawker Hartbees, 1936 65 60
796 45c. Short Empire "C" Class flying boat "Canopus", 1937 . . . . 65 60
797 45c. Miles Master II and Airspeed A.S 10 Oxford, 1940 . . . . 65 60
798 45c. North American Harvard Mk IIa, 1942 . . 65 60
799 45c. Short Sunderland flying boat, 1945 . . . . 65 60
800 45c. Avro Type 685 York, 1946 . . . . 65 60
801 45c. Douglas DC-7B, 1955 . 65 60
802 45c. Sikorsky S-55c helicopter, 1956 . . . . . 65 60
803 45c. Boeing 707-344, 1959 . . 65 60

312 Table Mountain Ghost Frog
313 Dragoons carrying Mail between Cape Town and False Bay, 1803

1993. Endangered Fauna. Multicoloured. (a) Face values as T **312**.
804 1c. Type **312** (I) 10 10
804c 1c. Type **312** (II) 20 20
805 2c. Smith's dwarf chameleon (I) 10 10
805c 2c. Smith's dwarf chameleon (II) 20 20
806 5c. Giant girdle-tailed lizard (I) 10 10
807 10c. Geometric tortoise (I) . 10 10
807c 10c. Geometric tortoise (II) 30 30
808 20c. Southern African hedgehog (I) 10 10
913 20c. Southern African hedgehog (II) 10 10
809 40c. Riverine rabbit (I) . . . 20 10
809c 40c. Riverine rabbit (II) . . 20 10
810 50c. Samango monkey (I) . 25 20
914 50c. Samango monkey (II) . 25 10
811 55c. Aardwolf (I) 20 10
811c 55c. Aardwolf (II) 30 30
812 60c. Cape hunting dog (I) . 40 20
915 60c. Cape hunting dog (II) . 30 10
813 70c. Roan antelope (I) . . . 40 25
813c 70c. Roan antelope (II) . . 30 20
814 75c. African striped weasel (I) 30 20
815 80c. Kori bustard (I) . . . 75 25
815a 85c. Lemon-breasted seedeater (I) 75 25
816 90c. Jackass penguin (I) . . 80 30
816c 90c. Jackass penguin (II) . . 70 30
817 1r. Wattled crane (I) 80 30
916 1r. Wattled crane (II) . . . 65 25
818 2r. Blue swallow (I) . . . . 1·00 55
818c 2r. Blue swallow (II) . . . . 1·00 55
819 5r. Martial eagle (I) . . . . 2·00 1·40
819c 5r. Martial eagle (II) . . . . 1·75 1·40

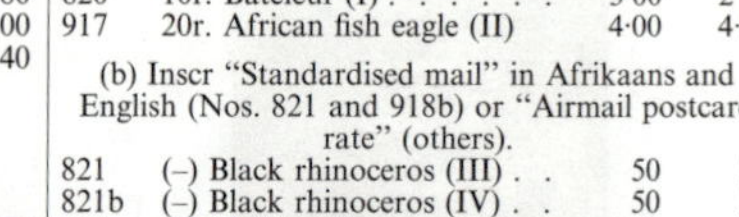

820 10r. Bateleur (I) . . . . . . 3·00 2·10
917 20r. African fish eagle (II) 4·00 4·25

(b) Inscr "Standardised mail" in Afrikaans and English (Nos. 821 and 918b) or "Airmail postcard rate" (others).
821 (–) Black rhinoceros (III) . . 50 25
821b (–) Black rhinoceros (IV) . . 50 35
821c (1r.) White rhinoceros (II) 50 30
821d (1r.) Buffalo (II) 50 30
821e (1r.) Lion (II) 50 30
821f (1r.) Leopard (II) 50 30
821g (1r.) African elephant (II) 50 30

I and III. Species name in Latin. II and IV. Species name in English, No. 821 has a small rhinoceros and No. 821b a larger rhinoceros; they were sold at 45c. at first but this was later increased to the prevailing rates.

For redrawn designs without frame and inscribed "South Africa" only, see Nos. 1029/44.

1993. National Stamp Day. Early 19th-century Postal Services. Multicoloured.
822 45c. Type **313** 30 25
823 65c. Ox wagon carrying Stellenbosch to Cape Town mail, 1803 . . . . 45 50
824 85c. Khoi-Khoin mail runners from Stellenbosch, 1803 . . . . 65 70
825 1r.05 Mounted postmen, 1804 80 90

314 Flowers from Namaqualand

1993. Tourism. Multicoloured.
826 85c. Type **314** (Afrikaans inscr) 65 70
827 85c. North Beach, Durban (English inscr) 65 70
828 85c. Lion (German inscr) . . 65 70
829 85c. "Appel Express" on Van Staden's Bridge (Dutch inscr) 65 70
830 85c. Gemsbok (antelope) (French inscr) 65 70

315 Grapes and Packing Bench

1994. Export Fruits. Multicoloured.
831 85c. Type **315** 55 50
832 90c. Apple and picker . . . 55 50
833 1r.05 Plum and fork-lift truck 65 60
834 1r.25 Orange and tractor with trailer 75 70
835 1r.40 Avocado and loading freighter 85 80

316 "Children of Different Races" (Nicole Davies)

1994. Peace Campaign. Children's Paintings. Multicoloured.
836 45c. Type **316** 25 20
837 70c. "Dove and Tree" (Robynne Lawrie) 40 40
838 95c. "Children and Dove" (Batami Nothmann) . . . 55 55
839 1r.15 "Multi-racial Crowd" (Karen Uys) 75 80

317 Pres. Mandela

1994. Inaug of President Nelson Mandela. Mult.
840 45c. Type **317** 45 20
841 70c. South African national anthems 80 60
842 95c. New national flag . . . 1·10 1·40
843 1r.15 Union Buildings, Pretoria . . . . 1·25 1·75

318 Tug "T.S. McEwen" towing "Winchester Castle" (liner), 1935

1994. Tugboats. Multicoloured.

844	45c. Type **318**	30	20
845	70c. "Sir William Hoy" with "Karanja" (liner), 1970	50	40
846	95c. "Sir Charles Elliott" and wreck of "Dunedin Star" (liner), 1942	65	55
847	1r.15 "Eland" and freighter at wharf, 1955	85	75
848	1r.35 "Pioneer" (paddle tug) and sailing ships, 1870	95	90
MS849	163 × 84 mm. Nos. 844/8	2·75	2·50

319 "Mother hands out Work" (Emile du Toit)

1994. International Year of the Family. Children's Paintings. Multicoloured.

850	45c. Type **319**	45	45
851	45c. "My Friends and I at Play" (Patrick Mackenzie)	45	45
852	45c. "Family Life" (Michelle du Pisani)	45	45
853	45c. "Sunday in Church" (Elizabeth Nel)	45	45
854	45c. "I visit my Brother in Hospital" (Zwelinzema Sam)	45	45

320 Hands holding Invoice and Bulk Mail Envelope

1994. National Stamp Day. Multicoloured.

855	50c. Type **320**	30	25
856	70c. Certified mail	40	40
857	95c. Registered mail	50	55
858	1r.15 Express Delivery mail	60	65

321 "Erica tenuifolia"

1994. Heathers. Multicoloured.

859	95c. Type **321**	65	65
860	95c. "Erica urna-viridis"	65	65
861	95c. "Erica decora"	65	65
862	95c. "Erica aristata"	65	65
863	95c. "Erica dichrus"	65	65

322 Warthogs (Eastern Transvaal) and Map (⅔-size illustration)

1995. Tourism. Multicoloured. (a) With face value.

864	50c. Type **322**	50	25
865	50c. Lost City resort (North-West Province)	50	25

(b) Inscr "Standardised mail" in English and Afrikaans

866	(60c.) White rhinoceros and calf (KwaZulu/Natal)	50	25
867	(60c.) Cape Town waterfront (Western Cape)	50	25
868	(60c.) Baobab tree (Northern Transvaal)	50	40
869	(60c.) Highland Route (Free State)	50	40
870	(60c.) Augrabies Falls (Northern Cape)	50	40
871	(60c.) Herd of elephants, Addo National Park (Eastern Cape)	50	40
872	(60c.) Union Buildings, Pretoria (Gauteng)	50	40

323 De Havilland D.H.9 Biplane and Cheetah D Jet Fighter

1995. Aviation Anniversaries. Multicoloured.

873	50c. Type **323** (75th anniv of South African Air Force)	55	30
874	95c. Vickers Vimy "Silver Queen II" (75th anniv of first Trans-African flight)	80	75

324 Player running with Ball and Silhouettes

1995. World Cup Rugby Championship, South Africa. Multicoloured.

875	(60c.) Type **324**	30	25
876	(60c.) Player running with ball and silhouettes (vert)	30	25
877	1r.15 Player taking ball from scrum (68 × 26½ mm)	75	85
MS878	109 × 61 mm. No. 876	75	75

Nos. 875/6 are inscribed "STANDARD POSTAGE" in English and Afrikaans.

325 Rural Water Purification System

1995. 50th Anniv of C.S.I.R. (technological research organization).

879	**325** (60c.) multicoloured	45	45

No. 879 is inscribed "Standardised mail" in English and Afrikaans.

326 Player with Ball

1995. South Africa's Victory in Rugby World Cup. Multicoloured.

880	(60c.) Type **326**	40	40
881	(60c.) South African player holding trophy aloft (vert)	40	40

Nos. 880/1 are inscribed "STANDARD POSTAGE" in English and Afrikaans.

327 Dr. John Gilchrist, South African Pilchards and "Africana" (oceanographic research ship)

328 Singapore Lion

1995. Centenary of Marine Science in South Africa.

882	**327** (60c.) multicoloured	30	30

No. 882 is inscribed "Standard Postage" in English and Afrikaans.

1995. "Singapore '95" International Stamp Exhibition. Sheet 71 × 55 mm.

MS883	**328** (60c.) multicoloured	75	1·00

No. **MS**883 is inscribed "STANDARD POSTAGE" in English and Afrikaans.

329 People building Flag Wall

1995. Masakhane Campaign.

884	**329** (60c.) multicoloured (34 × 24 mm)	20	20
884b	(60c.) multicoloured (26 × 20 mm)	20	20

Nos. 884 and 884b are inscribed "STANDARD POSTAGE" in English and Afrikaans.

330 Papal Arms

1995. Visit of Pope John Paul II.

885	**330** (60c.) multicoloured	55	30

No. 885 is inscribed "STANDARD POSTAGE" in English and Afrikaans.

331 Gandhi wearing Suit

332 Traditional African Postman

1995. 125th Birth Anniv (1994) of Mahatma Gandhi.

886	**331** (60c.) violet	65	25
887	– 1r.40 brown	85	85
MS888	71 × 71 mm. No. 887	1·25	1·40

DESIGN: 1r.40, Gandhi wearing dhoti.

No. 886 is inscribed "STANDARD POSTAGE" in English and Afrikaans.

1995. World Post Day.

889	**332** (60c.) multicoloured	30	30

No. 889 is inscribed "STANDARD POSTAGE" in English and Afrikaans.

1995. "Total Stampex '95" and "Ilsapex '98" Stamp Exhibitions. Sheet, 70 × 66 mm, containing T **332** and "ILSAPEX '98" logo. Imperf.

MS890	5r. multicoloured	2·00	2·25

333 "50" and U.N. Emblem

334 "Afrivoluta pringlei"

1995. 50th Annivs of United Nations and U.N.E.S.C.O. Multicoloured.

891	**333** (60c.) multicoloured	30	30
MS892	101 × 78 mm. (60c.) Traditional village (30 × 47 mm)	30	30

No. 891 is inscribed "STANDARD POSTAGE" in English and Afrikaans.

1995. Sea Shells. Multicoloured.

893	(60c.) Type **334**	35	35
894	(60c.) "Lyria africana"	35	35
895	(60c.) "Marginella mosaica"	35	35
896	(60c.) "Conus pictus"	35	35
897	(60c.) "Gypreaea fultoni"	35	35

Nos. 893/7 are inscribed "STANDARD POSTAGE" in English and Afrikaans.

No. 893 is inscribed "priglei" in error.

335 Map of Africa and Player

336 South African Player, Map and Trophy

1996. African Nations Football Championship, South Africa. Map and Players.

898	**335** (60c.) multicoloured ("RSA" in blue)	55	55
899	– (60c.) multicoloured ("RSA" in brown)	55	55
900	– (60c.) multicoloured ("RSA" in red)	55	55
901	– (60c.) multicoloured ("RSA" in grey)	55	55
902	– (60c.) multicoloured ("RSA" in green)	55	55
MS903	75 × 55 mm. (60c.) multicoloured (young player)	50	60

Nos. 898/903 are inscribed "STANDARD POSTAGE" in English and Afrikaans.

1996. South Africa's Victory in African Nations Football Championship.

904	**336** (60c.) multicoloured	40	30

No. 904 is inscribed "STANDARD POSTAGE" in English and Afrikaans.

337 Historical Buildings, Bloemfontein

1996. 150th Anniv of City of Bloemfontein.

905	**337** (60c.) multicoloured	50	20

No. 905 is inscribed "Standard Postage" in English and Afrikaans.

338 Rat

1996. "CHINA '96" 9th Asian International Stamp Exhibition, Peking. Sheet 109 × 85 mm.

MS906	**338** 60c. multicoloured	50	50

339 "Man in a Donkey Cart" (Gerard Sekoto)

1996. Gerard Sekoto (artist) Commemoration. Multicoloured.

907	1r. Type **339**	30	30
908	2r. "Song of the Pick"	80	80
MS909	108 × 70 mm. 2r. "Yellow Houses, Sophiatown" (detail) (vert)	1·00	1·10

340 Parliament Building, Cape Town

1996. "CAPEX '96" International Stamp Exhibition, Toronto. Sheet 72 × 49 mm.

MS910	**340** 2r. multicoloured	1·00	1·10

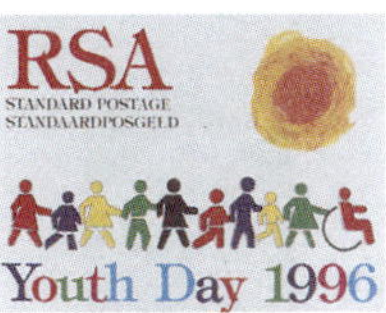

341 Children playing

1996. Youth Day.

911	**341** (60c.) multicoloured	30	20

No. 911 is inscribed "STANDARD POSTAGE" in English and Afrikaans.

342 Marathon Runners

1996. 75th Anniv of Comrades Marathon.
912 **342** (60c.) multicoloured . . . 30 20
No. 912 is inscribed "Standard postage" in English and Afrikaans.

343 Cycling

344 Constitutional Assembly Logo

1996. Olympic Games, Atlanta. Multicoloured.
919 (70c.) Type **343** 30 30
920 (70c.) Swimming 30 30
921 (70c.) Boxing 30 30
922 (70c.) Running 30 30
923 (70c.) Pole vaulting 30 30
924 1r.40 South African Olympic emblem 55 55
Nos. 919/24 are inscribed "STANDARD POSTAGE" in English and Afrikaans.

1996. New Democratic Constitution.
925 **344** (70c.) green, red and black 30 30
926 (70c.) blue, violet, and black 30 30
927 (70c.) violet, yellow and black 30 30
928 (70c.) blue, red and black 30 30
929 (70c.) red, yellow and black 30 30
Nos. 925/9 are inscribed "Standard Postage" in English and Afrikaans.

345 "Sea Pioneer" (bulk carrier)

1996. 50th Anniv of South African Merchant Marine. Multicoloured.
930 (70c.) Type **345** 75 65
931 (70c.) "Winterberg" (container ship) 75 65
932 1r.40 "Langkloof" (freighter) 1·10 95
933 1r.40 "Vaal" (liner) . . . . 1·10 95
MS934 102 × 63 mm. 2r. "Constantia" (freighter) and tug (71 × 30 mm) (inscr "SOUTH AFRICAN MERCHANT MARINE 1946–1996" on top margin) . . . . 1·00 1·00
No. **MS**934 also comes with the top margin inscription replaced by "Safmarine" and logo.
Nos. 930/1 are inscribed "Standard Postage" in English and Afrikaans.

346 "Xhosa Woman" (G. Pemba)

347 Postman delivering Letters

1996. National Women's Day.
935 **346** 70c. multicoloured 30 25

1996. World Post Day.
936 **347** 70c. multicoloured 30 25

348 Candles and Holly

1996. Christmas.
937 **348** 70c. multicoloured 30 25

349 "Liner "Oranje" at cape Town" (E. Wale) (⅔-size illustration)

1996. "Bloemfontein 150" National Stamp Show. Sheet 86 × 56 mm.
MS938 **349** 2r. multicoloured . . 1·25 1·25

350 Max Theiler (Medicine, 1951)

352 Lion

351 Early Motor Car

1996. South African Nobel Laureates.
939 **350** (70c.) violet and purple 45 45
940 – (70c.) green, purple and violet 45 45
941 – (70c.) purple and violet 45 45
942 – (70c.) green, purple and violet 45 45
943 – (70c.) violet and purple 45 45
944 – (70c.) violet and purple 45 45
945 – (70c.) green, purple and violet 45 45
946 – (70c.) purple and violet 45 45
947 – (70c.) green, purple and violet 45 45
948 – (70c.) violet and purple 45 45
DESIGNS: No. 940, Albert Luthuli (Peace, 1961); 941, Alfred Nobel; 942, Allan Cormack (Medicine, 1979); 943, Aaron Klug (Chemistry, 1982); 944, Desmond Tutu (Peace, 1984); 945, Nadine Gordimer (Literature, 1991); 946, Nobel Prizes symbol; 947, Nelson Mandela (Peace, 1993); 948, F. W. de Klerk (Peace, 1993).
Nos. 939/48 are inscribed "Standard Postage" in English and Afrikaans.

1997. Centenary of Motoring in South Africa.
949 **351** (70c.) multicoloured . . . 55 25
No. 949 is inscribed "STANDARD POSTAGE" in English and Afrikaans.

1997. "Hong Kong '97" International Stamp Exhibition. Sheet 82 × 68 mm.
MS950 **352** 3r. blue, gold and red 1·10 1·10

353 Vegetables and Water Pump

355 Election Day Poster

354 S.A.S. "Umkomaas" (minesweeper)

1997. National Water Conservation. Multicoloured.
951 (70c.) Type **353** 40 30
952 (70c.) Flowers and watering can 40 40
953 (70c.) Child in bath 40 40
954 (70c.) Building tools 40 40
955 (70c.) Water cart and stand pipe 40 40
Nos. 951/5 are inscribed "STANDARD POSTAGE".

1997. 75th Anniv of South African Navy. Multicoloured.
956 (70c.) Type **354** 60 60
957 (70c.) S.A.S. "Emily Hobhouse" (submarine) and S.A.S. "President Steyn" (frigate) 60 60
958 (70c.) S.A.S. "Kobie Coetsee" (fast attack craft) 60 60
959 (70c.) S.A.S. "Protea" (hydrographic survey ship) 60 60
Nos. 956/9 are inscribed "Standard Postage" in English and Afrikaans.

1997. Freedom Day. Each black and red.
960 (1r.) Type **355** 40 40
961 (1r.) People queueing 40 40
962 (1r.) People registering . . . 40 40
963 (1r.) Voting booth 40 40
964 (1r.) Woman placing vote in ballot box 40 40
Nos. 960/4, which are inscribed "STANDARD POSTAGE", were printed together, se-tenant, forming a composite design.

356 Brahman Bull

1997. Chinese New Year ("Year of the Ox"). "SAPDA '97" Stamp Exhibition, Johannesburg. Sheet 107 × 61 mm.
MS965 **356** 4r.50 multicoloured 1·00 1·00

357 Zulu Baskets

359 White-breasted Cormorant

358 Grocott's, Muirhead and Gowie Buildings, Grahamstown

1997. Year of Cultural Experiences. Multicoloured.
966 (1r.) Type **357** 40 40
967 (1r.) Southern Sotho figure 40 40
968 (1r.) South Ndebele figure . . 40 40
969 (1r.) Venda door 40 40
970 (1r.) Tsonga medicine gourd 40 40
971 (1r.) Wooden pot, Northern Cape 40 40
972 (1r.) Khoi walking stick . . . 40 40
973 (1r.) Tswana knife handle . . 40 40
974 (1r.) Xhosa pipe 40 40
975 (1r.) Swazi vessel 40 40
Nos. 966/75 are inscribed "Standard Postage".

1997. "Pacific '97" International Stamp Exhibition, San Francisco. Sheet 94 × 49 mm.
MS976 **358** 5r. multicoloured . . 1·25 1·25

1997. World Environment Day. Waterbirds. Multicoloured.
977 (1r.) Type **359** 40 40
978 (1r.) Hamerkop 40 40
979 (1r.) Lesser pied kingfisher ("Pied Kingfisher") 40 40
980 (1r.) Purple heron 40 40
981 (1r.) Black-headed heron . . 40 40
982 (1r.) African darter ("Darter") 40 40
983 (1r.) Green-backed heron . . 40 40
984 (1r.) White-face whistling duck ("White-faced Duck") 40 40
985 (1r.) Saddle-billed stork . . . 40 40
986 (1r.) Water dikkop 40 40
Nos. 977/86 are inscribed "STANDARD POSTAGE".

360 Double-headed Class 6E 1 Electric Locomotives

1997. Inaurguration of Revived Blue Train Service. Multicoloured.
987 (1r.20) Type **360** 70 70
988 (1r.20) Double-headed Class 6E 1 electric locomotives (different) 70 70
989 (1r.20) Double-headed Class 25NC steam locomotives, 1960s 70 70
990 (1r.20) Double-headed Class 34,900 diesel locomotives on Modder River bridge 70 70
991 (1r.20) Double-headed Class 34 diesel locomotives and baobab tree 70 70
Nos. 987/91 are inscribed "AIRMAIL POSTAGE RATE".

361 Nguni Breed

1997. Cattle Breeds. Multicoloured.
992 (1r.) Type **361** 50 50
993 (1r.) Bonsmara 50 50
994 (1r.) Afrikander 50 50
995 (1r.) Drakensberger 50 50
Nos. 992/5 are inscribed "Standard Postage" in English and Afrikaans.

362 Leopard Seal

1997. Antarctic Fauna. Multicoloured.
996 (1r.) Type **362** 35 25
997 1r.20 Antarctic skua 65 40
998 1r.70 King penguin . . . . . 1·00 70
No. 996 is inscribed "Standard Postage" in English and Afrikaans.

363 Enoch Sontonga and Verse from "Nkosi Sikelel'i Afrika"

1997. Heritage Day. Centenary of "Nkosi Sikele'i Afrika" (National Anthem). Multicoloured.
999 (1r.) Type **363** 50 50
1000 (1r.) As Type **363** but portrait at right 50 50
Nos. 999/1000 are inscribed "Standard Postage".

364 Horse-drawn Postcart delivering Mail

1997. "Cape Town '97" National Stamp Show. Sheet 85 × 64 mm.
MS1001 **364** 4r.50 multicoloured 1·25 1·25

365 Modern Postbox

366 Bethlehem

1997. World Post Day. Sheet, 108 × 69 mm.
MS1002 **365** (1 r.) multicoloured 50 50
No. **MS**1002 is inscribed "STANDARD POSTAGE".

1997. Christmas. 50th Anniv of S.A.N.T.A. (South African National Tuberculosis Association). Charity Labels. Multicoloured.
1003 (1r.) Type **366** 35 35
1004 (1r.) Cross of Lorraine and candles 35 35
1005 (1r.) Cross of Lorraine, angels and candles . . . 35 35
1006 (1r.) Angel kneeling before Cross of Lorraine . . . 35 35
1007 (1r.) Father Christmas carrying sack 35 35
1008 (1r.) Mary and Jesus 35 35
1009 (1r.) Christmas trees 35 35
1010 (1r.) Wise men on camels . . 35 35
1011 (1r.) Christmas bell 35 35
1012 (1r.) Child kneeling 35 35
Nos. 1003/12 are inscribed "STANDARD POSTAGE".

367 Black Rhinoceros 368 Tiger (woodcut)

1997. Endangered Fauna (3rd series). Redrawn values as 1993–97 issue and new designs (Nos. 1030/4), all without frame and inscr "South Africa" only as T **367**. Multicoloured. (a) Designs as Nos. 806/20, and some new values, redrawn.

1012a	5c. Giant girdle-tailed lizard	10	20
1013	10c. Geometric tortoise	10	20
1014	20c. Southern African hedgehog	10	20
1015	30c. Spotted hyena	10	20
1016	40c. Riverine rabbit	15	20
1017	50c. Samango monkey	15	10
1018	60c. Cape hunting dog	20	15
1019	70c. Roan antelope	20	20
1020	80c. Kori bustard	1·00	20
1021	90c. Jackass penguin	1·10	25
1022	1r. Wattled crane	1·00	25
1022a	1r.50 Tawny eagle (20 × 37 mm)	1·50	30
1023	2r. Blue swallow	1·25	45
1023a	2r.30 Cape vulture (20 × 37 mm)	1·50	45
1024	3r. Giraffe	1·75	65
1025	5r. Martial eagle	1·75	1·10
1026	10r. Bateleur (34 × 24 mm)	2·50	2·25
1028	20r. African fish eagle ("Fish Eagle") (34 × 24 mm)	4·50	4·25

(b) Inscr "Standard Postage" (No. 1029) or "standard postage" (others).

1029	(1r.) Type **367**	30	25
1030	(1r.) Eland (vert)	30	25
1031	(1r.10) Greater kudu (vert)	30	25
1032	(1r.10) Impala (vert)	30	25
1033	(1r.10) Waterbuck (vert)	30	25
1034	(1r.10) Blue wildebeest (vert)	30	25

(d) Inscr "Airmail Postcard".

1040	(1r.20) White rhinoceros	40	50
1041	(1r.20) Buffalo	40	50
1042	(1r.20) Lion	40	50
1043	(1r.20) Leopard	40	50
1044	(1r.20) African elephant	40	50

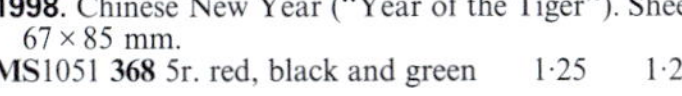

1998. Chinese New Year ("Year of the Tiger"). Sheet 67 × 85 mm.
MS1051 **368** 5r. red, black and green   1·25   1·25

369 "Rescue 8" (lifeboat)

1998. 30th Anniv (1997) of National Sea Rescue Institute.
1052 **369** (1r.) multicoloured   50   30

370 Leopard 371 Football Player

1998. "SAPDA '98" National Stamp Exhibition, Johannesburg. sheet 64 × 84 mm.
MS1053 **370** 5r. multicoloured   1·25   1·25

1998. World Cup Football Championship, France.
1054 **371** (1r.10) multicoloured   40   25
No. 1054 is inscribed "STANDARD POSTAGE".

372 Stone Age Hand Axe 373 Pale Chanting Goshawk

1998. Early South African History. Multicoloured.

1055	(1r.10) Type **372**	40	40
1056	(1r.10) Musuku (altar)	40	40
1057	(1r.10) San rock engravings	40	40
1058	(1r.10) Early iron age pot	40	40
1059	(1r.10) Khoekhoe pot	40	40
1060	(1r.10) Florisbad skull	40	40
1061	(1r.10) San rock painting	40	40
1062	(1r.10) Mapungubwe gold rhinoceros and pot	40	40
1063	(1r.10) Lydenburg head (ceremonial mask)	40	40
1064	(1r.10) Taung skull	40	40

Nos. 1055/64 are inscribed "standard postage".

1998. South African Raptors. Multicoloured.

1065	(1r.10) Type **373**	50	50
1066	(1r.10) Augur buzzard ("Jackal Buzzard")	50	50
1067	(1r.10) Lanner falcon	50	50
1068	(1r.10) Lammergeier ("Bearded Vulture")	50	50
1069	(1r.10) Black harrier	50	50
1070	(1r.10) Cape vulture	50	50
1071	(1r.10) Bateleur	50	50
1072	(1r.10) Spotted eagle owl	50	50
1073	(1r.10) White-headed vulture	50	50
1074	(1r.10) African fish eagle	50	50

Nos. 1065/74 are inscribed "standard postage".

1998. Endangered Fauna. Antelopes. Designs as Nos. 1030/4, but self-adhesive.

1075	(1r.10) Eland (vert)	50	50
1076	(1r.10) Greater kudu (vert)	50	50
1077	(1r.10) Impala (vert)	50	50
1078	(1r.10) Waterbuck (vert)	50	50
1079	(1r.10) Blue wildebeest (vert)	50	50

The above are inscribed "standard postage".

374 Shepherd's Tree

1998. Trees. Multicoloured.

1080	(1r.10) Type **374**	60	60
1081	(1r.10) Karee	60	60
1082	(1r.10) Baobab	60	60
1083	(1r.10) Umbrella thorn	60	60

Nos. 1080/3 are inscribed "Standard Postage".

375 Sandstone Cliffs, Cape Point

1998. "Explore South Africa" (1st series). Multicoloured. (a) Western Cape.

1084	(1r.30) Type **375**	80	65
1085	(1r.30) Robben Island	80	65
1086	(1r.30) Ostrich farming, Pinehurst Homestead	80	65
1087	(1r.30) Victoria and Alfred Waterfront, Capetown	80	65
1088	(1r.30) Homestead, Boschendal Wine Estate	80	65

(b) KwaZulu-Natal.

1089	(1r.30) Drakensberg waterfall	80	65
1090	(1r.30) Zulu women preparing food	80	65
1091	(1r.30) Eastern white pelicans and rhinoceros	80	65
1092	(1r.30) Rickshaw driver	80	65
1093	(1r.30) Indian dancers	80	65

Nos. 1084/8 and 1089/93 are inscribed "AIRMAIL POSTCARD".
See also Nos. 1338/42.

376 Angel 377 African Harrier Hawk

1998. Christmas. Multicoloured.

1094	(1r.10) Type **376**	60	60
1095	(1r.10) Christmas bell	60	60
1096	(1r.10) Present	60	60
1097	(1r.10) Christmas tree	60	60
1098	(1r.10) Star	60	60

Nos. 1094/8 are inscribed "STANDARD POSTAGE".

1998. World Post Day. Sheet 67 × 85 mm.
MS1099 **377** 5r. multicoloured   1·25   1·25

378 London Pictorial Essay, 1927 380 Emblem and Building

379 Cuvier's Beaked Whale

1998. "ILSAPEX '98" International Stamp Exhibition, Johannesburg. Sheet, 108 × 80 mm, containing T **378** and similar vert design.
MS1100 5r. green, red and cream (Type **378**); 5r. black, green and cream (as Type **378**, but "SOUTH AFRICA" at top)   2·00   2·25

1998. Endangered Species. Whales of the Southern Ocean. Multicoloured.

1101	(1r.30) Type **379**	75	55
1102	(1r.30) Minke whale	75	55
1103	(1r.30) Bryde's whale	75	55
1104	(1r.30) Pygmy right whale	75	55
MS1105	103 × 68 mm. 5r. Blue whale	1·50	1·50

Nos. 1101/4 are inscribed "airmail postcard".
No. **MS**1105 forms part of joint issue with Namibia and Norfolk Island.

1998. 50th Anniv of Universal Declaration of Human Rights.
1106 **380** (1r.10) multicoloured   55   35
No. 1106 is inscribed "Standard Postage".

381 Dennis Mail Van, 1913

1999. 125th Anniv of Universal Postal Union. Multicoloured.

1107	(1r.10) Type **381**	60	45
1108	(1r.10) Ford V8 post van, 1935	60	45
1109	(1r.10) Mobile Post Office, 1937	60	45
1110	(1r.10) Trojan Post Office van, 1927	60	45

Nos. 1107/10 are inscribed "Standard Postage".

382 Rabbit

1999. Chinese New Year ("Year of the Rabbit"). Sheet 85 × 67 mm.
MS1111 **382** 5r. multicoloured   1·25   1·25

383 "Discovery" (Scott)

1999. Famous Ships. Multicoloured.

1112	(1r.10) Type **383**	55	45
1113	(1r.10) "Heemskerk" (Tasman)	55	45
1114	(1r.10) H.M.S. "Endeavour" (Cook)	55	45
1115	(1r.10) H.M.S. "Beagle" (Darwin)	55	45

Nos. 1112/15 are inscribed "standard postage".

384 "Lawhill" (barque) 385 Traditional Nguni Love Token with AIDS Ribbon

1999. "Australia '99" International Stamp Exhibition, Melbourne. Sheet 65 × 85 mm.
MS1116 **384** 5r. multicoloured   1·25   1·25

1999. AIDS Awareness Campaign.

1117	**385** (1r.20) multicoloured (violet background)	50	50
1118	(1r.20) multicoloured (green background)	50	50

Nos. 1117/18 are inscribed "Standard Postage".

386 African Elephant

1999. "iBRA '99" International Stamp Exhibition, Nuremburg. Sheet 100 × 68 mm.
MS1119 **386** 5r. multicoloured   1·40   1·25

387 Class 19D Steam Locomotive, South African Railways 388 Nurse

1999. "SAPDA '99" Stamp Show, Johannesburg. Sheet 100 × 75 mm.
MS1120 **387** 5r. multicoloured   1·25   1·25

1999. Workers' Day. Multicoloured.

1121	(1r.20) Type **388**	45	45
1122	(1r.20) Cleaner with mop	45	45
1123	(1r.20) Forester with axe	45	45
1124	(1r.20) Farmer with spade	45	45
1125	(1r.20) Chef with sieve	45	45
1126	(1r.20) Fisherman with net	45	45
1127	(1r.20) Construction worker with scaffolding	45	45
1128	(1r.20) Miner with pick	45	45
1129	(1r.20) Postman with mail	45	45
1130	(1r.20) Road worker with pneumatic drill	45	45

389 President Thabo Mbeki 390 Nelson Mandela in Mantle of Order

1999. Inauguration of President Thabo Mbeki.
1131 **389** (1r.20) multicoloured   60   35
No. 1131 is inscribed "standard postage".

1999. 900th Anniv of Order of St. John of Jerusalem. sheet 108 × 68 mm.
MS1132 **390** 2r. multicoloured   75   75

391 Actress with Drama Masks

392 North Ndebele Wall Pattern

1999. 25th Anniv of Standard Bank National Arts Festival. Multicoloured.

1133 (1r.20) Type **391** 55 55
1134 (1r.20) Woman with roll of film 55 55
1135 (1r.20) Woman playing guitar 55 55
1136 (1r.20) Woman dancing . . 55 55
1137 (1r.20) Painter 55 55

Nos. 1133/7 are inscribed "STANDARD POSTAGE".

1999. "Explore South Africa" (2nd series). Mpumalanga and Northern Province. As T **375**. Multicoloured.

1138 (1r.70) Blyde River Canyon 45 35
1139 (1r.70) Lone Creek Falls, Sabie 45 35
1140 (1r.70) Ndebele women in traditional dress 45 35
1141 (1r.70) Pilgrim's Rest (historic town) 45 35
1142 (1r.70) Elephants, Kruger National Park 45 35

Nos. 1138/42 are inscribed "AIRMAIL POSTCARD".

1999. Traditional Wall Art. Designs showing sections of wall art. Multicoloured.

1143 (1r.20) Type **392** 40 40
1144 (1r.20) South Ndebele . . . 40 40
1145 (1r.20) Swazi 40 40
1146 (1r.20) Venda 40 40
1147 (1r.20) South Sotho 40 40
1148 (1r.20) Xhosa 40 40
1149 (1r.20) North Sotho 40 40
1150 (1r.20) Tsonga 40 40
1151 (1r.20) Zulu 40 40
1152 (1r.20) Tswana 40 40

Nos. 1143/52 are inscribed "STANDARD POSTAGE".

393 South African Rock Art Painting

395 Barn Swallow

394 Strelitzia reginae (flower)

1999. China '99 International Stamp Exhibition, Beijing. Sheet 154 × 85 mm.

MS1153 **393** 5r. multicoloured . . 1·25 1·25

1999. "JOPEX '99" National Stamp Exhibition, Johannesburg. Sheet 65 × 85 mm.

MS1154 **394** 5r. multicoloured . . 1·25 1·25

1999. Migratory Species of South Africa. Multicoloured.

1155 (1r.20) Type **395** 45 40
1156 (1r.20) Great white shark . . 45 40
1157 (1r.20) Lesser kestrel 45 40
1158 (1r.20) Common dolphin . . 45 40
1159 (1r.20) European bee-eater 45 40
1160 (1r.20) Loggerhead turtle . . 45 40
1161 (1r.20) Curlew sandpiper . . 45 40
1162 (1r.20) Wandering albatross 45 40
1163 (1r.20) Springbok 45 40
1164 (1r.20) Lesser flamingo . . . 45 40

Nos. 1155/64 are inscribed "Standard Postage".

396 Boers leaving for Commando

1999. Centenary of Anglo-Boer War (1st issue). Multicoloured.

1165 (1r.20) Type **396** 50 50
1166 (1r.20) British soldiers . . . 50 50

See also Nos. 2003/4, 1343/4 and **MS**1384.

397 Landscape

2000. New Millennium.

1167 **397** (1r.20) multicoloured . . 50 30

No. 1167 is inscribed "Standard Postage".

398 National Lottery Logo

399 Family inside Heart

2000. 1st National Lottery.

1168 **398** (1r.20) multicoloured . . 50 30

No. 1168 is inscribed "STANDARD POSTAGE".

2000. National Family Day.

1169 **399** (1r.30) multicoloured . . 50 30

No. 1169 is inscribed "Standard Postage".

400 Green Turaco ("Knysna Lourie")

2000. "The Stamp Show 2000" International Stamp Exhibition, London. Sheet 108 × 68 mm.

MS1170 **400** 4r.60 multicoloured 1·50 1·25

401 Banded Stream Frog

2000. Frogs of South Africa. Multicoloured.

1171 1r.30 Type **401** 50 50
1172 1r.30 Yellow-striped reed frog 50 50
1173 1r.30 Natal leaf-folding frog 50 50
1174 1r.30 Paradise toad 50 50
1175 1r.30 Table Mountain ghost frog 50 50
1176 1r.30 Banded rubber frog 50 50
1177 1r.30 Dwarf grass frog . . . 50 50
1178 1r.30 Long-toed tree frog . . 50 50
1179 1r.30 Namaqua rain frog . . 50 50
1180 1r.30 Bubbling kassina . . . 50 50

402 Forest Tree Frog

2000. "JUNASS 2000" National Junior Stamp Show, Baksburg. Sheet 108 × 68 mm.

MS1181 **402** 4r.60 multicoloured 1·25 1·25

403 Stalked Bulbine

404 Athelete with South African Flag

2000. Medicinal Plants. Multicoloured.

1182 1r.30 Type **403** 30 35
1183 1r.30 Wild dagga 30 35
1184 1r.30 Wild garlic 30 35
1185 1r.30 Pig's ear 30 35
1186 1r.30 Wild ginger 30 35
1187 2r.30 Red paintbrush . . . 50 55
1188 2r.30 Cancer bush 50 55
1189 2r.30 Yellow star 50 55
1190 2r.30 Bitter aloe 50 55
1191 2r.30 Sour fig 50 55

2000. Olympic Games, Sydney. Multicoloured.

1192 1r.30 Type **404** 30 25
1193 1r.50 Elana Meyer (medal winner, 1992) 30 35
1194 2r.20 Joshua Thugwane (medal winner, 1996) . . 50 50
1195 2r.30 Olympic rings and South African flag 55 55
1196 6r.30 Penny Heyns (medal winner, 1996) . . . . . 1·40 1·75

405 Globe and Peace Doves

2000. United Nations International Year of Peace.

1197 **405** 1r.30 multicoloured . . . 50 30

406 Robben Island

2000. U.N.E.S.C.O. World Heritage Sites. Mult.

1198 1r.30 Type **406** 35 25
1199 1r.30 Greater St. Lucia Wetland Park 35 25
1200 1r.30 Early skull from Sterkfontein 35 25

407 Dragon

2000. Chinese New Year ("Year of the Dragon"). Sheet 85 × 65 mm.

MS1201 **407** 4r.60 multicoloured 1·10 1·25

408 Heart and Envelope

2000. World Post Day.

1202 **408** 1r.30 multicoloured . . . 40 30

409 Sol Plaatje and Johanna Brandt

2000. Centenary of Anglo-Boer War (2nd issue). Authors. Multicoloured.

1203 1r.30 Type **409** 20 25
1204 4r.40 Arthur Conan Doyle and Winston Churchill . . 1·50 1·25

410 Palette Surgeonfish

2000. Flora and Fauna (1st issue). Multicoloured.

1205 5c. Type **410** 10 10
1206 10c. Clown surgeonfish ("Bluebanded Surgeon") 10 10
1207 20c. Regal angelfish 10 10
1208 30c. Emperor angelfish . . . 10 10
1209 40c. Picasso triggerfish ("Blackbar triggerfish") 10 10
1210 50c. Coral hind ("Coral rockcod") 10 10
1211 60c. Powder-blue surgeonfish 10 15
1212 70c. Thread-finned butterflyfish 10 15
1213 80c. Long-horned cowfish 10 15
1214 90c. Forceps butterflyfish ("Longnose butterflyfish") 15 20
1215 1r. Two-spined angelfish ("Coral Beauty") 15 20
1216 1r.30 Botterblom (vert) . . . 20 25
1217 1r.30 Blue marguerite (vert) 20 25
1218 1r.30 Karoo violet (vert) . . 20 25
1219 1r.30 Tree pelargonium (vert) 20 25
1220 1r.30 Black-eyed susy (vert) 20 25
1221 1r.40 Gold-banded forester 20 25
1222 1r.50 Brenton blue 25 30
1223 1r.90 Silver-barred charaxes 30 35
1224 2r. Lilac-breasted roller (vert) 30 35
1225 2r.30 Citrus butterfly . . . 35 40
1226 3r. Woodland kingfisher (vert) 45 50
1227 5r. White-fronted bee eater (vert) 75 80
1228 6r.30 Narrow blue-banded swallowtail ("Green-banded swallowtail") . . 95 1·00
1229 10r. African green pigeon (vert) . . . . 1·50 1·60
1230 12r.60 False-dotted border 1·90 2·00
1231 20r. Violet-crested turaco ("Purplecrested lourie") (vert) . . . . 3·00 3·25

(b) Designs as Nos. 1216/20, but smaller (20 × 25 mm). Self-adhesive.

1232 1r.30 As No. 1216 (inscr "Afrika Borwa") 20 25
1233 1r.30 As No. 1216 (inscr "Afrika Dzonga") 20 25
1234 1r.30 As No. 1217 (inscr "Ningizimu Afrika") . . . 20 25
1235 1r.30 As No. 1217 (inscr "Afrika Sewula") 20 25
1236 1r.30 As No. 1218 (inscr "Suid-Afrika") 20 25
1237 1r.30 As No. 1218 (inscr "Afrika Borwa") 20 25
1238 1r.30 As No. 1219 (inscr "Afrika Tshipembe") . . 20 25
1239 1r.30 As No. 1219 (inscr "Ningizimu Afrika") . . . 20 25
1240 1r.30 As No. 1220 (inscr "Afrika Borwa") 20 25
1241 1r.30 As No. 1220 (inscr "Mzantsi Afrika") 20 25

DESIGNS from 5c. to 1r. show fish, 1r.30 flowers, 1r.40 to 1r.90, 2r.30, 6r.30 and 12r.60 butterflies and the 2, 3, 5, 10 and 20r. birds.

See also Nos. 1268/1314 and 1389/93.

411 The Rain Bull

2001. South African Myths and Legends. Mult.

1242 1r.30 Type **411** 20 25
1243 1r.50 The Grosvenor Treasure 25 30
1244 2r.20 Seven Magic Birds . . 35 40
1245 2r.30 The Hole in the Wall 35 40
1246 6r.30 Van Hunks and the Devil . . . . 95 1·00

412 African Tree Snake

2001. Chinese New Year ("Year of the Snake") and "Hong Kong 2001" Stamp Exhibition. Sheet 65 × 85 mm.

MS1247 **412** 4r.60, multicoloured 70 75

413 Ernie Els (golf)

2001. South African Sporting Heroes. Multicoloured.

1248 1r.40 Type **413** 20 25
1249 1r.40 Lucas Radebe (soccer) 20 25
1250 1r.40 Francois Pienaar (rugby) 20 25
1251 1r.40 Terrence Parkin (swimming) 20 25
1252 1r.40 Rosina Magola (netball) 20 25

1253 1r.40 Hestrie Cloete (high-jumping) 20 25
1254 1r.40 Hezekiel Sepeng (athletics) 20 25
1255 1r.40 Jonty Rhodes (cricket) 20 25
1256 1r.40 Zanele Situ (paralymic javelin) 20 25
1257 1r.40 Vuyani Bungu (boxing) 20 25

414 Elephant

2001. Wildlife. Multicoloured. (a) Designs 34 × 26 mm.
1258 (2r.10) Type **414** 30 35
1259 (2r.10) Lion 30 35
1260 (2r.10) Rhinoceros 30 35
1261 (2r.10) Leopard 30 35
1262 (2r.10) Buffalo 30 35

(b) Designs 29 × 24 mm. Self-adhesive.
1263 (2r.10) Buffalo 30 35
1264 (2r.10) Leopard 30 35
1265 (2r.10) Rhinoceros 30 35
1266 (2r.10) Lion 30 35
1267 (2r.10) Type **414** 30 35

Nos. 1258/67 are inscribed "AIRMAIL POSTCARD RATE" and were initially valid for 2r.10.

2001. Flora and Fauna (2nd issue). Multicoloured. (a) As T **410**.
1268 50c. Coral hind ("Coral rockcook") 10 10
1269 60c. Powder-blue surgeonfish 10 15
1280 1r.40 Botterblom (vert) . . 20 25
1281 1r.40 Blue marguerite (vert) 20 25
1282 1r.40 Karoo violet (vert) 20 25
1283 1r.40 Tree pelargonium (vert) 20 25
1284 1r.40 Black-eyed susy (vert) 20 25
1285 1r.60 Yellow pansy butterfly 25 30
1286 1r.90 Large-spotted acraea 30 35
1286a 2r. Lilac-breasted roller (vert) 35 40
1287 2r.10 Koppe charaxes . . . 30 35
1288 2r.50 Common grass-yellow 40 45
1289 3r. Woodland kingfisher (vert) 45 50
1290 5r. White-fronted bee-eater (vert) 80 90
1291 7r. Southern milkweed . . 1·10 1·25
1292 10r. African green pigeon (vert) . . . . 1·50 1·60
1293 14r. Lilac-tip . . . . . 2·10 2·25
1294 20r. Purple-crested turacao ("Purplecrested lourie") (vert) . . . . 3·00 3·25

(b) Designs as Nos. 1280/4, but 20 × 25 mm and inscr "Standard Postage" instead of face value. Self-adhesive.
1295 (1r.40) As No. 1280 (inscr "Afrika Borwa") 20 25
1296 (1r.40) As No. 1280 (inscr "Afrika Dzonga") 20 25
1297 (1r.40) As No. 1281 (inscr "Ningizimu Afrika") . . . 20 25
1298 (1r.40) As No. 1281 (inscr "Afrika Sewula") 20 25
1299 (1r.40) As No. 1282 (inscr "Suid-Afrika") 20 25
1300 (1r.40) As No. 1282 (inscr "Afrika Borwa") 20 25
1301 (1r.40) As No. 1283 (inscr "Afrika Tshipembe") . . 20 25
1302 (1r.40) As No. 1283 (inscr "Ningizimu Afrika") . . . 20 25
1303 (1r.40) As No. 1284 (inscr "Afrika Borwa") 20 25
1304 (1r.40) As No. 1284 (inscr "Mzantsi Afrika") 20 25

Nos. 1285/8, 1291 and 1293 show butterflies.
Nos. 1295/1304 are inscribed "Standard Postage" and were initially valid for 1r.40.

(c) Designs as Nos. 1280/4, but 20 × 25 mm and inscr "Standard Postage" instead of face value. Self-adhesive.
1305 (1r.40) As No. 1280 (inscr "Afrika Borwa") 20 25
1306 (1r.40) As No. 1280 (inscr "Afrika Dzonga") 20 25
1307 (1r.40) As No. 1281 (inscr "Ningizimu Afrika") . . . 20 25
1308 (1r.40) As No. 1281 (inscr "Afrika Sewula") 20 25
1309 (1r.40) As No. 1282 (inscr "Suid-Afrika") 20 25
1310 (1r.40) As No. 1282 (inscr "Afrika Borwa") 20 25
1311 (1r.40) As No. 1283 (inscr "Afrika Tshipembe") . . 20 25
1312 (1r.40) As No. 1283 (inscr "Ningizimu Afrika") . . . 20 25
1313 (1r.40) As No. 1284 (inscr "Afrika Borwa") 20 25
1314 (1r.40) As No. 1284 (inscr "Mzantsi Afrika") 20 25

415 Gemsbok

2001. Kgalagadi Transfrontier Wildlife Park. Joint Issue with Botswana. Multicoloured.
1315 1r.40 Type **415** 20 25
1316 2r.50 Cheetah 40 45
1317 2r.90 Sociable weaver (bird) 45 50
1318 3r.60 Meercat 55 60
MS1319 114 × 78 mm. Nos. 1316/17 85 95

416 Adult holding Child's Hand

2001. "no excuse for child abuse" Campaign.
1320 **416** 1r.40 multicoloured . . . 20 25

417 Victims of Soweto Uprising

419 Conference Logo

418 Cape Horseshoe Bat

2001. 25th Anniv of Soweto Uprising.
1321 **417** 1r.40 multicoloured . . . 20 25

2001. Bats of South Africa. Multicoloured. Self-adhesive.
1322 1r.40 Type **418** 20 25
1323 1r.40 Welwitsch's hairy bat 20 25
1324 1r.40 Schreiber's long-fingered bat 20 25
1325 1r.40 Wahlberg's epauletted fruit bat 20 25
1326 1r.40 Short-eared trident bat 20 25
1327 1r.40 Common slit-faced bat 20 25
1328 1r.40 Egyptian fruit bat . . 20 25
1329 1r.40 Egyptian free-tailed bat (vert) 20 25
1330 1r.40 De Winton's long-eared bat 20 25
1331 1r.40 Large-eared free-tailed bat 20 25

Nos. 1322/31 were printed in sheetlets of 10 with the background forming a composite design. Descriptions of the various species are printed on the reverse of the backing paper.

2001. 3rd U.N. World Conference Against Racism, Durban.
1332 **419** 1r.40 mult (inscr as in T **419**) 20 25
1333 1r.40 mult (inscr "ningizimu afrika" and "kubeketelelana" at foot) 20 25
1334 1r.40 mult (inscr "suid-afrika") 20 25
1335 1r.40 mult (inscr "afrika tshipembe") 20 25
1336 1r.40 mult (inscr "afrika borwa" and "kutlwisiso" at foot) 20 25
1337 1r.40 mult (inscr "afrika dzonga") 20 25
1338 1r.40 mult (inscr "afrika sewula") 20 25
1339 1r.40 mult (inscr "afrika borwa" and "kgothlelelo" at foot) 20 25
1340 1r.40 mult (inscr "ningizimu afrika" and "ukubekezelelana" at foot) 20 25
1341 1r.40 mult (inscr "mzantsi afrika") . . 20 25
1342 – 2r.10 mult (logo and South Africans) . . . 30 35

420 Dominee J. D. Kestell

2001. Centenary of Anglo-Boer War (3rd issue). Angels of Mercy. Multicoloured.
1343 1r.40 Type **420** 20 25
1344 3r. Captain Thomas Crean V.C., R.A.M.C. 45 50

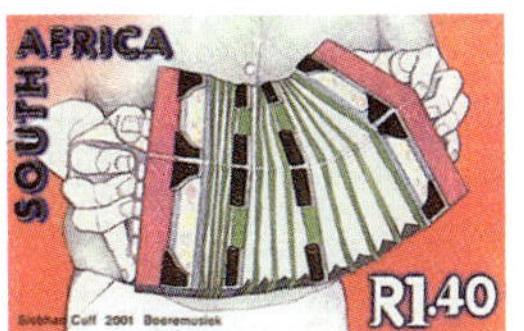

421 Boere Concertina

2001. Musical Instruments. Multicoloured.
1345 1r.40 Type **421** 20 25
1346 1r.90 Trumpet 30 35
1347 2r.50 Electric guitar 40 45
1348 3r. African drum 45 50
1349 7r. Cello . . . . 1·10 1·25

422 Fields of Flowers, Namaqualand

2001. Natural Wonders of South Africa. Multicoloured.
1350 (2r.10) Type **422** 30 35
1351 (2r.10) Cango Caves 30 35
1352 (2r.10) Richtersveld Desert 30 35
1353 (2r.10) Rocks on West Coast 30 35
1354 (2r.10) Snow covered mountains near Elliot . . 30 35
1355 (2r.10) Table Mountain . . 30 35
1356 (2r.10) Tsitsikamma Forest 30 35
1357 (2r.10) Augrabies Waterfall 30 35
1358 (2r.10) Cape Mountain Zebra 30 35
1359 (2r.10) Vineyards, Stellenbosch 30 35

Nos. 1350/9 are inscribed "Airmail Postcard Rate" and were initially valid at 2r.10 each.

423 Tree of Life decorated with Christmas Lights

2001. Christmas. Multicoloured.
1360 2r. Type **423** 30 35
1361 3r. Angel 45 50

424 Frame

2001. Greetings Stamps. Self-adhesive.
1362 **424** (1r.40) multicoloured . . 30 20

No. 1362 is inscribed "Standard Postage" and was initially valid for 1r.40.

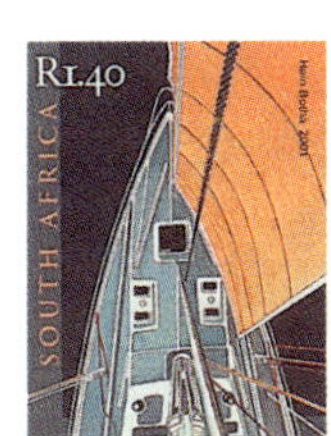

425 Class Volvo 60 Yacht

426 International Cricket Council Logo

2001. Volvo Round the World Ocean Race. Multicoloured.
1363 **425** 1r.40 multicoloured . . . 20 25
MS1364 55 × 85 mm. 6r. Volvo 60 yacht (horiz) 90 95

2001. Cricket World Cup (2003).
1365 **426** (1r.40) black, gold and silver 20 25

No. 1365 is inscribed "Standard Postage" and was initially valid for 1r.40.

427 Horse's Head

2001. Chinese New Year ("Year of the Horse").
1366 **427** 6r. multicoloured 90 95

428 Scalloped Hammerhead Sharks

2001. Marine Life. Multicoloured. Self-adhesive.
1367 1r.40 Type **428** 20 25
1368 1r.40 Loggerhead turtle (vert) 20 25
1369 1r.40 Clown triggerfish (vert) 20 25
1370 1r.40 Cape fur seals (vert) 20 25
1371 1r.40 Bottlenosed dolphins 20 25
1372 1r.40 Crowned seahorses (vert) 20 25
1373 1r.40 Blue-spotted ribbontail ray (vert) 20 25
1374 1r.40 Moorish idols 20 25
1375 1r.40 Octopus 20 25
1376 1r.40 Coral rock cod 20 25

Nos. 1367/76 were printed together, se-tenant, with the background forming a composite design. Descriptions of the various species are printed on the reverse of the backing paper.

429 Child laughing

2002. World Summit for Sustainable Development, Johannesburg. Multicoloured. Ordinary gum.
1377 (1r.40) Type **429** 20 25
1378 (1r.40) Globe in rainforest 20 25
1379 (1r.40) Trees in sunset . . . 20 25
1380 (3r.) Globe and South African landmarks (48 × 30 mm) 45 50

See also Nos. 1386/9.

2002. (b) Designs 20 × 25 mm. Self-adhesive.
1381 (1r.50) Type **429** 25 30
1382 (1r.50) As No. 1378 . . . . 25 30
1383 (1r.50) As No. 1379 . . . . 25 30

430 Earl Kitchener

2002. Centenary of Anglo-Boer War (4th issue). Treaty of Vereeniging. Sheet, 105×65 mm, containing T **430** and similar square design. Multicoloured.
MS1384 1r.50 Type **430**; 3r.30 Boer representative signing Treaty . . . 70 75

431 African Union Logo

2002. 1st African Union Summit, Durban.
1385 **431** 1r.50 multicoloured . . . 25 30

432 Water, Sanitation and Energy

2002. World Summit on Sustainable Development (2nd issue). Multicoloured.
1386 (1r.50) Type **432** 25 30
1387 (3r.) Child with hands raised to globe (Environment) 45 50
1388 (3r.30) Hands holding seedling (Food) 50 55

No. 1386 is inscribed "standard postage", No. 1387 "airmail postcard rate" and No. 1388 "international letter rate". The stamps were initially sold at the values quoted above.

2002. Flora and Fauna (3rd series). Moths. As T **410**. Multicoloured.
1389 1r.80 Emperor moth 25 30
1390 2r.20 Peach moth 35 40
1391 2r.80 Snouted tiger moth . . 40 45
1392 9r. False tiger moth . . . . 1·40 1·50
1393 16r. Moon moth . . . . . 2·40 2·50

OFFICIAL STAMPS

Prices for bilingual stamps are for mint pairs and used singles.

1926. Optd **OFFICIAL. OFFISIEEL.** (with full points). (a) On stamp of 1913.
O1 **3** 2d. purple . . . . 19·00 1·75

(b) On pictorial issues.
O2 **6** ½d. black and green . . . . 6·50 1·50
O3 **7** 1d. black and red . . . . . 3·50 50
O4 **8** 6d. green and orange . . . . £550 10·00

1928. Optd **OFFICIAL OFFISIEEL** (without full points).
O 7 **6** ½d. black and green (No. 42) . . . . . 2·25 35
O39 ½d. black and green (No. 114) 70 15
O 8 **7** 1d. black and red (No. 31) . . . . . 3·00 45
O21aw 1d. grey and red (No. 56) . . . . . 2·00 20
O22aw **22** 1½d. green and gold 26·00 80
O44 **34a** 1½d. green and buff . . 1·40 30
O 5a **11** 2d. grey and purple (No. 34) . . . . . 5·00 1·50
O14 2d. grey and lilac (No. 44) . . . . . 6·50 1·50
O15 2d. blue and violet (No. 44d) . . . . . £120 9·00
O30 2d. grey and purple (No. 58a) . . . . . 12·00 2·25
O36 **54** 2d. slate and violet . . 4·25 1·75
O45 **68** 2d. blue and violet . . 1·00 20
O16 **8** 6d. green and orange (No. 47) . . . . . 7·50 85
O46 6d. green and red (No. 119a) . . . . 1·00 35
O10 – 1s. brown and blue (No. 36) . . . . . 35·00 9·50
O47 – 1s. brown and blue (No. 120) . . . . . 5·50 2·00
O18a – 2s.6d. green and brown (No. 49) . . 48·00 8·50
O48 – 2s.6d. green and brown (No. 121) . . 8·50 3·50
O19 – 2s.6d. blue and brown (No. 49a) . . . . . 35·00 6·50
O50 – 5s. black and green (No. 64a) . . . . . 60·00 6·50
O51 – 10s. blue and brown (No. 39) . . . . . 75·00 22·00

POSTAGE DUE STAMPS

D 1

D 2

1914. Perf or roul.
D11 **D 1** ½d. black and green . . 80 1·75
D12 1d. black and red . . . 90 15
D13 1½d. black and brown . . 90 1·25
D14 2d. black and violet . . 1·00 70
D 4 3d. black and blue . . . 2·25 60
D 5 5d. black and brown . . 4·00 23·00
D16 6d. black and grey . . . 12·00 4·50
D 7 1s. red and black . . . 60·00 £150

1927.
D17 **D 2** ½d. black and green . . 1·00 3·25
D18 1d. black and red . . . 1·25 30
D19 2d. black and mauve . 1·25 30
D23 2d. black and purple . . 9·00 2·50
D20 3d. black and blue . . 8·50 23·00
D28 3d. indigo and blue . . 7·50 30
D21 6d. black and grey . . 21·00 4·50
D29 6d. green and brown . . 25·00 5·00
D29a 6d. green and orange . 12·00 3·00

D 3

D 5

1943.
D30 **D 3** ½d. green . . . . 11·00 30
D31 1d. red . . . . 10·00 10
D32 2d. violet . . . . 6·50 15
D33 3d. blue . . . . 48·00 1·25

The above mint prices are for horiz units of three.

1948. Frame as Type **D 2**, but with bolder figures of value and capital "D".
D34 ½d. black and green . . . . 6·00 11·00
D39 1d. black and red 70 30
D40 2d. black and violet . . . 50 20
D41 3d. indigo and blue . . . 4·50 2·25
D42 4d. turquoise and green . . 12·00 15·00
D43 6d. green and orange . . . 7·00 9·00
D44 1s. brown and purple . . . 12·00 15·00

1961.
D45 **D 5** 1c. black and red . . . . 20 3·50
D46 2c. black and violet . . . 35 3·50
D47 4c. turquoise and green 80 8·00
D48 5c. indigo and blue . . . 1·75 8·00
D49 6c. green and orange . . 6·50 8·50
D50 10c. sepia and brown . . 7·00 10·00

D 6

D 8

1961. (A) Inscr as in Type **D 6**; (B) English at top and left, Afrikans at bottom and right.
D59 **D 6** 1c. black and red (A) 20 55
D60 1c. black and red (B) 20 30
D61 2c. black and violet (A) 30 1·50
D53 2c. black and violet (B) 40 55
D54 4c. myrtle and green (A) . . . . 2·25 2·25
D54a 4c. myrtle and green (B) 12·00 22·00
D63 4c. black and green (A) 29·00 29·00
D64 4c. black and green (B) 29·00 29·00
D55 5c. indigo and blue (B) 2·00 4·25
D65 5c. black and blue (A) 50 50
D66 5c. black and blue (B) 50 50
D67 6c. green & salmon (A) 3·50 9·50
D68 6c. green and salmon (B) . . . . 3·50 9·50
D58 10c. sepia & brown (B) 2·75 1·75
D69 10c. black and brown (A) . . . . 1·00 2·75
D70 10c. black and brown (B) . . . . 1·00 2·75

1972.
D75 **D 8** 1c. green . . . . 50 2·25
D76 2c. orange . . . . . . 70 3·00
D77 4c. plum . . . . 1·75 3·50
D78 6c. yellow . . . . . . 1·75 4·75
D79 8c. blue . . . . 2·00 5·00
D80 10c. red . . . . 6·00 7·50

SOUTH ARABIAN FEDERATION Pt. 1

Comprising Aden and most of the territories of the former Western Aden Protectorate plus one from the Eastern Aden Protectorate. The South Arabian Federation became fully independent on 30 November 1967.

1963. 100 cents = 1 shilling.
1965. 1000 fils = 1 dinar.

1963. Cent of Red Cross. As T **63b** of St. Helena, but without portrait. Value in English and Arabic.
1 15c. red and black 30 30
2 1s.25 red and blue 70 95

2 Federal Crest

3 Federal Flag

1965.
3 **2** 5f. blue 20 10
4 10f. lavender 20 10
5 15f. green 20 10
6 20f. green 20 10
7 25f. brown 20 10
8 30f. bistre 20 10
9 35f. brown 20 10
10 50f. red 20 10
11 65f. green 30 30
12 75f. red 30 10
13 **3** 100f. multicoloured 30 10
14 250f. multicoloured . . . . . 5·00 1·00
15 500f. multicoloured . . . . . 9·00 1·00
16 1d. multicoloured . . . . . 16·00 12·00

4 I.C.Y. Emblem

1965. International Co-operation Year.
17 **4** 5f. purple and turquoise . . . 20 10
18 65f. green and lavender . . . 80 20

5 Sir Winston Churchill and St. Paul's Cathedral in Wartime

1966. Churchill Commem. Designs in black, cerise and gold with background in colours given.
19 **5** 5f. blue 10 10
20 10f. green 30 10
21 65f. brown 80 20
22 125f. violet . . . . 1·25 1·75

6 Footballer's Legs, Ball and Jules Rimet Cup

1966. World Cup Football Championship, England.
23 **6** 10f. multicoloured 50 10
24 50f. multicoloured . . . . . 1·50 20

7 W.H.O. Building

1966. Inaug of W.H.O. Headquarters, Geneva.
25 **7** 10f. black, green and blue . . 50 10
26 75f. black, purple and brown . 1·25 45

8 "Education"

1966. 20th Anniv of U.N.E.S.C.O.
27 **8** 10f. multicoloured 30 20
28 – 65f. yellow, violet and olive 1·25 1·40
29 – 125f. black, purple and orange . . . . 3·25 4·75

DESIGNS: 65f. "Science"; 125f. "Culture".

For later issues see **SOUTHERN YEMEN** and **YEMEN PEOPLE'S DEMOCRATIC REPUBLIC**.

SOUTH AUSTRALIA Pt. 1

A state of the Australian Commonwealth whose stamps it now uses.

12 pence = 1 shilling;
20 shillings = 1 pound.

1

1855. Imperf.
1 **1** 1d. green £3000 £425
9 2d. red . . . . £650 40·00
3 6d. blue £2000 £160
12 1s. orange £4000 £375

3

4

1858. Roul or perf.
20 **1** 1d. green . . . . 42·00 26·00
26 2d. red . . . . 50·00 3·00
112 **3** 3d. on 4d. blue . . . . . 75·00 18·00
138 4d. purple . . . . 45·00 2·75
141 **1** 6d. blue . . . . 50·00 2·00
118 **4** 8d. on 9d. brown . . . . 80·00 7·00
124 9d. purple . . . . 10·00 3·50
35 10d. on 9d. orange . . . . £200 32·00
38 **1** 1s. yellow . . . . £450 28·00
130 1s. brown . . . . 25·00 3·00
151 **3** 2s. red . . . . 24·00 10·00

The 3d., 8d. and 10d. are formed by surcharges: **3-PENCE**, **8 PENCE** and **TEN PENCE** (curved).

15

11

12

1868. Various frames.
191 **15** ½d. brown . . . . 2·75 30
173 **11** 1d. green . . . . 8·00 70
176 1d. red . . . . 3·75 20
177 **12** 2d. orange . . . . . . 4·50 10
178 2d. violet . . . . . . 3·25 10
229b – 2½d. on 4d. green . . . 8·00 1·75
192a – 3d. green . . . . . . 5·00 1·60
193 – 4d. violet . . . . . . 6·00 50
230a – 5d. on 6d. brown . . . 16·00 4·25
194 – 6d. blue . . . . 7·00 1·25

Nos. 230 and 231 are surch in figures over straight or curved line.

1882. Surch **HALF-PENNY** in two lines.
181 **11** ½d. on 1d. green . . . . . 11·00 6·00

19

24 G.P.O., Adelaide

22 Red Kangaroo

23

1886.

195a **19** 2s.6d. mauve . . . . . . 32·00 6·00
196a 5s. pink . . . . 42·00 14·00
197a 10s. green . . . . £100 40·00
198a 15s. brown £350 £140
199a £1 blue £250 £110

1894.

241 **24** ½d. green . . . . 1·50 50
236 **22** 2½d. violet . . . . 16·00 70
237 2½d. blue . . . . 4·50 1·00
238a **23** 5d. purple . . . . 6·50 70

1902. Inscr "POSTAGE" at top.
268 **19** 3d. green . . . . 5·50 2·00
269 4d. orange . . . . 8·50 2·00
270 6d. green . . . . 6·00 2·00
285 8d. blue . . . . 9·00 6·00
273 9d. red . . . . 8·00 3·50
274 10d. orange . . . . . . 12·00 7·50
303b 1s. brown . . . . . . 12·00 4·00
276a 2s.6d. violet . . . . . 23·00 11·00
290a 5s. red . . . . 42·00 28·00
278 10s. green . . . . . . £100 60·00
292a £1 blue £140 £100

OFFICIAL STAMPS

1874. Various postage issues optd **O.S.** A. Issue of 1858.
O 6 **1** 1d. green £1200 £100
O 7 **3** 3d. on 4d. blue £2000 £850
O17 4d. mauve . . . . 35·00 2·50
O19 **1** 6d. blue . . . . 55·00 4·50
O26 **4** 8d. on 9d. brown £1400 £650
O11 9d. purple £1000 £475
O33 **1** 1s. brown . . . . 29·00 5·50
O35 **3** 2s. red . . . . 65·00 10·00

B. Issues of 1868–82.
O60 **15** ½d. brown . . . . 16·00 4·75
O48 **11** ½d. on 1d. green . . . . . 60·00 14·00
O56 1d. green . . . . 10·00 1·25
O81 1d. red . . . . 12·00 1·60
O44 **12** 2d. orange . . . . 7·50 80
O82 2d. violet . . . . 12·00 80
O71 – 2½d. on 4d. green . . . . 35·00 10·00
O84 – 4d. violet . . . . 50·00 4·50
O72 – 5d. on 6d. brown . . . . 42·00 15·00
O67 – 6d. blue . . . . 25·00 3·00

C. Issue of 1886.
O86 **19** 2s.6d. violet £3000 £2250
O87 5s. pink £3000 £2250

D. Issue of 1894.
O80 **24** ½d. green . . . . 13·00 6·00
O75 **22** 2½d. blue . . . . 50·00 7·00
O74 **23** 5d. purple . . . . 65·00 10·00

SOUTH GEORGIA Pt. 1

An island in the Antarctic. From May 1980 to 1985 used stamps inscribed FALKLAND ISLANDS DEPENDENCIES and thereafter those of South Georgia and the South Sandwich Islands (q.v.).

1963. 12 pence = 1 shilling;
20 shillings = 1 pound.
1971. 100 pence = 1 pound.

1 Reindeer

1963.

1 **1** ½d. red . . . . 50 1·00
2 – 1d. blue . . . . 80 1·00
3 – 2d. blue . . . . 1·25 1·00
4 – 2½d. black . . . . 5·50 2·50
5 – 3d. bistre . . . . 2·75 30
6 – 4d. green . . . . 5·00 80
7 – 5½d. violet . . . . 2·50 30
8 – 6d. orange 75 50
9 – 9d. blue . . . . 5·00 2·00
10 – 1s. purple 75 30
11 – 2s. olive and blue . . . . 25·00 6·50
12 – 2s.6d. blue . . . . 24·00 4·00
13 – 5s. brown . . . . 22·00 4·00
14 – 10s. mauve . . . . 42·00 10·00
15 – £1 blue . . . . 85·00 48·00
16 – £1 black . . . . 10·00 16·00
DESIGNS—HORIZ: 2½d. King penguins and Bearded penguin ("Chinstrap Penguin"); 4d. Fin whale; 5½d. Southern elephant-seal; 9d. Whale-catcher; 1s. Leopard seal; 2s. Shackleton's Cross; 2s.6d. Wandering albatross; 5s. Southern elephant seal and South American fur seal; £1 (No. 15) Blue whale. VERT: 1d. South Sandwich Islands map; 2d. Sperm whale; 3d. South American fur seal; 6d. Light-mantled sooty albatross ("Sooty Albatross"); 10s. Plankton and krill; £1 (No. 16) King penguins.

1971. Decimal Currency. Nos. 1/14 surch.
18a ½p. on ½d. red . . . . 1·00 1·00
19 1p. on 1d. blue . . . . 1·50 55
55 1½p. on 5½d. violet . . . . . 90 1·75
21 2p. on 2d. blue 70 50
22 2½p. on 2½d. black . . . . . 2·25 40
23 3p. on 3d. bistre . . . . . . 1·00 50
24 4p. on 4d. green . . . . . . 1·00 50
25 5p. on 6d. orange . . . . . 2·00 30
26 6p. on 9d. blue . . . . . . 1·50 70
27 7½p. on 1s. purple . . . . . 1·50 70
63w 10p. on 2s. olive and blue . . 1·00 5·00
64w 15p. on 2s.6d. blue . . . . . 1·50 5·50
65w 25p. on 5s. brown . . . . . 1·00 5·50
66 50p. on 10s. mauve . . . . . 1·00 5·00

6 "Endurance" beset in Weddell Sea

1972. 50th Death Anniv of Sir Ernest Shackleton. Multicoloured.
32 1½p. Type **6** . . . . 1·00 1·50
33 5p. Launching of the longboat "James Caird" . . . . 1·25 2·00
34 10p. Route of the "James Caird" . . . . 1·75 2·25
35 20p. Sir Ernest Shackleton and the "Quest" . . . . 2·00 2·50

1972. Royal Silver Wedding. As T **103** of St. Helena, but with Elephant Seal and King Penguins in background.
36 5p. green 75 35
37 10p. violet 75 35

1973. Royal Wedding. As T **103a** of St. Helena. Background colours given. Multicoloured.
38 5p. brown 30 10
39 15p. lilac 40 20

8 Churchill and Westminster Skyline

1974. Birth Cent of Sir Winston Churchill. Mult.
40 15p. Type **8** . . . . 75 1·00
41 25p. Churchill and warship . . 1·00 1·00
MS42 122 × 98 mm. Nos. 40/1 . . 6·00 6·00

9 Captain Cook

10 "Discovery" and Biological Laboratory

1975. Bicentenary of Possession by Captain Cook.
43 2p. Type **9** . . . . 2·25 1·00
44 8p. H.M.S. "Resolution" (horiz) . . . . 3·50 1·50
45 16p. Possession Bay (horiz) . . 3·75 1·75

1976. 50th Anniv of "Discovery" Investigations. Multicoloured.
46 2p. Type **10** . . . . 1·50 45
47 8p. "William Scoresby" and water-sampling bottles . . . 1·75 60
48 11p. "Discovery II" and plankton net . . . . 2·00 65
49 25p. Biological station and krill . . . . 2·50 95

11 The Queen and Retinue after Coronation

1977. Silver Jubilee. Multicoloured.
50 6p. Visit by Prince Philip, 1957 50 30
51 11p. Queen Elizabeth and Westminster Abbey 70 35
52 33p. Type **11** 80 50

12 Fur Seal 13 H.M.S. "Resolution"

1978. 25th Anniv of Coronation.
67 – 25p. deep blue, blue and silver . . . . 35 1·10
68 – 25p. multicoloured . . . . 35 1·10
69 **12** 25p. deep blue, blue and silver . . . . 35 1·10
DESIGNS: No. 67, Panther of Henry VI; No. 68, Queen Elizabeth II.

1979. Bicentenary of Captain Cook's Voyages, 1768–79. Multicoloured.
70 3p. Type **13** . . . . 1·50 80
71 6p. "Resolution" and Map of South Georgia and S. Sandwich Isles showing route . . . . 1·50 70
72 11p. King penguin (from drawing by George Forster) 1·75 1·40
73 25p. Flaxman/Wedgwood medallion of Capt. Cook . . 2·00 1·75

SOUTH GEORGIA AND THE SOUTH SANDWICH ISLANDS Pt. 1

Under the new constitution, effective 3 October 1985, South Georgia and the South Sandwich Islands ceased to be dependencies of the Falkland Islands.

100 pence = 1 pound.

1986. 60th Birthday of Queen Elizabeth II. As T **145a** of St. Helena. Multicoloured.
153 10p. Four generations of Royal Family at Prince Charles's christening, 1948 35 50
154 24p. With Prince Charles and Lady Diana Spencer, Buckingham Palace, 1981 60 75
155 29p. In robes of Order of the British Empire, St. Paul's Cathedral, London 60 80
156 45p. At banquet, Canada, 1976 . . . . 80 1·00
157 58p. At Crown Agents Head Office London, 1983 . . . 1·00 1·25

25a Prince Andrew and Miss Sarah Ferguson at Ascot

26a I.G.Y. Logo

26 Southern Black-backed Gull ("Dominican Gull")

1986. Royal Wedding. Multicoloured.
158 17p. Type **25a** . . . . 75 1·00
159 22p. Wedding photograph . . 85 1·25
160 29p. Prince Andrew with Westland Lynx helicopter on board H.M.S. "Brazen" 1·50 1·50

1987. Birds. Multicoloured.
161 1p. Type **26** . . . . 1·00 1·50
162 2p. South georgia cormorant ("Blue-eyed cormorant") 1·25 1·75
163 3p. Snowy sheathbill ("Wattled Sheatbill") (vert) 1·50 2·00
164 4p. Skua antarctic ("Brown Skua") (vert) . . . . . 1·25 2·00
165 5p. Pintado petrel ("Coupe Pigeon") . . . . 1·25 2·00
166 6p. Georgian diving petrel ("South Georgia Diving Petrel") . . . . 1·25 2·00
167 7p. South Georgia pipit (vert) 1·50 2·00
168 8p. Georgian teal ("South Georgian Pintail") (vert) 1·50 2·00
169 9p. Fairy prion . . . . . . 1·50 2·00
170 10p. bearded penguin ("Chinstrap Penguin") . . 1·50 2·00
171 20p. Macaroni penguin (vert) 1·75 2·25
172 25p. Light-mantled sooty albatross (vert) . . . . . 1·75 2·25
173 50p. Giant petrel ("Southern Giant Petrel") (vert) . . . 2·00 2·50
174 £1 Wandering albatross . . . 2·25 3·75
175 £3 King penguin (vert) . . . 6·00 8·00

1987. 30th Anniv of International Geophysical Year.
176 **26a** 24p. black and blue . . . 70 55
177 – 29p. multicoloured . . . 75 60
178 – 58p. multicoloured . . . 1·40 1·25
DESIGNS: 29p. Grytviken; 58p. Glaciologist using hand-drill to take core sample.

27 "Gaimardia trapesina"

1988. Sea Shells. Multicoloured.
179 10p. Type **27** 65 30
180 24p. "Margarella tropidophoroides" . . . . 1·00 60
181 29p. "Trophon geversianus" 1·10 65
182 58p. "Chlanidota densesculpta" . . . . . . 1·60 1·25

1988. 300th Anniv of Lloyd's of London. As T **192** of Samoa.
183 10p. black and brown 60 40
184 24p. multicoloured 85 75
185 29p. black and green 90 80
186 58p. black and red . . . . . 1·40 1·60
DESIGNS—VERT: 10p. Queen Mother at opening of new Lloyd's building, 1957; 58p. "Horatio" (tanker) on fire, 1916. HORIZ: 24p. "Lindblad Explorer" (cruise liner); 29p. Whaling station, Leith Harbour.

28 Glacier Headwall

1989. Glacier Formations. Multicoloured.
187 10p. Type **28** 40 35
188 24p. Accumulation area . . . 80 70
189 29p. Ablation area 90 80
190 58p. Calving front . . . . . 1·60 1·40

29 Retracing Shackleton's Trek 30 "Brutus", Prince Olav Harbour

1989. 25th Anniv of Combined Services Expedition to South Georgia. Multicoloured.
191 10p. Type **29** 40 35
192 24p. Surveying at Royal Bay 90 70
193 29p. H.M.S. "Protector" (ice patrol ship) . . . . 1·00 80
194 58p. Raising Union Jack on Mount Paget . . . . . . 1·60 1·40

1990. 90th Birthday of Queen Elizabeth the Queen Mother. As T **161a** of St. Helena.
195 26p. multicoloured . . . . . 1·00 1·50
196 £1 black and blue . . . . . 2·75 3·50
DESIGNS—(21 × 36 mm): 26p. Queen Mother. (29 × 37 mm): King George VI and Queen Elizabeth with A.R.P. wardens, 1940.

1990. Wrecks and Hulks. Multicoloured.
197 12p. Type **30** 55 40
198 26p. "Bayard", Ocean Harbour . . . . 1·00 80
199 31p. "Karrakatta", Husvik 1·10 95
200 62p. "Louise", Grytviken . . 1·90 1·75

1991. 65th Birthday of Queen Elizabeth II and 70th Birthday of Prince Philip. As T **165a** of St. Helena. Multicoloured.
201 31p. Queen Elizabeth II . . . 1·40 1·75
202 31p. Prince Philip in Grenadier Guards uniform 1·40 1·75

31 Contest between two Bull Elephant Seals

1991. Elephant Seals. Multicoloured.
203 12p. Type **31** 50 50
204 26p. Adult elephant seal . . 1·00 1·00
205 29p. Seal throwing sand . . . 1·10 1·10
206 31p. Head of elephant seal 1·10 1·10
207 34p. Seals on beach . . . . 1·25 1·25
208 62p. Cow seal with pup . . . 2·00 2·00

1992. 40th Anniv of Queen Elizabeth II's Accession. As T **168a** of St. Helena. Multicoloured.
209 7p. Ice-covered mountains . . 40 40
210 14p. Zavodovski Island . . . 65 65
211 29p. Gulbrandsen Lake . . . 1·00 1·00
212 34p. Three portraits of Queen Elizabeth . . . . 1·10 1·25
213 68p. Queen Elizabeth II . . . 1·60 1·75

32 Adult Teal and Young Bird

1992. Endangered Species. Georgian Teal ("South Georgia Teal"). Multicoloured.
214 2p. Type **32** 50 20
215 6p. Adult with eggs 60 30
216 12p. Teals swimming 80 50
217 20p. Adult and two chicks . . 1·00 90

1992. 10th Anniv of Liberation. As T **169** of St. Helena. Multicoloured.
218 14p.+6p. King Edward Point 70 70
219 29p.+11p. "Queen Elizabeth 2" (liner) in Cumberland Bay . . . . 1·50 1·25
220 34p.+16p. Royal Marines hoisting Union Jack on South Sandwich Islands . . 1·90 1·60
221 68p.+32p. H.M.S. "Endurance" (ice patrol ship) and Westland Wasp helicopter . . . . 3·50 3·00
MS222 116 × 116 mm. Nos. 218/21 6·00 6·00

33 Disused Whale Factory, Grytviken

1993. Opening of South Georgia Whaling Museum. Multicoloured.
223 15p. Type **33** 55 60
224 31p. Whaler's lighter and whale bones . . . . 1·00 1·10
225 36p. Aerial view of King Edward Cove . . . . . . 1·25 1·40
226 72p. Museum building . . . 2·25 2·75

34 Pair of Swimming Penguins

1993. Macaroni Penguin. Multicoloured.
227 16p. Type **34** 60 45
228 34p. Group of penguins . . . 1·25 1·00
229 39p. Two juvenile penguins 1·40 1·25
230 78p. Two adult penguins . . 2·25 2·25

35 Hourglass Dolphin

1994. Whales and Dolphins. Multicoloured.
231 1p. Type **35** 65 70
232 2p. Southern right whale dolphin 80 80
233 5p. Long-finned pilot whale 1·25 1·00
234 8p. Southern bottlenose whale . . . . 1·40 1·00
235 9p. Killer whale . . . . . . 1·40 1·00
236 10p. Minke whale . . . . . 1·40 1·00
237 20p. Sei whale . . . . 1·75 1·25
238 25p. Humpback whale . . . . 1·75 1·25
239 50p. Southern right whale . . 2·75 1·75
240 £1 Sperm whale . . . . . . 3·75 3·00
241 £3 Fin whale . . . . 7·00 7·00
242 £5 Blue whale . . . . 11·00 11·00

1994. "Hong Kong '94" International Stamp Exhibition. Nos. 227/30 optd **HONG KONG '94** and emblem.
243 16p. Type **34** . . . . 80 1·25
244 34p. Group of penguins . . . 1·40 2·25
245 39p. Two juvenile penguins 1·60 2·50
246 78p. Two adult penguins . . 2·50 3·25

36 Bull Elephant Seals

1994. "Life in the Freezer". Scenes from the B.B.C. Natural History Unit series. Multicoloured.
247 17p. Type **36** 50 75
248 35p. Young fur seal (vert) . . 90 1·50
249 40p. Pair of grey-headed albatrosses . . . . 1·60 1·75
250 65p. King penguins in courtship display (vert) . . 2·50 2·75

37 Map of Jason Harbour

1994. Centenary of C. A. Larsen's First Voyage to South Georgia. Multicoloured.
251 17p. Type **37** 60 75
252 35p. "Castor" (whaling ship), 1886 . . . . 1·10 1·50
253 40p. "Hertha" (whaling ship), 1886 . . . . 1·25 1·60
254 65p. "Jason" (whaling ship), 1881 . . . . 2·25 1·75

1994. 50th Anniv of Second World War. As T **182a** of St. Helena. Multicoloured.
255 50p. H.M.S. "Queen of Bermuda" (armed merchant cruiser), Leith Harbour . . . . 1·75 2·25
256 50p. 4-inch coastal gun, Hansen Point . . . . . . 1·75 2·25
MS257 75 × 85 mm. £1 Reverse of 1939–45 war medal (vert) . . . 2·25 2·50
Nos. 255/6 were printed together, se-tenant, forming a composite design.

38 "Damien II" (research schooner)

1995. Sailing Ships. Multicoloured.
258 35p. Type **38** . . . . 1·25 1·75
259 40p. "Curlew" (cutter) . . . 1·40 1·75
260 76p. "Mischief" (yacht) . . . 2·25 2·75

39 Sir Ernest Shackleton and Ridge 2493

1996. 80th Anniv of Sir Ernest Shackleton's Trek across South Georgia. Multicoloured.
261 15p. Type **39** 85 90
262 20p. Frank Worsley and King Haakon Bay . . . . 90 1·00
263 30p. Map of route . . . . . 1·10 1·25
264 65p. Tom Crean and Manager's villa, Stromness whaling station . . . . . 1·40 1·75

40 Bearded Penguin swimming

1996. Bearded Penguins ("Chinstrap Penguins"). Multicoloured.
265 17p. Type **40** 55 55
266 35p. Mutual display 90 90
267 40p. Adult feeding chicks . . 1·10 1·10
268 76p. Feeding on krill . . . . 1·90 1·90

1997. Return of Hong Kong to China Sheet 130 × 90 mm, containing No. 268.
MS269 76p. Feeding on krill . . 2·00 2·25

1997. Golden Wedding of Queen Elizabeth and Prince Philip. As T **192a** of St. Helena. Multicoloured.
270 15p. Queen Elizabeth wearing red hat, 1996 . . . . 60 50
271 15p. Prince Philip in carriage-driving at Royal Windsor Horse Show 60 50
272 17p. Queen Elizabeth with show jumping team, 1993 70 55
273 17p. Prince Philip smiling . . 70 55
274 40p. Princess Anne on horseback and Queen Elizabeth . . . . 1·60 1·40
275 40p. Zara Phillips horse riding and Prince Philip . . 1·60 1·40
MS276 110 × 70 mm. £1.50 Queen Elizabeth and Prince Philip in landau (horiz) . . . . 3·50 3·75
Nos. 270/1, 272/3 and 274/5 respectively were printed together, se-tenant, with the backgrounds forming composite designs.

41 Reindeer

1998. Wildlife. Sheet, 138 × 84 mm, containing T **41** and similar horiz designs. Multicoloured.
MS277 35p. Type **41**; 35p. Antartic tern; 35p. Grey-headed albatross; 35p. King penguin; 35p. Prickly burr; 35p. Fur seal . . . . . . 6·50 5·00

1998. Diana, Princess of Wales Commemoration. Sheet, 145 × 70 mm, containing vert designs as T **194** of St. Helena. Multicoloured.
MS278 35p. Laughing, 1983; 35p. In eveing dress, 1996; 35p. Wearing red jacket, 1991; 35p. Wearing white jacket, 1996 (sold at £1.40 + 20p. charity premium) . . . . 3·50 3·50

42 "Explorer" (cruise ship)

1998. Tourism. Multicoloured.
279 30p. Type **42** . . . . 1·50 1·10
280 35p. Wandering albatross . . . 1·75 1·25
281 40p. Elephant seal . . . . . 1·75 1·25
282 65p. Post Office at King Edward Point . . . . . . 2·00 1·75

43 Grytviken and Sugartop Mountain

1999. Island Views. Multicoloured.
283 9p. Type **43** 75 60
284 17p. "Dias" and "Albatros" (abandoned sealing ships), Grytviken . . . . 1·00 85
285 35p. King Edward Point . . 1·40 1·25
286 40p. South Georgia from the sea . . . . 1·40 1·25
287 65p. Grytviken Church . . . 1·75 1·50

44 H.M.S. "Resolution" in Antartic, 1773

45 Bearded Penguins ("Chinstrap Penguins")

1999. "Australia '99" World Stamp Exhibition, Melbourne. Sheet 120 × 83 mm.
MS288 **44** £1.50 multicoloured 4·25 3·50

1999. "Queen Elizabeth the Queen Mother's Century". As T **199** of St. Helena. Multicoloured. (except 30p., £1).
289 25p. Visiting air-raid shelter, 1940 . . . . 1·00 80
290 30p. With grandchildren, 1970 (black) . . . . . . 1·10 90
291 35p. With Prince William, 1994 . . . . 1·25 1·00
292 40p. Presenting colour to Royal Anglian Regt . . . 1·40 1·10
MS293 145 × 70 mm. £1 Lady Elizabeth Boewes-Lyon, 1914, and funeral of Queen Victoria, 1901 (black) . . . . 3·00 3·50

1999. Birds. Multicoloured.
294 1p. Type **45** 10 10
295 2p. White-chinned petrel (horiz) 10 10
296 5p. Grey-backed storm petrel 10 10
297 10p. South Georgia pipit . . 20 25
298 11p. Grey-headed albatross (horiz) 20 25
299 30p. Blue petrel 60 65
300 35p. Black-browed albatross (horiz) 70 75
301 40p. Georgian diving petrel ("South Georgia Diving Petrel") (horiz) 80 85
302 50p. Macaroni penguin . . . 1·00 1·10
303 £1 Light-mantled sooty albatross (horiz) . . . . . 2·00 2·10
304 £3 Georgian teal ("South Georgia Pintail") (horiz) 6·00 6·25
305 £5 King penguin . . . . . . 10·00 10·50

46 Sunrise

1999. New Millennium. Multicoloured.
306 11p. Type **46** 65 65
307 11p. Grytviken Church . . . 65 65
308 11p. Nesting black-browed and grey-headed albatross 65 65
309 35p. Sunset . . . . 1·00 1·00
310 35p. Reindeer . . . . 1·00 1·00
311 35p. Macaroni penguins and chicks . . . . 1·00 1·00

47 Shackleton in "James Caird" crossing Scotia Sea

2000. Shackleton's Trans-Antarctic Expedition, 1914–17, Commemoration. Multicoloured.
312 35p. Type **47** . . . . 1·25 1·25
313 40p. Shackleton and party approaching Stromness Whaling Station . . . . . 1·40 1·40
314 65p. Shackleton's Cross at Hope Point . . . . 2·00 2·00

48 Prince William at Zurich Airport, 1994

2000. 18th Birthday of Prince William. Multicoloured.
315 25p. Type **48** . . . . 1·00 90
316 30p. Skiing in Klosters, Switzerland, 1994 . . . . 1·10 95
317 35p. Prince William in 1997 (horiz) . . . . 1·25 1·10
318 40p. Prince William waving, 1999 (horiz) . . . . . . 1·40 1·25
MS319 175 × 95 mm. 50p. In Parachute Regiment uniform, 1986 (horiz) and Nos. 315/18 7·50 6·00

49 King Penguins swimming

2000. King Penguins. Multicoloured.
320 37p. Type **49** . . . . 1·40 1·40
321 37p. Adult penguin with chicks . . . . 1·40 1·40
322 43p. Penguins courting . . . 1·60 1·60
323 43p. Penguins on nests . . . 1·60 1·60

50 R.F.A. *Tidespring* (tanker)

2001. Royal Fleet Auxiliary Vessels. Multicoloured.
324 37p. Type **50** . . . . 1·40 1·40
325 37p. R.F.A. *Sir Percivale* (landing ship) . . . . . . 1·40 1·40
326 43p. R.F.A. *Diligence* (maintenance ship) . . . . 1·60 1·60
327 43p. R.F.A. *Gold Rover* (tanker) . . . . 1·60 1·60

51 Mackerel Icefish

2001. 20th Anniv of Convention for the Conservation of Antarctic Marine Resources. Marine Life. Multicoloured.
328 33p. Type **51** 70 80
329 37p. Spiney back crab . . . 80 90
330 37p. Krill (vert) 80 90
331 43p. Blenny rockcod ("Toothfish") (vert) . . . . 90 1·00

2002. Golden Jubilee. As T **211** of St. Helena.
332 20p. brown, turquoise and gold 65 65
333 37p. multicoloured . . . . . 1·00 1·00
334 43p. black, turquoise and gold . . . . 1·25 1·25
335 50p. multicoloured . . . . . 1·50 1·50
MS336 162 × 95 mm. Nos. 332/5 and 50p. multicoloured . . . . . . 6·00 6·50

DESIGNS—HORIZ (as Type **211** of St. Helena): 20p. Queen Elizabeth with corgi, 1952; 37p. Queen Elizabeth and Prince Philip in evening dress; 43p. Princess Elizabeth looking at stamp album, 1946; 50p. Queen Elizabeth at garden party, 1999. VERT (38 × 51 mm.): 50p. Queen Elizabeth after Annigoni.

Designs as Nos. 332/5 in No. **MS**336 omit the gold frame around each stamp and the "Golden Jubilee 1952-2002" inscription.

52 Fin Whale

2002. South Atlantic Sea Mammals. Multicoloured.
337 10p. Type **52** 40 40
338 10p. Blue whale 40 40
339 20p. Sperm whale 60 60
340 37p. Head of leopard seal . . 85 90
341 37p. Leopard seal on ice floe 85 90
342 43p. Elephant seal . . . . . 1·00 1·10
MS343 90 × 67 mm. £1.50 Elephant seal . . . . 3·75 4·25

2002. Queen Elizabeth the Queen Mother Commemoration. As T **215** of St. Helena.
344 22p. brown, gold and purple 45 50
345 40p. multicoloured 80 85
346 45p. black, gold and purple 90 95
347 95p. multicoloured . . . . . 1·90 2·00
MS348 145 × 70 mm. Nos. 346/7 2·75 3·00

DESIGNS: 22p. Queen Elizabeth at British Red Cross Society, London; 40p. Queen Mother at Birthday Variety Show, 1990; 45p. Duchess of York and corgi, 1936; 95p. Queen Mother at Royal College of Music, 1989.

Designs in No. **MS**348 omit the "1900–2002" inscription and the coloured frame.

53 Antarctic Fur Seals on Ice

2002. Fur Seals. Multicoloured.
349 40p. Type **53** 80 85
350 40p. Fur seal underwater . . 80 85
351 45p. Fur seal in winter coat 90 95
352 45p. Competing males . . . 90 95

54 Pair of Grey-headed Albatrosses on Nest

2003. Endangered Species. Grey-headed Albatross. Multicoloured.
353 40p. Type **54** 40 45
354 45p. Adult with chick 90 95
355 45p. Two adults 90 95
356 70p. Grey-headed Albatross in flight . . . . 1·40 1·50

SOUTH KASAI Pt. 14

100 centimes = 1 franc.

Region of Zaire around the town of Bakwanga. The area was declared autonomous in 1960, during the upheaval following independence, but returned to the control of the central government in October 1962.

Various stamps of Belgian Congo were overprinted "ETAT AUTONOME DU SUD-KASAI" and some surcharged in addition with new values. These were put on sale at the Philatelic Bureau in Brussels and were also valid for use in South Kasai but no supplies were sent out.

1 Leopard's Head and "V"

2 A. D. Kalonji

1961.
1 **1** 1f. multicoloured 10 10
2 1f.50 multicoloured 10 10
3 3f.50 multicoloured 15 15
4 8f. multicoloured 25 25
5 10f. multicoloured 30 30

1961.
6 **2** 6f.50 brown, blue and black 20 20
7 9f. light brown, brown & black 25 25
8 14f.50 brown, green and black 40 40
9 20f. multicoloured . . . . . . 45 1·45

SOUTH RUSSIA Pt. 10

Stamps of various anti-Bolshevist forces and temporary governments in S. Russia after the revolution.

100 kopeks = 1 rouble.

A. KUBAN TERRITORY: COSSACK GOVERNMENT

1918. Arms type of Russia surch. Imperf or perf.
8 **22** 25k. on 1k. orange 25 45
2 50k. on 2k. green 15 25
23 70k. on 1k. orange 30 55
10 70k. on 5k. red 45 75
11 1r. on 3k. red 20 50
13 **23** 3r. on 4k. red . . . . . . 9·00 11·00
14 10r. on 4k. red . . . . . . 4·00 5·00
15 **10** 10r. on 15k. blue and purple 70 1·10
16 **22** 25r. on 3k. red . . . . . . 4·00 3·00
17 25r. on 7k. blue . . . . . . 30·00 60·00
18 **10** 25r. on 14k. red and blue 70·00 £100
19 25r. on 25k. mauve & green 35·00 65·00

1919. Postal Savings Bank stamps of Russia surch.
20 10r. on 1k. red on buff . . . 40·00 70·00
21 10r. on 5k. green on buff . . . 40·00 70·00
22 10r. on 10k. brown on buff . . 75·00 £225

B. DON TERRITORY: COSSACK GOVERNMENT

1919. Arms type of Russia surch in figures only. Imperf or perf.
25 **22** 25k. on 1k. orange 20 45
29 25k. on 2k. green 20 40
30 25k. on 3k. red 25 60
31 **23** 25k. on 4k. red 20 45
32 **22** 50k. on 7k. blue . . . . . 1·75 2·75

10 T. Ermak (16th century Cossack Ataman)
13

1919. Currency stamp with arms and seven-line print on back used for postage.
33 **10** 20k. green . . . . 18·00 £150

C. CRIMEA: REGIONAL GOVERNMENT

1919. Arms type of Russia surch **35 Kon**. Imperf.
34 **22** 35k. on 1k. orange 15 40

1919. Currency and postage stamp. Arms and inscription on back. Imperf.
35 **13** 50k. brown on buff . . . . 25·00 80·00

D. SOUTH RUSSIA: GOVERNMENT OF GENERAL DENIKIN

1919. Nos. G6 and G10 of Ukraine surch in figs.
36 **G 1** 35k. on 10s. brown . . . 15·00 30·00
37 **G 5** 70k. on 50s. red . . . . 30·00 50·00

15

16

1919. Imperf or perf.
38 **15** 5k. yellow 10 15
39 10k. green 10 15
40 15k. red 10 15
41 35k. blue 10 15
42 70k. blue 10 15
43 **16** 1r. red and brown 15 35
44 2r. yellow and lilac 35 55
45 3r. green and brown 35 60
46 5r. violet and blue . . . . 1·00 1·50
47 7r. pink and green . . . . 80 1·75
48 10r. grey and red . . . . . 1·50 2·00

Higher values similar to Type **16** are bogus.

E. SOUTH RUSSIA: GOVERNMENT OF GENERAL WRANGEL

5
пять
рублей.
(17)

ЮГЪ
РОССІИ.
100
рублей.
(18)

1920. Crimea issue. Surch with T **17**. (a) On Arms types of Russia. Imperf or perf.
52 **22** 5r. on 5k. red . . . . . . 2·00 3·75
54 **14** 5r. on 20k. red and blue . . 2·00 3·75

(b) On No. 41 of South Russia.
55 **15** 5r. on 35k. blue . . . . . . 7·50 12·00

1920. Arms type of Russia surch with T **18**.
56 **22** 100r. on 1k. orange . . . . 2·50

SOUTH WEST AFRICA Pt. 1

A territory in S.W. Africa formerly the German Colony of German South West Africa (q.v. in Volume 2). Administered by South Africa until 1990 when it became independent as Namibia.

1923. 12 pence = 1 shilling;
20 shillings = 1 pound.
1961. 100 cents = 1 rand.

NOTE. Stamps overprinted for South West Africa are always of South Africa, except where otherwise indicated."Bilingual" in heading indicates that the stamps are inscribed alternately in English and Afrikaans throughout the sheet, "Bilingual" is not repeated in the heading where bilingual stamps of South Africa are overprinted.Our prices for surch issues are for mint bilingual pairs and used single stamps of either inscription.

1923. Optd **South West Africa.** or **Zuid-West Afrika.** alternately
1 **2** ½d. green . . . . 2·50 1·00
2 1d. red . . . . 3·25 1·00
3 2d. purple . . . . 4·25 1·50
4 3d. blue . . . . 7·50 2·75
5 4d. orange and green . . . . 13·00 4·00
6 6d. black and violet . . . . 8·00 4·00
7 1s. yellow . . . . 23·00 5·00
8 1s.3d. violet . . . . 30·00 5·50
9 2s.6d. purple and green . . . 60·00 18·00
10 5s. purple and blue . . . . £140 50·00
11 10s. blue and green £1300 £400
12 £1 green and red £700 £250

1923. Optd **Zuidwest Afrika.** or **South West Africa.*** alternately.
16 **2** ½d. green . . . . 6·00 3·75
30 1d. red . . . . 3·25 1·40
18 2d. purple . . . . 5·50 1·25
19 3d. blue . . . . 5·00 1·25
20 4d. yellow and green . . . . 6·00 2·75
34 6d. black and violet . . . . 9·00 5·00
35 1s. yellow . . . . 11·00 5·00
36 1s.3d. violet . . . . 15·00 5·00
37 2s.6d. purple and green . . . 29·00 10·00
38 5s. purple and blue . . . . . 42·00 14·00
39 10s. blue and green . . . . . 65·00 20·00
40 £1 green and red . . . . . . £225 55·00

*The English overprint is the same, for the purposes of this catalogue, as that on Nos. 1/12.

1926. Optd **South West Africa.** (on stamps inscr in English) or **Suidwes Afrika.** (on stamps inscr in Afrikaans) alternately.
41 **6** ½d. black and green . . . . 3·75 1·00
42 **7** 1d. black and red . . . . . 3·00 80
49 **11** 2d. grey and purple . . . . 4·75 1·75
50 – 3d. black and red . . . . . 4·75 2·50
43 **8** 6d. green and orange . . . 25·00 7·00
51 – 1s. brown and blue . . . . 15·00 4·00
52 – 2s.6d. green and brown . . 35·00 13·00
53 – 5s. black and green . . . . 75·00 20·00
54 – 10s. blue and brown . . . . 65·00 20·00

1926. Optd **SOUTH WEST AFRICA** in two lines or **SUIDWES-AFRIKA** in one line. Imperf or perf.
44A **10** 4d. blue . . . . 75 3·00

1927. Optd as Nos. 41/2 and 43 but with Afrikaans opt on stamp inscr in English and vice versa.
45 **6** ½d. black and green . . . . 1·60 80
46 **7** 1d. black and red . . . . . 1·60 50
47 **8** 6d. green and orange . . . . 11·00 3·00

1927. Optd **SOUTH WEST AFRICA** in one line. Imperf.
48 **10** 4d. blue . . . . 6·00 19·00

1927. Optd **S.W.A.**
56 **2** 1s.3d. violet . . . . 1·25 6·50
57 £1 olive and red . . . . . . 90·00 £160

1927. Optd **S.W.A.**
58 **6** ½d. black and green . . . . 2·00 80
59 **7** 1d. black and red . . . . . 1·25 55
60 **11** 2d. grey and purple . . . . 9·00 1·50
61 – 3d. black and red . . . . . 6·00 3·25
62 – 4d. brown . . . . 15·00 7·00
63 **8** 6d. green and orange . . . 11·00 2·75
64 – 1s. brown and blue . . . . 20·00 5·00
65 – 2s.6d. green and brown . . 40·00 12·00
66 – 5s black and green . . . . 60·00 18·00
67 – 10s. blue and brown . . . . £100 28·00

1930. Air. Optd **S.W.A.**
72 **17** 4d. green . . . . 1·25 6·00
73 1s. orange . . . . 3·75 15·00

12 Kori Bustard

1931. Bilingual pairs.
74 **12** ½d. black and green . . . . 2·25 10
75 – 1d. blue and red . . . . . 2·25 10
76 – 2d. blue and brown 70 15
77 – 3d. dull blue and blue . . . 70 15
78 – 4d. green and purple . . . . 1·75 20
79 – 6d. blue and brown . . . . 1·50 20
80 – 1s. brown and blue . . . . 1·50 25
81 – 1s.3d. violet and yellow . . 7·50 50
82 – 2s.6d. red and grey . . . . 20·00 1·75
83 – 5s. green and brown . . . . 16·00 2·75

84 – 10s. brown and green 45·00 6·00
85 – £1 red and green 70·00 10·00
DESIGNS: 1d. Cape Cross; 2d. Bogenfels; 3d. Windhoek; 4d. Waterberg; 6d. Luderitz Bay; 1s. Bush scene; 1s.3d. Elands; 2s.6d. Mountain zebra and wildebeests; 5s. Herero huts; 10s. Welwitschia plant; £1 Okuwahaken Falls.

24 Fokker Monoplane over Windhoek

1931. Air. Bilingual pairs.
86 **24** 3d. brown and blue 25·00 2·50
87 – 10d. black and brown 35·00 5·00
DESIGN: 10d. Handley Page H.P.25 Hendon biplane over Windhoek.

26

1935. Silver Jubilee.
88 **26** 1d. black and red 1·00 25
89 2d. black and brown 1·00 25
90 3d. black and blue 7·50 18·00
91 6d. black and purple 3·00 10·00

1935. Voortrekker Memorial. Nos. 50/3 of South Africa optd **S.W.A.**
92 ½d.+½d. black and green 1·50 75
93 1d.+½d. black and pink 1·50 40
94 2d.+1d. green and purple 5·50 80
95 3d.+1½d. green and blue 16·00 4·00

27 Mail Transport **28**

1937. Bilingual pair.
96 **27** 1½d. brown 22·00 25

1937. Coronation. Bilingual pairs.
97 **28** ½d. black and green 40 15
98 1d. black and red 40 15
99 1½d. black and orange 40 15
100 2d. black and brown 40 15
101 3d. black and blue 50 15
102 4d. black and purple 50 10
103 6d. black and yellow 50 20
104 1s. black and grey 55 25

1938. Voortrekker Centenary Fund. Nos. 76/9 of South Africa optd **S.W.A.**
105 ½d.+½d. blue and green 8·00 1·75
106 1d.+1d. blue and red 20·00 1·00
107 1½d.+1½d. brown and green 22·00 2·75
108 3d.+3d. blue 45·00 6·50

1938. Voortrekker Commem. Nos. 80/1 of South Africa optd **S.W.A.**
109 1d. blue and red 10·00 1·50
110 1½d. blue and brown 13·00 1·75

1939. 250th Anniv of Landing of Huguenots in South Africa. Nos. 82/4 of South Africa optd **S.W.A.**
111 ½d.+½d. brown and green 13·00 1·10
112 1d.+1d. green and red 16·00 1·25
113 1½d.+1½d. green and purple 24·00 1·25

1941. War Effort. Nos. 88/94a of South Africa optd **SWA.**
114a ½d. green 65 15
115 1d. red 55 15
116 1½d. green 55 15
121 2d. violet 50 60
117 3d. blue 22·00 1·00
118 4d. brown 6·50 1·00
119 6d. orange 2·50 50
122 1s. brown 60 60
120 1s.3d. brown 11·00 1·25

1943. War Effort. Nos. 97/104 of South Africa optd **SWA.**
123 ½d. green (T) 50 10
124 1d. red (T) 2·00 10
125 1½d. brown (P) 50 10
126 2d. violet (P) 6·00 10
127 3d. blue (T) 3·25 45
129 4d. green (T) 2·00 45
128 6d. orange (P) 5·50 30
130b 1s. brown (P) 4·00 30

The units refered to above consist of pairs (P) or triplets (T).

1945. Victory. Nos. 108/10 of South Africa optd **SWA.**
131 1d. brown and red 25 10
132 2d. blue and violet 30 10
133 3d. blue 1·25 10

1947. Royal Visit. Nos. 111/13 of South Africa optd **SWA.**
134 1d. black and red 10 10
135 2d. violet 10 10
136 3d. blue 15 10

1948. Silver Wedding. No. 125 of South Africa optd **SWA.**
137 3d. blue and silver 1·00 10

1949. 75th Anniv of U.P.U. Nos 128/30 of South Africa optd **SWA.**
138 ½d. mauve 75 25
139 1½d. red 75 15
140 3d. blue 1·00 25

1949. Inauguration of Voortrekker Monument Pretoria. Nos. 131/3 of South Africa optd **S W A.**
141 1d. mauve 10 10
142 1½d. green 10 10
143 3d. blue 15 35

1952. Tercentenary of Landing of Van Riebeeck. Nos. 136/40 of South Africa optd **SWA.**
144 ½d. purple and sepia 10 50
145 1d. green 10 10
146 2d. violet 50 10
147 4½d. blue 30 2·75
148 1s. brown 75 20

33 Queen Elizabeth II and "Catophracies alexandri" **34** "Two Bucks" (rock painting)

1953. Coronation. Native Flowers.
149 **33** 1d. red 40 10
150 – 2d. green ("Bauhinia macrantha") 40 10
151 – 4d. mauve ("Caralluma nebrownii") 50 30
152 – 6d. blue ("Gloriosa virescens") 50 60
153 – 1s. brown ("Rhigozum tricholotum") 65 20

1954.
154 **34** 1d. red 30 10
155 – 2d. brown 35 10
156 – 3d. purple 1·25 10
157 – 4d. black 1·50 10
158 – 4½d blue 70 40
159 – 6d. green 70 70
160 – 1s. mauve 70 50
161 – 1s.3d. red 2·00 1·00
162 – 1s.6d. purple 2·00 50
163 – 2s.6d. brown 4·50 70
164 – 5s. blue 6·00 2·75
165 – 10s. green 32·00 15·00
DESIGNS—VERT: 2d. "White Lady" (rock painting); 4½d. Karakul lamb; 6d. Ovambo woman blowing horn; 1s. Ovambo woman; 1s. 3d. Herero woman; 1s. 6d. Ovambo girl; 2s. 6d. Lioness; 5s. Gemsbok; 10s. African elephant. HORIZ: 3d. "Rhinoceros Hunt" (rock painting); 4d. "White Elephant and Giraffe" (rock painting).

46 G.P.O., Windhoek **59** "Agricultural Development"

1961.
171 **46** ½c. brown and blue 60 10
172 – 1c. brown and lilac 15 10
173 – 1½c. violet and orange 20 10
174 – 2c. green and yellow 75 60
175 – 2½c. brown and blue 35 10
176 – 3c. blue and red 4·25 40
177 – 3½c. blue and green 85 15
209 – 4c. brown and blue 1·50 2·50
178 – 5c. red and blue 6·50 10
211 – 6c. sepia and yellow 7·00 9·00
179 – 7½c. brown and lemon 70 15
213 – 9c. blue and yellow 7·50 10·00
180 – 10c. blue and yellow 1·75 60
181 – 12½c. blue and yellow 60 40
182 – 15c. brown and blue 14·00 3·25
183 – 20c. brown and orange 4·00 30
184 – 50c. green and orange 6·00 1·50
185 – 1r. yellow, purple and blue 10·00 15·00

DESIGNS—VERT: 1c. Finger Rock; 1½c. Mounted Soldier Monument; 2c. Quivertree; 3c. Greater flamingoes and Swakopmund Lighthouse; 3½c. Fishing industry; 5c. Greater flamingo; 6c., 7½c. German Lutheran Church, Windhoek; 10c. Diamond; 20c. Topaz; 50c. Tourmaline; 1r. Heliodor. HORIZ: 2½c., 4c. S.W.A. House, Windhoek; 9c., 12½c. Fort Namutoni; 15c. Hardap Dam.
See also Nos. 224/26.

1963. Opening of Hardap Dam.
192 **59** 3c. brown and green 30 15

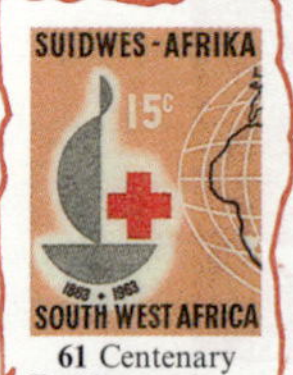

61 Centenary Emblem and part of Globe **62** Interior of Assembly Hall

1963. Centenary of Red Cross.
193 – 7½c. red, black and blue 4·00 5·00
194 **61** 15c. red, black and brown 6·00 8·00
DESIGN: 7½c. Centenary emblem and map.

1964. Opening of Legislative Assembly Hall, Windhoek.
195 **62** 3c. blue and orange 50 30

63 Calvin **64** Mail Runner of 1890

1965. 400th Death Anniv of Calvin (Protestant reformer).
196 **63** 2½c. purple and gold 50 15
197 15c. green and gold 2·25 3·75

1965. 75th Anniv of Windhoek.
198 **64** 3c. sepia and red 50 15
199 – 15c. brown and green 1·25 2·25
DESIGN: 15c. Kurt von Francois (founder).

66 Dr. H. Vedder **70** Pres. Swart

67 Camelthorn Tree

1966. 90th Birth Anniv of Dr. H. Vedder (philosopher and writer).
200 **66** 3c. green and orange 30 15
201 15c. brown and blue 70 40

1967. Verwoerd Commemoration.
217 **67** 2½c. black and green 15 10
218 – 3c. brown and blue 15 10
219 – 15c. brown and purple 55 45

DESIGNS—VERT: 3c. Waves breaking against rock; 15c. Dr. H. F. Verwoerd.

1968. Swart Commemoration. Inscr in German, Afrikaans or English.
220 **70** 3c. red, blue and black 30 15
221 – 15c. red, green and olive 1·00 1·25
DESIGN: 15c. Pres. and Mrs. Swart.

1970. Water 70 Campaign. As Nos. 299/300 of South Africa, but inscr "SWA".
222 2½c. green, blue and brown 50 30
223 3c. blue and buff 50 30

1970. As Nos. 171 etc, but with "POSGELD" "INKOMSTE" omitted and larger figure of value.
224 **46** ½c. brown and blue 1·50 30
225 – 1½c. violet and orange 13·00 16·00
226 – 2c. green and yellow 5·00 40

1970. 150th Anniv of Bible Society of South Africa. As Nos. 301/2 of South Africa. Inscr "SWA"
228 2½c. multicoloured 1·50 10
229 12½c. gold, black and blue 5·00 6·00

1971. "Interstex" Stamp Exhibition, Cape Town. As No. 303 of South Africa. Inscr "SWA".
230 5c. blue, black and yellow 3·25 1·50

1971. 10th Anniv of Antarctic Treaty. As No. 304 of South Africa. Inscr "SWA".
231 12½c. black, blue and red 20·00 16·00

1971. 10th Anniv of South African Republic. As Nos. 305/6 of South Africa. Inscr "SWA".
232 2c. flesh and red 3·25 75
233 4c. green and black 3·25 75

1972. Centenary of S.P.C.A. As No. 312 of South Africa. Inscr "SWA".
234 5c. multicoloured 3·00 1·00

73 "Red Sand-dunes, Eastern South-West Africa"

1973. Scenery. Paintings by Adolph Jentsch. Multicoloured.
235 2c. Type **73** 75 75
236 4c. "After the Rain" 85 1·00
237 5c. "Barren Country" 1·00 1·25
238 10c. "Schaap River" (vert) 1·25 1·75
239 15c. "Namib Desert" (vert) 2·25 3·25

74 "Sarcocaulon rigidum" **75** "Euphorbia virosa"

1973. Succulents. Multicoloured. (a) As T **74**.
241 1c. Type **74** 15 10
242a 2c. "Lapidaria margaretae" 20 10
243 3c. "Titanopsis schwantesii" 20 10
244 4c. "Lithops karasmontana" 25 10
245b 5c. "Caralluma lugardii" 50 20
246 6c. "Dinteranthus microspermus" 1·75 2·25
247 7c. "Conophytum gratum" 1·25 2·25
248 9c. "Huernia oculata" 65 50
249b 10c. "Gasteria pillansii" 40 30
250 14c. "Stapelia pedunculata" 1·75 2·75
251 15c. "Fenestraria aurantiaca" 65 30
252 20c. "Decabelone grandiflora" 4·75 3·50
253 25c. "Hoodia bainii" 4·25 3·00
(b) As T **75**.
254 30c. Type **75** 75 80
255a 50c. "Pachypodium namaquanum" (vert) 75 1·25
256 1r. "Welwitschia bainesii" 1·00 5·00

1973. As Nos. 241/2a and 245. Colours changed.
257 **18** 1c. black and mauve 70 60
258 – 2c. black and yellow 50 50
259a – 5c. black and red 1·00 60

76 Chat-shrikes **77** Giraffe, Antelope and Spoor

1974. Rare Birds. Multicoloured.
260 4c. Type **76** 3·25 1·00
261 5c. Peach-faced lovebirds 4·25 1·50
262 10c. Damaraland rock jumper 9·00 5·50
263 15c. Ruppell's parrots 12·00 9·50

1974. Twyfelfontein Rock-engravings. Mult.
264 4c. Type **77** 1·50 50
265 5c. Elephant, hyena, antelope and spoor 1·50 80
266 15c. Kudu cow (38 × 21 mm) 5·50 7·50

78 Cut Diamond **79** Wagons and Map of the Trek

1974. Diamond Mining. Multicoloured.
267 10c. Type **78** 4·00 5·00
268 15c. Diagram of shore workings 4·00 5·00

1974. Centenary of Thirstland Trek.
269 **79** 4c. multicoloured 75 1·00

80 Peregrine Falcon **81** Kolmannskop (ghost town)

1975. Protected Birds of Prey. Mult.
270 4c. Type **80** 2·00 1·25
271 5c. Verreaux's eagle 2·00 1·75
272 10c. Martial eagle 5·00 5·50
273 15c. Egyptian vulture 5·50 8·00

1975. Historic Monuments. Multicoloured.
274 5c. Type **81** 15 15
275 9c. "Martin Luther" (steam tractor) 30 60
276 15c. Kurt von Francois and Old Fort, Windhoek 50 75

82 "View of Luderitz"

1975. Otto Schroder (painter). Multicoloured.
277 15c. Type **82** 30 60
278 15c. "View of Swakopmund" 30 60
279 15c. "Harbour Scene" 30 60
280 15c. "Quayside, Walvis Bay" 30 60
MS281 122 × 96 mm. Nos. 277/80 1·00 3·50

83 Elephants

1976. Prehistoric Rock Paintings. Mult.
282 4c. Type **83** 35 15
283 10c. Rhinoceros 40 60
284 15c. Antelope 45 70
285 20c. Man with bow and arrow 55 1·00
MS286 121 × 95 mm. Nos. 282/5 1·50 4·00

84 Schwerinsburg

1976. Castles. Multicoloured.
287 10c. Type **84** 20 30
288 15c. Schloss Duwisib 30 50
289 20c. Heynitzburg 30 70

85 Large-toothed Rock Hyrax

1976. Fauna Conservation. Multicoloured.
290 4c. Type **85** 30 20
291 10c. Kirk's dik-dik 50 75
292 15c. Kuhl's tree squirrel 75 1·60

86 The Augustineum, Windhoek

1976. Modern Buildings.
293 **86** 15c. black and yellow 30 60
294 – 20c. black and yellow 40 80
DESIGN: 20c. Katutura Hospital, Windhoek.

87 Ovambo Water Canal System

1976. Water and Electricity Supply. Mult.
295 15c. Type **87** 30 50
296 20c. Ruacana Falls Power Station 40 75

88 Coastline, near Pomona

1977. Namib Desert. Multicoloured.
297 4c. Type **88** 15 15
298 10c. Bush and dunes, Sossusvlei 20 20
299 15c. Plain near Brandberg 35 35
300 20c. Dunes, Sperr Gebiet 40 40

89 Kraal

1977. The Ovambo People.
301 **89** 4c. multicoloured 10 10
302 – 10c. black, orange & brown 20 15
303 – 15c. multicoloured 25 20
304 – 20c. multicoloured 25 35
DESIGNS: 10c. Grain baskets; 15c. Pounding grain; 20c. Women in tribal dress.

90 Terminal Buildings

1977. J. G. Strijdom Airport, Windhoek.
305 **90** 20c. multicoloured 40 30

91 Drostdy, Luderitz

1977. Historic Houses. Multicoloured.
306 5c. Type **91** 15 10
307 10c. Woermannhaus, Swakopmund 25 30
308 15c. Neu-Heusis, Windhoek 30 35
309 20c. Schmelenhaus, Bethanie 40 40
MS310 122 × 96 mm. Nos. 306/9 1·00 2·00

92 Side-winding Adder

1978. Small Animals. Multicoloured.
311 4c. Type **92** 15 10
312 10c. Grant's desert golden mole 25 20
313 15c. Palmato gecko 25 25
314 20c. Namaqua chameleon 25 25

93 Ostrich Hunting

1978. The Bushmen. Each brown, stone and black.
315 4c. Type **93** 30 10
316 10c. Woman carrying ostrich eggs 30 20
317 15c. Hunters kindling fire 40 20
318 20c. Woman with musical instrument 40 30

94 Lutheran Church, Windhoek

1978. Historic Churches.
319 **94** 4c. black and brown 10 10
320 – 10c. black and brown 15 20
321 – 15c. black and pink 20 25
322 – 20c. black and blue 30 35
MS323 125 × 90 mm. Nos. 319/22 75 1·75
DESIGNS: 10c. Lutheran Church, Swakopmund; 15c. Rhenish Mission Church, Otjimbingwe; 20c. Rhenish Missionary Church, Keetmanshoop.

1978. Universal Suffrage. Nos. 244/5, 249b and 251/3 optd **ALGEMENE STEMREG** (Afrikaans), **UNIVERSAL SUFFRAGE** (English) or **ALLGEMEINES WAHLRECHT** (German).
324 4c. "Lithops karasmontana" 10 10
325 5c. "Caralluma lugardii" 10 10
326 10c. "Gasteria pillansii" 10 10
327 15c. "Fenestraria aurantiaca" 10 15
328 20c. "Decabelone grandiflora" 10 15
329 25c. "Hoodia bainii" 15 15
Nos. 324/9 were issued in se-tenant strips of three, each stamp in the strip being optd in either Afrikaans, English or German. The same prices apply for any of the three languages.

96 Greater Flamingo **98** Killer Whale

97 Silver Topaz

1979. Water Birds. Multicoloured.
330 4c. Type **96** 20 10
331 15c. White-breasted cormorant 35 25
332 20c. Chestnut-banded sand plover 35 35
333 25c. Eastern white pelican 35 40

1979. Gemstones. Multicoloured.
334 4c. Type **97** 30 10
335 15c. Aquamarine 65 20
336 20c. Malachite 70 25
337 25c. Amethyst 70 30

1980. Whales. Multicoloured.
338 4c. Type **98** 25 20
339 5c. Humpback whale (38 × 22 mm) 25 20
340 10c. Black right whale (38 × 22 mm) 35 30
341 15c. Sperm whale (58 × 22 mm) 45 75
342 20c. Fin whale (58 × 22 mm) 55 90
343 25c. Blue whale (88 × 22 mm) 65 1·25
MS344 202 × 95 mm. Nos. 338/43 2·75 5·00

99 Impala

1980. 25th Anniv of Division of Nature Conservation and Tourism. Antelopes. Mult.
345 5c. Type **99** 15 10
346 10c. Topi 15 10
347 15c. Roan antelope 25 15
348 20c. Sable antelope 25 20

100 Black-backed Jackal **101** Meerkat

1980. Wildlife. Multicoloured.
349 1c. Type **100** 15 10
350 2c. Hunting dog 15 10
351 3c. Brown hyena 15 10
352 4c. Springbok 15 10
353 5c. Gemsbok 15 10
354 6c. Greater kudu 15 10
355 7c. Mountain zebra (horiz) 40 20
356 8c. Cape porcupine (horiz) 20 10
357 9c. Ratel (horiz) 20 10
358 10c. Cheetah (horiz) 30 10
358a 11c. Blue wildebeest 40 30
358b 12c. African buffalo (horiz) 70 1·50
358c 14c. Caracal (horiz) 3·00 2·25
359 15c. Hippopotamus (horiz) 30 10
359b 16c. Warthog (horiz) 1·75 1·75
360 20c. Eland (horiz) 30 10
361 25c. Black rhinoceros (horiz) 50 20
362 30c. Lion (horiz) 50 20
363 50c. Giraffe 50 30
364 1r. Leopard 50 55
365 2r. African elephant 50 90

1980. Wildlife.
366 **101** 1c. brown 20 20
367 – 2c. blue 20 20
368 – 5c. green 30 30
DESIGNS: 2c. Savanna monkey; 5c. Chacma baboon.

102 Von Bach

1980. Water Conservation. Dams. Mult.
369 5c. Type **102** 10 10
370 10c. Swakoppoort 15 10
371 15c. Naute 15 20
372 20c. Hardap 15 25

103 View of Fish River Canyon

1981. Fish River Canyon.
373 – 5c. multicoloured 10 10
374 – 15c. multicoloured 15 20
375 – 20c. multicoloured 20 25
376 **103** 25c. multicoloured 20 30
DESIGNS: 5c. to 20c. Various views of Canyon.

104 "Aloe erinacea"

1981. Aloes. Multicoloured.
377 5c. Type **104** 15 10
378 15c. "Aloe viridiflora" 35 25
379 20c. "Aloe pearsonii" 40 25
380 25c. "Aloe littoralis" 50 30

105 Paul Weiss-Haus

1981. Historic Buildings of Luderitz.
381 5c. Type **105** 10 10
382 15c. Deutsche Afrika Bank 15 20
383 20c. Schroederhaus 20 30
384 25c. Altes Postamt 20 35
MS385 125 × 90 mm. Nos. 381/4 65 1·00

106 Salt Pan

1981. Salt Industry. Multicoloured.

386	5c. Type **106**	10	10
387	15c. Dumping and washing	20	20
388	20c. Loading by conveyor	25	30
389	25c. Dispatch to refinery	30	35

107 Kalahari Starred Tortoise ("Psammobates oculifer")

1982. Tortoises. Multicoloured.

390	5c. Type **107**	15	10
391	15c. Leopard tortoise ("Geochelone pardalis")	25	25
392	20c. Angulate tortoise ("Chersina angulata")	30	35
393	25c. Speckled padloper ("Homopus signatus")	40	45

108 Mythical Sea-monster

1982. Discoveries of South West Africa (1st series). Multicoloured.

394	15c. Type **108**	20	20
395	20c. Bartolomeu Dias and map of Africa showing voyage	40	30
396	25c. Dias' caravel	65	40
397	30c. Dias erecting commemorative cross, Angra das Voltas, 25 July 1488	70	45

See also Nos. 455/8.

109 Brandberg

1982. Mountains of South West Africa. Mult.

398	6c. Type **109**	10	10
399	15c. Omatako	20	20
400	20c. Die Nadel	25	30
401	25c. Spitzkuppe	30	35

110 Otjikaeva Headdress of Herero Woman

1982. Traditional Headdresses of South West Africa (1st series). Multicoloured.

402	6c. Type **110**	10	10
403	15c. Ekori headdress of Himba	20	35
404	20c. Oshikoma hair-piece and iipanda plaits of Ngandjera	25	45
405	25c. Omhatela headdress of Kwanyama	25	60

See also Nos. 427/30.

111 Fort Vogelsang

1983. Centenary of Luderitz.

406 **111**	6c. black and red	10	10
407 –	20c. black and brown	15	20
408 –	25c. black and brown	20	25
409 –	30c. black and purple	20	30
410 –	40c. black and green	25	50

DESIGNS—VERT (23 × 29 mm): 20c. Chief Joseph Fredericks; 30c. Heinrich Vogelsang (founder); 40c. Adolf Luderitz (colonial promoter). HORIZ (as T **111**): 25c. Angra Pequena.

112 Searching for Diamonds, Kolmanskop, 1908

1983. 75th Anniv of Discovery of Diamonds.

411 **112**	10c. deep brown & brown	15	15
412 –	20c. red and brown	30	40
413 –	25c. blue and brown	35	45
414 –	40c. black and brown	55	85

DESIGNS—HORIZ (34 × 19 mm): 20c. Digging for diamonds, Kolmanskop, 1908. VERT (19 × 26 mm): 25c. Sir Ernest Oppenheimer (industrialist); 40c. August Stauch (prospector).

113 "Common Zebras drinking" (J. van Ellinckhuijzen)

1983. Painters of South West Africa. Mult.

415	10c. Type **113**	15	15
416	20c. "Rossing Mountain" (H. Henckert)	20	30
417	25c. "Stampeding African Buffalo" (F. Krampe)	20	35
418	40c. "Erongo Mountains" (J. Blatt)	30	55

114 The Rock Lobster

1983. The Lobster Industry. Multicoloured.

419	10c. Type **114**	15	15
420	20c. Mother ship and fishing dinghies	20	30
421	25c. Netting lobsters from a dinghy	20	35
422	40c. Packing lobsters	30	55

115 Hohenzollern House

1984. Historic Buildings of Swakopmund.

423 **115**	10c. black and brown	15	15
424 –	20c. black and blue	20	25
425 –	25c. black and green	20	30
426 –	30c. black and brown	25	30

DESIGNS: 20c. Railway Station; 25c. Imperial District Bureau; 30c. Ritterburg.

1984. Traditional Headdresses of South West Africa (2nd series). As T **110**. Multicoloured.

427	11c. Eendjushi headdress of Kwambi	15	15
428	20c. Bushman woman	20	25
429	25c. Omulenda headdress of Kwaluudhi	20	35
430	30c. Mbukushu women	20	35

116 Map and German Flag

1984. Cent of German Colonization. Mult.

431	11c. Type **116**	25	15
432	25c. Raising the German flag, 1884	50	50
433	30c. German Protectorate boundary marker	50	60
434	45c. "Elizabeth" and "Leipzig" (German corvettes)	1·25	1·75

117 Sweet Thorn **118** Head of Ostrich

1984. Spring in South West Africa. Mult.

435	11c. Type **117**	15	15
436	25c. Camel thorn	20	35
437	30c. Hook thorn	20	35
438	45c. Candle-pod acacia	25	50

1985. Ostriches. Multicoloured.

439	11c. Type **118**	40	10
440	25c. Ostrich on eggs	60	30
441	30c. Newly-hatched chick and eggs	70	50
442	50c. Mating dance	90	75

119 Kaiserstrasse

1985. Historic Buildings of Windhoek.

443 **119**	12c. black and brown	15	10
444 –	25c. black and green	20	25
445 –	30c. black and brown	20	30
446 –	50c. black and brown	25	70

DESIGNS: 25c. Turnhalle; 30c. Old Supreme Court Building; 50c. Railway Station.

120 Zwilling Locomotive

1985. Narrow-gauge Railway Locomotives. Mult.

447	12c. Type **120**	25	10
448	25c. Feldspur side-tank locomotive	45	25
449	30c. Jung and Henschel side-tank locomotive	40	35
450	50c. Henschel Hd locomotive	60	60

121 Lidumu-dumu (keyboard instrument)

1985. Traditional Musical Instruments. Mult.

451	12c. Type **121**	10	10
452	25c. Ngoma (drum)	15	20
453	30c. Okambulumbumbwa (stringed instrument)	20	25
454	50c. //Gwashi (stringed instrument)	25	35

122 Erecting Commemorative Pillar at Cape Cross, 1486

1986. Discoverers of South West Africa (2nd series). Diogo Cao.

455 **122**	12c. black, grey and green	25	10
456 –	20c. black, grey and brown	40	25
457 –	25c. black, grey and blue	60	35
458 –	30c. black, grey and purple	70	60

DESIGNS: 20c. Diogo Cao's coat of arms; 25c. Caravel; 30c. Diogo Cao.

123 Ameib, Erongo Mountains

1986. Rock Formations. Multicoloured.

459	14c. Type **123**	35	15
460	20c. Vingerklip, near Outjo	40	25
461	25c. Petrified sand dunes, Kuiseb River	45	40
462	30c. Orgelpfeifen, Twyfelfontein	50	55

124 Model wearing Swakara Coat **125** Pirogue, Lake Liambezi

1986. Karakul Industry. Multicoloured.

463	14c. Type **124**	15	15
464	20c. Weaving karakul wool carpet	25	30
465	25c. Flock of karakul ewes in veld	25	45
466	30c. Karakul rams	30	60

1986. Life in the Caprivi Strip. Mult.

467	14c. Type **125**	30	15
468	20c. Ploughing with oxen	50	80
469	25c. Settlement in Eastern Caprivi	60	1·25
470	30c. Map of Caprivi Strip	1·00	2·00

126 "Gobabis Mission Station", 1863

1987. Paintings by Thomas Baines. Multicoloured.

471	14c. Type **126**	30	15
472	20c. "Outspan at Koobie", 1861	55	70
473	25c. "Outspan under Oomahaama Tree", 1862	70	1·25
474	30c. "Swakop River", 1861	80	2·00

127 "Garreta nitens" (beetle)

1987. Useful Insects. Multicoloured.

475	16c. Type **127**	40	15
476	20c. "Alcimus stenurus" (fly)	60	80
477	25c. "Anthophora caerulea" (bee)	75	1·50
478	30c. "Hemiempusa capensis" (mantid)	1·10	2·00

128 Okaukuejo

1987. Tourist Camps. Multicoloured.

479	16c. Type **128**	25	15
480	20c. Daan Viljoen	40	55
481	25c. Ai-Ais	45	1·25
482	30c. Hardap	50	1·40

129 Wreck of "Hope" (Dutch whaling schooner, 1804) **130** Bartolomeu Dias

1987. Shipwrecks. Multicoloured.

483	16c. Type **129**	50	15
484	30c. "Tilly" (brig), 1885	75	80
485	40c. "Eduard Bohlen" (steamer), 1909	1·00	2·00
486	50c. "Dunedin Star" (liner), 1942	1·25	2·50

1988. 500th Anniv of Discovery of Cape of Good Hope by Bartolomeu Dias. Multicoloured.

487	16c. Type **130**	35	15
488	30c. Caravel	70	55
489	40c. Map of South West Africa, c. 1502	80	70
490	50c. King Joao II of Portugal	80	75

131 Sossusvlei

1988. Landmarks of South West Africa. Multicoloured.

491	16c. Type **131**	30	15
492	30c. Sesriem Canyon	60	65
493	40c. Hoaruseb "clay castles"	70	1·25
494	50c. Hoba meteorite	80	1·50

132 First Postal Agency, Otyimbingue, 1888

1988. Centenary of Postal Service in South West Africa. Multicoloured.

495 16c. Type **132** 30 15
496 30c. Post Office, Windhoek, 1904 . . . . 60 55
497 40c. Mail-runner and map . . 70 75
498 50c. Camel mail, 1904 . . . 80 1·00

133 Herero Chat **134** Dr. C. H. Hahn and Gross-Barmen Mission

1988. Birds of South West Africa. Mult.

499 16c. Type **133** 80 25
500 30c. Gray's lark . . . . . . 1·25 80
501 40c. Ruppell's bustard . . . 1·40 1·25
502 50c. Monteiro's hornbill . . . 1·40 1·40

1989. Missionaries. Multicoloured.

503 16c. Type **134** 20 10
504 30c. Revd. J. G. Kronlein and Berseba Mission . . . 35 60
505 40c. Revd. F. H. Kleinschmidt and Rehoboth Mission 40 70
506 50c. Revd. J. H. Schmelen and Bethanien Mission . . 40 85

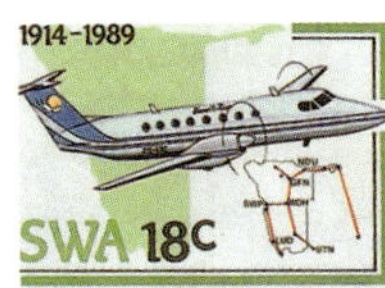

135 Beech Commuter 1900

1989. 75th Anniv of Aviation in South West Africa. Multicoloured.

507 18c. Type **135** 55 20
508 30c. Ryan Navion 90 60
509 40c. Junkers F-13 . . . . . 1·00 65
510 50c. Pfalz Otto biplane . . . 1·25 85

136 Barchan Dunes

1989. Namib Desert Sand Dunes. Mult.

511 18c. Type **136** 20 15
512 30c. Star dunes (36×20 mm) 30 40
513 40c. Transverse dunes 35 60
514 50c. Crescentic dunes (36×20 mm) 40 80

137 Ballot Box and Outline Map of South West Africa

1989. South West Africa Constitutional Election.

515 **137** 18c. brown and orange . . 15 15
516 35c. blue and green . . . 25 40
517 45c. purple and yellow . . 35 60
518 60c. green and ochre . . . 45 80

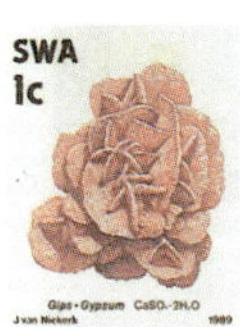

138 Gypsum **140** Arrow Poison

139 Oranjemund Alluvial Diamond Field

1989. Minerals. Multicoloured.

519 1c. Type **138** 15 30
520 2c. Fluorite 20 30
521 5c. Mimetite 30 30
522 7c. Cuprite 45 45
523 10c. Azurite 50 20
524 18c. Boltwoodite 70 10
525 20c. Dioptase 75 15
526 25c. Type **139** . . . . 1·25 15
527 30c. Tsumeb lead and copper complex . . . . 1·00 20
528 35c. Rosh Pinah zinc mine . 1·00 20
529 40c. Diamonds . . . . 1·25 30
530 45c. Wulfenite . . . . 1·00 30
531 50c. Uis tin mine . . . . . . 1·25 40
532 1r. Rossing uranium mine . . 1·75 1·00
533 2r. Gold . . . . 2·75 2·00

The 1, 2, 5, 7, 10, 18, 20, 40, 45c. and 2r. are vert as T **138**, and the remainder horiz as T **139**.

1990. Flora. Multicoloured.

534 18c. Type **140** 20 10
535 35c. Baobab flower 35 40
536 45c. Sausage tree flowers . . 40 50
537 60c. Devil's claw 45 90

OFFICIAL STAMPS

Prices are for pairs mint and for single stamps used.

1927. Pictorial and portrait (2d.) stamps alternately optd **OFFICIAL South West Africa.** or **OFFISIEEL Suidwes Afrika.**

O1 **6** ½d. black and green . . . . 70·00 30·00
O2 **7** 1d. black and red . . . . . 70·00 30·00
O3 **2** 2d. purple . . . . £160 45·00
O4 **8** 6d. green and orange . . . . 90·00 30·00

1929. Pictorial stamps alternately optd **OFFICIAL S.W.A.** or **OFFISIEEL S.W.A.** horizontally or vertically.

O 9 **6** ½d. black and green . . . 75 2·75
O10 1d. black and red . . . . 1·00 2·75
O11 **11** 2d. grey and purple . . . 1·00 3·25
O 8 **8** 6d. green and orange . . . 2·00 3·75

1931. Optd alternately **OFFICIAL** or **OFFISIEEL**.

O13 **12** ½d. black and green . . . 11·00 3·50
O14 – blue and red (No. 75) . . 1·00 3·50
O25 **27** 1½d. brown . . . . 24·00 5·00
O15 – 2d. blue and brown (No. 76) . . . . 2·25 2·25
O16 – 6d. blue and brown (No. 79) . . . . 3·25 3·25

POSTAGE DUE STAMPS

Prices for Nos. D1/46 are for pairs mint and for single stamps used.

1923. Optd **South West Africa.** or **Zuid-West Afrika.** alternately. (i) On Postage Due stamps of Transvaal.

D1 **D 1** 5d. black and violet . . . 4·00 11·00
D2 6d. black and brown . . . 17·00 11·00

(ii) On Postage Due stamps of South Africa.

D 6 **D 1** ½d. black and green . . 6·00 5·50
D 7 1d. black and pink . . . 7·00 6·00
D 8 1½d. black and brown . . 1·25 2·75
D 9 2d. black and violet . . 3·50 5·00
D12 3d. black and blue . . . 7·50 5·50
D 5 6d. black and grey . . . 26·00 13·00

1923. Optd **South West Africa.*** or **Zuidwest Afrika.**
(i) on Postage Due stamps of Transvaal.

D25 **D 1** 5d. black and violet . . 2·75 3·50
D14 6d. black and brown . . 21·00 20·00

(ii) On Postage Due stamps of South Africa.

D23 **D 1** ½d. black and green . . 3·00 6·50
D28 1d. black and pink . . . 2·00 1·60
D29 1½d. black and brown . . 4·50 6·50
D30 2d. black and violet . . 2·50 3·50
D31 3d. black and blue . . . 4·50 3·75
D20 6d. black and grey . . . 2·25 9·00

*The English overprint is the same, for the purposes of this catalogue, as that on the previous set.

1927. Optd **South West Africa.*** or **Suidwes Afrika.**
(a) On Postage Due stamps of Transvaal.

D33 **D 1** 5d. black and violet . . 19·00 23·00

(b) On Postage Due stamps of South Africa.

D39 **D 2** 1d. black and red . . . 1·00 2·25
D34 **D 1** 1½d. black and brown . . 1·00 3·25
D35 2d. black and violet . . 4·75 3·25
D37 3d. black and blue . . . 13·00 11·00
D38 6d. black and grey . . . 7·50 8·50

*The English overprint is the same, for the purposes of this catalogue, as that on Nos. D33 and D34/8 of the previous sets.

1928. Postage Due stamps of South Africa optd **S.W.A.** (a) On Nos. D4 and D16.

D40 **D 1** 3d. black and blue . . . 1·50 15·00
D41 6d. black and grey . . . 6·00 28·00

(b) On Nos. D 17 etc.

D42 **D 2** ½d. black and green . . 50 8·00
D43 1d. black and red . . . 50 3·25
D44 2d. black and mauve . . 50 4·50
D45 3d. black and blue . . . 2·25 26·00
D46 6d. black and grey . . . 1·50 20·00

D 3

1931. Size 19×23½ mm.

D47 **D 3** ½d. black and green . . 1·00 9·00
D48 1d. black and red . . . 1·00 1·25
D49 2d. black and violet . . 1·00 2·75
D50 3d. black and blue . . . 4·25 17·00
D51 6d. black and slate . . . 13·00 27·00

1959. As Type **D 3** but smaller, 17½×21 mm.

D55 1d. black and red . . . . . 1·50 3·00
D53 2d. black and violet . . . . 1·50 15·00
D56 3d. black and blue . . . . . 1·50 3·75

1961. As Nos. D55, etc. but values in cents.

D57 1c. black and turquoise . . . 70 3·75
D58 2c. black and red . . . . . 70 3·75
D59 4c. black and violet . . . . 70 6·00
D60 5c. black and blue . . . . . 1·00 4·25
D61 6c. black and green . . . . 1·25 6·50
D62 10c. black and yellow . . . 3·75 9·00

1972. As Type **D 8** of South Africa. Inscr "S.W.A."

D63 1c. green . . . . 75 5·00
D64 8c. blue . . . . 3·00 8·50

For subsequent issues see **NAMIBIA**.

SOUTHERN NIGERIA Pt. 1

A British possession on the west coast of Africa. In 1914 joined with Northern Nigeria to form Nigeria (q.v.).

12 pence = 1 shilling;
20 shillings = 1 pound.

1

1901.

1 **1** ½d. black and green . . . . . 1·75 2·25
2 1d. brown and red . . . . 1·40 1·50
3 2d. black and brown . . . . 3·25 3·75
4 4d. black and green . . . . 2·75 16·00
5 6d. black and purple . . . . 2·75 6·50
6 1s. green and black . . . . 8·00 26·00
7 2s.6d. black and brown . . . 45·00 80·00
8 5s. black and yellow . . . . 48·00 £100
9 10s. black and purple on yellow . . . . 90·00 £170

2 **3**

1903.

21 **2** ½d. black and green . . . 50 10
11 1d. black and red . . . . 1·25 70
23 2d. black and brown . . . 2·50 45
24 2½d. black and blue . . . 1·00 1·00
25 3d. brown and purple . . . 9·50 1·25
14 4d. black and green . . . 2·75 5·50
15 6d. black and purple . . . 4·00 8·00
28 1s. green and black . . . 3·25 3·50
29 2s.6d. black and brown . . 24·00 17·00
30 5s. black and yellow . . . 40·00 75·00
19 10s. black & purple on yell 29·00 90·00
32ab £1 green and violet £150 £190

1907.

33 **2** ½d. green . . . . 1·75 20
34ab 1d. red 75 10
35 2d. grey . . . . 2·50 70
36 2½d. blue . . . . 2·00 3·75
37 3d. purple on yellow . . . 2·00 30
38 4d. black and red on yellow . . . . 2·25 80
39 6d. purple . . . . 25·00 3·25
40 1s. black on green . . . . 7·00 40
41 2s.6d. black and red on blue . . . . 5·00 1·00
42 5s. green and red on yellow 38·00 48·00
43 10s. green and red on green . . . . 65·00 95·00
44 £1 purple and black on red £190 £225

1912.

45 **3** ½d. green . . . . 2·00 10
46 1d. red . . . . 1·75 10
47 2d. grey 75 85
48 2½d. blue . . . . 2·75 2·75
49 3d. purple on yellow . . . . 1·00 30
50 4d. black and red on yellow 1·25 2·00
51 6d. purple . . . . 1·25 1·25
52 1s. black on green . . . . . 2·75 75
53 2s.6d. black and red on blue 8·00 30·00
54 5s. green and red on yellow 20·00 75·00
55 10s. green and red on green 45·00 90·00
56 £1 purple and black on red £170 £225

SOUTHERN RHODESIA Pt. 1

A Br. territory in the N. part of S. Africa, S. of the Zambesi. In 1954 became part of the Central African Federation which issued its own stamps inscribed "Rhodesia and Nyasaland" (q.v.), until 1964 when it resumed issuing after the break-up of the Federation. In October 1964, Southern Rhodesia was renamed Rhodesia.

12 pence = 1 shilling;
20 shillings = 1 pound.

1

1924.

1 **1** ½d. green . . . . 2·00 10
2 1d. pink . . . . 1·60 10
3 1½d. brown . . . . 2·00 80
4 2d. black and grey . . . . 2·25 70
5 3d. blue . . . . 2·25 2·50
6 4d. black and red . . . . . 2·50 2·75
7 6d. black and mauve . . . . 2·00 3·75
8 8d. purple and green . . . . 11·00 42·00
9 10d. blue and pink . . . . . 11·00 48·00
10 1s. black and blue . . . . . 5·00 5·00
11 1s.6d. black and yellow . . . 19·00 32·00
12 2s. black and brown . . . . 17·00 17·00
13 2s.6d. black and brown . . . 30·00 60·00
14 5s. blue and green . . . . . 60·00 £110

2 King George V **3** Victoria Falls

1931.

15a **2** ½d. green 65 20
16b 1d. red 50 20
16d 1½d. brown . . . . 2·50 80
17 **3** 2d. black and brown . . . 4·00 1·40
18 3d. blue . . . . 10·00 11·00
19 **2** 4d. black and red . . . . . 1·25 1·50
20 6d. black and mauve . . . 2·25 3·00
21 8d. violet and green . . . . 1·75 3·25
21b 9d. red and green . . . . . 6·00 9·00
22 10d. blue and red . . . . . 7·00 2·25
23 1s. black and blue . . . . 2·00 2·50
24 1s.6d. black and yellow . . . 10·00 16·00
25 2s. black and brown . . . . 21·00 6·50
26a 2s.6d. blue and brown . . . 28·00 30·00
27 5s. blue and green . . . . . 48·00 48·00

4

1932.

29 **4** 2d. green and brown . . . . 3·75 1·00
30 3d. blue . . . . 4·00 1·75

5 Victoria Falls

1935. Silver Jubilee.

31 **5** 1d. green and red . . . . . 3·25 1·75
32 2d. green and brown . . . . 5·50 5·00
33 3d. violet and blue . . . . 5·50 10·00
34 6d. black and purple . . . . 8·00 14·00

1935. As Nos. 29/30, but inscr "POSTAGE AND REVENUE".

35a **4** 2d. green and brown . . . 1·75 10
35b 3d. blue . . . . 3·25 10

6 Victoria Falls and Railway Bridge

1937. Coronation.

36 **6** 1d. olive and red 60 70
37 2d. green and brown . . . . 60 1·50
38 3d. violet and blue . . . . . 3·25 7·00
39 6d. black and purple . . . . 1·75 3·25

7 King George VI

10 Cecil John Rhodes (after S. P. Kendrick)

8 British South Africa Co's Arms

1937.

40 **7** $\frac{1}{2}$d. green . . . 50 10
41 1d. red . . . 50 10
42 1$\frac{1}{2}$d. brown . . . 1·00 30
43 4d. orange . . . 1·50 10
44 6d. black . . . 1·50 50
45 8d. green . . . 2·00 2·25
46 9d. blue . . . 1·50 1·00
47 10d. purple . . . 2·25 2·75
48 1s. black and green . . . 1·75 10
49 1s.6d. black and yellow . . . 10·00 2·25
50 2s. black and brown . . . 14·00 55
51 2s.6d. blue and purple . . . 9·00 4·75
52 5s. blue and green . . . 18·00 2·25

1940. Golden Jubilee of British South Africa Company.

53 **8** $\frac{1}{2}$d. violet and green . . . 10 55
54 – 1d. blue and red . . . 10 10
55 **10** 1$\frac{1}{2}$d. black and brown . . . 15 80
56 – 2d. green and violet . . . 30 70
57 – 3d. black and blue . . . 30 1·50
58 – 4d. green and brown . . . 2·00 2·50
59 – 6d. brown and green . . . 50 2·00
60 – 1s. blue and green . . . 50 2·00

DESIGNS—HORIZ: 1d. Fort Salisbury, 1890; 2d. Fort Victoria; 3d. Rhodes makes peace, 1896; 1s. Queen Victoria, King George VI, Lobengula's kraal and Govt. House, Salisbury. VERT: 4d. Victoria Falls Bridge; 6d. Statue of Sir Charles Coghlan.

16 Mounted Pioneer

20 King George VI

17 Queen Elizabeth II when Princess, and Princess Margaret

1943. 50th Anniv of Occupation of Matabeleland.

61 **16** 2d. brown and green . . . 20 85

1947. Royal Visit.

62 **17** $\frac{1}{2}$d. black and green . . . 15 60
63 – 1d. black and red . . . 15 60

DESIGN: 1d. King George VI and Queen Elizabeth.

1947. Victory.

64 – 1d. red . . . 10 10
65 **20** 2d. slate . . . 10 10
66 – 3d. blue . . . 85 75
67 – 6d. orange . . . 30 1·25

PORTRAITS: 1d. Queen Elizabeth; 3d. Queen Elizabeth II when Princess; 6d. Princess Margaret.

1949. 75th Anniv of U.P.U. As T **33d/g** of St. Helena.

68 2d. green . . . 70 20
69 3d. blue . . . 80 3·25

23 Queen Victoria, Arms and King George VI

1950. Diamond Jubilee of S. Rhodesia.

70 **23** 2d. green and brown . . . 50 90

24 "Medical Services"

27 "Water Supplies"

1953. Birth Centenary of Cecil Rhodes. Inscr "RHODES CENTENARY".

71 **24** $\frac{1}{2}$d. blue and sepia . . . 15 2·00
72 – 1d. chestnut and green . . . 15 10
73 – 2d. green and violet . . . 15 10
74 **27** 4$\frac{1}{2}$d. green and blue . . . 75 2·75
75 – 1s. black and brown . . . 3·00 1·00

DESIGNS: 1d. "Agriculture"; 2d. "Building"; 4$\frac{1}{2}$d. "Water Supplies"; 1s. "Transport".

No. 74 also commemorates the Diamond Jubilee of Matabeleland.

1953. Rhodes Centenary Exhibition, Bulawayo. As No. 59 of Northern Rhodesia.

76 6d. violet . . . 30 75

30 Queen Elizabeth II

1953. Coronation.

77 **30** 2s.6d. red . . . 4·75 6·00

31 Sable Antelope

33 Rhodes's Grave

43 Balancing Rocks

1953.

78 **31** $\frac{1}{2}$d. grey and claret . . . 30 50
79 – 1d. green and brown . . . 30 10
80 **33** 2d. brown and violet . . . 30 10
81 – 3d. brown and red . . . 55 1·25
82 – 4d. red, green and blue . . . 3·25 20
83 – 4$\frac{1}{2}$d. black and blue . . . 2·50 3·50
84 – 6d. olive and turquoise . . . 3·00 75
85 – 9d. blue and brown . . . 3·00 3·50
86 – 1s. violet and blue . . . 1·25 10
87 – 2s. purple and red . . . 11·00 3·75
88 – 2s.6d. olive and brown . . . 4·25 4·00
89 – 5s. brown and green . . . 7·00 6·50
90 **43** 10s. brown and olive . . . 9·00 21·00
91 – £1 red and black . . . 14·00 27·00

DESIGNS—VERT (as Type **31**): 1d Tobacco planter. (As Type **33**): 6d. Baobab tree; 5s. Basket maker. HORIZ (as Type **33**): 3d. Farm worker; 4d. Flame lily; 4$\frac{1}{2}$d. Victoria Falls; 9d. Lion; 1s. Zimbabwe ruins; 2s. Birchenough Bridge; 2s.6d. Kariba Gorge. (As Type **43**): £1 Coat of arms.

45 Maize

50 Flame Lily

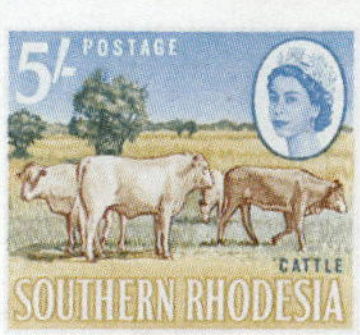

56 Cattle

1964.

92 **45** $\frac{1}{2}$d. yellow, green and blue . . . 20 2·00
93 – 1d. violet and ochre . . . 15 10
94 – 2d. yellow and violet . . . 60 10
95 – 3d. brown and blue . . . 20 10
96 – 4d. orange and green . . . 30 10
97 **50** 6d. red, yellow and green . . . 40 10
98 – 9d. brown, yellow and green . . . 2·50 1·50
99 – 1s. green and ochre . . . 3·25 20
100 – 1s.3d. red, violet and green . . . 3·00 10
101 – 2s. blue and ochre . . . 2·50 2·00
102 – 2s.6d. blue and red . . . 4·00 1·00
103 **56** 5s. multicoloured . . . 3·50 2·25
104 – 10s. multicoloured . . . 11·00 6·50
105 – £1 multicoloured . . . 6·00 16·00

DESIGNS—As Type **45**: 1d. African buffalo; 2d. Tobacco; 3d. Greater kudu; 4d. Citrus. As Type **50**: 9d. Ansellia orchid; 1s. Emeralds; 1s.3d. Aloe; 2s. Lake Kyle; 2s.6d. Tigerfish. As Type **56**: 10s. Helmeted guineafowl; £1 Coat of arms.

Similar designs inscribed "RHODESIA" are listed under that heading.

POSTAGE DUE STAMPS

1951. Postage due stamps of Great Britain optd **SOUTHERN RHODESIA**.

D1 **D 1** $\frac{1}{2}$d. green . . . 3·25 16·00
D2 1d. blue . . . 3·00 2·00
D3 2d. black . . . 2·50 1·75
D4 3d. violet . . . 2·75 2·75
D5 4d. blue . . . 1·75 3·50
D6 4d. green . . . £190 £550
D7 1s. blue . . . 2·50 3·75

For later issues see **RHODESIA**.

SOUTHERN YEMEN Pt. 19

PEOPLE'S REPUBLIC

Independent Republic comprising the areas formerly known as Aden, the Aden States and the South Arabian Federation.

From 30 November 1970, the country was renamed The People's Democratic Republic of Yemen.

1000 fils = 1 dinar.

1968. Stamps of South Arabian Federation optd **PEOPLE'S REPUBLIC OF SOUTHERN YEMEN** in English and Arabic.

1 **2** 5f. blue . . . 10 10
2 10f. blue . . . 10 10
3 15f. green . . . 10 10
4 20f. green . . . 10 10
5 25f. brown . . . 10 10
6 30f. bistre . . . 25 10
7 35f. brown . . . 20 20
8 50f. red . . . 35 30
9 65f. green . . . 40 35
10 75f. red . . . 55 45
11 **3** 100f. multicoloured . . . 80 60
12 250f. multicoloured . . . 1·60 1·40
13 500f. multicoloured . . . 3·25 2·50
14 1d. multicoloured . . . 8·50 6·00

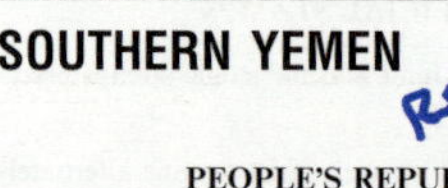

3 National Flag across Globe

1968. Independence. Multicoloured.

15 10f. Type **3** . . . 10 10
16 15f. Revolutionary (vert) . . . 10 10
17 50f. Aden harbour . . . 40 40
18 100f. Cotton-picking . . . 1·25 1·25

4 Girl Guides

1968. Aden Girl Guides' Movement.

19 – 10f. brown and blue . . . 25 25
20 – 25f. blue and brown . . . 35 35
21 **4** 50f. multicoloured . . . 65 65

DESIGNS—HORIZ: 10f. Guides around camp-fire. VERT: 25f. Brownies.

5 Revolutionary Soldier

1968. Revolution Day.

22 **5** 20f. brown and blue . . . 20 20
23 – 30f. brown and green . . . 25 25
24 – 100f. red and yellow . . . 85 85

DESIGNS—HORIZ: 30f. Radfan Mountains ("where first martyr fell"). VERT: 100f. Open book and torch ("Freedom, Socialism and Unity").

6 Sculptured Plaque "Assyrian influence")

1968. Antiquities.

25 – 5f. yellow and green . . . 10 10
26 – 35f. blue and purple . . . 35 35
27 **6** 50f. buff and blue . . . 75 65
28 – 65f. green and purple . . . 95 80

DESIGNS—VERT: 5f. King Yusdqil Far'am of Ausan (statue); 35f. Sculptured figure ("African-inspired"). HORIZ: 65f. Bull's head ("Moon God").

7 Martyrs' Monument, Aden

8 Albert Thomas Memorial, Geneva

1969. Martyrs' Day.

29 **7** 15f. multicoloured . . . 10 10
30 35f. multicoloured . . . 25 25
31 100f. multicoloured . . . 90 75

1969. 50th Anniv of I.L.O.

32 **8** 10f. brown, black and green . . . 10 10
33 25f. brown, black and mauve . . . 40 30

9 Teacher and Class

1969. International Literacy Day.

34 **9** 35f. multicoloured . . . 40 30
35 100f. multicoloured . . . 1·00 95

10 Mahatma Gandhi

1969. Birth Centenary of Mahatma Gandhi.

36 **10** 35f. purple and blue . . . 1·00 50

11 Yemeni Family

1969. Family Day.

37 **11** 25f. multicoloured . . . 35 25
38 75f. multicoloured . . . 95 70

12 U.N. Headquarters, New York

1969. United Nations Day.

39 **12** 20f. multicoloured . . . 20 15
40 65f. multicoloured . . . 70 55

13 Map and Flag

1969. 2nd Anniv of Independence. Multicoloured.

41		15f. Type **13**	20	20
42		35f. Type **13**	35	30
43		40f. Bulldozers (37 × 37 mm)	45	30
44		50f. As No. 43	65	45

14 Arab League Flag, Emblem and Map

1970. 25th Anniv of Arab League.

45	**14**	35f. multicoloured	40	30

15 Lenin

16 Palestinian Guerrilla

1970. Birth Centenary of Lenin.

46	**15**	75f. multicoloured	90	65

1970. Palestine Day. Multicoloured.

47		15f. Type **16**	15	10
48		35f. Guerrilla and attack on airliner	35	25
49		50f. Guerrillas and Palestinian flag (horiz)	75	45

17 New Headquarters Building, Berne

1970. Inauguration of New U.P.U. Headquarters Building, Berne.

50	**17**	15f. green and orange	25	15
51		65f. red and buff	55	50

18 Girl with Pitcher

1970. National Costumes. Multicoloured.

52		10f. Type **18**	25	15
53		15f. Woman in veil	30	25
54		20f. Girl in burnous	45	30
55		50f. Three Yemeni men	90	45

19 Dromedary and Calf

1970. Fauna. Multicoloured.

56		15f. Type **19**	25	20
57		25f. Goats	45	25
58		35f. Arabian oryx and kid	90	50
59		65f. Socotran dwarf cows	1·50	95

20 Torch and Flags

1970. 7th Revolution Day. Multicoloured.

60		25f. Type **20**	25	20
61		35f. National Front Headquarters (57 × 27 mm)	45	40
62		50f. Farmer and soldier (42 × 25 mm)	60	45

21 U.N. H.Q., New York, and Emblem

1970. 25th Anniv of United Nations.

63	**21**	10f. orange and blue	10	10
64		65f. mauve and blue	75	60

For later issues see **YEMEN PEOPLE'S DEMOCRATIC REPUBLIC**.

SPAIN Pt. 19

A kingdom in south-west Europe; a republic between 1873 and 1874, and from 1931 until 1939.

1850. 8½ (later 8) cuartos = 1 real.
1866. 80 cuartos = 100 centimos de escudo = 1 escudo.
1867. 1000 milesimas = 100 centimos de escudo = 80 cuartos = 1 escudo.
1872. 100 centimos = 1 peseta.
2002. 100 cents = 1 euro.

1 Queen Isabella II

2 Queen Isabella II

3 Queen Isabella II

1850. Imperf.

2	**1**	6c. black	£375	14·00
3		12c. lilac	£1700	£225
4	**2**	5r. red	£2000	£180
5		6r. blue	£2500	£650
6		10r. green	£3500	£1800

1851. Imperf.

9	**3**	6c. black	£200	2·30
10		12c. lilac	£3500	£150
11		2r. red	£16000	£8500
12		5r. pink	£2000	£170
13		6r. blue	£3000	£850
14		10r. green	£2250	£400

4

5

7 Arms of Castile and Leon

1852. Imperf.

16	**4**	6c. pink	£300	2·10
17		12c. purple	£1500	£120
18		2r. red	£13000	£4250
19		5r. green	£1800	90·00
20		6r. blue	£2750	£400

1853. Imperf.

22	**5**	6c. red	£350	2·50
23		12c. purple	£1700	£140
24		2r. red	£8500	£2500
25		5r. green	£1800	85·00
26		6r. blue	£2500	£350

1854. Imperf.

32	**7**	2c. green	£1600	£400
33		4c. red	£325	2·00
34		6c. red	£250	1·20
35		1r. blue	£2750	£275
36		2r. red	£1200	75·00
37		5r. green	£1200	85·00
38		6r. blue	£2000	£250

9

12

13

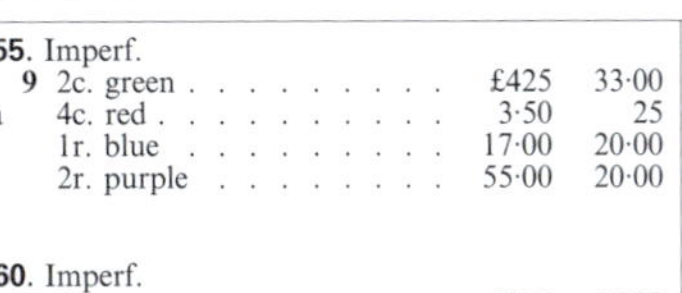

1855. Imperf.

54	**9**	2c. green	£425	33·00
55a		4c. red	3·50	25
61		1r. blue	17·00	20·00
57		2r. purple	55·00	20·00

1860. Imperf.

63	**12**	2c. green on green	£275	16·00
64		4c. orange on green	32·00	55
65		12c. red on buff	£275	8·75
66		19c. brown on brown	£2250	£1200
67		1r. blue on green	£225	9·75
68		2r. lilac on lilac	£300	8·50

1862. Imperf.

69a	**13**	2c. blue on yellow	29·00	10·50
70		4c. brown on brown	2·00	60
70b		4c. brown on white	18·00	4·75
71		12c. blue on pink	36·00	7·00
72		19c. red on lilac	£150	£160
72a		19c. red on white	£170	£190
73a		1r. brown on yellow	48·00	17·00
74		2r. green on pink	27·00	10·50

14

15

16

1864. Imperf.

75	**14**	2c. blue on lilac	41·00	15·00
75b		2c. blue on white	60·00	23·00
76b		4c. red on red	1·90	60
76c		4c. pink on white	14·00	11·00
77a		12c. green on pink	36·00	11·00
78		19c. lilac on lilac	£150	£140
79		1r. brown on green	£150	70·00
80		2r. blue on pink	36·00	11·00
80b		2r. blue on white	70·00	16·00

1865. Imperf.

81a	**15**	2c. red	£250	26·00
82		12c. pink and blue	£325	16·00
83		19c. pink and brown	£1200	£600
84		1r. green	£325	44·00
85		2r. mauve	£325	26·00
85c		2r. red	£375	55·00
85e		2r. yellow	£375	34·00

1865. Perf.

86	**15**	2c. red	£375	£100
87		4c. blue	29·00	60
88		12c. pink and blue	£425	46·00
89		19c. pink and brown	£2750	£1900
90		1r. green	£1400	£400
91		2r. lilac	£900	£170
91b		2r. orange	£1100	£250

1866. Perf.

92	**16**	2c. pink	£200	25·00
93a		4c. blue	33·00	60
94a		12c. orange	£190	9·75
95		19c. brown	£750	£350
96		10c. de e. green	£225	21·00
97		20c. de e. lilac	£150	16·00

1866. As T **14**, but dated "1866", and perf.

98		20c. de e. lilac	£850	55·00

19

25

26

1867. Inscr "CORREOS DE ESPANA". Various frames.

99a	**19**	2c. brown	£275	36·00
100		4c. blue	20·00	80
101a		12c. orange	£180	8·50
102		19c. pink	£1100	£325
150		19c. brown	£1700	£425
103		10c. de e. green	£200	19·00
104		20c. de e. lilac	95·00	8·00

1867. Various frames.

105	**25**	5m. green	33·00	13·50
106		10m. brown	33·00	17·00
107	**26**	25m. pink and blue	£190	20·00
145		25m. blue	£200	13·00
108		50m. brown	16·00	60
146a	**19**	50m. purple	19·00	45
147		100m. brown	£425	60·00
148		200m. green	£140	9·75

1868. Various stamps optd **HABILITADO POR LA NACION**.

109	**25**	5m. green	16·00	5·50
110		10m. brown	9·25	4·00
111	**26**	25m. pink and blue	31·00	12·00
151		25m. blue	27·00	9·25
112		50m. brown	7·00	4·00
152	**19**	50m. purple	7·75	3·00
153		100m. brown	60·00	27·00
154		200m. green	22·00	9·25
113		10c. de e. green	29·00	12·00
114		20c. de e. lilac	20·00	7·25
115		12c. orange	31·00	7·75
116		19c. pink	£300	£130
156		19c. brown	£600	£170

36

38a

38

1870.

172	**36**	1m. brown on buff	5·75	6·50
173		2m. black on buff	8·00	8·00
174		4m. brown	16·00	11·50
175		10m. red	19·00	5·25
176a		25m. mauve	55·00	5·50
177a		50m. blue	10·50	25
178b		100m. brown	29·00	5·00
179		200m. brown	29·00	5·00
180		400m. green	£250	23·00
181		12c. red	£225	7·00
182		19c. green	£325	£190
183a		1e.60m. lilac	£1300	£850
184		2e. blue	£1200	£500

1872. Imperf.

185	**38a**	¼c. blue	1·80	1·80
186	**38**	¼c. green	1·10	1·10
187	**38a**	¼c. green	15	10

1872. As T **25**, but currency in centavos de peseta and bottom panel inscr "COMUNICS".

192	**25**	2c. lilac	18·00	13·00
193		5c. green	£130	65·00

40 King Amadeo

41

42 Allegorical Figure of Peace

1872.

194	**40**	5c. pink	20·00	6·00
195b		6c. blue	£120	44·00
196		10c. lilac	£275	£225
197		10c. blue	5·50	25
199		12c. lilac	15·00	1·70
200		20c. lilac	£110	60·00
201		25c. brown	43·00	7·00
202		40c. brown	55·00	7·00
203		50c. green	70·00	8·00
204	**41**	1p. lilac	80·00	40·00
205		4p. brown	£475	£425
206		10p. green	£1700	£1800

1873.

207	**42**	2c. orange	16·00	6·50
208		5c. pink	31·00	6·50
209		10c. green	7·00	25
210		20c. black	85·00	23·00
211		25c. brown	30·00	5·75
212		40c. purple	33·00	6·50
213		50c. blue	13·00	5·50
214a		1p. lilac	43·00	30·00
215		4p. brown	£550	£425
216		10p. purple	£1800	£1800

43 Allegorical Figure of Justice

44

45 King Alfonso XII

1874.

217	**43**	2c. yellow	20·00	8·50
218a		5c. mauve	30·00	7·00
219		10c. blue	10·50	25
220		20c. green	£140	43·00
221		25c. brown	30·00	7·00
222a		40c. mauve	£350	8·00
223		50c. orange	£110	8·00
224		1p. green	75·00	38·00
225		4p. red	£600	£400
226		10p. black	£2500	£1800

1874.

227	**44**	10c. brown	20·00	60

1875.

228	**45**	2c. brown	17·00	8·50
229		5c. lilac	60·00	9·75
230		10c. blue	7·00	25
231		20c. brown	£225	£110
232		25c. pink	48·00	5·00
233		40c. brown	95·00	31·00
234		50c. mauve	£150	27·00
235		1p. black	£150	70·00
236		4p. green	£400	£400
237		10p. blue	£1300	£1400

46 King Alfonso XII

48

49

1876.

238	**46**	5c. brown	9·75	3·75
239		10c. blue	3·00	25

240 20c. green 17·00 13·00
241 25c. brown 6·50 3·25
242 40c. brown 60·00 80·00
250 50c. green 13·00 5·25
244 1p. blue 17·00 8·00
245 4p. purple 46·00 55·00
246 10p. red 95·00 £120

1878.

253 **48** 2c. mauve 23·00 9·75
254a 5c. yellow 36·00 9·75
255 10c. brown 6·50 30
256 20c. black £150 £110
257 25c. green 19·00 1·90
258 40c. brown £140 £130
259 50c. green 65·00 8·00
260 1p. grey 60·00 17·00
261 4p. violet £170 £110
262a 10p. blue £325 £325

1879.

263 **49** 2c. black 7·00 1·90
264 5c. green 11·50 70
265 10c. pink 9·25 25
266 20c. brown £100 11·00
267 25c. grey 12·00 25
268 40c. brown 23·00 3·50
269b 50c. yellow 95·00 3·75
270 1p. red £110 1·70
271 4p. grey £550 30·00
272 10p. bistre £1400 £190

50 King Alfonso XII **51** King Alfonso XII **52**

1882.

273 **50** 15c. pink 8·75 15
273b 15c. yellow 55·00 1·20
274 30c. mauve £250 3·50
275 75c. lilac £225 4·50

1889.

276 **51** 2c. green 4·00 25
289 2c. black 18·00 4·75
277 5c. blue 7·00 10
290 5c. green 80·00 1·90
278 10c. brown 11·50 10
291 10c. red £150 3·00
279 15c. brown 3·00 10
280 20c. green 29·00 1·60
281 25c. blue 10·50 10
282 30c. grey 46·00 2·30
283 40c. brown 46·00 1·90
284 50c. red 46·00 90
285 75c. orange £160 2·40
286 1p. purple 34·00 25
287 4p. red £500 26·00
288 10p. red £800 60·00

For 15c. yellow see No. O289.

1900.

292a **52** 2c. brown 3·00 15
293b 5c. green 5·25 15
294 10c. red 7·50 15
295 15c. black 13·50 15
296 15c. mauve 9·75 15
297 15c. violet 5·25 15
298 20c. black 31·00 1·60
299 25c. blue 5·00 15
300 30c. green 31·00 35
301 40c. bistre £110 3·00
302 40c. pink £250 3·25
303 50c. blue 31·00 40
304 1p. purple 29·00 30
305 4p. purple £225 17·00
306 10p. orange £225 50·00

54 Quixote setting out

1905. Tercentenary of Publication of Cervantes' "Don Quixote".

307 **54** 5c. green 1·50 80
308 – 10c. red 2·30 1·40
309 – 15c. violet 2·30 1·40
310 – 25c. blue 6·50 3·00
311 – 30c. green 38·00 6·50
312 – 40c. red 85·00 21·00
313 – 50c. grey 17·00 5·75
314 – 1p. red £250 60·00
315 – 4p. purple £100 60·00
316 – 10p. orange £160 £100

DESIGNS: 10c. Quixote attacking windmill; 15c. Meeting country girls; 25c. Sancho Panza tossed in a blanket; 30c. Don Quixote knighted by innkeeper; 40c. Tilting at the flock of sheep; 50c. On the wooden horse; 1p. Adventure with lions; 4p. In the bullock-cart; 10p. The enchanted lady.

64

66

67 G.P.O., Madrid

1909.

344 **64** 2c. brown 60 60
330 5c. green 1·30 10
331 10c. red 1·70 10
332 15c. violet 8·50 10
343 15c. yellow 4·25 10
334 20c. green 48·00 65
335 20c. violet 36·00 10
336 25c. blue 3·50 10
337 30c. green 8·50 10
338 40c. pink 13·50 35
339a 50c. blue 12·00 25
340 1p. red 30·00 25
341 4p. purple 70·00 9·75
342 10p. orange £100 20·00

1920. Air. Optd **CORREO AEREO**.

353 **64** 5c. green 1·10 80
354 10c. red 1·70 1·10
355 25c. blue 2·30 2·30
356 50c. blue 14·00 6·50
357 1p. red 40·00 28·00

1920. Imperf.

358 **66** 1c. green 20 10

1920. U.P.U. Congress, Madrid.

361 **67** 1c. black and green 15 10
362 2c. black and brown 15 10
363 5c. black and green 90 80
364 10c. black and red 90 80
365 15c. black and yellow 1·40 1·10
366 20c. black and violet 1·70 1·10
367 25c. black and blue 2·30 2·30
368 30c. black and green 6·25 3·50
369 40c. black and red 25·00 6·00
370 50c. black and blue 29·00 18·00
371 1p. black and pink 29·00 14·00
372 4p. black and brown 90·00 70·00
373 10p. black and orange £180 £140

68 **69**

1922.

374 **68** 2c. green 60 15
375 5c. purple 4·00 10
376 5c. red 1·70 10
377 10c. red 1·70 10
378a 10c. green 1·60 10
380 15c. blue 7·00 10
382 20c. violet 4·00 10
383a 25c. red 4·00 10
387 30c. brown 13·00 10
388 40c. blue 4·00 10
389 50c. orange 18·00 10
391 **69** 1p. grey 17·00 10
392 4p. red 75·00 3·50
393 10p. brown 30·00 13·00

70 Princesses Maria Cristina and Beatriz **71** King Alfonso XIII

1926. Red Cross.

394 **70** 1c. black 1·80 1·80
395 – 2c. blue 1·80 1·90
396 – 5c. purple 4·25 4·50
397 – 10c. green 3·75 4·00
398 **70** 15c. blue 1·40 1·70
399 – 20c. violet 1·40 1·70
400 **71** 25c. red 25 25
401 **70** 30c. green 34·00 36·00
402 – 40c. blue 20·00 21·00
403 – 50c. red 20·00 21·00
404 – 1p. grey 1·40 1·50
405 – 4p. red 1·10 1·10
406 **71** 10p. brown 1·10 1·10

DESIGNS—VERT: 2, 50c. Queen Victoria Eugenie as nurse; 5, 40c., 4p. Queen Victoria Eugenie; 10, 20c., 1p. Prince of the Asturias.

75 CASA-built Dornier Do-J Wal Flying Boat "Plus Ultra"

76 Route Map and Gallarza and Loriga's Breguet 19A2 Biplane

1926. Air. Red Cross and Trans-Atlantic and Madrid-Manila Flights

407 **75** 5c. violet and black 1·60 1·60
408 10c. black and blue 1·90 1·90
409 **76** 15c. blue and red 25 25
410 20c. red and green 25 25
411 **75** 25c. black and red 25 25
412 **76** 30c. brown and blue 25 25
413 40c. green and brown 25 25
414 **75** 50c. black and red 25 25
415 1p. green and black 2·30 2·30
416 **76** 4p. red and yellow 85·00 85·00

1927. 25th Anniv of Coronation. Red Cross stamps of 1926 variously optd or surch **17-V 1902 17-V 1927 A XIII** or **17-V-1902 17-V-1927 ALFONSO XIII** or **17 MAYO 17 1902 1927 ALFONSO XIII** with ornaments. (a) Postage stamps of Spain optd only.

417 **70** 1c. black 5·00 5·00
418 – 2c. blue 9·25 10·00
419 – 5c. purple 2·30 2·30
420 – 10c. green 60·00 60·00
421 **70** 15c. blue 1·60 1·60
422 – 20c. violet 3·50 3·50
423 **71** 25c. red 60 60
424 **70** 30c. green 90 90
425 – 40c. blue 90 90
426 – 50c. red 90 90
427 – 1p. grey 1·60 1·60
428 – 4p. red 9·25 10·00
429 **71** 10p. brown 34·00 36·00

(b) Postage stamps of Spain also surch with new value.

430 – 3c. on 2c. blue 8·50 8·50
431 – 4c. on 2c. blue 8·50 8·50
432 **71** 10c. on 25c. red 40 40
433 25c. on 25c. red 40 40
434 – 55c. on 2c. blue 80 80
435 – 55c. on 10c. green 50·00 50·00
436 – 55c. on 20c. violet 50·00 50·00
437 **70** 75c. on 15c. blue 60 60
438 75c. on 30c. green £180 £180
439 – 80c. on 5c. purple 44·00 44·00
440 – 2p. on 40c. blue 80 80
441 – 2p. on 1p. grey 80 80
442 – 5p. on 50c. red 1·50 1·50
443 – 5p. on 4p. red 2·20 2·20
444 **71** 10p. on 10p. brown 20·00 20·00

(c) Air stamps of Spain optd only.

445 **75** 5c. violet and black 1·40 1·40
446 10c. black and blue 3·00 3·00
447 **76** 15c. blue and red 25 25
448 20c. red and green 25 25
449 **75** 25c. black and red 25 25
450 **76** 30c. brown and blue 25 25
451 40c. green and brown 25 25
452 **75** 50c. black and red 25 25
453 1p. green and black 2·30 2·30
454 **76** 4p. red and yellow £100 £100

(d) Air stamps of Spain also surch with new value.

455 **75** 75c. on 5c. violet and black 4·50 4·50
456 75c. on 10c. black and blue 20·00 20·00
457 **76** 75c. on 25c. black and red 40·00 40·00
458 75c. on 50c. black and red 17·00 17·00

(e) Nos. 24/5 of Spanish Post Offices in Tangier.

460 1p. on 10p. violet 85·00 85·00
461 4p. bistre 32·00 32·00

(f) Nos. 122/3 of Spanish Morocco.

462 55c. on 4p. bistre 18·00 18·00
463 80c. on 10p. violet 18·00 18·00

(g) Nos. 34 and 35 of Cape Juby.

464 5p. on 4p. bistre 55·00 55·00
465 10p. on 10p. violet 32·00 32·00

(h) Nos. 231/2 of Spanish Guinea.

466 1p. on 10p. violet 18·00 18·00
467 2p. on 4p. bistre 18·00 18·00

(i) Nos. 23/4 of Spanish Sahara.

468 80c. on 10p. violet 25·00 25·00
469 2p. on 4p. bistre 18·00 18·00

82 Pope Pius XI and King Alfonso XIII

1928. Rome Catacombs Restoration Fund.

470 **82** 2c. black and violet 25 30
471 2c. black and purple 25 35
486 2c. red and black 35 35
487 2c. red and blue 35 35
472 3c. violet and black 25 30
473 3c. violet and blue 35 35
488 3c. blue and bistre 25 25
489 3c. blue and green 35 35
474 5c. violet and green 70 75
490 5c. red and purple 70 75
475 10c. black and green 1·10 1·20
491 10c. blue and green 1·10 1·20
476 15c. violet and green 4·25 4·50
492 15c. red and blue 4·25 4·50
477 25c. violet and red 4·25 4·50
493 25c. blue and brown 4·25 4·50
478 40c. black and blue 25 25
494 40c. red and blue 25 25
479 55c. violet and brown 25 25
495 55c. blue and brown 25 25
480 80c. black and red 25 25
496 80c. red and black 25 25
481 1p. violet and grey 25 25
497 1p. red and yellow 25 25
482 2p. black and brown 5·75 5·75
498 2p. blue and grey 5·75 5·75
483 3p. violet and pink 5·75 6·25
499 3p. red and violet 5·75 5·75
484 4p. black and purple 5·75 5·75
500 4p. red and purple 5·75 5·75
485 5p. violet and black 5·75 5·75
501 5p. blue and yellow 5·75 5·75

83 A Spanish Caravel, Seville in background **84** Miniature of Exhibition Poster

1929. Seville and Barcelona Exhibitions. Inscr "EXPOSICION GENERAL (or GRAL.) ESPANOLA".

502 **83** 1c. green 1·80 1·80
503 **84** 2c. green 25 25
504 – 5c. red 35 35
505 – 10c. green 35 35
506 **83** 15c. blue 65 65
507 **84** 20c. violet 45 45
508 **83** 25c. red 45 45
509 – 30c. brown 3·75 3·75
510 – 40c. blue 6·50 6·50
511 **84** 50c. orange 3·75 3·75
512 – 1p. grey 10·50 10·50
513 – 4p. purple 21·00 21·00
514 – 10p. brown 55·00 55·00

DESIGNS—VERT: 5, 30c., 1p. View of exhibition. HORIZ: 10, 40c., 4, 10p. Alfonso XIII and Barcelona.

87 "Spirit of St. Louis" over Coast

1929. Air. Seville and Barcelona Exhibitions.

515 **87** 5c. brown 5·00 4·75
516 10c. red 5·00 5·00
517 25c. blue 5·75 5·75
518 50c. violet 6·75 6·75
519 1p. green 32·00 32·00
520 4p. black 23·00 25·00

1929. Meeting of Council of League of Nations at Madrid. Optd **Sociedad de las Naciones LV reunion del Consejo Madrid.**

521 **66** 1c. green 60 60
522 **68** 2c. green 60 60
523 5c. red 60 60
524 10c. green 60 60
525 15c. blue 60 60
526 20c. violet 60 60
527 25c. red 60 60
528 30c. brown 2·30 2·30
529 40c. blue 2·30 2·30
530 50c. orange 2·30 2·30
531 **69** 1p. grey 12·00 12·00
532 4p. red 12·00 13·50
533 10p. brown 42·00 42·00

89 Class 4601 Steam Locomotive, 1924 **90** Stinson Junior over Congress Emblem

1930. 11th Int Railway Congress, Madrid.

534 **89** 1c. green (postage) 45 45
535 2c. green 45 45
536 5c. purple 45 45
537 10c. green 45 45
538 15c. blue 45 45
539 20c. violet 45 45
540 25c. red 45 45
541 30c. brown 1·70 1·70
542 40c. blue 1·60 1·60
543 50c. orange 3·50 3·50
544 – 1p. grey 4·25 4·25
545 – 4p. red 80·00 80·00
546 – 10p. brown £325 £325

DESIGN: 1p. to 10p. Class 1301 steam locomotive (1914) at points.

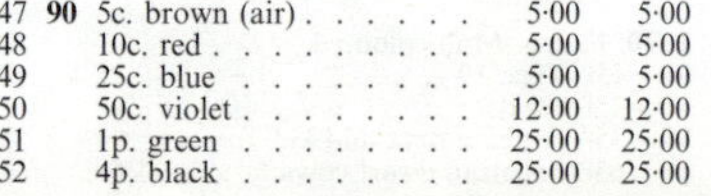

547 **90** 5c. brown (air) 5·00 5·00
548 10c. red 5·00 5·00
549 25c. blue 5·00 5·00
550 50c. violet 12·00 12·00
551 1p. green 25·00 25·00
552 4p. black 25·00 25·00

91 Francisco Goya (after Lopez) 92

93 "The Naked Maja"

1930. Death Cent of Goya (painter). (a) Postage.

No.	Type	Description	Unused	Used
553	**91**	1c. yellow	10	10
554		2c. brown	10	10
555	**92**	2c. green	10	10
556	**91**	5c. mauve	10	10
557	**92**	5c. violet	10	10
558	**91**	10c. green	15	20
559		15c. blue	10	15
560		20c. purple	10	15
561		25c. red	10	15
562	**92**	25c. red	25	30
563	**91**	30c. brown	4·50	5·00
564		40c. blue	4·50	5·00
565		50c. red	4·50	5·00
566		1p. black	5·75	5·50
567	**93**	1p. purple	80	90
568		4p. black	60	60
569		10p. brown	12·50	13·00

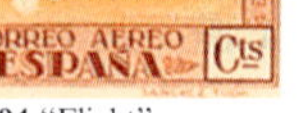

94 "Flight" 97 King Alfonso XIII

(b) Air. Designs show works by Goya, all with curious flying figures.

No.	Type	Description	Unused	Used
570	**94**	5c. yellow and red	10	15
571	–	5c. blue and green	10	15
572	–	10c. green and turquoise	10	15
573	–	15c. red and black	10	15
574	–	20c. red and blue	10	15
575	**94**	25c. red and purple	20	20
576	–	30c. violet and brown	35	35
577	–	40c. blue and ultramarine	35	35
578	–	50c. green and red	35	35
579	–	1p. violet and purple	35	40
580	–	4p. black and purple	2·30	2·30
581	–	4p. blue and light blue	2·30	2·30
582	–	10p. brown and sepia	8·50	8·50

DESIGNS—VERT: 5, 10, 20, 40c. Asmodeus and Cleofas; 1, 4 (581), 10p. Woman and dwarfs in flight. HORIZ: 30, 50c., 4p. (580), Weird flying methods.

1930.

No.	Type	Description	Unused	Used
583	**97**	2c. brown	10	10
584		5c. brown	65	10
585		10c. green	3·50	10
586		15c. green	11·00	10
587		20c. violet	6·25	60
588		25c. red	65	10
589		30c. red	13·50	1·60
590		40c. blue	19·00	65
592		50c. orange	19·00	1·30

98 The "Santa Maria" 99

100 "Santa Maria", "Pinta" and "Nina"

101 The Departure from Palos

1930. Columbus issue.

No.	Type	Description	Unused	Used
593	**98**	1c. brown	19·00	10
594		2c. green	25	10
595	**99**	2c. green	25	15
596	**98**	5c. purple	25	10
597	**99**	5c. purple	25	10
598		10c. green	90	90
599	**98**	15c. blue	90	90
600	**99**	20c. violet	1·30	1·30
601	**100**	25c. red	1·30	1·30
602	**101**	30c. brown, blue and sepia	6·25	6·25
603	**100**	40c. blue	5·25	5·25
604	**101**	50c. violet, blue and purple	8·25	8·25
605	**100**	1p. black	8·25	8·25
606	–	4p. black and blue	9·00	9·00
607	–	10p. brown and purple	37·00	41·00

DESIGNS—As Type **101**: 4, 10p. Arrival in America.

103 Monastery of La Rabida

104 Martin Pinzon

106 Columbus

1930. "Columbus" Air stamps (for Europe and Africa).

No.	Type	Description	Unused	Used
608	**103**	5c. red	10	15
609		5c. brown	10	15
610		10c. green	25	30
611		15c. violet	25	30
612		20c. blue	25	25
613	**104**	25c. red	25	25
614	–	30c. brown	1·80	1·80
615	**104**	40c. blue	1·80	1·80
616	–	50c. orange	1·80	1·80
617	**104**	1p. violet	1·80	1·80
618	**106**	4p. green	1·80	1·80
619		10p. brown	8·50	10·50

DESIGNS—As Type **104**: 30, 50c. Vincent Pinzon.

107 Monastery of La Rabida

108 Columbus 109 Columbus and the brothers Pinzon

1930. "Columbus" Air stamps (for America and Philippines).

No.	Type	Description	Unused	Used
620	**107**	5c. red	10	15
621		10c. green	10	10
622	**108**	25c. red	10	10
623		50c. grey	2·10	2·10
624		1p. brown	2·10	2·10
625	**109**	4p. blue	2·10	2·10
626		10p. purple	10·00	10·00

110 Arms of Bolivia and Paraguay

113 Sidar and Douglas 0-2-M Biplane 114 Breguet 19GR "Jesus del Gran Poder" over "Santa Maria"

1930. Spanish-American Exhibition. Views of pavilions of various countries.

No.	Type	Description	Unused	Used
627	**110**	1c. green (postage)	15	20
628	–	2c. brown (C. America)	15	20
629	–	5c. brown (Venezuela)	15	15
630	–	10c. green (Colombia)	25	25
631	–	15c. blue (Dominican Republic)	25	25
632	–	20c. violet (Uruguay)	25	30
633	–	25c. red (Argentina)	25	30
634	–	25c. red (Chile)	25	30
635	–	30c. purple (Brazil)	1·70	1·70
636	–	40c. blue (Mexico)	95	95
637	–	40c. blue (Cuba)	95	95
638	–	50c. orange (Peru)	1·70	1·70
639	–	1p. blue (U.S.A.)	2·30	2·30
640	–	4p. purple (Portugal)	28·00	32·00
641	–	10p. brown	2·20	2·20

The 10p. shows King Alfonso and Queen Victoria, maps of S. America and Spain, and the Giralda, Seville. The 2, 5c., 4, 10p. are vert.

No.	Type	Description	Unused	Used
643	–	5c. black (air)	80	80
644	–	10c. green	80	80
645	–	25c. blue	80	80
646	–	50c. blue	1·70	1·70
647	**113**	50c. black	1·70	1·70
648	–	1p. red	4·00	4·00
649	–	1p. purple	55·00	65·00
650	–	1p. green	3·00	4·00
651	**114**	4p. blue	5·50	7·50

DESIGNS—HORIZ: 5c. Alberto Santos Dumont and Wright Flyer I over Rio de Janeiro; 10c. Teodoro Fels and Douglas 0-2-M biplane; 25c. Dagoberto Godoy and Nieuport 17 biplane; 50c. Admiral Gago Coutinha, Sacadura Cabral and Fairey IIID seaplane; 1p. (650) Charles Lindbergh and "Spirit of St. Louis". VERT: 1p. (648/9) Jimenez Iglesias and Breguet 19GR "Jesus de Gran Poder".

115 121 The Fountain of the Lions

1930.

No.	Type	Description	Unused	Used
652	**115**	5c. black	5·75	10

1931. Optd **REPUBLICA**. (a) Postage.

No.	Type	Description	Unused	Used
660	**66**	1c. green	10	10
673	**97**	2c. brown	10	10
662		5c. brown	10	10
671	**115**	5c. black	1·60	1·60
675	**97**	10c. green	25	10
664		15c. green	60	60
677		20c. violet	40	40
678		25c. red	40	40
667		30c. red	4·25	4·25
668		40c. blue	1·40	1·40
669		50c. orange	1·40	1·40
670	**69**	1p. grey	7·25	7·25

(b) Air. On Nos. 353/6.

No.	Type	Description	Unused	Used
683	**64**	5c. green	8·25	8·25
684		10c. red	8·25	8·25
685		25c. blue	11·50	15
686		50c. blue	24·00	24·00

1931. Optd **Republica Espanola** in two lines continuously.

No.	Type	Description	Unused	Used
687	**97**	2c. brown	10	10
688		5c. brown	25	15
689		10c. green	25	15
690		15c. green	3·00	30
691		20c. violet	1·30	1·10
692		25c. red	40	25
693		30c. red	4·00	1·00
694		40c. blue	4·00	45
695		50c. orange	6·75	60
696	**69**	1p. grey	47·00	80

1931. 3rd Pan-American Postal Union Congress. (a) Postage.

No.	Type	Description	Unused	Used
697	**121**	5c. purple	10	10
698	–	10c. green	40	40
699	–	15c. violet	40	40
700	–	25c. red	40	40
701	–	30c. green	40	40
702	**121**	40c. blue	1·10	1·10
703	–	50c. red	1·10	1·10
704	–	1p. black	2·20	2·20
705	–	4p. purple	10·50	10·50
706	–	10p. brown	34·00	34·00

DESIGNS—VERT: 10, 25, 50c. Cordoba Cathedral. HORIZ: 15c., 1p. Alcantara Bridge, Toledo; 30c. Dr. F. Garcia y Santos; 4, 10p. Revolutionaries hoisting Republican flag, 14 April, 1931.

123 Royal Palace and San Francisco el Grande

(b) Air.

No.	Type	Description	Unused	Used
707	**123**	5c. purple	15	20
708		10c. green	15	20
709		25c. red	15	20
710	–	50c. blue	45	50
711	–	1p. violet	70	80
712	–	4p. black	9·25	9·25

DESIGNS—HORIZ: 50c., 1p. G.P.O. and Cibeles Fountain; 4p. Calle de Alcala.

125a Montserrat Arms 125b Airplane above Montserrat

1931. 900th Anniv of Montserrat Monastery.

No.	Type	Description	Unused	Used
713	**125a**	1c. green (postage)	1·30	1·40
714		2c. brown	80	60
715		5c. brown	90	80
716		10c. green	90	80
717	–	15c. green	1·30	95
718	–	20c. purple	3·00	2·20
719	–	25c. purple	4·00	3·25
720	–	30c. red	42·00	34·00
721	–	40c. blue	24·00	14·50
722	–	50c. orange	55·00	40·00
723	–	1p. blue	55·00	42·00
724	–	4p. mauve	£425	£375
725	–	10p. brown	£325	£325

DESIGNS: 15, 50c. Monks planning Monastery; 20, 30c. "Black Virgin" (full length); 25c., 1, 10p. "Black Virgin" (profile); 40c., 4p. Monastery.

No.	Type	Description	Unused	Used
726	**125b**	5c. brown (air)	45	45
727		10c. green	2·30	2·30
728		25c. purple	9·25	9·25
729		50c. orange	34·00	34·00
730		1p. blue	23·00	23·00

126 Blasco Ibanez 127 Pi y Margall 128 Joaquin Costa

129 Mariana Pineda 130 Nicolas Salmeron 131 Concepcion Arenal

132 Ruiz Zorilla 133 Pablo Iglesias 134 Ramon y Cajal

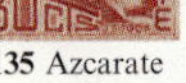

135 Azcarate 136 Jovellanos 137 Pablo Iglesias

138 Emilio Castelar 139 Pablo Iglesias 140 Velazquez

141 F. Salvoechea 142 Cuenca

1931.

738	**126**	2c. brown	10	10
731	**127**	5c. brown	3·00	25
740	**126**	5c. brown	10	10
741	**128**	10c. green	5·00	10
742	**129**	10c. green	10	10
744	**130**	15c. green	75	10
745	**131**	15c. green	25	10
747		15c. black	80	10
748	**127**	20c. violet	25	10
734	**133**	25c. red	24·00	55
750	**132**	25c. red	60	10
751	**133**	30c. red	2·10	10
752	**134**	30c. brown	7·75	1·40
753	**135**	30c. red	8·50	25
755	**136**	30c. red	10	10
756	**137**	30c. red	10	10
757	**139**	30c. red	1·30	45
758	**138**	40c. blue	10	10
759		40c. red	1·30	45
760	**139**	45c. red	10	10
761	**130**	50c. orange	31·00	45
762		50c. blue	1·10	50
763	**140**	50c. blue	10	10
764	**138**	60c. green	10	10
765	**141**	60c. blue	90	1·10
766		60c. orange	7·00	8·00
767c	**142**	1p. black	15	15
768c	–	4p. mauve	35	25
769c	–	10p. brown	60	60

DESIGNS—As Type **142**: 4p. Castle of Segovia; 10p. Sun Gate, Toledo.

143 144

1933. Imperf (1c.), perf (others).

770	**143**	1c. green	10	10
771		2c. brown	25	10
772	**144**	2c. brown	10	10
773	**143**	5c. brown	10	10
774		10c. green	10	10
775		15c. green	10	10
776a		20c. violet	10	10
777a		25c. mauve	10	10
778		30c. red	10	10

145 Cierva C.30A Autogyro over Seville

1935.

780	**145**	2p. blue	20	10

146 Lope De Vega's Book-plate 148 Scene from "Peribanez"

1935. 300th Death Anniv of Lope de Vega (author).

781	**146**	15c. green	6·75	30
782	–	30c. red	3·00	15
783	–	50c. blue	13·50	2·20
784	**148**	1p. black	23·00	1·60

DESIGN—As Type **146**: 30, 50c. Lope de Vega (after Tristan).

149 Old-time Map of the Amazon

1935. Iglesias' Amazon Expedition.

785	**149**	30c. red	2·20	75

150 M. Moya 153 Airplane over Press Association Building

151 House of Nazareth and Rotary Press

152 Pyrenean Eagle and Newspapers

1936. 40th Anniv of Madrid Press Association.

786	**150**	1c. red (postage)	15	40
787	–	2c. brown	15	20
788	–	5c. brown	15	20
789	–	10c. green	15	20
790	**150**	15c. green	15	20
791	–	20c. violet	15	20
792	–	25c. mauve	15	20
793	–	30c. red	15	20
794	**150**	40c. orange	45	15
795	–	50c. blue	25	15
796	–	60c. green	60	25
797	–	1p. black	60	30
798	**151**	2p. blue	7·50	3·50
799		4p. purple	7·50	5·75
800		10p. red	18·00	13·00

PORTRAITS: 2, 20, 50c. T. L. de Tena; 5, 25, 60c. J. F. Rodriguez; 10, 30c., 1p. A. Lerroux.
SIZES: 1c. to 10c. 22 × 27 mm; 15c. to 30c. 24 × 30 mm; 40c. to 1p. 26 × 31½ mm.

801	**152**	1c. red (air)	15	15
802	**153**	2c. brown	15	15
803	**152**	5c. brown	15	15
804	**153**	10c. green	15	15
805	–	15c. blue	15	20
806	**152**	20c. violet	15	20
807	**153**	25c. mauve	15	20
808	–	30c. red	15	15
809	**152**	40c. orange	45	30
810		50c. blue	35	25
811	**153**	60c. green	75	25
812	–	1p. black	75	25
813	–	2p. blue	5·00	3·25
814	–	4p. purple	5·50	5·00
815	–	10p. red	14·00	11·00

DESIGNS—VERT: 15, 30, 50c., 1p. Cierva C.30A autogyro over House of Nazareth. HORIZ: 2, 4, 10p. Don Quixote on wooden horse.

155 Gregorio Fernandez 156

1936. 300th Birth Anniv of Gregorio Fernandez (sculptor).

816	**155**	30c. red	1·30	85

1936. 1st National Philatelic Exhibition, Madrid. Imperf. (a) Postage.

817	**156**	10c. brown	38·00	43·00
818		15c. green	38·00	43·00

(b) Air. Optd **CORREO AEREO**.

819	**156**	10c. red	£140	£140
820		15c. blue	£140	£140

1936. Manila–Madrid Flight of Arnaiz and Calvo. Optd **VUELO MANILA MADRID 1936 ARNAIZ CALVO.**

821	**137**	30c. red	6·00	5·00

159 160a Republican Symbol

1937. Fiscal stamp of Austrias and Leon surch.

822	**159**	25c. on 5c. red	9·25	7·75
823		45c. on 5c. red	5·00	9·25
824		60c. on 5c. red	25	40
825		1p. on 5c. red	25	35

1938. Surch **45 centimos.**

826	**143**	45c. on 1c. green (imperf)	6·50	6·50
827		45c. on 1c. green (perf)	45	25
830		45c. on 2c. brown	17·00	15·00
831	**144**	45c. on 2c. brown	10	10
832	**126**	45c. on 2c. brown	35·00	35·00

1938.

833	**160a**	40c. pink	10	10
834		45c. red	10	10
835		50c. blue	10	10
836		60c. blue	45	25

1938. 7th Anniv of Republic. Nos. 308/9 surch **14 ABRIL 1938 VII Aniversario de la Republica** and values. (a) Postage.

837		45c. on 15c. violet	13·00	13·00

(b) Air. Additionally optd **CORREO AEREO.**

838		2p.50 on 10c. red	90·00	90·00

163 Defence of Madrid

1938. Defence of Madrid Relief Fund. (a) Postage.

839	**163**	45c.+2p. blue & lt blue	60	60

(b) Air. Surch **AEREO + 5 Pts.**

841	**163**	45c.+2p.+5p. blue and light blue	£225	£275

1938. Labour Day. Surch **FIESTA DEL TRABAJO 1 MAYO 1938** and values.

843	**54**	45c. on 15c. violet	3·00	3·00
844		1p. on 15c. violet	5·50	5·50

167 Statue of Liberty and Flags

1938. 150th Anniv of U.S. Constitution. (a) Postage.

845	**167**	1p. multicoloured	15·00	17·00

(b) Air. Surch **AEREO + 5 Pts.**

847	**167**	1p.+5p. multicoloured	£200	£225

169 172 Steelworks

1938. Red Cross. (a) Postage.

849	**169**	45c.+5p. red	45	45

(b) Air. Surch **+3 Pts. Aereo.**

850	**169**	45c.+5p.+3p. red	9·25	8·50

1938. Air. No. 719 surch with two airplanes, **CORREO AEREO** twice and value.

851		50c. on 25c. purple	31·00	29·00
852		1p. on 25c. purple	1·10	1·10
853		1p.25 on 25c. purple	1·10	1·10
854		1p.50 on 25c. purple	1·10	1·10
855		2p. on 25c. purple	31·00	29·00

1938. Workers of Sagunto.

856	**172**	45c. black	15	15
857	–	1p.25 blue	15	15

DESIGN: 1p.25, Blast furnace and air raid victims.

173 "Isaac Peral"

1938. Submarine Service.

857a	**173**	1p. blue	4·25	4·25
857b	–	2p. brown	8·50	8·50
857c	–	4p. orange	9·25	9·25
857d	–	6p. blue	20·00	20·00
857e	–	10p. purple	36·00	36·00
857f	–	15p. green	£375	£375

DESIGNS: 2, 6p. "Narciso Monturiol". 4, 10p. "B-2".

174 Troops on the Alert

1938. In Honour of 43rd Division. Perf or imperf.

858	**174**	25c. green	9·25	9·25
859	–	45c. brown	9·25	9·25

DESIGN—VERT: 45c. Two soldiers on guard.

1938. 2nd Anniv of Defence of Madrid. Optd **SEGUNDO ANIVERSARIO DE LA HEROICA DEFENSA DE MADRID 7 NOV. 1938.**

860	**163**	45c.+2p. blue and light blue	4·00	3·00

1938. No. 719 surch **2'50 PTAS.**, bars and ornaments.

861		2p.50 on 25c. purple	10	10

176a Man and Woman in Firing Position

1938. In honour of the Militia.

861b	**176a**	5c. brown	3·00	3·00
861c		10c. purple	3·00	3·00
861d		25c. green	3·00	3·00
861e	–	45c. red	3·00	3·00
861f	–	60c. blue	5·50	3·50
861g	–	1p.20 black	£110	£110
861h	–	2p. orange	34·00	34·00
861i	–	5p. brown	£200	£200
861j	–	10p. green	38·00	38·00

DESIGNS—HORIZ: 45, 60c., 1p.20, Militia with machine gun. VERT: 2, 5, 10p. Grenade-thrower.

NATIONAL STATE

The Civil War began on 17 July 1936. Until it ended on 1 April 1939, the stamps listed below were current only in areas held by the forces of General Franco.

177 Seville Cathedral 178 Xavier Castle, Navarre

1936. Junta of National Defence.

862	–	5c. brown	60	60
863	–	15c. green	60	50
864	**177**	25c. red	60	60
865	**178**	30c. red	60	60
867	–	1p. black	5·50	4·00

DESIGNS—VERT: 5c. Burgos Cathedral. HORIZ: 15c. Zaragoza Cathedral; 1p. Alcantara Bridge and Alcazar, Toledo.

179 180 Cordoba Cathedral

1936.
868 179 1c. green (imperf) 5·50 5·75
869 2c. brown 60 60
870 – 10c. green 60 60
871 – 50c. blue 14·00 10·50
872 180 60c. green 1·20 80
873 – 4p. lilac, red and yellow 55·00 32·00
874 – 10p. brown 55·00 32·00
DESIGNS (As T 180)—HORIZ: 10c. Salamanca University; 50c. Court of Lions, Granada; 10p. Troops disembarking at Algeciras. VERT: 4p. National flag at Malaga.

181 182

183 "El Cid" 184 Isabella the Catholic

1937.
875 181 1c. green (imperf) 10 10
876 182 2c. brown 10 10
902 183 5c. brown 10 10
879 10c. green 10 10
903 10c. red 10 10
896 15c. green 10 10
880 184 15c. black 10 15
881 20c. violet 35 15
882 25c. red 25 15
883 30c. red 45 10
885 40c. orange 2·10 15
886 50c. blue 1·80 10
887 60c. yellow 25 15
897 70c. blue 60 10
888 1p. blue 17·00 45
889 4p. mauve 21·00 4·75
891 183 10p. blue 32·00 18·00
See also No. 1113.

186 Santiago Cathedral 189

1937. Holy Year of Compostela.
905 – 15c. brown 1·10 1·00
906 186 30c. red 5·75 45
908 – 1p. orange and blue 18·00 3·25
DESIGNS—VERT: 15c. St. James of Compostela. HORIZ: 1p. Portico de la Gloria.

1937. Anti-tuberculosis Fund. Cross in red.
913 189 10c. blue and black 7·00 4·25

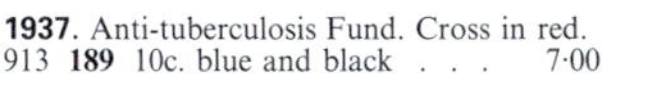

190 Ferdinand the Catholic 192

1938.
917 190 15c. green 1·40 15
918 20c. violet 9·25 2·10
919 25c. red 65 15
921 30c. red 4·50 10

1938. Air. Optd **correo aereo.**
922 190 50c. blue 90 60
923 1p. blue 3·00 60

1938. 2nd Anniv of National Uprising.
926 192 15c. green and light green 4·50 4·50
927 25c. red and pink 4·50 4·25
928 30c. blue and light blue 2·30 2·30
929 1p. brown and yellow 95·00 95·00

193 Isabella the Catholic 194

1938.
930 193 20c. violet 60 15
931 25c. red 6·25 60
932 30c. red 25 15
933 40c. mauve 25 10
934 50c. blue 26·00 2·20
935 1p. blue 9·25 90

1938. Anti-tuberculosis Fund. Cross in red.
940 194 10c. blue and black 4·50 1·80

195 Juan de la Cierva and Cierva C.30A Autogyro 196 General Franco

1939. Air.
1010 195 20c. orange 60 25
1011 25c. red 40 15
943 35c. mauve 60 25
1013 50c. brown 60 15
945 1p. blue 60 15
1015 2p. green 1·90 10
1016 4p. blue 6·50 25
1017 10p. violet 5·25 55

1939.
960 196 5c. brown 40 10
961 10c. red 1·80 65
962 15c. green 45 10
1114 20c. violet 10 10
1115 25c. purple 10 10
950 30c. red 25 15
1116 30c. blue 10 10
1117 35c. blue 25 10
951 40c. green 25 15
966 40c. grey 40 10
952 45c. red 2·10 1·90
1119 45c. blue 10 10
1120 50c. grey 10 10
1121 60c. orange 10 10
955 70c. blue 40 15
956 1Pts. black 12·50 10
974 1PTA. black 5·75 10
975 1PTS. grey 55·00 65
957 2Pts. brown 16·00 1·00
1124 2PTAS. brown 5·00 10
958 4Pts. purple £100 13·50
1125 4PTAS. red 11·00 10
959 10Pts. brown 48·00 32·00
978 10PTS. brown £130 3·50
1126 10PTAS. brown 1·90 45
For 10c. brown imperf, see No. 981.

197 "Spain" and Wreath of Peace

1939. Homage to the Army.
980 197 10c. blue 10 10

1939. Anti-tuberculosis Fund. Imperf.
981 196 10c. brown 10 15

198 Ruins of Belchite

1940. Zaragoza Cathedral Restoration Fund and 19th Centenary of Apparition of Virgin of El Pilar at Zaragoza. (a) Postage.
982 198 10c.+5c. brown and blue 10 15
983 – 15c.+10c. green and lilac 10 15
984 – 20c.+10c. blue & violet 10 15
985 – 25c.+10c. brown & red 10 15
986 – 40c.+10c. purple & grn 10 15
987 – 45c.+15c. red and blue 25 25
988 198 70c.+20c. black & brn 25 25
989 – 80c.+20c. violet and red 40 40
990 – 1p.+30c. purple & black 40 40
991 – 1p.40+40c. black & vio 34·00 34·00
992 – 1p.50+50c. purple & bl 45 45
993 – 2p.50+50c. blue & pur 45 45
994 – 4p.+1p. grey and lilac 11·00 11·00
995 – 10p.+4p. brown & blue £160 £160
DESIGNS—HORIZ: 15, 80c. Procession of the Rosary; 20c., 1p.50, El Pilar; 25c., 1p. Mother Rafols praying; 40c., 2p.50, Sanctuary of the Virgin; 45c., 1p.40, Oath of the besieged; 4p. Miracle of Calanda; 10p. Virgin appearing to St. James.

(b) Air.
996 25c.+5c. grey and purple 25 25
997 50c.+5c. violet and red 25 25
998 65c.+15c. blue and violet 25 25
999 70c.+15c. violet and grey 25 25
1000 90c.+20c. red and brown 25 30
1001 1p.20+30c. purple & violet 25 25
1002 1p.40+40c. brown & blue 25 25
1003 2p.+50c. violet and purple 40 40
1004 4p.+1p. purple and green 9·25 9·25
1005 10p.+4p. blue and brown £225 £225
DESIGNS—VERT: 25, 70c. Prayer during bombardment; 50c., 1p.40, Caravel and Image of the Virgin; 65, 90c. The Assumption; 1p.20, 2p. Coronation of the Virgin; 4p. "The Cave", after Goya; 10p. Bombing of Zaragoza Cathedral.

199 Gen. Franco 200 Knight and Cross of Lorraine

1940. Anti-tuberculosis Fund.
1006 199 10c. violet and red (post) 10 10
1007 20c.+5c. green and red 65 65
1008 40c.+10c. blue and red 90 35
1009 10c. pink and red (air) 85 85

1941. Anti-tuberculosis Fund.
1018 200 10c. black and red (post) 10 15
1019 20c.+5c. violet and red 60 30
1020 40c.+10c. grey and red 60 30
1021 10c. blue and red (air) 25 30

201 Gen. Franco 202 St. John of the Cross

1942.
1022 201 40c. brown 25 10
1023 75c. blue 4·25 50
1024a 90c. green 75 15
1025b 1p.35 violet 75 25

1942. 400th Birth Anniv of St. John of the Cross.
1026 202 20c. violet 70 10
1027 40c. orange 1·60 35
1028 75c. blue 1·80 1·90

203 Arms and Lorraine Cross

1942. Anti-T.B. Fund. Inscr "1942 43".
1029 203 10c. orange and red (postage) 10 10
1030 20c.+5c. brown and red 1·60 1·50
1031 40c.+10c. green and red 90 25
1032 – 10c. orange and red (air) 80 45
DESIGN—HORIZ: No. 1032, Lorraine Cross and two doves in flight.

204 St. James of Compostela 205

1943. Holy Year. Inscr "ANO SANTO 1943".
1033 204 20c. blue 25 20
1034 – 20c. red 25 15
1035 – 20c. lilac 25 15
1036 – 40c. brown 60 20
1037 205 40c. green 45 20
1038 – 40c. brown 60 20
1039 – 75c. blue 2·20 1·80
1040 – 75c. blue 2·75 1·90
1041 – 75c. blue 31·00 33·00
DESIGNS—VERT: Nos. 1034 and 1040. Details of pillars in Santiago Cathedral; No. 1036, St. James enthroned; No. 1038, Portal of Santiago Cathedral; No. 1039, Censer; No. 1041, Santiago Cathedral. HORIZ: No. 1035, Tomb of St. James.

206

1943. Anti-Tuberculosis Fund. Inscr "1943–1944".
1042 206 10c. violet & red (postage) 25 30
1043 20c.+5c. green and red 3·50 1·60
1044 40c.+10c. blue and red 2·30 1·20
1045 – 10c. violet and red (air) 1·00 1·10
DESIGN: No. 1045. Lorraine Cross and outline of bird.

207 10th-cent Tower 208 Arms of Soria

1944. Millenary of Castile. Arms designs as T 208 inscr "MILENARIO DE CASTILLA".
1046 207 20c. lilac 25 25
1047 208 20c. lilac 25 25
1048 – 20c. lilac 25 25
1049 – 40c. brown 3·00 60
1050 – 40c. brown 3·00 60
1051 – 40c. brown 2·50 60
1052 – 75c. blue 3·00 3·50
1053 – 75c. blue 3·00 3·50
1054 – 75c. blue 3·25 4·00
DESIGNS: No. 1048, Avila (Shield at left); No. 1049, Castile (Arms in centre); No. 1050, Segovia (Shield at left); No. 1051, Burgos (Shield at right); No. 1052, Avila (Shield at left); No. 1053, Fernan Gonzalez, founder of Castile (Helmet, bow and arrows at left); No. 1054, Santander (Shield at right).

209 "Dr. Thebussem" (M. P. de Figueroa, author and postal historian)

1944. Air. Stamp Day.
1055 209 5p. blue 17·00 15·00

210 211 Quevedo

1944. Anti-tuberculosis Fund. Inscr "1944 1945".
(a) Postage.
1056 210 10c. orange and red 10 15
1057 20c.+5c. black and red 25 30
1058 40c.+10c. violet & red 60 60
1059 80c.+10c. blue and red 8·50 9·00
(b) Air. Inscr "CORRESPONDENCIA AEREA".
1060 – 25c. orange and red 4·00 4·00
DESIGN—HORIZ: No. 1060, Hospital.

1945. 300th Death Anniv of Francisco de Quevedo (author).
1061 211 40c. brown 85 65

212 Conde de San Luis, Mail Vehicle of 1850 and Airplane

1945. Air. Stamp Day.
1062 212 10p. green 25·00 16·00

213 Carlos de Haya Gonzalez 214 J. Garcia Morato

1945. Air. Civil War Air Aces.
1063 **213** 4p. red . . . . 13·50 5·00
1064 **214** 10p. purple . . . . . . 30·00 6·00

215 St. George and Dragon **216** Lorraine Cross and Eagle

1945. Anti-T.B. Fund.
1065 **215** 10c. orge & red (postage) 20 20
1066 20c.+5c. green and red 25 15
1067 40c.+10c. violet and red 45 15
1068 80c.+10c. blue and red 12·50 8·50
1069 **216** 25c. red (air) . . . . . 1·80 1·40

217 E. A. de Nebrija (compiler of first Spanish Grammar) **219** Statue of Fray Bartolome de las Casas and native Indian

1946. Stamp Day and Day of the Race.
1070 **217** 50c. red (postage) . . . 65 20
1071 – 75c. blue 70 45
1072 **219** 5p.50 green (air) . . . . 3·75 2·50
DESIGN—As Type **217**: 75c. Salamanca University and signature of F. F. de Vitoria (founder of International Law).

220 Self-portrait of Goya **221** Woman and Child

1946. Birth Bicentenary of Goya (painter).
1073 **220** 25c. red 15 15
1074 50c. green 15 15
1075 75c. blue 95 60

1946. Anti-tuberculosis Fund. Dated "1946 1947".
1076 **221** 5c. violet and red (postage) 15 15
1077 10c. green and red 15 15
1078 – 25c. orange and red (air) 35 15
DESIGN—HORIZ: 25c. Eagle.

222 B. J. Feijoo y Montenegro

1947.
1079 **222** 50c. green 80 60

223 Don Quixote in Library **224** Don Quixote

1947. Stamp Day and 400th Birth Anniv of Cervantes.
1080 **223** 50c. brown (postage) . . 40 15
1081 **224** 75c. blue 70 40
1082 – 5p.50 violet (air) . . . . 7·00 4·00
DESIGN—HORIZ: 5p.50, Quixote on Wooden Horse (after Gustav Dore).

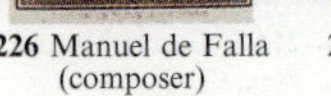

226 Manuel de Falla (composer) **228** Lorraine Cross

1947. Air.
1083 **226** 25p. purple . . . . . . 50·00 19·00
1084 – 50p. red . . . . £180 34·00
PORTRAIT: 50p. Ignacio Zuloaga (painter).

1947. Anti-tuberculosis Fund. Dated "1947 1948".
1085 **228** 5c. brown & red (postage) 15 15
1086 – 10c. blue and red 15 15
1087 – 25c. mauve and red (air) 35 15
DESIGNS—VERT: 10c. Deckchair in garden. HORIZ: 25c. Sanatorium.

229 General Franco **230** Hernando Cortes

1948.
1088 **229** 5c. brown 10 10
1088a 5c. green 10 10
1089 15c. green 20 10
1090 50c. brown 20 10
1091 80c. red . . . . 5·00 15

1948.
1092 **230** 35c. black . . . . 30 1·10
1093 – 70c. purple . . . . . . 3·00 1·90
PORTRAIT: 70c. M. Aleman (writer).

232 Gen. Franco and Castillo de la Mota **233** Ferdinand III of Castile

1948.
1094 **232** 25c. orange 10 10
1095 30c. green 10 10
1096 35c. green 10 10
1097 40c. brown 85 10
1099 45c. red 40 15
1100 50c. purple . . . . . . 1·40 10
1101 70c. violet . . . . . . 2·30 20
1102 75c. blue . . . . 2·20 15
1103 1p. red . . . . 7·00 10

1948. 700th Anniv of Institution of Castilian Navy.
1104 **233** 25c. violet 40 10
1105 – 30c. red (Admiral R. de Bonifaz) 20 10

235 Marquis of Salamanca **236** Series ABJ Diesel Railcar (1936) and Lockheed Constellation Airliner

1948. Stamp Day and Spanish Railway Centenary Inscr "F.F.C.C. ESPANOLES 1848 1948".
1106 **235** 50c. brown (postage) . . 75 10
1107 – 5p. green . . . . 3·00 15
1108 **236** 2p. red (air) . . . . . . 3·50 1·40
DESIGN—HORIZ: 5p. Garganta de Pancorbo Viaduct.

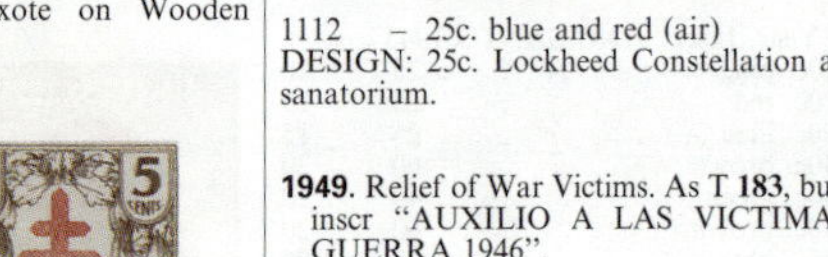

238 Aesculapius **240** Globe and Buildings

1948. Anti-tuberculosis Fund. Dated "1948 1949".
1109 **238** 5c. brown & red (postage) 15 15
1110 10c. green and red . . . 15 10
1111 50c.+10c. brown & red 1·30 85
1112 – 25c. blue and red (air) 60 30
DESIGN: 25c. Lockheed Constellation airliner over sanatorium.

1949. Relief of War Victims. As T **183**, but larger and inscr "AUXILIO A LAS VICTIMAS DE LA GUERRA 1946".
1113 5c. violet 25 10

1949. 75th Anniv of U.P.U.
1127 **240** 50c. brown (postage) . . 1·10 20
1128 75c. blue 80 35
1129 4p. green (air) 60 30

241 Galleon **242** San Juan de Dios and Leper

1949. Anti-tuberculosis Fund. Inscr "1949 1950".
1130 **241** 5c. violet & red (postage) 15 15
1131 10c. green and red . . . 15 10
1132 50c.+10c. brown & red 60 30
1133 – 25c. brown and red (air) 25 15
DESIGN: 25c. Bell.

1950. 400th Death Anniv of San Juan de Dios.
1134 **242** 1p. violet . . . . 18·00 5·75

243 Calderon de la Barca (dramatist) **244** Isabella II

1950. Portraits.
1135 **243** 5c. brown 10 10
1136 – 10c. purple 10 10
1137 – 15c. green 35 10
1138 – 20c. violet 60 10
1139 – 2p. blue . . . . 23·00 25
1140 – 4p.50 purple . . . . . . 1·90 1·10
PORTRAITS—VERT: 10c. Lope de Vega (author); 15c. Tirso de Molina (poet); 20c. Ruiz de Alarcon (author); 2p. Dr. Ramon y Cajal (physician); 4p.50, Dr. Ferran y Clua (bacteriologist).

1950. Stamp Centenary. Imperf. (a) Postage. Reproduction of T **1**.
1141 **244** 50c. violet . . . . 9·75 5·50
1142 75c. blue . . . . 9·75 5·50
1143 10p. green . . . . £150 95·00
1144 15p. red . . . . £150 95·00

(b) Air. Reproduction of T **2**.
1145 – 1p. purple . . . . 9·75 5·50
1146 – 2p.50 brown . . . . . . 9·75 5·50
1147 – 20p. blue £150 £100
1148 – 25p. green £150 £100

1950. Gen. Franco's Canary Is Visit. Nos. 1100 and 1103 surch **VISITA DEL CAUDILLO A CANARIAS OCTUBRE 1950 SOBRETASA: DIEZ CTS** and No. 1083 with **Correspondencia por avion** also.
1149 **232** 10c. on 50c. purple (postage) . . . . . . 60·00 60·00
1150 10c. on 1p. red . . . . 60·00 60·00
1151 **226** 10c. on 25p. purple (air) £550 £300

246 Candle and Conifer **247** Map

1950. Anti-T.B. Fund. Cross in red. Inscr "1950 1951".
1152 **246** 5c. violet (postage) . . . 10 10
1153 10c. green 10 10
1154 50c.+10c. brown . . . . 2·30 1·20
1155 – 25c. blue (air) 60 25
DESIGN: 25c. Dove and flowers.

1951. Air. 6th Conference of Spanish–American Postal Union.
1156 **247** 1p. blue . . . . 7·25 2·40

248 Isabella the Catholic **248a** St. Antonio Claret

1951. 5th Centenary of Birth of Isabella.
1157 **248** 50c. brown . . . . 1·00 35
1158 75c. blue . . . . 1·40 35
1159 90c. purple 65 30
1160 1p.50 orange . . . . . 15·00 6·50
1161 2p.80 olive . . . . . . 33·00 21·00

1951. Stamp Day.
1162 **248a** 50c. blue . . . . 5·25 3·00

249 Children on Beach **250** Isabella the Catholic

1951. Anti-tuberculosis Fund. Cross in red.
1163 **249** 5c. red (postage) 10 10
1164 10c. green 70 25
1165 – 25c. brown (air) 80 35
DESIGN: 25c. Nurse and child.

1951. Air. Stamp Day and 500th Birth Anniv of Isabella the Catholic.
1166 **250** 60c. green . . . . 7·75 40
1167 90c. yellow . . . . . . 1·00 55
1168 1p.30 red . . . . 11·00 5·75
1169 1p.90 sepia . . . . . . 7·75 6·00
1170 2p.30 blue . . . . 5·00 3·00

251 Ferdinand the Catholic **252** St. Maria Micaela

1952. 500th Birth Anniv of Ferdinand the Catholic.
1171 **251** 50c. green 90 25
1172 75c. blue . . . . 6·75 1·60
1173 90c. purple 60 25
1174 1p.50 orange . . . . . 16·00 6·75
1175 2p.80 brown . . . . . . 19·00 17·00

1952. 35th International Eucharistic Congress, Barcelona.
1176 **252** 90c. red (postage) . . . 10 10
1177 – 1p. green (air) . . . . . 4·25 35
DESIGN: 1p. "The Eucharist" (Tiepolo).

252a St. Francis Xavier **254** Nurse and Baby

1952. Air. 400th Death Anniv of St. Francis Xavier.
1178 **252a** 2p. blue . . . . 52·00 18·00

1952. Air. Stamp Day and 500th Anniv of Birth of Ferdinand the Catholic. As T **250** but interior scene and portrait of Ferdinand the Catholic.
1179 60c. green 25 15
1180 90c. orange 25 15
1181 1p.30 red 90 85
1182 1p.90 brown . . . . 3·25 2·30
1183 2p.30 blue . . . . 16·00 9·75

1953. Anti-tuberculosis Fund. Cross in red.
1184 **254** 5c. lake (postage) . . . 60 10
1185 10c. green . . . . 1·80 10
1186 – 25c. brown (air) . . . . 6·75 5·25
DESIGN: 25c. Girl and angel.

255 J. Sorolla (painter)

1953. Air.
1187 **255** 50p. violet . . . . . . £550 20·00

256 Bas-relief **257** Fray Luis de Leon

1953. Stamp Day and 700th Anniv of Salamanca University. Inscr "UNIVDAD DE SALAMANCA".
1188 **256** 50c. red 45 20
1189 **257** 90c. green . . . . 2·30 2·30
1190 – 2p. brown . . . . 20·00 4·00
DESIGN—As Type **185**—HORIZ: 2p. Salamanca University.

258 M. L. de Legazpi (founder of Manila)

259 "St. Mary Magdalene"

1953. Air. Signing of Filipino–Spanish Postal Convention.
1191 **258** 25p. black . . . . £140 30·00

1954. Death Tercentenary of Ribera (painter).
1192 **259** 1p.25 lake 10 10

260 St. James of Compostela

261 "Purity" (after Cano)

1954. Holy Year.
1193 **260** 50c. brown 60 20
1194 – 3p. blue . . . . 60·00 3·50
DESIGN: 3p. Santiago Cathedral.

1954. Marian Year.
1195 **261** 10c. red 10 10
1196 – 15c. green 10 10
1197 – 25c. violet 15 10
1198 – 30c. brown 15 10
1199 – 50c. green 75 10
1200 – 60c. black 15 10
1201 – 80c. green . . . . 4·00 10
1202 – 1p. violet . . . . 4·00 10
1203 – 2p. brown . . . . 1·20 20
1204 – 3p. blue . . . . 1·20 95
DESIGNS: 15c. Virgin of Begona, Bilbao; 25c. Virgin of the Abandoned, Valencia Cathedral; 30c. The "Black Virgin" of Montserrat; 50c. El Pilar Virgin, Zaragoza; 60c. Covadonga Virgin; 80c. Virgin of the Kings, Seville Cathedral; 1p. Almudena Virgin, Madrid; 2p. Virgin of Africa; 3p. Guadalupe Virgin.

262 M. Menendez Pelayo (historian)

263 Gen. Franco

1954. Stamp Day.
1205 **262** 80c. green . . . . 8·50 20

1955.
1206 **263** 10c. red 10 10
1207 15c. ochre 10 10
1208 20c. green 10 10
1209 25c. violet 10 10
1210 30c. brown 10 10
1211 40c. purple 10 10
1212 50c. brown 10 10
1213 60c. purple 10 10
1214 70c. green 15 10
1215 80c. turquoise 10 10
1216 1p. orange 10 10
1217 1p.40 mauve 15 15
1218 1p.50 turquoise 10 10
1219 1p.80 green 15 15
1220 2p. red . . . . 22·00 70
1221 2p. mauve 10 10
1222 3p. blue 10 10
1222a 4p. red 10 15
1223 5p. brown 15 10
1224 6p. black 15 10
1224a 7p. blue 10 10
1225 8p. violet 15 10
1226 10p. green 20 10
1226a 12p. green 10 10
1226b 20p. red 20 10

264 Torres Quevedo (engineer and inventor)

265 St. Ignatius of Loyola

1955. Air.
1229 – 25p. black . . . . 28·00 65
1230 **264** 50p. violet . . . . . . 9·75 1·90
PORTRAIT: 25p. Fortuny

1955. Stamp Day and 4th Centenary of Death of St. Ignatius of Loyola.
1231 **265** 25c. slate 20 20
1232 – 60c. ochre 80 35
1233 **265** 80c. green . . . . 3·00 35
DESIGN—HORIZ: 60c. St. Ignatius and Loyola Castle.

266 Lockheed L.1049 Super Constellation and Caravel

1955. Air.
1234 **266** 20c. green 10 10
1235 25c. violet 10 10
1236 50c. brown 10 15
1237 1p. red 10 15
1238 1p.10 green 15 20
1239 1p.40 mauve 15 15
1240 3p. blue 15 10
1241 4p.80 yellow 15 10
1242 5p. brown . . . . 1·50 15
1243 7p. mauve 75 15
1244 10p. green 75 20

267 "T-elecommunications"

269 "The Holy Family" (after El Greco)

1955. Centenary of Telegraphs in Spain.
1245 **267** 15c. brown 50 25
1246 80c. green . . . . 11·00 30
1247 3p. blue . . . . 20·00 95

1955. 500th Anniv of Canonization of St. Vincent Ferrer. As T **259** but portrait of the Saint (after C. Vilar).
1248 15c. ochre 50 25

1955. Christmas.
1249 **269** 80c. myrtle . . . . . . 5·75 60

270

272 The "Black Virgin"

271 "Ciudad de Toledo" (cargo liner)

1956. 20th Anniv of Civil War.
1250 **270** 15c. brown and bistre . . 20 20
1251 50c. olive and green . . 75 50
1252 80c. grey and mauve . . 7·75 30
1253 3p. blue and ultramarine 11·00 2·20

1956. 1st Floating Exhibition of National Products.
1254 **271** 3p. blue . . . . 5·50 2·20

1956. 75th Anniv of "Black Virgin" of Montserrat.
1255 **272** 15c. brown 10 15
1256 – 60c. purple 25 30
1257 **272** 80c. green 45 35
DESIGN—VERT: 60c. Montserrat Monastery.

273 Archangel Gabriel

274 "Statistics"

1956. Stamp Day.
1258 **273** 80c. green 60 40

1956. Centenary of Statistics in Spain.
1259 **274** 15c. ochre 40 35
1260 80c. green . . . . 5·00 65
1261 1p. red . . . . 5·00 55

275 Hermitage and Monument

276 Refugee Children

1956. 20th Anniv of Gen. Franco's Assumption of Office as Head of State.
1262 **275** 80c. green . . . . 5·50 40

1956. Hungarian Children's Relief.
1263 **276** 10c. lake 15 15
1264 15c. brown 15 15
1265 50c. sepia 40 25
1266 80c. green . . . . . . 4·75 30
1267 1p. red . . . . 4·75 25
1268 3p. blue . . . . 13·50 2·20

277 Apparition of the Sacred Heart

278 "The Great Captain"

1957. Stamp Day and Centenary Feast of the Sacred Heart.
1269 **277** 15c. brown 10 15
1270 60c. purple 25 15
1271 80c. green 25 15

1958. 5th Birth Cent of Gonzalves de Cordoba.
1272 **278** 1p.80 green 15 25

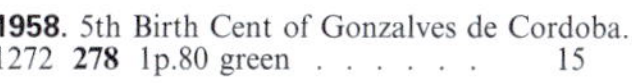

279 Francisco Goya after Lopez

280 Exhibition Emblem

1958. Stamp Day and Goya (painter) Commem. Frames in gold.
1273 – 15c. ochre 15 10
1274 – 40c. purple 15 15
1275 – 50c. green 15 15
1276 – 60c. purple 15 15
1277 – 70c. green 15 15
1278 **279** 80c. green 15 15
1279 – 1p. red 15 15
1280 – 1p.80 green 15 20
1281 – 2p. purple 35 35
1282 – 3p. blue 85 60
PAINTINGS—HORIZ: 15c. "The Sunshade"; 3p. "The Drinker". VERT: 40c. "The Bookseller's Wife"; 50c. "The Count of Fernan-Nunez"; 60c. "The Crockery Vendor"; 70c. "Dona Isabel Cobos de Porcel"; 1p. "The Carnival Doll"; 1p.80, "Marianito Goya"; 2p. "The Vintage".
For similar designs see Nos. 1301/10, 1333/42, 1391/1400, 1479/88, 1495/8, 1559/68, 1627/36, 1718/27, 1770/9, 1837/46, 1912/21, 1968/77, 2021/30, 2077/84, 2135/42 and 2204/11.

1958. Brussels International Exhibition.
1283 **280** 80c. brown, red and deep brown 20 20
1284 3p. blue, red and black 85 1·10

281 Emperor Charles V (after Strigell)

1958. 4th Death Cent of Emperor Charles V.
1287 **281** 15c. brown and ochre . . 15 15
1288 – 50c. olive and green . . 15 15
1289 – 70c. green and drab . . 15 20
1290 – 80c. green and brown . . 15 15
1291 **281** 1p. red and buff 20 10
1292 – 1p.80 emerald and green 15 30
1293 – 2p. purple and grey . . . 60 75
1294 – 3p. blue and brown . . . 1·60 2·00
PORTRAITS of Charles V: 50c., 1p.80, At Battle of Muhlberg (after Titian); 70c., 2p. (after Leoni); 80c., 3p. (after Titian).

282 Talgo II Articulated Train and Escorial

1958. 17th Int Railway Congress, Madrid. Inscr "XVII CONGRESO", etc.
1295 **282** 15c. ochre 15 15
1296 – 60c. plum 15 15
1297 – 80c. green 15 15
1298 **282** 1p. orange 60 15
1299 – 2p. purple 60 15
1300 – 3p. blue . . . . 2·20 1·20
DESIGNS—VERT: 60c., 2p. Class 1600 diesel-electric locomotive on viaduct, Despenaperros Gorge. HORIZ: 80c., 3p. Class 242F steam locomotive and Castillo de La Mota.

1959. Stamp Day and Velazquez Commem. Designs as T **279**. Frames in gold.
1301 15c. sepia 15 15
1302 40c. purple 15 10
1303 50c. olive 15 10
1304 60c. sepia 15 10
1305 70c. green 15 10
1306 80c. myrtle 15 15
1307 1p. brown 20 10
1308 1p.80 green 15 15
1309 2p. purple 40 25
1310 3p. blue 80 60
PAINTINGS—HORIZ: 15c. "The Drunkards". VERT: 40c. "The Spinners" (detail); 50c. "The Surrender of Breda"; 60c. "Las Meninas"; 70c. "Balthasar Don Carlos"; 80c. Self-portrait; 1p. "The Coronation of the Virgin"; 1p.80, "Aesop"; 2p. "The Forge of Vulcan"; 3p. "Menippus".

284 The Holy Cross of the Valley of the Fallen

1959. Completion of Monastery of the Holy Cross of the Valley of the Fallen.
1311 **284** 80c. green and brown . . 15 10

285 Mazarin and Luis de Haro (after tapestry by Lebrun)
286 Monastery from Courtyard

1959. 300th Anniv of Treaty of the Pyrenees.
1312 **285** 1p. brown and gold . . 10 10

1959. 50th Anniv of Entry of Franciscan Community into Guadeloupe Monastery.
1313 **286** 15c. brown 10 10
1314 – 80c. myrtle 20 10
1315 – 1p. red 20 10
DESIGNS: 80c. Exterior view of monastery; 1p. Entrance doors of church.

287 "The Holy Family" (after Goya)
288 Pass with Muleta

1959. Christmas.
1316 **287** 1p. brown 25 10

1960. Bullfighting.
1317 – 15c. brown and ochre (postage) 15 10
1318 – 20c. violet and blue . . . 15 10
1319 – 25c. black 15 10
1320 – 30c. brown and bistre . . 15 10
1321 – 50c. brown and violet . . 15 10
1322 – 70c. green and brown . . 15 10
1323 **288** 80c. emerald and green 15 15
1324 – 1p. brown and red . . . 15 10
1325 – 1p.40 purple and brown 15 15
1326 – 1p.50 green and blue . . 15 15
1327 – 1p.80 blue and green . . 15 15
1328 – 5p. red and brown . . . 60 55
1329 – 25c. dp pur & pur (air) 15 10
1330 – 50c. blue and turquoise 15 10
1331 – 1p. red and vermilion . . 20 15
1332 – 5p. violet and purple . . 60 45
DESIGNS—HORIZ: No. 1317, Fighting bull; No. 1318, Rounding-up bull; No. 1327, Placing darts from horseback; No. 1330, Pass with cape; No. 1332, Bull-ring. VERT: No. 1319, Corralling bulls at Pamplona; No. 1320, Bull entering ring; No. 1321, As No. 1330 (different pass); No. 1322, Banderillero placing darts; No. 1323/6, As Type **288** (different passes with muleta); No. 1328, Old-time bull-fighter; No. 1329, Village bull-ring; No. 1331, Dedicating the bull.

1960. Stamp Day and Murillo Commemoration. (painter). Designs as T **279**. Frames in gold.
1333 25c. violet 15 15
1334 40c. purple 15 10
1335 50c. olive 15 15
1336 70c. green 15 10
1337 80c. turquoise 15 15
1338 1p. brown 15 10
1339 1p.50 turquoise 15 10
1340 2p.50 red 15 15
1341 3p. blue . . . . 1·30 80
1342 5p. brown 40 35
PAINTINGS—VERT: 25c. "The Good Shepherd"; 40c. "Rebecca and Elizer"; 50c. "The Virgin of the Rosary"; 70c. "The Immaculate Conception"; 80c. "Children with Shells"; 1p. Self-portrait; 2p.50, "The Dice Game"; 3p. "Children Eating"; 5p. "Children with Coins". HORIZ: 1p.50, "The Holy Family with Bird".

289 "Christ of Lepanto"
290 Pelota Player

1960. International Philatelic Congress and Exhibition, Barcelona. Inscr "CIF".
1343 **289** 70c. lake & green (postage) . . . . . 1·50 1·20
1344 – 80c. black and sage . . . 1·50 1·20
1345 **289** 1p. purple and red . . . 1·50 1·40
1346 – 2p.50 slate and violet . . 1·50 1·40
1347 **289** 5p. sepia and bistre . . . 1·50 1·40
1348 – 10p. sepia and ochre . . 1·50 1·40
1349 **290** 1p. black and red (air) 4·75 3·25
1350 5p. red and brown . . . 4·75 3·25
1351 6p. red and purple . . . 4·75 3·25
1352 10p. red and green . . . 4·75 3·25
DESIGN—VERT: Nos. 1344, 1346, 1348, Church of the Holy Family, Barcelona.

291 St. John of Ribera
292 St. Vincent de Paul

1960. Canonization of St. John of Ribera.
1353 **291** 1p. brown 15 10
1354 2p.50 mauve 10 10

1960. Europa. 1st Anniv of European Postal and Telecommunications Conference. As T **144a** of Switzerland but size 38½ × 22 mm.
1355 1p. drab and green 75 20
1356 5p. red and brown . . . . 1·00 75

1960. 300th Death Anniv of St. Vincent de Paul.
1357 **292** 25c. violet 10 10
1358 1p. brown 15 10

293 Menendez de Aviles
294 Running

1960. 400th Anniv of Discovery and Colonization of Florida.
1359 **293** 25c. blue and light blue 15 15
1360 – 70c. green and orange 15 15
1361 – 80c. green and stone . . 15 15
1362 – 1p. brown and yellow . . 15 10
1363 **293** 2p. red and pink 30 20
1364 – 2p.50 mauve and green 50 20
1365 – 3p. blue and green . . . 3·00 80
1366 – 5p. brown and bistre . . 2·00 1·00
PORTRAITS: 70c., 2p.50, Hernando de Soto; 80c., 3p. Ponce de Leon; 1, 5p. Cabeza de Vaca.

1960. Sports.
1367 **294** 25c. brn and bl (postage) 15 15
1368 – 40c. orange and violet 15 10
1369 – 70c. red and green . . . 30 10
1370 – 80c. red and green . . . 25 15
1371 – 1p. green and red . . . 75 15
1372 **294** 1p.50 sepia and turquoise 30 20
1373 – 2p. green and purple . . 1·90 15
1374 – 2p.50 green and mauve 30 20
1375 – 3p. red and blue 75 30
1376 – 5p. blue and brown . . . 75 60
1377 – 1p.25 red and brown (air) 15 20
1378 – 1p.50 brown and violet 25 20
1379 – 6p. red and violet . . . 1·00 65
1380 – 10p. red and olive . . . 1·40 90
DESIGNS—HORIZ: 40c., 2p. Cycling; 70c., 2p.50, Football; 1, 5p. Hockey; 1p.25, 6p. Horse-jumping. VERT: 80c., 3p. Gymnastics; 1p.50 (air), 10p. Pelota.

295 Albeniz
296 Cloisters

1960. Birth Cent of Isaac Albeniz (composer).
1381 **295** 25c. violet 10 10
1382 1p. brown 10 10

1960. Samos Monastery.
1383 **296** 80c. turquoise and green 15 10
1384 – 1p. lake and brown . . . 1·10 15
1385 – 5p. sepia and bistre . . 1·30 90
DESIGNS—VERT: 1p. Fountain; 5p. Portico and facade.

297 "The Nativity" (Velazquez)
298 "The Flight to Egypt" (after Bayeu)

1960. Christmas.
1386 **297** 1p. brown 25 10

1961. World Refugee Year.
1387 **298** 1p. brown 20 10
1388 5p. brown 45 30

299 L. F. Moratin (after Goya)
301 Velazquez (Prado Memorial)

1961. Birth Bicentenary of Moratin (poet and dramatist).
1389 **299** 1p. red 10 10
1390 1p.50 turquoise 10 10

1961. Stamp Day and El Greco (painter) Commem. Designs as T **279**. Frames in gold.
1391 25c. purple 15 10
1392 40c. purple 15 15
1393 70c. green 20 15
1394 80c. turquoise 15 15
1395 1p. purple . . . . 2·30 10
1396 1p.50 turquoise 15 15
1397 2p.50 lake 20 15
1398 3p. blue . . . . 1·80 90
1399 5p. sepia . . . . 4·00 1·90
1400 10p. violet 50 35
PAINTINGS: 25c. "St. Peter"; 40c. Madonna (detail, "The Holy Family" ("Madonna of the Good Milk")); 70c. Detail of "The Agony in the Garden"; 80c. "Man with Hand on Breast"; 1p. Self-portrait; 1p.50, "The Baptism of Christ"; 2p.50, "The Holy Trinity"; 3p. "Burial of the Count of Orgaz"; 5p. "The Spoliation"; 10p. "The Martyrdom of St. Maurice".

1961. 300th Death Anniv of Velazquez.
1401 **301** 80c. green and blue . . 1·20 25
1402 – 1p. brown and red . . . 6·00 25
1403 – 2p.50 violet and blue . . 80 55
1404 – 10p. green and light green . . . . 8·50 1·90
PAINTINGS—VERT: 1p. "The Duke of Olivares"; 2p.50, "Princess Margarita". HORIZ: Part of "The Spinners".

302 "Stamp" and "Postmark"
303 Vazquez de Mella

1961. World Stamp Day.
1409 **302** 25c. black and red . . . 15 10
1410 1p. red and black . . . 1·00 10
1411 10p. green and purple . . 1·10 50

1961. Birth Centenary of Juan Vazquez de Mella (politician and writer).
1412 **303** 1p. red 40 10
1413 2p.30 purple 15 20

304 Gen. Franco
305 "Portico de la Gloria" (Cathedral of Santiago de Compostela)

1961. 25th Anniv of National Uprising. Mult.
1414 70c. Angel and flag 15 15
1415 80c. Straits of Gibraltar . . 15 15
1416 1p. Knight and Alcazar, Toledo 15 10
1417 1p.50 Victory Arch 15 10
1418 2p. Knight crossing River Ebro 15 15
1419 2p.30 Soldier, flag and troops 15 15
1420 2p.50 Shipbuilding 15 15
1421 3p. Steelworks 25 30
1422 5p. Map of Spain showing electric power stations (horiz) . . . . 2·20 1·10
1423 6p. Irrigation (woman beside dam) . . . . 1·70 1·60
1424 8p. Mine 70 90
1425 10p. Type **304** 60 70

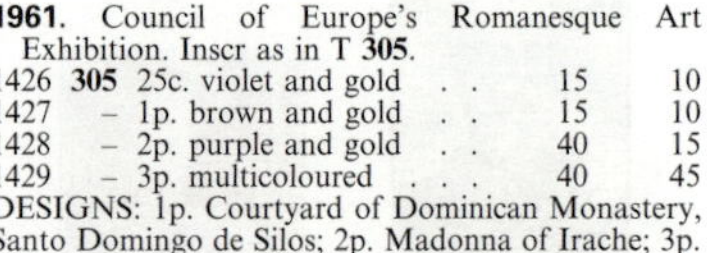

1961. Council of Europe's Romanesque Art Exhibition. Inscr as in T **305**.
1426 **305** 25c. violet and gold . . 15 10
1427 – 1p. brown and gold . . 15 10
1428 – 2p. purple and gold . . 40 15
1429 – 3p. multicoloured . . . 40 45
DESIGNS: 1p. Courtyard of Dominican Monastery, Santo Domingo de Silos; 2p. Madonna of Irache; 3p. "Christos Pantocrator" (from Tahull Church fresco).

306 L. de Gongora (after Velazquez)
308 Burgos Cathedral

307 Doves and C.E.P.T. Emblem

1961. 400th Birth Anniv of De Gongora (poet).
1430 **306** 25c. violet 10 10
1431 1p. brown 20 10

1961. Europa.
1432 **307** 1p. red 10 15
1433 5p. brown 40 40

1961. 25th Anniv of Gen. Franco as Head of State.
1434 **308** 1p. green and gold . . . 10 10

309 S. de Belalcazar
310 Courtyard

1961. Explorers and Colonizers of America (1st series).
1435 **309** 25c. violet and green . . 15 15
1436 – 70c. green and buff . . . 15 15
1437 – 80c. green and pink . . 15 10
1438 – 1p. blue and flesh . . . 45 15
1439 **309** 2p. red and blue . . . . 3·25 25
1440 – 2p.50 purple and mauve 85 45
1441 – 3p. blue and grey . . . 2·00 90
1442 – 5p. brown and yellow . . 2·00 1·10
PORTRAITS: 70c., 2p.50, B de Lezo; 80c., 3p. R. de Bastidas; 1, 5p. N. de Chaves.
See also Nos. 1515/22, 1587/94, 1683/90, 1738/45, 1810/17, 1877/84, 1947/51, 1997/2001 and 2054/8.

1961. Escorial.
1443 – 70c. green and turquoise 20 10
1444 **310** 80c. slate and green . . 15 15
1445 – 1p. red and brown . . . 50 15
1446 – 2p.50 purple and violet 25 15
1447 – 5p. sepia and ochre . . . 1·50 85
1448 – 6p. purple and blue . . . 2·20 2·00
DESIGNS—VERT: 70c. Patio of the Kings; 2p.50, Grand Staircase; 6p. High Altar. HORIZ: 1p. Monks' Garden; 5p. View of Escorial.

311 King Alfonso XII Monument
312 Santa Maria del Naranco Church

1961. 400th Anniv of Madrid as Capital of Spain.
1449 **311** 25c. purple and green . . 15 15
1450 – 1p. brown and bistre . . 25 15
1451 – 2p. purple and grey . . . 25 10
1452 – 2p.50 violet and red . . 15 15
1453 – 3p. black and blue . . . 55 45
1454 – 5p. blue and brown . . . 1·40 80

DESIGNS—VERT: 1p. King Philip II (after Pantoja); 5p. Plaza, Madrid. HORIZ: 2p. Town Hall, Madrid; 2p.50, Fountain of Cybele; 3p. Portals of Alcala Palace.

1961. 1200th Anniv of Oviedo.
1455 **312** 25c. violet and green . . 15 15
1456 – 1p. brown and bistre . . 30 10
1457 – 2p. sepia and purple . . 90 10
1458 – 2p.50 violet and purple 15 15
1459 – 3p. black and blue . . . 80 45
1460 – 5p. brown and green . . 80 75
DESIGNS: 1p. Fruela (portrait); 2p. Cross of the Angels; 2p.50, Alfonso II; 3p. Alfonso III; 5p. Apostles of the Holy Hall, Oviedo Cathedral.

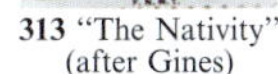

313 "The Nativity" (after Gines) **314** Cierva C.30A Autogyro

1961. Christmas.
1461 **313** 1p. plum 25 15

1961. 50th Anniv of Spanish Aviation.
1462 **314** 1p. violet and blue . . . 15 15
1463 – 2p. green and lilac . . . 25 15
1464 – 3p. black and green . . 1·30 75
1465 – 5p. purple and slate . . 3·00 1·30
1466 – 10p. brown and blue . . 1·30 60
DESIGNS—HORIZ: 2p. CASA-built Dornier Do-J Wal flying boat "Plus Ultra"; 3p. Breguet 19GR airplane "Jesus del Gran Poder" (Madrid-Manila Flight). VERT: 5p. Avro 504K biplane hunting great bustard; 10p. Madonna of Loreto (patron saint) and North American F-86F Sabre jet fighters.

315 Arms of Alava **316** "Ecstasy of St. Teresa" (Bernini)

1962. Arms of Provincial Capitals. Multicoloured.
1467 5p. Type **315** 10 15
1468 5p. Albacete 10 15
1469 5p. Alicante 25 25
1470 5p. Almeria 25 25
1471 5p. Avila 25 25
1472 5p. Badajoz 15 20
1473 5p. Baleares 15 20
1474 5p. Barcelona 15 25
1475 5p. Burgos 60 45
1476 5p. Caceres 40 30
1477 5p. Cadiz 50 40
1478 5p. Castellon de la Plana . . 4·50 1·90
See also Nos. 1542/53, 1612/23, 1692/1703 and 1756/64.

1962. Stamp Day and Zurbaran (painter) Commem. As T **279**. Frames in gold.
1479 25c. olive 15 20
1480 40c. purple 15 20
1481 70c. green 15 20
1482 80c. turquoise 15 20
1483 1p. sepia . . . . 7·00 25
1484 1p.50 turquoise 60 20
1485 2p.50 lake 60 20
1486 3p. blue . . . . 1·20 80
1487 5p. brown . . . . 3·00 1·80
1488 10p. olive . . . . 3·00 1·40
PAINTINGS—HORIZ: 25c. "Martyr". VERT: 40c. "Burial of St. Catalina"; 70c. "St. Casilda"; 80c. "Jesus crowning St. Joseph"; 1p. Self-portrait; 1p.50, "St. Hieronymus"; 2p.50, "Madonna of the Grace"; 3p. Detail from "Apotheosis of St. Thomas Aquinas"; 5p. "Madonna as a Child"; 10p. "The Immaculate Madonna".

1962. 4th Centenary of Teresian Reformation.
1489 – 25c. violet 10 10
1490 **316** 1p. brown 10 10
1491 – 3p. blue . . . . 1·10 35
DESIGNS—As Type **316**: 25c. St. Joseph's Monastery, Avila. (22 × 38½ mm): 3p. "St. Teresa of Avila" (Velazquez).

317 Mercury **318** St. Benedict

1962. World Stamp Day.
1492 **317** 25c. pink, purple & violet 15 15
1493 1p. yellow, brown and bistre 15 10
1494 10p. green and turquoise 1·70 90

1962. Rubens Paintings. As T **279**. Frames in gold.
1495 25c. violet 25 20
1496 1p. brown . . . . 1·00 20
1497 3p. turquoise . . . . 5·00 2·50
1498 10p. green . . . . 5·75 1·90
PAINTINGS—As Type **279**: 25c. Ferdinand of Austria; 1p. Self-portrait; 3p. Philip II. (26 × 39 mm): 10p. Duke of Lerma.

1962. 400th Death Anniv of Alonso Berruguete (sculptor). Sculptures by Berruguete.
1499 **318** 25c. mauve and blue . . 15 20
1500 – 80c. green and brown . . 20 20
1501 – 1p. red and stone . . . 40 20
1502 – 2p. mauve and stone . . 3·00 15
1503 – 3p. blue and mauve . . 1·20 95
1504 – 10p. brown and pink . . 1·20 1·10
SCULPTURES: 80c. "The Apostle"; 1p. "St. Peter"; 2p. "St. Christopher and Child Jesus"; 3p. "Ecce Homo"; 10p. "St. Sebastian".

319 El Cid (R. Diaz de Vivar), after statue by J. Cristobal **321** Throwing the Discus

320 Honey Bee and Honeycomb

1962. El Cid Campeador Commem. Inscr "EL CID".
1505 **319** 1p. drab and green . . . 15 20
1506 – 2p. violet and sepia . . . 1·30 20
1507 – 3p. green and blue . . . 4·00 2·20
1508 – 10p. green and yellow . . 2·50 1·30
DESIGNS—VERT: 2p. El Cid (equestrian statue by A. Huntington). HORIZ: 3p. El Cid's treasure chest; 10p. Oath-taking ceremony of Santa Gadea.

1962. Europa.
1509 **320** 1p. red 20 20
1510 5p. green . . . . 1·10 65

1962. 2nd Spanish–American Athletic Games, Madrid.
1511 **321** 25c. blue and pink . . . 15 15
1512 – 80c. green and yellow . . 20 15
1513 – 1p. brown and pink . . 15 10
1514 – 3p. blue and light blue 20 30
DESIGNS: 80c. Running; 1p. Hurdling; 3p. Start of sprint.

1962. Explorers and Colonizers of America (2nd series). As T **309**.
1515 25c. mauve and grey 15 20
1516 70c. green and pink 60 20
1517 80c. green and yellow . . . 45 20
1518 1p. brown and green 85 20
1519 2p. red and blue . . . . . 3·00 30
1520 2p.50 violet and brown . . 55 40
1521 3p. blue and pink . . . . . 7·25 1·80
1522 5p. brown and yellow . . . 3·50 2·20
PORTRAITS: 25c., 2p. A. de Mendoza; 70c., 2p.50, J. de Quesada; 80c., 3p. J. de Garay; 1, 5p. P. de la Gasca.

322 U.P.A.E. Emblem **323** "The Annunciation" (after Murillo)

1962. 50th Anniv of Postal Union of the Americas and Spain.
1523 **322** 1p. brown, grn & dp grn 10 10

1962. Mysteries of the Rosary.
1524 **323** 25c. brn & vio (postage) 15 15
1525 – 70c. turquoise and green 15 20
1526 – 80c. turquoise and olive 15 20
1527 – 1p. sepia and green . . . 4·50 65
1528 – 1p.50 blue and green . . 15 15
1529 – 2p. sepia and violet . . . 1·00 45
1530 – 2p.50 red and purple . . 15 20
1531 – 3p. black and violet . . 15 30
1532 – 5p. lake and brown . . . 80 60
1533 – 8p. black and purple . . 65 65
1534 – 10p. green and myrtle . . 65 35
1535 – 25c. violet and slate (air) 15 35
1536 – 1p. olive and purple . . 15 20
1537 – 5p. lake and purple . . . 55 35
1538 – 10p. yellow, green & grey . . . . 1·30 75
PAINTINGS—"Joyful Mysteries": No. 1525, "Visit of Elizabeth" (Correa); 1526, "The Birth of Christ" (Murillo); 1527, "Christ shown to the Elders" (Campana); 1528, "Jesus lost and found in the Temple" (unknown artist). "Sorrowful Mysteries": 1529, "Prayer on the Mount of Olives" (Giaquinto); 1530, "Scourging" (Cano); 1531, "The Crown of Thorns" (Tiepolo); 1532, "Carrying the Cross" (El Greco); 1533, "The Crucifixion" (Murillo). "Glorious Mysteries": 1534, "The Resurrection" (Murillo); 1535, "The Ascension" (Bayeu); 1536, "The Sending-forth of the Holy Ghost" (El Greco); 1537, "The Assumption of the Virgin" (Cerezo); 1538, "The Coronation of the Virgin" (El Greco).

324 "The Nativity" (after Pedro de Mena) **325** Campaign Emblem and Swamp

1962. Christmas.
1539 **324** 1p. olive 25 10

1962. Malaria Eradication.
1540 **325** 1p. black, yellow & green 10 10

326 Pope John and Dome of St. Peter's **327** "St. Paul" (after El Greco)

1962. Ecumenical Council, Vatican City (1st issue).
1541 **326** 1p. slate and purple . . 15 15
See also Nos. 1601 and 1755.

1963. Arms of Provincial Capitals. As T **315**. Multicoloured.
1542 5p. Ciudad Real 50 45
1543 5p. Cordoba . . . . 3·25 1·70
1544 5p. Coruna 50 65
1545 5p. Cuenca 50 45
1546 5p. Fernando Poo . . . . . 85 1·00
1547 5p. Gerona 10 15
1548 5p. Gran Canaria 15 25
1549 5p. Granada 25 40
1550 5p. Guadalajara 50 30
1551 5p. Guipuzcoa 10 15
1552 5p. Huelva 10 15
1553 5p. Huesca 10 15

1963. 1900th Anniv of Arrival of St. Paul in Spain.
1554 **327** 1p. sepia, olive and brown 20 15

328 Poblet Monastery **329** Mail Coach

1963. Poblet Monastery.
1555 **328** 25c. purple, sepia & green 15 15
1556 – 1p. orange and red . . . 40 15
1557 – 3p. blue and violet . . . 1·10 40
1558 – 5p. ochre and brown . . 2·25 1·30
DESIGNS—VERT: 1p. Tomb; 5p. Arch. HORIZ: 3p. Aerial view of monastery.

1963. Stamp Day and Ribera (painter) Commem. As T **279**. Frames in gold.
1559 25c. violet 15 15
1560 40c. purple 15 15
1561 70c. green 40 15
1562 80c. turquoise 40 10
1563 1p. brown 40 10
1564 1p.50 turquoise 40 10
1565 2p.50 red . . . . 2·20 15
1566 3p. blue . . . . 3·50 70
1567 5p. brown . . . . 11·50 2·40
1568 10p. brown and purple . . . 4·00 1·40
PAINTINGS: 25c. "Archimedes"; 40c. "Jacob's Flock"; 70c. "Triumph of Bacchus"; 80c. "St. Christopher"; 1p. Self-portrait; 1p.50, "St. Andrew"; 2p.50, "St. John the Baptist"; 3p. "St. Onofrius"; 5p. "St. Peter"; 10p. "The Madonna".

1963. Centenary of Paris Postal Conference.
1569 **329** 1p. multicoloured . . . 10 10

330 Globe

1963. World Stamp Day.
1570 **330** 25c. multicoloured . . . 15 10
1571 1p. multicoloured . . . 15 10
1572 10p. multicoloured . . . 95 50

331 "Give us this day our daily bread"

1963. Freedom from Hunger.
1573 **331** 1p. multicoloured . . . 15 15

332 Pillars and Globes

1963. Spanish Cultural Institutions Congress. Multicoloured.
1574 25c. Type **332** 10 15
1575 80c. "Santa Maria", "Pinta" and "Nina" 35 20
1576 1p. Columbus 35 10

333 Civic Seals **334** "St. Maria of Europe"

1963. 150th Anniv of San Sebastian.
1577 **333** 25c. blue and green . . . 10 15
1578 – 80c. red and purple . . 10 15
1579 – 1p. green and bistre . . 10 10
DESIGNS: 80c. City aflame; 1p. View of San Sebastian, 1836.

1963. Europa.
1580 **334** 1p. brown and bistre . . 15 15
1581 5p. sepia and green . . . 50 50

335 Arms of the Order of Mercy **336** Scenes from Parable of the Good Samaritan

1963. 75th Anniv of the Order of Mercy.
1582 **335** 25c. red, gold and black 10 15
1583 – 80c. sepia and green . . 10 15
1584 – 1p. purple and blue . . . 10 10
1585 – 1p.50 brown and blue . . 10 10
1586 – 3p. black and violet . . 10 20
DESIGNS: 80c. King Jaime I; 1p. Our Lady of Mercy; 1p.50, St. Pedro Nolasco; 3p. St. Raimundo de Penafort.

1963. Explorers and Colonizers of America (3rd series). As T **309**.
1587 25c. deep blue and blue . . 15 15
1588 70c. green and salmon . . . 15 15
1589 80c. green and cream . . . 45 15
1590 1p. blue and salmon 50 15
1591 2p. red and blue . . . . . 1·90 20
1592 2p.50 violet and flesh . . . 1·20 20

1593 3p. blue and pink . . . . . 2·50 1·30
1594 5p. brown and cream . . . 3·25 2·20
PORTRAITS: 25c., 2p. Brother J. Serra; 70c., 2p.50, Vasco Nunez de Balboa; 80c., 3p. J. de Galvez; 1, 5p. D. Garcia de Paredes.

1963. Red Cross Centenary.
1595 **336** 1p. violet, red and gold 10 15

337 "The Nativity" (after sculpture by Berruguete) **338** Fr. Raimundo Lulio

1963. Christmas.
1596 **337** 1p. green 10 10

1963. Famous Spaniards (1st series).
1597 **338** 1p. black & vio (postage) 15 10
1598 – 1p.50 violet and sepia . . 15 10
1599 – 25p. purple and red (air) 85 25
1600 – 50p. black and green . . 1·60 45
PORTRAITS: 1p.50, Cardinal Belluga; 25p. King Recaredo; 50p. Cardinal Cisneros.
See also Nos. 1714/17.

339 Pope Paul and Dome of St. Peter's

1963. Ecumenical Council, Vatican City (2nd issue).
1601 **339** 1p. black and turquoise 10 15

340 Alcazar de Segovia

1964. Tourist Series.
1602 – 40c. brown, blue & green 10 10
1603 – 50c. sepia and blue . . . 10 10
1604 – 70c. blue and green . . 10 10
1605 – 70c. brown and lilac . . 10 10
1606 – 80c. black and blue . . . 10 10
1607 **340** 1p. lilac and violet . . . 10 10
1608 – 1p. red and purple . . . 10 10
1609 – 1p. black and green . . 10 10
1610 – 1p. red and purple . . . 10 10
1611 – 1p.50 brown, green and blue 10 10
DESIGNS—HORIZ: No. 1602, Potes; 1604, Crypt of St. Isidore (Leon); 1608, Lion Court of the Alhambra (Granada); 1611, Gerona. VERT: 1603, Leon Cathedral; 1605, Costa Brava; 1606, "Christ of the Lanterns" (Cordoba); 1609, Drach Caves (Majorca); 1610, Mosque (Cordoba).
See also Nos. 1704/13, 1786/95, 1798/1805, 1860/6, 1867/74, 1933/42, 1985/9, 1993/6, 2035/9, 2040/5, 2311/6, 2379/84, 2466/7, 2575/8, 2696/2700, 2744/8, 2858/9, 2870/1 and 2915/18.

1964. Arms of Provincial Capitals. As T **315**. Multicoloured.
1612 5p. Ifni 10 10
1613 5p. Jaen 10 15
1614 5p. Leon 10 15
1615 5p. Lerida 10 15
1616 5p. Logrono 10 15
1617 5p. Lugo 10 15
1618 5p. Madrid 10 10
1619 5p. Malaga 10 15
1620 5p. Murcia 10 10
1621 5p. Navarra 10 15
1622 5p. Orense 10 15
1623 5p. Oviedo 10 15

341 Santa Maria Monastery

1964. Monastery of Santa Maria, Huerta.
1624 – 1p. bronze and green . . 10 10
1625 – 2p. sepia, black & turq 15 10
1626 **341** 5p. slate and violet . . . 1·40 55
DESIGNS—VERT: 1p. Great Hall; 2p. Cloisters.

1964. Stamp Day and Sorolla (painter) Commem. As T **279**. Frames in gold.
1627 25c. violet 15 15
1628 40c. purple 15 10
1629 70c. green 15 10
1630 80c. turquoise 15 15
1631 1p. brown 15 10
1632 1p.50 turquoise 15 10
1633 2p.50 mauve 15 10
1634 3p. blue 35 35
1635 5p. brown . . . . 1·30 1·10
1636 10p. green 60 30
PAINTINGS—VERT: 25c. "The Earthen Jar"; 70c. "La Mancha Types"; 80c. "Valencian Fisherwoman"; 1p. Self-portrait; 5p. "Pulling the Boat"; 10p. "Valencian Couple on Horse". HORIZ: 40c. "Castillan Oxherd"; 1p.50, "The Cattlepen"; 2p.50, "And people say fish is dear" (fish market); 3p. "Children on the Beach".

342 "25 Years of Peace"

1964. 25th Anniv of End of Spanish Civil War.
1637 **342** 25c. gold, green and black 15 10
1638 – 30c. red, blue and green 15 15
1639 – 40c. black and gold . . 15 15
1640 – 50c. multicoloured . . . 15 15
1641 – 70c. multicoloured . . . 15 10
1642 – 80c. multicoloured . . . 15 15
1643 – 1p. multicoloured . . . 20 10
1644 – 1p.50 olive, red and blue 15 15
1645 – 2p. multicoloured . . . 15 15
1646 – 2p.50 multicoloured . . 15 15
1647 – 3p. multicoloured . . . 80 90
1648 – 5p. red, green and gold 25 30
1649 – 6p. multicoloured . . . 40 45
1650 – 10p. multicoloured . . . 50 55
DESIGNS—VERT: 30c. Athletes ("Sport"); 50c. Apartment-houses ("National Housing Plan"); 1p. Graph and symbols ("Economic Development"); 1p.50, Rocks and tower ("Construction"); 2p.50, Wheatear and dam ("Irrigation"); 5p. "Tree of Learning" ("Scientific Research"); 10p. Gen. Franco. HORIZ: 40c. T.V. screen and symbols ("Radio and T.V."); 70c. Wheatears, tractor and landscape ("Agriculture"); 80c. Tree and forests ("Reafforestation"); 2p. Forms of transport ("Transport and Communications"); 3p. Pylon and part of dial ("Electrification"); 6p. Ancient buildings ("Tourism").

343 Spanish Pavilion at Fair **344** 6c. Stamp of 1850 and Globe

1964. New York World's Fair.
1651 **343** 1p. green and turquoise 15 10
1652 – 1p.50 brown and red . . 15 10
1653 – 2p.50 green and blue . . 15 10
1654 – 5p. red 25 30
1655 – 50p. blue and grey . . . 75 30
DESIGNS—VERT: 1p.50, Bullfighting; 2p.50, Castillo de la Mota; 5p. Spanish dancing; 50p. Pelota.

1964. World Stamp Day.
1656 **344** 25c. red and purple . . . 15 15
1657 1p. green and blue . . . 15 10
1658 10p. orange and red . . 30 30

345 Macarena Virgin **346** Medieval Ship

1964. Canonical Coronation of Macarena Virgin.
1659 **345** 1p. green and yellow . . 10 10

1964. Spanish Navy Commemoration.
1660 **346** 15c. slate and purple . . 10 15
1661 – 25c. grey and orange . . 10 15
1662 – 40c. grey and blue . . . 10 15
1663 – 50c. green and slate . . 10 15
1664 – 70c. violet and blue . . 10 15
1665 – 80c. blue and green . . 10 15
1666 – 1p. purple and brown . . 10 10
1667 – 1p.50 sepia and red . . 10 15
1668 – 2p. black and green . . 65 10
1669 – 2p.50 red and violet . . 15 10
1670 – 3p. blue and brown . . 15 15
1671 – 5p. blue and green . . . 80 90
1672 – 6p. violet and turquoise 70 75
1673 – 10p. red and orange . . 30 30
SHIPS—VERT: 25c. Carrack; 1p. Ship of the line "Santissima Trinidad"; 1p.50, Corvette "Atrevida". HORIZ: 40c. "Santa Maria"; 50c. Galley; 70c. Galleon; 80c. Xebec; 2p. Steam frigate "Isabel II"; 2p.50, Frigate "Numancia"; 3p. Destroyer "Destructor"; 5p. Isaac Peral's submarine; 6p. Cruiser "Baleares"; 10p. Cadet schooner "Juan Sebastian de Elcano".

347 Europa "Flower" **348** "The Virgin of the Castle"

1964. Europa.
1674 **347** 1p. ochre, red and green 25 20
1675 5p. blue, purple and green 95 85

1964. 700th Anniv of Reconquest of Jerez.
1676 **348** 25c. brown and buff . . 10 10
1677 1p. blue and grey . . . 10 10

349 Putting the Shot **350** "Adoration of the Shepherds" (after Zurbaran)

1965. Olympic Games, Tokyo and Innsbruck. Olympic rings in gold.
1678 **349** 25c. blue and orange . . 10 10
1679 – 80c. blue and green . . . 10 10
1680 – 1p. blue and light blue 10 10
1681 – 3p. blue and buff 15 20
1682 – 5p. blue and violet . . . 20 20
DESIGNS: 80c. Long jumping; 1p. Skiing (slalom); 3p. Judo; 5p. Throwing the discus.

1964. Explorers and Colonizers of America (4th series). As T **309**. Inscr "1964" at foot.
1683 25c. violet and blue 10 15
1684 70c. olive and pink 10 15
1685 80c. green and buff 25 20
1686 1p. violet and buff 25 10
1687 2p. olive and blue 25 10
1688 2p.50 purple and turquoise 20 20
1689 3p. blue and grey . . . . . 3·00 1·10
1690 5p. brown and cream . . . 1·90 1·10
PORTRAITS: 25c., 2p. D. de Almagro; 70c., 2p.50, F. de Toledo; 80c., 3p. T. de Mogrovejo; 1, 5p. F. Pizarro.

1964. Christmas.
1691 **350** 1p. brown 10 10

1965. Arms of Provincial Capitals. As T **315**. Multicoloured.
1692 5p. Palencia 10 10
1693 5p. Pontevedra 10 10
1694 5p. Rio Muni 10 10
1695 5p. Sahara 10 10
1696 5p. Salamanca 10 10
1697 5p. Santander 10 10
1698 5p. Segovia 10 10
1699 5p. Seville 10 10
1700 5p. Soria 10 10
1701 5p. Tarragona 10 10
1702 5p. Tenerife 10 10
1703 5p. Teruel 10 10

1965. Tourist Series. As T **340**.
1704 25c. black and blue 10 10
1705 30c. brown and turquoise . 10 10
1706 50c. purple and red 10 10
1707 70c. indigo and blue 10 10
1708 80c. purple and mauve . . . 10 10
1709 1p. mauve, red and sepia . . 10 10
1710 2p.50 purple and brown . . 10 10
1711 2p.50 olive and blue . . . 10 10
1712 3p. purple and purple . . . 10 10
1713 6p. violet and slate 10 10
DESIGNS—VERT: 25c. Columbus Monument, Barcelona; 30c. Santa Maria Church, Burgos; 50c. Synagogue, Toledo; 80c. Seville Cathedral; 1p. Cudillero Port; 2p.50, (No. 1710), Burgos Cathedral (interior); 3p. Bridge at Cambados (Pontevedra); 6p. Ceiling, Lonja (Valencia). HORIZ: 70c. Zamora; 2p.50, (No. 1711), Mogrovejo (Santander).

1965. Famous Spaniards (2nd series). As T **338**.
1714 25c. sepia and turquoise . . 10 15
1715 70c. deep blue and blue . . 10 20
1716 2p.50 sepia and bronze . . 10 15
1717 5p. bronze and green . . . 25 30
PORTRAITS: 25c. Donoso Cortes; 70c. King Alfonso X (the Saint); 2p.50, G. M. de Jovellanos; 5p. St. Dominic de Guzman.

1965. Stamp Day and J. Romero de Torres Commem. As T **279**. Frames in gold.
1718 25c. purple 10 10
1719 40c. purple 10 15
1720 70c. green 10 15
1721 80c. turquoise 10 15
1722 1p. brown 10 15
1723 1p.50 turquoise 10 10
1724 2p.50 mauve 10 15
1725 3p. blue 30 30
1726 5p. brown 30 25
1727 10p. green 45 30
PAINTINGS (by J. Romero de Torres): 25c. "Girl with Jar"; 40c. "The Song"; 70c. "The Virgin of the Lanterns"; 80c. "Girl with Guitar"; 1p. Self-portrait; 1p.50, "Poem of Cordoba"; 2p.50, "Marta and Maria"; 3p. "Poem of Cordoba" (different); 5p. "A Little Charcoal-maker"; 10p. "Long Live the Hair!".

351 Bull and Stamps **352** I.T.U. Emblem and Symbols

1965. World Stamp Day.
1728 **351** 25c. multicoloured . . . 10 10
1729 1p. multicoloured . . . 10 10
1730 10p. multicoloured . . . 35 40

1965. Centenary of I.T.U.
1731 **352** 1p. red, black and pink 10 10

353 Pilgrim **354** Spanish Knight and Banners

1965. Holy Year of Santiago de Compostela. Multicoloured.
1732 1p. Type **353** 10 10
1733 2p. Pilgrim (profile) 10 10

1965. 400th Anniv of Florida Settlement.
1734 **354** 3p. black, red and yellow 10 10

355 St. Benedict (after sculpture by Pereira) **356** Sports Palace, Madrid

1965. Europa.
1735 **355** 1p. green and emerald 10 15
1736 5p. violet and purple . . 35 30

1965. Int Olympic Committee Meeting, Madrid.
1737 **356** 1p. brown, gold and grey 10 10

1965. Explorers and Colonizers of America (5th series). As T **309**. Inscr "1965" at foot.
1738 25c. violet and green 10 15
1739 70c. brown and pink 10 15
1740 80c. green and cream 10 15
1741 1p. violet and buff 10 10
1742 2p. brown and blue 10 10
1743 2p.50 purple and turquoise 10 15
1744 3p. blue and grey 90 35
1745 5p. brown and yellow . . . 90 35
PORTRAITS: 25c., 2p. Don Fadrique de Toledo; 70c., 2p.50, Padre Jose de Anchieta; 80c., 3p. Francisco de Orellana; 1p., 5p. St. Luis Beltran.

357 Cloisters

1965. Yuste Monastery.
1746 **357** 1p. blue and sepia 10 10
1747 – 2p. sepia and brown 10 10
1748 – 5p. green and blue 20 20
DESIGNS—VERT: 2p. Charles V room. HORIZ: 5p. Courtyard.

358 Spanish 1r. Stamp of 1865 — **360** Madonna of Antipolo

359 "The Nativity" (after Mayno)

1965. Centenary of Spanish Perforated Stamps.
1749 **358** 80c. green and bronze 10 15
1750 – 1p. brown and purple 10 15
1751 – 5p. brown and sepia 10 10
DESIGNS: 1p. 1865 19c. stamp; 5p. 1865 2r. stamp.

1965. Christmas.
1752 **359** 1p. green and blue 10 10

1965. 400th Anniv of Christianity in the Philippines.
1753 **360** 1p. brown, black and buff 10 10
1754 – 3p. blue and grey 10 10
DESIGN: 3p. Father Urdaneta.

361 Globe — **362** Admiral Alvaro de Bazan

1965. 21st Ecumenical Council, Vatican City (3rd issue).
1755 **361** 1p. multicoloured 10 10

1966. Arms of Provincial Capitals. As T **315**. Multicoloured.
1756 5p. Toledo 10 10
1757 5p. Valencia 10 10
1758 5p. Valladolid 10 10
1759 5p. Vizcaya 10 10
1760 5p. Zamora 10 10
1761 5p. Zaragoza 10 10
1762 5p. Ceuta 10 10
1763 5p. Melilla 10 10
1764 10p. Spain ($26 \times 38\frac{1}{2}$ mm) 15 10

1966. Celebrities (1st series).
1765 **362** 25c. black and blue (postage) 10 15
1766 – 2p. violet and purple 10 10
1767 – 25p. bronze & green (air) 1·10 20
1768 – 50p. grey and blue 1·90 55
PORTRAITS: 2p. Benito Daza de Valdes (doctor); 25p. Seneca; 50p. St. Damaso.
See also Nos. 1849/52.

363 Exhibition Emblem — **364** Luno Church

1966. Graphic Arts Exn, "Graphispack", Barcelona.
1769 **363** 1p. green, blue and red 10 10

1966. Stamp Day and J. M. Sert Commem. Designs as T **279**. Frames in gold.
1770 25c. violet 10 10
1771 40c. purple 10 15
1772 70c. green 10 15
1773 80c. bronze 10 15
1774 1p. brown 10 10
1775 1p.50 blue 10 10
1776 2p.50 red 10 15
1777 3p. blue 10 15
1778 5p. sepia 10 15
1779 10p. green 10 15
PAINTINGS (by J. M. Sert)—VERT: 25c. "The Magic Ball"; 70c. "Christ Addressing the Disciples"; 80c. "The Balloonists"; 1p. Self-portrait; 1p.50, "Audacity"; 2p.50, "Justice"; 3p. "Jacob's Struggle with the Angel"; 5p. "The Five Parts of the World"; 10p. "St. Peter and St. Paul". HORIZ: 40c. "Memories of Toledo".

1966. 600th Anniv of Guernica. Multicoloured.
1780 80c. Type **364** 10 10
1781 1p. Arms of Guernica 10 10
1782 3p. "Tree of Guernica" 10 10

365 Postmarked 6 cuartos Stamp of 1850

1966. World Stamp Day.
1783 **365** 25c. multicoloured 10 15
1784 – 1p. multicoloured 10 15
1785 – 10p. multicoloured 15 25
DESIGNS—POSTMARKED STAMPS: 1p. 5r. stamp of 1850; 10p. 10r. stamp of 1850.

1966. Tourist Series. As T **340**.
1786 10c. emerald and green 10 10
1787 15c. bistre and green 10 10
1788 40c. brown and chestnut 10 10
1789 50c. purple and red 10 10
1790 80c. purple and mauve 10 10
1791 1p. turquoise and blue 10 10
1792 1p.50 black and blue 10 10
1793 2p. brown and blue 10 10
1794 3p. brown and blue 10 10
1795 10p. blue and turquoise 10 10
DESIGNS—VERT: 10c. Bohi waterfalls (Lerida); 40c. Sigena monastery (Huesca); 50c. Santo Domingo Church (Soria); 80c. Golden Tower (Seville); 1p. El Teide (Canaries); 10p. Church of St. Gregory (Valladolid). HORIZ: 15c. Torla (Huesca); 1p.50, Cathedral, Guadalupe; 2p. University, Alcala de Henares; 3p. La Seo Cathedral (Lerida).

366 Tree and Globe

1966. World Forestry Congress.
1796 **366** 1p. green, brown and deep brown 10 10

367 Crown and Anchor — **368** Butron Castle (Vizcaya)

1966. Naval Week, Barcelona.
1797 **367** 1p. blue and grey 10 10

1966. Spanish Castles (1st series).
1798 – 10c. sepia and blue 10 10
1799 – 25c. purple and violet 10 10
1800 – 40c. green and turquoise 10 10
1801 – 50c. blue and indigo 10 10
1802 – 70c. blue and ultramarine 10 10
1803 **368** 80c. green and violet 10 10
1804 – 1p. olive and brown 10 10
1805 – 3p. purple and red 10 10
CASTLES—HORIZ: 10c. Guadamur (Toledo); 25c. Alcazar (Segovia); 40c. La Mota (Medina del Campo); 50c. Olite (Navarra); 70c. Monteagudo (Murcia); 1p. Manzanares (Madrid). VERT: 3p. Almansa (Albacete).

369 Don Quixote, Dulcinea and Aldonza Lorenzo

1966. 4th World Psychiatric Congress, Madrid.
1806 **369** 1p.50 multicoloured 10 10

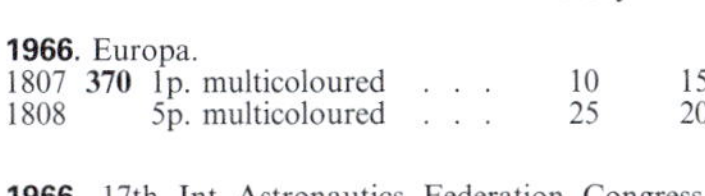

370 "Europa and the Bull" — **371** Horseman in the Sky

1966. Europa.
1807 **370** 1p. multicoloured 10 15
1808 5p. multicoloured 25 20

1966. 17th Int Astronautics Federation Congress, Madrid.
1809 **371** 1p.50 red, black and blue 10 10

1966. Explorers and Colonizers of America (6th series). As T **309**. Inscr "1966" at foot.
1810 30c. bistre and brown 10 15
1811 50c. red and green 10 10
1812 1p. violet and blue 10 10
1813 1p.20 slate and grey 10 15
1814 1p.50 myrtle and green 10 10
1815 3p. blue 10 10
1816 3p.50 violet and lilac 20 20
1817 6p. brown and buff 10 10
DESIGNS: 30c. A. de Mendoza; 50c. Title page of Dominican Fathers' "Christian Doctrine"; 1p. J. A. Manso de Velasco; 1p.20, Coins of Lima Mint (1699); 1p.50, M. de Castro y Padilla; 3p. Oruro Convent; 3p.50, M. de Amat; 6p. Inca postal runner.

372 R. del Valle Inclan — **373** Monastery Facade

1966. Spanish Writers.
1818 **372** 1p.50 green and black 10 15
1819 – 3p. violet and black 10 10
1820 – 6p. blue and black 10 10
WRITERS: 3p. Carlos Arniches; 6p. J. Benavente y Martinez.
See also Nos. 1888/91.

1966. St. Mary's Carthusian Monastery, Jerez.
1821 **373** 1p. indigo and blue 10 10
1822 – 2p. light green and green 10 10
1823 – 5p. plum and purple 10 10
DESIGNS—HORIZ: 2p. Cloisters; 5p. Gateway.

374 "The Nativity" (after P. Duque Cornejo) — **375** Alava Costume

1966. Christmas.
1824 **374** 1p.50 multicoloured 10 10

1967. Provincial Costumes. Multicoloured.
1825 6p. Type **375** 10 10
1826 6p. Albacete 10 10
1827 6p. Alicante 10 10
1828 6p. Almeria 10 10
1829 6p. Avila 10 10
1830 6p. Badajoz 10 10
1831 6p. Baleares 10 10
1832 6p. Barcelona 10 10
1833 6p. Burgos 10 10
1834 6p. Caceres 10 10
1835 6p. Cadiz 10 10
1836 6p. Castellon de la Plana 10 10
See also Nos. 1897/1908, 1956/67, 2007/18 and 2072/6.

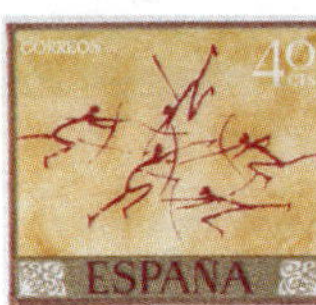

376 Archers

1967. Stamp Day. Cave Paintings. Multicoloured.
1837 40c. Type **376** 10 10
1838 50c. Boar-hunting 10 15
1839 1p. Trees (vert) 10 10
1840 1p.20 Bison 10 15
1841 1p.50 Hands 10 10
1842 2p. Hunter (vert) 10 15
1843 2p.50 Deer (vert) 10 10
1844 3p.50 Hunters 10 10
1845 4p. Chamois-hunters (vert) 10 15
1846 6p. Deer-hunter (vert) 10 10

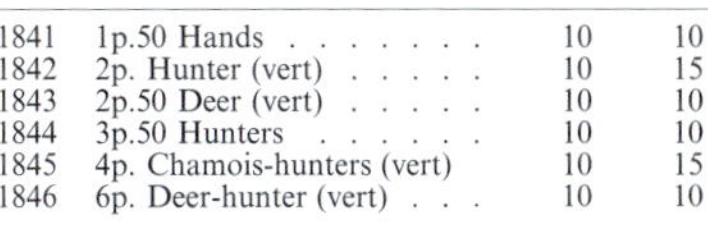

377 Cathedral, Palma de Mallorca, and Union Emblem

1967. Interparliamentary Union Congress, Palma de Mallorca.
1847 **377** 1p.50 green 10 10

378 Wilhelm Rontgen (physicist)

1967. Radiology Congress, Barcelona.
1848 **378** 1p.50 green 10 10

1967. Celebrities (2nd series). As T **362**.
1849 1p.20 violet and purple 10 10
1850 3p.50 purple 15 20
1851 4p. sepia and brown 10 10
1852 25p. grey and blue 20 10
PORTRAITS: 1p.20, Averroes (physician and philosopher); 3p.50, Acosta (poet); 4p. Maimonides (physician and philosopher); 25p. Andres Laguna (physician).

379 Cogwheels — **381** Spanish 5r. Stamp of 1850 with Numeral Postmark

380 Fair Building

1967. Europa.
1853 **379** 1p.50 green, brown & red 10 15
1854 6p. violet, blue & purple 10 10

1967. 50th Anniv of Valencia Int Samples Fair.
1855 **380** 1p.50 green 10 10

1967. World Stamp Day.
1856 **381** 40c. brown, blue & black 10 15
1857 – 1p.50 lake, black and green 10 15
1858 – 6p. blue, red and black 10 10
DESIGNS: 1p.50, Spanish 12c. stamp of 1850 with crowned "M" (Madrid) postmark; 6p. Spanish 6r. stamp of 1850 with "1.R." postmark.
See also Nos. 1927/8, 1980/1, 2032, 2091, 2150 and 2185.

382 Sleeping Vagrant and "Guardian Angel" — **383** I.T.Y. Emblem

1967. National Day for Caritas Welfare Organization.
1859 **382** 1p.50 multicoloured 10 10

1967. Tourist Series and Int Tourist Year.
1860 – 10c. black and blue 10 10
1861 – 1p. black and blue 10 10
1862 – 1p.50 black and brown 10 10
1863 – 2p.50 blue and turquoise 10 10
1864 **383** 3p.50 blue and purple 15 15
1865 – 5p. bronze and green 10 10
1866 – 6p. purple and mauve 10 10

DESIGNS: 10c. Betanzos Church (Corunna); 1p. St. Miguel's Tower (Palencia); 1p.50, Castellers (acrobats); 2p.50, Columbus Monument (Huelva); 5p. "Enchanted City" (Cuenca); 6p. Church of our Lady, Sanlucar (Cadiz).

1967. Spanish Castles (2nd series). As T **368**.
1867 50c. brown and grey 10 10
1868 1p. violet and grey 10 10
1869 1p.50 green and blue . . . 10 10
1870 2p. brown and red 10 10
1871 2p.50 brown and green . . . 10 10
1872 5p. blue and purple 10 10
1873 6p. sepia and brown 10 30
1874 10p. green and blue 15 10
CASTLES—HORIZ: 50c. Balsareny (Barcelona); 1p. Jarandilla (Caceres); 1p.50, Almodovar (Cordoba); 2p.50, Peniscola (Castellon); 5p. Coca (Segovia); 6p. Loarre (Huesca); 10p. Belmonte (Cuenca). VERT: 2p. Ponferrada (Leon).

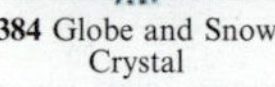

384 Globe and Snow Crystal

385 Map of the Americas, Spain and the Philippines

1967. 12th Int Refrigeration Congress, Madrid.
1875 **384** 1p.50 blue 10 10

1967. 4th Spanish, Portuguese, American and Philippine Municipalities Congress, Barcelona.
1876 **385** 1p.50 violet 10 10

1967. Explorers and Colonizers of America (7th series). As T **309**. Inscr "1967" at foot.
1877 40c. olive and orange . . . 10 10
1878 50c. agate and grey 10 15
1879 1p. mauve and blue 10 10
1880 1p.20 green and cream . . . 10 10
1881 1p.50 green and flesh . . . 10 10
1882 3p. violet and buff 10 10
1883 3p.50 blue and pink 20 20
1884 6p. brown 15 20
DESIGNS—VERT: 40c. J. Francisco de la Bodega y Quadra; 50c. Map of Nutka coast; 1p. F. A. Mourelle; 1p.50, E. J. Martinez; 3p.50, Cayetano Valdes y Florez. HORIZ: 1p.20, View of Nutka; 3p. Map of Californian coast; 6p. San Elias, Alaska.

387 Ploughing with Oxen

388 Main Portal, Veruela Monastery

1967. 2000th Anniv of Caceres. Multicoloured.
1885 1p.50 Statue and archway 10 10
1886 3p.50 Type **387** 10 10
1887 6p. Roman coins 10 10
Nos. 1885 and 1887 are vert.

1967. Anniversaries. Portraits as T **372**.
1888 1p.20 brown and black . . . 10 15
1889 1p.50 green and black . . . 10 15
1890 3p.50 violet and black . . . 15 15
1891 6p. blue and black 10 10
DESIGNS: 1p.20, P. de S. Jose Bethencourt (founder of Bethlehemite Order, 300th death anniv); 1p.50, Enrique Granados (composer, birth cent); 3p.50, Ruben Dario (poet, birth centenary); 6p. San Ildefonso, Archbishop of Toledo (after El Greco) (1900th death anniv).

1967. Veruela Monastery.
1892 **388** 1p.50 blue & ultramarine 10 10
1893 – 3p.50 grey and green . . 15 15
1894 – 6p. purple and brown . . 15 15
DESIGNS—HORIZ: 3p.50, Aerial view of monastery; 6p. Cloisters.

389 "The Canonization of San Jose de Calasanz" (from painting by Goya)

390 "The Nativity" (Salzillo)

1967. Bicentenary of Canonization of San Jose de Calasanz.
1895 **389** 1p.50 multicoloured . . 10 10

1967. Christmas.
1896 **390** 1p.50 multicoloured . . 10 10

1968. Provincial Costumes. As T **375**. Mult.
1897 6p. Ciudad Real 10 10
1898 6p. Cordoba 10 10
1899 6p. Coruna 10 10
1900 6p. Cuenca 10 10
1901 6p. Fernando Poo 10 10
1902 6p. Gerona 10 10
1903 6p. Las Palmas (Gran Canaria) 10 10
1904 6p. Granada 10 10
1905 6p. Guadalajara 10 10
1906 6p. Guipuzcoa 10 10
1907 6p. Huelva 10 10
1908 6p. Huesca 10 10

391 Slalom

1968. Winter Olympic Games, Grenoble. Multicoloured.
1909 1p.50 Type **391** 10 10
1910 3p.50 Bobsleighing (vert) . . 15 25
1911 6p. Ice hockey 10 15

1968. Stamp Day and Fortuny Commemoration As T **279**. Frames in gold.
1912 40c. purple 10 15
1913 50c. green 10 15
1914 1p. brown 10 10
1915 1p.20 violet 10 10
1916 1p.50 green 10 15
1917 2p. brown 10 10
1918 2p.50 red 10 10
1919 3p.50 brown 15 15
1920 4p. olive 10 15
1921 6p. blue 15 15
Fortuny Paintings—HORIZ: 40c. "The Vicarage"; 1p.20, "The Print Collector"; 6p. "Queen Christina". VERT: 50c. "Fantasia"; 1p. "Idyll"; 1p.50, Self-portrait; 2p. "Old Man Naked to the Sun"; 2p.50, "Typical Calabrian"; 3p.50, "Portrait of Lady"; 4p. "Battle of Tetuan".

392 Beatriz Galindo

1968. Famous Spanish Women. With background scenes.
1922 **392** 1p.20 brown and bistre 10 10
1923 – 1p.50 blue and turquoise 10 10
1924 – 3p.50 violet 15 15
1925 – 6p. black and blue . . . 10 10
WOMEN: 1p.50, Agustina de Aragon; 3p.50, Maria Pacheco; 6p. Rosalia de Castro.

393 Europa "Key"

1968. Europa.
1926 **393** 3p.50 gold, brn & blue 10 10

1968. World Stamp Day. As T **381**, but stamps and postmarks changed. Inscr "1968".
1927 1p.50 black, brown and blue 10 15
1928 3p.50 blue, black and green 10 10
DESIGNS: 1p.50, Spanish 6c. stamp of 1850 with Puebla (Galicia) postmark; 3p.50, Spanish 6r. stamp of 1850 with Serena postmark.

394 Emperor Galba's Coin

395 Human Rights Emblem

1968. 1900th Anniv of Foundation of Leon by VIIth Roman Legion.
1929 – 1p. brown and purple . . 10 10
1930 – 1p.50 brown and yellow 10 10
1931 **394** 3p.50 green and ochre 20 25
DESIGNS—VERT: 1p. Inscribed tile and town map of Leon (26 × 47 mm); 1p.50, Legionary with standard (statue).

1968. Human Rights Year.
1932 **395** 3p.50 red, green and blue 10 10

1968. Tourist Series. As T **340**.
1933 50c. brown 10 10
1934 1p.20 green 10 10
1935 1p.50 blue and green . . . 10 10
1936 2p. purple 10 10
1937 3p.50 purple 10 10
DESIGNS—VERT: 50c. Count Benavente's Palace, Baeza; 1p.50, Sepulchre, St. Vincent's Church, Avila; 3p.50, Main portal, Church of Santa Maria, Sanguesa (Navarra). HORIZ: 1p.20, View of Salamanca; 2p. "The King's Page" (statue), Siguenza Cathedral.

1968. Spanish Castles (3rd series). As T **368**.
1938 40c. sepia and blue 10 15
1939 1p.20 purple 10 10
1940 1p.50 black and bistre . . . 10 10
1941 2p.50 bronze and green . . 10 10
1942 6p. turquoise and blue . . 10 10
DESIGNS—HORIZ: 40c. Escalona; 1p.20, Fuensaldana; 1p.50, Penafiel; 2p.50, Villas and obroso. VERT: 6p. Frias.

396 Rifle-shooting

1968. Olympic Games, Mexico. Multicoloured.
1943 1p0. Type **396** 10 15
1944 1p.50 Horse-jumping . . . 10 15
1945 3p.50 Cycling 15 25
1946 6p. Yachting (vert) 15 15

1968. Explorers and Colonisers of America (8th series). As T **309** but inscr "1968" at foot.
1947 40c. blue and light blue . . 10 15
1948 1p. purple and blue 10 10
1949 1p.50 green and flesh . . . 10 10
1950 3p.50 blue and mauve . . . 20 20
1951 6p. brown and yellow . . . 20 20
DESIGNS—VERT: 40c. Map of Orinoco missions; 1p. Diego de Losada (founder of Caracas); 1p.50, Arms of the Losadas; 3p.50, Diego de Henares (builder of Caracas). HORIZ: 6p. Old plan of Santiago de Leon de Caracas.

397 Monastery Building

398 "The Nativity" (Barocci)

1968. Santa Maria del Parral Monastery.
1952 **397** 1p.50 lilac and blue . . . 10 10
1953 – 3p.50 brown & chocolate 20 15
1954 – 6p. brown and red . . . 20 15
DESIGNS—VERT: 3p.50, Cloisters; 6p. "Santa Maria del Parral".

1968. Christmas.
1955 **398** 1p.50 multicoloured . . 10 10

1969. Provincial Costumes. As T **375**. Mult.
1956 6p. Ifni 10 10
1957 6p. Jaen 10 10
1958 6p. Leon 10 10
1959 6p. Lerida 10 10
1960 6p. Logrono 10 10
1961 6p. Lugo 10 10
1962 6p. Madrid 10 10
1963 6p. Malaga 10 10
1964 6p. Murcia 10 10
1965 6p. Navarra 10 10
1966 6p. Orense 10 10
1967 6p. Oviedo 10 10

1969. Stamp Day and Alonso Cano Commem. Various paintings as T **279**. Frames gold: centre colours below.
1968 40c. red 10 15
1969 50c. green 10 15
1970 1p. sepia 10 15
1971 1p.50 green 10 15
1972 2p. brown 10 15
1973 2p.50 mauve 10 10
1974 3p. blue 10 10
1975 3p.50 purple 10 10
1976 4p. purple 10 10
1977 6p. blue 15 15
Alonso Cano paintings—VERT: 40c. "St. Agnes"; 50c. "St. Joseph"; 1p. "Christ supported by an Angel"; 1p.50, "Alonso Cano" (Velazquez); 2p. "The Holy Family"; 2p.50, "The Circumcision"; 3p. "Jesus and the Samaritan"; 3p.50, "Madonna and Child"; 6p. "The Vision of St. John the Baptist". HORIZ: 4p. "St. John Capistrano and St. Bernardin".

399 Molecules and Diagram

1969. 6th European Biochemical Congress.
1978 **399** 1p.50 multicoloured . . 10 10

400 Colonnade

1969. Europa.
1979 **400** 3p.50 multicoloured . . 10 15

1969. World Stamp Day. As T **381**.
1980 1p.50 black, red and green 10 15
1981 3p.50 green, red and blue 10 10
DESIGNS: 1p.50, Spanish 6c. stamp of 1851 with "A 3 1851" postmark; 3p.50, Spanish 10r. stamp of 1851 with "CORVERA" postmark.

401 Spectrum

1969. 15th Int Spectroscopical Conf, Madrid.
1982 **401** 1p.50 multicoloured . . 10 10

402 Red Cross Symbols and Globe

1969. 50th Anniv of League of Red Cross Societies.
1983 **402** 1p.50 multicoloured . . 10 10

403 Capital, Lugo Cathedral

1969. 300th Anniv of Dedication of Galicia to Jesus Christ.
1984 **403** 1p.50 brown, blk & grn 10 10

1969. Spanish Castles (4th series). As T **368**.
1985 1p. purple and green 10 15
1986 1p.50 blue and violet . . . 10 15
1987 2p.50 lilac and blue 10 10
1988 3p.50 brown and green . . . 20 20
1989 6p. drab and green 10 10
CASTLES—HORIZ: 1p. Turegano; 1p.50, Villalonso; 2p.50, Velez Blanco; 3p.50, Castilnovo; 6p. Torrelobaton.

404 Franciscan Friar and Child

405 Rock of Gibraltar

1969. Bicentenary of San Diego (California).
1990 **404** 1p.50 multicoloured . . 10 10

1969. Aid for Spanish "ex-Gibraltar" Workers.
1991 **405** 1p.50 blue 10 10
1992 – 2p. purple 10 10
DESIGN: 2p. Aerial view of Rock.

1969. Tourist Series. As T **340**.
1993 1p.50 green and turquoise 15 10
1994 3p. turquoise and green . . 10 10
1995 3p.50 blue and green . . . 10 10
1996 6p. violet and green 15 10
DESIGNS—HORIZ: 1p.50, Alcaniz (Teruel). VERT: 3p. Murcia Cathedral; 3p.50, "The Lady of Elche" (sculpture); 6p. Church of Our Lady of the Redonda, Logrono.

1969. Explorers and Colonizers of America (9th series). Chile. As T **309**. Inscr "1969" at foot.
1997 40c. brown on blue 10 15
1998 1p.50 violet on flesh 10 10
1999 2p. green on mauve 15 10
2000 3p.50 green on cream . . . 30 25
2001 6p. brown on cream . . . 25 20
DESIGNS—VERT: 40c. Convent of Santo Domingio, Santiago de Chile; 2p. Ambrosio O'Higgins; 3p.50, Pedro de Valdivia (founder of Santiago de Chile). HORIZ: 1p.50, Chilean Mint; 6p. Cal y Canto Bridge.

406 "Adoration of the Three Kings" (Maino)

1969. Christmas. Multicoloured.
2002 1p.50 Type **406** 10 10
2003 2p. "The Nativity" (Gerona Cathedral) 10 10

407 Las Huelgas Monastery

1969. Las Huelgas Monastery, Burgos.
2004 **407** 1p.50 slate and green . . 15 15
2005 – 3p.50 blue 35 55
2006 – 6p. olive and green . . . 20 30
DESIGNS—HORIZ: 3p.50, Tombs. VERT: 6p. Cloisters.

1970. Provincial Costumes. As T **375**. Multicoloured.
2007 6p. Palencia 10 10
2008 6p. Pontevedra 10 10
2009 6p. Sahara 10 10
2010 6p. Salamanca 10 10
2011 6p. Santa Cruz de Tenerife 10 10
2012 6p. Santander 10 10
2013 6p. Segovia 10 10
2014 6p. Seville 10 10
2015 6p. Soria 10 10
2016 6p. Tarragona 10 10
2017 6p. Teruel 10 10
2018 6p. Toledo 10 15

408 Blessed Juan of Avila (after El Greco)

409 "St. Stephen"

1970. Spanish Celebrities.
2019 **408** 25p. blue and lilac . . . 4·25 10
2020 – 50p. brown and orange 1·75 20
DESIGN: 25p. Type **408** (400th death anniv); 50p. Cardinal Rodrigo Ximenes de Rada (after J. de Borgena) (800th birth anniv).
See also Nos. 2129/31.

1970. Stamp Day and Luis de Morales Commem. Various paintings. Multicoloured.
2021 50c. Type **409** 10 15
2022 1p. "The Annunciation" . . 10 15
2023 1p.50 "Virgin and Child with St. John" 10 10
2024 2p. "Virgin and Child" . . 10 15
2025 3p. "The Presentation of the Infant Christ" 10 10
2026 3p.50 "St. Jerome" 10 15
2027 4p. "St. John of Ribera" . . 10 10
2028 5p. "Ecce Homo" 15 15
2029 6p. "Pieta" 15 15
2030 10p. "St. Francis of Assisi" 15 20
See also Nos. 2077/84, 2135/42, 2204/11, 2261/8, 2420/7, 2478/85, 2529/36 and 2585/90.

410 "Flaming Sun"

1970. Europa.
2031 **410** 3p.50 gold & ultramarine 10 15

1970. World Stamp Day. As T **381** but stamp and postmark changed.
2032 2p. red, black and green . . 10 10
DESIGN: 2p. Spanish 12c. stamp of 1860 with railway cachet.

411 Fair Building

1970. 50th Anniv of Barcelona Fair.
2033 **411** 15p. multicoloured . . . 20 10

412 Gen. Primo de Rivera

1970. Birth Cent of General Primo de Rivera.
2034 **412** 2p. green, brown and buff 10 10

1970. Spanish Castles (5th series). As T **368**.
2035 1p. black and blue 30 20
2036 1p.20 blue and turquoise . . 10 15
2037 3p.50 brown and green . . . 15 15
2038 6p. violet and brown . . . 20 10
2039 10p. brown and chestnut . . 75 15
CASTLES—HORIZ: 1p. Valencia de Don Juan; 1p.20, Monterrey; 3p.50, Mombeltran; 6p. Sadaba; 10p. Bellver.

1970. Tourist Series. As T **340**.
2040 50c. lilac and blue 10 10
2041 1p. brown and ochre . . . 10 15
2042 1p.50 green and blue . . . 10 10
2043 2p. blue and deep blue . . . 40 10
2044 3p.50 blue and violet . . . 15 10
2045 5p. brown and blue 75 15
DESIGNS—HORIZ: 50c. Alcazaba, Almeria; 1p. Malaga Cathedral; 2p. St. Francis' Convent, Orense. VERT: 1p.50, Our Lady of the Assumption, Lequeitio; 3p.50, The Lonja, Zaragoza; 5p. The Portalon, Vitoria.

413 17th-century Tailor

1970. International Tailoring Congress.
2046 **413** 2p. violet, red and brown 10 15

414 Diver on Map

1970. 12th European Swimming, Diving and Water-polo Championships, Barcelona.
2047 **414** 2p. brown, blue and green 10 10

415 Concha Espina

417 "The Adoration of the Shepherds" (El Greco)

416 Survey Map of Southern Spain and North Africa

1970. Spanish Writers.
2048 **415** 50c. blue, brown and buff 10 15
2049 – 1p. violet, green and drab 10 15
2050 – 1p.50 green, blue & drab 10 10
2051 – 2p. olive, green and buff 20 10
2052 – 2p.50 pur, vio & ochre 10 10
2053 – 3p.50 red, brown & lilac 10 10
WRITERS: 1p. Guillen de Castro; 1p.50, J. R. Jimenez; 2p. G. A. Becquer; 2p.50, Miguel de Unamuno; 3p.50, J. M. Gabriel y Galan.

1970. Explorers and Colonizers of America (10th series). Mexico. As T **309**.
2054 40c. green on light green . . 10 15
2055 1p.50 brown on blue 15 10
2056 2p. violet on cream 45 15
2057 3p.50 green on light green 15 10
2058 6p. blue on pink 25 10
DESIGNS—VERT: 40c. House in Queretaro; 2p. Vasco de Quiroga; 3p.50, F. Juan de Zumarraga; 6p. Morelia Cathedral. HORIZ: 1p.50, Cathedral, Mexico City.

1970. Centenary of Spanish Geographical and Survey Institute.
2059 **416** 2p. multicoloured . . . 10 10

1970. Christmas. Multicoloured.
2060 1p.50 Type **417** 10 10
2061 2p. "The Adoration of the Shepherds" (Murillo) . . 10 10

418 U.N. Emblem and New York Headquarters

1970. 25th Anniv of United Nations.
2062 **418** 8p. multicoloured . . . 10 10

419 Ripoll Monastery

420 Pilgrims' Route Map

1970. Ripoll Monastery.
2063 – 2p. purple and violet . . 45 15
2064 **419** 3p.50 purple and orange 10 10
2065 – 5p. green and slate . . . 85 20
DESIGNS: 2p. Entrance; 5p. Cloisters.

1971. Holy Year of Compostela (1st issue). "St. James in Europe".
2066 **420** 50c. brown and blue . . 10 10
2067 – 1p. black and brown . . 10 15
2068 – 1p.50 purple and green 20 15
2069 – 2p. brown and purple . . 15 10
2070 – 3p. deep blue and blue 20 15
2071 – 4p. olive 35 10
DESIGNS—VERT: 1p. Statue of St. Brigid, Vadstena (Sweden); 1p.50, St. Jacques' Church tower, Paris; 2p. "St. James" (carving from altar, Pistoia, Italy). HORIZ: 3p. St. David's Cathedral, Wales; 4p. Carving from Ark of Charlemagne (Aachen, West Germany).
See also Nos. 2105/11 and 2121/8.

1971. Provincial Costumes. As T **375**. Mult.
2072 6p. Valencia 10 15
2073 8p. Valladolid 15 20
2074 8p. Vizcaya 15 20
2075 8p. Zamora 15 25
2076 8p. Zaragoza 15 20

1971. Stamp Day and Ignacio Zuloaga Commem. Paintings as T **409**. Multicoloured.
2077 50c. "My Uncle Daniel" . . 10 15
2078 1p. "Segovia" (horiz) . . . 10 15
2079 1p.50 "The Duchess of Alba" 10 10
2080 2p. "Ignacio Zuloaga" (self-portrait) 20 10
2081 3p. "Juan Belmonte" . . . 20 15
2082 4p. "The Countess of Noailles" 10 10
2083 5p. "Pablo Uranga" 20 20
2084 8p. "Boatmen's Houses, Lerma" (horiz) 20 20

421 Amadeo Vives (composer)

1971. Spanish Celebrities. Multicoloured.
2085 1p. Type **421** 15 20
2086 2p. St. Teresa of Avila (mystic) 20 10
2087 8p. B. Perez Galdos (writer) 20 20
2088 15p. R. Menendez Pidal (writer) 15 15

422 Europa Chain

1971. Europa.
2089 **422** 2p. brown, violet and blue 45 15
2090 8p. brown, light green and green 35 30

1971. World Stamp Day. As T **381**, but with different stamp and postmark.
2091 2p. black, blue and green . . 10 10
DESIGN: 2p. Spanish 6c. stamp of 1850 with "A.s." postmark.

423 Gymnast on Vaulting-horse

1971. 9th European Male Gymnastics Cup Championships, Madrid. Multicoloured.
2092 1p. Type **423** 10 15
2093 2p. Gymnast on bar 10 15

424 Great Bustard

1971. Spanish Fauna (1st series). Mult.
2094 1p. Type **424** 20 25
2095 2p. Lynx 15 15
2096 3p. Brown bear 15 15
2097 5p. Red-legged partridge (vert) 35 25
2098 8p. Spanish ibex (vert) . . . 35 35
See also Nos. 2160/4, 2192/6, 2250/4, 2317/21, 2452/6 and 2579/83.

426 Legionaries in Battle

1971. 50th Anniv of Spanish Foreign Legion. Multicoloured.
2101 1p. Type **426** 10 15
2102 2p. Ceremonial parade 20 10
2103 5p. Memorial service 20 20
2104 8p. Officer and mobile column 25 25

1971. Holy Year of Compostela (2nd issue). "En Route to Santiago". As T **420**.
2105 50c. purple and blue 10 15
2106 6p. blue 15 15
2107 7p. purple and deep purple 40 15
2108 7p.50 red and purple 10 20
2109 8p. purple and green 20 20
2110 9p. violet and green 20 20
2111 10p. brown and green 30 10
DESIGNS—HORIZ: 50c. Pilgrims' route map of northern Spain; 7p.50, Cloisters, Najera Monastery; 9p. Eunate Monastery. VERT: 6p. "Pilgrims" (sculpture, Royal Hospital, Burgos); 7p. Gateway, St. Domingo de la Calzada Monastery; 8p. Statue of Christ, Puente de la Reina; 10p. Cross of Roncesvalles.

427 "Children of the World"

1971. 25th Anniv of U.N.I.C.E.F.
2112 **427** 8p. multicoloured 10 10

428 "Battle of Lepanto" (after L. Valdes)

1971. 400th Anniv of Battle of Lepanto.
2113 – 2p. green & brown (vert) 40 10
2114 **428** 5p. chocolate and brown 90 15
2115 – 8p. blue and red (vert) 60 60
DESIGNS: 2p. "Don John of Austria" (S. Coello); 8p. Standard of the Holy League.

429 Hockey Players

431 "The Nativity" (detail from altar, Avia)

430 De Havilland D.H.9B over Seville

1971. World Hockey Cup Championships, Barcelona.
2116 **429** 5p. multicoloured 45 10

1971. 50th Anniv of Spanish Airmail Services. Multicoloured.
2117 2p. Type **430** 25 15
2118 15p. Boeing 747-100 airliner over Madrid 25 15

1971. Christmas. Multicoloured.
2119 2p. Type **431** 10 10
2120 8p. "The Birth" (detail from altar, Saga) 10 10

1971. Holy Year of Compostela (3rd issue). As T **420**.
2121 1p. black and green 10 10
2122 1p.50 violet and purple 15 20
2123 2p. blue and green 75 10
2124 2p.50 violet and red 10 15
2125 3p. purple and red 40 15
2126 3p.50 green and pink 10 15
2127 4p. brown and blue 10 15
2128 5p. black and green 30 10
DESIGNS—VERT: 1p. Santiago Cathedral; 2p. Lugo Cathedral; 3p. Astorga Cathedral; 4p. San Tirso, Sahagun. HORIZ: 1p.50, Pilgrim approaching Santiago de Compostela; 2p.50, Villafranca del Bierzo; 3p.50, San Marcos, Leon; 5p. San Martin, Fromista.

1972. Spanish Celebrities. As T **408**.
2129 15p. green and brown 20 15
2130 25p. black and green 25 10
2131 50p. brown and red 45 10
CELEBRITIES: 15p. Emilia Pardo Bazan (novelist); 25p. Jose de Espronceda (poet); 50p. Fernan Gonzalez (first King of Castile).

432 Ski Jumping

433 Title-page of "Don Quixote" (1605)

1972. Winter Olympic Games, Sapporo, Japan. Multicoloured.
2132 2p. Type **432** 25 15
2133 15p. Figure skating (vert) 15 20

1972. International Book Year.
2134 **433** 2p. red and brown 10 10

1972. Stamp Day and Solana Commem. Paintings by Solana. As T **409**. Multicoloured.
2135 1p. "Clowns" (horiz) 10 20
2136 2p. "Solana and Family" (self-portrait) 30 10
2137 3p. "Blind Musician" 30 10
2138 4p. "Return of the Fishermen" 15 15
2139 5p. "Decorating Masks" 1·10 25
2140 7p. "The Bibliophile" 45 15
2141 10p. "Merchant Navy Captain" 45 15
2142 15p. "Pombo Reunion" (vert) 45 20

434 "Abies pinsapo"

435 "Europeans"

1972. Spanish Flora (1st series). Multicoloured.
2143 1p. Type **434** 10 15
2144 2p. Strawberry tree 25 15
2145 3p. Maritime pine 35 15
2146 5p. Holm oak 45 10
2147 8p. "Juniperus thurifera" 25 25
See also Nos. 2178/82, 2278/82 and 2299/303.

1972. Europa. Multicoloured.
2148 2p. Type **435** 1·60 15
2149 8p. "Communications" 50 35

436 Cordoba Pre-stamp Postmark

1972. World Stamp Day.
2150 **436** 2p. red, black and brown 10 15

1972. Spanish Castles (6th series). As T **368**.
2151 1p. brown and green 35 30
2152 2p. brown and green 65 10
2153 3p. brown and red 65 10
2154 5p. green and blue 65 20
2155 10p. violet and blue 2·50 20
CASTLES—VERT: 1p. Sajazarra. HORIZ: 2p. Santa Catalina; 3p. Biar; 5p. San Servando; 10p. Pedraza.

437 Fencing

1972. Olympic Games, Munich. Multicoloured.
2156 1p. Type **437** 10 15
2157 2p. Weightlifting (vert) 25 10
2158 5p. Rowing (vert) 15 10
2159 8p. Pole vaulting (vert) 20 20

438 Chamois

439 Brigadier M. A. de Ustariz

1972. Spanish Fauna (2nd series). Mult.
2160 1p. Pyrenean desman 10 15
2161 2p. Type **438** 15 10
2162 3p. Wolf 20 15
2163 5p. Egyptian mongoose (horiz) 45 20
2164 7p. Small-spotted genet (horiz) 30 15

1972. "Spain in the New World" (1st series). 450th Anniv of Puerto Rico. Multicoloured.
2165 1p. Type **439** 10 15
2166 2p. View of San Juan, 1870 (horiz) 20 10
2167 5p. View of San Juan, 1625 (horiz) 30 10
2168 8p. Map of Plaza de Bahia, 1792 (horiz) 30 40
See also Nos. 2212/5, 2271/4, 2338/41 and 2430/3.

440 Facade of Monastery

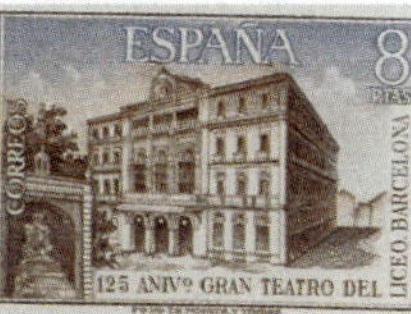

441 Grand Lyceum Theatre

1972. Monastery of St.Thomas, Avila.
2169 **440** 2p. green and blue 70 10
2170 – 8p. purple and brown 60 25
2171 – 15p. blue and purple 40 15
DESIGNS—VERT: 8p. Interior of monastery. HORIZ: 15p. Cloisters.

1972. 125th Anniv of Grand Lyceum Theatre, Barcelona.
2172 **441** 8p. brown and blue 20 15

442 "The Nativity"

1972. Christmas. Murals in Royal Collegiate Basilica of San Isidoro, Leon. Multicoloured.
2173 2p. Type **442** 10 10
2174 8p. "The Annunciation" 10 10

443 J. de Herrera and Escorial

1973. Spanish Architects (1st series).
2175 **443** 8p. green and sepia 45 10
2176 – 10p. blue and brown 1·40 15
2177 – 15p. blue and green 30 10
DESIGNS: 10p. J. de Villanueva and Prado; 15p. V. Rodriguez and Apollo Fountain, Madrid.
See also Nos. 2295/7.

444 "Apollonias canariensis"

1973. Spanish Flora (2nd series). Canary Islands. Multicoloured.
2178 1p. Type **444** 15 20
2179 2p. "Myrica faya" 45 15
2180 4p. "Phoenix canariensis" 15 15
2181 5p. "Ilex canariensis" 45 25
2182 15p. "Dracaena draco" 25 15
Nos. 2179/82 are vert.

445 Roman Mosaic

446 Iznajar Dam

1973. Europa.
2183 **445** 2p. multicoloured 40 15
2184 – 8p. blue, red and black 30 20
DESIGN—HORIZ (37×26 mm): 8p. Europa "Posthorn".

1973. World Stamp Day. As T **381**, but with different stamp and postmark.
2185 2p. red, blue and black 10 10
DESIGN: 2p. Spanish 6r. stamp of 1853 with Madrid postmark.

1973. 11th Congress of Int High Dams Commission, Madrid.
2186 **446** 8p. multicoloured 10 10

1973. Tourist Series. As T **340**.
2187 1p. brown and green 10 15
2188 2p. green and dark green 45 10
2189 3p. brown and light brown 45 10
2190 5p. violet and blue 1·40 20
2191 8p. red and green 55 20
DESIGNS—HORIZ: 1p. Gateway, Onate University, Guipuzcoa; 2p. Town Square, Lugo; 5p. Columbus' House, Las Palmas; 8p. Windmills, La Mancha. VERT: 3p. Llerena Square, Badajoz.

447 Black-bellied Sandgrouse

1973. Spanish Fauna (3rd series). Birds. Mult.
2192 1p. Type **447** 15 25
2193 2p. Black stork 25 15
2194 5p. Azure-winged magpie (vert) 45 45
2195 7p. Imperial eagle 50 15
2196 15p. Red-crested pochard (vert) 20 20

448 Hermandad Standard-bearer, Castile, 1488

1973. Spanish Military Uniforms (1st series). Multicoloured.
2197 1p. Type **448** 10 15
2198 2p. Mounted knight, Castile, 1493 (horiz) 40 15
2199 3p. Arquebusier, 1534 40 15
2200 7p. Mounted arquebusier, 1560 25 15
2201 8p. Infantry sergeant, 1567 25 20
See also Nos. 2225/7, 2255/9, 2290/4, 2322/6, 2410/14, 2441/5, 2472/6 and 2499/503.

449 Fishes in Net and Trawler

1973. World Fishing Fair and Congress, Vigo.
2202 **449** 2p. multicoloured . . . 10 10

450 Conference Building

1973. I.T.U. Conference, Torremolinos.
2203 **450** 8p. multicoloured . . . 10 10

1973. Stamp Day and Vicente Lopez Commem. Paintings. As T **409**. Multicoloured.
2204 1p. "Ferdinand VII" . . . 10 15
2205 2p. Self-portrait 20 15
2206 3p. "La Senora de Carvallo" 20 15
2207 4p. "M. de Castelldosrrius" 15 10
2208 5p. "Isabella II" 15 15
2209 7p. "Goya" 15 10
2210 10p. "Maria Amalia of Saxony" 20 15
2211 15p. "Felix Lopez, the Organist" 20 15

451 Leon Cathedral, Nicaragua

452 Pope Gregory XI receiving St. Jerome's Petition

1973. "Spain in the New World" (2nd series). Nicaragua. Multicoloured.
2212 1p. Type **451** 10 10
2213 2p. Subtiava Church 25 10
2214 5p. Colonial-style house (vert) 45 20
2215 8p. Rio San Juan Castle . . 25 15

1973. 600th Anniv of Order of St. Jerome.
2216 **452** 2p. multicoloured . . . 10 10

453 Courtyard

454 "The Nativity" (pillar capital, Silos)

1973. Monaster of Santo Domingo de Silos, Burgos.
2217 **453** 2p. purple and brown . . 40 10
2218 – 8p. purple and blue . . 15 10
2219 – 15p. blue and green . . 20 15
DESIGNS—HORIZ: 8p. Cloisters. VERT: 15p. "Three Saints" (statue).

1973. Christmas. Multicoloured.
2220 2p. Type **454** 10 10
2221 8p. "Adoration of the Kings" (bas-relief, Butrera) (horiz) 10 10

455 Map of Spain and the Americas

1973. 500th Anniv of Spanish Printing.
2222 **455** 1p. blue and green . . . 25 15
2223 – 7p. violet and blue . . . 15 15
2224 – 15p. green and purple . . 20 20

DESIGNS—VERT: 7p. "Teacher and pupils" (ancient woodcut); 15p. "Los Sinodales" (manuscript).

1974. Spanish Military Uniforms (2nd series). As T **448**. Multicoloured.
2225 1p. Mounted arquebusier, 1603 . . . . 10 15
2226 2p. Arquebusier, 1632 . . . 45 15
2227 3p. Mounted cuirassier, 1635 60 15
2228 5p. Mounted drummer, 1677 80 20
2229 9p. Musketeers, "Viejos Morados" Regiment, 1694 20 20

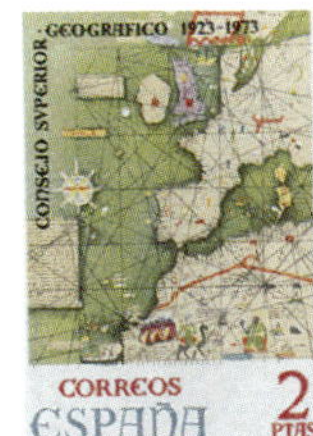

456 14th-century Nautical Chart

1974. 50th Anniv of Spanish Higher Geographical Council.
2230 **456** 2p. multicoloured . . . 10 10

457 Miguel Biada (construction engineer) and Locomotive "Mataro"

1974. 125th Anniv of Barcelona–Mataro Railway.
2231 **457** 2p. multicoloured . . . 10 15

458 Stamp Collector, Album and Magnifier

1974. "ESPANA 75" Int Stamp Exhibition, Madrid.
2232 **458** 2p. multicoloured . . . 10 15
2233 – 5p. blue, black and brown 30 30
2234 – 8p. multicoloured . . . 25 30
DESIGNS—DIAMOND (43×43 mm): 5p. Exhibition emblem; 8p. Globe and arrows.

459 "Woman with Offering"

1974. Europa. Stone Sculptures. Multicoloured.
2235 2p. Type **459** 45 15
2236 8p. "Woman from Baza" . . 20 20

460 2r. Stamp of 1854 with Seville Postmark

1974. World Stamp Day.
2237 **460** 2p. multicoloured . . . 10 10

461 Jaime Balmes (philosopher) and Monastery

462 Bramante's "Little Temple", Rome

1974. Spanish Celebrities.
2238 **461** 8p. brown and blue . . . 10 10
2239 – 10p. brown and red . . 50 30
2240 – 15p. blue and brown . . 15 10
DESIGNS: 10p. Pedro Poveda (educationalist) and mountain village; 15p. Jorge Juan (cosmographer and mariner) and shipyard.

1974. Centenary of Spanish Fine Arts Academy, Rome.
2241 **462** 5p. multicoloured . . . 15 20

463 Roman Aqueduct, Segovia

1974. Spain as a Province of the Roman Empire.
2242 **463** 1p. black and brown . . 10 10
2243 – 2p. brown and green . . 25 15
2244 – 3p. brown & light brown 10 10
2245 – 4p. blue and green . . . 10 10
2246 – 5p. purple and blue . . . 10 10
2247 – 7p. purple and green . . 10 15
2248 – 8p. green and red . . 10 15
2249 – 9p. brown and purple . . 10 15
DESIGNS—HORIZ: 2p. Roman Bridge, Alcantara; 3p. Martial (poet) giving public reading; 5p. Theatre, Merida; 7p. Ossio, 1st Bishop of Cordoba, addressing the Synod. VERT: 4p. Triumphal Arch, Bara; 8p. Ruins of Curia, Talavera la Vieja; 9p. Statue of Emperor Trajan.

464 Tortoise

1974. Spanish Fauna (4th series). Reptiles. Mult.
2250 1p. Type **464** 10 15
2251 2p. Chameleon 25 15
2252 5p. Gecko 50 50
2253 7p. Green lizard 35 20
2254 15p. Adder 15 15

1974. Spanish Military Uniforms (3rd series). As T **448**. Multicoloured.
2255 1p. Dismounted trooper, Hussars de la Muerte, 1705 . . . . 10 15
2256 2p. Officer, Royal Regiment of Artillery, 1710 . . . . 35 20
2257 3p. Drummer and fifer, Granada Regiment, 1734 35 15
2258 7p. Guidon-bearer, Numancia Dragoons, 1737 . . . . 30 20
2259 8p. Ensign with standard, Zamora Regiment, 1739 15 20

465 Swimmer making Rescue

1974. 18th World Life-saving Championships. Barcelona.
2260 **465** 2p. multicoloured . . . 10 15

1974. Stamp Day and Eduardo Rosales. Commemoration. Various paintings as T **409**. Multicoloured.
2261 1p. "Tobias and the Angel" 10 15
2262 2p. Self-portrait 15 20
2263 3p. "Testament of Isabella the Catholic" (horiz) . . . 10 20
2264 4p. "Nena" 10 15
2265 5p. "Presentation of Don Juan of Austria" (horiz) 15 10
2266 7p. "The First Steps" (horiz) 10 10
2267 10p. "St. John the Evangelist" 25 15
2268 15p. "St. Matthew the Evangelist" 15 25

466 Figure with Letter and Posthorns

1974. Centenary of U.P.U. Multicoloured.
2269 2p. Type **466** 10 15
2270 8p. U.P.U. Monument, Berne 10 10

467 Sobremonte's House, Cordoba

1974. "Spain in the New World" (3rd series). Argentina. Multicoloured.
2271 1p. Type **467** 10 10
2272 2p. Town Hall, Buenos Aires (1929) 30 10
2273 5p. Ruins of St. Ignacio de Mini (vert) 25 20
2274 10p. "The Gaucho" (M. Fierro) (vert) 20 20

468 "Nativity" (detail, Valdavia Church)

1974. Christmas. Church Fonts. Multicoloured.
2275 2p. Type **468** 10 10
2276 3p. "Adoration of the Kings", Valcobero Church (vert) 10 10
2277 8p. As No. 2276 . . . . . 10 10

469 "Teucrium lanigerum"

471 Spanish 6c. and 5p. Stamps of 1850 and 1975

470 Leyre Monastery

1974. Spanish Flora (3rd series). Multicoloured.
2278 1p. Type **469** 10 15
2279 2p. "Hypericum ericoides" 15 15
2280 4p. "Thymus longiflorus"
2281 5p. "Anthyllis onobrychioides" 20 20
2282 8p. "Helianthemum paniculatum" 15 15
The 1p. and 8p. are wrongly inscribed "Teucriun" and "Helianthemun" respectively.

1974. Leyre Monastery.
2283 **470** 2p. grey and green . . . 40 10
2284 – 8p. red and brown . . . 15 15
2285 – 15p. deep green and green 25 10
DESIGNS—VERT: 8p. Pillars and bas-relief. HORIZ: 15p. Crypt.

1975. 125th Anniv of Spanish Postage Stamps.
2286 **471** 2p. blue 25 40
2287 – 3p. brown and green . . 40 55
2288 – 8p. mauve and violet . . 1·00 40
2289 – 10p. green and purple . . 45 50
DESIGNS—HORIZ: 3p. Mail coach, 1850; 8p. Sail packet of West Indian service. VERT: 10p. St. Mark's Chapel.

1975. Spanish Military Uniforms (4th series). As T **448**. Multicoloured.
2290 1p. Toledo Regiment, 1750 15 15
2291 2p. Royal Corps of Artillery, 1762 . . . . 15 25
2292 3p. Queen's Regt of the Line, 1763 . . . . 1·60 20
2293 5p. Vitoria Regt of Fusiliers, 1766 . . . . 40 20
2294 10p. Dragoon of Sagunto Regt, 1775 . . . . 1·40 20

1975. Spanish Architects (2nd series). As T **443**.
2295 8p. olive and green 10 10
2296 10p. brown and red 35 10
2297 15p. black and brown . . . 15 10
ARCHITECTS: 8p. Antonio Gaudi and apartment building; 10p. Antonio Palacios and palace; 15p. Secundino Zuazo and block of flats.

473 Almonds

1975. Spanish Flora (4th series). Multicoloured.
2299 1p. Type **473** 10 15
2300 2p. Pomegranates (vert) . . 20 20
2301 3p. Oranges (vert) 20 15
2302 4p. Chestnuts (vert) 10 15
2303 5p. Apples (vert) 10 15

474 Woman and Pitcher, La Aranya

475 Early Leon Postmark

1975. Europa. Primitive Cave Paintings.
2304 **474** 3p. red, brown and stone 20 15
2305 – 12p. mauve, black & brn 25 20
DESIGN—HORIZ: 12p. Horse, Tito Bustillo.

1975. World Stamp Day.
2306 **475** 3p. multicoloured . . . 10 10

476 Emblem and Inscription

1975. 1st General Assembly of World Tourism Organization, Madrid.
2307 **476** 3p. blue 10 15

477 Farm Scene

1975. 25th Anniv of "Feria del Campo".
2308 **477** 3p. multicoloured . . . 10 10

478 Heads of Different Races

1975. International Women's Year.
2309 **478** 3p. multicoloured . . . 10 15

479 Virgin of Cabeza Sanctuary and Forces Emblems

1975. Defence of Virgin of Cabeza Sanctuary during Civil War Commemoration.
2310 **479** 3p. multicoloured . . . 10 15

1975. Tourist Series. As T **340**.
2311 1p. lilac and purple 10 10
2312 2p. deep brown and brown 10 15
2313 3p. black and blue 10 15
2314 4p. mauve and orange . . . 10 10
2315 5p. black and blue 15 15
2316 7p. indigo and blue 30 20
DESIGNS—HORIZ: 1p. Cervantes' cell, Argamasilla de Alba; 2p. St. Martin's Bridge, Toledo; 3p. St. Peter's Church, Tarrasa. VERT: 4p. Alhambra archway, Granada; 5p. Mijas village, Malaga; 7p. St. Mary's Chapel, Tarrasa.

480 Salamander Lizard

1975. Spanish Fauna (5th series). Reptiles and Amphibians. Multicoloured.
2317 1p. Type **480** 10 10
2318 2p. Triton lizard 20 15
2319 3p. Tree-frog 20 15
2320 6p. Toad 10 15
2321 7p. Frog 15 20

1975. Spanish Military Uniforms (5th series). As T **448**. Multicoloured.
2322 1p. Montesa Regt. 1788 . . 10 15
2323 2p. Asturias Regt of Fusiliers, 1789 . . . . . 40 20
2324 3p. Infantry of the Line, 1802 . . . . 15 15
2325 4p. Royal Corps of Artillery, 1803 . . . . . 10 20
2326 7p. Royal Engineers Regt, 1809 . . . . 15 20

481 Child

1975. Child Welfare.
2327 **481** 3p. multicoloured . . . 10 15

482 Scroll

1975. Latin Notaries' Congress, Barcelona.
2328 **482** 3p. multicoloured . . . 10 15

483 "Blessing the Birds"

1975. Stamp Day and Millenary of Gerona Cathedral. Beatitude Miniatures. Multicoloured.
2329 1p. Type **483** 10 15
2330 2p. "Angel and River of Life" (vert) 15 15
2331 3p. "Angel at Gates of Paradise" (vert) 15 10
2332 4p. "Fox seizing Cockerel" 10 10
2333 6p. "Daniel with the Lions" 10 10
2334 7p. "Blessing the Multitude" (vert) 20 20
2335 10p. "The Four Horsemen of the Apocalypse" (vert) 15 15
2336 12p. "Peacock and Snake" (vert) 15 15

484 Industry Emblems

1975. Spanish Industry.
2337 **484** 3p. violet and purple . . 10 15

485 El Cabildo, Montevideo

1975. "Spain in the New World" (4th series). 150th Anniv of Uruguayan Independence. Multicoloured.
2338 1p. Type **485** 10 10
2339 2p. Ox wagon 15 15
2340 3p. Fortress, St. Teresa . . 20 15
2341 8p. Cathedral, Montevideo (vert) 10 15

486 San Juan de la Pena Monastery

1975. San Juan de la Pena Monastery Commem.
2342 **486** 3p. brown and green . . 25 10
2343 – 8p. violet and mauve . . 10 15
2344 – 10p. red and mauve . . 20 15
DESIGNS—HORIZ: 8p. Cloisters. VERT: 10p. Pillars.

487 "Virgin and Child"

1975. Christmas. Navarra Art. Multicoloured.
2345 3p. Type **487** 10 10
2346 12p. "The Flight into Egypt" (horiz) 10 10

488 King Juan Carlos I

489 Virgin of Pontevedra

1975. Proclamation of King Juan Carlos I. Multicoloured.
2347 3p. Type **488** 10 10
2348 3p. Queen Sophia 10 10
2349 3p. King Juan Carlos and Queen Sophia (33 × 33 mm) 10 15
2350 12p. As No. 2349 . . . . . 10 15

1975. Holy Year of Compostela.
2351 **489** 3p. brown and orange 10 15

490 Mountain Scene and Emblems

491 Cosme Damian Churruca and "San Juan Nepomucendo"

1976. Centenary of Catalunya Excursion Centre.
2352 **490** 6p. multicoloured . . . 10 10

1976. Spanish Navigators.
2353 **491** 7p. black and brown . . 1·60 20
2354 – 12p. violet 20 15
2355 – 50p. brown and green . . 65 10
NAVIGATORS—VERT: 12p. Luis de Requesens. HORIZ: 50p. Juan Sebastian del Cano and "Vitoria".

492 Alexander Graham Bell and Telephone Equipment

1976. Telephone Centenary.
2356 **492** 3p. multicoloured . . . 10 15

493 Crossing the Road

1976. Road Safety. Multicoloured.
2357 1p. Type **493** 10 10
2358 3p. Dangerous driving (vert) 25 15
2359 5p. Wearing of seat-belts . . 15 15

494 St. George on Horseback

1976. 700th Anniv of St. George's Guardianship of Alcoy.
2360 **494** 3p. multicoloured . . . 10 15

495 Talavera Pottery

1976. Europa. Spanish Handicrafts. Multicoloured.
2361 3p. Type **495** 60 15
2362 12p. Camarinas lace-making 85 30

496 Spanish 1851 6r. Stamp with Coruna Postmark

1976. World Stamp Day.
2363 **496** 3p. red, blue and black 10 15

497 Coins

1976. Bimillenary of Zaragoza. Roman Antiquities.
2364 **497** 3p. brown and black . . 2·00 15
2365 – 7p. blue and black . . . 95 30
2366 – 25p. brown and black . . 45 10
DESIGNS—HORIZ: 7p. Plan of site and coin. VERT: 25p. Mosaic.

498 Rifle, 1757

1976. Bicentenary of American Revolution.
2367 **498** 1p. blue and brown 10 15
2368 – 3p. brown and green . . 90 15
2369 – 5p. green and brown . . 35 15
2370 – 12p. brown and green . . 35 25
DESIGNS: 3p. Bernado de Galvez and emblem; 5p. Richmond $1 banknote of 1861; 12p. Battle of Pensacola.

499 Customs-house, Cadiz

1976. Spanish Customs Buildings.
2371 **499** 1p. brown and black . . 15 10
2372 – 3p. brown and green . . 50 10
2373 – 7p. purple and brown . . 1·10 30
BUILDINGS: 3p. Madrid; 7p. Barcelona.

500 Savings Jar and "Industry"

1976. Spanish Post Office. Multicoloured.

2374		1p. Type **500**	10	10
2375		3p. Railway mail-sorting van	30	10
2376		6p. Mounted postman (horiz)	10	15
2377		10p. Automatic letter sorting equipment (horiz)	20	20

501 King Juan Carlos I, Queen Sophia and Map of the Americas

1976. Royal Visit to America (1st issue).

2378	**501**	12p. multicoloured	20	15

See also No. 2434.

1976. Tourist Series. As T **340**.

2379		1p. brown and blue	10	15
2380		2p. green and blue	60	15
2381		3p. chocolate and brown	40	10
2382		4p. blue and brown	20	15
2383		7p. brown and blue	75	40
2384		12p. purple and red	1·20	20

DESIGNS—HORIZ: 1p. Cloisters, San Marcos, Leon; 2p. Las Canadas, Tenerife; 4p. Cruz de Tejeda, Las Palmas; 7p. Gredos, Avila; 12p. La Arruzafa, Cordoba. VERT: 3p. Hospice of the Catholic Kings, Santiago de Compostela.

502 Rowing

1976. Olympic Games, Montreal. Multicoloured.

2385		1p. Type **502**	10	15
2386		2p. Boxing	25	20
2387		3p. Wrestling (vert)	20	15
2388		12p. Basketball (vert)	20	15

503 King Juan Carlos I

504 "Giving Blood"

1976.

2389	**503**	10c. orange	10	15
2390		25c. yellow	10	15
2391		30c. blue	10	15
2392		50c. purple	10	15
2393		1p. green	10	10
2394		1p.50 red	10	10
2395		2p. blue	10	10
2396		3p. green	10	10
2397		4p. turquoise	10	10
2398		5p. red	10	10
2399		6p. turquoise	10	10
2400		7p. olive	15	10
2401		8p. blue	15	10
2402		10p. red	15	10
2403		12p. brown	20	10
2403a		13p. brown	20	15
2403b		14p. orange	20	10
2404		15p. violet	25	10
2405		16p. brown	25	10
2405a		17p. blue	25	10
2406		19p. orange	25	10
2407		20p. red	25	10
2408		30p. green	35	10
2409		50p. red	80	15
2409a		60p. blue	70	15
2409b		75p. green	90	25
2409c		85p. grey	1·00	30
2409d	–	100p. brown	1·20	10
2409e	–	200p. green	2·30	10
2409f	–	500p. blue	5·50	60

Nos. 2409d/f are as Type **503**, but larger, 25×30 mm.

1976. Spanish Military Uniforms (6th series). As T **448**. Multicoloured.

2410		1p. Alcantara Regiment, 1815	10	15
2411		2p. Regiment of the line, 1821	70	15
2412		3p. Gala Engineers, 1825	25	15
2413		7p. Artillery Regiment, 1828	20	25
2414		25p. Light Infantry Regiment, 1830	25	15

1976. Blood Donors Publicity.

2415	**504**	3p. red and black	10	10

505 Batitales Mosaic

506 Parliament House, Madrid

1976. Bimillenary of Lugo.

2416	**505**	1p. purple and black	10	15
2417	–	3p. brown and black	15	15
2418	–	7p. red and green	40	25

DESIGNS: 3p. Old City Wall; 7p. Roman coins.

1976. 63rd Inter-Parliamentary Union Congress, Madrid.

2419	**506**	12p. brown and green	10	10

1976. Stamp Day and Luis Menendez Commemoration. Paintings as T **409**. Mult.

2420		1p. "Jug, Cherries, Plums and Cheese"	10	15
2421		2p. "Jar, Melon, Oranges and Savouries"	10	15
2422		3p. "Barrel, Pears and Melon"	10	15
2423		4p. "Pigeons, Basket and Bowl"	10	15
2424		6p. "Fish and Oranges" (horiz)	10	15
2425		7p. "Melon and Bread" (horiz)	25	25
2426		10p. "Jug, Plums and Bread" (horiz)	20	15
2427		12p. "Pomegranates, Apples and Grapes" (horiz)	25	20

507 "The Nativity"

508 Nicoya Church

1976. Christmas. Statuettes. Multicoloured.

2428		3p. Type **507**	55	10
2429		12p. St. Christopher carrying Holy Child (vert)	1·80	75

1976. "Spain in the New World" (5th series). Costa Rica. Multicoloured.

2430		1p. Type **508**	10	15
2431		2p. Juan Vazquez de Coronado	20	20
2432		3p. Orosi Mission (horiz)	10	15
2433		12p. Tomas de Acosta	20	15

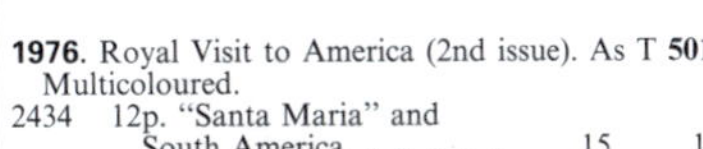

1976. Royal Visit to America (2nd issue). As T **501**. Multicoloured.

2434		12p. "Santa Maria" and South America	15	15

510 San Pedro de Alcantara Monastery

1976. Monastery of San Pedro de Alcantara.

2435	**510**	3p. brown and purple	25	15
2436	–	7p. purple and blue	10	20
2437	–	20p. chocolate and brown	25	15

DESIGNS—VERT: 7p. High Altar; 20p. San Pedro de Alcantara.

511 Hand releasing Doves

1976. Civil War Invalids' Association Commem.

2438	**511**	3p. multicoloured	10	10

512 Pablo Casals and Cello

1976. Birth Centenaries.

2439	**512**	3p. black and blue	10	15
2440	–	5p. green and red	10	15

DESIGN: 5p. Manuel de Falla and "Fire Dance".

1977. Spanish Military Uniforms (7th series). Vert designs as T **448**. Multicoloured.

2441		1p. Calatrava Regiment of Lancers, 1844	10	15
2442		2p. Engineers' Regiment, 1850	25	15
2443		3p. Light Infantry Regiment, 1861	10	15
2444		4p. Infantry of the Line, 1861	10	15
2445		20p. Horse Artillery, 1862	20	15

513 King James I and Arms of Aragon

1977. 700th Death Anniv of King James I.

2446	**513**	4p. brown and violet	10	15

514 Jacinto Verdaguer (poet)

516 Atlantic Salmon

515 King Charles III

1977. Spanish Celebrities.

2447	**514**	5p. red and purple	20	10
2448	–	7p. green and brown	15	20
2449	–	12p. green and blue	15	15
2450	–	50p. brown and green	45	15

DESIGNS: 7p. Miguel Servet (theologian and physician); 12p. Pablo Sarasate (violinist); 50p. Francisco Tarrega (guitarist).

1977. Bicentenary of Economic Society of the Friends of the Land.

2451	**515**	4p. brown and green	10	10

1977. Spanish Fauna (6th series). Freshwater Fishes. Multicoloured.

2452		1p. Type **516**	10	15
2453		2p. Brown trout (horiz)	10	15
2454		3p. European eel (horiz)	10	15
2455		4p. Common carp (horiz)	10	15
2456		6p. Barbel (horiz)	10	15

517 Skiing

1977. World Ski Championships, Granada.

2457	**517**	5p. multicoloured	10	10

518 La Cuadra, 1902

1977. Vintage Cars. Multicoloured.

2458		2p. Type **518**	10	10
2459		4p. Hispano Suiza, 1916	10	10
2460		5p. Elizade, 1915	10	15
2461		7p. Abadal, 1914	15	20

519 Donana

1977. Europa. Landscapes, National Parks. Multicoloured.

2462		3p. Type **519**	10	10
2463		12p. Ordesa	20	15

520 Plaza Mayor, Madrid and Stamps

1977. 50th Anniv of Philatelic Bourse on Plaza Mayor, Madrid.

2464	**520**	3p. green, red and violet	10	10

521 Enrique de Osso (founder)

1977. Centenary of Society of St. Theresa of Jesus.

2465	**521**	8p. multicoloured	10	10

1977. Tourist Series. As T **340**.

2466		1p. brown and orange	10	15
2467		2p. grey and brown	10	15
2468		3p. purple and blue	10	15
2469		4p. green and blue	10	15
2470		7p. grey and brown	10	15
2471		12p. brown and violet	10	10

DESIGNS—HORIZ: 1p. Toledo Gate, Ciudad Real; 2p. Roman Aqueduct, Almunecar; 7p. Ampudia Castle, Palencia; 12p. Bisagra Gate, Toledo. VERT: 3p. Jaen Cathedral; 4p. Bridge and Gate, Ronda Gorge, Malaga.

1977. Spanish Military Uniforms (8th series). As T **448**. Multicoloured.

2472		1p. Administration officer, 1875	10	15
2473		2p. Lancer, 1883	10	15
2474		3p. General Staff commander, 1884	10	15
2475		7p. Trumpeter, Divisional Artillery, 1887	15	25
2476		25p. Medical Corps officer, 1895	25	15

522 San Marino de la Cogalla (carving) and Early Castilian Manuscript

1977. Millenary of Castilian Language.
2477 **522** 5p. brown, green & pur . . . 10 10

1977. Stamp Day and F. Madrazo (painter) Commemoration. Portraits. As T **409**. Mult.
2478 1p. "The Youth of Florez" . . . 10 10
2479 2p. "Duke of San Miguel" . . . 10 15
2480 3p. "C. Coronado" 10 15
2481 4p. "Campoamor" 10 10
2482 6p. "Marquesa de Montelo" . . . 10 15
2483 7p. "Rivadeneyra" 10 15
2484 10p. "Countess of Vilches" . . . 10 15
2485 15p. "Gomez de Avellaneda" 15 15

523 West Indies Sailing Packet and Map of Mail Routes to America

1977. Bicentenary of Mail to the Indies, and "Espamer 77" Stamp Exhibition, Barcelona.
2486 **523** 15p. green and brown . . 20 25

524 St. Francis's Church

1977. Spanish–Guatemalan Relations. Guatemala City Buildings. Multicoloured.
2487 1p. Type **524** 10 15
2488 3p. High-rise flats 10 15
2489 7p. Government Palace . . 10 15
2490 12p. Monument, Columbus Square 10 15

525 Monastery Building

1977. St. Peter's Monastery, Cardena Commem.
2491 **525** 3p. grey and blue . . . 10 15
2492 – 7p. red and brown . . . 10 15
2493 – 20p. grey and green . . 20 10
DESIGNS: 7p. Cloisters; 20p. El Cid (effigy).

526 Adoration of the Kings

1977. Christmas. Miniatures from Manuscript "Romanico de Huesca". Multicoloured.
2494 5p. Type **526** 10 10
2495 12p. Flight into Egypt (vert) 10 10

527 Rohrbach Ro.VII Roland, 1927, and Douglas DC-10

1977. 50th Anniv of Iberia (State Airline).
2496 **527** 12p. multicoloured . . . 10 15

528 Crown Prince Felipe

529 Judo

1977. Felipe de Borbon, Prince of Asturias.
2497 **528** 5p. multicoloured . . . 10 10

1977. 10th World Judo Championships.
2498 **529** 3p. black, red and brown . . 10 10

1977. Spanish Military Uniforms (9th series). Multicoloured. Vert designs as T **448**.
2499 1p. Standard bearer, Royal Infantry Regiment, 1908 . . 10 15
2500 2p. Lieutenant-Colonel, Pavia Hussars', 1909 . . . 10 15
2501 3p. Lieutenant, Horse Artillery, 1912 . . . . . 10 15
2502 5p. Engineers' Captain, 1921 10 15
2503 12p. Captain-General of the Armed Forces, 1925 . . . 10 15

530 Hilarion Eslava (composer)

531 "The Deposition of Christ" (detail Juan de Juni)

1977. Spanish Celebrities.
2504 **530** 5p. black and purple . . 10 15
2505 – 8p. black and green . . 10 15
2506 – 25p. black and green . . 25 10
2507 – 50p. purple and brown . . 45 15
DESIGNS: 8p. Jose Clara (sculptor); 25p. Pio Baroja (writer); 50p. Antonio Machado (writer).

1978. Anniversaries of Artists.
2508 **531** 3p. multicoloured . . . 10 15
2509 – 3p. multicoloured . . . 10 15
2510 – 3p. mauve and violet . . 10 15
2511 – 5p. multicoloured . . . 10 15
2512 – 5p. multicoloured . . . 10 20
2513 – 5p. brown and black . . 10 15
2514 – 8p. multicoloured . . . 10 15
2515 – 8p. multicoloured . . . 10 15
2516 – 8p. pink and green . . . 10 15
DESIGNS—As T **531**. No. 2510, Portrait of Juan de Juni (sculptor, 400th death anniv); No. 2511, Detail of "Rape of the Sabines" (Rubens); No. 2513, Artist's palette and Ruben's signature; No. 2514, Detail of "Bacchanal" (Titian); No. 2516, Artist's palette and Titian's initial. 46 × 25 mm: No. 2509, Different detail of "Deposition of Christ" and sculptor's tools; No. 2512, Different detail of "Rape of the Sabines" and portrait of Rubens (400th birth anniv); No. 2515, Different detail of "Bacchanal" and portrait of Titian (500th birth anniv).

532 Edelweiss in the Pyrenees

1978. Protection of the Environment. Mult.
2517 3p. Type **532** 10 15
2518 5p. Brown trout and red-breasted merganser . . . 10 15
2519 7p. Forest (fire prevention) 10 10
2520 12p. Tanker, oil rig and industrial complex (protection of the sea) . . 10 10
2521 20p. Audouin's gull and Mediterranean monk seal (vert) 10 10

533 Palace of Charles V, Granada

1978. Europa.
2522 **533** 5p. green and light green 10 15
2523 – 12p. red and green . . . 10 15
DESIGN: 12p. Exchange building, Seville.

534 Council Emblem and Map of Spain

1978. Membership of the Council of Europe.
2524 **534** 12p. multicoloured . . . 10 10

535 Columbus Hermitage

1978. 500th Anniv of Las Palmas, Gran Canaria. Multicoloured.
2525 3p. 16th-century plan of city (horiz) 10 15
2526 5p. Type **535** 10 10
2527 12p. View of Las Palmas (16th century) (horiz) . . 10 10

536 Post Box, Stamp, U.P.U. Emblem and Postal Transport

1978. World Stamp Day.
2528 **536** 5p. green and deep green 10 10

1978. Stamp Day and Picasso Commemoration. As T **409**. Multicoloured.
2529 3p. "Portrait of Senora Canals" 10 10
2530 5p. Self-portrait 10 10
2531 8p. "Portrait of Jaime Sabartes" 10 10
2532 10p. "The End of the Number" 10 10
2533 12p. "Science and Charity" (horiz) 10 15
2534 15p. "Las Meninas" (horiz) 15 15
2535 20p. "The Pigeons" 20 15
2536 25p. "The Painter and Model" (horiz) 25 15

537 Jose de San Martin

1978. Latin-American Heroes.
2537 **537** 7p. brown and red . . . 10 10
2538 – 12p. violet and red . . . 10 10
DESIGNS: 12p. Simon Bolivar.

538 Flight into Egypt

1978. Christmas. Capitals from Santa Maria de Nieva. Multicoloured.
2539 5p. Type **538** 10 10
2540 12p. The Annunciation . . 10 10

539 Aztec Calendar

1978. Royal Visits to Mexico, Peru and Argentina. Multicoloured.
2541 5p. Type **539** 10 10
2542 5p. Macchu Piccu, Peru . . 10 10
2543 5p. Pre-Columbian pots, Argentina 10 15

540 Philip V

1978. Spanish Kings and Queens of the House of Bourbon.
2544 **540** 5p. red and blue 10 15
2545 – 5p. deep green and green 10 15
2546 – 8p. lake and blue 10 10
2547 – 10p. black and green . . 10 10
2548 – 12p. lake and brown . . 10 10
2549 – 15p. blue and green . . 15 15
2550 – 20p. blue and olive . . . 20 15
2551 – 25p. violet and blue . . 25 15
2552 – 50p. brown and red . . 45 20
2553 – 100p. violet and blue . . 90 55
DESIGNS: 5p. (No. 2545), Luis I; 8p. Ferdinand VI; 10p. Charles III; 12p. Charles IV; 15p. Ferdinand VII; 20p. Isabel II; 25p. Alfonso XII; 50p. Alfonso XIII; 100p. Juan Carlos I.

541 Miniatures from Bible

1978. Millenary of Consecration of Third Basilica of Santa Maria, Ripoll.
2554 **541** 5p. multicoloured . . . 10 15

542 Flag, First Lines of Constitution and Cortes Building

1978. New Constitution.
2555 **542** 5p. multicoloured . . . 10 10

543 Car and Oil Drop

545 Jorge Manrique (poet)

544 St. Jean Baptiste de la Salle (founder)

1979. Energy Conservation. Multicoloured.
2556 5p. Type **543** 10 15
2557 8p. Insulated house and thermometer 10 15
2558 10p. Hand removing electric plug 10 15

1979. Centenary of Brothers of the Christian Schools in Spain.
2559 **544** 5p. brown, blue & mauve 10 15

1979. Spanish Celebrities.
2560 **545** 5p. brown and green . . 10 15
2561 – 8p. blue and red 10 15
2562 – 10p. violet and brown . . 10 15
2563 – 20p. green and bistre . . 20 15
DESIGNS: 8p. Fernan Caballero (novelist); 10p. Francisco Villaespesa (poet); 20p. Gregorio Maranon (writer).

546 Running and Jumping

1979. Sport for All.
2564 **546** 5p. red, green and black . . . 10 15
2565 – 8p. blue, ochre and black . . . 10 15
2566 – 10p. brown, blue & black 10 15
DESIGNS: 8p. Football, running, skipping and cycling; 10p. Running.

547 School Library (child's drawing)

1979. International Year of the Child.
2567 **547** 5p. multicoloured . . . 10 15

548 Cabinet Messenger and Postilion, 1761 **549** Wave Pattern and Television Screen

1979. Europa.
2568 **548** 5p. deep brown and brown on yellow . . . 10 15
2569 – 12p. green and brown on yellow 10 15
DESIGN—HORIZ: 12p. Manuel de Ysasi (postal reformer).

1979. World Telecommunications Day. Mult.
2570 5p. Type **549** 10 15
2571 8p. Satellite and receiving aerial (horiz) 10 15

550 First Bulgarian Stamp and Exhibition Hall

1979. "Philaserdica 79" Stamp Exhibition, Sofia.
2572 **550** 12p. multicoloured . . . 10 15

551 Tank, "Roger de Lauria" (destroyer) and Hawker Siddeley Matador Jet Fighter

1979. Armed Forces Day.
2573 **551** 5p. multicoloured . . . 10 15

552 King receiving Messenger

1979. Stamp Day.
2574 **552** 5p. multicoloured . . . 10 15

1979. Tourist Series. As T **340**.
2575 5p. lilac and blue 10 15
2576 8p. brown and blue 10 15
2577 10p. green and myrtle . . . 10 15
2578 20p. sepia and brown . . . 20 15
DESIGNS—VERT: 5p. Daroca Gate, Zaragoza; 8p. Gerona Cathedral; 10p. Interior of Carthusian Monastery Church, Granada; 20p. Portal of Marques de Dos Aguas Palace, Valencia.

553 Turkey Sponge

1979. Spanish Fauna (7th series). Invertebrates. Multicoloured.
2579 5p. Type **553** 10 15
2580 7p. Crayfish 10 15
2581 8p. Scorpion 10 15
2582 20p. Starfish 20 15
2583 25p. Sea anemone 25 15

554 Antonio Gutierrez

1979. Defence of Tenerife, 1797.
2584 **554** 5p. multicoloured . . . 10 15

1979. Stamp Day and J. de Juanes (painter) Commemoration. Religious Paintings as T **409**. Multicoloured.
2585 8p. "Immaculate Conception" 10 15
2586 10p. "Holy Family" 10 15
2587 15p. "Ecce Homo" 15 15
2588 20p. "St. Stephen in the Synagogue" 20 15
2589 25p. "The Last Supper" (horiz) 25 15
2590 50p. "Adoration of the Mystic Lamb" (horiz) . . 45 15

555 Cathedral and Statue of Virgin and Child, Zaragoza

1979. 8th Mariological Congress, Zaragoza.
2591 **555** 5p. multicoloured . . . 10 15

556 St. Bartholomew's College, Bogota

1979. Latin-American Architecture.
2592 **556** 7p. green, blue and brown 10 15
2593 – 12p. indigo, purple & brn 10 15
DESIGN: 12p. University of San Marcos, Lima.

557 Hands and Governor's Palace, Barcelona

1979. Catalonian Autonomy.
2594 **557** 8p. multicoloured . . . 10 15

558 Autonomy Statute

1979. Basque Autonomy.
2595 **558** 8p. multicoloured . . . 10 15

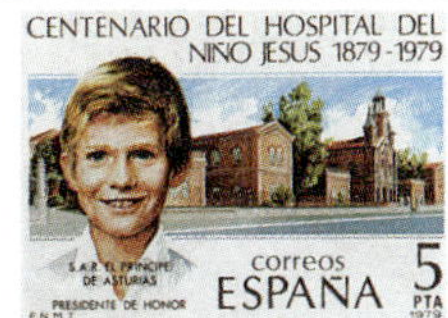

559 Prince of Asturias and Hospital

1979. Centenary of Hospital of the Child Jesus, Madrid.
2596 **559** 5p. multicoloured . . . 10 15

560 Barcelona Tax Stamp, 1929

1979. 50th Anniv of Barcelona Exhibition Tax Stamps.
2597 **560** 5p. multicoloured . . . 10 15

561 The Nativity

1979. Christmas. Capitals from San Pedro el Viejo, Huesca. Multicoloured.
2598 8p. Type **561** 10 15
2599 19p. Flight into Egypt . . . 10 15

562 Charles I

1979. Spanish Kings of the House of Hapsburg.
2600 **562** 15p. green and blue . . 15 15
2601 – 20p. blue and mauve . . 20 15
2602 – 25p. violet and brown . 25 15
2603 – 50p. brown and green . . 45 30
2604 – 100p. mauve and brown . 90 40
DESIGNS: 20p. Philip II; 25p. Philip III; 50p. Philip IV; 100p. Charles II.

563 Olive Plantation and Harvester

1979. International Olive Oil Year.
2605 **563** 8p. multicoloured . . . 10 15

564 Electric Train

1980. Public Transport.
2606 **564** 3p. lake and brown . . . 10 15
2607 – 4p. blue and brown . . . 10 15
2608 – 5p. green and brown . . 10 15
DESIGNS: 4p. Motorbus; 5p. Underground train.

565 Steel Products

1980. Spanish Exports (1st series). Multicoloured.
2609 5p. Type **565** 10 15
2610 8p. Tankers 10 15
2611 13p. Footwear 15 15
2612 19p. Industrial machinery 20 15
2613 25p. Factory buildings, bridge and symbols of technology 25 30
See also Nos. 2653/5.

566 Federico Garcia Lorca

1980. Europa. Writers.
2614 **566** 8p. violet and green . . 10 15
2615 – 19p. brown and green . . 20 15
DESIGN: 19p. J. Ortega y Gasset.

567 Footballers

1980. World Cup Football Championship, Spain (1982) (1st issue). Multicoloured.
2616 8p. Type **567** 20 15
2617 19p. Football and flags . . 10 15
See also Nos. 2640/1, 2668/9 and 2683/4.

568 Armed Forces

1980. Armed Forces Day.
2618 **568** 8p. multicoloured . . . 10 15

569 Bourbon Arms, Ministry of Finance, Madrid

1980. Public Finances under the Bourbons.
2619 **569** 8p. deep brown & brown 10 15

570 Helen Keller

1980. Birth Centenary of Helen Keller.
2620 **570** 19p. red and green . . . 20 15

572 King Alfonso XIII and Count of Maceda at Exhibition

571 Postal Courier (14th century)

1980. Stamp Day.
2621 **571** 8p. brown, stone and red 10 15

1980. 50th Anniv of First National Stamp Exhibition.
2622 **572** 8p. multicoloured . . . 1·60 65

573 Altar of the Virgin, La Palma Cathedral
574 Ramon Perez de Ayala

1980. 300th Anniv of Appearance of the Holy Virgin at La Palma.
2623 **573** 8p. brown and black . . 10 15

1980. Birth Centenary of Ramon Perez de Ayala (writer).
2624 **574** 100p. green and brown 90 30

576 Juan de Garay and Founding of Buenos Aires (after Moreno Carbonero)

1980. 400th Anniv of Buenos Aires.
2626 **576** 19p. blue, green and red 20 15

578 Palace of Congresses, Madrid
579 "Nativity" (mural from Church of Santa Maria de Cuina, Oza de los Rios)

1980. European Security and Co-operation Conference, Madrid.
2628 **578** 22p. multicoloured . . . 20 15

1980. Christmas. Multicoloured.
2629 10p. Type **579** 10 15
2630 22p. "Adoration of the Kings" (doorway of Church of St. Nicholas of Cines, Oza de los Rios) (horiz) 20 15

580 Pedro Vives and Farman H.F.III Biplane

1980. Aviation Pioneers. Multicoloured.
2631 5p. Type **580** 10 15
2632 10p. Benito Loygorri and Farman H.F.20 type biplane 10 15
2633 15p. Alfonso de Orleans and Caudron G-3 . . . . . . 15 15
2634 22p. Alfredo Kindelan and biplane 20 20

581 Games Emblem and Skier

1981. Winter University Games.
2635 **581** 30p. multicoloured . . . 25 15

582 "Homage to Picasso" (Joan Miro)

1981. Birth Centenary of Pablo Picasso (artist).
2636 **582** 100p. multicoloured . . 90 20

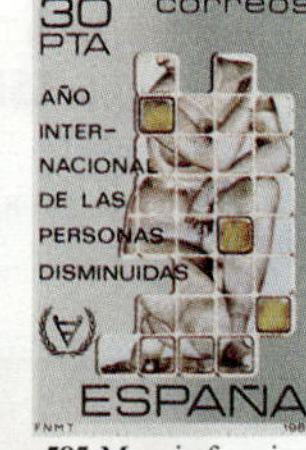

583 Newspaper, Camera, Notepaper and Pen

1981. The Press.
2637 **583** 12p. multicoloured . . . 10 15

584 Map of Galicia, Arms and National Anthem
585 Mosaic forming Human Figure

1981. Galician Autonomy.
2638 **584** 12p. multicoloured . . . 10 15

1981. International Year of Disabled Persons.
2639 **585** 30p. multicoloured . . . 25 15

586 Heading Ball
588 King Juan Carlos reviewing Army

587 La Jota (folk dance)

1981. World Cup Football Championship (1982) (2nd issue). Multicoloured.
2640 12p. Type **586** 10 15
2641 30p. Kicking ball (horiz) . . 25 15

1981. Europa.
2642 **587** 12p. black and brown . . 10 15
2643 – 30p. deep lilac and lilac 25 15
DESIGN: 30p. Procession of the Virgin of Rocio.

1981. Armed Forces Day.
2644 **588** 12p. multicoloured . . . 10 15

589 Gabriel Miro (writer)
590 Messenger (14th-century woodcut)

1981. Spanish Celebrities.
2645 **589** 6p. violet and green . . 10 15
2646 – 12p. brown and violet 10 15
2647 – 30p. green and brown . . 25 15
DESIGNS: 12p. Francisco de Quevedo (writer); 30p. St. Benedict.

1981. Stamp Day.
2648 **590** 12p. pink, brown & green 10 15

591 Map of the Balearic Islands (from Atlas of Diego Homem, 1563)

1981. Spanish Islands. Multicoloured.
2649 7p. Type **591** 10 15
2650 12p. Map of the Canary Islands (from map of Mateo Prunes, 1563) . . . 10 15

592 Alfonso XII, Juan Carlos and Arms

1981. Century of Public Prosecutor's Office.
2651 **592** 50p. brown, green & blue 25 15

593 King Sancho VI of Navarre with Foundation Charter

1981. 800th Anniv of Vitoria.
2652 **593** 12p. multicoloured . . . 10 15

594 Citrus Fruit

1981. Spanish Exports (2nd series). Multicoloured.
2653 6p. Type **594** 10 15
2654 12p. Wine 10 15
2655 30p. CASA C-212 Aviocar airplane, car and lorry . . 25 15

595 Foodstuffs

1981. World Food Day.
2656 **595** 30p. multicoloured . . . 25 15

597 Congress Palace, Buenos Aires

1981. "Espamer 81" International Stamp Exhibition, Buenos Aires.
2658 **597** 12p. red and blue . . . 10 15

598 "Adoration of the Kings" (from Cervera de Pisuerga)

1981. Christmas. Multicoloured.
2659 12p. Type **598** 10 15
2660 30p. "Nativity" (from Paredes de Nava) 25 15

599 Plaza de Espana, Seville

1981. Air.
2661 **599** 13p. green and blue . . 15 15
2662 – 20p. blue and brown . . 15 15
DESIGN: 20p. Rande Bridge, Ria de Vigo.

600 Telegraph Operator

1981. Postal and Telecommunications Museum, Madrid.
2663 **600** 7p. green and brown . . 10 20
2664 – 12p. brown and violet 10 20
DESIGN: 12p. Post wagon.

601 Royal Mint, Seville

1981. Financial Administration by the Bourbons in Spain and the Indies.
2666 **601** 12p. brown and grey . . 10 15

602 Iparraguirre
603 Publicity Poster by Joan Miro

1981. Death Centenary of Jose Maria Iparraguirre.
2667 **602** 12p. blue and black . . 10 15

1982. World Cup Football Championship, Spain (3rd issue). Multicoloured.
2668 14p. Type **603** 15 15
2669 33p. World Cup trophy and championship emblem . . 30 15

604 Andres Bello (author and philosopher) (birth bicent)
605 St. James of Compostela (Codex illustration)

1982. Anniversaries (1981).
2670 **604** 30p. deep green and green 25 15
2671 – 30p. green and blue . . 25 15
2672 – 50p. violet and black . . 45 15

DESIGNS: No. 2671, J. R. Jimenez (author, birth centenary); 2672, P. Calderon (playwright, 300th death anniv).

1982. Holy Year of Compostela.
2673 **605** 14p. multicoloured . . . 15 15

606 Manuel Fernandez Caballero

608 Swords, Arms and Flag

607 Arms, Seals and Signatures (Unification of Spain, 1479)

1982. Masters of Operetta (1st series). As T **606** (2674, 2676, 2678) or T **625** (others). Multicoloured.
2674 3p. Type **606** 10 15
2675 3p. Scene from "Gigantes y Cabezudos" (horiz) . . . 10 15
2676 6p. Amadeo Vives Roig . . 10 15
2677 6p. Scene from "Maruxa" (horiz) 10 15
2678 8p. Tomas Breton y Hernandez 10 15
2679 8p. Scene from "La Verbena de la Paloma" (horiz) . . 10 15
See also Nos. 2713/8 and 2772/7.

1982. Europa. Multicoloured.
2680 14p. Type **607** 15 15
2681 33p. Symbolic ship, Columbus map of "La Spanola" and signature (Discovery of America) 30 15

1982. Armed Forces Day and Centenary of General Military Academy.
2682 **608** 14p. multicoloured . . . 15 15

609 Tackling

1982. World Cup Football Championship, Spain (4th issue). Multicoloured.
2683 14p. Type **609** 15 20
2684 33p. Goal 30 30

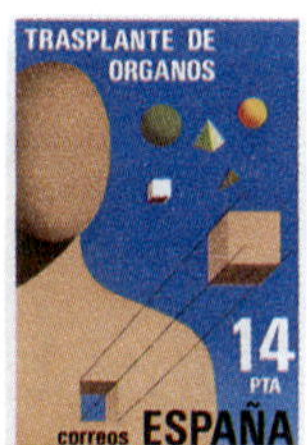

610 "St. Andrew and St. Francis"

612 "Transplants"

611 Map of Tenerife and Letter

1982. Air. Paintings by El Greco. Multicoloured.
2686 13p. Type **610** 15 15
2687 20p. "St. Thomas" 20 15

1982. Stamp Day.
2688 **611** 14p. multicoloured . . . 15 15

1982. Organ Transplants.
2689 **612** 14p. multicoloured . . . 15 15

613 White Storks and Diesel Locomotive

1982. 23rd International Railway Congress, Malaga. Multicoloured.
2690 9p. Type **613** 10 15
2691 14p. Steam locomotive "Antigua" (37 × 26 mm) 15 15
2692 33p. Steam locomotive "Montana" (wrongly inscr "Santa Fe") (37 × 26 mm) 30 15

614 La Fortaleza, San Juan

1982. "Espamer 82" Stamp Exhibition, San Juan, Puerto Rico.
2693 **614** 33p. blue and lilac . . . 30 15

615 St. Theresa of Avila (sculpture by Gregorio Hernandez)

1982. 400th Death Anniv of St. Theresa of Avila.
2694 **615** 33p. brown, blue and green 30 15

616 Pope John Paul II

1982. Papal Visit.
2695 **616** 14p. blue and brown . . 15 15

1982. Tourist Series. As T **340**.
2696 4p. blue and grey 10 15
2697 6p. grey and blue 10 15
2698 9p. lilac and blue 10 15
2699 14p. lilac and blue 15 15
2700 33p. brown and red 30 15
DESIGNS—VERT: 4p. Arab water-wheel, Alcantarilla; 9p. Dying Christ, Seville; 14p. St. Martin's Tower, Teruel; 33p. St. Andrew's Gate, Villalpando. HORIZ: 6p. Bank of Spain, Madrid.

617 "Adoration of The Kings" (sculpture, Covarrubias Collegiate Church)

1982. Christmas. Multicoloured.
2701 14p. Type **617** 15 15
2702 33p. "The Flight into Egypt" (painting) 30 15

618 "The Prophet"

619 St. John Bosco (founder) and Children

1982. Birth Centenary of Pablo Gargallo (sculptor).
2703 **618** 14p. green and blue . . 15 15

1982. Centenary of Salesian Schools in Spain.
2704 **619** 14p. multicoloured . . . 15 15

620 Arms of Spain

1983.
2705 **620** 14p. multicoloured . . . 15 15

621 Sunrise over Andalusia

1983. Andalusian Autonomy.
2706 **621** 14p. multicoloured . . . 20 15

622 Arms of Cantabria, Mountains and Monuments

1983. Cantabrian Autonomy.
2707 **622** 14p. multicoloured . . . 15 15

623 National Police

1983. State Security Forces. Multicoloured.
2708 9p. Type **623** 10 15
2709 14p. Civil Guard 15 15
2710 33p. Superior Police Corps 30 20

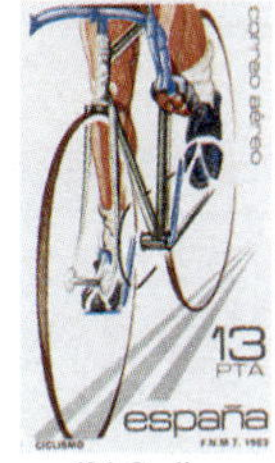

624 Cycling

1983. Air. Sports. Multicoloured.
2711 13p. Type **624** 15 15
2712 20p. Bowling (horiz) 20 15

625 Scene from "La Parranda"

1983. Masters of Operetta (2nd series). As T **625** (2714, 2716, 2718) or T **606** (others). Multicoloured.
2713 4p. Francisco Alonso (vert) 10 15
2714 4p. Type **625** 10 15
2715 6p. Jacinto Guerrero (vert) 10 15
2716 6p. Scene from "La Rosa del Azafran" 10 15
2717 9p. Jesus Guridi (vert) . . . 15 15
2718 9p. Scene from "El Caserio" 15 15

626 Cervantes and Scene from "Don Quixote"

1983. Europa.
2719 **626** 16p. red and green . . . 15 15
2720 – 38p. sepia and brown . . 40 25
DESIGN: 38p. Torres Quevedo and Niagara cable-car.

LAS COMUNICACIONES
AÑO MUNDIAL DE
38 PTA
correos
ESPAÑA

627 Francisco Salzillo (artist)

628 W.C.Y. Emblem

1983. Spanish Celebrities.
2721 **627** 16p. purple and green . . 15 15
2722 – 38p. blue and brown . . 40 15
2723 – 50p. blue and brown . . 45 15
2724 – 100p. brown and violet 90 25
DESIGNS: 38p. Antonio Soler (composer); 50p. Joaquin Turina (composer); 100p. St. Isidro Labrador (patron saint of Madrid).

1983. World Communications Year.
2725 **628** 38p. multicoloured . . . 40 15

629 Leaves

1983. Riojan Autonomy.
2726 **629** 16p. multicoloured . . . 10 15

DIA DE LAS FUERZAS ARMADAS
16 PTA
ESPAÑA correos

630 Army Monument, Burgos

1983. Armed Forces Day.
2727 **630** 16p. multicoloured . . . 15 15

631 Burgos Setter

1983. Spanish Dogs.
2728 **631** 10p. blue, brown and red 10 15
2729 – 16p. multicoloured . . . 15 15
2730 – 26p. multicoloured . . . 30 30
2731 – 38p. multicoloured . . . 40 15
DESIGNS: 16p. Spanish mastiff; 26p. Ibiza spaniel; 38p. Navarrese basset.

632 Juan-Jose and Fausto Elhuyar y de Suvisa

1983. Anniversaries. Multicoloured.
2732 16p. Type **632** (bicentenary of discovery of wolfram) . . . 15 15
2733 38p. Scout camp (75th anniv of Boy Scout Movement) 40 20
2734 50p. University of Zaragoza (400th anniv) 50 15

633 Arms of Murcia

1983. Murcian Autonomy.
2735 **633** 16p. multicoloured . . . 20 15

634 Covadonga Basilica and Victory Cross

1983. Autonomy of Asturias.
2736 **634** 14p. multicoloured . . . 20 15

635 National Statistical Institute, Madrid

1983. 44th International Institute of Statistics Congress.
2737 **635** 38p. multicoloured . . . 40 15

636 Roman Horse-drawn Mail Cart

1983. Stamp Day.
2738 **636** 16p. pink and brown . . 25 40

637 Palace and Arms of Valencia

1983. Valencian Autonomy.
2739 **637** 16p. multicoloured . . . 20 15

638 Seville (Illustration from "Floods of Guadalquivir" by Francisco Palomo)

1983. America–Spain.
2740 **638** 38p. violet and blue . . 40 20

639 "Biblical King" (Leon Cathedral)

1983. Stained Glass Windows. Multicoloured.
2741 10p. Type **639** 10 15
2742 16p. "Epiphany" and Gerona Cathedral 20 15
2743 38p. "St. James" and Santiago de Compostela Hospital 40 15

1983. Tourist Series. As T **340**.
2744 3p. blue and green 10 15
2745 6p. indigo 10 15
2746 16p. violet and red 15 15
2747 38p. red and brown 40 25
2748 50p. red and brown 45 20
DESIGNS: 3p. Church and tower, Llivia, Gerona; 6p. Santa Maria del Mar, Barcelona; 16p. Ceuta Cathedral; 38p. Bridge gateway, Melilla; 50p. Charity Hospital, Seville.

640 "Nativity" (altarpiece, Tortosa) 641 Indalecio Prieto

1983. Christmas. Multicoloured.
2749 16p. Type **640** 15 15
2750 38p. "Adoration of the Kings" (altarpiece, Vich) 40 30

1983. Birth Centenary of Indalecio Prieto (politician).
2751 **641** 16p. brown and black . . 15 15

642 Worker falling from Scaffolding

1984. Safety at Work. Multicoloured.
2752 7p. Type **642** 10 15
2753 10p. Burning factory and extinguisher 10 15
2754 16p. Electric plug and wiring, cutters, gloved hands and warning sign 15 15

643 Tree

1984. Extremaduran Autonomy.
2755 **643** 16p. multicoloured . . . 20 15

644 Burgos Cathedral and Coat of Arms

1984. 1500th Anniv of Burgos City.
2756 **644** 16p. brown and blue . . 15 15

645 Carnival Dancer, Santa Cruz, Tenerife

1984. Festivals. Multicoloured.
2757 16p. Type **645** 20 15
2758 16p. Carnival figure and fireworks, Valencia . . . 20 15

646 "Man" (Leonardo da Vinci)

1984. Man and Biosphere.
2759 **646** 38p. multicoloured . . . 40 25

647 Map and Flag of Aragon and "Justice"

1984. Aragon Autonomy.
2760 **647** 16p. multicoloured . . . 20 15

649 F.I.P. Emblem

1984. 53rd International Philatelic Federation Congress, Madrid.
2762 **649** 38p. red and violet . . . 40 20

650 Bridge

1984. Europa.
2763 **650** 16p. red 15 15
2764 38p. blue 40 30

651 Monument to the Alcantara Cazadores Regiment, Valladolid (Mariano Benlliure)

1984. Armed Forces Day.
2765 **651** 17p. multicoloured . . . 15 15

652 Arms of Canary Islands

1984. Autonomy of Canary Islands.
2766 **652** 16p. multicoloured . . . 20 15

653 Arms of Castilla-La Mancha 655 "James III confirming Grants"

654 King Alfonso X, the Wise, of Castile and Leon (700th death anniv)

1984. Autonomy of Castilla-La Mancha.
2767 **653** 17p. multicoloured . . . 20 15

1984. Anniversaries.
2768 **654** 16p. red, blue and black 20 15
2769 – 38p. blue, red and black 40 25
DESIGN: 38p. Ignacio Barraquer (opthalmologist, birth centenary).

1984. Autonomy of Balearic Islands.
2770 **655** 17p. multicoloured . . . 20 15

656 Running before Bulls

1984. Pamplona Festival, San Fermin.
2771 **656** 17p. multicoloured . . . 20 15

1984. Masters of Operetta (3rd series). Horiz designs as T **625** (2772, 2775/6) or vert designs as T **606** (others). Multicoloured.
2772 6p. Scene from "El Nino Judio" 10 15
2773 6p. Pablo Luna 10 15
2774 7p. Ruperto Chapi 10 15
2775 7p. Scene from "La Revoltosa" 10 15
2776 10p. Scene from "La Reina Mora" 10 15
2777 10p. Jose Serrano 10 15

657 Bronze of Swimmer ready to Dive

1984. Olympic Games, Los Angeles. Mult.
2778 1p. Roman quadriga (horiz) 10 15
2779 2p. Type **657** 10 15
2780 5p. Bronze of two wrestlers (horiz) 10 15
2781 8p. "The Discus-thrower" (statue, Miron) 10 15

658 Arms and Map of Navarra

1984. Autonomy of Navarra.
2782 **658** 17p. multicoloured . . . 20 15

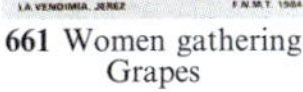

659 Cyclist **661** Women gathering Grapes

660 Arms (Levante Building Salamanca University)

1984. International Cycling Championship, Barcelona.
2783 **659** 17p. multicoloured . . . 15 15

1984. Autonomy of Castilla y Leon.
2784 **660** 17p. multicoloured . . . 20 15

1984. Vintage Festival, Jerez.
2785 **661** 17p. multicoloured . . . 20 15

662 Egeria on Donkey and Map of Middle East

1984. 1600th Anniv of Nun Egeria's Visit to Middle East.
2786 **662** 40p. multicoloured . . . 40 25

663 Arab Courier

1984. Stamp Day.
2787 **663** 17p. multicoloured . . . 15 15

664 Father Junipero Serra

1984. Death Bicentenary of Father Junipero Serra (missionary).
2788 **664** 40p. red and blue . . . 40 25

665 "Adoration of the Kings" (Miguel Moguer) (Campos altarpiece)

1984. Christmas. Multicoloured.
2789 17p. "Nativity" (15th-century retable) (horiz) 15 15
2790 40p. Type **665** 40 25

666 Arms, Buildings and Trees

1984. Autonomy of Madrid.
2791 **666** 17p. multicoloured . . . 20 15

667 Flags and Andean Condor

1985. 15th Anniv (1984) of Andes Pact.
2792 **667** 17p. multicoloured . . . 15 15

668 "Virgin of Louvain" (attr Jan Gossaert) **669** College Porch and Tympanum

1985. "Europalia 85 Espana" Festival.
2793 **668** 40p. multicoloured . . . 40 20

1985. 500th Anniv of Santa Cruz College, Valladolid University.
2794 **669** 17p. yellow, brown & red 15 15

670 Flames and "Olymphilex '85"

1985. "Olymphilex 85" International Olympic Stamps Exhibition, Lausanne.
2795 **670** 40p. red, yellow & black 40 20

671 Havana Cathedral

1985. "Espamer '85" International Stamp Exhibition, Havana, Cuba.
2796 **671** 40p. blue and purple . . 40 20

672 Couple in Traditional Dress on Horseback

1985. April Fair, Seville.
2797 **672** 17p. multicoloured . . . 20 15

673 Heads as Holder for Flames

1985. International Youth Year.
2798 **673** 17p. green, black and red 15 15

674 Moors and Christians fighting

1985. Festival of Moors and Christians, Alcoy.
2799 **674** 17p. multicoloured . . . 20 15

675 Don Antonio de Cabezon (organist)

1985. Europa.
2800 **675** 18p. red, black and blue on yellow 20 15
2801 – 45p. red, black and green on yellow 40 25
DESIGN: 45p. Musicians of National Youth Orchestra.

676 Capitania General Headquarters, La Coruna

1985. Armed Forces Day.
2802 **676** 18p. multicoloured . . . 20 15

677 Carlos III's Arms, 1785 Decree and "Santissima Trinidad" (ship of the line)

1985. Bicentenary of National Flag. Mult.
2803 18p. Type **677** 20 15
2804 18p. State arms, 1978 constitution and lion (detail from House of Deputies) 20 15

678 Sunflower and Bird

1985. World Environment Day.
2805 **678** 17p. multicoloured . . . 15 15

679 Monstrance in Decorated Street **680** King Juan Carlos I

1985. Corpus Christi Festival, Toledo.
2806 **679** 18p. multicoloured . . . 20 15

1985.

2807	**680**	10c. blue	10	15
2808		50c. green	10	15
2809		1p. blue	10	10
2810		2p. green	10	10
2811		3p. brown	10	10
2812		4p. bistre	10	10
2813		5p. purple	10	10
2814		6p. brown	10	10
2815		7p. violet	15	10
2816		7p. green	10	10
2817		8p. grey	10	10
2818		10p. red	10	10
2819		12p. red	10	10
2820		13p. blue	15	10
2821		15p. green	15	10
2822		17p. orange	15	10
2823		18p. green	20	10
2824		19p. brown	20	10
2825		20p. mauve	20	10
2825a		25p. green	25	15
2825b		27p. mauve	50	15
2826		30p. blue	25	10
2827		45p. green	40	10
2828		50p. blue	45	15
2828a		55p. brown	50	15
2829		60p. red	55	15
2830		75p. mauve	70	15

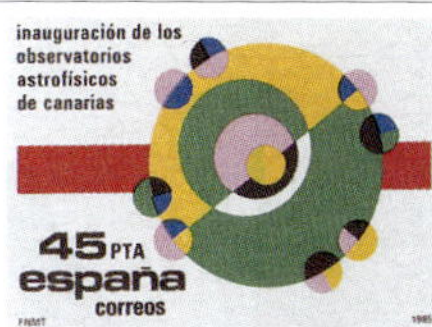

681 Planetary System

1985. Inauguration of Astrophysical Observatories, Canary Islands.
2831 **681** 45p. multicoloured . . . 40 25

682 Ataulfo Argenta (conductor)

1985. European Music Year. Multicoloured.
2832 12p. Type **682** 10 15
2833 17p. Tomas Luis de Victoria (composer) 20 15
2834 45p. Fernando Sor (guitarist and composer) 40 25

683 Bernal Diaz del Castillo (conquistador)

1985. Celebrities.
2835 **683** 7p. red, black and green on yellow 10 30
2836 – 12p. red, black and blue on yellow 10 15
2837 – 17p. green, red and black on yellow 20 15
2838 – 45p. green, black and brown on yellow . . . 45 20
DESIGNS: 12p. Esteban Terradas (mathema-tician); 17p. Vicente Aleixandre (poet); 45p. Leon Felipe Camino (poet).

684 Canoeist

1985. "Descent down the Sella" Canoe Festival, Asturias.
2839 **684** 17p. multicoloured . . . 20 15

685 Monk returning with Rotulet to Savigni Abbey, 1122 **686** Ribbon Exercise

1985. Stamp Day.
2840 **685** 17p. multicoloured . . . 20 15

1985. 12th World Rhythmic Gymnastics Championship, Valladolid. Multicoloured.
2841 17p. Type **686** 15 15
2842 45p. Hoop exercise 40 20

688 "Virgin and Child" (Escalas Chapel, Seville Cathedral)

690 Subalpine Warbler

689 "Nativity" (detail of altarpiece by Ramon de Mur)

1985. Stained Glass Windows. Multicoloured.
2844 7p. Type **688** 10 15
2845 12p. Monk (Toledo Cathedral) 10 15
2846 17p. King Enrique II of Castile and Leon (Alcazar of Segovia) 15 15

1985. Christmas. Multicoloured.
2847 17p. Type **689** 15 15
2848 45p. "Adoration of the Magi" (embroidered frontal, after Jaume Huguet) 40 20

1985. Birds. Multicoloured.
2849 6p. Type **690** 10 15
2850 7p. Rock thrush 10 15
2851 12p. Spotless starling . . . 15 15
2852 17p. Bearded reedling . . . 25 15

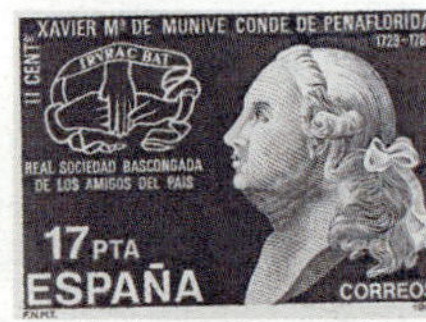
691 Count of Penaflorida

1985. Death Bicentenary of Count of Penaflorida (founder of Economic Society of Friends of the Land).
2853 **691** 17p. blue 15 15

692 Royal Palace, Madrid

1986. Admission of Spain and Portugal to European Economic Community. Multicoloured.
2854 7p. Type **692** 10 15
2855 17p. Map and flags of member countries 15 15
2856 30p. Hall of Columns, Royal Palace 25 20
2857 45p. Flags of Portugal and Spain uniting with flags of other members 50 30

1986. Tourist Series. As T **340**.
2858 12p. black and red 10 15
2859 35p. brown and blue 55 20
DESIGNS: 12p. Lupiana Monastery, Guadalajara; 35p. Balcony of Europe, Nerja.

693 Merino

1986. 2nd World Conference on Merinos.
2860 **693** 45p. multicoloured . . . 40 20

694 "Revellers" (detail, F. Hohenleiter)

1986. Cadiz Carnival.
2861 **694** 17p. multicoloured . . . 20 15

695 Helmets and Flower

1986. International Peace Year.
2862 **695** 45p. multicoloured . . . 40 20

696 Organ Pipes

1986. Religious Music Week, Cuenca.
2863 **696** 17p. multicoloured . . . 20 15

697 "Swearing in of Regent, Queen Maria Cristina" (detail, Joaquin Sorolla y Bastida)

1986. Centenary of Chambers of Commerce, Industry and Navigation.
2864 **697** 17p. black and green . . 15 15

698 Man with Suitcase

1986. Emigration.
2865 **698** 45p. multicoloured . . . 40 25

699 Boy and Birds

1986. Europa. Multicoloured.
2866 17p. Type **699** 15 15
2867 45p. Woman watering young tree 45 30

700 Our Lady of the Dew

1986. Our Lady of the Dew Festival, Rocio, near Almonte.
2868 **700** 17p. multicoloured . . . 20 15

701 Capitania General Building, Tenerife

1986. Armed Forces Day.
2869 **701** 17p. multicoloured . . . 15 15

1986. Tourist Series. As T **340**. Multicoloured.
2870 12p. black and blue 10 15
2871 35p. brown and blue 35 25
DESIGNS: 12p. Ciudad Rodrigo Cathedral, Salamanca; 35p. Calella lighthouse, Barcelona.

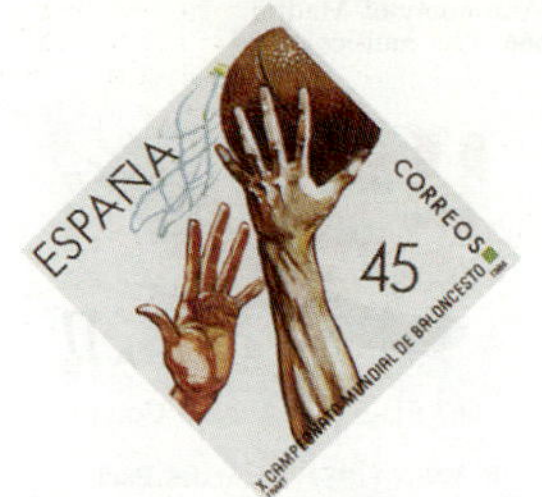
702 Hands and Ball

1986. 10th World Basketball Championship.
2872 **702** 45p. multicoloured . . . 40 20

703 Francisco Loscos (botanist)

704 Apostles awaiting Angels carrying Virgin's Soul

1986. Celebrities.
2873 **703** 7p. green and black . . 10 15
2874 – 11p. red and black . . . 10 15
2875 – 17p. brown and black . . 15 15
2876 – 45p. purple, orange and black 40 25
DESIGNS: 11p. Salvador Espriu (writer); 17p. Azorin (Jose Martinez Ruiz) (writer); 45p. Juan Gris (artist).

1986. Elche Mystery Play.
2877 **704** 17p. multicoloured . . . 20 15

705 Swimmer

1986. 5th World Swimming, Water Polo, Leap and Synchronous Swimming Championships.
2878 **705** 45p. multicoloured . . . 40 25

706 Pelota Player

1986. 10th World Pelota Championship.
2879 **706** 17p. multicoloured . . . 20 15

707 King's Messenger with Letter summoning Nobleman to Court

1986. Stamp Day.
2880 **707** 17p. multicoloured . . . 15 15

709 Aristotle

1986. 500th Anniv (1992) of Discovery of America by Columbus (1st issue). Designs showing historic figures and prophecies of discovery of New World.
2882 **709** 7p. black and mauve . . 10 15
2883 – 12p. black and lilac . . . 10 15
2884 – 17p. black and yellow . . 15 15
2885 – 30p. black and mauve . . 25 20
2886 – 35p. black and green . . 30 20
2887 – 45p. black and orange . . 40 15
DESIGNS: 12p. Seneca and quote from "Medea"; 17p. St. Isidoro of Seville and quote from "Etymologies"; 30p. Cardinal Pierre d'Ailly and quote from "Imago Mundi"; 35p. Mayan and quote from "Chilam Balam" books; 45p. Conquistador and quote from "Chilam Balam" books.
See also Nos. 2932/7, 2983/8, 3035/40, 3079/82, 3126/9, 3175/6 and 3190.

710 Gaspar de Portola

711 "Holy Family" (detail, Diego de Siloe)

1986. Death Bicentenary of Gaspar de Portola (first Governor of California).
2888 **710** 22p. blue, red and black 20 15

1986. Christmas. Wood Carvings. Multicoloured.
2889 19p. Type **711** 20 15
2890 48p. "Nativity" (detail, Toledo Cathedral altarpiece, Felipe de Borgona) (horiz) 45 15

712 Abd-er Rahman II and Cordoba Mosque

1986. Hispanic Islamic Culture.
2891 **712** 7p. brown and red . . . 10 15
2892 – 12p. brown and red . . 10 15
2893 – 17p. blue and black . . 15 15
2894 – 45p. green and black . . 40 15
DESIGNS: 12p. Ibn Hazm (writer) and burning book; 17p. Al-Zarqali (astronomer) and azophea (astrolabe); 45p. King Alfonso VII of Castile and Leon and scholars of Toledo School of Translators.

713 "The Good Curate"

1986. Birth Centenary of Alfonso Castelao (artist and writer).
2895 **713** 32p. multicoloured . . . 30 20

714 Chateau de la Muette (headquarters)

1987. 25th Anniv of Organization for Economic Co-operation and Development.
2896 **714** 48p. multicoloured . . . 45 20

715 Abstract Shapes

1987. "Expo 92" World's Fair, Seville (1st issue). Multicoloured.
2897 19p. Type **715** 20 15
2898 48p. Moon surface, Earth and symbol 80 15
See also Nos. 2941/2, 2951/2, 3004/7, 3052/5, 3094/7, 3143 and 3148/71.

716 Francisco de Vitoria

1987. 500th Birth Anniv of Francisco de Vitoria (jurist).
2899 **716** 48p. brown 50 15

717 18th-century Warship and Standard Bearer

718 University

1987. 450th Anniv of Marine Corps.
2900 **717** 19p. multicoloured . . . 20 15

1987. Centenary of Deusto University.
2901 **718** 19p. red, green and black 20 15

719 Breastfeeding Baby

1987. U.N.I.C.E.F. Child Survival Campaign.
2902 **719** 19p. brown and deep brown 20 15

720 Crowd

721 15th-century Pharmacy Jar, Manises

1987. 175th Anniv of Constitution of Cadiz. Multicoloured.
2903 25p. Type **720** 25 25
2904 25p. Crowd and herald on steps 25 25
2905 25p. Dignitaries on dais . . 25 25
2906 25p. Crown and Constitution 25 25
Nos. 2903/6 were printed together, se-tenant, the first three stamps forming a composite design showing "The Promulgation of the Constitution of 1812" by Salvador Viniegra.

1987. Ceramics. Multicoloured.
2907 7p. Type **721** 10 15
2908 14p. 20th-century glazed figure, Sargadelos 15 15
2909 19p. 18th-century vase, Buen Retiro 20 15
2910 32p. 20th-century pot, Salvatierra de los Barros 30 25
2911 40p. 18th-century jar, Talavera 40 30
2912 48p. 18–19th century jug, Granada 45 30

722 "Procession at Dawn, Zamora" (Gallego Marquina)

723 Bilbao Bank, Madrid (Saenz de Oiza)

1987. Holy Week Festivals. Multicoloured.
2913 19p. Type **722** 20 15
2914 48p. Gate of Pardon, Seville Cathedral and "Passion" (statue by Martinez Montanes) 60 15

1987. Tourist Series. As T **340**.
2915 14p. green and blue 15 15
2916 19p. deep green and green 20 15
2917 40p. brown 40 20
2918 48p. black 45 30

DESIGNS—HORIZ: 14p. Ifach Rock, Calpe, Alicante; 19p. Ruins of Church of Santa Maria d'Ozo, Pontevedra; 40p. Palace of Sonanes, Villacarriedo, Santander. VERT: 48p. 11th-century monastery of Sant Joan de les Abadesses, Gerona.

1987. Europa. Architecture.
2919 **723** 19p. multicoloured . . . 20 15
2920 – 48p. brown, bistre & grn 45 20
DESIGN—HORIZ: 14p. National Museum of Roman Art, Merida (Rafael Moneo).

724 Horse's Head and Harnessed Pair

1987. Jerez Horse Fair.
2921 **724** 19p. multicoloured . . . 20 15

725 Carande

1987. Birth Centenary of Ramon Carande (historian and Honorary Postman).
2922 **725** 40p. black and brown . . 40 20

726 Numbers on Pen Nib

1987. Postal Coding.
2923 **726** 19p. multicoloured . . . 20 15

727 Arms and School

1987. 75th Anniv of Eibar Armoury School.
2924 **727** 20p. multicoloured . . . 20 15

728 Batllo House Chimneys (Antonio Gaudi)

1987. Nomination of Barcelona as 1992 Olympic Games Host City. Multicoloured.
2925 32p. Type **728** 30 20
2926 65p. Athletes 65 30

729 Festival Poster (Fabri)

1987. 25th Pyrenees Folklore Festival, Jaca.
2927 **729** 50p. multicoloured . . . 50 15

730 Monturiol (after Marti Alsina) and Diagrams of Submarine "Ictineo"

1987. Death Cent of Narcis Monturiol (scientist).
2928 **730** 20p. black and brown . . 20 15

731 Detail from Jaime II of Majorca's Law appointing Couriers

1987. Stamp Day.
2929 **731** 20p. multicoloured . . . 20 15

734 Amerigo Vespucci

1987. 500th Anniv (1992) of Discovery of America by Columbus (2nd issue). Explorers. Multicoloured.
2932 14p. Type **734** 15 15
2933 20p. King Ferdinand and Queen Isabella the Catholic and arms on ships 20 15
2934 32p. Juan Perez and departing ships 30 15
2935 40p. Juan de la Cosa and ships 40 15
2936 50p. Map, ship and Christopher Columbus . . 45 15
2937 65p. Native on shore, approaching ships and Martin Alonzo and Vincente Yanez Pinzon 60 20

735 Star and Baubles

736 Macho (self-sculpture)

1987. Christmas. Multicoloured.
2938 20p. Type **735** 20 15
2939 50p. Zambomba and tambourine 45 20

1987. Birth Centenary of Victorio Macho (sculptor).
2940 **736** 50p. brown and black . . 45 20

1987. "Expo '92" World's Fair, Seville (2nd issue). As Nos. 2897/8 but values changed. Multicoloured.
2941 20p. Type **715** 20 15
2942 50p. As No. 2898 . . . . . 45 15

737 Queen Sofia

739 Speed Skating

738 Campoamor

1988. 50th Birthdays of King Juan Carlos I and Queen Sofia. Each brown, yellow and violet.
2943 20p. Type **737** 20 15
2944 20p. King Juan Carlos I . . 20 15

1988. Birth Centenary of Clara Campoamor (politician and women's suffrage campaigner).
2945 **738** 20p. multicoloured . . . 20 15

1988. Winter Olympic Games, Calgary.
2946 **739** 45p. multicoloured . . . 40 15

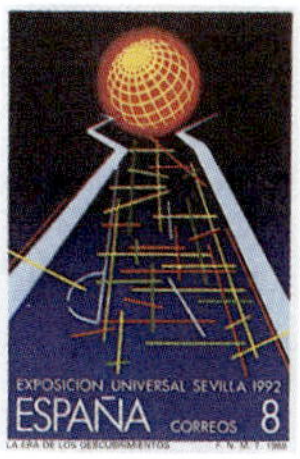

740 "Christ tied to the Pillar" (statue) and Valladolid Cathedral

742 Globe and Stylized Roads

741 Ingredients for and Dish of Paella

1988. Holy Week Festivals. Multicoloured.
2947 20p. Type **740** 20 15
2948 50p. Float depicting Christ carrying the Cross, Malaga 45 15

1988. Tourist Series. Multicoloured.
2949 18p. Type **741** 20 15
2950 45p. Covadonga National Park (70th anniv of National Parks) 35 15

1988. "Expo '92" World's Fair, Seville (3rd issue).
2951 8p. Type **742** 15 15
2952 45p. Compass rose and globe (horiz) 40 15

743 18th-Century Valencian Chalice

744 Francis of Taxis (organiser of European postal service, 1505)

1988. Glassware. Multicoloured.
2953 20p. Type **743** 20 15
2954 20p. 18th-century pitcher, Cadalso de los Vidrios, Madrid 20 15
2955 20p. 18th-century crystal sweet jar, La Granja de San Ildefonso 20 15
2956 20p. 18th-century Andalusian two-handled jug, Castril 20 15
2957 20p. 17th-century Catalan four-spouted jug 20 15
2958 20p. 20th-century bottle, Balearic Islands 20 15

1988. Stamp Day.
2959 **744** 20p. violet and brown 20 15

745 Pablo Iglesias (first President)

1988. Centenary of General Workers' Union.
2960 **745** 20p. multicoloured . . . 20 15

746 Steam Locomotive, 1837, Cuba

1988. Europa. Transport and Communications.
2961 **746** 20p. red and black . . . 20 15
2962 – 50p. green and black . . 45 20
DESIGN: 50p. Light telegraph, Philippines, 1818.

747 Monnet **749** Couple in Granada

748 Emblem

1988. Birth Cent of Jean Monnet (statesman).
2963 **747** 45p. blue 40 20

1988. Centenary of 1888 Universal Exhibition, Barcelona.
2964 **748** 50p. multicoloured . . . 50 20

1988. International Festival of Music and Dance, Granada.
2965 **749** 50p. multicoloured . . . 50 15

750 Bull

1988. "Expo 88" World's Fair, Brisbane.
2966 **750** 50p. multicoloured . . . 45 15

751 "Virgin of Hope"

1988. Coronation of "Virgin of Hope", Malaga.
2967 **751** 20p. multicoloured . . . 20 15

753 Orreo (agricultural store), Cantabria

1988. Tourist Series.
2969 **753** 18p. green, brown & blue 20 15
2970 – 45p. black, brn & ochre 35 15
DESIGN: 45p. Dulzaina (wind instrument), Castilla y Leon.

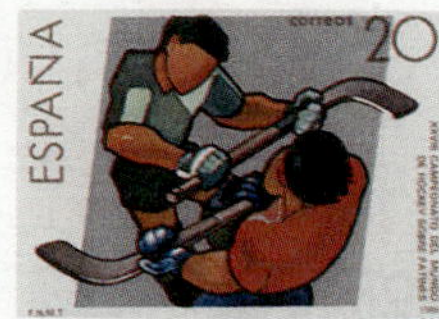

754 Players

1988. 28th World Roller Skate Hockey Championship, La Coruna.
2971 **754** 20p. multicoloured . . . 20 15

755 Congress Emblem **756** "Olympic" Class Yacht

1988. 1st Spanish Regional Homes and Centres World Congress, Madrid.
2972 **755** 20p. multicoloured . . . 15 15

1988. Olympic Games, Seoul.
2973 **756** 50p. multicoloured . . . 45 15

757 Borrell II, Count of Barcelona

1988. Millenary of Catalonia.
2974 **757** 20p. multicoloured . . . 20 15

758 King Alfonso IX of Leon (detail of Codex of "Toxos Outos")

1988. 800th Anniv of 1st Leon Parliament.
2975 **758** 20p. multicoloured . . . 20 15

759 Emblem on Band around Peace Year Stamps

1988. 25th Anniv of Spanish Philatelic Associations Federation.
2976 **759** 20p. multicoloured . . . 20 15

760 Games Emblem

1988. Olympic Games, Barcelona (1992) (1st issue). Designs showing stylized representations of sports. Multicoloured.
2977 8p. Type **760** 10 25
2978 20p.+5p. Athletics 25 50
2979 45p.+5p. Badminton 55 70
2980 50p.+5p. Basketball 55 75
See also Nos. 3008/11, 3031/3, 3056/8, 3076/8, 3098/3100, 3123/5, 3144/6, 3180/2 and 3183/5.

761 Palace of the Generality, Valencia, and Seal of Jaime I **762** Manuel Alonso Martinez (statesman)

1988. 750th Anniv of Re-conquest of Valencia by King Jaime I of Aragon.
2981 **761** 20p. multicoloured . . . 20 15

1988. Centenary of Civil Code.
2982 **762** 20p. multicoloured . . . 20 15

763 Hernan Cortes and Quetzalcoatl Serpent

1988. 500th Anniv (1992) of Discovery of America by Columbus (3rd issue). Each red, blue and orange.
2983 10p. Type **763** 10 15
2984 10p. Vasco Nunez de Balboa and waves 10 15
2985 20p. Francisco Pizarro and guanaco 20 15
2986 20p. Ferdinand Magellan, Juan Sebastian del Cano and globe 20 15
2987 50p. Alvar Nunez Cabeza de Vaca and river 50 25
2988 50p. Andres de Urdaneta and maritime currents . . 50 30

764 Enrique III of Castile and Leon (first Prince of Asturias)

1988. 600th Anniv of Title of Prince of Asturias.
2989 **764** 20p. multicoloured . . . 20 15

765 Snowflakes

1988. Christmas. Multicoloured.
2990 20p. Type **765** 20 15
2991 50p. Shepherd carrying sheep (vert) 45 15

766 Cordoba Mosque

1988. U.N.E.S.C.O. World Heritage Sites.
2992 **766** 18p. brown 20 15
2993 – 20p. blue 20 15
2994 – 45p. brown 45 20
2995 – 50p. green 55 20
DESIGNS—VERT: 20p. Burgos Cathedral. HORIZ: 45p. San Lorenzo Monastery, El Escorial; 50p. Alhambra, Granada.

767 Representation of Political Parties

1988. 10th Anniv of Constitution.
2996 **767** 20p. multicoloured . . . 20 15

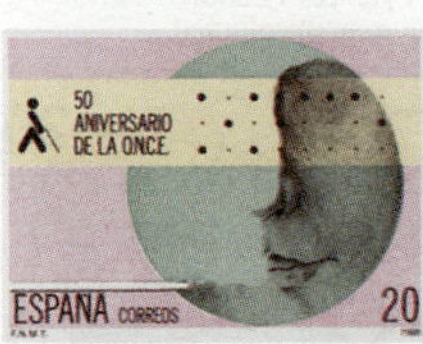

769 Blind Person

1988. 50th Anniv of National Organization for the Blind.
2998 **769** 20p. multicoloured . . . 20 15

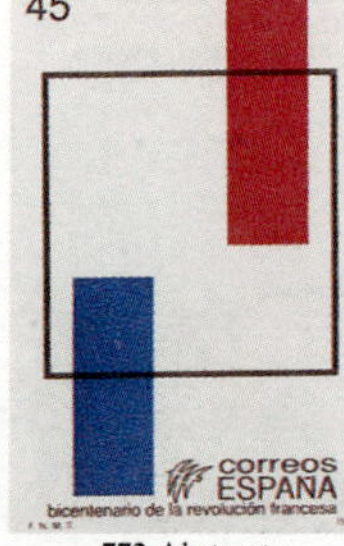

770 Luis de Granada **772** Abstract

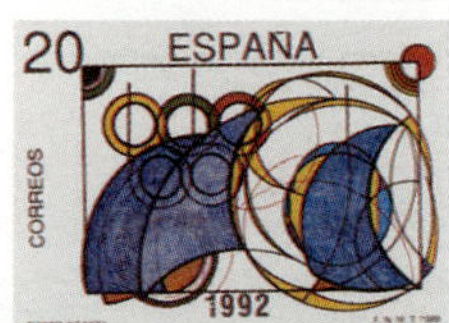

771 Olympic Rings and Sails (Natalia Barrio Fernandez)

1988. 400th Death Anniv of Brother Luis de Granada (mystic).
2999 **770** 20p. multicoloured . . . 20 15

1989. Children's Stamp Designs. Multicoloured.
3000 20p. Type **771** 20 15
3001 20p. Magnifying glass on stamp (Jose Luis Villegas Lopez) (vert) 20 15

1989. Bicentenary of French Revolution.
3002 **772** 45p. red, blue and black 40 15

773 Maria de Maeztu

1989. 107th Birth Anniv of Maria de Maeztu (educationist).
3003 **773** 20p. multicoloured . . . 20 15

774 London, 1851

1989. "Expo '92" World's Fair, Seville (4th issue). Great Exhibitions. Multicoloured.
3004 8p.+5p. Type **774** 10 15
3005 8p.+5p. Paris, 1889 . . . . 10 15
3006 20p.+5p. Brussels, 1958 . . 25 20
3007 20p.+5p. Osaka, 1970 . . . 25 20

1989. Olympic Games, Barcelona (1992) (2nd issue). As T **760**. Multicoloured.
3008 8p.+5p. Handball 15 20
3009 18p.+5p. Boxing 25 35
3010 20p.+5p. Cycling 25 40
3011 45p.+5p. Show jumping . . 50 70

775 Uniforms, 1889

1989. Centenary of Post Office.
3012 **775** 20p. multicoloured . . . 20 15

776 International Postal Service Treaty, 1601 — 777 Entrance Door

1989. Stamp Day.
3013 **776** 20p. black 20 15

1989. Cordon House, Burgos.
3014 **777** 20p. black 20 15

778 Skittles — 781 Manuscript and Portrait

779 European Flag

1989. Europa. Children's Toys. Multicoloured.
3015 40p. Type **778** 40 15
3016 50p. Spinning top 45 15

1989. Spanish Presidency of European Economic Community.
3017 **779** 45p. multicoloured . . . 40 15

1989. Birth Centenary of Gabriela Mistral (poet).
3019 **781** 50p. multicoloured . . . 50 15

782 Flags forming Ballot Box

1989. European Parliament Elections.
3020 **782** 45p. multicoloured . . . 40 15

783 Catalonia

1989. Lace. Typical designs from named region.
3021 **783** 20p. blue and brown . . 20 15
3022 – 20p. blue and brown . . 20 15
3023 – 20p. blue 20 15
3024 – 20p. blue 20 15
3025 – 20p. blue and brown . . 20 15
3026 – 20p. blue and brown . . 20 15
DESIGNS: No. 3022, Andalucia; 3023, Extremadura; 3024, Canary Islands; 3025, Castilla-La Mancha; 3026, Galicia.

784 Pope John Paul II and Youths

1989. 3rd Papal Visit.
3027 **784** 50p. green, brown & blk 50 15

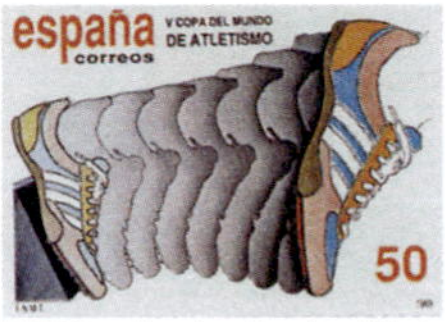

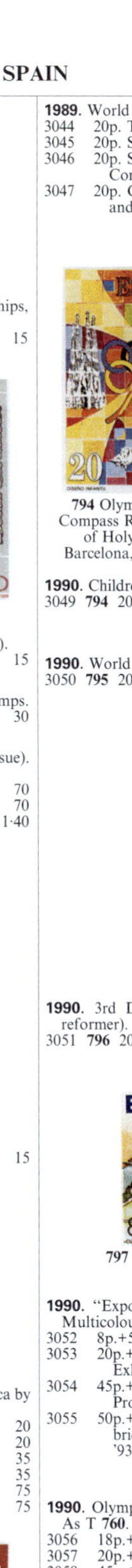

785 Foot leaving Starting Block

1989. World Cup Athletics Championships, Barcelona.
3028 **785** 50p. multicoloured . . . 50 15

786 Chaplin — 787 1p. Stamp

1989. Birth Centenary of Charlie Chaplin (actor).
3029 **786** 50p. multicoloured . . . 50 15

1989. Centenary of First King Alfonso XIII Stamps.
3030 **787** 50p. brown, grey and red 50 30

1989. Olympic Games, Barcelona (1992) (3rd issue). As T **760**.
3031 18p.+5p. Fencing 55 70
3032 20p.+5p. Football 55 70
3033 45p.+5p. Gymnastics . . . 1·10 1·40

788 Fr. Andres Manjon (founder)

1989. Centenary of Ave Maria Schools.
3034 **788** 20p. multicoloured . . . 20 15

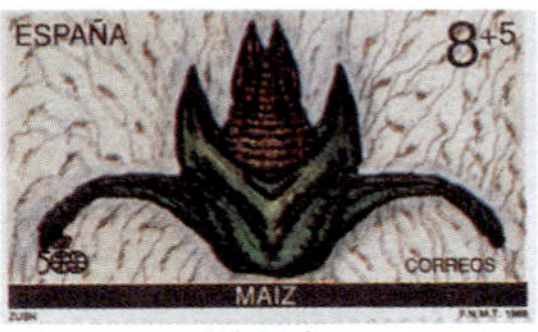

789 Maize

1989. 500th Anniv (1992) of Discovery of America by Columbus (4th issue). Multicoloured.
3035 8p.+5p. Type **789** 15 20
3036 8p.+5p. Cacao nut 15 20
3037 20p.+5p. Tomato 25 35
3038 20p.+5p. Horse 25 35
3039 50p.+5p. Potato 50 75
3040 50p.+5p. Turkey 50 75

790 Inca irrigating Corn (from "New Chronicle" by Waman Puma) — 791 "Navidad 89"

1989. America. Pre-Columbian Life.
3041 **790** 50p. multicoloured . . . 50 15

1989. Christmas. Multicoloured.
3042 20p. Type **791** 20 15
3043 45p. Girl with Christmas present (horiz) 40 15

792 Altamira Caves

1989. World Heritage Sites. Multicoloured.
3044 20p. Type **792** 20 15
3045 20p. Segovia Aqueduct . . . 20 15
3046 20p. Santiago de Compostela 20 15
3047 20p. Guell Park and Palace and Mila House 20 15

794 Olympic Rings, Compass Rose, Church of Holy Family, Barcelona, and Seville — 795 Getxo City Hall and Competitor

1990. Children's Stamp Design.
3049 **794** 20p. multicoloured . . . 20 15

1990. World Cyclo-cross Championship, Getxo.
3050 **795** 20p. multicoloured . . . 20 15

796 Victoria Kent

1990. 3rd Death Anniv of Victoria Kent (prison reformer).
3051 **796** 20p. lilac 20 15

797 Curro (mascot) flying over Path of Discoveries

1990. "Expo '92" World's Fair, Seville (5th issue). Multicoloured.
3052 8p.+5p. Type **797** 15 30
3053 20p.+5p. Curro and Exhibition building . . . 25 45
3054 45p.+5p. Curro and view of Project Cartuja '93 . . . 60 65
3055 50p.+5p. Curro crossing bridge in Project Cartuja '93 . . . . 65 75

1990. Olympic Games, Barcelona (1992) (4th issue). As T **760**. Multicoloured.
3056 18p.+5p. Weightlifting . . . 25 30
3057 20p.+5p. Hockey 25 45
3058 45p.+5p. Judo 55 55

798 Rafael Alvarez Sereix (Honorary Postman)

1990. Stamp Day.
3059 **798** 20p. flesh, brown & green 20 15

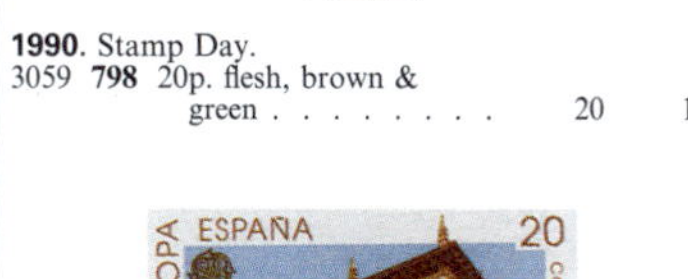

799 Vitoria Post Office

1990. Europa. Post Office Buildings.
3060 20p. Type **799** 20 15
3061 50p. Malaga Post Office (vert) 45 20

800 "Hispasat" Communications Satellite

1990. 125th Anniv of I.T.U.
3062 **800** 8p. multicoloured . . . 10 15

801 Door Knocker, Aragon

1990. Wrought Ironwork. Each black, grey and red.
3063 20p. Type **801** 20 15
3064 20p. Door knocker, Andalucia 20 15
3065 20p. Pistol, Catalonia . . . 20 15
3066 20p. Door knocker, Castilla-La Mancha 20 15
3067 20p. Mirror with lock, Galicia 20 15
3068 20p. Basque fireback 20 15

803 "Charity" (Lopez Alonso) — 805 Poster

1990. Anniversaries.
3070 **803** 8p. multicoloured . . . 10 15
3071 – 20p. multicoloured . . . 25 15
3072 – 45p. orange and brown 50 35
3073 – 50p. red and blue . . . 55 30
DESIGNS—VERT: 8p. Type **803** (bicent of arrival in Spain of Daughters of Charity); 50p. Page of book (500th anniv of publication of "Tirant lo Blanch" by Joanot Martorell and Marti Joan de Galba). HORIZ: 20p. Score of "Leilah" and Jose Padilla (composer, birth centenary (1989)); 45p. Palace of Kings of Navarre (900th anniv of grant of privileges to Estella).

1990. 17th International Historical Sciences Congress, Madrid.
3075 **805** 50p. multicoloured . . . 45 15

1990. Olympic Games, Barcelona (1992) (5th issue). As T **760**. Multicoloured.
3076 8p.+5p. Wrestling 15 25
3077 18p.+5p. Swimming 30 30
3078 20p.+5p. Baseball 40 55

806 Caravel and Compass Rose

1990. 500th Anniv of Discovery of America by Columbus (5th issue). Multicoloured.
3079 8p.+5p. Type **806** 10 20
3080 8p.+5p. Caravels 10 20
3081 20p.+5p. Caravel 25 40
3082 20p.+5p. Galleons 25 40

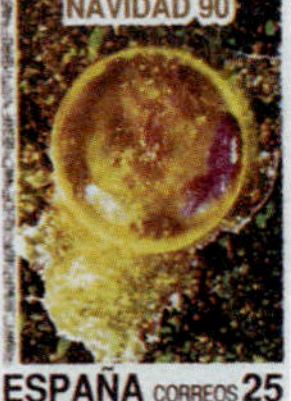

807 Puerto Rican Todys — 808 Sun

1990. America. The Natural World.
3083 **807** 50p. multicoloured . . . 45 30

1990. Christmas. Details of "Cosmic Poem" by Jose Antonio Sistiaga. Multicoloured.
3084 25p. Type **808** 25 15
3085 45p. Moon (horiz) 40 15

810 Tourism Logo (Joan Miro)
811 Church of St. Miguel de Lillo, Oviedo

1990. European Tourism Year.
3087 **810** 45p. multicoloured . . . 40 15

1990. World Heritage Sites. Multicoloured.
3088 20p. Type **811** 20 20
3089 20p. St. Peter's Tower, Teruel 20 20
3090 20p. Bujaco Tower, Caceres (horiz) 20 20
3091 20p. St. Vincent's Church, Avila (horiz) 20 20

812 Conductor and Orchestra

1990. Spanish National Orchestra.
3092 **812** 25p. green, turq & blk 25 15

813 Maria Moliner

1991. 10th Death Anniv of Maria Moliner (philologist).
3093 **813** 25p. multicoloured . . . 25 20

814 La Cartuja (Santa Maria de las Cuevas Monastery)

1991. "Expo 92" World's Fair, Seville (6th issue). Views of Seville. Multicoloured.
3094 15p.+5p. Type **814** 20 25
3095 25p.+5p. The Auditorium 30 45
3096 45p.+5p. La Cartuja bridge 55 60
3097 55p.+5p. La Barqueta bridge 65 85

1991. Olympic Games, Barcelona (1992) (6th series). As T **760**.
3098 15p.+5p. grey, black and red 25 30
3099 25p.+5p. multicoloured . . 30 45
3100 45p.+5p. multicoloured . . 55 65
DESIGNS: 15p. Modern pentathlon; 25p. Canoeing; 45p. Rowing.

815 Olympic Rings and Yachts

817 Juan de Tassis y Peralta (Chief Courier to Kings Philip III and IV)

1991. Children's Stamp Design.
3101 **815** 25p. multicoloured . . . 25 20

1991. Stamp Day.
3103 **817** 25p. black 25 20

819 Dish Aerials, INTA-NASA Earth Station, Robledo de Chavela

1991. Europa. Europe in Space. Multicoloured.
3105 25p. Type **819** 25 15
3106 45p. "Olympus I" telecommunications satellite 45 15

820 Brother Luis Ponce de Leon (translator and poet, 400th death anniv)
822 Choir (after mural mosaic, Palau de la Musica)

821 Apollo Fountain

1991. Anniversaries.
3107 – 15p. multicoloured . . . 15 15
3108 **820** 15p. orange, red & black 15 15
3109 – 25p. multicoloured . . . 25 15
3110 – 25p. multicoloured . . . 25 15
DESIGNS—HORIZ: No. 3107, Table and chair (400th death anniv of St. John of the Cross). VERT: No. 3109, Banner and cap (500th birth anniv of St. Ignatius de Loyola (founder of Society of Jesus)); 3110, Abd-er Rahman III, Emir of Cordoba (1100th birth anniv).

1991. Madrid. European City of Culture (1st issue). Multicoloured.
3111 15p.+5p. Type **821** 20 25
3112 25p.+5p. "Don Alvaro de Bazan" (statue, Mariano Benlliure) 30 45
3113 45p.+5p. Bank of Spain . . 50 70
3114 55p.+5p. Cloisters, St. Isidro Institute 60 80
See also Nos. 3195/8.

1991. Centenary of Orfeo Catala (Barcelona choral group).
3115 **822** 25p. multicoloured . . . 25 25

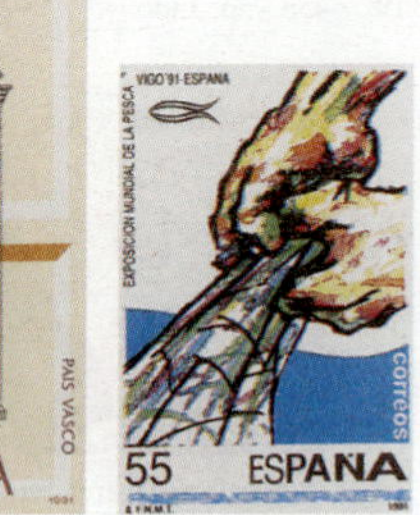

823 Basque Drug Cupboard
824 Hands holding Net

1991. Furniture. Multicoloured.
3116 25p. Type **823** 25 15
3117 25p. Kitchen dresser, Castilla y Leon 25 15
3118 25p. Chair, Murcia 25 15
3119 25p. Cradle, Andalucia . . . 25 15
3120 25p. Travelling chest, Castilla-La Mancha . . . 25 15
3121 25p. Bridal chest, Catalonia 25 15

1991. World Fishing Exhibition, Vigo.
3122 **824** 55p. multicoloured . . . 55 20

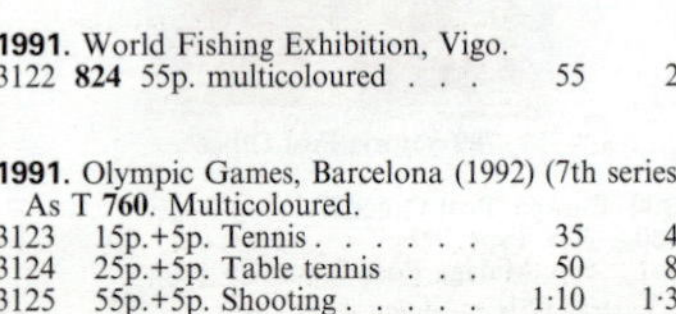

1991. Olympic Games, Barcelona (1992) (7th series). As T **760**. Multicoloured.
3123 15p.+5p. Tennis 35 40
3124 25p.+5p. Table tennis . . . 50 85
3125 55p.+5p. Shooting . . . . . 1·10 1·30

825 Garcilaso de la Vega (Spanish-Inca poet)

1991. 500th Anniv of Discovery of America by Columbus (6th issue). Multicoloured.
3126 15p.+5p. Type **825** 20 30
3127 25p.+5p. Pope Alexander VI 30 50
3128 45p.+5p. Luis de Santangel (banker) 50 75
3129 55p.+5p. Brother Toribio Motolinia (missionary) . . 60 95

826 Nocturlabe
827 "Nativity" (from "New Chronicle" by Guaman Poma de Ayala)

1991. America. Voyages of Discovery.
3130 **826** 55p. brown and purple 55 20

1991. Christmas.
3131 **827** 25p. buff and brown . . 25 15
3132 – 45p. multicoloured . . . 45 15
DESIGN: 45p. "Nativity" (16th-century Russian icon).

829 Alcantara Gate, Toledo
830 Gen. Carlos Ibanez de Ibero (cartographer)

1991. World Heritage Sites.
3134 **829** 25p. agate and brown . . 30 15
3135 – 25p. black and brown . . 30 15
3136 – 25p. brown and blue . . 30 15
3137 – 25p. violet and green . . 30 15
DESIGNS—VERT: No. 3135, Casa de las Conchas, Salamanca. HORIZ: No. 3136, Seville Cathedral; 3137, Aeonio (flower) and Garajonay National Park, Gomera.

1991. Anniversaries and Events. Multicoloured.
3138 25p. Type **830** (death centenary) 25 15
3139 55p. "Las Palmas" (Antarctic survey ship) (signing of Antarctic Treaty protocol of Madrid declaring the Antarctic a nature reserve) 55 20

831 Margarita Xirgu

1992. 23rd Death Anniv of Margarita Xirgu (actress).
3140 **831** 25p. brown and red . . 25 20

832 "Expo 92, Seville"

1992. Children's Stamp Design.
3141 **832** 25p. multicoloured . . . 25 20

833 Pedro Rodriguez, Count of Campomanes (administrator and postal consultant)

1992. Stamp Day.
3142 **833** 27p. multicoloured . . . 30 20

834 Spanish Pavilion

1992. "Expo '92" World's Fair, Seville (7th issue).
3143 **834** 27p. grey, black & brown 30 20

1992. Olympic Games, Barcelona (8th issue). As T **760**. Multicoloured.
3144 15p.+5p. Archery 30 40
3145 25p.+5p. Sailing 45 55
3146 55p.+5p. Volleyball . . . . 90 1·10

836 Cable-cars

1992. "Expo '92" World's Fair, Seville (8th issue). Multicoloured.
3148 17p. Exhibition World Trade Centre 25 25
3149 17p. Type **836** 25 25
3150 17p. Fourth Avenue 25 25
3151 17p. Barqueta entrance . . 25 25
3152 17p. Nature pavilion 25 25
3153 17p. Bioclimatic sphere . . 25 25
3154 17p. Alamillo bridge 25 25
3155 17p. Press centre 25 25
3156 17p. Pavilion of the 15th century 25 25
3157 17p. Expo harbour 25 25
3158 17p. Tourist train 25 25
3159 17p. One-day entrance ticket showing bridge 25 25
3160 27p. Santa Maria de las Cuevas Carthusian monastery 40 25
3161 27p. Palisade 40 25
3162 27p. Monorail 40 25
3163 27p. Avenue of Europe . . 40 25
3164 27p. Pavilion of Discovery 40 25
3165 27p. Auditorium 40 25
3166 27p. First Avenue 40 25
3167 27p. Square of the Future 40 25
3168 27p. Italica entrance 40 25
3169 27p. Last avenue 40 25
3170 27p. Theatre 40 25
3171 27p. Curro (official mascot) 40 25

837 Wheelchair Sports

1992. Paralympic (Physically Handicapped) Games, Barcelona.
3173 **837** 27p. multicoloured . . . 30 20

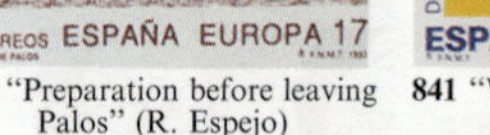

839 "Preparation before leaving Palos" (R. Espejo)

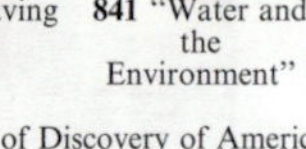

841 "Water and the Environment"

1992. Europa. 500th Anniv of Discovery of America by Columbus (7th issue).
3175 **839** 17p. multicoloured . . . 20 15
3176 – 45p. grey and brown . . 50 15
DESIGN: 45p. Map of the Americas, Columbus's fleet and Monastery of Santa Maria de La Rabida.

1992. World Environment Day.
3178 **841** 27p. blue and yellow . . 30 15

842 "Albertville", Olympic Rings and "Barcelona"

1992. Winter Olympic Games, Albertville, and Summer Games, Barcelona.
3179 **842** 45p. multicoloured . . . 50 20

843 Victorious Athlete

845 Cobi holding Magnifying Glass and Stamp Album

844 Olympic Stadium

1992. Olympic Games, Barcelona (9th issue). Multicoloured.
3180 17p.+5p. Type **843** 25 30
3181 17p.+5p. Cobi (official mascot) 25 30
3182 17p.+5p. Olympic torch (horiz) 25 30

1992. Olympic Games, Barcelona (10th issue). Multicoloured.
3183 27p.+5p. Type **844** 35 55
3184 27p.+5p. San Jordi sports arena 35 55
3185 27p.+5p. I.N.E.F. sports university 35 55

1992. "Olymphilex 92" International Stamp Exhibition, Barcelona. Multicoloured.
3186 17p.+5p. Type **845** 25 30
3187 17p.+5p. Church of the Holy Family, Barcelona, and exhibition emblem . . 25 30

846 Athletes

1992. Paralympic (Mentally Handicapped) Games, Madrid.
3188 **846** 27p. blue and red . . . 30 20

848 Quarterdeck of "Santa Maria"

1992. America. 500th Anniv of Discovery of America by Columbus (8th issue).
3190 **848** 60p. brown, cinnamon and ochre 60 25

849 Luis Vives (philosopher)

850 Helmet of Mercury and European Community Emblem

1992. Anniversaries. Multicoloured.
3191 17p. Type **849** (500th birth anniv) 20 25
3192 27p. Pamplona Choir (centenary) (horiz) 30 25

1992. European Single Market.
3193 **850** 45p. blue and yellow . . 50 20

851 "Nativity" (Obdulia Acevedo)

852 Municipal Museum

1992. Christmas.
3194 **851** 27p. multicoloured . . . 30 20

1992. Madrid, European City of Culture (2nd issue). Multicoloured.
3195 17p.+5p. Type **852** 25 30
3196 17p.+5p. Queen Sofia Art Museum 25 30
3197 17p.+5p. Prado Museum . . 25 30
3198 17p.+5p. Royal Theatre . . 25 30

854 Bird, Sun, Leaves and Silhouettes

855 Maria Zambrano

1993. Public Services. Protection of the Environment.
3200 **854** 28p. blue and green . . 35 15

1993. 2nd Death Anniv of Maria Zambrano (writer).
3201 **855** 45p. multicoloured . . . 55 30

856 Figures and Blue Cross

857 Segovia

1993. Public Services. Health and Sanitation.
3202 **856** 65p. blue and green . . 85 20

1993. Birth Centenary of Andres Segovia (guitarist).
3203 **857** 65p. black and brown . . 85 15

858 Post-box, Cadiz, 1908

1993. Stamp Day.
3204 **858** 28p. multicoloured . . . 40 2·75

859 Parasol Mushroom ("Lepiota procera")

861 Road Safety

1993. Fungi (1st series). Multicoloured.
3205 17p. Type **859** 30 15
3206 17p. Caesar's mushroom ("Amanita caesarea") . . 30 15
3207 28p. "Lactarius sanguifluus" 30 15
3208 28p. The charcoal burner ("Russula cyanoxantha") 30 15
See also Nos. 3256/9 and 3312/13.

1993. Public Services.
3210 **861** 17p. green and red . . . 30 15

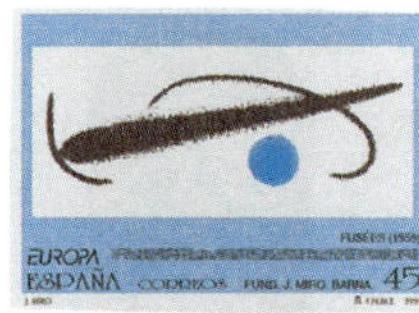

863 "Fusees"

1993. Europa. Contemporary Art. Paintings by Joan Miro.
3212 **863** 45p. black and blue . . 55 15
3213 – 65p. multicoloured . . . 85 40
DESIGN—VERT: 65p. "La Bague d'Aurore".

864 "Translation of Body from Palestine to Galicia" (detail of altarpiece, Santiago de Compostela Cathedral)

1993. St. James's Holy Year (1st issue). Mult.
3214 17p. Type **864** 30 15
3215 28p. "Discovery of St. James's tomb by Bishop Teodomiro" (miniature from "Tumbo A" (codex)) 40 15
3216 45p. "St. James" (illuminated initial letter from Bull issued by Pope Alexander III declaring Holy Years of St. James) 55 20
See also No. 3218.

865 Letters, Map and Satellite

1993. World Telecommunications Day.
3217 **865** 28p. multicoloured . . . 40 15

866 Bagpipe Player (Isaac Diaz Pardo)

867 King Juan Carlos I

1993. St. James's Holy Year (2nd issue).
3218 **866** 28p. multicoloured . . . 40 15

1993.
3220 **867** 1p. blue and gold . . . 10 10
3221 2p. green and gold . . 10 15
3222 10p. red and gold . . . 10 10
3222b 15p. green and gold . . 20 15
3223 16p. brown and gold . . 15 15
3224 17p. orange and gold . . 20 15
3225 18p. turquoise and gold 25 15
3226 19p. brown and gold . . 25 15
3226a 20p. mauve and gold . . 25 15
3227 21p. green and gold . . 25 15
3229 28p. brown and gold . . 35 15
3230 29p. green and gold . . 35 15
3231 30p. blue and gold . . 35 15
3232 32p. green and gold . . 35 15
3233 35p. red and gold . . . 35 15
3234 45p. green and gold . . 55 15
3235 55p. brown and gold . . 70 15
3236 60p. red and gold . . . 70 30
3237 65p. orange and gold . . 75 15
3238 70p. red and gold . . . 70 20

868 "Water and the Environment"

869 Count of Barcelona (after Ricardo Macarrion)

1993. World Environment Day.
3240 **868** 28p. multicoloured . . . 40 15

1993. Juan de Borbon, Count of Barcelona (King Juan Carlos's father) Commemoration.
3241 **869** 28p. multicoloured . . . 40 15

870 Tank Locomotive

1993. Centenary of Igualada–Martorell Railway.
3242 **870** 45p. green and black . . 55 15

871 "The Mint" (lithograph, Pic de Leopold, 1866)

1993. Cent of National Coin and Stamp Mint.
3243 **871** 65p. blue 85 35

872 Alejandro Malaspina (navigator)

1993. Explorers. Multicoloured.
3244 45p. Type **872** 55 25
3245 65p. Jose Celestino Mutis (naturalist) (vert) 85 35

873 "Road to Santiago"

1993. Children's Stamp Design.
3246 **873** 45p. multicoloured . . . 55 20

874 Black Stork

1993. America. Endangered Animals.
3247 **874** 65p. black and orange 85 35
3248 – 65p. black and red . . . 85 35
DESIGN: No. 3248, Lammergeier.

875 Old and Young Hands

1993. European Year of Senior Citizens and Solidarity between Generations.
3249 **875** 45p. multicoloured . . . 55 20

876 Star and Three Wise Men

1993. Christmas. Multicoloured.
3250 17p. Type **876** 25 15
3251 28p. Holy Family (vert) . . 40 20

877 Guillen

1993. Birth Centenary of Jorge Guillen (poet).
3252 **877** 28p. green 40 20

878 Santa Maria de Poblet Monastery, Tarragona

1993. World Heritage Sites.
3253 **878** 50p. brown, blue & green 70 20

879 Luis Bunuel and Camera

1994. Spanish Cinema (1st series). Multicoloured.
3254 29p. Type **879** 40 15
3255 55p. Segundo de Chomon and scene from "Goblin House" 70 20
See also Nos. 3308/9 and 3419/20.

1994. Fungi (2nd series). As T **859**. Multicoloured.
3256 18p. Cep ("Boletus edulis") 25 15
3257 18p. Satan's mushroom ("Boletus satanas") . . . 25 15
3258 29p. Death cap ("Amanita phalloides") 40 20
3259 29p. Saffron milk cap ("Lactarius deliciosus") 40 20

880 Cinnabar

1994. Minerals (1st series).
3260 **880** 29p. multicoloured . . . 40 20
3261 – 29p. multicoloured . . . 40 20
3262 – 29p. multicoloured . . . 40 20
3263 – 29p. black and blue . . . 40 20
DESIGNS: 3261, Blende (inscr "Esfalerita"); 3262, Pyrites; 3263, Galena.
See also Nos. 3314/16 and 3366/7.

881 Barristers' Mailbox, Barcelona

1994. Stamp Day.
3264 **881** 29p. brown and cinnamon 40 15

882 Worker (detail of sculpture), I.L.O. Building, Geneva.

1994. 75th Anniv of I.L.O., Geneva.
3265 **882** 65p. multicoloured . . . 85 30

883

1994. 90th Birth Anniv of Salvador Dali (painter). Multicoloured.
3266 18p. Type **883** 25 15
3267 18p. "Portrait of Gala" (horiz) 25 15
3268 29p. "Port Alguer" 35 15
3269 29p. "The Great Masturbator" (horiz) . . 35 15
3270 55p. "The Bread Basket" . . 70 35
3271 55p. "Soft Self-portrait" . . 70 35
3272 65p. "Galatea of the Spheres" 90 35
3273 65p. "The Enigma without End" (horiz) 90 35

884 Pla

1994. 13th Death Anniv of Josep Pla (writer).
3274 **884** 65p. green and red . . . 85 35

885 "Martyrdom of St. Andrew" (Peter Paul Rubens)
886 "Foundation of Santa Cruz de Tenerife" (Gonzalez Mendez)

1994. 400th Anniv of Carlos de Amberes Foundation (philanthropic organization).
3275 **885** 55p. multicoloured . . . 70 35

1994. Anniversaries. Multicoloured.
3276 18p. Type **886** (500th anniv of city) 25 15
3277 29p. Sancho IV's Foundation Charter at Alcala, 1293 (700th anniv of Complutense University, Madrid) (horiz) 40 20

887 Severo Ochoa (biochemist)

1994. Europa. Discoveries. Multicoloured.
3278 55p. Type **887** (research into DNA) 70 35
3279 65p. Miguel Catalan (spectrochemist) (research into atomic structures) . . . 85 35

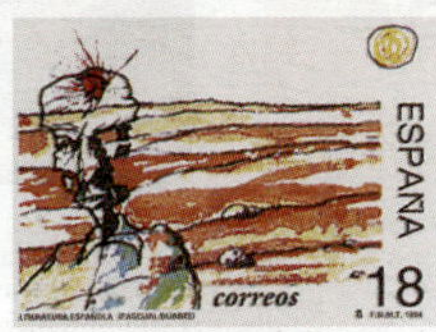

888 "Family of Pascual Duarte"

1994. Spanish Literature. Works of Camilo Jose Cela. Multicoloured.
3280 18p. Type **888** 25 15
3281 29p. Walker and horse rider ("Journey to Alcarria") 40 20

889 Sancho I Ramirez

1994. 900th Death Anniv of King Sancho I Ramirez of Aragon (3282) and 500th Anniv of Treaty of Tordesillas (defining Portuguese and Spanish spheres of influence) (others).
3282 **889** 18p. red, yellow and blue 25 20
3283 – 29p. multicoloured . . . 40 20
3284 – 55p. green, orange and brown 70 30
DESIGN—HORIZ: 29p Compass rose and arms of Tordesillas; 55p. Treaty House, Tordesillas.

891 "Giralda" (yacht)

893 Knight of Swords (14th-century Catalan deck)

892 Forum Caryatid and Tablet bearing Roman Name of Merida

1994. Ships sailed by Count of Barcelona. Multicoloured.
3286 16p. Type **891** 25 15
3287 29p. "Saltillo" (schooner) 40 15

1994. World Heritage Site. Merida.
3288 **892** 55p. brn, cinnamon & red 70 35

1994. Playing Card Museum, Vitoria. Multicoloured.
3289 18p. Type **893** 25 15
3290 29p. Jack of Clubs (Catalan Tarot deck, 1900) 40 20
3291 55p. King of Cups (Spanish deck by Juan Barbot, 1750) 70 35
3292 65p. "Mars", Jack of Diamonds (English deck by Stopforth, 1828) . . . 85 40

894 Globe and Douglas DC-8

1994. America. Postal Transport.
3293 **894** 65p. multicoloured . . . 75 35

895 Civil Guard (150th anniv)

1994. Public Services.
3294 – 18p. red and blue . . . 25 20
3295 **895** 29p. multicoloured . . . 40 20
DESIGN—As T **854**: 18p. Underground train (75th anniv of Madrid Metro).

896 Map of Member Countries

1994. 40th Anniv of Western European Union.
3296 **896** 55p. multicoloured . . . 70 35

897 Running

1994. Centenary of International Olympic Committee. Spanish Olympic Gold Medal Sports. Multicoloured.
3297 29p. Type **897** 40 20
3298 29p. Cycling 40 20
3299 29p. Skiing 40 20
3300 29p. Football 40 20
3301 29p. Show jumping 40 20
3302 29p. Hockey 40 20
3303 29p. Judo 40 20
3304 29p. Swimming 40 20
3305 29p. Archery 40 20
3306 29p. Yachting 40 20
See also Nos. 3332/45 and 3373/81.

898 "Adoration of the Kings" (detail of Ripoll altarpiece, Esteve Bover)

1994. Christmas.
3307 **898** 29p. multicoloured . . . 40 20

899 "Belle Epoque" (dir. Fernando Trueba)

1995. Spanish Cinema (2nd series). Film posters. Multicoloured.
3308 30p. Type **899** 40 25
3309 60p. "Volver a Empezar" (dir. Jose Luis Garci) . . 85 40

900 Logrono

1995. 900th Anniv of Logrono Law Code.
3310 **900** 30p. multicoloured . . . 40 25

902 Shaggy Ink Cap

1995. Fungi (3rd series). Multicoloured.
3312 19p. Type **902** 30 20
3313 30p. "Dermocybe cinnamomea" 40 20

1995. Minerals (2nd series). As T **880**. Mult.
3314 30p. Aragonite 40 25
3315 30p. Advanced Mining Engineering Technical School and Mining Museum, Madrid 40 25
3316 30p. Dolomite 40 25

903 19th-century Lion's Head Letter Box

1995. Stamp Day.
3317 **903** 30p. brown and green . . 40 20

904 Goicoechea and Talgo Train

1995. Birth Centenary of Alejandro Goicoechea (inventor of Talgo articulated train).
3318 **904** 30p. multicoloured . . . 40 25
3319 – 60p. blue and brown . . 85 40
DESIGN: 60p. Goicoechea and "Virgen del Pilar" articulated train.

905 Globe as Tree on Hand

1995. European Nature Conservation Year.
3320 **905** 60p. multicoloured . . . 80 40

907 Angel (from illuminated manuscript)

1995. 900th Anniv of Monastery of Liebana. Multicoloured.
3322 30p. Type **907** 40 25
3323 60p. Liebana landscape . . 85 40

908 Miguel Hernandez and part of "El Nino Yuntero"

1995. Literature.
3324 **908** 19p. multicoloured . . . 30 20
3325 – 30p. blue, green and black 40 25
DESIGN—VERT: 30p. Juan Valera and scene from "Juanita la Larga".

909 Marti

1995. Death Centenary of Jose Marti (Cuban poet).
3326 **909** 60p. multicoloured . . . 85 40

910 Captain Trueno

1995. Comic Strip Characters. Multicoloured.
3327 30p. Type **910** 40 25
3328 60p. Carpanta (vert) 85 35

911 Chain and Laurel Twig

1995. Europa. Peace and Freedom.
3329 **911** 60p. multicoloured . . . 85 45

912 Lumiere Brothers

1995. Centenary of Motion Pictures.
3330 **912** 19p. brown 25 15

913 Typewriter, Pen and Camera

1995. Centenary of Madrid Press Association.
3331 **913** 30p. multicoloured . . . 40 25

1995. Spanish Olympic Silver Medal Sports. As T **897**. Multicoloured.
3332 30p. Type **897** 40 25
3333 30p. Basketball 40 25
3334 30p. Boxing 40 25
3335 30p. As No. 3300 . . . . . 40 25
3336 30p. Gymnastics 40 25
3337 30p. As No. 3301 . . . . . 40 25
3338 30p. As No. 3302 . . . . . 40 25
3339 30p. Canoeing 40 25
3340 30p. Polo 40 25
3341 30p. Rowing 40 25
3342 30p. Tennis 40 25
3343 30p. Shooting 40 25
3344 30p. As No. 3306 . . . . . 40 25
3345 30p. Water polo 40 25

914 King Juan Carlos I at National Assembly, 1986

1995. Anniversaries. Multicoloured.
3346 60p. Type **914** (50th anniv of U.N.O.) 85 45
3347 60p. Anniversary emblem, globes and wheat ears (50th anniv of F.A.O.) (vert) 85 45
3348 60p. Emblem and coloured bands (20th anniv of World Tourism Organization) 85 45

915 Presidency Emblem

916 Spotlight on Woman

1995. Spanish Presidency of the European Union.
3349 **915** 60p. red, yellow and blue 85 45

1995. 4th U.N. Conference on Women, Peking.
3350 **916** 60p. multicoloured . . . 75 45

918 Entrance to Hospital de la Azabacheria

1995. 500th Anniv of University of Santiago de Compostela.
3352 **918** 30p. multicoloured . . . 35 25

919 Royal Monastery of Santa Maria, Guadalupe

1995. World Heritage Sites.
3353 **919** 60p. brown 70 40
3354 – 60p. multicoloured . . . 70 40
DESIGN—HORIZ: No. 3354, Route map of Spanish section of road to Santiago de Compostela and statue of pilgrim.

921 Red-crested pochard, Mallard and Lagoon of La Mancha

1995. America. Environmental Protection.
3356 **921** 60p. multicoloured . . . 70 40

922 La Cueva de Menga, Malaga (Bronze Age)

1995. Archaeology. Multicoloured.
3357 30p. Type **922** 40 25
3358 30p. La Taula de Torralba (c. 700 B.C.) 40 25

924 "Adoration of the Kings" (capital, Collegiate Church, San Martin de Elines)

1995. Christmas.
3360 **924** 30p. multicoloured . . . 35 25

925 King Juan Carlos

1995. 20th Anniv of Accession of King Juan Carlos I.
3361 **925** 1000p. violet . . . . . 10·50 2·40
See also Nos. 3408/11.

926 Cordoba Station, Plaza de Armas, Seville (venue)

1995. "Espamer" Spanish–Latin American and "Aviation and Space" Stamp Exhibitions, Seville. Multicoloured.
3362 60p. Type **926** 70 40
3363 60p. Dr. Lorenzo Galindez de Carvajal (Master Courier of the Indies and Terra Firma of the Ocean Sea, 1514) 70 40

927 "Leaving Mass at Pilar de Zaragoza" (first Spanish film, 1896)

1996. Centenary of Motion Pictures.
3364 **927** 30p. brown, mauve and black 35 25
3365 – 60p. multicoloured . . . 70 45
DESIGN: 60p. "Bienvenido, Mister Marshall!" (poster).

928 Miner's Lamp

1996. Minerals (3rd series). Multicoloured.
3366 30p. Type **928** 35 25
3367 60p. Amber fluorite 70 45

929 Jose Mathe Aragua (General Director) and Telegraph Tower

1996. Stamp Day. 150th Anniv of Madrid–Irun Telegraph Signal Line.
3368 **929** 60p. green and red . . . 70 45

930 Columbus (statue), "B" and Arch of Triumph

1996. 10th Anniv (1995) of Start of Barcelona Urbanization Programme.
3369 **930** 30p. multicoloured . . . 35 25

931 Brown Bear with Cubs

935 Carmen Amaya (flamenco dancer)

933 Scales

1996. Endangered Species.
3370 **931** 30p. multicoloured . . . 35 25

1996. 400th Anniv of Madrid Bar Assocation.
3372 **933** 19p. multicoloured . . . 25 20

1996. Spanish Olympic Bronze Medal Sports. As T **897**. Multicoloured. Dated "1996".
3373 30p. Type **897** 35 25
3374 30p. As No. 3334 . . . . . 35 25
3375 30p. As No. 3299 . . . . . 35 25
3376 30p. As No. 3302 . . . . . 35 25
3377 30p. As No. 3304 . . . . . 35 25
3378 30p. As No. 3339 . . . . . 35 25
3379 30p. As No. 3342 . . . . . 35 25
3380 30p. As No. 3343 . . . . . 35 25
3381 30p. As No. 3306 . . . . . 35 25

1996. Europa. Famous Women.
3383 **935** 60p. multicoloured . . . 70 45

936 El Jabato (Victor Mora and Francisco Darnis)

937 "General Don Antonio Ricardos"

1996. Comic Strip Characters. Multicoloured.
3384 19p. Type **936** 25 20
3385 30p. Reporter Tribulete (Guillermo Cifre) (horiz) 35 25

1996. 250th Birth Anniv of Francisco de Goya (artist). Multicoloured.
3386 19p. Type **937** 25 20
3387 30p. "The Milkmaid of Bordeaux" 35 25
3388 60p. "Boys with Mastiffs" (horiz) 75 40
3389 130p. "3rd of May 1808 in Madrid" (horiz) . . . . . 1·60 65

938 Magnifying Glass and Stamp Album

1996. 50th Anniv of Philatelic Service.
3390 **938** 30p. multicoloured . . . 35 25

939 Jose Monge Cruz (Camaron de la Isla)

1996. Flamenco Artistes.
3391 **939** 19p. multicoloured . . . 25 20
3392 – 30p. purple and red . . 35 20
DESIGN—HORIZ: 30p. Lola Flores.

940 Lanuza Market, Zaragoza (Felix Navarro Perez)

1996. 19th International Architects Congress, Barcelona. Metallic Buildings.
3393 **940** 30p. multicoloured . . . 35 25

941 Gerardo Diego and Pen (poet, birth centenary)

1996. Anniversaries.
3394 **941** 19p. violet and red . . . 25 20
3395 – 30p. multicoloured . . . 35 25
3396 – 60p. black, red and blue 70 45
DESIGNS—HORIZ: 30p. Joaquin Costa and birthplace (politician and historian, 150th birth anniv). VERT: 60p. The five senses (50th anniv of U.N.I.C.E.F.).

942 Naveta (tomb) des Tudons, Minorca

1996. Archaeology. Multicoloured.
3397 30p. Type **942** 35 20
3398 30p. Cabezo de Alcala de Azila, Teruel 35 25

944 Salamancan Costumes

945 Albaicin Quarter, Granada

1996. America. Traditional Costumes.
3400 **944** 60p. multicoloured . . . 70 45

1996. World Heritage Sites.
3401 **945** 19p. blue 25 20
3402 – 30p. purple 35 25
3403 – 60p. blue 70 45
DESIGNS—HORIZ: 30p. Tiberiades Square and statue of Maimonides (centre of Cordova). VERT: 60p. Deer, Donana National Park.

946 Oviedo Cathedral, Leopoldo Alas and Quotation from "La Regenta"

947 "Nativity" (Fernando Gallego)

1996. Literature.
3404 **946** 30p. blue and purple . . 35 25
3405 – 60p. blue and purple . . 70 45
DESIGN—HORIZ: 60p. Scene from "Don Juan Tenorio" by Jose Zorrilla.

1996. Christmas.
3406 **947** 30p. multicoloured . . . 35 25

1996. King Juan Carlos I.
3408 **925** 100p. brown . . . . . . 1·00 30
3409 200p. green . . . . . . 2·00 55
3410 300p. purple . . . . . 3·00 65
3411 500p. blue . . . . 5·00 1·40

949 Genet

950 Exhibition Poster (Jose Sanchez)

1997. Endangered Species.
3416 **949** 32p. multicoloured . . . 35 20

1997. "Juvenia '97" National Youth Stamp Exhibition, El Puerto de Santa Maria.
3417 **950** 32p. multicoloured . . . 35 25

951 Stone Post Box, Madrid

1997. Stamp Day.
3418 **951** 65p. blue and red . . . 70 50

952 "The Journey to Nowhere" (dir. Fernando Fernan)

953 La Caprichosa and Bano de Diana Waterfalls, Monastery of Piedra Park

1997. Spanish Cinema (3rd series). Posters. Multicoloured.
3419 21p. Type **952** 25 20
3420 32p. "The South" (dir. Victor Erice) 35 20

1997. World Water Day.
3421 **953** 65p. multicoloured . . . 70 50

955 Vizcaya Bridge

1997. Anniversaries. Metal Structures. Mult.
3423 32p. Type **955** (centenary of Engineering School, Bilbao) 35 25
3424 194p. Atocha railway station and AVE locomotive (fifth anniv of AVE high speed train) . . . . 2·00 1·10

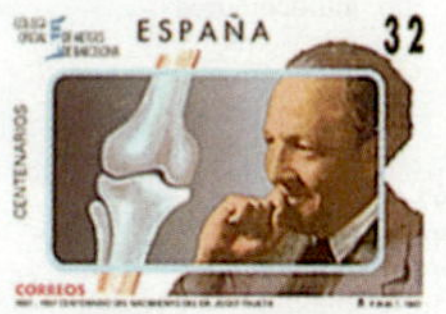

956 Joint and Trueta

1997. Birth Centenary of Josep Trueta i Raspall (orthopaedic surgeon).
3425 **956** 32p. multicoloured . . . 35 25

957 Prince and Princess, Castle and Forest

958 Lazaro with Blind Beggar

1997. Europa. Tales and Legends.
3426 **957** 65p. multicoloured . . . 70 50

1997. Spanish Literature.
3427 **958** 21p. black and green . . 25 20
3428 – 32p. brown and blue . . 35 25
DESIGNS—VERT: 21p. Type **958** ("Life of Lazarillo de Tormes and his Fortunes and Setbacks"). HORIZ: 32p. Jose Maria Peman and character El Seneca.

959 Anxel Fole (writer) (after Siro Lopez Lorenzo)

1997. Galician Literature Day.
3429 **959** 65p. multicoloured . . . 70 45

960 The Ulysses Family (Mariano Benejam)

1997. Comic Strip Characters. Multicoloured.
3430 21p. Type **960** 25 10
3431 32p. The Masked Warrior (Manuel Gago) 35 25

961 Manolete (Manuel Rodriguez Sanchez) (matador)

1997. Anniversaries. Multicoloured.
3432 32p. Type **961** (50th death anniv) 35 25
3433 65p. Charlie Rivel (Josep Andreu i Lasserre) (clown, birth centenary (1996)) . . 70 50

963 Championship Poster (Manel Esclusa)

1997. 30th Men's European Basketball Championship, Barcelona, Girona and Badalona.
3435 **963** 65p. multicoloured . . . 70 50

964 Cibeles Fountain, Madrid

1997. North Atlantic Co-operation Council Summit, Madrid.
3436 **964** 65p. multicoloured . . . 70 50

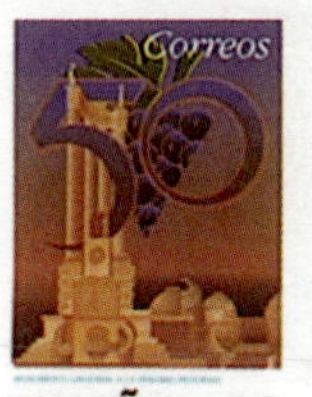

965 Grape Harvest Monument (Jose Esteve Edo)

966 Antonio Canovas del Castillo (author of 1876 Constitution)

1997. 50th Anniv of Grape Harvest Festival, Requena.
3437 **965** 32p. multicoloured . . . 35 25

1997. Anniversaries. Multicoloured.
3438 21p. Type **966** (death centenary) 25 20
3439 32p. Roman coin and arrival of "Virgin of the Assumption" (statue) (2000th anniv of Elche) 35 25
3440 65p. Ships attacking city (after contemporary painting) (bicentenary of defence of Tenerife) (horiz) 70 50

967 Blue Ribbon

968 Mariano Benlliure and "Breath of Life"

1997. Campaign for Peaceful Co-existence.
3441 **967** 32p. blue and black . . 35 25

1997. Spanish Art.
3442 **968** 32p. multicoloured . . . 35 35
3443 – 65p. black and stone . . 70 70
DESIGNS: 32c. Type **968** (sculptor, 50th death anniv); 65c. "Basque Rower" (photograph by Jose Ortiz Echague).

969 Net and Boat

1997. 4th World Fishing Fair, Vigo.
3444 **969** 32p. blue, deep blue and gold 35 35

970 City

1997. Anniversaries.
3445 **970** 21p. multicoloured . . . 25 20
3446 – 32p. multicoloured . . . 35 25
3447 – 65p. violet and red . . . 70 50
DESIGNS—VERT: 21p. Type **970** (500th anniv of Spanish administration of Melilla); 32p. St. Pascual Baylon (after Vincente Carducho) (centenary of proclamation as World Patron of Eucharistic Congresses). HORIZ: 65p. Ausias March (after Jacomart) (poet, 600th birth anniv).

971 San Julian de los Prados Church, Oviedo

1997. World Heritage Sites.
3448 **971** 21p. brown, blue and green 25 20
3449 – 32p. brown, blue and green 35 25
DESIGN: 32p. Santa Cristina de Lena.

972 Emblem **974** Postman

1997. 29th Annual Congress of International Transport and Communications Museums Association, Madrid.
3450 **972** 140p. multicoloured . . 1·50 65

1997. America. Postal Delivery.
3452 **974** 65p. multicoloured . . . 70 50

975 Miguel Fleta (tenor) **976** Town Arms

1997. Re-opening of Royal Theatre, Madrid.
3453 **975** 21p. brown 25 20
3454 – 32p. brown 35 25
DESIGNS: 21p. Type **975** (birth centenary); 32p. Theatre facade.

1997. 500th Anniv of San Cristobal de la Laguna, Tenerife.
3455 **976** 32p. multicoloured . . . 35 25

977 Emblem

1997. 6th World Downs Syndrome Congress, Madrid.
3456 **977** 65p. blue and yellow . . 70 50

978 School

1997. 150th Anniv of Cordoba Veterinary School.
3457 **978** 21p. green and blue . . 25 20

979 "Adoration of the Kings" (detail, Pedro Berruguete)

1997. Christmas.
3458 **979** 32p. multicoloured . . . 35 25

980 New Gate, Ribadavia

1997. Jewish Quarters.
3459 **980** 21p. brown and black . . 25 30
3460 – 32p. violet and black . . 35 30
3461 – 32p. brown and black . . 35 30
3462 – 65p. violet and black . . 70 50
DESIGNS: No. 3460, Women's Gallery, Cordoba Synagogue; 3461, Facade of 15th-century building, St. Anthony's Quarter, Caceres; 3462, Street, El Call, Girona.

981 Ball in Net **982** Emblem

1997. Spanish Sporting Success. Zarra's Winning Goal in Spain v England Match, World Cup Football Championship, Brazil, 1950.
3463 **981** 32p. multicoloured . . . 75 30

1998. St. James's Holy Year (1999).
3464 **982** 35p. orange, grey and black 35 20

983 Lynx **985** Clever and Smart (Francisco Ibanez)

984 Club Flag and Emblem

1998. Endangered Species.
3465 **983** 35p. multicoloured . . . 35 20

1998. Centenary of Athletic Bilbao Football Club.
3466 **984** 35p. multicoloured . . . 35 25

1998. Comic Strip Characters. Multicoloured.
3467 35p. Type **985** 35 25
3468 70p. Zipi and Zape (Josep Escobar) (horiz) 70 50

986 Gredos Parador

1998. 70th Anniv of Paradores (state hotels).
3469 **986** 35p. multicoloured . . . 35 25

987 St. Philip's Fort and Harbour, Ceuta

1998. 3rd Anniv of Autonomy of Ceuta and Melilla. Multicoloured.
3470 150p. Type **987** . . . . . 1·60 90
3471 150p. Plaza de Menendez Pelayo, Melilla (horiz) . . 1·60 90

988 1898 Generation

1998. 1898 Generation of Spanish Writers.
3472 **988** 70p. multicoloured . . . 70 50
The writers depicted are Azorin, Pio Baroja, Miguel de Unamuno, Ramiro de Maeztu, Antonio Machado and Valle Inclan.

989 Pedro Abarca de Bolea, Count of Aranda **990** "The Celestine" (Fernando de Rojas)

1998. Death Bicentenary of Pedro Abarca de Bolea, Count of Aranda (politician).
3473 **989** 35p. multicoloured . . . 35 25

1998. Spanish Literature.
3474 **990** 35p. deep green and green 35 25
3475 – 70p. green and red . . . 70 50
DESIGN: 70p. "Fortunata and Jecinta" (Benito Perez Galdos).

991 Royal Barge

1998. Ship Paintings by Carlos Broschi from "Royal Celebrations in Reign of Fernando VI". Multicoloured.
3476 35p. Type **991** 35 25
3477 70p. Tajo xebec (for court officials) 70 50

992 St. John's Bonfires, Alicante

1998. Europa. National Festivals.
3478 **992** 70p. multicoloured . . . 70 50

993 Jimenez Diaz

1998. Centenary of Professional Institute of Doctors of Madrid and Birth Centenary of Carlos Jimenez Diaz (physician).
3479 **993** 35p. black and blue . . 35 25

994 Felix Rodriguez de la Fuente (naturalist, 70th anniv)

1998. Birth Anniversaries.
3480 **994** 35p. multicoloured . . . 35 25
3481 – 70p. orange and red . . 70 50
DESIGN—VERT: 70p. Fofo (Alfonso Aragon) (clown, 75th anniv).

995 Philip II (after Antonio Moro) **996** Lorca

1998. 400th Death Anniv of King Philip II.
3482 **995** 35p. multicoloured . . . 35 25

1998. Birth Centenary of Federico Garcia Lorca (writer).
3483 **996** 35p. multicoloured . . . 35 25

997 Antonio Manso Fernandez and 1978 Queen Isabel II Stamp

1998. Spanish Engravers.
3484 **997** 35p. brown, blue and deep blue 35 25
3485 – 70p. purple, blue and black 70 50
DESIGN: 70p. Jose Luis Sanchez Toda and 1935 Mariana Pineda stamp.

998 Spanish and Philippine Flags, Cebu Basilica (after M. Miguel) and "Holy Child" (statuette)

1998. Centenary of Philippine Independence.
3486 **998** 70p. multicoloured . . . 70 50

999 "Foster Brothers" (sculpture, Aniceto Marinas)

1998. Spanish Art.
3487 **999** 35p. multicoloured . . . 35 25

1000 "Union of the Oceans"

1998. "Expo '98" World's Fair, Lisbon.
3488 **1000** 70p. multicoloured . . 70 50

1001 Computer, Computer Disk and Letter

1998. 20th International Data Protection Conference, Santiago de Compostela.
3489 **1001** 70p. multicoloured . . 70 50

1003 Fortified City, Cuenca

1998. World Heritage Sites.
3491 **1003** 35p. brown and blue . . 35 25
3492 – 70p. brown and red . . 70 50
DESIGN: 70p. Silk Exchange, Valencia.

1004 Man writing with Quill

1998. School Correspondence Programme. Scenes from "Don Quixote" (novel by Cervantes). Multicoloured.
3493 20p. Type **1004** 25 20
3494 20p. Man reading book . . 25 20
3495 20p. Priest dubbing Quixote 25 20
3496 20p. Quixote riding off at dawn (angel blowing trumpet) 25 20
3497 20p. Man beating Quixote with stick 25 20
3498 20p. Investigator burning books 25 20
3499 20p. Quixote and Sancho on horseback 25 20
3500 20p. Quixote and horse on sail of windmill 25 20
3501 20p. Quixote watching Sancho fly through air . . 25 20
3502 20p. Quixote charging through flock of sheep . . 25 20
3503 20p. Quixote and galley slaves 25 20
3504 20p. Quixote piercing goat-skins of wine 25 20
3505 20p. Quixote in cage 25 20
3506 20p. Quixote and Sancho on knees and woman on donkey 25 20
3507 20p. Quixote on foot holding sword to Knight of the Mirrors 25 20
3508 20p. Lion escaping cage . . 25 20
3509 20p. Quixote attacking birds 25 20
3510 20p. Quixote on wooden horse 25 20
3511 20p. Sancho as governor at meal 25 20
3512 20p. Quixote surprised in bed by Dona Rodriguez 25 20
3513 20p. Sancho and donkey . . 25 20
3514 20p. Quixote and Sancho looking over lake 25 20
3515 20p. Quixote on horse holding sword to Knight of the White Moon . . . 25 20
3516 20p. Quixote and Sancho returning home at night 35 25

1005 Angel Ganivet (writer, death centenary)

1998. Anniversaries.
3517 **1005** 35p. brown and violet 70 35
3518 – 70p. brown and blue . . 35 50
DESIGN—VERT: 70p. Giralda Tower, Seville (800th anniv).

1006 Ladies' Tower and El Partal Gardens, Alhambra, Granada

1998. Aga Khan 1998 Architecture Award.
3519 **1006** 35p. brown and green 70 35

1007 U.P.U. Emblem

1998. World Stamp Day.
3520 **1007** 70p. blue and green . . 70 55

1008 Maria Guerrero (actress) and Scene from "The Lioness of Castille" by Francisco Villaespesa

1998. America. Famous Women.
3521 **1008** 70p. multicoloured . . 35 50

1009 Steam Locomotive "Mataro" (1848) and Euromed Electric Train (1998)

1998. 150th Anniv of Spanish Railways.
3522 **1009** 35p. blue and black . . 35 25

1010 Antarctic Base

1998. 10th Anniv of Juan Carlos I Antarctic Base.
3523 **1010** 35p. multicoloured . . 00 65

1012 Chestnut Seller

1998. Christmas. Multicoloured.
3525 35p. Type **1012** 35 25
3526 70p. "Wedding of Virgin Mary and Joseph" (detail of capital from Oviedo Cathedral) 70 55

1013 Juan de Onate (expedition leader)

1998. 400th Anniv of Foundation of Spanish Province of New Mexico. Multicoloured.
3527 35p. Type **1013** 35 25
3528 70p. Map and arms of New Mexico 70 55

1014 House, Hervas

1998. Jewish Quarters.
3529 **1014** 35p. purple and blue . . 35 30
3530 – 35p. green and blue . . 35 30
3531 – 70p. purple and blue . . 70 50
3532 – 70p. green and blue . . 70 50
DESIGNS: No. 3530, Bust of Benjamin Tudela (travel writer); 3531, Corpus Christi Church (former synagogue), Segovia; 3532, Santa Maria la Blanca synagogue, Toledo.

1015 Alaior and Mt. Toro

1998. U.N.E.S.C.O. Biosphere Reserve, Minorca.
3533 **1015** 35p. multicoloured . . 35 25

1016 Bust of Plato and Ancient Greek Amphora

1998. 30th Anniv of Spanish Olympic Academy.
3534 **1016** 70p. multicoloured . . 70 55

1017 Angel Sanz Briz (diplomat)

1998. 50th Anniv of Universal Declaration of Human Rights. Multicoloured.
3535 35p. Type **1017** 35 25
3536 70p. Fingerprints forming heart (painting, Javier Valmaseda Calvo) 70 50

1018 Mare and Foal

1998. "Espana 2000" International Stamp Exhibition (1st issue). La Cartuja-Hierro del Bocado Horses. Multicoloured.
3537 20p. Type **1018** (emblem bottom right) 25 15
3538 20p. Type **1018** (emblems top left and top right) . . 25 15
3539 35p. Brown horse (emblem top right) 35 20
3540 35p. As No. 3538 (emblem bottom left) 35 20
3541 70p. Horse's head (emblems bottom left and bottom right) 60 50
3542 70p. As No. 3541 (emblem top left) 60 50
3543 100p. Mare and foal (different) (emblems top left and top right) . . 90 55
3544 100p. As No. 3543 (emblem bottom right) 90 55
3545 150p. Grey (emblem bottom left) . . . . 1·40 75
3546 150p. As No. 3545 (emblem top right) . . . . . . 1·40 75
3547 185p. Two white horses (emblem top left) . . . . 1·60 1·10
3548 185p. As No. 3547 (emblems bottom left and bottom right) . . . . 1·60 1·10
See also Nos. 3612/23 and 3662/3.

1019 Giant Lizard, El Hierro Island

1999. Endangered Species. Multicoloured.
3549 35p. Type **1019** 35 30
3550 70p. Osprey (vert) 70 55
3551 100p. Manx shearwater . . 1·10 55

1020 Stone Cross, Perelada, Galicia

1021 Poster (Antoni Tapies)

1999. St. James's Holy Year. Multicoloured.
3552 35p. Type **1020** 35 20
3553 70p. Figure of St. James on tympanum, St. James's Church, Sanguesa, Navarra (horiz) 70 35
3554 100p. Stone cross and Cizur bridge, Pamplona, Navarra . . . . 1·10 45
3555 185p. Jurisdictional stone pillar, Boadilla del Camino, Palencia . . . . 1·90 90

1999. Centenary of Barcelona Football Club.
3556 **1021** 35p. multicoloured . . 35 25

1022 "Alaior" (Aroa Vidal)

1999. "Juvenia'99" National Youth Stamp Exhibition, Alaior, Minorca.
3557 **1022** 35p. black, red and yellow 35 25

1023 Police Moped, Helicopter and Men in Protective Suits

1999. 175th Anniv of Spanish Police Force.
3558 **1023** 35p. multicoloured . . 35 25

1025 Radio Transmitter and Receiver

1999. 50th Anniv of Spanish Amateur Radio Union.
3560 **1025** 70p. multicoloured . . 70 50

1026 Emblem and Athletes

1999. 7th World Athletics Championship, Seville.
3561 **1026** 70p. multicoloured . . 70 50

1027 Monfrague Nature Park, Caceres, and Wild Cat

1999. Europa. Parks and Gardens.
3562 **1027** 70p. multicoloured . . 70 50

1028 Underground Train

1999. 75th Anniv of Barcelona Metro.
3563 **1028** 70p. multicoloured . . 70 50

1029 "King Solomon" (detail of reredos from Becerril de Campos Church)

1999. "The Ages of Man" Exhibition, Palencia. Multicoloured.
3564 35p. Type **1029** 35 25
3565 70p. Detail of choir railing, Palencia Cathedral . . . 70 50

1030 European Community Flag

1999. The Euro (European single currency). Showing maps of the participating countries and the appropriate exchange rate. Multicoloured.
3566 166p. Type **1030** . . . . . 1·50 1·20
3567 166p. Germany . . . . . . 1·50 1·20
3568 166p. Austria . . . . 1·50 1·20
3569 166p. Belgium . . . . . . 1·50 1·20
3570 166p. Spain . . . . 1·50 1·20
3571 166p. Finland . . . . 1·50 1·20
3572 166p. France . . . . 1·50 1·20
3573 166p. Netherlands . . . . . 1·50 1·20
3574 166p. Republic of Ireland . . 1·50 1·20
3575 166p. Italy . . . . 1·50 1·20
3576 166p. Luxembourg . . . . 1·50 1·20
3577 166p. Portugal . . . . . . 1·50 1·20

1031 Footballers and Club Badge

1999. Real Club Recreativo (Royal Recreation Club) of Huelva.
3578 **1031** 35p. multicoloured . . 35 25

1032 Dona Urraca (Jorge (Miguel Bernet Toledano))

1035 Cangas de Onis Parador (former Monastery of San Pedro de Villanueva)

1034 Attack of Dutch Navy (after De Bry) and Arms of Las Palmas

1999. Comic Strip Characters. Multicoloured.
3579 35p. Type **1032** 35 25
3580 70p. El Coyote (Jose Mallorqui and Francisco Batet) 70 50

1999. 400th Anniv of Defence of Las Palmas, Gran Canaria.
3582 **1034** 70p. black and yellow 70 50

1999. Paradores (state hotels).
3583 **1035** 35p. multicoloured . . 35 25

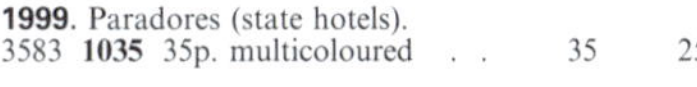

1036 Old Bridge

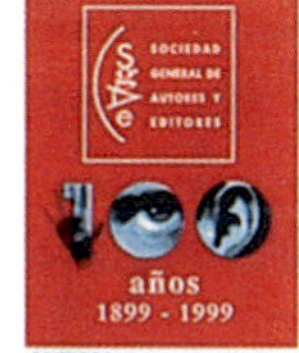
1037 Society and Anniversary Emblems

1999. 800th Anniv of Granting of Township Rights to Balmaseda.
3584 **1036** 35p. multicoloured . . 35 30

1999. Centenary of Society of Authors and Publishers.
3585 **1037** 70p. multicoloured . . 70 50

1038 Illuminated Fountain

1999. Birth Centenary of Carles Buigas (engineer).
3586 **1038** 70p. multicoloured . . 70 50

1039 Queen Isabel II, Geological Map of Spain and Founding Decree

1999. 150th Anniv of Spanish Technical Institute of Geology and Mining.
3587 **1039** 150p. multicoloured . . 1·60 1·10

1040 El Cid (after Vela Zanetti)

1042 "The Jester Don Sebastian de Morra"

1041 "Winter"

1999. 900th Death Anniv of El Cid (Rodrigo Diaz de Vivar).
3588 **1040** 35p. multicoloured . . 35 25

1999. Spanish Art. Paintings by Vela Zanetti. Multicoloured.
3589 70p. Type **1041** 70 35
3590 150p. "The Harvest" (vert) 1·60 90

1999. 400th Birth Anniv of Diego de Silva Velazquez (artist). Multicoloured.
3591 35p. Type **1042** 35 25
3592 70p. "A Sibyl" 70 50

1043 Emblem, Couple, Man and Baby

1999. International Year of the Elderly.
3593 **1043** 35p. multicoloured . . 35 25

1044 Oix Castle

1999. Catalan Lower Pyrenees Region.
3594 **1044** 70p. brown and blue . . 70 50

1045 St. Millan of Yuso Monastery, La Rioja

1999. World Heritage Sites.
3595 **1045** 35p. brown, green and blue 35 25
3596 – 70p. brown, green and blue 70 35
DESIGN: 70p. St. Millan of Suso Monastery, La Rioja.

1046 U.P.U. Monument, Berne

1999. Stamp Day. 125th Anniv of Universal Postal Union.
3597 **1046** 70p. multicoloured . . 70 50

1047 First Spanish Stamp, 1850

1999. School Correspondence Programme. Designs showing a stamp performing various activities. Multicoloured.
3598 20p. Type **1047** 25 15
3599 20p. Watching airliner taking off over city . . . 25 15
3600 20p. As postman delivering letter 25 15
3601 20p. Writing letter 25 15
3602 20p. Reading book 25 15
3603 20p. With bird, butterfly and fish (nature) 25 15
3604 20p. Viewing historical buildings (heritage) . . . 25 15
3605 20p. Painting portrait 25 15
3606 20p. With football, tennis racquet and sailboard . . 25 15
3607 20p. With baton, cello and saxophone 25 15
3608 20p. Holding magnifying glass over 40c. stamp . . 25 15
3609 20p. On horseback 25 15

1048 Dove on Hand

1999. America. A New Millennium without Arms.
3610 **1048** 70p. multicoloured . . 70 50

1049 "The Money Changer and his Wife" (Marinus Reymerswaele)

1999. National Money Museums Congress, Madrid.
3611 **1049** 70p. brown and blue . . 70 50

1050 Horse and Rider

1999. "Espana 2000" International Stamp Exhibition, Madrid (2nd issue). La Cartuja-Hierro del Bocado Horses. Paintings by Jose Manuel Gomez. Multicoloured.
3612 20p. Type **1050** (emblem bottom right) 25 15
3613 20p. Type **1050** (emblem top left) 25 15
3614 35p. Exhibition emblem and horses (emblems top left and right) 35 20
3615 35p. As No. 3614 (emblems top left and right but transposed) 35 20
3616 70p. Exhibition emblem (emblems bottom left and right) 70 30
3617 70p. As No. 3616 (emblems bottom left and right but transposed) 70 30
3618 100p. White horses (emblem top right) . . . . . . 1·10 40
3619 100p. As No. 3618 (emblem bottom left) . . . . . 1·10 40
3620 150p. Heads of two white horses (emblem bottom left) . . . . 1·40 50
3621 150p. As No. 3620 (emblem top right) . . . . 1·40 50
2622 185p. Men inspecting horse (emblem top left) . . . . 1·25 25
3623 185p. As No. 3622 (emblem bottom right) . . . . . 1·60 65

1051 "The Epiphany" (altarpiece, Toledo Cathedral)

1999. Christmas. Multicoloured.
3624 35p. Type **1051** 35 25
3625 70p. "Christmas" (Isabel Guerra) (horiz) 70 50

1052 King Juan Carlos and 1850 12c. Stamp

2000. 150th Anniv of First Spanish Stamp. Mult.
3626 35p. Type **1052** 35 20
3627 35p. King Juan Carlos and 6c. stamp 35 20
3628 35p. King Juan Carlos and 5r. stamp 35 20
3629 35p. King Juan Carlos and 6r. stamp 35 20
3630 35p. Anniversary emblem and 6c. stamp 35 20
3631 35p. King Juan Carlos and 10r. stamp 35 20
3632 35p. King Juan Carlos and State arms 35 20

1053 Apollo

2000. Endangered Butterflies. Multicoloured.
3633 35p. Type **1053** 35 20
3634 70p. *Agriades zullichi* . . . 70 50

1054 Virgin Mary and Baby Jesus (xylographic engraving, Juan Luschner)

1055 "Charles V as Sovereign Master of the Order of the Golden Fleece" (anon)

2000. 500th Anniv of the Monastery of Santa Maria of Montserrat Printing House.
3635 **1054** 35p. multicoloured . . 35 25

2000. 500th Birth Anniv of King Charles V, Holy Roman Emperor. Multicoloured.
3636 35p. Type **1055** 35 25
3637 70p. "Charles V" (Corneille da la Haye) 70 25

1056 The Virgin de al Majestad (12th-century statue), Astorga Cathedral

2000. "The Age of Man" Exhibition, Astorga, Leon. Multicoloured.
3639 70p. Type **1056** 70 25
3640 100p. 12th-century Lignum Crucis and 10th-century Arab perfume bottle) . . 1·00 20

1057 Sos del Rey Catolico, Saragossa

2000. Paradores (state hotels).
3641 **1057** 35p. multicoloured . . 35 25

1058 Lleida University

2000. University Anniversaries.
3642 **1058** 35p. brown and mauve 35 25
3643 – 70p. brown and blue . . 70 30
DESIGNS: 35p. Type **1058** (700th anniv); 70p. Valencia (500th anniv (1999)).

1059 Emblem

1060 Maria de las Mercedes (painting, Ricardo Macarron)

2000. Centenary of Reial Club Deportiu Espanyol Football Club, Barcelona.
3644 **1059** 35p. multicoloured . . 35 25

2000. Maria de las Mercedes de Borbon y Orleans (mother of King Juan Carlos I) Commemoration.
3645 **1060** 35p. multicoloured . . 35 25

1061 "Building Europe"

2000. Europa.
3646 **1061** 70p. multicoloured . . 70 30

1062 Emblem

2000. World Mathematics Year (3648) and Science (others). Multicoloured.
3647 35p. Type **1062** (300th anniv of Royal Academy of Medicine, Seville) 35 25
3648 70p. Julio Rey Pastor (mathematician) (painting, Pedro Piug Adam) and mathematical equation . . 70 25
3649 100p. School of Pharmacy, Granada (150th anniv) (vert) . . . . 1·10 55
3650 185p. Prince Felipe Science Museum, Valencia . . . . 1·60 1·30

1063 Hermenegilda and Leovigilda (Manuel Vazquez Gallego)

2000. Comic Strip Characters. Multicoloured.
3651 35p. Type **1063** 35 25
3652 70p. Roberto Alcazar and Pedrin (Eduardo Vano and Juan Bautista Puerto Belda) (vert) 70 50

1064 Guggenheim Museum

2000. 700th Anniv of Bilbao.
3653 **1064** 70p. multicoloured . . 70 50

1065 "Prayer in the Garden" (detail, Francisco Salzillo)

2000. Spanish Art.
3654 **1065** 70p. multicoloured . . 70 50

1067 Wild Pine (*Pinus silvestris*)

2000. Trees (1st series). Multicoloured.
3656 70p. Type **1067** 70 50
3657 150p. Holm oak (*Quercus ilex*) . . . . 1·50 85
See also Nos. 3757/8 and 3837/8.

1068 Fire Walking, San Pedro Manrique, Soria

2000. Festivals (1st series). Multicoloured.
3658 35p. Type **1068** 35 25
3659 70p. Rearing horse, crowd and flag (700th anniv of Chivalry Festival of San Juan, Ciudadela, Menorca) 70 50
See also Nos 3760/1.

1069 Escriva

2000. 25th Death Anniv of Josemaria Escriva de Balaguer (founder of Opus Dei (religious organization)).
3660 **1069** 70p. black and orange 70 50

1071 Horse and Emblem

2000. "Espana 2000" International Stamp Exhibition, Madrid (3rd issue). La Carbija-Hierro de Bocado Horses. Multicoloured.
3662 20p. Type **1071** (emblem bottom right) 25 15
3663 20p. Type **1071** (emblems top right) 25 15
3664 35p. Horse on beach (emblem top right) . . . 35 20
3665 35p. As No. 3664 (emblem bottom left) 35 20
3666 70p. Galloping horses and horse's head (emblems bottom left and right) . . 70 35
3667 70p. As No. 3666 (emblem top left) 70 35
3668 100p. Two horses' heads (emblems top left and right) . . . . 1·10 45
3669 100p. As No. 3668 (emblem bottom right) . . . . . 1·10 45
3670 150p. Horse and horse's head (emblem bottom left) 1·60 70
3671 150p. As No. 3671 (emblem top right) . . . . . . 1·60 70
3672 185p. Horse outside stable (emblem top left) . . . 1·90 90
3673 185p. As No. 3672 (emblems bottom left and right) . . 1·90 90
Nos. 3662/73 were issued together in se-tenant sheetlets of 12 stamps. Two different emblems were each printed twice in orange within the sheet, occurring in each case at the intersection of four stamps so that each stamp carries only part of one or two emblems as described in brackets.

1072 Las Medulas, Leon

2000. U.N.E.S.C.O. World Heritage Sites.
3674 **1072** 35p. multicoloured . . 35 25
3675 – 70p. brown and blue (vert) 70 50
3676 – 150p. red and brown 1·50 1·10
DESIGNS: 70p. Mount Perdido, Pyrenees; 150p. Catalan Music Palace, Barcelona.

1073 Atapuercan Man wearing Football Scarf

2000. School Correspondence Programme (1st series). Spanish History. Multicoloured.
3677 20p. Type **1073** 25 15
3678 20p. Cave artists, Altamira 25 15
3679 20p. Phoenician ship 25 15
3680 20p. Question marks in Roman helmets (Tartessos) 25 15
3681 20p. Celtic and Iberian men 25 15
3682 20p. "The Lady of Elche" listening to music 25 15
3683 20p. Elephant on low-loader (Carthage) (first Punic war) 25 15
3684 20p. Romans 25 15
3685 20p. Viriathus (leader) attacking Roman (uprising in northern Spain) 25 15
3686 20p. Roman preparing to kick football into net full of Numanians (fall of the city of Numantia) . . . 25 15
3687 20p. Aqueduct of Segova . . 25 15
3688 20p. Roman facing Vandal, Suevian and Alani (invasion, 409) 25 15
3689 20p. Visigoth kings Teodoredo I, Wallia, Sigerico and Ataulfo . . . 25 15
3690 20p. King Recaredo I (conversion to Christianity, 589) 25 15
3691 20p. Map showing extent of Arab rule (conquest by Arab forces, 711) 25 15
3692 20p. Pelayo (Visigoth soldier), Covadonga, 722 (victory over the Moors) 25 15
3693 20p. Horseman (discovery of Tomb of the Apostle, 813) 25 15
3694 20p. Kings (union of Castille and Navarre) 25 15
3695 20p. Death of El Cid (soldier), 1099 . . . . . 25 15
3696 20p. Battle of Las Navas de Tolosa represented by chess game 25 15
3697 20p. Accession of Alfonso X (1252) 25 15
3698 20p. Enrique II and slain Pedro I foundation of House of Trastamara (Kingdom of Castille and Leon), 1396 . . . . . . 25 15
3699 20p. Monk with magnifying glass (The Inquisition, established 1478) 25 15
3700 20p. Two crowns (unification of Kingdoms of Castile and Aragon 1479) 25 15
See also Nos. 3775/86 and 3882/93.

1075 Boy putting up Poster

1076 Portrait and Treble Clef

2000. America. A.I.D.S. Awareness.
3702 **1075** 70p. multicoloured . . 70 50

2000. 1st Death Anniv of Alfred Kraus (tenor).
3703 **1076** 70p. multicoloured . . 70 50

1077 The Adoration of Jesus (triptych) (Cristiane Hemmerich)

1078 Building Facade

2000. Christmas. Multicoloured.
3704 35p. Type **1077** 40 25
3705 70p. "Birth of Christ" (Conrad von Soest) . . . 70 50

2000. Millenary of Santa María la Real Church, Aranda de Duero.
3706 **1078** 35p. brown 40 25

1079 Couple in Orange Grove (*Etre Naranjos*, Vicente Blasco Ibanez)

2000. Literature.
3707 35p. Type **1079** 40 25
3708 70p. Troubadour with lute, figures and castle (*La Venganza de Don Mendo*, Pedro Munzo Seca) . . . 70 35
3709 100p. Soldiers (*El Alcalde Zalamea*, Pedro Calaeron de la Barca) . . . . . . 1·00 50

1080 "Tribute to Broker" (sculpture) (Francisco Lopez Hernandez) and Emblem

1081 Firefighters

2001. 75th Anniv of Brokers' Schools.
3710 **1080** 40p. multicoloured . . 40 20

2001.
3711 **1081** 75p. multicoloured . . 70 45

1082 Soldier, Building and Emblem

2001. 150th Anniv of Infantry College, Toledo.
3712 **1082** 120p. multicoloured . . 1·10 35

1083 Emblem

2001. Campaign Against Domestic Violence.
3713 **1083** 155p. multicoloured . . 1·40 45

1084 First Post Box in Spain, Mayorga (1793)

2001. Stamp Day.
3714 **1084** 155p. black . . . . . . 1·40 45

1085 Young Couple and Yacht

2001. "Juvenia 2001" Youth Stamp Exhibition, Cadiz.
3715 **1085** 12p. multicoloured . . 1·10 25

1086 Plasencia Hotel (former monastery of San Vicente Ferrer)

2001. Paradores (state hotels).
3716 **1086** 40p. multicoloured . . 40 20

1087 Joaquin Rodrigo (composer, birth centenary)

2001. Personalities.
3717 **1087** 40p. violet 40 20
3718 – 75p. brown and blue . . 70 45
DESIGNS: 75p. Rafael Alberti (poet and dramatist, first death anniv).

1088 Zuda Castle, Tortosa

1089 Books forming Flower

2001. Castles. Multicoloured.
3719 40p. Type **1088** 40 20
3720 75p. Castle of El Cid, Jadraque (horiz) 70 30
3721 155p. San Fernando Castle, Figueres (horiz) . . . . . 1·40 45
3722 260p. Montesquiu Castle (horiz) . . . . 2·40 75

2001. World Book Day.
3723 **1089** 40p. multicoloured . . 40 20

1090 Dornier Do-J Wal Flying Boat, *Plus Ultra* and Map of South America

2001. 75th Anniv of Spanish Aviation. Multicoloured.
3724 40p. Type **1090** (flight from Palos de Fontera, Spain to Buenos Aires, 1926) . . 40 25
3725 75p. Breguet 19A2 and map of Europe (flight by Gallariza and Loruga from Madrid to Manilla, 1926) 70 35
3726 155p. Dornier flying boat and map of Africa (flight from Melilla to Santa Isabel, Equatorial Guinea, 1926) . . . . 1·40 50
3727 260p. C-295 (transport) (commemorative flight) . . 2·20 80
Nos. 3724/7 were issued together, se-tenant, the backgrounds forming the composite design of a map.

1091 Decorated Ceiling and Emblem

1092 King Juan Carlos I

2001. 154th Anniv of Liceu Theatre.
3728 **1091** 120p. multicoloured . . 1·10 35

2001.
3729 5p. red and silver . . . 10 15
3730 **1092** 40p. green and silver . . 40 15
3744 75p. violet and silver 70 35
3748 100p. brown and silver 90 20

1093 Garden

1094 Church Facade (church of San Martino, Noia)

2001. Europa. Water Resources.
3750 **1093** 75p. multicoloured . . 70 35

2001. Architecture.
3751 **1094** 40p. brown and blue . . 40 20
3752 – 75p. multicoloured . . 70 20
3753 – 155p. blue and brown 1·30 25
DESIGNS: 75p. Tui Cathedral, Pontevedra; 155p. Dovecote, Villaconcha, Frechilla.

1095 Peninsula, Marina and Bay

2001. Luarca.
3754 **1095** 40p. multicoloured . . 40 20

1096 De Castro (statue, Juan de Bologna) and School of Our Lady of Antigua

2001. 400th Death Anniv of Cardinal Rodrigo de Castro (Supreme Counsellor of The Inquisition).
3755 **1096** 40p. multicoloured . . 40 20

1097 Children and Calf (*Adios Corderia*, Leopoldo Alas ("Clarin"))

2001. Literature.
3756 **1097** 75p. multicoloured . . 50 20

2001. Trees (2nd series). As T **1067**. Multicoloured.
3757 40p. Olive 40 20
3758 75p. Beech 70 30

1098 Emblem and Shield

2001. 25th Anniv of Copa del Rey Football Championship.
3759 **1098** 40p. multicoloured . . 40 15

1099 Hooded Dancer being pelted with Tomatoes, Zaragoza

2001. Festivals (2nd series). Multicoloured.
3760 40p. Type **1099** 40 15
3761 70p. Giants, Barcelona (vert) 75 25

1100 Gracian

2001. 400th Birth Anniv of Baltasar Gracian (philosopher and writer).
3762 **1100** 120p. multicoloured . . 1·10 30

1101 Our Lady of Calva (statue), Zamora Cathedral

1102 Boy looking up (Grandmothers' Day)

2001. "Ages of Man Exhibition", Zamora.
3763 **1101** 120p. mauve and red 1·10 30
3764 – 155p. red and black . . 1·40 40
DESIGN: 155p. Cupola and cathedral.

2001. Social Activities. Multicoloured.
3765 40p. Type **1102** 40 15
3766 75p. Nun and building (Servants of Jesus for Charity (social relief organization)) 70 45

1103 View of City (½-size illustration)

2001. Salamanca, European City of Culture, 2002 .
3767 **1103** 75p. multicoloured . . 70 30

1104 Covadonga Basilica

2001. Centenary of Consecration of Basilica of Covadonga.
3768 **1104** 40p. multicoloured . . 40 15

1105 Emblem

2001. Formation of State Post and Telegraph Company.
3769 **1105** 40p. multicoloured . . 40 20

1107 Musicians

1108 Children encircling Globe

2001. Birth Millenary of St. Dominic of Silos (Benedictine monk and abbot).
3771 **1107** 40p. multicoloured . . 40 20

2001. United Nations Year of Dialogue among Civilizations.
3773 **1108** 120p. multicoloured . . 1·10 35

1109 Grasses, Ses Salines Nature Reserve

2001. America. U.N.E.S.C.O. World Heritage Sites.
3774 **1109** 155p. multicoloured . . 1·40 40

2001. School Correspondence Programme. Spanish History (2nd series). As T **1073** but with currency inscribed in both euros and pesetas. Multicoloured.
3775 25p. Christopher Columbus juggling eggs (discovery of America, 1492) 25 10
3776 25p. Spanish and Portuguese boys each holding balloons showing maps (Treaty of Tordesillas, 1494) 25 10
3777 25p. King Carlos I of Spain (elected Emperor Charles V, 1519) 25 10
3778 25p. Hernan Cortes and Mexican musicians (conquest of Mexico, 1519) 25 10
3779 25p. Juan Sebastian Elcano (first circumnavigation of globe, 1522) 25 10
3780 25p. Inca city and bull on mountain (Francisco Pizarro's conquest of Peru, 1532) 25 10
3781 25p. King Felipe II with globe shaped as map of Spain (accession, 1556) . . 25 10
3782 25p. King Felipe II drawing plans (commencement of Monastery San Lorenzo de El Escorial, 1563) . . . 25 10
3783 25p. Severed arm attacking Turk (Battle of Lepanto, 1571) 25 10
3784 25p. St John of the Cross, St. Teresa of Avila and El Greco being drawn up into spacecraft 25 10
3785 25p. Lope de Vega Carpio using his open skull as inkwell (Spanish playwright, died 1593) . . 25 10
3786 25p. King Felipe III surrounded by buckets collecting water (accession, 1598) 25 10

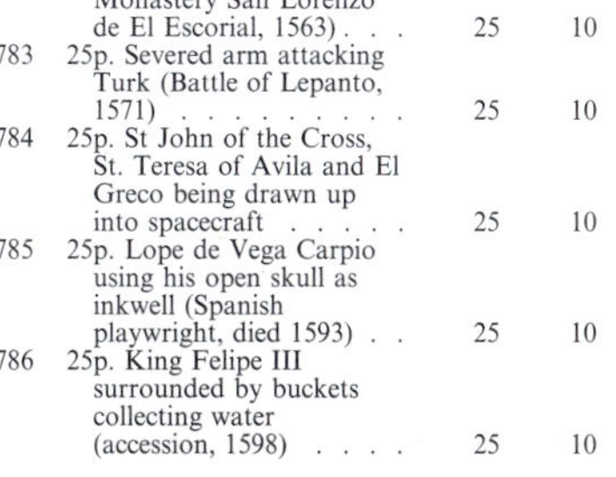

1111 "Virgin and Child" (Alfredo Roldan)

2001. Christmas. Religious Paintings. Mult.
3788 40p. Type **1111** 30 10
3789 75p. "The Shepherd's Adoration" (Jusepe de Ribera) 55 25
MS3790 106 × 133 mm. Nos. 3788/9 together with Nos. 3082/3 of Germany . . . . 3·25 1·50

1112 Music Score

2001. 125th Birth Anniv of Manuel de Falla (composer).
3791 **1112** 75p. multicoloured . . 60 25

1113 Man driving Car

2001. 75th Birth Anniv of Josep Coll (cartoonist). Multicoloured.
3792 40p. Type **1113** 30 10
3793 75p. Man and dog 55 25

1114 Cano

1115 Woman and Flowers

2001. 55th Birth Anniv of Carlos Cano (singer).
3794 **1114** 40p. black 30 10

2001. International Volunteers' Day.
3795 **1115** 120p. multicoloured . . 90 35

1116 12th-century Church of San Climent, Taull (Lleida)

2001. UNESCO. World Heritage Sites. Multicoloured.
3796 40p. Type **1116** 30 10
3797 40p. El Misteri d'Elx (religious festival at Elche cathedral) 30 10
3798 40p. Sant Pau Hospital, Barcelona 30 10
3799 40p. Map of St. Cristobal, La Laguna 30 10
3800 40p. Archeological excavations, Atapuerca . . 30 10
3801 40p. Protected palm trees, Elche 30 10
3802 40p. La Foncalada (medieval monument), Oviedo 30 10
3803 40p. Roman walls, Lugo . . 30 10
3804 40p. Cave painting, Cueva de los Caballos, Albocacer, Castellon . . . 30 10
3805 40p. Dalt Villa, Eivissa, Ibiza 30 10
3806 40p. Roman amphitheatre, Tarraco 30 10
3807 40p. Renaissance university building, Alcala de Henares 30 10

1117 Map and Postal Emblem (Postal Service)

2001. 150th Anniv of Ministry of Public Works.
3808 **1117** 40p. multicoloured . . 30 10
3809 – 75p. lilac, black and blue 55 20
3810 – 120p. blue, green and black 90 35
3811 – 155p. multicoloured . . 1·20 50
3812 – 260p. multicoloured . . 1·90 75
DESIGNS: Maps showing-75p. Ports; 120p. Railways; 155p. Airports; 260p. Motorways

1118 Crown Prince Felipe de Borbon

1119 King Juan Carlos I

2001. Silver Jubilee of King Juan Carlos I. Sheet 125 × 80 mm. containing T **1118** and similar multicoloured designs.
MS3813 Type **1118**; 40p. Infanta Elena; 40p. Arms; 40p. Infanta Cristina; 75p. King Juan Carlos; 75p. Queen Sofia; 260p. Palace (49 × 28 mm) . . . . 4·25 1·70

New Currency 100 cents = 1 euro

2002.
3814 **1119** 1c. black and silver 10 10
3818 5c. blue and silver . . . 10 10
3823 10c. green and silver . . 15 10
3826 25c. red and silver . . . 35 10
3827 50c. green and silver . . 70 30
3828 75c. purple and silver 1·10 45
3829 €1 green and silver . . 1·40 55
3830 €2 red and silver . . . 3·00 1·20

1120 Emblem

2002. Spanish Presidency of European Union.
3835 **1120** 25c. red, black and yellow 35 10
3836 50c. red, yellow and black 70 30

1121 Sabina

2002. Trees (3rd series). Multicoloured.
3837 50c. Type **1121** 70 30
3838 75c. Elm . . . . 1·10 45

1122 Orchids

1124 Father Francisco Piquer (founder)

1123 Emblem

2002. Flowers.Depicting paintings by Eduardo Naranjo. Multicoloured. Self-adhesive.
3839 25c. Type **1122** 35 10
3840 25c. Gardenia in vase . . . 35 10
3841 25c. Hands holding white rose 35 10
3842 25c. Iris 35 10
3843 25c. Two white orchid blooms 35 10
3844 25c. Pink-tinged rose in vase 35 10
3845 25c. Two pink orchid blooms 35 10
3846 25c. Three pink orchid blooms on one stem . . . 35 10

2002. "Espana 2002" International Youth Stamp Exhibition, Salamanca (1st issue). Multicoloured.
3847 50c. Type **1123** 70 30
MS3848 80 × 105 mm. £1.80 Salamanca Cathedral . . . . . 2·50 1·00
See also Nos. 2913/22.

2002. 300th Anniv of Caja Madrid Savings Bank.
3849 **1124** 25c. multicoloured . . . 35 10

1125 Anniversary Emblem

2002. Centenary of Real Madrid Football Club.
3850 **1125** 75c. yellow and grey . . 1·10 45

1126 Town Hall Portico, Tarazona

2002. "PHILAIBERIA '02" Spanish-Portuguese Stamp Exhibition, Tarazona. Sheet 106 × 80 mm.
MS3851 multicoloured . . . . . 3·00 1·20

1127 Mon

1128 Stylized Coin

2002. Birth Centenary (2001) of Alejandro Mon (politician).
3852 **1127** 25c. multicoloured . . . 35 10

2002. "Homage to the Peseta".
3853 **1128** 25c. multicoloured . . . 35 10

1129 Canon do Sil, Ribeira Sacra

1130 Cadets on Parade, 1886

2002. Nature. Multicoloured.
3854 75c. Type **1129** . . . . . . 1·10 45
3855 €2.10 Cabo de Gata, Nijer Park, Almeria (horiz) . . 3·00 1·20

2002. 75th Anniv of Military Academy, Zaragoza.
3856 **1130** 25c. multicoloured . . . 35 10

1131 Emblem

2002. Centenary of Real Union Irun Football Club.
3857 **1131** 50c. multicoloured . . . 70 30

1132 Tweezers, Stamp and Magnifying Glass

2002. Stamp Day.
3858 **1132** 25c. multicoloured . . . 35 10

1133 Banyeres de Mariola Castle, Alicante

2002. Castles.
3859 **1133** 25c. brown and blue . . 35 10
3860 – 50c. black 70 30
3861 – 75c. black . . . . . . 1·10 45
DESIGNS: 50c. Soutomaior Castle, Pontevedra; 75c. Calatorao Castle, Zaragoza.

1134 View across River

2002. Anniversaries. Multicoloured.
3862 75c. Type **1134** (1200th anniv of Tuleda) . . . . . 1·10 45
3863 €1.80 View through pillars (millennium of St. Cugat Monastery) . . . . 2·50 1·00

1135 Luis Cernuda

2002. Birth Anniversaries. Multicoloured.
3864 50c. Type **1135** (poet, centenary) 70 30
3865 50c. Dr. Federico Rubio and nurses (175th anniv) . . . 70 30

1136 Clown (Sara Blanco Quintas)

2002. Europa. The Circus.
3866 **1136** 50c. multicoloured . . . 70 30

1137 Soldiers on Horseback

2002. Bicentenary of Inclusion of Menorca under Spanish Rule.
3867 **1137** 50c. multicoloured . . . 70 30

1138 Driving

2002. World Equestrian Games, Jerez. Mult.
3868 25c. Type **1138** 35 10
3869 25c. Hunting 35 10
3870 25c. Dressage 35 10
3871 25c. Reining 35 10
3872 25c. Acrobats 35 10
3973 75c. Racing 35 10
3874 €1.80 Show jumping . . . 2·50 1·00

1139 Maria de las Dolores

2002. 108th Death Anniv of Maria "La Dolores" de las Dolores.
3875 **1139** 50c. multicoloured . . . 70 30

1140 Plaza Mayor, Salamanca

2002. "EXFILNA 2002" National Stamp Exhibition, Salamanca. European City of Culture. Sheet 155 × 94 mm, containing T **1140** and similar horiz design. Multicoloured (€1.80) or orange and blue (others).
MS3876 Type **1140**; 25c. Centre view of Plaza; 25c. Right side of Plaza; €1.80 Aerial view of Plaza . . 3·75 1·50

1141 Rohrbach R-VIII Aircraft, 1927

2002. 75th Anniv of IBERIA Airlines. Multicoloured.
3877 25c. Type **1141** 35 10
3878 50c. Boeing 747 . . . . . . 70 30

1142 Grapes (Rias Baixas)
1143 Grapes and Glass of Red Wine (Rioja)

2002. Wine Regions (1st series).
3879 **1142** 25c. multicoloured . . . 35 10

2002. Wine Regions (2nd series). Multicoloured.
3880 50c. Type **1143** 70 30
3881 75c. Grapes, wine bottle and glass of sherry (Manzanilla) . . . . . . 1·10 45

2002. School Correspondence Programme. Spanish History (3rd series). As T **1073** but with currency inscribed in euros. Multicoloured.
3882 10c. Man being knighted with pen (*Don Quixote* by Miguel de Cervantes) . . 15 10
3883 10c. Felipe IV and the Count-Duke of Olivares (accession, 1621) 15 10
3884 10c. Quevedo and Gongora pulling on rope of words (literary rivalry) 15 10
3885 10c. Velazquez (artist) sitting at easel 15 10
3886 10c. Carlos II and witch holding apple 15 10
3887 10c. Man rolling out carpet and Felipe V (start of War of the Spanish Succession) 15 10
3888 10c. Fernando VI (accession, 1746) 15 10
3889 10c. Carlos III holding architectural drawings (accession, 1759) 15 10
3890 10c. Bull and toreador (Riot of Esquilanche) 15 10
3891 10c. Book escaping from bird cage 15 10
3892 10c. Carlos IV (accession, 1788) and Napoleon . . . 15 10
3893 10c. Manuel de Godoy (politician) and open door 15 10

1144 Temple Expiatori de la Sagrada Famíla, Barcelona

2002. 150th Birth Anniv of Antonio Gaudi (architect).
3894 **1144** 50c. blue and black . . 70 30

1145 Musicians

2002. Music. Designs depicting paintings by G. Dominguez. Multicoloured. Self-adhesive.
3895 25c. Type **1145** . . . . . .
3896 25c. Vase of flowers and lute 35 10
3897 25c. Woman holding lute . . 35 10
3898 25c. Flowers and open book of music 35 10
3899 25c. Vase of flowers, clock and violin 35 10
3900 25c. Man holding lute with woman 35 10
3901 25c. Flowers, violin, compass and sheet music 35 10
3902 25c. Woman wearing blue dress holding lute 35 10

1146 Alphabet Jigsaw Puzzle

2002. America. Education and Literacy Campaign.
3903 **1146** 75c. multicoloured . . . 1·10 45

1147 Cordoba Mosque and Silhouette of Almanzor

2002. Death Millenary of Abu Amir Muhammad al-Ma'afiri (Almanzor) (Arab ruler).
3904 **1147** 75c. multicoloured . . . 1·10 45

1148 Basket
1149 Cupola, Aranjuez

2002. Dijous Bo Fair, Inca, Mallorca.
3905 **1148** 75c. multicoloured . . . 1·10 45

2002. UNESCO. World Heritage Sites. Multicoloured.
3906 25c. Type **1149** 35 10
3907 25c. Santa Maria church, Calatayud, Aragon . . . 35 10
3908 50c. San Martin church, Teruel, Aragon 70 30
3909 75c. Santa Maria church, Tobed, Aragon . . . . . 1·10 45
3910 €1.80 Santa Tecla church, Cervera de la Canada, Aragon . . . . 2·50 1·00
3911 €2.10 San Pablo church, Zaragoza, Aragon . . . . 3·00 1·20

1150 Alcaniz (former Monastery of Calatrava)

2002. Paradores (state hotels).
3912 **1150** 25c. multicoloured . . . 35 10

1151 Capitan Alatriste (Arturo Perez-Reverte)

2002. "Espana 2002" International Youth Stamp Exhibition, Salamanca (2nd issue). Multicoloured.
(a) Self-adhesive gum.
3913 50c. As No. 3847 . . . . . 70 30
3914 75c. Type **1151** (comic strip character) . . . . 1·10 45
3915 75c. Television screen and emblem (television) . . . 1·10 45
3916 75c. Hand and record (music) . . . . 1·10 45
3917 75c. Radio and music score (radio) . . . . 1·10 45
3918 75c. Cyclist, skier and football (sport) . . . . 1·10 45
3919 75c. Person holding camera (the press) . . . . . . 1·10 45
3920 75c. Film clapper board (film) . . . . 1·10 45
3921 €1.80 Salamanca Cathedral (vert) . . . . 2·50 1·00

2002. (b) Ordinary gum.
MS3922 Six sheets 79 × 106 mm (g) or 106 × 79 mm (others) (a) 75c. As No. 3920; (b) 75c. As No. 3915; (c) 75c. As 3919; (d) 75c. As 3917; (e) 75c. As 3918; (f) 75c. As 3916; (g) 75c. As 3914 Set of 6 sheets . . 7·50 3·00

1152 San Jorge Church, Alicante

2002.
3923 **1152** 75c. multicoloured . . . 1·10 45

1153 Cruceiro do Hio (crucifix) (Jose Cervino) Hio, Galicia

2002. Historical Monuments. Multicoloured.
3924 50c. Type **1153** 70 30
3925 50c. Herreria de Compludo (smithy), Leon (horiz) . . 70 30

1154 Mary (detail, stained glass window)
1155 "Adoration of Kings" (Carlos Munoz de Pablos) (alterpiece, Calzadilla de Barros Church)

2002. 140th Anniv of St. Mary's Cathedral, Vitoria-Gasteiz. Sheet 106 × 79 mm.
MS3926 multicoloured 70 30

2002. Christmas. Multicoloured.
3927 25c. Type **1155** 35 10
3928 50c. "Maternity" (Goyo Dominguez) 70 30

EXPRESS LETTER STAMPS

E 53 Pegasus and Arms

1905.
E308 E **53** 20c. red . . . . 37·00 90

E 77 Spanish Royal Family

1926. Red Cross.
E417 E **77** 20c. purple and deep purple . . . . 7·00 7·00

1927. 25th Anniv of Coronation. No. E417 optd **17-V-1902 17-V-1927 ALFONSO XIII.**
E459 E **77** 20c. purple and deep purple . . . . 6·25 6·25

E 88 Gazelle
E 89

1929. Seville and Barcelona Exhibitions.
E521 E **88** 20c. brown . . . . . . 16·00 16·00

1929.
E522 E **89** 20c. red . . . . 15·00 3·00

1929. Optd **Sociedad de las Naciones LV reunion del Consejo Madrid.**
E534 E **89** 20c. red . . . . 14·00 14·00

1930. Optd **URGENCIA.**
E535 E **89** 20c. red . . . . 13·50 3·00

E 91 Class 7201 Electric Locomotive

1930. 11th Int Railway Congress, Madrid.
E553 E **91** 20c. red . . . . 48·00 48·00

1930. "Goya" types optd **URGENTE**.
E570 **91** 20c. mauve (postage) . . 25 25
E583 – 20c. brown and blue (as No. 574) (air) 25 25

1930. "Columbus" type optd **URGENTE**.
E608 **99** 20c. purple . . . . 1·80 1·80

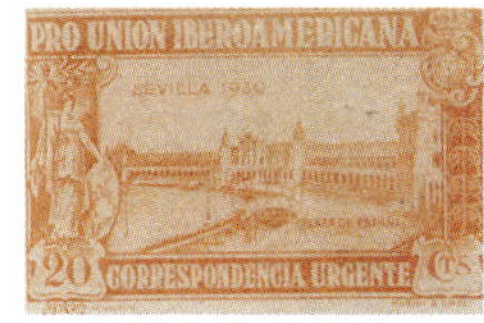

E 113 Seville Exhibition

1930. Spanish–American Exhibition.
E643 E **113** 20c. orange 45 45

1931. Optd **REPUBLICA**.
E660 E **89** 20c. red (No. E535) . . 3·50 3·50
E672 20c. red (No. E522) . . 6·75 2·30

1931. Optd **Republica Espanola** in two lines continuously.
E697 E **89** 20c. red (No. E522) . . 6·75 2·30

E 126
E 152 Newspaper Boy

E 145

1931. 900th Anniv of Montserrat Monastery.
E731 E **126** 20c. red . . . . . . 22·00 23·00

1934.
E779 E **145** 20c. red 15 15

1936. 40th Anniv of Madrid Press Association.
E801 E **152** 20c. red 25 25

E 185 Pegasus

1937.
E906 E **185** 20c. brown 1·10 40

E 198 Pegasus

1939.
E1022 E **198** 25c. red 10 10

E 199

1940. 19th Centenary of Apparition of Virgin of El Pilar at Zaragoza.
E1006 E **199** 25c.+5c. red & buff 25 25

E 270 "Speed"

E 271 Centaur

1956.
E1250 E **270** 2p. red 10 10
E1251 3p. red 10 10
E1252 E **271** 4p. mauve and black 10 10
E1253 E **270** 5p. red 10 10
E1254 E **271** 6p.50 red and violet 10 10

E 425 Roman Chariot

1971.
E2099 E **425** 10p. green, blk & red 10 10
E2100 – 15p. blue, black & red 15 10
DESIGN—VERT: 15p. Letter encircling globe.

E 862 Communications

1993. Public Services.
E3211 E **862** 180p. red and yellow 2·50 25

FRANK STAMPS

F 36

F 50

1869. For use on "Cartilla Postal de Espana" (book) by Senor Castell.
F172 F **36** (–) blue 65·00 50·00

1881. For use on book by A. F. Duro.
F273 F **50** (–) black on buff 44·00 18·00

F 163

1938. For use by Agencia Filatelica Oficial, Barcelona.
F839 F **163** (–) blue 00 4·00
F840 (–) lilac 00 4·00
F841 (–) green 00 4·00
F842 (–) brown 00 4·00
F843 (–) black 00 4·00

OFFICIAL STAMPS

O 9

O 10

1854. Imperf.
O46 O **9** ½ onza black on orange 2·20 2·30
O47 1 onza black on pink 3·00 3·50
O48 4 onza black on green 8·00 9·75
O49 1 libra black on blue 55·00 60·00
The face values of Nos. O46/53 are expressed in onzas (ounces) and libra (pound) which refer to the maximum weight for which each value could prepay postage.

1855. Imperf.
O50 O **10** ½ onza black on yellow 1·70 2·00
O55 1 onza black on pink 1·70 2·00
O52 4 onza black on green 3·25 4·00
O53 1 libra black on blue 16·00 20·00

O 52

1895. For use by Members of Chamber of Deputies.
O289 **51** 15c. yellow 8·00 3·25
O290 O **52** (–) pink 5·75 1·90
O291 (–) blue 19·00 6·75

O 66 National Library

O 67 Cervantes (from painting by J. de Jauregui)

O 68 Statue of Cervantes by A. Sola

1916. Death Tercentenary of Cervantes. (a) For use by Members of the Chamber of Deputies.
O353 – (–) black and violet 95 95
O354 O **66** (–) black and green 95 95
O355 O **67** (–) black and violet 95 95
O356 O **68** (–) black and red 95 95
(b) For use by Members of the Senate.
O357 – (–) black and green 95 95
O358 O **66** (–) black and red 95 95
O359 O **67** (–) black and brown 95 95
O360 O **68** (–) black and brown 95 95
DESIGN—As Type O **66**: Chamber of Deputies.

1931. 3rd Pan-American Postal Union Congress. T **121** etc optd **Oficial**.
O707 5c. purple 25 25
O708 10c. green 25 25
O709 15c. violet 25 25
O710 25c. red 25 25
O711 30c. green 25 25
O712 40c. blue 40 45
O713 50c. orange 40 45
O714 1p. grey 45 45
O715 4p. mauve 10·50 10·50
O716 10p. brown 25·00 25·00
Air. T **123** etc optd **OFICIAL**.
O717 5c. brown 15 15
O718 10c. green 15 15
O719 25c. red 15 15
O720 50c. blue 15 15
O721 1p. lilac 15 15
O722 4p. grey 4·00 4·00

WAR TAX STAMPS

W 42

W 48

W 49

1874. The 5c. perf or imperf.
W217 W **42** 5c. de p. black 9·25 1·00
W218 10c. de p. blue 12·50 1·80

1875. As Type W **42**, but large figures in bottom corners.
W228a 5c. de p. green 5·50 60
W229 10c. de p. mauve 11·50 3·00

1876. 2nd Carlist War (1873–76) and Cuban War (1868–78).
W253 W **48** 5c. de p. green 4·00 60
W254 10c. de p. blue 4·00 60
W255 25c. de p. black 30·00 11·50
W256 1p. lilac £375 80·00
W257 5p. pink £550 £225

1877. Cuban War (1868–78).
W258 W **49** 15c. de p. purple 20·00 60
W259 50c. de p. yellow £550 75·00

1897. Cuban War of Independence (1895–98). Inscr "1897–1898" (15c.) or "1897 A 1898" (others).
W289 5c. green 3·00 1·90
W290 10c. green 3·00 1·90
W291 15c. green £375 £200
W292 20c. green 7·00 3·25

W 52

W 53

W 163

1898. Cuban War of Independence (1895–98) and Spanish-American War (1898). Inscr "1898–99".
W293 W **52** 5c. black 2·30 2·00
W294 10c. black 2·30 2·00
W295 15c. black 47·00 9·75
W296 20c. black 4·00 3·25

1898. Cuban War of Independence (1895–98) and Spanish-American War (1898).
W297 W **53** 5c. black 8·00 60

1938.
W839 W **163** 10c. red 45 1·20
W840 20c. blue 45 80
W841 60c. pink 1·60 3·00
W842 1p. blue 45 95
W843 2p. green 45 95
W844 10p. blue 2·30 4·75
Nos. W842/3 have coloured figures of value on white backgrounds.

SPANISH GUINEA Pt. 19

A Spanish colony consisting of the islands of Fernando Poo, Annobon and the Corisco Islands off the west coast of Africa and Rio Muni on the mainland. In 1959 it was divided into the two Spanish Overseas Provinces of Fernando Poo and Rio Muni.

100 centimos = 1 peseta.

1902. "Curly Head" key-type inscr "GUINEA ESPANOLA 1902".
1 Z 5c. green 9·00 3·00
2 10c. grey 9·00 3·00
3 25c. red 65·00 29·00
4 50c. brown 65·00 27·00
5 75c. lilac 65·00 27·00
6 1p. red £100 27·00
7 2p. green £120 £140
8 5p. red £190 £140

1903. Fiscal stamps inscr "POSESIONES ESPANOLAS DE AFRICA OCCIDENTAL", surch **HABILITADO PARA CORREOS 10 cen de peseta**.
9 10c. on 25c. black £350 £150
10 10c. on 50c. orange 90·00 27·00
11 10c. on 1p.25 pink £600 £275
12 10c. on 2p. red £650 £400
13a 10c. on 2p.50 brown £950 £600
14a 10c. on 5p. black £1000 £350
15 10c. on 10p. brown £850 £350
16 10c. on 5p. lilac £650 £350
17 10c. on 25p. blue £650 £350
18 10c. on 50p. brown £850 £500
19 10c. on 70p. violet £950 £500
20 10c. on 100p. green £1300 £600

1903. "Curly Head" key-type inscr "GUINEA CONTIAL-ESPANOLA PARA 1903".
21 Z ¼c. black 90 70
22 ½c. green 90 70
23 1c. purple 90 65
24 2c. green 90 65
25 3c. brown 90 65
26 4c. red 90 65
27 5c. black 90 65
28 10c. brown 1·50 70
29 15c. blue 5·50 5·50
30 25c. orange 5·50 5·50
31 50c. red 9·75 12·00
32 75c. lilac 14·00 12·00
33 1p. green 22·00 18·00
34 2p. green 22·00 18·00
35 3p. red 60·00 25·00
36 4p. blue 70·00 42·00
37 5p. purple £130 65·00
38 10p. red £225 85·00

1905. "Curly Head" key-type inscr as above but dated "1905".
39 Z 1c. black 15 10
40 2c. green 15 10
41 3c. red 15 10
42 4c. green 15 10
43 5c. brown 15 10
44 10c. red 90 60
45 15c. brown 3·00 1·90
46 25c. brown 3·00 1·90
47 50c. blue 6·50 4·25
48 75c. orange 7·00 4·25
49 1p. red 7·00 4·25
50 2p. lilac 16·00 9·25
51 3p. green 42·00 19·00
52 4p. green 42·00 27·00
53 5p. red 70·00 30·00
54 10p. blue £120 90·00

1905. No. 19/34 of Elobey optd **CONTINENTAL GUINEA CORREOS ASSOBLA**.
55 Z 1c. pink 5·50 2·40
56 2c. purple 5·50 2·40
57 3c. black 5·50 2·40
58 4c. red 5·50 2·40
59 5c. green 5·50 2·40
60 10c. green 11·00 7·00
61 15c. lilac 20·00 10·00
62 25c. red 20·00 10·00
63 50c. orange 27·00 12·50
64 75c. blue 32·00 14·50
65 1p. brown 60·00 28·00
66 2p. brown 85·00 20·00
67 3p. red £120 42·00
68 4p. red £450 £150
69 5p. green £450 £150
70 10p. red £1900 £800

1907. As Nos. 18/33 of Rio de Oro, but inscr "GUINEA CONTIAL ESPANOLA".
71 1c. green 45 15
72 2c. blue 45 15
73 3c. lilac 45 15
74 4c. green 45 15
75 5c. red 45 15
76 10c. bistre 2·75 1·10
77 15c. brown 2·00 70
78 25c. blue 2·00 70
79 50c. brown 2·00 70
80 75c. green 2·00 70
81 1p. orange 3·50 1·25
82 2p. brown 6·50 5·50
83 3p. black 6·50 5·50
84 4p. red 8·25 5·50
85 5p. green 8·50 8·00
86 10p. purple 13·00 10·00

1908. Surch **HABILITADO PARA** and value in figures and **CTMS**.
87 **3** 05c. on 1c. green 4·00 2·50
88 05c. on 2c. blue 4·00 2·50
89 05c. on 3c. lilac 4·00 2·50
90 05c. on 4c. green 4·00 2·50
91 05c. on 10c. bistre 4·00 2·50
92 15c. on 10c. bistre 18·00 10·50

1909. Fiscal stamps inscr "TERRITORIOS ESPANOLES DEL AFRICA OCCIDENTAL", surch **HABILITADO PARA CORREOS 10 cen de peseta**.
93 10c. on 50c. green 80·00 55·00
94 10c. on 1p.25 violet £225 65·00
95 10c. on 2p. brown £600 £400
96 10c. on 5p. mauve £600 £400
97 10c. on 25p. brown £800 £550
98 10c. on 50p. red £2750 £1500
99 10c. on 75p. pink £2750 £1500
100 10c. on 100p. orange £2750 £1500

1909. As Nos. 47/59 of Rio de Oro, but inscr "TERRITORIOS ESPANOLES DEL GOLFO DE GUINEA".
101 1c. brown 10 10
102 2c. red 10 10
103 5c. green 85 10
104 10c. red 25 10
105 15c. brown 25 10
106 20c. mauve 45 25
107 25c. blue 45 25
108 30c. brown 50 10
109 40c. red 30 10
110 50c. lilac 30 10
111 1p. green 9·25 4·75
112 4p. orange 2·25 3·00
113 10p. orange 2·25 3·00

1911. Nos. 101/13 optd **GUINEA 1911** in oval.
114 1c. brown 25 25
115 2c. red 25 25
116 5c. green 1·00 30
117 10c. red 65 40
118 15c. brown 1·00 75
119 20c. mauve 1·25 1·10
120 25c. blue 1·60 2·10
121 30c. brown 2·25 2·75
122 40c. red 2·40 3·00
123 50c. lilac 4·00 4·50
124 1p. green 35·00 12·00
125 4p. orange 37·00 11·50
126 10p. orange 22·00 23·00

1912. As Nos. 73/85 of Rio de Oro, but inscr "TERRS. ESPANOLES DEL GOLFO DE GUINEA".
127 1c. black 10 10
128 2c. brown 10 10
129 5c. green 10 10
130 10c. red 20 10
131 15c. red 20 10
132 20c. red 35 10
133 25c. blue 20 10
134 30c. red . . . . 2·25 1·40
135 40c. red . . . . 1·50 75
136 50c. orange . . . . 1·10 30
137 1p. lilac . . . . 1·50 90
138 4p. mauve . . . . 3·25 1·90
139 10p. green . . . . 7·00 7·00

1914. As Nos. 86/98 of Rio de Oro, but inscr as 1912 issue.
140 1c. violet 15 10
141 2c. red 15 15
142 5c. green 15 10
143 10c. red 15 15
144 15c. purple 15 15
145 20c. brown 50 35
146 25c. blue 20 20
147 30c. brown 90 35
148 40c. green 90 35
149 50c. red 40 25
150 1p. orange . . . . 1·00 1·40
151 4p. red . . . . 3·75 3·00
152 10p. brown . . . . 4·75 5·50

1917. Nos. 127/39 optd **1917**.
153 1c. black . . . . 70·00 45·00
154 2c. brown . . . . 70·00 45·00
155 5c. green 25 15
156 10c. orange 25 15
157 15c. purple 25 15
158 20c. red 25 15
159 25c. blue 10 15
160 30c. red 25 20
161 40c. pink 40 25
162 50c. orange 20 15
163 1p. brown 40 25
164 4p. violet . . . . 5·50 3·25
165 10p. green . . . . 5·50 3·25

1918. Stamps of 1912 surch **HTADO 1917** and value in figures and words.
166 **11** 5c. on 40c. pink . . . . . 25·00 8·50
167 10c. on 4p. violet . . . . . 25·00 8·50
168 15c. on 20c. red . . . . . 45·00 15·00
169 25c. on 10p. green . . . . 45·00 15·00

12 **13** **14** Nipa House

1919.
170 **12** 1c. violet 70 30
171 2c. red 70 30
172 5c. red 70 30
173 10c. purple . . . . 1·10 30
174 15c. brown . . . . 1·10 30
175 20c. blue . . . . 2·10 65
176 25c. green . . . . 1·10 65
177 30c. orange . . . . 1·10 65
178 40c. orange . . . . 3·00 65
179 50c. red . . . . 3·00 65
180 1p. green . . . . 3·00 2·00
181 4p. red . . . . 6·00 7·25
182 10p. brown . . . . 11·00 14·00

1920. As Nos. 125/37 of Rio de Oro, but inscr as T **12**.
183 1c. brown 15 15
184 2c. red 15 15
185 5c. green 15 15
186 10c. red 15 15
187 15c. orange 15 15
188 20c. yellow 15 15
189 25c. blue 40 25
190 30c. green . . . . 24·00 15·00
191 40c. brown 35 25
192 50c. purple . . . . 1·10 25
193 1p. brown . . . . 1·10 35
194 4p. red . . . . 3·50 3·75
195 10p. violet . . . . 5·00 7·50

1922.
196 **13** 1c. brown 40 20
197 2c. red 40 20
198 5c. green 40 20
199 10c. red . . . . 2·75 90
200 15c. orange 40 20
201 20c. mauve . . . . 1·90 80
202 25c. blue . . . . 3·00 90
203 30c. violet . . . . 2·75 1·10
204 40c. blue . . . . 2·10 45
205 50c. red . . . . 2·10 45
206 1p. green . . . . 2·10 45
207 4p. brown . . . . 8·50 10·00
208 10p. yellow . . . . 17·00 19·00

1925.
209 **14** 5c. blue and brown 20 10
210 10c. blue and green 20 20
211 15c. black and red 20 15
212 20c. black and violet . . . 20 20
213 25c. black and red 45 20
214 30c. black and orange . . 45 20
215 40c. black and blue 45 20
216 50c. black and red 45 20
217 60c. black and brown . . . 50 20
218 1p. black and violet . . . 1·75 20
219 4p. black and blue . . . . 4·50 1·90
220 10p. black and green . . . 9·00 4·50

1926. Red Cross stamps of Spain optd **GUINEA ESPANOLA**.
221 – 5c. brown . . . . 8·00 8·00
222 – 10c. green . . . . 8·00 8·00
223 **70** 15c. violet . . . . 1·75 1·75
224 – 20c. purple . . . . 1·75 1·75
225 **71** 25c. red . . . . 1·75 1·75
226 **70** 30c. green . . . . 1·75 1·75
227 – 40c. blue 35 35
228 – 50c. red 35 35
229 **71** 60c. green 35 35
230 – 1p. red 35 35
231 – 4p. bistre . . . . 1·50 1·50
232 **71** 10p. violet . . . . 5·50 5·50

1929. Seville and Barcelona Exhibition stamps of Spain (1929) optd **GUINEA**.
233 5c. red 25 25
234 10c. green 25 25
235 15c. blue 25 25
236 20c. violet 25 25
237 25c. red 25 25
238 30c. brown 25 25
239 40c. blue 40 40
240 50c. orange 40 40
241 1p. grey . . . . 7·50 7·50
242 4p. red . . . . 16·00 16·00
243 10p. brown . . . . 30·00 30·00

17 Porter **24** **26** Gen. Franco

1931.
244 **17** 1c. green 10 10
245 2c. brown 10 10
246 5c. black 10 10
318 5c. grey . . . . 1·90 10
247 10c. green 10 10
248 15c. black 15 10
290 15c. green . . . . 2·75 10
249 20c. lilac 15 10
250 – 25c. red 15 10
251 – 30c. red 20 10
252 – 40c. blue 65 45
320 – 40c. green 70 10
253 – 50c. orange . . . . 1·50 1·00
292 – 50c. blue . . . . 6·00 50
254 – 80c. blue . . . . 2·75 1·60
255 – 1p. black . . . . 4·50 3·75
256 – 4p. mauve . . . . 30·00 17·00
257 – 5p. brown . . . . 12·50 12·50
DESIGNS: 25c. to 50c. Native drummers; 80c. to 5p. King Alfonso XIII and Queen Victoria.

1931. Optd **REPUBLICA ESPANOLA** horiz.
258 **17** 1c. green 10 10
259 2c. brown 10 10
260 5c. grey 15 10
261 10c. green 15 10
262 15c. blue 15 10
263 20c. violet 15 10
264 – 25c. red 15 10
265 – 30c. red 35 20
266 – 40c. blue . . . . 1·40 40
267 – 50c. orange . . . . 9·00 5·25
268 – 80c. blue . . . . 2·75 1·50
269 – 1p. black . . . . 9·50 3·25
270 – 4p. red . . . . 16·00 10·00
271 – 5p. brown . . . . 16·00 10·00

1933. Optd **Republica Espanola**.
272 **17** 1c. green 10 10
273 2c. brown 10 10
274 5c. grey 15 10
275 10c. green 15 10
276 15c. blue 15 10
277 20c. violet 40 15
278 – 25c. red 35 20
279 – 30c. red 35 20
280 – 40c. blue . . . . 2·75 60
281 – 50c. orange . . . . 9·75 3·25
282 – 80c. blue . . . . 4·75 2·75
283 – 1p. black . . . . 10·00 2·75
284 – 4p. red . . . . 32·00 13·00
285 – 5p. brown . . . . 38·00 13·00

1937. Surch **HABILITADO 30 Cts.**
293 30c. on 40c. (No. 252) . . . 3·25 1·90
294 30c. on 40c. (No. 266) . . . 13·00 3·00
295 30c. on 40c. (No. 280) . . . 50·00 15·00

1939. Stamps of Spain, 1937, optd **Territorios Espanoles del Golfo de Guinea** in script type.
296 **183** 10c. green . . . . 1·40 40
297 **184** 15c. black . . . . 1·40 40
298 20c. violet . . . . 3·25 1·40
299 25c. red . . . . 3·25 1·40

1939. Surch **Habilitado 40 cts.**
300 40c. on 80c. (No. 268) . . . 10·50 6·50
301 40c. on 80c. (No. 282) . . . 10·50 3·75

1940. Fiscal stamps as T **24** inscr "ESPECIAL MOVIL", "TIMBRE MOVIL" or "IMPUESTO SOBRE CONTRATOS" and surch or optd **Habilitado Correos.**
302 5c. red . . . . 4·00 1·25
304 5c. on 35c. green . . . . . . 5·00 1·60
307 10c. on 75c. brown . . . . . 6·00 2·10
308 15c. on 1p.50 violet . . . . 5·00 2·00
305 25c. on 60c. brown . . . . . 5·00 2·00
306 50c. on 75c. brown . . . . . 6·00 2·10
310 1p. bistre . . . . 75·00 30·00
303 1p. on 15c. green . . . . . . 19·00 6·00
316 1p. on 17p. red . . . . 38·00 12·00
315 1p. on 40p. green . . . . . . 10·00 3·50

1940.
311 **26** 5c. brown . . . . 2·75 70
312 40c. blue . . . . 3·50 70
314 50c. green . . . . 4·75 70

1941. Air. Fiscal stamp as T **24** inscr "IMPUESTO SOBRE CONTRATOS" surch **Habilitado para Correo Aereo Intercolonial Una Peseta** and bar.
317a 1p. on 17p. red . . . . . . 28·00 7·00

1942. No. 249 surch **Habilitado 3 Pesetas.**
321 **17** 3p. on 20c. violet . . . . . 11·00 1·40
1939,

1942. Stamps of Spain, 1939, optd **Golfo de Guinea.**
322 **196** 1PTA. black 35 15
323 4PTAS. pink . . . . 7·50 65

1942. Air. Air stamp of Spain optd **Golfo de Guinea.**
324 **195** 1p. blue . . . . 1·50 20

1943. Stamp of Spain, 1939, optd **Territorios espanoles del Golfo de Guinea.**
325 **196** 2PTAS. brown 95 15

1948. Air. Ministerial Visit. No. 323 optd **CORREO AEREO Viaje Ministerial 10-19 Enero 1948.**
326 **196** 4PTAS. pink . . . . . . 10·00 2·75

1949. Nos. 322 and 325 surch **Habilitado para** and value in words.
327 **196** 5c. on 1PTA. black . . . 20 10
328 15c. on 2PTAS. brown . . 20 10

33 Natives in Pirogue

1949. 75th Anniv of U.P.U.
329 **33** 4p. violet . . . . 1·75 65

34 Count Argalejo and San Carlos Bay

1949. Air. Colonial Stamp Day.
330 **34** 5p. green . . . . 1·75 65

35 San Carlos Bay **36** Manuel Iradier y Bulfy

1949.
331 **35** 2c. brown 20 10
332 – 5c. violet 20 10
333 – 10c. blue 20 10
334 – 15c. green 20 10
335 **35** 25c. brown 20 10
336 – 30c. yellow 20 10
337 – 40c. green 20 10
338 – 45c. purple 20 10
339 **35** 50c. orange 20 10
340 – 75c. blue 20 10
341 – 90c. green 20 10
342 – 1p. black . . . . 1·50 20
343 **35** 1p.35 violet . . . . 5·50 1·10
344 – 2p. brown . . . . 15·00 2·50
345 – 5p. mauve . . . . 20·00 8·00
346 **35** 10p. brown . . . . 80·00 30·00
DESIGNS: 5, 30, 75c., 2p. Benito River rapids; 10, 40, 90c., 5p. Coast scene and Clarence Peak, Fernando Poo; 15, 45, 1p. Niepan, Benito River.

1950. Air. Colonial Stamp Day.
347 **36** 5p. brown . . . . 2·75 65

37 Hands and Natives **38** Mt. Mioco

1951. Native Welfare.
348 **37** 50c.+10c. blue 20 15
349 1p.+25c. green . . . . . . 11·00 3·75
350 6p.50+1p.65 orange . . . 2·75 1·75

1951. Air.
351 – 25c. yellow 20 20
352 **38** 50c. mauve 20 20
353 – 1p. green 20 20
354 – 2p. blue 35 20
355 **38** 3p.25 violet . . . . 1·00 20
356 – 5p. sepia . . . . 6·00 3·00
357 – 10p. red . . . . 24·00 7·00
DESIGNS: 25c., 2, 10p. Benito Rapids; 1, 5p. Santa Isabel Bay.

1951. Air. 500th Birth Anniv of Isabella the Catholic. As T **9a** of Spanish Sahara.
358 5p. blue . . . . 19·00 4·00

39 Leopard **40** Native and Map

1951. Colonial Stamp Day.
359 **39** 5c.+5c. brown 10 10
360 10c.+5c. orange 10 10
361 60c.+15c. olive 20 15

1951. International West African Conference.
362 **40** 50c. orange 20 10
363 5p. blue . . . . 7·00 90

41 Native Man **42** "Crinum giganteum"

1952.
364 **41** 5c. brown 10 10
365 50c. olive 10 10
366 5p. violet . . . . 2·10 10

1952. Native Welfare Fund.
367 **42** 5c.+5c. brown 10 10
368 50c.+10c. black 10 10
369 2p.+30c. blue . . . . . . 1·25 60

43 Ferdinand the Catholic **44** Brown-cheeked Hornbills

1952. Air. 500th Birth Anniv of Ferdinand the Catholic.
370 **43** 5p. brown . . . . 25·00 5·00

1952. Colonial Stamp Day.
371 **44** 5c.+5c. brown 40 20
372 10c.+5c. purple 45 35
373 60c.+15c. green 80 60

45 Native Musician **46** Native Woman and Dove

1953. Native Welfare Fund. Inscr "PRO INDIGENAS 1953".
374 **45** 5c.+5c. lake 10 10
375 – 10c.+5c. purple 10 10

376 **45** 15c. olive 10 10
377 – 60c. brown 10 10
DESIGN: 10, 60c. Musician facing right.

1953.
378 **46** 5c. orange 10 10
379 10c. purple 10 10
380 60c. brown 10 10
381 – 1p. lilac 80 10
382 – 1p.90 green 2·10 20
DESIGN: 1, 1p.90, Native drummer.

47 "Tragocephala nobilis" (longhorn beetle)

48 Hunting with Bow and Arrow

1953. Colonial Stamp Day. Inscr "DIA DEL SELLO COLONIAL 1953".
383 **47** 5c.+5c. blue 15 10
384 – 10c.+5c. purple 25 10
385 **47** 15c. green 35 15
386 – 60c. brown 35 15
DESIGN: 10, 60c. African giant swallowtail (butterfly).

1954. Native Welfare Fund. Inscr "PRO-INDIGENAS 1954".
387 **48** 5c.+5c. lake 10 10
388 – 10c.+5c. lilac 10 10
389 **48** 15c. green 10 10
390 – 60c. brown 20 10
DESIGN: 10, 60c. Native hunting elephant with spear.

49 Turtle

1954. Colonial Stamp Day. Inscr "DIA DEL SELLO COLONIAL 1954".
391 **49** 5c.+5c. red 10 10
392 – 10c.+5c. purple 10 10
393 **49** 15c. green 10 10
394 – 60c. brown 20 10
DESIGN: 10, 60c. Barbelled houndshark (fish).

50 M. Iradier y Bulfy

51 Native Priest

1955. Birth Centenary of Iradier (explorer).
395 **50** 60c. brown 15 10
396 1p. violet 2·75 25

1955. Centenary of Apostolic Prefecture in Fernando Poo.
397 **51** 10c.+5c. purple 10 10
398 – 25c.+10c. violet 10 10
399 **51** 50c. olive 15 10
DESIGN: 25c. "Baptism".

52 Footballers

53 El Pardo Palace, Madrid

1955. Air.
400 **52** 25c. grey 10 10
401 50c. olive 10 10
402 1p.50 brown 85 10
403 4p. red 2·75 25
404 10p. green 1·60 25

1955. Treaty of Pardo, 1778.
405 **53** 5c. brown 10 10
406 15c. red 10 10
407 80c. green 10 10

54 Moustached Monkeys

55 "Orquidea"

1955. Colonial Stamp Day. Inscr "DIA DEL SELLO COLONIAL 1955".
408 **54** 5c.+5c. lake and brown 10 15
409 – 15c.+5c. sepia and lake 10 15
410 **54** 70c. blue and slate 15 10
DESIGN—HORIZ: 15c. Talapoin and young.

1956. Native Welfare Fund. Inscr "PRO INDIGENAS 1956".
411 **55** 5c.+5c. olive 10 10
412 – 15c.+5c. ochre 10 10
413 **55** 20c. turquoise 10 10
414 – 50c. brown 10 10
DESIGN: 15, 50c. "Strophantus kombe".

56 Arms of Santa Isabel

57 Grey Parrot

1956. Colonial Stamp Day. Inscr "DIA DEL SELLO 1956".
415 **56** 5c.+5c. brown 10 10
416 – 15c.+5c. violet 10 10
417 **56** 70c. green 10 10
DESIGN—HORIZ: 15c. Arms of Bata and natives.

1957. Native Welfare Fund. Inscr "PRO INDIGENAS 1957".
418 **57** 5c.+5c. purple 15 10
419 – 15c.+5c. ochre 25 15
420 **57** 70c. green 55 35
DESIGN—HORIZ: 15c. Grey parrot in flight.

58 "Flight"

1957. Air. 30th Anniv of Spain–Fernando Poo Flight by "Atlantida" Seaplane Squadron.
421 **58** 25p. sepia and bistre 8·00 85

59 African Elephant and Calf

1957. Colonial Stamp Day.
422 **59** 10c.+5c. mauve 10 10
423 – 15c.+5c. brown 10 10
424 **59** 20c. turquoise 10 10
425 – 70c. green 15 10
DESIGN—VERT: 15, 70c. African elephant trumpeting.

60 Doves and Arms of Valencia and Santa Isabel

1958. "Aid for Valencia".
426 **60** 10c.+5c. brown 10 10
427 15c.+10c. ochre 10 10
428 50c.+10c. brown 10 10

61 Boxing

1958. Sports.
429 **61** 5c. brown 10 10
430 – 10c. brown 10 10
431 – 15c. brown 10 10
432 – 80c. green 10 10
433 **61** 1p. red 10 10
434 – 2p. purple 20 10
435 – 2p.30 lilac 35 10
436 – 3p. blue 35 10
DESIGNS—VERT: 10c., 2p. Basketball; 80c., 3p. Running. HORIZ: 15c., 2p.30, Long jumping.

62 Missionary holding Cross

63 African Monarchs

1958. Native Welfare Fund. Inscr "1883 PRO-INDIGENAS 1958".
437 **62** 10c.+5c. brown 10 10
438 – 15c.+5c. ochre 10 10
439 **62** 20c. turquoise 10 10
440 – 70c. green 10 10
DESIGN: 15, 70c. The Crucifixion.

1958. Colonial Stamp Day. Inscr "1958".
441 **63** 10c.+5c. red 10 10
442 – 25c.+10c. violet 30 10
443 – 50c.+10c. olive 35 15
DESIGNS: 25, 50c. Different views of butterflies on plants.

64 Digitalis

65 Boy on "Penny-farthing" Cycle

1959. Child Welfare Fund. Floral designs as T **64**. Inscr "PRO-INFANCIA 1959".
444 **64** 10c.+5c. lake 10 10
445 – 15c.+5c. ochre 10 10
446 – 20c. myrtle 10 10
447 **64** 70c. green 10 10
DESIGN: 15, 20c. Castor bean.

1959. Colonial Stamp Day. Inscr "1959".
448 **65** 10c.+5c. lake 10 10
449 – 20c.+5c. myrtle 10 10
450 – 50c.+20c. olive 10 10
DESIGNS: 20c. Racing cyclists; 50c. Winning cyclist.

EXPRESS LETTER STAMP

E **38** Fernando Poo

1951.
E358 E **38** 25c. red 20 15

SPANISH MOROCCO Pt. 9

100 centimos = 1 peseta.

I. SPANISH POST OFFICES IN MOROCCO.

Nos. 2/150, except Nos. 93/8 and 124/37 are all stamps of Spain overprinted.

1903. Optd **CORREO ESPANOL MARRUECOS.**
2 **38a** ½c. green 15 10

1903. Optd **CORREO ESPANOL MARRUECOS.**
3 **52** 2c. brown 1·00 1·00
4 5c. green 1·10 55
5 10c. red 1·50 20
6 15c. violet 2·00 60
7 20c. black 7·25 2·75
8 25c. blue 65 60
9 30c. green 4·50 2·75
10 40c. pink 8·00 4·50
11 50c. blue 4·50 4·25
12 1p. purple 9·50 6·50
13 4p. purple 24·00 11·00
14 10p. orange 24·00 27·00

1908. Stamps of Spain handstamped **TETUAN.**
15 **38a** ½c. green 12·50 5·25
16 **52** 2c. brown 50·00 19·00
17 5c. green 65·00 30·00
18 10c. red 65·00 32·00
19 15c. violet 65·00 32·00
20 20c. black £225 £170
21 25c. blue £100 55·00
22 30c. green £250 £100
23 40c. bistre £325 £170

1908. Nos. 2/5 and 7/8 handstamped **TETUAN.**
24 **38a** ½c. green 20·00 13·00
25 **52** 2c. brown £170 95·00
26 5c. green £160 50·00
27 10c. red £160 50·00
28 20c. grey £375 £170
29 25c. blue £140 48·00

1909. Optd **CORREO ESPANOL MARRUECOS.**
30 **64** 2c. brown 45 15
31 5c. green 2·40 55
32 10c. red 3·00 15
33 15c. violet 7·00 30
34 20c. green 17·00 70
35 25c. blue £110
36 30c. green 5·50 30
37 40c. pink 5·50 30
38 50c. blue 9·50 9·00
39 1p. lake 21·00 18·00
40 4p. purple £110
41 10p. orange £110

After the appearance of Nos. 42/54 for the Spanish Protectorate in 1914, the use of Nos. 30/41 was restricted to Tangier.

II. SPANISH PROTECTORATE (excluding Tangier).

1914. Optd **MARRUECOS.**
42 **38a** ½c. green 10 10
43 **64** 2c. brown 10 10
44 5c. green 25 20
45 10c. red 25 20
46 15c. violet 1·00 80
47 20c. green 1·90 1·40
48 25c. blue 1·90 1·10
49 30c. green 3·75 1·90
50 40c. pink 8·75 2·75
51 50c. blue 4·50 1·90
52 1p. red 4·50 2·75
53 4p. purple 22·00 19·00
54 10p. orange 32·00 25·00

1915. Optd **PROTECTORADO ESPANOL EN MARRUECOS.**
55 **38a** ½c. green 10 10
56 **64** 2c. brown 15 15
57 5c. green 45 15
58 10c. red 35 15
59 15c. violet 50 15
60 20c. green 1·25 25
61 25c. blue 1·25 25
62 30c. green 1·40 35
63 40c. pink 2·40 35
64 50c. blue 4·00 25
65 1p. red 4·00 35
66 4p. purple 28·00 18·00
67 10p. orange 40·00 21·00

1916. Optd **ZONA DE PROTECTORADO ESPANOL EN MARRUECOS.**
68 **38a** ½c. green 25 10
69 **66** 1c. green 1·25 15
70 **64** 2c. brown 1·10 25
71 5c. green 4·50 25
72 10c. red 6·00 25
73 15c. orange 6·25 25
74 20c. violet 8·50 15
75 25c. blue 18·00 3·00
76 30c. green 24·00 20·00
77 40c. red 22·00 60
78 50c. blue 11·50 30
79 1p. red 26·00 2·25
80 4p. purple 40·00 29·00
81 10p. orange 90·00 65·00

1920. Optd **PROTECTORADO ESPANOL EN MARRUECOS** perf through centre and each half surch in figures and words.
82 **64** 10c.+10c. on 20c. green 3·25 1·60
83 15c.+15c. on 30c. green 8·00 6·00

1920. No. E68 perf through centre, and each half surch **10 centimos.**
E84 **53** 10c.+10c. on 20c. red 9·50 6·00

1920. Fiscal stamps showing figure of Justice, bisected and surch **CORREOS** and value.
93 5c. on 5p. blue 7·00 1·40
94 5c. on 10p. green 15 10
95 10c. on 25p. green 15 10
96 10c. on 50p. grey 30 20
97 15c. on 100p. red 30 20
98 15c. on 500p. red 9·25 4·75

1923. Optd **ZONA DE PROTECTORADO ESPANOL EN MARRUECOS.**
101 **68** 2c. green 65 10
102 5c. purple 65 10
103 10c. green 2·50 10
105 15c. blue 2·50 10
106 20c. violet 5·50 10
107 25c. red 11·00 1·25
108 40c. blue 11·50 4·00

109 50c. orange 29·00 7·00
110 **69** 1p. grey 45·00 4·00

1926. Red Cross stamps optd **ZONA PROTECTORADO ESPANOL**.
111 **70** 1c. orange 6·50 6·50
112 – 2c. red 9·50 9·50
113 – 5c. brown 3·25 3·25
114 – 10c. green 3·25 3·25
115 **70** 15c. violet 60 60
116 – 20c. purple 60 60
117 **71** 25c. red 60 60
118 **70** 30c. green 60 60
119 – 40c. blue 15 15
120 – 50c. red 15 15
121 – 1p. red 15 15
122 – 4p. bistre 60 60
123 **71** 10p. violet 2·40 2·40

11 Mosque of Alcazarquivir

12 Moorish Gateway, Larache

1928.
124 **11** 1c. red 10 10
126 2c. violet 25 20
127 3c. blue 10 10
128 10c. green 10 10
129 15c. brown 30 10
130 **12** 20c. olive 30 10
131 25c. red 30 10
132 30c. brown 1·10 10
133 40c. blue 1·50 10
134 50c. purple 3·00 10
135 – 1p. green 4·50 25
136 – 2p.50 purple 14·50 6·00
137 – 4p. blue 8·00 1·50
DESIGNS—HORIZ: 1p. Well at Alhucemas; 2p.50, Xauen; 4p. Tetuan.

1929. Seville–Barcelona Exhibition stamps, Nos. 502/14 optd **PROTECTORADO MARRUECOS**.
138 1c. blue 20 20
139 2c. green 20 20
140 5c. red 20 20
141 10c. green 20 20
142 15c. blue 20 20
143 20c. violet 20 20
144 25c. red 20 20
145 30c. brown 55 55
146 40c. blue 55 55
147 50c. orange 55 55
148 1p. grey 4·75 4·75
149 4p. red 11·00 11·00
150 10p. brown 23·00 23·00

14 Xauen

15 Market-place, Larache

1933.
151 **14** 1c. red 10 10
152 – 2c. green 10 10
153 – 5c. mauve 10 10
154 – 10c. green 25 25
155 – 15c. yellow 1·40 30
156 **14** 20c. green 55 30
157 – 25c. red 14·50 40
165 – 25c. violet 80 10
158 – 30c. lake 4·25 30
166 – 30c. red 12·00 20
159 **15** 40c. blue 9·50 30
167 – 40c. red 6·25 30
160 – 50c. red 28·00 7·50
168 – 50c. blue 6·25 30
169 – 60c. green 6·25 30
161 – 1p. grey 10·00 30
170 – 2p. lake 32·00 8·50
162 – 2p.50 brown 18·00 7·50
163 – 4p. green 18·00 7·50
164 – 5p. black 24·00 7·50
DESIGNS—HORIZ: 2c., 1p. Xauen; 5c., 2p.50, Arcila; 25c. (No. 157), 5p. Sultan and bodyguard; 30c. (No. 166), 50c. (No. 168), 2p. Forest at Ketama. VERT: 10c., 30c. (No. 158), Tetuan; 15c., 4p. Alcazarquivir; 25c. (No. 165), 40c. (No. 167), Wayside scene at Arcila.

See also Nos. 177/83 and 213/6.

1936. Air. No. 157 surch with new value and **18-7-36**.
171 25c.+2p. on 25c. red 25·00 5·75

1936. Surch.
172 – 1c. on 4p. blue (137) 25 15
173 – 2c. on 2p.50 pur (136) 25 15
174 **12** 5c. on 25c. red (131) 15 15
175 – 10c. on 1p. green (135) 7·25 3·50
176 **E 12** 15c. on 20c. black 6·00 1·90

1937. Pictorials as T **14/15**.
177 1c. green 10 10
178 2c. mauve 10 10
179 5c. orange 15 10
180 15c. violet 15 10
181 30c. red 40 20
182 1p. blue 4·25 30
183 10p. brown 50·00 24·00
DESIGNS—VERT: 1, 15c. Caliph and Viziers; 30c. Tetuan; 1p. Arcila; 10p. Caliph on horseback. HORIZ: 2c. Bokoia; 5c. Alcazarquivir.

18 Legionaries

19 General Franco

1937. 1st Anniv of Civil War.
184 – 1c. blue 10 10
185 **18** 2c. brown 10 10
186 – 5c. mauve 10 10
187 – 10c. green 10 10
188 – 15c. blue 10 10
189 – 20c. purple 10 10
190 – 25c. mauve 10 10
191 – 30c. red 10 10
192 – 40c. orange 10 10
193 – 50c. blue 10 10
194 – 60c. green 10 10
195 – 1p. violet 10 10
196 – 2p. blue 8·00 7·50
197 – 2p.50 black 8·00 7·50
198 – 4p. brown 8·00 7·50
199 – 10p. black 8·00 7·50
DESIGNS—VERT: 1c. Sentry; 5c. Trooper; 10c. Volunteers; 15c. Colour bearer; 20c. Desert halt; 25c. Ifni mounted riflemen; 30c. Trumpeters; 40c. Cape Juby Camel Corps; 50c. Infantryman; 60c., 1, 2, 4p. Sherifian Guards; 2p.50, Cavalryman. HORIZ: 10p. "Road to Victory".

1937. Obligatory Tax. Disabled Soldiers in N. Africa.
200 **19** 10c. brown 70 20
201 10c. blue 70 20

20 Yellow-billed Stork over Mosque

22 Soldier on Horseback

1938. Air.
203 – 5c. brown 10 10
204 **20** 10c. green 25 10
205 – 25c. red 10 10
206 – 40c. blue 2·00 70
207 – 50c. mauve 10 10
208 – 75c. blue 10 10
209 – 1p. brown 10 10
210 – 1p.50 violet 1·75 40
211 – 2p. red 40 10
212 – 3p. black 1·40 30
DESIGNS—VERT: 5c. Mosque de Baja, Tetuan; 25c. Straits of Gibraltar; 40c. Desert natives; 1p. Mounted postman; 1p.50, Farmers; 2p. Sunset; 3p. Shadow of airplane over city. HORIZ: 50c. Airplane over Tetuan; 75c. Airplane over Larache.

1939. Pictorials as T **14**.
213 5c. orange 15 10
214 10c. green 15 10
215 15c. brown 35 10
216 20c. blue 35 10
DESIGNS: 5c. "Carta de Espana"; 10c. "Carta de Marruecos"; 15c. Larache; 20c. Tetuan.

1940. Pictorials as T **14**, inscr "ZONA" on back.
217 1c. brown 10 10
218 2c. olive 10 10
219 5c. blue 15 15
220 10c. lilac 15 15
221 15c. green 15 15
222 20c. violet 15 15
223 25c. sepia 15 15
224 30c. green 15 15
225 40c. green 15 15
226 45c. orange 1·25 15
227 50c. brown 50 15
228 70c. blue 50 15
229 1p. brown and blue 1·60 15
230 2p.50 green and brown 9·50 3·50
231 5p. sepia and purple 1·60 20
232 10p. brown and olive 17·00 6·50
DESIGNS—VERT: 1c. Postman; 2c. Pillar-box; 5c. Winter landscape; 10c. Alcazar street; 15c. Castle wall, Xauen; 20c. Palace sentry, Tetuan; 25c. Caliph on horseback; 30c. Market-place, Larache; 40c. Gateway, Tetuan; 45c. Gateway, Xauen; 50c. Street, Alcazarquivir; 70c. Post Office; 1p. Spanish War veterans.

1940. 4th Anniv of Civil War. Nos. 184/99 optd **17-VII-940 40 ANIVERSARIO**.
233 1c. blue 50 50
234 2c. brown 50 50
235 5c. mauve 50 50
236 10c. green 50 50
237 15c. blue 50 50
238 20c. purple 50 50
239 25c. mauve 50 50
240 30c. red 50 50
241 40c. orange 80 80
242 50c. blue 80 80
243 60c. green 80 80
244 1p. violet 80 80
245 2p. blue 32·00 32·00
246 2p.50 black 32·00 32·00
247 4p. brown 32·00 32·00
248 10p. black 32·00 32·00

1941. Obligatory Tax for Disabled Soldiers.
249 **22** 10c. green 4·00 25
250 10c. pink 4·00 25
251 10c. red 4·00 25
252 10c. blue 2·00 10

23 Larache

25 General Franco

1941.
253 **23** 5c. brown and deep brown 10 10
263 – 5c. blue 10 10
254 – 10c. deep red and red 15 10
255 – 15c. yellow and green 15 10
256 – 20c. blue and deep blue 35 10
264 – 40c. brown 15·00 20
257 – 40c. red and purple 95 10
DESIGNS: 5c. blue, 10c. Alcazarquivir; 15, 40c. brown, Larache market; 20c. Moorish house; 40c. purple, Gateway, Tangier.

1942. Air. New designs as T **14**, optd **Z**.
258 5c. blue 20 15
259 10c. brown 20 15
260 15c. green 20 15
261 90c. red 20 15
262 5p. black 80 40
DESIGNS—VERT: 5c. Atlas mountains; 10c. Mosque at Tangier; 15c. Velez fortress; 90c. Sanjurjo harbour; 5p. Straits of Gibraltar.

1943. Obligatory Tax for Disabled Soldiers.
265 **25** 10c. grey 8·00 15
266 10c. blue 8·00 15
267 10c. brown 8·00 15
268 10c. violet 8·00 15
283 10c. brown and mauve 8·00 15
284 10c. green and orange 8·00 15
295 10c. brown and blue 8·00 15
296 10c. lilac and grey 8·00 15

26 Homeward Bound

1944. Agricultural Scenes.
269 – 1c. blue and brown 20 10
270 – 2c. green 10 10
271 **26** 5c. black and brown 10 10
272 – 10c. orange and blue 10 10
273 – 15c. green 10 10
274 – 20c. black and red 10 10
275 – 25c. brown and blue 15 10
276 – 30c. blue and green 75 25
277 – 40c. purple and brown 10 10
278 **26** 50c. brown and blue 35 10
279 – 75c. blue and green 40 10
280 – 1p. brown and blue 40 10
281 – 2p.50 blue and black 5·50 2·25
282 – 10p. black and orange 9·25 5·25
DESIGNS—HORIZ: 1, 30c. Ploughing; 2, 40c. Harvesting; 10, 75c. Threshing; 15c., 1p. Vegetable garden; 20c., 2p.50, Gathering oranges; 25c., 10p. Shepherd and flock.

27 Dyers

28 Sanatorium

1946. Craftsmen.
285 – 1c. brown and purple 10 10
286 **27** 2c. violet and green 10 10
287 – 10c. blue and orange 10 10
288 **27** 15c. green and blue 10 10
289 – 25c. blue and green 10 10
290 – 40c. brown and blue 10 10
291 **27** 45c. red and black 40 10
292 **27** 1p. blue and green 45 10
293 – 2p.50 green and orange 1·25 40
294 – 10p. grey and blue 2·50 1·90
DESIGNS: 1, 10, 25c. Potters; 40c. Blacksmiths; 1p. Cobblers; 2p.50, Weavers; 10p. Metal workers.

1946. Anti-T.B. Fund.
297 – 10c. green and red 10 10
298 **28** 25c. brown and red 10 10
299 – 25c.+5c. violet and red 10 10
300 – 50c.+10c. blue and red 20 15
301 – 90c.+10c. brown and red 50 35
DESIGNS: 10c. Emblem and arabesque ornamentation; 25c.+5c. Mountain roadway; 50c.+10c. Fountain; 90c.+10c. Wayfarers.

29 Sanatorium

30 Steam Goods Train

1947. Anti-T.B. Fund.
302 – 10c. blue and red 10 10
303 **29** 25c. brown and red 10 10
304 – 25c.+5c. lilac and red 10 10
305 – 50c.+10c. blue and red 20 20
306 – 90c.+10c. brown and red 50 50
DESIGNS: 10c. Emblem, mosque and palm tree; 25c.+5c. Hospital ward; 50c.+10c. Nurse and children; 90c.+10c. Arab swordsman.

1948. Transport and Commerce.
307 **30** 2c. brown and violet 10 10
308 – 5c. violet and red 10 10
309 – 15c. green and blue 10 10
310 – 25c. green and black 10 10
311 – 35c. black and blue 10 10
312 – 50c. violet and orange 10 10
313 – 70c. blue and green 10 10
314 – 90c. green and red 10 10
315 – 1p. violet and blue 35 30
316 **30** 2p.50 green and purple 7·50 7·50
317 – 10p. blue and black 3·00 1·50
DESIGNS: 5, 35c. Road transport; 15, 70c. Urban market; 25, 90c. Rural market; 50c., 1p. Camel caravan; 10p. "Arango" (freighter) at quay.

31 Emblem

32 Herald

1948. Anti-T.B. Fund.
318 **31** 10c. green and red 10 10
319 – 25c. green and red 1·25 60
320 **32** 50c.+10c. purple and red 15 10
321 – 90c.+10c. black and red 80 40
322 – 2p.50+50c. brown & red 6·50 3·00
323 – 5p.+1p. violet and red 10·00 5·50
DESIGNS: 25c. Airplane over sanatorium; 90c. Arab swordsman; 2p.50, Natives sitting in the sun; 5p. Airplane over Ben Karrich.

33 Market Day

34 Caliph on Horseback

1949. Air.
324 – 5c. green and purple 10 10
325 **33** 10c. mauve and black 10 10
326 – 30c. grey and blue 10 10
327 – 1p.75 blue and black 10 10
328 **33** 3p. black and blue 20 10
329 – 4p. red and black 40 25
330 – 6p.50 brown and green 1·10 25
331 – 8p. blue and mauve 2·00 45
DESIGNS—VERT: 5c., 1p.75, Straits of Gibraltar; 30c., 4p. Kebira Fortress; 6p.50, Arrival of mail plane; 8p. Galloping horseman.

1949. Caliph's Wedding Celebrations.
332 **34** 50c.+10c. red (postage) 20 20
333 – 1p.+10c. black (air) 70 30
DESIGN: 1p. Wedding crowds in palace grounds.

35 Emblem

36 Postman, 1890

1949. Anti-T.B. Fund.

No.	Type	Description	Unused	Used
334	**35**	5c. green and red	10	10
335	–	10c. blue and red	10	10
336	–	25c. black and red	50	20
337	–	50c.+10c. brown and red	25	10
338	–	90c.+10c. green and red	70	20

DESIGNS: 10c. Road to recovery; 25c. Palm tree and tower; 50c. Flag and followers; 90c. Moorish horseman.

1950. 75th Anniv of U.P.U.

No.	Type	Description	Unused	Used
339	**36**	5c. blue and brown	10	10
340	–	10c. black and blue	10	10
341	–	15c. green and black	10	10
342	–	35c. black and violet	10	10
343	–	45c. mauve and red	15	15
344	**36**	50c. black and green	10	10
345	–	75c. blue and deep blue	10	10
346	**36**	90c. red and black	10	10
347	–	1p. green and purple	10	10
348	–	1p.50 blue and red	40	10
349	–	5p. purple and black	70	15
350	–	10p. blue and violet	19·00	18·00

DESIGNS: 10, 45c., 1p. Mounted postman; 15c., 1p.50, Mail coach; 35, 75c., 5p. Mail van; 10p. Steam mail train.

37 Morabito

38 Hunting

1950. Anti-T.B. Fund.

No.	Type	Description	Unused	Used
351	–	5c. black and red	10	10
352	–	10c. green and red	10	10
353	–	25c. blue and red	55	30
354	–	50c.+10c. brown and red	20	10
355	**37**	90c.+10c. green and red	1·25	65

DESIGNS: 5c. Arab horseman; 10c. Fort; 25c. Sanatorium; 50c. Crowd at Fountain of Life.

1950.

No.	Type	Description	Unused	Used
356	**38**	5c. mauve and brown	10	10
357	–	10c. grey and red	10	10
358	**38**	50c. sepia and green	10	10
359	–	1p. red and violet	35	10
360	–	5p. violet and red	55	10
361	–	10p. red and green	2·00	50

DESIGNS: 10c., 1p. Hunters and hounds; 5p. Fishermen; 10p. Carabo (fishing boat).

39 Emblem

40 Mounted Riflemen

1951. Anti-T.B. Fund.

No.	Type	Description	Unused	Used
362	**39**	5c. green and red	10	10
363	–	10c. blue and red	10	10
364	–	25c. black and red	60	35
365	–	50c.+10c. brown and red	10	10
366	–	90c.+10c. blue and red	25	15
367	–	1p.+5p. blue and red	8·00	3·50
368	–	1p.10+25c. sepia and red	2·75	1·75

DESIGNS: 10c. Natives and children; 25c. Airplane over Nubes; 50c. Moorish horsemen; 90c. Riverside fortress; 1p. Brig "Hernan Cortes"; 1p.10, Airplane over caravan.

1952.

No.	Type	Description	Unused	Used
369	**40**	5c. brown and blue	10	10
370	–	10c. mauve and sepia	10	10
371	–	15c. green and black	10	10
372	–	20c. purple and green	10	10
373	–	25c. blue and red	10	10
374	–	35c. orange and olive	10	10
375	–	45c. red	10	10
376	–	50c. green and red	10	10
377	–	75c. blue and purple	10	10
378	–	90c. purple and blue	10	10
379	–	1p. brown and blue	10	10
380	–	5p. blue and red	1·25	30
381	–	10p. black and green	1·90	40

DESIGNS—HORIZ: 10c. Grooms leading horses; 15c. Parade of horsemen; 20c. Peasants; 25c. Monastic procession; 35c. Native band; 45c. Tribesmen; 50c. Natives overlooking roof tops; 75c. Inside a tea house; 90c. Wedding procession; 1p. Pilgrims on horseback; 5p. Storyteller and audience; 10p. Natives talking.

41 Road to Tetuan

1952. Air. Tetuan Postal Museum Fund.

No.	Type	Description	Unused	Used
382	**41**	2p. blue and black	10	10
383	–	4p. red and black	30	10
384	–	8p. green and black	40	25
385	–	16p. brown and black	2·00	80

DESIGNS: 4p. Moors watching airplane; 8p. Horseman and airplane; 16p. Shadow of airplane over Tetuan.

42 Natives at Prayer

43 Sidi Saidi

1952. Anti-T.B. Fund. Frame in red.

No.	Type	Description	Unused	Used
386	**42**	5c. green	10	10
387	–	10c. brown	10	10
388	–	25c. blue	30	20
389	–	50c.+10c. black	10	10
390	–	60c.+25c. green	60	35
391	–	90c.+10c. purple	55	30
392	–	1p.10+25c. violet	1·60	75
393	–	5p.+2p. black	4·00	2·00

DESIGNS: 10c. Beggars outside doorway; 25c. Airplane over cactus; 50c. Natives on horseback; 60c. Airplane over palms; 90c. Hilltop fortress; 1p.10, Airplane over agaves; 5p. Mounted warrior.

1953. Air.

No.	Type	Description	Unused	Used
394	–	35c. red and blue	15	10
395	**43**	60c. green and lake	15	10
396	–	1p.10 black and blue	25	10
397	–	4p.50 brown and lake	85	20

DESIGNS: 35c. Carabo (fishing boat); 1p.10, Le Yunta (ploughing); 4p.50, Fortress, Xauen.

1953. Air. No. 208 surch **50**.

No.	Type	Description	Unused	Used
398		50c. on 75c. blue	30	10

1953. Anti-T.B. Fund. As T **32** but inscr "PRO TUBERCULOSOS 1953". Frame in red.

No.	Type	Description	Unused	Used
400		5c. green	10	10
401		10c. purple	10	10
402		25c. green	70	40
403		50c.+10c. violet	10	10
404		60c.+25c. brown	1·40	80
405		90c.+10c. black	45	25
406		1p.10+25c. brown	2·50	1·25
407		5p.+2p. blue	8·75	5·00

DESIGNS: 5c. Herald; 10c. Moorish horseman; 25c. Airplane over Ben Karrich; 50c. Mounted warrior; 60c. Airplane over sanatorium; 90c. Moorish horseman; 1p.10, Airplane over sea; 5p. Arab swordsman.

46

47 Water-carrier

1953.

No.	Type	Description	Unused	Used
408	**46**	5c. red	10	10
409		10c. green	10	10

1953. 25th Anniv of 1st Pictorial Stamps of Spanish Morocco.

No.	Type	Description	Unused	Used
410	–	25c. purple and green	10	10
411	**47**	50c. green and red	10	10
412	–	90c. orange and blue	10	10
413	–	1p. green and brown	10	10
414	–	1p.25 mauve and green	10	10
415	–	2p. blue and purple	25	15
416	**47**	2p.50 orange and grey	55	20
417	–	4p.50 green and mauve	3·25	45
418	–	10p. black and green	3·75	90

DESIGNS—VERT: 35c., 1p.25, Mountain women; 90c., 2p. Mountain tribesmen; 1, 4p.50, Veiled Moorish women; 10p. Arab dignitary.

1954. Anti-T.B. Fund. As T **32**, but inscr "PRO TUBERCULOSOS 1954". Frame in red.

No.	Type	Description	Unused	Used
419		5c. turquoise	10	10
420		5c.+5c. purple	60	20
421		10c. sepia	10	10
422		25c. blue	15	15
423		50c.+10c. green	60	30
424		5p.+2p. black	7·50	3·75

DESIGNS: 5c. Convent; 5c.+5c. White stork on a tower; 10c. Moroccan family; 25c. Airplane over Spanish coast; 50c. Father and child; 5p. Chapel.

48 Saida Gate

49 Celebrations

1955. Frames in black.

No.	Type	Description	Unused	Used
425	–	15c. green	10	10
426	**48**	25c. purple	10	10
427	–	80c. blue	10	10
428	**48**	1p. mauve	20	10
429	–	15p. turquoise	2·40	85

DESIGNS: 15c., 80c. Queen's Gate; 15p. Ceuta Gate.

1955. 30th Anniv of Caliph's Accession.

No.	Type	Description	Unused	Used
430	**49**	15c. olive and brown	10	10
431	–	25c. lake and purple	10	10
432	–	30c. green and sepia	10	10
433	**49**	70c. green and myrtle	10	10
434	–	80c. brown and olive	10	10
435	–	1p. brown and blue	10	10
436	**49**	1p.80 violet and black	20	10
437	–	3p. grey and blue	20	10
438	–	5p. brown and myrtle	1·10	35
439	–	15p. green and brown	2·50	1·25

DESIGNS: 25c., 80c., 3p. Caliph's portrait; 30c., 1, 5p. Procession; 15p. Coat of Arms.

EXPRESS LETTER STAMPS

Express Letter Stamps of Spain overprinted.

1914. Optd **MARRUECOS**.

No.	Type	Description	Unused	Used
E55	E **53**	20c. red	3·75	1·90

1915. Optd **PROTECTORADO ESPANOL EN MARRUECOS**.

No.	Type	Description	Unused	Used
E68	E **53**	20c. red	3·25	1·40

1923. Optd **ZONA DE PROTECTORADO ESPANOL EN MARRUECOS**.

No.	Type	Description	Unused	Used
E111	E **53**	20c. red	9·50	8·25

1926. Red Cross. Optd **ZONA PROTECTORADO ESPANOL**.

No.	Type	Description	Unused	Used
E124	E **77**	20c. black and blue	2·50	2·50

E **12** Moorish Courier

E **16**

1928.

No.	Type	Description	Unused	Used
E138	E **12**	20c. black	3·00	2·75

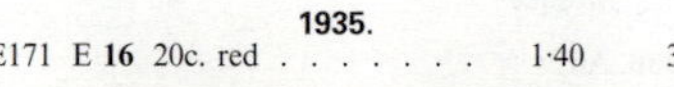

1935.

No.	Type	Description	Unused	Used
E171	E **16**	20c. red	1·40	30

E **19** Moorish Courier

E **21**

1937. 1st Anniv of Civil War.

No.	Type	Description	Unused	Used
E200	E **19**	20c. red	10	10

1940.

No.	Type	Description	Unused	Used
E233	E **21**	25c. red	30	20

1940. No. E200 optd as Nos. 233/48 and surch also.

No.	Type	Description	Unused	Used
E249	E **19**	25c. on 20c. red	10·00	10·00

E **37** Air Mail 1935

E **41** Moorish Courier

1950. 75th Anniv of U.P.U.

No.	Type	Description	Unused	Used
E351	E **37**	25c. black and red	19·00	18·00

1952.

No.	Type	Description	Unused	Used
E382	E **41**	25c. red	10	10

E **48** Moorish Courier

E **49** Tangier Gate

1953. 25th Anniv of First Pictorial Stamps of Spanish Morocco.

No.	Type	Description	Unused	Used
E419	E **48**	25c. mauve and blue	20	15

1955.

No.	Type	Description	Unused	Used
E430	E **49**	2p. violet and black	15	10

For later issues see **MOROCCO**.

SPANISH POST OFFICES IN TANGIER Pt. 9

See note below No. 41 of Spanish P.O.s in Morocco, concerning the exclusive use of Nos. 30/41 in Tangier after 1914.

Postage stamps of Spain overprinted.

1921. Optd **CORREO ESPANOL MARRUECOS.**
1 **66** 1c. green . . . 15 10
2 **64** 2c. brown . . . £300
3 15c. yellow . . . 1·10 10
4 20c. violet . . . 1·90 10

1939. Optd as 1921.
5 **68** 2c. green . . . 3·75 15
6 5c. purple . . . 3·75 15
7 5c. red . . . 3·75 15
8a 10c. green . . . 4·25 15
10 20c. violet . . . 7·50 15
11 50c. orange . . . 32·00 6·50
12 **69** 10p. brown . . . 4·25 4·25

1926. Red Cross stamps optd **CORREO ESPANOL TANGER.**
13 **70** 1c. orange . . . 6·25 6·25
14 – 2c. red . . . 6·25 6·25
15 – 5c. grey . . . 3·00 3·00
16 – 10c. green . . . 3·00 3·00
17 **70** 15c. violet . . . 1·25 1·25
18 – 20c. purple . . . 1·25 1·25
19 **71** 25c. red . . . 1·25 1·25
20 **70** 30c. olive . . . 1·25 1·25
21 – 40c. blue . . . 25 25
22 – 50c. brown . . . 25 25
23 – 1p. red . . . 55 55
24 – 4p. brown . . . 55 55
25 **71** 10p. lilac . . . 3·00 3·00

1929. Seville–Barcelona Exhibition stamps, Nos. 504/14 optd **TANGER.**
27 5c. red . . . 25 25
28 10c. green . . . 25 25
29 15c. blue . . . 25 25
30 20c. violet . . . 25 25
31 25c. red . . . 25 25
32 30c. brown . . . 25 25
33 40c. blue . . . 70 70
34 50c. orange . . . 70 70
35 1p. grey . . . 7·00 7·00
36 4p. red . . . 19·00 19·00
37 10p. brown . . . 28·00 28·00

1930. Optd as 1921.
38 **97** 10c. green . . . 2·40 30
39 15c. turquoise . . . £110 1·25
40 20c. violet . . . 2·50 50
41 30c. red . . . 2·75 1·25
42 40c. blue . . . 10·00 6·50

1933. Optd **MARRUECOS.**
43 **143** 1c. green (imperf) . . . 15 15
44 2c. brown . . . 15 15
45 **127** 5c. brown . . . 15 15
46 **128** 10c. green . . . 15 15
47 **130** 15c. blue . . . 15 15
48 **127** 20c. violet . . . 15 15
49 **132** 25c. red . . . 15 15
50 **133** 30c. red . . . 45·00 5·50
51 **138** 40c. blue . . . 25 15
52 **130** 50c. orange . . . 60 15
53 **138** 60c. green . . . 60 15
54 **142** 1p. black . . . 60 25
55 – 4p. mauve . . . 1·60 2·40
56 – 10p. brown . . . 2·40 5·50

1937. Optd **TANGER.**
58 **143** 1c. green (imperf) . . . 30 15
59 2c. brown . . . 30 15
60 **127** 5c. brown . . . 30 15
61 **128** 10c. green . . . 30 15
62 **130** 15c. blue . . . 40 15
63 **127** 20c. violet . . . 40 40
64 **132** 25c. red . . . 40 40
65 **136** 30c. red . . . 40 15
66 **138** 40c. blue . . . 1·10 50
67 **130** 50c. orange . . . 3·25 50
68 **142** 1p. black . . . 6·00 3·00
69 – 4p. mauve (No. 768c) . . . £160
70 – 10p. brown (No. 769c) . . . £200

1938. Optd **Correo Espanol Tanger.**
71 **143** 5c. brown . . . 1·60 90
72 10c. green . . . 1·60 90
73 15c. green . . . 1·60 90
74 20c. violet . . . 1·60 60
75 25c. mauve . . . 1·60 60
76 30c. red . . . 6·50 3·00
77 **160a** 40c. red . . . 3·25 1·40
78 45c. red . . . 1·10 40
79 50c. blue . . . 1·10 40
80 60c. blue . . . 3·25 1·40
81 **145** 2p. blue . . . 20·00 8·00
82 – 4p. mauve (No. 768c) . . . 20·00 8·00

1938. Air. Optd **Correo Aereo TANGER.**
83 **143** 25c. mauve . . . 85 45
84 **160a** 50c. blue . . . 85 45

1938. Air. Optd **CORREO AEREO TANGER.**
86 **142** 1p. black . . . 85 45
85 **145** 2p. blue . . . 6·50 2·50
87 – 4p. mauve (No. 768c) . . . 6·50 2·50
88 – 10p. brown (No. 769c) . . . 48·00 30·00

1939. Optd **Tanger.**
89 **143** 5c. brown . . . 60 40
90 10c. green . . . 60 40
91 15c. green . . . 60 40
92 20c. violet . . . 60 40
93 25c. mauve . . . 60 40
94 30c. red . . . 60 40
95 **160a** 40c. red . . . 60 40
96 45c. red . . . 60 40
97 50c. blue . . . 1·60 1·00
98 60c. blue . . . 80 40
99 **142** 1p. black . . . 1·10 60
100 **145** 2p. blue . . . 21·00 12·50
101 – 4p. mauve (No. 768c) . . . 21·00 12·50
102 – 10p. brown (No. 769c) . . . 21·00 12·50

1939. Air. Optd **Via Aerea Tanger.**
103 **143** 5c. brown . . . 85 80
104 10c. green . . . 85 80
105 15c. green . . . 80 65
106 20c. violet . . . 80 65
107 25c. mauve . . . 80 65
108 30c. red . . . 1·40 95
109 **160a** 40c. red . . . 38·00
110 45c. red . . . 40 40
111 50c. blue . . . 80·00
112 60c. blue . . . 80·00 16·00
113 **142** 1p. black . . . 25·00
114 – 4p. mauve (No. 768c) . . . 40·00 24·00
115 – 10p. brown (No. 769c) . . . £110

1939. Air. Express Letter stamp optd **Via Aerea Tanger.**
116 E **145** 20c. red . . . 2·75 1·40

1939. Various fiscal types inscr "DERECHOS CONSULARES ESPANOLES" optd **Correo Tanger.**
117 50c. pink . . . 17·00 17·00
118 1p. pink . . . 4·25 4·25
119 2p. pink . . . 4·25 4·25
120 5p. red and green . . . 4·75 4·25
121 10p. red and violet . . . 20·00 20·00

1939. Air. Various fiscal types inscr "DERECHOS CONSULARES ESPANOLES" optd **Correo Aereo Tanger.**
122 1p. blue . . . 48·00 48·00
123 2p. blue . . . 48·00 48·00
124 5p. blue . . . 80·00 80·00
125 10p. blue . . . 6·00 6·00

15 Moroccan Woman

16 Douglas DC-3

1948.
126 – 1c. green . . . 10 10
127 – 2c. orange . . . 10 10
128 – 5c. purple . . . 10 10
129 – 10c. blue . . . 10 10
130 – 20c. sepia . . . 10 10
131 – 25c. green . . . 10 10
132 – 30c. grey . . . 25 10
133 – 45c. red . . . 25 10
134 **15** 50c. red . . . 25 10
135 – 75c. blue . . . 50 10
136 – 90c. green . . . 40 10
137 – 1p.35 red . . . 1·75 30
138 **15** 2p. violet . . . 3·25 30
139 – 10p. green . . . 3·75 60

DESIGNS: 1, 2c. Woman's head facing right; 5, 25c. Palm tree; 10, 20c. Woman's head facing left; 30c., 1p.35, Old map of Tangier; 45c., 10p. Street scene; 75, 90c. Head of Moor.

1949. Air.
140 – 20c. brown . . . 50 10
141 **16** 25c. red . . . 50 10
142 – 35c. green . . . 50 10
143 – 1p. violet . . . 1·50 10
144 **16** 2p. green . . . 2·50 30
145 – 10p. purple . . . 3·50 1·10

DESIGNS: 20c., 1p. Lockheed Constellation and map; 35c., 10p. Boeing 377 Stratocruiser in clouds.

EXPRESS LETTER STAMPS

Express Letter Stamps of Spain overprinted.

1926. Red Cross. Optd **CORREO ESPANOL TANGER.**
E26 E **77** 20c. black and blue . . . 3·00 3·00

1933. No. E17 optd **MARRUECOS.**
EE57 **145** 20c. red . . . 1·10 35

E **17** Courier

1949.
E146 E **17** 25c. red . . . 55 30

SPANISH SAHARA Pt. 9

Former Spanish territory on the north-west coast of Africa, previously called Rio de Oro. Later divided between Morocco and Mauritania.

100 centimos = 1 peseta.

1 Tuareg and Camel

1924.
1 **1** 5c. green . . . 1·50 40
2 10c. green . . . 1·50 40
3 15c. blue . . . 1·50 40
4 20c. violet . . . 1·50 65
5 25c. red . . . 1·50 65
6 30c. brown . . . 1·50 65
7 40c. blue . . . 1·50 65
8 50c. orange . . . 1·50 65
9 60c. purple . . . 1·50 65
10 1p. red . . . 7·50 3·50
11 4p. brown . . . 38·00 17·00
12 10p. purple . . . 85·00 50·00

1926. Red Cross stamps of Spain optd **SAHARA ESPANOL.**
13 – 5c. grey . . . 7·00 7·00
14 – 10c. green . . . 7·00 7·00
15 **70** 15c. violet . . . 2·25 2·25
16 – 20c. purple . . . 2·25 2·25
17 **71** 25c. red . . . 2·25 2·25
18 **70** 30c. olive . . . 2·25 2·25
19 – 40c. blue . . . 15 15
20 – 50c. brown . . . 15 15
21 **71** 60c. green . . . 15 15
22 – 1p. red . . . 15 15
23 – 4p. brown . . . 1·90 1·90
24 **71** 10p. lilac . . . 5·00 5·00

1929. Seville and Barcelona Exn stamps of Spain. Nos. 504/14, optd **SAHARA.**
25 5c. red . . . 15 15
26 10c. green . . . 15 15
27 15c. blue . . . 15 15
28 20c. violet . . . 15 15
29 25c. red . . . 15 15
30 30c. brown . . . 15 15
31 40c. blue . . . 40 40
32 50c. orange . . . 40 40
33 1p. grey . . . 2·40 2·40
34 4p. red . . . 18·00 18·00
35 10p. brown . . . 35·00 35·00

1931. Optd **Republica Espanola.**
36 **1** 5c. green . . . 45 40
37 10c. green . . . 45 40
38 15c. blue . . . 45 40
39 20c. violet . . . 45 40
40 25c. red . . . 55 40
41 30c. brown . . . 55 40
42 40c. blue . . . 2·75 60
43 50c. orange . . . 2·75 1·40
44 60c. purple . . . 2·75 1·40
45 1p. red . . . 2·75 1·40
46 4p. brown . . . 26·00 14·00
47 10p. purple . . . 50·00 28·00

1941. Stamps of Spain optd **SAHARA ESPANOL.**
47a **181** 1c. green . . . 1·40 1·40
47b **182** 2c. brown . . . 1·40 1·40
48 **183** 5c. brown . . . 40 40
49 10c. red . . . 1·40 1·40
50 15c. green . . . 40 40
51 **196** 20c. violet . . . 40 40
52 25c. red . . . 95 80
53 30c. blue . . . 95 95
54 40c. green . . . 40 40
55 50c. blue . . . 5·00 1·25
56 70c. blue . . . 3·50 1·90
57 1PTA. black . . . 16·00 2·50
58 2PTAS. brown . . . 90·00 60·00
59 4PTAS. red . . . £200 £140
60 10PTS. brown . . . £650 £225

6 Dorcas Gazelles

7 Ostriches

1943.
61 **6** 1c. mauve & brown (postage) . . . 10 10
62 – 2c. blue and green . . . 10 10
63 – 5c. blue and red . . . 10 10
64 **6** 15c. green and myrtle . . . 10 10
65 – 20c. brown and mauve . . . 10 10
66 **6** 40c. mauve and purple . . . 10 10
67 – 45c. red and purple . . . 15 15
68 – 75c. blue and indigo . . . 15 15
69 **6** 1p. brown and red . . . 65 65
70 – 3p. green and violet . . . 1·25 1·25
71 – 10p. black and sepia . . . 21·00 18·00

DESIGNS—VERT: 2, 20, 45c., 3p. Camel caravan; 5, 75c., 10p. Camel troups.

72 **7** 5c. brown and red (air) . . . 40 40
73 – 25c. olive and green . . . 20 15
74 **7** 50c. turquoise and blue . . . 40 40
75 – 1p. blue and mauve . . . 50 25
76 **7** 1p.40 blue and green . . . 40 40
77 – 2p. brown and purple . . . 85 85
78 **7** 5p. mauve and brown . . . 2·00 1·25
79 – 6p. green and blue . . . 18·00 16·00

DESIGN: 25c., 1, 2, 6p. Airplane and camels.

8 Boy carrying Lamb

9 Diego de Herrera

1950. Child Welfare.
80 **8** 50c.+10c. brown . . . 20 15
81 1p.+25c. red . . . 9·75 5·25
82 6p.50+1p.65 green . . . 5·25 1·60

1950. Air. Colonial Stamp Day.
83 **9** 5p. violet . . . 2·75 1·00

9a Woman and Dove

9b General Franco

1951. Air. 500th Birth Anniv of Isabella the Catholic.
84 **9a** 5p. green . . . 21·00 6·50

1951. Visit of General Franco.
85 **9b** 50c. orange . . . 10 10
86 1p. brown . . . 25 20
87 5p. turquoise . . . 30·00 11·00

10 Dromedary and Calf

11 Native Woman

1951. Colonial Stamp Day.
88 **10** 5c.+5c. brown . . . 10 10
89 10c.+5c. orange . . . 10 10
90 60c.+15c. olive . . . 30 10

1952. Child Welfare Fund.
91 **11** 5c.+5c. brown . . . 10 10
92 50c.+10c. black . . . 10 10
93 2p.+30c. blue . . . 1·40 95

12 Morion, Sword and Banner

13 Head of Ostritch

1952. Air. 500th Birth Anniv of Ferdinand the Catholic.
94 **12** 5p. brown . . . 25·00 6·50

1952. Colonial Stamp Day.
95 **13** 5c.+5c. brown . . . 10 10
96 10c.+5c. red . . . 15 10
97 60c.+15c. green . . . 35 20

14 "Geography"

15 Woman Musician

1953. 75th Anniv of Royal Geographical Society.
98 **14** 5c. red 10 10
99 35c. green 10 10
100 60c. brown 20 10

1953. Child Welfare Fund. Inscr "PRO INFANCIA 1953".
101 **15** 5c.+5c. brown 10 10
102 – 10c.+5c. purple 10 10
103 **15** 15c. olive 10 10
104 – 60c. brown 15 10
DESIGN: 10, 60c. Native man musician.

16 Red Scorpionfish

1953. Colonial Stamp Day. Inscr "DIA DEL SELLO COLONIAL 1953".
105 **16** 5c.+5c. violet 10 10
106 – 10c.+5c. green 10 10
107 **16** 15c. olive 10 10
108 – 60c. orange 25 20
DESIGN—HORIZ: 10, 60c. Zebra seabreams.

17 Hurdlers

1954. Child Welfare Fund. Inscr "PRO INFANCIA 1954".
109 **17** 5c.+5c. brown 10 10
110 – 10c.+5c. violet 10 10
111 **17** 15c. green 10 10
112 – 60c. brown 10 10
DESIGN—VERT: 10, 60c. Native runner.

18 Atlantic Flyingfish

1954. Colonial Stamp Day. Inscr "DIA DEL SELLO COLONIAL 1954".
113 **18** 5c.+5c. red 10 10
114 – 10c.+5c. purple 10 10
115 **18** 15c. green 10 10
116 – 60c. brown 25 20
DESIGN—HORIZ: 10, 60c. Gilthead seabream.

19 E. Bonelli

1955. Birth Centenary of Bonelli (explorer).
117 **19** 10c.+5c. purple 10 10
118 – 25c.+10c. violet 10 10
119 **19** 50c. olive 15 15
DESIGN: 25c. Bonelli and felucca.

20 Scimitar Oryx

21 "Antirrhinum ramosissimum"

1955. Colonial Stamp Day. Inscr "DIA DEL SELLO COLONIAL 1955".
120 **20** 5c.+5c. brown 10 10
121 – 15c.+5c. bistre 10 10
122 **20** 70c. green 15 10
DESIGN: 15c. Scimitar oryx's head.

1956. Child Welfare Fund. Inscr "PRO-INFANCIA 1956".
123 **21** 5c.+5c. olive 10 10
124 – 15c.+5c. ochre 10 10
125 **21** 20c. turquoise 10 10
126 – 50c. brown 10 10
DESIGN: 15, 50c. "Sesuvium portulacastrum" (wrongly inscr "Sesiviun").

22 Arms of Aaiun and Native on Camel

23 Dromedaries

1956. Colonial Stamp Day. Inscr "DIA DEL SELLO 1956".
127 **22** 5c.+5c. black and violet 10 10
128 – 15c.+5c. green and ochre 10 10
129 **22** 70c. brown and green 10 10
DESIGN—VERT: 15c. Arms of Villa Cisneros and native chief.

1957. Animals.
130 **23** 5c. violet 10 10
131 – 15c. ochre 30 20
132 – 50c. brown 10 10
133 **23** 70c. green 70 10
134 – 80c. turquoise 1·50 20
135 – 1p.80 mauve 70 20
DESIGNS: 15, 80c. Ostrich; 50c., 1p.80, Dorcas gazelle.

24 Golden Eagle

25 Head of Striped Hyena

1957. Child Welfare Fund. Inscr "PRO-INFANCIA 1957".
136 **24** 5c.+5c. brown 15 10
137 – 15c.+5c. bistre 30 10
138 **24** 70c. green 55 25
DESIGN: 15c. Tawny eagle in flight.

1957. Colonial Stamp Day. Inscr "DIA DEL SELLO 1957".
139 **25** 10c.+5c. purple 10 10
140 – 15c.+5c. ochre 10 10
141 **25** 20c. green 10 10
142 – 70c. myrtle 15 10
DESIGN: 15, 70c. Striped hyena.

26 White Stork and Arms of Valencia and Aaiun

27 Cervantes

1958. Aid for Valencia.
143 **26** 10c.+5c. brown 10 10
144 15c.+10c. ochre 15 15
145 50c.+10c. brown 40 30

1958. Child Welfare Fund. Inscr "1958".
146 **27** 10c.+5c. brown & chest 10 10
147 – 15c.+5c. myrtle & orange 10 10
148 – 20c. green and brown 10 10
149 **27** 70c. blue and green 10 10
DESIGNS—VERT: 15c. Don Quixote and Sancho Panza on horseback. HORIZ: 20c. Don Quixote and the lion.

28 Hoopoe Lark

29 Lope de Vega (author)

1958. Colonial Stamp Day. Inscr "1958".
150 **28** 10c.+5c. red 20 10
151 – 25c.+10c. violet 55 25
152 – 50c.+10c. olive 90 45
DESIGNS—HORIZ: 25c. Hoopoe lark feeding young. VERT: 50c. Fulvous babbler.

1959. Child Welfare Fund. Inscr "PRO INFANCIA 1959".
153 **29** 10c.+5c. olive and brown 10 10
154 – 15c.+5c. brown and bistre 10 10
155 – 20c. sepia and green 10 10
156 **29** 70c. myrtle and green 10 10
DESIGNS—Characters from the comedy "The Star of Seville": 15c. Spanish lady; 20c. Caballero.

30 Grey Heron

31 Sahara Postman

1959. Birds.
157 **30** 25c. violet 15 15
158 – 50c. green 15 15
159 – 75c. sepia 20 15
160 **30** 1p. red 25 15
161 – 1p.50 green 35 15
162 – 2p. purple 2·25 15
163 **30** 3p. blue 2·25 15
164 – 5p. brown 4·25 15
165 – 10p. olive 12·50 8·75
DESIGNS: 50c., 1p.50, 5p. Northern sparrow hawk; 75c., 2, 10p. Herring gull.

1959. Colonial Stamp Day. Inscr "1959".
166 **31** 10c.+5c. brown and red 10 10
167 – 20c.+5c. brown and green 10 10
168 – 50c.+20c. slate and olive 10 10
DESIGNS: 20c. Postman tendering letters; 50c. Camel postman.

32 F. de Quevedo (writer)

33 Leopard

1960. Child Welfare Fund. Inscr "PRO-INFANCIA 1960".
169 **32** 10c.+5c. purple 10 10
170 – 15c.+5c. bistre 30 30
171 – 35c. green 10 10
172 **32** 80c. turquoise 10 10
DESIGNS—VERT: (representing Quevedo's works): 15c. Winged railway wheel and hour-glass; 25c. Man in plumed hat wearing cloak and sword.

1960. Stamp Day. Inscr "1960".
173 **33** 10c.+5c. mauve 10 10
174 – 20c.+5c. myrtle 10 10
175 – 30c.+10c. brown 55 40
176 – 50c.+20c. brown 25 10
DESIGNS: 20c. Fennec fox; 30c. Golden eagle defying leopard; 50c. Red fox.

34 Houbara Bustard

35 Cameleer and Airplane

1961.
177 **34** 25c. violet 10 10
178 – 50c. brown 10 10
179 **34** 75c. dull purple 15 10
180 – 1p. red 20 10
181 **34** 1p.50 green 25 10
182 – 2p. mauve 1·25 10
183 **34** 3p. blue 1·40 45
184 – 5p. brown 2·00 60
185 **34** 10p. olive 4·50 2·50
DESIGN: 50c., 1, 2, 5p. Feral rock doves.

1961. Air.
186 **35** 25p. sepia 3·25 85

36 Dorcas Gazelle

37

1961. Child Welfare. Inscr "PRO-INFANCIA 1961".
187 **36** 10c.+5c. red 10 10
188 – 25c.+10c. violet 10 10
189 **36** 80c.+20c. green 10 10
DESIGN: 25c. One dorcas gazelle.

1961. 25th Anniv of Gen. Franco as Head of State.
190 – 25c. grey 10 10
191 **37** 50c. olive 10 10
192 – 70c. green 10 10
193 **37** 1p. orange 10 10
DESIGNS—VERT: 25c. Map; 70c. Aaiun Chapel.

38 A. Fernandez de Lugo

39 "Neurada procumbres linn"

1961. Stamp Day. Inscr "DIA DEL SELLO 1961".
194 **38** 10c.+5c. salmon 10 10
195 – 25c.+10c. plum 10 10
196 **38** 30c.+10c. brown 10 10
197 – 1p.+10c. orange 10 10
PORTRAIT: 25c., 1p. D. de Herrera.

1962. Flowers.
198 **39** 25c. violet 10 10
199 – 50c. sepia 10 10
200 – 70c. green 10 10
201 **39** 1p. orange 10 10
202 – 1p.50 turquoise 30 10
203 – 2p. purple 1·10 10
204 **39** 3p. blue 1·90 30
205 – 10p. olive 4·00 1·40
FLOWERS: 50c., 1p.50, 10p. "Anabasis articulata moq"; 70c., 2p. "Euphorbia resinifera".

40 Hoefler's Butterflyfish

42 Seville Cathedral

41 Goats

1962. Child Welfare.
206 **40** 25c. violet 10 10
207 – 50c. green 10 10
208 **40** 1p. brown 20 15
DESIGN—HORIZ: 50c. Dungat groupers.

1962. Stamp Day.
209 **41** 15c. green 10 10
210 – 35c. purple 10 10
211 **41** 1p. brown 15 10
DESIGN: 35c. Sheep.

1963. Seville Flood Relief.
212 **42** 50c. olive 15 10
213 1p. brown 10 10

43 Cameleer and Camel

44 Dove in Hands

1963. Child Welfare. Inscr "PRO-INFANCIA 1963".
214 – 25c. violet 10 10
215 **43** 50c. grey 10 10
216 – 1p. red 15 10
DESIGN: 25c., 1p. Three camels.

1963. "For Barcelona".
217 **44** 50c. turquoise 10 10
218 1p. brown 10 10

45 John Dory

1964. Stamp Day. Inscr "DIA DEL SELLO 1963".
219 **45** 25c. violet 15 10
220 – 50c. olive 20 10
221 **45** 1p. brown 30 15
FISH—VERT: 50c. Plain bonito.

46 Striped Hawk Moth
47 Mounted Dromedary and Microphone

1964. Child Welfare.
222 **46** 25c. violet 10 10
223 – 50c. olive 20 10
224 **46** 1p. red 40 15
DESIGN—VERT: 50c. Goat moths.

1964.
225 **47** 25c. purple 10 10
226 – 50c. olive 10 10
227 – 70c. green 10 10
228 **47** 1p. purple 10 10
229 – 1p.50 turquoise 10 10
230 – 2p. turquoise 15 10
231 – 3p. blue 20 15
232 – 10p. lake 1·40 65
DESIGNS: 50c., 1p.50, 3p. Flute-player; 70c., 2, 10p. Women drummer.

48 Barbary Ground Squirrel

1964. Stamp Day.
233 – 50c. olive 10 10
234 **48** 1p. lake 10 10
235 – 1p.50 green 10 10
DESIGN—VERT: 50c., 1p.50, Eurasian red squirrel eating.

49 Doctor tending Patient, and Hospital

1965. 25th Anniv of End of Spanish Civil War.
236 – 50c. olive 10 10
237 **49** 1p. red 10 10
238 – 1p.50 blue 10 10
DESIGNS—VERT: 50c. Saharan woman; 1p.50, Desert installation and cameleer.

50 "Anthia sexmaculata" (ground beetle)
51 Handball

1965. Child Welfare. Insects.
239 **50** 50c. blue 10 10
240 – 1p. green 10 10
241 **50** 1p.50 brown 15 10
242 – 3p. blue 1·25 60
INSECTS—VERT: 1, 3p. "Blepharopsis mendica" (praying mantis).

1965. Stamp Day.
243 **51** 50c. red 10 10
244 – 1p. purple 10 10
245 **51** 1p.50 blue 10 10
DESIGN: 1p. Arms of Spanish Sahara.

52 Bows of "Rio de Oro"

1966. Child Welfare.
246 **52** 50c. olive 10 10
247 1p. brown 10 10
248 – 1p.50 green 15 10
DESIGN: 1p.50, Freighter "Fuerta Ventura".

53 Big-eyed Tuna
54 Fig

1966. Stamp Day.
249 **53** 10c. blue and yellow 10 10
250 – 40c. grey and salmon 10 10
251 **53** 1p.50 brown and green 10 10
252 – 4p. purple and green 25 20
DESIGN—VERT: 40c., 4p. Ocean sunfish.

1967. Child Welfare.
253 **54** 10c. yellow and blue 10 10
254 – 40c. purple and green 10 10
255 **54** 1p.50 yellow and green 10 10
256 – 4p. orange and blue 15 10
DESIGN: 40c., 4p. Lupin.

55 Quay, Aaiun

1967. Inauguration of Sahara Ports.
257 **55** 1p.50 brown and blue 10 10
258 – 4p. ochre and blue 20 10
DESIGN: 4p. Port of Villa Cisneros.

56 Ruddy Shelduck

1968. Stamp Day.
259 **56** 1p. brown and green 60 35
260 – 1p.50 mauve and black 95 65
261 – 3p.50 lake and brown 1·10 1·50
DESIGNS—VERT: 1p.50, Greater flamingo. HORIZ: 3p.50, Rufous scrub robin.

56a Scorpio (scorpion)
57 Dove, and Stamp within Posthorn

1968. Child Welfare. Signs of the Zodiac.
262 **56a** 1p. mauve on yellow 10 10
263 – 1p.50 brown on pink 10 10
264 – 2p.50 violet on yellow 15 15
DESIGNS: 1p.50, Capricorn (goat); 2p.50, Virgo (virgin).

1968. Stamp Day.
265 **57** 1p. blue and purple 10 10
266 – 1p.50 green and light green 10 10
267 – 2p.50 blue and orange 15 10
DESIGNS: 1p.50, Postal handstamp, stamps and letter; 2p.50, Saharan postman.

58 Head of Dorcas Gazelle

1969. Child Welfare.
268 **58** 1p. brown and black 10 10
269 – 1p.50 brown and black 15 10
270 – 2p.50 brown and black 20 10
271 – 6p. brown and black 30 10
DESIGNS: 1p.50, Dorcas gazelle tending young; 2p.50, Dorcas gazelle and camel; 6p. Dorcas gazelle leaping.

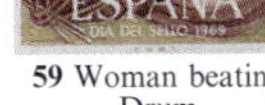

59 Woman beating Drum
61 Dorcas Gazelle and Arms of El Aaiun

60 "Grammodes boisdeffrei" (moth)

1960. Stamp Day.
272 **59** 50c. brown and bistre 15 10
273 – 1p.50 turquoise and green 15 10
274 – 2p. blue and brown 15 30
275 – 25p. brown and green 80 25
DESIGNS—VERT: 1p.50, Man playing flute. HORIZ: 2p. Drum and mounted cameleer; 25p. Flute.

1970. Child Welfare. As T **58**.
276 50c. ochre and blue 10 10
277 2p. brown and blue 15 10
278 2p.50 ochre and blue 20 10
279 6p. ochre and blue 30 10
DESIGNS: 50c. Fennec fox; 2p. Fennec fox walking; 2p.50, Head of fennec fox; 6p. Fennec fox family.

1970. Stamp Day. Butterflies. Multicoloured.
280 50c. Type **60** 10 10
281 1p. Type **60** 10 10
282 2p. African monarch 25 10
283 5p. As 2p. 60 15
284 8p. Spurge hawk moth 90 20

1971. Child Welfare.
285 **61** 1p. multicoloured 10 10
286 – 2p. green and olive 10 10
287 – 5p. blue, brown and grey 15 10
288 – 25p. green, grey and blue 70 15
DESIGNS—VERT: 25p. Smara Mosque. HORIZ: 2p. Tourist inn, Aaiun; 5p. Assembly House, Aaiun.

63 Trumpeter Finch

1971. Stamp Day. Multicoloured.
290 1p.50 Type **63** 30 30
291 2p. Type **63** 40 40
292 5p. Cream-coloured courser 70 70
293 24p. Lanner falcon 2·25 2·00

64 Seated Woman
65 Tuareg Woman

1972. Saharan Nomads.
294 **64** 1p. black, pink and blue 10 10
295 – 1p.50 slate, lilac and brown 10 10
296 – 2p. black, flesh and green 10 10
297 **64** 5p. purple, olive and green 10 10
298 – 8p. violet, green and black 20 10
299 – 10p. green, grey and black 30 10
300 – 12p. multicoloured 35 20
301 – 15p. multicoloured 40 30
302 – 24p. multicoloured 90 50
DESIGNS: 1p.50, 2p. Squatting nomad; 8, 10p. Head of nomad; 12p. Woman with bangles; 15p. Nomad with rifle; 24p. Woman displaying trinkets.

1972. Child Welfare. Multicoloured.
303 8p. Type **65** 20 10
304 12p. Tuareg elder 30 15

66 Mother and Child

1972. Stamp Day. Multicoloured.
305 4p. Type **66** 15 10
306 15p. Nomad 40 15

67 Sahara Desert

1973. Child Welfare. Multicoloured.
307 2p. Type **67** 10 10
308 7p. City Gate, El Aaiun 15 10

68 Villa Cisneros

1973. Stamp Day. Multicoloured.
309 2p. Type **68** 10 10
310 7p. Tuareg (vert) 15 10

69 U.P.U. Monument, Berne
70 Archway, Smara Mosque

1974. Centenary of Universal Postal Union.
311 **69** 15p. multicoloured 35 15

1974. Child Welfare. Multicoloured.
312 1p. Type **70** 10 10
313 2p. Villa Cisneros Mosque 15 10

71 Desert Eagle Owl

1974. Stamp Day. Multicoloured.
314 2p. Type **71** 1·00 75
315 5p. Lappet-faced vulture 2·00 2·00

72 "Espana" Emblem and Spanish Sahara Stamp
74 Tuareg Elder

73 Desert Conference

1975. "Espana 75" International Stamp Exhibition, Madrid.
316 **72** 8p. yellow, blue and black 15 10

1975. Child Welfare. Multicoloured.
317 1p.50 Type **73** 10 10
318 3p. Desert oasis 10 10

1975.
319 **74** 3p. purple, green and black 10 10

EXPRESS LETTER STAMPS

1943. Design as No. 63, inscr "URGENTE".
E80 25c. red and myrtle 65 65

E **62** Despatch-rider

1971.
E289 E **62** 10p. brown and red 35 20

SPANISH WEST AFRICA Pt. 9

100 centimos = 1 peseta.

Issues for use in Ifni and Spanish Sahara.

1 Native

2 Isabella the Catholic

1949. 75th Anniv of U.P.U.
1 **1** 4p. green 1·75 85

1949. Air. Colonial Stamp Day.
2 **2** 5p. brown 1·50 85

3 Tents

1950.
3 **3** 2c. brown 10 10
4 – 5c. violet 10 10
5 – 10c. blue 10 10
6 – 15c. black 15 10
7 **3** 25c. brown 15 10
8 – 30c. yellow 10 10
9 – 40c. olive 10 10
10 – 45c. red 10 10
11 **3** 50c. orange 10 10
12 – 75c. blue 15 15
13 – 90c. green 10 10
14 – 1p. grey 10 10
15 **3** 1p.35 violet 55 40
16 – 2p. sepia 1·00 85
17 – 5p. mauve 10·00 3·00
18 **3** 10p. brown 20·00 13·00
DESIGNS: 5, 30, 75c., 2p. Palm trees, Lake Tinzgarrentz; 10, 40, 90c., 5p. Camels and irrigation; 15, 45c., 1p. Camel transport.

8 Camel Train

1951. Air.
19 – 25c. yellow 30 10
20 **8** 50c. mauve 15 10
21 – 1p. green 35 10
22 – 2p. blue 65 10
23 **8** 3p.25 violet 1·25 45
24 – 5p. sepia 11·00 1·50
25 – 10p. red 23·00 18·00
DESIGNS: 25c., 2, 10p. Desert camp; 1, 5p. Four camels.

EXPRESS LETTER STAMP

E **10** Port Tilimenzo

1951.
E26 E **10** 25c. red 1·10 30

SRI LANKA Pt. 1

Ceylon became a republic within the British Commonwealth on 22 May 1972 and changed its name to Sri Lanka (= "Resplendent Island").

100 cents = 1 rupee.

208 National Flower and Mountain of the Illustrious Foot

1972. Inaug of Republic of Sri Lanka.
591 **208** 15c. multicoloured 30 30

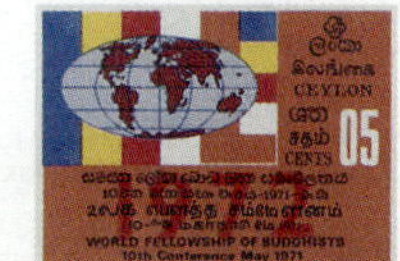

209 Map of World with Buddhist Flag

1972. 10th World Fellowship of Buddhists Conf.
592 **209** 5c. multicoloured 30 60

210 Book Year Emblem **211** Emperor Angelfish

1972. International Book Year.
593 **210** 20c. orange and brown 20 50

1972. Fishes. Multicoloured.
594 2c. Type **211** 10 1·00
595 5c. Green chromide 10 1·00
596 30c. Skipjack tuna 1·25 30
597 2r. Black ruby barb 3·50 5·25

212 Memorial Hall

1973. Opening of Bandaranaike Memorial Hall.
598 **212** 15c. cobalt and blue 30 30

213 King Vessantara giving away his Children

1973. Rock and Temple Paintings. Mult.
599 35c. Type **213** 35 10
600 50c. The Prince and the grave-digger 40 10
601 90c. Bearded old man 60 85
602 1r.55 Two female figures 70 2·00
MS603 115 × 141 mm. Nos. 599/602 2·75 3·00

214 Bandaranaike Memorial Conference Hall

215 Prime Minster Bandaranaike

1974. 20th Commonwealth Parliamentary Conf, Colombo.
604 **214** 85c. multicoloured 30 30

1974.
605 **215** 15c. multicoloured 15 10

216 "U.P.U." and "100"

1974. Centenary of U.P.U.
606 **216** 50c. multicoloured 1·00 75

217 Sri Lanka Parliament Building

1975. Inter-Parliamentary Meeting.
607 **217** 1r. multicoloured 30 50

218 Sir Ponnambalam Ramanathan (politician)

219 D. J. Wimalasurendra (engineer)

1975. Ramanathan Commemoration.
608 **218** 75c. multicoloured 30 80

1975. Wimalasurendra Commemoration.
609 **219** 75c. black and blue 30 80

220 Mrs. Bandaranaike, Map and Dove

221 Ma-ratmal

1975. International Women's Year.
610 **220** 1r.15 multicoloured 2·25 1·25

1976. Indigenous Flora. Multicoloured.
611 25c. Type **221** 10 10
612 50c. Binara 10 10
613 75c. Daffodil orchid 15 15
614 10r. Diyapara 3·00 4·50
MS615 153 × 153 mm. Nos. 611/14 11·00 14·00

222 Mahaweli Dam

1976. Mahaweli River Diversion.
616 **222** 85c. turquoise, bl & azure 30 80

223 Dish Aerial

1976. Opening of Satellite Earth Station, Padukka.
617 **223** 1r. multicoloured 65 85

224 Conception of the Buddha

1976. Vesak. Multicoloured.
618 5c. Type **224** 10 70
619 10c. King Suddhodana and the astrologers 10 70
620 1r.50 The astrologers being entertained 90 80
621 2r. The Queen in a palanquin 1·00 85
622 2r.25 Royal procession 1·10 1·75
623 5r. Birth of the Buddha 1·60 3·00
MS624 161 × 95 mm. Nos 618/23 9·50 13·00
Nos. 618/23 show paintings from the Dambava Temple.

225 Blue Sapphire

1976. Gems of Sri Lanka. Multicoloured.
625 60c. Type **225** 4·25 30
626 1r.15 Cat's eye 6·50 1·50
627 2r. Star sapphire 7·00 3·25
628 5r. Ruby 9·50 11·00
MS629 152 × 152 mm. Nos. 625/8 30·00 25·00

226 Prime Minister Mrs. S. Bandaranaike **227** Statue of Liberty

1976. Non-aligned Summit Conf, Colombo.
630 **226** 1r.15 multicoloured 25 50
631 2r. multicoloured 40 1·00

1976. Bicent of American Revolution.
632 **227** 2r.25 blue and indigo 65 1·50

228 Bell, Early Telephone and Telephone Lines

229 Maitreya (pre-carnate Buddha)

1976. Centenary of Telephone.
633 **228** 1r. multicoloured 60 20

1976. Centenary of Colombo Museum. Mult.
634 50c. Type **229** 25 15
635 1r. Sundara Murti Swami (Tamil psalmist) 30 30
636 5r. Tara (goddess) 2·25 4·50

230 Kandyan Crown **231** Sri Rahula Thero (poet)

1977. Regalia of the Kings of Kandy. Mult.

637		1r. Type **230**	50	40
638		2r. Throne and footstool	1·10	3·00

1977. Sri Rahula Commemoration.

639	**231**	1r. multicoloured	75	75

232 Sir Ponnambalam Arunachalam

233 Brass Lamps

1977. Sir Ponnambalam Arunachalam (social reformer) Commemoration.

640	**232**	1r. multicoloured	50	65

1977. Handicrafts. Multicoloured.

641	20c. Type **233**	15	15
642	25c. Jewellery box	15	15
643	50c. Caparisoned elephant	30	20
644	5r. Mask	1·60	3·25
MS645	205 × 89 mm. Nos. 641/4	3·50	4·25

234 Siddi Lebbe (author and educationist)

235 Girl Guide

1977. Siddi Lebbe Commemoration.

646	**234**	1r. multicoloured	30	60

1977. 60th Anniv of Sri Lanka Girl Guides Association.

647	**235**	75c. multicoloured	85	30

236 Parliament Building and "Wheel of Life"

237 Youths Running

1978. Election of New President.

648	**236**	15c. gold, green & emerald	20	10

For similar design in a smaller format, see Nos. 680/c.

1978. National Youth Service Council.

649	**237**	15c. multicoloured	30	50

238 Prince Siddhartha's Renunciation

1978. Vesak. Rock Carvings from Borobudur Temple.

650	**238**	15c. buff, brown and blue	75	30
651	–	50c. buff, brown and blue	1·00	1·50

DESIGN: 50c. Prince Siddhartha shaving his hair.

1978. Surch.

652	5c. on 90c. Bearded old man (No. 601)	2·00	3·25
653	10c. on 35c. Type **213**	50	50
654	25c. on 15c. Type **215**	4·25	4·25
655	25c. on 15c. Type **236**	4·25	4·25
656	25c. on 15c. Type **237**	4·25	4·25
657	1r. on 1r.55 Two female figures (No. 602)	1·25	45

240 Veera Puran Appu

241 "Troides helena"

1978. 130th Death Anniv of Veera Puran Appu (revolutionary).

658	**240**	15c. multicoloured	20	20

1978. Butterflies. Multicoloured.

659	25c. Type **241**	55	10
660	50c. "Cethosia nietneri"	1·00	10
661	5r. "Kallima horsfieldi"	1·75	1·25
662	10r. "Papilio polymnestor"	1·75	2·50
MS663	203 × 147 mm. Nos. 659/62	11·00	7·00

1979. No. 486 of Ceylon surch **SRI LANKA 15.**

664	15c. on 10c. green	2·25	1·75

243 Prince Danta and Princess Hema Mala bringing the Sacred Tooth Relic from Kalinga

244 Piyadasa Sirisena

1979. Vesak. Kelaniya Temple Paintings. Mult.

665	25c. Type **243**	10	10
666	1r. Theri Sanghamitta bringing the Bodhi Tree branch to Sri Lanka	15	15
667	10r. King Kirti Sri Rajasinghe offering fan of authority to the Sangha Raja	1·50	2·75
MS668	120 × 80 mm. Nos. 665/7	2·00	3·00

1979. Piyadasa Sirisena (writer) Commem.

669	**244**	1r.25 multicoloured	40	40

245 Wrestlers

246 Dudley Senanayake

1979. Wood Carvings from Embekke Temple.

670	**245**	20r. brown, ochre & green	1·00	1·25
671	–	50r. agate, yellow & green	1·50	2·75

DESIGN: 50r. Dancer.

1979. Dudley Senanayake (former Prime Minister) Commemoration.

672	**246**	1r.25 green	15	20

247 Mother with Child

1979. International Year of the Child. Mult.

673	5c. Type **247**	10	10
674	3r. Superimposed heads of children of different races	40	1·00
675	5r. Children playing	50	1·10

248 Ceylon 1857 6d. Stamp and Sir Rowland Hill

1979. Death Centenary of Sir Rowland Hill.

676	**248**	3r. multicoloured	30	1·00

249 Conference Emblem and Parliament Building

1979. International Conference of Parliamentarians on Population and Development, Colombo.

677	**249**	2r. multicoloured	70	1·25

250 Airline Emblem on Aircraft Tail-fin

251 Coconut Tree

1979. Inauguration of "Airlanka" Airline.

678	**250**	3r. black, blue and red	80	1·75

1979. 10th Anniv of Asian and Pacific Coconut Community.

679	**251**	2r. multicoloured	70	1·50

1979. As No. 648, but 20 × 24 mm.

680	**236**	25c. gold, green and emerald	30	20
680a		50c. gold, green and emerald	2·50	10
680b		60c. gold, green and emerald	8·00	1·25
680c		75c. gold, green and emerald	10	10

252 Swami Vipulananda

253 Inscription and Crescent

1979. Swami Vipulananda (philosopher) Commem.

681	**252**	1r.25 multicoloured	30	30

1979. 1500th Anniv of Hegira (Mohammedan religion).

682	**253**	3r.75 black, deep green and green	35	1·75

254 "The Great Teacher" (Institute emblem)

255 Ceylon Blue Magpie

1979. 50th Anniv of Institute of Ayurveda (school of medicine).

683	**254**	15c. multicoloured	30	60

1979. Birds (1st series). Multicoloured.

684	10c. Type **255**	10	1·00
685	15c. Ceylon hanging parrot	1·00	10
686	75c. Ceylon whistling thrush	15	15
687	1r. Ceylon spurfowl	15	15
688	5r. Yellow-fronted barbet	75	1·75
689	10r. Yellow-tufted bulbul	75	1·75
MS690	151 × 151 mm. Nos. 684/9	4·75	4·75

See also Nos. 827/30, 985/8 and 1242/5.

256 Rotary International Emblem and Map of Sri Lanka

257 A. Ratnayake

1980. 75th Anniv of Rotary International and 50th Anniv of Sri Lanka Rotary Movement.

691	**256**	1r.50 multicoloured	70	1·75

1980. 80th Birth Anniv of A. Ratnayake (politician).

692	**257**	1r.25 green	20	30

1980. No. 680 surch **.35**.

693	**236**	35c. on 25c. gold, green and emerald	15	15

259 Tank and Stupa (symbols of Buddhist culture)

260 Colonel Olcott

1980. 60th Anniv of All Ceylon Buddhist Congress. Multicoloured.

694	10c. Type **259**	25	1·25
695	35c. Bo-leaf wheel and fan	25	20

1980. Centenary of Arrival of Colonel Olcott (campaigner for Buddhism).

696	**260**	2r. multicoloured	80	1·75

261 Patachara's Journey through Forest

262 George E. de Silva

1980. Vesak. Details from Temple Paintings, Purvaramaya, Kataluwa. Multicoloured.

697	35c. Type **261**	30	15
698	1r.60 Patachara crossing river	1·25	2·25

1980. George E. de Silva (politician) Commem.

699	**262**	1r.60 multicoloured	30	30

263 Dalada Maligawa

1980. U.N.E.S.C.O.—Sri Lanka Cultural Triangle Project.

700	**263**	35c. claret	15	40
701	–	35c. grey	15	40
702	–	35c. red	15	40
703	–	1r.60 olive	45	1·10
704	–	1r.60 green	45	1·10
705	–	1r.60 brown	45	1·10
MS706		215 × 115 mm. Nos. 700/5	1·40	3·25

DESIGNS: No. 701, Dambulla; 702, Alahana Pirivena; 703, Jetavanarama; 704, Abhayagiri; 705, Sigiri.

264 Co-operation Symbols

266 The Holy Family

265 Lanka Mahila Samiti Emblem

1980. 50th Anniv of Co-operative Department.

707	**264**	20c. multicoloured	10	30

1980. 50th Anniv of Lanka Mahila Samiti (Rural Women's Movement).

708	**265**	35c. violet, red and yellow	15	50

1980. Christmas. Multicoloured.

709	35c. Type **266**	10	10
710	3r.75 The Three Wise Men	60	1·75
MS711	125 × 75 mm. Nos. 709/10	1·00	2·00

267 Colombo Public Library

1980. Opening of Colombo Public Library.

712	**267**	35c. multicoloured	10	10

268 Flag of Walapane Disawa **269** Fishing Cat

1980. Ancient Flags.
713 **268** 10c. black, green & purple 10 10
714 – 25c. black, yellow & purple 10 10
715 – 1r.60 black, yellow & purple 15 20
716 – 20r. black, yellow & purple . . . . 85 2·50
MS717 215 × 140 mm. Nos. 713/16 1·00 2·75
DESIGNS: 25c. Flag of the Gajanayaka Huduhumpola, Kandy; 1r.60, Sinhala royal flag; 20r. Sinhala royal flag, Ratnapura.

1981. Animals. Multicoloured.
718 2r.50 on 1r.60 Type **269** . . . 25 15
719 3r. on 1r.50 Golden palm civet 25 20
720 4r. on 2r. Indian-spotted chevrotain 25 30
721 5r. on 3r.75 Rusty-spotted cat 35 45
MS722 165 × 89 mm. Nos. 718/21 1·00 2·25
Nos. 718/21 are previously unissued stamps surcharged as in T **269**.
For stamps with revised face values see Nos. 780/3.

270 Heads and Houses on Map of Sri Lanka **271** Sri Lanka Light Infantry Regimental Badge

1981. Population and Housing Census.
723 **270** 50c. multicoloured . . . . 75 1·00

1981. Centenary of Sri Lanka Light Infantry.
724 **271** 2r. multicoloured . . . . 1·00 1·00

272 Panel from "The Great Stupa" in Honour of the Buddha, Sanci, India, 1st-century A.D. **274** Rev. Polwatte Sri Buddadatta

273 St. John Baptist de la Salle

1981. Vesak.
725 **272** 35c. black, dp green & green 10 10
726 – 50c. multicoloured 10 10
727 – 7r. black and pink . . . . 1·50 3·50
MS728 147 × 108mm. Nos. 725/7 3·50 3·75
DESIGNS: 50c. Silk banner representing a Bodhisattva from "Thousand Buddhas", Tun-Huang, Central Asia; 7r. Bodhisattva from Fondukistan, Afghanistan.

1981. 300th Anniv of De La Salle Brothers (Religious Order of the Brothers of the Christian Schools).
729 **273** 2r. pink, light blue & blue 1·25 2·00

1981. National Heroes.
730 **274** 50c. brown . . . . 50 1·00
731 – 50c. pink . . . . 50 1·00
732 – 50c. mauve . . . . 50 1·00
DESIGNS: No. 731, Rev. Mohottiwatte Gunananda; 732, Dr. Gnanaprakasar (each a scholar, writer and Buddhist campaigner).

275 Dr. Al-Haj T. B. Jayah **276** Dr. N. M. Perera

1981. Dr. Al-Haj T. B. Jayah (statesman) Commemoration.
733 **275** 50c. green . . . . 60 1·00

1981. Dr. N. M. Perera (campaigner for social reform) Commemoration.
734 **276** 50c. red . . . . 60 1·00

277 Stylized Disabled Person and Globe

1981. International Year for Disabled Persons.
735 **277** 2r. red, black and grey . . 1·10 1·75

278 Hand placing Vote into Ballot Box

1981. 50th Anniv of Universal Franchise. Mult.
736 50c. Type **278** 25 15
737 7r. Ballot box and people forming map of Sri Lanka (vert) . . . . 1·75 2·75

279 T. W. Rhys Davids (founder)

1981. Centenary of Pali Text Society.
738 **279** 35c. stone, dp brown & brown 70 30

280 Federation Emblem and "25"

1981. 25th Anniv of All-Ceylon Buddhist Students' Federation.
739 **280** 2r. black, yellow and red 1·00 1·00

281 "Plan for Happiness" **282** Dove Symbol with Acupuncture Needle and "Yin-Yang" (Chinese universe duality emblem)

1981. Population and Family Planning.
740 **281** 50c. multicoloured . . . . 75 1·00

1981. World Acupuncture Congress.
741 **282** 2r. black, yellow & orange 2·75 3·25

283 Union and Sri Lanka Flags

1981. Royal Visit.
742 **283** 50c. multicoloured 50 25
743 5r. multicoloured . . . . 1·75 3·50
MS744 165 × 90 mm. Nos. 742/3 2·25 3·50

284 "Conserve our Forests" **285** Sir James Peiris

1981. Forest Conservation.
745 **284** 35c. multicoloured 15 10
746 – 50c. brown and stone . . 20 20
747 – 5r. multicoloured . . . . 1·90 3·75
MS748 180 × 90 mm. Nos. 745/7 1·50 3·75
DESIGNS: 50c. "Plant a tree"; 5r. Jak (tree).

1981. Birth Centenary of Sir James Peiris (politician).
749 **285** 50c. brown 60 85

286 F. R. Senanayaka **287** Philip Gunawardhane

1982. Birth Centenary of F. R. Senanayaka (national hero).
750 **286** 50c. brown . . . . 60 1·00

1982. 10th Death Anniv of Philip Gunawardhane (politician).
751 **287** 50c. red . . . . 60 1·00

288 Department of Inland Revenue Building, Colombo **289** Rupavahini Emblem

1982. 50th Anniv of Department of Inland Revenue.
752 **288** 50c. black, blue & orange 60 1·00

1982. Inauguration of Rupavahini (national television service).
753 **289** 2r.50 yellow, brn & grey 2·25 3·25

290 Cricketer and Ball **292** Mother breast-feeding Child

291 "Obsbeckia wightiana"

1982. 1st Sri Lanka–England Test Match, Colombo.
754 **290** 2r.50 multicoloured . . . 4·00 4·00

1982. Flowers. Multicoloured.
755 35c. Type **291** 10 10
756 2r. "Mesua nagassarium" . . 20 20
757 7r. "Rhodomyrtus tomentosa" . . . . 50 1·25
758 20r. "Phaius tancarvilleae" 1·40 3·50
MS759 180 × 110 mm. Nos.755/8 6·00 7·50

1982. Food and Nutrition Policy Planning.
760 **292** 50c. multicoloured . . . . 1·00 1·25

293 Conference Emblem

1982. World Hindu Conference.
761 **293** 50c. multicoloured . . . . 85 1·00

294 King Vessantara giving away Magical, Rain-making White Elephant

1982. Vesak. Legend of Vessantara Jataka. Details of Cloth Painting from Arattana Rajamaha Vihara (temple), Hanguranketa, District of Nuwara Eliya. Multicoloured.
762 35c. Type **294** 45 10
763 40c. King Vessantara with family in Vankagiri Forest 55 15
764 2r.50 Vessantara giving away his children as slaves . . . 2·00 2·25
765 5r. Vessantara and family returning to Jetuttara in royal chariot . . . . . 2·75 3·50
MS766 160 × 115 mm. Nos. 762/5 7·00 7·00

295 Parliament Buildings, Sri Jayawardanapura

1982. Opening of Parliament Building Complex, Sri Jayawardanapura, Kotte.
767 **295** 50c. multicoloured . . . . 85 1·00

296 Dr. C. W. W. Kannangara **298** Dr. G. P. Malalasekara

297 Lord Baden-Powell

1982. Dr. C. W. W. Kannangara ("Father of Free Education") Commemoration.
768 **296** 50c. green . . . . 85 1·00

1982. 125th Birth Anniv of Lord Baden-Powell.
769 **297** 50c. multicoloured . . . . 1·75 1·00

1982. Dr. G. P. Malalasekara (founder of World Fellowship of Buddhists) Commemoration.
770 **298** 50c. green . . . . 85 1·00

299 Wheel encircling Globe

1982. World Buddhist Leaders Conference.
771 **299** 50c. multicoloured . . . . 1·00 1·25

300 Wildlife

1982. World Environment Day.
772 **300** 50c. multicoloured . . . . 1·90 1·25

301 Sir Waitialingam Duraiswamy

303 Rev. Weliwita Sri Saranankara Sangharaja

302 Y.M.C.A. Emblem

1982. Sir Waitialingam Duraiswamy (statesman and educationalist) Commemoration.
773 **301** 50c. deep brown and brown . . . . 85 1·00

1982. Centenary of Colombo Y.M.C.A.
774 **302** 2r.50 multicoloured . . . 3·00 4·00

1982. Rev. Weliwita Sri Saranankara Sangharaja (Buddhist leader) Commemoration.
775 **303** 50c. brown and orange . . 85 1·00

304 Maharagama Sasana Sevaka Samithiya Emblem

1982. 25th Anniv of Maharagama Sasana Sevaka Samithiya (Buddhist Social Reform Movement).
776 **304** 50c. multicoloured . . . . 85 1·00

305 Dr. Robert Koch

1982. Centenary of Robert Koch's Discovery of Tubercle Bacillus.
777 **305** 50c. multicoloured . . . . 2·00 1·50

306 Sir John Kotelawala

307 Eye Donation Society and Lions Club Emblems

1982. 2nd Death Anniv of Sir John Kotelawala.
778 **306** 50c. green . . . . 85 1·00

1982. World-Wide Sight Conservation Project.
779 **307** 2r.50 multicoloured . . . 3·00 4·00

1982. As Nos. 718/21 but without surcharges and showing revised face values.
780 2r.50 Type **269** 25 20
781 3r. Golden palm civet* . . . 3·25 3·25
1081 3r. Golden palm civet* . . . 1·40 30
782 4r. Indian-spotted chevrotain 25 30
783 5r. Rusty-spotted cat . . . 30 30
*No. 781 has the face value and inscriptions in brown, No. 1081 in black.

308 1859 4d. Rose and 1948 15c. Independence Commemorative

1982. 125th Anniv of First Postage Stamps. Mult.
784 50c. Type **308** 50 50
785 2r.50 1859 1s.9d. green and 1981 50c. "Just Society" stamp . . . . 1·75 2·75
MS786 59 × 84 mm. Nos. 784/5 (sold at 5r.) . . . . 2·00 3·00

309 Goonetilleke

1983. 4th Death Anniv of Sir Oliver Goonetilleke (statesman).
787 **309** 50c. grey, brown and black . . . . 60 1·00

310 Sarvodaya Emblem

1983. 25th Anniv of Sarvodaya Movement.
788 **310** 50c. multicoloured . . . . 1·00 1·00

311 Morse Key, Radio Aerial and Amateur Radio Society Emblem

1983. Amateur Radio Society.
789 **311** 2r.50 multicoloured . . . 2·75 4·00

312 Customs Co-operation Council Emblem and Sri Lanka Flag

1983. 30th Anniv of International Customs Day.
790 **312** 50c. multicoloured 50 40
791 5r. multicoloured . . . . 3·00 5·50

313 Bottle-nosed Dolphin

1983. Marine Mammals.
792 **313** 50c. black, blue and green 40 20
793 – 2r. multicoloured 60 80
794 – 2r.50 black, blue and grey 1·75 2·00
795 – 10r. multicoloured . . . . 4·00 6·50
DESIGNS: 2r. Dugongs; 2r.50, Humpback whale; 10r. Sperm whale.

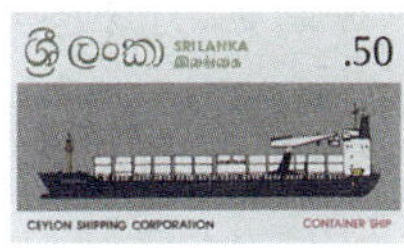
314 "Lanka Athula" (container ship)

1983. Ships of the Ceylon Shipping Corporation. Multicoloured.
796 50c. Type **314** 25 15
797 2r.50 Map of routes 90 70
798 5r. "Lanka Kalyani" (freighter) . . . . 1·25 1·60
799 20r. "Tammanna" (tanker) 2·00 5·50

315 Woman with I.W.D. Emblem and Sri Lanka Flag

1983. International Women's Day. Mult.
800 50c. Type **315** 20 25
801 5r. Woman, emblem, map and symbols of progress 80 2·50

316 Waterfall

1983. Commonwealth Day. Multicoloured.
802 50c. Type **316** 10 10
803 2r.50 Tea plucking 15 25
804 5r. Harvesting rice 25 40
805 20r. Decorated elephants . . 80 2·00

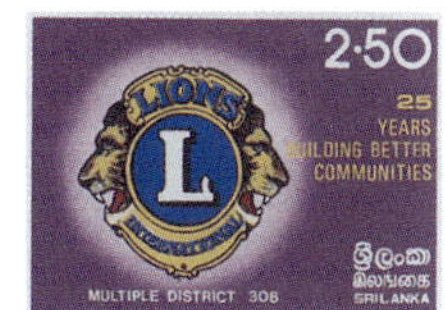
317 Lions Club International Badge

1983. 25th Anniv of Lions Club International in Sri Lanka.
806 **317** 2r.50 multicoloured . . . 2·50 2·50

318 "The Dream of Queen Mahamaya"

1983. Vesak. Life of Prince Siddhartha at Gotami Vihara. Multicoloured.
807 35c. Type **318** 10 10
808 50c. "Prince Siddhartha given to Maha Brahma" 10 10
809 5r. "Prince Siddhartha and the Sleeping Dancers"' . . 85 1·50
810 10r. "The Meeting with Mara" . . . . 1·40 3·00
MS811 150 × 90 mm. Nos. 807/10 2·00 4·00

319 First Telegraph Transmission, Colombo to Galle, 1858

1983. 125th Anniv of Telecommunications in Sri Lanka (2r.) and World Communications Year (10r.). Multicoloured.
812 2r. Type **319** 50 60
813 10r. World Communications Year emblem . . . . . . 2·25 4·25

320 Henry Woodward Amarasuriya (philanthropist)

1983. National Heroes.
814 **320** 50c. green 30 90
815 – 50c. blue 30 90
816 – 50c. mauve 30 90
817 – 50c. green 30 90
DESIGNS: No. 815, Father Simon Perera (historian); 816, Charles Lorenz (lawyer and newspaper editor); 817, Noordeen Abdul Cader (first President of All-Ceylon Muslim League).

321 Family and Village

1983. Gam Udawa (Village Re-awakening Movement). Multicoloured.
818 50c. Type **321** 10 25
819 5r. Village view . . . . . . 40 1·75

322 Caravan of Bulls

1983. Transport. Multicoloured.
820 35c. Type **322** 10 10
821 2r. Steam train . . . . 2·00 1·75
822 2r.50 Ox and cart . . . . . 1·00 2·00
823 5r. Ford motor car . . . . . 2·25 4·00

323 Sir Tikiri Banda Panabokke

1983. 20th Death Anniv of Adigar Sir Tikiri Banda Panabokke.
824 **323** 50c. red . . . . 85 1·00

324 C. W. Thamotheram Pillai

325 Arabi Pasha

1983. C. W. Thamotheram Pillai (Tamil scholar) Commemoration.
825 **324** 50c. brown . . . . 85 1·00

1983. Centenary of Banishment of Arabi Pasha (Egyptian nationalist).
826 **325** 50c. green . . . . 1·00 1·00

326 Sri Lanka Wood Pigeon

1983. Birds (2nd series). Multicoloured.
827 25c. Type **326** . . . . . . 60 1·00
828 35c. Large Sri Lanka white-eye 60 50
829 2r. Sri Lanka dusky blue flycatcher 70 40
829a 7r. As 35c. 50 30
830 20r. Ceylon coucal . . . . 1·00 2·75
MS831 183 × 93 mm. Nos. 827/9 and 830 . . . . 2·25 6·50

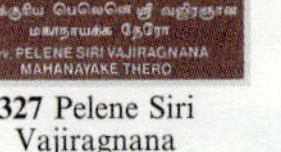

327 Pelene Siri Vajiragnana

328 Mary praying over Jesus and St. Joseph welcoming Shepherds

1983. Pelene Siri Vajiragnana (scholar) Commem.
832 **327** 50c. brown . . . . 1·25 1·25

1983. Christmas.
833 **328** 50c. multicoloured 10 15
834 5r. multicoloured . . . . 25 1·50
MS835 85 × 141 mm. Nos. 833/4 65 2·00

1983. No. 680a surch **.60**.
836 **236** 60c. on 50c. gold, green and emerald . . . . . 3·00 1·75

331 Paddy Field, Globe and F.A.O. Emblem

1984. World Food Day.
838 **331** 3r. multicoloured . . . . 40 1·50

332 Modern Tea Factory

1984. Centenary of Colombo Tea Auctions. Mult.
839 1r. Type **332** 15 15
840 2r. Logo 30 45
841 5r. Girl picking tea . . . . . 75 1·75
842 10r. Auction in progress . . 1·50 3·25

333 Students and University

1984. 4th Anniv of Mahapola Scheme for Development and Education. Multicoloured.
843 60c. Type **333** 10 15
844 1r. Teacher with Gnana Darsana class 10 15
845 5r.50 Student with books and microscope . . . . 35 1·50
846 6r. Mahapola lamp symbol 40 1·50

334 King Daham Sonda instructing Angels

1984. Vesak. The Story of King Daham Sonda from Ancient Casket Paintings. Multicoloured.
847 35c. Type **334** 15 10
848 60c. Elephant paraded with gift of gold 40 25
849 5r. King Daham Sonda leaps into mouth of God Sakra 1·25 2·50
850 10r. God Sakra carrying King Daham Sonda . . . 1·60 4·00
MS851 154 × 109 mm. Nos. 847/50 1·75 3·25

335 Development Programme Logo

336 Dodanduwe Siri Piyaratana Tissa Mahanayake Thero (Buddhist scholar)

1984. Sri Lanka Lions Clubs' Development Programme.
852 **335** 60c. multicoloured . . . . 1·40 1·00

1984. National Heroes.
853 **336** 60c. bistre 30 75
854 – 60c. green 30 75
855 – 60c. green 30 75
856 – 60c. red 30 75
857 – 60c. brown 30 75
DESIGNS: No. 854, G. P. Wickremarachchi (physician); 855, Sir Mohamed Macan Markar (politician); 856, Dr. W. Arthur de Silva (philanthropist); 857, K. Balasingham (lawyer).

337 Association Emblem

1984. Centenary of Public Service Mutual Provident Association.
858 **337** 4r.60 multicoloured . . . 50 1·75

338 Sri Lanka Village

1984. 6th Anniv of "Gam Udawa" (Village Re-awakening Movement).
859 **338** 60c. multicoloured 30 65

339 World Map showing A.P.B.U. Countries

1984. 20th Anniv of Asia-Pacific Broadcasting Union.
860 **339** 7r. multicoloured . . . . 2·00 3·25

340 Drummers and Elephant carrying Royal Instructions

1984. Esala Perahera (Procession of the Tooth), Kandy. Multicoloured.
861 4r.60 Type **340** . . . . . . 1·10 1·90
862 4r.60 Dancers and elephants 1·10 1·90
863 4r.60 Elephant carrying Tooth Relic . . . . 1·10 1·90
864 4r.60 Custodian of the Sacred Tooth and attendants . . . 1·10 1·90
MS865 223 × 108 mm. Nos. 861/4 3·75 7·00
Nos. 861/4 were printed together, se-tenant, forming a composite design.

341 "Vanda memoria Ernest Soysa" (orchid)

342 Symbolic Athletes and Stadium

1984. 50th Anniv of Ceylon Orchid Circle. Mult.
866a 60c. Type **341** . . . . . . 1·00 1·25
867a 4r.60 "Acanthephippium bicolor" . . . . 2·00 3·75
868a 5r. "Vanda tessellata var. rufescens" . . . . 1·25 3·75
869 10r. "Anoectochilus setaceus" . . . . 4·00 6·00
MS870 115 × 110 mm. Nos. 866/9 7·00 10·00

1984. 1st National School Games.
871 **342** 60c. black, grey and blue 1·75 1·50

343 D. S. Senanayake, Temple and Fields

1984. Birth Centenary of D. S. Senanayake (former Prime Minister). Multicoloured.
872 35c. Type **343** 10 10
873 60c. Senanayake and statue 10 10
874 4r.60 Senanayake and irrigation project 35 50
875 6r. Senanayake and House of Representatives 40 60

344 Lake House

345 Agricultural Workers and Globe

1984. 150th Anniv of "Observer" Newspaper.
876 **344** 4r.60 multicoloured . . . 2·00 3·25

1984. 20th Anniv of World Food Programme.
877 **345** 7r. multicoloured . . . . 1·50 1·25

346 College Emblem

347 Dove and Stylized Figures

1984. Cent of Baari Arabic College, Weligama.
878 **346** 4r.60 green, turquoise & blue . . . . 1·25 3·00

1985. International Youth Year. Multicoloured.
879 4r.60 Type **347** 50 60
880 20r. Dove, stylized figures and flower . . . . 2·00 3·00

348 Religious Symbols

349 College Crest

1985. World Religion Day.
881 **348** 4r.60 multicoloured . . . 2·00 2·75

1985. 150th Anniv of Royal College, Colombo.
882 **349** 60c. yellow and blue . . . 15 25
883 – 7r. multicoloured . . . . 1·75 3·25
DESIGN: 7r. Royal College.

350 Banknotes, Buildings, Ship and "Wheel of Life"

351 Wariyapola Sri Sumangala Thero

1985. 5th Anniv of Mahapola Scheme.
884 **350** 60c. multicoloured . . . . 1·00 1·25

1985. Wariyapola Sri Sumangala Thero (Buddhist priest and patriot) Commemoration.
885 **351** 60c. brown, yellow & black . . . . 70 1·00

352 Victoria Dam

1985. Inaug of Victoria Hydro-electric Project. Multicoloured.
886 60c. Type **352** 75 50
887 7r. Map of Sri Lanka enclosing dam and power station (vert) . . . . . . 4·25 5·50

353 Cover of 50th Edition of International Buddhist Annual, "Vesak Sirisara"

354 Ven. Waskaduwe Sri Subhuthi (priest and scholar)

1985. Centenary of Vesak Poya Holiday. Mult.
888 35c. Type **353** 10 10
889 60c. Buddhists worshipping at temple 10 10
890 6r. Buddhist Theosophical Society Headquarters, Colombo . . . . 60 1·00
891 9r. Buddhist flag . . . . . 1·25 2·00
MS892 180 × 110 mm. Nos. 888/91 4·00 6·00

1985. Personalities.
893 **354** 60c. black, orange & brown 30 65
894 – 60c. black, orange & mauve 30 65
895 – 60c. black, orange & brown 30 65
896 – 60c. black, orange & green 30 65
DESIGNS: No. 894, Revd. Fr. Peter A. Pillai (educationist and social reformer); 895, Dr. Senarath Paranavitane (scholar); 896, A. M. Wapche Marikar (architect and educationist).

355 Stylized Village and People

356 Emblem

1985. Gam Udawa '85 (Village Re-awakening Movement).
897 **355** 60c. multicoloured . . . . 1·00 1·00

1985. 50th Anniv of Colombo Young Poets' Association.
898 **356** 60c. multicoloured . . . . 1·00 1·25

357 Kothmale Dam and Reservoir

1985. Inauguration of Kothmale Hydro-electric Project. Multicoloured.
899 60c. Type **357** 65 25
900 6r. Kothmale Power Station 2·50 3·50

358 Federation Logo

359 Breast-feeding

1985. 10th Asian and Oceanic Congress of Obstetrics and Gynaecology.
901 **358** 7r. multicoloured . . . . 3·25 3·75

1985. U.N.I.C.E.F. Child Survival and Development Programme. Multicoloured.
902 35c. Type **359** 30 10
903 60c. Child and oral rehydration salts 45 30
904 6r. Weighing child (growth monitoring) . . . . 2·25 3·25
905 9r. Immunization . . . . . . 2·75 4·75
MS906 99 × 180 mm. Nos. 902/5 4·00 6·00

360 Blowing Indian Chank Shell

1985. 10th Anniv of World Tourism Organization. Multicoloured.
907 1r. Type **360** 20 10
908 6r. Parliamentary Complex, Jayawardhanapura, Kotte 80 90
909 7r. Tea plantation . . . . . . 90 1·10
910 10r. Ruwanveliseya (Buddhist shrine), Anuradhapura . . 1·40 1·75
MS911 179 × 89 mm. Nos. 907/10 2·75 2·75

361 Casket containing Land Grant Deed

362 Koran and Map of Sri Lanka

1985. 50th Anniv of Land Development Ordinance.
912 **361** 4r.60 multicoloured . . . 2·00 3·00

1985. Translation of The Koran into Sinhala.
913 **362** 60c. violet and gold . . . 1·50 1·25

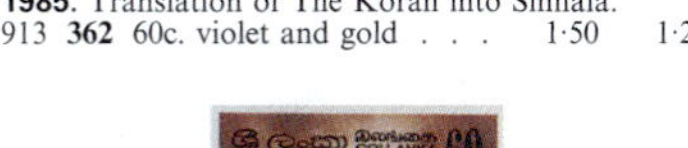

363 "Our Lady of Matara" Statue

1985. Christmas. Multicoloured.
914 60c. Type **363** 30 15
915 9r. "Our Lady of Madhu" Statue . . . . 1·50 2·50
MS916 180 × 100 mm. Nos. 914/15 5·50 7·00

1985. Nos. 680b, 780, 828, 860 and 879 surch.
917 **236** 75c. on 60c. gold, green and emerald 10 10
918 **347** 1r. on 4r.60 mult . . . . 4·00 2·75
919 **339** 1r. on 7r. multicoloured 6·00 2·75
920 **269** 5r.75 on 2r.50 mult . . . 3·50 1·50
921 – 7r. on 35c. mult (No. 828) 4·50 1·25

365 Linked Arms and Map of S.A.A.R.C. Countries

1985. 1st Summit Meeting of South Asian Association for Regional Co-operation, Dhaka, Bangladesh. Multicoloured.
922 60c. Type **365** . . . . 3·50 6·00
923 5r.50 Logo and flags of member countries . . . . 3·50 3·75

366 "Viceroy Special" Train

1986. Inaugural Run of "Viceroy Special" Train from Colombo to Kandy.
924 **366** 1r. multicoloured . . . . 60 1·50

367 Girl and Boy Students

1986. 6th Anniv of Mahapola Scheme.
925 **367** 75c. multicoloured 50 60

368 Wijewardena

1986. Birth Centenary of D. R. Wijewardena (newspaper publisher).
926 **368** 75c. brown and green . . 30 60

369 Ven. Welitara Gnanatillake Maha Nayake Thero

370 Red Cross Flag and Personnel

1986. Ven. Welitara Gnanatillake Maha Nayake Thero (scholar) Commemoration.
927 **369** 75c. multicoloured 70 80

1986. 50th Anniv of Sri Lanka Red Cross Society.
928 **370** 75c. multicoloured . . . . 2·00 1·75

371 Comet depicted as Goddess visiting Sun-god

372 Woman lighting Lamp

1986. Appearance of Halley's Comet. Mult.
929 50c. Type **371** 10 20
930 75c. Comet and constellations of Scorpius and Sagittarius 10 20
931 6r.50 Comet's orbit . . . . . 30 1·40
932 8r.50 Edmond Halley . . . . 55 1·90
MS933 180 × 115 mm. Nos. 929/32 4·75 9·00

1986. Sinhalese and Tamil New Year. Mult.
934 50c. Type **372** 10 20
935 75c. Woman and festive foods 10 20
936 6r.50 Women playing drum 30 1·75
937 8r.50 Anointing and making offerings at temple . . . . 55 2·25
MS938 178 × 108 mm. Nos. 934/7 1·75 5·50

373 The King donating Elephant to the Brahmin

1986. Vesak. Wall paintings from Samudragiri Temple, Mirissa. Multicoloured.
939 50c. Type **373** 10 20
940 75c. The Bodhisattva in the Vasavarthi heaven 10 20
941 5r. The offering of milk rice by Sujatha . . . . 40 1·75
942 10r. The offering of parched corn and honey by Thapassu and Bhalluka . . 50 2·50

374 Ven. Kalukondayave Sri Prajnasekhara Maha Nayake Thero (Buddhist leader and social refomer)

375 Stylized Village and People

1986. National Heroes. Multicoloured.
943 75c. Type **374** 15 70
944 75c. Brahmachari Walisinghe Harischandra (social reformer) (birth centenary) 15 70
945 75c. Martin Wickramasinghe (author and scholar) . . . 15 70
946 75c. G. G. Ponnambalam (politician) 15 70
947 75c. A. M. A. Azeez (Islamic scholar) (75th birth anniv) 15 70

1986. Gam Udawa '86 (Village Re-awakening Movement).
948 **375** 75c. multicoloured . . . . 1·50 1·75

376 Co-op Flag and Emblem

377 Arthur V. Dias

1986. 75th Anniv of Sri Lanka Co-operative Movement.
949 **376** 1r. multicoloured . . . . 75 1·75

1986. Birth Centenary of Arthur V. Dias (philanthropist).
950 **377** 1r. brown and blue . . . 1·50 2·00

378 Bull Elephant

1986. Sri Lanka Wild Elephant. Multicoloured.
951 5r. Type **378** . . . . 8·00 6·00
952 5r. Cow elephant and calf . . 8·00 6·00
953 5r. Cow elephant . . . . . . 8·00 6·00
954 5r. Elephants bathing . . . . 8·00 6·00

379 Congress Logo

381 Anniversary Logo

380 Map showing Route of Cable and Telephone Receiver

1986. 2nd Indo-Pacific Congress on Legal Medicine and Forensic Sciences.
955 **379** 8r.50 multicoloured . . . 2·25 3·00

1986. SEA-ME-WE Submarine Cable Project.
956 **380** 5r.75 multicoloured . . . 3·75 2·75

1986. 25th Anniv of Dag Hammarskjold Award.
957 **381** 2r. multicoloured . . . . 1·00 1·00

382 Logo on Flag

383 Logo

1986. 2nd National School Games.
958 **382** 1r. multicoloured . . . . 2·75 1·90

1986. 60th Anniv of Surveyors' Institute of Sri Lanka.
959 **383** 75c. brown & light brown 60 1·00

384 College Building and Crest

1986. Centenary of Ananda College, Colombo.
960 **384** 75c. multicoloured 10 10
961 – 5r. multicoloured 30 70
962 – 5r.75 multicoloured . . . 35 70
963 – 6r. red, gold and lilac . . 40 1·00
DESIGNS: 5r. Sports field and college crest; 5r.75, Col. H. S. Olcott (founder), Ven. Migettuwatte Gunananda, Ven. Hikkaduwe Sri Sumangala (Buddhist leaders) and Buddhist flag; 6r. College flag.

385 Mangrove Swamp

1986. Mangrove Conservation. Multicoloured.
964 35c. Type **385** 60 20
965 50c. Mangrove tree 70 30
966 75c. Germinating mangrove flower 80 30
967 6r. Fiddler crab . . . . . . 5·50 7·00

386 Family and Housing Estate

1987. International Year of Shelter for the Homeless.
968 **386** 75c. multicoloured . . . . 1·75 50

387 Ven. Ambagahawatte Indasabhawaragnanasamy Thero

388 Proctor John de Silva

1987. Ven. Ambagahawatte Indasabhawaragnanasamy Thero (Buddhist monk) Commemoration.
969 **387** 5r.75 multicoloured . . . 2·50 1·00

1987. Proctor John de Silva (playwright) Commemoration.
970 **388** 5r.75 multicoloured . . . 70 70

389 Mahapola Logo and Aspects of Communication

1987. 7th Anniv of Mahapola Scheme.
971 **389** 75c. multicoloured . . . . 75 1·25

390 Dr. R. L. Brohier

1987. Dr. Richard L. Brohier (historian and surveyor) Commemoration.
972 **390** 5r.75 multicoloured . . . 2·00 1·40

391 Tyre Corporation Building, Kelaniya, and Logo

1987. 25th Anniv of Sri Lanka Tyre Corporation.
973 **391** 5r.75 black, red and orange 50 50

392 Logo

1987. Centenary of Sri Lanka Medical Association.
974 **392** 5r.75 brown, yellow and black . . . . 2·00 2·75

393 Clasped Hands, Farmer and Paddy Field

396 Girls playing on Swing

1987. Inauguration of Farmers' Pension and Social Security Benefit Scheme.
975 **393** 75c. multicoloured . . . . 1·00 1·25

394 Exhibition Logo

1987. Mahaweli Maha Goviya Contest and Agro Mahaweli Exhibition.
976 **394** 75c. multicoloured 30 30

395 Young Children with W.H.O. and Immunization Logos

1987. World Health Day.
977 **395** 1r. multicoloured . . . . 2·50 50

1987. Sinhalese and Tamil New Year. Mult.
978 75c. Type **396** 10 10
979 5r. Girls with oil lamp and sun symbol 50 50

397 Lotus Lanterns

1987. Vesak. Multicoloured.
980 50c. Type **397** 10 10
981 75c. Octagonal lanterns . . . 10 10
982 5r. Star lanterns 35 30
983 10r. Gok lanterns 60 65
MS984 150 × 90 mm. Nos. 980/3 1·00 1·00

398 Emerald-collared Parakeet ("Layard's Parakeet")

1987. Birds (3rd series). Multicoloured.
985A 50c. Type **398** 50 10
986A 1r. Legge's flowerpecker . . 75 10
987A 5r. Ceylon white-headed starling ("Sri Lanka White-headed Starling") 1·10 1·50
988A 10r. Ceylon jungle babbler ("Sri Lanka Rufous Babbler") . . . . . . 1·40 2·50
MS989A 140 × 80 mm. Nos. 985A/8A . . . . 4·50 4·50

399 Ven. Heenatiyana Sri Dhammaloka Maha Nayake Thero (Buddhist monk)

1987. National Heroes. Multicoloured.
990 75c. Type **399** 40 40
991 75c. P. de S. Kularatne (educationist) 40 40
992 75c. M. C. Abdul Rahuman (legislator) 40 40

400 Peasant Family and Village

1987. Gam Udawa '87 (Village Re-awakening Movement).
993 **400** 75c. multicoloured 30 30

401 "Mesua nagassarium"

1987. Forest Conservation. Multicoloured.
994 75c. Type **401** 10 10
995 5r. Elephants in forest . . . 1·25 1·25

402 Dharmaraja College, Crest and Col. Olcott (founder)

1987. Centenary of Dharmaraja College, Kandy.
996 **402** 75c. multicoloured . . . . 2·00 30

403 Youth Sevices Logo

1987. 20th Anniv of National Youth Services.
997 **403** 75c. multicoloured 20 20

404 Arm holding Torch and Mahaweli Logo

405 Open Bible and Logo

1987. Mahaweli Games.
998 **404** 75c. multicoloured . . . . 2·50 2·00

1987. 175th Anniv of Ceylon Bible Society.
999 **405** 5r.75 multicoloured . . . 40 40

406 Hurdler and Committee Symbol

1987. 50th Anniv of National Olympic Committee.
1000 **406** 10r. multicoloured . . . 2·50 1·25

407 Madonna and Child, Flowers and Oil Lamp

408 Sir Ernest de Silva

1987. Christmas. Multicoloured.
1001 75c. Type **407** 10 10
1002 10r. Christ Child in manger, star and dove 35 40
MS1003 145 × 82 mm. Nos. 1001/2 60 70

1987. Birth Centenary of Sir Ernest de Silva (philanthropist and philatelist).
1004 **408** 75c. multicoloured . . . 30 30

409 Society Logo

410 University Flag and Graduates

1987. 150th Anniv of Kandy Friend-in-Need Society.
1005 **409** 75c. multicoloured . . . 30 30

1987. 1st Convocation of Buddhist and Pali University.
1006 **410** 75c. multicoloured . . . 30 30

411 Father Joseph Vaz

412 Wheel of Dhamma, Dagaba and Bo Leaf

1987. 300th Anniv of Arrival of Father Joseph Vaz in Kandy.
1007 **411** 75c. multicoloured . . . 30 30

1988. 30th Anniv of Buddhist Publication Society, Kandy.
1008 **412** 75c. multicoloured . . . 30 30

413 Dharmayatra Lorry

414 Society Logo

1988. 5th Anniv of Mahapola Dharmayatra Service.
1009 **413** 75c. multicoloured . . . 30 30

1988. Centenary of Ceylon Society of Arts.
1010 **414** 75c. multicoloured . . . 30 30

415 National Youth Centre, Maharagama

416 Citizens with National Flag and Map of Sri Lanka

1988. Opening of National Youth Centre, Maharagama.
1011 **415** 1r. multicoloured . . . . 2·75 30

1988. 40th Anniv of Independence. Multicoloured.
1012 75c. Type **416** 10 10
1013 8r.50 "40" in figures and lion emblem 90 90

417 Graduates, Clay Lamp and Open Book

419 Ven. Weligama Sri Sumangala Maha Nayake Thero

418 Bus and Logo

1988. 8th Anniv of Mahapola Scheme.
1014 **417** 75c. multicoloured . . . 20 20

1988. 30th Anniv of Sri Lanka Transport Board.
1015 **418** 5r.75 multicoloured . . . 55 55

1988. Ven. Weligama Sri Sumangala Maha Nayake Thero (Buddhist monk) Commemoration.
1016 **419** 75c. multicoloured . . . 20 20

420 Regimental Colour

1988. Centenary of Regiment of Artillery.
1017 **420** 5r.75 multicoloured . . . 2·50 80

421 Chevalier I. X. Pereira

423 Father Ferdinand Bonnel (educationist)

422 Invitation to the Deities and Brahmas

1988. Birth Centenary of Chevalier I. X. Pereira (politician).
1018 **421** 5r.75 multicoloured . . . 30 30

1988. Vesak. Paintings from Narendrarama Rajamaha Temple, Suriyagoda. Multicoloured.
1019 50c. Type **422** 15 15
1020 75c. Bodhisathva at the Seventh Step 15 15
MS1021 150 × 92 mm. Nos. 1019/20 1·00 1·00

1988. National Heroes. Multicoloured.
1022 75c. Type **423** 15 15
1023 75c. Sir Razik Fareed (politician) 15 15
1024 75c. W. F. Gunawardhana (scholar) 15 15
1025 75c. Edward Nugawela (politician) 15 15
1026 75c. Chief Justice Sir Arthur Wijeyewardene 15 15

424 Stylized Figures and Re-awakened Village

1988. 10th Anniv of Gam Udawa (Village Re-awakening Movement).
1027 **424** 75c. multicoloured . . . 20 20

425 Maliyadeva College, Kurunegala, and Crest

1988. Cent of Maliyadeva College, Kurunegala.
1028 **425** 75c. multicoloured . . . 20 20

426 M. J. M. Lafir, Billiard Game and Trophy

1988. Mohamed Junaid Mohamed Lafir (World Amateur Billiards Champion, 1973) Commem.
1029 **426** 5r.75 multicoloured . . . 30 30

427 Flags of Australia and Sri Lanka, Handclasp and Map of Australia

1988. Bicentenary of Australian Settlement.
1030 **427** 8r.50 multicoloured . . . 50 50

428 Ven. Kataluwe Sri Gunaratana Maha Nayake Thero

429 Athlete, Rice and Hydro-electric Dam

1988. Ven. Kataluwe Sri Gunaratana Maha Nayake Thero (Buddhist monk) Commemoration.
1031 **428** 75c. multicoloured . . . 20 20

1988. Mahaweli Games.
1032 **429** 75c. multicoloured . . . 20 20

430 Athletics

431 Outline Map of Sri Lanka and Anniversary Logo

1988. Olympic Games, Seoul. Multicoloured.
1033 75c. Type **430** 10 10
1034 1r. Swimming 10 10
1035 5r.75 Boxing 40 40
1036 8r.50 Map of Sri Lanka and logos of Olympic Committee and Seoul Games 70 70
MS1037 181 × 101 mm. Nos. 1033/6 1·10 1·40

1988. 40th Anniv of W.H.O.
1038 **431** 75c. multicoloured . . . 20 20

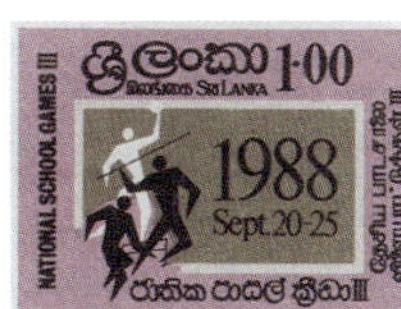

432 Games Logo

1988. 3rd National School Games.
1039 **432** 1r. black, gold and mauve . . . . 2·00 25

433 Mahatma Gandhi

1988. 40th Death Anniv of Mahatma Gandhi.
1040 **433** 75c. multicoloured . . . 65 20

434 Globe with Forms of Transport and Communications

1988. Asia-Pacific Transport and Communications Decade.
1041 **434** 75c. multicoloured . . . 35 10
1042 – 5r.75 mauve, blue & blk 1·40 1·00
DESIGN: 5r.75, Antenna tower with dish aerials and forms of transport.

435 Woman with Rice Sheaf and Hydro-electric Project

1988. Commissioning of Randenigala Project. Multicoloured.
1043 75c. Type **435** 10 10
1044 5r.75 Randenigala Dam and reservoir 45 45

436 Handicrafts and Centre Logo in Cupped Hands

437 Angel, Dove, Olive Branch and Globe

1988. Opening of Gramodaya Folk Art Centre, Colombo.
1045 **436** 75c. multicoloured . . . 20 20

1988. Christmas. Multicoloured.
1046 75c. Type **437** 10 10
1047 8r.50 Shepherds and Star of Bethlehem 50 60
MS1048 175 × 100 mm. Nos. 1046/7 60 60

438 Dr. E. W. Adikaram

439 Open Book in Tree and Children reading

1988. Dr. E. W. Adikaram (educationist) Commemoration.
1049 **438** 75c. multicoloured . . . 20 20

1989. 10th Anniv of Free Distribution of School Text Books.
1050 **439** 75c. multicoloured . . . 20 20

440 Wimalaratne Kumaragama

441 Logo and New Chamber of Commerce Building

1989. Poets of Sri Lanka. Multicoloured.
1051 75c. Type **440** 15 15
1052 75c. G. H. Perera 15 15
1053 75c. Sagara Palansuriya . . 15 15
1054 75c. P. B. Alwis Perera . . 15 15

1989. 150th Anniv of Ceylon Chamber of Commerce.
1055 **441** 75c. multicoloured . . . 20 20

442 Bodhisatva at Lunch and Funeral Pyre

1989. Vesak. Wall Paintings from Medawala Monastery, Harispattuwa. Multicoloured.
1056 50c. Type **442** 10 10
1057 75c. Rescue of King Vessantara's children by god Sakra 10 10
1058 5r. Bodhisatva ploughing and his son attacked by snake 30 35
1059 5r.75 King Vessantara giving away his children 30 35
MS1060 150 × 90 mm. Nos. 1056/9 75 75

443 Parawahera Vajiragnana Thero (Buddhist monk)

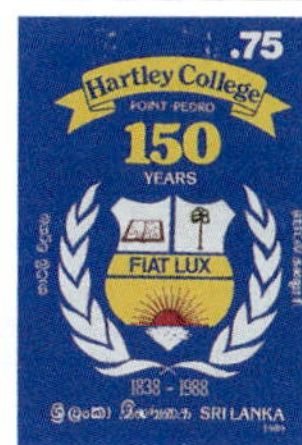

444 College Crest

1989. National Heroes. Multicoloured.
1061 75c. Type **443** 15 15
1062 75c. Fr. Maurice Jacques Le Goc (educationist) 15 15
1063 75c. Hemapala Munidasa (author) 15 15
1064 75c. Ananda Samarakoon (composer) 15 15
1065 75c. Simon Casie Chitty (scholar) (horiz) 15 15

1989. 150th Anniv of Harley College, Point-Pedro (1988).

1066 **444** 75c. multicoloured . . . 20 20

445 Dramachakra, Lamp, Buddhist Flag and Map

1989. Establishment of Ministry of Buddha Sasana.
1067 **445** 75c. multicoloured . . . 20 20

446 Hands holding Brick and Trowel, House and Family

1989. Gam Udawa '89 (Village Re-awakening Movement).
1068 **446** 75c. multicoloured . . . 20 20

447 Two Families and Hand turning Cogwheel

448 Dunhinda Falls

1989. Janasaviya Development Programme.
1069 **447** 75c. multicoloured . . . 20 20
1070a 1r. multicoloured . . . 10 10

1989. Waterfalls. Multicoloured.
1071 75c. Type **448** 10 10
1072 1r. Rawana Falls 10 10
1073 5r.75 Laxapana Falls . . . 45 45
1074 8r.50 Diyaluma Falls . . . 60 60

449 Rev. James Chater (missionary) and Baptist Church

1989. 177th Anniv of Baptist Church in Sri Lanka.
1075 **449** 5r.75 multicoloured . . . 30 30

450 Bicentenary Logo

1989. Bicentenary of French Revolution.
1076 **450** 8r.50 black, blue and red 70 70

451 Old and New Bank Buildings and Logo

452 Water Lily, Dharma Chakra and Books

1989. 50th Anniv of Bank of Ceylon. Mult.
1077 75c. Type **451** 10 10
1078 5r. "Bank of Ceylon orchid and logo" 45 45

1989. State Literary Festival.
1079 **452** 75c. multicoloured . . . 20 20

453 Wilhelm Geiger

454 H. V. Perera, Q.C.

1989. Wilhelm Geiger (linguistic scholar) Commemoration.
1080 **453** 75c. multicoloured . . . 20 20

1989. Constitutional Pioneers. Multicoloured.
1082 75c. Type **454** 20 20
1083 75c. Prof. Ivor Jennings . . 20 20

455 Sir Cyril de Zoysa

456 Map of South-east Asia and Telecommunications Equipment

1989. Sir Cyril de Zoysa (Buddhist philanthropist) Commemoration.
1084 **455** 75c. multicoloured . . . 20 20

1989. 10th Anniv of Asia-Pacific Telecommunity.
1085 **456** 5r.75 multicoloured . . . 50 50

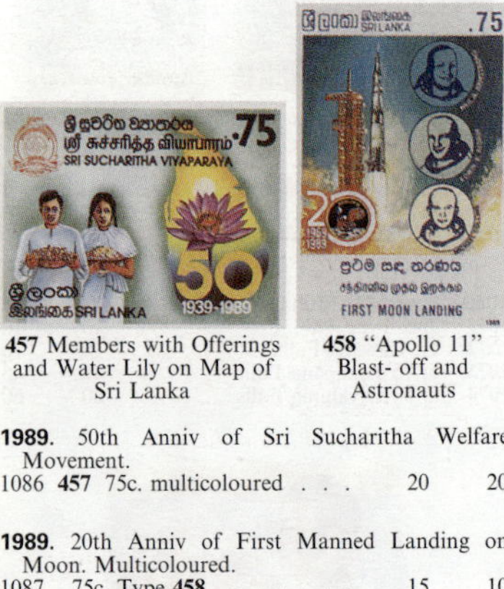

457 Members with Offerings and Water Lily on Map of Sri Lanka

458 "Apollo 11" Blast- off and Astronauts

1989. 50th Anniv of Sri Sucharitha Welfare Movement.
1086 **457** 75c. multicoloured . . . 20 20

1989. 20th Anniv of First Manned Landing on Moon. Multicoloured.
1087 75c. Type **458** 15 10
1088 1r. Armstrong leaving lunar module "Eagle" 20 10
1089 2r. Astronaut on Moon . . 35 30
1090 5r.75 Lunar surface and Earth from Moon 60 70
MS1091 100 × 160 mm. Nos. 1087/90 . . . . 1·40 1·40

459 Shepherds

460 Ven. Sri Devananda Nayake Thero

1989. Christmas. Multicoloured.
1092 75c. Type **459** 10 10
1093 8r.50 Magi with gifts . . . 60 2·00
MS1094 160 × 100 mm. Nos. 1092/3 1·25 2·00

1989. Ven. Sri Devananda Nayake Thero (Buddhist monk) Commemoration.
1095 **460** 75c. multicoloured . . . 30 20

461 College Building, Crest and Revd. William Ault (founder)

1989. 175th Anniv of Methodist Central College, Batticaloa.
1096 **461** 75c. multicoloured . . . 20 20

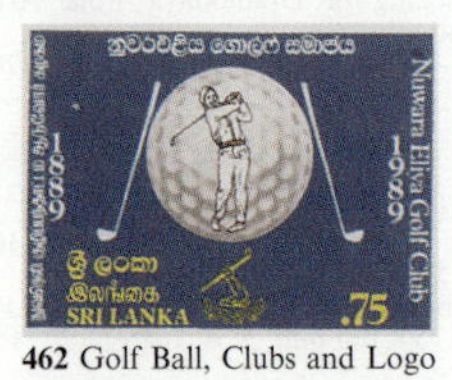

462 Golf Ball, Clubs and Logo

1989. Cent of Nuwara Eliya Golf Club. Mult.
1097 75c. Type **462** . . . . . . 1·75 25
1098 8r.50 Course and club house 5·00 4·00

463 "Raja"

464 College Building and G. Wickremarachchi (founder)

1989. "Raja" Royal Ceremonial Elephant, Kandy Commemoration.
1099 **463** 75c. multicoloured . . . 2·75 65

1989. 60th Anniv of Gampaha Wickremarachchi Institute of Ayurveda Medicine.
1100 **464** 75c. multicoloured . . . 20 20

465 Ven. Udunuwara Sri Sarananda Thero

467 Cardinal Thomas Cooray

466 Diesel Train on Viaduct, Ella–Demodara Line

1989. Ven. Udunuwara Sri Sarananda Thero (Buddhist monk) Commemoration.
1101 **465** 75c. multicoloured . . . 20 20

1989. 125 Years of Sir Lanka Railways. Mult.
1102 75c. Type **466** 50 20
1103 2r. Diesel train at Maradana Station 90 25
1104 3r. Steam train and semaphore signal . . . . 1·10 40
1105 7r. Steam train leaving station, 1864 . . . . . . 1·40 70

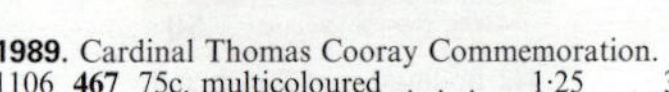

1989. Cardinal Thomas Cooray Commemoration.
1106 **467** 75c. multicoloured . . . 1·25 30

468 Farmer and Wife with Dagaba and Dam

1989. Agro Mahaweli Development Programme.
1107 **468** 75c. multicoloured . . . 20 20

469 Justin Wijayawardena

470 Ven. Induruwe Uttarananda Mahanayake Thero

1990. Justin Wijayawardena (scholar) Commem.
1108 **469** 1r. multicoloured . . . . 2·00 25

1990. Surch.
1108a 25c. on 5r.75 King Vessantara giving away his children (No. 1059) 40 20
1109a 1r. on 75c. Type **447** . . . 1·40 1·25

1990. 4th Death Anniv of Ven. Induruwe Uttarananda Mahanayake Thero (Buddhist theologian).
1109 **470** 1r. multicoloured . . . . 1·40 1·25

471 Two Graduates, Lamp and Open Book

1990. 9th Anniv of Mahapola Scheme.
1110 **471** 75c. multicoloured . . . 20 20

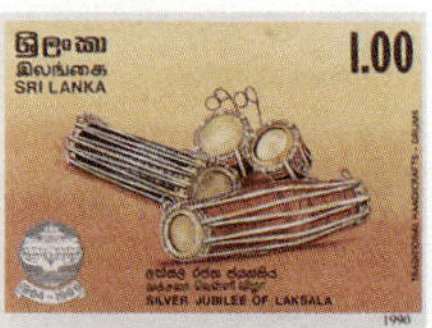

472 Traditional Drums

1990. 25th Anniv of Laksala Traditional Handicrafts Organization. Multicoloured.
1111 1r. Type **472** 20 10
1112 2r. Silverware 35 15
1113 3r. Lacquerware 50 20
1114 8r. Dumbara mats . . . . . 1·10 1·10

473 King Maha Prathapa visiting Queen Chandra

1990. Vesak. Wall Paintings from Buduraja Maha Viharaya, Wewurukannala. Multicoloured.
1115 75c. Type **473** 10 10
1116 1r. Execution of Prince Dharmapala 10 10
1117 2r. Prince Mahinsasaka with the Water Demon 20 20
1118 8r. King Dahamsonda with the God Sakra disguised as a demon 70 70
MS1119 160 × 99 mm. Nos. 1115/18 1·00 1·00

474 Father T. Long (educationist)

476 Gold Reliquary

475 Janasaviya Workers

1990. National Heroes. Multicoloured.
1120 1r. Type **474** 40 25
1121 1r. Prof. M. Ratnasuriya (37 × 25 mm) 40 25
1122 1r. D. Wijewardene (patriot) (37 × 25 mm) 40 25
1123 1r. L. Manjusri (artist) (37 × 25 mm) 40 25

1990. 12th Anniv of Gam Udawa and Opening of Janasaviya Centre, Pallekele.
1124 **475** 1r. multicoloured . . . . 1·50 30

1990. Cent of Department of Archaeology.
1125 **476** 1r. black and yellow . . 30 10
1126 – 2r. black and grey . . . 50 15
1127 – 3r. black, green & brown 70 35
1128 – 8r. black and brown . . 1·40 1·25
DESIGNS: 2r. Statuette of Ganesh; 3r. Terrace of the Bodhi-tree, Isurumuniya Vihara; 8r. Inscription of King Nissankamalla.

477 Male Tennis Player at Left

1990. 75th Anniv of Sri Lanka Tennis Association. Multicoloured.
1129 1r. Type **477** 65 65
1130 1r. Male tennis player at right 65 65
1131 8r. Male tennis players . . . 2·25 2·25
1132 8r. Female tennis players . . 2·25 2·25
Nos. 1129/30 and 1131/2 were each printed together, se-tenant, each pair forming a composite design of a singles (1r.) or doubles (8r.) match.

478 Spotted Loach

479 Rukmani Devi

1990. Endemic Fishes. Multicoloured.
1133 25c. Type **478** 10 10
1134 2r. Spotted gourami ("Ornate paradise fish") 40 10
1135 8r. Mountain labeo . . . . 95 1·00
1136 20r. Cherry barb . . . . . 1·75 3·00
MS1137 150 × 90 mm. Nos. 1133/6 2·75 3·75

1990. 12th Death Anniv of Rukmani Devi (actress and singer).
1138 **479** 1r. multicoloured . . . . 2·25 1·00

480 Innkeeper turning away Mary and Joseph

1990. Christmas. Multicoloured.
1139 1r. Type **480** 40 10
1140 10r. Adoration of the Magi 3·25 3·75
MS1141 190 × 114 mm. Nos. 1139/40 3·50 3·75

481 Health Worker talking to Villagers

1990. World AIDS Day. Multicoloured.
1142 1r. Type **481** 50 15
1143 8r. Emblem and Aids virus 2·25 3·00

482 Main College Building and Flag

483 Peri Sundaram

1990. 50th Anniv of Dharmapala College, Pannipitiya.
1144 **482** 1r. multicoloured . . . . 2·00 90

1990. Birth Centenary of Peri Sundaram (lawyer and politician).
1145 **483** 1r. brown and green . . 2·00 90

484 Letter Box, Galle, 1904

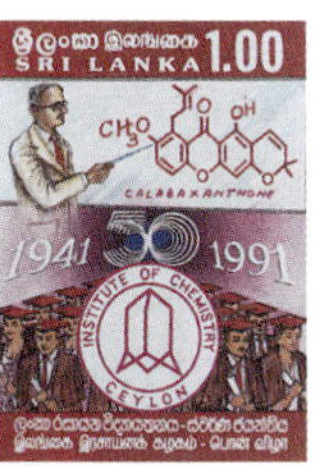

485 Chemical Structure Diagram, Graduating Students and Emblem

1990. 175th Anniv of Sri Lanka Postal Service. Multicoloured.
1146 1r. Type **484** 45 10
1147 2r. Mail runner, 1815 . . . 85 30
1148 5r. Mail coach, 1832 . . . . 1·50 1·75
1149 10r. Nuwara-Eliya Post Office, 1894 . . . . . . 2·25 3·25

1991. 50th Anniv of Institute of Chemistry.
1150 **485** 1r. multicoloured . . . . 2·00 90

486 Kastavahana on Royal Elephant

1991. Vesak. Temple Paintings from Karagampitiya Subodarama. Multicoloured.
1151 75c. Type **486** 25 10
1152 1r. Polo Janaka in prison 25 10
1153 2r. Two merchants offering food to Buddha 55 35
1154 11r. Escape of Queen . . . 2·50 4·50
MS1155 150 × 90 mm. Nos. 1151/4 3·50 4·50

487 Narada Thero (Buddhist missionary)

488 Society Building

1991. National Heroes. Multicoloured.
1156 1r. Type **487** 50 50
1157 1r. Wallewatta Silva (novelist) 50 50
1158 1r. Sir Muttu Coomaraswamy (lawyer and politician) 50 50
1159 1r. Dr. Andreas Nell (ophthalmic surgeon) . . 50 50

1991. Centenary of Maha Bodhi Society.
1160 **488** 1r. multicoloured . . . . 1·25 80

489 Women working at Home

1991. 13th Anniv of Gam Udawa Movement.
1161 **489** 1r. multicoloured . . . . 2·00 80

490 Globe and Plan Symbol

492 Ven. Henpitagedera Gnanaseeha Nayake Thero

491 17th-century Map and Modern Satellite Photo of Sri Lanka

1991. 40th Anniv of Colombo Plan.
1162 **490** 1r. violet and blue . . . 2·25 80

1991. 190th Anniv of Sri Lanka Survey Department.
1163 **491** 1r. multicoloured . . . . 1·75 80

1991. 10th Death Anniv of Ven. Nayak Henpitagedera Gnanaseeha Nayake Thero (Buddhist theologian).
1164 **492** 1r. multicoloured . . . . 1·75 80

493 Police Officers of 1866 and 1991 with Badge

1991. 125th Anniv of Sri Lanka Police Force.
1165 **493** 1r. multicoloured . . . . 1·00 60

494 Kingswood College

1991. Centenary of Kingswood College, Kandy.
1166 **494** 1r. multicoloured 50 30

495 The Annunciation

496 Early Magneto Telephone

1991. Christmas. Multicoloured.
1167 1r. Type **495** 20 20
1168 10r. The Presentation of Jesus in the Temple . . . 1·10 2·00
MS1169 90 × 150 mm. Nos. 1167/8 1·25 2·00

1991. Inauguration of Sri Lankan Telecom Corporation. Multicoloured.
1170 1r. Type **496** 20 10
1171 2r. Manual switchboard and telephonist 25 15
1172 8r. Satellite communications system . . . . 55 1·40
1173 10r. Fibre optics cable and mobile phone . . . . . 70 1·40

497 S.A.A.R.C. Logo and Bandaranaike Memorial Hall

1991. 6th South Asian Association for Regional Co-operation Summit, Colombo. Multicoloured.
1174 1r. Type **497** 15 10
1175 8r. Logo and hall surrounded by national flags . . . . 45 1·25

498 "Pancha" (Games mascot)

1991. 5th South Asian Federation Games. Mult.
1176 1r. Type **498** 25 10
1177 2r. Games logo 45 20
1178 4r. Sugathadasa Stadium . . 85 1·00
1179 11r. Asia map on globe and national flags . . . . . . 1·75 3·00

499 Crate, Boeing 747-300/400 Airliner and Container Ship

1992. Exports Year.
1180 **499** 1r. multicoloured . . . . 1·50 80

500 Plucking Tea

501 General Ranjan Wijeratne

1992. 125th Anniv of Tea Industry. Mult.
1181 1r. Type **500** 40 10
1182 2r. Healthy family, tea and tea estate 70 20
1183 5r. Ceylon tea symbol . . . 2·00 2·00
1184 10r. James Taylor (founder) 2·50 3·50

1992. 1st Death Anniv of General Ranjan Wijeratne.
1185 **501** 1r. multicoloured 30 20

502 Olcott Hall, Mahinda College

1992. Centenary of Mahinda College, Galle.
1186 **502** 1r. multicoloured 20 20

503 Newstead College and Logo

1992. 175th Anniv (1991) of Newstead Girls' College, Negombo.
1187 **503** 1r. multicoloured 20 20

504 Student and Oil Lamp

506 Ven. Devamottawe Amarawansa (Buddhist missionary)

505 Sama's Parents leaving for Forest

1992. 11th Anniv of Mahapola Scholarship Fund.
1188 **504** 1r. multicoloured 20 20

1992. Vesak Festival. Sama Jataka Paintings from Kottimbulwala Cave Temple. Multicoloured.
1189 75c. Type **505** 15 10
1190 1r. Sama and parents in forest 15 10
1191 8r. Sama leading blind parents . . . . 1·10 1·50
1192 11r. Sama's parents grieving for wounded son . . . . 1·50 2·25
MS1193 151 × 91 mm. Nos. 1189/92 2·40 3·75

1992. National Heroes. Multicoloured.
1194 1r. Type **506** 15 20
1195 1r. Richard Mirando (Buddhist philanthropist) 15 20
1196 1r. Gate Mudaliyar N. Canaganayagam (Buddhist social reformer) 15 20
1197 1r. Abdul Azeez (Moorish social reformer) 15 20

507 Map of Sri Lanka, Flag and Symbol

508 Family in House

1992. 2300th Anniv of Arrival of Buddhism in Sri Lanka.
1198 **507** 1r. multicoloured 20 20

1992. 14th Anniv of Gam Udawa Movement.
1199 **508** 1r. multicoloured 20 20

509 Postal Activities and Award

510 Narilata Mask

1992. Postal Service Awards. Multicoloured.
1200 1r. Type **509** 30 10
1201 10r. Medals and commemorative cachet . . 2·25 2·75

1992. Kolam Dance Masks. Multicoloured.
1202 1r. Type **510** 15 10
1203 2r. Mudali mask 25 10
1204 5r. Queen mask 50 70
1205 10r. King mask . . . . . . 90 1·60
MS1206 150 × 90 mm. N0os. 1202/5 1·25 2·00

511 19th and 20th-century Players and Match of 1838

512 Running

1992. 160th Anniv of Cricket in Sri Lanka.
1207 **511** 5r. multicoloured . . . . 2·25 2·00

1992. Olympic Games, Barcelona. Multicoloured.
1208 1r. Type **512** 20 10
1209 11r. Shooting . . . . 1·25 1·75
1210 13r. Swimming . . . . . . 1·60 2·25
1211 15r. Weightlifting . . . . . 1·75 2·50
MS1212 91 × 151 mm. Nos. 1208/11 4·00 6·00

513 Vijaya Kumaratunga

514 College Building and Crest

1992. Vijaya Kumaratunga (actor) Commem.
1213 **513** 1r. multicoloured 30 20

1992. Centenary of Al-Bahjathhul Ibraheemiyyah Arabic College.
1214 **514** 1r. multicoloured 30 20

515 Official Church Seal

516 Nativity

1992. 350th Anniv of Dutch Reformed Church in Sri Lanka.
1215 **515** 1r. black, green & yellow 1·00 40

1992. Christmas. Multicoloured.
1216 1r. Type **516** 15 10
1217 9r. Family going to church 1·60 2·00
MS1218 150 × 90 mm. Nos. 1216/17 1·50 2·25

517 Fleet of Columbus

1992. 500th Anniv of Discovery of America by Columbus. Multicoloured.
1219 1r. Type **517** 50 10
1220 11r. Columbus landing in New World . . . . . . 1·25 1·50
1221 13r. Wreck of "Santa Maria" . . . . 1·50 2·00
1222 15r. Columbus reporting to Queen Isabella and King Ferdinand . . . . 1·50 2·25
MS1223 155 × 95 mm. Nos. 1219/22 3·75 5·50

1992. No. 684 surch **2.00**.
1224 **255** 2r. on 10c. multicoloured 2·00 50

519 Ven. Sumedhankara Thero and Dagoba

1992. Birth Centenary of Ven. Dambagasare Sumedhankara Nayake Thero.
1225 **519** 1r. multicoloured 20 20

520 University Logo, Students and Building

1992. 50th Anniv of University Education in Sri Lanka (1st issue).
1226 **520** 1r. multicoloured 20 20
See also No. 1227.

521 University of Colombo Building and Logo

1993. 50th Anniv of University Education in Sri Lanka (2nd issue).
1227 **521** 1r. multicoloured 75 20

522 College Building and Crest

1993. Centenary of Zahira College, Colombo.
1228 **522** 1r. multicoloured 75 30

523 Magandiya being presented to Buddha

524 Girl Guide, Badge and Camp

1993. Vesak Festival. Verses from the "Dhammapada". Multicoloured.
1229 75c. Type **523** 15 10
1230 1r. Kisa Gotami carrying her dead baby 20 10
1231 3r. Patachara and her dying family 50 70
1232 10r. Angulimala praying . . 1·00 1·75
MS1233 180 × 101 mm. Nos. 1229/32 1·25 2·00

1993. 75th Anniv of Sri Lanka Girl Guides Association. Multicoloured.
1234 1r. Type **524** 50 10
1235 5r. Girl Guide activities . . 1·25 1·75

525 Ven. Yagirala Pagnananda Maha Nayaka Thero (scholar)

526 Family arriving at New Home

1993. National Heroes. Multicoloured.
1236 1r. Type **525** 30 30
1237 1r. Charles de Silva (politician) 30 30
1238 1r. Wilmot A. Perera (politician) 30 30
1239 1r. Abdul Caffoor (philanthropist) 30 30

1993. "Gam Udawa '93".
1240 **526** 1r. multicoloured . . . . 1·25 30

527 Consumer Movement Flag and Logo

1993. 50th Anniv (1992) of Co-operative Consumer Movement.
1241 **527** 1r. multicoloured . . . . 1·50 30

528 Ashy-headed Laughing Thrush

1993. Birds (4th series). Multicoloured.
1242 3r. Type **528** 40 20
1243 4r. Brown-capped jungle babbler ("Ceylon Brown-capped Babbler") 40 20
1244 5r. Red-faced malkoha . . . 50 50
1245 10r. Ceylon grackle ("Ceylon Hill-Mynah") 95 1·25
MS1246 151 × 121 mm. Nos. 1242/5 2·25 3·00

529 Talawila Church

1993. 150th Anniv of Talawila Church.
1247 **529** 1r. multicoloured . . . . 1·00 30

530 Rosette and Mail Delivery

531 College and Flag

1993. Sri Lanka Post Excellent Service Awards.
1248 **530** 1r. multicoloured . . . . 1·00 30

1993. Centenary of Musaeus College.
1249 **531** 1r. multicoloured . . . . 1·50 30

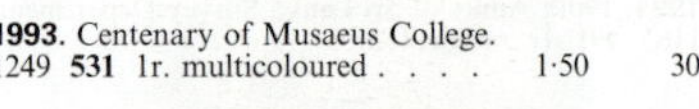

532 Presentation of Jesus in the Temple

1993. Christmas. Multicoloured.
1250 1r. Type **532** 10 10
1251 17r. Boy Jesus with the Jewish teachers . . . . . 1·00 2·00
MS1252 180 × 102 mm. Nos. 1250/1 1·00 2·00

533 Healthy Youth and Drug Addict

1993. Youth and Health Campaign.
1253 **533** 1r. multicoloured 50 30

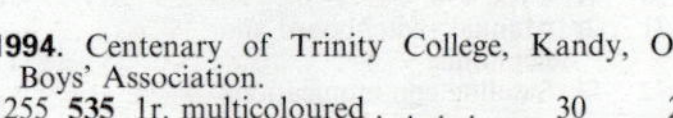

534 Maradana Technical College Building and Emblems

535 Trinity College Logo

1993. Centenary of Technical Education.
1254 **534** 1r. multicoloured . . . . 1·00 30

1994. Centenary of Trinity College, Kandy, Old Boys' Association.
1255 **535** 1r. multicoloured 30 20

536 College Flag

1994. 150th Anniv of St. Thomas' College, Matara.
1256 **536** 1r. brown and blue . . . 30 20

537 Ven. Siyambalangamuwe Sri Gunaratana Thero

1994. Ven. Siyambalangamuwe Sri Gunaratana Thero (educationist) Commemoration.
1257 **537** 1r. multicoloured . . . . 1·25 30

538 College Building and Arms

1994. 125th Anniv of St. Joseph's College, Trincomalee.
1258 **538** 1r. multicoloured 30 20

539 Man distributing Water

1994. Vesak Festival. Dasa Paramita (Ten Virtues). Multicoloured.
1259 1r. Type **539** 10 10
1260 2r. Man and elephant . . . 80 40
1261 5r. Man surrounded by women 90 90
1262 17r. Ruler with snake charmer . . . . 2·00 3·00
MS1263 162/88 mm. Nos. 1259/62 2·75 4·00

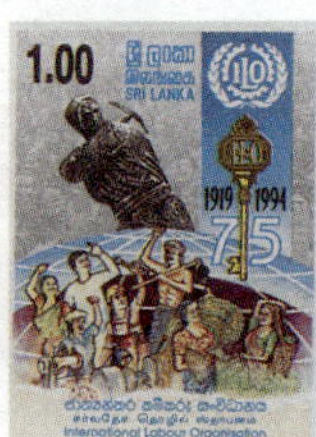

540 I.L.O. Monument, Geneva, Logo and Workers

1994. 75th Anniv of I.L.O.
1264 **540** 1r. multicoloured 70 30

541 Mahakavindra Dhammaratana Thero (Buddhist theologian)

1994. National Heroes. Multicoloured.
1265 1r. Type **541** 15 20
1266 1r. Ranasinghe Premadasa (former President) 15 20
1267 1r. Dr. Colvin de Silva (trade union leader) . . . 15 20
1268 1r. E. Periyathambipillai (Tamil poet) 15 20

542 Conference Logo

1994. 13th International Federation of Social Workers World Conference, Colombo.
1269 **542** 8r. multicoloured . . . . 1·75 1·75

543 Ven. Sri Somaratana Thero and Temple

1994. 10th Death Anniv of Ven. Sri Somaratana Thero (Buddhist religious leader).
1270 **543** 1r. multicoloured . . . . 1·00 30

544 Communication Technology and Logo

1994. "INFOTEL LANKA '94" International Computers and Telecommunications Exhibition.
1271 **544** 10r. multicoloured . . . 1·75 2·00

545 Veddah Tribesman stringing Bow

546 Luca Pacioli (pioneer), Logo and Equipment inside "500"

1994. Year of Indigenous People (1993). Mult.
1272 1r. Type **545** 20 10
1273 17r. Veddah artist and rock paintings . . . . 2·75 3·25

1994. 500th Anniv of Accountancy.
1274 **546** 1r. multicoloured . . . . 1·00 30

547 Society Emblem

1994. Centenary of Wildlife and Nature Society of Sri Lanka.
1275 **547** 1r. green and black . . . 15 10
1276 – 2r. multicoloured 50 20
1277 – 10r. multicoloured . . . 1·50 1·60
1278 – 17r. multicoloured . . . 2·00 3·00
MS1279 130 × 96 mm. Nos. 1275/8 3·25 4·50
DESIGNS: 2r. Horned lizard; 10r. Giant squirrel; 17r. Sloth bear.

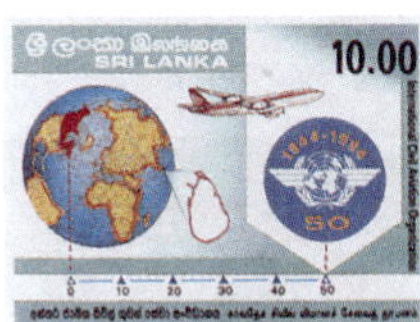

548 Airliner, I.C.A.O. Logo and Globe

1994. 50th Anniv of I.C.A.O.
1280 **548** 10r. multicoloured . . . 2·25 2·25

549 Christmas Crib

1994. Christmas. Multicoloured.
1281 1r. Type **549** 10 10
1282 17r. St. Joseph's carpentry workshop, Nazareth . . . 2·00 2·50
MS1283 145 × 81 mm. Nos. 1281/2 1·50 2·50

550 Map of Sri Lanka and Aspects of Science

1994. 50th Anniv of Sri Lankan Association for the Advancement of Science.
1284 **550** 1r. multicoloured . . . . 1·75 40

551 College Building and Arms

1994. Cent of Richmond College Old Boys' Assn.
1285 **551** 1r. black, red and blue 20 20

552 "Dendrobium maccarthiae"

554 Blue Water Lily

553 Father Joseph Vaz and Pope John Paul II

1994. 60th Anniv of Orchid Circle of Ceylon. Multicoloured.
1286 50c. Type **552** 20 10
1287 1r. "Cottonia peduncularis" 25 10
1288 5r. "Bulbophyllum wightii" 55 50
1289 17r. "Habenaria crinifera" 1·10 2·00
MS1290 127 × 95 mm. Nos. 1286/9 2·25 2·75

1995. Papal Visit and Beatification of Father Joseph Vaz.
1291 **553** 1r. multicoloured . . . . 1·75 40

1995.
1292 **554** 1r. multicoloured 40 10

555 College Building and Arms

1995. Centenary of St. Joseph's College, Colombo.
1293 **555** 1r. multicoloured 70 20

556 Sirimavo Bandaranaike and National Flag

1995. Election of Sirimavo Banadaranaike as Prime Minister.
1294 **556** 2r. multicoloured . . . . 1·25 70

557 Man offering Water to Crew of Outrigger Canoe

558 14th-century Map of Sri Lanka and Society Arms

1995. Vesak Festival. Dasa Paramita (Ten Virtues). Multicoloured.
1295 1r. Type **557** 15 10
1296 2r. Catching falling man . . 20 15
1297 10r. Teacher with students 80 1·00
1298 17r. Stopping man digging 1·50 2·00
MS1299 170 × 90 mm. Nos. 1295/8 2·25 3·00

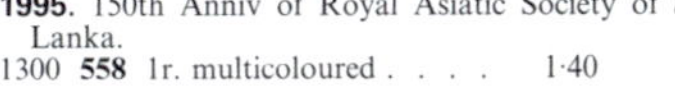

1995. 150th Anniv of Royal Asiatic Society of Sri Lanka.
1300 **558** 1r. multicoloured . . . . 1·40 50

559 Abdul Cader

1995. 120th Birth Anniv of Abdul Cader (lawyer).
1301 **559** 2r. multicoloured . . . . 1·00 60

560 College Building

1995. Centenary of St. Aloysius's College, Galle.
1302 **560** 2r. multicoloured . . . . 1·00 60

561 Tikiri Ilangaratna

1995. Tikiri Bandara Ilangaratna (politician and author) Commemoration.
1303 **561** 2r. multicoloured . . . . 1·00 60

562 Lamps and Schools Flag

1995. Centenary of Dhamma Schools Movement.
1304 **562** 2r. multicoloured . . . . 1·00 60

563 G.P.O. Building

1995. Centenary of General Post Office, Colombo.
1305 **563** 1r. multicoloured 70 20

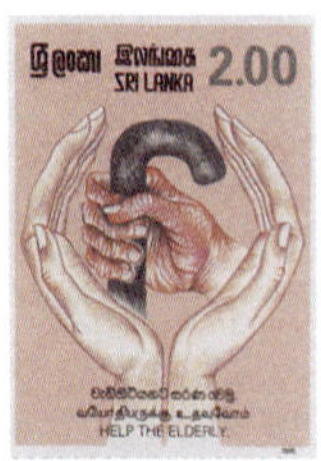

564 Young Hands surrounding Old Hand

1995. International Day for the Elderly.
1306 **564** 2r. multicoloured . . . . 1·00 60

565 Sri Lankan Parliament Building and C.P.A. Logo

1995. 41st Commonwealth Parliamentary Conf, Colombo.
1307 **565** 2r. multicoloured . . . . 1·00 60

566 Anniversary Emblem and Map of Sri Lanka

567 Money falling into Globe Money Box

1995. 50th Anniv of United Nations.
1308 **566** 2r. multicoloured . . . . 1·00 70

1995. 71st Anniv of World Thrift Day and 110th Anniv of National Savings Bank.
1309 **567** 2r. multicoloured . . . . 1·00 60

568 Diocesan Arms of Colombo and Kurunegala

1995. Christmas. 150th Anniv of Anglican Diocese of Colombo. Multicoloured.
1310 2r. Type **568** 20 10
1311 20r. Nativity scene and hands surrounding map 2·00 2·50
MS1312 150 × 90 mm. Nos. 1310/11 2·00 3·00

569 Flags of Member Countries

570 School Emblem

1995. 10th Anniv of South Asian Association for Regional Co-operation.
1313 **569** 2r. multicoloured . . . . 1·25 70

1996. 175th Anniv of Vincent Girls' High School, Batticaloa.
1314 **570** 2r. multicoloured . . . 1·00 60

571 Little Basses Lighthouse

572 Traditional Sesath (umbrellas)

1996. Lighthouses. Multicoloured.
1315 50c. Type **571** 20 15
1316 75c. Great Basses 25 15
1317 2r. Devinuwara 35 15
1317a 2r.50 As 2r. 35 25
1318 20r. Galle . . . . 1·50 2·00
MS1319 151 × 91 mm. Nos. 1315/17 and 1318 . . . . 1·75 2·50

1996. Traditional Handicrafts. Multicoloured.
1320 25c. Type **572** 10 10
1321 8r.50 Pottery 40 35
1322 10r.50 Mats 55 60
1323 17r. Lace . . . . 75 1·10
MS1324 150 × 90 mm. Nos. 1320/3 2·00 2·50

573 School Emblem and Trees

1996. Centenary of Chundikuli Girls' College, Jaffna.
1325 **573** 2r. multicoloured . . . . 1·00 60

574 Upaka and Capa

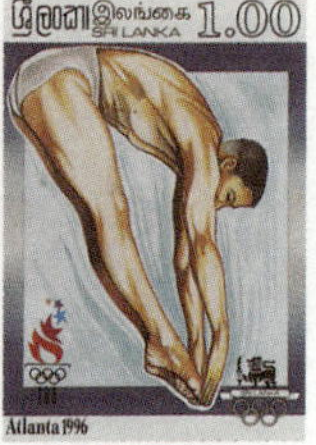
575 Diving

1996. Vesak Festival. Multicoloured.
1326 1r. Type **574** 15 10
1327 2r. Dantika and elephant . . 40 15
1328 5r. Subha removing her eye 60 60
1329 10r. Punna and the Brahmin 85 1·00
MS1330 170 × 90 mm. Nos. 1326/9 1·50 2·00

1996. Olympic Games, Atlanta. Multicoloured.
1331 1r. Type **575** 20 10
1332 2r. Tennis 60 10
1333 5r. Rifle shooting (horiz) . . 85 80
1334 17r. Running (horiz) . . . . 1·50 2·50

576 Bowler

1996. Sri Lanka's Victory in World Cup Cricket Tournament. Multicoloured.
1335 2r. Type **576** 45 25
1336 10r.50 Wicket-keeper . . . 80 80
1337 17r. Batsman . . . . 1·25 1·60
1338 20r. World Cup trophy . . 1·40 1·75
MS1339 150 × 90 mm. Nos. 1335/8 3·00 4·00

577 Main Building, Jaffna Central College

1996. 180th Anniv of Jaffna Central College.
1340 **577** 2r. multicoloured . . . . 1·00 60

578 Globe in Flowers and White Dove

579 Jesus washing the Disciples' Feet

1996. 50th Anniv of U.N.E.S.C.O.
1341 **578** 2r. multicoloured . . . . 1·25 70

1996. Christmas. Murals by David Paynter from Trinity College Chapel, Kandy. Multicoloured.
1342 2r. Type **579** 10 10
1343 17r. Parable of the Good Samaritan . . . . . . 90 1·25
MS1344 150 × 90 mm. Nos. 1342/4 1·00 1·50

580 Cupped Hands holding Child

581 Swami Vivekananda and Globe

1996. 50th Anniv of U.N.I.C.E.F.
1345 **580** 5r. multicoloured 50 70

1997. Centenary of Swami Vivekananda's Visit to Sri Lanka.
1346 **581** 2r.50 multicoloured . . . 50 50

1997. No. 1317 surch **2.50**.
1347 2r.50 on 2r. multicoloured 1·75 50

586 Venerable Welivitiye Sorata Thero (scholar)

589 Thuparama Stupa, 3rd-century B.C.

1997. National Heroes (1st series). Multicoloured.
1351 2r. Type **586** 50 50
1352 2r. Mahagama Sekera (writer and artist) 50 50
1353 2r. Dr. S. A. Wickremasinghe (physician) 50 50
1354 2r. Lt. Gen. Denzil Kobbekaduwa 50 50
See also Nos. 1373/6.

1997. No. 1322 surch **11.00**.
1355 11r. on 10r.50 multicoloured 2·25 2·25

1997. Vesak Festival. Anauradhapura Sites. Mult.
1357 1r. Type **589** 10 10
1358 2r.50 Ruwanvalisaya stupa, 61–137 B.C. 15 10
1359 3r. Abhayagiri Dagaba, 103–102 B.C. 15 15
1360 17r. Jethavana Dagaba, 276–303 A.D. . . . . . . 80 1·00
MS1361 170 × 90 mm. Nos. 1357/60 1·00 1·50

590 Don Johannes Kumarage

1997. Birth Centenary of D. J. Kumarage (Buddhist teacher).
1362 **590** 2r.50 multicoloured . . . 1·00 60

591 "Munronia pinnata"

1997. Medicinal Herbs. Multicoloured.
1363 2r.50 Type **591** 20 10
1364 14r. "Rauvolfia serpentina" 80 1·00

592 Tourist Board Logo, Airliner and Holiday Resorts

1997. Visit Sri Lanka.
1365 **592** 20r. multicoloured . . . 2·00 2·50

1997. No. 1321 surch **1.00**.
1366 1r. on 8r.50 Pottery . . . . 2·50 30

594 Lyre Head Lizard

1997. Reptiles. Multicoloured.
1367 2r.50 Type **594** 10 10
1368 5r. Boie's roughside (snake) 20 20
1369 7r. Common Lanka skink 55 70
1370 20r. Great forest gecko . . 60 1·00
MS1371 170 × 90 mm. Nos. 1367/70 1·25 1·60

595 St. Servatius' College, Matara

1997. Centenary of St. Servatius' College, Matara.
1372 **595** 2r.50 multicoloured . . . 30 20

1997. National Heroes (2nd series). As T **586**. Multicoloured.
1373 2r.50 Sri Indasara Nayake Thero (Buddhist leader) 15 20
1374 2r.50 Abdul Aziz (trade union leader) 15 20
1375 2r.50 Prof. Subramaniam Vithiananthan 15 20
1376 2r.50 Vivienne Goonewardene (politician) 15 20

596 The Nativity

1997. Christmas. Multicoloured.
1377 2r.50 Type **596** 10 10
1378 20r. Visit of the Three Kings 90 1·25
MS1379 170 × 90 mm. Nos. 1377/8 1·00 1·25

597 Young Men's Buddhist Association Building, Colombo

1998. Centenary of Young Men's Buddhist Association, Colombo.
1380 **597** 2r.50 multicoloured . . . 20 15

598 Sri Jayawardenapura Vidyalaya School

1998. 175th Anniv of Sri Jayawardenapura Vidyalaya School, Kotte.
1381 **598** 2r.50 multicoloured . . . 20 15

599 Children and Mathematical Symbols

1998. 50th Anniv of Independence. Multicoloured.
1382 2r. Type **599** 25 10
1383 2r.50 Flag and 1949 4c. Independence stamp (38 × 28 mm) 35 30
1384 2r.50 People with technological and industrial symbols 35 30
1385 5r. Dancers with arts and music symbols 40 45
1386 10r. Women with cultural and historical symbols . . 60 80

600 Scouts raising Flag and Jamboree Logo

601 W.H.O. Emblem in "50" and Flag of Sri Lanka

1998. 5th National Scout Jamboree, Kandy. Mult.
1387 2r.50 Type **600** 35 10
1388 17r. Scout saluting and Jamboree emblem . . . . 1·50 2·00

1998. 50th Anniv of W.H.O.
1389 **601** 2r.50 multicoloured . . . 40 15

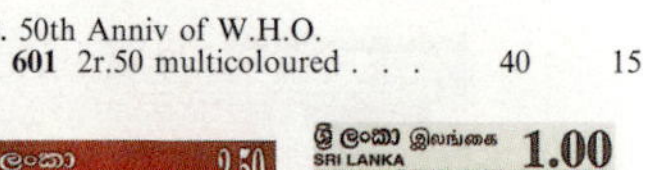
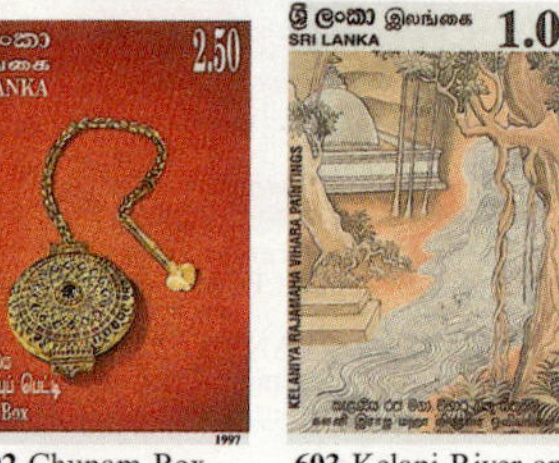
602 Chunam Box

603 Kelani River and Stupa

1998. Traditional Jewellery and Crafts. Mult.
1390 2r.50 Type **602** 20 10
1391 5r. Agate necklace 30 20
1392 10r. Bangle and hairpin . . 50 60
1393 17r. Sigiri ear-ring . . . . . 80 1·25
MS1394 151 × 91 mm. Nos. 1390/3 1·50 2·00

1998. Vesak Festival. Wall Paintings from Kelaniya Temple. Multicoloured.
1395 1r. Type **603** 10 10
1396 2r.50 Crown Prince Mahanaga and his court on way to Magampura . . 20 10
1397 4r. Mahanaga and wife with baby Yatala Tissa 35 30
1398 17r. Prince Mahanaga with King's minister . . . . 80 1·10
MS1399 170 × 90 mm. Nos. 1395/8 1·25 1·75

604 School Building and Emblem

1998. 175th Anniv of St. John's College, Jaffna.
1400 **604** 2r.50 multicoloured . . . 20 15

605 Elephants in River

1998. Elephants. Multicoloured.
1401 2r.50 Type **605** 35 15
1402 10r. Cow and calf 60 50
1403 17r. Family group 80 90
1404 50r. Bull elephant . . . . . 1·50 3·00
MS1405 105 × 90 mm. Nos. 1401/4 2·50 3·00

606 S.A.A.R.C. Flags and Logo

1998. 10th Anniv of South Asian Association for Regional Co-operation.
1406 **606** 2r.50 multicoloured . . . 40 15

607 William Gopallawa

1998. William Gopallawa (first President of Sri Lanka) Commemoration.
1407 **607** 2r.50 multicoloured . . . 30 15

608 Satellite and Computer

1998. Year of Information Technology.
1408 **608** 2r.50 multicoloured . . . 30 15

609 Ven. Kotahene Pannakitti Nayaka Thero (Buddhist scholar)

610 Flag of Sri Lanka and Lions Club Emblem

1998. Distinguished Personalities. Multicoloured.
1409 2r.50 Type **609** 20 20
1410 2r.50 Prof. Ediriweera Sarachchandra (scholar) 20 20
1411 2r.50 Sir Nicholas Attygalle (medical pioneer) 20 20
1412 2r.50 Dr. Samuel Fisk Green (Tamil scholar) . . 20 20

1998. Lions Clubs International 26th South Asia, Africa and Middle East Forum, Colombo.
1413 **610** 2r.50 multicoloured . . . 1·00 50

611 "50" and Meteorological Symbols

1998. 50th Anniv of Department of Meteorology.
1414 **611** 2r.50 multicoloured . . . 40 15

612 Virgin Mary and the Infant Jesus

613 S. W. Bandaranaike as a Young Man

1998. Christmas. Multicoloured.
1415 2r.50 Type **612** 10 10
1416 20r. The Annunciation . . . 90 1·25
MS1417 90 × 150 mm. Nos. 1415/16 1·00 1·25

1999. Birth Centenary of S. W. Bandaranaike. Multicoloured.
1418 3r.50 Type **613** 50 50
1419 3r.50 Bandaranaike as Prime Minister 50 50
MS1420 81 × 100 mm. Nos. 1418/19 1·00 1·25

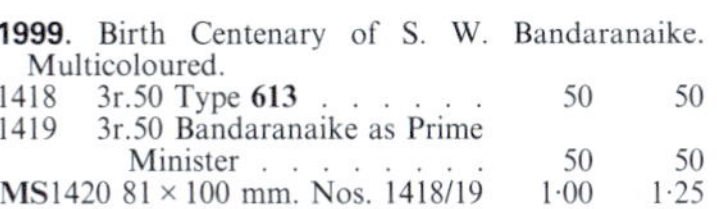

614 Traditional Dancer

615 Sir Arthur C. Clarke (author) and Spacecraft

1999.

1422 **614** 1r. brown 10 10
1423 2r. blue 10 10
1424 3r. purple 10 10
1425 3r.50 blue 10 10
1426 4r. red 10 10
1427 5r. green 10 10
1428 10r. violet 15 20
1429 13r.50 red 15 20
1430 17r. green 20 25
1431 20r. brown 25 30
1431a – 50r. brown and orange 65 70
1431b – 100r. brown and ochre 1·25 1·40
1431c – 200r. lavender and blue 2·50 2·75

DESIGNS—(25 × 30mm): 50, 100 and 200r. As T **614** but with background of scroll work.
The 5r. to 20r. are larger, 21 × 26 mm.

1999. 50 Years of Communication Improvement. Multicoloured.
1432 3r.50 Type **615** 35 35
1433 3r.50 Sir Arthur C. Clarke with spacecraft orbiting Earth 35 35
Nos. 1432/3 were printed together, se-tenant, forming a composite design.

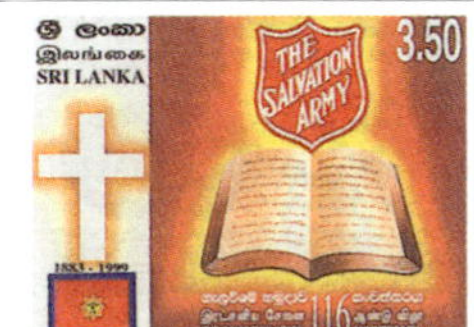

616 Salvation Army Badge, Bible and Cross

1999. 116th Anniv of Salvation Army in Sri Lanka.
1434 **616** 3r.50 multicoloured . . . 25 20

617 Activities of British Council

618 "Birth of Prince Siddhartha"

1999. 50th Anniv of British Council.
1435 **617** 3r.50 multicoloured . . . 25 20

1999. Vesak Festival. Multicoloured.
1436 2r. Type **618** 10 10
1437 3r.50 "The Enlightenment" 15 15
1438 13r.50 "The Maha Parinirvana" 45 60
1439 17r. Celebrating Vesak . . . 55 80
MS1440 151 × 90 mm. Nos. 1436/9 1·00 1·25

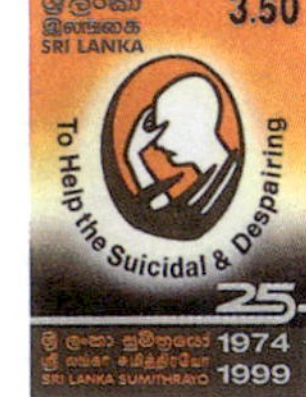

619 Dish Aerial and Transmitting Tower

620 Sumithrayo Logo

1999. 20th Anniv of Independent Television.
1441 **619** 3r.50 multicoloured . . . 20 15

1999. 25th Anniv of Sumithrayo (humanitarian charity).
1442 **620** 3r.50 multicoloured . . . 20 15

621 Scene from "Handaya" and Camera Crew

623 Hector Kobbekaduwa

622 Vidyodaya Pirivena

1999. 50 Years of Sri Lankan Cinema. Mult.
1443 3r.50 Type **621** 10 10
1444 4r. Scene from "Nidhanaya" and film societies' emblems 10 10
1445 10r. Scene from "Gamperaliya" and camera crew 30 30
1446 17r. Two scenes from "Kadawunu Poronduwa" 85 1·25
MS1447 109 × 183 mm. Nos. 1443/6 1·00 1·25

1999. 125th Anniv of Vidyodaya Pirivena (Buddhist education foundation).
1448 **622** 3r.50 multicoloured . . . 20 15

1999. Hector Kobbekaduwa (former Minister of Agriculture and Lands) Commemoration.
1449 **623** 3r.50 multicoloured . . . 20 15

624 Hands holding Emblem, Fountain Pen and Magazine

1999. Centenary of *Bhakthi Prabodanaya* (religious magazine).
1450 **624** 3r.50 multicoloured . . . 20 15

625 Army Emblem and Flags

626 Emblem and Scenery within Segments of Circle

1999. 50th Anniv of Sri Lankan Army.
1451 **625** 3r.50 multicoloured . . . 35 20

1999. 50th Anniv of Sri Lankan National Commission for U.N.E.S.C.O.
1452 **626** 13r.50 multicoloured . . 1·00 1·25

627 Two Children on Globe within Hands

628 Ven. Balangoda Ananda Maitreya

1999. 10th Anniv of United Nations Rights of the Child Convention.
1453 **627** 3r.50 multicoloured . . . 60 30

1999. Ven. Balangoda Ananda Maitreya (Buddhist monk and teacher).
1454 **628** 3r.50 multicoloured . . . 20 15

629 The Nativity

1999. Christmas. Multicoloured.
1455 3r.50 Type **629** 15 10
1456 20r. Visit of Three Wise Men . . . . 85 1·00
MS1457 150 × 90 mm. Nos. 1455/6 1·00 1·25

630 Sunil Santha

632 Dr. Pandithamani Kanapathipillai

1999. 85th Birth Anniv of Sunil Santha (musician and teacher).
1458 **630** 3r.50 multicoloured . . . 60 30

1999. No. 1317a surch **2.00**.
1459 2r. on 2r.50 Devinawara Lighthouse . . . . 1·50 55

1999. Birth Centenary of Dr. Pandithamani Kanapathipillai (Tamil scholar).
1460 **632** 3r.50 multicoloured . . . 50 25

633 Emblem, Figures and Inscriptions

1999. Bicentenary of State Audit Department.
1461 **633** 3r.50 multicoloured . . . 50 25

634 Dr. Badiudin Mahmud

635 "Christian Family" (David Paynter)

1999. 95th Birth Anniv of Dr. Badiudin Mahmud (Islamic polititian).
1462 **634** 3r.50 multicoloured . . . 50 25

1999. Sri Lankan Paintings. Multicoloured.
1463 3r.50 Type **635** 15 10
1464 4r. "Sri Lankan Woman" (Justin Daraniyagala) . . 15 10
1465 17r. "Waiting for the Fishermen" (Ivan Peries) 60 70
1466 20r. "Composing the 'Tripitaka'" (Soliyas Mendis) 70 85
MS1467 150 × 91 mm. Nos. 1463/6 1·25 1·50

636 Kumar Anandan swimming Palk Strait

1999. Sporting Achievements. Multicoloured.
1468 1r. Type **636** 15 10
1469 3r.50 Batsman and trophy (One Day Cricket World Champions, 1996) (vert) 20 10
1470 13r.50 Athletics (vert) . . . 75 1·00

637 Striped Albatross (butterfly)

638 Doves at Nest and Religious Symbols

1999. Butterflies. Multicoloured.
1471 3r.50 Type **637** 25 10
1472 13r.50 Ceylon tiger 60 60
1473 17r. Two-spot grass yellow 75 80
1474 20r. Great orange tip . . . 90 95
MS1475 90 × 148 mm. Nos. 1471/4 2·00 2·25

2000. New Millennium. Multicoloured.
1476 10r. Type **638** 40 25
1477 100r. Girl reading within hands, Scales of Justice and Red Cross . . . . . 2·50 3·00
1478 100r. Man using computer, airliner and dish aerial . . 2·50 3·00
1479 100r. People within open cupped hands . . . . 2·50 3·00
MS1480 148 × 90 mm. Nos. 1476/9 6·50 7·50

639 Cathedral Church, Kurunagala

2000. 50th Anniv of Diocese of Kurunagala.
1481 **639** 13r.50 multicoloured . . 70 80

640 College Logo and Figures around Globe

2000. 125th Anniv of Wesley College, Colombo.
1482 **640** 3r.50 multicoloured . . . 20 15

641 Buddhist Monk and Temple

2000. Centenary of Saddharmakara Pirivena (Buddhist college), Panadura.
1483 **641** 3r.50 multicoloured . . . 20 15

642 Boulder Coral

2000. Corals. Multicoloured.
1484 3r.50 Type **642** 25 10
1485 13r.50 Blue-tipped coral . . 60 65
1486 14r. Brain-boulder coral . . 60 65
1487 22r. Elk-horn coral . . . . 80 1·00
MS1488 148 × 90 mm. Nos. 1484/7 1·50 2·00

643 Arrival of Cutting from Jaya Sri Maha Bodhi (sacred tree)

2000. Vesak Festival. Multicoloured.
1489 2r. Type **643** 10 10
1490 3r.50 King Devanampiyatissa carrying Jaya Sri Maha Bodhi 15 10
1491 10r. Venerating the Java Sri Maha Bodhi 45 55
1492 13r.50 Planting the cutting at Anuradhapura 60 75
MS1493 98 × 166 mm. Nos 1489/92 1·00 1·25

644 Bar Association Logo and Courts

2000. 25th Anniv of Sri Lanka Bar Association.
1494 **644** 3r.50 multicoloured . . . 20 15

645 C.W.E. Emblem and People in Supermarket

2000. 50th Anniv of Co-operative Wholesale Establishment.
1495 **645** 3r.50 multicoloured . . . 20 15

2000. No. 1135 surch **.50**.
1496 50c. on 8r. Mountain labeo 1·00 75

647 St. Patrick's College

2000. 150th Anniv of St. Patrick's College, Jaffna.
1497 **647** 3r.50 multicoloured . . . 50 20

648 Surveyors at Work

2000. Bicentenary of Survey Department, Sri Lanka.
1498 **648** 3r.50 multicoloured . . . 20 15

649 Central Bank of Sri Lanka

2000. 50th Anniv of Central Bank of Sri Lanka.
1499 **649** 3r.50 multicoloured . . . 20 15

650 Dr. Maria Montessori

2000. 130th Birth Anniv of Dr. Maria Montessori (educator).
1500 **650** 3r.50 multicoloured . . . 20 15

651 "2" with Olympic Rings and Maps

2000. Olympic Games, Sydney. Multicoloured.
1501 10r. Type **651** 30 40
1502 10r. Running 30 40
1503 10r. Olympic flame 30 40
1504 10r. Hurdling 30 40
MS1505 172 × 96 mm. Nos. 1501/4 1·10 1·40

652 Association Flag and Conference Hall

2000. 50th Anniv of All Ceylon Young Men's Muslim Association Conference.
1506 **652** 3r.50 multicoloured . . . 20 15

653 Beach, Hotel and Bay-headed Bee Eaters

2000. 25th Anniv of Modern Hotel Industry.
1507 **653** 10r. multicoloured . . . 70 50

654 Airliner, Ship and Globe

2000. 50th Anniv of Dept of Immigration and Emigration.
1508 **654** 3r.50 multicoloured . . . 30 15

655 Saumiyamoorthy Thondaman

656 Baddegama Siri Piyaratana Nayake Thero (Buddhist educator)

2000. Saumiyamoorthy Thondaman (politician) Commemoration.
1509 **655** 3r.50 multicoloured . . . 20 15

2000. Distinguished Personalities. Multicoloured.
1510 3r.50 Type **656** 20 20
1511 3r.50 Aluthgamage Simon de Silva (novelist) 20 20
1512 3r.50 Desigar Ramanujam (trade unionist) 20 20

657 Journey to Bethlehem

2000. Christmas. Multicoloured.
1513 2r. Type **657** 15 10
1514 17r. The Nativity . . . . . 85 1·00
MS1515 150 × 91 mm. Nos. 1513/14 1·00 1·25

658 Lalith Athulathmudali

2000. Lalith Athulathmudali (politician) Commem.
1516 **658** 3r.50 multicoloured . . . 15 10

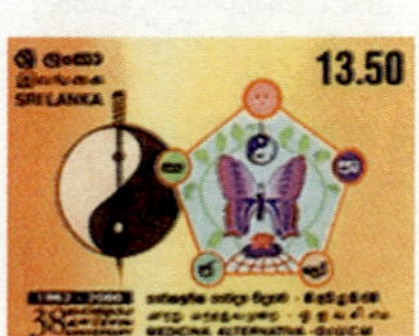

659 Five Elements and Butterfly

2000. 38th Anniv of Medicina Alternativa (alternative medicine society).
1517 **659** 13r.50 multicoloured . . 50 55

660 Chapel of Hope of the World

2000. Centenary of Ladies' College, Colombo.
1518 **660** 3r.50 multicoloured . . . 15 10

661 Patrol Boat

2000. 50th Anniv of Sri Lanka Navy.
1519 **661** 3r.50 multicoloured . . . 40 15

662 Peliyagoda Vidyalankara Pirivena Building

2000. 125th Anniv of Peliyagoda Vidyalankara Pirivena (Buddhist university).
1520 **662** 3r.50 multicoloured . . . 15 10

663 Bishop's College

2001. 125th Anniv of Bishop's College, Colombo.
1521 **663** 3r.50 multicoloured . . . 15 10

664 St. Thomas' College

2001. 150th Anniv of St. Thomas' College, Mount Lavinia.
1522 **664** 3r.50 multicoloured . . . 15 10

665 Woman with Basket of Vegetables and Logo

2001. 70th Anniv of Lanka Mahili Samiti (rural women's society).
1523 **665** 3r.50 multicoloured . . . 15 10

666 Air Force Crest and Aircraft

2001. 50th Anniv of Sri Lanka Air Force.
1524 **666** 3r.50 multicoloured . . . 40 20

667 St. Lawrence's School

2001. Centenary (2000) of St. Lawrence's School, Wellawatta.
1525 **667** 3r.50 multicoloured . . . 15 10

668 Bernard Soysa

669 Nagadeepa Stupa, Jaffna

2001. Bernard Soysa (politician) Commemoration.
1526 **668** 3r.50 multicoloured . . . 15 10

2001. Vesak Festival. Buddhist shrines. Mult.
1527 2r. Type **669** 10 10
1528 3r.50 Muthiyangana Chaithya, Badulla 10 10
1529 13r.50 Kirivehera Stupa, Kataragama 40 50
1530 17r. Temple of the Tooth, Kandy 55 70
MS1531 179 × 99 mm. Nos. 1527/30 1·00 1·25

670 "Hansa Jataka" (George Keyt) ($\frac{1}{2}$-size illustration)

2001. Birth Centenary of George Keyt (painter).
1532 **670** 13r.50 multicoloured . . 50 60

671 Gold Kahavanu Coin (9th century)

2001. Sri Lanka Coins. Multicoloured.
1533 3r.50 Type **671** 15 10
1534 13r.50 Silver coin of Vijayabahu I (11th-12th century) 40 40
1535 17r. Copper Sethu coin from Jaffna (13th-14th century) 55 65
1536 20r. Silver commemorative five rupee coin (1957) . . 65 75
MS1537 155 × 95 mm. Nos. 1533/6 1·50 2·00

672 Colombo Plan Emblem

674 Lance-Corporal Gamini Kularatne and Attack on Tank

673 Flags of Sri Lanka and U.S.A.

2001. 50th Anniv of Colombo Plan.
1538 **672** 10r. multicoloured . . . 30 40

2001. 150th Anniv of Bi-lateral Relations with U.S.A.
1539 **673** 10r. multicoloured . . . 30 40

2001. 10th Death Anniv of Gamini Kularatne (war hero).
1540 **674** 3r.50 multicoloured . . . 15 10

2001. No. 630 surch.
1541 **226** 5r. on 1r.15 multicoloured 10 10
1542 10r. on 1r.15 multicoloured 15 20

676 Prince and Princess of Wales Colleges, Moratuwa

2001. 125th Anniv of Prince and Princess of Wales Colleges, Moratuwa.
1543 **676** 3r.50 multicoloured . . . 15 10

677 Congress Building

2001. All-Ceylon Buddhist Congress National Awards Ceremony.
1544 **677** 3r.50 multicoloured . . . 40 20

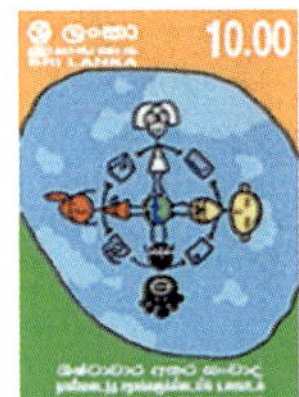
678 Children encircling Globe

679 Hand protecting Globe from Harmful Rays

2001. U.N. Year of Dialogue among Civilizations.
1545 **678** 10r. multicoloured . . . 30 40

2001. 13th Meeting of the Montreal Protocol Group (protection of Ozone Layer), Colombo.
1546 **679** 13r.50 multicoloured . . 40 50

680 Ramakrishna Mission Students' Home, Batticaloa

2001. 75th Anniv of Ramakrishna Mission Students' Home, Batticaloa.
1547 **680** 3r.50 multicoloured . . . 15 10

681 Daul Drummer

2001. Drummers.
1548 **680** 1r. red 10 10
1549 – 2r. green 10 10
1550 – 3r. brown 10 10
1551 – 3r.50 blue 10 10
1552 – 4r. pink 10 10
1553 – 5r. orange 10 10
1554 – 10r. violet 15 20
1555 – 13r.50 violet 15 20
1556 – 17r. blue 20 25
1557 – 20r. orange 25 30

DESIGNS: (18 × 23 mm.)–1r. to 3r.50, Type **680**. (23 × 28 mm.)–4r. to 10r. Kandyan drummer; 13r.50 to 20r. Low Country drummer.

682 Bandaranaike Memorial International Conference Hall, Colombo

2001. 25th Anniv of S.W.R.D. Bandaranaike National Memorial Foundation.
1558 **682** 3r.50 multicoloured . . . 15 10

683 Jesus with Children

2001. Christmas. Multicoloured.
1559 3r.50 Type **683** 10 10
1560 17r. Angel Gabriel appearing to Mary . . . 20 25
MS1561 150 × 120 mm. Nos. 1559/60 30 35

684 Conical Wart Pygmy Tree-frog

2001. 4th World Congress of Herpetology. Frogs. Multicoloured.
1562 3r.50 Type **684** 10 10
1563 13r.50 Sharp-snout saddle tree-frog 15 20
1564 17r. Round-snout pygmy tree-frog 20 25
1565 20r. Sri Lanka wood frog 25 30
MS1566 180 × 120 mm. Nos. 1562/5 70 80

685 St. Bridget's Convent

2002. Centenary of St. Bridget's Convent, Colombo.
1567 **685** 3r.50 multicoloured . . . 10 10

686 Front Page from First Edition of Ceylon Government Gazette, 1802

2002. Bicentenary of Ceylon Government Gazette.
1568 **686** 3r.50 multicoloured . . . 10 10

687 Prime Minister D. Senanayake

2002. 50th Death Anniv of D. Senanayake (first Sri Lankan Prime Minister).
1569 **687** 3r.50 multicoloured . . . 10 10

688 Gamini Dissanayake and Victoria Dam

2002. 60th Birth Anniv of Gamini Dissanayake (former government minister)
1570 **688** 3r.50 multicoloured . . . 10 10

POSTAL FISCALS

1952. As T **57** but inscr " REVENUE" at sides.
F1 10r. green and orange . . . . 60·00 28·00

F 1 Republic Crest

1979. As Type F **1** but with additional Sinhala and Tamil inscriptions on either side of crest.
F2 20r. green . . . . 5·00 2·75
F3 50r. violet . . . . 13·00 7·00
F4 100r. red . . . . 23·00 22·00

1984.
F8 F **1** 100r. purple . . . . 2·00 3·00

1998.
F 9 F **1** 50r. orange 65 70
F10 100r. brown . . . . . . 1·25 1·40

STELLALAND Pt. 1

A temporary Boer republic annexed by the British in 1885 and later incorporated in Br. Bechuanaland.

12 pence = 1 shilling;
20 shillings = 1 pound.

1 Arms of the Republic

1884.
1 **1** 1d. red £180 £325
2 3d. orange . . . . 21·00 £325
3 4d. blue . . . . 21·00 £350
4 6d. mauve . . . . 21·00 £350
5 1s. green . . . . 42·00 £600

1885. Surch **Twee**.
6 **1** 2d. on 4d. blue £3500

STRAITS SETTLEMENTS Pt. 1

A British Crown colony which included portions of the mainland of the Malay Peninsula and islands off its coasts, and the island of Labuan off the N. coast of Borneo.

100 cents = 1 dollar (Straits).

1867. Stamps of India surch with crown and value.
1 **11** $1\frac{1}{2}$c. on $\frac{1}{2}$a. blue . . . . . . 85·00 £200
2 2c. on 1a. brown . . . . . . £110 80·00
3 3c. on 1a. brown . . . . . . £120 85·00
4 4c. on 1a. brown £225 £250
5 6c. on 2a. orange £550 £225
6 8c. on 2a. orange . . . . . £170 42·00
7 12c. on 4a. green £900 £300
8 24c. on 8a. red . . . . £375 80·00
9 32c. on 2a. orange . . . . . £325 90·00

1869. No. 1 with "THREE HALF" deleted and "2" written above in manuscript.
10 **11** 2 on $1\frac{1}{2}$c. on $\frac{1}{2}$c. blue . . . £8500 £3750

5

8

9

1867.
11 **5** 2c. brown . . . . 25·00 4·00
98 4c. red . . . . 4·00 1·25
66a 6c. lilac . . . . 2·00 3·25
52 8c. orange . . . . 3·00 1·00
15 12c. blue . . . . 95·00 6·50
68a 24c. green . . . . 4·25 3·75
69 **8** 30c. red . . . . 8·00 8·00
70 **9** 32c. red . . . . 8·50 9·00
71 96c. grey . . . . 75·00 45·00

1879. Surch in words.
20 **5** 5c. on 8c. orange . . . . . 90·00 £140
21 **9** 7c. on 32c. red . . . . 95·00 £130

1880. Surch in figures and words.
47 **5** 5c. on 4c. red £225 £250
42 5c. on 8c. orange £100 £120
44 10c. on 6c. lilac . . . . . 55·00 6·00
45a 10c. on 12c. blue . . . . . 45·00 9·00
23 **8** 10c. on 30c. red . . . . . . £275 65·00

1880. Surch in figures only.
33 **8** "10" on 30c. red . . . . . . £150 50·00

18

19

1882.
63a **5** 2c. pink . . . . 6·00 85
64 4c. brown . . . . 22·00 1·25
65 **18** 5c. blue . . . . 11·00 1·00
99 5c. brown . . . . 3·75 1·00
100 5c. mauve . . . . 2·25 2·00
101 **5** 8c. blue . . . . 4·50 50
53 **19** 10c. grey . . . . 4·50 1·25
102 **5** 12c. purple . . . . 10·00 8·50

1883. Surch in words in one line horiz (No. 109) or vert.
57 **5** 2c. on 8c. orange . . . . . £100 65·00
59 **9** 2c. on 32c. orange £550 £160
109 **18** 4c. on 5c. red 75 30

1883. Surch with figures over words in two lines.
61 **5** 2c. on 4c. red . . . . . . 75·00 85·00
62 2c. on 12c. blue £225 £120
82 **18** 3c. on 5c. blue £110 £225
84 3c. on 5c. purple £180 £190
106 4c. on 5c. brown . . . . 2·75 4·75
73 4c. on 5c. blue (A)* . . . £100 90·00
107 4c. on 5c. blue (B)* . . . 3·25 13·00
108b **5** 4c. on 8c. blue . . . . . 80 1·00
74 8c. on 12c. blue £325 £120
75 8c. on 12c. purple £275 £120

*(A) "Cents" in italics. (B) "cents" (with small "c") in roman type.

1884. Surch **TWO CENTS** vert.
76 **18** 2c. on 5c. blue £110 £120

1884. No. 75 additionally surch with large figure **8**.
80 **5** 8 on 8c. on 12c. purple £225 £250

1885. Surch with words in one line and thick bar.
93 **5** 1c. on 8c. green 1·00 1·50
83a **9** 3c. on 32c. purple 1·25 1·00
94 3c. on 32c. red 2·25 70

1887. Surch **2 Cents** in one line.
85 **18** 2c. on 5c. blue 22·00 60·00

1891. Surch **10 CENTS** in one line and thin bar.
86 **5** 10c. on 24c. green 3·00 1·25

1891. Surch with words in two lines and thin bar.
88 **5** 1c. on 2c. red 2·00 3·75
89 1c. on 4c. brown 5·00 5·50
90 1c. on 6c. lilac 1·40 4·75
91 1c. on 8c. orange 1·00 1·25
92 1c. on 12c. purple 5·00 9·00
87 **9** 30c. on 32c. orange 7·00 3·50

33 37

1892.
95 **33** 1c. green 3·00 70
96 3c. red 11·00 40
97b 3c. brown 4·25 60
103c 25c. purple and green 22·00 6·00
104 50c. olive and red 20·00 2·50
105 $5 orange and red £300 £250

1902.
110 **37** 1c. green 2·50 3·00
111 3c. purple and orange 4·50 20
112 4c. purple on red 4·75 30
113 5c. purple 5·50 85
157 5c. orange 2·75 2·00
114 8c. purple on blue 3·50 20
132 10c. purple & black on yellow 7·00 80
159 10c. purple on yellow 6·50 1·00
116 25c. purple and green 11·00 6·00
161 25c. purple 13·00 7·00
117 30c. grey and red 18·00 8·00
162 30c. purple and yellow 38·00 4·00
118 50c. green and red 20·00 20·00
164 50c. black on green 5·00 4·50
136a $1 green and black 45·00 18·00
165 $1 black and red on blue 14·00 5·00
120 $2 purple and black 65·00 70·00
166 $2 green and red on yellow 24·00 24·00
138a $5 green and orange £180 £140
167 $5 green and red on green £110 75·00
139 $25 green and black £1400 £1400

39 42

46 47

1903.
127 **39** 1c. green 2·75 10
128 3c. purple 2·25 30
153 3c. red 2·00 10
125 4c. purple on red 4·25 30
154 4c. red 5·50 2·50
155 4c. purple 5·50 10
131a **42** 8c. purple on blue 21·00 2·75
158 8c. blue 3·50 50
160 **46** 21c. purple 6·50 35·00
163 45c. black on green 2·50 4·00
168 **47** $25 purple and blue £1300 £1000

1907. Stamps of Labuan (Crown type) optd **Straits Settlements**. (10c.) or **STRAITS SETTLEMENTS** (others) or surch in words also.
141 **18** 1c. black and purple 60·00 £170
142a 2c. black and green £170 £300
143 3c. black and brown 20·00 85·00
144 4c. on 12c. black & yellow 2·25 6·00
145 4c. on 16c. green & brown 4·25 8·00
146 4c. on 18c. black & brown 2·75 6·50
147 8c. black and orange 2·75 8·00
148 10c. brown and black 7·00 8·00
149 25c. green and blue 14·00 38·00
150 50c. purple and lilac 15·00 70·00
151 $1 red and orange 45·00 £110

48 54

52 53

1912.
193 **48** 1c. green 6·00 1·25
196a 3c. red 2·25 10
197 4c. purple 1·50 60
225 **54** 5c. orange 1·50 15
227 **52** 6c. purple 2·00 15
201 8c. blue 1·25 80
202 **54** 10c. purple on yellow 1·50 1·00
204 **53** 21c. purple 4·75 9·50
234b **54** 25c. purple and mauve 5·00 1·75
235a 30c. purple and orange 2·00 1·25
208b **53** 45c. black on green 3·25 13·00
238 **54** 50c. black on green 1·75 40
239 $1 black and red on blue 6·00 65
240 $2 green and red on yellow 10·00 8·00
240a $5 green and red on green 85·00 32·00
240b – $25 purple and blue on blue £650 £120

No. 240b is as Type **47** but with head of King George V.

1917. Surch **RED CROSS 2c.**
216 **48** 2c. on 3c. red 2·25 25·00
217 2c. on 4c. purple 3·00 25·00

1919.
218 **48** 1c. black 50 10
219 **52** 2c. green 50 10
220 2c. brown 7·00 2·50
221 **48** 3c. green 1·50 80
198 4c. red 1·75 15
223 4c. violet 60 10
224 4c. orange 1·00 10
226 **54** 5c. brown 2·75 10
227 **52** 6c. red 2·00 15
230 **54** 10c. blue 1·75 2·50
232 **52** 12c. blue 1·00 20
236a **53** 35c. purple and orange 3·50 5·50
237 35c. red and purple 10·00 7·00

1922. Optd **MALAYA–BORNEO EXHIBITION**.
250 **48** 1c. black 2·75 12·00
251 **52** 2c. green 2·25 14·00
252 **48** 4c. red 3·00 27·00
243 **54** 5c. orange 5·00 19·00
244 **52** 8c. blue 1·75 7·50
254 **54** 10c. blue 2·25 25·00
245 25c. purple and mauve 3·25 30·00
246 **53** 45c. black on green 3·00 26·00
255 **54** $1 black and red on blue 19·00 £120
248 $2 green and red on yellow 26·00 £110
249 $5 green and red on green £225 £400

1935. Silver Jubilee. As T **32a** of St. Helena.
256 5c. blue and grey 3·00 30
257 8c. green and blue 3·00 3·25
258 12c. brown and blue 3·00 3·75
259 25c. grey and purple 3·25 5·00

57 58

1936.
260 **57** 1c. black 1·00 20
261 2c. green 1·00 70
262 4c. orange 2·00 70
263 5c. brown 1·00 30
264 6c. red 1·25 1·10
265 8c. grey 1·50 70
266 10c. purple 1·75 60
267 12c. blue 2·00 2·50
268 25c. purple and red 1·25 50
269 30c. purple and orange 1·25 3·25
270 40c. red and purple 1·25 2·50
271 50c. black and green 4·50 1·25
272 $1 black and red on blue 19·00 1·75
273 $2 green and red 40·00 10·00
274 $5 green and red on green 85·00 10·00

1937. Coronation. As T **32b** of St. Helena.
275 4c. orange 30 10
276 8c. grey 70 10
277 12c. blue 1·25 60

1937.
278 **58** 1c. black 5·50 10
279 2c. green 18·00 20
294 2c. orange 2·00 10·00
295 3c. green 4·25 4·00
280 4c. orange 16·00 20
281 5c. brown 20·00 30
282 6c. red 11·00 50
283 8c. grey 38·00 10
284 10c. purple 8·00 10
285 12c. blue 8·00 50
298 15c. blue 6·00 10·00
286 25c. purple and red 42·00 1·10
287 30c. purple and orange 23·00 2·00
288 40c. red and purple 11·00 2·25
289 50c. black on green 11·00 10
290 $1 black and red on blue 15·00 20
291 $2 green and red 32·00 5·50
292 $5 green and red on green 25·00 3·50

For Japanese issues see **JAPANESE OCCUPATION OF MALAYA** and for British military administration see **MALAYA**.

POSTAGE DUE STAMPS

D 1

1924.
D1 **D 1** 1c. violet 5·50 6·50
D2 2c. black 3·25 1·25
D3 4c. green 2·00 4·75
D4 8c. red 4·50 55
D5 10c. orange 6·00 85
D6 12c. blue 7·00 65

For later issues see **MALAYAN POSTAL UNION**.

SUDAN Pt. 1; Pt. 14

A territory in Africa, extending south from Egypt towards the Equator, jointly administered by Gt. Britain and Egypt until 1954 when the territory was granted a large measure of self-government. Became independent on 1 January 1956.

1897. 1000 milliemes = 100 piastres = £1 Sudanese.
1993. dinar.

1897. Stamps of Egypt optd **SOUDAN** in English and Arabic.
1 **18** 1m. brown 2·00 2·00
3 2m. green 1·25 1·75
4 3m. yellow 1·40 1·50
5 5m. red 2·00 70
6 **10** 1p. blue 7·00 2·00
7 – 2p. orange 48·00 16·00
8 – 5p. grey 45·00 17·00
9 **18** 10p. mauve 30·00 38·00

2 Arab Postman 6

1898.
18 **2** 1m. brown and red 1·25 65
19 2m. green and brown 1·75 10
20 3m. mauve and green 2·25 25
21 4m. blue and brown 1·50 2·50
22 4m. red and brown 1·50 75
23 5m. red and black 2·00 10
24 1p. blue and brown 2·25 30
25 2p. black and blue 24·00 1·75
44 2p. purple and orange 1·50 10
44b 3p. brown and blue 2·75 10
44c 4p. blue and black 3·50 10
45 5p. brown and green 1·25 10
45b 6p. blue and black 6·00 1·25
45c 8p. green and black 6·00 2·50
46 10p. black and mauve 3·50 10
46b 20p. blue 3·50 10

1903. Surch **5 Milliemes.**
29 **2** 5m. on 5p. brown and green 6·50 9·50

1921.
37 **6** 1m. black and orange 70 10
38 2m. yellow and brown 60 10
39 3m. mauve and green 70 10
40 4m. green and brown 60 10
41 5m. brown and black 60 10
42 10m. red and black 1·50 10
43 15m. blue and brown 1·50 10

For stamps as Type **2** and **6** with different Arabic inscriptions see issue of 1948.

1931. Air. Nos. 41/2 and 44 optd **AIR MAIL**.
47 **6** 5m. brown and black 35 70
48 10m. red and black 85 10·00
49 **2** 2p. purple and yellow 85 7·50

10 Statue of General Gordon

1931. Air.
49b **10** 3m. green and brown 2·50 6·50
50 5m. black and green 1·00 10
51 10m. black and red 1·00 20
52 15m. brown 40 10
53 2p. black and orange 30 10
53d 2½p. mauve and blue 3·00 10
54 3p. black and grey 60 15
55 3½p. black and violet 1·50 80
56 4½p. brown and grey 10·00 15·00
57 5p. black and blue 1·00 30
57c 7½p. green 4·00 10·00
57d 10p. brown and blue 9·00 1·75

1932. Air. Surch **2½ 2½ AIR MAIL** and value in Arabic figures.
58 **2** 2½p. on 2p. purple and orange 1·40 3·50

12 General Gordon (after C. Ouless) 13 Gordon Memorial College, Khartoum

1935. 50th Death Anniv of Gen. Gordon.
59 **12** 5m. green 35 10
60 10m. brown 85 25
61 13m. blue 85 9·50
62 15m. red 1·75 25
63 **13** 2p. blue 1·25 20
64 5p. orange 1·25 40
65 10p. purple 7·50 8·50
66 – 20p. black 22·00 50·00
67 – 50p. brown 80·00 £110

DESIGN—(44 × 20 mm): 20, 50p. Gordon Memorial Service, Khartoum.

1935. Air. Stamps of 1931 surch in English and Arabic.
74 **10** 5m. on 2½p. mauve and blue 3·50 10
68 15m. on 10m. black and red 40 10
69 2½p. on 3m. green & brown 85 5·50
70 2½p. on 5m. black and green 50 1·50
75 3p. on 3½p. black and violet 35·00 48·00
71 3p. on 4½p. brown and grey 1·75 16·00
76 3p. on 7½p. green 7·00 6·50
77 5p. on 10p. brown and blue 1·75 4·75
72 7½p. on 4½p. brown and grey 6·50 48·00
73 10p. on 4½p. brown and grey 6·50 48·00

1940. No. 42 surch **5 Mills.** and in Arabic.
78 **6** 5m. on 10m. red and black 60 30

1940. Nos. 41 surch **4½ PIASTRES** and No. 45c surch **4½ Piastres** in English and Arabic.
79 **6** 4½p. on 5m. brown and black 48·00 6·00
80 **2** 4½p. on 8p. green and black 40·00 9·00

20 Tuti Island, R. Nile near Khartoum

1941.
81 **20** 1m. black and orange 1·50 4·00
82 2m. orange and brown 1·50 4·00
83 3m. mauve and green 1·50 20
84 4m. green and brown 80 60
85 5m. brown and black 30 10
86 10m. red and black 8·00 2·00
87 15m. blue and brown 1·00 10
88 2p. purple and yellow 5·50 60
89 3p. brown and blue 1·00 10
90 4p. blue and black 1·25 10
91 5p. brown and green 5·00 9·00
92 6p. blue and black 18·00 40
93 8p. green and black 14·00 45
94 10p. black and violet 55·00 75
95 20p. blue 50·00 32·00

The piastre values are larger, 30 × 25 mm.

22 Arab Postman 23 Arab Postman

1948.
96 **22** 1m. black and orange 35 3·50
97 2m. orange and brown 80 4·50
98 3m. mauve and green 30 4·00
99 4m. green and brown 50 30
100 5m. brown and black 5·50 2·00
101 10m. red and black 5·50 10
102 15m. blue and brown 5·00 10
103 **23** 2p. purple and yellow 7·50 2·50
104 3p. brown and blue 6·50 30
105 4p. blue and black 4·00 1·75
106 5p. orange and green 4·00 2·50
107 6p. blue and black 4·50 3·00
108 8p. green and black 4·50 3·00
109 10p. black and mauve 11·00 4·00
110 20p. blue 4·50 30
111 50p. red and blue 6·50 2·50

In this issue the Arabic inscriptions below the camel differ from those in Types **2** and **6**.

24 Arab Postman

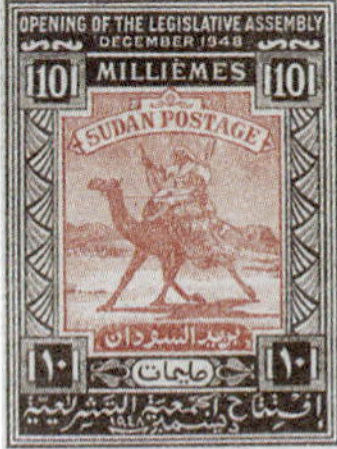
25 Arab Postman

1948. Golden Jubilee of "Camel Postman" design.

112	24	2p. black and blue	20	10

1948. Opening of Legislative Assembly.

113	25	10m. red and black	50	10
114		5p. orange and green . . .	1·00	1·50

26 Blue Nile Bridge, Khartoum

1950. Air.

115	26	2p. black and green . . .	4·50	1·50
116	–	2½p. blue and orange . . .	75	1·25
117	–	3p. purple and blue	3·00	1·25
118	–	3½p. sepia and brown . . .	2·00	3·00
119	–	4p. brown and blue	1·25	2·75
120	–	4½p. black and blue . . .	2·50	3·75
121	–	6p. black and red	2·00	3·25
122	–	20p. black and purple . . .	2·25	5·50

DESIGNS: 2½p. Kassala Jebel; 3p. Sagia (water wheel); 3½p. Port Sudan; 4p. Gordon Memorial College; 4½p. "Gordon Pasha" (Nile mail boat); 6p. Suakin; 20p. G.P.O. Khartoum.

34 Ibex

35 Cotton Picking

1951.

123	34	1m. black and orange . . .	1·50	1·50
124	–	2m. black and blue	1·75	1·00
125	–	3m. black and green . . .	6·50	3·50
126	–	4m. black and green . . .	1·50	3·50
127	–	5m. black and purple . . .	2·25	10
128	–	10m. black and blue . . .	30	10
129	–	15m. black and brown . . .	3·50	10
130	35	2p. blue	30	10
131	–	3p. brown and blue	6·50	10
132	–	3½p. green and brown . . .	2·00	10
133	–	4p. blue and black	1·25	10
134	–	5p. brown and green . . .	50	10
135	–	6p. blue and black	8·00	2·50
136	–	8p. blue and brown	13·00	3·00
137	–	10p. black and green . . .	1·50	10
138	–	20p. turquoise and black	5·00	2·00
139	–	50p. red and black	13·00	2·00

DESIGNS—VERT (As Type 34): 2m. Whale-headed stork ("Shoebill");, 3m. Giraffe; 4m. Baggara girl; 5m. Shilluk warrior; 10m. Hadendowa; 15m. Policeman. (As Type 35): 50p. Camel postman. HORIZ (As Type 35): 3p. Ambatch reed canoe; 3½p. Nuba wrestlers; 4p. Weaving; 5p. Saluka farming; 6p. Gum tapping; 8p. Darfur chief; 10p. Stack Laboratory; 20p. Nile lechwe (antelope).

51 Camel Postman

52 "Independent Sudan"

1954. Self-Government.

140	51	15m. brown and green . .	50	1·25
141		3p. blue and indigo	50	1·90
142		5p. black and purple . . .	50	1·50

Stamps as Type 51 but dated "1953" were released in error at the Sudan Agency in London. They had no postal validity.

1956. Independence Commemoration.

143	52	15m. orange and purple . .	15	10
144		3p. orange and blue . . .	35	15
145		5p. orange and green . . .	50	35

53 Globe on Rhinoceros (Badge of Sudan)

54 Sudanese Soldier and Farmer

1958. Arab Postal Congress, Khartoum.

146	53	15m. orange and purple . .	20	10
147		3p. orange and blue . . .	35	15
148		5p. orange and green . . .	80	35

1959. 1st Anniv of Army Revolution.

149	54	15m. yellow, blue & brown	15	10
150		3p. multicoloured	50	20
151		55m. multicoloured	65	40

1960. Inauguration of Arab League Centre, Cairo. As T **154a** of Syria.

152		15m. black and green	15	10

55 Refugees

56 Football

1960. World Refugee Year.

153	55	15m. blue, black and brown	15	15
154		55m. red, black and sepia	55	45

1960. Olympic Games, Rome.

155	56	15m. multicoloured	20	10
156		3p. multicoloured	45	25
157		55m. multicoloured	65	35

57 Forest

58 King Ta'rhaqa

1960. 5th World Forestry Congress, Seattle.

158	57	15m. green, brown and red	15	10
159		3p. green, brown and deep green	35	20
160		55m. multicoloured	60	35

1961. Sudanese Nubian Monuments Preservation Campaign.

161	58	15m. brown and green . .	20	10
162		3p. violet and orange . . .	35	20
163		55m. brown and blue . . .	60	35

59 Girl with Book

60 "The World United against Malaria"

1961. "50 Years of Girls' Education in the Sudan".

164	59	15m. mauve, purple & blue	15	10
165		3p. blue, orange and black	40	20
166		55m. brown, green & black	55	40

1962. Malaria Eradication.

167	60	15m. violet, blue and black	15	10
168		55m. green, emerald & blk	50	35

60a League Centre, Cairo and Emblem

1962. Arab League Week.

169	60a	15m. orange	15	10
170		55m. turquoise	45	35

62 Republican Palace

63 Nile Felucca

64 Camel Postman

65 Campaign Emblem and "Millet" Cobs

1962.

185	62	5m. blue	10	10
186	–	10m. purple and blue . .	10	10
187	–	15m. purple, orange & bistre	10	10
188	62	2p. purple	10	10
189	–	3p. brown and green . . .	20	10
190	–	35m. brown, dp brown & green	55	10
191	–	4p. mauve, red and blue	55	10
192	–	55m. black and green . .	55	20
193	–	6p. brown and blue . . .	65	20
194	–	8p. green	65	20
195	63	10p. brown, bistre and blue	80	35
196	–	20p. green and bronze . .	1·75	55
194a	–	25p. brown and green . .	10	10
197	–	50p. green, blue and black	4·75	1·25
469	64	£S1 brown and green . .	9·25	4·25
198	–	£S5 green and brown . .	11·00	1·75
199	63	£S10 orange and green . .	22·00	3·75

DESIGNS: As Type 62—HORIZ: 15m. "Tabbaque" (food cover); 55m., 6, 25p. Cattle; 8p. Date palms. VERT: 10m., 3p. Cotton picking; 35m., 4p. Wild game. As Type 63—HORIZ: 20p., £S5 Bohein Temple; 50p. Sennar Dam.

1963. Freedom from Hunger.

226	65	15m. green and brown . .	15	15
227		55m. violet, lilac and blue	55	35

66 Centenary Emblem and Medallions

67 "Knight"

1963. Centenary of Red Cross.

228	66	15m. multicoloured	35	15
229		55m. multicoloured	65	35

1964. Nubian Monuments Preservation. Frescoes from Faras Church, Nubia. Multicoloured.

230	15m. Type **67**	20	15
231	30m. "Saint" (horiz)	35	20
232	55m. "Angel"	85	55

68 Sudan Map

69 Chainbreakers and Mrs. E. Roosevelt

1964. New York World's Fair. Multicoloured.

233	15m. Khashm el Girba Dam	10	10
234	3p. Sudan Pavilion	20	15
235	55m. Type **68**	50	30

Nos. 233/4 are horiz.

1964. 80th Birth Anniv of Mrs. Eleanor Roosevelt (Human Rights pioneer).

236	69	15m. blue and black . . .	10	10
237		3p. violet and black . . .	30	15
238		55m. brown and black . .	45	30

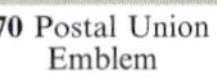
70 Postal Union Emblem

71 I.T.U. Symbol and Emblems

1964. 10th Anniv of Arab Postal Unions' Permanent Bureau.

239	70	15m. black, gold and red	10	10
240		3p. black, gold and green	30	15
241		55m. black, gold and violet	45	30

1965. Centenary of I.T.U.

242	71	15m. brown and gold . . .	10	10
243		3p. black and gold	30	15
244		55m. green and gold . . .	45	30

72 Gurashi (martyr) and Demonstrators

1965. 1st Anniv of 21 October Revolution.

245	72	15m. black and brown . .	10	10
246		3p. black and red	20	15
247		55m. black and grey . . .	45	30

73 I.C.Y. Emblem

74 El Siddig El Mahdi

1965. International Co-operation Year.

248	73	15m. lilac and black . . .	10	10
249		3p. green and black . . .	20	15
250		55m. red and black	45	30

1966. 5th Death Anniv of Imam El Siddig El Mahdi.

251	74	15m. violet and blue . . .	35	15
252		3p. brown and orange . .	50	35
253		55m. brown and grey . . .	1·10	60

75 M. Zaroug (politician)

1966. Mubarak Zaroug Commemoration.

254	75	15m. olive and pink . . .	35	15
255		3p. green and light green	50	35
256		55m. brown and chestnut	1·10	55

76 W.H.O. Building

77 Crests of Upper Nile, Blue Nile and Kassala Provinces

1966. Inaug of W.H.O. Headquarters, Geneva.

257	76	15m. blue	10	10
258		3p. purple	20	15
259		55m. brown	45	30

1967. "The Month of the South".

260	77	15m. multicoloured	10	10
261	–	3p. multicoloured	20	10
262	–	55m. multicoloured	80	40

DESIGNS (Crests of): 3p. Equatoria, Kordofan and Khartoum Provinces; 55m. Bahr El Gazal, Darfur and Northern Provinces.

78 Giraffe and Tourist Emblem

79 Handclasp Emblem

1967. International Tourist Year.
263 **78** 15m. multicoloured 20 10
264 3p. multicoloured 45 25
265 55m. multicoloured 70 25

1967. Arab Summit Conference, Khartoum.
266 **79** 15m. multicoloured 10 10
267 3p. green and orange . . . 20 10
268 55m. violet and yellow . . 45 20

80 P.L.O. Shoulder Flash

1967. Palestine Liberation Organization.
269 **80** 15m. multicoloured 10 10
270 3p. multicoloured 20 10
271 55m. multicoloured 45 20

81 Mohamed Nur El Din

1968. Nur El Din (politician) Commemoration.
272 **81** 15m. green and blue . . . 35 15
273 3p. bistre and blue . . . 50 30
274 55m. ultramarine and blue 1·10 50

82 Abdullahi El Fadil El Mahdi

1968. Abdullahi El Fadil El Mahdi (Ansar leader) Commemoration.
275 **82** 15m. violet and blue . . . 35 15
276 3p. green and blue 50 30
277 55m. green and orange . . 1·10 50

83 Ahmed Yousif Hashim

1968. 10th Death Anniv of Ahmed Yousif Hashim (journalist).
278 **83** 15m. brown and green . . 35 10
279 3p. brown and blue 50 10
280 55m. violet and blue . . . 1·10 30

84 Mohamed Ahmed El Mardi

1968. Mohamed Ahmed El Mardi (politician) Commemoration.
281 **84** 15m. ultramarine and blue 35 15
282 3p. orange, blue and pink 50 35
283 55m. brown and blue . . . 1·10 55

85 Douglas DC-3 Airliner

1968. 20th Anniv of Sudan Airways. Mult.
284 15m. Type **85** 10 10
285 2p. De Havilland Dove . . . 20 10
286 3p. Fokker Friendship . . . 40 20
287 55m. Hawker Siddeley Comet 4C 65 45

87 Anniversary and Bank Emblems

1969. 5th Anniv of African Development Bank.
288 **87** 2p. black and gold 15 10
289 4p. red and gold 30 15
290 65m. green and gold . . . 45 20

88 I.L.O. Emblem

1969. 50th Anniv of Int Labour Organization.
291 **88** 2p. black, red and blue . . 15 10
292 4p. black, blue and yellow 30 15
293 65m. black, mauve & green 45 20

89 "Solidarity of the People"

1970. 1st Anniv of 25 May Revolution (1st issue).
294 **89** 2p. multicoloured . . . .
295 4p. multicoloured . . . .
296 65m. multicoloured . . .
Set of 3 . . . . 50·00

Nos. 294/6 were withdrawn on day of issue (25 May) as being unsatisfactory. They were later replaced by Nos. 297/9 and the 1st issue may be easily distinguished by the figures of value which appear on the extreme left of the design.

90 "Solidarity of the People"

1970. 1st Anniv of 25 May Revolution (2nd issue).
297 **90** 2p. brown, green and red 15 10
298 4p. blue, green and red . . 35 15
299 65m. green, blue and red 50 25

91 Map of Egypt, Libya and Sudan

92 I.E.Y. Emblem

1971. 1st Anniv of Tripoli Charter.
300 **91** 2p. green, black and red 20 10

1971. International Education Year.
301 **92** 2p. multicoloured 15 10
302 4p. multicoloured 30 10
303 65m. multicoloured 45 20

93 Laurel and Bayonets on Star

94 Emblems of Arab League and Sudan Republic

1971. 2nd Anniv of 25 May Revolution.
304 **93** 2p. black, green and yellow 15 10
305 4p. black, green and blue 35 15
306 10½p. black, green and grey 60 35

1972. 25th Anniv of Arab League.
307 **94** 2p. black, yellow and green 15 10
308 4p. multicoloured 35 15
309 10½p. multicoloured 70 35

95 U.N. Emblem and Text

96 Cogwheel Emblem

1972. 25th Anniv of United Nations.
310 **95** 2p. green, orange and red 15 10
311 4p. blue, orange and red 35 15
312 10½p. black, orange and red 70 40

1972. World Standards Day.
313 **96** 2p. multicoloured 15 10
314 4p. multicoloured 40 20
315 10½p. multicoloured . . . 85 55

97 Sudanese Arms and Pres. Nemery

1972. Presidential Elections.
316 **97** 2p. multicoloured 15 10
317 4p. multicoloured 35 15
318 10½p. multicoloured . . . 70 40

98 Arms and Emblem

1972. Socialist Union's Founding Congress.
319 **98** 2p. black, yellow and blue 10 10
320 4p. mauve, yellow and black 20 15
321 10½p. black, yellow & green 65 25

99 Airmail Envelope and A.P.U. Emblem

1972. 10th Anniv of African Postal Union (1971).
322 **99** 2p. multicoloured 10 10
323 4p. multicoloured 20 15
324 10½p. multicoloured . . . 80 30

100 Provincial Emblems

1973. National Unity.
325 **100** 2p. multicoloured 10 10
326 – 4p. brown and black . . . 20 10
327 – 10½p. green, orange & silver 80 35

DESIGNS—HORIZ: 4p. Revolutionary Council. VERT: 10½p. Entwined trees.

101 Emperor Haile Selassie of Ethiopia

1973. 80th Birthday of Emperor Haile Selassie.
328 **101** 2p. multicoloured 20 15
329 4p. multicoloured 50 20
330 10½p. multicoloured . . . 1·10 45

102 President Nasser

1973. 3rd Death Anniv of Pres. Nasser.
331 **102** 2p. black 10 10
332 4p. black and green . . . 20 10
333 10½p. black and violet . . 65 35

103 Ancient Gateway

1973. 10th Anniv of World Food Programme.
334 **103** 2p. multicoloured 10 10
335 4p. multicoloured 20 10
336 10½p. multicoloured . . . 80 45

104 Scout Emblem

1973. World Scout Conference, Nairobi and Addis Ababa.
337 **104** 2p. multicoloured 30 10
338 4p. multicoloured 45 20
339 10½p. multicoloured . . . 95 55

105 Interpol Emblem

1974. 50th Anniv of International Criminal Police Organization (Interpol).
340 **105** 2p. multicoloured 10 10
341 4p. multicoloured 30 15
342 10½p. multicoloured . . . 70 35

106 K.S.M. Building, Khartoum University

1974. 50th Anniv of Faculty of Medicine, Khartoum University.
343 **106** 2p. multicoloured 15 10
344 4p. green, brown and red 35 10
345 10½p. red, brown and green 70 45

107 African Postal Union Emblem

1974. Centenary of Universal Postal Union. Mult.
346 2p. Type **107** 10 10
347 4p. Arab Postal Union emblem 20 15
348 10½p. Universal Postal Union emblem 80 35

108 A. A. Latif and A. F. Elmaz (revolution leaders)

1975. 50th Anniv of 1924 Revolution.

349	**108**	2½p. green and blue	10	10
350		4p. red and blue	20	10
351		10½p. brown and blue	80	35

109 Bank and Commemorative Emblems

1975. 10th Anniv of African Development Bank.

352	**109**	2½p. multicoloured	10	10
353		4p. multicoloured	20	10
354		10½p. multicoloured	80	35

110 Earth Station and Camel Postman

1976. Inauguration of Satellite Earth Station.

355	**110**	2½p. multicoloured	15	10
356		4p. multicoloured	30	15
357		10½p. multicoloured	65	35

111 Woman, Flag and IWY Emblem

1976. International Women's Year.

358	**111**	2½p. multicoloured	10	10
359		4p. multicoloured	30	15
360		10½p. multicoloured	70	35

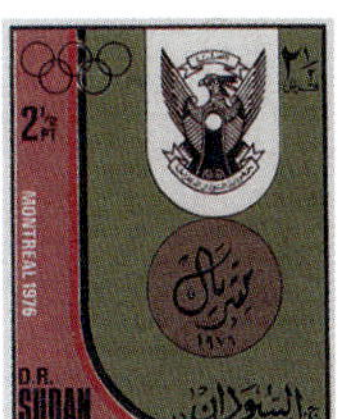

112 Arms of Sudan and "Gold Medal"

113 "Unity"

1976. Olympic Games, Montreal.

361	**112**	2½p. multicoloured	40	10
362		4p. multicoloured	45	20
363		10½p. multicoloured	1·10	55

1977. 5th Anniv of National Unity.

364	**113**	2½p. red, black and blue	10	10
365		4p. red, black and green	20	15
366		10½p. red, black and brown	65	30

114 Archbishop Capucci

1977. Archbishop Capucci's Imprisonment Commemoration.

367	**114**	2½p. black	45	10
368		4p. black and green	65	20
369		10½p. black and red	1·10	45

115 Fair Emblem and Flags

1978. International Fair, Khartoum.

370	**115**	3p. multicoloured	20	10
371		4p. multicoloured	35	15
372		10½p. multicoloured	55	25

117 Commemorative and A.P.U. Emblems

1978. Silver Jubilee of Arab Postal Union.

373	**117**	3p. black, silver and red	15	10
374		4p. black, silver and green	30	10
375		10½p. black, silver and blue	65	35

118 Jinnah and Sudanese Flag

1978. Birth Cent of Mohammed Ali Jinnah (first Governor-General of Pakistan).

376	**118**	3p. multicoloured	20	10
377		4p. multicoloured	35	15
378		10½p. multicoloured	55	25

119 Desert Scene

1978. U.N. Conference on Desertification.

379	**119**	3p. black, yellow and green	20	10
380		4p. black, pink and green	35	15
381		10½p. black, brown & green	85	45

120 Lion God Apedemek and O.A.U. Emblem

1978. 15th African Summit Conference, Khartoum.

382	**120**	3p. black, yellow & purple	15	10
383		4p. black, yellow and blue	30	15
384		10½p. black, yellow & green	55	30

121 Sudanese Flag

122 I.B.E. and U.N.E.S.C.O. Emblems

1979. 10th Anniv of May Revolution.

385	**121**	3½p. multicoloured	15	10
386		6p. multicoloured	35	15
387		13p. multicoloured	60	30

1980. 50th Anniv of International Bureau of Education (1979).

388	**122**	4½p. black and orange	20	15
389		8p. black and green	45	25
390		15½p. black and blue	90	40

123 I.Y.C. Emblem and Hands carrying Child

1980. International Year of the Child (1979).

391	**123**	4½p. multicoloured	20	15
392		8p. multicoloured	40	25
393		15½p. multicoloured	70	40

124 National Flag, Arms and Sudanese Warrior

1982. 25th Anniv of Independence.

396	**124**	60m. multicoloured	20	10
397		120m. multicoloured	45	20
398		250m. multicoloured	90	45

125 Hands reaching for F.A.O. Emblem on Map of Sudan

1983. World Food Day.

399	**125**	60m. blue, green and black	20	10
400	–	120m. green, black and red	45	20
401	–	250m. green, black and red	90	45

DESIGNS: 120m. F.A.O. emblem, crops and cattle; 250m. Emblem, crops and cattle on map of Sudan.

126 Commission Emblem

127 Warrior on Horseback

1984. 25th Anniv of Economic Commission for Africa.

402	**126**	10p. lilac and silver	20	15
403		25p. blue and silver	55	35
404		40p. green and silver	1·00	60

1984. Centenary of Shaykan Battle, Kordofan.

405	**127**	10p. multicoloured	20	15
406		25p. multicoloured	55	35
407		40p. multicoloured	90	50

128 Sudan Olympic Committee Emblem

129 Emblem and Flags

1984. 1st Olympic Week.

408	**128**	10p. multicoloured	20	15
409		25p. multicoloured	60	30
410		40p. multicoloured	1·10	55

1984. 2nd Anniv of Sudan–Egypt Co-operation Treaty.

411	**129**	10p. multicoloured	20	15
412		25p. multicoloured	55	35
413		40p. multicoloured	90	50

130 Institute Emblem

131 Map and Broken Chain

1985. 50th Anniv of Bakht Erruda Teacher Training Institute, Edduim Town.

414	**130**	10p. multicoloured	20	15
415		25p. multicoloured	55	35
416		40p. multicoloured	90	50

1986. 1st Anniv of 6 April Rising.

417	**131**	5p. black, green and brown	10	10
418		25p. black, green and blue	55	30
419		40p. black, green and brown	90	45

132 Fishermen hauling in Nets

1988. World Food Day (1986).

420	**132**	25p. black, silver and brown	40	15
421	–	30p. green and black	45	15
422	–	50p. multicoloured	55	35
423	–	75p. black, deep blue and blue	1·00	45
424	–	300p. blue, black and silver	3·50	1·40

DESIGNS—VERT: 30p. Two fishes. HORIZ: 50p. Plant and globe; 75p. Outline of fish and waves; 300p. Shoal of fish.

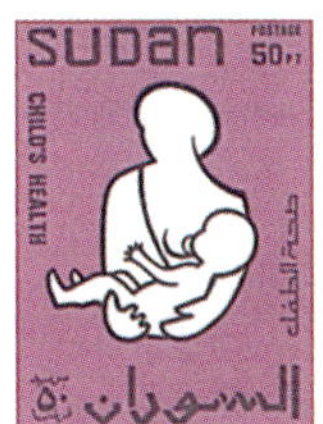

133 Mother breast-feeding Baby

134 Emblem

1988. Child Health Campaign.

426	**133**	50p. black and mauve	55	20
427	–	75p. multicoloured	85	35
428	–	100p. multicoloured	1·10	45
429	–	150p. multicoloured	1·60	65

DESIGNS—HORIZ: No. 427, Mother spoon-feeding child; 428, Child being given oral vaccination; 429, Children on scales.

1988. 30th Anniv of Sudan Red Crescent.

431	**134**	40p. black, yellow and red	40	30
432	–	100p. black, red and green	90	60
433	–	150p. black, red and blue	1·25	80

DESIGNS: 100p. Candle; 150p. Figure with crescent on head.

135 Anniversary Emblem

1988. 75th Anniv of Bank of Khartoum. Mult.

434		40p. Type **135**	40	20
435		100p. Bubbles and medal	90	45
436		150p. Inscription and emblem	1·25	65

136 Plough

1988. World Food Day. The Small Farmer. Mult.

437	40p. Type **136**	40	20
438	100p. Farmer ploughing	90	45
439	150p. Farmer drawing water from river	1·25	65

137 Emblem 138 Crowd of Youths

1989. "Freedom of Palestine".

440 **137**	100p. multicoloured	50	20
441	150p. multicoloured	80	35
442	200p. multicoloured	95	55

1989. Palestinian "Intifada" Movement.

443 **138**	100p. multicoloured	50	20
444	150p. multicoloured	80	35
445	200p. multicoloured	95	55

139 Emblem

1989. 25th Anniv of African Development Bank.

446 **139**	100p. green, black & silver	50	20
447	150p. blue, black and silver	80	35
448	200p. purple, black & sil	95	55

140 Map 142 Pied Hornbill ("Zande Hornbill")

141 Leopard

1990. 34th Anniv of Independence.

449 **140**	50p. blue and yellow	20	10
450	100p. brown and yellow	50	20
451	150p. mauve and yellow	80	35
452	200p. mauve and yellow	1·00	55

1990. Mammals. Multicoloured.

453	25p. Type **141**	15	10
454	50p. African elephant	35	20
455	75p. Giraffe (vert)	45	35
456	100p. White rhinoceros	60	45
457	125p. Addax (vert)	65	55

1990. Birds. Multicoloured.

458	25p. Type **142**	25	10
459	50p. Marabou stork	60	20
460	75p. Crested bustard ("Buff-crested Bustard")	85	35
461	100p. Saddle-bill stork ("Saddle-bill")	1·10	50
462	150p. Waldrapp ("Bald-headed Ibis")	1·50	60

143 Mardoum Dance

1990. Traditional Dances. Multicoloured.

463	25p. Type **143**	15	10
464	50p. Zandi dance (vert)	35	20
465	75p. Kambala dance (vert)	45	35
466	100p. Nubian dance (vert)	60	45
467	125p. Sword dance	65	55

1990. No. 195 surch with new value in Arabic.

468 **63**	£S1 on 10p. brown, bistre & blue	2·50	1·50

146 Flag

1991. 1st Anniv of "National Salvation Revolution".

470 **146**	150p. multicoloured	75	55
471	200p. multicoloured	1·00	75
472	250p. multicoloured	1·25	1·00
473	£S5 multicoloured	2·50	2·10
474	£S10 multicoloured	5·00	4·50

147 Whale-headed Stork ("Shoebill") 148 Camel Postman

1991. (a) As T **147**. Multicoloured.

475	25p. Type **147**	10	10
476	50p. Sunflower	10	10
477	75p. Collecting gum arabic	35	20
478	100p. Cotton	50	35
479	125p. South African crowned crane	60	40
480	150p. Kenana Sugar Co Ltd (29½ × 25 mm)	75	50
481	175p. Secretary bird (24 × 30½ mm)	85	60
482	£S2 Atbara Cement Factory (29½ × 25 mm)	95	70
483	250p. King Taharka (statue) (26 × 37 mm)	1·25	90
484	£S3 Republican Palace (26 × 37 mm)	1·50	1·10
485	£S4 Hug (scent container) (24 × 30½ mm)	1·90	1·40
486	£S5 Gabanah (coffee pot) (24 × 30½ mm)	2·40	2·00
	(b) As T **148**. Multicoloured.		
487	£S8 Lionfish (horiz)	3·75	3·00
488	£S10 Goat, ox and camel (horiz)	4·75	4·00
489	£S15 Nubian ibex	7·25	6·25
490	£S20 Type **148**	9·75	8·00

150 Campaign Emblem (151)

1991. Pan-African Campaign against Rinderpest.

507 **150**	£S1 black and green	50	35
508	£S2 violet and green	95	60
509	£S5 orange and green	2·40	1·40

1993. Various stamps handstamped as T **151**.

510 –	1d. on 100p. multicoloured (No. 478)	2·50	1·75
511 –	2d. on £S2 mult (No. 482)	5·00	3·25
512 **147**	2¼d. on 25p. multicoloured (No. 475)	6·25	3·75
513 –	3d. on £S3 mult (No. 484)	7·75	4·75
514 –	4d. on £S4 mult (No. 485)	10·00	6·50

152 Emblem 153 Arabic Script and Hearts

1993. 500th Anniv of Fung Sultanate and Abdalab Islamic Shaikhdom. Multicoloured.

515	£S4 Type **152**	60	40
516	£S5 Arabic script on bottle	75	50
517	750p. Arabic script in cartouche and helmet (horiz)	1·10	75

Nos. 515/17 were sold at 4, 5 and 7½ dinars respectively.

1993. International Human Rights Day.

518 **153**	£S4 multicoloured	60	40
519 –	£S5 multicoloured	75	50
520 –	750p. black, green and red	1·10	75

DESIGNS—HORIZ: £S5 Rainbow breaking through chains. VERT: 750p. Rose and Arabic script.

Nos. 518/20 were sold at 4, 5 and 7½ dinars respectively.

154 Feeding Young 155 Olympic Flag

1994. The Wild Ass. Multicoloured.

521	4d. Type **154**	15	10
522	8d. Adult	35	20
523	10d. Adult galloping	70	25
524	15d. Head of adult	1·10	60

1994. Cent of International Olympic Committee.

525 **155**	5d. multicoloured	20	10
526	7d. multicoloured	30	20
527	15d. multicoloured	85	35

156 Anniversary Emblem (157)

1994. 50th Anniv of I.C.A.O.

528 **156**	5d. purple, yellow & black	20	10
529	7d. brown, yellow & black	30	20
530	15d. blue, yellow and black	60	35

1995. Various stamps handstamped as T **157**.

531	2½d. on 25p. green and brown (No. 194a)	1·75	1·25
532	15d. on 150p. multicoloured (No. 480)	45	25
533	20d. on 75p. multicoloured (No. 477)	60	35

158 Goalkeeper 159 Map and Emblem

1995. World Cup Football Championship, U.S.A. (1994). Multicoloured.

534	4d. Type **158**	10	10
535	5d. Type **158**	15	10
536	7d. Player in green shirt	15	10
537	8d. As No. 536 but red shirt	20	10
538	10d. Player heading ball	25	15
539	15d. Brazilian player	40	25
540	20d. German player	50	30
541	25d. American player	60	35
542	35d. As No. 537	85	50

1995. 50th Anniv of Arab League.

544 **159**	15d. green and black	25	15
545	25d. blue and black	40	25
546	30d. violet and black	45	25

160 Emblem 162 Rahman

1996. Common Market for Eastern and Southern Africa.

547 **160**	15d. multicoloured	15	10
548	25d. multicoloured	25	15
549	30d. multicoloured	35	20

1997. 42nd Death Anniv of Abdel Rahman al Mahadi.

557 **162**	25d. black and violet	20	10
558	35d. black and red	25	15
559	50d. black and brown	40	25

163 Hands reaching to Dove 164 Stripes

1997. Peace.

560 **163**	5d. multicoloured	10	10

1997. 25th Anniv of Police Force.

561 **164**	25d. multicoloured	20	10
562	35d. multicoloured	25	15
563	50d. silver, green and black	40	25

165 Mosque (166)

1997. 5th Anniv of Reconstruction of Sheikh Quriballa's Mosque, Omdurman. Multicoloured.

564	25d. Type **165**	20	10
565	35d. Close-up of facade	25	15
566	50d. Distant view of facade (vert)	40	25

1997. Nos. 476, 483 and 487 surch as T **166**.

567	5d. on 50p. multicoloured	10	10
568	25d. on 250p. multicoloured	20	10
569	35d. on £S8 multicoloured	25	15

The size of surcharge differs for each value.

167 Emblem and Outline of Africa 168 Faras Church Fresco (detail)

1998. 18th Anniv of Pan-African Postal Union.

570 **167**	25d. multicoloured	15	10
571	35d. multicoloured	20	10
572	50d. multicoloured	30	20

1998. Archaeological Finds. Multicoloured.

573	50d. Type **168**	30	20
574	50d. Drinking cup	30	20
575	50d. Faras Church fresco (different)	30	20
576	60d. Decorated dish (2000 B.C.)	40	25
577	75d. Statue of King Natakamani (vert)	45	25
578	75d. Meroe decorated pot (4000 B.C.)	45	25
579	100d. Bowl (2000 B.C.)	60	35

169 Arab Postman Design 170 Soldier with Flag and Cannon

1998. Centenary of First Sudanese Stamp.

580 **169**	100d. multicoloured	60	35

1999. Centenary of Battle of Kerreri.

581 **170**	75d. multicoloured	35	25
582	100d. multicoloured	50	30
583	150d. multicoloured	75	45

171 Factory Ruins 172 Elderly Women and Children

1999. 1st Anniv of Bombing of Shifa Pharmaceutical Factory. Multicoloured.

584	75d. Type **171**	35	25
585	100d. Shifa emblem (22 × 27 mm)	50	30
586	150d. Effects of bombing	75	45

1999. International Year of the Elderly Person. Multicoloured.

587	75d. Type **172**	40	25
588	100d. Emblem (vert)	55	35
589	150d. Elderly man and children	80	50

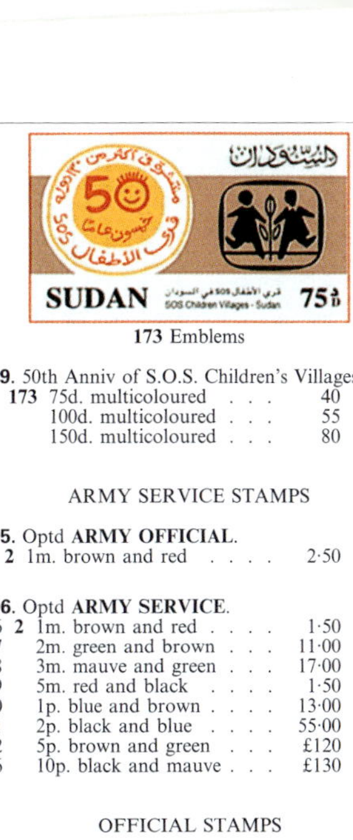

173 Emblems

1999. 50th Anniv of S.O.S. Children's Villages.
590 **173** 75d. multicoloured . . . 40 25
591 100d. multicoloured . . . 55 35
592 150d. multicoloured . . . 80 50

ARMY SERVICE STAMPS

1905. Optd **ARMY OFFICIAL**.
A1 **2** 1m. brown and red . . . . 2·50 2·00

1906. Optd **ARMY SERVICE**.
A 6 **2** 1m. brown and red . . . . 1·50 20
A 7 2m. green and brown . . . 11·00 1·00
A 8 3m. mauve and green . . . 17·00 40
A 9 5m. red and black . . . . 1·50 10
A10 1p. blue and brown . . . . 13·00 15
A11 2p. black and blue . . . . 55·00 13·00
A12 5p. brown and green . . . £120 65·00
A16 10p. black and mauve . . . £130 £350

OFFICIAL STAMPS

1902. Optd **O.S.G.S.**
O 5 **2** 1m. brown and red 50 10
O 6 3m. mauve and green . . . 2·50 15
O 7 5m. red and black . . . . 2·50 10
O 8 1p. blue and brown . . . . 2·50 10
O 9 2p. black and blue . . . . 22·00 20
O10 5p. brown and green . . . 2·00 30
O 4 10p. black and mauve . . . 13·00 24·00

1936. Optd **S.G.**
O32 **6** 1m. black and orange . . 2·50 9·50
O33 2m. yellow and brown . . 1·00 4·25
O34 3m. mauve and green . . 3·00 10
O35 4m. green and brown . . 3·50 2·75
O36 5m. brown and black . . 2·25 10
O37 10m. red and black . . 1·00 10
O38 15m. blue and brown . . 7·50 30
O39 2p. purple and orange . . 14·00 10
O39b 3p. brown and blue . . 6·00 2·75
O39c 4p. blue and black . . . 27·00 4·25
O40 5p. brown and green . . . 17·00 10
O40b 6p. blue and black . . . . 8·00 7·00
O40c **2** 8p. green and black . . . 5·50 28·00
O41 10p. black and mauve . . 30·00 10·00
O42 20p. blue . . . . 28·00 22·00

1948. Optd **S.G.**
O43 **22** 1m. black and orange . . 30 3·75
O44 2m. orange and brown . . 1·25 10
O45 3m. mauve and green . . 3·00 6·50
O46 4m. green and brown . . 3·00 4·25
O47 5m. brown and black . . 3·00 10
O48 10m. red and black . . . 3·00 1·50
O49 15m. blue and brown . . 3·00 10
O50 **23** 2p. purple and yellow . . 3·00 10
O51 3p. brown and blue . . . 3·00 10
O52 4p. blue and black . . . . 3·00 10
O53 5p. orange and green . . . 3·50 10
O54 6p. blue and black . . . . 3·00 10
O55 8p. green and black . . . 3·00 2·25
O56 10p. black and mauve . . . 4·50 20
O57 20p. blue . . . . 4·50 25
O58 50p. red and blue . . . . 65·00 60·00

1950. Air. Nos. 115/22 optd **S.G.**
O59 2p. black and green . . . . 15·00 3·25
O60 2½p. blue and orange . . . . 1·50 1·75
O61 3p. purple and blue . . . . 80 1·00
O62 3½p. sepia and brown . . . . 80 7·00
O63 4p. brown and blue . . . . 80 7·50
O64 4½p. black and blue . . . . 4·00 17·00
O65 6p. black and red . . . . . 1·00 4·25
O66 20p. black and purple . . . 4·00 12·00

1951. Nos. 123/39 optd **S.G.**
O67 1m. black and orange . . . 40 3·75
O68 2m. black and blue 50 85
O69 3m. black and green . . . . 3·50 15·00
O70 4m. black and green . . . . 10 5·50
O71 5m. black and purple . . . 10 10
O72 10m. black and blue 10 10
O73 15m. black and brown . . . 30 10
O74 2p. blue 10 10
O75 3p. brown and blue . . . . 7·50 10
O76 3½p. green and brown . . . 25 10
O77 4p. blue and black 60 10
O78 5p. brown and green 25 10
O79 6p. blue and black . . . . 50 2·75
O80 8p. blue and brown 55 10
O81 10p. black and green 50 10
O82 20p. turquoise and black . . 1·25 30
O83 50p. red and black . . . . 3·50 1·25

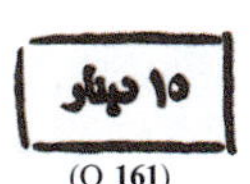
(O 65 "S.G.") (O 161)

1962. Nos. 171/84 optd with Type O **65** (larger on 10p. to £S10).
O185 **62** 5m. blue 10 10
O186 – 10m. purple and blue . . . 10 10
O187 – 15m. purple, orge & bis . . 10 10
O188 **62** 2p. violet 10 10
O189 – 3p. brown and green . . 45 10
O190 – 35m. brown, deep brown and green . . 55 20
O191 – 4p. purple, red and blue . . 65 20
O192 – 55m. brown and green . . 90 20
O193 – 6p. brown and blue . . 90 35
O194 – 8p. green . . . . 1·10 55
O222 **63** 10p. brown, black & blue . . . . 1·10 55
O223 – 20p. green and olive . . 2·75 90
O223a – 25p. brown and green . . 10 10
O224 – 50p. green, blue & black . 4·50 2·00
O198 **64** £S1 brown and green . . 14·00 9·00
O226 – £S5 green and brown . . 6·50 4·00
O227 **63** £S10 orange and blue . . 14·00 8·50

1991. Nos. 475/90 optd similarly to Type O **65**.
O491 25p. multicoloured 10 10
O492 50p. multicoloured 10 10
O493 75p. multicoloured 35 20
O494 100p. multicoloured 45 20
O495 125p. multicoloured 55 25
O496 150p. multicoloured 65 30
O497 175p. multicoloured 80 50
O498 £S2 multicoloured 90 60
O499 250p. multicoloured . . . . 1·10 75
O500 £S3 multicoloured . . . . 1·25 90
O501 £S4 multicoloured . . . . 1·75 1·25
O502 £S5 multicoloured . . . . 2·10 1·50
O503 £S8 multicoloured . . . . 3·50 3·00
O504 £S10 multicoloured . . . . 4·25 3·50
O505 £S15 multicoloured . . . . 6·50 5·50
O506 £S20 multicoloured . . . . 8·50 7·00

1996. Nos. O494, O496, O498 and O500/2 handstamped. (a) As Type O **161**.
O550 2d. on £S2 multicoloured
O551 3d. on £S3 multicoloured
O552 4d. on £S4 multicoloured
O553 5d. on £S5 multicoloured
O554 15d. on 100p. multicoloured
O555 15d. on 150p. multicoloured

(b) As T **151**.
O556 2d. on £S2 multicoloured

POSTAGE DUE STAMPS

1897. Postage Due Stamps of Egypt optd **SOUDAN** in English and Arabic.
D1 **D 23** 2m. green . . . . 1·75 5·00
D2 4m. purple . . . . . . 1·75 5·00
D3 1p. blue . . . . 10·00 3·50
D4 2p. orange . . . . . . 10·00 7·00

D 1 Gunboat "Zafir"

D 2 Gunboat "Zafir"

1901.
D 5 **D 1** 2m. black and brown . . 55 60
D10 4m. brown and green . . 1·00 80
D11 10m. green and mauve . 1·25 1·60
D 8 20m. blue and red . . . 3·25 3·25

1948.
D12 **D 2** 2m. black and brown . . 1·00 35·00
D13 4m. brown and green . . 2·00 32·00
D14 10m. green and mauve . 18·00 20·00
D15 20m. blue and red . . . 18·00 32·00

The Arabic inscription in Type D **2** differs from that in Type D **1**.

SUNGEI UJONG Pt. 1

A native state of the Malay Peninsula, later incorporated in Negri Sembilan.

100 cents = 1 dollar (Straits).

1878. Stamp of Straits Settlements optd with Crescent, Star and **SU** in an oval.
1 **5** 2c. brown £2000 £2250

1881. Stamps of Straits Settlements optd **SUNGEI UJONG**.
28 **5** 2c. brown . . . . 42·00 95·00
43 2c. red . . . . 7·00 10·00
22 4c. red £1200 £1300
34 4c. brown £225 £300
24 8c. orange £1400 £1100
26 **19** 10c. grey £475 £475

1882. Stamps of Straits Settlements optd **S.U.** (2c. with or without stops).
13 **5** 2c. brown £275 £325
14 4c. red £2500 £2500

1891. Stamp of Straits Settlements surch **SUNGEI UJONG Two CENTS**.
49 **5** 2c. on 24c. green £140 £160

35 Tiger

37 Tiger

1891.
50 **35** 2c. red . . . . 28·00 29·00
51 2c. orange . . . . 1·75 4·25
55 **37** 3c. purple and red . . . . . 8·00 2·50
52 **35** 5c. blue . . . . 5·00 6·00

1894. Surch in figures and words.
53 **35** 1c. on 5c. green . . . . . . 1·00 70
54 3c. on 5c. red . . . . 2·50 4·75

SURINAM Pt. 4; Pt. 20

A Netherlands colony on the north-east coast of South America. In December 1954 Surinam became an autonomous state within the Kingdom of the Netherlands. Became an independent state in November 1975.

100 cents = 1 gulden.

1 King William III

3

1873. No gum.
25 **1** 1c. grey . . . . 2·50 2·50
26 2c. yellow . . . . 1·40 1·40
14 2½c. red . . . . 1·40 1·40
15 3c. green . . . . 20·00 16·00
16 5c. lilac . . . . 17·00 5·50
17 10c. bistre . . . . 3·50 3·50
27 12½c. blue . . . . 16·00 7·25
18 15c. grey . . . . 22·00 7·00
19 20c. green . . . . 35·00 29·00
20 25c. blue . . . . 85·00 9·00
22 30c. brown . . . . 35·00 35·00
23 40c. brown . . . . 32·00 29·00
12 50c. brown . . . . 30·00 18·00
28 1g. grey and brown . . . . . 50·00 50·00
13 2½g. brown and green . . . . 70·00 65·00

The gulden values are larger.

1890.
44 **3** 1c. grey . . . . 2·00 1·25
45 2c. brown . . . . 3·00 2·40
46 2½c. red . . . . 2·40 2·00
47 3c. green . . . . 5·50 3·75
48 5c. blue . . . . 25·00 1·25

1892. Surch **2½ CENT.**
53 **1** 2½c. on 50c. brown . . . . . £275 11·00

5

6 Queen Wilhelmina

1892. No gum.
56 **5** 2½c. black and yellow . . . . 1·60 90

1892.
63 **6** 10c. bistre . . . . 40·00 3·00
64 12½c. mauve . . . . 45·00 5·75
65 15c. grey . . . . 4·00 2·50
66 20c. green . . . . 4·25 3·00
67 25c. blue . . . . 10·00 3·75
68 30c. brown . . . . 5·50 4·00

1898. Surch **10 CENT.**
69 **1** 10c. on 12½c. blue . . . . . 25·00 3·50
70 10c. on 15c. grey . . . . . . 65·00 50·00
71 10c. on 20c. green . . . . . 4·75 4·75
72 10c. on 25c. blue . . . . . . 10·50 6·00
74 10c. on 30c. brown . . . . . 4·75 4·75

1900. Stamps of Netherlands surch **SURINAME** and value.
77 **13** 50c. on 50c. red and green . . 22·00 7·50
78 **11** 1g. on 1g. green . . . . . . 20·00 12·50
79 2½g. on 2½g. lilac . . . . . 16·00 10·50

1900. Surch.
83 **1** 25c. on 40c. brown . . . . . 2·75 2·50
84 25c. on 50c. brown . . . . . 2·75 1·90
86 50c. on 1g. grey and brown . 30·00 27·00
82 50c. on 2½g. brown and green £140 £150

11 (shaded background)

12

1902.
87 **11** ½c. lilac 90 75
88 1c. green . . . . 1·90 1·25
89 2c. brown . . . . 10·00 3·50
90 2½c. green . . . . 4·50 35
91 3c. yellow . . . . 7·25 4·25
92 5c. red . . . . 4·25 35
93 7½c. grey . . . . 15·00 7·00
94 **12** 10c. slate . . . . 10·00 90
95 12½c. blue . . . . 3·75 30
96 15c. brown . . . . 26·00 9·00
97 20c. green . . . . 25·00 4·50
98 22½c. green and brown . . . 19·00 10·50
99 25c. violet . . . . 17·00 1·10
100 30c. brown . . . . 40·00 7·75
101 50c. brown . . . . 32·00 7·75

13

1907.
102 **13** 1g. purple . . . . 50·00 14·50
103 2½g. slate . . . . 50·00 50·00

14

17

1909. Roul or perf. No gum.
104 **14** 5c. red . . . . 10·00 8·25

1911. Surch with crown and value.
106 **3** ½c. on 1c. grey . . . . . . 1·60 1·00
107 ½c. on 2c. brown . . . . . 9·00 7·25
108 **6** 15c. on 25c. blue . . . . . 65·00 55·00
109 20c. on 30c. brown . . . . 9·50 7·25
110 – 30c. on 2½g. on 2½g. purple (No. 79) £120 £100

1912. No gum.
113 **17** ½c. lilac 95 95
114 2½c. green 95 95
115 5c. red . . . . 7·25 7·25
116 12½c. blue . . . . 9·00 9·00

18 (unshaded background)

19

20 21

1913. With or without gum.
117 **18** ½c. lilac 35 30
118 1c. green 35 20
119 1½c. blue 35 20
120 2c. brown . . . . 1·40 1·25
121 2½c. green 90 20
122 3c. yellow 75 55
123 3c. green . . . . 2·75 2·40
125 4c. blue . . . . 7·25 4·25
126 5c. pink . . . . 1·50 20
127 5c. green . . . . 1·90 90
128 5c. violet . . . . 1·40 20
129 6c. buff . . . . 2·50 2·40
130 6c. red . . . . 2·00 50
131 7½c. brown . . . . 1·00 35
132 7½c. red . . . . 1·25 35
133 7½c. yellow . . . . 8·00 8·00
134 10c. lilac . . . . 4·50 4·50
135 10c. red . . . . 3·50 55
136 **19** 10c. red . . . . 1·25 55
137 12½c. blue . . . . 1·60 55
138 12½c. red . . . . 1·90 2·00
139 15c. green 55 65
140 15c. blue . . . . 6·75 4·25
142 20c. blue . . . . 2·10 1·90
143 20c. green . . . . 3·00 2·75
144 22½c. orange . . . . 2·50 2·40
145 25c. mauve . . . . 3·50 35
146 30c. grey . . . . 4·25 1·00
147 32½c. violet and orange . . . 13·50 17·00
148 35c. blue and orange . . . 4·50 4·50
149 **20** 50c. green . . . . 4·00 75
150 1g. brown . . . . 5·25 55
151 1½g. purple . . . . 30·00 30·00
152a 2½g. pink . . . . 26·00 24·00

1923. Queen's Silver Jubilee.
169a **21** 5c. green 90 65
170 10c. red . . . . 1·40 1·40
171 20c. blue . . . . 3·00 2·50
172a 50c. orange . . . . 16·00 19·00
173 1g. purple . . . . 23·00 12·50
174 2g.50 grey . . . . 65·00 £190
175 5g. brown . . . . 80·00 £225

1925. Surch.
176 **18** 3c. on 5c. green 90 90
177 **19** 10c. on 12½c. red . . . . . 1·75 1·60

180 12½c. on 22½c. orange 22·00 24·00
178 15c. on 12½c. blue 1·25 1·25
179 15c. on 20c. blue 1·25 1·25

1926. Postage Due stamps surch **Frankeerzegel 12½ CENT SURINAME.** (a) In three lines with bars.
181 D 6 12½c. on 40c. mve & blk 2·50 2·50

(b) In four lines without bars.
182 D 6 12½c. on 40c. lilac 24·00 24·00

28 29

1927.
183 **28** 10c. red 80 35
184 12½c. orange 1·60 1·60
185 15c. blue 1·90 55
186 20c. blue 1·90 75
187 21c. brown 15·00 14·50
188 22½c. brown 7·25 9·00
189 25c. purple 2·50 65
190 30c. green 2·50 1·00
191 35c. sepia 2·75 2·75

1927. Green Cross Fund. Various designs incorporating green cross.
192 **29** 2c.+2c. green and slate 1·10 1·00
193 – 5c.+3c. green and purple 1·10 1·00
194 – 10c.+3c. green and red 1·90 1·60

1927. Unissued Marine Insurance stamps (as Type M **22** of Netherlands but inscr "SURINAME") surch **FRANKEER ZEGEL** and value.
195 3c. on 15c. green 40 35
196 10c. on 60c. red 40 35
197 12½c. on 75c. brown 40 35
198 15c. on 1g.50 blue 2·10 2·00
199 25c. on 2g.25 brown 4·75 4·25
200 30c. on 4½g. black 10·50 8·50
201 50c. on 7½g. red 4·50 4·25

32 Indigenous Disease
33 The Good Samaritan

1928. Governor Van Heemstrastichting Medical Foundation Fund.
202 **32** 1½c.+1½c. blue 5·00 4·50
203 2c.+2c. green 5·00 4·50
204 5c.+3c. violet 5·00 4·50
205 7½c.+2½c. red 5·00 4·50

1929. Green Cross Fund.
206 **33** 1½c.+1½c. green 6·25 6·25
207 2c.+2c. red 6·25 6·25
208 5c.+3c. blue 6·25 6·25
209 6c.+4c. black 6·25 6·25

1930. No. 132 surch **6**.
210 **18** 6c. on 7½c. red 1·90 95

35 Mercury and Posthorn
37 Mother and Child

1930. Air.
276 **35** 10c. red 2·50 35
212 15c. blue 3·25 65
213 20c. green 10 20
214 40c. red 20 30
215 60c. purple 50 35
216 1g. black 1·25 1·40
217 1½g. brown 1·40 1·60
281 2½g. yellow 12·50 11·00
282 5g. green £275 £300
283 10g. bistre 30·00 45·00

1931. Air. "Dornier 10" Flight. Optd **Vlucht Do. X 1931.**
218 **35** 10c. red 18·00 15·00
219 15c. blue 19·00 15·00
220 20c. green 19·00 15·00
221 40c. red 28·00 23·00
222 60c. purple 55·00 50·00
223 1g. black 70·00 60·00
224 1½g. brown 70·00 65·00

1931. Child Welfare.
225 **37** 1½c.+1½c. black 4·50 4·00
226 2c.+2c. red 4·50 4·00
227 5c.+3c. blue 4·50 4·00
228 6c.+4c. green 4·50 4·00

37a William I (after Key)
38 "Supplication"

1933. 400th Birth Anniv of William I of Orange.
229 **37a** 6c. red 5·50 1·60

1935. Bicent of Moravian Mission in Surinam.
230 **38** 1c.+½c. brown 2·25 1·90
231 2c.+1c. blue 2·25 1·90
232 – 3c.+1½c. green 2·75 2·50
233 – 4c.+2c. orange 2·75 2·50
234 – 5c.+2½c. black 3·00 3·00
235 **38** 10c.+5c. red 3·00 3·00
DESIGN: 3, 4, 5c. Cross and clasped hands.

39 "Johannes van Walbeeck" (galleon)
40 Queen Wilhelmina

1936.
236 **39** ½c. brown 25 30
237 1c. green 35 20
238 1½c. blue 50 35
239 2c. brown 55 30
240 2½c. green 25 20
241 3c. blue 55 35
242 4c. orange 55 65
243 5c. grey 55 20
244 6c. red 2·25 1·75
245 7½c. purple 25 20
246 **40** 10c. red 75 20
247 12½c. green 3·00 1·25
248 15c. blue 1·10 55
249 20c. orange 1·90 55
250 21c. black 2·75 2·75
251 25c. red 2·00 90
252 30c. purple 3·00 90
253 35c. bistre 3·50 3·50
254 50c. green 3·50 1·60
255 1g. blue 6·50 2·00
256 1g.50 brown 18·00 14·50
257 2g.50 red 11·00 7·25
Nos. 254/7 are larger, 22 × 33 mm.

41 "Infant Support"

1936. Child Welfare.
258 **41** 2c.+1c. green 2·25 2·25
259 3c.+1½c. blue 2·25 2·25
260 5c.+2½c. black 3·00 3·00
261 10c.+5c. red 3·00 3·00

42 "Emancipation"
42a Surinam Girl

1938. 75th Anniv of Liberation of Slaves in Surinam and Paramaribo Girls' School Funds.
262 **42** 2½c.+2c. green 1·75 1·40
263 **42a** 3c.+2c. black 1·75 1·40
264 5c.+3c. brown 1·90 1·60
265 7½c.+5c. blue 1·90 1·60

42b Queen Wilhelmina
44 Creole

1938. 40th Anniv of Coronation.
266 **42b** 2c. violet 35 30
267 7½c. red 90 90
268 15c. blue 2·40 2·25

1940. Social Welfare Fund.
269 **44** 2½c.+2c. green 2·50 1·90
270 – 3c.+2c. red 2·50 1·90
271 – 5c.+3c. blue 2·50 1·90
272 – 7½c.+5c. red 2·50 1·90
DESIGNS: 3c. Javanese woman; 5c. Hindu woman; 7½c. Indian woman.

44a Netherlands Coat of Arms
44b Queen Wilhelmina

1941. Prince Bernhard and "Spitfire" Funds.
273 **44a** 7½c.+7½c. blue & orge 2·50 2·75
274 15c.+15c. blue and red 3·00 3·00
275 1g.+1g. blue and grey 23·00 20·00

1941.
342 **44b** 12½c. blue 90 20
284 15c. blue 18·00 6·25

1942. Red Cross. Surch with red cross and new values.
289 **39** 2c.+2c. brown (postage) 1·90 1·90
291 2½c.+2c. green 1·90 1·90
292 7½c.+5c. purple 1·90 1·90
293 **35** 10c.+5c. red (air) 4·25 1·25

44d Dutch Royal Family

1943. Birth of Princess Margriet.
294 **44d** 2½c. orange 55 50
295 7½c. red 55 10
296 15c. black 2·40 1·90
297 40c. blue 3·00 2·10

1945. Surch.
298 **39** ½c. on 1c. green 10 20
299 1½c. on 7½c. purple 25 20
300 2½c. on 7½c. purple 1·90 2·00
301 **40** 2½c. on 10c. red 1·00 30
302 5c. on 10c. red 65 50
303 7½c. on 10c. red 75 50

1945. Air. Surch.
304 **35** 22½c. on 60c. purple 80 80
305 1g. on 2½g. yellow 12·50 12·00
306 5g. on 10g. bistre 18·00 19·00

1945. National Welfare Fund. Surch **CENT VOOR HET NATIONAAL STEUNFONDS** and premium.
307 **49** 7½c.+5c. orange 3·25 2·25
308 **50** 15c.+10c. brown 2·50 2·25
309 20c.+15c. green 2·50 2·25
310 22½c.+20c. grey 2·50 2·25
311 40c.+35c. red 2·50 2·25
312 60c.+50c. violet 2·50 2·25

49 Sugar-cane Train

50 Queen Wilhelmina
51 Queen Wilhelmina
53 Star

1945.
313 – 1c. red 30 30
314 – 1½c. red 1·00 1·00
315 – 2c. violet 50 35
316 – 2½c. brown 50 35
317 – 3c. green 1·00 55
318 – 4c. brown 1·00 65
319 – 5c. blue 1·00 30
320 – 6c. olive 1·90 1·25
321 **49** 7½c. orange 65 30
322 **50** 10c. blue 1·25 20
323 15c. brown 1·60 30
324 20c. green 2·75 20
325 22½c. grey 3·00 75
326 25c. red 8·50 3·50
327 30c. olive 8·25 50
328 35c. blue 13·50 5·75
329 40c. red 8·25 30
330 50c. red 8·25 30
331 60c. violet 8·25 75
332 **51** 1g. brown 10·00 30
333 1g.50 lilac 9·00 65
334 2g.50 brown 17·00 75
335 5g. red 35·00 10·00
336 10g. orange 90·00 19·00
DESIGNS—As Type **49**: 1c. Bauxite mine, Moengo; 1½c. Natives in canoes; 2c. Native and stream; 2½c. Road in Coronie; 3c. River Surinam near Berg en Dal; 4c. Government Square, Paramaribo; 5c. Mining gold; 6c. Street in Paramaribo.

1946. Air. Anti-tuberculosis Fund. Surch **LUCHT POST** and premium.
340 **50** 10c.+40c. blue 1·10 1·10
341 15c.+60c. brown 1·10 1·10

1947. Anti-leprosy Fund.
343 **53** 7½c.+12½c. orange (postage) 2·75 2·40
344 12½c.+37½c. blue 2·75 2·40
345 22½c.+27½c. grey (air) 2·75 2·40
346 27½c.+47½c. green 2·75 2·40

54
54a Queen Wilhelmina

1948.
347 **54** 1c. red 20 20
348 1½c. purple 20 20
349 2c. violet 30 20
350 2½c. green 1·25 20
351 3c. green 20 20
352 4c. brown 20 20
353 5c. blue 1·25 20
355 **54a** 5c. blue 35 20
356 6c. green 90 65
354 **54** 7½c. orange 2·75 1·10
357 **54a** 7½c. red 35 20
358 10c. blue 55 20
359 12½c. blue 1·00 90
360 15c. brown 1·50 35
361 17½c. purple 1·60 1·25
362 20c. green 1·25 20
363 22½c. blue 1·25 65
364 25c. red 1·25 30
365 27½c. red 1·25 20
366 30c. green 1·60 20
367 37½c. brown 2·50 1·75
368 40c. purple 1·90 30
369 50c. orange 2·00 30
370 60c. violet 2·00 35
371 70c. black 2·25 55

54b Queen Wilhelmina
54c Queen Juliana

1948. Queen Wilhelmina's Golden Jubilee.
372 **54b** 7½c. orange 80 65
373 12½c. blue 80 65

1948. Accession of Queen Juliana.
374 **54c** 7½c. orange 2·75 2·50
375 12½c. blue 2·75 2·50

55 Women of Netherlands and Surinam
55a Posthorns and Globe

1949. Air. 1st K.L.M. Flight on Paramaribo–Amsterdam Service.
376 **55** 27½c. brown 6·00 2·75

1949. 75th Anniv of U.P.U.
377 **55a** 7½c. red 6·00 2·75
378 27½c. blue 6·00 2·00

56 Marie Curie

1950. Cancer Research Fund.
379 **56** 7½c.+7½c. violet 14·50 7·75
380 – 7½c.+22½c. green 14·50 7·75

381 – 27½c.+12½c. blue . . . . . 14·50 7·75
382 **56** 27½c.+97½c. brown . . . . 14·50 7·75
PORTRAIT: Nos. 380/1, Wilhelm Rontgen.

1950. Surch **1 Cent** and bars.
383 **49** 1c. on 7½c. orange 80 65

57a Queen Juliana **57b** Queen Juliana

1951.
395 **57a** 10c. blue 40 20
396 15c. brown 95 30
397 20c. turquoise . . . . . 2·40 20
398 25c. red . . . . 1·60 35
399 27½c. lake . . . . 1·40 20
400 30c. green . . . . 1·40 35
401 35c. olive . . . . 1·60 1·00
402 40c. mauve . . . . 1·90 35
403 50c. orange . . . . . . 2·40 35
404 **57b** 1g. brown . . . . 24·00 35

1953. Netherlands Flood Relief Fund. Nos. 374/5 surch **STORMRAMP NEDERLAND 1953** and premium.
405 12½c.+7½c. on 7½c. orange . . 2·75 2·50
406 20c.+10c.on 12½c. blue . . . 2·75 2·50

60 Fisherman **61** Surinam Stadium

1953.
407 – 2c. brown 20 20
408 **60** 2½c. green 30 20
409 – 5c. grey 30 20
410 – 6c. blue . . . . 1·60 1·10
411 – 7½c. violet 20 20
412 – 10c. red 20 20
413 – 12½c. blue . . . . 1·60 1·25
414 – 15c. red 60 30
415 – 17½c. brown . . . . . . 2·50 1·90
416 – 20c. green 50 20
417 – 25c. green . . . . 2·40 75
DESIGNS—HORIZ: 2c. Native shooting fish; 10c. Woman gathering fruit. VERT: 5c. Bauxite mine; 6c. Log raft; 7½c. Ploughing with buffalo; 12½c. Brown hoplo (fish); 15c. Blue and yellow macaw; 17½c. Nine-banded armadillo; 20c. Poling pirogue; 25c. Iguana.

1953. Sports Week.
419 **61** 10c.+5c. red . . . . 10·00 7·25
420 15c.+7½c. brown . . . . . 10·00 7·25
421 30c.+15c. green . . . . . 10·00 7·25

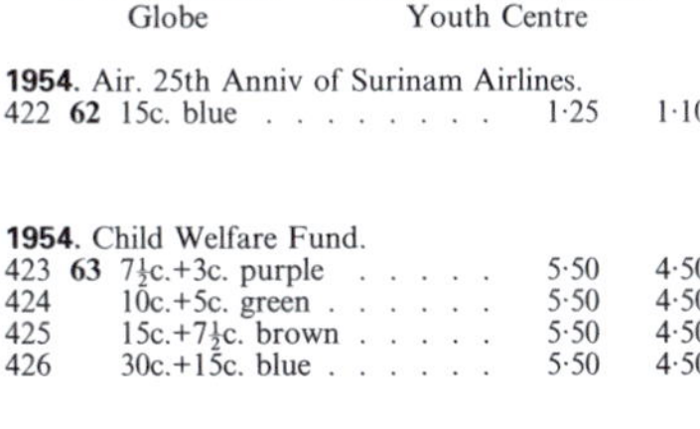

62 Posthorn and Globe **63** Native Children and Youth Centre

1954. Air. 25th Anniv of Surinam Airlines.
422 **62** 15c. blue . . . . 1·25 1·10

1954. Child Welfare Fund.
423 **63** 7½c.+3c. purple . . . . . 5·50 4·50
424 10c.+5c. green . . . . . . 5·50 4·50
425 15c.+7½c. brown . . . . . 5·50 4·50
426 30c.+15c. blue . . . . . . 5·50 4·50

63a Queen Juliana

1954. Ratification of Statute for the Kingdom.
427 **63a** 7½c. purple 55 55

64 Doves of Peace **65** Gathering Bananas

1955. 10th Anniv of Liberation of Netherlands and War Victims Relief Fund.
428 **64** 7½c.+3½c. red . . . . . . 2·40 2·40
429 15c.+8c. blue . . . . . . 2·40 2·40

1955. 4th Caribbean Tourist Assn Meeting.
430 **65** 2c. green . . . . 1·60 1·25
431 – 7½c. yellow . . . . 2·50 1·90
432 – 10c. brown . . . . 2·50 1·90
433 – 15c. blue . . . . 2·75 1·90
DESIGNS: 7½c. Pounding rice; 10c. Preparing cassava; 15c. Fishing.

66 Caduceus and Globe **67** Queen Juliana and Prince Bernhard

1955. Surinam Fair.
434 **66** 5c. blue 40 35

1955. Royal Visit.
435 **67** 7½c.+2½c. olive 55 55

68 Flags and Caribbean Map **69** Facade of 19th-century Theatre

1956. 10th Anniv of Caribbean Commission.
447 **68** 10c. blue and red 30 30

1958. 120th Anniv of "Thalia" Amateur Dramatic Society.
448 **69** 7½c.+3c. blue and black . . 50 50
449 – 10c.+5c. purple & black . . 50 50
450 – 15c.+7½c. green & black . . 50 50
451 – 20c.+10c. orange & black 50 50
DESIGNS: 10c. Early 20th-century theatre; 15c. Modern theatre; 20c. Performance on stage.

1959. No. 399 surch **8 C.**
452 8c. on 27½c. red 20 20

71 Queen Juliana **72** Symbolic Plants

1959.
453 **71** 1g. purple . . . . 1·50 20
454 1g.50 brown . . . . 2·25 50
455 2g.50 red . . . . 3·00 30
456 5g. blue . . . . 6·00 30

1959. 5th Anniv of Ratification of Statute for the Kingdom.
457 **72** 20c. multicoloured . . . . 2·50 1·50

73 Wooden Utensils

1960. Surinam Handicrafts.
458 **73** 8c.+4c. multicoloured . . . 90 90
459 – 10c.+5c. red, blue & brn 90 90
460 – 15c.+7c. green, brn & red 90 90
461 – 20c.+10c. multicoloured . . 90 90
DESIGNS: 10c. Indian chief's headgear; 15c. Clay pottery; 20c. Wooden stool.

74 Boeing 707

1960. Opening of Zanderij Airport Building.
462 – 8c. blue . . . . 1·10 1·10
463 – 10c. green . . . . 1·60 1·60
464 – 15c. red . . . . 1·60 1·60
465 – 20c. lilac . . . . 2·00 2·00
466 **74** 40c. brown . . . . 2·75 2·75
DESIGNS: 8c. Charles Lindbergh's seaplane, 1929; 10c. Fokker "De Snip", 1934; 15c. Cessna 170A, 1954; 20c. Lockheed Super Constellation, 1957.

75 "Uprooted Tree" **76** Surinam Flag

1960. World Refugee Year.
467 **75** 8c.+4c. green and brown 20 20
468 10c.+5c. green and blue . . 20 20

1960. Freedom Day. Multicoloured.
469 10c. Type **76** 55 55
470 15c. Coat-of-arms (30 × 26 mm) 55 55

77 Putting the Shot **78** Bananas

1960. Olympic Games, Rome.
471 **77** 8c.+4c. brown, blk & grey 80 65
472 – 10c.+5c. brown, blk & orge 80 65
473 – 15c.+7c. brown, blk & vio 1·00 90
474 – 20c.+10c. brown, blk & bl 1·00 90
475 – 40c.+20c. brown, blk & grn 1·10 90
DESIGNS: 10c. Basketball; 15c. Running; 20c. Swimming; 40c. Football.

1961. Local Produce.
476 **78** 1c. yellow, black and green 15 10
477 – 2c. green, black and yellow 15 10
478 – 3c. brown, black & choc 15 10
479 – 4c. yellow, black and blue 15 10
480 – 5c. red, black and brown 15 10
481 – 6c. yellow, black and green 15 10
482 – 8c. yellow, black and blue 15 10
DESIGNS: 2c. Citrus fruit; 3c. Cocoa; 4c. Sugar-cane; 5c. Coffee; 6c. Coconuts; 8c. Rice.

79 Treasury **80** Commander Shepard, Rocket and Globe

1961. Surinam Buildings. Multicoloured.
483 10c. Type **79** 30 20
484 15c. Court of Justice 25 20
485 20c. Concordia Masonic Lodge 30 20
486 25c. Neve Shalom Synagogue 55 40
487 30c. Lock Gate, Nieuw Amsterdam . . . . 1·50 1·25
488 35c. Government Building . . 1·50 1·40
489 40c. Governor's House . . . 80 65
490 50c. Legislative Assembly . . 80 30
491 60c. Old Dutch Reform Church 90 90
492 70c. Fort Zeelandia (1790) . . 90 1·00
The 10, 15, 20 and 30c. are vert and the rest horiz.

1961. Air. "Man in Space". Multicoloured.
493 15c. Globe and astronaut in capsule 90 90
494 20c. Type **80** 90 90

81 Girl Scout saluting **82** Dag Hammarskjold

1961. Caribbean Girl Scout Jamborette. Mult.
495 8c.+2c. Semaphoring (horiz) 45 35
496 10c.+3c. Type **81** 45 35
497 15c.+4c. Brownies around a "toadstool" (horiz) 45 35
498 20c.+5c. Campfire sing-song 55 50
499 25c.+6c. Lighting fire (horiz) 50 50

1962. Dag Hammarskjold Memorial Issue.
500 **82** 10c. black and blue 20 20
501 20c. black and violet . . . 20 20

82a Queen Juliana and Prince Bernhard

1962. Royal Silver Wedding.
502 **82a** 20c. green 30 30

83 "Hibiscus rosa sinensis" **84** Campaign Emblem

1962. Red Cross Fund. Flowers in natural colours. Background colours given.
503 **83** 8c.+4c. olive 50 30
504 – 10c.+5c. blue 50 30
505 – 15c.+6c. brown 50 30
506 – 20c.+10c. violet 50 30
507 – 25c.+12c. turquoise 50 30
FLOWERS: 10c. "Caesalpinia pulcherrima"; 15c. "Heliconia psittacorum"; 20c. "Lochnera rosea"; 25c. "Ixora macrothyrsa".

1962. Malaria Eradication.
508 **84** 8c. red 20 20
509 10c. blue 20 20

85 Stoelmans Guesthouse

1962. Opening of New Hotels. Multicoloured.
510 10c. Type **85** 35 35
511 15c. Torarica Hotel 35 35

86 Sisters' Residence **87** Wildfowl

1962. Nunnery and Hospital of the Deaconesses. Multicoloured.
512 10c. Type **86** 35 35
513 20c. Hospital building . . . 35 35

1962. Animal Protection Fund.
514 **87** 2c.+1c. red and blue . . . 30 20
515 – 8c.+2c. red and black . . . 30 20
516 – 10c.+3c. black and green 30 20
517 – 15c.+4c. black and red . . 30 20
ANIMALS: 8c. Dog; 10c. Donkey; 15c. Horse.

88 Emblem in Hands

1963. Freedom from Hunger.
518 **88** 10c. red 20 20
519 – 20c. blue 20 20
DESIGN—VERT: 20c. Tilling the land.

89 "Freedom"

1963. Centenary of Abolition of Slavery in Dutch West Indies.
520 **89** 10c. black and red 20 20
521 20c. black and green . . . 20 20

90 Indian Girl **90a** William of Orange at Scheveningen

1963. Child Welfare Fund.
522 **90** 8c.+3c. green 30 20
523 – 10c.+4c. brown 30 20
524 – 15c.+10c. blue 30 20
525 – 20c.+10c. red 30 20
526 – 40c.+20c. purple 30 20
PORTRAITS OF CHILDREN: 10c. Bush negro; 15c. Hindustani; 20c. Indonesian; 40c. Chinese.

1963. 150th Anniv of Kingdom of the Netherlands.
528 **90a** 10c. black, bistre and blue 20 20

91 North American X-15

1964. Aeronautical and Astronomical Foundation, Surinam.
529 3c.+2c. sepia and lake . . . 40 20
530 8c.+4c. sepia, indigo & blue 40 20
531 10c.+5c. sepia and green . . 40 20
532 15c.+7c. sepia and brown . . 40 20
533 20c.+10c. sepia and violet . . 40 20
DESIGNS: 3, 15c. Type **91**; 8c. Foundation flag; 10, 20c. Agena B-Ranger rocket.

92 "Camp Fire" **93** Skipping

1964. Scout Jamborette, Paramaribo, and 40th Anniv of Surinam Boy Scouts Association.
534 **92** 3c.+1c. lt yell, yell & bis 40 20
535 8c.+4c. brn, bl & dp bl . . 40 20
536 10c.+5c. brn, red & dp red 40 20
537 20c.+10c. brn, grn & bl . . 40 20

1964. Child Welfare.
538 **93** 8c.+3c. blue 20 20
539 – 10c.+4c. red 20 20
540 – 15c.+9c. green 20 20
541 – 20c.+10c. purple 20 20
DESIGNS: 10c. Children swinging; 15c. Child on scooter; 20c. Child with hoop.

94 Crown and Wreath **95** Expectant Mother ("Prenatal Care")

1964. 10th Anniv of Statute of the Kingdom.
543 **94** 25c. multicoloured 20 20

1965. 50th Anniv of "Het Groene Kruis" (The Green Cross).
544 **95** 4c.+2c. green 20 20
545 – 10c.+5c. brown and green 20 20
546 – 15c.+7c. blue and green . . 20 20
547 – 25c.+12c. violet and green 20 20
DESIGNS: 10c. Mother and baby ("Infant care"); 15c. Young girl ("Child care"); 25c. Old man ("Care in old age").

96 Abraham Lincoln **97** I.C.Y. Emblem

1965. Death Centenary of Abraham Lincoln.
548 **96** 25c. purple and bistre . . . 20 20

1965. International Co-operation Year.
549 **97** 10c. orange and blue . . . 20 20
550 15c. red and blue 20 20

98 Surinam Waterworks **99** Bauxite Mine, Moengo

1965. Air. Size 25 × 18 mm.
551 **98** 10c. green 20 20
552 – 15c. ochre 20 20
553 – 20c. green 20 20
554 – 25c. indigo 25 20
555 – 30c. turquoise 25 20
556 – 35c. red 30 20
557 – 40c. orange 30 20
558 – 45c. red 30 20
559 – 50c. red 30 20
560 **98** 55c. green 30 20
561 – 65c. yellow 35 30
562 – 75c. blue 35 30
DESIGNS: 15, 65c. Brewery; 20c. River scene; 25, 75c. Timber yard; 30c. Bauxite mine; 35, 50c. Poelepantje Bridge; 40c. Shipping; 45c. Jetty.
For same designs but size 22 × 18 mm, see Nos. 843a/h.

1965. Opening of Brokopondo Power Station.
563 **99** 10c. ochre 20 20
564 – 15c. green 20 20
565 – 20c. blue 20 20
566 – 25c. red 20 20
DESIGNS: 15c. Alum-earth works, Paranam; 20c. Power station and dam, Afobaka; 25c. Aluminium smeltery, Paranam.

100 Girl with Leopard **101** Red-breasted Blackbird

100a "Help them to a safe haven" (Queen Juliana)

1965. Child Welfare.
567 **100** 4c.+4c. black, turquoise and green 20 20
568 – 10c.+5c. black, brown and light brown 20 20
569 – 15c.+7c. black, orange and red 20 20
570 – 25c.+10c. black, blue and cobalt 20 20
DESIGNS: 10c. Boy with monkey; 15c. Girl with tortoise; 25c. Boy with rabbit.

1966. Intergovernmental Committee for European Migration (I.C.E.M.) Fund.
572 **100a** 10c.+5c. green & black 20 20
573 25c.+10c. red and black 20 20

1966. Birds. Multicoloured.
575 1c. Type **101** 30 20
576 2c. Great kiskadee 30 20
577 3c. Silver-beaked tanager . . 30 20
578 4c. Ruddy ground dove . . . 30 20
579 5c. Blue-grey tanager . . . 30 20
580 6c. Straight-billed hermit . . 30 20
581 8c. Turquoise tanager . . . 30 20
582 10c. Pale-breasted thrush . . 30 20

102 Hospital Building **103** Father P. Donders

1966. Opening of Central Hospital, Paramaribo. Multicoloured.
583 10c. Type **102** 20 20
584 15c. Different view 20 20

1966. Centenary of Redemptorists Mission.
585 **103** 4c. black and brown . . . 20 20
586 – 10c. black, brown and red 20 20
587 – 15c. black and ochre . . . 20 20
588 – 25c. black and lilac . . . 20 20
DESIGNS: 10c. Batavia Church, Coppename; 15c. Mgr. J. B. Swinkels; 25c. Paramaribo Cathedral.

104 Mary Magdalene and Disciples **105** "Century Tree"

1966. Easter Charity.
589 **104** 10c.+5c. black, red and gold 20 20
590 15c.+8c. black, violet and blue 20 20
591 20c.+10c. black, yellow and blue 20 20
592 25c.+12c. black, green and gold 20 20
593 30c.+15c. black, blue and gold 20 20
On Nos. 590/3 the emblems at bottom left differ for each value. These represent various welfare organizations.

1966. Centenary of Surinam Parliament.
594 **105** 25c. black, green and red 20 20
595 30c. black, red and green 20 20

106 TV Mast, Eye and Globe **107** Boys with Bamboo Gun

1966. Inauguration of Surinam Television Service.
596 **106** 25c. red and blue 20 20
597 30c. red and brown . . . 20 20

1966. Child Welfare. Multicoloured.
598 10c.+5c. Type **107** 15 15
599 15c.+8c. Boy pouring liquid on another 20 20
600 20c.+10c. Children rejoicing 20 20
601 25c.+12c. Children on merry-go-round 20 20
602 30c.+15c. Children decorating room 20 20
The designs symbolize New Year's Eve, the End of Lent, Liberation Day, Queen's Birthday and Christmas respectively.

108 Mining Bauxite, 1916 **109** "The Good Samaritan"

1966. 50th Anniv of Surinam Bauxite Industry.
604 **108** 20c. black, orange & yell 20 20
605 – 25c. black, orange and blue 20 20
DESIGN: 25c. Modern bauxite plant.

1967. Easter Charity. Printed in black, background colours given.
606 **109** 10c.+5c. yellow 20 20
607 – 15c.+8c. blue 20 20
608 – 20c.+10c. ochre 20 20
609 – 25c.+12c. pink 20 20
610 – 30c.+15c. green 20 20
DESIGNS: 15 to 30c. Various episodes illustrating the parable of "The Good Samaritan".

110 Central Bank

1967. 10th Anniv of Surinam Central Bank.
611 **110** 10c. black and yellow . . 15 10
612 – 25c. black and lilac . . . 15 10
DESIGN: 25c. Aerial view of Central Bank.

111 Amelia Earhart and Lockheed 10E Electra Airplane **112** Siva Nataraja and Ballerina's Foot

1967. 30th Anniv of Visit of Amelia Earhart to Surinam.
613 **111** 20c. red and yellow . . . 15 10
614 25c. green and yellow . . 15 10

1967. 20th Anniv of Surinam Cultural Centre. Multicoloured.
615 10c. Type **112** 15 10
616 25c. "Bashi-Lele" mask and violin scroll 15 10

113 Fort Zeelandia, Paramaribo (c. 1670) **114** Stilt-walking

1967. 300th Anniv of Treaty of Breda. Mult.
617 10c. Type **113** 25 20
618 20c. Nieuw Amsterdam (c. 1660) 25 20
619 25c. Breda Castle (c. 1667) 25 20

1967. Child Welfare. Multicoloured.
620 10c.+5c. Type **114** 30 20
621 15c.+8c. Playing marbles . . 30 20
622 20c.+10c. Playing dibs . . . 30 20
623 25c.+12c. Kite-flying 30 20
624 30c.+15c. "Cooking" game 30 20

115 "Cross of Ashes" **116** W.H.O. Emblem

1968. Easter Charity.
626 10c.+5c. grey and violet . . . 30 20
627 15c.+8c. green and red . . . 30 20
628 20c.+10c. green and yellow 30 20
629 25c.+12c. black and grey . . 30 20
630 30c.+15c. brown and yellow 30 20
DESIGNS: 10c. Type **115** (Ash Wednesday); 15c. Palm branches (Palm Sunday); 20c. Cup and wafer (Maundy Thursday); 25c. Cross (Good Friday); 30c. Symbol of Christ (Easter).

1968. 20th Anniv of W.H.O.
631 **116** 10c. blue and purple . . . 10 10
632 25c. violet and blue . . . 20 20

117 Chandelier, Reformed Church **119** Map of Joden Savanne

118 Missionary Shop, 1768

1968. 300th Anniv of Reformed Church, Paramaribo.
633 **117** 10c. blue 10 10
634 – 25c. green 20 20
DESIGN: 25c. No. 633 reversed; chandelier on left.

1968. Bicentenary of Evangelist Brothers' Missionary Store, G. Kersten and Co.
635 **118** 10c. black and yellow . . 10 10
636 – 25c. black and blue . . . 20 20
637 – 30c. black and mauve . . 20 20
DESIGNS: 25c. Paramaribo Church and Kersten's store, 1868; 30c. Kersten's modern store, Paramaribo.

1968. Restoration of Joden Savanne Synagogue. Multicoloured.
638 20c. Type **119** 35 35
639 25c. Synagogue, 1685 . . . . 35 35
640 30c. Gravestone at Joden Savanne, dated 1733 . . . 35 35

120 Playing Hopscotch
121 Western Hemisphere illuminated by Full Moon

1968. Child Welfare.
641 **120** 10c.+5c. black & brown 30 20
642 – 15c.+8c. black and blue 30 20
643 – 20c.+10c. black & pink 30 20
644 – 25c.+12c. black & green 30 20
645 – 30c.+15c. black & lilac . . 30 30
DESIGNS: 15c. Forming "pyramids"; 20c. Playing ball; 25c. Handicrafts; 30c. Tug-of-war.

1969. Easter Charity.
647 **121** 10c.+5c. blue & lt blue . . 30 30
648 15c.+8c. grey & yellow . . 30 30
649 20c.+10c. turq & green . . 30 30
650 25c.+12c. brown & buff 30 30
651 30c.+15c. violet & grey 30 30

122 Cayman
123 Mahatma Gandhi

1969. Opening of Surinam Zoo, Paramaribo. Mult.
652 10c. Type **122** . . . . 50 3·00
653 20c. Common squirrel-monkey (vert) 50 30
654 25c. Nine-banded armadillo 50 30

1969. Birth Centenary of Mahatma Gandhi.
655 **123** 25c. black and red 30 30

124 I.L.O. Emblem
125 Pillow Fight

1969. 50th Anniv of Int Labour Organization.
656 **124** 10c. green and black . . . 20 20
657 25c. red and black 30 20

1969. Child Welfare.
658 10c.+5c. purple and blue . . 30 20
659 15c.+8c. brown and yellow 30 20
660 20c.+10c. blue and grey . . . 30 20
661 25c.+12c. blue and pink . . . 30 20
662 30c.+15c. brown and green 30 20
DESIGNS: 10c. Type **125**; 15c. Eating contest; 20c. Pole-climbing; 25c. Sack-race; 30c. Obstacle-race.

126 Queen Juliana and "Sunlit Road"

1969. 15th Anniv of Statute for the Kingdom.
664 **126** 25c. multicoloured 30 25

127 "Flower"
128 "1950–1970"

1970. Easter Charity. "Wonderful Nature". Mult.
665 10c.+5c. Type **127** 50 50
666 15c.+8c. "Butterfly" 50 50
667 20c.+10c. "Bird" 50 50
668 25c.+12c. "Sun" 50 50
669 30c.+15c. "Star" 50 50

1970. 20th Anniv of Secondary Education in Surinam.
670 **128** 10c. yellow, green and brown 15 15
671 25c. yellow, blue and green 15 15

129 New U.P.U. Headquarters Building
130 U.N. "Diamond"

1970. New U.P.U. Headquarters Building.
672 **129** 10c. violet, blue & turq 15 15
673 – 25c. black and red 20 20
DESIGN: 25c. Aerial view of H.Q. Building.

1970. 25th Anniv of United Nations.
674 **130** 10c. multicoloured 20 20
675 25c. multicoloured 20 20

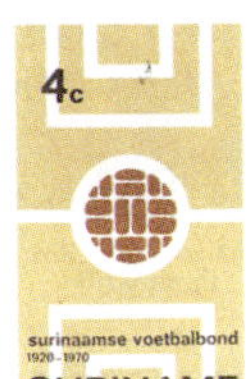

131 Aircraft over Paramaribo Town Plan
132 Football Pitch (ball in centre)

1970. "40 Years of Inland Airmail Flights".
676 **131** 10c. grey, ultramarine & blue 40 30
677 – 20c. grey, red and yellow 40 30
678 – 25c. grey, red and pink 40 30
DESIGNS: As Type **131**, but showing different background maps—20c. Totness; 25c. Nieuw-Nickerie.

1970. 50th Anniv of Surinam Football Association.
679 **132** 4c. brown, yellow & black 30 20
680 – 10c. brown, olive and black 30 20
681 – 15c. brown, green & black 30 20
682 – 25c. brown, green & black 30 20
DESIGNS: As Type **132**, but with ball: 10c. in "corner"; 15c. at side ("throw-in"); 25c. at top ("goal").

133 Beethoven (1786)
134 Grey Heron

1970. Child Welfare. Birth Bicentenary of Beethoven (composer).
683 **133** 10c.+5c. yellow, drab and green 55 50
684 – 15c.+8c. yellow, drab and red 55 50
685 – 20c.+10c. yellow, drab and blue 55 50
686 – 25c.+12c. yellow, drab and orange 55 50
687 – 30c.+15c. yellow, drab and violet 55 50
DESIGNS—Beethoven: 15c. 1804; 20c. 1812; 25c. 1814; 30c. 1827.

1971. 25th Anniv of Netherlands–Surinam–Netherlands Antilles Air Service. Multicoloured.
689 15c. Type **134** 45 35
690 20c. Greater flamingo 45 35
691 25c. Scarlet macaw 45 35

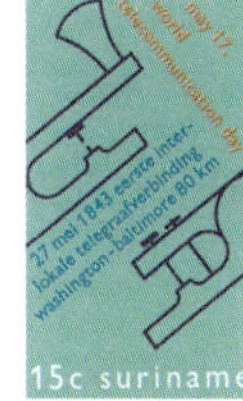

135 Donkey and Palm
136 Morse Key

1971. Easter. The Bible Story. Multicoloured.
692 10c.+5c. Type **135** 50 50
693 15c.+8c. Cockerel 50 50
694 20c.+10c. Lamb 50 50
695 25c.+12c. Crown of Thorns 50 50
696 30c.+15c. Sun ("The Resurrection") 50 50

1971. World Telecommunications Day. Mult.
697 15c. Type **136** 35 35
698 20c. Telephones 35 35
699 25c. Lunar module and telescope 35 35
EVENTS: 15c. First national telegraph, Washington–Baltimore, 1843; 20c. First international telephone communication, England–Sweden, 1926; 25c. First interplanetary television communication, Earth–Moon, 1969.

137 Prince Bernhard
138 Population Map

1971. Prince Bernhard's 60th Birthday.
700 **137** 25c. multicoloured 30 30

1971. 50th Anniv of 1st Census and Introduction of Civil Registration.
701 **138** 15c. blue, black and red 20 20
702 30c. red, black and blue 30 30
DESIGN: 30c. "Individual" representing civil registration.

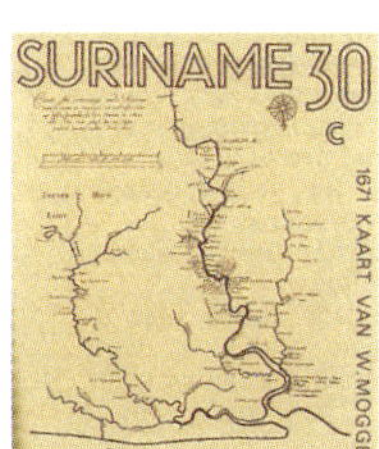

139 William Mogge's Map of Surinam

1971. 300th Anniv of First Surinam Map.
703 **139** 30c. brown on yellow . . 55 50

140 Leap-frog
141 Plan of Albina

1971. Child Welfare. Details from Brueghel's "Children's Games". Multicoloured.
704 10c.+5c. Type **140** 50 50
705 15c.+8c. Strewing flowers . . 50 50
706 20c.+10c. Rolling hoop . . . 50 50
707 25c.+12c. Playing ball . . . 50 50
708 30c.+15c. Stilt-walking . . . 50 50

1971. 125th Anniv of Albina Settlement.
710 **141** 15c. black on blue 35 35
711 – 20c. black on green . . . 35 35
712 – 25c. black on yellow . . . 35 35
DESIGNS—HORIZ: 20c. Albina and River Marowijne. VERT: 25c. August Kappler (naturalist and founder).

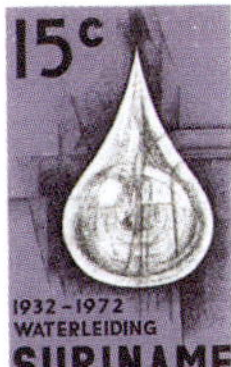

142 Drop of Water
143 Easter Candle

1972. 40th Anniv of Surinam Waterworks.
713 **142** 15c. black and violet . . . 30 30
714 – 30c. black and blue . . . 35 35
DESIGN: 30c. Water tap.

1972. Easter Charity. Multicoloured.
715 10c.+5c. Type **143** 50 50
716 15c.+8c. "Christ teaching the Apostles" 50 50
717 20c.+10c. Hands holding cup ("Christ in Gethsemane") 50 50
718 25c.+12c. Fishes in net ("Miracle of the Fishes") 50 50
719 30c.+15c. Pieces of silver ("Judas's Betrayal") . . . 50 50

144 "Eucyane bicolor"
145 Air-letter Motif

1972. Moths and Butterflies. Multicoloured.
720 15c. Type **144** 25 20
721 20c. Gold drop 25 20
722 25c. Orange swallowtail . . . 25 20
723 30c. White tailed page . . . 30 20
724 35c. "Stalachtis calliope" . . 30 20
725 40c. "Stalachtis phlegia" . . 30 20
726 45c. Malachite 30 20
727 50c. Spear-winged cattle heart 40 20
728 55c. Red anartia 55 55
729 60c. Five continent butterfly 55 75
730 65c. Doris 65 35
731 70c. "Nessaea obrinus" . . . 65 55
732 75c. Cracker 65 35

1972. 50th Anniv of 1st Airmail in Surinam.
733 **145** 15c. red and blue 20 20
734 30c. blue and red 30 30

146 Doll and Toys (kindergarten)
147 Giant Tree

1972. Child Welfare. Multicoloured.
735 10c.+5c. Type **146** 50 50
736 15c.+8c. Clock and abacus (primary education) . . . 50 50
737 20c.+10c. Blocks (primary education) 50 50
738 25c.+12c. Molecule complex (secondary education) . . 50 50
739 30c.+15c. Wrench and blue-print (technical education) 50 50

1972. 25th Anniv of Surinam Forestry Commission.
741 **147** 15c. brown and yellow . . 25 20
742 – 20c. brown, black and blue 25 20
743 – 30c. chocolate, brn & grn 30 35
DESIGNS: 20c. Aerial transport of logs; 30c. Planting tree.

148 "The Storm on the Lake"
149 Hindu Peasant Woman

1973. Easter Charity. Jesus's Life and Death. Mult.
744 10c.+5c. Type **148** 50 50
745 15c.+8c. "Washing the Disciples' Feet" 50 50
746 20c.+10c. "Jesus taken to Execution" 50 50

747 25c.+12c. The Cross 50 50
748 30c.+15c. "The Men of Emmaus" 50 50

1973. Centenary of Arrival of Indian Immigrants in Surinam.
749 **149** 15c. violet and yellow . . 30 30
750 – 25c. red and grey 30 30
751 – 30c. orange and blue . . 35 35
DESIGNS: 25c. J. F. A. Cateau van Rosevelt, Head of Department of Immigration, holding map; 30c. Symbols of immigration.

150 Queen Juliana

1973. Silver Jubilee of Queen Juliana's Reign.
752 **150** 30c. black, orange & silver 65 55

151 Florence Nightingale and Red Cross

152 Interpol Emblem

1973. 30th Anniv of Surinam Red Cross.
753 **151** 30c.+10c. multicoloured 75 75

1973. 50th Anniv of International Criminal Police Organization (Interpol). Multicoloured.
754 15c. Type **152** 20 20
755 30c. Emblem within passport stamp 30 30

153 Flower

154 Carrier-pigeons

1973. Child Welfare.
756 **153** 10c.+5c. multicoloured . . 50 50
757 – 15c.+8c. green, brown and emerald 50 50
758 – 20c.+10c. violet, blue and green 50 50
759 – 25c.+12c. multicoloured 50 50
760 – 30c.+15c. multicoloured 50 50
DESIGNS: 15c. Tree; 20c. Dog; 25c. House; 30c. Doll.

1973. Stamp Centenary.
762 **154** 15c. green and blue . . . 20 20
763 – 25c. multicoloured 30 30
764 – 30c. multicoloured . . . 50 50
DESIGNS: 25c. Postman; 30c. Map and postal routes.

155 "Quassia amara"

156 Nurse and Blood Transfusion Equipment

1974. Easter Charity Flowers. Multicoloured.
765 10c.+5c. Type **155** 55 50
766 15c.+8c. "Passiflora quadrangularis" 55 50
767 20c.+10c. "Combretum rotundifolium" 55 50
768 25c.+12c. "Cassia alata" . . 55 50
769 30c.+15c. "Asclepias curassavica" 55 50

1974. 75th Anniv of Surinam Medical School. Multicoloured.
770 15c. Type **156** 20 20
771 30c. Microscope slide and oscilloscope scanner . . . 30 30

157 Aerial Crop-spraying

158 Commemorative Text superimposed on Early Newspaper

1974. 25th Anniv of Mechanized Agriculture. Multicoloured.
772 15c. Type **157** 20 30
773 30c. Fertilizer plant 20 30

1974. Bicentenary of Surinam's "Weekly Wednesday" Newspaper.
774 **158** 15c. multicoloured 20 20
775 30c. multicoloured 30 30

159 Scout and Tent

160 G.P.O., Paramaribo

1974. "50 Years of Scouting in Surinam". Mult.
776 10c.+5c. Type **159** 45 35
777 15c.+8c. Jamboree emblem 45 35
778 20c.+10c. Scouts and badge 45 35

1974. Centenary of Universal Postal Union.
779 **160** 15c. black and brown . . . 20 20
780 – 30c. black and blue . . . 30 30
DESIGN: 30c. G.P.O., Paramaribo (different view).

161 Girl with Fruit

1974. Child Welfare.
781 **161** 10c.+5c. green, emerald and pink 50 50
782 – 15c.+8c. brown, mauve and green 50 50
783 – 20c.+10c. yellow, orange and mauve 50 50
784 – 25c.+12c. brown, lilac and yellow 50 50
785 – 30c.+15c. cobalt, blue and lilac 50 50
DESIGNS: 15c. Birds and nest; 20c. Mother and child with flower; 25c. Young boy in cornfield; 30c. Children at play.

162 Panning for Gold

163 "I am the Good Shepherd"

1975. Centenary of Prospecting Concession Policy.
787 **162** 15c. brown and bistre . . 20 20
788 – 30c. purple and red . . . 30 30
DESIGN: 30c. Claws of modern excavator.

1975. Easter Charity.
789 **163** 15c.+5c. yellow and green 50 50
790 – 20c.+10c. yellow and blue 50 50
791 – 30c.+15c. yellow and red 50 50
792 – 35c.+20c. blue and violet 50 50
DESIGNS—Quotations from the New Testament: 20c. "I do not know the man"; 30c. "He is not here; He has been raised again"; 35c. "Because you have seen Me you have found faith. Happy are they who never saw Me and yet have found faith".

164 "Looking to Equality, Education and Peace"

165 "Weights and Measures"

1975. International Women's Year.
793 **164** 15c.+5c. blue and green 50 50
794 30c.+15c. violet & mve . . 50 50

1975. Centenary of Metre Convention.
795 **165** 15c. multicoloured . . . 35 35
796 25c. multicoloured . . . 35 35
796a 30c. multicoloured . . . 35 35

166 Caribbean Water Jug

167 "Labour and Technology"

1975. Child Welfare. Multicoloured.
797 15c.+5c. Type **166** 50 50
798 20c.+10c. Indian arrowhead 50 50
799 30c.+15c. "Maluana" (protection against evil spirits) 50 50
800 35c.+20c. Indian arrowhead (different) 50 50

1975. Independence. "Nation in Development". Multicoloured.
802 25c. Type **167** 20 20
803 50c. Open book ("Education and Art") 50 50
804 75c. Hands with ball ("Physical Training") . . . 70 70

168 Central Bank, Paramaribo

169 "Oncidium lanceanum"

1975.
805 **168** 1g. black, mauve & purple 90 25
806 $1\frac{1}{2}$g. black, orange & brn 1·50 25
807 $2\frac{1}{2}$g. black, red and brown 2·75 35
808 5g. black, emerald & green . . . . 5·50 55
809 10g. black, blue & dp blue 11·00 1·10

1976. Surinam Orchids. Multicoloured.
809 1c. Type **169** 10 10
810 2c. "Epidendrum stenopetalum" 10 10
811 3c. "Brassia lanceana" . . . 10 10
812 4c. "Epidendrum ibaguense" 10 10
813 5c. "Epidendrum fragans" . . 10 10

170 Surinam Flag

171 "Feeding the Hungry"

1976. Multicoloured.
814 25c. Type **170** 30 30
815 35c. Surinam arms 35 35

1976. Easter. Paintings in Alkmaar Church. Mult.
816 20c.+10c. Type **171** 30 30
817 25c.+15c. "Visiting the Sick" 35 35
818 30c.+15c. "Clothing the Naked" 40 40
819 35c.+15c. "Burying the Dead" 45 55
820 50c.+25c. "Refreshing the Thirsty" 70 80

172 Semicircle Angelfish

1976. Fishes. Multicoloured.
822 1c. Type **172** (postage) . . 10 10
823 2c. Diadem squirrelfish . . . 10 10
824 3c. Zebra goby 10 10
825 4c. Queen triggerfish 10 10
826 5c. Black-barred soldierfish 10 10
827 35c. Teardrop butterflyfish (air) 50 40
828 60c. Flame angelfish 90 65
829 95c. Red-tailed butterflyfish 1·40 1·00

173 Early Telephone and Switchboard

1976. Telephone Centenary.
830 20c. Type **173** 25 20
831 35c. Globe, satellite and modern telephone 40 35

174 "Anansi Tori" (A. Baag)

1976. Paintings by Surinam Artists. Mult.
832 20c. Type **174** 25 20
833 30c. "Surinam Now" (R. Chang) 35 30
834 35c. "Lamentation" (N. Hatterman) (vert) . . . 45 40
835 50c. "Chess-players" (Q. Jan Telting) 60 55

175 "Join or Die" (Franklin's "Divided Snake" poster of 1754)

1976. Bicentenary of American Revolution.
836 **175** 20c. black, green & cream 25 20
837 60c. black, red and cream 75 75

176 Pekinese

177 "Ionopsis utricularioides"

1976. Child Welfare. Pet Dogs.
838 20c.+10c. Type **176** 40 40
839 25c.+10c. Alsatian 45 45
840 30c.+10c. Dachshund 55 55
841 35c.+15c. Surinam breed . . 60 60
842 50c.+25c. Mongrel 85 85

1976. As Nos. 551/7 and new values but size 22 × 18 mm.
843a – 5c. brown 10 10
843b **98** 10c. green 15 10
843c – 20c. green 25 15
843d – 25c. blue 25 15
843e – 30c. green 30 15
843f – 35c. red 35 20
843g – 40c. orange 50 25
843h – 60c. red 75 35
NEW VALUES: 5c. Brewery; 60c. Jetty.

1977. Surinam Orchids. Multicoloured.
844 20c. Type **177** 30 25
845 30c. "Rodiguezia secunda" 45 40

846	35c. "Oncidium pusillum"	50	45
847	55c. "Sobralia sessulis"	75	65
848	60c. "Octomeria surinamensis"	80	70

178 Javanese Costume

179 Triptych, left panel (Jan Mostaert)

1977. Surinam Costumes (1st series). Mult.

849	10c. Type **178**	15	10
850	15c. Forest Negro	20	15
851	35c. Chinese	40	35
852	60c. Creole	75	65
853	75c. Aborigine Indian	95	85
854	1g. Hindustani	1·25	1·25

DESIGNS: 15c. to 1g. Various women's festival costumes.

See also Nos. 906/11.

1977. Easter. Multicoloured.

855	20c.+10c. Type **179**	25	30
856	25c.+15c. Right panel	35	40
857	30c.+15c. Right panel	40	45
858	35c.+15c. Centre panel (30 × 38 mm.)	50	55
859	50c.+25c. Left panel	70	80

The 20c. and 25c. show the triptych closed, the 30c. and 50c. show designs on the reverse of the doors, and the 35c. shows the centre panel.

180 Green Honeycreeper

1977. Air. Birds. Multicoloured.

860	20c. Red-breasted blackbird	60	35
861	25c. Type **180**	70	40
862	30c. Paradise tanager	75	45
863	40c. Spot-tailed nightjar	90	55
864	45c. Yellow-backed tanager	95	60
865	50c. White-tailed goldenthroat	1·00	70
866	55c. Grey-breasted sabrewing	1·10	75
867	60c. Caica parrot (vert)	1·10	80
868	65c. Red-billed toucan (vert)	1·25	90
869	70c. Crimson-hooded manakin (vert)	1·40	95
870	75c. Hawk-headed parrot (vert)	1·50	1·00
871	80c. Spangled cotinga (vert)	1·75	1·10
872	85c. Black-tailed trogon (vert)	1·90	1·25
872a	90c. Orange-winged amazon (vert)	1·75	1·10
873	95c. Black-banded owl (vert)	2·00	1·40

181 Candy Basslet

1977. Fishes. Multicoloured.

875	1c. Type **181** (postage)	10	10
876	2c. Queen angelfish	10	10
877	3c. Yellow-headed jawfish	10	10
878	4c. Porkfish	10	10
879	5c. Royal gramma	10	10
880	60c. Banded butterflyfish (air)	75	65
881	90c. Spot-finned hogfish	1·10	95
882	120c. Cherub angelfish	1·75	1·40

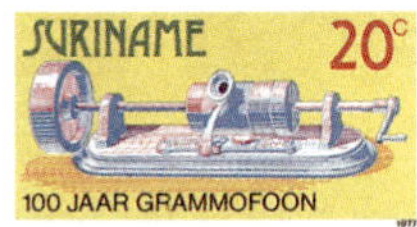

182 Edison's Phonograph, 1877

1977. Centenary of Sound Reproduction. Mult.

883	20c. Type **182**	25	20
883a	60c. Modern gramophone turntable	75	75

183 Paddle Steamer "Curacao"

185 Dog

1977. 150th Anniv of Regular Passenger Steam Service with Netherlands.

884	**183** 5c. blue and light blue	25	10
885	– 15c. red and orange	45	15
886	– 30c. black and ochre	40	35
887	– 35c. black and olive	50	40
888	– 60c. black and lilac	80	70
889	– 95c. green and light green	1·75	1·75

DESIGNS: 15c. Hellevoetsluis port; 30c. Chart of steamer route from Hellevoetsluis to Paramaribo; 35c. Log of "Curacao"; 60c. Chart of Paramaribo and 1852 postmark; 95c. Passenger liner "Stuyvesant".

1977. Surch.

890	– 1c. on 25c. mult (No. 722)	10	10
891	**144** 4c. on 15c. multicoloured	10	10
892	– 4c. on 30c. mult (No. 723)	10	10
893	– 5c. on 40c. mult (No. 725)	10	10
894	– 10c. on 75c. mult (No. 732)	15	15

The word "LUCHTPOST" ("AIR-MAIL") on the original stamp is obliterated by bars.

1977. Child Welfare. Multicoloured.

895	20c.+10c. Type **185**	30	35
896	25c.+15c. Monkey	40	45
897	30c.+15c. Rabbit	45	50
898	35c.+15c. Cat	50	55
899	50c.+25c. Parrot	75	80

186 "Passiflora quadrangularis"

187 Javanese Costumes

1978. Flowers. Multicoloured.

901	20c. Type **186**	25	20
902	30c. "Centropogon surinamensis"	35	30
903	55c. "Gloxinia perennis"	65	55
904	60c. "Hydrocleys nymphoides"	70	60
905	75c. "Clusia grandiflora"	85	75

1978. Surinam Costumes (2nd series). Mult.

906	10c. Type **187**	15	10
907	20c. Forest Negro	25	20
908	35c. Chinese	40	35
909	60c. Creole	75	60
910	75c. Aborigine Indian	85	75
911	1g. Hindustani	1·25	1·25

188 Cross and Halo

189 Municipal Church, 1783

1978. Easter Charity.

912	**188** 20c.+10c. multicoloured	30	35
913	– 25c.+15c. brown, yellow and red	45	50
914	– 30c.+15c. brown, red and yellow	50	55
915	– 35c.+15c. brown, violet and red	55	60
916	– 60c.+30c. brown, yellow and green	1·00	1·10

DESIGNS: 25c. Serpent and cross; 30c. Blood and lamb; 35c. Passover dish and chalice; 60c. Eclipse and crucifix.

1978. Bicentenary of Church of Evangelistic Brothers Community.

917	**189** 10c. brown, black and blue	10	10
918	– 20c. black and grey	20	20
919	– 55c. black and purple	55	55
920	– 60c. black and orange	70	70

DESIGNS: 20c. Brother Johannes King, 1830–1899; 55c. Modern Municipal Church; 60c. Brother Johannes Raillard, 1939–1954.

190 Golden-eyed Cichlid

192 Coconuts

1978. Tropical Fish. Multicoloured.

921	1c. Type **190** (postage)	10	10
922	2c. Banded leporinus	10	10
923	3c. X-ray tetra	10	10
924	4c. Golden pencilfish	10	10
925	5c. Agila rivulus	10	10
926	60c. Two-spotted astyanax (air)	85	75
927	90c. Blue-spotted corydoras	1·25	1·10
928	120c. River hatchetfish	1·75	1·50

1978. Fruits. Multicoloured.

930	5c. Type **192**	10	10
931	10c. Citrus	10	10
932	15c. Papaya	15	15
933a	20c. Bananas	15	15
934	25c. Sour-sop	25	25
934b	30c. Cacao	25	25
935	35c. Water melons	35	35

193 Children's Heads and Kittens

194 Daedalus and Icarus

1978. Child Welfare.

936	**193** 20c.+10c. multicoloured	25	30
937	– 25c.+15c. multicoloured	35	40
938	– 30c.+15c. multicoloured	40	45
939	– 35c.+15c. multicoloured	40	45
940	– 60c.+30c. multicoloured	80	90

DESIGNS: 25c. to 60c. Different designs showing kittens at play.

1978. 75th Anniv of First Powered Flight. Mult.

942	20c. Type **194**	25	20
943	60c. Wright Flyer I (horiz)	60	50
944	95c. Douglas DC-8-63 (horiz)	85	70
945	125c. Concorde (horiz)	1·25	1·25

195 Black Curassow

196 "Rodriguezia candida"

1979. Air.

946	**195** 5g. purple	8·00	6·00

1979. Orchids. Multicoloured.

947	10c. Type **196**	15	10
948	20c. "Stanhopea grandiflora"	25	20
949	35c. "Scuticaria steelei"	40	35
950	60c. "Bollea violacea"	65	60

197 Javanese Dance

198 Church, Chalice and Cross

1979. Dancing Costumes. Multicoloured.

951	5c. Type **197**	10	10
952	10c. Forest Negro	10	10
953	15c. Chinese	20	15
954	20c. Creole	20	20
955	25c. Aborigine Indian	25	20
956	25c. Hindustani	35	35

1979. Easter Charity.

957	**198** 20c.+10c. multicoloured	25	30
958	– 30c.+15c. multicoloured	35	40
959	– 35c.+15c. multicoloured	40	45
960	– 40c.+20c. multicoloured	45	50
961	– 60c.+30c. multicoloured	70	80

DESIGNS: 30c. to 60c. Different churches.

199 Spotted Drum

1979. Fishes. Multicoloured.

962	1c. Type **199** (postage)	10	10
963	2c. Barred cardinalfish	10	10
964	3c. Porkfish	10	10
965	5c. Spanish hogfish	10	10
966	35c. Yellow-tailed damselfish	45	40
967	60c. White-spotted filefish (air)	75	70
968	90c. Long-spined squirrelfish	1·10	1·00
969	120c. Rock beauty	1·50	1·40

200 Javanese Wooden Head

1979. Art Objects. Multicoloured.

970	20c. Type **200**	20	20
971	35c. American Indian hair ornament	30	30
972	60c. Javanese horse's head	55	55

201 S.O.S. Children's Village and Emblem

202 Sir Rowland Hill

1979. International Year of the Child. Mult.

973	20c. Type **201**	20	15
974	60c. Different view of Village, and emblem	55	55

1979. Death Centenary of Sir Rowland Hill.

975	**202** 1g. green and yellow	1·00	1·00

203 Bird, Running Youth and Blood Transfusion Bottle

204 Javanese

1979. Child Welfare.

976	**203** 20c.+10c. blk, vio & red	25	30
977	30c.+15c. blk, red & vio	40	45
978	35c.+15c. multicoloured	45	50
979	40c.+20c. multicoloured	50	55
980	60c.+30c. multicoloured	70	80

1980. Children's Costumes. Multicoloured.

982	10c. Type **204**	10	10
983	15c. Forest Negro	15	15
984	25c. Chinese	25	20
985	60c. Creole	55	55
986	90c. Indian	80	80
987	1g. Hindustani	85	85

205 Handshake and Rotary Emblem

206 Church Interior

1980. 75th Anniv of Rotary International. Each blue and yellow.

988	20c. Type **205**	20	20
989	60c. Globe and Rotary emblem	50	50

1980. Easter Charity. Various Easter symbols.

990	**206** 20c.+10c. multicoloured	25	30
991	– 30c.+15c. multicoloured	40	45
992	– 40c.+20c. multicoloured	50	55
993	– 50c.+25c. multicoloured	60	70
994	– 60c.+30c. multicoloured	70	80

207 Mail Coach

208 Weightlifting

1980. "London 1980" International Stamp Exhibition.
995 **207** 50c. yellow, black and blue 40 40
996 – 1g. yellow, black & purple 80 80
997 – 2g. pink, black & turq . . 1·60 1·60
DESIGNS: 1g. Sir Rowland Hill; 2g. People posting letters.

1980. Olympic Games, Moscow.
999 **208** 20c. multicoloured . . . 20 20
1000 – 30c. multicoloured . . . 25 25
1001 – 50c. green, yellow and red 40 40
1002 – 75c. multicoloured . . . 60 60
1003 – 150c. multicoloured . . . 1·25 1·25
DESIGNS: 30c. Diving; 50c. Gymnastics; 75c. Basketball; 150c. Running.

209 Arawana

210 Anansi disguised as Spider

1980. Tropical Fishes. Multicoloured.
1005 10c. Type **209** (postage) . . 10 10
1006 15c. Colossoma 15 15
1007 25c. Garnet tetra 30 20
1008 30c. False rummy-nosed tetra 35 25
1009 45c. Red-spotted tetra . . . 50 40
1010 60c. Red discus (air) 70 55
1011 75c. Flag acara 80 65
1012 90c. Wimple piranha . . . 95 75

1980. Child Welfare. "The Story of Anansi and his Creditors".
1013 **210** 20c.+10c. bistre and yellow 30 35
1014 – 25c.+15c. yellow, brown and orange 35 40
1015 – 30c.+15c. brown, red and orange 40 45
1016 – 35c.+15c. green, light green and yellow . . . 45 50
1017 – 60c.+30c. multicoloured 80 90
DESIGNS—(Anansi in various disguises): 25c. Bear; 30c. Cockerel; 35c. Hunter; 60c. Beetle.

212 Old Woman reading

SURINAME 20C
Passiflora laurifolia
Naar Maria Sibylle Merian

213 "Passiflora laurifolia"

1980. Welfare of the Aged. Multicoloured.
1020 25c.+10c. Type **212** 30 35
1021 50c.+15c. Old man tending flowers 50 60
1022 75c.+20c. Grandfather and grandchildren 80 90

1981. Flower Drawings by Maria Sibylle Merian. Multicoloured.
1023 20c. Type **213** 20 20
1024 30c. "Aphelandra pectinata" 30 25
1025 60c. "Caesalpinia pulcherrima" 55 55
1026 75c. "Hibiscus mutabilis" 70 70
1027 1g.25 "Hippeastrum puniceum" . . . . 1·25 1·25

214 Justice and Text "Renewal of the Governmental and Political Order"

SURINAME
20+10c
PAASWELDADIGHEID

215 Christ with Jug

1981. The Four Renewals.
1028 – 30c. yellow, brown and deep yellow 25 25
1029 – 60c. orange, brown & red 50 50
1030 – 75c. green, deep green and olive 60 60
1031 **214** 1g. deep yellow, green and yellow 80 80
DESIGNS: 30c. "Renewal of the Economic Order"; 60c. "Renewal of the Educational Order"; 75c. "Renewal of the Social Order".

1981. Easter Charity. Multicoloured.
1033 20c.+10c. Type **215** 25 30
1034 30c.+15c. Christ and pointing hand 40 45
1035 50c.+25c. Christ and Roman soldier 60 65
1036 60c.+30c. Christ wearing crown of thorns 70 80
1037 75c.+35c. Christ and Mary 80 90

218 "Phyllomedusa hypochondrialis"

1981. Frogs. Multicoloured.
1040 40c. Type **218** (postage) . . 40 35
1041 50c. "Leptodactylus pentadactylus" 45 40
1042 60c. "Hyla boans" 55 50
1043 75c. "Phyllomedusa burmeisteri" (vert) (air) 70 65
1044 1g. "Dendrobates tinctorius" (vert) 90 85
1045 1g.25 "Bufo guttatus" (vert) 1·25 1·25

219 Deaf Child

1981. International Year of Disabled Persons.
1046 **219** 50c. yellow and green . . 40 40
1047 – 100c. yellow and green 80 80
1048 – 150c. yellow and red . . 1·25 1·25
DESIGNS: 100c. Child reading braille; 150c. Woman in wheelchair.

220 Planter's House on the Parakreek River

221 Indian Girl

1981. Illustrations to "Journey to Surinam" by P. I. Benoit. Multicoloured.
1049 20c. Type **220** 20 20
1050 30c. Sarameca Street, Paramaribo 25 25
1051 75c. Negro hamlet, Paramaribo 60 60
1052 1g. Fish market, Paramaribo 80 80
1053 1g.25 Blaauwe Berg Cascade 1·00 1·00

1981. Child Welfare. Multicoloured.
1055 20c.+10c. Type **221** 25 30
1056 30c.+15c. Negro girl 40 45
1057 50c.+25c. Hindustani girl . . 60 70
1058 60c.+30c. Javanese girl . . . 70 80
1059 75c.+35c. Chinese girl . . . 80 90

222 Satellites orbiting Earth

1982. Peaceful Uses of Outer Space. Mult.
1061 35c. Type **222** 35 30
1062 65c. Space shuttle 60 55
1063 1g. U.S.–Russian space link 85 85

223 "Caretta caretta"

224 Pattern from Stained Glass Window

1982. Turtles. Multicoloured.
1064 5c. Type **223** (postage) . . . 10 10
1065 10c. "Chelonia mydas" . . 10 10
1066 20c. "Dermochelys coriacea" 20 20
1067 25c. "Eretmochelys imbricata" 25 25
1068 35c. "Lepidochelys olivacea" 30 30
1069 65c. "Platemys platycephala" (air) . . . 60 60
1070 75c. "Phrynops gibba" . . . 75 75
1071 125c. "Rihnoclemys punctularia" . . . . . . 1·10 1·10

1982. Easter. Stained-glass Windows, Church of Saints Peter and Paul, Paramaribo.
1072 **224** 20c.+10c. multicoloured 25 30
1073 – 35c.+15c. multicoloured 40 45
1074 – 50c.+25c. multicoloured 60 70
1075 – 65c.+30c. multicoloured 75 85
1076 – 75c.+35c. multicoloured 80 90
DESIGNS: 35c. to 75c. Different patterns.

225 Lions Emblem

SURINAME 35c
Zaligverklaring Pater Donders

226 Father Donders with the Sick

1982. 25th Anniv of Surinam Lions Club.
1077 **225** 35c. multicoloured . . . 30 30
1078 70c. multicoloured . . . 60 60

1982. Beatification of Father Peter Donders.
1079 **226** 35c. multicoloured . . . 30 30
1080 – 65c. silver, black and red 50 50
DESIGN: 65c. Portrait, birthplace, Tilburg, and map of South America.

227 Stamp Designer

228 Dr. Robert Koch

1982. "Philexfrance 82" International Stamp Exhibition, Paris. Multicoloured.
1082 50c. Type **227** 40 40
1083 100c. Stamp printing . . . 80 80
1084 150c. Stamp collector . . . 1·25 1·25

1982. Cent of Discovery of Tubercle Bacillus.
1086 **228** 35c. yellow and green . . 35 30
1087 – 65c. orange and brown 60 55
1088 – 150c. light blue, blue and red . . . . 1·50 1·50
DESIGNS: 65c. Dr. Koch and microscope; 150c. Dr. Koch and Bacillus.

229 Sugar Mill

230 Cleaning Tools and Flag

1982. Cent of Marienburg Sugar Company.
1089 **229** 35c. yellow, green and black 30 30
1090 – 65c. orange and brown 50 50
1091 – 100c. light blue, blue and black . . . . 2·10 2·10
1092 – 150c. lilac and purple . . 1·25 1·25
DESIGNS: 65c. Workers in cane fields; 100c. Sugar-cane railway; 150c. Mill machinery.

1982. Child Welfare. "Keep Surinam Tidy" (children's paintings). Multicoloured.
1093 20c.+10c. Type **230** 25 30
1094 35c.+15c. Man with barrow 40 45
1095 50c.+25c. Litter bin and cleaning tools 60 70
1096 65c.+30c. Spraying weeds 75 85
1097 75c.+35c. Litter bin 85 95

231 Municipal Church, Paramaribo

1982. 250th Anniv of Moravian Church Mission in the Caribbean.
1099 **231** 35c. multicoloured . . . 30 30
1100 – 65c. light blue, black and blue 50 50
1101 – 150c. multicoloured . . . 1·25 1·25
DESIGNS—HORIZ: 65c. Aerial view of St. Thomas Monastery. VERT: 150c. Johann Leonhardt Dober (missionary).

232 "Erythrina fusca"

1983. Flower Paintings by Maria Sibylle Merian. Multicoloured.
1102 1c. Type **232** 10 10
1103 2c. "Ipomoea acuminata" . 10 10
1104 3c. "Heliconia psittacorum" 10 10
1105 5c. "Ipomoea" 10 10
1106 10c. "Herba non denominata" 10 10
1107 15c. "Anacardium occidentale" 15 15
1108 20c. "Inga edulis" (vert) . . 20 15
1109 25c. "Abelmoschus moschatus" (vert) . . . 25 20
1110 30c. "Argemone mexicana" (vert) 30 25
1111 35c. "Costus arabicus" (vert) 35 30
1112 45c. "Muellera frutescens" (vert) 45 45
1113 65c. "Punica granatum" (vert) 60 60

233 Scout Anniversary Emblem

234 Dove of Peace

1983. Year of the Scout.
1114 **233** 40c. mauve, violet & green 45 40
1115 – 65c. lt grey, blue & grey 70 60
1116 – 70c. multicoloured . . . 80 70
1117 – 80c. blue, lt green & green 85 80
DESIGNS: 65c. Lord Baden-Powell; 70c. Tent and campfire; 80c. Axe in tree trunk.

1983. Easter. Multicoloured.
1118 **234** 10c.+5c. Type 15 15
1119 15c.+5c. Bread 20 25
1120 25c.+10c. Fish 30 35
1121 50c.+25c. Eye 60 70
1122 65c.+30c. Chalice . . . 75 85

235 Drawing by Raphael

1983. 500th Birth Anniv of Raphael.
1123 **235** 5c. multicoloured 10 10
1124 – 10c. multicoloured . . . 10 10
1125 – 40c. multicoloured . . . 35 35
1126 – 65c. multicoloured . . . 60 60
1127 – 70c. multicoloured . . . 65 65
1128 – 80c. multicoloured . . . 70 70
DESIGNS: 10c. to 80c. Drawings by Raphael.

236 1c. Coin

237 "25" on Map of Surinam

1983. Coins and Banknotes. Multicoloured.
1129 5c. Type **236** 10 10
1130 10c. 5c. coin 10 10
1131 40c. 10c. coin 45 40
1132 65c. 25c. coin 65 65
1133 70c. 1g. note 70 70
1134 80c. 2½g. note . . . . . . 1·50 90

1983. 25th Anniv of Department of Construction. Multicoloured.
1135 25c. Type **237** 25 25
1136 50c. Construction vehicles on map 45 45

238 "Papilio anchisiades"

239 Montgolfier Balloon "Le Martial", 1783

1983. Butterfly Paintings by Maria Sibylle Merian. Multicoloured.
1137 1c. Type **238** 10 10
1138 2c. "Urania leilus" 10 10
1139 3c. "Morpho deidamia" . . . 10 10
1140 5c. "Thysania agrippina" . . 10 10
1141 10c. "Morpho sp." 20 10
1142 15c. "Philaethria dido" . . 30 20
1143 20c. "Morpho menelaus" (horiz) 40 25
1144 25c. "Protoparce rustica" (horiz) 50 30
1145 30c. "Rothschildia aurota" (horiz) 60 40
1146 35c. "Phoebis sennae" (horiz) 80 50
1147 45c. "Papilio androgeos" (horiz) 90 70
1148 65c. "Dupo vitis" (horiz) . . 1·40 1·00

1983. Bicentenary of Manned Flight. Mult.
1149 5c. Type **239** 10 10
1150 10c. Montgolfier balloon (1st manned free flight by D'Arlandes and Pilatre de Rozier, 1783) 10 10
1151 40c. Charles's hydrogen balloon, 1783 . . . . . . 40 40
1152 65c. Balloon "Armand Barbes", 1870 . . . . . . 65 65
1153 70c. Balloon "Double Eagle II" (transatlantic flight, 1978) 70 70
1154 80c. Hot-air balloons at International Balloon Festival, Albuquerque, U.S.A. 75 75

240 Calabash Pitcher 241 Martin Luther

1983. Child Welfare. Caribbean Artifacts. Mult.
1155 10c.+5c. Type **240** 15 15
1156 15c.+5c. Umari (headdress) 15 20
1157 25c.+10c. Maraka (medicine man's rattle) 20 35
1158 50c.+25c. Manari (sieve) . . 60 70
1159 65c.+30c. Pasuwa/pakara (basket) 70 80

1983. 500th Birth Anniv of Martin Luther (Protestant reformer).
1161 **241** 25c. yellow, brown and black 20 20
1162 – 50c. pink, purple & black 40 40
DESIGN: 50c. Selling of indulgences.

242 "Catasetum discolor" 243 Atlantic Turkey Wing

1983. Orchids. Multicoloured.
1163 5c. Type **242** 10 10
1164 10c. "Menadenium labiosum" 10 10
1165 40c. "Comparettia falcata" 45 40
1166 50c. "Rodriguezia decora" 70 60
1167 70c. "Oncidium papilio" . . 80 70
1168 75c. "Epidendrum porpax" 85 75

1984. Sea Shells. Multicoloured.
1169 40c. Type **243** 45 45
1170 65c. American prickly cockle 80 80
1171 70c. Sunrise tellin 80 80
1172 80c. Knorr's worm shell . . 95 95

244 Cross and Flower 245 Sikorsky S-40 Flying Boat

1984. Easter. Multicoloured.
1173 10c.+5c. Type **244** 15 15
1174 15c.+5c. Cross and gate of cemetery 15 20
1175 25c.+10c. Candle flames . . 30 35
1176 50c.+25c. Cross and crown of thorns 60 70
1177 65c.+30c. Lamp 70 80

1984. 40th Anniv of I.C.A.O. Multicoloured.
1178 35c. Type **245** 40 40
1179 65c. Surinam Airways De Havilland Twin Otter 200/300 . . . . 85 85

246 Running 247 Emblem of 8th Caribbean Scout Jamboree

1984. Olympic Games, Los Angeles. Multicoloured.
1180 2c. Type **246** 10 10
1181 3c. Javelin, discus and long jump 10 10
1182 5c. Massage 10 10
1183 10c. Rubbing with ointment 10 10
1184 15c. Wrestling 15 15
1185 20c. Boxing 20 20
1186 30c. Horse-racing 30 30
1187 35c. Chariot-racing 35 35
1188 45c. Temple of Olympia . . 40 40
1189 50c. Entrance to Stadium, Olympia 45 45
1190 65c. Stadium, Olympia . . . 60 60
1191 75c. Zeus 70 70

1984. 60th Anniv of Scouting in Surinam. Mult.
1193 30c.+10c. Type **247** 40 40
1194 35c.+10c. Scout saluting . . 50 50
1195 50c.+10c. Scout camp . . . 65 65
1196 90c.+10c. Campfire and map 95 95

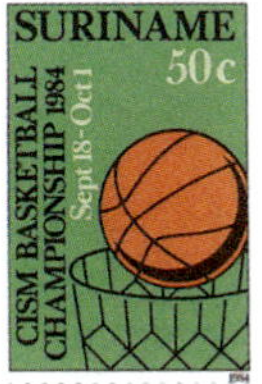

248 Ball entering Basket 249 Red Square, Moscow

1984. International Military Sports Council Basketball Championship. Multicoloured.
1197 50c. Type **248** 50 45
1198 90c. Ball leaving basket . . 85 75

1984. World Chess Championship, Moscow.
1199 **249** 10c. brown 10 10
1200 – 15c. green and light green 15 15
1201 – 30c. light brown & brown 30 30
1202 – 50c. brown and purple . . 50 50
1203 – 75c. brown & light brown 80 80
1204 – 90c. green and blue . . . 90 90
DESIGNS: 15c. Knight, king and pawn on board; 30c. Gary Kasparov; 50c. Start of game and clock; 75c. Anatoly Karpov; 90c. Position during Andersen–Kizeritski game.

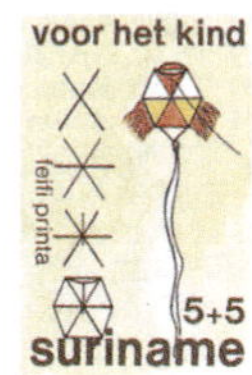

250 Children collecting Milk from Cow 251 Kite

1984. World Food Day. Multicoloured.
1206 50c. Type **250** 50 45
1207 90c. Platter of food 85 75

1984. Child Welfare. Multicoloured.
1208 5c.+5c. Type **251** 10 10
1209 10c.+5c. Kites 15 15
1210 30c.+10c. Pingi-pingi-kasi (game) 40 40
1211 50c.+25c. Cricket 85 85
1212 90c.+30c. Peroen, peroen (game) . . . . 1·10 1·10

252 Leaf Cactus

1985. Cacti. Multicoloured.
1215 5c. Type **252** 10 10
1216 10c. Melocactus 10 10
1217 30c. Pillar cactus 25 25
1218 50c. Fig cactus 45 45
1219 75c. Night queen 70 70
1220 90c. Segment cactus 80 80

253 "Peace" and Star 254 Crosses

1985. 5th Anniv of Revolution. Multicoloured.
1221 5c. Type **253** 10 10
1222 30c. "Unity in labour" and manual workers 20 20
1223 50c. "5 years of Steadfastness" and flower 40 40
1224 75c. "Progress" and wheat as flower 60 60
1225 90c. "Unity", flower and dove 70 70

1985. Easter. Multicoloured.
1227 5c.+5c. Type **254** 10 10
1228 10c.+5c. Crosses (different) 10 10
1229 30c.+15c. Sun's rays illuminating crosses . . . 30 30
1230 50c.+25c. Crosses (different) 55 65
1231 90c.+30c. Crosses and leaves (Resurrection) 75 85

255 Emblem 256 U.N. Emblem and State Arms

1985. 75th Anniv of Chamber of Commerce and Industry.
1232 **255** 50c. yellow, green and red 40 40
1233 – 90c. green, blue & yellow 70 70
DESIGN: 90c. Chamber of Commerce building.

1985. 40th Anniv of U.N.O.
1234 **256** 50c. multicoloured . . . 40 40
1235 90c. multicoloured . . . 70 70

257 Sugar-cane Train (detail of 1945 stamp)

1985. Railway Locomotives.
1236 **257** 5c. orange and blue . . 10 10
1237 – 5c. green, red and blue 10 10
1238 – 10c. multicoloured . . . 20 15
1239 – 10c. multicoloured . . . 20 15
1240 – 20c. multicoloured . . . 45 30
1241 – 20c. multicoloured . . . 45 30
1242 – 30c. multicoloured . . . 80 45
1243 – 30c. multicoloured . . . 80 45
1244 – 50c. multicoloured . . . 1·40 80
1245 – 50c. multicoloured . . . 1·40 80
1246 – 75c. multicoloured . . . 1·75 1·25
1247 – 75c. multicoloured . . . 1·75 1·25
DESIGNS: No. 1237, Monaco 3f. Postage due train stamp; 1238, Steam locomotive "Dam"; 1239, Modern electric railcars; 1240, Steam locomotive No. 3737, Netherlands; 1241, Electric railcar Type IC-III, Netherlands; 1242, Stephenson's "Rocket"; 1243, TGV express train, France; 1244, Stephenson "Adler", Germany; 1245, Double-deck UB2N train, France; 1246, "General", U.S.A.; 1247, "Hikari" express train, Japan.

258 American Purple Gallinule 259 German Letterbox, 1900

1985. Birds. Multicoloured.
1248 1g. Type **258** . . . . 1·25 1·00
1249 1g.50 Rufescent tiger heron 1·60 1·40
1250 2g.50 Scarlet ibis . . . . 3·00 2·50
1251 5g. Guianan cock of the rock . . . . 3·75 3·00
1252 10g. Harpy eagle . . . . . 8·00 7·00

1985. Old Letterboxes. Multicoloured.
1254 15c. Type **259** 15 15
1255 30c. French letterbox, 1900 20 20
1256 50c. English pillar box, 1932 35 35
1257 90c. Dutch letterbox, 1850 55 55

260 Emblem on Map 261 Studying

1985. 25th Anniv of Evangelical Brotherhood in Surinam.
1258 **260** 30c.+10c. multicoloured 30 30
1259 – 50c.+10c. red, yellow and brown 45 45
1260 – 90c.+20c. yellow, brown and red 75 75
DESIGNS: 50c. Different population groups around cross and clasped hands emblem; 90c. List of work undertaken by Brotherhood.

1985. Child Welfare. Multicoloured.
1261 5c.+5c. Type **261** 10 10
1262 10c.+5c. Writing alphabet on board 15 15
1263 30c.+10c. Writing 30 30
1264 50c.+25c. Reading 55 55
1265 90c.+30c. Thinking 80 80

1985. Victory of Kasparov in World Chess Championship. No. 1201 optd **KACTTAPOB Wereldkampioen 9 nov. 1985.**
1267 30c. light brown and brown 30 20

263 Agriculture 264 "Epidendrum ciliare"

1985. 10th Anniv of Independence.
1268 **263** 50c. yellow and green . . 40 40
1269 – 90c. orange and brown 70 70
DESIGN: 90c. Industry.

1986. Orchids. Multicoloured.
1271 5c. Type **264** 35 35
1272 15c. "Cycnoches chlorochilon" . . . . . . 1·10 1·10
1273 30c. "Epidendrum anceps" 1·75 1·75
1274 50c. "Epidendrum vespa" 3·25 3·25

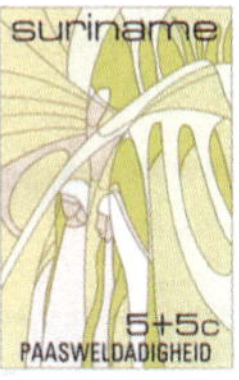

265 Bayeux Tapestry (detail) 266 Couple and Palm Leaves

1986. Appearance of Halley's Comet. Mult.
1275 50c. Type **265** 35 35
1276 110c. Comet 75 75

1986. Easter.
1277 **266** 5c.+5c. multicoloured . . 10 10
1278 10c.+5c. multicoloured 15 15
1279 30c.+15c. multicoloured 30 30
1280 50c.+25c. multicoloured 55 55
1281 90c.+30c. multicoloured 80 80

1986. Nos. 1244/5 surch.
1282 15c. on 50c. multicoloured 1·25 90
1283 15c. on 50c. multicoloured 1·25 90

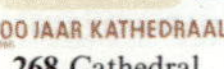

268 Cathedral

270 National Forestry Emblem

1986. Centenary of St. Peter and St. Paul's Cathedral, Paramaribo.
1284 **268** 30c.+10c. brown and ochre 30 30
1285 – 50c.+10c. brown and red 50 50
1286 – 110c.+30c. deep brown and brown . . . . . 1·10 1·10
DESIGNS: 50c. Relief of St. Peter and St. Paul; 110c. Font.

1986. 150th Anniv of Finance Building. No. 1133 surch **30 c 150 jaar FINANCIENGEBOUW**.
1287 30c. on 70c. multicoloured 30 30

1986. Centenary of Foresters' Court Charity. Mult.
1288 50c.+20c. Type **270** 60 60
1289 110c.+30c. First Court building . . . . 1·25 1·25

271 Emblem

1986. 50th Anniv of Surinam Shipping Line. Mult.
1290 50c. Type **271** 40 40
1291 110c. Container ship "Saramacca" . . . . . . 2·75 1·10

1986. No. 862 surch **15ct.**
1292 15c. on 30c. multicoloured 70 25

273 Children playing Hopscotch

1986. Child Welfare. Multicoloured.
1293 5c.+5c. Type **273** 10 10
1294 10c.+5c. Ballet class 15 15
1295 30c.+10c. Children boarding library bus 35 35
1296 50c.+25c. Boys at display of craftwork 65 65
1297 110c.+30c. Children in class 1·10 1·10

274 Red Howler

1987. Monkeys. Multicoloured.
1299 35c. Type **274** 30 30
1300 60c. Night monkey 55 55
1301 110c. Common squirrel-monkey 85 85
1302 120c. Red uakari 90 90

275 Emblem

1987. Centenary of Esperanto (invented language). Multicoloured.
1303 60c. Type **275** 55 55
1304 110c. Dove holding "Esperanto" banner across world map 85 85
1305 120c. L. L. Zamenhof (inventor) 90 90

1987. Various stamps surch.
1306 – 10c. on 85c. multicoloured (No. 872) 70 20
1307 – 10c. on 95c. multicoloured (No. 873) 70 20
1308 **168** 50c. on 1½g. black, orange and brown . . 45 45
1309 60c. on 2½g. black, red and brown 55 55

277 "Crucifixion"

278 Mushroom (Brownie emblem)

1987. Easter. Etchings by Rembrandt. Each light mauve, mauve and black.
1310 5c.+5c. Type **277** 10 10
1311 10c.+5c. "Christ on the Cross" 15 15
1312 35c.+15c. "Descent from the Cross" 35 35
1313 60c.+30c. "Christ carried to His Tomb" 65 65
1314 110c.+50c. "Entombment of Christ" . . . . 1·10 1·10

1987. 40th Anniv of Surinam Girl Guides.
1315 **278** 15c.+10c. mult 20 20
1316 – 60c.+10c. mult 50 50
1317 – 110c.+10c. mult 80 80
1318 – 120c.+10c. green, black and yellow 90 90
DESIGNS: 60c. Cloverleaf and star (Guide emblem); 110c. Campfire (Rangers emblem) on Guide trefoil; 120c. Ivy leaves (Captain's emblem).

279 Football

280 Commission Emblem

1987. 10th Pan-American Games, Indianapolis.
1319 **279** 90c. blue, green and brown 80 80
1320 – 110c. blue, light blue and brown 90 90
1321 – 150c. blue, mauve and brown . . . . 1·25 1·25
DESIGNS: 110c. Swimming; 150c. Basketball.

1987. 40th Anniv of Forestry Commission. Mult.
1322 90c. Type **280** 80 80
1323 120c. Loading tree trunks for export 95 95
1324 150c. Green-winged macaw in forest . . . . 2·50 1·25

282 Boy and Tents

283 Banana

1987. International Year of Shelter for the Homeless (90, 120c.) and Centenary of Salvation Army in the Caribbean Territory (150c.). Multicoloured.
1331 90c. Type **282** 70 70
1332 120c. Shanty town and man 85 85
1333 150c. William and Catherine Booth and emblem . . . 1·10 1·10

1987. Fruits. Multicoloured.
1334 10c. Type **283** 10 10
1335 15c. Cacao bean 15 15
1336 20c. Pineapple 15 15
1337 25c. Papaya 20 20
1338 35c. China orange 30 30

284 Jacob Degen's Balloon-assisted "Ornithopter", 1808

1987. Aircraft. Multicoloured.
1339 25c. Type **284** 20 20
1340 25c. Microlight airplane . . 20 20
1341 35c. Ellehammer II, 1906 . . 30 30
1342 35c. Concorde 30 30
1343 60c. Fokker F.VII (inscr "F.7"), 1924 . . . . . . 50 50
1344 60c. Fokker F28 Friendship 50 50
1345 90c. Fokker monoplane "Haarlem Spin", 1910 . . 75 75
1346 90c. Douglas DC-10 . . . . 75 75
1347 110c. Lockheed 9 Orion, 1932 . . . . 80 80
1348 110c. Boeing 747 . . . . . 80 80
1349 120c. 1967 Amelia Earhart 25c. stamp 95 95
1350 120c. 1978 Douglas DC-8-63 95c. stamp 95 95

285 Herring-bone Design

287 Ganges Gavial

1987. Child Welfare. Indian Weaving.
1351 **285** 50c.+25c. green & blk 65 65
1352 – 60c.+30c. orange and black 70 70
1353 – 110c.+50c. red & black 1·25 1·25
DESIGNS: 60c. Tortoise-back design; 110c. Concentric diamonds design.

1987. Nos. 869 and 805 surch.
1356 – 25c. on 70c. mult 75 40
1357 **168** 35c. on 1g. black, mauve and purple 60 60

1988. Reptiles. Multicoloured.
1358 50c. Type **287** 40 40
1359 60c. Nile crocodile 50 50
1360 90c. Black cayman 70 70
1361 110c. Mississippi alligator 80 80

288 Javanese Costumes

290 Cross and Chalice

1988. Wedding Costumes. Multicoloured.
1362 35c. Type **288** 30 30
1363 60c. Bushman 50 50
1364 80c. Chinese 65 65
1365 110c. Creole 80 80
1366 120c. Amerindian 85 85
1367 130c. Hindustan 90 90

1988. Various stamps surch.
1368 – 60c. on 75c. mult (No. 1246) . . . . . 1·75 1·25
1369 – 60c. on 75c. mult (No. 1247) . . . . . 1·75 1·25
1370 **168** 125c. on 10g. black, blue and deep blue . . . . 1·75 1·75

1988. Easter.
1371 **290** 50c.+25c. mult 65 65
1372 60c.+30c. mult 75 75
1373 110c.+50c. mult . . . . 1·40 1·40

291 Relay

292 Abaisa Monument

1988. Olympic Games, Seoul. Multicoloured.
1374 90c. Type **291** 80 80
1375 110c. Football 90 90
1376 120c. Pole vaulting . . . . 1·00 1·00
1377 250c. Tennis . . . . 2·00 2·00

1988. 125th Anniv of Abolition of Slavery. Mult.
1379 50c. Type **292** 50 50
1380 110c. Kwakoe monument 90 90
1381 120c. Anton de Kom's house . . . . 1·10 1·10

293 Combine Harvester

294 Egypt 1906 4m. Stamp

1988. 10th Anniv of International Agricultural Development Fund. "For a World without Hunger". Multicoloured.
1382 105c. Type **293** 90 90
1383 110c. Fishing 95 95
1384 125c. Cultivation . . . . . 1·25 1·25

1988. "Filacept" International Stamp Exhibition, The Hague.
1385 **294** 120c. red, black & orange . . . . 1·00 1·00
1386 – 150c. green, black & blue 1·25 1·25
1387 – 250c. red, black & deep red . . . . 2·25 2·25
DESIGNS: No. 1386, Netherlands 1952 10c. Stamp Centenary stamp; 1387, Surinam 1949 7½c. U.P.U. stamp.

295 Anniversary Emblem

296 Symbolic Representation of Butterfly Stroke

1988. 125th Anniv of Red Cross. Multicoloured.
1389 60c.+30c. Type **295** 85 85
1390 120c.+60c. Anniversary emblem and red cross in blood drop . . . . 1·60 1·60

1988. Anthony Nesty, Seoul Olympic Gold Medal Winner for 100 m Butterfly.
1391 **296** 110c. multicoloured . . . 95 95

297 "Man and Animal"

1988. 25th Anniv of Child Welfare Stamps. Mult.
1392 50c.+25c. Type **297** 70 70
1393 60c.+30c. "The Child in Nature" 85 85
1394 110c.+50c. Children helping each other ("Stop Drugs") 1·50 1·50

1988. Nos. 1238/9 and 1244/5 surch.
1396 2c. on 10c. mult (No. 1238) 55 60
1397 2c. on 10c. mult (No. 1239) 55 60
1398 3c. on 50c. mult (No. 1244) 55 60
1399 3c. on 50c. mult (No. 1245) 55 60

299 Otter on Rock

300 "The Passion" (left wing)

1989. Otters. Multicoloured.
1400 10c. Type **299** 10 10
1401 20c. Two otters 20 10
1402 25c. Two otters (different) 25 25
1403 30c. Otter with fish 50 30
1404 185c. Two otters (vert) (air) 1·60 1·60

1989. Easter. Altarpiece by Tamas of Koloszvar. Multicoloured.
1405 60c.+30c. Type **300** 85 85
1406 105c.+50c. "Crucifixion" (centre panel) (28 × 36 mm) . . . . . . 1·50 1·50
1407 110c.+55c. "Resurrection" (right wing) . . . . . . 1·50 1·50

301 Mercedes Touring Car, 1930

1989. Motor Cars. Multicoloured.
1408 25c. Type **301** 15 15
1409 25c. Mercedes Benz "300 E", 1985 . . . . 15 15
1410 60c. Daimler, 1897 . . . . 40 40
1411 60c. Jaguar "Sovereign", 1986 . . . . 40 40
1412 90c. Renault "Voiturette", 1898 . . . . 60 60
1413 90c. Renault "25 TX", 1989 60 60
1414 105c. Volvo "Jacob", 1927 70 70
1415 105c. Volvo "440", 1989 . . 70 70
1416 110c. Left-half of 1961 1f. Monaco stamp 75 75

1417	110c. Right-half of 1961 1f. Monaco stamp	75	75
1418	120c. Toyota "AA", 1936	80	80
1419	120c. Toyota "Corolla" saloon, 1988	80	80

303 Joseph Nicephore Niepce (pioneer)

304 Jade Statuette

1989. 150th Anniv of Photography. Mult.

1421	60c. Type **303**	40	40
1422	110c. First camera using daguerreotype process	75	75
1423	120c. Louis Jacques Mande Daguerre (inventor of daguerreotype process)	80	80

1989. America. Pre-Columbian Artifacts. Mult.

1424	60c. Type **304**	40	40
1425	110c. Statuette of pregnant woman	75	75

305 1976 25c. Surinam Stamp

306 "Children Helping Each Other" (Gianna Karg)

1989. "World Stamp Expo '89" International Stamp Exhibition, Washington, D.C. Mult.

1426	110c. Type **305**	75	75
1427	150c. 1950 3c. U.S.A. White House stamp	1·00	1·00
1428	250c. 1976 60c. Surinam "Divided Snake" stamp	1·75	1·75

1989. Child Welfare. Children's Paintings. Mult.

1430	60c.+30c. Type **306**	60	60
1431	105c.+50c. "Child and Nature" (Tamara Busropan)	1·00	1·00
1432	110c.+55c. "In the School Bus" (Cindy Kross)	1·10	1·10

307 Local Emblem

308 Temple

1990. International Literacy Year. Multicoloured.

1434	60c. Type **307**	40	40
1435	110c. I.L.Y. emblem	75	75
1436	120c. Emblems and boy reading	80	80

1990. 60th Anniv of Arya Dewaker Temple.

1437	**308**	60c. brown, red and black	40	40
1438		110c. violet and black	75	75
1439		200c. green and black	1·40	1·40

309 Mary and Baby Jesus

310 Surinam 1930 10c. Air Stamp

1990. Easter. Multicoloured.

1440	60c.+30c. Type **309**	55	55
1441	105c.+50c. Jesus teaching	90	90
1442	110c.+55c. Jesus's body taken from cross	1·00	1·00

1990. "Stamp World London 90" International Stamp Exhibition, London, and 150th Anniv of the Penny Black. Multicoloured.

1443	110c. Type **310**	65	65
1444	200c. Penny Black	1·25	1·25
1445	250c. G.B. 1929 2½d. Postal Union Congress stamp	1·50	1·50

311 Couple carrying Goods

313 Swamp

312 Pomegranate

1990. Centenary of Javanese Immigration. Mult.

1447	60c. Type **311**	35	35
1448	110c. Woman	65	65
1449	120c. Man	70	70

1990. Flowers. Paintings by Maria Sibylle Merian. Multicoloured.

1450	25c. Type **312**	15	15
1451	25c. Passion flower	15	15
1452	35c. "Hippeastrum puniceum"	20	20
1453	35c. Sweet potato	20	20
1454	60c. Rose of Sharon	35	35
1455	60c. Jasmine	35	35
1456	105c. Blushing hibiscus	60	60
1457	105c. "Musa serapionis"	60	60
1458	110c. Frangipani	65	65
1459	110c. "Hibiscus diversifolius"	65	65
1460	120c. Annatt ("Bixa orellana")	70	70
1461	120c. Dwarf poinciana ("Caesalpinia pulcherima")	70	70

1990. America. Natural World.

1462	**313**	60c. multicoloured	35	35
1463		110c. multicoloured	65	65

314 Anniversary Emblem

315 Fish and Flag as Map

1990. Centenary of Organization of American States.

1464	**314**	100c. multicoloured	65	65

1990. 15th Anniv of Independence. Multicoloured.

1465	10c. Type **315**	15	10
1466	60c. Passion flower and flag as map	35	35
1467	110c. Dove and flag as map	65	65

316 Painting by Janneke Fleskens

1990. Child Welfare. The Child in Nature. Paintings by children named. Multicoloured.

1468	60c.+30c. Type **316**	55	55
1469	105c.+50c. Tahlita Zuiverloon	90	90
1470	110c.+55c. Samuel Jensen	1·00	1·00

317 Green Aracari

1991. Birds. Multicoloured.

1472	10c. Type **317**	10	10
1473	15g. Blue and yellow macaw	9·75	9·75
1542	25g. Barn owl	19·00	19·00

318 Christ carrying Cross

319 Shipping Company Store

1991. Easter. Multicoloured.

1474	60c.+30c. Type **318**	60	60
1475	105c.+50c. Christ wearing crown of thorns	1·00	1·00
1476	110c.+55c. Woman cradling Christ's body	1·10	1·10

1991. Buildings.

1478	**319**	35c. black, blue & lt blue	20	20
1479	–	60c. black, green and emerald	40	40
1480	–	75c. black, yell & lemon	50	50
1481	–	105c. black, orange and light orange	70	70
1482	–	110c. black, pink and red	70	70
1483	–	200c. black, deep mauve and mauve	1·25	1·25

DESIGNS: 60c. Upper class house; 75c. House converted into Labour Inspection offices; 105c. Plantation supervisor's house; 110c. Ministry of Labour building; 200c. Houses.

320 Puma

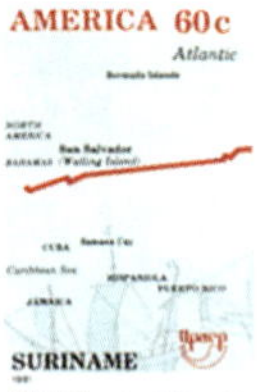

321 Route Map to Bahamas via San Salvador

1991. The Puma. Multicoloured.

1484	10c. Type **320** (postage)	10	10
1485	20c. Stalking	15	15
1486	25c. Stretching	15	15
1487	30c. Licking nose	20	20
1488	125c. Lying down (horiz) (air)	80	80
1489	500c. Leaping (horiz)	3·25	3·25

1991. America. Voyages of Discovery. Each red, blue and black.

1490	60c. Type **321**	80	80
1491	110c. Route map from Canary Islands	1·40	1·40

Nos. 1490/1 were printed together, se-tenant, forming a composite design.

322 Green Tree Boa ("Corallus caninus")

1991. Snakes. Multicoloured.

1492	25c. Type **322**	15	15
1493	25c. Garden tree boa ("Corallus enydris")	15	15
1494	35c. Boa constrictor	20	20
1495	35c. Bushmaster ("Lachesis muta")	20	20
1496	60c. South American rattlesnake ("Crotalus durissus")	40	40
1497	60c. Surinam coral snake ("Micrurus surinamensis")	40	40
1498	75c. Mussurana ("Clelia cloelia")	50	50
1499	75c. Anaconda ("Eunectes murinus")	50	50
1500	110c. Rainbow boa ("Epicrutes cenchris")	70	70
1501	110c. Sipo ("Chrironius carinatus")	70	70
1502	200c. Black and yellow rat snake ("Spilotes pullatus")	1·25	1·25
1503	200c. Vine snake ("Oxybelis argenteus")	1·25	1·25

323 Child in Wheelchair

324 "Cycnoches haagii"

1991. Child Welfare. Multicoloured.

1504	60c.+30c. Type **323**	60	60
1505	105c.+50c. Trees and girl	1·10	1·00
1506	110c.+55c. Girls playing in yard	1·10	1·10

1992. Orchids. Multicoloured.

1508	50c. Type **324**	30	30
1509	60c. "Lycaste cristata"	40	40
1510	75c. "Galeandra dives" (horiz)	50	50
1511	125c. "Vanilla mexicana"	80	80
1512	150c. "Cyrtopodium glutiniferum"	1·00	1·00
1513	250c. "Gongora quinquenervis"	1·60	1·60

325 Crucifixion

327 Basketball

1992. Easter. Multicoloured.

1514	60c.+30c. Type **325**	70	70
1515	105c.+50c. Women taking away Christ's body	1·10	1·10
1516	110c.+55c. The Resurrection	1·25	1·25

1992. Olympic Games, Barcelona. Multicoloured.

1518	35c. Type **327**	25	25
1519	60c. Volleyball	45	45
1520	75c. Sprinting	55	55
1521	125c. Football	95	95
1522	150c. Cycling	1·10	1·10
1523	250c. Swimming	1·90	1·90

328 Emblems

1992. 50th Anniv of Young Women's Christian Association.

1525	**328**	60c. multicoloured	45	45
1526		250c. multicoloured	1·90	1·90

1992. Nos. 1236/7 surch **1 c.**

1527	1c. on 5c. orange and blue	65	65
1528	1c. on 5c. green, red and blue	65	65

330 Nau

331 Matzeliger and Shoe-lasting Machine

1992. 500th Anniv of Expulsion of Jews from Spain.

1529	**330**	250c. multicoloured	2·50	2·50

1992. 140th Birth Anniv of Jan E. Matzeliger (inventor).

1530	**331**	60c. multicoloured	45	45
1531		250c. multicoloured	1·90	1·90

332 Amerindian Ornament

333 Tree with Child's Face

1992. America. 500th Anniv of Discovery of America by Columbus.

1532	**332**	60c. multicoloured	45	45
1533		250c. multicoloured	1·90	1·90

1992. Child Welfare. Multicoloured.

1534	60c.+30c. Type **333**	70	70
1535	105c.+50c. Tree with child's face beside flower	1·10	1·10
1536	110c.+55c. Children hanging from tree	1·25	1·25

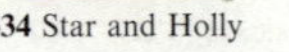

334 Star and Holly
336 "Costus arabicus"

1992. Christmas. Multicoloured.
1538 10c. Type **334** 10 10
1539 60c. Candle 45 45
1540 250c. Parcels . . . . . . 1·90 1·90
1541 400c. Crown . . . . . . 3·00 3·00

1993. Air. No. 865 surch **35 ct.**
1543 35c. on 50c. multicoloured 25 25

1993. Medicinal Plants. Multicoloured.
1544 50c. Type **336** 40 40
1545 75c. "Quassia amara" . . . 55 55
1546 125c. "Combretum rotundifolium" (horiz) . . 95 95
1547 500c. "Bixa orellana" (horiz) 3·75 3·75

337 Christ and Cross
339 90r. "Bull's Eye" Stamp

338 Long-horned Beetle ("Macrodontia cervicornis")

1993. Easter. Multicoloured.
1548 60c.+30c. Type **337** 70 70
1549 110c.+50c. Crucifixion . . . 1·25 1·25
1550 125c.+60c. Resurrection . . 1·40 1·40

1993. Insects. Multicoloured.
1551 25c. Type **338** 20 20
1552 25c. Locust 20 20
1553 35c. Weevil ("Curculionidae") 25 25
1554 35c. Grasshopper ("Acrididae") 25 25
1555 50c. Goliath beetle ("Euchroma gigantea") 40 40
1556 50c. Bush cricket ("Tettigonidae") 40 40
1557 100c. "Tettigonidae" 75 75
1558 100c. Scarab beetle ("Phanaeus festivus") . . 75 75
1559 175c. Cricket ("Grylllidae") 1·25 1·25
1560 175c. Dung beetle ("Phanaeus lancifer") . . 1·25 1·25
1561 220c. "Tettigonidae" (different) . . . . . . 1·60 1·60
1562 220c. Longhorn beetle ("Batus barbicornis") . . 1·60 1·60

1993. 150th Anniv of First Brazilian Stamps and "Brasiliana 93" International Stamp Exhibition, Rio de Janeiro.
1563 **339** 50c. black and violet . . 40 40
1564 – 250c. black and blue . . 1·90 1·90
1565 – 500c. black and green . . 3·75 3·75
DESIGNS: 250c. 60r. "Bull's eye" stamp; 500c. 30r. "Bull's eye" stamp.

340 Dwarf Cayman
341 Afro-Caribbean Angel

1993. America. Endangered Animals.
1567 **340** 50c. multicoloured . . . 40 40
1568 100c. multicoloured . . . 75 75

1993. Christmas. Multicoloured.
1569 25c. Type **341** 20 20
1570 45c. Asian angel 35 35
1571 50c. Oriental angel 40 40
1572 150c. Amerindian angel . . 1·10 1·10

342 Hopscotch
344 Sambura

1993. Child Welfare. Children's Games.
1573 **342** 25g.+10g. brown & grn 25 25
1574 – 35g.+10g. brown & blue 35 35
1575 – 50g.+25g. brown & grn 55 55
1576 – 75g.+25g. brown & blue 75 75
DESIGNS: 35g. Hopscotch (different); 50g. Djoel (variant of hopscotch); 75g. Djoel (different).

1993. Nos. 1252 and 1473 surch **f 5.-**.
1578 5g. on 10g. multicoloured 3·75 3·75
1579 5g. on 15g. multicoloured 3·75 3·75

1994. Traditional Drums. Multicoloured.
1580 25g. Type **344** 20 20
1581 50g. Apinti 40 40
1582 75g. Terbangan 60 60
1583 100g. Dhol 80 80

345 Roseate Spoonbill

1994.
1584 **345** 1300g. multicoloured . . 10·00 10·00

1994. Air. No value expressed. Nos. 864 and 866/7 optd **Port Paye.**
1585 (–) on 45c. multicoloured 35 35
1586 (–) on 55c. multicoloured 45 45
1587 (–) on 60c. multicoloured 55 55

347 Smoking Chimneys
348 Goalkeeper's Gloves and Ball

1994. Environmental Protection. Multicoloured.
1588 50g. Type **347** 40 40
1589 350g. Dead fish in polluted sea . . . . 2·75 2·75

1994. World Cup Football Championship, U.S.A. Multicoloured.
1590 100g. Type **348** 30 30
1591 250g. Boot on ball 80 80
1592 300g. Goal net on ball . . . 95 95

349 Anniversary Emblem

1994. Cent of International Olympic Committee.
1594 **349** 250g. multicoloured . . 80 80

350 "Dulcedo sp."

1994. Butterflies. Multicoloured.
1595 25g. Type **350** 10 10
1596 25g. "Ithomia sp." 10 10
1597 30g. "Danaus sp." (brown wings) 10 10
1598 30g. "Danaus sp." (black and gold wings) . . . 10 10
1599 45g. "Bithijs sp." 15 15
1600 45g. "Echenais sp." . . . 15 15
1601 75g. White peacock ("Anartia jatrophae") . . 25 25
1602 75g. Caribbean buckeye ("Junonia evarete") . . 25 25
1603 250g. Small postman ("Heliconius erato") . . . 80 80
1604 250g. "Heliconius sp." . . . 80 80
1605 300g. "Parides sp." 95 95
1606 300g. "Eurytides sp." . . . 95 95

351 Netherlands 1943 Stamp Day Issue

1994. "Fepapost 94" European Stamp Exhibition, The Hague. Multicoloured.
1607 250g. Type **351** 80 80
1608 300g. Surinam 1936 1c. stamp 95 95

352 Canoe and Airplane

1994. America. Postal Transport. Multicoloured.
1610 50g. Type **352** 15 15
1611 400g. Donkey-cart and motor van . . . . 1·25 1·25

353 Mother reading to Children
354 Hands and Globes

1994. Christmas. Multicoloured. (a) Value indicated by letter "A".
1612 A Angel hovering over pine forest 25 25

(b) With face value.
1613 250g. Type **353** 80 80
1614 625g. Woman praying . . . 2·00 2·00

1995. Centenary of Volleyball. Multicoloured.
1616 375g. Type **354** . . . . . 1·25 1·25
1617 650g. Balls . . . . 2·10 2·10

355 "Stachytarpheta jamaicense"

1995. Medicinal Plants. Multicoloured.
1619 30g. Type **355** 10 10
1620 30g. "Ruellia tuberosa" . . 10 10
1621 50g. Sweet basil ("Ocimum sanctum") 15 15
1622 50g. "Peperomia pellucida" 15 15
1623 75g. "Phyllanthus amarus" 25 25
1624 75g. "Portulaca oleracea" 25 25
1625 250g. "Wulffia baccata" . . 80 80
1626 250g. Sesame ("Sesamum indicum") 80 80
1627 500g. Blood flower ("Asclepias curassavica") 1·60 1·60
1628 500g. "Heliotropium indicum" . . . . . . 1·60 1·60
1629 600g. "Wedelia tribolata" 1·90 1·90
1630 600g. "Lantana camara" . . 1·90 1·90

356 Jaguarundi
357 Emblem, Dove and "50"

1995. Big Cats. Multicoloured.
1631 25g. Type **356** (postage) . . 10 10
1632 30g. Head of jaguarundi . . 10 10
1633 50g. Tiger cat 15 15
1634 100g. Head of tiger cat . . . 30 30
1635 1000g. Tree ocelot (air) . . 3·25 3·25
1636 1200g. Head of tree ocelot 3·75 3·75

1995. 50th Anniv of U.N.O. Multicoloured.
1637 135g. Type **357** 45 45
1638 740g. As T **357** but dove flying towards right . . . 2·40 2·40

358 Emblem

1995. Centenary of Surinam Police Force.
1639 **358** 875g. multicoloured . . 2·75 2·75

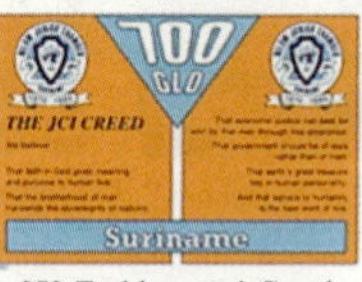

359 Emblem and Creed

1995. 25th Anniv of Nilom Junior Chamber.
1640 **359** 700g. orange, blue and deep blue . . . . . . 2·25 2·25

360 Channel-billed Toucan

1995. Birds. Multicoloured.
1641 1780g. Type **360** . . . . . 5·75 5·75
1642 2225g. Rufous-throated sapphire . . . . 7·00 7·00
1643 2995g. Hoatzin . . . . . . 9·50 9·50
See also Nos. 1679/81, 1736/9, 1767/70 and 1826/7.

361 Waterfall
362 Shepherds and Star of Bethlehem

1995. America. Environmental Protection. Mult.
1644 135g. Forest floor 45 45
1645 1500g. Type **361** . . . . . 4·75 4·75

1995. Christmas. Multicoloured.
1646 70g. Type **362** 20 20
1647 135g. Joseph with Mary on donkey 45 45
1648 295g. Three wise men bearing gifts 95 95
1649 1000g. Wise men adoring child Jesus (horiz) . . . . 3·25 3·25

363 Jester and Bird
365 Hawk-headed Parrot

364 "Cyrtopodium cristatum"

1995. Paintings by Corneille. Multicoloured.
1651 135g. Type **363** 45 45
1652 615g. Jester and cat . . . . 1·90 1·90

1996. Flowers. Multicoloured.
1653 10g. Type **364** 10 10
1654 10g. "Epidendrum cristatum" 10 10
1655 75g. "Cochleanthes guianensis" 25 25
1656 75g. "Otostylis lepida" . . . 25 25
1657 135g. "Catasetum longifolium" 40 40
1658 135g. "Rudolfiella aurantiaca" 40 40
1659 250g. "Encyclia granitica" 75 75
1660 250g. "Maxillaria splendens" 75 75
1661 300g. "Brassia caudata" . . 90 90
1662 300g. "Catasetum macrocarpum" 90 90
1663 750g. "Maxillaria rufescens" 2·25 2·25
1664 750g. "Vanilla grandiflora" 2·25 2·25

1996.
1665 **365** 2000g. multicoloured . . 6·00 6·00

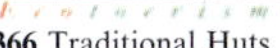
366 Traditional Huts

367 Radio Apparatus

1996. Eco-tourism. Multicoloured.

1666	70g. Type **366**	20	20
1667	70g. Butterfly on leaf	20	20
1668	135g. Men in traditional costumes	40	40
1669	135g. Woman hand-spinning	40	40

1996. Centenary of Guglielmo Marconi's Patented Wireless-Telegraph. Multicoloured.

1670	135g. Type **367**	40	40
1671	615g. Marconi and world map (horiz)	1·90	1·90

368 Basketball

370 Women

1996. Olympic Games, Atlanta. Multicoloured.

1672	70g. Type **368**	20	20
1673	135g. Running	40	40
1674	195g. Badminton	60	60
1675	200g. Swimming	60	60
1676	900g. Cycling	2·75	2·75
1677	1000g. Hurdling	3·00	3·00

1996. Birds. As T **360**. Multicoloured.

1679	75g. Green kingfisher	25	25
1680	160g. Bat falcon	50	50
1681	1765g. Red-legged honey-creeper	5·25	5·25

1996. America. Traditional Costumes. Mult.

1682	135g. Type **370**	40	40
1683	990g. Young women	3·00	3·00

Nos. 1682/3 were issued together, se-tenant, forming a composite design.

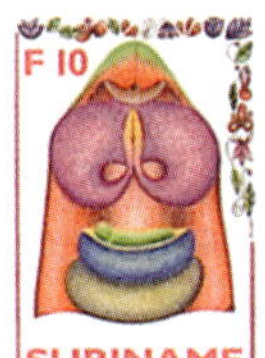

371 Mother praying over Child in Crib

373 Brown Dog and Injured Boy

1996. Christmas. Multicoloured.

1684	10g. Type **371**	10	10
1685	70g. Mother kneeling beside child	20	20
1686	135g. Mother with backpack kneeling beside "eye" on mouth/cushion	40	40
1687	285g. Mother playing with child on floor	85	85
1688	750g. Mother and child rocking on floor	2·25	2·25

1996. Nos. 1603/6 surch.

1690	50g. on 250g. mult (No. 1603)	15	15
1691	50g. on 250g. mult (No. 1604)	15	15
1692	100g. on 300g. mult (No. 1605)	30	30
1693	100g. on 300g. mult (No. 1606)	30	30

1996. No value expressed. Nos. 1648/9 optd **Port Paye**.

1694	(–) on 295g. multicoloured	1·40	1·40
1695	(–) on 1000g. multicoloured	1·40	1·40

1996. Child Welfare. Paintings by Jan Telting. Multicoloured.

1696	135g. Type **373**	40	40
1697	865g. White dog and injured boy	2·75	2·75

374 August Kappier (founder)

375 Inauguration of Aluminium Smelter, Paranam, 1965

1996. 150th Anniv of Town of Albina.

1698	**374**	875g. multicoloured	2·75	2·75

1996. 80th Anniv of Bauxite Industry. Paintings by Michel Pawiroredjo. Multicoloured.

1699	10g. Type **375**	10	10
1700	70g. Drilling blasting holes, Moengo, 1947	20	20
1701	130g. Labourers' huts, Moengo, 1919	40	40
1702	150g. Loading "Tarpon" with alumina, Paranam, 1995	45	45
1703	160g. Construction of dam and power station, 1960	50	50
1704	730g. "Moengo" (schooner), 1922	2·25	2·25

376 Von Stephan

1997. Death Centenary of Heinrich von Stephan (founder of U.P.U.).

1705	**376**	275g. multicoloured	85	85
1706		475g. multicoloured	1·40	1·40

377 Weeper Capuchin ("Cebus nigrivittatus")

1997. Primates. Multicoloured.

1707	25g. Type **377**	10	10
1708	25g. Black-capped capuchin ("Cebus apella")	10	10
1709	75g. Yellow-handed marmoset ("Saguinus midas")	25	25
1710	75g. Black spider monkey ("Ateles paniscus")	25	25
1711	100g. Black-handed spider monkey ("Ateles geoffroyi panamensis")	30	30
1712	100g. Black-handed spider monkey ("Ateles geoffroyi frontatus")	30	30
1713	275g. Bald uakari ("Cacajao calvus")	85	85
1714	275g. Hendee's woolly monkey ("Lagothrix flavicauda")	85	85
1715	300g. Bare-faced tamarin ("Saguinus bicolor")	90	90
1716	300g. Cotton-headed tamarin ("Saguinus oedipus")	90	90
1717	725g. Red howler monkey ("Alouatta seniculus")	2·25	2·25
1718	725g. Common squirrel monkey ("Saimiri sciureus")	2·25	2·25

378 Earhart, Airplane and Finch

379 "Selenipedium steyermarkii"

1997. Linda Finch's Reconstruction of Amelia Earhart's Last Flight.

1719	**378**	275g. multicoloured	85	85

1997. Orchids. Multicoloured.

1720	25g. Type **379**	10	10
1721	50g. "Phragmipedium schlimii"	15	15
1722	75g. "Criosanthes arietina"	25	25
1723	200g. "Cypripedium margaritaceum"	60	60
1724	775g. "Paphiopedilum gratrixianum"	2·40	2·40

380 Museum

382 Great Mosque, Isfahan, Iran

1997. 50th Anniv of Surinam Museum.

1725	**380**	625g. multicoloured	1·90	1·90

1997. Mosques. Multicoloured.

1727	50g. Type **382**	15	15
1728	125g. Dome of the Rock, Jerusalem	40	40
1729	175g. Ulugh Beg's Mosque, Samarkand, Uzbekistan	55	55
1730	225g. Taj Mahal, Agra, India	70	70
1731	275g. Mosque on Keizerstraat, Paramaribo, Surinam	85	85
1732	325g. Suleiman Mosque, Istanbul, Turkey	1·00	1·00

383 Tower

384 Child's Face (left side)

1997. 17th Anniv of State Oil Company. Mult.

1734	50g. Type **383**	15	15
1735	125g. Oil derrick and butterfly	40	40
1736	275g. Tank	85	85
1737	275g. Pressure gauge in field	85	85

1997. Birds. As T **360**. Multicoloured.

1738	50g. Spectacled owl	15	15
1739	125g. Rufous pigeon	40	40
1740	275g. Blaack-crested antshrike	85	85
1741	3150g. Red-crested finch	9·50	9·50

1997. Child Welfare. Multicoloured.

1742	50g. Type **384**	15	15
1743	100g. Child's face (right side)	30	30
1744	175g. Child with shoulder-length hair (left side)	55	55
1745	225g. Child with shoulder-length hair (right side)	70	70
1746	350g. Faces of the two children	1·10	1·10

385 Madonna and Child

386 Motor Cycle Courier

1997. Christmas. Multicoloured.

1748	125g. Type **385**	40	40
1749	225g. Children and baby	70	70
1750	450g. Angel and candle	1·40	1·40

1997. America. Postal Workers. Multicoloured.

1752	170g. Type **386**	50	50
1753	230g. Postal worker carrying parcel	70	70

387 "Alcandor"

1998. Butterflies. Multicoloured.

1754	50g. Type **387**	15	15
1755	50g. "Achilles"	15	15
1756	75g. "Alphenor"	25	25
1757	75g. "Ceres"	25	25
1758	100g. "Cecropia"	30	30
1759	100g. "Helenor"	30	30
1760	175g. "Promothea"	55	55
1761	175g. "Cassiae"	55	55
1762	275g. "Ino"	85	85
1763	275g. "Phidippus"	85	85
1764	725g. "Palamedes"	2·25	2·25
1765	725g. "Helenor"	2·25	2·25

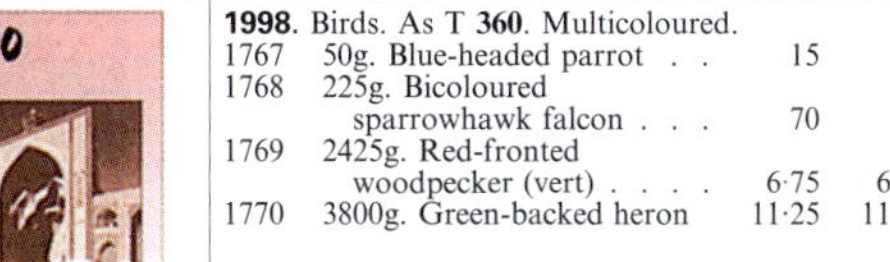

1998. Birds. As T **360**. Multicoloured.

1767	50g. Blue-headed parrot	15	15
1768	225g. Bicoloured sparrowhawk falcon	70	70
1769	2425g. Red-fronted woodpecker (vert)	6·75	6·75
1770	3800g. Green-backed heron	11·25	11·25

388 Immigrants and Lala Rooch (painting)

1998. 125th Anniv of Arrival of First Hindu Immigrants. Multicoloured.

1771	175g. Type **388**	55	55
1772	200g. "Baba and Mai" (statue) (first immigrants from India)	65	65

389 Tanden Temple, Sri Lanka

390 Sophie Redmond

1998. Temples. Multicoloured.

1773	50g. Type **389**	15	15
1774	75g. Golden Pagoda, Myanmar (vert)	20	20
1775	275g. Swayambhunath, Nepal (vert)	85	85
1776	325g. Borobudur, Indonesia	95	95
1777	400g. Phra Kaew, Thailand (vert)	1·25	1·25
1778	450g. Peking, China (vert)	1·40	1·40

1998. America. Famous Women. Multicoloured.

1780	400g. Type **390**	1·25	1·25
1781	1000g. Grace Ruth Schneiders-Howard	2·75	2·75

391 1951 20c. Queen Juliana Stamp

1998. International Stamp Exhibition, The Hague, Netherlands. Multicoloured.

1782	400g. Type **391**	1·25	1·25
1783	800g. 1946 12½c. Queen Wilhelmina stamp	2·50	2·50

392 "Canawaima" (ferry)

1998. Surinam–Guyana Ferry.

1785	**392**	275g. multicoloured	85	85
1786		400g. multicoloured	1·25	1·25

393 Holy Family

394 Boy flying Kite

1998. Christmas. Multicoloured.

1787	50g. Type **393**	15	15
1788	325g. Angel with banner, Holy Family and stable of animals	95	95
1789	400g. Holy family and animals	1·25	1·25
1790	1225g. Nativity	3·50	3·50

1998. Child Welfare. Multicoloured.

1792	375g. Type **394**	1·00	1·00
1793	400g. Girl flying kite	1·25	1·25
1794	1225g. Child holding kite	3·50	3·50

395 Mother and Child and Food

1998. 50th Anniv of W.H.O. "Mother and Child Care". Multicoloured.

No.	Description	Mint	Used
1795	400g. Type **395**	1·25	1·25
1796	1000g. Mother and baby	2·75	2·75

396 "Heliconia pastazae"

1999. Flora. Multicoloured.

No.	Description	Mint	Used
1797	50g. Type **396**	10	10
1798	50g. "Heliconia caribaea 'Kawauchi'"	10	10
1799	200g. "Heliconia rostrata"	30	30
1800	200g. "Heliconia 'Sexy Pink'"	30	30
1801	300g. "Heliconia collinsiana"	45	45
1802	300g. "Heliconia wagneriana"	45	45
1803	400g. "Heliconia 'Jaded Forest'"	60	60
1804	400g. "Heliconia 'Bihai-nappi'"	60	60
1805	750g. "Heliconia 'Golden Torch'"	1·10	1·10
1806	750g. "Heliconia latispatha 'Red Yellow Gyro'"	1·10	1·10
1807	1300g. "Heliconia 'Sexy Pink'" (different)	2·00	2·00
1808	1300g. "Heliconia 'Nappi Yellow'"	2·00	2·00

397 Katwijk Plantation

398 Greater Flamingo

1999. Plantation Houses.

No.	Type	Description	Mint	Used
1809	397	75g. black	10	10
1810	–	300g. purple and black	45	45
1811	–	400g. yellow and black	60	60
1812	–	2225g. blue and black	3·25	3·25

DESIGNS: 300g. Sorgvliet Plantation; 400g. Peperpot Plantation; 2225g. Speiringshoek Plantation.

1999. Endangered Species. Multicoloured.

No.	Description	Mint	Used
1813	75g. Type **398**	10	10
1814	375g. Orang-utan	55	55
1815	450g. Elephant	70	70
1816	500g. Whale	75	75
1817	850g. Frog	1·25	1·25
1818	900g. Rhinoceros	1·25	1·25
1819	1600g. Giant panda	2·50	2·50
1820	7250g. Tiger	11·00	11·00

399 Coppename Bridge

400 STINASU Emblem

1999. Coppename Bridge.

No.	Type	Description	Mint	Used
1821	399	850g. green, lt grn & blk	1·25	1·25
1822		2250g. blue, dp bl & blk	3·50	3·50

1999. Conservation. Multicoloured.

No.	Description	Mint	Used
1823	850g. Type **400** (30th anniv of Surinam Nature Protection Society)	1·25	1·25
1824	2650g. Map and rainforest (first anniv of Surinam Central Forest Nature Reserve)	4·00	4·00

1999. Birds. As T **360**. Multicoloured.

No.	Description	Mint	Used
1826	1000g. Blue-grey tanager	1·50	1·50
1827	5500g. Wattled jacana	8·00	8·00

401 Earth, Letter and Satellite

402 Gun firing Streamers and Flowers

1999. 125th Anniv of Universal Postal Union. Multicoloured.

No.	Description	Mint	Used
1828	950g. Type **401**	1·40	1·40
1829	1000g. Satellite, letter and ringed planet	1·50	1·50

1999. America. A Millennium without Arms. Mult.

No.	Description	Mint	Used
1830	1000g. Type **402**	1·50	1·50
1831	2250g. Flowers	3·50	3·50

Nos. 1830/1 were issued together, se-tenant, forming a composite design.

403 Star over Stable

404 Child's Painting

1999. Christmas. Multicoloured.

No.	Description	Mint	Used
1832	500g. Type **403**	75	75
1833	850g. Christmas tree	1·25	1·25
1834	900g. Angel	1·25	1·25
1835	1000g. Candle	1·50	1·50

1999. Child Welfare.

No.	Type	Description	Mint	Used
1837	404	1100g. multicoloured	1·60	1·60
1838	–	1400g. multicoloured	2·10	2·10
1839	–	1600g. multicoloured	2·40	2·40

DESIGNS: 1400g. to 1600g. Different children's paintings.

405 Tennis Players, House and Car (Tahirih van Kanten)

406 One Way Sign

2000. "Stampin' the Future". Children's Drawings. Multicoloured.

No.	Description	Mint	Used
1841	1000g. Type **405**	1·40	1·40
1842	2500g. Sunflower (Tirsa Braaf) (vert)	3·50	3·50

2000. Traffic Signs (1st series).

No.	Type	Description	Mint	Used
1843	406	2000g. multicoloured	2·75	2·75

See also Nos. 1858, 1861, 1868 and 1874.

407 Watermelon

2000. Tropical Fruits. Multicoloured.

No.	Description	Mint	Used
1844	50g. Type **407** (postage)	10	10
1845	50g. Papaya (*Carica papaya*)	10	10
1846	175g. Mango (*Mangifera indica*)	25	25
1847	175g. Mangosteen (*Garcinia mangostana*)	25	25
1848	200g. Banana (*Musa nana*)	30	30
1849	200g. Grapefruit (*Citrus paradisi*)	30	30
1850	250g. *Punika granatum*	35	35
1851	250g. Pineapple (*Ananas comosus*)	35	35
1852	325g. Coconut (*Cocos nucifera*)	45	45
1853	325g. Giant granadilla (*Passiflora quadrangularis*)	45	45
1854	5000g. Sweet orange (*Citrus sinensis*) (air)	7·00	7·00
1855	5000g. Avocado (*Persea gratissima*)	7·00	7·00

408 Red-billed Whistling Duck

409 Double Bend Sign

2000. Birds. Multicoloured.

No.	Description	Mint	Used
1856	1100g. Type **408**	1·50	1·50
1857	4425g. Ringed kingfisher	6·00	6·00

2000. Traffic Signs (2nd series).

No.	Type	Description	Mint	Used
1858	409	2000g. multicoloured	3·00	3·00

410 Bridge over Suriname River

411 No Overtaking

2000.

No.	Type	Description	Mint	Used
1859	410	1100g. multicoloured	1·60	1·60
1860		1700g. multicoloured	2·50	2·50

2000. Traffic Signs (3rd series).

No.	Type	Description	Mint	Used
1861	411	2000g. multicoloured	3·00	3·00

413 Running

2000. Olympic Games, Sydney. Multicoloured.

No.	Description	Mint	Used
1863	1100g. Type **413**	1·60	1·60
1864	1100g. Football	1·60	1·60
1865	3900g. Swimming	5·50	5·50
1866	3900g. Tennis	5·50	5·50

414 Roundabout Ahead

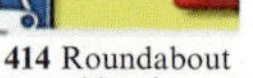

415 Foot stamping on "AIDS"

2000. Traffic Signs (4th series).

No.	Type	Description	Mint	Used
1868	414	2000g. multicoloured	3·00	3·00

2000. America. AIDS Awareness Campaign. Multicoloured.

No.	Description	Mint	Used
1869	1100g. Type **415**	1·60	1·60
1870	6400g. Stylized figures holding condoms (vert)	9·00	9·00

416 Star of Bethelehem

417 No Parking

2000. Christmas. Multicoloured.

No.	Description	Mint	Used
1871	1100g. Type **416**	1·60	1·25
1872	3900g. Mary and Jesus	6·00	4·75
MS1873	72 × 51 mm. 3000g. Three Kings bearing gifts	4·50	3·50

2000. Traffic (5th series).

No.	Type	Description	Mint	Used
1874	417	2000g. multicoloured	3·00	2·40

418 Currency Notes

419 Emblem

2000. 25th Anniv of International Philatelic Agency for Surinam Stamps. Multicoloured.

No.	Description	Mint	Used
1875	125g. Type **418**	10	10
1876	5900g. Stamps	9·00	7·25
MS1877	75 × 73 mm. Nos. 1875/7	9·00	9·00

2000. 25th Anniv of Independence.

No.	Type	Description	Mint	Used
1878	419	1100g. multicoloured	1·60	1·25
1879		4900g. multicoloured	7·50	6·00

420 Toddler

2000. Child Care. Multicoloured.

No.	Description	Mint	Used
1880	1100g. Type **420**	1·60	1·25
1881	3900g. Baby at breast	6·00	4·75
MS1882	72 × 51 mm. 2000g. Baby	3·00	2·40

2000. Nos. 1551/2 surch **F 3100**.

No.	Description	Mint	Used
1883	3100g. on 35c. multicoloured	4·75	3·75
1884	3100g. on 35c. multicoloured	4·75	3·75

POSTAGE DUE STAMPS

D 2

D 6

1885.

No.	Type	Description	Mint	Used
D36b	D 2	2½c. mauve and black	2·00	2·00
D37b		5c. mauve and black	6·25	6·25
D38a		10c. mauve and black	£100	75·00
D39a		20c. mauve and black	6·25	6·25
D40b		25c. mauve and black	7·25	7·25
D41b		30c. mauve and black	2·75	2·75
D42b		40c. mauve and black	4·00	4·00
D43b		50c. mauve and black	2·25	2·25

1892.

No.	Type	Description	Mint	Used
D57	D 6	2½c. mauve and black	35	35
D58b		5c. mauve and black	90	90
D59		10c. mauve and black	16·00	12·00
D60b		20c. mauve and black	1·90	1·25
D61b		25c. mauve and black	7·00	5·75
D62		40c. mauve and black	2·10	2·50

1911.

No.	Type	Description	Mint	Used
D111b	D 2	10c. on 30c. mve & blk	85·00	85·00
D112b		10c. on 50c. mve & blk	£110	£110

1913.

No.	Type	Description	Mint	Used
D153	D 6	½c. lilac	20	20
D154		1c. lilac	20	20
D155		2c. lilac	20	20
D156		2½c. lilac	20	20
D157		5c. lilac	20	20
D158		10c. lilac	20	20
D159a		12c. lilac	20	20
D160a		12½c. lilac	20	10
D161		15c. lilac	30	30
D162a		20c. lilac	55	50
D163		25c. lilac	30	20
D164a		30c. lilac	20	35
D165		40c. lilac	9·75	9·50
D166a		50c. lilac	90	70
D167a		75c. lilac	90	90
D168a		1g. lilac	1·10	90

D 52

D 68

1945.

No.	Type	Description	Mint	Used
D337	D 52	1c. purple	55	35
D338		5c. purple	4·00	1·40
D339		25c. purple	9·00	20

1950. As Type D **121** of Netherlands.

No.	Description	Mint	Used
D384	1c. purple	1·60	1·60
D385	2c. purple	2·75	2·00
D386	2½c. purple	2·75	1·75
D387	5c. purple	3·50	35
D388	10c. purple	2·40	35
D389	15c. purple	6·75	2·25
D390	20c. purple	1·90	3·00
D391	25c. purple	22·00	30
D392	50c. purple	27·00	1·50
D393	75c. purple	40·00	30·00
D394	1g. purple	28·00	6·00

1956.

No.	Type	Description	Mint	Used
D436	D 68	1c. purple	10	10
D437		2c. purple	35	20
D438		2½c. purple	35	35
D439		5c. purple	35	35
D440		10c. purple	35	35
D441		15c. purple	55	50

D442 20c. purple 55 55
D443 25c. purple 65 20
D444 50c. purple 1·60 35
D445 75c. purple 2·25 1·00
D446 1g. purple 3·00 70

1987. Various stamps optd **TE BETALEN**.
D1325 65c. mult (No. 868) 1·75 50
D1326 65c. mult (No. 1132) 50 50
D1327 80c. mult (No. 1134) 1·75 60
D1328 90c. mult (No. 872a) 1·75 70
D1329 95c. mult (No. 873) 2·00 75
D1330 1g. mult (No. 1248) 2·00 75

SWAZILAND Pt. 1

A kingdom in the eastern part of S. Africa. Its early stamps were issued under joint control of Gt. Britain and the S. Africa Republic. Incorporated into the latter state in 1895 it was transferred in 1906 to the High Commissioner for S. Africa. Again issued stamps in 1933. Achieved Independence in 1968.

1961. 100 cents = 1 rand.
1974. 100 cents = 1 lilangeni (plural: emalangeni)

1889. Stamps of Transvaal optd **Swazieland**.
10 18 ½d. grey 7·50 16·00
1 1d. red 17·00 16·00
5 2d. bistre 17·00 15·00
6 6d. blue 20·00 40·00
3 1s. green 10·00 13·00
7 2s.6d. yellow £225 £250
8 5s. blue £140 £180
9 10s. brown £4500 £3000

2 King George V

7 Swazi Married Woman

1933.
11 2 ½d. green 30 30
12 1d. red 30 20
13 2d. brown 30 45
14 3d. blue 45 2·50
15 4d. red 2·75 3·00
16 6d. mauve 1·25 1·00
17 1s. olive 1·50 2·75
18 2s.6d. violet 15·00 22·00
19 5s. grey 30·00 48·00
20 10s. brown 80·00 £100

1935. Silver Jubilee. As T **32a** of St. Helena.
21 1d. blue and red 50 1·50
22 2d. blue and black 50 1·25
23 3d. brown and blue 55 5·00
24 6d. grey and purple 65 1·50

1937. Coronation. As T **32b** of St. Helena.
25 1d. red 50 1·50
26 2d. brown 50 20
27 3d. blue 50 50

1938. As T **2**, but with portraits of King George VI and inscr "SWAZILAND" only below portrait.
28a ½d. green 30 2·75
29a 1d. red 1·00 1·75
30b 1½d. blue 30 1·00
31a 2d. brown 30 50
32b 3d. blue 3·50 4·75
33a 4d. orange 50 1·40
34b 6d. purple 4·50 1·50
35a 1s. olive 1·25 65
36a 2s.6d. violet 14·00 2·50
37b 5s. grey 26·00 13·00
38a 10s. brown 6·50 6·00

1945. Victory stamps of South Africa (inscr alternately in English or Afrikaans) optd **Swaziland**.
39 55 1d. brown and red 55 10
40 – 2d. blue and violet (No. 109) 55 10
41 – 3d. blue (No. 110) 55 20
Unused prices are for bilingual pairs, used prices for single stamps in either language.

1947. Royal Visit. As Nos. 32/5 of Basutoland.
42 1d. red 10 10
43 2d. green 10 10
44 3d. blue 10 10
45 1s. mauve 10 10

1948. Silver Wedding. As T **33b/c** of St. Helena.
46 1½d. blue 50 10
47 10s. purple 23·00 27·00

1949. 75th Anniv of U.P.U. As T **33d/g** of St. Helena.
48 1½d. blue 15 10
49 3d. blue 1·75 2·50
50 6d. mauve 30 60
51 1s. olive 30 70

1953. Coronation. As T **33h** of St. Helena.
52 2d. black and brown 20 20

1956.
53 – ½d. black and orange 10 10
54 – 1d. black and green 10 10
55 7 2d. black and brown 30 10
56 – 3d. black and red 20 10
57 – 4½d. black and blue 60 10
58 – 6d. black and mauve 50 10
59 – 1s. black and olive 20 10
60 – 1s.3d. black and sepia 1·00 2·50
61 – 2s.6d. green and red 1·00 2·00
62 – 5s. violet and grey 7·50 2·75
63 7 10s. black and violet 15·00 13·00
64 – £1 black and turquoise 38·00 27·00
DESIGNS—HORIZ: ½d., 1s. Havelock asbestos mine; 1d., 2s.6d. Highveld view. VERT: 3d., 1s.3d. Swazi courting couple; 4½d., 5s. Swazi warrior in ceremonial dress; 6d., £1 Greater kudu.

1961. Stamps of 1956 surch in new currency.
65 ½c. on ½d. black and orange 3·25 4·25
66 1c. on 1d. black and green 10 1·50
67 2c. on 2d. black and brown 10 1·75
68 2½c. on 2d. black and brown 10 1·00
69 2½c. on 3d. black and red 10 10
70 3½c. on 2d. black and brown 10 1·00
71 4c. on 4½d. black and blue 10 10
72 5c. on 6d. black and mauve 10 10
73 10c. on 1s. black and olive 25·00 3·00
74 25c. on 2s.6d. green and red 30 65
75 50c. on 5s. violet and grey 30 60
76 1r. on 10s. black and violet 1·50 60
77a 2r. on £1 black and turquoise 4·50 8·50

1961. As 1956 but values in new currency.
78 ½c. black and orange (as ½d.) 10 1·00
79 1c. black and green (as 1d.) 10 10
80 2c. black and brown (as 2d.) 10 2·25
81 2½c. black and red (as 3d.) 15 10
82 4c. black and blue (as 4½d.) 15 1·25
83 5c. black and mauve (as 6d.) 70 15
84 10c. black and olive (as 1s.) 15 10
85 12½c. black and sepia (as 1s.3d.) 1·25 40
86 25c. green and red (as 2s.6d.) 2·75 3·75
87 50c. violet and grey (as 5s.) 2·00 1·40
88 1r. black and violet (as 10s.) 4·25 10·00
89 2r. black and turquoise (as £1) 9·50 11·00

15 Swazi Shields

31 Goods Train and Map of Swaziland Railway

1962.
90 15 ½c. black, brown and buff 10 10
91 – 1c. orange and black 10 10
92 – 2c. green, black and olive 10 1·00
93 – 2½c. black and red 10 10
94 – 3½c. green and grey 10 40
95 – 4c. black and turquoise 10 10
96 – 5c. black, red and deep red 70 10
97 – 7½c. brown and buff 80 50
98 – 10c. black and blue 3·50 20
99 – 12½c. red and olive 1·25 3·00
100 – 15c. black and mauve 1·50 70
101 – 20c. black and green 40 90
102 – 25c. black and blue 50 70
103 – 50c. black and red 12·00 4·25
104 – 1r. green and ochre 2·50 2·25
105 – 2r. red and blue 14·00 9·00
DESIGNS—VERT: 1c. Battle axe; 2c. Forestry; 2½c. Ceremonial headdress; 3½c. Musical instrument; 4c. Irrigation; 5c. Long-tailed whydah ("Widowbird"); 7½c. Rock paintings; 10c. Secretary bird; 12½c. Pink arum; 15c. Swazi married woman; 20c. Malaria control; 25c. Swazi warrior; 1r. Aloes. HORIZ: 50c. Southern ground hornbill ("Ground Hornbill"); 2r. Msinsi in flower.

1963. Freedom from Hunger. As T **63a** of St. Helena.
106 15c. violet 50 15

1963. Cent of Red Cross. As T **63b** of St. Helena.
107 2½c. red and black 30 10
108 15c. red and blue 70 90

1964. Opening of Swaziland Railway.
109 31 2½c. green and purple 55 10
110 3½c. blue and olive 55 1·00
111 15c. orange and brown 70 70
112 25c. yellow and blue 85 80

1965. Cent of I.T.U. As T **64a** of St. Helena.
113 2½c. blue and bistre 15 10
114 15c. purple and red 35 20

1965. I.C.Y. As T **64b** of St. Helena.
115 ½c. purple and turquoise 10 10
116 15c. green and lavender 40 20

1966. Churchill Commemoration. As T **64c** of St. Helena.
117 ½c. blue 10 1·25
118 2½c. green 20 10
119 15c. brown 45 25
120 25c. violet 70 70

1966. 20th Anniv of U.N.E.S.C.O. As T **64f/h** of St. Helena.
121 2½c. multicoloured 10 10
122 7½c. yellow, violet and olive 40 60
123 15c. black, purple and orange 65 1·25

32 King Sobhuza II and Map

1967. Protected State.
124 32 2½c. multicoloured 10 10
125 – 7½c. multicoloured 15 15
126 32 15c. multicoloured 20 30
127 – 25c. multicoloured 25 40
DESIGN—VERT: 7½, 25c. King Sobhuza II.

1967. 1st Conferment of University Degrees. As Nos. 234/7 of Botswana.
128 2½c. sepia, blue and orange 10 10
129 7½c. sepia, blue and turquoise 15 15
130 15c. sepia, blue and red 25 30
131 25c. sepia, blue and violet 30 35

35 Incwala Ceremony

1968. Traditional Customs.
132 35 3c. silver, red and black 10 10
133 – 10c. multicoloured 10 10
134 35 15c. gold, red and black 15 20
135 – 25c. multicoloured 15 20
DESIGN—VERT: 10, 25c. Reed dance.

1968. No. 96 surch **3c**.
136 3c. on 5c. black, red & dp red 1·25 10

38 Cattle Ploughing

1968. Independence.
137 38 3c. multicoloured 10 10
138 – 4½c. multicoloured 10 35
139 – 17½c. multicoloured 15 60
140 – 25c. slate, black and gold 45 80
MS141 180 × 162 mm. Nos. 137/40 each × 5 14·00 22·00
DESIGNS: 4½c. Overhead cable carrying asbestos; 17½c. Cutting sugar cane; 25c. Iron ore mining and railway map.

1968. Nos. 90/105 optd **INDEPENDENCE 1968** and No. 93 additionally surch **3 c**.
142 15 ½c. black, brown and buff 10 10
143 – 1c. orange and black 10 10
144 – 2c. green, black and olive 10 10
145a – 2½c. black and red 1·50 10
146 – 3c. on 2½c. black and red 10 10
147 – 3½c. green and grey 15 10
148 – 4c. black and turquoise 10 10
149 – 5c. black, red and deep red 3·50 10
150 – 7½c. brown and buff 50 10
151 – 10c. black and blue 3·75 10
152 – 12½c. red and olive 25 55
153 – 15c. black and mauve 25 1·00
154 – 20c. black and green 75 1·75
155 – 25c. black and blue 35 1·00
159 – 50c. black and red 3·50 5·00
157 – 1r. green and ochre 2·00 4·50
160 – 2r. red and blue 5·00 5·00

43 Porcupine

1969. Multicoloured.
161 ½c. Caracal 10 10
162 1c. Type **43** 10 10
163 2c. Crocodile 20 10
164 3c. Lion 60 10
165 3½c. African elephant 75 10
166 5c. Bush pig 30 10
167 7½c. Impala 35 10
168 10c. Chacma baboon 45 10
169 12½c. Ratel 70 3·50
170 15c. Leopard 1·25 70
171 20c. Blue wildebeest 95 60
172 25c. White rhinoceros 1·40 1·75
173 50c. Common zebra 1·50 3·25
174 1r. Waterbuck (vert) 3·00 6·50
175 2r. Giraffe (vert) 8·00 11·00
Nos. 164/5 are larger, 35 × 24½ mm.
For designs as Nos. 174/5, but in new currency, see Nos. 219/20.

44 King Sobhuza II and Flags

1969. Swaziland's Admission to the U.N. Multicoloured.
176 3c. Type **44** 10 10
177 7½c. King Sobhuza II, U.N. Building and emblem 15 10
178 12½c. As Type **44** 25 10
179 25c. As 7½c. 40 40

46 Athlete, Shield and Spears

47 "Bauhinia galpinii"

1970. 9th Commonwealth Games. Multicoloured.
180 3c. Type **46** 10 10
181 7½c. Runner 20 10
182 12½c. Hurdler 25 10
183 25c. Procession of Swaziland competitors 35 40

1971. Flowers. Multicoloured.
184 3c. Type **47** 20 10
185 10c. "Crocosmia aurea" 20 10
186 15c. "Gloriosa superba" 30 25
187 25c. "Watsonia densiflora" 40 70

48 King Sobhuza II in Ceremonial Dress

49 U.N.I.C.E.F. Emblem

1971. Golden Jubilee of King Sobhuza II's Accession. Multicoloured.
188 3c. Type **48** 10 10
189 3½c. Sobhuza II in medallion 10 10
190 7½c. Sobhuza II attending Incwala ceremony 15 10
191 25c. Sobhuza II and aides at opening of Parliament 30 35

1972. 25th Anniv of U.N.I.C.E.F.
192 49 15c. black and lilac 15 20
193 – 25c. black and green 20 55
DESIGN: 25c. As Type **49**, but inscription rearranged.

50 Local Dancers

1972. Tourism. Multicoloured.
194 3½c. Type **50** 10 10
195 7½c. Swazi beehive hut 15 15
196 15c. Ezulwini Valley 20 50
197 25c. Fishing, Usutu River 65 1·25

51 Spraying Mosquitoes

1973. 25th Anniv of W.H.O. Multicoloured.
198 3½c. Type **51** 20 10
199 7½c. Anti-malaria vaccination 40 70

52 Mining

1973. Natural Resources. Multicoloured.
200 3½c. Type **52** 55 10
201 7½c. Cattle 25 15
202 15c. Water 30 20
203 25c. Rice 35 50

53 Coat of Arms

1973. 5th Anniv of Independence.
204 **53** 3c. pink and black 10 10
205 – 10c. multicoloured 15 10
206 – 15c. multicoloured 30 75
207 – 25c. multicoloured . . . . 40 1·40
DESIGNS: 10c. King Sobhuza II saluting; 15c. Parliament buildings; 25c. National Somhlolo stadium.

54 Flags and Mortar-board **55** King Sobhuza as College Student

1973. 10th Anniv of University of Botswana, Lesotho and Swaziland. Multicoloured.
208 7½c. Type **54** 20 10
209 12½c. University campus . . 25 10
210 15c. Map of Southern Africa 30 20
211 25c. University badge 40 35

1974. 75th Birth Anniv of King Sobhuza II. Multicoloured.
212 3c. Type **55** 10 10
213 9c. King Sobhuza in middle-age 10 10
214 50c. King Sobhuza at 75 years of age 70 60

56 New Post Office, Lobamba

1974. Centenary of U.P.U. Multicoloured.
215 4c. Type **56** 10 10
216 10c. Mbabane Temporary Post Office, 1902 . . . . . 15 15
217 15c. Carrying mail by cableway 30 50
218 25c. Mule-drawn mail-coach 40 70

1975. As Nos. 174/5, but in new currency.
219 1e. Waterbuck . . . . 50 2·00
220 2e. Giraffe . . . . 1·10 4·00

57 Umcwasho Ceremony

1975. Swazi Youth. Multicoloured.
221 3c. Type **57** 10 10
222 10c. Butimba (hunting party) 15 10
223 15c. Lusekwane (sacred shrub) (horiz) 40 40
224 25c. Goina Regiment 60 70

58 Control Tower, Matsapa Airport

1975. 10th Anniv of Internal Air Service. Multicoloured.
225 4c. Type **58** 30 10
226 5c. Fire engine 70 20
227 15c. Douglas DC-3 . . . . . 1·25 1·40
228 25c. Hawker Siddeley H.S.748 . . . . 2·00 2·00

1975. Nos. 167 and 169 surch.
230 3c. on 7½c. Impala . . . . . 75 1·00
231 6c. on 12½c. Ratel . . . . . 1·50 2·00

60 Elephant Symbol

1975. International Women's Year.
232 **60** 4c. grey, black and blue . . 10 10
233 – 5c. multicoloured 10 10
234 – 15c. multicoloured 30 60
235 – 25c. multicoloured 50 90
DESIGNS—HORIZ: 5c. Queen Labotsibeni. VERT: 15c. Craftswoman; 25c. "Women in Service".

61 African Black-headed Oriole ("Black-headed Oriole")

1976. Birds. Multicoloured.
236 1c. Type **61** . . . . 75 2·25
237 2c. African green pigeon ("Green Pigeon") (vert) 80 2·25
238 3c. Green-winged pytilia ("Melba Finch") . . . . 1·00 1·00
239 4c. Violet starling ("Plum-coloured Starling") (vert) 80 15
240 5c. Black-headed heron (vert) . . . . 90 1·50
241 6c. Common stonechat ("Stonechat") (vert) . . . 1·50 2·25
242 7c. Chorister robin chat ("Chorister Robin") (vert) 1·40 2·50
243 10c. Four-coloured bush-shrike ("Gorgeous Bush Shrike") (vert) . . . . 1·50 1·50
244 15c. Black-collared barbet (vert) . . . . 2·25 55
245 20c. Grey heron (vert) . . . 3·25 2·00
246 25c. Giant kingfisher (vert) 3·50 2·00
247 30c. Verreaux's eagle ("Black Eagle") (vert) . . 3·50 2·50
248a 50c. Red bishop (vert) . . . 90 1·00
249a 1e. Pin-tailed whydah (vert) 1·75 2·50
250a 2e. Lilac-breasted roller . . 2·00 5·00

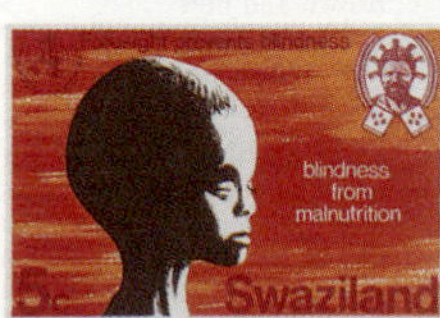

62 Blindness from Malnutrition

1976. Prevention of Blindness. Mult.
251 5c. Type **62** 25 10
252 10c. Infected retina 30 10
253 20c. Blindness from trachoma 60 65
254 25c. Medicines 65 85

63 Marathon **64** Footballer Shooting

1976. Olympic Games, Montreal. Mult.
255 5c. Type **63** 15 10
256 6c. Boxing 20 30
257 20c. Football 45 45
258 25c. Olympic torch and flame 55 65

1976. F.I.F.A. Membership. Multicoloured.
259 4c. Type **64** 20 10
260 6c. Heading 20 10
261 20c. Goalkeeping 50 25
262 25c. Player about to shoot . . 50 30

65 Alexander Graham Bell and Telephone

1976. Centenary of Telephone.
263 **65** 4c. multicoloured 10 10
264 – 5c. multicoloured 10 10
265 – 10c. multicoloured 10 10
266 – 15c. multicoloured 20 20
267 – 20c. multicoloured 25 30
Nos. 264/7 as Type **65**, but showing different telephones.

66 Queen Elizabeth II and King Sobhuza II

1977. Silver Jubilee. Multicoloured.
268 20c. Type **66** 15 15
269 25c. Coronation Coach at Admiralty Arch 15 15
270 50c. Queen in coach 20 40

67 Matsapa College

1977. 50th Anniv of Police Training. Mult.
271 5c. Type **67** 10 10
272 10c. Policemen and women on parade 50 20
273 20c. Royal Swaziland Police badge (vert) 70 95
274 25c. Dog handling . . . . . 80 1·10

68 Animals and Hunters

1977. Rock Paintings. Multicoloured.
275 5c. Type **68** 25 10
276 10c. Four dancers in a procession 30 10
277 15c. Man with cattle 40 20
278 20c. Four dancers 45 30
MS279 103×124 mm. Nos. 275/8 2·00 2·75

69 Timber, Highveld Region

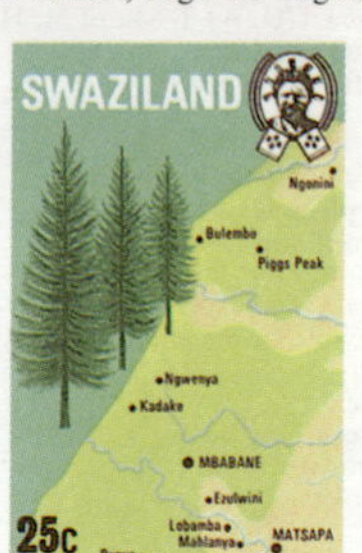

70 Timber, Highveld Region

1977. Maps of the Regions. Multicoloured.
280 5c. Type **69** 40 10
281 10c. Pineapple, Middleveld 50 10
282 15c. Orange and lemon, Lowveld 70 65
283 20c. Cattle, Lubombo region 85 95
MS284 87×103 mm. Four 25c. designs as T **70**, together forming a composite map of Swaziland 1·40 1·60

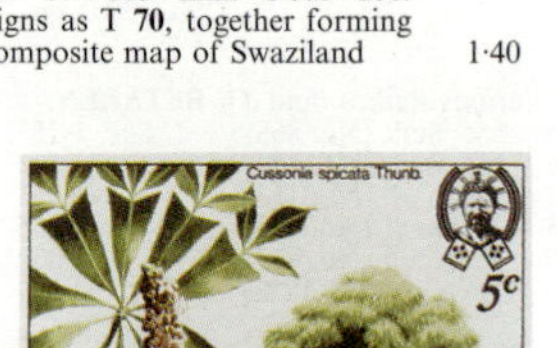

71 Cabbage Tree

1978. Trees of Swaziland.
285 **71** 5c. green, brown and black 15 15
286 – 10c. multicoloured 20 15
287 – 20c. multicoloured . . . . 45 1·25
288 – 25c. multicoloured . . . . 55 1·40
DESIGNS: 10c. Marula; 20c. Kiaat; 25c. Lucky bean-tree.

72 Rural Electrification at Lobamba

1978. Hydro-electric Power.
289 **72** 5c. black and brown . . . 10 10
290 – 10c. black and green . . . 15 10
291 – 20c. black and blue . . . 25 30
292 – 25c. black and purple . . . 30 35
DESIGNS: 10c. Edwaleni Power Station; 20c. Switchgear, Magudza Power Station; 25c. Turbine Hall, Edwaleni.

73 Elephant **75** Defence Force

74 Clay Pots

1978. 25th Anniv of Coronation.
293 – 25c. blue, black and green 15 25
294 – 25c. multicoloured 15 25
295 **73** 25c. blue, black and green 15 25
DESIGNS: No. 293, Queen's Lion; No. 294, Queen Elizabeth II.

1978. Handicrafts (1st series). Multicoloured.
296 5c. Type **74** 10 10
297 10c. Basketwork 10 10
298 20c. Wooden utensils 15 15
299 30c. Wooden pot 25 30
See also Nos. 310/13.

1978. 10th Anniv of Independence. Mult.
300 4c. Type **75** 15 10
301 6c. The King's Regiment . . 15 10
302 10c. Tinkabi tractor (agricultural development) 15 10
303 15c. Water-pipe laying (self-help scheme) 25 10
304 25c. Sebenta adult literacy scheme 30 25
305 50c. Fire emergency service 1·25 50

76 Archangel Gabriel appearing before Shepherds

1978. Christmas. Multicoloured.
306 5c. Type **76** 10 10
307 10c. Wise men paying homage to infant Jesus . . 10 10

308 15c. Archangel Gabriel warning Joseph 10 10
309 25c. Flight into Egypt . . . 20 20

1979. Handicrafts (2nd series). As T **74**. Mult.
310 5c. Sisal bowls 10 10
311 15c. Pottery 15 10
312 20c. Basket work 20 15
313 30c. Hide shield 30 20

77 Prospecting at Phophonyane

1979. Centenary of Discovery of Gold in Swaziland.
314 **77** 5c. gold and blue 25 10
315 – 15c. gold and brown . . . 45 20
316 – 25c. gold and green 65 30
317 – 50c. gold and red . . . . 90 1·25
DESIGNS: 15c. Early 3-stamp battery mill; 25c. Cyanide tanks at Piggs Peak; 50c. Pouring off molten gold.

78 "Girls at the Piano"

1979. International Year of the Child. Paintings by Renoir. Multicoloured.
318 5c. Type **78** 10 10
319 15c. "Madame Charpentier and her Children" 25 10
320 25c. "Girls picking Flowers" 35 15
321 50c. "Girl with Watering Can" 70 55
MS322 123 × 135 mm. Nos. 318/21 1·25 1·75

79 1933 1d. Carmine Stamp and Sir Rowland Hill

1979. Death Centenary of Sir Rowland Hill. Multicoloured.
323 10c. 1945 3d. Victory commemorative 15 10
324 20c. Type **79** 25 25
325 25c. 1968 25c. Independence commemorative 25 30
MS326 115 × 90 mm. 50c. 1956 6d. Great kudu antelope definitive 75 85

80 Obverse and Reverse of 5 Cents

1979. Coins.
327 **80** 5c. black and brown . . . 15 10
328 – 10c. black and blue . . . 20 10
329 – 20c. black and green . . . 35 20
330 – 50c. black and orange . . 50 50
331 – 1e. black and cerise . . . 75 1·00
DESIGNS: 10c. Obverse and reverse of 10 cents; 20c. Obverse and reverse of 20 cents; 50c. Reverse of 50 cents; 1e. Reverse of 1 lilangeni.

81 Big Bend Post Office

1979. Post Office Anniversaries.
332 **81** 5c. multicoloured 10 10
333 – 15c. multicoloured 15 10
334 – 20c. black, green and red . . 20 15
335 – 50c. multicoloured 40 60

DESIGNS AND COMMEMORATIONS—HORIZ: 5c. Type **81** (25th anniv of Posts and Telecommunications Services); 20c. 1949 75th anniv of U.P.U. 1s. stamp (10th anniv of U.P.U. membership); 50c. 1974 Centenary of U.P.U. 25c. stamp (10th anniv of U.P.U membership). VERT: 15c. Microwave antenna, Mount Ntondozi (25th anniv of Posts and Telecommunications Services).

82 Map of Swaziland

83 "Brunsvigia radulosa"

1980. 75th Anniv of Rotary International.
336 **82** 5c. blue and gold 25 10
337 – 15c. blue and gold 45 10
338 – 50c. blue and gold 50 55
339 – 1e. blue and gold . . . . 85 1·25
DESIGNS: 15c. Vitreous cutter and optical illuminator; 50c. Scroll; 1e. Rotary Head-quarters, Evanston, U.S.A.

1980. Flowers. Multicoloured.
340A 1c. Type **83** 10 10
341A 2c. "Aloe suprafoliata" . . 10 10
342A 3c. "Haemanthus magnificus" 10 10
343A 4c. "Aloe marlothii" . . . 10 10
344A 5c. "Dicoma zeyheri" . . . 10 10
345A 6c. "Aloe kniphofioides" . . 15 30
346A 7c. "Cyrtanthus bicolor" . . 10 10
347A 10c. "Eucomis autumnalis" (horiz) 20 10
348A 15c. "Leucospermum gerrardii" (horiz) 15 10
349A 20c. "Haemanthus multiflorus" (horiz) . . . 30 25
350A 30c. "Acridocarpus natalitius" (horiz) 20 20
351A 50c. "Adenium swazicum" (horiz) 20 30
352A 1e. "Protea simplex" . . . 35 60
353A 2e. "Calodendrum capense" 1·10 1·25
354A 5e. "Gladiolus ecklonii" . . 1·50 3·00
Nos. 347A/51A are 42 × 45 mm and Nos. 352A/4A 28 × 38 mm.
Nos. 340A/1A, 343A, 345A, 347A and 349A come with and without date imprint.

84 Mail Runner

1980. "London 1980" International Stamp Exhibition. Multicoloured.
355 10c. Type **84** 15 10
356 20c. Post Office mail truck 25 15
357 25c. Mail sorting office . . . 30 20
358 50c. Ropeway conveying mail at Bulembu 70 70

85 Scaly

1980. River Fishes. Multicoloured.
359 5c. Type **85** 25 10
360 10c. Silver catfish ("Silver barbel") 25 10
361 15c. Tiger fish 40 15
362 30c. Brown squeaker 50 30
363 1e. Red-breasted tilapia ("Bream") . . . . 60 1·40

86 Oribi

1980. Wildlife Conservation. Multicoloured.
364 5c. Type **86** 15 10
365 10c. Nile crocodile (vert) . . 30 10
366 50c. Temminck's ground pangolin 75 70
367 1e. Leopard (vert) . . . . . 1·60 1·50

87 Public Bus Service

1981. Transport. Multicoloured.
368 5c. Type **87** 10 10
369 25c. Royal Swazi National Airways 25 15
370 30c. Swaziland United Transport 30 20
371 1e. Swaziland Railway . . . 1·25 1·75

88 Mantenga Falls

1981. Tourism. Multicoloured.
372 5c. Type **88** 10 10
373 15c. Mananga Yacht Club . . 15 10
374 30c. White rhinoceros in Mlilwane Game Sanctuary 40 30
375 1e. Gambling equipment (casinos) . . . . 1·10 1·60

89 Prince Charles on Hike

91 "Physical Recreation"

90 Installation of King Sobhuza II, 22 December 1921

1981. Royal Wedding. Multicoloured.
376 10c. Wedding bouquet from Swaziland 10 10
377 25c. Type **89** 15 10
378 1e. Prince Charles and Lady Diana Spencer 40 70

1981. Diamond Jubilee of King Sobhuza II. Multicoloured.
379 5c. Type **90** 10 10
380 10c. Royal Visit, 1947 . . . 10 10
381 15c. King Sobhuza II and Coronation of Queen Elizabeth II, 1953 . . . . 15 15
382 25c. King Sobhuza taking Royal Salute, Independence, 1968 . . . . 15 15
383 30c. King Sobhuza in youth 20 20
384 1e. King Sobhuza and Parliament Buildings . . . 50 90

1981. 25th Anniv of Duke of Edinburgh Award Scheme. Multicoloured.
385 5c. Type **91** 10 10
386 20c. "Expeditions" 10 10
387 50c. "Skills" 25 25
388 1e. Duke of Edinburgh in ceremonial dress 50 80

92 Disabled Person in Wheelchair

1981. International Year of Disabled Persons. Multicoloured.
389 5c. Type **92** 30 10
390 15c. Teacher with disabled child (vert) 50 15
391 25c. Disabled craftsman (vert) 75 20
392 1e. Disabled driver in invalid carriage . . . . 2·25 1·75

93 "Papilio demodocus"

1981. Butterflies. Multicoloured.
393 5c. Type **93** 50 10
394 10c. "Charaxes candiope" . . 50 10
395 50c. "Papilio nireus" . . . . 1·50 85
396 1e. "Terias desjardinsii" . . . 2·00 2·00

94 Man holding a Flower after discarding Cigarettes

95 Male Pel's Fishing Owl

1982. Pan-African Conference on Smoking and Health. Multicoloured.
397 5c. Type **94** 50 85
398 10c. Smoker and non-smoker 60 90

1982. Wildlife Conservation (1st series). Pel's Fishing Owl. Multicoloured.
399 35c. Type **95** . . . . 8·00 4·00
400 35c. Female Pel's fishing owl at nest . . . . 8·00 4·00
401 35c. Pair of Pel's fishing owls 8·00 4·00
402 35c. Pel's fishing owl, nest and eggs . . . . 8·00 4·00
403 35c. Adult Pel's fishing owl with youngster . . . . . 8·00 4·00
See also Nos. 425/29 and 448/52.

96 Swaziland Coat of Arms

1982. 21st Birthday of Princess of Wales. Mult.
404 5c. Type **96** 10 10
405 20c. Princess leaving Eastleigh Airport, Southampton 80 10
406 50c. Bride at Buckingham Palace 90 30
407 1e. Formal portrait . . . . . 2·25 85

97 Irrigation

1982. Sugar Industry. Multicoloured.
408 5c. Type **97** 10 10
409 20c. Harvesting 25 15
410 30c. Mhlume mills 35 25
411 1e. Sugar transportation by train . . . . 1·00 1·60

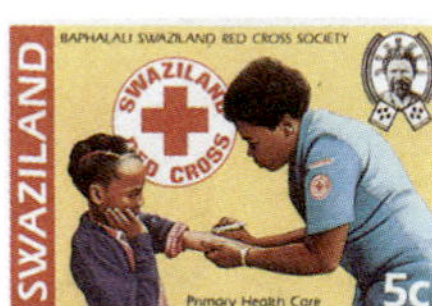

98 Doctor with Child

1982. Swaziland Red Cross Society (Baphaladi). Multicoloured.
412 5c. Type **98** 10 10
413 20c. Juniors carrying stretcher 25 15
414 50c. Disaster relief 55 70
415 1e. Henri Dunant (founder of Red Cross) . . . . 1·25 2·25

99 Taking the Oath

1982. 75th Anniv of Boy Scout Movement. Multicoloured.
416 5c. Type **99** 10 10
417 10c. Hiking and exploration 15 10
418 25c. Community development 30 30
419 75c. Lord Baden-Powell . . . 1·00 1·25
MS420 107 × 109 mm. 1e. World Scout badge . . . . 1·00 1·40

100 Satellite View of Earth
102 Montgolfier Balloon

1982. Commonwealth Day. Multicoloured.
421 6c. Type **100** 10 10
422 10c. King Sobhuza II 10 10
423 50c. Swazi woman and beehive huts (horiz) 35 55
424 1e. Spraying sugar crops (horiz) . . . . 70 1·00

1983. Wildlife Conservation (2nd series). Lammergeier. As T **95**. Multicoloured.
425 35c. Adult male . . . . . . 2·50 2·50
426 35c. Pair . . . . 2·50 2·50
427 35c. Nest and egg . . . . . 2·50 2·50
428 35c. Female at nest . . . . 2·50 2·50
429 35c. Adult bird with fledgling 2·50 2·50

101 Swaziland National Football Team

1983. Tour of Swaziland by English Football Clubs. Three sheets, 101 × 72 mm, each containing one 75c. stamp as T **101**. Multicoloured.
MS430 75c. Type **101**; 75c. Tottenham Hotspur; 75c. Manchester United Set of 3 sheets 1·50 3·00

1983. Bicentenary of Manned Flight. Mult.
431 5c. Type **102** 10 10
432 10c. Wright brothers' Flyer I (horiz) 15 10
433 25c. Fokker Fellowship (horiz) 30 35
434 50c. Bell XS-1 (horiz) 60 65
MS435 73 × 73 mm. 1e. Space shuttle "Columbia" . . . . 1·00 1·40

103 Dr. Albert Schweitzer (Peace Prize, 1952)

1983. 150th Birth Anniv of Alfred Nobel. Multicoloured.
436 6c. Type **103** . . . . 1·75 50
437 10c. Dag Hammarskjold (Peace Prize, 1961) 70 15
438 50c. Albert Einstein (Physics Prize, 1921) . . . . . . 3·50 1·75
439 1e. Alfred Nobel . . . . . . 3·75 4·25

104 Maize

1983. World Food Day. Multicoloured.
440 6c. Type **104** 15 10
441 10c. Rice 15 10
442 50c. Cattle herding 80 90
443 1e. Ploughing . . . . 1·40 2·50

105 Women's College

1984. Education. Multicoloured.
444 5c. Type **105** 10 10
445 15c. Technical training school 15 15
446 50c. University 35 60
447 1e. Primary school . . . . . 65 1·10

106 Male on Ledge

1984. Wildlife Conservation (3rd series). Bald Ibis. Multicoloured.
448 35c. Type **106** . . . . . . 3·00 3·00
449 35c. Male and female . . . . 3·00 3·00
450 35c. Bird and egg . . . . . 3·00 3·00
451 35c. Female on nest of eggs 3·00 3·00
452 35c. Adult and fledgling . . . 3·00 3·00

107 Mule-drawn Passenger Coach

1984. Universal Postal Union Congress, Hamburg. Multicoloured.
453 7c. Type **107** 30 10
454 15c. Ox-drawn post wagon 45 15
455 50c. Mule-drawn mail coach 90 75
456 1e. Bristol to London mail coach . . . . 1·40 1·40

108 Running

1984. Olympic Games, Los Angeles. Multicoloured.
457 7c. Type **108** 10 20
458 10c. Swimming 10 10
459 50c. Shooting 45 85
460 1e. Boxing . . . . 90 1·75
MS461 100 × 70 mm. Nos. 457/60 2·75 4·50

109 "Suillus bovinus"

1984. Fungi. Multicoloured.
462 10c. Type **109** . . . . . . 1·50 30
463 15c. "Langermannia gigantea" (vert) . . . . . 2·50 55
464 50c. "Trametes versicolor" ("Coriolus versicolor") (vert) . . . . 2·75 2·75
465 1e. "Boletus edulis" . . . . 3·25 5·25

110 King Sobhuza opening Railway, 1964

1984. 20th Anniv of Swaziland Railways. Multicoloured.
466 10c. Type **110** 30 15
467 25c. Type 15A locomotive at Siweni Yard 55 40
468 30c. Container loading, Matsapha Station 55 40
469 1e. Locomotive No. 268 leaving Alto Tunnel . . . 1·25 2·25
MS470 144 × 74 mm. Nos. 466/9 2·75 6·00

1985. Nos. 340, 342, 343, 345 and 346 surch.
471a 10c. on 4c. "Aloe marlothii" 50 10
472 15c. on 7c. "Cyrtanthus bicolor" 60 20
473 20c. on 3c. "Haemanthus magnificus" 50 15
474 25c. on 6c. "Aloe kniphofioides" 60 20
475 30c. on 1c. Type **83** 70 20
476 30c. on 2c. "Aloe suprafoliata" . . . . . . 2·75 3·75

112 Rotary International Logo and Map of World

1985. 80th Anniv of Rotary International. Multicoloured.
477 10c. Type **112** 40 10
478 15c. Teacher and handicapped children . . . 80 20
479 50c. Youth exchange . . . . 1·10 1·00
480 1e. Nurse and children . . . 2·50 2·75

113 Male Southern Ground Hornbill
114 The Queen Mother in 1975

1985. Birth Bicentenary of John J. Audubon (ornithologist). Southern Ground Hornbills. Multicoloured.
481 25c. Type **113** . . . . 2·25 3·25
482 25c. Male and female ground hornbills . . . . 2·25 3·25
483 25c. Female at nest . . . . . 2·25 3·25
484 25c. Ground hornbill in nest, and egg . . . . 2·25 3·25
485 25c. Adult and fledgling . . . 2·25 3·25

1985. Life and Times of Queen Elizabeth the Queen Mother. Multicoloured.
486 10c. The Queen Mother in South Africa, 1947 . . . 25 10
487 15c. With the Queen and Princess Margaret, 1985 (from photo by Norman Parkinson) 25 10
488 50c. Type **114** 90 75
489 1e. With Prince Henry at his christening (from photo by Lord Snowdon) . . . . . 1·10 1·75
MS490 91 × 73 mm. 2e. Greeting Prince Andrew . . . . 2·50 1·75

115 Buick "Tourer"

1985. Century of Motoring. Multicoloured.
491 10c. Type **115** 50 10
492 15c. Four cylinder Rover . . 70 20
493 50c. De Dion Bouton . . . . 1·75 2·00
494 1e. "Model T" Ford . . . . 2·25 4·00

116 Youths building Bridge over Ravine

1985. International Youth Year (10, 50c.) and 75th Anniv of Girl Guide Movement (others). Multicoloured.
495 10c. Type **116** 15 10
496 20c. Girl Guides in camp . . 20 15
497 50c. Youth making model from sticks . . . . 45 1·00
498 1e. Guides collecting brushwood . . . . 80 2·00

117 Halley's Comet over Swaziland

1986. Appearance of Halley's Comet.
499 **117** 1e.50 multicoloured . . . 2·75 4·00

1986. 60th Birthday of Queen Elizabeth II. As T **145a** of St. Helena. Multicoloured.
500 10c. Christening of Princess Anne, 1950 . . . . 10 10
501 30c. On Palace balcony after wedding of Prince and Princess of Wales, 1981 . . 15 25
502 45c. Royal visit to Swaziland, 1947 . . . . 15 30
503 1e. At Windsor Polo Ground, 1984 . . . . 30 70
504 2e. At Crown Agents Head Office, London 1983 . . . 60 1·40

118 King Mswati III
119 Emblems of Round Table and Project Orbis (eye disease campaign)

1986. Coronation of King Mswati III.
505 **118** 10c. black and gold . . . 35 25
506 – 20c. multicoloured 70 30
507 – 25c. multicoloured 80 35
508 – 30c. multicoloured 90 50
509 – 40c. multicoloured . . . . 2·75 2·00
510 – 2e. multicoloured . . . . 3·75 7·00
DESIGNS—HORIZ: 20c. Prince with King Sobhuza II at Incwala ceremony; 25c. At primary school; 30c. At school in England; 40c. Inspecting guard of honour at Matsapha Airport; 2e. Dancing the Simemo.

1986. 50th Anniv of Round Table Organization. Designs showing branch emblems. Multicoloured.
511 15c. Type **119** 25 10
512 25c. Ehlanzeni 51 . . . . . . 35 20
513 55c. Mbabane 30 . . . . . . 75 60
514 70c. Bulembu 54 . . . . . . 85 1·40
515 2e. Manzini 44 . . . . 1·75 3·25

120 "Precis hierta"

1987. Butterflies (1st series). Multicoloured.
516 10c. Type **120** . . . . 55 1·25
517 15c. "Hamanumida daedalus" 65 1·00
518 20c. "Charaxes boueti" . . . 65 90
519 25c. "Abantis paradisea" . . 65 1·50
520 30c. "Acraea anemosa" . . . 65 70
521 35c. "Graphium leonidas" . . 65 75
522 45c. "Graphium antheus" . . 70 1·50
523 50c. "Precis orithya" 70 85
524 55c. "Pinacopteryx eriphia" 70 85
525 70c. "Precis octavia" . . . . 80 1·40
526 1e. "Mylothris chloris" . . . 1·00 2·75
527 5e. "Colotis regina" 75 80
528 10e. "Spindasis natalensis" 1·50 1·60
For these designs and similar 5c. with different portrait of King Mswati III, see Nos. 606/17.

121 Two White Rhinoceroses
122 Hybrid Tea Rose "Blue Moon"

1987. White Rhinoceros. Multicoloured.
529 15c. Type **121** . . . . 2·00 45
530 25c. Female and calf . . . . 2·75 1·00
531 45c. Rhinoceros charging . . 4·25 3·25
532 70c. Rhinoceros wallowing . . 6·50 7·50

1987. Garden Flowers. Multicoloured.
533 15c. Type **122** . . . . 1·00 20
534 35c. Rambler rose "Danse du feu" . . . . 2·00 80
535 55c. Pompon dahlia "Odin" 2·25 1·50
536 2e. "Lilium davidii var. willmottiae" . . . . . . 6·50 10·00

1987. Royal Ruby Wedding. Nos. 501/4 optd **40TH WEDDING ANNIVERSARY**.
537 30c. On Palace balcony after wedding of Prince and Princess of Wales, 1981 . . 20 20
538 45c. Royal visit to Swaziland, 1947 . . . . 30 30
539 1e. At Windsor Polo Ground, 1984 . . . . 50 1·25
540 2e. At Crown Agents Head Office, London, 1983 . . . 75 2·25

123 "Zabalius aridus" (grasshopper)

1988. Insects. Multicoloured.
541 15c. Type **123** . . . . 1·25 15
542 55c. "Callidea bohemani" (shieldbug) . . . . 2·50 85
543 1e. "Phymateus viridipes" (grasshopper) . . . . . . 4·25 4·25
544 2e. "Nomadacris septemfasciata" (locust) . . 6·50 8·50

124 Athlete with Swazi Flag and Olympic Stadium

1988. Olympic Games, Seoul. Multicoloured.
545 15c. Type **124** 60 10
546 35c. Taekwondo . . . . . . 1·10 45
547 1e. Boxing . . . . 1·50 2·25
548 2e. Tennis . . . . 3·25 5·00

125 Savanna Monkey

1989. Small Mammals. Multicoloured.
549 35c. Type **125** . . . . 1·50 30
550 55c. Large-toothed rock hyrax . . . . 2·00 75
551 1e. Zorilla . . . . 3·50 4·00
552 2e. African wild cat . . . . 6·00 8·00

126 Dr. David Hynd (founder of Swazi Red Cross)

1989. 125th Anniv of Int Red Cross. Mult.
553 15c. Type **126** 20 15
554 60c. First aid training 55 40
555 1e. Sigombeni Clinic . . . . 90 1·10
556 2e. Refugee camp . . . . . 1·40 2·25

127 King Mswati III with Prince of Wales, 1987

1989. 21st Birthday of King Mswati III. Mult.
557 15c. Type **127** 10 10
558 60c. King with Pope John Paul II, 1988 . . . . . . 30 35
559 1e. Introduction of Crown Prince to people, 1983 . . 50 55
560 2e. King Mswati III and Queen Mother . . . . . . 95 1·00

128 Manzini to Mahamba Road

1989. 25th Anniv of African Development Bank. Multicoloured.
561 15c. Type **128** 10 10
562 60c. Microwave Radio Receiver, Mbabane 30 40
563 1e. Mbabane Government Hospital . . . . 50 1·00
564 2e. Ezulwini Power Station switchyard . . . . 95 2·00

129 International Priority Mail Van

1990. "Stamp World London 90" International Stamp Exhibition. Multicoloured.
565 15c. Type **129** 15 10
566 60c. Facsimile service operators 40 40
567 1e. Rural post office . . . . 75 1·00
568 2e. Ezulwini Earth Station . . 1·40 2·50
MS569 105 × 85 mm. 2e. Mail runner . . . . 2·25 3·25

1990. 90th Birthday of Queen Elizabeth the Queen Mother. As T **161a** of St. Helena.
570 75c. multicoloured 50 50
571 4e. black and green . . . . . 2·25 3·50
DESIGNS—21 × 36 mm: 75c. Queen Mother. 29 × 37 mm: 4e. King George VI and Queen Elizabeth visiting Civil Resettlement Unit, Hatfield House.

130 Pictorial Teaching

1990. International Literacy Year. Mult.
572 15c. Type **130** 10 10
573 75c. Rural class 45 45
574 1e. Modern teaching methods 60 1·00
575 2e. Presentation of certificates 1·10 2·00

131 Rural Water Supply

133 Lobamba Hot Spring

1990. 40th Anniv of United Nations Development Programme. "Helping People to Help Themselves". Multicoloured.
576 60c. Type **131** 35 35
577 1e. Seed multiplication project . . . . 60 1·10
578 2e. Low-cost housing project 1·25 2·25

1990. Nos. 519/20, 522 and 524 surch.
579 10c. on 25c. "Abantis paradisea" 30 30
580 15c. on 30c. "Acraea anemosa" 40 40
580a 15c. on 45c. "Graphium antheus" . . . . 16·00 16·00
581 20c. on 45c. "Graphium antheus" 40 40
582 40c. on 55c. "Pinacopteryx eriphia" 55 55

1991. National Heritage. Multicoloured.
583 15c. Type **133** 25 10
584 60c. Sibebe Rock 65 45
585 1e. Jolobela Falls . . . . . 1·00 1·25
586 2e. Mantjolo Sacred Pool . . 1·75 2·25
MS587 80 × 60 mm. 2e. Usushwana river . . . . 2·25 3·00

134 King Mswati III making Speech

1991. 5th Anniv of King Mswati III's Coronation. Multicoloured.
588 15c. Type **134** 25 10
589 75c. Butimba Royal Hunt . . 70 60
590 1e. King and visiting school friends, 1986 . . . . . . 1·00 1·25
591 2e. King opening Parliament 1·75 2·50

1991. 65th Birthday of Queen Elizabeth II and 70th Birthday of Prince Philip. As T **165a** of St. Helena. Multicoloured.
592 1e. Prince Philip . . . . . . 1·25 1·50
593 2e. Queen Elizabeth II . . . 1·50 1·75

135 "Xerophyta retinervis"

136 Father Christmas arriving with Gifts

1991. Indigenous Flowers. Multicoloured.
594 15c. Type **135** 50 10
595 75c. "Bauhinia galpinii" . . . 1·25 80
596 1e. "Dombeya rotundifolia" 1·50 1·60
597 2e. "Kigelia africana" . . . . 2·25 3·25

1991. Christmas. Multicoloured.
598 20c. Type **136** 15 10
599 70c. Singing carols 65 50
600 1e. Priest reading from Bible 80 1·25
601 2e. The Nativity . . . . . . 1·50 2·50

137 Lubombo Flat Lizard

1992. Reptiles (1st series). Multicoloured.
602 20c. Type **137** 90 20
603 70c. Natal hinged tortoise . . 2·25 1·50
604 1e. Swazi thick-toed gecko . . 2·75 2·75
605 2e. Nile monitor . . . . . . 3·75 5·50
See also Nos. 658/61.

138 "Precis hierta"

1992. Butterflies (2nd series). Nos. 516/26 and new value (5c.) showing different portrait of King Mswati III. Multicoloured.
606 5c. "Colotis antevippe" . . . 10 10
607 10c. Type **138** 10 10
608 15c. "Hamanumida daedalus" 10 10
609 20c. "Charaxes boueti" . . . 10 10
610 25c. "Abantis paradisea" . . 10 10
611 30c. "Acraea anemosa" . . . 10 10
612 35c. "Graphium leonidas" . . 10 10
613 45c. "Graphium antheus" . . 10 10
614 50c. "Precis orithya" 10 10
615 55c. "Pinacopteryx eriphia" 10 10
616 70c. "Precis octavia" 10 15
617 1e. "Mylothris chloris" . . . 15 20

139 Missionaries visiting King Sobhuza II and Queen Lomawa

140 Calabashes

1992. Centenary of Evangelical Alliance Missions. Multicoloured.
620 20c. Type **139** 40 10
621 1e. Pioneer missionaries . . . 2·00 2·50

1993. Archaeological and Contemporary Artifacts. Multicoloured.
622 20c. Type **140** 45 10
623 70c. Contemporary cooking pot . . . . 1·10 85
624 1e. Wooden bowl and containers . . . . 1·50 1·75
625 2e. Quern for grinding seeds 2·50 3·50

141 King Mswati III as Baby

142 Male and Female Common Waxbills

1993. 25th Birthday of King Mswati III and 25th Anniv of Independence. Mult.
626 25c. Type **141** 20 10
627 40c. King Mswati III addressing meeting 25 20
628 1e. King Sobhuza II receiving Instrument of Independence . . . . . . 75 1·10
629 2e. King Mswati III delivering Coronation speech . . . . 1·40 2·25

1993. Common Waxbill. Multicoloured.
630 25c. Type **142** 40 20
631 40c. Waxbill and eggs in nest 55 25
632 1e. Waxbill on nest . . . . . 1·25 1·50
633 2e. Waxbill feeding chicks . . 2·00 2·75

143 Classroom and Practical Training

144 "Agaricus arvensis"

1994. 25th Anniv of U.S. Peace Corps in Swaziland. Multicoloured.
634 25c. Type **143** 20 10
635 40c. Rural water supply . . . 30 20
636 1e. Americans and Swazis in traditional costumes . . . 1·25 1·25
637 2e. Swazi–American co-operation . . . . 1·40 2·25

1994. Fungi. Multicoloured.
638 30c. Type **144** 90 50
639 40c. "Boletus edulis" . . . . 1·00 50
640 1e. "Russula virescens" . . . 2·25 1·75
641 2e. "Armillaria mellea" . . . 3·00 3·50

145 Emblem and Airliner on Runway

1994. 50th Anniv of I.C.A.O. Multicoloured.
642 30c. Type **145** 30 10
643 40c. Control tower and dish aerial 35 20
644 1e. Crash tenders . . . . . . 75 1·10
645 2e. Air traffic controllers . . 1·25 2·25

146 Wooden Bowls

147 Harvesting Maize

1995. Handicrafts. Multicoloured.
646 35c. Type **146** 35 20
647 50c. Chicken nests 55 35
648 1e. Leather crafts 80 90
649 2e. Wood carvings . . . . . 1·50 2·00

1995. 50th Anniv of F.A.O. Multicoloured.
650 35c. Type **147** 20 20
651 50c. Planting vegetables . . . 30 35
652 1e. Herd of cattle 50 75
653 2e. Harvesting sorghum . . . 90 1·75

148 Green Turaco

1995. Turacos ("Louries"). Multicoloured.

654	35c. Type **148**	40	30
655	50c. Green turaco in flight	55	45
656	1e. Violet-crested turaco	80	1·00
657	2e. Livingstone's turaco	1·25	2·00

1996. Reptiles (2nd series). As T **137** with King's portrait at right. Multicoloured.

658	35c. Chameleon	40	20
659	50c. Rock monitor	55	35
660	1e. African python	75	85
661	2e. Tree agama	1·25	2·00

149 Waterberry

1996. Trees. Multicoloured.

662	40c. Type **149**	20	15
663	60c. Sycamore fig	25	20
664	1e. Stem fruit	45	80
665	2e. Wild medlar	90	1·60

150 Mahamba Methodist Church

1996. Historic Monuments. Multicoloured.

666	40c. Type **150**	30	15
667	60c. Colonial Secretariat, Mbabane	40	20
668	1e. King Sobhuza II Monument, Lobamba	70	85
669	2e. First High Court Building, Hlatikulu	1·25	1·75

151 Children in Class

1996. 50th Anniv of U.N.I.C.E.F. Multicoloured.

670	40c. Type **151**	15	15
671	60c. Child being inoculated (vert)	20	20
672	1e. Child on crutches (vert)	40	60
673	2e. Mother and children (vert)	80	1·40

152 Klipspringer **153** Umgaco Costume

1997. Mammals. Multicoloured.

674	50c. Type **152**	30	20
675	70c. Grey duiker	35	30
676	1e. Antbear (horiz)	50	70
677	2e. Cape clawless otter (horiz)	80	1·40

1997. Traditional Costumes. Multicoloured.

678	50c. Type **153**	20	15
679	70c. Sigeja cloak	30	25
680	1e. Umdada kilt	45	55
681	2e. Ligcebesha costume	75	1·10

154 Olive Toad

1998. Amphibians. Multicoloured.

682	55c. Type **154**	20	15
683	75c. African bullfrog	30	25
684	1e. Water lily frog	45	60
685	2e. Bushveld rain frog	75	1·10

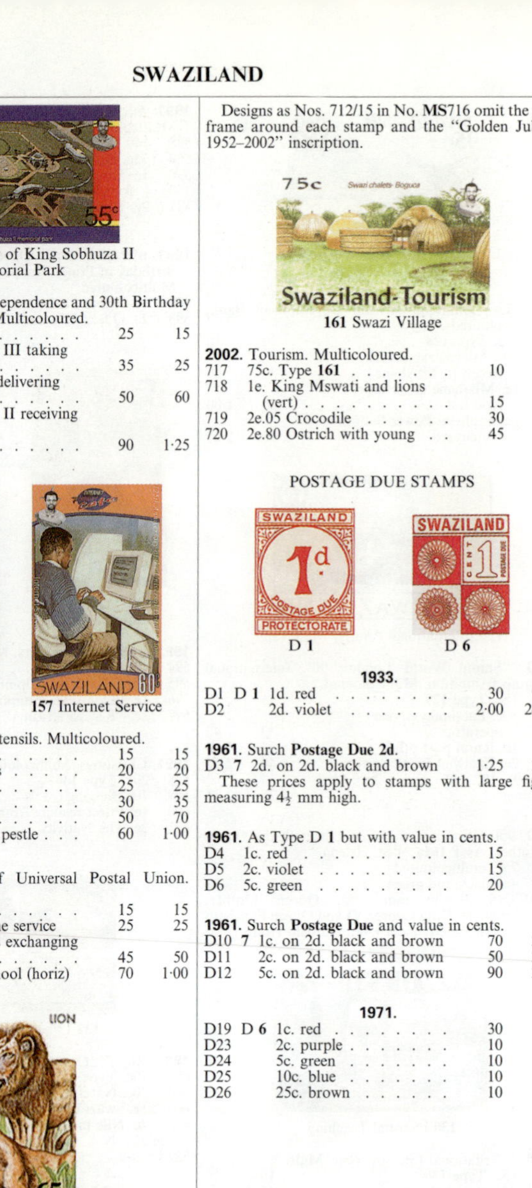

155 Aerial View of King Sobhuza II Memorial Park

1998. 30th Anniv of Independence and 30th Birthday of King Mswati III. Multicoloured.

686	55c. Type **155**	25	15
687	75c. King Mswati III taking oath (vert)	35	25
688	1e. King Mswati delivering speech	50	60
689	2e. King Sobhuza II receiving Instrument of Independence	90	1·25

156 Grinding Stone **157** Internet Service

1999. Local Culinary Utensils. Multicoloured.

690	60c. Type **156**	15	15
691	75c. Stirring sticks	20	20
692	80c. Clay pot	25	25
693	95c. Swazi spoons	30	35
694	1e.75 Beer cups	50	70
695	2e.40 Mortar and pestle	60	1·00

1999. 125th Anniv of Universal Postal Union. Multicoloured.

696	60c. Type **157**	15	15
697	80c. Cellular phone service	25	25
698	1e. Two post vans exchanging mail (horiz)	45	50
699	2e.40 Training school (horiz)	70	1·00

158 Lion and Lioness

2000. Wildlife. Multicoloured.

700	65c. Type **158**	25	10
701	90c. Leopard (horiz)	35	20
702	1e.50 Rhinoceros (horiz)	80	70
703	2e.50 Buffalo	85	1·10

159 Oribi with Young

2001. Endangered Species. Antelopes. Mult.

704	65c. Type **159**	20	10
705	90c. Oribi buck	25	20
706	1e.50 Young klipspringers	45	55
707	2e.50 Male and female klipspringers	65	85

160 Fighting Forest Fires

2001. Environment Protection. Multicoloured.

708	70c. Type **160**	20	10
709	95c. Tree planting	25	15
710	2e.05 Construction of Maguga Dam	50	60
711	2e.80 Building embankment	65	85

2002. Golden Jubilee. As T **211** of St. Helena.

712	70c. agate, violet and gold	20	10
713	95c. multicoloured	25	10
714	2e.05 agate, violet and gold	50	60
715	2e.80 multicoloured	65	85
MS716	162×95 mm. Nos. 715/15 and 22e.50 multicoloured	6·00	7·00

DESIGNS—HORIZ (as T **211** of St. Helena): 70c. Princess Elizabeth, Prince Philip, and children, 1951; 95c. Queen Elizabeth in blue and white beret; 2e.05, Queen Elizabeth in evening dress; 2e80, Queen Elizabeth on visit to Norway, 2001. VERT (38×51 mm): 50p. Queen Elizabeth after Annigoni.

Designs as Nos. 712/15 in No. **MS**716 omit the gold frame around each stamp and the "Golden Jubilee 1952–2002" inscription.

161 Swazi Village

2002. Tourism. Multicoloured.

717	75c. Type **161**	10	10
718	1e. King Mswati and lions (vert)	15	10
719	2e.05 Crocodile	30	35
720	2e.80 Ostrich with young	45	50

POSTAGE DUE STAMPS

D 1 D 6

1933.

No.	Type	Description		
D1	D 1	1d. red	30	9·00
D2		2d. violet	2·00	24·00

1961. Surch **Postage Due 2d.**

No.	Type	Description		
D3	7	2d. on 2d. black and brown	1·25	2·75

These prices apply to stamps with large figure measuring 4½ mm high.

1961. As Type **D 1** but with value in cents.

D4	1c. red	15	1·10
D5	2c. violet	15	1·10
D6	5c. green	20	1·10

1961. Surch **Postage Due** and value in cents.

No.	Type	Description		
D10	7	1c. on 2d. black and brown	70	2·75
D11		2c. on 2d. black and brown	50	2·75
D12		5c. on 2d. black and brown	90	2·25

1971.

No.	Type	Description		
D19	D 6	1c. red	30	1·50
D23		2c. purple	10	10
D24		5c. green	10	10
D25		10c. blue	10	10
D26		25c. brown	10	10

SWEDEN Pt. 11

A kingdom of N. Europe, united to Norway till 1905.

1855. 48 skilling banco = 1 riksdaler.
1858. 100 ore = 1 riksdaler.
1875. 100 ore = 1 krona.

1 2 3

1855.

1 1 3s. green £5500 £225
2 4s. blue £1000 44·00
3 6s. grey £6500 £800
4 8s. orange £3500 £400
5 24s. red £5000 £1300

1858.

6b 1 5ore green £150 12·50
7 9ore purple £375 £170
8a 12ore blue £170 1·60
9 24ore orange £400 18·00
10a 30ore brown £400 20·00
11b 50ore red £550 65·00

1862.

12c 2 3ore brown £100 9·25
13 3 17ore purple £600 £100
14 17ore grey £750 £600
15b 20ore red £190 11·00

4 5 6 King Oscar II

1872.

29 4 2ore orange 1·70 3·75
30 3ore brown 10·50 11·50
31 4ore grey 27·00 85
32 5ore green 65·00 45
33a 6ore mauve 23·00 34·00
20 6ore green £750 42·00
34 6 10ore pink 60·00 35
21a 4 12ore blue 23·00 50
35 20ore red £110 45
23a 24ore yellow 47·00 16·00
36 30ore brown £190 75
37 50ore red £150 2·40
26 5 1r. blue and bistre £750 55·00
38 1k. blue and bistre 95·00 1·60

No. 26 has the value expressed as one riksdaler and No. 38 one krona.

1889. Surch **10 10 TIO ORE** and Arms.

39 4 10ore on 12ore blue 2·30 3·25
40 10ore on 24ore yellow 7·75 21·00

9 10 Oscar II 11

1891.

41 9 1ore blue and brown 1·10 40
42a 2ore yellow and blue 4·00 35
43 3ore orange and brown 55 85
44a 4ore blue and red 6·00 30
45c 10 5ore green 2·75 15
46 8ore purple 3·00 85
47 10ore red 3·75 15
48 15ore brown 25·00 15
49 20ore blue 25·00 15
56 25ore orange 25·00 2·75
51a 30ore brown 60·00 15
53 50ore grey 95·00 25
54 11 1k. grey and red £150 1·10

13 G.P.O., Stockholm 14 15 Gustav V

1903. Opening of new Post Office.

57 13 5k. blue £300 20·00

1910.

65 14 1ore black 15 15
66 2ore orange 15 15
67 3ore brown 15 20
68 4ore mauve 15 15
69 15 5ore green 1·70 15
70 7ore green 30 15
71 8ore purple 30 25
72 10ore red 2·20 15
73 12ore purple 30 15
74 15ore brown 4·75 15
75 20ore blue 7·75 15
76 25ore orange 30 15
77 27ore blue 35 50
78 30ore brown 19·00 15
79 35ore violet 17·00 15
80 40ore green 24·00 15
81 50ore grey 55·00 15
82 55ore blue £1100 £3250
83 65ore green 60 1·30
84 80ore black £1100 £3250
85 90ore green 55 40
63 1k. black on yellow 65·00 35
64 5k. purple on yellow 2·00 2·20

1916. Clothing Fund for Mobilized Reservists ("Landstorm"). (a) Postage stamps surch **FRIMARKE LANDSTORMEN** and value in figures and words round Arms.

86a 4 5+5 on 2ore orange 3·50 4·75
86b 5+5 on 3ore brown 3·50 4·75
86c 5+5 on 4ore grey 3·50 4·75
86d 5+5 on 5ore green 3·50 4·75
86e 5+5 on 6ore mauve 3·50 4·75
86f 10+10 on 12ore blue 3·50 4·75
86g 10+10 on 20ore red 3·50 4·75
86h 10+10 on 24ore yellow 3·50 4·75
86i 10+10 on 30ore brown 3·50 4·75
86j 10+10 on 50ore red 3·50 4·75

(b) Postage Due stamps surch **FRIMARKE SVERIGE** in frame round Arms, **LANDSTORMEN** and value in figures and words.

86k D 6 5+5 on 1ore black 31·00 6·25
86l 5+5 on 3ore red 6·25 3·50
86m 5+5 on 5ore brown 7·50 4·00
86n 5+10 on 6ore orange 4·50 4·50
86o 5+15 on 12ore red 46·00 17·00
86p 10+20 on 20ore blue 12·50 14·50
86q 10+40 on 24ore mauve 55·00 60·00
86r 10+20 on 30ore green 4·75 4·75
86s 10+40 on 50ore brown 20·00 22·00
86t 10+90 on 1k. blue and brown £130 £250

(c) No. 57 surch **FRIMARKE ORE 10 ORE FRIMARKE LANDSTORMEN KR. 4,90** and Arms.

86u 13 10 ore+4k.90 on 5k. blue £100 £250

1917. Surch in figures only.

87 15 7 on 10ore red 25 20
88 12 on 25ore orange 1·90 25
89 12 on 65ore green 80 75
90 27 on 55ore blue 60 1·10
91 27 on 65ore green 1·20 2·40
92 27 on 80ore black 65 1·10
93 1.98k. on 5k. purple on yell 1·00 3·75
94 2.12k. on 5k. purple on yell 1·40 4·25

1918. Landstorm Fund. Nos. 8ba/j surch.

94a 4 7+3 on 5ore on 2ore 7·75 7·50
94b 7+3 on 5ore on 3ore 2·10 1·10
94c 7+3 on 5ore on 4ore 2·10 1·10
94d 7+3 on 5ore on 5ore 2·10 1·10
94e 7+3 on 5ore on 6ore 2·10 1·10
94f 12+8 on 10ore on 12ore 2·10 1·10
94g 12+8 on 10ore on 20ore 2·10 1·10
94h 12+8 on 10ore on 24ore 2·10 1·10
94i 12+8 on 10ore on 30ore 2·10 1·10
94j 12+8 on 10ore on 50ore 2·10 1·10

19 Arms 20 Lion (after sculpture by B. Foucquet)

21 Gustav V 22 Emblem of Swedish Post

1920.

95A 19 3ore red 25 25
96Bb 20 5ore green 1·00 1·40
97A 5ore brown 5·25 25
98B 10ore green 2·30 50
99A 10ore violet 4·25 25
102a 21 10ore red 8·50 6·75
103 15ore purple 30 30
104a 20ore blue 41·00 2·10
100A 20 25ore orange 12·00 30
101A 30ore brown 35 25
105A 22 35ore yellow 49·00 30
106A 40ore green 36·00 1·10
107A 45ore brown 1·00 45
108A 60ore purple 18·00 20
109A 70ore brown 55 1·80
110A 80ore green 35 25
111A 85ore green 4·00 25
112A 90ore blue 65·00 25
113A 1k. orange 7·00 25
114A 110ore blue 55 20
115A 115ore brown 8·75 25
116A 120ore black 60·00 40
117A 120ore mauve 13·00 40
118A 140ore black 45 20
119A 145ore green 7·50 55

23 Gustavus II Adolphus 24 Gustav V (after portrait by E. Osterman) 25 Gustavus Vasa

1920. Tercentenary of Swedish Post between Stockholm and Hamburg.

120A 23 20ore blue 3·25 25

1920. Air. Official stamps surch **LUFTPOST** and value.

120a O 17 10 on 3ore brown 2·25 3·50
120b 20 on 2ore yellow 3·75 5·25
120c 50 on 4ore lilac 15·00 17·00

1921.

121 24 15ore violet 18·00 20
122a 15ore red 9·50 25
123 15ore brown 4·25 20
124 20ore violet 30 20
125 20ore red 20·00 25
126 20ore orange 30 40
128 25ore red 65 1·20
129 25ore blue 14·00 20
131 25ore orange 33·00 25
133 30ore brown 22·00 20
134 30ore blue 5·50 25
135 35ore purple 14·50 20
136 40ore blue 35 45
137 40ore green 36·00 60
138 45ore brown 4·00 45
139a 50ore black 1·50 35
140 85ore green 10·50 75
141 115ore brown 11·00 1·10
142 145ore green 7·50 1·00

1921. 400th Anniv of Liberation of Sweden.

143 25 20ore violet 8·25 16·00
144 110ore blue 50·00 4·75
145 140ore black 28·00 4·75

26 Old City, Stockholm 27 Gustav V

1924. 8th Congress of U.P.U.

146 26 5ore brown 1·70 1·90
147 10ore green 1·80 1·90
148 15ore violet 1·80 1·50
149 20ore red 10·50 8·75
150 25ore orange 15·00 14·50
151 30ore blue 14·50 14·00
152 35ore black 18·00 18·00
153 40ore green 26·00 19·00
154 45ore brown 31·00 27·00
155 50ore grey 27·00 22·00
156 60ore purple 42·00 36·00
157 80ore green 34·00 33·00
158 27 1k. green 60·00 65·00
159 2k. red £150 £170
160 5k. blue £275 £325

28 Post Rider and Friedrichsafen FF-49 Seaplane 29 Carrier-pigeon

1924. 50th Anniv of U.P.U.

161 28 5ore brown 2·75 2·75
162 10ore green 2·75 3·75
163 15ore violet 2·50 1·90
164 20ore red 19·00 19·00
165 25ore orange 25·00 21·00
166 30ore blue 24·00 21·00
167 35ore black 31·00 34·00
168 40ore green 28·00 20·00
169 45ore brown 39·00 25·00
170 50ore grey 46·00 37·00
171 60ore purple 48·00 47·00
172 80ore green 40·00 22·00
173 29 1k. green 70·00 60·00
174 2k. red £150 50·00
175 5k. blue £275 £160

29a King Gustav V 29c Night Flight by Junkers F-13 (with skis) over Stockholm

1928. 70th Birthday of King Gustav V and Cancer Research Fund.

175a 29a 5(+5)ore green 2·20 3·75
175b 10(+5)ore violet 2·20 3·75
175c 15(+5)ore red 2·30 2·75
175d 20(+5)ore orange 3·75 1·90
175e 25(+5)ore blue 3·75 2·30

1930. Air.

175f 29c 10ore blue 35 40
175g 50ore violet 90 1·10

30 Royal Palace, Stockholm 31 Death of Gustavus Adolphus at Lutzen

1931.

176 30 5k. green 95·00 7·00

1932. Death Tercentenary of Gustavus Adolphus.

177 31 10ore violet 1·80 25
178a 15ore red 2·40 55
179 25ore blue 5·25 45
180 90ore green 31·00 1·20

32 Allegory of Thrift 33 Stockholm Cathedral

1933. 50th Anniv of Swedish Postal Savings Bank.

181 32 5ore green 2·20 60

1935. 500th Anniv of First Swedish Parliament. Stockholm Buildings.

182a – 5ore green 3·00 50
183 – 10ore violet 3·50 2·40
184 33 15ore red 3·50 20
185 – 25ore blue 7·25 50
186 – 35ore purple 11·50 1·60
187 – 60ore purple 18·00 1·00

DESIGNS: 5ore Old City Hall; 10ore Exchange; 25ore House of the Nobility; 35ore Houses of Parliament; 60ore Arms of Engelbrekt and representatives of the Four Estates.

35 A. Oxenstierna (after D. Dumonstier) 38 Junkers W.34 over Scandinavia

1936. Tercentenary of Swedish Post.

188 35 5ore green 1·30 25
189 – 10ore violet 1·60 60
190 – 15ore red 2·50 25
191 – 20ore blue 9·00 3·25
192 – 25ore blue 5·75 35
193 – 30ore brown 19·00 2·10
194 – 35ore mauve 5·50 1·20
195 – 40ore green 6·75 1·60
196 – 45ore green 7·75 1·00
197 – 50ore grey 25·00 1·90
198 – 60ore purple 30·00 50
199 – 1k. blue 8·75 5·25

DESIGNS: 10ore Early courier; 15ore Post rider; 20ore Sailing packet "Hiorten"; 25ore Paddle-steamer "Constitutionen"; 30ore Mail coach; 35ore Arms; 40ore Class F steam locomotive and mail train; 45ore A. W. Roos (Postmaster General 1867–89); 50ore Motor bus and trailer; 60ore Liner "Gripsholm"; 1k. Junkers Ju 52/3m seaplane.

For similar designs, but dated "1972" at foot, see Nos. 700/4.

1936. Inauguration of Bromma Aerodrome.

200 38 50ore blue 4·00 5·75

39 E. Swedenborg (after P. Krafft) 40 Governor Printz and Red Indian

1938. 250th Birth Anniv of Swedenborg.

201 39 10ore violet 1·40 20
202 100ore green 4·75 1·00

1938. 300th Anniv of Founding of New Sweden, U.S.A.

203 40 5ore green 75 30
204 – 15ore brown 90 45
205 – 20ore red 1·50 55
206 – 30ore blue 4·50 60
207 – 60ore purple 7·25 30

DESIGNS: 15ore Emigrant ships "Calmare Nyckel" and "Fagel Grip"; 20ore Swedish landing in America; 30ore First Swedish church, Wilmington; 60ore Queen Christina (after S. Bourdon).

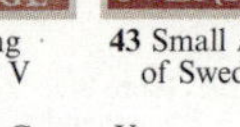

41 King Gustav V **42** King Gustav V **43** Small Arms of Sweden

1938. 80th Birthday of King Gustav V.

208	41	5ore green	1·00	25
209		15ore brown	1·00	25
210		30ore blue	13·00	70

1939.

234	42	5ore green	35	10
299		5ore orange	10	15
235		10ore violet	10	10
300		10ore green	15	15
236b		15ore brown	35	25
237		20ore red	15	10
238		25ore orange	75	15
301		25ore violet	70	15
239		30ore blue	30	10
240		35ore purple	50	15
241		40ore green	45	10
242		45ore brown	45	10
243		50ore grey	2·40	15
301a	43	50ore grey	1·20	20
302		55ore brown	45	15
221		60ore red	95	15
302a		65ore green	45	20
302b		70ore blue	1·70	1·00
302c		75ore brown	1·40	55
303		80ore green	40	15
222		85ore green	40	15
303a		85ore brown	2·75	1·10
223		90ore blue	50	15
224		1k. orange	50	10
303b		1k.05 blue	50	20
304		1k.10 violet	2·75	15
225		1k.15 brown	45	15
226		1k.20 purple	1·80	15
304a		1k.20 blue	1·30	1·50
305		1k.40 green	50	20
227		1k.45 green	2·10	55
305a		1k.50 purple	75	70
305b		1k.50 brown	50	15
305c		1k.70 red	70	15
306		1k.75 blue	6·00	5·50
306a		1k.80 blue	50	40
306b		1k.85 blue	1·00	70
306c		2k. purple	60	15
306ca		2k. mauve	50	15
306d		2k.10 blue	5·25	20
306e		2k.15 green	2·30	30
306f		2k.30 brown	3·50	20
306g		2k.50 green	75	15
306h		2k.55 red	1·70	1·60
306i		2k.80 red	85	20
306j		2k.85 orange	2·30	2·50
306k		3k. blue	85	15

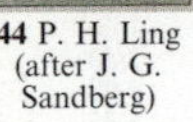

44 P. H. Ling (after J. G. Sandberg) **45** Carl von Linne (Linnaeus) (after A. Roslin) **47** Carl Michael Bellman

1939. Death Centenary of P. H. Ling (creator of "Swedish Drill").

228	44	5ore green	30	15
229		25ore brown	90	25

1939. Bicent of Swedish Academy of Sciences.

230a	–	10ore violet	1·70	40
231	45	15ore brown	15	20
232	–	30ore blue	8·75	40
233	45	50ore grey	11·00	75

PORTRAIT: 10ore, 30ore J. J. Berzelius (after O. J. Sodermark).

1940. Birth Bicent of C. M. Bellman (poet).

244	47	5ore green	15	20
245		35ore red	55	40

48 Johan Tobias Sergel (self-portrait bust) **49** Reformers presenting Bible to Gustavus Vasa

1940. Birth Bicent of J. T. Sergel (sculptor).

246a	48	15ore brown	3·25	30
247		50ore grey	14·50	85

1941. 400th Anniv of First Authorized Version of Bible in Swedish.

248	49	15ore brown	15	20
249		90ore blue	16·00	70

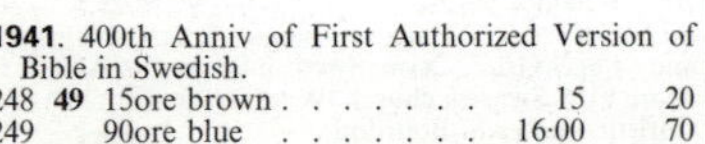

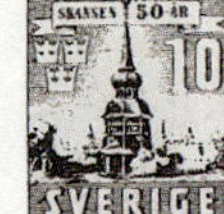

50 Hasjo Belfry **50a** Royal Palace, Stockholm

1941. 50th Anniv of Foundation of Skansen Open-air Museum.

250a	50	10ore violet	1·80	35
251		60ore purple	7·25	30

1941.

252	50a	5k. blue	1·40	20

51 A. Hazelius **52** St. Bridget (from altar painting, Vasteras Cathedral)

1941. Artur Hazelius (founder of Skansen Museum).

253	51	5ore green	40	20
254		1k. orange	5·75	2·00

1941. 550th Anniv of Canonization of St. Bridget (Foundress of Brigittine Order of Our Saviour).

255	52	15ore brown	20	20
256		120ore purple	20·00	8·50

53 Mute Swans **54** King Gustavus III (after A. Roslin)

1942.

257a	53	20k. blue	3·25	30

1942. 150th Anniv of National Museum, Stockholm.

258	54	20ore red	75	15
259	–	40ore green	16·00	75

PORTRAIT: 40ore Carl Gustaf Tessin (architect and chancery president) (after Gustav Lundberg).

55 Count Rudenschold and Nils Mansson **56** Carl Wilhelm Scheele

1942. Centenary of Institution of National Elementary Education.

260a	55	10ore red	20	25
261		90ore blue	2·30	3·75

1942. Birth Bicent of C. W. Scheele (chemist).

262	56	5ore green	15	15
263		60ore red	5·75	30

57 King Gustav V **58** Rifle Assn Badge

1943. 85th Birthday of King Gustav V.

264	57	20ore red	50	30
265		30ore blue	90	1·80
266		60ore purple	1·10	2·10

1943. 50th Anniv of National Voluntary Rifle Association.

267	58	10ore purple	15	10
268		90ore blue	3·00	30

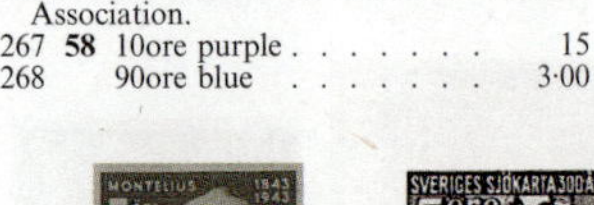

59 O. Montelius (after E. Stenberg) **60** First Swedish Navigators' Chart

1943. Birth Centenary of Oscar Montelius (archaeologist).

269	59	5ore green	15	15
270		120ore purple	5·25	1·70

1944. Tercent of First Swedish Marine Chart.

271	60	5ore green	20	15
272		60ore red	3·25	35

61 "Smalands Lejon" (ship of the line)

1944. Swedish Fleet (Tercentenary of Battle of Femern).

273	61	10ore violet	20	30
274	–	20ore red	35	15
275	–	30ore blue	45	65
276	–	40ore green	85	95
277	–	90ore grey	7·00	1·50

DESIGNS—27 × 22½ mm: 30ore "Kung Karl" (ship of the line); 40ore Stern of "Amphion" (royal yacht); 90ore "Gustav V" (cruiser). 18½ × 20½ mm: 20ore Admiral C. Fleming (after L. Pasch).

See also Nos. 517/22.

62 Red Cross **63** Press Symbols

1945. 80th Anniv of Swedish Red Cross and Birthday of Prince Carl.

278	62	20ore red	50	15

1945. Tercentenary of Swedish Press.

279	63	5ore green	25	15
280		60ore red	3·75	25

64 Viktor Rydberg (after A. Edelfelt) **65** Oak Tree, Savings Banks' Symbol

1945. 50th Death Anniv of Viktor Rydberg (author).

281	64	20ore red	25	15
282		90ore blue	3·75	25

1945. 125th Anniv of Swedish Savings Banks.

283	65	10ore violet	25	20
284		40ore green	85	75

66 Cathedral Model **67** Lund Cathedral

1946. 800th Anniv of Lund Cathedral.

285	66	15ore brown	55	25
286	67	20ore red	25	15
287	66	90ore blue	6·25	50

68 Mare and Foal **69** Tegner (after bust by J. N. Bystrom) **70** A. Nobel

1946. Centenary of Swedish Agricultural Show.

288	68	5ore green	25	15
289		60ore red	3·25	20

1946. Death Centenary of Esaias Tegner (poet).

290	69	10ore violet	25	15
291		40ore green	1·00	40

1946. 50th Death Anniv of Alfred Nobel (scientist and creator of Nobel Foundation).

292	70	20ore red	55	15
293		30ore blue	1·50	35

71 E. G. Geijer (after J. G. Sandberg) **72** King Gustav V **73** Ploughman and Skyscraper

1947. Death Centenary of Erik Gustav Geijer (historian, philosopher, poet and composer).

294	71	5ore green	25	15
295		90ore blue	3·00	20

1947. Forty Years Reign of King Gustav V.

296	72	10ore violet	25	20
297		20ore red	25	20
298		60ore purple	85	1·10

1948. Centenary of Swedish Pioneers in U.S.A.

307	73	15ore brown	25	15
308		30ore blue	30	40
309		1k. orange	1·00	70

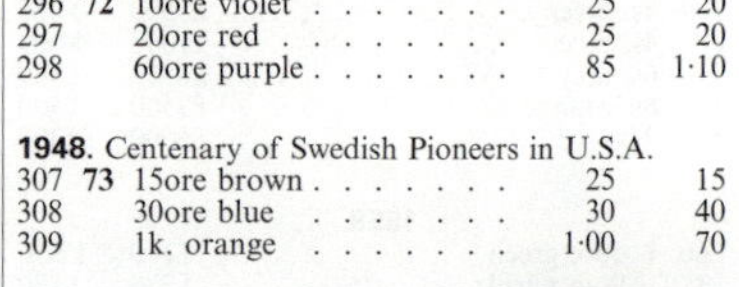

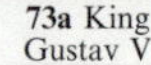

73a King Gustav V **74** J. A. Strindberg (after R. Bergh) **75** Gymnasts

1948. King Gustav V's 90th Birthday, and Youth Fund.

309a	73a	10ore+10ore green	40	45
309b		20ore+10ore red	40	60
309c		30ore+10ore blue	30	50

1949. Birth Centenary of Strindberg (dramatist).

310	74	20ore red	25	15
311		30ore blue	55	55
312		80ore green	2·10	40

1949. 2nd Lingiad, Stockholm.

313	75	5ore blue	25	25
314		15ore brown	25	20

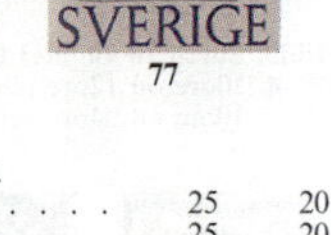

76 Globe and Hand Writing **77**

1949. 75th Anniv of U.P.U.

315	76	10ore green	25	20
316		20ore red	25	20
317	77	30ore blue	25	40

78 King Gustav VI Adolf **79** Christopher Polhem (after G. E. Schroder) **80**

1951. (a) Coloured lettering and figures.

318	78	10ore green	15	15
318b		10ore brown	10	15
319		15ore brown	15	25
388		15ore red	15	15
320		20ore red	15	20
391		20ore black	30	15
322a		25ore black	40	30
323		25ore red	85	20
324a		25ore blue	15	15
392		25ore brown	55	25
393		30ore blue	30	15
326		30ore brown	30	30
326a		30ore red	3·75	15
327		40ore blue	35	20
328		40ore green	40	25

(b) White lettering and figures.

429	78	15ore red	15	15
430		20ore black	20	15
431a		25ore brown	15	15
432a		30ore blue	50	15
433		30ore violet	35	15
433b		30ore red	50	70
434		35ore violet	50	15
435a		35ore blue	35	15
436		35ore black	50	20
437		40ore green	35	15
438a		40ore blue	20	15
439a		45ore orange	50	15
439b		45ore blue	50	15
440		50ore green	40	20
440a		50ore green	25	20
440c		55ore red	35	15
441		60ore red	40	50
441a		65ore blue	60	15
441c		70ore mauve	50	15
441d		85ore purple	60	25

1951. Death Bicentenary of Polhem (engineer).

329a	**79**	25ore black	30	30
330		45ore brown	25	30

1951.

383	**80**	5ore red	20	15
386		10ore blue	10	15
387a		10ore brown	10	20
389		15ore green	10	20
390a		15ore brown	15	40

81 Olavus Petri Preaching

81a King Gustav VI Adolf

1952. 400th Death Anniv of Petri (reformer).

332	**81**	25ore black	15	25
333		1k.40 brown	1·70	45

1952. 70th Birthday of King Gustav VI Adolf and Culture Fund.

333a	**81a**	10ore+10ore green	15	30
333ba		25ore+10ore red	15	40
333c		40ore+10ore blue	20	35

82 Ski Jumping

83 Stockholm, 1650

1953. 50th Anniv of Swedish Athletic Assn.

334	**82**	10ore green	25	20
335	–	15ore brown	25	45
336	–	40ore blue	85	1·00
337	–	1k.40 mauve	2·75	70

DESIGNS—HORIZ: 1k.40, Wrestling. VERT: 15ore Ice hockey; 40ore Slingball.

1953. 700th Anniv of Stockholm.

338	**83**	25ore blue	15	15
339	–	1k.70 red	1·60	45

DESIGN: 1k.70, Seal of Stockholm, 1296 (obverse and reverse).

84 "Radio"

85 Skier

1953. Cent of Telecommunications in Sweden.

340	–	25ore blue ("Telephones")	15	20
341	**84**	40ore green	80	1·00
342	–	60ore red ("Telegraphs")	1·70	1·80

1954. World Skiing Championships.

343	**85**	20ore grey	20	25
344	–	1k. blue (Woman skier)	4·25	90

86 Anna Maria Lenngren (after medallion, J. T. Sergel)

87 Rock-carvings

88

1954. Birth Bicentenary of Anna Maria Lenngren (poetess).

345	**86**	20ore grey	15	20
346		65ore brown	2·30	1·80

1954.

347	**87**	50ore grey	15	15
348		55ore red	65	20
349		60ore red	20	15
350		65ore green	90	15
351		70ore orange	35	15
352		75ore brown	1·50	20
353		80ore green	35	15
355		90ore blue	35	15
356		95ore violet	1·80	2·10

1955. Centenary of First Swedish Postage Stamps.

362	**88**	25ore blue	15	15
363		40ore green	85	25

89 Swedish Flag

91 P. D. A. Atterbom (after Fogelberg)

1955. National Flag Day.

364	**89**	10ore yellow, blue & green	15	15
365		15ore yellow, blue and red	20	25

1955. Cent of First Swedish Postage Stamps and "Stockholmia" Philatelic Exn. As T **1** but with two rules through bottom panel.

366	**1**	3ore green	1·20	3·50
367		4ore blue	1·20	3·50
368		6ore grey	1·20	3·50
369		8ore yellow	1·20	3·50
370		24ore orange	1·20	3·50

Nos. 366/70 were sold only at the exhibition in single sets, at 2k.45 (45ore face + 2k. entrance fee).

1955. Death Centenary of Atterbom (poet).

371	**91**	20ore blue	15	20
372		1k.40 brown	2·00	40

92 Greek Horseman, (from Parthenon frieze)

92a Whooper Swans

1956. 16th Olympic Games Equestrian Competitions, Stockholm.

373	**92**	20ore red	20	20
374		25ore blue	20	15
375		40ore green	1·60	1·40

1956. Northern Countries' Day.

376	**92a**	25ore red	15	20
377		40ore blue	40	45

93 Railway Construction

94 Trawler in Distress and Lifeboat

1956. Centenary of Swedish Railways.

378	**93**	10ore green	35	20
379	–	25ore blue	20	20
380	–	40ore orange	1·80	2·20

DESIGNS: 25ore Steam locomotive, "Fryckstad" and passenger carriage; 40ore Type XOa5 electric train on Arsta Bridge, Stockholm.

1957. 50th Anniv of Swedish Life Saving Service.

381	**94**	30ore blue	1·60	20
382		1k.40 red	2·75	1·00

95 Galleon and "Gripsholm II"

96 Bell 47G Helicopter with Floats

1958. Postal Services Commemoration.

395	**95**	15ore red	15	20
396	**96**	30ore blue	15	20
397	**95**	40ore green	2·30	2·10
398	**96**	1k.40 brown	2·40	80

97 Footballer

98 Bessemer Tilting-furnace

1958. World Cup Football Championship.

399	**97**	15ore red	40	20
400		20ore green	30	20
401		1k.20 blue	1·10	55

1958. Centenary of Swedish Steel Industry.

402	**98**	30ore blue	15	20
403		170ore brown	2·75	60

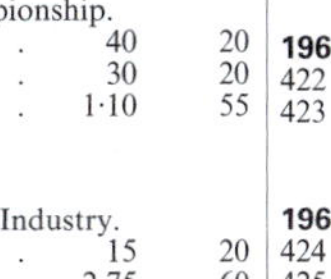

99 Selma Lagerlof (after bust by G. Malmquist)

100 Overhead Power Lines

1958. Birth Centenary of Selma Lagerlof (writer).

404	**99**	20ore red	15	20
405		30ore blue	15	20
406		80ore green	55	70

1959. 50th Anniv of Swedish State Power Board.

407	**100**	30ore blue	20	20
408	–	90ore red	2·40	1·80

DESIGN—HORIZ: 90ore Dam sluice-gates.

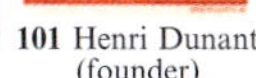

101 Henri Dunant (founder)

102 Heidenstam

1959. Red Cross Centenary.

409	**101**	30ore+10ore red	40	45

1959. Birth Centenary of Verner von Heidenstam (poet).

410	**102**	15ore red	55	20
411		1k. black	2·00	60

103 Forest Trees

104 S. Arrhenius

1959. Centenary of Crown Lands and Forests Administration.

412	**103**	30ore green	90	20
413	–	1k.40 red	2·30	45

DESIGN: 1k.40, Forester felling tree.

1959. Birth Centenary of Arrhenius (chemist).

414	**104**	15ore brown	15	20
415		1k.70 blue	2·30	30

105 Anders Zorn (self-portrait)

106 "Uprooted Tree"

1960. Birth Cent of Zorn (painter and etcher).

416	**105**	30ore grey	15	20
417		80ore brown	2·10	1·20

1960. World Refugee Year.

418	**106**	20ore brown	15	20
419	–	40ore violet	20	20

DESIGN—VERT: 40ore Refugees.

107 Target-shooting

108 G. Froding

1960. Centenary of Voluntary Shooting Organization.

420	**107**	15ore red	15	20
421	–	90ore blue	2·10	1·10

DESIGN: 90ore Organization members marching, 1860.

1960. Birth Centenary of Gustav Froding (poet).

422	**108**	30ore brown	15	20
423		1k.40 green	1·80	25

1960. Europa. As T **144a** of Switzerland.

424		40ore blue	30	30
425		1k. red	25	30

109 H. Branting

109a Douglas DC-8

1960. Birth Centenary of Hjalmar Branting (statesman).

426	**109**	15ore red	15	20
427		1k.70 blue	1·90	30

1961. 10th Anniv of Scandinavian Airlines System.

428	**109a**	40ore blue	20	20

111 "Coronation of Gustav III" (after Pilo)

1961. 250th Birth Anniv of Carl Gustav Pilo (painter).

442	**111**	30ore brown	15	20
443		1k.40 blue	2·30	75

112 J. Alstromer (after bust by P. H. l'Archeveque)

113 Printing Works and Library

1961. Death Bicentenary of Jonas Alstromer (industrial reformer).

444	**112**	15ore purple	15	20
445		90ore blue	1·00	1·20

1961. Tercentenary of Royal Library Regulation.

446	**113**	20ore red	15	20
447		1k. blue	3·00	60

114 Motif on Runic Stone at Oland

115 Nobel Prize Winners of 1901

1961.

448	**114**	10k. purple	13·50	50

1961. Nobel Prize Winners of 1901.

449	**115**	20ore red	15	20
450		40ore blue	15	20
451		50ore green	15	20

See also Nos. 458/9, 471/2, 477/8, 488/9, 523/4, 546/7 and 573/4.

116 Postman's Footprints

117 Code, Voting Instrument and Mallet

1962. Cent of Swedish Local Mail Delivery Service.

452	**116**	30ore violet	15	20
453		1k.70 red	2·20	30

1962. Centenary of Municipal Laws.

454	**117**	30ore blue	15	20
455		2k. red	2·30	20

118 St. George and Dragon, Storkyrkan ("Great Church"), Stockholm

119 Ice Hockey Player

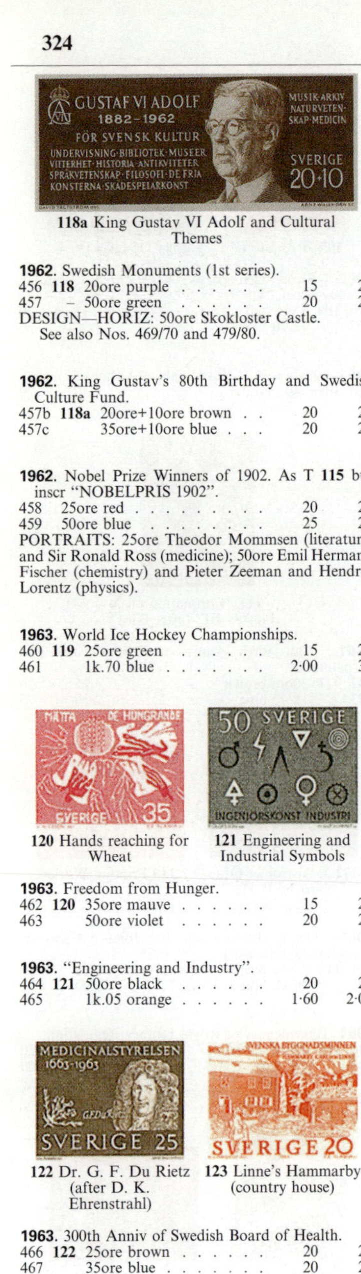

118a King Gustav VI Adolf and Cultural Themes

1962. Swedish Monuments (1st series).
456 **118** 20ore purple 15 20
457 – 50ore green 20 20
DESIGN—HORIZ: 50ore Skokloster Castle.
See also Nos. 469/70 and 479/80.

1962. King Gustav's 80th Birthday and Swedish Culture Fund.
457b **118a** 20ore+10ore brown . . 20 25
457c 35ore+10ore blue . . . 20 25

1962. Nobel Prize Winners of 1902. As T **115** but inscr "NOBELPRIS 1902".
458 25ore red 20 20
459 50ore blue 25 20
PORTRAITS: 25ore Theodor Mommsen (literature) and Sir Ronald Ross (medicine); 50ore Emil Hermann Fischer (chemistry) and Pieter Zeeman and Hendrik Lorentz (physics).

1963. World Ice Hockey Championships.
460 **119** 25ore green 15 20
461 1k.70 blue . . . . 2·00 30

120 Hands reaching for Wheat
121 Engineering and Industrial Symbols

1963. Freedom from Hunger.
462 **120** 35ore mauve 15 20
463 50ore violet 20 20

1963. "Engineering and Industry".
464 **121** 50ore black 20 20
465 1k.05 orange . . . . . . 1·60 2·00

122 Dr. G. F. Du Rietz (after D. K. Ehrenstrahl)
123 Linne's Hammarby (country house)

1963. 300th Anniv of Swedish Board of Health.
466 **122** 25ore brown 20 25
467 35ore blue 20 20
468 2k. red . . . . 2·20 40

1963. Swedish Monuments (2nd series).
469 **123** 20ore red 15 20
470 50ore green 20 20

1963. Nobel Prize Winners of 1903. As T **115** but inscr "NOBELPRIS 1903".
471 25ore green 40 45
472 50ore brown 30 15
PORTRAITS: 25ore Svante Arrhenius (chemistry), Niels Ryberg Finsen (medicine) and Bjornstjerne Bjornson (literature); 50ore Antoine Henri Becquerel and Pierre and Marie Curie (physics).

124 Motif from Poem "Elie Himmelsfard"

125 Seal of Archbishop Stefan

1964. Birth Centenary of E. A. Karlfeldt (poet).
473 **124** 35ore blue 25 15
474 1k.05 red . . . . 2·10 2·75

1964. 800th Anniv of Archbishopric of Uppsala.
475 **125** 40ore green 10 15
476a 60ore brown 20 25

1964. Nobel Prize Winners of 1904. As T **115** but inscr "NOBELPRIS 1904".
477 30ore blue 20 20
478 40ore red 55 20
PORTRAITS: 30ore Jose Echegaray y Eizaguirre and Frederic Mistral (literature) and J. W. Strutt (Lord Rayleigh) (physics); 40ore Sir William Ramsay (chemistry) and Ivan Petrovich Pavlov (medicine).

126 Visby Town Wall

127 Posthorns
128 Telecommunications

1965. Swedish Monuments (3rd series).
479 **126** 30ore mauve 15 20
480 2k. blue . . . . 2·10 20

1965.
481 **127** 20ore blue and yellow . . 15 15

1965. Centenary of I.T.U.
482 **128** 60ore violet 20 20
483 1k.40 blue . . . . 1·50 75

129 Prince Eugen (after D. Tagtstrom)

130 F. Bremer (after O. J. Sodermark)

1965. Birth Centenary of Prince Eugen (painter).
484 **129** 40ore black 15 15
485 1k. brown . . . . 2·20 25

1965. Death Centenary of Fredrika Bremer (novelist).
486 **130** 25ore violet 10 20
487 3k. green . . . . 2·50 25

1965. Nobel Prize Winners of 1905. As T **115** but inscr "NOBELPRIS 1905".
488 30ore blue 20 20
489 40ore red 25 20
PORTRAITS: 30ore Philipp von Lenard (physics) and Johann von Baeyer (chemistry); 40ore Robert Koch (medicine) and Henryk Sienkiewicz (literature).

131 N. Soderblom
132 Skating

1966. Birth Centenary of Nathan Soderblom, Archbishop of Uppsala.
490 **131** 60ore brown 20 20
491 80ore green 65 20

1966. World Men's Speed Skating Championships, Gothenburg.
492 **132** 5ore red 10 20
493 25ore green 25 30
494 40ore blue 35 50

133 Entrance Hall, National Museum

134 Ale's Stones, Ship Grave, Kaseberga

1966. Centenary of Opening of National Museum Building.
495 **133** 30ore violet 15 20
496 2k.30 green 70 80

1966.
498 – 35ore brown and blue . . 15 15
499 **134** 3k.50 grey 90 15
500 – 3k.70 violet . . . . . . 1·00 15
501 – 4k.50 red . . . . 1·30 20
502 – 7k. red and blue . . . . 1·90 30
DESIGNS—HORIZ: 35ore Fjeld (mountains); 7k. Gripsholm Castle. VERT: 3k.70, Lion Fortress, Gothenburg; 4k.50, Uppsala Cathedral (interior).

135 Louis de Geer (advocate of reform)

1966. Cent of Representative Assembly Reform.
510 **135** 40ore blue 15 20
511 3k. red . . . . 2·75 45

136 Theatre Stage
137 Almqvist (after C. P. Mazer)

1966. Bicentenary of Drottningholm Theatre.
512 **136** 5ore red on pink 10 15
513 25ore bistre on pink . . . 10 15
514 40ore purple on pink . . 30 45

1966. Death Centenary of Carl Almqvist (writer).
515 **137** 25ore mauve 15 20
516 1k. green . . . . 1·60 80

1966. National Cancer Fund. Swedish Ships. Designs as T **61**, but with imprint "1966" at foot.
517 10ore red 15 30
518 15ore red 15 30
519 20ore green 15 30
520 25ore blue 15 25
521 30ore red 15 30
522 40ore red 15 30
SHIPS—HORIZ: 10ore "Smalands Lejon"; 15ore "Calmare Nyckel" and "Fagel Grip"; 20ore "Hiorten"; 25ore "Constitutionen"; 30ore "Kung Karl"; 40ore Stern of "Amphion".

1966. Nobel Prize Winners of 1906. As T **115** but inscr "NOBELPRIS 1906".
523 30ore red 20 20
524 40ore green 30 20
PORTRAITS: 30ore Sir Joseph John Thomson (physics) and Giosue Carducci (literature); 40ore Henri Moissan (chemistry) and Camillo Golgi and Santiago Ramon y Cajal (medicine).

138 Handball

139 "E.F.T.A."

1967. World Handball Championships.
525 **138** 45ore blue 15 20
526 2k.70 mauve . . . . . . 2·00 1·00

1967. European Free Trade Assn (E.F.T.A.).
527 **139** 70ore orange 20 20

140 Table Tennis Player

141 Axeman and Beast

1967. World Table Tennis Championships, Stockholm.
528 **140** 35ore mauve 15 20
529 90ore blue 85 40

1967. Iron Age Helmet Decorations, Oland.
530 **141** 10ore blue and brown . . 10 20
531 – 15ore brown and blue . . 15 20
532 – 30ore mauve and brown . 15 20
533 – 35ore brown and mauve . 15 25
DESIGNS: 15ore Man between two bears; 30ore "Lion man" putting enemy to flight; 35ore Two warriors.

142 "Solidarity"

144 18th-century Post-rider

143 "Keep to the Right"

1967. Finnish Settlers in Sweden.
534 **142** 10ore multicoloured . . . 10 15
535 35ore multicoloured . . . 15 20

1967. Adoption of Changed Rule of the Road.
536 **143** 35ore black, yellow & blue 15 20
537 45ore black, yellow & grn 15 15

1967.
538 **144** 5ore black and red . . . 10 10
539 – 10ore black and blue . . 10 10
539b – 20ore black on flesh . . 15 15
540 – 30ore red and blue . . . 15 15
541 – 40ore blue, green & black 15 20
541b – 45ore black and blue . . 15 15
542 – 90ore brown and blue . . 25 15
543 – 1k. green 25 15
DESIGNS—As T **144**. VERT: 10ore "Svent Skepp" (warship); 20ore "St. Stephen" (ceiling painting, Dadesjo Church, Smaland); 30ore Angelica plant on coast. HORIZ: 40ore Haverud Aqueduct, Dalsland Canal. $27\frac{1}{2} \times 22\frac{1}{2}$ mm: 45ore Floating logs; 90ore Elk; 1k. Dancing cranes.

145 King Gustav VI Adolf

146 Berwald, Violin and Music

1967. 85th Birthday of King Gustav VI Adolf.
544 **145** 45ore blue 15 20
545 70ore green 20 20

1967. Nobel Prize Winners 1907. As T **115**, but inscr "NOBELPRIS 1907".
546 35ore red 45 40
547 45ore blue 20 20
PORTRAITS: 35ore Eduard Buchner (chemistry) and Albert Abraham Michelson (physics); 45ore Charles Louis Alphonse Laveran (medicine) and Rudyard Kipling (literature).

1968. Death Centenary of Franz Berwald (composer).
548 **146** 35ore black and red . . . 20 20
549 2k. black, blue and yellow 2·20 40

147 Bank Seal

148 Butterfly Orchids

1968. 300th Anniv of Bank of Sweden.
550 **147** 45ore blue 15 20
551 70ore black on orange . . 20 20

1968. Wild Flowers.
552 **148** 45ore green 80 30
553 – 45ore green 80 30
554 – 45ore red and green . . . 80 30
555 – 45ore green 80 30
556 – 45ore green 80 30
DESIGNS: No. 553, Wood anemone; 554, Wild rose; 555, Wild cherry; 556, Lily of the valley.

149 University Seal

150 Ecumenical Emblem

1968. 300th Anniv of Lund University.
557 **149** 10ore blue 10 20
558 35ore red 25 35

1968. 4th General Assembly of World Council of Churches, Uppsala.
559 **150** 70ore purple 20 25
560 90ore blue 60 20

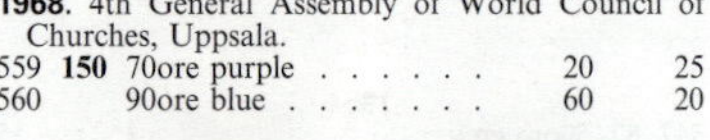

151 "The Universe"

152 "Orienteer" crossing Forest

1968. Centenary of the People's College.
561 **151** 45ore red 15 20
562 2k. blue . . . . 2·00 20

1968. World Orienteering Championships, Linkoping.
563 **152** 40ore red and violet . . . 20 20
564 2k.80 violet and green . . 1·50 1·60

153 "The Tug of War" (wood-carving by Axel Petersson)

154 Red Fox

1968. Birth Centenary of Axel Petersson ("Doderhultarn").
565 **153** 5ore green 10 15
566 25ore brown 35 80
567 45ore brown and sepia . . 10 15

1968. Bruno Liljefors' Fauna Sketches.
568 – 30ore blue 60 50
569 – 30ore black 60 50
570 **154** 30ore brown 60 35
571 – 30ore brown 60 50
572 – 30ore blue 60 50
DESIGNS: No. 568, Arctic hare; 569, Greater black-backed gull; 571, Golden eagle and carrion crows; 572, Stoat.

1968. Nobel Prize Winner of 1908. As T **115**, but inscr "NOBELPRIS 1908".
573 35ore red 30 30
574 45ore green 25 20
PORTRAITS: 35ore Ilya Mechnikov and Paul Ehrlich (medicine) and Lord Rutherford (chemistry); 45ore Gabriel Lippman (physics) and Rudolf Eucken (literature).

154a Viking Ships

155 "The Worker" (A. Amelin)

1969. 50th Anniv of Northern Countries Union.
575 **154a** 45ore brown 20 20
576 70ore blue 75 75

1969. 50th Anniv of I.L.O.
577 **155** 55ore red 15 20
578 70ore blue 50 35

156 Colonnade

157 A. Engstrom with Eagle Owl (self-portrait)

1969. Europa.
579 **156** 70ore multicoloured . . . 95 40
580 1k. multicoloured 95 25

1969. Birth Centenary of Albert Engstrom (painter and writer).
581 **157** 35ore black 15 20
582 55ore blue 20 20

159 Tjorn Bridges

160 Helmeted Figure (carving)

1969. Tjorn Bridges.
584 **159** 15ore blue on blue . . . 70 40
585 – 30ore green and black on blue 70 40
586 – 55ore black and blue on blue 70 35
DESIGNS—As T **159**: 30ore Tjorn Bridges (different). 41 × 19 mm: 55ore Tjorn Bridges (different).

1969. Warship "Wasa" Commemoration.
587 **160** 55ore red 40 35
588 – 55ore brown 40 35
589 – 55ore blue 40 45
590 – 55ore brown 40 35
591 – 55ore red 40 35
592 – 55ore blue 40 45
DESIGNS—As T **160**: No. 588, Crowned lion's head (carving); 590, Lion's head (carving); 591, Carved support. 46 × 28 mm: No. 589, Ship's coat-of-arms; 592, Ship of the line "Wasa", 1628.

161 H. Soderberg (writer)

163 "The Adventures of Nils" by S. Lagerlof (illus by J. Bauer)

162 Lighthouses and Lightship "Cyklop"

1969. Birth Centenaries of Hjalmar Soderberg and Bo Bergman.
593 **161** 45ore brown on cream . . 15 20
594 – 55ore green on green . . 20 20
DESIGN—HORIZ: 55ore Bo Bergman (poet).

1969. 300th Anniv of Swedish Lighthouse Service.
595 **162** 30ore black, red and grey 15 20
596 55ore black, orange & blue 15 20

1969. Swedish Fairy Tales.
597 – 35ore brown, red & orange . . . . 1·30 1·20
598 **163** 35ore brown . . . . . . 1·30 1·20
599 – 35ore brown, red & orange . . . . 1·30 1·20
600 – 35ore brown . . . . . . 1·30 1·20
601 – 35ore red and orange . . 1·30 1·20
DESIGNS: No. 597, "Pelle's New Suit" written and illus by Elsa Beskow; 599, "Pippi Longstocking" by A. Lindgren (illus by I. Vang Nyman); 600, "Vill-Vallareman, the Shepherd" (from "With Pucks and Elves" illus by J. Bauer); 601, "The Cat's Journey" written and illus by I. Arosenius.

164 Emil Kocher (medicine) and Wilhelm Ostwald (chemistry)

165 Weathervane, Soderala Church

1969. Nobel Prize Winners of 1909.
602 **164** 45ore green 45 30
603 – 55ore black on flesh . . . 35 20
604 – 70ore black 45 50
DESIGNS: 55ore Selma Lagerlof (literature); 70ore Guglielmo Marconi and Ferdinand Braun (physics).

1970. Swedish Forgings.
605 **165** 5ore green and brown . . 30 25
606 – 10 green and brown . . . 30 25
607 – 30 ore black and green . . 30 25
608 – 55 ore brown and green 30 25
DESIGNS—As T **165**: 10ore As Type **165**, but design and country name/figures of value in reverse order; 30ore Memorial Cross, Eksharad Churchyard. 24 × 44 mm: 55ore 14th-century door, Bjorksta Church.

166 Seal of King Magnus Ladulas

167 River Ljungan

1970.
609 **166** 2k.55 blue on cream . . 65 45
610a – 3k. blue on cream . . . 80 15
611a – 5k. green on cream . . . 1·20 15
DESIGNS: 3k. Seal of Duke Erik Magnusson; 5k. Great Seal of Erik IX.

1970. Nature Conservation Year.
612 **167** 55ore multicoloured . . . 20 15
613 70ore multicoloured . . . 45 45

168 View of Kiruna

1970. Sweden within the Arctic Circle.
614 **168** 45ore brown 40 50
615 – 45ore blue 40 50
616 – 45ore green 40 50
617 – 45ore brown 40 50
618 – 45ore blue 40 50
DESIGNS: No. 615, Winter landscape and skiers; 616, Lake and Lapp hut, Stora National Park; 617, Reindeer herd; 618, Rocket-launching.

170 Chinese Palace, Drottningholm

171 Lumber Trucks

1970. Historic Buildings.
619 – 55ore green 15 15
620 **170** 2k. multicoloured . . . 1·00 15
DESIGN—21 × 27½ mm: 55ore Glimmingehus (15th-century castle).

1970. Swedish Trade and Industry.
621 **171** 70ore brown and blue 1·30 1·70
622 – 70ore blue, brown & pur 1·30 1·70
623 – 70ore purple and blue 1·30 1·70
624 – 70ore blue and purple 1·30 1·70
625 – 70ore blue and purple 1·30 1·50
626 – 70ore brown and purple 1·30 1·70
627a – 1k. black on cream . . . 35 20
DESIGNS—As Type **171**: No. 623, Ship's propeller; 624, Dam and Class Dm3 electric locomotive; 626, Technician and machinery. 44 × 20 mm: No. 622, Loading freighter at quayside; 625, Mine and electric ore train. 26 × 20 mm: No. 627a, Miners at coal face.

173 Three Hearts

1970. 25th Anniv of United Nations.
628 **173** 55ore red, yellow and black 20 20
629 – 70ore green, yellow & blk 25 35
DESIGN: 70ore Three four-leaved clovers.

174 Blackbird

175 Paul Heyse (literature)

1970. Christmas. Birds. Multicoloured.
630 30ore Type **174** 70 70
631 30ore Great tit 70 70
632 30ore Northern bullfinch . . 70 70
633 30ore Western greenfinch . . 70 70
634 30ore Blue tit 70 70

1970. Nobel Prize Winners of 1910.
635 **175** 45ore violet 65 40
636 – 55ore blue 50 20
637 – 70ore black 70 75
PORTRAITS: 55ore Otto Wallach (chemistry) and Johannes van der Waals (physics); 70ore Albrecht Kossel (medicine).

176 Ferry "Storskar" and Royal Palace, Stockholm

178 Kerstin Hesselgren (suffragette)

1971.
638 **176** 80ore black and blue . . 35 15
639 – 4k. black . . . . 1·00 20
639a – 6k. blue . . . . 1·50 20
DESIGN: 4k. 16th-century "Blood Money" coins; 6k. Gustav Vasa's dollar.

1971. 50th Anniv of Swedish Women's Suffrage.
640 **178** 45ore violet on green . . 15 20
641 1k. brown on yellow . . . 45 20

179 Arctic Terns

180 "The Prodigal Son" (painting, Sodra Rada Church)

1971. Nordic Help for Refugees Campaign.
642 **179** 40ore red 40 20
643 55ore blue 40 20

1971.
644 **180** 15ore green on green . . 10 20
645 – 25ore blue and brown . . 15 20
646 – 25ore blue and brown . . 15 20
DESIGNS—HORIZ (Panels from Grodinge Tapestry, Swedish Natural History Museum): No. 645, Griffin; 646, Lion.

182 Container Port, Gothenburg

1971.
647 **182** 55ore violet and blue . . 20 20
648 – 60ore brown on cream . . 25 25
649 – 75ore green on green . . 20 15
DESIGNS—28 × 23 mm: 60ore Timber-sledge; 75ore Windmills, Oland.

184 Musical Score

186 "The Three Wise Men"

185 "The Mail Coach" (E. Schwab)

1971. Bicent of Swedish Royal Academy of Music.
650 **184** 55ore purple 20 20
651 85ore green 25 20

1971.
652 **185** 1k.20 multicoloured . . . 45 15

1971. Gotland Stone-masons' Art.
653 **186** 5ore violet and brown . . 25 25
654 – 10ore violet and green . . 25 25
655 – 55ore green and brown 25 20
656 – 65ore brown and violet 25 20
DESIGNS—As T **186**: 10ore "Adam and Eve". 40 × 21 mm: 55ore "Winged Knight" and "Samson and the Lion"; 65ore "The Flight into Egypt".

187 Child beside Lorry Wheel

188 State Sword of Gustavus Vasa, c. 1500

1971. Road Safety.
657 **187** 35ore black and red . . . 15 20
658 65ore blue and red . . . 30 20

1971. Swedish Crown Regalia. Multicoloured.
659 65ore Type **188** 45 25
660 65ore Sceptre of Erik XIV, 1561 . . . . 45 25
661 65ore Crown of Erik XIV, 1561 . . . . 45 25
662 65ore Orb of Erik XIV, 1561 45 25
663 65ore Anointing horn of Karl IX, 1606 . . . . 45 25

189 Santa Claus and Gifts

190 "Nils Holgersson on Goose" (from "The Wonderful Adventures of Nils" by Selma Lagerlof)

1971. Christmas. Traditional Prints.
664 **189** 35ore red . . . . 1·00 1·00
665 – 35ore blue . . . . 1·00 1·00
666 – 35ore purple . . . . . . 1·00 1·00
667 – 35ore blue . . . . 1·00 1·00
668 – 35ore green . . . . . . 1·00 1·00
DESIGNS: No. 665, Market scene; 666, Musical evening; 667, Skating; 668, Arriving for Christmas service.

1971.
669 **190** 65ore blue on cream . . . 20 15

191 Maurice Maeterlinck (literature)

192 Fencing

1971. Nobel Prize Winners of 1911.
670 **191** 55ore orange 30 25
671 – 65ore green 55 20
672 – 85ore red 55 45
DESIGNS: 65ore Allvar Gullstrand (medicine) and Wilhelm Wien (physics); 85ore Marie Curie (chemistry).

1972. Sportswomen.
673 **192** 55ore purple 55 55
674 – 55ore blue 55 55
675 – 55ore green 55 55
676 – 55ore purple 55 55
677 – 55ore blue 55 55
DESIGNS: No. 674, Diving; 675, Gymnastics; 676, Tennis; 677, Figure-skating.

193 L. J. Hierta (newspaper editor, statue by C. Eriksson)

195 Roe Deer

1972. Anniversaries of Swedish Cultural Celebrities.
678 **193** 35ore multicoloured . . . 15 20
679 – 50ore violet 20 20
680 – 65ore blue 25 20
681 – 85ore multicoloured . . . 35 35
DESIGNS AND ANNIVERSARIES—VERT: 35ore (death cent); 85ore G. Stiernhielm (poet 300th death anniv) (portrait by D. K. Ehrenstrahl). HORIZ: 50ore F. M. Franzen (poet and hymn-writer, birth bicent) (after K. Hultstrom); 65ore Hugo Alfven (composer, birth cent) (granite bust by C. Milles).

1972.
682 **195** 95ore brown on cream . . 25 15

196 Glass-blowing

1972. Swedish Glass Industry.
683 **196** 65ore black 70 45
684 – 65ore blue 70 45
685 – 65ore red 70 45
686 – 65ore black 70 45
687 – 65ore blue 70 45
DESIGNS: No. 684, Glass-blowing (close-up); 685, Shaping glass; 686, Handling glass vase; 687, Bevelling glass vase.

197 Horses, Borgholm Castle (after N. Kreuger)

1972. Tourism in South-east Sweden.
688 **197** 55ore brown on cream . . 25 35
689 – 55ore blue on cream . . . 25 35
690 – 55ore brown on cream . . 25 35
691 – 55ore green on cream . . 25 35
692 – 55ore blue on cream . . . 25 35
DESIGNS: No. 689, Oland Bridge and sailing barque "Meta"; 690, Kalmar Castle; 691, Salmon-fishing, Morrumsan; 692, Cadet schooner "Falken", Karlskrona Naval Base.

198 Conference Emblem and Motto, "Only One Earth"

1972. U.N. Environment Conservation Conference, Stockholm.
693 **198** 65ore blue and red on cream 25 20
694 – 85ore mult on cream . . 45 35
DESIGN—28 × 45 mm: 85ore "Spring" (wooden relief by B. Hjorth).

199 Junkers F-13

201 Early Courier

200 Reindeer and Sledge (woodcut from "Lapponia")

1972. Swedish Mailplanes.
695 **199** 5ore lilac 10 20
696 – 15ore blue 10 30
697 – 25ore blue 10 30
698 – 75ore green 30 25
DESIGNS—45 × 19 mm: 15ore Junkers Ju 52/3m; 25ore Friedrichshafen FF-49 seaplane; 75ore Douglas DC-3.

1972. Centenary of "Lapponia" (book by J. Schefferus).
699 **200** 1k.40 red and blue . . . 40 15

1972. "Stockholmia 74" Stamp Exhibition (1st issue) and Birth Centenary of Olle Hjortzberg (stamp designer).
700 **201** 10ore red 25 45
701 – 15ore green 40 35
702 – 40ore blue 40 45
703 – 50ore brown 35 35
704 – 60ore blue 40 35
DESIGNS: 15ore Post-rider; 40ore Steam train; 50ore Motor bus and trailer; 60ore Liner "Gripsholm".
See also Nos. 779/82.

202 Figurehead of Royal Yacht "Amphion" (Per Ljung)

203 Christmas Candles (J. Wikstrom)

1972. Swedish 18th-century Art.
705 – 75ore green 45 30
706 – 75ore brown 45 30
707 **202** 75ore red 45 30
708 – 75ore red 45 30
709 – 75ore black, brown and red 45 30
710 – 75ore black, blue & purple 45 30
DESIGNS—59 × 24 mm: No. 705, "Stockholm" (F. Martin); 706, "The Forge" (P. Hillestrom). As T **202**: No. 708, "Quadriga" (Sergel). 28 × 37 mm: No. 709, "Lady with a Veil" (A. Roslin); 710, "Sophia Magdalena" (C. G. Pilo).

1972. Christmas. Multicoloured.
711 45ore Type **203** 25 20
712 45ore Father Christmas (E. Flygh) 25 20
713 75ore Carol singers (S. Hagg) (40 × 23 mm) 35 20

204 King Gustav VI Adolf

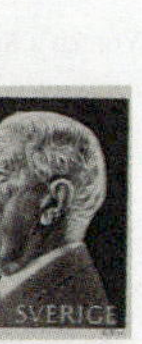

205 King Gustav with Book

1972.
714 **204** 75ore blue 20 15
715 1k. red 25 15

1972. King Gustav VI Adolf's 90th Birthday.
716 **205** 75ore blue . . . . 80 1·70
717 – 75ore green . . . . . . 80 1·70
718 – 75ore red . . . . 80 1·70
719 – 75ore blue . . . . 80 1·70
720 – 75ore green . . . . . . 80 1·70
DESIGNS: No. 717, Chinese objets d'art; 718, Opening Parliament; 719, Greek objets d'art; 720, King Gustav tending flowers.

206 Alexis Carrel (medicine)

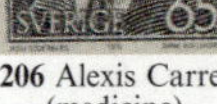

207 "Tintomara" Stage Set (B-R. Hedwall)

1972. Nobel Prize Winners of 1912.
721 – 60ore brown 45 35
722 **206** 65ore blue 55 35
723 – 75ore violet 65 20
724 – 1k. brown 80 20
DESIGNS—HORIZ: 60ore Paul Sabatier and Victor Grignard (chemistry). VERT: 75ore Nils Gustav Dalen (physics); 1k. Gerhart Hauptmann (literature).

1973. Bicentenary of Swedish Royal Theatre.
725 **207** 75ore green 20 15
726 – 1k. purple 30 20
DESIGN—41 × 23 mm: 1k. "Orpheus" (P. Hillestrom).

208 Modern Mail Coach, Vietas

210 Horse (bas relief)

209 Vasa Ski Race

1973.
727 – 60ore black on yellow . . 20 20
728 **208** 70ore orange, blue & green 20 20
DESIGN: 60ore Mail bus, 1923.

1973. Tourism in Dalecarlia.
729 **209** 65ore green 25 30
730 – 65ore green 25 40
731 – 65ore black 25 40
732 – 65ore green 25 40
733 – 65ore red 25 40
DESIGNS: No. 730, "Going to the Church in Mora" (A. Zorn); 731, Church stables in Rattvik; 732, "The Great Pit"; 733, "Mid-summer Dance" (B. Nordenberg).

1973. Gottland Picture Stones.
734 **210** 5ore purple 10 15
735 – 10 blue 10 15
DESIGN: 10ore Viking longship (bas relief).

211 "Row of Willows" (P. Persson)

1973. Swedish Landscapes.
736 **211** 40ore brown 15 15
737 – 50ore black and brown 20 15
738 – 55ore green on cream . . 20 20
DESIGNS—20 × 28 mm: 50ore "View of Trosa" (R. Ljunggren). 27 × 23 mm: 55ore "Spring Birches" (O. Bergman).

212 Lumberman

213 Observer reading Thermometer

1973. 75th Anniv of Swedish Confederation of Trade Unions.
739 **212** 75ore red 20 20
740 1k.40 blue 40 20

1973. Centenary of I.M.O./W.M.O. and Swedish Meteorological Organizations.
741 **213** 65ore green 55 20
742 – 65ore blue and black . . 55 25
DESIGN: No. 742, U.S. satellite weather picture.

214 Nordic House, Reykjavik

1973. Nordic Countries' Postal Co-operation.
743 **214** 75ore multicoloured . . . 35 20
744 1k. multicoloured 45 20

215 C. P. Thunberg, Japanese Flora and Scene

1973. Swedish Explorers.
745 **215** 1k. brown, green and blue 65 75
746 – 1k. multicoloured 65 75
747 – 1k. brown, green and blue 65 75
748 – 1k. multicoloured 65 75
749 – 1k. multicoloured 65 75
DESIGNS: No. 746, Anders Sparrman and Tahiti; 747, Adolf Erik Nordenskiold and the "Vega"; 748, Salomon Andree and wreckage of balloon "Ornen"; 749, Sven Hedin and camels.

216 Team of Oxen

217 Grey Seal

1973. Centenary of Nordic Museum.
750 **216** 75ore black . . . . . . 85 1·20
751 – 75ore brown . . . . . . 85 1·20
752 – 75ore black . . . . . . 85 1·20
753 – 75ore purple . . . . . . 85 1·20
754 – 75ore brown . . . . . . 85 1·20
DESIGNS: No. 751, Braking flax; 752, Potato-planting; 753, Baking bread; 754, Spring sowing.

1973. "Save Our Animals".
755 **217** 10ore green 10 20
756 – 20ore violet 10 15
757 – 25ore blue 10 15
758 – 55ore blue 10 20
759 – 65ore violet 15 15
760 – 75ore green 20 25
DESIGNS: 20ore Peregrine falcon; 25ore Lynx; 55ore European otter; 65ore Wolf; 75ore White-tailed sea eagle.

218 King Gustav VI Adolf

220 "Goosegirl" (E. Josephson)

219 "Country Dance" (J. Nilsson)

1973. King Gustav VI Adolf Memorial Issue.
761 **218** 75ore blue 20 20
762 1k. purple 25 20

1973. Christmas. Peasant Paintings. Mult.
763 45ore Type **219** 30 20
764 45ore "The Three Wise Men" (A. Clemetson) 30 20
765 75ore "Gourd Plant" (B. A. Hansson) (23 × 28 mm) . . 1·30 20
766 75ore "The Rider" (K. E. Jonsson) (23 × 28 mm) . . 1·30 20

1973. Ernst Josephson Commemoration.
767 **220** 10k. multicoloured . . . 2·40 15

221 A. Werner (chemistry) and H. Kamerlingh-Onnes (physics)

1973. Nobel Prize Winners 1913.
768 **221** 75ore violet 40 20
769 – 1k. brown 50 20
770 – 1k.40 green 50 20
DESIGNS—VERT: 1k. Charles Robert Richet (medicine); 1k.40, Rabindranath Tagore (literature).

222 Ski Jumping

1974. "Winter Sports on Skis".

771	222	65ore green	35	35
772	–	65ore blue	35	40
773	–	65ore green	35	35
774	–	65ore red	35	40
775	–	65ore blue	35	40

DESIGNS: No 772, Cross-country (man); 773, Relay-racing; 774, Downhill-racing; 775, Cross-country (woman).

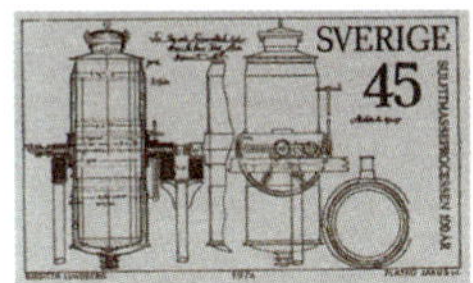

223 Ekman's Sulphite Pulping Machine

1974. Swedish Anniversaries.

776	223	45ore brown on grey	15	20
777	–	60ore green	20	30
778	–	75ore red	20	20

DESIGNS AND EVENTS: 45ore Type **223** (centenary of first sulphite pulp plant, Bergvik); 60ore Hans Jarta and part of Government Act (birth bicent); 75ore Samuel Owen and engineers (birth bicent).

224 U.P.U. Congress Stamp of 1924

1974. "Stockholmia '74" Stamp Exn (2nd issue).

779	224	20ore green	10	25
780		25ore blue	10	25
781		30ore brown	10	25
782		35ore red	10	25

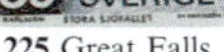

225 Great Falls

226 "Figure in a Storm" (B. Marklund)

1974.

784	225	35ore black and blue	15	20
785	–	75ore brown	20	20

DESIGN—HORIZ: 75ore Ystad (town).

1974. Europa. Sculptures.

786	226	75ore purple	65	20
787	–	1k. green	75	25

DESIGN: 1k. Picasso statue (from "Les Dames de Mougins"), Kristinehamn.

227 King Carl XVI Gustav

228 Central Post Office, Stockholm

1974.

788	227	75ore green	20	15
789		90ore blue	25	15
790		1k. purple	25	15
791		1k.10 red	30	15
792		1k.30 green	35	20
793		1k.40 blue	35	15
794		1k.50 mauve	40	15
795		1k.70 orange	45	20
796		2k. brown	50	20

1974. Centenary of Universal Postal Union.

800	228	75ore purple	75	15
801	–	75ore purple	75	20
802	–	1k. green	35	20

DESIGNS—As Type **228**: No. 801, Interior of Central Post Office, Stockholm. 40 × 24 mm: No. 802, Rural postman.

229 Regatta

1974. Tourism on Sweden's West Coast.

803	229	65ore red	25	35
804	–	65ore blue	25	35
805	–	65ore green	25	35
806	–	65ore green	25	35
807	–	65ore brown	25	35

DESIGNS: No. 804, Vinga Lighthouse; 805, Varberg Fortress; 806, Seine fishing; 807, Mollosund.

230 "Mr. Simmons" (A. Fridell)

231 Thread and Spool

1974. Centenary of Publicists' Club (Swedish press, radio and television association).

808	230	45ore black	15	20
809		1k.40 purple	45	20

1974. Swedish Textile and Clothing Industry.

810	231	85ore violet	25	20
811	–	85ore black and orange	25	20

DESIGN: No. 811, Stylized sewing-machine.

232 Deer

1974. Christmas. Mosaic Embroideries of Mythical Creatures. Each blue, red and green (45ore) or multicoloured (75ore).

812	45ore Type **232**	55	60
813	45ore Griffin	55	60
814	45ore Lion	55	60
815	45ore Griffin	55	60
816	45ore Unicorn	55	60
817	45ore Horse	55	60
818	45ore Lion	55	60
819	45ore Griffin	55	60
820	45ore Lion	55	60
821	45ore Lion-like creature	55	60
822	75ore Deer-like creature	20	20

No. 813 is facing right and has inscr at top, No. 815 faces left with similar inscr and No. 819 has inscr at bottom.

No. 814 has the inscr at top, No. 818 has it at the foot of the design, the lion having blue claws, No. 820 has similar inscr, but white claws.

Nos. 812/22 were issued together, se-tenant, forming a complete design.

233 Tanker "Bill"

1974. Swedish Shipping. Each blue.

823	1k. Type **233**	45	55
824	1k. "Snow Storm" (liner)	45	55
825	1k. "Tor" and "Atle" (ice-breakers)	45	55
826	1k. "Skanes" (train ferry)	45	55
827	1k. Tugs "Bill", "Bull" and "Starkodder"	45	55

234 Max von Laue (physics)

235 Sven Jerring (first announcer), Children and Microphone

1974. Nobel Prize Winners of 1914.

828	234	65ore red	25	25
829	–	70ore green	25	30
830	–	1k. blue	55	20

DESIGNS:—70ore Theodore William Richards (chemistry); 1k. Richard Barany (medicine).

1974. 50th Anniv of Swedish Broadcasting Corporation.

831	235	75ore blue and brown	40	20
832	–	75ore blue and brown	40	20

DESIGN: No. 832, Television camera at Parliamentary debate.

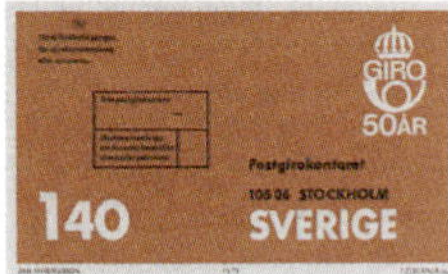

236 Giro Envelope

1975. 50th Anniv of Swedish Postal Giro Office.

833	236	1k.40 black and brown	40	20

237 Male and Female Engineers

238 Bronze Helmet Decoration, Vendel

1975. International Women's Year.

834	237	75ore green	20	20
835	–	1k. purple	25	20

DESIGN—VERT: 1k. Jenny Lind (singer) (portrait by O. J. Sodermark).

1975. Archaeological Discoveries.

836	238	10ore red	15	15
837	–	15ore green	15	15
838	–	20ore violet	15	15
839	–	25ore yellow	15	15
840	–	55ore brown	20	15

DESIGNS: 15ore Iron sword hilt and chapel, Vendel; 20ore Iron shield buckle, Vendel; 25ore Embossed gold plates (Gold Men), Eketorp Fortress, Oland; 55ore Iron helmet, Vendel.

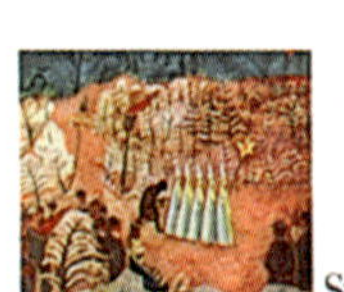

239 "New Year's Eve at Skansen" (Eric Hallstrom)

1975. Europa. Paintings. Multicoloured.

841	90ore Type **239**	35	20
842	1k.10 "Inferno" (August Strindberg) (vert)	45	20

240 Metric Tape-measure (centenary of Metre Convention)

241 Western European Hedgehog

1975. Anniversaries.

843	240	55ore blue	15	20
844	–	70ore sepia and brown	20	25
845	–	75ore violet	20	25

DESIGNS AND EVENTS—44 × 27 mm: 70ore Peter Hernqvist (founder) and title-page of his book "Comprehensive Thesis on Glanders in Horses" (bicent of Swedish Veterinary Service). 24 × 31 mm: 75ore "Folke Filbyter" (birth centenary of Carl Milles (sculptor)).

1975.

846	241	55ore black	20	20
847	–	75ore red	20	20
848	–	1k.70 blue	50	20
849	–	2k. purple	65	20
850	–	7k. green	1·70	20

DESIGNS—HORIZ: 75ore Key-fiddler; 1k.70, Western capercaillie ("cock of the woods"). VERT: 2k. Rok stone (ancient inscribed rock), Ostergotland; 7k. Ballet dancers (from "Romeo and Juliet").

242 Village Buildings, Skelleftea

1975. European Architectural Heritage Year.

851	242	75ore black	20	30
852	–	75ore red	20	30
853	–	75ore black	20	30
854	–	75ore red	20	30
855	–	75ore blue	20	30

DESIGNS: No. 852, Engelsberg iron-works, Vastmanland; 853, Gunpowder tower, Visby, Gotland; 854, Iron-mine, Falun; 855, Rommehed military barracks, Dalecarlia.

243 Fire Brigade

1975. "Watch, Guard and Help". Public Services.

856	243	90ore red	25	25
857	–	90ore blue	25	25
858	–	90ore red	25	25
859	–	90ore blue	25	25
860	–	90ore green	25	25

DESIGNS: No. 857, Customs service; 858, Police service; 859, Ambulance and hospital service; 860, Shipwreck of "Merkur" (Sea rescue service).

244 "Fryckstad"

1975. Swedish Steam Locomotives.

861	244	5ore green	20	15
862	–	5ore blue	20	15
863	–	90ore green	45	15

DESIGNS—As Type **244**: No. 862, "Gotland". 49 × 22 mm: 90ore "Prins August".

245 Canoeing

246 "Madonna" (sculpture), Vikiau church, Gotland

1975. Scouting. Multicoloured.

864	90ore Type **245**	25	25
865	90ore Camping	25	25

1975. Christmas. Religious Art.

866	246	55ore multicoloured	15	20
867	–	55ore multicoloured	20	25
868	–	55ore multicoloured	20	25
869	–	90ore brown	30	20
870	–	90ore red	45	20
871	–	90ore blue	45	20

DESIGNS—VERT: No. 867, "Birth of Christ" (embossed copper), Broddetorp church, Vastergotland; 868, "The Sun" (embossed copper), Broddetorp church, Vastergotland; 869, "Mourning Mary" (sculpture), Oja church, Gotland. HORIZ: Noore 870, 871, "Jesse at Foot of Christ's genealogical tree" (retable), Lofta church, Smaland.

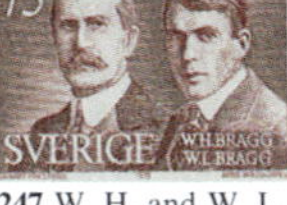

247 W. H. and W. L. Bragg (physics)

248 Bronze Coiled Snake Brooch, Vendel

1975. Nobel Prize Winners of 1915.

872	247	75ore purple	20	25
873	–	90ore blue	25	20
874	–	1k.10 green	40	35

DESIGNS: 90ore Richard Willstatter (chemistry); 1k.10, Romain Rolland (literature).

1976.

875	248	15ore bistre	10	10
876	–	20ore green	10	10
877	–	30ore purple	15	15
878	–	85ore blue	20	20
879	–	90ore blue	20	15
880	–	1k. purple	10	15
881	–	1k.90 green	50	30
882	–	9k. deep green and green	2·10	20

DESIGNS—21 × 19 mm: 20ore Pilgrim badge. 28 × 21 mm: 30ore Drinking horn; 85ore Common guillemot and razorbills. 28 × 23 mm: 1k.90, "Cave of the Winds" (sculpture) (Eric Grate). 21 × 28 mm: 90ore Chimney sweep; 1k. Bobbin lace-making; 9k. "Girl's Head" (wood-carving) (Bror Hjorth).

249 Early and Modern Telephones

250 Wheat and Cornflower Seed

1976. Telephone Centenary.

883	249	1k.30 mauve	35	20
884		3k.40 red	85	35

1976. Swedish Seed-testing Centenary.

885	250	65ore brown	15	20
886	–	65ore green and brown	15	20

DESIGN: No. 886, Viable and non-viable plants.

251 Lapp Spoon

253 Ship's Wheel and Cross

252 "View from Ringkallen" (H. Osslund)

1976. Europa. Handicrafts.

887	**251**	1k. black, pink and blue	35	20
888	–	1k.30 multicoloured . . .	45	30

DESIGN: 1k.30, Tile stove (from aquarelle by C. Slania).

1976. Tourism. Angermanland.

889	**252**	85ore green	25	30
890	–	85ore blue	25	30
891	–	85ore brown	25	30
892	–	85ore blue	25	30
893	–	85ore red	25	30

DESIGNS: No. 890, Tug towing timber; 891, Hay-drying racks; 892, Granvagsnipan; 893, Seine-net fishing.

1976. Centenary of Swedish Seamen's Church.

894	**253**	85ore blue	20	25

254 Torgny Segerstedt and "Goteborg Handels-och Sjofarts-tidning"

1976. Birth Centenary of Torgny Segerstedt (newspaper editor).

895	**254**	1k.90 black and brown . .	55	25

255 King Carl XVI Gustav and Queen Silvia

257 Hands and Cogwheels

256 John Ericsson (marine propeller)

1976. Royal Wedding.

896	**255**	1k. red	20	15
897		1k.30 green	35	30

1976. Swedish Technological Pioneers. Mult.

898	1k.30 Type **256**	45	50
899	1k.30 Helge Palmcrantz (hay maker)	45	50
900	1k.30 Lars Magnus Ericsson (telephone improvements)	45	50
901	1k.30 Sven Wingquist (ball bearing)	45	50
902	1k.30 Gustaf de Laval (milk separator and reaction turbine)	45	45

1976. Industrial Safety.

903	**257**	85ore orange and violet	20	20
904		1k. green and brown . . .	25	20

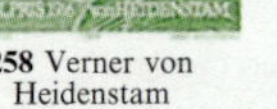

258 Verner von Heidenstam

259 "Archangel Michael Destroying Lucifer" (Flemish prayer book)

1976. Literature Nobel Prize Winner of 1916.

905	**258**	1k. green	25	20
906		1k.30 blue	45	30

1976. Christmas. Mediaeval Book Illustrations. Multicoloured.

907	65ore Type **259**	15	20
908	65ore "St. Nicholas awakening Children from Dead" (Flemish prayer book)	15	20
909	1k. "Mary visiting Elizabeth" (Austrian prayer book) . .	25	20
910	1k. "Prayer to the Virgin" (Austrian prayer book) . .	25	20

Nos. 909/10 are vert, 26 × 44 mm.

260 Water-lilies

261 Tawny Owl

1977. Nordic Countries Co-operation in Nature Conservation and Environment Protection.

911	**260**	1k. multicoloured	25	20
912		1k.30 multicoloured . . .	35	35

1977.

913	**261**	45ore green	15	20
914	–	70ore blue	20	20
915	–	1k.40 brown	40	25
916	–	2k.10 brown	55	20

DESIGNS—23 × 29 mm: 70ore Norwegian cast-iron stove decoration. 41 × 21 mm: 1k.40, Gotland ponies. 28 × 22 mm: 2k.10, Tailor.

262 "Politeness"

264 Gustavianum Building

263 Skating

1977. Birth Centenary of Oskar Andersson (cartoonist).

917	**262**	75ore black	20	25
918		3k.80 red	1·00	25

1977. Keep-fit Activities.

919	**263**	95ore blue	20	25
920	–	95ore green	20	30
921	–	95ore red	20	25
922	–	95ore green	20	30
923	–	95ore blue	20	25

DESIGNS: No. 920, Swimming; 921, Cycling; 922, Jogging; 923, Badminton.

1977. 500th Anniv of Uppsala University.

924	**264**	1k.10 black, yellow & blue	25	15

265 Winter Forest Scene

1977. Europa. Landscapes. Multicoloured.

925	1k.10 Type **265**	40	20
926	1k.40 Rapadalen valley, Sarek	55	65

266 Calle Schewen at Breakfast

267 Blackberries

1977. Tourism. Roslagen. Poem "Calle Schewen Waltz" by E. Taube.

927	**266**	95ore green	20	30
928	–	95ore violet	20	30
929	–	95ore black and red . . .	20	30
930	–	95ore blue	20	30
931	–	95ore red	20	30

DESIGNS: No. 928, Black-headed gull; 929, Calle Schewen dancing; 930, Fishing; 931, Sunset.

1977. Wild Berries. Multicoloured.

932	75ore Type **267**	30	30
933	75ore Cowberries	30	30
934	75ore Cloudberries	30	30
935	75ore Bilberries	30	30
936	75ore Strawberries	30	30

268 Horse-drawn Tram

1977. Public Transport.

937	**268**	1k.10 green	30	35
938	–	1k.10 blue	30	35
939	–	1k.10 blue	30	35
940	–	1k.10 blue	30	35
941	–	1k.10 green	30	35

DESIGN: No. 938, Electric tram; 939, Ferry "Djurgarden 6"; 940, Articulated bus; 941, Underground train, Stockholm.

269 H. Pontoppidan and K. A. Gjellerup (literature)

270 Erecting Sheaf for Birds

1977. Nobel Prize Winners of 1917.

942	**269**	1k.10 brown	40	20
943	–	1k.40 green	50	45

DESIGN: 1k.40, Charles Glover Barkla (physics).

1977. Christmas. Seasonal Customs.

944	**270**	75ore violet	20	25
945	–	75ore orange	20	25
946	–	75ore green	20	20
947	–	1k.10 green	20	20
948	–	1k.10 red	20	20
949	–	1k.10 blue	25	20

DESIGNS: No. 945, Making gingersnaps; 946, Bringing in the Christmas tree; 947, Preparing the traditional fish dish; 948, Making straw goats for the pantomime; 949, Candle-making.

271 Brown Bear

272 Orebro Castle

1978.

950	**271**	1k.15 brown	25	15
951	–	2k.50 blue	65	15

DESIGN: 2k.50, "Space without Affiliation" (sculpture by Arne Jones).

1978. Europa.

952	**272**	1k.30 green	40	20
953	–	1k.70 red	55	50

DESIGN—VERT: 1k.70, Doorway, Orebro Castle.

273 Pentecostal Meeting

1978. Independent Christian Associations.

954	**273**	90ore purple	30	45
955	–	90ore black	30	45
956	–	90ore violet	30	45
957	–	90ore green	30	45
958	–	90ore purple	30	45

DESIGNS: No. 955, Minister with children (Swedish Missionary Society); 956, Communion Service, Ethiopia (Evangelical National Missionary Society); 957, Baptism (Baptist Society); 958, Salvation Army band.

274 Brosarp Hills

1978. Travels of Carl Linne (botanist).

959	**274**	1k.30 black	30	30
960	–	1k.30 blue	30	35
961	–	1k.30 purple	30	30
962	–	1k.30 red	30	30
963	–	1k.30 blue	30	30
964	–	1k.30 purple	30	30

DESIGNS—58 × 23 mm: No. 960, Pied avocets. 27 × 23 mm: No. 961, Grindstone production (after J. W. Wallander); 962, "Linnaea borealis". 27 × 36 mm: No. 963, Red limestone cliff; 964, Linnaeus wearing Lapp dress and Dutch doctor's hat, and carrying Lapp drum (H. Kingsbury).

275 Glider over Alleberg Plateau

1978. Tourism. Vastergotland.

965	**275**	1k.15 green	30	30
966	–	1k.15 red	30	30
967	–	1k.15 blue	30	30
968	–	1k.15 grey	30	25
969	–	1k.15 black and purple . .	30	30

DESIGNS: No. 966, Common cranes; 967, Fortress on Lacko Island Skara; 968, Rock tomb, Luttra; 969, "Traders of South Vastergotland" (sculpture, N. Sjogren).

276 Diploma and Laurel Wreath

1978. Centenary of Stockholm University.

970	**276**	2k.50 green on brown . .	60	25

277 "The Homecoming" (Carl Kylberg)

1978. Paintings by Swedish Artists. Mult.

971	90ore Type **277**	25	20
972	1k.15 "Standing Model seen from Behind" (Karl Isakson)	35	20
973	4k.50 "Self-portrait with a Floral Wreath" (Ivar Arosenius)	1·20	45

278 Northern Arrow

280 "Russula decolorans"

279 Coronation Carriage, 1699

1978.

974	**278**	10k. mauve	1·90	15

1978.

975	**279**	1k.70 red on buff	50	45

1978. Edible Mushrooms. Multicoloured.

976	1k.15 Type **280**	30	40
977	1k.15 Common puff-ball ("Lycoperdon perlatum")	30	40
978	1k.15 Parasol mushroom ("Macrolepiota procera")	30	40
979	1k.15 Chanterelle ("Cantharellus cibarius")	30	40
980	1k.15 Cep ("Boletus edulis")	30	40
981	1k.15 Cauliflower clavaria ("Ramaria botrytis") . . .	30	40

281 Dalecarlian Horse

282 Fritz Haber (chemistry)

1978. Christmas. Old Toys.

982	**281**	90ore multicoloured . . .	20	20
983	–	90ore multicoloured . . .	20	20

984 – 90ore green and red . . . 20 15
985 – 1k.30 multicoloured . . . 35 20
986 – 1k.30 multicoloured . . . 35 20
987 – 1k.30 blue 35 15
DESIGNS—VERT: No. 983, Swedish Court doll; 984, Meccano; 987, Teddy bear. HORIZ: No. 985, Tops; 986, Equipage with water barrel (metal toy).

1978. Nobel Prize Winners of 1918.
988 **282** 1k.30 brown 45 20
989 – 1k.70 black 55 50
DESIGN: 1k.70, Max Planck (physics).

283 Bandy Players fighting for Ball

1979. Bandy.
990 **283** 1k.05 blue 25 20
991 2k.50 orange 65 20

284 Child in Gas-mask 285 Wall Hanging

1979. International Year of the Child.
992 **284** 1k.70 blue 55 45

1979.
993 **285** 4k. blue and red 95 15

286 Carrier Pigeon and Hand with Quill 287 Sledge-boat

1979. Rebate Stamp.
994 **286** (1k.) yellow, black and blue 85 15
No. 994 was only issued in booklets of 20 sold at 20k. in exchange for tokens distributed to all households in Sweden. Valid for inland postage only, they represented a rebate of 30ore on the normal rate of 1k.30.

1979. Europa.
995 **287** 1k.30 black and green . . 70 25
996 – 1k.70 black and brown . . 85 65
DESIGN: 1k.70, Hand using telegraph key.

288 Felling Tree

1979. Farming.
997 **288** 1k.30 black, red & green 30 30
998 – 1k.30 green and black 30 30
999 – 1k.30 green and black 30 30
1000 – 1k.30 brown and green 30 30
1001 – 1k.30 red, black & green 30 30
DESIGNS: No. 998, Sowing; 999, Cows; 1000, Harvesting; 1001, Ploughing.

289 Tourist Launch "Juno"

1979. Tourism. Gota Canal.
1002 **289** 1k.15 violet 35 40
1003 – 1k.15 green 35 40
1004 – 1k.15 purple 35 40
1005 – 1k.15 red 35 40
1006 – 1k.15 violet 35 40
1007 – 1k.15 green 35 40
DESIGNS—As T **289**: No. 1003, Borenshult lock. 27 × 23½ mm: No. 1004, Hajstorp roller bridge; 1005, Opening lock gateore 27 × 36½ mm: No. 1006, Motor barge "Wilhelm Tham" in lock; 1007, Kayak in lock.

290 "Aeshna cyanea" (dragonfly) 291 Workers leaving Sawmills

1979. Wildlife.
1008 **290** 60ore violet 30 25
1009 – 65ore green 35 20
1010 – 80ore green 45 30
DESIGNS—41 × 21 mm: 65ore Northern pike. 27 × 22 mm: 80ore Green spotted toad.

1979. Centenary of Sundsvall Strike.
1011 **291** 90ore brown and red . . 25 25

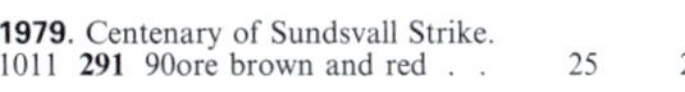

292 Banner 293 J. J. Berzelius

1979. Cent of Swedish Temperance Movement.
1012 **292** 1k.30 multicoloured . . 40 25

1979. Birth Bicentenaries of J. J. Berzelius (chemist) and J. O. Wallin (poet and hymn-writer).
1013 **293** 1k.70 brown and green 45 45
1014 – 4k.50 blue . . . . 1·20 35
DESIGN: 4k.50, J. O. Wallin and hymn numbers.

295 Atlantic Herrings and Growth Marks

1979. Marine Research.
1016 **295** 1k.70 green and blue . . 45 50
1017 – 1k.70 brown 45 50
1018 – 1k.70 green and blue . . 45 50
1019 – 1k.70 brown 45 50
1020 – 1k.70 green and blue . . 45 50
DESIGNS: No. 1017, Acoustic survey of sea-bed; 1018, Plankton bloom; 1019, Echo-sounding chart of Baltic Sea, October 1978; 1020, Fishery research ship "Argos".

296 Ljusdal Costume

1979. Peasant Costumes and Jewellery.
1021 **296** 90ore multicoloured . . 30 15
1022 – 90ore multicoloured . . 30 20
1023 – 90ore blue 30 20
1024 – 1k.30 multicoloured . . 35 20
1025 – 1k.30 multicoloured . . 35 20
1026 – 1k.30 red 35 15
DESIGNS: As T **296**: No. 1022, Osteraker costume. 21 × 27 mm: No. 1023, Brooch from Jamtland; 1026, Brooch from Smaland. 23 × 40 mm: No. 1024, Goinge church dress; 1025, Mora church dress.

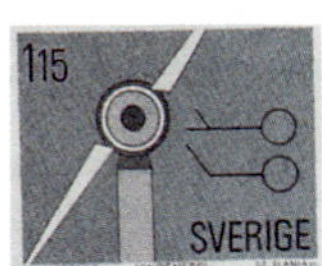

297 Jules Bordet (chemistry) 298 Wind Power

1979. Nobel Prize Winners of 1919.
1027 **297** 1k.30 mauve 40 25
1028 – 1k.70 blue 50 65
1029 – 2k.50 green 60 25
DESIGNS: 1k.70, Johannes Stark (physics); 2k.50, Carl Spitteler (literature).

1980. Renewable Energy Sources.
1030 **298** 1k.15 blue 40 30
1031 – 1k.15 buff and green . . 40 30
1032 – 1k.15 orange 40 30
1033 – 1k.15 green 40 30
1034 – 1k.15 green and blue . . 40 30
DESIGNS: No. 1031, Biological energy; 1032, Solar energy; 1033, Geothermal energy; 1034, Wave energy.

299 King Carl XVI Gustav and Crown Princess Victoria 300 Child's Hand in Adult's

1980. New Order of Succession to Throne.
1035 **299** 1k.30 blue 35 20
1036 1k.70 red 45 40

1980. Care.
1037 **300** 1k.40 brown 35 20
1038 – 1k.60 green 40 20
DESIGN: 1k.60, Aged hand clasping stick.

301 Squirrel 302 Elise Ottesen-Jensen (pioneer of birth control)

1980. Rebate Stamp.
1039 **301** (1k.) yellow, blue & black 80 15
No. 1039 was only issued in booklets of 20 sold at 20k. on production of tokens distributed to all households in Sweden.

1980. Europa.
1040 **302** 1k.30 green 55 20
1041 – 1k.70 red 60 60
DESIGN: 1k.70, Joe Hill (member of workers' movement).

303 Tybling Farm, Tyby

1980. Tourism. Halsingland.
1042 **303** 1k.15 red 45 30
1043 – 1k.15 blue and purple . . 45 30
1044 – 1k.15 green 45 30
1045 – 1k.15 purple 45 30
1046 – 1k.15 blue 45 30
DESIGNS: No. 1043, Old iron works, Iggesund; 1044, Blaxas ridge, Forsa; 1045, Banga farm, Alfta; 1046, Sunds Canal, Hudiksvall.

304 Chair from Scania (1831) 305 Motif from film "Diagonal Symphony"

1980. Nordic Countries' Postal Co-operation.
1047 **304** 1k.50 green 40 20
1048 – 2k. brown 55 35
DESIGN: 2k. Cradle from North Bothnia (19th century).

1980. Birth Bicentenary of Viking Eggeling (film-maker).
1049 **305** 3k. blue 75 20

307 Bamse 308 "Necken" (Ernst Josephson)

1980. Christmas. Swedish Comic Strips.
1051 **307** 1k.15 blue and red . . . 35 20
1052 – 1k.15 multicoloured . . 30 20
1053 – 1k.50 black 40 20
1054 – 1k.50 multicoloured . . 40 20
DESIGNS—As T **307** but VERT: No. 1052, Karlsson; 1053, Adamson. 40 × 23 mm: No. 1054, Kronblom.

1980.
1055 **308** 8k. brown, black and blue . . . . 1·90 65

309 Knut Hamsun (literature) 310 Angel blowing Horn

1980. Nobel Prize Winners of 1920.
1056 **309** 1k.40 blue 35 35
1057 – 1k.40 red 35 35
1058 – 2k. green 45 45
1059 – 2k. brown 45 45
DESIGNS: No. 1057, August Krogh (medicine); 1058, Charles-Edouard Guillaume (physics); 1059, Walther Nernst (chemistry).

1980. Christmas.
1060 **310** 1k.25 brown and blue . . 35 20

311 Ernst Wigforss 312 Thor catching Midgard Serpent

1981. Birth Centenary of Ernst Wigforss (politician).
1061 **311** 5k. red . . . . 1·20 25

1981. Norse Mythology.
1062 **312** 10ore black 10 15
1063 – 15ore red 10 15
1064 – 50ore red 15 15
1065 – 75ore green 25 15
1066 – 1k. black 30 15
DESIGNS: 15ore Heimdall blowing horn; 50ore Freya riding boar; 75ore Freya in carriage drawn by cats; 1k. Odin on eight-footed steed.

313 Gyr Falcon 314 Troll

1981.
1067 **313** 50k. brown, black & blue . . . . 10·50 90

1981. Europa.
1068 **314** 1k.50 blue and red . . . 50 20
1069 – 2k. red and green . . . 65 25
DESIGN: 2k. The Lady of the Woods.

315 Blind Boy feeling Globe 316 Arms of Bohuslan

1981. International Year of Disabled Persons.
1070 **315** 1k.50 green 40 20
1071 3k.50 violet 65 35

1981. Rebate stamps. Arms of Swedish Provinces (1st series). Multicoloured.
1072 1k.40 Ostergotland 80 15
1073 1k.40 Jamtland 80 15
1074 1k.40 Dalarna 80 15
1075 1k.40 Type **316** 80 15
See also Nos. 1112/15, 1153/6, 1189/92, 1246/9 and 1302/5.

317 King Carl XVI Gustav 318 Boat from Bohuslan

1981.
1076 **317** 1k.65 green 45 15
1077 – 1k.75 blue 45 25
1077a **317** 1k.80 blue 45 15
1077b 1k.90 red 50 20
1078 2k.40 purple 65 25
1078a – 2k.40 green 65 55

1078b **317** 2k.70 purple 70 30
1078c – 3k.20 red 80 35
DESIGN: 1k.75, 2k.40 (1078a), 3k.20, Queen Silvia.

1981. Provincial Sailing Boats.
1079 **318** 1k.65 blue 45 30
1080 – 1k.65 blue 45 30
1081 – 1k.65 blue 45 30
1082 – 1k.65 blue 45 30
1083 – 1k.65 blue 45 30
1084 – 1k.65 blue 45 30
DESIGNS: No. 1080, Boat from Blekinge; 1081, Boat from Norrbotten; 1082, Boat from Halsingland; 1083, Boat from Gotland; 1084, Boat from West Skane.

319 "Night and Day"

320 Par Lagerkvist riding Railway Trolley with Father (illustration from "Guest of Reality")

1981.
1085 **319** 1k.65 violet 40 15

1981.
1086 **320** 1k.50 green 40 20

321 Electric Locomotive

1981. "Sweden in the World".
1087 **321** 2k.40 red 55 55
1088 – 2k.40 red 55 55
1089 – 2k.40 purple 55 55
1090 – 2k.40 violet 55 55
1091 – 2k.40 blue 55 55
1092 – 2k.40 blue 55 55
DESIGNS—As T **321**: No. 1088, Scania trucks with rock drilling equipment; 1089, Birgit Nilsson (opera singer) and Sixten Ehrling (conductor); 1090, North Sea gas rig. 19 × 23 mm: No. 1091, Bjorn Borg (tennis player); 1092, Ingemar Stenmark (skier).

322 Baker's Sign

324 Wooden Bird

1981. Business Mail.
1093 **322** 2k.30 brown . . . . . . 1·40 55
1094 – 2k.30 brown . . . . . . 1·40 55
DESIGN: No. 1094, Pewterer's sign.

1981. Christmas.
1096 **324** 1k.40 red 35 20
1097 – 1k.40 green 35 20
DESIGN: No. 1097, Wooden bird (different).

325 Albert Einstein (physics)

1981. Nobel Prize Winners of 1921.
1098 **325** 1k.35 red 35 35
1099 – 1k.65 green 45 20
1100 – 2k.70 blue 55 55
DESIGNS: 1k.65, Anatole France (literature); 2k.70, Frederick Soddy (chemistry).

326 Knight on Horseback

327 Impossible Triangle

1982. Birth Centenary of John Bauer (illustrator of fairy tales).
1101 **326** 1k.65 blue, yellow & lilac 40 25
1102 – 1k.65 multicoloured 40 25
1103 – 1k.65 black and yellow 40 25
1104 – 1k.65 yellow and lilac . . 40 25

DESIGNS: No. 1102, "What a wretched pale creature, said the Troll Woman"; 1103, "The Princess beside the Forest Lake"; 1104, "Now it is already twilight Night".

1982.
1105 **327** 25ore brown 15 15
1106 – 50ore brown 15 15
1107 – 75ore blue 20 20
1108 – 1k.35 blue 35 20
1109 – 5k. purple . . . . . . 1·20 15
DESIGNS: 50, 75ore, Impossible figures (different); 1k.35, Newspaper distributor; 5k. "Graziella wonders if she could be a Model" (etching, Carl Larsson).

328 Villages before and after Land Reform

1982. Europa.
1110 **328** 1k.65 green and black 1·30 20
1111 – 2k.40 green 60 55
DESIGN—26 × 22 mm: 2k.40, Anders Celsius.

1982. Rebate Stamps. Arms of Swedish Provinces (2nd series). As T **316**. Multicoloured.
1112 1k.40 Dalsland 80 15
1113 1k.40 Oland 80 15
1114 1k.40 Vastmanland 80 15
1115 1k.40 Halsingland 80 15

329 Elin Wagner

330 Burgher House

1982. Birth Centenary of Elin Wagner (novelist).
1116 **329** 1k.35 brown on grey . . 35 25

1982. Centenary of Museum of Cultural History, Lund.
1117 **330** 1k.65 brown 50 15
1118 – 2k.70 brown 65 40
DESIGN: 2k.70, Embroidered lace.

331 Lateral Mark

1982. New International Buoyage System.
1119 **331** 1k.65 blue and green . . 55 20
1120 – 1k.65 green and blue . . 55 20
1121 – 1k.65 deep blue and blue 55 20
1122 – 1k.65 blue and green . . 55 20
1123 – 1k.65 deep blue and blue 55 20
DESIGNS: No. 1120, Cardinal mark and Sweden–Finland ferry "Sally"; 1121, Racing yachts and special mark; 1122, Safe-water mark; 1123, Pilot boat, isolated danger mark and lighthouse.

332 Scene from "The Emigrants" (film)

1982. Living Together.
1124 **332** 1k.65 green 40 20
1125 – 1k.65 purple 40 20
1126 – 1k.65 blue 40 20
1127 – 1k.65 red 40 20
DESIGNS: No. 1125, Vietnamese boat people in factory; 1126, Immigrants examining local election literature; 1127, Three girls arm-in-arm.

334 Angel

1982. Christmas. Medieval Glass Paintings from Lye Church. Multicoloured.
1129 1k.40 Type **334** 45 35
1130 1k.40 "The Child in the Temple" 45 35
1131 1k.40 "Adoration of the Magi" 45 35
1132 1k.40 "Tidings to the Shepherds" 45 35
1133 1k.40 "The Birth of Christ" 45 35

335 Quantum Mechanics (Niels Bohr, 1922)

1982. Nobel Prize Winners for Physics.
1134 **335** 2k.40 blue 55 60
1135 – 2k.40 red 55 60
1136 – 2k.40 green 55 60
1137 – 2k.40 lilac 55 60
1138 – 2k.40 red 55 60
DESIGNS: No. 1135, Fuse distribution (Erwin Schrodinger, 1933); 1136, Wave pattern (Louis de Broglie, 1929); 1137, Electrons (Paul Dirac, 1933); 1138, Atomic model (Werner Heisenberg, 1932).

336 Horse Chestnut

337 Ferlin (statue by K. Bejemark)

1983. Fruits.
1139 **336** 5ore brown 10 10
1140 – 10ore green 10 10
1141 – 15ore red 10 10
1142 – 20ore blue 15 15
DESIGNS: 10ore Norway maple; 15ore Dog rose; 20ore Blackthorn.

1983. 85th Birth Anniv of Nils Ferlin (poet).
1143 **337** 6k. green . . . . 1·40 15

338 Peace March

340 Family Cycling in Countryside

339 Lead Type

1983. Centenary of Swedish Peace Movement.
1144 **338** 1k.35 blue 35 20

1983. 500th Anniv of Printing in Sweden.
1145 **339** 1k.65 black and brown on stone 40 25
1146 – 1k.65 black, green and red on stone 40 25
1147 – 1k.65 brown and black on stone 40 25
1148 **339** 1k.65 black and brown on stone 40 25
1149 – 1k.65 brown, green and black on stone . . . 40 25
DESIGNS: No. 1146, Ox plough (illustration from "Dialogus creaturarum" by Johan Snell, 1483); 1147, Title page of Karl XII's Bible, 1703; 1148, 18th-century alphabet books; 1149, Laser photocomposition.

1983. Nordic Countries' Postal Co-operation. "Visit the North".
1150 **340** 1k.65 green 40 20
1151 – 2k.40 blue and brown . . 60 40
DESIGN: 2k.40, Yachts at Stockholm.

341 Benjamin Franklin and Great Seal of Sweden

1983. Bicentenary of Sweden–U.S.A. Treaty of Amity and Commerce.
1152 **341** 2k.70 blue, brown & blk 70 40

1983. Rebate Stamps. Arms of Swedish Provinces (3rd series). As T **316**. Multicoloured.
1153 1k.60 Vastergotland 80 15
1154 1k.60 Medelpad 80 15
1155 1k.60 Gotland 80 15
1156 1k.60 Gastrikland 80 15

342 Costume Sketch by Fernand Leger for "Creation du Monde"

343 Essay for Unissued Stamp, 1885

1983. Europa.
1157 1k.65 chocolate and brown 75 20
1158 2k.70 blue . . . . 1·20 70
DESIGNS: 1k.65, Type **342** (Swedish Ballet); 2k.70, J. P. Johansson's adjustable spanner.

1983. "Stockholmia 86" International Exhibition (1st issue). Oscar II stamp designs by Max Mirowsky.
1159 **343** 1k. blue 60 40
1160 – 2k. red 60 45
1161 – 3k. blue 60 55
1162 – 4k. green 60 65
DESIGNS: 2k. Issued stamp of 1885; 3k. Essay for unissued stamp, 1891; 4k. Issued stamp of 1891.
See also Nos. 1199/1202, 1252/5, 1285/8 and 1310/13.

344 Greater Karlso

345 Freshwater Snail

1983.
1163 **344** 1k.60 blue 50 15
1164 **345** 1k.80 green 45 15
1165 – 2k.10 green 45 15
DESIGN—22 × 27 mm: 2k.10, Arctic fox.

346 Bergman

347 Helgeandsholmen, 1580 (after Franz Hogenberg) and Riksdag

1983. Birth Centenary of Hjalmar Bergman (novelist and dramatist).
1166 **346** 1k.80 blue 45 20
1167 – 1k.80 multicoloured . . 45 25
DESIGN: No. 1167, Jac the Clown (novel character).

1983. Return of Riksdag (Parliament) to Helgeandsholmen Island, Stockholm.
1168 **347** 2k.70 purple and blue . . 70 40

348 Red Cross

350 Dancing round the Christmas Tree

1983. Swedish Red Cross.
1169 **348** 1k.50 red 40 20

1983. Christmas. Early Christmas Cards. Multicoloured.
1171 1k.60 Type **350** 40 25
1172 1k.60 Straw goats 40 25
1173 1k.60 The Christmas table 40 25
1174 1k.60 Carrying Christmas presents on pole 40 25

351 Electrophoresis (Arne Tiselius, 1948)

1983. Nobel Prize Winners for Chemistry.
1175 **351** 2k.70 black 65 70
1176 – 2k.70 violet 65 70
1177 – 2k.70 mauve 65 70

1178 – 2k.70 violet 65 70
1179 – 2k.70 black 65 70
DESIGNS: No. 1176, Radioactive isotopes (George de Hevesy, 1943); 1177, Electrolytic dissociation (Svante Arrhenius, 1903); 1178, Colloids (Theodor Svedberg, 1926); 1179, Fermentation of sugar (Hans von Euler-Chelpin, 1929).

352 Three Crowns (detail from Postal Savings Receipt)

1984. Centenary of Postal Savings.
1180 **352** 100ore orange 20 20
1181 – 1k.60 violet 40 40
1182 – 1k.80 mauve 50 20
DESIGNS: 1k.60, 1k.80, Postal Savings badge.

353 Bridge

1984. Europa. 25th Anniv of European Post and Telecommunications Conference.
1183 **353** 1k.80 red 50 20
1184 2k.70 blue . . . . 1·10 70

354 Norway Lemming
355 Paraffin Stove (F. W. Lindqvist)

1984. Swedish Mountain World.
1185 **354** 1k.90 brown 45 20
1186 – 1k.90 blue 45 20
1187 – 2k. green 50 15
1188 – 2k.25 black 75 45
DESIGNS: No. 1186, Musk ox; 1187, Garden angelica; 1188, Tolpagorni mountain.

1984. Rebate Stamps. Arms of Swedish Provinces (4th series). As T **316**. Multicoloured.
1189 1k.60 Sodermanland 80 15
1190 1k.60 Blekinge 80 15
1191 1k.60 Vasterbotten 80 15
1192 1k.60 Skane 80 15

1984. "Made in Sweden". Centenary of Patent Office. Patented Swedish Inventions.
1193 **355** 2k.70 red 60 70
1194 – 2k.70 lilac 60 70
1195 – 2k.70 green 60 70
1196 – 2k.70 green 60 70
1197 – 2k.70 lilac 60 70
1198 – 2k.70 blue 60 70
DESIGNS: No. 1194, "ASEA IRB 6" industrial robot for arc welding; 1195, Vacuum cleaner (Axel Wennergren); 1196, "AQ 200" inboard/outboard engine; 1197, Integrated circuit; 1198, Tetrahedron container.

356 King Erik XIV (after S. van der Meulen) and Letter to Queen Elizabeth I of England
358 Genetic Symbols forming "100"

357 Jonkoping

1984. "Stockholmia 86" International Stamp Exhibition (2nd issue).
1199 **356** 1k. brown, blue and ultramarine 50 40
1200 – 2k. multicoloured . . . 60 45
1201 – 3k. multicoloured . . . 65 60
1202 – 4k. multicoloured . . . 75 65

DESIGNS: 2k. Erik Dahlbergh (architect) (after J. H. Stromer) and letter to Sten Bielke (Paymaster General), 1674; 3k. Feather letter, 1843; 4k. Harriet Bosse and letter from her husband, August Strindberg, 1905.

1984. Old Towns. 17th-century views by M. Karl (1207) or Erik Dahlbergh (others).
1203 **357** 1k.90 blue 45 35
1204 – 1k.90 brown 45 35
1205 – 1k.90 blue 45 40
1206 – 1k.90 brown 45 40
1207 – 1k.90 blue 45 40
1208 – 1k.90 brown 45 40
DESIGNS: No. 1204, Karlstad; 1205, Gavle; 1206, Sigtuna; 1207, Norrkoping; 1208, Vadstena.

1984. Centenary of Fredrika Bremer Association (for promotion of male/female equal rights).
1209 **358** 1k.50 purple 40 20
1210 6k.50 red . . . . 1·60 45

359 "Viking" in Orbit

1984. Launch of Swedish "Viking" Satellite.
1211 **359** 1k.90 ultramarine, blue and deep blue 50 20
1212 – 3k.20 green, yellow and black 80 70
DESIGN: 3k.20, Dish aerial and rocket pad at Esrange space station.

361 Hawfinch ("Coccothraustes coccothraustes")

1984. Christmas. Birds. Multicoloured.
1214 1k.60 Type **361** 40 30
1215 1k.60 Bohemian waxwing ("Bombycilla garrulus") 40 30
1216 1k.60 Great-spotted woodpecker ("Dendrocopos major") 40 30
1217 1k.60 Eurasian nuthatch ("Sitta europaea") 40 30

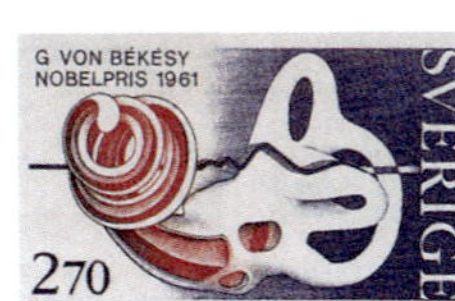

362 Inner Ear (Georg von Bekesy, 1961)

1984. Nobel Prize Winners for Medicine.
1218 **362** 2k.70 blue, black and red 65 65
1219 – 2k.70 blue and black . . 65 65
1220 – 2k.70 red, black and blue 65 65
1221 – 2k.70 blue and black . . 65 65
1222 – 2k.70 red, black and blue 65 65
DESIGNS: No. 1219, Nerve cell activation (John Eccles, Alan Hodgkin and Andrew Huxley, 1963); 1220, Nerve cell signals (Bernard Katz, Ulf von Euler and Julius Axelrod, 1970); 1221, Functions of the brain (Roger Sperry, 1981); 1222, Eye (David Hubel and Torsten Wiesel, 1981).

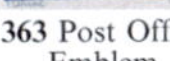

363 Post Office Emblem
364 King Carl XVI Gustav

1985.
1223 **363** 1k.60 blue 45 20
1224 1k.70 violet 50 20
1326 1k.80 purple 55 20
1225 2k.50 yellow 65 20
1226 2k.80 green 80 40
1327 3k.20 brown 85 60
1227 4k. red 90 20
1328 6k. turquoise . . . . . 1·40 30

1985.
1228 **364** 2k. black 50 15
1229 2k.10 blue 60 15
1230 2k.20 blue 55 20
1230a 2k.30 green 55 20
1230b 2k.50 purple 65 20
1231 2k.70 brown 70 35
1232 2k.90 green 75 35
1233 3k.10 brown 80 45
1234 – 3k.20 blue 80 60
1235 **364** 3k.30 purple . . . . . 1·30 50
1236 – 3k.40 red 85 40
1237 – 3k.60 green 90 50

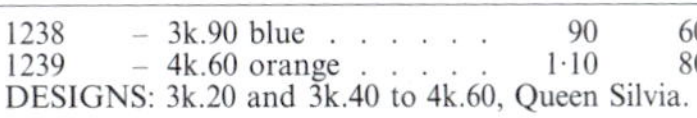
1238 – 3k.90 blue 90 60
1239 – 4k.60 orange . . . . . 1·10 80
DESIGNS: 3k.20 and 3k.40 to 4k.60, Queen Silvia.

365 Hazel Dormouse ("Muscardinus avellanarius")
366 Jan-Ove Waldner

1985. Nature.
1240 **365** 2k. brown and black . . 50 20
1241 – 2k. orange and black . . 50 20
1242 – 2k.20 red 55 15
1243 – 3k.50 red and green . . 85 20
DESIGNS: No. 1241, Char ("Salvelinus salvelinus"); 1242, Black vanilla orchid ("Nigritella nigra"); 1243, White water-lily ("Nymphaea alba frosea").

1985. World Table Tennis Championships, Gothenburg.
1244 **366** 2k.70 blue 75 35
1245 – 3k.20 mauve 85 60
DESIGN: 3k.20, Cai Zhenhua (Chinese player).

1985. Rebate Stamps. Arms of Swedish Provinces (5th series). As T **316**. Multicoloured.
1246 1k.80 Narke 80 15
1247 1k.80 Angermanland . . . 80 15
1248 1k.80 Varmland 80 15
1249 1k.80 Smaland 80 15

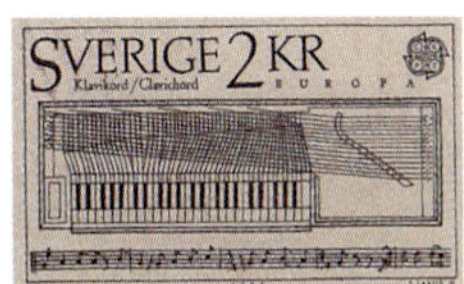

367 Clavichord

1985. Europa. Music Year.
1250 **367** 2k. purple on buff . . . 1·90 20
1251 – 2k.70 brown on buff . . 65 60
DESIGN—28 × 24 mm: 2k.70, Keyed fiddle.

368 "View of Slussen" (Sigrid Hjerten)
369 Syl Hostel, 1920

1985. "Stockholmia 86" International Stamp Exhibition (3rd issue). Multicoloured.
1252 2k. Type **368** 60 50
1253 2k. "Skeppsholmen, Winter" (Gosta Adrian-Nilsson) 60 50
1254 3k. "A Summer's Night by Riddarholmen Canal" (Hilding Linnqvist) . . . 70 60
1255 4k. "Klara Church Tower" (Otte Skold) 80 65

1985. Centenary of Swedish Touring Club.
1256 **369** 2k. blue and black . . . 50 20
1257 – 2k. black and blue . . . 50 20
DESIGN—58 × 24 mm: No. 1257, "Af Chapman" (youth hostel in Stockholm).

370 Canute and Helsingborg
371 Nilsson's Music Shop Sign

1985. 900th Anniv of Saint Canute's Deed of Gift to Lund.
1258 – 2k. blue and black . . . 50 20
1259 **370** 2k. red and black . . . 50 20
DESIGN: No. 1258, Canute and Lund Cathedral.

1985. Trade Signs.
1260 **371** 10ore blue 10 15
1261 – 20ore brown 10 15
1262 – 20ore brown 10 15
1263 – 50ore blue 20 15
1264 – 2k. green 85 15
DESIGNS: No. 1261, Erik Johansson's furrier's sign; 1262, O. L. Sjowals's coppersmith's sign; 1263, Bodecker's hatter's sign; 1264, Berggren's shoemaker's sign.

372 "Otryades" (Johan Tobias Sergel)

1985. 250th Anniv of Royal Academy of Fine Arts.
1265 **372** 2k. blue 50 20
1266 – 7k. brown . . . . 1·70 50
DESIGN—20 × 28 mm: 7k. "Baron Carl Fredrik Adelcrantz" (former Academy president) (Alexander Roslin).

373 Fox and Geese
374 Birger Sjoberg (writer)

1985. Board Games.
1267 **373** 50ore blue 15 15
1268 – 60ore green 15 15
1269 – 70ore yellow 20 20
1270 – 80ore red 20 20
1271 – 90ore mauve 20 20
1272 – 3k. purple 65 15
DESIGNS—As T **373**: 60k. Dominoes; 70k. Ludo; 80k. Chinese checkers; 90k. Backgammon. 23 × 28 mm: 3k. Chess.

1985. Birth Centenaries.
1273 – 1k.60 red and black . . 40 30
1274 **374** 4k. green . . . . 1·00 20
DESIGN—40 × 24 mm: 1k.60, Per Albin Hansson (politician).

376 "Annunciation"
377 American Deep South Scene (William Faulkner, 1949)

1985. Christmas. Medieval Church Frescoes by Albertus Pictor.
1276 **376** 1k.80 blue, brown and red 45 25
1277 – 1k.80 brown, blue and red 45 25
1278 – 1k.80 brown, blue and red 45 25
1279 – 1k.80 blue, brown and red 45 25
DESIGNS: No. 1277, "Birth of Christ"; 1278, "Adoration of the Magi"; 1279, "Mary as the Apocalyptic Virgin".

1985. Nobel Prize Winners for Literature.
1280 **377** 2k.70 green 70 70
1281 – 2k.70 brown, blue and green 70 70
1282 – 2k.70 green and brown 70 70
1283 – 2k.70 green and blue . . 70 70
1284 – 2k.70 brown and blue . . 70 70
DESIGNS: No. 1281, Icelandic scene (Halldor Kiljan Laxness, 1955); 1282, Guatemalan scene (Miguel Angel Asturias, 1967); 1283, Japanese scene (Yasunari Kawabata, 1968); 1284, Australian scene (Patrick White, 1973).

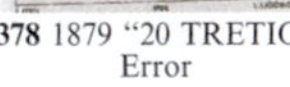

378 1879 "20 TRETIO" Error
379 Eiders ("Somateria mollissima")

1986. "Stockholmia 86" International Stamp Exhibition (4th issue).
1285 **378** 2k. orange, purple & grn 70 50
1286 – 2k. multicoloured . . . 70 45
1287 – 3k. purple, blue and green 75 65
1288 – 4k. multicoloured . . . 75 75
DESIGNS: No. 1286, Sven Ewert (engraver); 1287, Magnifying glass and United States 1938 Scandinavian Settlement 3c. stamp; 1288, Boy soaking stamps.

1986. Water Birds.
1289 **379** 2k.10 blue and brown . . 50 20
1290 – 2k.10 brown 50 20
1291 – 2k.30 blue 55 20
DESIGNS: No. 1290, Whimbrel ("Numenius phaeopus"); 1291, Black-throated diver ("Gavia arctica").

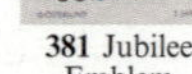

380 Swedish Academy Emblem

381 Jubilee Emblem

1986. Bicentenaries of Swedish Academy and Royal Swedish Academy of Letters, History and Antiquities.

1292 **380** 1k.70 green and red on grey 40 40
1293 – 1k.70 blue and purple on grey 40 40

DESIGN: No. 1293, Royal Swedish Academy emblem.

1986. 350th Anniv of Post Office.

1294 **381** 2k.10 blue and yellow . . 55 15

382 Palme

383 Carl Gustav Birdwatching

1986. Olof Palme (Prime Minister) Commemoration.

1295 **382** 2k.10 purple 55 75
1296 2k.90 black 80 75

1986. 40th Birthday of King Carl XVI Gustav.

1297 **383** 2k.10 black and green 60 35
1298 – 2k.10 gold, mauve and blue 60 35
1299 – 2k.10 deep blue and blue 60 35
1300 – 2k.10 gold, blue and deep blue 60 35
1301 – 2k.10 black and mauve 60 35

DESIGNS: Nos. 1298, 1300, Crowned cypher; 1299, King presenting Nobel Prize for Literature to Czeslaw Milosz; 1301, King and family during summer holiday at Solliden Palace.

1986. Rebate Stamps. Arms of Swedish Provinces (6th series). As T **316**. Multicoloured.

1302 1k.90 Harjedalen 80 20
1303 1k.90 Uppland 80 20
1304 1k.90 Halland 80 20
1305 1k.90 Lappland 80 20

384 Uppsala

385 Forest and Car Fumes

1986. Nordic Countries' Postal Co-operation. Twinned Towns.

1306 **384** 2k.10 green, chestnut and brown 55 20
1307 – 2k.90 green, red & brown 70 55

DESIGN: 2k.90, Eskilstuna.

1986. Europa. Each black, green and red.

1308 2k.10 Type **385** . . . . . 1·10 20
1309 2k.90 Forest and industrial pollution 65 65

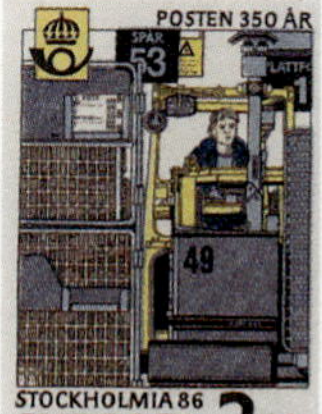
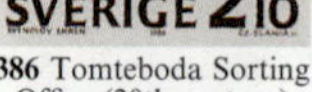

386 Tomteboda Sorting Office (20th-century)

388 Olive Branch sweeping away Weapons

1986. "Stockholmia 86" International Stamp Exhibition (5th issue). Multicoloured.

1310 2k.10 19th-century railway sorting carriage . . . . 1·30 2·10
1311 2k.10 Type **386** . . . . . 1·30 2·10
1312 2k.90 17th-century farmhand postal messenger . . . . 1·30 2·10
1313 2k.90 18th-century post office . . . . 1·30 2·10

1986. International Peace Year (1315) and 25th Anniv of Amnesty International (1316).

1315 **388** 3k.40 green and black 80 85
1316 – 3k.40 red and black . . 80 80

DESIGN: No. 1316, Emblem above broken manacles.

389 Bertha von Suttner (founder of Austrian Society of Peace Lovers, 1905)

1986. Nobel Prize Winners for Peace.

1317 **389** 2k.90 black, red and blue 75 75
1318 – 2k.90 black and red . . 75 75
1319 – 2k.90 black, brown and blue 75 75
1320 – 2k.90 brown and black 75 75
1321 – 2k.90 red, black and blue 75 75

DESIGNS: No. 1318, Carl von Ossietzky (anti-Nazi fighter and concentration camp victim, 1935); 1319, Albert Luthuli (South African anti-apartheid leader, 1960); 1320, Martin Luther King (American civil rights leader, 1964); 1321, Mother Teresa (worker amongst poor of Calcutta, 1979).

390 Mail Van

391 Clouded Apollo ("Parnassius mnemosyne")

1986. Christmas. Designs showing a village at Christmas. Multicoloured.

1322 1k.90 Type **390** 45 25
1323 1k.90 Postman on cycle delivering mail 45 25
1324 1k.90 Children and sledge loaded with parcels . . . 45 25
1325 1k.90 Christmas tree, man carrying parcel and child posting letter 45 25

Nos. 1322/5 were printed together, se-tenant, forming a composite design.

1987. Threatened Species of Meadows and Pastures.

1331 **391** 2k.10 black, green and purple 50 20
1332 – 2k.10 black, green and purple 50 20
1333 – 2k.50 brown 65 15
1334 – 4k.20 green and yellow 95 20

DESIGNS: 2k.10 (1332), Field gentian ("Gentianella campestris"); 2k.50, Leather beetle ("Osmoderma eremita"); 4k.20, Arnica ("Arnica montana").

392 SAAB-Fairchild SF-340

393 Boys flying over Rooftops ("Karlsson")

1987. Swedish Aircraft.

1335 **392** 25k. purple . . . . . . 5·50 55

1987. Rebate Stamps. Characters from Children's Books by Astrid Lindgren. Multicoloured.

1336 1k.90 Type **393** 85 15
1337 1k.90 Girl holding doll ("Bullerby Children") . . 85 15
1338 1k.90 Girls dancing ("Madicken") 85 15
1339 1k.90 Boys on horse ("Mio, Min Mio") 85 15
1340 1k. Boy doing handstand ("Nils Karlsson-Pyssling") 85 15
1341 1k.90 Emil picking cherries ("Emil") 85 15
1342 1k.90 "Ronja the Robber's Daughter" 85 15
1343 1k.90 "Pippi Longstocking" 85 15
1344 1k.90 Dragon ("Brothers Lionheart") 85 15
1345 1k.90 "Lotta" 85 15

394 Hans Brask, Bishop of Linkoping (sculpture, Karl-Olav Bjork)

395 Stockholm City Library (Gunnar Asplund)

1987. Town Anniversaries. Each brown, blue and black.

1346 2k.10 Type **394** (700th anniv) 50 45
1347 2k.10 Nykoping Castle (800th anniv) 50 45

1987. Europa. Architecture.

1348 **395** 2k.10 brown and blue . . 1·00 20
1349 3k.10 brown and green 70 65
1350 – 3k.10 purple and green 70 65

DESIGN: No. 1350, Marcus Church (Sigurd Lewerentz).

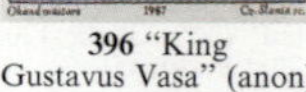

396 "King Gustavus Vasa" (anon)

398 Clowns

397 Raoul Wallenberg (rescuer of Hungarian Jews) and Prisoners

1987. 450th Anniv of Gripsholm Castle.

1351 **396** 2k.10 multicoloured . . 50 25
1352 – 2k.10 multicoloured . . 50 25
1353 – 2k.10 multicoloured . . 50 25
1354 – 2k.10 brown, black and blue 50 25

DESIGNS: No. 1352, "Blue Tiger" (David Klocker Ehrenstrahl); 1353, "Hedvig Charlotta Nordenflycht" (after Johan Henrik Scheffel); 1354, "Gripsholm Castle" (lithograph, Carl Johan Billmark).

1987. "In the Service of Humanity".

1355 **397** 3k.10 blue 65 70
1356 – 3k.10 green 65 70
1357 – 3k.10 brown 65 70

DESIGNS: No. 1356, Dag Hammarskjold (U.N. Secretary-General, 1953–1961); 1357, Folke Bernadotte (leader of "white bus" relief action to rescue prisoners, 1945).

1987. Stamp Day. Bicentenary of Circus in Sweden. Multicoloured.

1358 2k.10 Type **398** 60 65
1359 2k.10 Reino riding one-wheel cycle on wire . . . 60 65
1360 2k.10 Acrobat on horseback 60 65

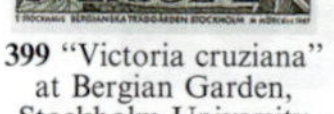

399 "Victoria cruziana" at Bergian Garden, Stockholm University

400 Porridge left for the Grey Christmas Elf

1987. Bicentenary of Swedish Botanical Gardens.

1361 **399** 2k.10 green, deep green and blue 50 25
1362 – 2k.10 green and brown 50 25
1363 – 2k.10 deep green, green and blue 50 25
1364 – 2k.10 yellow, brown and green 50 25

DESIGNS: No. 1362, Uppsala University Baroque Garden plan and Carl Harleman (architect); 1363, Rock garden, Gothenburg Botanical Garden; 1364, "Liriodendron tulipifera", Lund Botanical Garden.

1987. Christmas. Folk Customs. Multicoloured.

1365 2k. Type **400** 45 30
1366 2k. Staffan ride (watering horses in North-running spring on Boxing Day) . . 45 30
1367 2k. Christmas Day sledge race home from church 45 30
1368 2k. Northern bullfinches on corn sheaf 45 30

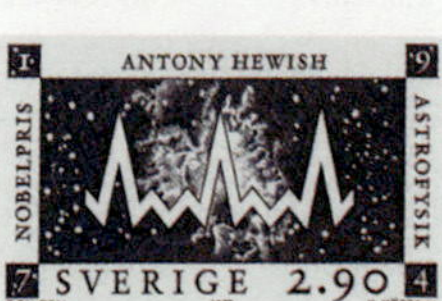

401 Pulsars (Antony Hewish, 1974)

1987. Nobel Prize Winners for Physics.

1369 **401** 2k.90 blue 65 65
1370 – 2k.90 black 65 65
1371 – 2k.90 blue 65 65
1372 – 2k.90 blue 65 65
1373 – 2k.90 black 65 65

DESIGNS: No. 1370, Formula of maximum white dwarf star mass (S. Chandrasekhar, 1983); 1371, Heavy atom nuclei construction (William Fowler, 1983); 1372, Temperature of cosmic background radiation (A. Penzias and R. Wilson, 1978); 1373, Radio telescopes receiving radio waves from galaxy (Martin Ryle, 1974).

402 Lake Hjalmaren Fishing Skiff

404 White-tailed Sea Eagle ("Haliaetus albicilla")

403 Bishop Hill and Erik Jansson (founder)

1988. Inland Boats. Each purple on buff.

1374 3k.10 Type **402** 70 70
1375 3k.10 Lake Vattern market boat 70 70
1376 3k.10 River Byske logging boat 70 70
1377 3k.10 Lake Asnen rowing boat 70 70
1378 3k.10 Lake Vanern ice boat 70 70
1379 3k.10 Lake Lockne church longboat 70 70

1988. 350th Anniv of New Sweden (settlement in America).

1380 – 3k.60 multicoloured . . 85 80
1381 **403** 3k.60 multicoloured . . 85 80
1382 – 3k.60 brown 85 80
1383 – 3k.60 blue and brown . . 85 80
1384 – 3k.60 blue, yellow and red 85 80
1385 – 3k.60 black, blue and red 85 80

DESIGNS—As T **403**: No. 1380, Map, settlers, Indians, "Calmare Nyckel" and "Fagel Grip". 27 × 23 mm: No. 1382, Carl Sandburg (American poet) and Jenny Lind (Swedish soprano); 1383, Charles Lindbergh (aviator) and Ryan NYP Special "Spirit of St. Louis". 27 × 37 mm: No. 1384, Alan Bean (astronaut) on Moon with Hasselblad camera; 1385, Ice hockey.

1988. Coastal Wildlife.

1386 **404** 2k.20 brown and red . . 50 20
1387 – 2k.20 brown and blue . . 50 20
1388 – 4k. black, brown and green . . . . 1·00 25

DESIGNS: No. 1387, Grey seal ("Halichoerus gryphus"); 1388, European eel ("Anguilla anguilla").

405 Daisies and Bluebells

406 Detail of "Creation" Stained Glass Window (Bo Beskow), Skara Cathedral

1988. Rebate stamps. Midsummer Festival. Multicoloured.

1389 2k. Type **405** 85 20
1390 2k. Garlanded longboat . . 85 20
1391 2k. Children making garlands 85 20
1392 2k. Raising the maypole . . 85 20
1393 2k. Fiddlers 85 20
1394 2k. "Norrskar" (tourist launch) 85 20
1395 2k. Couples dancing 85 20
1396 2k. Accordianist 85 20
1397 2k. Archipelago with decorated landing stage 85 20
1398 2k. Bouquet of seven wild flowers 85 20

1988. Anniversaries.

1399 **406** 2k.20 multicoloured . . 55 20
1400 – 4k.40 red on brown . . 1·00 30
1401 – 8k. red, green and black 1·80 70

DESIGNS: 2k.20, Type **406** (millenary of Skara). 23 × 41 mm: 4k.40, "Falun Copper Mine" (Pehr Hillestrom) (700th anniv of Stora Kopparberg (mining company)); 8k. Scene from play "The Queen's Diamond Ornament" (bicentenary of Royal Dramatic Theatre, Stockholm).

407 "Self-portrait" (Nils Dardel)

408 X2 High-speed Train

1968. Swedish Artists in Paris. Multicoloured.
1402 2k.20 Type **407** 50 45
1403 2k.20 "Autumn, Gubbhuset" (Vera Nilsson) (40 × 43 mm) . . 50 45
1404 2k.20 "Self-Portrait" (Isaac Grunewald) 50 45
1405 2k.20 "Visit to an Eccentric Lady" (Nils Dardel) . . . 50 45
1406 2k.20 "Soap Bubbles" (Vera Nilsson) (40 × 43 mm) . . 50 45
1407 2k.20 "The Singing Tree" (Isaac Grunewald) 50 45

1988. Europa. Transport and Communications.
1408 **408** 2k.20 blue, orange and brown . . . . 1·00 20
1409 3k.10 blue, black and purple 75 75
1410 – 3k.10 black and purple 75 75
DESIGN: No. 1410, Narrow-gauge steam locomotive.

409 Common Swift

410 Andersson

1988.
1411 **409** 20k. purple and mauve 4·25 55

1988. Birth Centenary of Dan Andersson (poet). Each violet, green and blue.
1412 2k.20 Type **410** 50 30
1413 2k.20 Lake, Finnmarken (58 × 24 mm) 50 30

411 Players

412 Angel and Shepherds

1988. Swedish Football. Multicoloured.
1414 2k.20 Type **411** 60 70
1415 2k.20 Three players 60 70
1416 2k.20 Women players . . . 60 70

1988. Christmas. Multicoloured.
1417 2k. Type **412** 45 25
1418 2k. Horse and angel 45 25
1419 2k. Birds singing in trees . . 45 25
1420 2k. Three wise men 45 25
1421 2k. Holy Family 45 25
1422 2k. Shepherds and sheep . . 45 25
Nos. 1417/22 were printed together, se-tenant, forming a composite design.

413 Archaeologist, Carbon 14 Dating Graph and Tutankhamun

414 Nidingen 1946 Concrete and 1832 Twin Lighthouses

1988. Nobel Prize Winners for Chemistry. Mult.
1423 3k.10 Type **413** (Willard Frank Libby, 1960) . . . 70 70
1424 3k.10 Plastics molecules (Karl Ziegler and Giulio Natta, 1963) 70 70
1425 3k.10 Electron microscope (Aaron Klug, 1982) . . . 70 70
1426 3k.10 Landscape and symbols (Ilya Prigogine, 1977) 70 70

1989. Lighthouses.
1427 **414** 1k.90 green, brown and black 45 20
1428 – 2k.70 blue, red and deep blue 70 45
1429 – 3k.80 brown, deep blue and blue 90 55
1430 – 3k.90 black, red & brown . . . . 1·00 65
DESIGNS: 2k.70, Soderarm stone lighthouse; 3k.80, Sydostbrotten caisson lighthouse; 3k.90, Sandhammaren iron lighthouse.

415 Wolverine ("Gulo gulo")

1989. Animals in Threatened Habitats.
1431 **415** 2k.30 brown, orange and green 50 20
1432 – 2k.30 brown, green and orange 50 20
1433 – 2k.40 brown, chocolate and red 55 20
1434 – 2k.60 agate, brown and orange 60 50
1435 – 3k.30 deep green, green and brown 70 60
1436 – 4k.60 black, green and orange . . . . 1·00 40
DESIGNS: 2k.30 (1432), Ural owl ("Strix uralensis"); 2k.40, Lesser spotted woodpecker ("Dendrocopos minor"); 2k.60, Dunlin ("Calidris alpina schinzii"); 3k.30, Common tree frog ("Hyla arborea"); 4k.60, Red-breasted flycatcher ("Ficedula parva").

416 Globe Arena

1989. Opening of Globe Arena, Stockholm. Mult.
1437 2k.30 Type **416** 50 25
1438 2k.30 Ice hockey 50 25
1439 2k.30 Gymnastics 50 25
1440 2k.30 Pop concert 50 25

417 Woman's Woollen Bib Front

418 Sailing

1989. Nordic Countries' Postal Co-operation. Traditional Lapp Costumes.
1441 2k.30 Type **417** 60 20
1442 3k.30 Man's belt pouch . . 80 60

1989. Rebate stamps. Summer Activities. Mult.
1443 2k.10 Type **418** 80 25
1444 2k.10 Beach ball 80 25
1445 2k.10 Cycling 80 25
1446 2k.10 Canoeing 80 25
1447 2k.10 Fishing 80 25
1448 2k.10 Camping 80 25
1449 2k.10 Croquet 80 25
1450 2k.10 Badminton 80 25
1451 2k.10 Gardening 80 25
1452 2k.10 Sand castle, bucket and spade 80 25

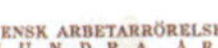

419 "Protest March" (Nils Kreuger)

420 Playing with Boats

1989. Centenary of Swedish Labour Movement.
1453 **419** 2k.30 black and red . . 55 15

1989. Europa. Children's Games and Toys.
1454 **420** 2k.30 brown 90 20
1455 3k.30 mauve 75 75
1456 – 3k.30 green 75 75
DESIGN: No. 1456, Girl riding kick-sled.

421 Lounger (Varnamo)

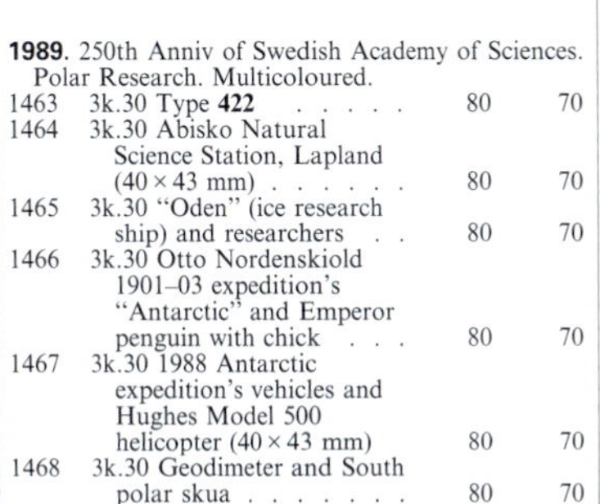

422 Researcher in Greenland and Temperature Curve

1989. Industries of Smaland Towns. Each mauve, orange and red.
1457 2k.30 Type **421** 50 55
1458 2k.30 Tools for self-assembly furniture (Almhult) 50 55
1459 2k.30 Sewing machine and embroidery (Huskvarna) 50 55
1460 2k.30 Blowing glass (Afors) 50 55
1461 2k.30 Coathanger hook and clothes-peg spring (Gnosjo) 50 55
1462 2k.30 Match (Jonkoping) . . 50 55

1989. 250th Anniv of Swedish Academy of Sciences. Polar Research. Multicoloured.
1463 3k.30 Type **422** 80 70
1464 3k.30 Abisko Natural Science Station, Lapland (40 × 43 mm) 80 70
1465 3k.30 "Oden" (ice research ship) and researchers . . 80 70
1466 3k.30 Otto Nordenskiold 1901–03 expedition's "Antarctic" and Emperor penguin with chick . . . 80 70
1467 3k.30 1988 Antarctic expedition's vehicles and Hughes Model 500 helicopter (40 × 43 mm) 80 70
1468 3k.30 Geodimeter and South polar skua 80 70

423 Eagle Owl

1989.
1469 **423** 30k. brown, black & mve 5·75 45

424 Arctic Rhododendron ("Rhododendron lapponicum")

425 Jamthund

1989. National Parks (1st series).
1470 **424** 2k.40 mauve, green & bl 55 25
1471 – 2k.40 mauve and green 55 25
1472 – 4k.30 red, black and blue 1·00 75
DESIGNS—HORIZ: No. 1471, Calypso ("Calypso bulbosa"). VERT: No. 1472, Black guillemots at Bla Jungfrun.
See also Nos. 1486/90.

1989. Centenary of Swedish Kennel Club. Mult.
1473 2k.40 Type **425** 75 85
1474 2k.40 Hamilton foxhound 75 85
1475 2k.40 Vastgota sheep dog 75 85

426 Decorated Tree

427 Vinegar Flies (T. H. Morgan, 1933)

1989. Christmas. Multicoloured.
1476 2k.10 Type **426** 55 25
1477 2k.10 Candelabra and food 55 25
1478 2k.10 Star, poinsettia and tureen 55 25
1479 2k.10 Decorated tree and straw goat 55 25
1480 2k.10 Girl watching television 55 25
1481 2k.10 Family with present 55 25
Nos. 1476/81 were issued together, se-tenant, forming a composite design.

1989. Nobel Prize Winners for Medicine.
1482 **427** 3k.60 brown, yellow & bl 80 80
1483 – 3k.60 yellow, blue & red 80 80
1484 – 3k.60 multicoloured . . 80 80
1485 – 3k.60 multicoloured . . 80 80
DESIGNS: No. 1483 X-ray diffractogram and D.N.A. molecule (Francis Crick, James Watson and Maurice Wilkins, 1962); 1484, D.N.A. molecule cut by restriction enzyme (W. Arber, D. Nathans and H. O. Smith, 1978); 1485, Maize kernels (Barbara McClintock, 1983).

428 Angso

429 Lumberjack

1990. National Parks (2nd series).
1486 **428** 2k.50 blue, green and red 55 20
1487 – 2k.50 red, green and blue 55 20
1488 – 3k.70 blue, brown & grn 85 25
1489 – 4k.10 blue, green & brn 95 80
1490 – 4k.80 green, brown & bl 1·20 90
DESIGNS: No. 1487, Pieljekaise; 1488, Muddus; 1489, Padjelanta; 1490, Sanfjallet.

1990. Centenary of Industrial Safety Inspectorate.
1491 **429** 2k.50 blue and brown . . 65 20

430 Postal Museum, Stockholm

431 Carved Bone Head and Cast Dragon Head

1990. Europa. Post Office Buildings.
1492 **430** 2k.50 brown, orange & bl 85 25
1493 – 3k.80 blue, yellow and brown 85 85
1494 – 3k.80 brown, blue and yellow 85 85
DESIGNS: No. 1493, Sollebrunn Post Office; 1494, Vasteras Post Office.

1990. Vikings. Multicoloured.
1495 2k.50 Type **431** 55 55
1496 2k.50 Returning Viking longships (34 × 29 mm) . . 55 55
1497 2k.50 Wooden houses (34 × 29 mm) 55 55
1498 2k.50 Bronze figurine of God of Fertility and silver cross 55 55
1499 2k.50 Crosier and gold embroidered deer 55 55
1500 2k.50 Vikings in roundship (34 × 29 mm) 55 55
1501 2k.50 Viking disembarking (34 × 29 mm) 55 55
1502 2k.50 Viking swords 55 55
Nos. 1496/7 and 1500/1 form a composite design.

432 Worker collecting Pollen

433 Prow of "Wasa" and Museum

1990. Rebate stamps. Honey Bees. Multicoloured.
1503 2k.30 Type **432** 90 25
1504 2k.30 Worker on bilberry 90 25
1505 2k.30 Worker flying back to hive 90 25
1506 2k.30 Beehive 90 25
1507 2k.30 Bees building honeycombs 90 25
1508 2k.30 Drone 90 25
1509 2k.30 Queen 90 25
1510 2k.30 Swarm on branch . . 90 25
1511 2k.30 Beekeeper collecting frame 90 25
1512 2k.30 Pot of honey 90 25

1990. Opening of New "Wasa" (17th-century ship of the line) Museum.
1513 **433** 2k.50 black and red . . 75 20
1514 – 4k.60 blue and red . . 1·10 70
DESIGNS: 4k.60, Stern of "Wasa" and museum.

434 Endurance Event

1990. World Equestrian Games, Stockholm. Mult.
1515 3k.80 Type **434** 90 85
1516 3k.80 Mark Todd on Carisma jumping wall (3-day event) 90 85
1517 3k.80 John Whitaker on Next Milton jumping fence (show jumping) . . 90 85
1518 3k.80 Louise Nathorst (dressage) 90 85
1519 3k.80 Team vaulting 90 85
1520 3k.80 Pahlsson brothers driving four-in-hand . . . 90 85

435 Papermaking, 1600 **436** "Dearest Brothers, Sisters and Friends"

1990. Centenary of Swedish Pulp and Paper Industry. Multicoloured.
1521 2k.50 Type **435** 55 40
1522 2k.50 Crown watermark . . 55 40
1523 2k.50 Foreign newspapers using Swedish newsprint 55 40
1524 2k.50 Rolls of paper 55 40

1990. 250th Birth Anniv of Carl Michael Bellman (poet) (1525/7) and Birth Centenary of Evert Taube (poet) (1528/30). Designs showing illustrations of their poems.
1525 **436** 2k.50 brown and black 60 55
1526 – 2k.50 multicoloured . . 60 55
1527 – 2k.50 black, blue and red 60 55
1528 – 2k.50 multicoloured . . 60 55
1529 – 2k.50 multicoloured . . 60 55
1530 – 2k.50 multicoloured . . 60 55
DESIGNS—As Type **436**: No. 1527, "Fredman in the Gutter"; 1528, "Happy Baker of San Remo"; 1530, "Violava". 40 × 43 mm: 1526, "Proud City"; 1529, "At Sea".

437 Oved Castle

1990.
1531 **437** 40k. brown, black and red . . . . 7·50 30

438 Moa Martinson **439** Box Camera with Bellows

1990. Birth Centenary of Moa Martinson (novelist).
1532 **438** 2k.50 black and red . . 60 25
1533 – 2k.50 black and violet 60 25
DESIGN: No. 1533, Fredrika and Sofi bathing (from "Women and Apple Trees").

1990. Photography. Multicoloured.
1534 2k.50 Type **439** 70 75
1535 2k.50 August Strindberg (self-photograph) 70 75
1536 2k.50 Modern 35 mm camera 70 75

440 Cumulus Clouds **441** Christmas Cactus ("Schlumbergera x buckleyi")

1990. Clouds.
1537 **440** 4k.50 multicoloured . . 1·10 25
1538 – 4k.70 black and blue . . 1·20 85
1539 – 4k.90 blue, green & brn 1·20 90
1540 – 5k.20 blue & ultramarine 1·30 80
DESIGNS: 4k.70, Cumulonimbus; 4k.90, Cirus uncinus; 5k.20, Altocumulus lenticularis.

1990. Christmas. Flowers. Multicoloured.
1541 2k.30 Type **441** 60 30
1542 2k.30 Christmas rose ("Helleborus niger") . . . 60 30
1543 2k.30 Azalea ("Rhododenron simsii") 60 30
1544 2k.30 Amaryllis ("Hippeastrum × hortorum") 60 30
1545 2k.30 Hyacinth ("Hyacinthus orientalis") 60 30
1546 2k.30 Poinsettia ("Euphorbia pulcherrima") 60 30

442 Par Lagerkvist (1951)

1990. Nobel Prize Winners for Literature.
1547 **442** 3k.80 blue 85 85
1548 – 3k.80 red 85 85
1549 – 3k.80 green 85 80
1550 – 3k.80 violet 85 80
DESIGNS: No. 1548, Ernest Hemingway (1954); 1549, Albert Camus (1957); 1550, Boris Pasternak (1958).

443 Heath of Wels ("Silurus glanis") and Young **444** "Carta Marina", 1572 (Olaus Magnus)

1991. Freshwater Fishes.
1551 **443** 2k.50 black, green & brn 60 20
1552 – 2k.50 black, green & brn 60 20
1553 – 5k. black, blue and brown . . . . 1·10 25
1554 – 5k.40 black, violet & red 1·30 90
1555 – 5k.50 brown and green 1·30 35
1556 – 5k.60 black, blue & orge 1·40 85
DESIGNS: No. 1552, Wels (different); 1553, Spined loach ("Cobitis taeina"); 1554, Gudgeon ("Gobio gobio"); 1555, Stone loach ("Noemacheilus barbataulus"); 1556, Sunbleak ("Leucaspius delineatus").
Nos. 1551/2 form a composite design of two catfish.

1991. Maps. Multicoloured.
1557 5k. Type **444** . . . . . . 1·10 1·10
1558 5k. Sweden, Denmark and Norway, 1662 (A. Bureus and J. Blaeu) (40 × 43 mm) . . . . . . 1·10 1·10
1559 5k. Star globe, 1759 (Anders Akerman) . . . . 1·10 1·10
1560 5k. Relief map of Areskutan, 1938 . . . . 1·10 1·10
1561 5k. Stockholm old town, 1989 (40 × 43 mm) . . . . 1·10 1·10
1562 5k. Bed-rock map of Areskutan, 1984 . . . . 1·10 1·10

445 Queen Silvia **447** Seglora Church

446 Drottningholm Palace (after Erik Dahlbergh)

1991.
1564 – 2k.80 blue 75 20
1565 – 2k.90 green 70 20
1566 – 3k.20 violet 80 20
1568 **445** 5k. purple . . . . 1·20 30
1569 6k. red . . . . 1·30 20
1570 6k.50 violet . . . . 1·60 55
DESIGN: 2k.80 to 3k.20, King Carl XVI Gustav.

1991. Royal Residence at Drottningholm Palace.
1576 **446** 25k. brown, black & grn 5·00 65

1991. Rebate stamps. Centenary of Skansen Park, Stockholm. Multicoloured.
1577 2k.40 Type **447** 65 25
1578 2k.40 Celebration of Swedish Flag and National Days at Skansen 65 25
1579 2k.40 Wedding at Skansen 65 25
1580 2k.40 Animals, Skansen Zoo 65 25

448 Park Entrance **449** Polar Bears

1991. Centenary of Public Amusement Parks. Each blue.
1581 2k.50 Type **448** 60 30
1582 2k.50 Dancers and violinist 60 30

1991. Nordic Countries' Postal Co-operation. Tourism. Animals in Kolmarden Zoo.
1583 **449** 2k.50 black, brown & bl 65 25
1584 – 4k. red and purple . . . 90 60
DESIGN: 4k. Dolphins and trainer.

450 "Hermes" Rocket

1991. Europa. Europe in Space. Multicoloured.
1585 4k. Type **450** . . . . . . 1·00 85
1586 4k. "Freja" Northern Lights research satellite . . . . 1·00 85
1587 4k. "Tele-X" television satellite . . . . 1·00 85

451 Magda Julin (figure skating, Antwerp, 1920)

1991. Olympic Games Gold Medallists (1st issue). Multicoloured.
1588 2k.50 Type **451** 55 40
1589 2k.50 Toini Gustafsson (cross-country skiing, Grenoble, 1968) 55 40
1590 2k.50 Agneta Andersson and Anna Olsson (canoeing, Los Angeles, 1984) 55 40
1591 2k.50 Ulrika Knape (high diving, Munich, 1972) . . 55 40
See also Nos. 1619/22 and 1635/8.

452 Spetal Mine, Norberg (after Carl David af Uhr)

1991. Bergslagen Iron Industry. Multicoloured.
1592 2k.50 Type **452** 65 45
1593 2k.50 Walloon smithy, Forsmark Mill (after J. Wilhem Wallender) . . 65 45
1594 2k.50 Forge (27 × 24 mm) . . 65 45
1595 2k.50 Foundry (after Johann Ahlback) (27 × 24 mm) . . 65 45
1596 2k.50 Dannemora Mine (after Elias Martin) (27 × 37 mm) 65 45
1597 2k.50 Pershyttan Mill (27 × 37 mm) 65 45

453 Stromsholm Castle

1991.
1598 **453** 10k. green and black . . 1·90 25

454 Lena Philipsson **455** Close-up of Gustav III

1991. Rock and Pop Music. Multicoloured.
1599 2k.50 Type **454** 55 50
1600 2k.50 Roxette (duo) 55 50
1601 2k.50 Jerry Williams 55 50

1991. 70th Birthday of Czeslaw Slania (engraver). Designs showing "Coronation of King Gustav III" by Carl Gustav Pilo.
1602 **455** 10k. blue . . . . 2·20 1·30
1603 – 10k. violet . . . . . . 2·20 1·30
1604 – 10k. black . . . . 2·20 1·30
DESIGNS—As T **455**: No. 1603, Close-up of lowering of crown onto King's head. 76 x 44mm: 1604, Complete picture.

456 "Mans and Mari from Spring to Winter" (Kaj Beckman)

1991. Christmas. Illustrations from children's books. Multicoloured.
1605 2k.30 Type **456** 50 30
1606 2k.30 Family dancing round Christmas tree ("Peter and Lottas's Christmas", Elsa Beskow) 50 30
1607 2k.30 Dressed cat by Christmas tree ("Pettersson gets a Christmas Visit", Sven Nordqvist) 50 30
1608 2k.30 Girl by bed ("Little Anna's Christmas Present", Lasse Sandberg) 50 30

457 Henri Dunant (founder of Red Cross), 1901

1991. Nobel Prize Winners for Peace.
1609 **457** 4k. red 90 70
1610 – 4k. green 90 95
1611 – 4k. blue 90 70
1612 – 4k. lilac 90 70
DESIGNS: No. 1610, Albert Schweitzer (medical missionary), 1953; 1611, Alva Myrdal (disarmament negotiator), 1982; 1612, Andrei Sakharov (human rights activist), 1975.

458 Mulle, the Forest Elf, with Children **459** Roe Buck

1992. Centenary of Outdoor Life Association.
1613 **458** 2k.30 brown, red & grn 55 20

1992. Wildlife.
1614 **459** 2k.80 brown, agate & grn 70 20
1615 – 2k.80 agate, brn & grn 70 20
1617 – 6k. brown and agate . . 1·40 50
1618 – 7k. brown and green . . 1·60 50
DESIGNS—As T **459**: No. 1615, Roe deer ("Capreolus capreolus") with fawn. 20 × 28 mm: No. 1617, Eurasian red squirrel ("Sciurus vulgaris"); 1618, Elk ("Alces alces").

1992. Olympic Games Gold medallists (2nd issue). As T **451**. Multicoloured.
1619 2k.80 Gunde Svan (cross-country skiing, Sarajevo, 1984, and Calgary, 1988) 65 45
1620 2k.80 Thomas Wassberg (cross-country skiing, Lake Placid, 1980, and Sarajevo, 1984) 65 35
1621 2k.80 Tomas Gustafson (speed skating, Sarajevo, 1984, and Calgary, 1988) 65 35
1622 2k.80 Ingemar Stenmark (slalom, Lake Placid, 1980) 65 35

460 Gunnar Nordahl (Sweden)

461 1855 3s. Green

1992. European Football Championship, Sweden. Each blue and green.
1623 2k.80 Type **460** 70 20
1624 2k.80 Lothar Matthaus (Germany) and Tomas Brolin (Sweden) 70 20

1992. Stamp Year.
1625 **461** 2k.80 green, yellow & blk . . . . 1·10 1·60
1626 4k.50 green, yellow & blk . . . . 1·10 1·60
1627 – 5k.50 yellow, grey & blk 1·10 1·10
DESIGN: 5k.50, 1857 3s. yellow error.

462 "Sprengtporten" (frigate), 1785

463 Rabbit (Emma Westerberg)

1992. Europa. 500th Anniv of Discovery of America by Columbus. Multicoloured.
1628 4k.50 Type **462** . . . . . 1·10 1·10
1629 4k.50 "Superb" (brig), 1855 1·10 1·10
1630 4k.50 "Big T" (yacht) (competitor in Discovery Race) . . . . 1·10 1·10

1992. Rebate stamps. Centenary of "Kamratposten" (children's magazine) showing children's drawings. Multicoloured.
1631 2k.50 Type **463** 55 25
1632 2k.50 Horses (Helena Johansson) 55 25
1633 2k.50 Kitten (Sabina Ostermark) 55 25
1634 2k.50 Elephant (Hanna Bengtsson) 55 25

1992. Olympic Games Gold Medallists (3rd series). As T **451**. Multicoloured.
1635 5k.50 Gunnar Larsson (swimming, Munich, 1972) 1·30 1·00
1636 5k.50 Bernt Johansson (cycling, Montreal, 1976) 1·30 1·00
1637 5k.50 Anders Garderud (steeplechase, Montreal, 1976) . . . . 1·30 1·10
1638 5k.50 Gert Fredriksson (canoeing, London, 1948) 1·30 1·10

464 Karlberg Castle

1992.
1639 **464** 20k. black, green and blue . . . . 4·00 35

465 Hand holding Flower

466 Gustaf Dalen's Sun Valve and First Automated Lighthouse, Gasfeten

1992. Greetings Stamps. Multicoloured.
1640 2k.80 Type **465** 65 30
1641 2k.80 Wedge of cheese ("Lyckans ost") 65 30
1642 2k.80 New-born baby ("Lev val!") 65 30
1643 2k.80 Writing with feather ("Gratulerar") 65 30

1992. Centenary of Patent and Registration Office.
1644 **466** 2k.80 black and blue . . 65 20

467 Riksdag (Parliament), Helgeandsholmen Island

1992. 88th Interparliamentary Union Conference, Stockholm.
1645 **467** 2k.80 violet on buff . . 70 20

468 "Kitchen Maid" (Rembrandt)

469 Plateosaurus

1992. Bicentenary of National Museum of Fine Arts. Multicoloured.
1646 5k.50 Type **468** . . . . . 1·20 1·10
1647 5k.50 "Triumph of Venus" (Francois Boucher) (40 × 44 mm) . . . . . 1·20 1·10
1648 5k.50 "Portrait of a Girl" (Albrecht Durer) . . . . 1·20 1·10
1649 5k.50 Rorstrand vase decorated by Erik Wahlberg . . . . 1·20 1·10
1650 5k.50 "Seine Motif" (Carl Fredrik Hill) (40 × 44 mm) 1·20 1·10
1651 5k.50 "Sergel in his Studio" (Carl Larsson) . . . . . 1·20 1·10

1992. Prehistoric Animals. Mult.
1652 2k.80 Type **469** 75 70
1653 2k.80 Crocodile ("Thoracosaurus scanicus") 75 70
1654 2k.80 Woolly-haired rhino ("Coelodonta antiquitatis") 75 70
1655 2k.80 Mammoth ("Mammuthus primigenius") 75 70

470 Volvo "PV831", 1950

471 Osprey ("Pandion haliaetus")

1992. Swedish Cars.
1656 **470** 4k. blue 90 45
1657 – 4k. green and blue . . . 90 45
DESIGN: No. 1657 Saab "92", 1950.

1992. Birds of the Baltic.
1658 **471** 4k.50 black and blue . . 1·00 85
1659 – 4k.50 brown, black & bl 1·00 85
1660 – 4k.50 deep brown, brown and blue . . . 1·00 95
1661 – 4k.50 black, brown & bl 1·00 85
DESIGNS: No. 1659, Black-tailed godwit ("Limosa limosa"); 1660, Goosander ("Mergus merganser"); 1661, Common shelducks ("Tadorna tadorna").

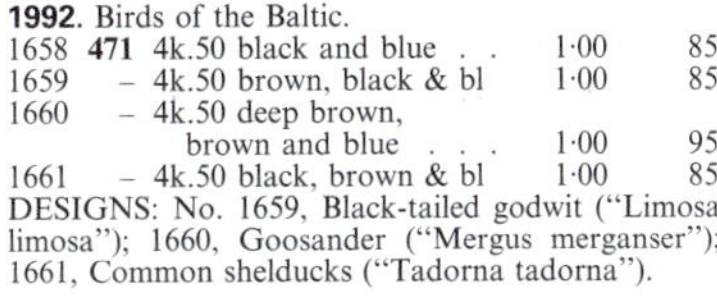

472 "Meeting of Joachim and Anna"

473 Walcott

1992. Christmas. Icons. Multicoloured.
1662 2k.30 Type **472** 50 30
1663 2k.30 "Madonna and Child" 50 30
1664 2k.30 "Archangel Gabriel" (head) 50 30
1665 2k.30 "Saint Nicholas" (½-length portrait) 50 30

1992. Award of Nobel Literature Prize to Derek Walcott.
1666 **473** 5k.50 purple, blue & brn 1·20 80
1667 – 5k.50 purple, brown & bl 1·20 80
DESIGN: No. 1667, Palm trees, ocean and text.

474 Brown Bear Cubs

1993. Wildlife.
1668 **474** 2k.90 brown and black 75 20
1669 – 2k.90 brown and black 75 20
1671 – 3k. multicoloured . . . 50 45
1672 – 5k.80 black, grey & brn 1·40 35
1673 – 12k. brown, blue and red 2·50 1·00
DESIGNS—As T **474**: No. 1669, Brown bear. 27 × 21 mm: No. 1671, Polecat; 1672, Wolf. 21 × 27 mm: No. 1673, Lynx.

475 "Big Bird" Glider (World Gliding Championships, Borlange)

476 Gooseberries ("Ribes uva-crispa")

1993. Int Sports Championships in Sweden. Mult.
1674 6k. Type **475** . . . . . . 1·30 1·20
1675 6k. Martin Kornbakk (World Wrestling Championships, Stockholm) . . . . . . 1·30 1·20
1676 6k. Jorgen Persson (World Table Tennis Championships, Gothenburg) . . . . . . 1·30 1·20
1677 6k. Lars Erik Andersson (European Bowling Championships, Malmo) 1·30 1·20
1678 6k. Per Carlen (World Handball Championships, Gothenburg) . . . . . . 1·30 1·20
1679 6k. Marie Helene Westin (World Cross-country Skiing Championships, Falun) . . . . 1·30 1·20
Nos. 1675/9 show Swedish competitors.

1993. Fruits.
1680 **476** 2k.40 green 55 20
1681 – 2k.40 green 55 25
1682 – 2k.40 red 55 25
DESIGNS: No. 1681, Pears ("Pryus communis"); 1682, Cherries ("Prunus avium").

477 The Creation (relief, Uppsala Cathedral)

478 "Poseidon" (Carl Milles)

1993. 400th Anniv of Uppsala Convocation.
1683 **477** 2k.90 violet and buff . . 65 40
1684 – 2k.90 red and buff . . 65 40
DESIGN: No. 1684, Uppsala Cathedral before fire of 1702.

1993. Nordic Countries' Postal Co-operation. Tourism. Tourist Attractions in Gothenburg.
1685 **478** 3k.50 green, yellow & bl 85 45
1686 – 3k.50 indigo, yellow and blue 85 45
DESIGN: No. 1686, Liseberg Loop (fairground ride).

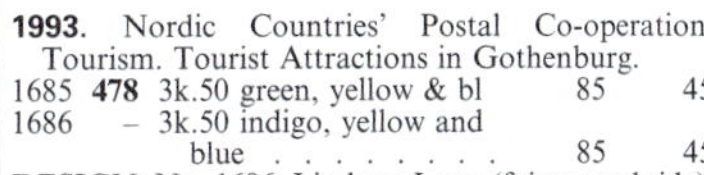

479 Ox-eye Daisies

480 "Oguasark" (Olle Baertling)

1993. Rebate stamps. Flowers. Multicoloured.
1687 2k.60 Type **479** 65 20
1688 2k.60 Poppies 65 20
1689 2k.60 Buttercups 65 20
1690 2k.60 Harebells 65 45

1993. Europa. Contemporary Art. Multicoloured.
1691 5k. Type **480** . . . . . . 1·20 95
1692 5k. "Ade-Ledic-Nander II" (Oyvind Fahlstrom) (horiz) . . . . 1·20 90
1693 5k. "The Cubist Chair" (Otto Carlsund) . . . . . 1·20 95

481 Swallowtail ("Papilio machaon")

1993. Butterflies. Multicoloured.
1694 6k. Type **481** . . . . . . 1·40 1·00
1695 6k. Camberwell beauty ("Nymphalis antiopa") . . 1·40 1·00
1696 6k. Moorland clouded yellow ("Colias palaeno") 1·40 1·00
1697 6k. Scarce fritillary ("Euphydryas maturna") 1·40 1·00

482 Fireworks ("Hurray")

1993. Greetings Stamps. Multicoloured.
1698 2k.90 Type **482** 70 25
1699 2k.90 "Hor av Dig" ("Get in touch") 70 30
1700 2k.90 "Tycker om Dig" ("I like you") 70 25
1701 2k.90 "Lycka Till" ("Good luck") 70 30

483 Red-breasted Merganser ("Mergus serrator")

1993. Sea Birds. Multicoloured.
1702 5k. Type **483** . . . . . . 1·10 85
1703 5k. Velvet scoter ("Melanitta fusca") . . . . 1·10 85
1704 5k. Tufted duck ("Aythya fuligula") . . . . 1·10 85
1705 5k. Eider ("Somateria mollissima") . . . . . . 1·10 95

484 Surveyor, 1643 (cover of Johan Mansson's nautical book)

485 King Carl Gustav

1993. 350th Anniv of Hydrographic Service.
1706 **484** 2k.90 brown, blue & blk 70 25
1707 – 2k.90 brown, blue & blk 70 25
DESIGN: No. 1707, Survey ship "Nils Stromcrona", 1993.

1993. 20th Anniv of Accession of King Carl XVI Gustav and Queen Silvia's 50th Birthday.
1708 8k. Type **485** . . . . . . 1·40 1·50
1709 10k. King Carl Gustav wearing medals . . . . . 2·50 1·90

1710 10k. Queen Silvia . . . . . 2·50 1·90
1711 12k. Family group and Stockholm and Drottningholm Palaces (75 × 44 mm) . . . . . . 3·00 2·50

486 Plaited Heart **487** Stockholm City Hall

1993. Christmas.
1712 **486** 2k.40 green 55 20
1713 – 2k.40 red 55 20
DESIGN: No. 1713, Straw goat.

1993. Award of Nobel Literature Prize to Toni Morrison.
1714 **487** 6k. red and blue . . . . 1·30 90
1715 – 6k. brown and red . . . . 1·30 90
DESIGN: No. 1715, Toni Morrison.

488 Victoria Plums **489** North Sweden Horse's Head

1994. Fruits.
1716 **488** 2k.80 multicoloured . . 70 20
1717 – 2k.80 multicoloured . . 70 30
1718 – 2k.80 light green & green 70 30
DESIGNS: No. 1717, Opal plums; 1718, "James Grieve" apples.

1994. Domestic Animals (1st series).
1719 **489** 3k.20 brown, agate and red 75 20
1720 – 3k.20 brown, agate and red 75 20
1721 – 3k.20 black, brown & bl 80 20
1722 – 6k.40 black and green 1·50 40
DESIGNS—VERT: No. 1720, North Sweden horses in harness. HORIZ: 1721, Gotland sheep; 1722, Mountain cow.
See also Nos. 1787/91 and 1802/3.

490 Mother Svea and European Union Emblem **491** Siamese

1994. Single European Market.
1723 **490** 5k. blue . . . . 1·20 35

1994. Cats. Multicoloured.
1724 4k.50 Type **491** . . . . . 1·00 80
1725 4k.50 Persian . . . . . . 1·00 80
1726 4k.50 European . . . . . . 1·00 85
1727 4k.50 Abyssinian . . . . . 1·00 75

492 Illustration from "Le Roman de la Rose"

1994. Franco-Swedish Cultural Relations. Multicoloured.
1728 5k. Type **492** . . . . . . 1·10 95
1729 5k. Swedish and French flags . . . . 1·10 1·10
1730 5k. Sketch by De la Vallee of Knight's House (40 × 43 mm) . . . . . . 1·10 1·10
1731 5k. "Household Chores" (Pehr Hillestrom) . . . . 1·10 1·10
1732 5k. "Banquet for Gustav III at the Trianon, 1784" (Niclas Lafrensen the younger) (40 × 43 mm) . . 1·10 1·10
1733 5k. "Carl XIV Johan" (Francois Gerard) . . . . 1·10 1·10

493 Martin Dahlin during Match

1994. World Cup Football Championship, U.S.A.
1734 **493** 3k.20 blue and red . . . 80 35

494 Wild Rose ("Rosa dumalis") **495** Lunar Module "Eagle" and Astronauts

1994. Roses. Multicoloured.
1735 3k.20 Type **494** 95 20
1736 3k.20 "Rosa alba maxima" 95 20
1737 3k.20 "Tuscany Superb" . . 95 20
1738 3k.20 "Peace" 95 20
1739 3k.20 "Four Seasons" . . . 95 20

1994. 25th Anniv of First Manned Moon Landing.
1740 **495** 6k.50 orange, black & bl 1·50 1·00

496 Iris Vase (Gunnar Wennerberg), 1897 **497** Cat ("Love and Kisses")

1994. 150th Annivs of Stockholm College of Arts, Crafts and Design and of Swedish Society of Crafts and Design. Multicoloured.
1741 6k.50 Type **496** . . . . . 1·50 1·30
1742 6k.50 Wallpaper (Uno Ahren) and Chair (Carl Malmsten), 1917 . . . . 1·50 1·30
1743 6k.50 Aralia cloth, 1920, and cabinet, 1940 (Josef Frank) . . . . 1·50 1·30
1744 6k.50 Crystal bowl engraved with fireworks design (Edward Hald), 1921 . . 1·50 1·30
1745 6k.50 Silver water jug, 1941, and sketch of coffee pot, 1970s (Wiwen Nilsson) . . 1·50 1·30
1746 6k.50 Linen towel (Astrid Sampe), plate (Stig Lindberg) and cutlery (Sigurd Persson), 1955 . . 1·50 1·30

1994. Greetings Stamps. Multicoloured.
1747 3k.20 Type **497** 75 20
1748 3k.20 Snail ("You've got time") 75 20
1749 3k.20 Frog ("You're lovely just as you are") . . . 75 25
1750 3k.20 Dog ("Hi there!") . . 75 25

498 Musicians (sketch, Johan Silvius) and Opening Bars of "Drottningholm Music" **499** Sepo Raty (javelin)

1994. 300th Birth Anniv of Johan Helmich Roman (composer) (1751) and Inauguration of Gothenburg Opera House (1752).
1751 **498** 3k.20 brown and blue . . 80 25
1752 – 3k.20 multicoloured . . 80 20
DESIGN: No. 1752, Opera House (designed Jan Izikowitz) and opening bars of opera "Aniara" by Karl Birger (inaugural programme).

1994. Sweden-Finland Athletics Meeting, Stockholm. Multicoloured.
1753 4k.50 Type **499** . . . . . 1·00 90
1754 4k.50 Patrik Sjoberg (high jump) . . . . 1·00 90

500 Erland Nordenskiold (South America) **501** Caspian Tern ("Sterna caspia")

1994. Europa. Swedish Explorers. Multicoloured.
1755 5k.50 Type **500** . . . . . . 1·20 1·20
1756 5k.50 Eric von Rosen (Africa) . . . . 1·20 1·20
1757 5k.50 Sten Bergman (Asia and Australasia) . . . . 1·20 1·20

1994. Endangered Birds. Multicoloured.
1758 5k.50 Type **501** . . . . . . 1·30 1·10
1759 5k.50 White-tailed sea eagle ("Haliaeetus albicilla") . . 1·30 1·10
1760 5k.50 White-backed woodpecker ("Dendrocopos leucotos") 1·30 1·10
1761 5k.50 Lesser white-fronted goose ("Anser erythropus") . . . . . . 1·30 1·10

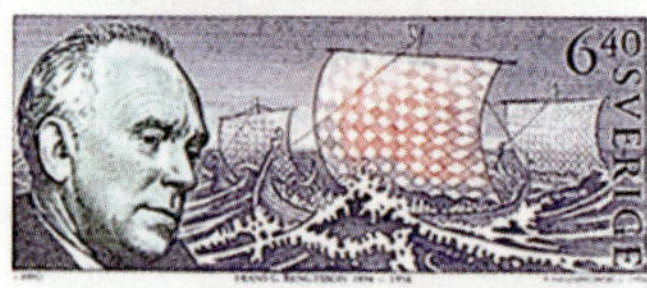

502 Bengtsson and Illustration from "The Longships" (novel)

1994. Birth Centenary of Frans Bengtsson (writer).
1762 **502** 6k.40 violet, red and black . . . . 1·50 70

503 "Ja" ("Yes") **504** "The Annunciation"

1994. European Union Membership Referendum (1st issue). Multicoloured.
1763 3k.20 Type **503** 80 25
1764 3k.20 "Nej" ("No") 80 25
See also Nos. 1785/6.

1994. Christmas. Details from Askeby altarpiece. Multicoloured.
1765 2k.80 Type **504** 65 20
1766 2k.80 "Flight into Egypt" 65 20

505 Erik Axel Karlfeldt (1931) **506** King Carl XVI Gustav

1994. Swedish Winners of the Nobel Literature Prize.
1767 **505** 4k.50 brown, dp bl & bl 1·00 70
1768 – 5k.50 deep brn, bl & brn 1·30 90
1769 – 6k.50 brn, dp grn & grn 1·50 1·20
DESIGNS: 5k.50, Eyvind Johnson (1974); 6k.50, Harry Martinsson (1974).

1995.
1772 **506** 3k.70 red 90 25
1773 3k.85 black . . . . . . 1·00 25
1775 – 6k. green . . . . . . 1·30 65
1776 – 7k.50 purple . . . . . 1·70 85
1777 – 8k. red . . . . 1·70 80
DESIGN: 6k., 7k.50, 8k. Queen Silvia.

1995. European Union Membership Referendum (2nd issue). Designs as Nos. 1763/4 but colours and values changed. Multicoloured.
1785 3k.70 Type **503** 85 25
1786 3k.70 "Nej" ("No") 85 25

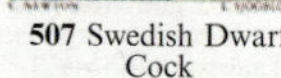

507 Swedish Dwarf Cock **508** Strawberries

1995. Domestic Animals (2nd series).
1787 **507** 3k.10 brown, chocolate and red 80 35
1788 – 3k.70 chestnut, brown and red 85 20
1789 – 3k.70 chestnut, brown and red 85 20
DESIGNS—VERT: No. 1788, Red poll cow; 1789, Goat.

1995. Berries.
1790 **508** 3k.35 red, green and black on cream . . . 1·30 25
1791 – 3k.35 black, green and purple on cream . . . 75 30
1792 – 3k.35 red, green and black on cream . . . 75 30
DESIGNS: No. 1791, Blackberries; 1792, Raspberries.

509 Cottage with Allotment, Sodermanland

1995. Traditional Buildings (1st series). Rural Houses. Multicoloured.
1793 3k.70 Type **509** 75 25
1794 3k.70 Soldier's smallholding, Skanegard 75 25
1795 3k.70 17th-century farmhouse, Scania 75 25
1796 3k.70 19th-century farmhouse, Jamtland . . 75 25
1797 3k.70 18th-century manor house, Dalarna 75 25
See also Nos. 1856/64, 1905/10 and 1961/5.

510 Jesus, Walt Whitman and Socrates **511** Scanian Geese

1995. Europa. Peace and Freedom. "Love, Peace and Labour" (wooden relief, Bror Hjorth). Multicoloured.
1798 5k. Type **510** . . . . . . 1·20 1·00
1799 5k. Lumumba, Albert Schweitzer and people of different races . . . . . 1·20 1·00
1800 6k. Type **510** . . . . . . 1·30 1·20
1801 6k. As No. 1799 . . . . . 1·30 1·20

1995. Domestic Animals.
1802 **511** 7k.40 deep brown, brown and green . . . 1·70 50
1803 – 7k.50 brown, green and blue . . . . 1·80 90
DESIGN: 7k.50, Swedish yellow duck.

512 Members' Flags forming "EU"

1995. Admission of Sweden to European Union.
1804 **512** 6k. multicoloured . . . 1·40 65

513 Ice Hockey

1995. World Ice Hockey Championship, Stockholm and Gavle (1805) and World Athletics Championships, Gothenburg (1806). Mult.
1805 3k.70 Type **513** . . . . 1·00 25
1806 3k.70 Erica Johansson (1992 junior long jump champion) (27½ × 28 mm) 90 20

514 Rock Speedwell **515** "Wilhelm Tham" (motor barge) on Gota Canal

1995. Mountain Flowers. Multicoloured.
1807 3k.70 Type **514** 90 20
1808 3k.70 Cloudberry (white flowers) 90 20
1809 3k.70 Mountain heath (pink flowers) and black bearberry 90 20
1810 3k.70 Alpine arnica (yellow flowers) and crowberry 90 20

1995. Nordic Countries' Postal Co-operation. Tourism.
1811 **515** 5k. green 1·10 80
1812 – 5k. violet 1·10 80
DESIGN: No. 1812, Moored yacht, Lake Vattern.

516 English Horse-drawn Tram, Gothenburg

1995. Trams.
1813 **516** 7k.50 red 1·70 1·40
1814 – 7k.50 purple 1·70 1·40
1815 – 7k.50 green 1·70 1·40
1816 – 7k.50 lilac 1·70 1·40
1817 – 7k.50 blue 1·70 1·50
DESIGNS: No. 1814, Electric tram, Norrkoping; 1815, Commuter tram, Helsingborg; 1816, Narrow gauge tram, Kiruna; 1817, Mustang tram, Stockholm.

517 "Non-Violence" (sculpture, Carl Frederik Reutersward) (U.N. Building, New York)

1995. 50th Anniv of U.N.O.
1818 **517** 3k.70 deep blue and blue 1·20 20

518 "The Ball is Yours!" (Mikael Angesjo)

519 Maria Akraka

1995. Greetings Stamps. Winning Entries in Children's Drawing Competition. Multicoloured.
1819 3k.70 Type **518** 90 20
1820 3k.70 Happy man saying "Hello" (Erica Sandstrom) 90 20
1821 3k.70 Teddy bear saying "I miss you" (Linda Nordenhem) 90 20
1822 3k.70 Shy mussel saying "Hello" (Christoffer Stenbom) 90 25

1995. World Athletics Championships, Gothenburg.

1823 **519** 7k.50 multicoloured 1·70 1·10

520 "Soldier Bom" (1948)

1995. Centenary of Motion Pictures. Scenes from Swedish Films. Multicoloured.
1824 6k. Type **520** 1·30 1·10
1825 6k. "Sir Arne's Treasure" (1919) 1·30 1·10
1826 6k. "Wild Strawberries" (1957) 1·30 1·10
1827 6k. "House of Angels" (1992) 1·30 1·10
1828 6k. "One Summer of Happiness" (1951) 1·30 1·10
1829 6k. "The Apple War" (1971) 1·30 1·10

521 Nilsson

522 Bronze Figures (Bronze Age)

1995. Birth Centenary of Fritiof Nilsson (writer).
1830 **521** 3k.70 blue and red 85 20

1995. Ancient Treasures from Museum of National Antiquities, Stockholm. Multicoloured.
1831 3k.70 Type **522** 85 75
1832 3k.70 Gold collar (400–550 A.D.) 85 70
1833 3k.70 Pendant (400–550 A.D.) 85 70
1834 3k.70 Bronze drum (Bronze Age) 85 70

523 Uraniborg Observatory

524 Santa Candlestick, Varmland

1995. 450th Birth Anniv of Tycho Brahe (astronomer). Multicoloured.
1835 5k. Type **523** 1·30 70
1836 6k. Instrument for measuring positions in Space 1·40 90

1995. Christmas. Candlesticks. Multicoloured.
1837 3k.35 Type **524** 85 25
1838 3k.35 Apple candlestick, Smaland 85 30
1839 3k.35 Wrought iron candlestick, Dalarna 85 25
1840 3k.35 Three-armed candlestick, Bergslagen 85 30

525 Nobel and Will

1995. Centenary of Nobel Prize Trust Fund. Multicoloured.
1841 6k. Type **525** 1·50 1·30
1842 6k. Nobel's home in Paris 1·50 1·30
1843 6k. Laboratory, Bjorkborn Manor, Karlskoga 1·50 1·30
1844 6k. Medal and award ceremony for Wilhelm Rontgen, 1901 1·50 1·20

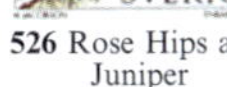
526 Rose Hips and Juniper

527 West European Hedgehog ("Erinaceus europaeus")

1996. Winter Berries. Multicoloured.
1845 3k.50 Type **526** 85 40
1846 3k.50 Cowberries and sloes 85 45
1847 3k.50 Holly 85 45
1848 7k.50 Rowan 1·80 90

1996. Wildlife.
1849 **527** 1k. sepia, brown and green 20 20
1850 – 3k.20 multicoloured 85 35
1851 – 3k.85 multicoloured 90 25
1854 – 3k.85 green, olive and black 90 30
1852 – 7k.70 brown, deep brown and chocolate 1·70 60
DESIGNS—VERT: No. 1850, Eurasian beaver ("Castor fiber"). HORIZ: No. 1851, Stoat ("Mustela erminea"); 1852, Red fox ("Vulpes vulpes"); 1854, European otter ("Lutra lutra").

528 Postal Sorters and Modern Mail Carriage

1996. Discontinuation of Mail Sorting on Train Travelling Post Offices.
1855 **528** 6k. black, blue and red 1·40 95

529 Post Office and Railway Station, Halsingland

1996. Traditional Buildings (2nd series). Business and Commercial Premises. Multicoloured.
1856 3k.85 Type **529** 85 65
1857 3k.85 Motala Assembly Hall, Ostergotland 85 50
1858 3k.85 Parish storehouse, Smaland (27 × 23 mm) 85 50
1859 3k.85 Octagonal log barn, Vasterbotten (27 × 23 mm) 85 50
1860 3k.85 Sheep shelter, Gotland (27 × 36 mm) 85 50
1861 3k.85 Old Town Hall, Lidkoping (27 × 36 mm) 85 50

530 King Carl Gustav opening Tyresta National Park, 1993

531 Karin Kock (politician)

1996. 50th Birthday of King Carl XVI Gustaf. Multicoloured.
1862 10k. Type **530** 2·20 1·70
1863 10k. In Bernadotte Gallery with painting of King Karl XIV Johan 2·20 1·90
1864 10k. With King Albert of Belgium, 1994 2·20 1·70
1865 20k. With royal family, 1995 (76 × 43 mm) 4·25 3·00

1996. Europa. Famous Women.
1866 **531** 6k. brown and red 1·30 1·10
1867 – 6k. blue and red 1·30 1·10
DESIGN: No. 1867, Astrid Lindgren (children's writer).

532 "Summer" (Sven X:et Erixson)

1996. Summer Paintings. Multicoloured.
1868 3k.85 Type **532** 85 30
1869 3k.85 "Summer Evening in Stora Nassa" (Roland Svensson) 85 30
1870 3k.85 "On The Island" (Eric Hallstrom) 85 30
1871 3k.85 "Rallarros" (Thage Nordholm) 85 30
1872 3k.85 "On the Bridge" (Ragnar Sandberg) 85 30

533 Annika Sorenstam

534 Theatre Masks

1996. Golf.
1873 **533** 3k.50 green on cream 85 50

1996. Greetings Stamps.
1874 **534** 3k.85 multicoloured 1·00 35
1875 – 3k.85 blue, yellow and black 1·00 35
1876 – 3k.85 violet, yellow and black 1·00 35
1877 – 3k.85 red, black and pink 1·00 35
DESIGNS: No. 1875, Hearts forming four-leaved clover ("Be Happy!"); 1876, Heart within posthorn; 1877, Girl and hearts ("Do you remember me?").

535 Cep ("Boletus edulis")

536 Grass Slopes, Haga Park

1996. Fungi. Multicoloured.
1878 3k.85 Type **535** 90 20
1879 5k. "Russula integra" 1·10 55
1880 5k. Chanterelle ("Cantherellus cibarius") 1·10 55
1881 5k. Death trumpets ("Craterellus cornucopioides") 1·10 55
1882 5k. Shaggy ink caps ("Coprinus comatus") 1·10 55

1996. The Ecopark, Stockholm. Multicoloured.
1883 7k.50 Type **536** 1·50 1·40
1884 7k.50 Copper tents, Haga Park 1·50 1·40
1885 7k.50 Rosendal Palace 1·50 1·40
1886 7k.50 Herons, Isbladskarret Swamp 1·50 1·40

537 Errand Boy, 1930s

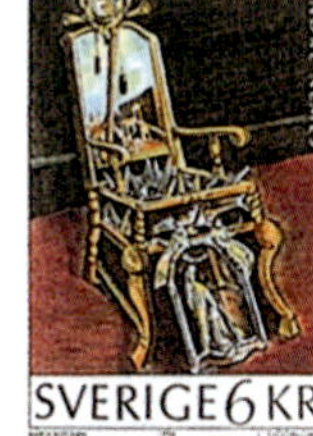

538 "Baroque Chair" (Endre Nemes)

1996. Four Decades of Youth. Multicoloured.
1887 3k.85 Type **537** 95 1·10
1888 3k.85 Hippy, 1960s 95 1·30
1889 3k.85 Zoot-suiter, 1940s 95 1·10
1890 3k.85 Biker, 1950s 95 1·30

1996. Art.
1891 **538** 6k. multicoloured 1·40 95

539 The Annunciation

1996. Christmas. Illustrations from 15th-century Book of Hours. Multicoloured.
1892 3k.50 Type **539** 80 40
1893 3k.50 Nativity 80 35
1894 3k.50 Adoration of the Wise Men 80 40

540 Sune Bergstrom (1982)

1996. Swedish Winners of the Nobel Physiology and Medicine Prize.
1895 **540** 5k. black, blue and green 1·30 80
1896 – 5k. black and green 1·30 80
1897 – 5k. black, blue and green 1·30 80
1898 – 5k. blue, green and black 1·30 80
DESIGNS: No. 1896, Bengt Samuelsson (1982); 1897, Hugo Theorell (1955); 1898, Ragnar Granit (1967).

541 Wolverine ("Gulo gulo")

543 Roses forming Heart

542 Queen Margareta, Coronation Document and Erik of Pommern

1997. Wildlife.
1899 **541** 3k.20 black, green and blue 80 55
1900 – 3k.50 black, green and red 85 50
1901 – 7k.70 black, red and green 1·80 85
DESIGNS—HORIZ: 3k.50, Snowy owl ("Nyctea scandiaca"). VERT: 7k.70, White stork ("Ciconia ciconia").

1997. 600th Anniv of Kalmar Union (of Sweden, Denmark and Norway).
1902 **542** 3k.85 blue 70 40

1997. Greetings Stamps.
1903 **543** 3k.85 multicoloured (red roses) 80 35
1904 3k.85 multicoloured (pink roses) 80 35

544 Dalby Church

1997. Traditional Buildings (3rd series). Churches. Multicoloured.
1905 3k.85 Type **544** 85 60
1906 3k.85 Vendel 85 60
1907 3k.85 Hagby (27 × 23 mm) 85 65
1908 3k.85 Overtornea (27 × 23 mm) 85 65
1909 3k.85 Varnhem (27 × 37 mm) 85 65
1910 3k.85 Ostra Amtervik (27 × 23 mm) 85 65

545 Cockerel

546 King Carl XVI Gustav

1997. Easter. Inscr "INRIKES BREV". Mult.
1911 (5k.) Type **545** . . . . . . 1·10 45
1912 (5k.) Daffodils . . . . . . 1·10 45
Nos. 1911/12 were for use on domestic first class mail.

1997. Inscr "INRIKES BREV".
1913 **546** (5k.) blue 90 25
No. 1913 was for use on domestic first class mail.

547 Arctic Fox ("Alopex lagopus")

548 Siberian Iris ("Iris sibirica")

1997. Wildlife (2nd series). (a) Inscr "EKONOMIBREV".
1914 **547** (4k.50) black, brn & bl 90 45

(b) Inscr "BREV INRIKES" (1915/16) or "INRIKES BREV" (1917).
1915 – (5k.) brown, black & grn 1·20 25
1916 – (5k.) black and blue . . . 1·20 30
1917 – (5k.) black and red . . . . 1·20 30
DESIGNS: No. 1915, Przewalski's horses; 1916, Snow leopard; 1917, Snow leopard cubs.
No. 1914 was for use on domestic second class mail and Nos. 1915/17 on domestic first class mail.

1997. Garden Flowers. Inscr "INRIKES BREV". Multicoloured.
1918 (5k.) Type **548** . . . . . . 1·10 25
1919 (5k.) Honeysuckle ("Lonicera periclymenum") . . . . . 1·10 25
1920 (5k.) Columbine ("Aquilegia vulgaris") . . . . 1·10 25
1921 (5k.) Day lily ("Hemerocallis flava") . . . . 1·10 25
1922 (5k.) Pansy ("Viola wittrockiana") . . . . 1·10 25
Nos. 1918/22 were for use on domestic first class mail.

549 Common Pheasant ("Phasianus colchicus")

1997. Pheasants. Multicoloured
1923 2k. Type **549** 50 25
1924 2k. Lady Amherst's pheasants ("Chrysolophus amherstiae") 50 25

550 Figurehead from "Carl XIII" (ship of the line)

1997. Inauguration of Naval Museum, Karlskrona.
1925 **550** 6k. blue, brown and red 1·40 80

551 Troll with Treasure Chest ("The Troll and the Gnome Boy")

552 18th-century Compass Rose (Sven Billing)

1997. Europa. Tales and Legends. Illustrations by John Bauer. Multicoloured.
1926 7k. Type **551** . . . . . . 1·90 1·20
1927 7k. Trolls gazing at fairy ("The Boy and the Trolls or the Adventure") . . . 1·90 1·20
1928 7k. Boy before troll ("The Fearless Boy") . . . . . 1·90 1·20

1997. 18th International Cartographic Conference, Stockholm. Multicoloured.
1929 7k. Type **552** . . . . . . 1·70 75
1930 8k. Compass rose, 1568 (from atlas by Diego Homem) . . . . 1·70 85

553 Lesser Panda

554 Bridge

1997. Inscr "FORENINGSBREV".
1931 **553** (3k.50) choc, brn & red 85 55
No. 1931 was for use on bulk rate mail from societies.

1997. Inauguration of High Coast Suspension Bridge. Inscr "INRIKES Brev".
1932 **554** (5k.) blue, green & dp bl 1·30 30
No. 1932 was for use on domestic first class mail.

555 Elk and Mountains

1997. Greeting Stamps. Elk. Inscr "INRIKES BREV".
1933 **555** (5k.) multicoloured . . . 1·10 35
1934 – (5k.) multicoloured . . . 1·10 35
1935 – (5k.) multicoloured . . . 1·10 35
1936 – (5k.) multicoloured . . . 1·10 35
1937 – (5k.) black, yellow and red . . . . 1·10 35
1938 – (5k.) black and red . . . 1·10 35
DESIGNS: No. 1934, Elk-shaped bar code; 1935, Striped elk; 1936, Running elk; 1937, Running elk (different); 1938, Elk and young.
Nos. 1933/8 were for use on domestic first class mail.

556 "Gallery of the Muses" (Peter Hillerstrom)

1997. Gustav III's Museum of Antiquities, Stockholm. Multicoloured.
1939 8k. Type **556** . . . . . . 1·70 1·50
1940 8k. "Endymion" . . . . . . 1·70 1·40

557 Volvo "Duett", 1958

1997. Cars. Inscr "INRIKES BREV". Mult.
1941 (5k.) Type **557** . . . . . . 1·10 90
1942 (5k.) Chevrolet "Bel Air", 1955 . . . . 1·10 90
1943 (5k.) Porsche "356", 1959 1·10 90
1944 (5k.) Citroen "B11", 1952 1·10 90
1945 (5k.) Saab "Monte Carlo" (Erik Carlsson's rally car) 1·10 90
1946 (5k.) Jaguar "E-type", 1961 1·10 90
Nos. 1941/6 were for use on domestic first class mail.

558 Alfred Nobel (founder of Prize Fund)

1997. The Nobel Prize.
1947 **558** 7k. black and pink . . . 1·60 1·10
1948 – 7k. black and grey . . . 1·60 1·10
DESIGN: No. 1948, Paul Karrer and molecular structure of Vitamin A (Chemistry Prize, 1937).

559 Heart

1997. Christmas Gingerbread Biscuits. Each brown, ochre and silver on yellow. Inscr "JULPOST".
1949 (3k.50) Type **559** 90 55
1950 (3k.50) Pigs 90 55
1951 (3k.50) Gingerbread men . . 90 50

560 Angels with Pipe and Lute

1997. Christmas. Angels from altarpiece, Litslena Church. Multicoloured.
1952 6k. Type **560** . . . . . . 1·30 95
1953 6k. Angels with pipes and harp . . . . 1·30 95

561 Tiger's Head

1998. Wildlife Photographs by Jan Lindblad. Inscr "FORENINGSBREV". Multicoloured.
1954 (3k.50) Type **561** 85 50
1955 (3k.50) Two tigers on rock 85 50
Nos. 1954/5 were for use on bulk rate mail from societies.

562 "Sponge Sculpture" (Yves Klein)

563 Heart with Love Birds

1998. Modern Art. Inscr "INRIKES BREV". Multicoloured.
1956 (5k.) Type **562** . . . . . . 1·10 70
1957 (5k.) "Skeppsholmen" (Goran Gidenstam) . . . 1·10 70
1958 (5k.) "Monogram" (Robert Rauschenberg) . . . . 1·10 70
Nos. 1956/8 were for use on domestic first class mail.

1998. St. Valentine's Day. Inscr "INRIKES Brev".
1959 **563** (5k.) red and green . . . 1·10 35
1960 (5k.) mauve and blue . . 1·10 35
Nos. 1959/60 were for use on domestic first class mail.

564 Fire Station, Gavle

1998. Traditional Buildings (4th series). Town Houses. Inscr "INRIKES BREV". Multicoloured.
1961 (5k.) Type **564** . . . . . 1·10 35
1962 (5k.) Shoe shop, Askersund 1·10 35
1963 (5k.) Fish and delicatessen market hall, Goteborg . . 1·10 35
1964 (5k.) Red Mill Cinema, Halmstad . . . . 1·10 35
1965 (5k.) Stads Hotel, Eksjo . . 1·10 35
Nos 1961/5 were for use on domestic first class mail.

565 Apron, Dalarna

566 Confederation Building, Stockholm (after Birger Lundquist)

1998. Handicrafts. (a) Inscr "EKONOMI BREV INRIKES".
1966 **565** (4k.50) scarlet, blk & red 95 35

(b) Inscr "INRIKES BREV".
1967 – (5k.) black and brown . . 1·20 30

(c) With face value.
1968 – 8k. orange, violet and red 1·40 1·50
1969 – 8k. violet and red . . . . 1·40 1·50
DESIGNS: No. 1967, Iron candlestick, Skane; 1968, Lumberjack's woollen glove; 1969, Decorative wooden box.
No. 1966 was for use on domestic second class mail and No. 1967 on domestic first class mail.

1998. Centenary of Swedish Confederation of Trade Unions. Inscr "Inrikes BREV".
1970 **566** (5k.) black, stone & red 1·20 20
No. 1970 was for use on domestic first class mail.

567 Queen Kristina and Memorial Medal

1998. 350th Anniv of Peace of Westphalia.
1971 **567** 7k. green and red . . . 1·50 95

568 Marsh Violet

1998. Wetland Flowers. Inscr "BREV INRIKES". Multicoloured.
1972 (5k.) Type **568** . . . . . . 1·10 25
1973 (5k.) Great willow herb . . 1·10 25
Nos. 1972/3 were for use on domestic first class mail.

569 The Royal Palace

1998. Stockholm, Cultural Capital of Europe, Multicoloured. (a) Inscr "INRIKES BREV".
1974 (5k.) Type **569** . . . . . . 1·10 55
1975 (5k.) Archipelago ferries . . 1·10 55
1976 (5k.) Fisherman in front of Opera House (31 × 26 mm) . . . . . . 1·10 55
1977 (5k.) Yachts (31 × 26 mm) 1·10 55
1978 (5k.) Open-air swimming (31 × 39 mm) . . . . . 1·10 55
1979 (5k.) City Hall (31 × 39 mm) 1·10 55

(b) With face value.
1980 7k. Type **569** . . . . . . 1·60 1·20
1981 7k. As No. 1975 . . . . . 1·60 1·20
Nos. 1974/9 were for use on domestic first class mail.

570 "Albatros" (cruise ship) in Stadsgard Harbour

1998. Nordic Countries, Postal Co-operation. Shipping.
1982 **570** 6k. multicoloured . . . 1·40 70

571 Paper Moon and Plate of Crayfish ("Crayfish Party")

572 King Carl XVI Gustav and Coat of Arms

1998. Europa. National Festivals. Multicoloured.
1983 7k. Type **571** . . . . . . 1·60 1·20
1984 7k. Children dancing around midsummer pole . . . . 1·60 1·20

1998. 25th Anniv of Accession of King Carl XVI Gustav. Inscr "INRIKES BREV".
1985 **572** (5k.) purple, green and red . . . . 1·20 25
No. 1985 was for use on domestic first class mail.

573 Moberg and Characters from "The Emigrants" (novel)

1998. Birth Centenary of Vilhelm Moberg (writer). Inscr "BREV INRIKES".
1986 **573** (5k.) multicoloured . . . 1·30 40
No. 1986 was for use on domestic first class mail.

574 Princess Cake

1998. Greetings Stamps. Pastries. Inscr "BREV". Multicoloured.
1987 (5k.) Type **574** . . . . . . 1·10 50
1988 (5k.) Gustav Adolf pastry 1·10 50
1989 (5k.) Napoleon pastry . . . 1·10 50
1990 (5k.) Mocha cake . . . . . 1·10 50
1991 (5k.) National pastry . . . 1·10 50
1992 (5k.) Lent bun . . . . . . 1·10 50
Nos. 1987/92 were for use on domestic first class mail.

575 "Flowers in the window" (Carl Larsson)

1998. The Twentieth Century (1st series). 1900–1938. Inscr "INRIKES BREV". Multicoloured.
1993 (5k.) Type **575** . . . . . . 1·20 75
1994 (5k.) Stockholm Stadium and poster (Olympic Games, 1912) . . . . . . 1·20 75
1995 (5k.) Porjus hydro-electric power station and electric iron-ore. train on Lulea (Sweden)–Narvik (Norway) railway line . . 1·20 75
1996 (5k.) Zip, ball-bearing, vacuum cleaner and refrigerator (Swedish inventions) . . . . 1·20 75
1997 (5k.) Map of trans-ocean shipping routes and liner 1·20 75
1998 (5k.) Sven Jerring (first Swedish radio reporter) 1·20 75
1999 (5k.) Jazz musicians and Charleston dancers . . . 1·20 75
2000 (5k.) Ellen Key (writer and suffragist) and Kerstin Hesselgren (first woman member of parliament) . . 1·20 75
2001 (5k.) Arne Borg (swimmer) and Gillis Grafstrom (figure skater) (Olympic and world champions) . . 1·20 75
2002 (5k.) Ernst Rolf (entertainer) 1·20 75
Nos. 1993/2002 were for use on domestic first class mail.
See also Nos. 2026/35 and 2083/92.

576 Nadine Gordimer (1991)

577 "King Sigismund of Sweden and Poland" (Studio of Rubens)

1998. The Nobel Literature Prize.
2003 **576** 6k. violet and blue . . . 90 85
2004 – 6k. violet and red . . . 90 85
DESIGN: No. 2004, Sigrid Undset (1928).

1998. 400th Anniv of Battle of Stangebro.
2005 **577** 7k. multicoloured . . . 1·10 95

578 Hyacinths

579 King Gustav Vasa 1 Daler, 1540

1998. Christmas. Flowers. (a) No value expressed. Inscr "Julpost". Size 21 × 28 mm. Multicoloured.
2006 (4k.) Type **578** 80 30
2007 (4k.) Mistletoe 65 35
2008 (4k.) Amaryllis 65 35

(b) With face value. Size 23 × 27½ mm.
2009 6k. Lingonberry wreath . . 90 70
2010 6k. Azaleas 90 70

1999. Coins. (a) Inscr "Ekonomibrev".
2011 **579** (4k.50) green 80 35

(b) Inscr "Brev inrikes".
2012 – (5k.) blue 90 25
DESIGN: No. 2012, King Carl XIV John 1 riksdaler, 1831–43.
No. 2011 was for use on domestic second class mail and No. 2012 on domestic first class mail.

580 Harbour and Katarina Lift, Stockholm

581 Easter Egg and Rabbit

1999. Centenary of Co-operative Union. Inscr "INRIKES BREV".
2013 **580** (5k.) multicoloured . . . 90 40
No. 2013 was for use on domestic first class mail.

1999. Easter. Inscr "INRIKES Brev". Mult.
2014 (5k.) Type **581** 30 40
2015 (5k.) Easter eggs and chicks 30 40
Nos. 2014/15 were for use on domestic first class mail.

582 Rabbit cooking

1999. Rabbits. Drawings by Eva Eriksson from "Little Sister Rabbit" by Ulf Nilsson. Inscr "INRIKES BREV" Multicoloured.
2016 (5k.) Type **582** 80 45
2017 (5k.) Rabbit feeding baby rabbit 80 45
2018 (5k.) Rabbits dancing . . . 80 45
2019 (5k.) Rabbits running through grass 80 45
Nos. 2016/19 were for use on domestic first class mail.

583 "East Indies" (anon)

1999. "Australia 99" International Stamp Exhibition, Melbourne. Paintings of Ships. Multicoloured.
2020 8k. Type **583** . . . . . 1·20 1·40
2021 8k. "Mary Anne" (brigantine) (Folke Sjogren) . . . . 1·20 1·50
2022 8k. "Beatrice" (barque) (A. V. Gregory) . . . . . . 1·20 1·40
2023 8k. "Australic" (steamship) (T. G. Purvis) . . . . . 1·20 1·50

584 Pontoon "Swan" at Dresund Bridge

1999. Construction of Oresund Bridge between Sweden and Denmark. (a) Inscr "INRIKES BREV". Multicoloured.
2024 (5k.) Type **584** 90 45

(b) With face value
2025 6k. Bridge under construction (different) . . 1·00 90
No. 2024 was for use on domestic first class mail.

585 Eva Dahlbeck and Gunnar Bjornstrand in "Smiles of a Summer Night" (director Ingmar Bergman), 1955

1999. The Twentieth Century (2nd series). 1939–1969. Inscr "INRIKES BREV". Multicoloured.
2026 (5k.) Type **585** 75 60
2027 (5k.) Vallingby (first satellite town of Stockholm) . . . 75 60
2028 (5k.) Ulla Billquist and scene from "My Soldier somewhere in Sweden" (song) (emergency military service, 1939–45) 75 60
2029 (5k.) Cobra telephone (L.M. Ericsson), three-point seat belt (Nils Bohlins), high voltage cables and Tetra Pak milk carton (Swedish inventions) 75 60
2030 (5k.) Douglas DC-4 airliner (first scheduled flight of state airline SAS) 75 60
2031 (5k.) Jester, Carl-Gustaf Lindstedt, host of "Hyland's Corner", and Prime Minister Tage Erlander (television) . . . 75 60
2032 (5k.) Demonstrators, girl wearing optical-patterned dress and pop group Hep Stars (the 60s) 75 60
2033 (5k.) Volvo Amazon Car and family camping (leisure time) 75 60
2034 (5k.) Ingemar Johansson (world heavy-weight boxing champion), Mora-Nisse Karlsson (skier) and Gunder Hagg (athlete) . . 75 60
2035 (5k.) Alice Babs (jazz singer) and Jussi Bjorling (opera tenor) 75 60
Nos. 2026/35 were for use on domestic first class mail.

586 Postman's Bicycle

587 Pyramidal Orchid ("Salepsrot")

1999. Bicycles. (a) Inscr "FORENINGSBREV".
2036 **586** (3k.50) bl, ultram & yell 80 55

(b) Inscr "INRIKES BREV".
2037 – (5k.) multicoloured 90 35

(c) With face value.
2038 – 6k. blue, purple and black 1·00 90
2039 – 8k. green, lt green & red 1·30 1·20
DESIGNS: No. 2037, Racing cyclist; 2038, City bike; 2039, Bike messenger.
No. 2036 was for use on bulk rate mail from societies; No. 2037 for use on domestic first class mail.

1999. Orchids. Inscr "INRIKES BREV". Multicoloured.
2040 (5k.) Type **587** 80 30
2041 (5k.) Lady's slipper ("Guckusko") 80 30
2042 (5k.) Marsh helleborine ("Karrknipprot") 80 30
2043 (5k.) Green-winged orchid ("Goknycklar") 80 30
Nos. 2040/3 were for use on domestic first class mail.

588 Plant Shoot

589 Eurasian Pygmy Owl and Tyresta National Park

1999. 50th Anniv of Council of Europe.
2044 **588** 7k. multicoloured . . . 1·20 85

1999. Europa. Parks and Gardens. Multicoloured.
2045 7k. Type **589** . . . . . . 1·50 1·30
2046 7k. Pink helleborine and Gotska Sandon National Park . . . . 1·50 1·30

590 Peacock ("Inachis io")

1999. Butterflies. Multicoloured.
2047 6k. Type **590** . . . . . . 95 1·10
2048 6k. Blue argus ("Junonia orithya") . . . . 95 1·10
2049 6k. Common eggfly ("Hypolimnas bolina") . . 95 1·10
2050 6k. Red admiral ("Vanessa atalanta") . . . . 95 1·10

591 "Pisces"

1999. Signs of the Zodiac. Inscr "INRIKES Brev".
2051 **591** (5k.) blue, ultram and orge 90 45
2052 – (5k.) multicoloured . . . 90 45
2053 – (5k.) blue, ultram and orge 90 45
2054 – (5k.) multicoloured . . . 90 45
2055 – (5k.) blue, ultram and orge 90 45
2056 – (5k.) multicoloured . . . 90 45
2057 – (5k.) multicoloured . . . 90 45
2058 – (5k.) blue, ultram and orge 90 45
2059 – (5k.) orange, ultram and bl 90 45
2060 – (5k.) blue, ultram and orge 90 45
2061 – (5k.) orange, ultram and bl 90 45
2062 – (5k.) blue, ultram and orge 90 45
DESIGNS: No. 2052, "Aries"; 2053, "Taurus"; 2054, "Gemini"; 2055, "Cancer"; 2056, "Aquarius"; 2057, "Virgo"; 2058, "Libra"; 2059, "Scorpio"; 2060, "Sagittarius"; 2061, "Capricorn"; 2062, "Leo".
Nos. 2051/62 were for use on domestic first class mail.

592 Auguste Beernaert (Prime Minister of Belgium 1884–94), 1909

594 "Nativity"

593 Thorleifs

1999. Belgian Winners of Nobel Peace Prize.
2063 **592** 7k. blue and gold . . . 1·10 1·30
2064 – 7k. red and gold . . . . 1·10 1·30
DESIGN: No. 2064, Henri la Fontaine (President of International Peace Bureau), 1913.

1999. Swedish Dance Bands. Inscr "INRIKES BREV". Multicoloured.
2065 (5k.) Type **593** 75 50
2066 (5k.) Arvingara 75 50

2067 (5k.) Lotta Engbergs . . . 75 50
2068 (5k.) Sten and Stanley . . . 75 50
Nos. 2065/8 were for use on domestic first class mail.

1999. Christmas. Stained-glass Windows (2069/71) and Wood Sculptures (2072/3). Multicoloured. (a) Inscr "JULPOST".
2069 (4k.) Type **594** 80 35
2070 (4k.) "Nativity" (different) 75 35
2071 (4k.) "Adoration of the Wise Men" 75 35

(b) With face value. Size 27½ × 30 mm.
2072 6k. Crowned Madonna with child 90 70
2073 6k. Madonna (in white cloak) and child 90 70
Nos. 2069/71 were for use on domestic first class mail.

595 Sun rising over Heligholmen

596 Watch Mechanism

1999. Dawning of New Millennium. Multicoloured.
2074 5k. Type **595** . . . . . . 1·30 90
2075 5k. Sun rising over coast at Gotland . . . . 1·30 1·00

2000. Recovery of King Karl XII's Pocket Watch. (a) Inscr "EKONOMIBREV".
2076 **596** (4k.50) blue 80 30

(b) Inscr "INRIKES BREV".
2077 – (5k.) brown 90 20
DESIGN: 5k. Watch face.
No. 2076 was for use on domestic second class mail and No. 2077 on domestic first class mail.

597 Heart

2000. Valentine's Day. Inscr "INRIKES BREV". Multicoloured.
2078 (5k.) Type **597** 80 45
2079 (5k.) Scribbled line in heart 80 45
Nos. 2078/9 were for use on domestic first class mail.

598 Dragon

2000. Chinese New Year. Year of the Dragon. Illustrations from "The Little Dragon with Red Eyes" by Astrid Lindgren. Inscr "INRIKES BREV". Multicoloured.
2080 (5k.) Type **598** 80 50
2081 (5k.) Dragon with basket . . 80 50
2082 (5k.) Dragon flying 80 50
Nos. 2080/2 were for use on domestic first class mail.

599 Modern Art, Stockholm Underground Railway

2000. The Twentieth Century (3rd series). 1970–1999. Inscr "INRIKES BREV". Multicoloured.
2083 (5k.) Type **599** 80 55
2084 (5k.) Swedish soldiers in United Nations peace-keeping force 80 55
2085 (5k.) Computer screen, mouse and voice-activated mobile phone (Swedish inventions) 80 55
2086 (5k.) Cullberg Ballet dancer and Hans Alfredson and Tage Danielsson (sketch writers) 80 55
2087 (5k.) Jonkoping Railway Station and high-speed train 80 55
2088 (5k.) Punk and Abba (pop group) 80 55
2089 (5k.) European flag and map of Europe (European Union membership, 1994) 80 55
2090 (5k.) Couple in orchard (film "The Apple War, 1971") 80 55
2091 (5k.) Pernilla Wiberg (slalom skier), Ingemar Stenmark (downhill skier) and Björn Borg (tennis player) . . . 80 55
2092 (5k.) Child in womb (photograph, Lennart Nilsson) 80 55
Nos. 2083/92 were for use on domestic first class mail.

600 Parent and Child walking through Forest (public access)

2000. Swedish Forests. Multicoloured. (a) Inscr "Foreningsbrev".
2093 (3k.80) Type **600** 70 55

(b) Inscr "INRIKES BREV".
2094 (5k.) Felled trees and elk (forestry) 80 40
2095 (5k.) Western capercaillie in fir forest 80 70

(c) With face value.
2096 6k. Birch trees . . . . . . 1·00 60
No. 2093 was for use on bulk rate mail from societies. Nos. 2094/5 were for use on domestic first class mail.

602 Oresund Bridge

2000. Inauguration of Oresund Link (Sweden–Denmark road and rail system). (a) Inscr "INRIKES BREV".
2098 **602** (5k.) black, bl & ultram 90 30

(b) Size 58 × 24 mm.
2099 – 6k. multicoloured . . . . 1·00 1·10
2100 – 6k. ultramarine and green 1·00 1·20
DESIGNS: No. 2099, Oresund Bridge; 2100, Map of Oresund Region.
No. 2098 was for use on domestic first class mail.

603 " A Peck of Apples"

604 " Building Europe"

2000. Modern Paintings by Philip von Schantz. Inscr "INRIKES BREV". Multicoloured.
2101 (5k.) Type **603** 80 45
2102 (5k.) "A Bowl of Blueberries" 80 45
Nos. 2101/2 were for use on domestic first class mail.

2000. Europa.
2103 **604** 7k. multicoloured . . . 1·20 1·10

605 Hurdling

2000. Olympic Games, Sydney. Multicoloured.
2104 8k. Type **605** . . . . . . 1·20 1·50
2105 8k. Archery . . . . 1·20 1·50
2106 8k. Wind surfing . . . . 1·20 1·50
2107 8k. Beach volleyball . . . . 1·20 1·50

606 Red Sun and Clouds

2000. Weather. Inscr "INRIKES BREV". Multicoloured. Self-adhesive.
2108 (5k.) Type **606** 75 45
2109 (5k.) Lightning 75 50
2110 (5k.) Black clouds 75 50
2111 (5k.) Northern lights 75 50
2112 (5k.) Rainbow 75 50
2113 (5k.) Blue sky and white clouds 75 45
Nos. 2108/13 were for use on domestic first class mail.

607 King Carl Gustaf XVI

608 Wislawa Szymborska (poet), 1996

2000. (a) Inscr "INRIKES Brev".
2114 **607** (5k.) blue 90 30

(b) With face value.
2115 – 8k. red . . . . 1·30 1·30
DESIGN: 8k. Queen Silvia.
No. 2114 was for use on domestic first class mail.

2000. Nobel Prize Winners for Literature.
2120 **608** 7k. purple and green . . 1·10 1·20
2121 – 7k. green and purple . . 1·10 1·20
DESIGN: No. 2121, Nelly Sachs (author), 1966.

609 Teddy Bear and Doll

2000. Children's Toys. Booklet stamps. Inscr "BREV". Multicoloured.
2122 (5k.) Type **609** 85 60
2123 (5k.) Skipping rope, marbles and tin soldier 85 60
2124 (5k.) Toy horses pulling cart, doll and flag 85 60
2125 (5k.) Toy cars and policeman 85 60
2126 (5k.) Railway carriages and porter 85 60
2127 (5k.) Modern toys 85 60
Nos. 2122/27 were for use on domestic first class mail.

610 Elves drinking

611 Farming

612 Gammelstad Church Village

2000. Christmas. Traditional Songs (2128/32) or Snowflakes (2133/4) (others). (a) No value expressed. Inscr "JULPOST".
2128 (4k.30) Type **610** 80 65
2129 (4k.30) Children dancing around tree (vert) 70 50
2130 (4k.30) Three gingerbread men (vert) 70 50
2131 (4k.30) Fox running (vert) 70 50
2132 (4k.30) Children dancing around candles (vert) . . 70 50

(b) With face value. Size 28 × 29 mm.
2133 6k. silver and blue (face value in blue) 95 70
2134 6k. silver and blue (face value in white) 95 70
DESIGNS: Nos. 2133/34 Snowflakes.
Nos. 2128/32 were for use on domestic first class mail.

2001. U.N.E.S.C.O. World Heritage Sites. Rock Carvings, Tanum. (a) Inscr "EKONOMIBREV".
2135 **611** (4k.50) blue on grey . . 80 65

(b) Inscr "INRIKES BREV".
2136 – (5k.) red on grey 90 55

(c) With face value 35 × 28 mm.
2137 6k. Type **612** 95 85
2138 6k. Karlskrona Naval Base 95 1·10
2139 6k. Interior of Drottningholm Palace Theatre . . . . 95 1·10
2140 6k. Ironworks, Engelsberg 95 1·10
DESIGN: No. 2136, Men in ships.
No. 2135 was for use on domestic second class mail and No. 2136 on domestic first class mail.

613 Rosa

614 Children with Golden Retriever

2001. Chinese New Year. Year of the Snake. Depicting scenes from *Nelson the Snake* (book) by Ulf Stark. Multicoloured. Inscr "INRIKES BREV".
2141 (5k.) Type **613** 80 75
2142 (5k.) Nelson coiled on rock 80 75
Nos. 2141/2 were for use on domestic first class mail.

2001. Working Dogs. Multicoloured. Inscr "INRIKES BREV".
2143 (5k.) Type **614** 80 80
2144 (5k.) German shepherds hunting in snow 80 85
2145 (5k.) Labrador guide dog with blind woman 80 85
2146 (5k.) Dachshunds and man 80 80

615 Northern Lapwing (*Vanellus vanellus*)

617 Waterways of Northern Sweden

616 Yellow Egg

2001. Birds. (a) Inscr "FORENINGSBREV".
2147 **615** (3k.80) blue, green and brown 70 60

(b) Inscr "INRIKES Brev".
2148 – (5k.) blue and black . . . 90 55

(c) With face value.
2149 – 6k. green, black and orange . . . . 1·00 90
2150 – 7k. purple, brown and green . . . . 1·20 1·00
DESIGNS: No. 2148, Black-billed magpie (*Pica pica*); 2149, Herring gull (*Larus argentatus*); 2150, Long-tailed tit (*Aegithalos caudatus*).
No. 2147 was for use on bulk rate mail from societies and No. 2148 for use on domestic first class mail.

2001. Easter. Multicoloured. Self-adhesive. Inscr "INRIKES Brev".
2151 (5k.) Type **616** 80 55
2152 (5k.) Purple egg 80 55
2153 (5k.) Chick 80 55
Nos. 2151/3 were for use on domestic first class mail.

2001. Europa. Water Resources.
2154 **617** 7k. blue, green and black 1·10 1·30
2155 – 7k. blue, green and black 1·10 1·30
2156 – 7k. multicoloured . . . 1·10 1·30
2157 – 7k. multicoloured . . . 1·10 1·30
DESIGNS: No. 2155, Waterways of Southern Sweden; 2156, Freighter entering lock, Trollhatte Canal; 2157 *Juno* (canal boat) leaving lock, Trollhatte Canal.

618 Obverse of Medals and Alfred Nobel (founder)

2001. Centenary of Nobel Prizes (1st issue). Each yellow and brown.
2158 8k. Type **618** . . . . 1·20 1·40
2159 8k. Reverse of medal for Medicine . . . . 1·20 1·40
2160 8k. Reverse of medal for Physics and Chemistry . . 1·20 1·50
2161 8k. Reverse of medal for Literature . . . . 1·20 1·40
See also Nos. 2172/3.

619 Lo-Johansson 620 Fern Leaf Peony

2001. Birth Centenary of Ivar Lo-Johansson (writer). Each indigo, red and blue. Inscr "INRIKES BREV".
2162 (5k.) Type **619** 80 70
2163 (5k.) "The Last Vanload of Furniture of the Agricultural Labourers, 1945" (Svenolov Ehren) 80 70
Nos. 2162/3 were for use on domestic first class mail.

2001. Peonies. Multicoloured. Inscr "INRIKES brev".
2164 (5k.) Type **620** . . . . . . 1·40 55
2165 (5k.) Garden peony "Monsieur Jules Elie" . . 1·40 55
2166 (5k.) Herbaceous peony . . 1·40 55
2167 (5k.) Common peony . . . 1·40 55
2168 (5k.) Tree peony . . . . . 1·40 55
Nos. 2164/8 were for use on domestic first class mail.

621 Eurasian Perch (*Perca fluviatilis*)

2001. Fishes. Illustrations by Wilhelm von Wright from *The Fishes of Scandinavia*. Inscr "INRIKES Brev". Multicoloured. Self-adhesive.
2169 (5k.) Type **621** 80 60
2170 (5k.) Bream (*Abramis brama*) 80 60
2171 (5k.) Four-horned sculpin (*Triglopsis quadricornis*) 80 60
Nos. 2169/71 were for use on domestic first class mail.

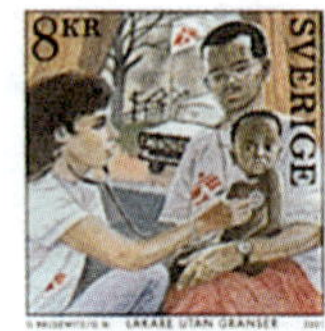
622 Doctors (Medicins sans Frontiers (1999))

2001. Centenary of Nobel Prize (2nd issue). Organizations. Peace Prize Winners. Multicoloured.
2172 8k. Type **622** . . . . 1·20 1·40
2173 8k. Relief workers distributing food (Red Cross (1901, 1917, 1944 and 1963)) . . . . 1·20 1·40

623 Solander

2001. 230th Anniv of Daniel Solander's (botanist) Voyage on H.M.S. *Endeavour*. Multicoloured.
2174 8k. Type **623** . . . . 1·20 1·40
2175 8k. Plant and H.M.S. *Endeavour* . . . . 1·20 1·50

624 Inline Skater and Wall with Graffiti (Emelie Kilstrom) 626 Christmas Tree

625 Otto Lilienthal and Biplane Glider, 1895

2001. Design a Stamp Prize Winners. Inscr "BREV INRIKES". Multicoloured.
2176 (5k.) Type **624** 85 65
2177 (5k.) Letter dropping through letter-box (Thomas Frohling) . . . 85 65
Nos. 2176/7 were for use on domestic first class mail.

2001. Aviation. Multicoloured.
2178 5k. Type **625** 85 85
2179 5k. DFS Weihl glider and emblem of Royal Swedish Flying Club 85 85
2180 5k. SAAB J 29, 1962 . . . 85 85
2181 5k. Freidrichshafen FF49, 1920 . . . . 85 85
2182 5k. Ultra-light trike, 1999 85 85
2183 5k. Douglas DC-3, 1938 . . 85 85

2001. Christmas. Decorations (2184/9) or Presents (2190/1). Multicoloured. (a) Inscr "julpost" (i) Ordinary gum.
2184 (4k.50) Type **626** 75 70

(ii) Size 26 × 20 mm. Self-adhesive.
2185 (4k.50) Star 75 70
2186 (4k.50) Home-made candy 75 70
2187 (4k.50) Angel 75 70
2188 (4k.50) Heart-shaped decoration 75 70
2189 (4k.50) Cone filled with sweets 75 70

(b) With face value. Size 26 × 29 mm. Ordinary gum.
2190 6k. Goat-shaped parcel . . 1·00 85
2191 6k. Christmas tree-shaped parcel . . . . 1·00 85
Nos. 2184/9 were for domestic first class mail.

627 Hockey Players 628 Children riding Horse

2002. World Ice Hockey Championship, Sweden. Inscr "INRIKES BREV".
2192 **627** (5k.) multicoloured . . . 85 70
No. 2192 was for use on domestic first class mail.

2002. Year of the Horse. Showing illustrations from Fairhair the Horse (cartoon character) by Bertil Almquist. Multicoloured. Inscr "INRIKES BREV".
2193 (5k.) Type **628** 85 70
2194 (5k.) Child leading Fairhair 85 70
Nos. 2193/4 were for use on domestic first class mail.

629 Couple in Bed

2002. Illustrations from *Love and Miss Terrified* by Joanna Dranger (book). Self-adhesive.
2195 **629** (5k.) pink, mauve and orange 85 70
2196 (5k.) mauve, pink and orange 85 70
2197 (5k.) orange, mauve and pink 85 70
Nos. 2195/7 were for use on domestic first class mail.

630 Osprey (*Pandion haliaetus*)

2002.
2198 **630** 10k. brown and blue . . 1·60 1·40

631 Scientists, Ship and Seabird

2002. Swedish Antarctic Expedition (1901–03). Multicoloured.
2199 10k. Type **631** . . . . . . 1·60 2·10
2200 10k. Icebergs, ship and gentoo penguin . . . . . 1·60 2·10

632 Pippi Longstocking (Ingrid Vang Nyman)

2002. Astrid Lindgren (children's writer) Commemoration. Depicting book illustrations by named artists.
2201 **632** 5k. multicoloured . . . 75 45
2202 – 5k. multicoloured . . . 75 45
2203 – 5k. multicoloured . . . 75 45
2204 – 5k. brown and black . . 75 45
2205 – 5k. multicoloured . . . 75 45
2206 – 5k. multicoloured . . . 75 45
2207 – 5k. multicoloured . . . 75 45
DESIGNS: No. 2202, Karlsson Pa Taket (Ilon Wikland); 2206, Lotta Pa Brakmakargatan (I. Wikland); 2207, Madicken (I. Wikland). 24 × 31 mm-No. 2203, Broderna Lejonhjarta (I. Wikland); 2205, Emil I Lonneberga (Bjorn Berg). 27 × 31 mm—No. 2204, Astrid Lindgren.

633 Cross (pendant, Birka) 634 Visby

2002. World Heritage Sites. (a) Birka and Hovgarden. (i) Inscr "FORENINGS BREV".
2208 **633** (3k.80) lilac 60 35

(ii) Inscr "EKONOMI BREV".
2209 (4k.50) blue 70 40

(iii) Inscr "INRIKES BREV".
2210 (5k.) brown and mauve . . 75 45
DESIGNS: No. 2209, Runic stone, Hovgarden; 2210, Face-shaped pendant, Birka.

(b) Visby. Multicoloured. Inscr "INRIKES BREV".
2211 (5k.) Type **634** 75 45
2212 (5k.) Part of town wall . . . 75 45
2213 (5k.) Burmeister building . . 75 45
2214 (5k.) Ruins of St. Catherine's Church . . 75 45
No. 2208 was for use on bulk rate mail from societies, No. 2209 was for domestic second class mail and Nos. 2210/14 were for domestic first class mail.

635 "Vadersolstavlan"

2002. 750th Anniv of Stockholm. (a) Inscr "INRIKES BREV".
2215 **635** (5k.) green and mauve 75 45

(b) With face value. Size 30 × 31 mm.
2216 10k. mauve . . . . 1·50 90
DESIGN: 10k. Stadsholmen Island ("Vadersolstavlan" (detail))

636 "Structure" (Takashi Naraha) 637 Charlie Rivel (clown)

2002. Nordic Countries' Postal Co-operation. Modern Art. Sculptures. Multicoloured.
2217 8k. Type **636** . . . . 1·20 70
2218 8k. "Sprung From" (Pal Svensson) . . . . 1·20 70

2002. Europa. Circus. Multicoloured.
2219 8k. Type **637** . . . . 1·20 70
2220 8k. Clown with child (Clowns without Borders) 1·20 70
2221 8k. Man in balloon (Cirkus Cirkor) . . . . 1·20 70
2222 8k. Elephant and rider (Cirkus Scott) . . . . . 1·20 70

638 "Rain Forest" (glass vase) (Marie and Ola Hoglund)

2002. Artistic Crafts. Joint Issue with New Zealand. Multicoloured.
2223 10k. Type **638** . . . . . . 1·50 90
2224 10k. Flax basket (Willa Rogers) . . . . 1·50 90
Nos. 2223/4 are additionally inscr "JOINT ISSUE SWEDEN–NEW ZEALAND".

639 Haro Warehouse

640 Lighthouse and Cliffs

2002. Bohuslan Province. Inscr "INRIKES BREV". (a) Ordinary gum.
2225 **639** (5k.) multicoloured . . . 75 45

(b) Multicoloured. Self-adhesive.
2226 (5k.) Type **640** . . . . . .
2227 (5k.) Lighthouse, rocks and birds 75 45
2228 (5k.) Yacht and waterfront houses 75 45
2229 (5k.) Dinghy with outboard engine 75 45
Nos. 2225/9 were for use on domestic first class mail.

641 Police Chief

2002. Centenary of *Gronkopings Veckoblad* (satirical newspaper). Inscr "INRIKES Brev". Each blue, buff and red.
2230 (5k.) Type **641** 75 45
2231 (5k.) Postman 75 45
Nos. 2230/1 were for use on domestic first class mail.

642 Charles Emil Hagdahl and Cajsa Warg

2002. Swedish Gastronomy. Chefs. Inscr "INRIKES BREV". Multicoloured.
2232 (5 k.) Type **642** 75 45
2233 (5k.) Marit "Hiram" Huldt 75 45
2234 (5k.) Tore Wretman 75 45
2235 (5k.) Leif Mannerstrom . . 75 45
2236 (5k.) Gert Klotzke 75 45
2237 (5k.) Christer Lingstrom . . 75 45
Nos. 2232/7 were for use on domestic first class mail.

643 The Royal Palace, Stockholm

2002. Palaces. Joint Issue with Thailand. Multicoloured.
2238 5k. Type **643** 75 45
2239 5k. Dusit Maha Prasat Throne Hall 75 45

644 Hakan Carlqvist (motocross)

2002. Motorcycle Sports. Multicoloured.
2240 5k. Type **644** 75 45
2241 5k. Sten Lundin (motocross) 75 45
2242 5k. Anders Eriksson (enduro) 75 45
2243 5k. Ulf Karlsson (trial) . . . 75 45

2244 5k. Ove Fundin (speedway) 75 45
2245 5k. Tony Rickardsson (speedway) 75 45
2246 5k. Peter Linden (road racing) 75 45
2247 5k. Varg-Olle Nygren (road racing) 75 45

645 Karl-Bertil Jonsson and Father 646 Kiruna Church

2002. Christmas. Karl-Bertil Jonsson's Christmas (animated film by Per Ahlin). Scenes from the film. Inscr "julpost" Multicoloured. (a) Ordinary gum.
2248 (4k. 50) Type **645** 70 20
Nos. 2248/52 were for domestic first class mail.

(b) Self-adhesive gum.
2249 (4k.50) With sack of presents 70 20
2250 (4k.50) Asleep wearing cap with feather 70 20
2251 (4k.50) Sdhaking hands with man 70 20
2252 (4k.50) Surrounded by family 70 20

2002. Christmas. Churches. Multicoloured.
2253 8k. Type **646** 1·20 70
2254 8k. Habo 1·20 70
2255 8k. Sundborns 1·20 70
2256 8k. Tensta 1·20 70

OFFICIAL STAMPS

O 6

O 17

1874.
O27 O **6** 2ore orange 1·00 1·30
O28 a 3ore bistre 1·00 1·70
O29 c 4ore grey 2·10 40
O30 a 5ore green 1·80 40
O31 a 6ore lilac 29·00 39·00
O32 6ore grey £250 70·00
O33 b 10ore red 1·90 25
O34 a 12ore blue 50·00 7·75
O35 a 20ore red £170 1·50
O36 20ore blue 3·75 25
O37 a 24ore yellow 60·00 11·00
O38ca 30ore brown 17·50 45
O39 a 50ore red £120 18·00
O40 50ore grey 14·50 1·00
O41 d 1k. blue and bistre 7·25 1·30

1889. Surch **TJENSTE FRIMARKE**, two crowns, and **TIO 10 ORE** on scroll.
O42 O **6** 10ore on 12ore blue 10·00 10·00
O43 10ore on 24ore yellow 15·00 16·00

1910.
O 87 O **17** 1ore black 30 30
O101 2ore yellow 20 70
O102 3ore brown 30 45
O103 4ore lilac 20 20
O104 5ore green 20 15
O105 7ore green 40 60
O 91 8ore purple 45 65
O107 10ore red 20 15
O108 12ore red 20 20
O109 15ore brown 30 20
O110 20ore blue 25 15
O111 25ore orange 85 30
O112 30ore brown 45 25
O113 35ore violet 65 45
O114 50ore grey 1·20 1·30
O 98 1k. black on yellow 7·75 5·25
O 99 5k. purple on yellow 9·75 3·00

POSTAGE DUE STAMPS

D 6

1874.
D27 a D **6** 1ore black 1·90 2·00
D28ab 3ore red 4·00 4·00
D29ba 5ore brown 2·75 2·75
D30 a 6ore yellow 3·25 2·75
D31 12ore red 6·00 3·25
D32 a 20ore blue 3·25 2·75
D33 24ore lilac 39·00 33·00
D34 b 24ore grey 11·50 15·00
D35 b 30ore green 4·00 3·00
D36 a 50ore brown 6·25 3·50
D37 a 1k. blue and bistre 31·00 17·00

SWITZERLAND Pt. 8

A federal republic in central Europe between France, Germany and Italy.

100 rappen = 1 franken.
100 centimes = 1 franc.
100 centesimi = 1 franco.

These are expressions of the same currency in three languages.
For the issues under the Cantonal Administrations of Basel, Geneva and Zurich, see Stanley Gibbons' Part 8 (Italy and Switzerland) Catalogue.

1 6

1850. Imperf. (a) Inscr "ORTS-POST".
1 **1** 2½r. black and red £2000 £1000

(b) Inscr "POSTE LOCALE".
3 **1** 2½r. black and red £1600 £950

1850. As T **1** but inscr "RAYON I", "II" or "III". Imperf.
6 **1** 5r. red, black and blue (I) £1200 £325
13 5r. red and blue (I) £425 85·00
10 10r. red, black and yellow (II) £700 80·00
24 15rp. red (III) £1600 75·00
21 15 cts. red (III) £8000 £500

1854. Imperf.
46 **6** 2r. grey £140 £300
47a 5r. brown £120 10·50
48 10r. blue £130 8·00
49a 15r. pink £225 29·00
50 20r. orange £275 38·00
51 40r. green £250 36·00
38a 1f. lilac £800 £600

7 9 10

1862. Perf.
52 **7** 2c. grey 44·00 1·70
61 2c. brown 1·60 65
61a 2c. bistre 1·60 60
53 3c. black 6·25 47·00
54b 5c. brown 1·70 25
55 10c. blue £225 25
62 10c. pink 1·90 35
63 15c. yellow 2·20 18·00
56a 20c. orange £200 2·50
64 25c. green 1·30 1·20
57 30c. red £750 18·00
65a 30c. blue £1500 £160
58 40c. green £750 27·00
66 40c. grey 1·50 60·00
67 50c. purple 35·00 18·00
59 60c. bronze £500 65·00
60a 1f. gold £700 £180

1882.
126Bd **9** 2c. brown 65 10
127Bc 3c. brown 1·10 1·60
128Bd 5c. purple 11·50 30
196a 5c. green 3·50 10
130Be 10c. red 2·30 15
131Be 12c. blue 4·00 10
132A 15c. yellow 95·00 9·75
133Bc 15c. violet 31·00 85

1882.
214 **10** 20c. orange 1·70 1·10
146B 25c. green 8·25 55
207 25c. blue 5·00 60
202 30c. brown 4·75 1·10
209 40c. grey 23·00 4·00
150B 50c. blue 30·00 2·20
218 50c. green 5·50 1·00
152B 1f. purple 41·00 1·80
219 1f. red 21·00 3·25
154B 3f. brown £120 15·00

11

1900. 25th Anniv of U.P.U.
191 **11** 5c. green 2·75 60
189 10c. red 7·00 65
190 25c. blue 13·00 8·50

15 Tell's Son

16

17

1907.
225 **15** 2c. yellow 30 25
226 3c. brown 20 5·00
227 5c. green 2·30 15
228 **16** 10c. red 1·40 15
229 12c. brown 30 1·70
230 15c. mauve 3·75 7·00

1908.
232 **17** 20c. yellow and red 1·10 30
233 25c. blue and deep blue 1·90 20
234 30c. green and brown 1·90 20
235 35c. yellow and green 1·90 2·20
236 40c. yellow and purple 9·75 30
238 40c. blue 1·50 15
239 40c. green 23·00 20
240a 50c. green and deep green 6·25 15
241 60c. brown 6·50 20
242 70c. yellow and brown 50·00 5·00
243 70c. buff and violet 13·00 1·00
244 80c. buff and grey 7·00 40
245 1f. green and purple 4·75 25
246 3f. yellow and bistre £170 85

18 Cord in front of Shaft

19

1908.
247 **18** 2c. bistre 20 50
248 3c. violet 20 6·75
249 5c. green 2·00 15
250 **19** 10c. red 55 15
251 12c. brown 70 25
252 15c. mauve 16·00 45

20a Cord behind Shaft

21 William Tell

1910.
260 **20a** 2c. brown 10 15
261 2½c. purple 15 65
262 2½c. bistre on buff 30 1·60
254 3c. violet 10 15
255 3c. brown 10 20
256 3c. blue on buff 2·40 4·50
263 5c. green 1·10 15
264 5c. orange on buff 10 20
265 5c. grey on buff 10 15
266 5c. purple on buff 10 20
267 5c. green on buff 30 20
258 7½c. grey 1·40 20
259 7½c. green on buff 30 1·90

1914.
279 **21** 10c. red on buff 35 20
280 10c. green on buff 10 15
282 10c. violet on buff 1·20 20
283 12c. brown on buff 35 2·40
284 13c. green on buff 1·20 20
285 15c. purple on buff 2·00 15
286 15c. red on buff 2·50 1·40
287 20c. purple on buff 1·80 15
289 20c. red on buff 20 15
291 25c. red on buff 60 35
292 25c. brown on buff 4·25 80
293 30c. blue on buff 6·50 15

22 The Mythen

1914. Mountain Views.
294 **22** 3f. green £550 2·75
295 3f. red 70·00 45
296 – 5f. blue 30·00 1·10
297 – 10f. mauve £110 1·50
337 – 10f. green 00 29·00
DESIGNS: 5f. The Rutli; 10f. The Jungfrau and girl holding shield.

1915. Surch.
298 **20a** 1c. on 2c. brown 10 55
307 2½c. on 3c. brown 10 35
308 3c. on 2½c. bistre on buff 10 1·50
309 5c. on 2c. brown 10 2·40
310 5c. on 7½c. grey 10 25
312 5c. on 7½c. green on buff 15 5·25
313 **21** 10c. on 13c. green on buff 15 1·40
299 **19** 13c. on 12c. brown 10 5·25
300 **21** 13c. on 12c. brn on buff 15 60
314a 20c. on 15c. purple on buff 6·25 3·25
315 **17** 20c. on 25c. bl & dp bl 15 25
301 80c. on 70c. yell & brn 23·00 8·50

1919. Air. Optd with wings and propeller.
302 **17** 30c. green and brown £100 £900
303 50c. green and deep green 32·00 95·00

31

32

33

1919. Peace Celebrations.
304 **31** 7½c. green and black 60 1·20
305 **32** 10c. yellow and red 90 5·25
306 **33** 15c. yellow and violet 1·70 1·20

35 Monoplane

36 Pilot

37

38 Biplane

39 Icarus

40

1923. Air.
316 **35** 15c. green and red . . . . 2·50 4·50
317a 20c. green and deep green 70 4·25
318 25c. grey and blue . . . . 7·50 12·00
319 **36** 35c. cinnamon and brown 16·00 34·00
320a **37** 35c. brown and ochre . . 15·00 32·00
321 **36** 40c. lilac and violet . . . 10·50 34·00
322a **37** 40c. blue and green . . . 39·00 55·00
323 **38** 45c. red and blue . . . . 1·40 4·25
324a 50c. grey and red . . . . 11·00 10·50
325a **39** 65c. blue and deep blue 7·25 10·00
326 75c. orange and purple . . 14·00 42·00
327a 1f. lilac and purple . . . 36·00 25·00
328a **40** 2f. chestnut, sepia & brn 60·00 55·00

41

42 Seat of First U.P.U. Congress

1924.
329 **41** 90c. red, dp green & grn 10·50 35
330 1f.20 red, lake and pink 5·75 1·40
331 1f.50 red, blue & turq . . 25·00 1·50
332a 2f. red, black and grey . . 55·00 1·70

1924. 50th Anniv of U.P.U.
333 – 20c. red 45 90
334 **42** 30c. blue . . . . 95 4·00
DESIGN: 20c. As T **42** but with different frame.

43 The Mythen

1931.
335 **43** 3f. brown . . . . 41·00 1·60

44 Symbol of Peace

45 "After the Darkness, Light"

46 Peace and the Air Post

1932. International Disarmament Conference.
338 **44** 5c. green (postage) 15 15
339 10c. orange 20 10
340 20c. mauve 25 10
341 30c. blue . . . . 2·10 60
342 60c. brown . . . . 14·50 3·00
343 **45** 1f. grey and blue . . . . . 15·00 4·50

344 **46** 15c. lt green & green (air) 40 1·60
345 20c. pink and red . . . . 1·00 2·20
346 90c. light blue and blue . . 5·75 24·00

47 Louis Favre (engineer)

48 Staubbach Falls

1932. 50th Anniv of St. Gotthard Railway.
347 **47** 10c. brown 10 15
348 – 20c. red 20 15
349 – 30c. blue . . . . 40 1·10
DESIGNS: 20c. Alfred Escher (President of Railway); 30c. Emil Welti (surveyor).

1934. Landscapes.
350 **48** 3c. green . . . . 25 1·70
351 – 5c. green 20 10
352 – 10c. mauve 45 10
353 – 15c. orange . . . . 40 1·30
354 – 20c. red 50 10
355 – 25c. brown . . . . 6·50 4·25
356 – 30c. blue . . . . 20·00 45
DESIGNS: 5c. Mt. Pilatus; 10c. Chillon Castle and Dents du Midi; 15c. Grimsel Pass; 20c. St. Gotthard Railway, Biaschina Gorge; 25c. Viamala Gorge; 30c. Rhine Falls, Schaffhausen.
For redrawn designs, see Nos. 368 etc.

1935. Air. Surch.
358 **35** 10 on 15c. green and red 5·75 32·00
359 **46** 10 on 15c. light green and green 50 35
360 10 on 20c. pink and red . . 55 1·60
381 **39** 10 on 65c. blue & deep blue 30 35
361 **46** 30 on 90c. light blue & blue . . . . 3·00 9·50
362 40 on 20c. pink and red . . 4·00 10·50
363 40 on 90c. light blue & blue . . . . 3·00 10·50

51 Freiburg Cowherd

52 Staubbach Falls

1936. National Defence Fund.
364 **51** 10c.+5c. violet 35 55
365 20c.+10c. red . . . . . . 65 2·50
366 30c.+10c. blue . . . . . . 3·00 13·00

1936. As T **48** but redrawn with figure of value lower down. Various landscapes.
368A **52** 3c. green 15 15
369A – 5c. green 15 10
489 – 5c. brown 25 10
370Ad – 10c. purple 65 15
372A – 10c. brown 10 10
490 – 10c. green 30 10
373A – 15c. orange 30 45
374Ac – 20c. red (Railway) . . . 4·75 15
375A – 20c. red (Lake) 20 10
491 – 20c. brown 35 10
376A – 25c. brown 65 90
492 – 25c. red . . . . 1·60 1·20
377A – 30c. blue . . . . 1·20 15
378A – 35c. green . . . . 1·30 1·10
379A – 40c. grey . . . . 7·75 15
494 – 40c. blue . . . . 23·00 35
DESIGNS: 5c. Mt. Pilatus; 10c. Chillon Castle and Dents du Midi; 15c. Grimsel Pass; 20c. (374d) St. Gotthard Railway, Biaschina Gorge; 20c. (Nos. 375, 491) Lake Lugano and Mt. San Salvatore; 25c. (No. 376) Viamala Gorge; 25c. (No. 492) National Park; 30c. Rhine Falls, Schaffhausen; 35c. Mt. Neufalkenstein and Klus; 40c. Mt. Santis and Lake Seealp.

53 Mobile P.O.

1937. For Mobile P.O. Mail.
380 **53** 10c. yellow and black . . . 25 25

55 International Labour Bureau

1938.
382 **55** 20c. red and buff 20 15
383 – 30c. blue and light blue . . 30 15
384 – 60c. brown and buff . . . 1·50 1·30
385 – 1f. black and buff . . . . 6·25 10·00
DESIGNS: 30c. Palace of League of Nations; 60c. Inner courtyard of Palace of League of Nations; 1f. International Labour Bureau (different).

1938. Air. Special Flights. Surch **1938 "PRO AERO" 75 75** and bars.
386 **38** 75c. on 50c. green and red † 4·75

60 William Tell's Chapel

1938. National Fete. Fund for Swiss Subjects Abroad.
387 **60** 10c.+10c. violet & yellow 40 45

61 First Act of Federal Parliament

1938.
388A **61** 3f. brown on blue . . . 10·50 4·00
388C 3f. brown on buff . . . 6·00 35
389A – 5f. blue on blue . . . . 11·00 2·50
389C – 5f. blue on buff . . . . 5·00 25
390B – 10f. green on blue . . . 23·00 90
390C – 10f. green on buff . . . 8·75 1·25
DESIGNS: 5f. "The Assembly at Stans"; 10f. Polling booth.

62 Symbolical of Swiss Culture

64 Crossbow and Floral Branch

1939. National Exhibition, Zurich. Inscr in French (F.), German (G.) or Italian (I.). F.
391 – 10c. violet 30 15
392 **62** 20c. red . . . . 2·50 30
393 – 30c. blue and buff . . . . 2·75 5·75

G.
391 – 10c. violet 30 10
392 **62** 20c. red 40 10
393 – 30c. blue and buff . . . . 2·10 1·10

I.
391 – 10c. violet 25 15
392 **62** 20c. red . . . . 1·50 35
393 – 30c. blue and buff . . . . 1·75 5·00
DESIGNS: 10c. Group symbolic of Swiss Industry and Agriculture; 30c. Piz Rosegg and Tschirva Glacier.

1939. National Exhibition, Zurich. Inscr in French (F.), German (G.) or Italian (I.). F.
394Fa **64** 5c. green . . . . 65 1·60
395Fb 10c. brown . . . . . . 65 2·10
396Fc 20c. red . . . . 1·25 1·90
397F 30c. blue . . . . 2·40 7·25

G.
394Ga **64** 5c. green . . . . 60 1·75
395Ga 10c. brown 50 65
396Ga 20c. red . . . . 1·10 1·10
397G 30c. blue . . . . 3·00 5·25

I.
394I **64** 5c. green . . . . 80 2·00
395Ib 10c. brown . . . . . . 75 1·25
396Ia 20c red . . . . 25 3·50
397I 30c. blue . . . . 2·75 5·25

65 Laupen Castle

1939. National Fete. Fund for Destitute Mothers.
398 **65** 10c.+10c. brn, grey & red 25 40

66 Geneva

1939. 75th Anniv of Geneva (Red Cross) Convention.
399 **66** 20c. red and buff 30 20
400 30c. blue, grey and red . . 45 1·10

67 "Les Rangiers"

68 "William Tell" (Ferdinand Hodler)

1940. National Fete and Red Cross Fund. Memorial designs inscr "FETE NATIONALE 1940" in German (5c., 20c.), Italian (10c.) and French (30c.).
401 – 5c.+5c. black and green . . 25 90
402 – 10c.+5c. black & orange 25 30
403 – 20c.+5c. black and red . . 2·20 60
404 **67** 30c.+10c. black and blue 1·30 4·75
DESIGNS—Battle Memorials: 5c. Sempach; 10c. Giornico; 20c. Calven.

1941. Historical Designs.
405 – 50c. blue on green . . . . 4·25 10
406 **68** 60c. brown on cinnamon 6·25 10
407 – 70c. purple on mauve . . 2·75 45
408 – 80c. black on grey . . . . 1·10 10
408a – 80c. black on mauve . . . 2·30 30
409 – 90c. red on pink . . . . 1·10 10
409a – 90c. red on buff . . . . . 3·25 95
410 – 1f. green on green . . . . 1·40 10
411 – 1f.20 purple on grey . . . 1·90 15
411a – 1f.20 purple on lilac . . . 3·25 55
412 – 1f.50 blue on buff . . . . 2·00 40
413 – 2f. red on pink . . . . . 2·75 40
413a – 2f. red on cream . . . . 6·00 30
DESIGNS—(Works of art): 50c. "Oath of Union" (James Vibert); 70c. "Kneeling Warrior" (Ferdinand Hodler); 80c. "Dying Ensign" (Hodler); 90c. "Standard Bearer" (Niklaus Deutsch). Portraits: 1f. Col. Louis Pfyffer; 1f.20, George Jenatsch; 1f.50, Lt. Gen. Francois de Reynold; 2f. Col. Joachim Forrer.

69 Ploughing

1941. Agricultural Development Plan.
414 **69** 10c. brown and buff . . . 10 15

70 The Jungfrau

1941. Air. Landscapes.
415 **70** 30c. blue on orange . . . 85 15
415a – 30c. grey on orange . . . 7·25 9·00
416 – 40c. grey on orange . . . 85 15
416a – 40c. blue on orange . . . 36·00 1·50
417 – 50c. green on orange . . 1·10 15
418 – 60c. brown on orange . . 1·50 15
419 – 70c. violet on orange . . 1·20 30
420 – 1f. green on buff . . . . 2·30 35
421 – 2f. red on buff . . . . . 7·25 1·70
422 – 5f. blue on buff . . . . . 24·00 9·25
DESIGNS: 40f. Valais; 50c. Lac Leman; 60c. Alpstein; 70c. Ticino; 1f. Lake Lucerne; 2f. Engadin; 5f. Churfirsten.

1941. Air. Special (Buochs–Payerne) Flights. No. 420 with "PRO AERO 28.V.1941" added.
423 1f. green on buff . . . . . . 5·75 16·00

71 Chemin Creux near Kussnacht

1941. National Fete and 650th Anniv of Swiss Confederation.
424 – 10c.+10c. blue, red & yell 30 50
425 **71** 20c.+10c. scarlet, red and buff 50 70
DESIGN: 10c. Relief map of Lake Lucerne with Arms of Uri, Schwyz and Unterwalden.

72 Arms of Berne, Masons laying Cornerstone and Knight

1941. 750th Anniv of Berne.
426 **72** 10c. multicoloured 10 25

73 "To survive collect salvage"

1942. Salvage Campaign. Inscr in French (F.), German (G.) or Italian (I.). Value and coat of arms in red, tablets in blue. F.
427F **73** 10c. brown . . . . 7·50 2·50

G.
427G **73** 10c. brown 20 20

I.
427I **73** 10c. brown . . . . 8·00 2·50
INSCRIPTIONS: (G) "Zum Durchhalten/Alstoffe sammeln"; (I) "PER RESISTERE/RACCOGLIETE/LA ROBA VECCHIA".

74 View of Old Geneva

75 Soldiers' Memorial at Forch, near Zurich

1942. National Fete, National Relief Fund and Bimillenary of Geneva.

428 **74** 10c.+10c. black, yellow and red 35 45

429 **75** 20c.+10c. red and yellow 45 85

76

1943. Cent of Swiss Cantonal Postage Stamps.

430 **76** 10c.(4+6) black 10 10

77 Intragna (Ticino)

78 Apollo of Olympia

1943. National Fete and Youth's Vocational Training Fund.

431 **77** 10c.+10c. black, buff and red 35 50

432 – 20c.+10c. red and buff . . 40 80

DESIGN: 20c. Federal Palace, Berne.

1943. Air. Special Flights. 30th Anniv of First Flight across Alps by Oscar Bider. As No. 432, optd **PRO AERO 13.VII.1943** and value.

433 1f. red and buff . . . . . 2·20 8·00

1944. Olympic Games Jubilee.

434 **78** 10c. black and orange . . 20 45

435 20c. black and red 30 45

436 30c. black and blue . . . . 75 6·75

79 Heiden

1944. National Fete and Red Cross Fund.

437 **79** 5c.+5c. green, buff & red 35 1·50

438 – 10c.+10c. grey, buff and red 35 35

439 – 20c.+10c. red and buff . . 35 55

440 – 30c.+10c. blue, buff and red . . . . 2·40 12·00

DESIGNS: 10c. St. Jacques on the R. Birs; 20c. Castle Ruins, Mesocco; 30c. Basel.

80 Haefeli DH-3 Biplane

81 Symbolical of Faith, Hope and Charity

1944. Air. 25th Anniv of National Air Post.

441 **80** 10c. brown and green . . . 10 20

442 – 20c. red and stone 25 20

443 – 30c. ultramarine and blue 50 65

444 – 1f.50 agate, brown and red 7·25 14·50

AIRCRAFT: 20c. Fokker F.VIIb/3m; 30c. Lockheed 9B Orion; 1f.50, Douglas DC-3.

1945. War Relief Fund.

445 **81** 10c.+10c. green, black and grey 50 30

446 20c.+60c. red, black and grey . . . . 2·50 4·75

82 Trans "Peace to men of good will"

83 Olive Branch

1945. Peace. Inscr "PAX".

447 **82** 5c. green and grey 10 20

448 10c. brown and grey . . . 35 15

449 20c. red and grey 45 15

450 30c. blue and grey . . . . 80 2·30

451 40c. orange and grey . . . 3·00 8·25

452 **83** 50c. red and buff . . . . . 4·25 16·00

453 – 60c. grey and light grey . . 4·75 5·75

454 – 80c. green and buff . . . . 8·75 60·00

455 – 1f. blue and buff . . . . . 11·00 65·00

456 – 2f. brown and buff . . . . 42·00 £130

457 – 3f. green on buff . . . . . 49·00 46·00

458 – 5f. brown on buff £150 £225

459 – 10f. violet on buff . . . . £150 90·00

DESIGNS—As Type **83**: 60c. Keys; 80c. Horn of plenty; 1f. Dove; 2f. Spade and flowers in ploughed field. 38 × 21 mm: 3f. Crocuses; 5f. Clasped hands; 10f. Aged couple.

1945. Red Cross. As T **82**, but red cross and "5+10" in centre of stamp.

460 5c.+10c. green 75 60

85 Silk Weaving

1945. National Fete.

461 **85** 5c.+5c. green and red . . . 90 1·50

462 – 10c.+10c. brown, grey and red 80 40

463 – 20c.+10c. red and buff . . 1·00 45

464 – 30c.+10c. blue, grey and red . . . . 10·50 21·00

DESIGNS: 10, 20c. Jura and Emmental farmhouses; 30c. Timbered house.

86 J. H. Pestalozzi

87 Zoglig Instructional Glider

1946. Birth Bicentenary of J. H. Pestalozzi (educational reformer).

465 **86** 10c. purple 20 15

1946. Air. Special (Lausanne, Lucerne, Locarno) Flights.

466 **87** 1f.50 red and grey . . . . 23·00 22·00

88 Cheese-making

89 Chalet in Appenzell

1946. National Fete and Fund for Swiss Citizens Abroad.

467 **88** 5c.+5c. green and red . . . 70 2·00

468 – 10c.+10c. brown, buff and red 65 55

469 **89** 20c.+10c. red and buff . . 85 55

470 – 30c.+10c. blue, grey and red . . . . 5·75 7·25

DESIGNS: 10c. Chalet in Vaud; 30c. Chalet in Engadine.

90 Douglas DC-4 Airliner, Statue of Liberty and St. Peter's Cathedral, Geneva

1947. Air. 1st Geneva–New York "Swissair" Flight.

472 **90** 2f.50 deep blue, blue & red 11·50 15·00

92 Rorschach Station

1947. National Fete. Professional Education of Invalids and Anti-cancer Funds. Inscr "I VIII 1947". Arms in red.

473 – 5c.+5c. green . . . . . . 70 1·90

474 **92** 10c.+10c. black and buff 80 50

475 – 20c.+10c. red and buff . . 1·20 50

476 – 30c.+10c. blue and grey . . 6·00 8·75

DESIGNS: 5c. Platelayers; 20c. Luen-Castiel station; 30c. Fluelen station.

93 "Limmat" (first locomotive in Switzerland)

1947. Centenary of Swiss Federal Railways.

477 **93** 5c. green, yellow and black 25 30

478 – 10c. black and brown . . . 30 15

479 – 20c. red, buff and lake . . 35 15

480 – 30c. blue, grey & light blue 1·40 1·30

DESIGNS: 10c. Class C5/62-10-0 steam locomotive, 1913; 20c. Type Ae8/14 electric locomotive crossing Melide Causeway; 30c. Lorraine Bridge, Berne.

95 Sun of St. Moritz

96 Ice Hockey

1948. 5th Winter Olympic Games.

481 **95** 5c.+5c. brown, yell & grn 50 1·40

482 – 10c.+10c. blue, light blue and brown 55 85

483 **96** 20c.+10c. yellow, black and purple . . . . 85 1·60

484 – 30c.+10c. black, light blue and blue . . . . 2·30 5·00

DESIGN: 10c. Snow crystals; 30c. Ski-runner.

97 Johann Rudolf Wettstein

1948. Tercentenary of Treaty of Westphalia and Centenaries of the Neuchatel Revolution and Swiss Federation.

485 **97** 5c. green and deep green 20 30

486 – 10c. black and grey 20 15

487 – 20c. red and pink 30 15

488 – 30c. blue, grey and brown 75 1·10

DESIGNS: 10c. Neuchatel Castle; 20c. Symbol of Helvetia; 30c. Symbol of Federal State.

99 Frontier Guard

1948. National Fete and Anti-Tuberculosis Fund. Coat of arms in red.

495 **99** 5c.+5c. green 55 85

496 – 10c.+10c. slate and grey . . 50 45

497 – 20c.+10c. red and buff . . 50 50

498 – 30c.+10c. blue and grey . . 3·50 4·25

DESIGNS: 10c., 20c., 30c. Typical houses in Fribourg, Valais and Ticino respectively.

101 Glider

1949. Air. Special (La Chaux-de-Fonds–St. Gallen–Lugano) Flights.

499 **101** 1f.50 purple and yellow 32·00 34·00

102 Posthorn

1949. Centenary of Federal Post.

500 **102** 5c. yellow, pink and grey 20 30

501 – 20c. yellow, violet and grey 40 20

502 – 30c. yellow, brown & grey 60 5·75

DESIGNS: 20c. Mail coach drawn by five horses; 30c. Postal motor coach and trailer.

103 Main Motif of U.P.U. Monument, Berne

1949. 75th Anniv of U.P.U.

503 **103** 10c. green 20 20

504 – 25c. purple . . . . 55 6·25

505 – 40c. blue . . . . 80 2·30

DESIGNS: 25c. Globe and ribbon; 40c. Globe and pigeons.

104 Postman

1949. National Fete and Youth Fund. T **104** and designs as T **89**, but dated "I. VIII. 1949". Arms in red.

506 **104** 5c.+5c. purple . . . . . 65 1·20

507 – 10c.+10c. green & buff . . 60 55

508 – 20c.+10c. brown & buff 75 60

509 – 40c.+10c. blue & lt blue 4·25 7·00

DESIGNS—Typical houses in: 10c. Basel; 20c. Lucerne; 40c. Prattigau.

106 High-tension Pylons

107 Railway Viaducts over River Sitter, near St. Gall

1949. Landscapes.

510 **106** 3c. black . . . . 3·75 3·75

511 **107** 5c. orange 45 10

512 – 10c. green 30 10

513 – 15c. turquoise 45 15

514a – 20c. purple . . . . . . £4750 55·00

515 – 25c. red 60 10

516 – 30c. green 75 10

517 – 35c. brown . . . . . . 1·70 55

518 – 40c. blue . . . . 1·70 10

519 – 50c. grey . . . . 2·75 10

520 – 60c. green . . . . 7·50 10

521 – 70c. violet . . . . 2·75 20

DESIGNS: 10c. Rack railway, Rochers de Naye; 15c. Rotary snowplough; 20c. Grimsel Reservoir; 25c. Lake Lugano and Melide railway causeway; 30c. Verbois hydro-electric power station; 35c. Alpine road (Val d'Anniviers); 40c. Rhine harbour, Basel; 50c. Suspension railway, Santis; 60c. Railway viaduct, Landwasser; 70c. Survey mark, Finsteraarhorn.

110 First Federal Postage Stamps

111 Putting the Weight

1950. National Fete, Red Cross Fund and Centenary of First Federal Postage Stamps. T **110** and designs, as T **111**, inscr "I. VIII. 1950". Coat of arms in red.

522 **110** 5c.+5c. black 60 65
523 **111** 10c.+10c. green & grey . . 1·10 60
524 – 20c.+10c. green & grey . . 1·10 65
525 – 30c.+10c. mauve & grey 6·25 15·00
526 – 40c.+10c. blue and grey 7·50 8·00

DESIGNS: 20c. Wrestling; 30c. Sprinting; 40c. Rifle-shooting.

112 Arms of Zurich

113 Valaisan Polka

1951. National Fete, Mothers' Fund and 600th Anniv of Zurich. Coat of arms in red.

527 **112** 5c.+5c. black 55 45
528 **113** 10c.+10c. green & grey . . 85 50
529 – 20c.+10c. green & grey . . 1·20 65
530 – 30c.+10c. mauve & grey 6·25 11·00
531 – 40c.+10c. blue and grey 7·75 7·50

DESIGNS—As Type **113**: 20c. Flag-swinging; 30c. "Hornussen" (game); 40c. Blowing alphorn.

114 "Telegraph"

116 River Doubs

115 Arms of Glarus and Zug

1952. Centenary of Swiss Telecommunications.

532 **114** 5c. orange and yellow . . 40 45
533 – 10c. green and pink . . . 50 10
534 – 20c. mauve and lilac . . . 75 10
535 – 40c. blue and light blue 3·00 2·75

DESIGNS: 10c. "Telephone"; 20c. "Radio"; 40c. "Television".

1952. Pro Patria. Cultural Funds and 600th Anniv of Glarus and Zug joining Confederation.

536 **115** 5c.+5c. red and black . . 50 70
537 **116** 10c.+10c. green and cream 45 40
538 – 20c.+10c. purple & pink 50 40
539 – 30c.+10c. brown & buff 4·25 5·25
540 – 40c.+10c. blue & lt blue 5·00 4·75

DESIGNS—As T **116**: 20c. St. Gotthard Lake; 30c. River Moesa; 40c. Marjelen Lake.

1953. Pro Patria. Emigrants' Fund and 600th Anniv of Berne joining Confederation.

541 5c.+5c. red and black 70 75
542 10c.+10c. green and cream 30 35
543 20c.+10c. purple and pink 40 40
544 30c.+10c. brown and buff . . 2·75 6·75
545 40c.+10c. blue & light blue 3·75 4·75

DESIGNS—As T **115**: 5c. Arms of Berne (inscr "BERN 1353"). As T **116** (inscr "PRO PATRIA 1953"): 10c. Rapids, R. Reuss; 20c. Lake Sihl; 30c. Aqueduct, Bisse; 40c. Lac Leman.

119 Zurich Airport

1953. Inauguration of Zurich Airport.

546 **119** 40c. blue, grey and red . . 3·50 4·75

120 Alpine Postal Coach and Winter Landscape

1953. For Mobile P.O. Mail.

547 **120** 10c. yellow, green and emerald 20 10
548 – 20c. yellow, red and scarlet 35 10

DESIGN: 10c. Alpine postal coach and summer landscape.

121 Ear of Wheat and Flower

122 Rhine Map and Steering Wheel

1954. Publicity Issue.

549 **121** 10c. multicoloured 65 15
550 – 20c. multicoloured 95 15
551 **122** 25c. green, blue and red 1·60 2·00
552 – 40c. blue, yellow and black . . . . 2·75 1·20

DESIGNS—HORIZ: 10c. Type **121** (Agricultural Exhibition, Lucerne); 20c. Winged spoon (Cooking Exhibition, Berne); 40c. Football and world map (World Football Championship). VERT: 25c. Type **122** (50th anniv of navigation of River Rhine).

123 Opening Bars of "Swiss Hymn"

1954. Pro Patria. Youth Fund and Death Centenary of Father Zwyssig (composer of "Swiss Hymn").

553 **123** 5c.+5c. green 65 75
554 – 10c.+10c. green & turq . . 30 35
555 – 20c.+10c. purple and cream 40 35
556 – 30c.+10c. brown & buff 2·75 6·75
557 – 40c.+10c. deep blue and blue . . . . 5·25 4·75

DESIGNS: 10c. Lake Neuchatel; 20c. Maggia River; 30c. Taubenloch Gorge Waterfall; Schuss River; 40c. Lake Sils.

124 Lausanne Cathedral

125 Alphorn Blower

1955. Publicity Issue. Inscr "1955".

558 **124** 5c. multicoloured 75 20
559 – 10c. multicoloured 75 10
560 **125** 20c. brown and red . . . 1·00 10
561 – 40c. pink, black and blue 1·90 1·20

DESIGNS—HORIZ: 5c. Type **124** (National Philatelic Exhibition, Lausanne); 10c. Vaud girl's hat (Vevey Winegrowers' Festival); 40c. Car steering-wheel (25th International Motor Show, Geneva). VERT: 20c. Type **125** (Alpine Herdsman and Costume Festival, Interlaken).

126 Federal Institute of Technology, Zurich

1955. Pro Patria. Mountain Population Fund and Centenary of Federal Institute of Technology.

562 **126** 5c.+5c. grey 75 70
563 – 10c.+10c. green and cream 75 35
564 – 20c.+10c. red and pink . . 80 35
565 – 30c.+10c. brown & buff 6·00 4·75
566 – 40c.+10c. blue and light blue . . . . 6·00 4·00

DESIGNS: 10c. Grandfey railway viaduct over River Saane, near Fribourg; 20c. Lake Aegeri; 30c. Lake Grappelensee; 40c. Lake Bienne.

127 "Road Safety"

128 Fokker F.VIIb/3m and Douglas DC-6 Aircraft

1956. Publicity Issue. Inscr "1956".

567 – 5c. yellow, black and green 50 20
568 – 10c. black, green and red 80 10
569 **127** 20c. multicoloured 90 10
570 **128** 40c. blue and red . . . . 3·00 1·00

DESIGNS—HORIZ: 5c. First postal motor coach (50th anniv of postal motor coach service); 10c. Electric train emerging from Simplon Tunnel and Stockalper Palace (50th anniv of opening of Simplon Tunnel).

The 40c. commemorates the 25th anniv of Swissair.

129 Rose, Scissors and Tape-measure

130 Printing Machine's Inking Rollers

1956. Pro Patria. Swiss Women's Fund. T **129** and design as T **116** but inscr "PRO PATRIA 1956".

571 **129** 5c.+5c. green 65 75
572 – 10c.+10c. emerald and green 60 30
573 – 20c.+10c. purple & pink 65 50
574 – 30c.+10c. brown and light brown . . . . 4·25 4·75
575 – 40c.+10c. blue and light blue . . . . 4·25 3·75

DESIGNS: 10c. R. Rhone at St. Maurice; 20c. Katzensee; 30c. R. Rhine at Trin; 40c. Walensee.

1957. Publicity Issue. Inscr "1957".

576 **130** 5c. multicoloured 35 10
577 – 10c. brown, green & turq 2·30 10
578 – 20c. grey and red 70 10
579 – 40c. multicoloured . . . . 2·00 70

DESIGNS: 10c. Electric train crossing bridge over River Ticino (75th anniv of St. Gotthard Railway); 20c. Civil Defence shield and coat of arms ("Civil Defence"); 40c. Munatius Plancus, Basel and Rhine (2000th anniv of Basel).

The 5c. commemorates "Graphic 57" International Exhibition, Lausanne.

131 Shields of Switzerland and the Red Cross

132 "Charity"

1957. Pro Patria. Swiss Red Cross and National Cancer League Funds. Cross in red.

580 **131** 5c.+5c. red and grey . . . 50 60
581 **132** 10c.+10c. purple & grn 50 25
582 20c.+10c. grey and red . . 65 25
583 30c.+10c. blue & brown 3·50 4·00
584 40c.+10c. brown & blue 3·50 3·25

133 Symbol of Unity

1957. Europa.

585 **133** 25c. red 75 20
586 40c. blue . . . . 3·25 45

134 Nyon Castle (2000th anniv of Nyon)

1958. Publicity Issue. Inscr "1958".

587 **134** 5c. violet, buff and green 35 15
588 – 10c. myrtle, red and green 35 10
589 – 20c. red, lilac and vermilion 70 10
590 – 40c. multicoloured . . . . 3·00 95

DESIGNS: 10c. Woman's head with ribbons (Saffa Exhibition, Zurich); 20c. Crossbow (25th anniv as symbol of Swiss manufacture); 40c. Salvation Army bonnet (75th anniv of Salvation Army in Switzerland).

135 "Needy Mother" 136 Fluorite

1958. Pro Patria. For Needy Mothers. T **135** and designs showing minerals, rocks and fossils as T **136**. Inscr "PRO PATRIA 1958".

591 5c.+5c. purple 60 45
592 10c.+10c. yellow, grn & blk 60 25
593 20c.+10c. bistre, red & blk 65 45
594 30c.+10c. purple, brn & blk 3·25 3·50
595 40c.+10c. blue, ultram & blk 3·25 2·50

DESIGNS: 20c. "Lytoceras fimbriatus" ammonite; 30c. Garnet; 40c. Rock crystal.

137 Atomic Symbol

1958. 2nd U.N. Atomic Conference, Geneva.

596 **137** 40c. red, blue and cream 50 25

138 Modern Transport

139 "Swiss Citizens Abroad"

1959. Publicity Issue. Inscr "1959".

597 5c. multicoloured 35 15
598 10c. yellow, grey and green 45 10
599 20c. multicoloured 90 10
600 50c. blue, violet and light blue . . . . 1·30 85

DESIGNS: 5c. Type **138** (opening of "The Swiss House of Transport and Communications"); 10c. Lictor's fasces of the Coat of Arms of St. Gall and posthorn (NABAG—National Philatelic Exhibition, St. Gall); 20c. Owl, hare and fish (Protection of Animals); 50c. J. Calvin, Th. de Beze and University building (4th centenary of University of Geneva).

1959. Pro Patria. For Swiss Citizens Abroad. T **139** and other designs showing minerals, rocks and fossils as T **136**, and inscr "PRO PATRIA 1959".

601 5c.+5c. red and grey 45 50
602 10c.+10c. multicoloured . . . 70 30
603 20c.+10c. multicoloured . . . 80 35
604 30c.+10c. violet, brn & blk 2·40 2·10
605 40c.+10c. blue, turquoise and black . . . . 2·40 2·00

DESIGNS: 10c. Agate; 20c. Tourmaline; 30c. Amethyst; 40c. Fossilized giant salamander.

140 "Europa"

142 "Campaign against Cancer"

1959. Europa.

606 **140** 30c. red 65 10
607 50c. blue 75 15

1959. European P.T.T. Conference, Montreux. Optd **REUNION DES PTT D'EUROPE 1959**.

608 **140** 30c. red . . . . 26·00 7·75
609 50c. blue . . . . 26·00 7·75

1960. Publicity Issue. Inscr "1460–1960" (20c.) or "1960" (50c., 75c.).

610 10c. red, light green and green 75 15
611 20c. multicoloured 90 15
612 50c. yellow, ultramarine & blue 90 55
613 75c. red, black and blue . . . 4·00 4·75

DESIGNS: 10c. Type **142** (50th anniv of Swiss National League for Cancer Control); 20c. Charter and sceptre (500th anniv of Basel University); 50c. "Uprooted tree" (World Refugee Year); 75c. Douglas DC-8 jetliner ("Swissair enters the jet age").

143 15th-century Schwyz Cantonal Messenger

143a Lausanne Cathedral

1960. Postal History and "Architectural Monuments" (1st series).

614 – 5c. blue 10 10
615 **143** 10c. green 15 10
616 – 15c. red 10 10
617 – 20c. mauve 30 10
618 **143a** 25c. green 45 10
619p – 30c. red 35 10
620 – 35c. red 90 75
621 – 40c. purple 50 10
622 – 50c. blue 90 10
623 – 60c. red 70 10
624 – 70c. orange . . . . . . 1·20 45
625 – 75c. blue . . . . 1·50 60
626 – 80c. purple 90 10
627 – 90c. green . . . . . . 1·10 10
628 – 1f. orange . . . . . . 1·70 10
629 – 1f.20 red . . . . . . 1·90 15
632 – 1f.30 brown on lilac . . 1·40 15
630 – 1f.50 green . . . . . . 2·40 25
633 – 1f.70 purple on lilac . . 1·80 15

631 – 2f. blue . . . . 4·00 50
634 – 2f.20 green on green . . 2·40 40
635 – 2f.80 orange on orange . 3·00 35

DESIGNS—HORIZ: 5c. 17th-century Fribourg Cantonal messenger; 15c. 17th-century mule-driver; 20c. 19th-century mounted postman; 1f. Fribourg Town Hall; 1f.20, Basel Gate, Solothurn; 1f.50, Ital Reding's house, Schwyz; 1f.70, 2f., 2f.20, Abbey Church, Einsiedeln. VERT: 30c. Grossmunster, Zurich; 35c., 1f.30, Woodcutters Guildhall, Bienne; 40c. St. Peter's Cathedral, Geneva; 50c. Spalentor (gate), Basel; 60c. Clock Tower, Berne; 70c. Collegiate Church of St. Peter and St. Stephen, Bellinzona; 75c. Kapellbrucke (bridge) and Wasserturm, Lucerne; 80c. St. Gall Cathedral; 90c. Munot Fort, Schaffhausen; 2f.80, as 70c. but redrawn without bell-tower.

See also Nos. 698/713 and 1276.

144 Symbols of Occupational Trades

144a Conference Emblem

1960. Pro Patria. For Swiss Youth. T **144** and other designs showing minerals, rocks and fossils as T **136** and inscr "PRO PATRIA 1960".

636 – 5c.+5c. multicoloured . . 75 60
637 – 10c.+10c. pink, green and black 75 30
638 – 20c.+10c. yellow, purple and black 80 30
639 – 30c.+10c. blue, brown and black . . . . 3·50 2·75
640 **144** 50c.+10c. gold & blue . . 3·25 2·75

DESIGNS: 5c. Smoky quartz; 10c. Orthoclase (feldspar); 20c. Devil's toenail (fossil shell); 30c. Azurite; 50c. Type **144** ("50 Years of National Day Collection").

1960. Europa.

642 **144a** 30c. red 45 10
643 50c. blue 70 20

145 "Aid for Development"

1961. Publicity Issue.

644 **145** 5c. red, blue and grey . . 60 20
645 – 10c. yellow and blue . . . 60 10
646 – 20c. multicoloured . . . . 1·20 20
647 – 50c. red, green and blue 2·20 75

DESIGNS: 5c. Type **145** ("Aid to countries in process of development"); 10c. Circular emblem ("Hyspa" Exhibition of 20th-century Hygiene, Gymnastics and Sport, Berne); 20c. Hockey stick (World and European Ice Hockey Championships, Geneva and Lausanne); 50c. Map of Switzerland with telephone centres as wiring diagram (inauguration of Swiss fully automatic telephone service).

146 "Cultural Works of Eternity"

147 Doves

1961. Pro Patria. For Swiss Cultural Works, T **146** and other designs showing minerals, rocks and fossils as T **136** and inscr "PRO PATRIA 1961".

648 5c.+5c. blue 45 40
649 10c.+10c. purple, green and black 60 30
650 20c.+10c. red, blue and black 60 30
651 30c.+10c. blue, orange and black . . . . 1·70 2·30
652 50c.+10c. bistre, blue and black . . . . 1·70 2·20

DESIGNS: 10c. Fluorite; 20c. Glarone rabbitfish; 30c. Lazulite; 50c. Fossilized fern.

1961. Europa.

653 **147** 30c. red 40 10
654 50c. blue 50 20

148 St. Matthew

149 W.H.O. Emblem and Mosquito

1961. Wood Carvings from St. Oswald's Church, Zug.

655 **148** 3f. red . . . . 4·00 20
656 – 5f. blue . . . . 6·00 10
657 – 10f. brown . . . . 9·00 45
658 – 20f. red . . . . 17·00 1·90

DESIGNS: 5f. St. Mark; 10f. St. Luke; 20f. St. John.

1962. Publicity Issue.

659 – 5c. multicoloured 70 20
660 – 10c. bistre, purple and green 50 10
661 – 20c. multicoloured 80 15
662 **149** 50c. green, mauve and blue 85 45

DESIGNS: 5c. Electric train (introduction of Trans-Europe Express); 10c. Oarsman (World Rowing Championship, Lucerne); 20c. Jungfraujoch and Monch (50th anniv of Jungfraujoch rack railway station); 50c. Type **149** (malaria eradication).

150 Rousseau

151 Schwyz Gold Ducat

1962. Pro Patria. For Swiss Old People's Homes and Cultural Works.

663 **150** 5c.+5c. blue 15 20
664 – 10c.+10c. blue, black and green 25 25
665 **151** 20c.+10c. yellow, black and red 35 35
666 – 30c.+10c. green, blue and red . . . . 70 1·60
667 – 50c.+10c. violet, black and blue . . . . 75 1·40

COINS—As Type **151**: 10c. Obwalden silver-half taler; 30c. Uri batzen; 50c. Nidwalden batzen.

152 Europa "Tree"

1962. Europa.

668 **152** 30c. orange, yellow & brn 60 30
669 50c. blue, green and brown 65 40

153 Campaign Emblem (Freedom from Hunger)

1963. Publicity Issue.

670 – 5c. brown, red and blue 70 20
671 – 10c. red, grey and green 40 10
672 – 20c. lake, red and grey . . 1·50 15
673 **153** 30c. yellow, brown & green . . . . 1·40 1·10
674 – 50c. red, silver and blue 1·00 55
675 – 50c. multicoloured . . . 1·00 60

DESIGNS: No. 670, Boy scout (50th anniv of Swiss Boy Scout League); 671, Badge (Swiss Alpine Club cent); 672, Luegelkinn Viaduct (50th anniv of Lotschberg Railway); 674, Jubilee Emblem (Red Cross cent); 675, Hotel des Postes, Paris, 1863 (Paris Postal Conference).

154 Dr. Anna Heer (nursing pioneer)

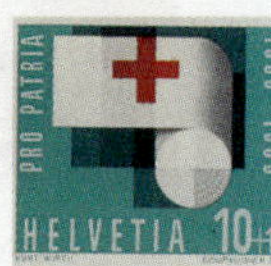

155 Roll of Bandage

1963. Pro Patria. For Swiss Medical and Refugee Aid. T **154** and other designs as T **155** showing Red Cross activities. Inscr "PRO PATRIA 1963".

676 5c.+5c. blue 20 25
677 10c.+10c. red, grey and green 25 15
678 20c.+10c. multicoloured . . . 30 20
679 30c.+10c. multicoloured . . . 90 1·20
680 50c.+10c. red, indigo & blue 1·10 1·20

DESIGNS: 20c. Gift parcel; 30c. Blood plasma; 50c. Red Cross brassard.

156 Glider and Jet Aircraft

1963. Air. 25th Anniv of Swiss "Pro Aero" Foundation. Berne–Locarno or Langenbruck–Berne (helicopter feeder) Special Flights.

681 **156** 2f. multicoloured . . . . 3·00 3·25

157 "Co-operation"

158 Exhibition Emblem

1963. Europa.

682 **157** 50c. brown and blue . . . 55 25

1963. Swiss National Exhibition, Lausanne.

683 **158** 10c. green and olive . . . 20 10
684 20c. red and brown . . . 15 10
685 – 50c. blue, grey and red . . 45 25
686 – 75c. violet, grey and red 55 45

DESIGNS: 50c. "Outlook" (emblem on globe and smaller globe); 75c. "Insight" (emblem on large globe).

159 Great St. Bernard Tunnel

1964. Publicity Issue.

687 5c. blue, red and green . . . 20 15
688 10c. green and blue 25 10
689 20c. multicoloured 50 10
690 50c. multicoloured 85 45

DESIGNS: 5c. Type **159** (Opening of Great St. Bernard Road Tunnel); 10c. Ancient "god of the waters" (Protection of water supplies); 20c. Swiss soldiers of 1864 and 1964 (Centenary of Swiss Association of Non-commissioned Officers); 50c. Standards of Geneva and Swiss Confederation (150th anniv of arrival of Swiss in Geneva).

160 Johann Georg Bodmer (inventor)

161 Europa "Flower"

1964. Pro Patria. For Swiss Mountain Aid and Cultural Funds. T **160** and vert designs of Swiss coins as T **151**. Inscr "PRO PATRIA 1964".

691 5c.+5c. blue 10 15
692 10c.+10c. drab, black & grn 15 15
693 20c.+10c. blue, black & mve 25 20
694 30c.+10c. blue, black & orge 35 55
695 50c.+10c. yellow, brn & bl 70 75

COINS: 10c. Zurich copper; 20c. Basel "doppeldicken"; 30c. Geneva silver thaler; 50c. Berne half gold florin.

1964. Europa.

696 **161** 20c. red 35 10
697 50c. blue 55 20

1964. "Architectural monuments" (2nd series). As T **143a**.

698 5c. mauve 10 10
699 10c. blue 10 10
700 15c. brown 20 10
701 20c. green 25 10
702 30c. red 30 10
703 50c. blue 50 10
704 70c. brown 75 10
705 1f. green . . . . 1·00 10
706 1f.20 red . . . . 1·20 15
707 1f.30 blue . . . . 1·50 55
708 1f.50 green . . . . 1·60 20
709 1f.70 red . . . . 1·90 70
710 2f. orange . . . . 2·10 20
711 2f.20 green . . . . 2·75 55
712 2f.50 green . . . . 2·75 25
713 3f.50 purple . . . . 3·75 30

DESIGNS—HORIZ: 5c. Lenzburg Castle; 10c. Freuler Mansion, Nafels; 15c. Mauritius Church, Appenzell; 20c. Planta House, Samedan; 30c. Town Square, Gais; 50c. Neuchatel Castle and Collegiate Church. VERT: 70c. Lussy "Hochhus", Wolfenschiessen; 1f. Riva San Vitale Church; 1f.20, Payerne Abbey Church; 1f.30, St. Pierre-de Clages Church; 1f.50, Gateway, Porrentruy; 1f.70, Frauenfeld Castle; 2f. Castle Seedorf (Uri); 2f.20, Thomas Tower and Arch, Liestal; 2f.50, St. Oswald's Church, Zug; 3f.50, Benedictine Abbey, Engelberg.

162 Swiss 5r. Stamp of 1854 with "Lozenge" Cancellation

1965. Publicity Issue.

714 – 5c. black, red and blue . . 10 10
715 **162** 10c. brown, blue and green 10 10
716 – 20c. multicoloured 25 10
717 – 50c. red, black and blue 50 35

DESIGNS, etc: 5c. Nurse and patient ("Nursing"); 10c. Type **162** ("NABRA 1965" National Stamp Exhibition, Berne); 20c. WAC Officer (25th anniv of Women's Army Corps); 50c. World telecommunications map (centenary of I.T.U.).

163 Father T. Florentini

164 Fish-tailed Goose ("Evil")

1965. Pro Patria. For Swiss Abroad and Art Research. Inscr "PRO PATRIA 1965".

719 **163** 5c.+5c. blue 10 10
720 **164** 10c.+10c. multicoloured 10 10
721 – 20c.+10c. multicoloured 25 10
722 – 30c.+10c. brown & blue 40 35
723 – 50c.+10c. blue & brown 55 40

DESIGNS—As Type **164**: (Ceiling paintings in St. Martin's Church, Zillis (Grisons): 20c. One of the magi journeying to Herod; 30c. Fishermen; 50c. The Temptation of Christ.

165 Swiss Emblem and Arms of Cantons

1965. 150th Anniv of Entry of Valais, Neuchatel and Geneva into Confederation.

724 **165** 20c. multicoloured 25 10

166 Matterhorn

167 Europa "Sprig"

1965. Mobile P.O. Issue.

725 **166** 10c. multicoloured 25 10
726 30c. multicoloured 65 60

The 30c. is inscr "CERVIN".

1965. Europa.

727 **167** 50c. green and blue . . . 60 20

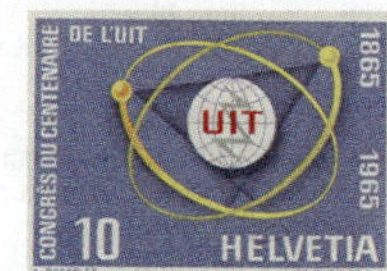

168 I.T.U. Emblem and Satellites

1965. I.T.U. Centenary Congress, Montreux. Multicoloured.

728 10c. Type **168** 10 10
729 30c. Symbols of world telecommunications 30 25

169 Figure Skating

1965. World Figure Skating Championships, Davos.

730 **169** 5c. multicoloured 10 10

170 River Kingfisher

171 H. Federer (author)

1966. Publicity Issue. Multicoloured.

731 10c. Type **170** 20 10
732 20c. Mercury's helmet and laurel twig 25 10
733 50c. Phase in nuclear fission and flags 45 20

PUBLICITY EVENTS: 10c. Preservation of natural beauty; 20c. 50th Swiss Industrial Fair, Basel (MUBA); 50c. International Institute for Nuclear Research (CERN).

1966. Pro Patria. For Aid to Mothers. Inscr "PRO PATRIA 1966".

734 **171** 5c.+5c. blue 10 10
735 – 10c.+10c. multicoloured 10 10
736 – 20c.+10c. multicoloured 25 15

737 – 30c.+10c. multicoloured 40 35
738 – 50c.+10c. multicoloured 55 40
DESIGNS—As Type **164**: ("The Flight to Egypt" from ceiling paintings in St. Martin's Church, Zillis (Grisons)): 10c. Joseph's dream; 20c. Joseph on his way; 30c. Virgin and Child; 50c. Angel pointing the way.

172 Society Emblem

173 Europa "Ship"

1966. 50th Anniv of New Helvetic Society for Swiss Abroad.
739 **172** 20c. red and blue 20 10

1966. Europa.
740 **173** 20c. red 25 10
741 50c. blue 50 20

174 Finsteraarhorn

1966. "Swiss Alps".
742 **174** 10c. multicoloured 10 10

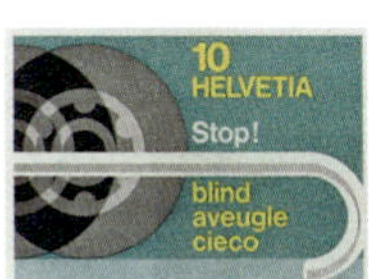
175 White Stick and Motor-car Wheel (Welfare of the Blind)

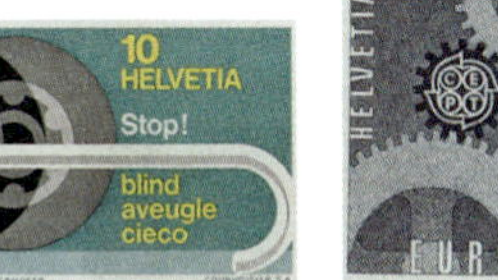
176 C.E.P.T. Emblem and Cogwheels

1967. Publicity Issue.
743 **175** 10c. multicoloured 10 10
744 – 20c. multicoloured 25 10
DESIGN: 20c. Flags of European Free Trade Area countries (abolition of E.F.T.A. tariffs).

1967. Europa.
745 **176** 30c. blue 30 10

177 Theodor Kocher (surgeon)

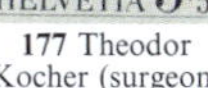
178 Cogwheel and Swiss Emblem

1967. Pro Patria. For National Day Collection. Inscr "PRO PATRIA 1967".
746 **177** 5c.+5c. blue 10 10
747 – 10c.+10c. multicoloured 10 10
748 – 20c.+10c. multicoloured 25 10
749 – 30c.+10c. multicoloured 40 35
750 – 50c.+10c. multicoloured 55 40
DESIGNS—As Type **164**: (Ceiling paintings in St. Martin's Church, Zillis (Grisons)): 10c. Annunciation to the Shepherds; 20c. Christ and the woman of Samaria; 30c. Adoration of the Magi; 50c. Joseph seated on throne.

1967. Publicity Issue. Multicoloured.
751 10c. Type **178** 10 10
752 20c. Hour-glass and Sun 20 10
753 30c. San Bernardino highway 35 10
754 50c. "OCTI" emblem 50 20
PUBLICITY EVENTS: 10c. 50th anniv of Swiss Week; 20c. 50th anniv of Aged People Foundation; 30c. Opening of San Bernardino road tunnel; 50c. 75th anniv of Central Office for International Railway Transport (OCTI).

179 "Mountains" and Swiss Emblem

1968. Publicity Issue.
755 10c. multicoloured 10 10
756 20c. yellow, brown and blue 25 10
757 30c. blue, ochre and brown 30 10
758 50c. red, turquoise and blue 55 20
DESIGNS AND EVENTS: 10c. T **179** (50th anniv of Swiss Women's Alpine Club); 20c. Europa "key" (Europa); 30c. Staunton rook and chessboard (18th Chess Olympiad, Lugano); 50c. Dispatch "satellites" and aircraft tail-fin (inauguration of new Geneva Air Terminal).

180 "Maius"

181 Protective helmet

1968. Pro Patria. For National Day Collection. Inscr "PRO PATRIA 1968".
759 **180** 10c.+10c. multicoloured 10 10
760 – 20c.+10c. multicoloured 25 15
761 – 30c.+10c. multicoloured 35 10
762 – 50c.+20c. multicoloured 55 50
DESIGNS (Stained-glass panels in the rose window, Lausanne Cathedral): 20c. "Leo"; 30c. "Libra"; 50c. "Pisces" (symbols of the months and signs of the zodiac).

1968. Publicity Issue. Multicoloured.
763 10c. Type **181** 10 10
764 20c. Geneva and Zurich stamps of 1843 25 10
765 30c. Part of Swiss map 30 10
766 50c. "Six Stars" (countries) and anchor 45 25
PUBLICITY EVENTS: 10c. 50th anniv of Swiss Accident Insurance Company; 20c. 125th anniv of Swiss stamps; 30c. 25th anniv of Swiss Territorial Planning Society; 50c. Centenary of Rhine Navigation Act.

182 Guide Camp and Emblem

1969. Publicity Issue. Multicoloured.
767 10c. Type **182** 25 10
768 20c. Pegasus constellation 25 10
769 30c. Emblem of Comptoir Suisse 30 10
770 50c. Emblem of Gymnaestrade 45 30
771 2f. Haefeli DH-3 biplane and Douglas DC-8 jetliner 2·00 1·40
EVENTS: 10c. 50th anniv of Swiss Girl Guides' Federation; 20c. Opening of first Swiss Planeta-rium, Lucerne; 30c. 50th anniv of Comptoir Suisse, Lausanne; 50c. 5th Gymnaestrada, Basel; 2f. 50th anniv of Swiss Airmail Services.

183 Colonnade

184 "St. Francis of Assisi preaching to the Birds" (Abbey-church, Konigsfelden)

1969. Europa.
772 **183** 30c. multicoloured 35 10
773 50c. multicoloured 50 40

1969. Pro Patria. For National Day Collection. Stained-glass Windows. Multicoloured.
774 10c.+10c. Type **184** 10 10
775 20c.+10c. "The People of Israel drinking" (Berne Cathedral) 25 15
776 30c.+10c. "St. Christopher" (Laufelfingen Church, Basle) 35 20
777 50c.+20c. "Madonna and Child" (St. Jacob's Chapel, Grapplang, Flums) 55 45

185 Kreuzberge

186 Huldrych Zwingli (Protestant reformer)

1969. Publicity and "Swiss Alps" Issues. Multicoloured.
778 20c. Type **185** 30 10
779 30c. Children crossing road 30 10
780 50c. Hammersmith 50 25
EVENTS: 30c. Road Safety campaign for children; 50c. 50th anniv of I.L.O.

1969. Swiss Celebrities.
781 **186** 10c. violet 10 10
782 – 20c. green 25 10
783 – 30c. red 35 10
784 – 50c. blue 45 35
785 – 80c. brown 80 80
CELEBRITIES: 20c. General Henri Guisan; 30c. Francesco Borromini (architect); 50c. Othmar Schoeck (composer); 80c. Germaine de Stael (writer).

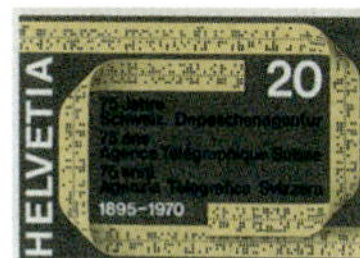
187 Telex Tape

188 "Flaming Sun"

1970. Publicity Issue. Multicoloured.
786 20c. Type **187** 20 10
787 30c. Fireman saving child 45 10
788 30c. "Chained wing" emblem 30 10
789 50c. U.N. emblem 50 25
790 80c. New U.P.U. Headquarters 90 95
EVENTS: 20c. 75th anniv of Swiss Telegraphic Agency; 30c. (No. 787), Centenary of Swiss Firemen's Assn; 30c. (No. 788), 50th anniv of "Pro Infirmis" Foundation; 50c. 25th anniv of U.N. Organization; 80c. Inauguration of new U.P.U. headquarters, Berne.

1970. Europa.
791 **188** 30c. red 30 10
792 50c. blue 55 25

1970. Pro Patria. For National Day Collection. Glass paintings by contemporary artists. As T **184** but inscr "1970". Multicoloured.
793 10c.+10c. "Sailor" (G. Casty) 10 15
794 20c.+10c. Architectonic composition (Celestino Piatti) 25 15
795 30c.+10c. "Bull" symbol of Marduk, from "The Four Elements" (Hans Stocker) 35 15
796 50c.+20c. "Man and Woman" (Max Hunziker and Karl Ganz) 55 45

189 Footballer (75th Anniv of Swiss Football Association)

190 Numeral

1970. Publicity and "Swiss Alps" (30c.) Issue. Multicoloured.
797 10c. Type **189** 25 10
798 20c. Census form and pencil (Federal Census) 20 10
799 30c. Piz Palu, Grisons 35 10
800 50c. Conservation Year Emblem (Nature Conservation Year) 45 35

1970. Coil Stamps.
801 **190** 10c. red 10 10
802 20c. green 25 10
803 50c. blue 55 30

191 Female Gymnasts ("Youth and Sport")

193 Europa Chain

1971. Publicity Issue.
804 **191** 10c. multicoloured 20 25
805 – 10c. multicoloured 20 25
806 – 20c. multicoloured 25 10
807 – 30c. multicoloured 30 10
808 – 50c. brown and blue 50 25
809 – 80c. multicoloured 85 65
DESIGNS AND EVENTS: 10c. (No. 805), Male athletes ("Youth and Sport" constitutional amendment); 20c. Stylized rose (child welfare); 30c. "Rayon II" stamp of 1850 and basilisk ("NABA" Philatelic Exhibition, Basel); 50c. "Co-operation" symbol (aid for technical development); 80c. "Intelsat 4" (I.T.U. Space Conference).

1971. Europa.
811 **193** 30c. yellow and mauve 30 10
812 50c. yellow and blue 50 20

1971. Pro Patria. For National Day Collection. Contemporary Glass Paintings. As T **184**.
813 10c.+10c. "Religious Abstract", (J. F. Comment) 10 10
814 20c.+10c. "Cockerel", (J. Prahin) 25 15
815 30c.+10c. "Fox", (K. Volk) 35 15
816 50c.+20c. "Christ's Passion" (B. Schorderet) 60 55

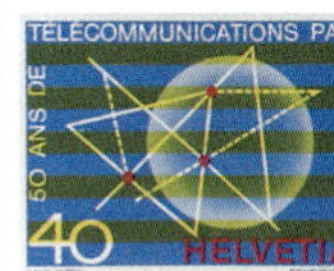
194 "Telecommunications Services" (50th anniv of Radio-Suisse)

195 Alexandre Yersin (bacteriologist)

1971. Publicity and "Swiss Alps" (30c.).
817 – 30c. purple, grey & mauve 35 10
818 **194** 40c. multicoloured 40 35
DESIGN: 30c. Les Diablerets, Vaud.

1971. Famous Physicians.
819 **195** 10c. green 10 10
820 – 20c. green 20 10
821 – 30c. red 30 10
822 – 40c. blue 45 45
823 – 80c. purple 80 80
PHYSICIANS: 20c. Auguste Forel (psychiatrist); 30c. Jules Gonin (ophthalmologist); 40c. Robert Koch (German bacteriologist); 80c. Frederick Banting (Canadian physiologist).

196 Warning Triangle and Wrench (75th Annivs of Motoring Organisations)

1972. Publicity Issue.
824 **196** 10c. multicoloured 10 10
825 – 20c. multicoloured 25 10
826 – 30c. orange, red & carmine 30 10
827 – 40c. violet, green and blue 50 30
DESIGNS AND EVENTS: 20c. Signal-box switch table (125th anniv of Swiss Railways); 30c. Stylized radio waves and girl's face (50th anniv of Swiss Broadcasting); 40c. Symbolic tree (50th "Swiss Citizens Abroad" Congress).

197 Swissair Boeing 747-100 Jetliner

198 "Communications"

1972. Air. Pro Aero Foundation and 50th Annivs of North Atlantic and Int Airmail Services.
828 **197** 2f.+1f. multicoloured 2·50 1·90

1972. Europa.
829 **198** 30c. multicoloured 30 10
830 40c. multicoloured 45 20

199 Late Stone Age Harpoon Heads

200 Civil Defence Emblem

1972. Pro Patria. For National Day Collection. Archaeological Discoveries (1st series). Mult.
831 10c.+10c. Type **199** 20 15
832 20c.+10c. Bronze water-vessel, c. 570 B.C. 35 15
833 30c.+10c. Gold bust of Marcus Aurelius, 2nd cent A.D. 50 20
834 40c.+20c. Alemannic disc. 7th-cent A.D. 55 65
See also Nos. 869/72, 887/90 and 901/4.

1972. Publicity and "Swiss Alps" (20c.) Issue. Multicoloured.
835 10c. Type **200** 10 10
836 20c. Spannorter 30 15
837 30c. Sud Aviation Alouette III rescue helicopter 40 10
838 40c. The "Four Elements" (53 × 31 mm) 45 30
SUBJECTS: 10c. Swiss Civil Defence; 20c. Tourism; 30c. Swiss Air Rescue Service; 40c. Protection of the environment.

201 Alberto Giacometti (painter)

202 Dish Aerial

1972. Swiss Celebrities.
839 **201** 10c. black and buff 10 10
840 – 20c. black and bistre 25 10
841 – 30c. black and pink 30 10
842 – 40c. black and blue 45 25
843 – 80c. black and purple 80 80
PORTRAITS: 20c. Charles Ramuz (novelist); 30c. Le Corbusier (architect); 40c. Albert Einstein (physicist); 80c. Arthur Honegger (composer).

1973. Publicity Issue. Multicoloured.
844 15c. Type **202** 20 20
845 30c. Quill pen 30 10
846 40c. Interpol emblem 45 25
EVENTS: 15c. Construction of Satellite Earth Station, Leuk-Brentjong; 30c. Centenary of Swiss Association of Commercial Employees; 40c. 50th anniv of International Criminal Police Organisation (Interpol).

203 Sottoceneri

204 Toggenburg Inn Sign

1973.
847 **203** 5c. blue and stone . . . 10 10
848 – 10c. green and purple . . 10 10
849 – 15c. blue and orange . . 20 10
850 – 25c. violet and green . . 25 20
851 – 30c. violet and red . . . 30 10
852 – 35c. violet and orange . . 50 30
853 – 40c. grey and blue . . . 40 10
854 – 50c. green and orange . . 50 10
855 – 60c. brown and grey . . 65 10
856 – 70c. green and purple . . 75 10
857 – 80c. red and green . . . 85 15
858 – 1f. purple . . . . . . 1·10 10
859 – 1f.10 blue . . . . . . 1·20 15
860 – 1f.20 red . . . . . . 1·30 1·00
861 **204** 1f.30 orange . . . . . 1·60 25
862 – 1f.50 green . . . . . 1·70 15
863 – 1f.70 grey . . . . . . 1·10 40
864 – 1f.80 red . . . . . . 2·00 20
865 – 2f. blue . . . . . . 2·20 20
866 – 2f.50 brown . . . . . 2·75 35
866a – 3f. red . . . . 3·25 40
866b – 3f.50 green . . . . . 3·75 70
DESIGNS—VERT: 10c. Grisons; 15c. Central Switzerland; 25c. Jura; 30c. Simmental; 35c. Houses, Central Switzerland; 40c. Vaud; 50c. Valais; 60c. Engadine; 70c. Sopraceneri; 80c. Eastern Switzerland. HORIZ: 1f. Rose window, Lausanne Cathedral; 1f.10, Gallus portal, Basel Cathedral; 1f.20, Romanesque capital, St.-Jean-Baptiste Church, Grandson; 1f.50, Medallion, St. Georgen Monastery, Stein am Rhein; 1f.70, Roman Capital, St.-Jean-Baptiste Church, Grandson; 1f.80, Gargoyle, Berne Cathedral; 2f. Oriel, Schaffhausen; 2f.50, Weathercock, St. Ursus Cathedral, Solothurn; 3f. Font, St. Maurice Church, Saanen; 3f.50, Astronomical clock, Berne.

205 Europa "Posthorn"

1973. Europa.
867 **205** 25c. yellow and red . . . 30 25
868 40c. yellow and blue . . . 40 20

1973. Pro Patria. For National Day Collection. Archaeological Discoveries (2nd series). As T **199**, but horiz. Multicoloured.
869 15c.+5c. Rauraric jar 25 25
870 30c.+10c. Head of a Gaul (bronze) 40 15
871 40c.+20c. Almannic "Fish" brooches 65 65
872 60c.+20c. Gold bowl . . . . 1·00 95

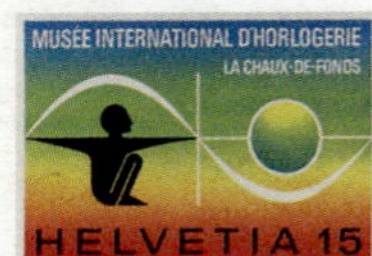

206 Horological Emblem

1973. Publicity Issue. Multicoloured.
873 15c. Type **206** 20 20
874 30c. Skiing emblem 30 10
875 40c. Face of child 40 20
SUBJECTS: 15c. Inaug (1974) of Int Horological Museum, Neuchatel; 30c. World Alpine Skiing Championships, St. Moritz (1974); 40c. "Terre des Hommes" (Child-care organization).

207 Global Hostels

209 "Continuity" (Max Bill)

1974. Publicity Issue. Multicoloured.
876 15c. Type **207** 15 10
877 30c. Gymnast and hurdlers . . 30 10
878 40c. Pistol and target 40 25
SUBJECTS: 15c. "50 Years of Swiss Youth Hostels"; 30c. Centenary of Swiss Workmen's Gymnastics and Sports Assn (S.A.T.U.S.); 40c. World Shooting Championships, 1974.

1974. Europa. Swiss Sculptures.
880 **209** 30c. black and red 30 10
881 – 40c. brown, blue and black 45 35
DESIGN: 40c. "Amazone" (Carl Burckhardt).

210 Eugene Borel (first Director of International Bureau, U.P.U.)

211 View of Berne

1974. Centenary of U.P.U.
882 **210** 30c. black and pink . . . 30 15
883 – 40c. black and grey . . . 45 25
884 – 80c. black and green . . . 85 75
DESIGNS: 40c. Heinrich von Stephan (founder of U.P.U.); 80c. Montgomery Blair (U.S. Postmaster-General and initiator of 1863 Paris Postal Conference).

1974. 17th U.P.U. Congress, Lausanne. Mult.
885 30c. Type **211** 30 20
886 30c. View of Lausanne . . . 30 20

1974. Pro Patria. For National Day Collection. Archaeological Discoveries (3rd series). As T **199** but horiz. Multicoloured.
887 15c.+5c. Glass bowl 25 25
888 30c.+10c. Bull's head (bronze) 40 15
889 40c.+20c. Gold brooch . . . 65 60
890 60c.+20c. "Bird" vessel (clay) 95 90

212 "Oath of Allegiance" (sculpture) (W. Witschi)

1974. Publicity Issue.
891 **212** 15c. deep green, green and lilac 20 15
892 – 30c. multicoloured 30 10
893 – 30c. multicoloured 30 10
EVENTS AND COMMEMORATIONS: No. 891, Centenary of Federal Constitution; No. 892, Foundation emblem (Aid for Swiss Sport Foundation); No. 893, Posthorn and "postal transit" arrow (125th anniv of Federal Posts).

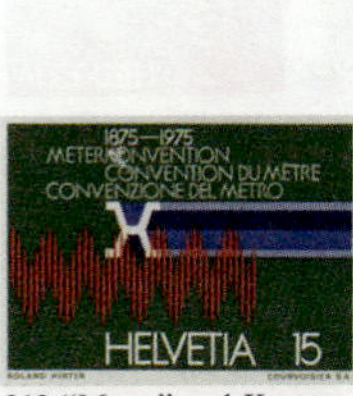

213 "Metre" and Krypton Line

214 "The Monch" (F. Hodler)

1975. Publicity Issue.
894 **213** 15c. orange, blue and green 20 25
895 – 30c. brown, purple & yell 30 10
896 – 60c. red, black and blue 60 40
897 – 90c. multicoloured . . . 1·00 70
DESIGNS AND EVENTS: 15c. Centenary of International Metre Convention; 30c. Heads of women (International Women's Year); 60c. Red Cross flag and barbed-wire (Conference on Humanitarian International Law, Geneva); 90c. Astra airship "Ville de Lucerne", 1910 ("Aviation and Space Travel" Exhibition, Transport and Communications Museum, Lucerne).

1975. Europa. Paintings. Multicoloured.
898 30c. Type **214** 35 15
899 50c. "Still Life with Guitar" (R. Auberjonois) 55 40
900 60c. "L'effeuilleuse" (M. Barraud) 70 50

1975. Pro Patria. Archaeological Discoveries. (4th series). As T **199**. Multicoloured.
901 15c.+10c. Gold brooch, Oron-le-Chatel 25 25
902 30c.+20c. Bronze head of Bacchus, Avenches 45 25
903 50c.+20c. Bronze daggers, Bois-de-Vaux, Lausanne . . 70 80
904 60c.+25c. Glass decanter, Maralto 85 75

215 "Eliminate Obstacles!"

1975. Publicity Issue.
905 **215** 15c. black, green and lilac 20 20
906 – 30c. black, rosine and red 30 10
907 – 50c. brown and bistre . . 60 45
908 – 60c. multicoloured 70 40
DESIGNS: 30c. Organization emblem (Inter-confessional Pastoral Care by Telephone Organization); 50c. European Architectural Heritage Year emblem; 60c. Beat Fischer von Reichenbach (founder) (300th anniv of Fischer postal service).

216 Forest Scene (Federal Forest Laws Cent)

217 Floral Embroidery

1976. Publicity Issue.
909 **216** 20c. multicoloured 20 20
910 – 40c. multicoloured 40 20
911 – 40c. black, orange & pur 40 20
912 – 80c. black and blue . . . 85 75
DESIGNS: No. 910, Fruit and vegetables (campaign to promote nutriments as opposed to alcohol); No. 911, African child (fight against leprosy); No. 912, Early and modern telephones (telephone centenary).

1976. Europa. Handicrafts.
913 **217** 40c. yellow, brown & pink 40 15
914 – 80c. blue, red and stone 80 55
DESIGN: 80c. Decorated pocket watch.

218 Kyburg Castle, Zurich

1976. Pro Patria. Swiss Castles (1st series). Multicoloured.
915 20c.+10c. Type **218** 30 30
916 40c.+20c. Grandson, Vaud 60 25
917 40c.+20c. Murten, Fribourg 60 35
918 80c.+40c. Bellinzona, Ticino 1·40 1·50
See also Nos. 932/5, 955/8 and 977/80.

219 Roe Deer Fawn, Barn Swallow and Frog (World Fed. for Protection of Animals)

1976. Publicity Issue.
919 **219** 20c. black, brown & green 25 25
920 – 40c. black, yellow and red 45 15
921 – 40c. multicoloured 45 15
922 – 80c. red, violet and blue 90 55
DESIGNS: No. 920, "Sun" and inscription ("Save Energy" campaign); No. 921, St. Gotthard mountains (Swiss Alps); No. 922, Skater (World Speed Skating Championships, Davos).

220 Oskar Bider and Bleriot XI

1977. Swiss Aviation Pioneers.
923 **220** 40c. black, mauve and red 45 15
924 – 80c. black, purple and blue 80 60
925 – 100c. black, green & bistre . . . . 1·00 80
926 – 150c. black, brown & grn 1·50 1·40
DESIGNS: 80c. Eduard Spelterini and balloon basket; 100c. Armand Dufaux and Dufaux IV biplane; 150c. Walter Mittelholzer and Dornier Do-B Merkur seaplane "Switzerland".

221 Blue Cross (society for care of alcoholics, cent)

1977. Publicity Issues.
927 **221** 20c. blue and brown . . . 20 15
928 – 40c. multicoloured 40 10
929 – 80c. multicoloured 80 55
DESIGNS: 40c. Festival emblem (Vevey vintage festival); 80c. Balloons carrying letters ("Juphilex 1977" youth stamp exhibition, Berne).

222 St. Ursanne

1977. Europa. Landscapes. Multicoloured.
930 40c. Type **222** 40 15
931 80c. Sils-Baselgia 80 60

1977. Pro Patria. Swiss Castles (2nd series). As T **218**. Multicoloured.
932 20c.+10c. Aigle, Vaud . . . 30 30
933 40c.+20c. Pratteln, Basel-Landschaft 55 25
934 70c.+30c. Sargans, St. Gallen 90 1·00
935 80c.+40c. Hallwil, Aargau . . 1·10 1·10

223 Factory Worker

1977. Publicity Issue. Multicoloured.
936 20c. Type **223** 20 20
937 40c. Ionic capital 40 15
938 80c. Association emblem and butterfly 85 55
EVENTS: 20c. Centenary of Federal Factories Act; 40c. Protection of cultural monuments; 80c. Swiss Footpaths Association.

224 Sternsingen, Bergun

225 Mailcoach Route Plate, Vaud Canton

1977. Regional Folk Customs.
939 **224** 5c. green 10 10
940 – 10c. red 10 10
941 – 20c. orange 20 10
941b – 25c. brown 40 25
941c – 30c. green 35 15
942 – 35c. green 45 20
943 – 40c. purple 50 10
943c – 45c. blue 65 60
944 – 50c. red 55 10
944b – 60c. brown 80 55
945 – 70c. lilac 80 10
946 – 80c. blue 95 25
947 – 90c. brown . . . . . . 1·00 30
DESIGNS: 10c. Sechselauten, Zurich; 20c. Silvesterklause, Herisau; 25c. Chesstete, Solothurn; 30c. Rollelibutzen, Alstatten; 35c. Gansabhauet, Sursee; 40c. Escalade, Geneva; 45c. Klausjagen, Kussnacht; 50c. Archetringele, Laupen; 60c. Schnabelgeissen, Ottenbach; 70c. Processioni storiche, Mendrisio; 80c. Vogel Gryff, Basel; 90c. Roitschaggata, Lotschental.

1978. Publicity Issue. Multicoloured.
948 20c. Type **225** 25 10
949 40c. View of Lucerne 40 10
950 70c. Title page of book "Melusine" 75 60
951 80c. Stylized camera and lens 85 60
EVENTS: 20c. "Lemanex '78" National Stamp Exhibition; 40c. 800th anniv of Lucerne; 70c. 500th anniv of Printing at Geneva; 80c. 2nd International Triennial Exhibition of Photography, Fribourg.

227 Stockalper Palace, Brig

228 Abbe Joseph Bovet (composer)

1978. Europa.
953 **227** 40c. multicoloured 45 10
954 – 80c. blue, brown and black 90 60
DESIGN: 80c. Old Diet Hall, Berne.

1978. Pro Patria. Swiss Castles (3rd series). As T **218**.
955 20c.+10c. Hagenwil, Thurgau 35 30
956 40c.+20c. Burgdorf, Berne . . 50 20
957 70c.+30c. Tarasp, Graubunden . . . . 1·00 1·10
958 80c.+40c. Chillon, Vaud . . . 1·30 1·30

1978. Celebrities.
959 **228** 20c. green 25 15
960 – 40c. purple 45 10
961 – 70c. grey 75 55
962 – 80c. blue 85 55
DESIGNS: 40c. Henri Dunant (founder of Red Cross); 70c. Carl Gustav Jung (psychiatrist); 80c. Auguste Piccard (physicist).

229 Worker wearing Goggles

1978. Safety at Work. Multicoloured.
963 40c. Type **229** 45 20
964 40c. Worker wearing respirator 45 20
965 40c. Worker wearing safety helmet 45 20

230 Arms of Switzerland and Jura

1978. Creation of Canton of Jura.
966 **230** 40c. red, black and stone 45 10

231 Rainer Maria Rilke (writer) **232** Othmar H. Ammann and Verrazano Narrows Bridge

1979. Celebrities.
967 **231** 20c. green 25 15
968 – 40c. red 45 10
969 – 70c. brown 75 55
970 – 80c. blue 85 55
DESIGNS: 40c. Paul Klee (artist); 70c. Herman Hesse (novelist and poet); 80c. Thomas Mann (novelist).

1979. Publicity Issue. Multicoloured.
971 20c. Type **232** 20 15
972 40c. Target and marker . . . 45 10
973 70c. Hot-air balloon "Esperanto" 75 60
974 80c. Aircraft tail fins 85 55
SUBJECTS: 20c. Birth centenary of O. H. Ammann (engineer); 40c. 50th Federal Riflemen's Festival, Lucerne; 70c. World Esperanto Congress, Lucerne; 80c. Basel-Mulhouse Airport.

233 Old Letter Box, Basel **234** Gold Stater

1979. Europa.
975 **233** 40c. multicoloured 45 15
976 – 80c. blue, lt blue & stone 85 65
DESIGN: 80c. Alpine relay station on the Jungfraujoch.

1979. Pro Patria. Swiss Castles (4th series). As T **218**. Multicoloured.
977 20c.+10c. Oron, Vaud . . . 30 30
978 40c.+20c. Spiez, Berne . . . 50 25
979 70c.+30c. Porrentruy, Jura 80 95
980 80c.+40c. Rapperswil, St. Gallen . . . . 1·10 1·20

1979. Publicity Issue. Multicoloured.
981 20c. Type **234** 25 15
982 40c. Child on dove (horiz) . . 45 10
983 70c. Morse key and satellite (horiz) 75 50
984 80c. "Ariane" rocket 85 50

EVENTS: 20c. Centenary of Swiss Numismatic Society; 40c. International Year of the Child; 70c. 50th anniv of Swiss Radio Amateurs; 80c. European Space Agency.

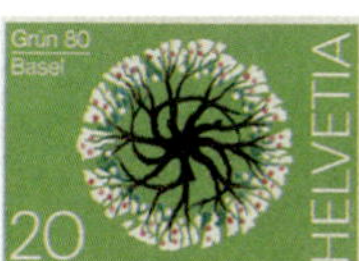

235 Tree in Blossom **236** Johann Konrad Kern (politician)

1980. Publicity Issue. Multicoloured.
985 20c. Type **235** 25 10
986 40c. Carved milk vessel . . . 45 10
987 70c. Winterthur Town Hall 70 55
988 80c. Pic-Pic motor car . . . 80 60
SUBJECTS: 20c. Horticultural and Landscape Gardening Exhibition, Basel; 40c. 50th anniv of Arts and Crafts Centre; 70c. Centenary of Society for Swiss Art History; 80c. 50th International Motor Show, Geneva.

1980. Europa.
989 **236** 40c. flesh, black and pink 45 10
990 – 80c. flesh, black and blue 85 55
DESIGN: 80c. Gustav Adolf Hasler (communications pioneer).

237 Mason and Carpenter **238** Girocheque and Letter Box

1980. Pro Patria. Trade and Craft Signs. Mult.
991 20c.+10c. Type **237** 30 30
992 40c.+20c. Barber 65 20
993 70c.+30c. Hatter . . . . . . 1·00 1·20
994 80c.+40c. Baker . . . . . . 1·20 1·00

1980. Swiss P.T.T. Services.
995 **238** 20c. multicoloured 25 20
996 – 40c. multicoloured 50 10
997 – 70c. brown, black and lilac 70 50
998 – 80c. multicoloured 80 55
DESIGNS: 40c. Postbus; 70c. Transfer roller (50th anniv of P.T.T. postage stamp printing office); 80c. Flowers and telephone (centenary of telephone in Switzerland).

239 Weather Chart

1980. Publicity Issue. Multicoloured.
999 20c. Type **239** 25 20
1000 40c. Figures and cross . . . 45 25
1001 80c. Motorway sign 90 85
SUBJECTS: 20c. Centenary of Swiss Meteorological Office; 40c. Centenary of Swiss Trades Union Federation; 80c. Opening of St. Gotthard road tunnel.

240 Granary from Kiesen

1981. Publicity Issue. Multicoloured.
1002 20c. Type **240** 25 15
1003 40c. Disabled figures 45 10
1004 70c. "The Parish Clerk" (Albert Anker) (vert) . . 75 65
1005 80c. Theodolite and rod . . 80 55
1006 110c. Tail of DC9-81 . . . 1·10 85
SUBJECTS: 20c. Ballenberg Open-air Museum; 40c. International Year of Disabled Persons; 70c. 150th birth anniv of Albert Anker (artist); 80c. 16th International Federation of Surveyors Congress, Montreux; 110c. 50th anniv of Swissair.

241 Figure leaping from Earth **242** Dancing Couple

1981. 50th Anniv of Swissair.
1007 **241** 2f.+1f. lilac, violet and yellow . . . . 2·40 2·10

1981. Europa. Multicoloured.
1008 40c. Type **242** 45 10
1009 80c. Stone putter 90 60

243 Aarburg Post Office Sign, 1685 **244** Seal of Fribourg

1981. Pro Patria. Postal Signs. Multicoloured.
1010 20c.+10c. Type **243** 35 40
1011 40c.+20c. Mail coach sign of Fribourg Cantonal Post 65 25
1012 70c.+30c. Gordola Post office sign (Ticino Cantonal Post) . . . . . 1·00 1·30
1013 80c.+40c. Splugen post office sign . . . . 1·20 1·10

1981. 500th Anniv of Covenant of Stans.
1014 **244** 40c. red, black and brown 45 15
1015 – 40c. green, black and purple 45 15
1016 – 80c. brown, black and blue 85 60
DESIGNS: 40c. (No. 1015) Seal of Solothurn; 80c. Old Town Hall, Stans.

245 Voltage Regulator from Jungfrau Railway's Power Station

1981. Publicity Issue. Multicoloured.
1017 20c. Type **245** 25 15
1018 40c. Crossbow quality seal 45 10
1019 70c. Group of youths . . . 75 60
1020 1f.10 Mosaic . . . . 1·20 80
SUBJECTS: 20c. Opening of Technorama of Switzerland, Winterthur (museum of science and technology); 40c. 50th anniv of Organization for Promotion of Swiss Products and Services; 70c. 50th anniv of Swiss Association of Youth Organizations; 1f.10, Restoration of St. Peter's Cathedral, Geneva.

246 Class C4/5 Steam Locomotive

1982. Centenary of St. Gotthard Railway.
1021 **246** 40c. black and purple . . 45 15
1022 – 40c. multicoloured . . . 45 15
DESIGN: No. 1022, Class Re 6/6 electric locomotive.

247 Hoteliers Association Emblem

1982. Publicity Issue. Multicoloured.
1023 20c. Type **247** 25 15
1024 40c. Flag formed by four Fs 45 10
1025 70c. Gas flame encircling emblem 75 55
1026 80c. Lynx and scientific instruments 80 55
1027 110c. Retort . . . . 1·10 80
SUBJECTS: 20c. Centenary of Swiss Hoteliers Association; 40c. 150th anniv of Swiss Gymnastics Association; 70c. 50th anniv of International Gas Union; 80c. 150th anniv of Natural History Museum, Berne; 110c. Centenary of Swiss Society of Chemical Industries.

248 "Swearing Oath of Eternal Fealty, Rutli Meadow" (detail of mural, Heinrich Danioth)

1982. Europa. Multicoloured.
1028 40c. Type **248** 45 20
1029 80c. Treaty of 1291 founding Swiss Confederation 85 55

249 "The Sun", Willisau **250** "Aquarius" and Old Berne

1982. Pro Patria. Inn Signs (1st series). Multicoloured.
1030 20c.+10c. Type **249** 25 30
1031 40c.+20c. "On the Wave", St. Saphorin 65 15
1032 70c.+30c. "The Three Kings", Rheinfelden . . . 85 1·10
1033 80c.+40c. "The Crown", Winterhur . . . . 1·00 95
See also Nos. 1056/9.

1982. Signs of the Zodiac and Landscapes.
1034 **250** 1f. multicoloured . . . 1·00 10
1035 – 1f.10 brown, blue & vio 1·10 10
1036 – 1f.20 green, blue & brn 1·30 20
1036a – 1f.40 multicoloured . . 1·70 1·30
1037 – 1f.50 bl, azure & orge 1·60 20
1038 – 1f.60 multicoloured . . 1·90 85
1039 – 1f.70 cobalt, brn & bl 1·80 15
1040 – 1f.80 brn, grn & dp grn 2·00 1·10
1041 – 2f. cobalt, brown & blue . . . . 2·50 1·80
1042 – 2f. cobalt, brown & blue . . . . 2·10 30
1042a – 2f.50 red, grn & dp grn 2·75 50
1043 – 3f. red, green and black 3·00 30
1044 – 4f. green, violet & purple . . . . 4·25 60
1045 – 4f.50 ochre, blue & brn 4·75 1·20
DESIGNS: 1f.10, "Pisces" and Nax near Sion; 1f.20, "Aries" and the Graustock, Obwalden; 1f.40, "Gemini" and Bischofszell; 1f.50, "Taurus" and Basel Cathedral; 1f.60, "Gemini" and Schonengrund; 1f.70, "Cancer" and Wetterhorn; 1f.80, "Leo" and Areuse Gorge; 2f. (1041), "Virgo" and Aletsch Glacier; 2f. (1042), "Virgo" and Schwarzsee above Zermatt; 2f.50, "Libra" and Fechy; 3f. "Scorpio" and Corippo; 4f. "Sagittarius" and Glarus; 4f.50, "Capricorn" and Schuls.

251 Articulated Tram

1982. Publicity Issue. Multicoloured.
1046 20c. Type **251** 40 15
1047 40c. Salvation Army singer and guitarist 50 10
1048 70c. Dressage rider 75 65
1049 80c. Emblem 80 60
SUBJECTS: 20c. Centenary of Zurich trams; 40c. Centenary of Salvation Army in Switzerland; 70c. World Dressage Championship, Lausanne; 80c. 14th International Water Supply Association Congress, Zurich.

252 Eurasian Perch **253** Jost Burgi's Celestial Globe, 1594

1983. Publicity Issue. Multicoloured.
1050 20c. Type **252** 30 15
1051 40c. University of Zurich . . 45 10
1052 70c. Teleprinter tape forming "JP" 75 65
1053 80c. Micrometer and cycloidal computer drawing 85 55
EVENTS: 20c. Centenary of Swiss Fishing and Pisciculture Federation; 40c. 150th anniv of University of Zurich; 70c. Centenary of Swiss Journalists' Federation; 80c. Centenary of Swiss Machine Manufacturers' Association.

1983. Europa.
1054 **253** 40c. orange, pink and brown 45 15
1055 – 80c. green, blue and black 90 70
DESIGN: 80c. Niklaus Riggenbach's rack and pinion railway, 1871.

1983. Pro Patria. Inn Signs (2nd series). As T **249**. Multicoloured.
1056 20c.+10c. "The Lion", Heimiswil 35 35
1057 40c.+20c. "The Cross", Sachseln 65 20

1058 70c.+30c. "The Jug", Lenzburg Castle 1·00 1·20
1059 80c.+40c. "The Cavalier", St. George 1·20 1·10

254 Seal, 1832–48 **255** Gallo-Roman Capital, Martigny

1983. 150th Anniv of Basel-Land Canton.
1060 **254** 40c. multicoloured 45 15

1983. Publicity Issue.
1061 **255** 20c. orange and black 25 15
1062 – 40c. multicoloured 60 10
1063 – 70c. multicoloured 85 70
1064 – 80c. multicoloured 85 55
DESIGNS: 20c. Type **255** (Bimillenary of Octodurus/Martigny); 40c. Bernese shepherd-dog and Schwyz hunting dog (Centenary of Swiss Kennel Club); 70c. Cyclists (Centenary of Swiss Cyclists and Motor Cyclists Federation); 80c. Carrier pigeon and world map (World Communications Year).

256 Pre-stamp Cover, 1839 **257** Bridge

1984. Publicity Issue. Multicoloured.
1065 25c. Type **256** 30 20
1066 50c. Collegiate Church clock and buildings 55 15
1067 80c. Olympic rings and Lausanne 1·00 65
SUBJECTS: 25c. National Stamp Exhibition, Zurich; 50c. 1100th anniv of Saint-Imier; 80c. Permanent headquarters of International Olympic Committee at Lausanne.

1984. Europa. 25th Anniv of European Posts and Telecommunications Conference.
1068 **257** 50c. purple, red and crimson 60 20
1069 80c. ultramarine, blue and deep blue 95 65

258 Hexagonal Stove from Rosenburg Mansion, Stans **260** Burning Match

1984. Pro Patria. Tiled Stoves. Multicoloured.
1070 35c.+15c. Type **258** 50 50
1071 50c.+20c. Winterthur stove (by Hans Heinrich Pfau) Freuler Palace, Nafels 70 40
1072 70c.+30c. Box-stove (by Rudolf Stern) from Plaisance, Riaz 95 1·10
1073 80c.+40c. Frame-modelled stove (by Leonard Racle) 1·30 1·20

1984. Fire Prevention.
1075 **260** 50c. multicoloured 55 15

261 Railway Conductor's Equipment **262** Ernest Ansermet (orchestral conductor)

1985. Publicity Issue. Multicoloured.
1076 35c. Type **261** (cent of Train Staff Association) 65 25
1077 50c. Stone with Latin inscription (2000 years of Rhaeto-Romanic culture) 55 15
1078 70c. Rescue of man (cent of International Lake Geneva Rescue Society) 80 60
1079 80c. Grande Dixence dam (International Large Dams Congress, Lausanne) 95 65

1985. Europa. Music Year. Multicoloured.
1080 50c. Type **262** 65 20
1081 80c. Frank Martin (composer) 90 75

263 Music Box, 1895

1985. Pro Patria. Musical Instruments. Mult.
1082 25c.+10c. Type **263** 50 50
1083 35c.+15c. 18th-century box rattle 65 60
1084 50c.+20c. Emmental necked zither (by Peter Zaugg), 1828 80 25
1085 70c.+30c. Drum, 1571 1·10 1·20
1086 80c.+40c. 20th-century diatonic accordion 1·30 1·20

264 Baker

1985. Publicity Issue. Multicoloured.
1087 50c. Type **264** (centenary of Swiss Master Bakers' and Confectioners' Federation) 60 15
1088 70c. Cross on abstract background (50th anniv of Swiss Radio International) 80 65
1089 80c. Geometric pattern and emblem (Postal, Telegraph and Telephone International World Congress, Interlaken) 85 60

265 Intertwined Ropes

1986. Publicity Issue.
1090 **265** 35c. multicoloured 45 25
1091 – 50c. deep brown, brown and red 55 15
1092 – 80c. orange, green and black 90 65
1093 – 90c. multicoloured 1·00 55
1094 – 1f.10 multicoloured 1·20 1·20
DESIGNS: 35c. Type **265** (50th anniv of Swiss Workers' Relief Organization); 50c. Battle site on 1698 map (600th anniv of Battle of Sempach); 80c. Statuette of Mercury (2000th anniv of Roman Chur); 90c. Gallic head (2000th anniv of Vindonissa); 1f.10, Roman coin of Augustus (2000th anniv of Zurich).

266 Sportsmen **267** Woman's Head

1986. Pro Sport.
1095 **266** 50c.+20c. mult 85 65

1986. Europa. Multicoloured.
1096 50c. Type **267** 55 20
1097 90c. Man's head 1·10 75

268 "Bridge in the Sun" (Giovanni Giacometti) **269** Franz Mail Van

1986. Pro Patria. Paintings. Multicoloured.
1098 35c.+15c. Type **268** 60 65
1099 50c.+20c. "The Violet Hat" (Cuno Amiet) 90 25
1100 80c.+40c. "After the Funeral" (Max Buri) 1·40 1·40
1101 90c.+40c. "Still Life" (Felix Vallotton) 1·50 1·30

1986. The Post Past and Present.
1102 **269** 5c. yellow, purple and red 55 15
1103 – 10c. dp grn, grn & orge 50 10
1104 – 20c. orange, brown & bl 20 15
1105 – 25c. dp blue, bl & yell 55 40
1106 – 30c. grey, black & yellow 40 15
1107 – 35c. lake, red and yellow 70 25
1108 – 45c. blue, black & brown 50 30
1109 – 50c. violet, green & pur 55 15
1110 – 60c. orange, yellow & brn 65 30
1111 – 75c. green, dp grn & red 85 70
1112 – 80c. indigo, blue & brn 1·50 50
1113 – 90c. olive, brown & green 1·70 80
DESIGNS: 10c. Mechanized parcel sorting; 20c. Mule post; 25c. Letter cancelling machine; 30c. Stagecoach; 35c. Post Office counter clerk; 45c. Paddle-steamer "Stadt Luzern", 1830s; 50c. Postman; 60c. Loading mail bags onto airplane; 75c. 17th-century mounted courier; 80c. Town postman, 1900s; 90c. Interior of railway mail sorting carriage.

270 Stylized Doves (International Peace Year)

1986. Publicity Issue. Multicoloured.
1115 35c. Type **270** 45 40
1116 50c. Sun behind snow-covered tree (50th anniv of Swiss Winter Relief Fund) 55 15
1117 80c. Symbols of literature and art (cent of Berne Convention for protection of literary and artistic copyright) 1·00 75
1118 90c. Red Cross, Red Crescent and symbols of aggression (25th Int Red Cross Conference meeting, Geneva) 95 70

271 Mobile Post Office

1987. Publicity Issue. Multicoloured.
1119 35c. Type **271** (50th anniv of mobile post offices) 50 25
1120 50c. Lecturers of the seven faculties (450th anniv of Lausanne University) 55 15
1121 80c. Profile, maple leaf and logarithmic spiral (150th anniv of Swiss Engineers' and Architects' Association) 95 65
1122 90c. Boeing 747-300/400 jetliner and electric train (Geneva Airport rail link) 1·20 75
1123 1f.10 Symbolic figure and water (2000th anniv of Baden thermal springs) 1·30 1·20

272 "Scarabaeus" (Bernhard Luginbuhl)

1987. Europa. Sculpture. Multicoloured.
1124 50c. Type **272** 55 20
1125 90c. "Carnival Fountain", Basel (Jean Tinguely) 1·20 85

273 Wall Cabinet, 1764

1987. Pro Patria. Rustic Furniture. Multicoloured.
1126 35c.+15c. Type **273** 60 65
1127 50c.+20c. 16th-century chest 80 30
1128 80c.+40c. Cradle, 1782 1·40 1·50
1129 90c.+40c. Wardrobe, 1698 1·50 1·40

274 Butcher cutting Chops **275** Zug Clock Tower

1987. Publicity Issue. Multicoloured.
1130 35c. Type **274** (centenary of Swiss Master Butchers' Federation) 45 45
1131 50c. Profiles on stamps (50th anniv of Stamp Day) 60 20
1132 90c. Cheesemaker breaking up curds (centenary of Swiss Dairying Association) 1·00 70

1987. Bicentenary of Tourism. Multicoloured.
1133 50c. Type **275** 60 15
1134 80c. St. Charles's church, Negrentino, Prugiasco/Blenio valley 90 65
1135 90c. Witches Tower, Sion 1·00 70
1136 1f.40 Jorgenberg Castle, Waltensburg/Vuorz, Surselva 1·60 1·70

1987. Flood Victims Relief Fund. No. 1109 surch **7.9.87 +50** and clasped hands.
1138 50c.+50c. violet, grn & pur 1·60 1·00

277 Society Emblem

1988. Publicity Issue. Multicoloured.
1139 25c. Type **277** (cent of Swiss Women's Benevolent Society) 30 25
1140 35c. Brushing woman's hair (centenary of Swiss Master Hairdressers' Association) 40 40
1141 50c. St. Fridolin banner and detail of Aegidius Tschudy's manuscript (600th anniv of Battle of Naefels) 60 15
1142 80c. Map and farming country seen from Beromunster radio tower (European Campaign for Rural Areas) 95 75
1143 90c. Girl playing shawm (50th anniv of Lucerne Int Music Festival) 1·00 70

278 Junkers Ju 52/3m "Auntie Ju" flying past Matterhorn **279** Rudolf von Neuenburg

1988. 50th Anniv of Pro Aero Foundation.
1144 **278** 140c.+60c. mult 2·50 2·50

1988. Pro Patria. Minnesingers. Multicoloured.
1145 35c.+15c. Type **279** 65 70
1146 50c.+20c. Rudolf von Rotenburg 90 40
1147 80c.+40c. Johannes Hadlaub 1·40 1·40
1148 90c.+40c. Hardegger 1·50 1·50

280 Arrows on Map of Europe

281 Snap Link

1988. Europa. Transport and Communications.
1149 **280** 50c. bistre, emerald and green 55 20
1150 – 90c. lilac, green and violet . . . . 1·10 70
DESIGN: 90c. Computer circuit on map of Europe.

1988. Publicity Issue. Multicoloured.
1151 35c. Type **281** (50th anniv of Swiss Accident Prevention Office) 45 35
1152 50c. Drilling letters (cent of Swiss Metalworkers' and Watchmakers' Association) 55 20
1153 80c. Triangulation pyramid, theodolite and map (150th anniv of Swiss Federal Office of Topography) . . 95 80
1154 90c. International Red Cross Museum, Geneva (inauguration) . . . . . 1·10 80

282 "Meta" (Jean Tinguely)

1988. Modern Art.
1155 **282** 90c. multicoloured . . . 2·75 2·10

283 Army Postman

1989. Publicity Issue. Multicoloured.
1156 25c. Type **283** (centenary of Swiss Army postal service) 35 30
1157 35c. Fontaine du Sauvage and Porte au Loup, Delemont (700th anniv of granting of town charter) 45 45
1158 50c. Eye and composite wheel (cent of Public Transport Association) . . 65 20
1159 80c. Class GE 4/4 electric locomotive on viaduct (centenary of Rhaetian Railway) . . . . 1·20 95
1160 90c. St. Bernard dog and hospice (2000th anniv of Great St. Bernard Pass) 1·00 70

284 King Friedrich II presenting Berne Town Charter (Bendicht Tschachtlan Chronicle)

285 Hopscotch

1989. Pro Patria. Medieval Chronicles. Mult.
1161 35c.+15c. Type **284** 65 70
1162 50c.+20c. Adrian von Bubenberg watching troops entering Murten (Diebold Schilling's Berne Chronicle) 90 35
1163 80c.+40c. Messenger presenting missive to Council of Zurich (Gerold Edlibach Chronicle) . . . 1·40 1·60
1164 90c.+40c. Schilling presenting Chronicle to Council of Lucerne (Diebold Schilling's Lucerne Chronicle) . . . 1·60 1·60

1989. Europa. Children's Games. Multicoloured.
1165 50c. Type **285** 60 25
1166 90c. Blind-man's buff . . . 1·20 90

286 Bricklayer

287 Testing Device

1989. Occupations.
1168 **286** 2f.75 purple, blk & yell 2·75 1·60
1169 – 2f.80 yellow, brn & bl 3·25 1·30
1170 – 3f. blue, dp brown & brn 3·00 1·30
1171 – 3f.60 orange, brn & pur 3·75 2·40
1173 – 3f.75 deep green, green and light green . . . . 3·75 2·75
1174 – 4f. multicoloured . . . . 4·00 1·40
1175 – 5f. ultram, stone & bl . . 6·25 1·40
1176 – 5f.50 grey, red and mauve . . . . 5·50 3·00
DESIGNS: 2f.80, Cook; 3f. Carpenter; 3f.60, Pharmacist; 3f.75, Fisherman; 4f. Vine grower; 5f. Cheesemaker; 5f.50, Dressmaker.

1989. Publicity Issue. Multicoloured.
1181 35c. Type **287** (cent of Swiss Electrotechnical Association) 45 35
1182 50c. Family on butterfly (50th anniv of Swiss Travel Fund) 55 15
1183 80c. "Wisdom" and "Science" (bronze statues) (centenary of Fribourg University) 95 70
1184 90c. Audio tape (1st anniv of National Sound Archives) . . . . . . 1·00 70
1185 1f.40 Bands of colour forming bridge (centenary of Inter-parliamentary Union) . . . . 1·60 1·50

288 Exercises

1989. Pro Sport.
1186 **288** 50c.+20c. mult . . . . . 1·00 95

289 1882 5c. and 50c. Stamps and Emblem

290 Cats

1990. Publicity Issue. Multicoloured.
1187 25c. Type **289** (centenary of Union of Swiss Philatelic Societies) 35 20
1188 35c. Electric locomotive and electric double-deck railcar (inauguration of Zurich Rapid Transit System) 50 35
1189 50c. Mountain farmer (50th anniv of Assistance for Mountain Communities) 55 15
1190 90c. Ice hockey players (A-series World Ice Hockey Championships, Berne and Fribourg) . . . . . 1·00 70

1990. Animals. Multicoloured.
1192 10c. Cow 10 10
1193 50c. Type **290** 55 10
1194 70c. Rabbit 80 25
1195 80c. Barn owls 90 25
1196 100c. Horse and foal . . . 1·10 25
1197 110c. Geese . . . . 1·20 35
1198 120c. Dog . . . . 1·30 65
1199 140c. Sheep . . . . 1·60 90
1200 150c. Goats . . . . 1·70 90
1201 160c. Turkey . . . . 1·80 1·20
1202 170c. Donkey . . . . 1·90 90
1203 200c. Chickens . . . . . . 1·90 85

291 Flyswats and Starch Sprinklers Seller

292 Lucerne Post Office

1990. Pro Patria. Street Criers. Engravings by David Herrliberger. Multicoloured.
1205 35c.+15c. Type **291** 65 70
1206 50c.+20c. Clock seller . . . 90 30
1207 80c.+40c. Knife grinder . . 1·40 1·50
1208 90c.+40c. Couple selling pinewood sticks . . . . . 1·60 1·60

1990. Europa. Post Office Buildings. Mult.
1209 50c. Type **292** 65 20
1210 90c. Geneva Post Office . . 1·00 60

293 Conrad Ferdinand Meyer (writer)

294 Anniversary Emblem and Crosses

1990. Celebrities.
1211 **293** 35c. black and green . . 45 35
1212 – 50c. black and blue . . . 55 15
1213 – 80c. black and yellow . . 85 75
1214 – 90c. black and pink . . 1·00 65
DESIGNS: 50c. Angelika Kauffmann (painter); 80c. Blaise Cendrars (writer); 90c. Frank Buchser (painter).

1990. 700th Anniv (1991) of Swiss Confederation (1st issue).
1215 50c. Type **294** 60 20
1216 90c. Emblem and crosses (different) . . . . 1·10 85
See also Nos. 1219/22 and 1224.

296 Figures on Jigsaw Pieces

1990. Population Census.
1218 **296** 50c. multicoloured . . . 60 20

297 "700 JAHRE"

298 Alps and City Skyline

1991. 700th Anniv of Swiss Confederation (2nd issue). Multicoloured.
1219 50c. Type **297** 70 40
1220 50c. "700 ONNS" 70 40
1221 50c. "700 ANS" 70 40
1222 50c. "700 ANNI" 70 40
Nos. 1219/22 were issued together, se-tenant, forming a composite design of the Swiss cross in the centre.

1991. 800th Anniv of Berne.
1223 **298** 80c. multicoloured . . . 95 50

299 Federal Palace, Berne, and Capitol, Washington

1991. 700th Anniv of Swiss Confederation (3rd issue). Swiss Emigration to U.S.A.
1224 **299** 160c. multicoloured . . . 1·70 1·00

300 Jettison of "Ariane" Rocket Friction Protection Jacket

301 Abstract

1991. Europa. Europe in Space. Multicoloured.
1225 50c. Type **300** 60 35
1226 90c. Orbit of Halley's Comet, "Giotto" space probe and its trajectory 1·10 85

1991. Pro Patria. Modern Art. Multicoloured.
1227 50c.+20c. Type **301** 80 35
1228 70c.+30c. Artist's monogram 1·10 1·30
1229 80c.+40c. "Labyrinth" . . . 1·40 1·40
1230 90c.+40c. "Man and Beast" 1·50 1·60

302 Stone Bridge, Lavertezzo

1991. Bridges. Multicoloured.
1231 50c. Type **302** 55 15
1232 70c. Wooden Neubrugg, Bremgarten 80 70
1233 80c. Koblenz-Felsenau iron truss railway bridge over River Aar . . . . 1·00 65
1234 90c. Ganter concrete bridge, Simplon Pass . . . . . . 1·00 65

303 P.T.T. Employees

304 Lake Moesola

1991. Centenary of Swiss Postal, Telephone and Telegraph Officials' Union.
1235 **303** 80c. multicoloured . . . 90 50

1991. Mountain Lakes.
1236 **304** 50c. multicoloured . . . 50 10
1237 – 80c. brown, red & purple 85 20
DESIGN: 80c. Fishing boat moored at jetty on Melchsee.
See also No. 1257.

305 Mouth of River Rhine and Caspian Tern

306 Map of Americas and "Santa Maria"

1992. Publicity Issue. Multicoloured.
1238 50c. Type **305** (centenary of Treaty for International Regulation of the Rhine) 55 40
1239 80c. Family (50th anniv of Pro Familia) 85 35
1240 90c. Chemical formula and model of difluorobutane molecule (centenary of International Chemical Nomenclature Conference, Geneva) 90 85

1992. Europa. 500th Anniv of Discovery of America by Columbus. Multicoloured.
1241 50c. Type **306** 60 25
1242 90c. Route map of first voyage and sketch for statue of Columbus (Vincenzo Vela) . . . . . 1·20 80

307 Skier

308 1780s Earthenware Plate, Heimberg

1992. Sierre Int Comics Festival. Mult.
1243 50c. Type **307** 60 25
1244 80c. Mouse-artist drawing strip . . . . 1·00 70
1245 90c. Love-struck man holding bunch of stamp-flowers behind back . . . 1·20 90

1992. Pro Patria. Folk Art. Multicoloured.
1246 50c.+20c. Type **308** 80 40
1247 70c.+30c. Paper cut-out by Johann Jakob Hauswirth 1·20 1·30
1248 80c.+40c. Maplewood cream spoon, Gruyeres . . . . 1·40 1·30
1249 90c.+40c. Carnation from 1780 embroidered saddle cloth, Grisons . . . . . 1·50 1·50

309 Flags and Alps

310 Clowns on Trapeze

1992. Alpine Protection Convention.
1250 **309** 90c. multicoloured . . . 1·00 65

1992. The Circus. Multicoloured.
1251 50c. Type **310** 60 25
1252 70c. Sealion with Auguste the clown 95 70
1253 80c. Chalky the clown and elephant . . . . 1·00 45
1254 90c. Harlequin and horse . . 1·20 85

311 Sport Pictograms

1992. Pro Sport.
1255 **311** 50c.+20c. black & blue 1·30 85

312 Train and Map

313 "A" (first class) Mail

1992. Centenary (1993) of Central Office for International Rail Carriage.
1256 **312** 90c. multicoloured . . . 1·10 85

1993.
1257 – 60c. dp blue, yellow & bl 60 20
1258 **313** 80c. red, orange and scarlet 85 20
DESIGN: 60c. Lake Tanay.

314 Zurich and Geneva 1843 Stamps

315 Paracelsus (after Augustin Hirschvogel) (500th birth anniv)

1993. 150th Anniv of Swiss Postage Stamps. Multicoloured.
1259 60c. Type **314** 70 30
1260 80c. Postal cancellation (stamps for postage) . . . 95 65
1261 100c. Magnifying glass (stamp collecting) . . . . 1·30 80

1993. Publicity Issue.
1262 **315** 60c. brown, grey and blue 70 30
1263 – 80c. multicoloured . . . 1·00 60
1264 – 180c. multicoloured . . . 2·10 2·00
DESIGNS—VERT: 80c. Discus thrower (from Greek vase) (inauguration of Olympic Museum, Lausanne). HORIZ: 180c. Worker's head (cent of International Metalworkers' Federation).

316 "Hohentwiel" (lake steamer) and Flags

317 Interior of Media House, Villeurbanne, France

1993. Lake Constance European Region.
1265 **316** 60c. multicoloured . . . 85 45

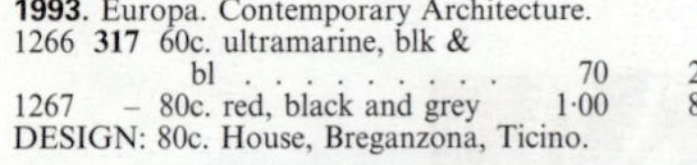

1993. Europa. Contemporary Architecture.
1266 **317** 60c. ultramarine, blk & bl 70 25
1267 – 80c. red, black and grey 1·00 80
DESIGN: 80c. House, Breganzona, Ticino.

318 Appenzell Dairyman's Earring

1993. Pro Patria. Folk Art. Multicoloured.
1268 60c.+30c. Type **318** . . . . 1·00 75
1269 60c.+30c. Fluhli enamelled glass bottle, 1738 . . . . 1·00 75
1270 80c.+40c. Driving cows to summer pasture (detail of mural, Sylvestre Pidoux) 1·40 1·50
1271 100c.+40c. Straw hat ornaments . . . . 1·50 1·70

319 "Work No. 095" (Emma Kunz)

320 Kapell Bridge and Water Tower, Lucerne

1993. Paintings by Swiss Women Artists. Mult.
1272 60c. Type **319** 75 35
1273 80c. "Great Singer Lilas Goergens" (Aloise) (33 × 33 mm) . . . . . . 1·00 60
1274 100c. "Under the Rain Cloud" (Meret Oppenheim) (33 × 33 mm) 1·20 90
1275 120c. "Four Spaces with Horizontal Bands" (Sophi Taeuber-Arp) (33 × 33 mm) . . . . . . 1·50 1·50

1993. Kapell Bridge Restoration Fund.
1276 **320** 80c.+20c. carmine and red . . . . 1·70 1·70

321 Hieroglyphic, Cuneiform and Roman Scripts

1994. "Books and the Press" Exhibition, Geneva. Multicoloured.
1277 60c. Type **321** 70 35
1278 80c. Gothic letterpress script 95 60
1279 100c. Modern electronic fonts . . . . 1·20 1·00

322 Athletes

1994. Publicity Issue. Multicoloured.
1280 60c. Type **322** (50th Anniv of National Sports School, Magglingen) . . . 70 45
1281 80c. Jakob Bernoulli (mathematician) (after Nicolas Bernoulli) and formula and diagram of the law of large numbers (Int Mathematicians' Congress, Zurich) 95 65
1282 100c. Heads, Unisource emblem, globe and flags (collaboration of Swiss, Dutch and Swedish telecommunications companies) . . . . 1·10 85
1283 180c. Radar image, airliner and globe (50th anniv of I.C.A.O.) . . . . 2·10 1·80

323 Footballers

324 "Trieste" (bathyscaphe)

1994. World Cup Football Championship, U.S.A., and Cent (1995) of Swiss Football Association.
1284 **323** 80c. multicoloured . . . 90 55

1994. Europa. Discoveries and Inventions. Vehicles used by Auguste Piccard in Stratospheric and Deep-sea Explorations. Multicoloured.
1285 60c. Type **324** 80 45
1286 100c. "F.N.R.S." (stratosphere balloon) . . 1·70 1·20

325 Neuchatel Weight-driven Clock (Jacques Matthey-Jonais)

326 Symbolic Condom

1994. Pro Patria. Folk Art. Multicoloured.
1287 60c.+30c. Type **325** . . . . 1·00 75
1288 60c.+30c. Embroidered pomegranate on linen . . 1·00 55
1289 80c.+40c. Mould for Krafli pastry . . . . 1·40 1·60
1290 100c.+40c. Paper-bird cradle mobile . . . . 1·60 1·80

1994. Anti-AIDS Campaign.
1291 **326** 60c. multicoloured . . . 85 30

327 Simenon and his Home, Echandens Castle, Lausanne

1994. 5th Death Anniv of Georges Simenon (novelist).
1292 **327** 100c. multicoloured . . . 1·10 75

328 "Swiss Electricity"

1995. Publicity Issue.
1293 **328** 60c. multicoloured . . . 75 30
1294 – 60c. blue and black . . . 75 30
1295 – 80c. multicoloured . . . 1·00 70
1296 – 180c. multicoloured . . . 2·20 1·60
DESIGNS—HORIZ: No. 1293, Type **328** (centenary of Swiss Association of Electricity Producers and Distributors); 1295, "(sda ats)" (centenary of Swiss News Agency); 1296, "ONU UNO" (50th anniv of U.N.O.). VERT: No. 1294, Wrestlers (centenary of Swiss Wrestling Association and National Wrestling and Alpine Herdsmen's Festival, Chur).

329 European Beaver

330 Cream Pail, 1776

1995. Endangered Animals. Multicoloured.
1297 60c. Type **329** 80 30
1298 80c. Map butterfly . . . . 1·10 60
1299 100c. Green tree frog . . . 1·40 90
1300 120c. Little owl . . . . . . 1·70 1·60

1995. Pro Patria. Folk Art. Multicoloured.
1301 60c.+30c. Type **330** . . . . 1·10 55
1302 60c.+30c. Neuchatel straw hat . . . . 1·10 75
1303 80c.+40c. Detail of chest lock, 1580 . . . . 1·40 1·60
1304 100c.+40c. Langnau ceramic sugar bowl . . . . 1·60 1·80

331 Couple and Dove

1995. Europa. Peace and Freedom.
1305 **331** 60c. blue and cobalt . . 75 45
1306 – 100c. brown and ochre 1·20 90
DESIGN: 100c. Europa with Zeus as bull.

333 Coloured Ribbons woven through River

1995. Switzerland–Liechtenstein Co-operation.
1308 **333** 60c. multicoloured . . . 70 40
No. 1308 was valid for use in both Switzerland and Liechtenstein (see No. 1106 of Liechtenstein).

334 "The Vocation of Andre Carrel" (1925)

1995. Centenary of Motion Pictures. Multicoloured.
1309 60c. Type **334** 85 35
1310 80c. "Anna Goldin – The Last Witch" 95 55
1311 150c. "Pipilotti's Mistakes – Absolution" . . . . . . 1·80 1·50

335 Ear, Eye and Mouth

336 "A" (first class) Mail

1995. "Telecom 95" International Telecommunications Exhibition, Geneva.
1312 **335** 180c. multicoloured . . . 1·90 1·10

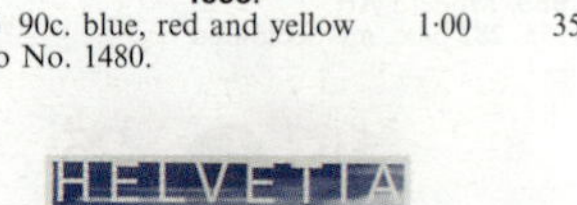

1995.
1313 **336** 90c. blue, red and yellow 1·00 35
See also No. 1480.

337 Emblem

1996. Publicity Issue. Multicoloured.
1314 70c. Type **337** (centenary of Touring Club of Switzerland) 80 45
1315 70c. Heart (50th anniv of charity organizations) . . 95 55
1316 90c. Brass band (30th Federal Music Festival, Interlaken) . . . . 1·10 70
1317 90c. Young girls (centenary of Pro Filia (girls' aid society)) . . . . 1·00 70
1318 180c. Jean Piaget (child psychologist, birth centenary) . . . . 2·10 1·80

338 Coloured Ribbons and "Bern 96" Gymnastic Festival Emblem

339 Corinna Bille (writer)

1996. Pro Sport.
1319 **338** 70c.+30c. multicoloured 1·00 1·20

1996. Europa. Famous Women. Multicoloured.
1320 70c. Type **339** 80 45
1321 110c. Iris von Roten-Meyer (feminist writer) . . . . . 1·70 1·00

340 Magdalena Chapel, Wolfenschiessen, and Cross

341 Olympic Rings

1996. Pro Patria. Heritage. Multicoloured.
1322 70c.+35c. Type **340** . . . . 1·10 75
1323 70c.+35c. Underground sawmill and workshop, Col-des-Roches . . . . . 1·10 95
1324 90c.+40c. Baroque baths, Pfafers . . . . 1·50 1·60
1325 110c.+50c. Roman road and milestone, Great St. Bernhard . . . . . . 1·70 1·90

1996. Centenary of Modern Olympic Games.
1326 **341** 180c. multicoloured . . . 2·00 1·70

342 Representation of 1995 "A" Mail Stamp

343 Musical Movement and Mechanical Ring (Isaac-Daniel Piguet)

1996. Guinness World Record for Largest "Living" Postage Stamp represented by Human Beings (arrangement of people to represent stamp design).
1327 **342** 90c. multicoloured . . . 1·50 1·10

1996. Bicentenary of Antoine Favre-Salomon's Invention of the Metal Teeth System for Music Boxes. Multicoloured.
1328 70c. Type **343** 85 40
1329 90c. "Basso-piccolo mandolin" cylinder music box (Eduard Jaccard) . . 1·10 65
1330 110c. Station automaton (Paillard & Co) . . . . . 1·40 1·00
1331 180c. Kalliope disc music box . . . . 2·20 1·90

344 Pattern

345 "The Golden Cow" (Daniel Ammann)

1996. Greetings Stamps. Multicoloured. Self-adhesive.
1332 90c. Type **344** . . . . . . 1·30 1·20
1333 90c. Mottled pattern . . . . 1·30 1·20
1334 90c. Coil pattern . . . . . 1·30 1·20
1335 90c. Flower and leaf pattern 1·30 1·20

1996. Winning Entries in Stamp Design Competition.
1336 **345** 70c. gold and blue . . . 80 50
1337 – 90c. multicoloured . . . 1·10 70
1338 – 110c. multicoloured . . . 1·30 95
1339 – 180c. brown, black and blue . . . . 2·10 2·00
DESIGNS: 90c. "Wake with a Smile" (Max Sprick); 110c. "Leaves" (Elena Emma-Pugliese); 180c. "Dove" (Rene Conscience).

346 Globi delivering Mail

347 Venus of Octodurus

1997. Globi (cartoon character by Robert Lips).
1340 **346** 70c. multicoloured . . . 75 40

1997. Gallo-Roman Works of Art. Multicoloured.
1341 70c. Type **347** (from Forum Claudii Vallensium (now Martigny)) 80 55
1342 90c. Bust of Bacchus (from Augusta Raurica (now Augst)) . . . . 1·10 85
1343 110c. Ceramic fragment showing "Victory" (from Iulio Magus (now Schleitheim)) . . . . . . 1·20 1·10
1344 180c. Mosaic showing female theatrical mask (from Vallon) . . . . . 2·10 2·10
Each stamp is inscribed with the name of the Foundation bearing responsibility for the preservation of the respective archaeological sites.

348 Class 460 Series 2000 Electric Locomotive

1997. 150th Anniv of Zurich–Barden Railway. Multicoloured.
1345 70c. Type **348** 80 55
1346 90c. Electric "Red Arrow" railcar set, 1935 . . . . . 1·10 90
1347 1f.40 Pullman coach, 1930s 1·60 1·70
1348 1f.70 "Limmat", 1847 (first locomotive in Switzerland) 2·20 2·20

349 Douglas DC-4 "Grand Old Lady" over Globe

1997. 50th Anniv of Swissair's North Atlantic Service.
1349 **349** 180c. multicoloured . . . 2·00 1·70

350 Farmland

351 "Devil and the Goat" (painting by Heinrich Danioth on rock face of Schollenen Gorge)

1997. Publicity Issue. Multicoloured.
1350 70c. Type **350** (centenary of Swiss Farmers' Union) . . 80 55
1351 90c. Street plan (centenary of Swiss Municipalities' Union) . . . . 1·00 85

1997. Europa. Tales and Legends. The Devil's Bridge.
1352 **351** 90c. brown and yellow 95 75

352 St. Valbert's Church, Soubey (Jura)

353 Clouds (Air)

1997. Pro Patria. Heritage and Landscapes. Mult.
1353 70c.+35c. Type **352** . . . . 1·10 90
1354 70c.+35c. Culture mill, Lutzelfluh (Berne) . . . . 1·10 90
1355 90c.+40c. Ittingen Charterhouse (Thurgau) 1·40 1·60
1356 110c.+50c. Casa Patriziale, Russo (Ticino) . . . . . 1·80 1·90

1997. Energy 2000 (energy efficiency programme). The Elements. Multicoloured.
1357 70c. Type **353** 80 55
1358 90c. Burning wood (Fire) . . 1·10 90
1359 110c. Water droplets (Water) . . . . 1·30 1·10
1360 180c. Pile of soil (Earth) . . 2·10 2·10

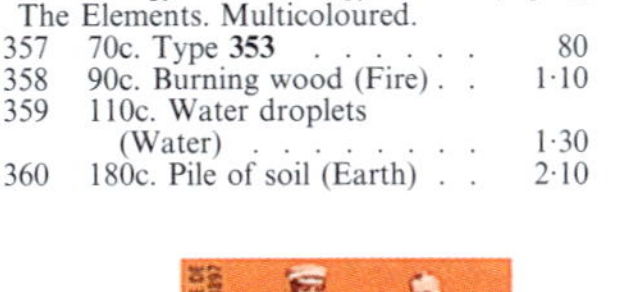

354 King Rama V and President Adolf Deucher

1997. Centenary of Visit of King Rama V of Siam.
1361 **354** 90c. multicoloured . . . 95 85

355 Paul Karrer and Molecular Structure of Vitamin A

1997. The Nobel Prize.
1362 **355** 90c. black and grey . . . 1·10 90
1363 – 110c. black and purple 1·30 1·10
DESIGNS: 90c. Type **355** (Chemistry Prize, 1937); 110c. Alfred Nobel (founder of Prize Fund).

356 Woman and Boy (German)

1997. "The Post keeps Us in Touch".
1364 **356** 70c. black, red and blue 95 70
1365 – 70c. black, yellow and blue 95 70
1366 – 70c. black, yellow and green 95 70
1367 – 70c. black, green and red 95 70
DESIGNS: No. 1365, Boy wearing baseball cap with woman (French); 1366, Young couple (Italian); 1367, Girl and man (Romansch).

357 Postal Service Emblem

1998. Separation of Swiss Post and Swisscom (telecommunications).
1368 **357** 90c. black, yellow and red 90 70
1369 – 90c. deep blue, blue and red 90 70
DESIGN: No. 1369, Swisscom emblem.

358 Arrows

1998. Bicentenary of Declaration of Helvetic Republic and 150th Anniv of Swiss Federal State. Multicoloured.
1370 90c. Type **358** . . . . . . 1·00 85
1371 90c. Face value at bottom right . . . . 1·00 85
1372 90c. Face value at top left 1·00 85
1373 90c. Face value at top right 1·00 85

359 Winter Olympics 2006

1998. Swiss Candidacy for Winter Olympic Games.
1374 **359** 90c. multicoloured . . . 1·00 85

360 Elderly Couple

361 "On Top of the Simplon Pass"

1998. Publicity Issues. Multicoloured.
1375 70c. Type **360** (Old Age and Survivor's Insurance) . . 80 60
1376 70c. National Museum, Prangins Castle (centenary of Swiss National Museum, Zurich, and inauguration of Prangins branch) 80 55
1377 90c. Fingerprints (centenary of St. Gallen University) 1·10 75

1998. Paintings by Jean-Frederic Schnyder. Multicoloured.
1378 10c. Type **361** 15 15
1379 20c. "Snowdrift near Neuthal" 25 20
1380 50c. "Franches Montagnes" 55 50
1381 70c. "Two Horses" 80 40
1382 90c. "En Route" 90 25
1383 110c. "Winter Morning by the Alpnachersee" . . . . 1·20 55
1385 140c. "Zug" . . . . 1·60 1·10
1386 170c. "Olive Grove" . . . . 1·70 1·20
1387 180c. "Near Reutigen" . . . 1·90 1·40

362 St. Gall, Rhine Valley

363 Lanterns

1998. Pro Patria. Heritage and Landscapes. Mult.
1390 70c.+35c. Type **362** . . . . 1·10 95
1391 70c.+35c. Round church, Saas Balen . . . . . . 1·10 95
1392 90c.+40c. Forest, Bodmeren 1·50 1·50
1393 90c.+40c. The old Refuge (museum), St. Gotthard 1·50 1·50
1394 110c.+50c. Smithy, Corcelles 1·80 2·00

1998. Europa. National Festivals. National Day.
1395 **363** 90c. multicoloured . . . 1·00 85

364 In-line Skating

1998. Sports. Multicoloured. Self-adhesive.
1396 70c. Type **364** 60 60
1397 70c. Snow-boarding 60 60
1398 70c. Mountain biking . . . 60 60
1399 70c. Basketball 60 60
1400 70c. Beach volleyball . . . 60 60

365 Bridge 24, Slender West Lake, Yangzhou, China

1998. Lakes. Multicoloured.
1401 20c. Type **365** 55 55
1402 70c. Chillon Castle, Lake Geneva 55 60

366 Emblem and Face

1998. 50th Anniv of Universal Declaration of Human Rights.
1404 **366** 70c. multicoloured . . . 85 80

367 Christmas Wrapping

1998. Christmas.
1405 **367** 90c. multicoloured . . . 1·00 90

368 Postman with Letter and Posthorn on Globe

1999. 150th Anniv of Swiss Postal Service.
1406 **368** 90c. multicoloured . . . 85 80

369 Little Pingu carrying Parcel

370 Vieux Bois falls in Love at First Sight

1999. Youth Stamps. Pingu (cartoon character). Multicoloured.
1407 70c. Type **369** 85 65
1408 90c. Papa Pingu driving snowmobile . . . . . . 1·10 90

1999. Birth Bicentenary of Rodolphe Topffer (cartoonist). Scenes from "The Love of Monsieur Vieux Boris". Multicoloured. Self-adhesive.
1409 90c. Type **370** 80 85
1410 90c. Vieux Bois declares his love 80 85
1411 90c. Vieux Bois jumps in air with joy, knocking over furniture 80 85
1412 90c. Vieux Bois helping his love over wall 80 85
1413 90c. Wedding of Vieux Bois 80 85

371 "Breitling Orbiter 3"

1999. 1st World Circumnavigation by Balloon, by Bertrand Piccard and Brian Jones.
1414 **371** 90c. multicoloured . . . 1·00 70

372 Envelope Flap

1999. 125th Anniv of Universal Postal Union.
1415 **372** 20c. yellow and black . . 35 35
1416 – 70c. black, red and yellow 95 95
DESIGN—55 × 29 mm: 70c. U.P.U. emblem on card in envelope.
Nos. 1415/16 were issued together, se-tenant, forming a composite design.

373 Jester and Clown 374 Chestnuts from Malcantone

1999. Publicity Issue.
1417 **373** 70c. multicoloured . . . 95 70
1418 – 90c. multicoloured . . . 1·00 90
1419 – 90c. multicoloured . . . 1·00 90
1420 – 1f.10 red and black . . . 1·20 1·10
DESIGNS: No. 1417, Type **373** (50th anniv of SOS Children's Villages); 1418, Sketch of giant puppets (Wine-growers' Festival, Vevey); 1419, Flags of member countries and emblem (50th anniv of Council of Europe); 1420, Red Cross and emblem (50th anniv of Geneva Conventions).

1999. Pro Patria. Heritage and Landscapes. Mult.
1421 70c.+35c. Type **374** . . . . 1·10 95
1422 70c.+35c. La Sarraz Castle 1·10 95
1423 90c.+40c. "Uri" (lake steamer) . . . . 1·50 1·50
1424 110c.+50c. St. Christopher carrying Baby Jesus (detail of fresco, St. Paul's Chapel, Rhazuns) . . . . 1·90 1·90

375 Ibex Horns (National Park, Engadine)

1999. Europa. Parks and Gardens.
1425 **375** 90c. black and blue . . . 1·00 80

377 Children holding Pictures

1999. Publicity Issue. Multicoloured.
1427 70c. Type **377** (Children's Rights) 75 55
1428 90c. Carl Lutz (Swiss diplomat in Budapest during Second World War) (24th death anniv) 1·00 75
1429 1f.10 Chemical model of ozone and globe (birth bicentenary of Christian Schönbein (chemist)) . . . 1·20 1·00
1430 180c. "Midday in the Alps" (death centenary of Giovanni Segantini (painter)) . . . . 2·00 1·90

378 Schollenen Gorge Monument, Suvorov and Soldiers

1999. Bicentenary of General Aleksandr Suvorov's Crossing of the Alps. Multicoloured.
1431 70c. Type **378** 70 65
1432 110c. Suvorov vanguard (after engraving by L. Hess) passing Lake Klontal . . . . 1·20 1·10

379 Christmas Bauble

1999. Christmas.
1433 **379** 90c. multicoloured . . . 1·00 80

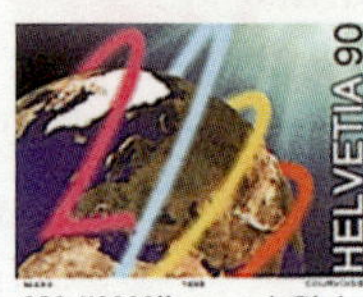

380 "2000" around Globe

1999. Year 2000.
1434 **380** 90c. multicoloured . . . 1·80 1·30

381 Cyclist 382 Alphorn Player

2000. Centenary of International Cycling Union.
1435 **381** 70c. multicoloured . . . 80 70

2000. Snow Storms. Multicoloured.
1436 10c. Type **382** 10 10
1437 20c. Fondue 25 25
1438 30c. Jugs and grapes on tray 40 40
1439 50c. Mountain goat 60 55
1440 60c. Clock 70 70
1441 70c. St. Bernards 80 80
See also No. 1479.

384 "frau" and Emblem

2000. Centenary of National Council of Women.
1443 **384** 70c. multicoloured . . . 80 50

385 "Building Europe" 386 Town Square, Nafels

2000. Europa.
1444 **385** 90c. multicoloured . . . 95 95

2000. Pro Patria. "Townscapes 2000" (rejuvenation projects). Multicoloured.
1445 70c.+35c. Type **386** . . . . 1·20 1·10
1446 70c.+35c. Main road, Tengia . . . . 1·20 1·10
1447 90c.+40c. Main road, Brugg 1·60 1·40
1448 90c.+40c. Marketplace, Carouge . . . . 1·60 1·40

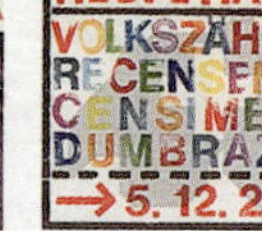

387 Payerne Church and Violin 389 Emblem

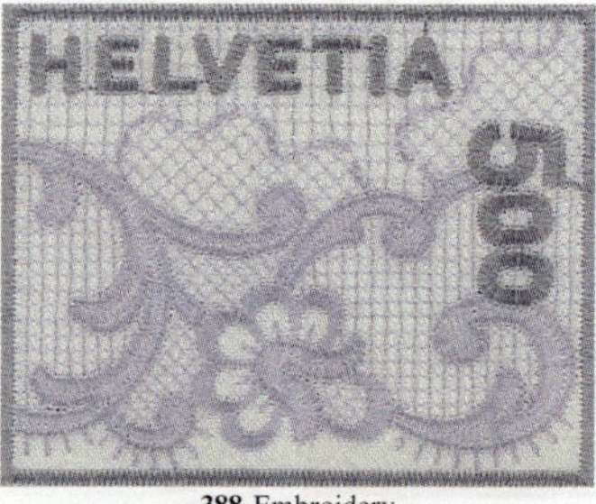

388 Embroidery

2000. Tourism. Multicoloured (except 1451, blue, turquoise and red).
1449 90c. Willisan farmhouse and horse . . . . 1·10 45
1450 100c. *La Suisse* (lake steamer) and woman looking over Lake Geneva 1·20 70
1451 110c. Kleine Matterhorn glacier and skier . . . . 1·70 1·50
1452 120c. Type **387** . . . . . 1·40 1·00
1453 130c. St. Saphorin Church and bottle of wine . . . . 1·40 15
1454 180c. National spring and bather, Vals . . . . . . 2·00 1·30
1455 200c. Landscape and walker 2·20 90
1456 220c. Bus and children . . . 2·50 1·90
1457 300c. Stone bridge and mountain bike . . . . . 3·25 65
1459 400c. Airplane fin and man with suitcase . . . . . 4·50 3·25

2000. St. Gallen Embroidery. Self-adhesive.
1460 **388** 5f. cobalt and blue . . . 8·75 8·75

2000. Population Census.
1462 **389** 70c. multicoloured . . . 80 65

390 "Alien from Outer Space" (Yannick Kehrli)

2000. "Stampin' the Future". Winning Entries in Children's International Painting Competition. Multicoloured. Self-adhesive.
1463 70c. Type **390** 50 65
1464 70c. "Looks below the Sun" (Charlotte Battig) 50 65
1465 70c. "The Perfect World" (Sandra Dobler) 50 65
1466 70c. "My Town" (Stephanie Aerschmann) 50 65

391 Swimming

2000. Olympic Games, Sydney. Multicoloured. Self-adhesive.
1467 90c. Type **391** 95 95
1468 90c. Cycling 95 95
1469 90c. Running 95 95

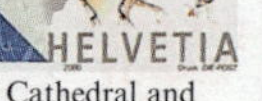
392 Cathedral and Horsemen 393 Dresden-style Tree Decoration

2000. Stamp Day.
1470 **392** 70c. multicoloured . . . 80 65

2000. Christmas.
1471 **393** 90c. multicoloured . . . 1·20 80

394 Alice Rivaz

2001. Anniversaries.
1472 **394** 70c. multicoloured . . . 80 60
1473 – 90c. multicoloured . . . 1·00 80
1474 – 110c. red, grey and black 1·20 1·30
1475 – 130c. multicoloured . . . 1·40 1·50
DESIGNS—As Type **394**:70c. Type **394** (writer, birth centenary); 110c. "CARITAS" and jigsaw pieces (centenary of Caritas (Christian charity organization)); 130c. Refugees (50th Anniv of United Nations High Commissioner for Refugees). Size 39 × 30 mm: 90c. Airplane (centenary of Aero-Club of Switzerland).

395 Flowers and Envelope

2001. Greetings Stamp.
1476 **395** 90c. multicoloured . . . 95 50

396 Woman's Head

2001. Anniversary and Event. Multicoloured.
1477 70c. Type **396** (re-opening of Vela Museum, Ligornetto) 80 80
1478 90c. Chocolate segment (centenary of Chocosuisse) 1·00 1·00
No. 1478 is impregnated with the scent of chocolate.

2001. Self-adhesive Stamps.
1479 — 70c. mult (as No. 1441) 80 80
1480 **336** 90c. blue, orge & lemon 95 1·00

397 Italian Theatre, La Chaux-de-Fonds

2001. Pro Patria. Cultural Heritage.
1481 70c.+35c. black, orange and red . . . . 1·20 1·20
1482 70c.+35c. black, brown and green . . . . 1·20 1·20
1483 90c.+40c. black, brown and lemon . . . . 1·60 1·60
1484 90c.+40c. multicoloured . . 1·60 1·60
DESIGNS: No. 1482, Hauterive Monastery; 1483, Leuk Castle; 1484, Rorschach Granary.

398 Water

2001. Europa. Water Resources.
1485 **398** 90c. multicoloured . . . 95 95

399 Blue Rainbow Fish

2001. Illustrations from *Rainbow Fish* (book by Martin Pfister). Multicoloured.
1486 70c. Type **399** 65 25
1487 90c. Purple rainbow fish . . . 80 50

400 Straits Rhododendron (*Melastoma malabathricum*)

401 "The Birth of Venus"

2001. Switzerland–Singapore Joint Issue. Flowers. Sheet 98 × 68 mm, containing T **400** and similar horiz designs. Multicoloured.
MS1488 70c. Type **400**; 90c. *Saraca cauliflora*; 110c. Edelweiss (*Leontopodium alpinum*); 130c. Gentian (*Gentiana clusii*) . . . 3·75 3·75

2001. Death Centenary of Arnold Bocklin (artist).
1489 **401** 180c. multicoloured . . . 1·70 1·50

402 Buildings (Beat Kehrli)

403 Gablonz-style Christmas Tree Ornament

2001. Stamp Day. Winning entry in stamp design competition.
1490 **402** 70c. multicoloured . . . 65 25

2001. Christmas.
1491 **403** 90c. multicoloured . . . 80 50

404 Ladder, Wall and Stars

2002. Escalade (festival) (celebrating 400th anniv of defeat of Savoyard attack on the city), Geneva.
1492 **404** 70c. multicoloured . . . 65 25

405 "E" and Towers, Biel

2002. "Expo '02" National Exhibition, Biel, Murten, Neuchatel and Yverdon-les-Bains (1st issue). Each featuring "Arteplage" (exhibition platform) of each host town. Multicoloured.
1493 70c. Type **405** 65 25
1494 70c. Reversed "P" and Monolith, Murten 65 25
1495 70c. "O", pebble-shaped construction over water, Neuchatel 65 25
1496 70c. "2" and artificial cloud, Yverdon-les-Bains 65 25
See also No. **MS**1509.

406 RABDe 500 InterCity Tilting Train (ICN)

2002. Centenary of Swiss Federal Railways (SBB) (national railway operator). Multicoloured.
1497 70c. Type **406** 65 25
1498 90c. InterCity 2000 double-deck train 80 50
1499 120c. Railcar, Lucerne–Lenzburg Seetal line . . . 1·10 1·00
1500 130c. 119 Re 460 locomotive 1·20 1·10

407 Facade

2002. Centenary of Federal Parliament Building.
1501 **407** 90c. multicoloured . . . 80 50

408 Augusta A-109-K2 Helicopter and Hawker 800B Air Ambulance

2002. 50th Anniv of Swiss Air Rescue (Rega).
1502 **408** 180c. multicoloured . . . 1·70 1·50

409 Clown

2002. Europa. Circus. Multicoloured.
1503 70c. Type **409** 65 25
1504 90c. Clown (different) . . . 80 50

410 Bruzella, Ticino Canton

2002. Pro Patria. Water Mills Preservation. Water mills. Multicoloured.
1505 70c. + 35c. Type **410** . . . 95 50
1506 70c. + 35c. Oberdorf, Basel Canton 95 50
1507 90c. + 40c. Lussery-Villars, de Vaud Canton . . . . 1·20 1·20
1508 90c. + 40c. Buren a. d. Aare, Berne Canton . . . 1·20 1·20

411 "X"

2002. "Expo '02", 6th National Exhibition, Biel, Murten, Neuchatel and Yverdon-les-Bains (2nd issue). Sheet 95 × 70 mm.
MS1509 **411** 90c. multicoloured 85 85

412 Two Teddies (Switzerland, c. 1950)

413 Emblem

2002. Centenary of the Teddy Bear. Multicoloured. Self-adhesive.
1510 90c. White teddy with pink bow (France, 1925) (26 × 26 mm, round) . . . 80 50
1511 90c. Type **412** 80 50
1512 90c. Teddy with grey-brown bow (Germany, 1904) (22 × 32 mm, oval) . . . 80 50
1513 90c. "Philibert", Swiss Post Teddy (Switzerland, 2002) (26 × 22 mm, rectangle) 80 50
1514 90c. Teddy with grey paws (England, c. 1920) (26 × 26 mm, round) . . . 80 50

2002. Switzerland's Acccession to the United Nations.
1515 **413** 90c. multicoloured . . . 80 50

414 Emperor Dragonfly (*Anax imperator*)

2002. Insects. Multicoloured.
1516 10c. Type **414** 10 10
1517 20c. Dark green fritillary (*Mesoacidalia aglaja*) . . 20 10
1518 50c. Alpine longhorn beetle (*Rosalia alpina*) 45 20
1519 100c. Striped bug (*Graphosoma lineatum*) . . 90 55

415 Printing Press (copper engraving, Abraham Bosse)

2002. Swiss Post Stamp Printers, Berne Commemoration.
1520 **415** 70c. multicoloured . . . 65 25

416 Ladybird on Leaf (½-size illustration)

2002. Greeting Stamp. Self-adhesive.
1521 **416** 90c. multicoloured . . . 80 50

417 Quartz

2002. Minerals. Multicoloured.
1522 200c. Type **417** . . . . . . 1·90 1·60
1523 500c. Titanite . . . . 4·50 4·25

418 Kingfisher and Jura Water Engineering System (Michele Berri)

419 Bohemian Cardboard Tree Decoration, c. 1900

2002. Stamp Day. Winning Entry in Stamp Design Competition.
1535 **418** 70c. multicoloured . . . 65 25

2002. Christmas.
1536 **419** 90c. multicoloured . . . 80 50

420 Skier

2002. World Alpine Skiing Championship, St. Moritz.
1537 **420** 90c. multicoloured . . . 80 50

FRANK STAMPS

Issued to charity hospitals for free transmission of their mails.

F 21

F 49 Deaconess

1911. With control figures at top.
F268 **F 21** 2c. red and green . . . 3·50 1·70
F269 3c. red and green . . . 2·40 25
F270 5c. red and green . . . 85 10
F271 10c. red and green . . 1·00 10
F272 15c. red and green . . 20·00 2·75
F273 20c. red and green . . 2·50 40

1935. With or without control figures.
F358A **F 49** 5c. green . . . . . . 4·00 20
F359A – 10c. violet . . . . . 4·00 15
F360A – 20c. red . . . . . . 4·50 25
DESIGNS: 10c. Sister of the Ingenbohl Order; 20c. Henri Dunant (founder of Red Cross).

OFFICIAL STAMPS

1918. Optd **Industrielle Kriegs-wirtschaft**.
O308 **20a** 3c. brown . . . . . . 4·00 24·00
O300 5c. green . . . . . . 7·75 30·00
O310 7½c. grey . . . . . . 4·00 18·00
O303 **21** 10c. red on buff . . . . 10·50 37·00
O304 15c. purple on buff . . 10·50 43·00
O313 **17** 20c. yellow and red . . 8·00 42·00
O314 25c. blue and deep blue 8·00 42·00
O315 30c. green and brown 13·50 70·00

1938. Optd with Geneva Cross.
O381A **52** 3c. green 10 25
O382A – 5c. green (No. 369) . . 10 20
O383A – 10c. purple (No. 370) 95 35
O384A – 15c. orange (No. 373) 40 1·20
O385A – 20c. red (No. 375) . . . 45 20
O386A – 25c. brown (No. 376) 45 1·10
O387A – 30c. blue (No. 377) . . 55 55
O388A – 35c. green (No. 378) . . 55 1·20
O389A – 40c. grey (No. 379) . . 55 35
O390 **17** 50c. green and deep green . . . . . . 95 1·10
O391 60c. brown . . . . . 1·30 1·80
O392 70c. buff and violet . . 1·30 3·25
O393 80c. buff and grey . . 1·40 2·30
O395 **41** 90c. red, dp green & green . . . . . . 1·50 2·75
O394 **17** 1f. green and purple . . 1·50 2·30
O396 **41** 1f.20 red, lake and pink 1·50 3·25
O397 1f.50 red, blue & turquoise . . . . 2·50 4·75
O398 – 2f. red, black and grey 3·00 5·25

1942. Optd **Officiel**. (a) Landscape designs of 1936.
O427 **52** 3c. green . . . . 25 1·20
O428 – 5c. green 35 20
O430 – 10c. brown 25 30
O431 – 15c. orange . . . . . 60 1·20
O432 – 20c. red (Lake) 60 20
O433 – 25c. brown . . . . . . 60 2·00
O434 – 30c. blue 80 35
O435 – 35c. green . . . . . . 1·10 2·10
O436 – 40c. grey . . . . . . 1·10 35

(b) Historical designs of 1941.
O437 – 50c. blue on green . . . 5·00 3·50
O438 **68** 60c. brown on brown . . 4·75 2·50
O439 – 70c. purple on mauve . . 5·50 6·50
O440 – 80c. black on grey . . . 1·40 1·10
O441 – 90c. red on pink . . . . 1·60 90
O442 – 1f. green on green . . . 1·70 1·70
O443 – 1f.20 purple on grey . . 1·90 2·10
O444 – 1f.50 blue on buff . . . 3·50 2·50
O445 – 2f. red on pink . . . . 3·50 3·25

1950. Landscape designs of 1949 optd **Officiel**.
O522 **107** 5c. orange 50 40
O523 – 10c. green 90 40
O524 – 15c. turquoise . . . . . 9·25 11·00
O525 – 20c. purple . . . . . . 2·75 25
O526 – 25c. red . . . . 4·50 6·00
O527 – 30c. green . . . . . . 3·50 1·90
O528 – 35c. brown . . . . . . 4·75 8·25
O529 – 40c. blue . . . . . . 3·50 1·00
O530 – 50c. grey . . . . . . 5·75 4·50
O531 – 60c. green . . . . . . 7·50 4·75
O532 – 70c. violet . . . . . . 19·00 16·00

For Swiss stamps overprinted for the use of officials of the League of Nations, International Labour Office and other special U.N. Agencies having their headquarters at Geneva, see sub- section INTERNATIONAL ORGANIZATIONS SITUATED IN SWITZERLAND.

POSTAGE DUE STAMPS

D 10 D 21 D 41

1878.
D 89 **D 10** 1c. blue . . . . . . 2·00 75
D 90 2c. blue . . . . . . 1·40 65
D 98B 3c. blue . . . . . . 8·00 4·50
D 92a 5c. blue . . . . . . † —
D 99B 5c. blue . . . . . . 12·00 4·75
D100B 10c. blue . . . . . £150 2·50
D101A 20c. blue . . . . . £180 1·70
D102A 50c. blue . . . . . £350 7·25
D 96 100c. blue . . . . . £450 5·00
D 97 500c. blue . . . . . £400 8·50
Nos. D89 and D92a have raised backgrounds behind the figure of value.

1883. Numerals in red.
D268 **D 10** 1c. green 15 60
D181C 3c. green . . . . . 7·25 4·75
D269B 5c. green 80 85
D270A 10c. green . . . . . 2·50 1·60
D271B 20c. green . . . . . 2·50 3·00
D204B 50c. green . . . . . 26·00 3·00
D205B 100c. green . . . . . 60·00 1·40
D187B 500c. green . . . . £120 12·00
The above were issued in a wide range of shades from pale turquoise to olive between 1883 and 1910. A detailed list of these appears in the Stanley Gibbons Part 8 (Italy and Switzerland) Catalogue.

1910.
D274 **D 21** 1c. green and red . . . 10 15
D275 3c. green and red . . . 10 15
D276 5c. green and red . . . 10 10
D277 10c. green and red . . 10·00 10
D278 15c. green and red . . 2·20 18·00
D279 20c. green and red . . 12·00 10
D280 25c. green and red . . 95 40
D281 30c. green and red . . 70 15
D282 50c. green and red . . 1·20 45

1916. Surch.
D299 **D 21** 5 on 3c. red and green 10 20
D300 10 on 1c. red and green . . . . . . 25 6·00

D301 10 on 3c. red and green . . . . . . 30 1·10
D302 20 on 50c. red & green . . . . . . 70 1·10

1924.
D329 D 41 5c. red and green . . 50 10
D330 10c. red and green . . 2·10 10
D331 15c. red and green . . 1·60 35
D332a 20c. red and green . . 5·25 10
D333 25c. red and green . . 2·10 25
D334 30c. red and green . . 2·10 40
D335 40c. red and green . . 2·75 35
D336 50c. red and green . . 00 3·25

1937. Surch.
D380 D 41 5 on 15c. red and green . . . . 85 2·50
D381 10 on 30c. red & green 85 1·10
D382 20 on 50c. red & green 1·60 3·00
D383 40 on 50c. red & green 2·25 7·75

D 54

1938.
D384A D 54 5c. red 30 10
D385A 10c. red 45 10
D386A 15c. red . . . . . . 95 2·00
D387A 20c. red 90 10
D388A 25c. red . . . . . . 1·10 1·80
D389A 30c. red . . . . . . 1·20 80
D390A 40c. red . . . . . . 47·00 25·00
D391A 50c. red . . . . . . 1·60 1·60

POSTCARD STAMPS

P 1 Tourism Emblem

2002. Self-adhesive gum. No value expressed.
P1 P 1 (1f.30) multicoloured . . . 1·20 50
P2 (1f.80) multicoloured . . . 1·70 85

No. P1 was for use only on postcards sent to countries within Europe and No. P2 to overseas countries. They were not valid for use on other mail or in combination with other stamps.

"PRO JUVENTUTE" CHARITY STAMPS

PREMIUMS. All "Pro Juventute" stamps are sold at an additional premium which goes to Benevolent Societies. Until 1937 these premiums were not shown on the stamps, but were as follows:

2c. for all 3c. franking values; 5c. for all 5, 7½, 10, 15 and 20c. values and 10c. for all 30 and 40c. values.

From 1937, when the premium first appeared on the designs, we show it in the catalogue listing.

C 1 Helvetia and Matterhorn

C 2 Appenzell

1913. Children's Fund.
J1 C 1 5c. green . . . . 2·50 4·25

1915. Children's Fund.
J1a C 2 5c. green on buff . . . . 2·75 5·50
J2 – 10c. red on buff . . . . . 80·00 55·00
DESIGN: 10c. Girl from Lucerne.

C 4 Berne

C 6 Valais

C 9 Uri

1916. Children's Fund.
J3 – 3c. violet on buff . . . . . 5·75 23·00
J4 C 4 5c. green on buff £38000 £19000
J5 – 10c. red on buff £3750 £850
DESIGNS: 3, 10c. Girls of Freiburg and Vaud.

1917. Children's Fund.
J6 C 6 3c. violet on buff . . . . . 4·25 33·00
J7 – 5c. green on buff £4000 £850
J8 – 10c. red on buff £2500 £550
DESIGNS: 5c. Man of Unterwalden; 10c. Girl of Ticino.

1918. Children's Fund. Dated "1918".
J9 C 9 10c. red, yellow and black on buff . . . . . 6·75 £70000
J10 – 15c. multicoloured on buff 9·00 6·50
ARMS: 15c. Geneva.

1919. Children's Fund. As Type C 9 but dated "1919". Cream paper.
J11 7½c. red, grey and black . . . £1900 £225
J12 10c. green, red and black . . . £2000 £400
J13 15c. red, violet and black . . 3·75 3·75
ARMS: 7½c. Nidwalden; 10c. Vaud; 15c. Obwalden.

1920. Children's Fund. As Type C 9 but dated "1920". Cream paper.
J14 7½c. red, grey and black . . . £1200 £160
J15 10c. blue, red and black . . . 4·50 7·75
J16 15c. red, blue, violet and black . . . . 2·30 3·25
ARMS: 7½c. Schwyz; 10c. Zurich; 15c. Ticino.

1921. Children's Fund. As Type C 9 but dated "1921". Cream paper.
J17 10c. red, black and green . . 60 1·70
J18 20c. multicoloured . . . . 2·00 2·00
J19 40c. red and blue . . . . 6·75 26·00
ARMS: 10c. Valais; 20c. Berne; 40c. Switzerland.

1922. Children's Fund. As Type C 9 but dated "1922". Cream paper.
J20 5c. orange, blue and black . . £8500 £425
J21 10c. green and black . . . . 75 1·30
J22 20c. violet, blue and black . . £9000 £650
J23 40c. blue, red and black . . . £1600 80·00
ARMS: 5c. Zug; 10c. Freiburg; 20c. Lucerne; 40c. Switzerland.

1923. Children's Fund. As Type C 9 but dated "1923". Cream paper.
J24 5c. orange and black . . . . 40 2·50
J25 10c. multicoloured . . . . . £500 60·00
J26 20c. multicoloured . . . . . £500 31·00
J27 40c. blue, red and black . . . £700 £110
ARMS: 5c. Basel; 10c. Glarus; 20c. Neuchatel; 40c. Switzerland.

1924. Children's Fund. As Type C 9 but dated "1924". Cream paper.
J28 5c. black and lilac £800 £180
J29 10c. red, green and black . . £375 95·00
J30 20c. black, yellow and red . . £850 85·00
J31 30c. red, blue and black . . . £700 75·00
ARMS: 5c. Appenzell; 10c. Solothurn; 20c. Schaffhausen; 30c. Switzerland.

1925. Children's Fund. As Type C 9 but dated "1925". Cream paper.
J32 5c. green, black and violet . . £900 £100
J33 10c. black and green . . . . £300 80·00
J34 20c. multicoloured . . . . . £250 23·00
J35 30c. red, blue and black . . . £190 28·00
ARMS: 5c. St. Gall; 10c. Appenzell-Ausser-Rhoden; 20c. Graubunden; 30c. Switzerland.

1926. Children's Fund. As Type C 9 but dated "1926". Cream paper.
J36 5c. multicoloured . . . . . . £325 42·00
J37 10c. green, black and red . . . £600 65·00
J38 20c. red, black and blue . . . 25 55
J39 30c. blue, red and black . . . £950 £650
ARMS: 5c. Thurgau; 10c. Basel; 20c. Aargau; 30c. Switzerland and Lion of Lucerne.

C 40 Forsaken Orphan

C 42 J. H. Pestalozzi

C 43 J. H. Pestalozzi

1927. Children's Fund. Dated "1927".
J40 C 40 5c. purple & yell on grey £2750 £300
J41 – 10c. green & pink on green £12000 £5000
J42 C 42 20c. red £2750 £700
J43 C 43 30c. blue and black . . . £3750 £600
DESIGN—As Type C 40: 40c. Orphan at Pestalozzi School.

C 44 Lausanne

C 47 J. H. Dunant

1928. Children's Fund. Dated "1928".
J44 C 44 5c. red, purple and black on buff £1900 £190
J45 – 10c. red, green and black on buff £1900 £160
J46 – 20c. black, yellow and red on buff 20 50
J47 C 47 30c. blue and red . . . . 1·10 3·25
DESIGNS—As Type C 44: 10c. Arms of Winterthur; 20c. Arms of St. Gall.

C 48 Mt. San Salvatore, Lake Lugano

1929. Children's Fund. Dated "1929".
J48 C 48 5c. red and violet . . . 10 60
J49 – 10c. blue and brown . . 15 35
J50 – 20c. blue and red 20 35
J51 – 30c. blue . . . . 1·00 5·75
DESIGNS: 10c. Mt. Titlis, Lake Engstlen; 20c. Mt. Lyskamm from Riffelberg; 30c. Nicholas de Flue.

C 50 Freiburg

C 51 A. Bitzius—"Jeremias Gotthelf"

1930. Children's Fund. Dated "1930".
J52 C 50 5c. blue, black and green on buff 15 65
J53 – 10c. multicoloured on buff 15 35
J54 – 20c. multicoloured on buff 20 40
J55 C 51 30c. blue . . . . 1·10 3·25
ARMS—As Type C 51: 10c. Altdorf; 20c. Schaffhausen.

C 52 St. Moritz and Silvaplana Lakes

1931. Children's Fund. Dated "1931".
J56 C 52 5c. green 30 70
J57 – 10c. violet 25 40
J58 – 20c. red 40 40
J59 – 30c. blue . . . . 4·00 8·75
DESIGNS: 10c. The Wetterhorn; 20c. Lac Leman; 30c. Alexandre Vinet.

C 54 Flag swinging

C 56 Vaud

C 59 A. von Haller

1932. Children's Fund. Dated "1932".
J60 C 54 5c. red and green 50 90
J61 – 10c. orange 60 90
J62 – 20c. red 65 85
J63 – 30c. blue . . . . 1·90 3·75
DESIGNS: 10c. Putting the weight; 20c. Wrestlers; 30c. Eugen Huber.

1933. Children's Fund. Dated "1933".
J64 C 56 5c. green and buff . . . 30 80
J65 – 10c. violet and buff . . . 30 40
J66 – 20c. scarlet and buff . . 45 50
J67 – 30c. blue . . . . 1·80 4·00
DESIGNS: 10c. Swiss girl from Berne; 20c. Swiss girl from Ticino; 30c. Father Gregoire Girard.

1934. Children's Fund. Dated "1934".
J68 – 5c. green and buff . . . 30 95
J69 – 10c. violet and buff . . . 35 40
J70 – 20c. red and buff . . . 40 45
J71 C 59 30c. blue . . . . 1·70 4·00
SWISS GIRL DESIGNS—As Type C 56: 5c. Appenzell; 10c. Valais; 20c. Graubunden.

C 61 Stefano Franscini

C 62 H. G. Nageli

1935. Children's Fund. Dated "1935".
J72 – 5c. green and buff . . . 25 95
J73 – 10c. violet and buff . . . 30 40
J74 – 20c. red and buff 35 65
J75 C 61 30c. blue . . . . 2·00 4·25
SWISS GIRL DESIGNS—As Type C 56: 5c. Basel; 10c. Lucerne; 20c. Geneva.

1936. Children's Fund.
J76 C 62 5c. green 30 35
J77 – 10c. purple and buff . . . 35 35
J78 – 20c. red and buff 35 70
J79 – 30c. blue and buff . . . 2·75 13·00
SWISS GIRL DESIGNS—As Type C 56: 10c. Neuchatel; 20c. Schwyz; 30c. Zurich.

C 64 Gen. Henri Dufour

C 66 "Youth"

1937. Children's Fund.
J80 C 64 5c.+5c. green 10 15
J81 – 10c.+5c. purple 10 15
J82 C 66 20c.+5c. red, buff and silver 60 30
J83 – 30c.+10c. blue, buff and silver . . . . 95 3·25
DESIGNS: 10c. Nicholas de Flue; 30c. as Type C 66, but girl's head facing other way.

C 67 Salomon Gessner

C 69 Gen. Herzog

1938. Children's Fund. Dated "1938".
J84 C 67 5c.+5c. green 20 20
J85 – 10c.+5c. violet & buff . . 20 20
J86 – 20c.+5c. red and buff . . 20 20
J87 – 30c.+10c. blue & buff . . 1·00 2·50
SWISS GIRL DESIGNS—As Type C 56: 10c. St. Gall; 20c. Uri; 30c. Aargau.

1939. Children's Fund.
J88 C 69 5c.+5c. green 15 20
J89 – 10c.+5c. violet & buff . . 25 20
J90 – 20c.+5c. red and buff . . 30 45
J91 – 30c.+10c. blue & buff . . 1·30 4·25
SWISS GIRL DESIGNS—As Type C 56: 10c. Freibourg; 20c. Nidwalden; 30c. Basel.

C 71 Gottfried Keller

C 73 Johann Kasper Lavater

1940. Children's Fund. Dated "1940".
J92 C 71 5c.+5c. green 15 15
J93 – 10c.+5c. brown & buff . . 20 15
J94 – 20c.+5c. red and buff . . 30 20
J95 – 30c.+10c. blue & buff . . 1·00 5·25
SWISS GIRL DESIGNS—As Type C 56: 10c. Thurgau; 20c. Solothurn; 30c. Zug.

1941. Children's Fund. Bicentenary of Birth of Lavater (philosopher) and of Death of Richard (clockmaker). Dated "1941".
J96 C 73 5c.+5c. green 15 15
J97 – 10c.+5c. brown & buff . . 20 20
J98 – 20c.+5c. red and buff . . 25 20
J99 – 30c.+10c. blue . . . . . 90 3·50
DESIGNS—As Type C 56: 10c., 20c. Girls in national costumes of Schaffhausen and Obwalden. As Type C 73: 30c. Daniel Jean Richard.

C 74 Niklaus Riggenbach (rack railway pioneer)

1942. Children's Fund. Dated "1942".
J100 C 74 5c.+5c. green 15 20
J101 – 10c.+5c. brn & buff . . . 25 25
J102 – 20c.+5c. red and buff . . 25 20
J103 – 30c.+10c. blue . . . . . 1·10 3·25
DESIGNS: 10c. and 20c. Girls in national costumes of Appenzell Ausser-Rhoden and Glarus; 30c. Conrad Escher von der Linth (statesman).

C 75 Emanuel von Fellenberg C 76 Silver Thistle

1943. Death Centenary of Philip Emanuel von Fellenberg (economist).

J104 C 75 5c.+5c. green 15 20
J105 C 76 10c.+5c. green, buff and grey . . . . 30 10·00
J106 – 20c.+5c. red, yellow and pink . . . . . 20 2·30
J107 – 30c.+10c. blue, light blue and black . . . 2·40 2·50

FLOWERS: As Type C 76: 20c. "Ladies slipper"; 30c. Gentian.

C 77 Numa Droz C 78 Ludwig Forrer

1944. Birth Centenary of Droz (statesman).

J108 C 77 5c.+5c. green . . . . . 4·50 £275
J109 – 10c.+5c. olive, yellow and green . . . . . 20 75·00
J110 – 20c.+5c. red, yellow and grey . . . . . . 20 50·00
J111 – 30c.+10c. blue, grey and blue 25 £2250

DESIGNS: 10c. Edelweiss; 20c. Martagon lily; 30c. "Aquilegia alpina".

1945. Children's Fund. Centenary of Births of Ludwig Forrer (statesman) and Susanna Orelli (social reformer). Dated "1945".

J112 C 78 5c.+5c. green . . . . . 8·50 £275
J113 – 10c.+10c. brown . . . 10·00 £850
J114 – 20c.+10c. red, pink and yellow 65 20
J115 – 30c.+10c. blue, mauve and grey . . . . . . 2·30 4·75

DESIGNS: 10c. Susanna Orelli; 20c. Alpine dog rose; 30c. Spring crocus.

C 79 Rudolf Toepffer C 80 Jacob Burckhardt (historian)

1946. Death Centenary of Rudolf Toepffer (author and painter). Type C 79 and floral designs inscr "PRO JUVENTUTE 1946".

J116 C 79 5c.+5c. green 20 15
J117 – 10c.+10c. green, grey and orange 40 20
J118 – 20c.+10c. red, grey and yellow 50 25
J119 – 30c.+10c. blue, grey and mauve . . . . . 2·10 4·25

DESIGNS—As Type C 76: 10c. Narcissus; 20c. Houseleek; 30c. Blue thistle.

1947. Children's Fund. Type C 80 and floral designs inscr "PRO JUVENTUTE 1947".

J120 C 80 5c.+5c. green 25 15
J121 – 10c.+10c. black, yellow and grey £275 £190
J122 – 20c.+10c. brown, orange and grey . . £650 55·00
J123 – 30c.+10c. blue, pink and grey . . . . . . £1700 43·00

DESIGNS—As Type C 76: 10c. Alpine primrose; 20c. Orange lily; 30c. Cyclamen.

C 81 Gen. U. Wille C 82 Nicholas Wengi

1948. Children's Fund. Type C 81 and floral designs as Type C 76. Dated "1948".

J124 C 81 5c.+5c. purple . . . . £110 20·00
J125 – 10c.+10c. green, yellow and grey £180 £190
J126 – 20c.+10c. brown, red and buff 50 20
J127 – 40c.+10c. blue, yellow and grey . . . . . . 2·10 4·25

FLOWERS: 10c. Yellow foxglove; 20c. Rust-leaved Alpine rose; 40c. Lily of Paradise.

1949. Children's Fund. Type C 82 and floral designs inscr "PRO JUVENTUTE 1949".

J128 C 82 5c.+5c. red 30 15
J129 – 10c.+10c. green, grey and yellow 40 20
J130 – 20c.+10c. brown, blue and buff 50 20
J131 – 40c. blue, mauve and yellow . . . . 2·40 3·25

DESIGNS—As Type C 76: 10c. "Pulsatilla alpina"; 20c. Alpine clematis; 40c. Superb pink.

C 83 General Theophil Sprecher von Bernegg C 84 Red Admiral Butterfly

1950. Children's Fund. Inscr "PRO JUVENTUTE 1950".

J132 C 83 5c.+5c. brown 30 20
J133 C 84 10c.+10c. mult 60 25
J134 – 20c.+10c. black, blue and orange . . . . . £110 2·40
J135 – 30c.+10c. brown, grey and mauve . . . . . £110 1·40
J136 – 40c.+10c. yellow, brown and blue . . . . . . 65·00 19·00

DESIGNS: 20c. Clifden's nonpareil (moth); 30c. Honey bee; 40c. Moorland clouded yellow (butterfly).

C 85 Johanna Spyri (authoress) C 86 "Portrait of a Boy" (Anker)

1951. Children's Fund. Type C 85 and various insects as Type C 84. Inscr "PRO JUVENTUTE 1951".

J137 C 85 5c.+5c. purple . . . . £100 10·50
J138 – 10c.+10c. blue & grn £140 2·00
J139 – 20c.+10c. black, cream and mauve . . . . . £120 6·25
J140 – 30c.+10c. black, orange and green . . . . . £600 49·00
J141 – 40c.+10c. brown, red and blue . . . . . . £110 6·25

INSECTS: 10c. Banded agrion (dragonfly); 20c. Scarce swallowtail (butterfly); 30c. Orange-tip (butterfly); 40c. Viennese emperor moth.

1952. Children's Fund. Type C 86 and insects as Type C 84. Inscr "PRO JUVENTUTE 1952".

J142 C 86 5c.+5c. red £475 £325
J143 – 10c.+10c. orange, black and green £950 £150
J144 – 20c.+10c. cream, black and mauve . . . . . £700 46·00
J145 – 30c.+10c. blue, black and brown . . . . . 3·25 6·00
J146 – 40c.+10c. buff, brown and blue . . . . . . 3·25 5·00

INSECTS: 10c. Seven-spotted ladybird; 20c. Marbled white (butterfly); 30c. Chalk-hill blue (butterfly); 40c. Oak eggar moth.

1953. Children's Fund. Portraits as Type C 86 and insects as Type C 84. Inscr "PRO JUVENTUTE 1953".

J147 5c.+5c. red 30 15
J148 10c.+10c. pink, brown and green 40 25
J149 20c.+10c. black, buff and mauve 45 25
J150 30c.+10c. black, red & grn 3·75 5·50
J151 40c.+10c. blue . . . . . . 4·00 4·25

DESIGNS: 5c. "Portrait of a girl" (Anker); 10c. Black arches moth; 20c. Camberwell beauty (butterfly); 30c. "Purpureus kaehleri" (longhorn beetle); 40c. F. Hodler (self-portrait).

1954. Children's Fund. Portrait as Type C 85 and insects as Type C 84. Inscr "PRO JUVENTUTE 1954".

J152 5c.+5c. brown 30 15
J153 10c.+10c. multicoloured . . 40 20
J154 20c.+10c. multicoloured . . 85 30
J155 30c.+10c. multicoloured . . 17·00 45
J156 40c.+10c. multicoloured . . 36·00 2·40

DESIGNS: 5c. Jeremias Gotthelf (novelist) (after Albert Bitzius); 10c. Garden tiger moth; 20c. Buff-tailed bumble bee; 30c. "Ascalaphus libelluloides" (owl-fly); 40c. Swallowtail (butterfly).

1955. Children's Fund. Portrait as Type C 85 and insects as Type C 84. Inscr "PRO JUVENTUTE 1955".

J157 5c.+5c. purple . . . . . . 60·00 2·30
J158 10c.+10c. multicoloured . . 55·00 14·50
J159 20c.+10c. multicoloured . . 28·00 2·20
J160 30c.+10c. multicoloured . . £1300 £100
J161 40c.+10c. black red & blue £300 14·50

DESIGNS: 5c. C. Pictet-de-Rochemont; 10c. Peacock (butterfly); 20c. Great horntail; 30c. Yellow tiger moth; 40c. Apollo (butterfly).

1956. Children's Fund. Portrait as Type C 85 and insects as Type C 84. Inscr "PRO JUVENTUTE 1956".

J162 5c.+5c. purple . . . . . . £130 10·50
J163 10c.+10c. deep green, red and green 40 15
J164 20c.+10c. multicoloured . . 45 15
J165 30c.+10c. blue, indigo and yellow . . . . 2·40 3·50
J166 40c.+10c. yellow, brn & bl 2·40 3·00

DESIGNS: 5c. Carlo Maderno (architect); 10c. Common burnet (moth); 20c. Lesser purple emperor (butterfly); 30c. Blue ground beetle; 40c. Large white (butterfly).

1957. Children's Fund. Portrait as Type C 85 and insects as Type C 84. Inscr "PRO JUVENTUTE 1957".

J167 5c.+5c. purple 30 15
J168 10c.+10c. multicoloured . . 40 15
J169 20c.+10c. yellow, brown and mauve 50 15
J170 30c.+10c. emerald, green and purple . . . . 3·25 3·25
J171 40c.+10c. multicoloured . . 3·00 2·10

DESIGNS: 5c. L. Euler (mathematician); 10c. Clouded yellow (butterfly); 20c. Magpie moth; 30c. Rose chafer (beetle); 40c. Rosy underwing (moth).

C 92 Albrecht von Haller (naturalist) C 93 Pansy

1958. Children's Fund. Type C 92 and flowers as Type C 93. Inscr "PRO JUVENTUTE 1958".

J172 C 92 5c.+5c. purple 25 15
J173 C 93 10c.+10c. yellow, brown and green 35 15
J174 – 20c.+10c. mult 50 15
J175 – 30c.+10c. mult . . . . 2·40 2·30
J176 – 40c.+10c. mult . . . . 2·40 2·00

FLOWERS: 20c. Chinese aster; 30c. Morning Glory; 40c. Christmas rose.

1959. Children's Fund. Portrait as Type C 92 and flowers as Type C 93. Inscr "PRO JUVENTUTE 1959".

J177 5c.+5c. purple 25 15
J178 10c.+10c. multicoloured . . 40 15
J179 20c.+10c. red, green and purple 50 15
J180 30c.+10c. multicoloured . . 2·20 2·00
J181 50c.+10c. multicoloured . . 2·20 2·20

DESIGNS: 5c. Karl Hilty (lawyer); 10c. Marsh marigold; 20c. Poppy; 30c. Nasturtium; 50c. Sweet pea.

1960. Children's Fund. Portrait as Type C 92 and flowers as Type C 93. Inscr "PRO JUVENTUTE 1960".

J182 5c.+5c. blue 35 10
J183 10c.+10c. yellow, drab and green 35 15
J184 20c.+10c. green, brown and mauve 40 15
J185 30c.+10c. green, blue and brown . . . . 2·20 2·50
J186 50c.+10c. yellow, grn & bl 2·30 2·50

DESIGNS: 5c. Alexandre Calame (painter); 10c. Dandelion; 20c. Phlox; 30c. Larkspur; 50c. Thorn apple.

1961. Children's Fund. Portrait as Type C 92 and flowers as Type C 93. Inscr "PRO JUVENTUTE 1961".

J187 5c.+5c. blue 15 15
J188 10c.+10c. multicoloured . . 26·00 1·50
J189 20c.+10c. multicoloured . . 30 15
J190 30c.+10c. multicoloured . . 1·10 1·80
J191 50c.+10c. multicoloured . . 1·60 1·70

DESIGNS: 5c. J. Furrer (first President of Swiss Confederation); 10c. Sunflower; 20c. Lily-of-the-Valley; 30c. Iris; 50c. Silverweed.

C 97 "Child's World" C 98 Mother and Child

1962. Children's Fund. 50th Anniv of Pro Juventute Foundation. Inscr "1912–1962".

J192 – 5c.+5c. multicoloured 35·00 20·00
J193 C 97 10c.+10c. red & green 28·00 7·50
J194 C 98 20c.+10c. mult . . . 3·25 80
J195 – 30c.+10c. red, mauve and yellow . . . . 3·25 30·00
J196 – 50c.+10c. yellow, brown and blue . . . . . . 85 1·70

DESIGNS—As Type C 97: 5c. Apple blossom; 30c. "Child's World" (child in meadow); 50c. Forsythia.

1963. Children's Fund. Portrait as Type C 86 and flowers as Type C 93. Inscr "PRO JUVENTUTE 1963".

J197 5c.+5c. blue . . . . 3·50 15
J198a 10c.+10c. multicoloured . . 95 55
J199a 20c.+10c. red, green and carmine 95 55
J200 30c.+10c. multicoloured . . 3·00 1·20
J201 50c.+10c. purple, green and blue . . . . 4·25 3·25

DESIGNS: 5c. "Portrait of a Boy" (Anker); 10c. Oxeye daisy; 20c. Geranium; 30c. Cornflower; 50c. Carnation.

1964. Children's Fund. Portrait as Type C 86 and flowers as Type C 93. Inscr "PRO JUVENTUTE 1964".

J202 5c.+5c. blue 10 10
J203 10c.+10c. orange, yellow and green . . . . 70·00 65·00
J204 20c.+10c. red, green and carmine 20 10
J205 30c.+10c. purple, green and brown 45 50
J206 50c.+10c. multicoloured . . £170 65·00

DESIGNS: 5c. "Portrait of a Girl" (Anker); 10c. Daffodil; 20c. Rose; 30c. Red clover; 50c. White water-lily.

C 101 Western European Hedgehogs C 102 Roe Deer

1965. Children's Fund. Animals. Inscr "PRO JUVENTUTE 1965".

J207 C 101 5c.+5c. ochre, brown and red 10 10
J208 – 10c.+10c. mult . . . . 60·00 2·75
J209 – 20c.+10c. blue, brown and chestnut 20 10
J210 – 30c.+10c. blue, black and yellow 45 40
J211 – 50c.+10c. black, brown and blue . . 50 40

ANIMALS: 10c. Alpine marmots; 20c. Red deer; 30c. Eurasian badgers; 50c. Arctic hares.

1966. Children's Fund. Animals. As Type C 101 but inscr "PRO JUVENTUTE 1966". Mult.

J212 5c.+5c. Stoat 10 10
J213 10c.+10c. Eurasian red squirrel 10 10
J214 20c.+10c. Red fox 20 10
J215 30c.+10c. Brown hare . . . 7·75 3·75
J216 50c.+10c. Chamois . . . . 4·75 4·75

1967. Children's Fund. Animals. Inscr "PRO JUVENTUTE 1967". Multicoloured.

J217 10c.+10c. Type C 102 . . . 18·00 19·00
J218 20c.+10c. Pine marten . . . 20 10
J219 30c.+10c. Ibex 45 10
J220 50c.+10c. European otter . . 9·00 3·00

1968. Children's Fund. Birds. As Type C 102 but inscr "1968". Multicoloured.

J221 10c.+10c. Western capercaillie £140 £275
J222 20c.+10c. Northern bullfinch 30 £13000
J223 30c.+10c. Woodchat shrike £11000 £4500
J224 50c.+20c. Firecrest . . . . £100 15·00

1969. Children's Fund. Birds. As Type C 102. Inscr "1969". Multicoloured.

J225 10c.+10c. Eurasian goldfinch 20 15
J226 20c.+10c. Golden oriole . . 30 15
J227 30c.+10c. Wallcreeper . . . 45 30
J228 50c.+20c. Jay 70 55

1970. Children's Fund. Birds. As Type C 102. Inscr "1970". Multicoloured.

J229 10c.+10c. Blue tits 20 10
J230 20c.+10c. Hoopoe 30 15
J231 30c.+10c. Great spotted woodpecker . . . . . . 5·75 60·00
J232 50c.+20c. Great crested grebes 65 65

1971. Children's Fund. Birds. As Type C 102. Inscr "1971". Multicoloured.

J233 10c.+10c. Common redstarts 20 10
J234 20c.+10c. Bluethroats . . . 30 15
J235 30c.+10c. Peregrine falcon 45 15
J236 40c.+20c. Mallards 65 60

C 104 "McGredy's Sunset" Rose C 105 Chestnut

1972. Children's Fund. Roses. Multicoloured.

J237 10c.+10c. Type C 104 . . . 3·25 25
J238 20c.+10c. "Miracle" 30 15

J239 30c.+10c. "Papa Meilland" 50 25
J240 40c.+20c. "Madame Dimitriu" 80 80
See also Nos. J258/61 and J279/82.

1973. Children's Fund. "Fruits of the Forest". Multicoloured.
J241 15c.+5c. Type C **105** 20 10
J242 30c.+10c. Cherries 40 10
J243 40c.+20c. Blackberries 60 45
J244 60c.+20c. Bilberries 80 95
See also Nos. J245/8, J250/3 and J254/7.

1974. Children's Fund. "Fruits of the Forest". Poisonous Plants. As Type C **105**. Inscr "1974". Multicoloured.
J245 15c.+10c. Daphne 25 10
J246 30c.+20c. Belladonna 45 10
J247 50c.+20c. Laburnum 75 80
J248 60c.+25c. Mistletoe 90 75

1975. Children's Fund. As Type C **105**. Inscr "1975". Multicoloured.
J249 10c.+5c. "Post-Brent" (postman's hamper) 20 15
J250 15c.+10c. Hepatica 25 15
J251 30c.+20c. Rowan 45 10
J252 50c.+20c. Yellow deadnettle 70 75
J253 60c.+25c. Sycamore 8·00 3·50

1976. Children's Fund. "Fruits of the Forest". As Type C **105**. Inscr "1976". Multicoloured.
J254 20c.+10c. Barberry 30 15
J255 40c.+20c. Black elder 55 20
J256 40c.+20c. Lime 55 20
J257 80c.+40c. Lungwort 13·00 2·75

1977. Children's Fund. Roses. As Type C **104**. Inscr "1977". Multicoloured.
J258 20c.+10c. "Rosa foetida bicolor" 30 10
J259 40c.+20c. "Parfum de l'Hay" 55 10
J260 70c.+30c. "R. foetida persiana" 1·00 1·10
J261 80c.+40c. "R. centifolia muscosa" 1·10 1·00

C **106** Arms of Aarburg

C **107** Letter Balance

1978. Children's Fund. Arms of the Communes (1st series). Multicoloured.
J262 20c.+10c. Type C **106** 25 10
J263 40c.+20c. Gruyeres 55 10
J264 70c.+30c. Castasegna 95 1·00
J265 80c.+40c. Wangen 1·00 90
See also Nos. J266/9, J270/3 and J274/7.

1979. Children's Fund. Arms of the Communes (2nd series). As Type C **106**. Multicoloured.
J266 20c.+10c. Cadro 25 10
J267 40c.+20c. Rute 50 10
J268 70c.+30c. Schwamendingen 95 1·10
J269 80c.+40c. Perroy 1·00 90

1980. Children's Fund. Arms of the Communes (3rd series). As Type C **106**. Multicoloured.
J270 20c.+10c. Cortaillod 25 10
J271 40c.+20c. Sierre 55 10
J272 70c.+30c. Scuol 95 1·10
J273 80c.+40c. Wolfenschiessen 1·10 90

1981. Children's Fund. Arms of the Communes (4th series). As Type C **106**. Multicoloured.
J274 20c.+10c. Uffikon 25 20
J275 40c.+20c. Torre 55 20
J276 70c.+30c. Benken 95 1·10
J277 80c.+40c. Preverenges 1·10 95

1982. Children's Fund. Type C **107** and roses as Type C **104**. Multicoloured.
J278 10c.+10c. Type C **107** 20 20
J279 20c.+10c. "La Belle Portugaise" 30 20
J280 40c.+20c. "Hugh Dickson" 55 20
J281 70c.+30c. "Mermaid" 1·00 1·10
J282 80c.+40c. "Madame Caroline" 1·20 85

C **108** Kitchen Stove, c. 1850

C **109** Heidi and Goat (Johanna Spyri)

1983. Children's Fund. Toys. Multicoloured.
J283 20c.+10c. Type C **108** 30 15
J284 40c.+20c. Rocking horse, 1826 60 15
J285 70c.+30c. Doll, c. 1870 95 1·10
J286 80c.+40c. Steam locomotive, c. 1900 1·10 1·00

1984. Children's Fund. Characters from Children's Books. Multicoloured.
J287 35c.+15c. Type C **109** 55 50
J288 50c.+20c. Pinocchio and kite (Carlo Collodi) 65 20
J289 70c.+30c. Pippi Longstocking (Astrid Lindgren) 1·10 1·20
J290 80c.+40c. Max and Moritz on roof (Wilhelm Busch) 1·40 1·10

1985. Children's Fund. Characters from Children's Books. As Type C **109**. Multicoloured.
J291 35c.+15c. Hansel, Gretel and Witch 50 50
J292 50c.+20c. Snow White and the Seven Dwarfs 70 20
J293 80c.+40c. Red Riding Hood and Wolf 1·10 1·10
J294 90c.+40c. Cinderella and Prince Charming 1·20 1·20

C **110** Teddy Bear

C **111** Girl carrying Pine Branch and Candle

1986. Children's Fund. Toys. Multicoloured.
J295 35c.+15c. Type C **110** 65 60
J296 50c.+20c. Spinning top 75 25
J297 80c.+40c. Steamroller 1·20 1·40
J298 90c.+40c. Doll 1·30 1·20

1987. Children's Fund. Child Development. Pre-school Age. Multicoloured.
J299 25c.+10c. Type C **111** 45 35
J300 35c.+15c. Mother breast-feeding baby 60 65
J301 50c.+20c. Toddler playing with bricks 75 25
J302 80c.+40c. Children playing in sand 1·20 1·20
J303 90c.+40c. Father with child on his shoulders 1·30 1·10

C **112** Learning to Read

C **113** Community Work

1988. Children's Fund. Child Development. School Age. Multicoloured.
J304 35c.+15c. Type C **112** 60 65
J305 50c.+20c. Playing triangle 75 25
J306 80c.+40c. Learning arithmetic 1·30 1·40
J307 90c.+40c. Drawing 1·40 1·20

1989. Children's Fund. Child Development. Adolescence. Multicoloured.
J308 35c.+15c. Type C **113** 60 65
J309 50c.+20c. Young couple (friendship) 65 30
J310 80c.+40c. Boy at computer screen (vocational training) 1·30 1·40
J311 90c.+40c. Girl in laboratory (higher education and research) £3500 £4500

C **114** Building Model Ship (hobbies)

C **115** Ramsons

1990. Child Development. Leisure Activities. Mult.
J312 35c.+15c. Type C **114** 60 60
J313 50c.+20c. Youth group 65 30
J314 80c.+40c. Sport 1·40 1·50
J315 90c.+40c. Music 1·50 1·30

1991. Woodland Flowers. Multicoloured.
J316 50c.+25c. Type C **115** 80 30
J317 70c.+30c. Wood cranesbill 1·10 1·20
J318 80c.+40c. Nettle-leaved bellflower 1·30 1·10
J319 90c.+40c. Few-leaved hawkweed 1·40 1·40

C **116** Melchior (wood puppet)

1992. Christmas (J320) and Trees (others). Mult.
J320 50c.+25c. Type C **116** 80 40
J321 50c.+25c. Beech 80 40
J322 70c.+30c. Norway maple 1·20 1·30
J323 80c.+40c. Pedunculate oak 1·20 1·20
J324 90c.+40c. Norway spruce 1·40 1·30
Nos. J321/4 show silhouette of tree and close-up of its leaves and fruit.

C **117** Christmas Wreath

C **118** Candles

1993. Christmas (J325) and Woodland Plants (others). Multicoloured.
J325 60c.+30c. Type C **117** 95 65
J326 60c.+30c. Male fern 95 65
J327 80c.+40c. Guelder rose 1·40 1·30
J328 100c.+50c. "Mnium punctatum" 1·70 1·80

1994. Christmas (J329) and Fungi (others). Mult.
J329 60c.+30c. Type C **118** 95 70
J330 60c.+30c. Wood blewit 95 70
J331 80c.+40c. Red boletus 1·40 1·40
J332 100c.+50c. Shaggy pholiota 1·70 1·70

C **119** Detail of "The Annunciation" (Bartolome Murillo)

1995. Christmas (J333) and Wildlife (others). Mult.
J333 60c.+30c. Type C **119** 95 80
J334 60c.+30c. Brown trout 95 80
J335 80c.+40c. Grey wagtail 1·40 1·50
J336 100c.+50c. Spotted salamander 1·70 1·80

C **120** Shooting Star and Constellations

1996. Christmas (J337) and Wildlife (others). Mult.
J337 70c.+35c. Type C **120** 1·20 95
J338 70c.+35c. European graylings (fish) 1·20 95
J339 90c.+45c. Crayfish 1·40 1·40
J340 110c.+55c. European otter 1·80 1·70

C **121** Mistletoe

1997. Christmas (J341) and Wildlife (others). Mult.
J341 70c.+35c. Type C **121** 1·20 1·10
J342 70c.+35c. Three-spined stickleback 1·20 1·00
J343 90c.+45c. Yellow-bellied toad 1·40 1·30
J344 110c.+55c. Ruff 1·80 1·60

C **122** Christmas Bell

1998. Christmas (J345) and Wildlife (others). Mult.
J345 70c.+35c. Type C **122** 1·20 1·00
J346 70c.+35c. Ramshorn snail 1·20 1·00
J347 90c.+45c. Great crested grebe 1·50 1·30
J348 110c.+55c. Pike 1·80 1·60

C **123** Children and Snowman (Margaret Strub)

1999. Christmas (J349) and Illustrations from "Nicolo the Clown" (picture book by Verena Pavoni) (others). Multicoloured.
J349 70c.+35c. Type C **123** 1·10 1·00
J350 70c.+35c. Nicolo holding guitar 1·10 1·00
J351 90c.+45c. Nicolo with his father 1·40 1·40
J352 110c.+55c. Nicolo with donkey 1·70 1·70

C **124** Santa Claus

C **125** Santa Claus and Cat

2000. Christmas. Illustrations from *Little Albert* (book) by Albert Manser. Multicoloured.
J353 70c.+35c. Type C **124** 1·30 1·20
J354 70c.+35c. Boys sitting on fence and girl 1·30 1·20
J355 90c.+45c. Little Albert with umbrella 1·60 1·60
J356 90c.+45c. Children sledging 1·60 1·60

2001. Illustrations from Children's Books. Multicoloured.
J357 70c. + 35c. Type C **125** (*What's Santa Claus Doing?* (text by Karin von Oldersausen, illustrations by Gabi Fluck)) 1·00 50
J358 70c. + 35c. Leopold the leopard in tree (*Leopold and the Sun* by Stephan Brülhart) 1·00 50
J359 90c. + 45c. Bear on scooter (*Honey Bear by S. Brulhart*) 1·25 1·25
J360 90c. + 45c. Tom the monkey in tree (*Leopold and the Sun*) 1·25 1·25

C **126** "Christmas rose"

2002. Roses. Multicoloured.
J361 70c. + 35c. Type C **126** 1·00 50
J362 70c. + 35c. "Ingrid Bergman" 1·00 50
J363 90c. + 45c. "Belle Vaudoise" 1·25 1·25
J364 90c. + 45c. "Charmian" 1·25 1·25
J365 130c. + 65c. "Fruhlingsgold" 1·80 1·80
No. J361 is impregnated with the fragrance of cinnamon and cloves and Nos. J362/5 with the perfume of roses.

INTERNATIONAL ORGANIZATIONS SITUATED IN SWITZERLAND

The stamps listed under this heading were issued by the Swiss Post Office primarily for the use of officials of the Organizations named, situated in Geneva.

These stamps could not be legitimately obtained unused before Feburary 1944.

A. LEAGUE OF NATIONS

1922. Optd **SOCIETE DES NATIONS**.
LN 1 **20a** 2½c. bistre on buff — 40
LN 2 3c. blue on buff — 4·50
LN 3 5c. orange on buff — 2·10
LN 4 5c. grey on buff — 2·10
LN 5 5c. purple on buff — 1·20
LN 5a 5c. green on buff — 13·00
LN 6 7½c. green on buff — 30
LN 7 **21** 10c. green on buff — 35
LN 8 10c. violet on buff — 95
LN 9 15c. red on buff — 70
LN10 20c. purple on buff — 3·75
LN11 20c. red on buff — 1·50
LN13 25c. red on buff — 75
LN14 25c. brown on buff — 9·25
LN15 **17** 30c. green and brown — 7·25
LN16 **21** 30c. blue on buff — 4·25
LN17 **17** 35c. yellow and green — 3·75
LN18 40c. blue — 1·00
LN19 40c. green and mauve — 6·50
LN20a 50c. green & dp green 50 6·25
LN21 60c. brown 00 80
LN22a 70c. buff and violet 15·00 14·00
LN23a 80c. buff and grey 1·20 1·90

LN24a 41 90c. red, dp green & grn — 9·25
LN25a 17 1f. green and purple — 5·00
LN26b 41 1f.20 red, lake and pink 2·50 3·50
LN27a 1f.50 red, bl & turq 2·50 9·25
LN28a 2f. red, black and grey 3·00 9·00
LN29 22 3f. red — 17·00
LN29a 43 3f. brown — £100
LN30 – 5f. blue (No. 296) — 38·00
LN32 – 10f. mauve (No. 297) — 75·00
LN33 – 10f. green (No. 337) — 85·00

1932. International Disarmament Conference. Optd **SOCIETE DES NATIONS.**
LN34 **44** 5c. green — 10·50
LN35 10c. orange — 95
LN36 20c. mauve — 95
LN37 30c. blue — 31·00
LN38 60c. brown — 9·00
LN39 **45** 1f. grey and blue — 7·50

1934. Landscape designs of 1934 optd **SOCIETE DES NATIONS.**
LN40 **48** 3c. green — 30
LN41 – 5c. green — 40
LN42 – 15c. orange — 80
LN43 – 25c. brown — 11·00
LN44 – 30c. blue — 95

1937. Landscape designs of 1936 optd **SOCIETE DES NATIONS.**
LN45A **52** 3c. green 10 20
LN46A – 5c. green 20 20
LN47Ac – 10c. purple — 70
LN49 – 10c. brown 50 45
LN50A – 15c. orange 30 40
LN51A – 20c. red (railway) — 1·50
LN51Ac – 20c. red (lake) 75 80
LN52A – 25c. brown 45 65
LN53A – 30c. blue 45 55
LN54A – 35c. green 45 65
LN55A – 40c. grey 70 80

1938. Nos. 382/5 optd **SOCIETE DES NATIONS.**
LN56 **55** 20c. red and buff — 1·20
LN57 – 30c. blue and light blue — 1·90
LN58 – 60c. brown and buff — 3·50
LN59 – 1f. black and buff — 6·00

1938. Nos. 382/5 optd **SERVICE DE LA SOCIETE DES NATIONS** in circle.
LN60 **55** 20c. red and buff — 1·40
LN61 – 30c. blue and light blue — 2·50
LN62 – 60c. brown and buff — 4·50
LN63 – 1f. black and buff 00 7·50

1939. Nos. 388c/90c optd **SOCIETE DES NATIONS.**
LN64 **61** 3f. brown on buff 3·50 6·25
LN65 – 5f. blue on buff 5·00 8·50
LN66 – 10f. green on buff 8·00 19·00

1944. Optd **COURRIER DE LA SOCIETE DES NATIONS.** (a) Landscape designs of 1936.
LN67 **52** 3c. green 20 25
LN68 – 5c. green 20 25
LN69 – 10c. brown 20 20
LN70 – 15c. orange 30 30
LN71 – 20c. red (lake) 45 55
LN72 – 25c. brown 55 70
LN73 – 30c. blue 60 75
LN74 – 35c. green 60 1·00
LN75 – 40c. grey 65 1·30

(b) Historical designs of 1941.
LN76 – 50c. blue on green 1·10 2·00
LN77 **68** 60c. brown on brown 1·40 2·40
LN78 – 70c. purple on mauve 1·50 2·20
LN79 – 80c. black on grey 1·30 2·00
LN80 – 90c. red on pink 1·30 2·00
LN81 – 1f. green on green 1·50 2·30
LN82 – 1f.20 purple on grey 2·00 3·25
LN83 – 1f.50 blue on buff 2·20 3·75
LN84 – 2f. red on pink 2·75 4·50

(c) Parliament designs of 1938.
LN85 **61** 3f. brown on buff 4·50 8·75
LN86 – 5f. blue on buff 7·00 12·00
LN87 – 10f. green on buff 12·50 23·00

B. INTERNATIONAL LABOUR OFFICE

Optd **S.d.N. Bureau international du Travail** (Nos. LB1/47).

1923.
LB 1 **20a** 2½c. bistre on buff — 20
LB 2 3c. blue on buff — 70
LB 3 5c. orange on buff — 35
LB 4 5c. purple on buff — 15
LB 5 7½c. green on buff — 20
LB 6 **21** 10c. green on buff — 30
LB 8 15c. red on buff — 55
LB 9 20c. purple on buff — 7·00
LB10 20c. red on buff — 3·00
LB11 25c. red on buff — 65
LB12 25c. brown on buff — 1·60
LB13 **17** 30c. green and brown — 31·00
LB14 **21** 30c. blue on buff — 1·10
LB15 **17** 35c. yellow and green — 5·00
LB16 40c. blue — 65
LB17 40c. green and mauve — 7·25
LB18a 50c. green & deep green 1·20 3·25
LB19 60c. brown 90 1·10
LB20a 70c. buff and violet 1·20 19·00
LB21 80c. buff and grey 6·25 1·00
LB22 **41** 90c. red, dp grn & grn — 2·50
LB23 **17** 1f. green and purple 00 1·40
LB24b **38** 1f.20 red, lake and pink 12·00 3·25
LB25a 1f.50 red, bl & turq 2·00 8·25
LB26a 2f. red, black and grey 2·50 22·00
LB27 **22** 3f. red — 14·00
LB27a **43** 3f. brown — £120
LB28 – 5f. blue (No. 296) — 22·00
LB30 – 10f. mauve (No. 297) — 90·00
LB31 – 10f. green (No. 337) — 90·00

1932. International Disarmament Conference.
LB32 **44** 5c. green — 70
LB33 10c. orange — 60
LB34 20c. mauve — 85
LB35 30c. blue — 4·25
LB36 60c. brown — 4·25
LB37 **45** 1f. grey and blue — 6·00

1937. Landscape design of 1934.
LB38 **48** 3c. green — 3·00

1937. Landscape designs of 1936.
LB39A **52** 3c. green 20 25
LB40A – 5c. green 20 25
LB41B – 10c. purple 00 1·20
LB41e – 10c. brown 30 30
LB42A – 15c. orange 30 25
LB43A – 20c. red (railway) — 1·10
LB43c – 20c. red (lake) 55 75
LB44A – 25c. brown 50 65
LB45A – 30c. blue 50 60
LB46A – 35c. green 50 85
LB47A – 40c. grey 80 90

1938. Nos. 382/5 optd **S.d.N. Bureau international du Travail.**
LB48 **55** 20c. red and buff — 75
LB49 – 30c. blue and light blue — 1·40
LB50 – 60c. brown and buff — 2·75
LB51 – 1f. black and buff — 4·50

1938. Nos. 382/5 optd **SERVICE DU BUREAU INTERNATIONAL DU TRAVAIL** in circle.
LB52 **55** 20c. red and buff — 2·00
LB53 – 30c. blue and light blue — 1·70
LB54 – 60c. brown and buff — 3·75
LB55 – 1f. black and buff — 3·75

1939. Nos. 388c/90c optd **S.d.N. Bureau international du Travail.**
LB56 **61** 3f. brown on buff 3·00 5·50
LB57 – 5f. blue on buff 4·00 9·75
LB58 – 10f. green on buff 6·75 14·50

1944. Optd **COURRIER DU BUREAU INTERNATIONAL DU TRAVAIL.** (a) Landscape designs of 1936.
LB59 **52** 3c. green 20 20
LB60 – 5c. green 20 25
LB61 – 10c. brown 30 30
LB62 – 15c. orange 40 50
LB63 – 20c. red (lake) 45 60
LB64 – 25c. brown 50 70
LB65 – 30c. blue 75 1·00
LB66 – 35c. green 80 1·20
LB67 – 40c. grey 85 1·40

(b) Historical designs of 1941.
LB68 – 50c. blue on green 2·30 3·75
LB69 **68** 60c. brown on brown 2·30 3·00
LB70 – 70c. purple on mauve 2·75 2·50
LB71 – 80c. black on grey 65 70
LB72 – 90c. red on pink 65 70
LB73 – 1f. green on green 85 75
LB74 – 1f.20 purple on grey 1·00 80
LB75 – 1f.50 blue on buff 1·20 85
LB76 – 2f. red on pink 1·70 1·20

(c) Parliament designs of 1938.
LB77 **61** 3f. brown on buff 3·75 3·00
LB78 – 5f. blue on buff 5·50 5·00
LB79 – 10f. green on buff 11·50 14·00

1950. Landscape designs of 1949 optd **BUREAU INTERNATIONAL DU TRAVAIL.**
LB80 **107** 5c. orange 2·75 2·75
LB81 – 10c. green 2·75 4·75
LB82 – 15c. turquoise 3·50 3·00
LB83 – 20c. purple 3·50 5·75
LB84 – 25c. red 3·75 4·50
LB85 – 30c. green 4·00 5·75
LB86 – 35c. brown 4·00 5·00
LB87 – 40c. blue 4·00 5·25
LB88 – 50c. grey 5·50 5·25
LB89 – 60c. green 6·50 7·00
LB90 – 70c. violet 8·00 9·50

LB 4 Miners (bas-relief)

1952. Inscr as in Type LB 4.
LB91 LB 4 5c. purple 10 10
LB92 10c. green 10 10
LB94 – 20c. red 1·10 55
LB95 – 30c. orange 10 20
LB96 LB 4 40c. blue 1·40 1·20
LB97 50c. blue 20 30
LB98 – 60c. brown 30 25
LB99 – 2f. purple 80 70
DESIGN—HORIZ: 20, 30, 60c., 2f. Globe, flywheel and factory chimney.

1969. Pope Paul's Visit to Geneva. No. LB95 optd **Visite du Pape Paul VI Geneve 10 juin 1969.**
LB100 30c. orange 05 15

LB 6 New Headquarters Building

1974. Inaug of New I.L.O. Headquarters, Geneva.
LB101 LB 6 80c. multicoloured 70 60

LB 7 Man at Lathe

1975.
LB102 LB 7 30c. brown 25 25
LB103 – 60c. blue 45 40
LB104 – 90c. brown, red & grn 70 65
LB105 – 100c. green 80 65
LB106 – 120c. ochre and brown 60 75
DESIGNS: 60c. Woman at drilling machine; 90c. Welder and laboratory assistant; 100c. Surveyor with theodolite; 120c. Apprentice and instructor with slide rule.

LB 8 Keys

1994. 75th Anniv of I.L.O.
LB107 LB 8 180c. multicoloured 1·40 1·60

C. INTERNATIONAL EDUCATION OFFICE

1944. Optd **COURRIER DU BUREAU INTERNATIONAL D'EDUCATION.** (a) Landscape designs of 1936.
LE1 **52** 3c. green 20 40
LE2 – 5c. green 50 95
LE3 – 10c. brown 55 1·20
LE4 – 15c. orange 50 1·10
LE5 – 20c. red (lake) 50 1·10
LE6 – 25c. brown 50 1·10
LE7 – 30c. blue 85 1·50
LE8 – 35c. green 75 1·40
LE9 – 40c. grey 95 1·70

(b) Historical designs of 1941.
LE10 – 50c. blue on green 5·25 7·75
LE11 **68** 60c. brown on brown 5·25 7·75
LE12 – 70c. purple on mauve 5·25 7·75
LE13 – 80c. black on grey 55 1·20
LE14 – 90c. red on pink 65 1·30
LE15 – 1f. green on green 75 1·50
LE16 – 1f.20 purple on grey 95 1·80
LE17 – 1f.50 blue on buff 1·20 3·00
LE18 – 2f. red on pink 1·90 2·75

(c) Parliament designs of 1938.
LE19 **61** 3f. brown on buff 4·50 12·00
LE20 – 5f. blue on buff 6·75 19·00
LE21 – 10f. green on buff 10·00 27·00

1946. Optd **BIE** vert.
LE22 **86** 10c. purple 15 25

Optd **BUREAU INTERNATIONAL D'EDUCATION** (Nos. LE23/39).

1948. Landscape designs of 1936.
LE23 5c. brown 1·70 2·00
LE24 10c. green 1·90 2·10
LE25 20c. brown 1·70 2·00
LE26 25c. red 1·70 2·00
LE27 30c. blue 1·90 2·10
LE28 40c. blue 1·70 2·00

1950. Landscape designs of 1949.
LE29 **107** 5c. orange 70 75
LE30 – 10c. green 90 90
LE31 – 15c. turquoise 90 95
LE32 – 20c. purple 3·00 3·00
LE33 – 25c. red 6·75 8·75
LE34 – 30c. green 6·75 7·75
LE35 – 35c. brown 4·50 6·00
LE36 – 40c. blue 4·75 5·75
LE37 – 50c. grey 5·50 6·00
LE38 – 60c. green 6·50 7·50
LE39 – 70c. violet 7·50 8·75

LE 3 Globe on Books

1958. Inscr as in Type LE 3.
LE40 LE 3 5c. purple 10 10
LE41 10c. green 10 10
LE43 – 20c. red 20 15
LE44 – 30c. orange 30 25
LE45 LE 3 40c. blue 2·20 1·80
LE46 50c. blue 45 35
LE47 – 60c. brown 55 45
LE48 – 2f. purple 1·50 1·30
DESIGN—VERT: 20, 30, 60c., 2f. Pestalozzi Monument, Yverdon.

D. WORLD HEALTH ORGANIZATION

1948. Optd **ORGANISATION MONDIALE DE LA SANTE.** (a) Landscape designs of 1936.
LH1 5c. brown (No. 489) 2·00 1·20
LH2 10c. green (No. 490) 2·50 2·50
LH3 20c. brown (No. 491) 2·30 2·50
LH4 25c. red (No. 492) 2·50 2·75
LH5 40c. blue (No. 494) 3·00 2·40

(b) Landscape designs of 1949.
LH 6 **107** 5c. orange 70 35
LH 7 – 10c. green 1·40 1·20
LH 8 – 15c. turquoise 1·80 90
LH 9 – 20c. purple 5·25 3·50
LH10 – 25c. red 5·50 5·50
LH11 – 30c. green 2·50 3·25
LH12 – 35c. brown 2·75 4·50
LH13 – 40c. blue 2·50 1·10
LH14 – 50c. grey 3·50 3·75
LH15 – 60c. green 3·50 3·75
LH16 – 70c. violet 5·50 3·25

(c) Historical designs of 1941 (Nos. 408/13).
LH17 80c. black on grey 1·10 1·40
LH18 90c. red on pink 6·25 3·00
LH19 1f. green on green 1·30 1·60
LH20 1f.20 purple on grey 7·75 7·75
LH21 1f.50 blue on buff 17·00 8·50
LH22 2f. red on pink 3·50 2·40

(d) Parliament designs of 1938.
LH23 **61** 3f. brown on buff 36·00 21·00
LH24 – 5f. blue on buff 7·75 5·50
LH25 – 10f. green on buff 75·00 38·00

LH 2 Staff of Aesculapius

1957.
LH26 LH 2 5c. purple 10 10
LH27 10c. green 10 10
LH29 20c. red 15 15
LH30 30c. orange 25 25
LH31 40c. blue 1·60 1·60
LH32 50c. blue 35 35
LH33 60c. brown 40 40
LH34 2f. purple 1·20 1·20

1962. Malaria Eradication. Optd **ERADICATION DU PALUDISME.**
LH35 LH 2 50c. blue 15 25

LH 4 Staff of Aesculapius

1975.
LH36 LH 4 30c. green, purple and pink 25 25
LH37 60c. yellow, blue and light blue 50 45
LH38 90c. yellow, violet and light violet 75 65
LH39 100c. blue, brown and orange 80 75
LH40 140c. green, turquoise and red 1·20 1·20

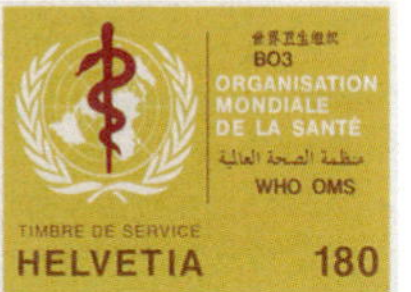

LH 5 Staff of Aesculapius

1995.
LH41 LH 5 180c. yellow, brown and red 1·50 1·60

E. INTERNATIONAL REFUGEES ORGANIZATION

Optd **ORGANISATION INTERNATIONALE POUR LES REFUGIES.**

1950. (a) Landscape designs of 1949.
LR1 **107** 5c. orange 10·00 7·50
LR2 – 10c. green 11·00 8·00
LR3 – 20c. purple 10·00 7·50

LR4 – 25c. red 11·00 8·00
LR5 – 40c. blue 10·50 7·50

(b) Historical designs of 1941 (Nos. 408/13).

LR6 80c. black on grey 10·00 11·50
LR7 1f. green on green 9·50 6·00
LR8 2f. red on pink 9·50 6·00

F. WORLD METEOROLOGICAL ORGANIZATION

LM 1 "The Elements" LM 2 W.M.O. Emblem

1956. Inscr as in Type LM 1.

LM1 LM 1 5c. purple 10 10
LM2 10c. green 10 10
LM4 – 20c. red 15 15
LM5 – 30c. orange 25 25
LM6 LM 1 40c. blue 1·30 1·80
LM7 50c. blue 35 35
LM8 – 60c. brown 40 40
LM9 – 2f. purple 1·40 1·20
DESIGN: 20, 30, 60c., 2f. Weathervane.

1973. Cent of World Meteorological Organization.

LM10 LM 2 30c. red 25 25
LM11 40c. blue 35 35
LM12 – 80c. violet and gold 65 60
LM13 LM 2 1f. brown 80 70
DESIGN: 80c. Emblem and "OMI OMM 1873 1973".

G. UNIVERSAL POSTAL UNION

LP 1 U.P.U. Monument, Berne LP 2 "Letter Post"

1957. Inscr as in Type LP 1.

LP1 LP 1 5c. purple 10 10
LP2 – 10c. green 10 10
LP4 – 20c. red 15 15
LP5 – 30c. orange 25 25
LP6 LP 1 40c. blue 1·30 1·70
LP7 50c. blue 35 35
LP8 – 60c. brown 40 50
LP9 LP 1 2f. purple 1·40 1·70
DESIGN: 10, 20, 30, 60c. Pegasus (sculpture).

1976.

LP10 LP 2 40c. purple, blue and claret 35 35
LP11 – 80c. multicoloured 60 60
LP12 – 90c. multicoloured 75 75
LP13 – 100c. multicoloured 75 75
LP14 – 120c. multicoloured 1·00 1·00
LP15 – 140c. grey, blue and red 1·30 1·30
DESIGNS: 80c. "Parcel Post"; 90c. "Financial Services"; 100c. Technical co-operation; 120c. Carrier pigeon, international reply coupon and postal money order; 140c. Express Mail Service.

The 120 and 140c. are additionally inscribed "TIMBRE DE SERVICE".

LP 3 Computer, Mail Sacks and Globe

1995.

LP16 LP 3 180c. multicoloured 1·60 1·60

LP 4 Hand reaching for Rainbow

1999. 125th Anniv of Universal Postal Union. Multicoloured.

LP17 20c. Type LP 4 20 20
LP18 70c. Hand holding rainbow 65 65

H. UNITED NATIONS

1950. Optd NATIONS UNIES OFFICE EUROPEEN. (a) Landscape designs of 1949.

LU 1 107 5c. orange 55 1·30
LU 2 – 10c. green 70 1·10
LU 3 – 15c. turquoise 1·20 1·50
LU 4 – 20c. purple 1·60 2·30
LU 5 – 25c. red 2·50 3·50
LU 6 – 30c. green 2·50 3·50
LU 7 – 35c. brown 5·25 7·25
LU 8 – 40c. blue 3·25 2·75
LU 9 – 50c. grey 4·25 6·25
LU10 – 60c. green 5·00 7·50
LU11 – 70c. violet 5·00 7·25

(b) Historical designs of 1941 (Nos. 408/13).

LU12 80c. black on grey 8·25 6·25
LU13 90c. red on pink 8·25 6·25
LU14 1f. green on green 8·25 6·25
LU15 1f.20 purple on grey 8·25 8·25
LU16 1f.50 blue on buff 8·75 14·00
LU17 2f. red on pink 8·75 10·50

(c) Parliament designs of 1938.

LU18 61 3f. brown on buff 75·00 60·00
LU19 – 5f. blue on buff 75·00 60·00
LU20 – 10f. green on buff £110 95·00

LU 2 LU 4

1955. 10th Anniv of U.N.O.

LU21 LU 2 40c. blue and yellow 1·80 2·10

1955. Nos. LU22/3 and LU27/8 are as Type LU 2 but without dates.

LU22 – 5c. purple 10 10
LU23 – 10c. green 10 10
LU25 LU 4 20c. red 15 15
LU26 30c. orange 25 20
LU27 – 40c. blue 2·20 2·30
LU28 – 50c. blue 40 25
LU29 LU 4 60c. brown 35 35
LU30 2f. purple 90 90

1960. World Refugee Year. Nos. LU25 and LU28 optd **ANNEE MONDIALE DU REFUGIE 1959 1960**.

LU31 20c. red 10 15
LU32 50c. blue 15 25

LU 6 Palace of Nations, Geneva

1960. 15th Anniv of U.N.O.

LU33 LU 6 5f. blue 2·30 3·00

LU 7 LU 8 UNCSAT Emblem

1962. Opening of U.N. Philatelic Museum, Geneva.

LU34 LU 7 10c. green and red 10 10
LU35 – 30c. red and blue 10 15
LU36 LU 7 50c. blue and red 15 25
LU37 – 60c. brown and green 15 30
DESIGN—HORIZ: 30, 60c. As Type LU 4 but inscr "ONU MUSEE PHILATELIQUE".

1963. U.N. Scientific and Technological Conf, Geneva.

LU38 LU 8 50c. red and blue 25 30
LU39 – 2f. green and purple 60 1·10
DESIGN—HORIZ: 2f. As Type LU 4, but with emblem.

From 1969 stamps for the Geneva Headquarters were issued by the United Nations (q.v.).

I. INTERNATIONAL TELECOMMUNICATION UNION

LT 1 Transmitting Aerial LT 2 New H.Q. Building

1958. Inscr as in Type LT 1.

LT1 LT 1 5c. purple 10 10
LT2 10c. green 10 10
LT4 – 20c. red 20 15
LT5 – 30c. orange 30 25
LT6 LT 1 40c. blue 1·50 1·70
LT7 50c. blue 45 35
LT8 – 60c. brown 55 45
LT9 – 2f. purple 1·80 1·30
DESIGN: 20, 30, 60c., 2f. Receiving aerials.

1973. Inaug of New I.T.U. Headquarters, Geneva.

LT10 LT 2 80c. black and blue 65 60

LT 3 Boeing 747 Jetliner and Ocean Liner

1976. World Telecommunications Network.

LT11 – 40c. blue and red 35 30
LT12 LT 3 90c. violet, blue & yellow 75 65
LT13 – 1f. red, green & yellow 80 80
DESIGNS: 40c. "Sound waves"; 1f. Face and microphone in television screen.

LT 4 Optical Fibre Cables

1988.

LT14 LT 4 1f.40 multicoloured 1·20 1·30

LT 5 Emblem emitting Radio Signals

1994. 100 Years of Radio.

LT15 LT 5 1f.80 multicoloured 1·50 1·60

LT 6 "a b c" and X-ray of Bone Joint ("Teleeducation")

1999. Multicoloured.

LT16 10c. Type LT 6 10 10
LT17 100c. Arrow and X-ray of bone joint ("Telemedicine") 90 90

J. WORLD INTELLECTUAL PROPERTY ORGANIZATION

LV 1 WIPO Seal

1989. Multicoloured.

LV1 40c. Type LV 1 45 40
LV2 50c. Face and symbolic representation of intellect 60 55
LV3 80c. WIPO building, Geneva 90 85
LV4 100c. Hand pressing buttons, retort and cogwheel (industrial property) 1·20 1·00
LV5 120c. Head, ballet dancer, cello and book (copyright) 1·40 1·30

K. INTERNATIONAL OLYMPIC COMMITTEE

LW 1 Olympic Rings

2000. Olympic Games, Sydney. Self-adhesive.

LW1 LW 1 20c. multicoloured 30 30
LW2 70c. multicoloured 1·00 1·00

SYRIA Pt. 6; Pt. 19

A country at the E. end of the Mediterranean Sea, formerly Turkish territory. Occupied by the Allies in 1918 and administered under French Military Occupation. An Arab kingdom was set up in the Aleppo and Damascus area during 1919, but the Emir Faisal came into conflict with the French and was defeated in July 1920. In April 1920, the Mandate was offered to France, becoming effective in September 1923. Separate governments were established for the Territories of Damascus, Aleppo, the Alaouites (including Latakia), Great Lebanon and the Jebel Druze. Syria became a republic in 1934, and the Mandate ended with full Independence in 1942.

In 1958 the United Arab Republic was formed which comprised Egypt and Syria but separate stamps were issued for each territory as they employed different currencies. In 1961 Syria left the U.A.R. and the Syrian Arab Republic was established.

1919. 40 paras = 10 milliemes = 1 piastre.
1920. 100 centimes (or centiemes) = 1 piastre; 100 piastres = 1 Syrian Pound.

A. FRENCH MILITARY OCCUPATION.

1919. Stamps of France surch **T. E. O.** and value in "MILLIEMES" or "PIASTRES".

1 11 1m. on 1c. grey £160 £160
2 2m. on 2c. purple £450 £450
3 3m. on 3c. orange £200 £200
4 15 4m. on 15c. green 45·00 45·00
5 18 5m. on 5c. green 28·00 32·00
6 1p. on 10c. red 32·00 30·00
7 2p. on 25c. blue 22·00 20·00
8 13 5p. on 40c. red and blue 27·00 27·00
9 9p. on 50c. brown and lilac 60·00 60·00
10 10p. on 1f. red and yellow 85·00 85·00

1919. Nos. 9/13a and 19/23 of French Post Offices in the Turkish Empire ("Blanc", "Mouchon" and "Merson" key-types inscr "LEVANT") optd **T. E. O.** or surch in "MILLIEMES" also.

11 A 1m. on 1c. grey 2·25 1·90
12 2m. on 2c. purple 1·75 2·00
13 3m. on 3c. red 3·00 2·75
14 B 4m. on 15c. red 1·75 2·50
15 A 5m. on 5c. green 1·60 1·25
16 B 1p. on 25c. blue 1·50 1·00
17 C 2p. on 50c. brown and lilac 1·75 3·25
18 4p. on 1f. red and green 4·00 3·25
19 8p. on 2f. lilac and buff 9·75 8·00
20 20p. on 5f. blue and buff £250 £225

1920. Stamps of France surch **O. M. F. Syrie** and value in "MILLIEMES" or "PIASTRES".

25 11 1m. on 1c. grey 95 2·25
26 2m. on 2c. purple 1·60 3·25
27 18 3m. on 5c. green 1·90 2·75
28 5m. on 10c. red 95 2·25
29 13 20p. on 5f. blue and buff 75·00 80·00

1920. Stamps of France surch **O. M. F. Syrie** and value. (a) Value in "CENTIMES" or "PIASTRES".

31 11 25c. on 1c. grey 2·25 2·50
32 50c. on 2c. purple 1·75 2·50
33 75c. on 3c. orange 2·00 2·75
35 18 1p. on 5c. green 2·25 30
36 2p. on 10c. red 1·75 1·60
37 2p. on 25c. blue 2·00 55
38 3p. on 25c. blue 2·25 2·75
39 15 5p. on 15c. green 2·25 3·00
40 13 10p. on 40c. red and blue 3·50 3·50
41 25p. on 50c. brown and lilac 4·00 4·00
42 50p. on 1f. red and yellow 24·00 25·00
44 100p. on 5f. blue and buff 45·00 50·00

(b) Value in "CENTIEMES".

45 11 25c. on 1c. grey 1·25 75
46 50c. on 2c. purple 1·25 30
47 75c. on 3c. orange 2·00 3·00

1920. Air. Nos. 35 and 39/40 optd **POSTE PAR AVION** in frame.

57 18 1p. on 5c. green £160 42·00
58 15 5p. on 15c. green £250 50·00
59 13 10p. on 40c. red and blue £350 80·00

1921. Issued at Damascus. Nos. K88/95 of Arab Kingdom surch **O. M. F. Syrie** and value in "CENTIEMES" or "PIASTRES".

60 K 3 25c. on 1m. brown 5·50 4·00
61 50c. on $\frac{2}{10}$p green 5·00 4·25

62 1p.on $\frac{3}{10}$p. yellow . . . . 4·75 4·75
63 K 4 1p. on 5m. red . . . . . 6·50 5·50
64a 2p. on 5m. red . . . . 7·00 6·75
65 K 3 3p. on 1p. blue . . . . 10·00 6·25
66 5p. on 2p. green . . . . 10·50 11·00
67 10p. on 5p. purple . . . 12·50 10·50
68 25p. on 10p. grey . . . 14·50 18·00

1921. Stamps of France surch **O. M. F. Syrie** and value in "CENTIEMES" or "PIASTRES" (in two lines).
69 **18** 25c. on 5c. green . . . . . 2·25 1·40
70 50c. on 10c. red 80 20
71 **15** 75c. on 15c. green . . . . . 90 1·25
72 **18** 1p. on 20c. red . . . . . 2·25 15
73 **13** 2p. on 40c. red and blue . . 2·00 20
74 3p. on 60c. violet and blue 2·50 35
75 5p. on 1f. red and yellow . . 4·00 3·75
76 10p. on 2f. orange and green . . . . 5·50 5·50
77 25p. on 5f. blue and buff . . £100 £100
See also Nos. 81/5.

1921. Air. Nos. 72 and 75/6 optd **POSTE PAR AVION** in frame.
78 **18** 1p. on 20c. red . . . . . . 85·00 40·00
79 **13** 5p. on 1f. red and yellow . . £375 £160
80 10p. on 2f. orange and green £350 £160

1921. Stamps of France surch **O.M.F. Syrie** and value in "PIASTRES" in one line.
81 **13** 2p. on 40c. red and blue . . 2·00 25
82 3p. on 60c. violet and blue 2·25 35
83 5p. on 1f. red and yellow . . 8·50 6·50
84 10p. on 2f. orange and green . . . . 12·50 11·50
85 25p. on 5f. blue and buff . . 10·50 13·50

1921. Air. Nos. 72 and 75/6 optd **AVION**.
86 **18** 1p. on 20c. red . . . . . . 55·00 23·00
87 **13** 5p. on 1f. red and yellow . . £130 42·00
88 10p. on 2f. orange and green . . . . £160 50·00

1922. Air. Stamps of France surch **Poste par Avion O. M. F. Syrie** and value.
89 **13** 2p. on 40c. red and blue . . 22·00 30·00
90 3p. on 60c. violet and blue 26·00 30·00
91 5p. on 1f. red and yellow . . 28·00 32·00
92 10p. on 2f. orange and green . . . . 24·00 32·00

1922. Stamps of France surch **O. M. F. Syrie** and value in "CENTIEMES" or "PIASTRES".
93 **11** 10c. on 2c. purple . . . . 2·25 2·75
94 **18** 10c. on 5c. orange . . . . 1·60 3·00
95 25c. on 5c. orange . . . . 1·40 35
96 50c. on 10c. green . . . . 2·00 20
96a 1,25p. on 25c. blue . . . . 2·25 55
96b 1,50p. on 30c. orange . . . 2·50 1·10
96c **13** 2,50p. on 50c. brn & lilac 2·25 1·50
96d **15** 2,50p. on 50c. blue . . . . 2·50 35

B. ARAB KINGDOM.

Prior to the issues listed below, the Kingdom used stamps of Turkey variously overprinted. These are listed in Part 19 (Middle East) of the Stanley Gibbons Catalogue.

K 3 K 4

1920. As Type K **3** and Type K **4**.
K88 K **3** 1m. brown (22 × 17 mm) 10 65
K89 $\frac{2}{10}$ p. green (27 × 21 mm) 45 30
K90 $\frac{3}{10}$ p. yellow (27 × 21 mm) 20 20
K91 K **4** 5m. red 20 20
K92 K **3** 1p. blue (27 × 21 mm) . . 20 10
K93 2p. green (27 × 21 mm) 1·90 60
K94 5p. purple (32 × 35 mm) 2·50 1·25
K95 10p. grey (32 × 35 mm) 2·50 1·90
For 1p. black as Type K **3**, see Postage Due No. KD96.

1920. Independence Commemoration Optd with Arabic inscription.
K98 K **4** 5m. red £350 £200

C. FRENCH MANDATED TERRITORY.

Issues for Lebanon and Syria.

Nos. 97/174 are all stamps of France surch.

1923. (a) Surch **Syrie Grand Liban** in two lines and value.
97 **11** 10c. on 2c. purple 30 65
98 **18** 25c. on 5c. orange . . . . 1·00 2·00
99 50c. on 10c. green . . . . 1·40 60
100 **15** 75c. on 15c. green . . . . 1·90 2·75
101 **18** 1p. on 20c. brown . . . . 2·50 1·25
102 1,25p. on 25c. blue . . . . 2·00 2·00
103 1,50p. on 30c. orange . . . 1·25 2·00
104 1,50p. on 30c. red . . . . 1·00 2·50
105 **15** 2,50p. on 50c. blue . . . . 1·50 75
(b) Surch **Syrie-Grand Liban** in one line and value.
106 **13** 2p. on 40c. red and blue 2·25 70
107 3p. on 60c. violet and blue 2·50 3·25
108 5p. on 1f. red and yellow 3·25 3·75

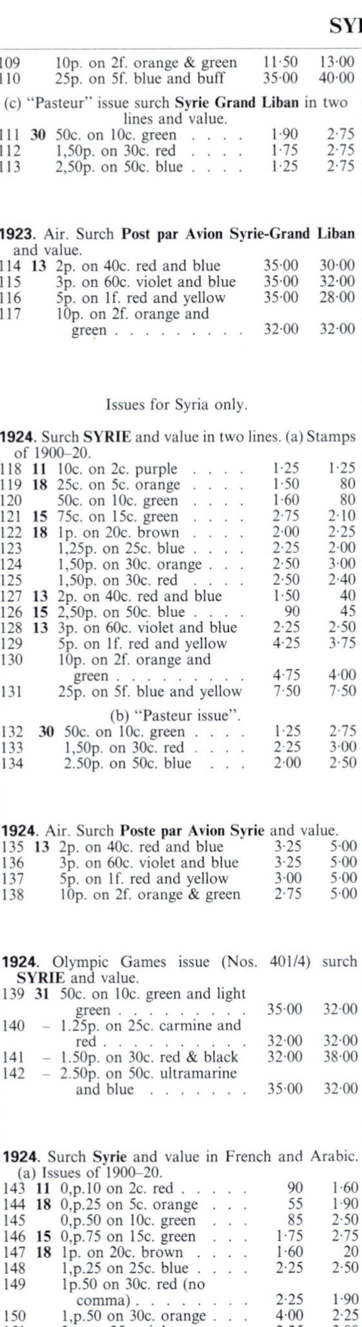

109 10p. on 2f. orange & green 11·50 13·00
110 25p. on 5f. blue and buff 35·00 40·00
(c) "Pasteur" issue surch **Syrie Grand Liban** in two lines and value.
111 **30** 50c. on 10c. green . . . . 1·90 2·75
112 1,50p. on 30c. red . . . . 1·75 2·75
113 2,50p. on 50c. blue . . . . 1·25 2·75

1923. Air. Surch **Post par Avion Syrie-Grand Liban** and value.
114 **13** 2p. on 40c. red and blue 35·00 30·00
115 3p. on 60c. violet and blue 35·00 32·00
116 5p. on 1f. red and yellow 35·00 28·00
117 10p. on 2f. orange and green . . . . 32·00 32·00

Issues for Syria only.

1924. Surch **SYRIE** and value in two lines. (a) Stamps of 1900–20.
118 **11** 10c. on 2c. purple . . . . 1·25 1·25
119 **18** 25c. on 5c. orange . . . . 1·50 80
120 50c. on 10c. green . . . . 1·60 80
121 **15** 75c. on 15c. green . . . . 2·75 2·10
122 **18** 1p. on 20c. brown . . . . 2·00 2·25
123 1,25p. on 25c. blue . . . . 2·25 2·00
124 1,50p. on 30c. orange . . . 2·50 3·00
125 1,50p. on 30c. red . . . . 2·50 2·40
127 **13** 2p. on 40c. red and blue 1·50 40
126 **15** 2,50p. on 50c. blue 90 45
128 **13** 3p. on 60c. violet and blue 2·25 2·50
129 5p. on 1f. red and yellow 4·25 3·75
130 10p. on 2f. orange and green . . . . 4·75 4·00
131 25p. on 5f. blue and yellow 7·50 7·50
(b) "Pasteur issue".
132 **30** 50c. on 10c. green . . . . 1·25 2·75
133 1,50p. on 30c. red . . . . 2·25 3·00
134 2.50p. on 50c. blue . . . 2·00 2·50

1924. Air. Surch **Poste par Avion Syrie** and value.
135 **13** 2p. on 40c. red and blue 3·25 5·00
136 3p. on 60c. violet and blue 3·25 5·00
137 5p. on 1f. red and yellow 3·00 5·00
138 10p. on 2f. orange & green 2·75 5·00

1924. Olympic Games issue (Nos. 401/4) surch **SYRIE** and value.
139 **31** 50c. on 10c. green and light green . . . . 35·00 32·00
140 – 1.25p. on 25c. carmine and red . . . . 32·00 32·00
141 – 1.50p. on 30c. red & black 32·00 38·00
142 – 2.50p. on 50c. ultramarine and blue . . . . 35·00 32·00

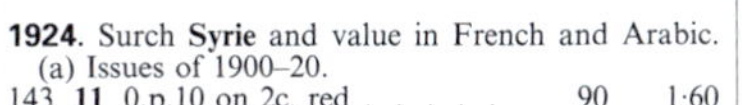

1924. Surch **Syrie** and value in French and Arabic. (a) Issues of 1900–20.
143 **11** 0,p.10 on 2c. red . . . . . 90 1·60
144 **18** 0,p.25 on 5c. orange . . . 55 1·90
145 0,p.50 on 10c. green . . . 85 2·50
146 **15** 0,p.75 on 15c. green . . . 1·75 2·75
147 **18** 1p. on 20c. brown . . . . 1·60 20
148 1,p.25 on 25c. blue . . . . 2·25 2·50
149 1p.50 on 30c. red (no comma) . . . . 2·25 1·90
150 1,p.50 on 30c. orange . . . 4·00 2·25
151 2p. on 35c. violet . . . . . 2·25 3·00
152 **13** 2p. on 40c. red and blue 2·75 85
153 2p. on 45c. green and blue 5·75 6·75
154 3p. on 60c. violet and blue 2·50 2·25
155 **15** 3p. on 60c. violet . . . . 2·75 3·50
156 4p. on 85c. red . . . . . 1·60 2·75
157 **13** 5p. on 1f. red and yellow 2·50 3·25
158 10p. on 2f. orange & green 3·75 4·25
159 25p. on 5f. blue and buff 3·75 4·25
(b) "Pasteur" issue.
160 **30** 0,p.50 on 10c. green . . . 1·00 25
161 0p.75 on 15c. green . . . . 2·75 3·00
162 1,p.50 on 30c. red . . . . 2·25 2·50
163 2p. on 45c. red . . . . . 2·50 3·00
164 2p.50 on 50c. blue . . . . 1·75 1·25
165 4p. on 75c. blue . . . . . 2·50 3·50
(c) Olympic Games Issue (Nos. 401/4).
166 **31** 0,p.50 on 10c. green and light green . . . . . . 35·00 32·00
167 – 1p.25 on 25c. carmine and red . . . . 32·00 32·00
168 – 1p.50 on 30c. red & black 32·00 38·00
169 – 2p.50 on 50c. ultramarine and blue . . . . 35·00 32·00
(d) Ronsard stamp.
170 **35** 4p. on 75c. blue on blue 75 3·00

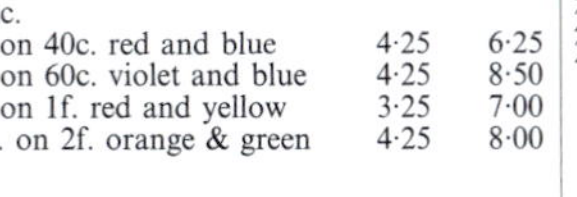

1924. Air. Surch **Syrie Avion** and new value in French and Arabic.
171 **13** 2p. on 40c. red and blue 4·25 6·25
172 3p. on 60c. violet and blue 4·25 8·50
173 5p. on 1f. red and yellow 3·25 7·00
174 10p. on 2f. orange & green 4·25 8·00

16 Hama

17 Merkab

18 Damascus

1925. Views.
175 **16** 0p.10 violet 15 85
176 **17** 0p.25 black . . . . 70 1·40
177 – 0p.50 green 30 25
178 – 0p.75 red . . . . 65 1·60
179 **18** 1p. purple 75 15
180 – 1p.25 green . . . . 2·50 2·50
181 – 1p.50 pink 35 15
182 – 2p. brown . . . . 2·25 35
183 – 2p.50 blue . . . . 1·75 1·10
184 – 3p. brown . . . . 1·00 15
185 – 5p. violet 80 15
186 – 10p. purple . . . . 3·00 85
187 – 25p. blue . . . . 3·50 3·25
DESIGNS—As Type **17**: 0p.50, Alexandretta; 0p.75, Hama; 1p.25, Latakia; 1p.50, Damascus; 2, 25p. Palmyra (different views); 2p.50, Kalat Yamoun; 3p. Bridge of Daphne; 5, 10p. Aleppo (different views).

1925. Air. Nos. 182 and 184/6 optd **AVION** in French and Arabic.
188 2p. brown . . . . 2·25 3·75
189 3p. brown . . . . 1·75 3·75
190 5p. violet . . . . 1·00 2·75
191 10p. purple . . . . 1·75 3·00

1926. Air. Nos. 182 and 184/6 optd with Bleriot XI airplane.
192 2p. brown . . . . 2·75 2·75
193 3p. brown . . . . 1·00 2·25
194 5p. violet . . . . 2·25 2·75
195 10p. purple . . . . 2·25 3·50

1926. War Refugees Fund. Nos. 176 etc and 192/5 surch **Secours aux Refugies Afft** and value in French and Arabic.
196 **17** 0p.25 on 0p.25 black (postage) . . . . . . 2·00 3·25
197 – 0p.25 on 0p.50 green . . . 2·50 3·75
198 – 0p.25 on 0p.75 red . . . . 95 3·25
199 **18** 0p.50 on 1p. purple . . . 1·75 3·25
200 – 0p.50 on 1p.25 green . . . 2·75 4·25
201 – 0p.50 on 1p.50 pink . . . 1·60 3·25
202 – 0p.75 on 2p. brown . . . 2·50 4·25
203 – 0p.75 on 2p.50 blue . . . 2·50 3·75
204 – 1p. on 3p. brown . . . . 1·75 3·50
205 – 1p. on 5p. violet . . . . 1·75 3·25
206 – 2p. on 10p. purple . . . . 1·90 3·75
207 – 5p. on 25p. blue . . . . 1·75 4·25
208 – 1p. on 2p. brown (air) . . 3·00 4·50
209 – 2p. on 3p. brown . . . . 2·00 4·50
210 – 3p. on 5p. violet . . . . 2·00 3·50
211 – 5p. on 10p. purple . . . . 2·00 3·75

1926. No. 175 etc surch with new value in English and Arabic.
221 05 on 0p.10 violet . . . . . 20 1·00
222 1p. on 3p. brown . . . . . 2·25 1·10
223 2p. on 1p.25 green . . . . 2·75 60
212 3p.50 on 0p.75 red . . . . 1·25 2·25
224 4p. on 0p.25 black . . . . 1·75 15
215 4p.50 on 0p.75 red 60 75
216 6p. on 2p.50 blue . . . . 1·25 1·50
217 7p.50 on 2p.50 blue . . . . 1·00 45
218 12p. on 1p.25 green . . . . 2·25 2·25
219 15p. on 25p. blue . . . . 1·25 30
220 20p. on 1p.25 green . . . . 3·00 3·50

1929. Air. Nos. 177 etc, optd with Bleriot XI airplane or surch also in English and Arabic.
225 0p.50 green . . . . 60 1·25
226 1p. purple . . . . 1·75 1·75
227 2p. on 1p.25 green . . . . 3·00 3·25
228 15p. on 25p. blue . . . . . 3·25 4·00
229 25p. blue . . . . 6·00 4·75

1929. Damascus Industrial Exhibition. Nos. 177 etc and various air stamps optd **EXPOSITION INDUSTRIELLE DAMAS 1929** in French and Arabic.
230 0p.50 green (postage) . . . . 2·75 2·75
231 1p. purple . . . . 2·50 2·75
232 1p.50 pink . . . . 2·75 2·75
233 3p. brown . . . . 2·50 3·25
234 5p. violet . . . . 3·25 2·75
235 10p. purple . . . . 3·25 3·50
236 25p. blue . . . . 3·00 3·50
237 0p.50 green (No. 225) (air) 2·75 3·75
238 1p. purple (No. 226) 2·75 3·75
239 2p. brown (No. 192) . . . . 2·75 3·75
240 3p. brown (No. 193) . . . . 2·25 3·50
241 5p. violet (No. 194) . . . . 2·25 4·00
242 10p. purple (No. 195) . . . . 2·50 4·00
243 25p. blue (No. 229) . . . . 2·50 4·00

26 Hama

27 Damascus

1930. Views.
244 **26** 0p.10 mauve . . . . 75 2·25
244b 0p.10 purple . . . . 15 1·25
245 – 0p.20 blue . . . . 40 1·50
245a – 0p.20 red . . . . 75 1·75
246 – 0p.25 green . . . . 1·50 1·50
246a – 0p.25 violet . . . . . . 1·50 2·00
247 – 0p.50 violet 55 15
247a – 0p.75 red . . . . 1·10 1·00
248 – 1p. green . . . . 1·75 15
248a – 1p. brown . . . . 1·75 15
249 – 1p.50 brown . . . . . . 7·25 3·50
249a – 1p.50 green . . . . . . 1·75 50
250 – 2p. violet . . . . 2·25 15
251 – 3p. green . . . . 2·25 1·75
252 **27** 4p. orange . . . . 1·10 15
253 – 4p.50 red . . . . 2·00 55
254 – 6p. black . . . . 1·25 95
255 – 7p.50 blue . . . . 2·25 25
256 – 10p. brown . . . . 2·75 45
257 – 15p. green . . . . 3·00 85
258 – 25p. purple . . . . 2·50 1·50
259 – 50p. brown . . . . 20·00 15·00
260 – 100p. red . . . . 85·00 40·00
DESIGNS—As Type **26**: 0p.20, Aleppo; 0p.25, Hama (different). As Type **27**: 0p.50, Alexandretta; 0p.75, 4p.50, Homs; 1p., 7p.50, Aleppo (different); 1p.50, 100p. Damascus (different); 2, 10p. Antioch; 3p. Bosra; 5p. Sednaya; 15p. Hama; 25p. St. Simeon; 50p. Palmyra.

28 River Euphrates

1931. Air. Views with Potez 29-4 biplane.
261 – 0p.50 yellow (Homs) . . . 95 1·60
261a – 0p.50 brown (Homs) . . . 1·90 2·00
262 – 1p. brown (Damascus) . . 1·60 1·90
263 **28** 2p. blue . . . . 2·75 2·75
264 – 3p. green (Palmyra) . . . 1·75 1·40
265 – 5p. purple (Deir-el-Zor) 1·00 1·25
266 – 10p. blue (Damascus) . . 1·25 1·25
267 – 15p. red (Aleppo citadel) 2·25 1·40
268 – 25p. orange (Hama) . . . 3·50 2·25
269 – 50p. black (Zebdani) . . . 3·50 3·50
270 – 100p. mauve (Telebisse) 4·00 3·00

D. REPUBLIC UNDER FRENCH MANDATE.

29 Parliament House, Damascus

30 Aboulula el Maari

31 Farman F.190 Airplane over Bloudan

1934. Establishment of Republic.
271 **29** 0p.10 green (postage) . . . 1·60 1·75
272 0p.20 black . . . . 1·25 1·60
273 0p.25 red . . . . 1·60 1·60
274 0p.50 blue . . . . 1·25 2·00
275 0p.75 purple . . . . 1·60 1·90
276 **30** 1p. red . . . . 3·25 4·00
277 1p.50 green . . . . 5·25 4·75
278 2p. brown . . . . 4·50 5·00
279 3p. blue . . . . 40·00 8·00
280 4p. violet . . . . 5·00 5·00
281 4p.50 red . . . . 6·50 6·25
282 5p. blue . . . . 4·75 5·75
283 6p. brown . . . . 5·00 5·25
284 7p.50 blue . . . . 6·50 6·00
285 – 10p. brown . . . . 8·25 9·00
286 – 15p. blue . . . . 10·00 10·00
287 – 25p. red . . . . 21·00 24·00
288 – 50p. brown . . . . 40·00 40·00
289 – 100p. red . . . . 32·00 35·00
DESIGNS—As Type **30**: Nos. 285/7, President Mohammed Ali Bey el-Abed; 288/9, Sultan Saladin.

290 **31** 0p.50 brown (air) . . . . 2·75 3·25
291 1p. green . . . . 2·25 2·25
292 2p. blue . . . . 2·50 2·75
293 3p. red . . . . 2·50 2·50
294 5p. purple . . . . 3·75 3·50
295 10p. violet . . . . 29·00 30·00
296 15p. brown . . . . 30·00 27·00
297 25p. blue . . . . 42·00 35·00
298 50p. black . . . . 50·00 45·00
299 100p. brown . . . . 85·00 70·00

1936. Damascus Fair. Optd **1936 FOIRE DE DAMAS** in Arabic and French. (a) Postage stamps of 1930.
300 – 0p.50 violet . . . . 2·50 3·00
301 – 1p. brown . . . . 2·75 3·50
302 – 2p. violet . . . . 2·25 3·00
303 – 3p. green . . . . 2·25 2·75
304 **27** 4p. orange . . . . 3·00 3·50
305 – 4p.50 red . . . . 3·25 3·50
306 – 6p. green . . . . 2·25 2·75

No.	Type	Description	Unused	Used
307	–	7p. blue	3·00	3·50
308	–	10p. brown	4·25	4·50
		(b) Air stamps of 1931.		
309	–	0p.50 brown	3·00	4·50
310	–	1p. brown	2·50	3·75
311	28	2p. blue	2·25	4·75
312	–	3p. green	2·75	4·75
313	–	5p. purple	3·50	4·25

33 Exhibition Pavilion

1937. Air. Paris International Exhibition.

No.	Type	Description	Unused	Used
314	33	½p. green	1·75	2·00
315		1p. green	2·50	2·75
316		2p. brown	2·00	2·00
317		3p. red	1·75	2·75
318		5p. orange	3·00	3·00
319		10p. green	4·75	7·75
320		15p. blue	6·00	9·25
321		25p. violet	6·00	9·25

34 Savoia Marchetti S-73 over Aleppo

1937. Air.

No.	Type	Description	Unused	Used
322	34	½p. violet	15	60
323	–	1p. black	1·00	1·10
324	34	2p. green	1·75	1·50
325	–	3p. blue	1·50	1·75
326	34	5p. mauve	2·00	1·10
327	–	10p. brown	1·60	1·25
328	34	15p. brown	2·50	2·25
329	–	25p. blue	4·50	6·00

DESIGN: 1, 3, 10, 25p. Potez 62 airplane over Damascus.

1938. Stamps of 1930 surch in English and Arabic.

No.	Type	Description	Unused	Used
330		0p.25 on 0p.75 red	15	1·10
331		0p.50 on 1p.50 green	50	65
332		2p. on 7p.50 blue	85	55
333		2p.50 on 4p. orange	65	20
334		5p. on 7p.50 blue	1·25	40
335		10p. on 50p. brown	1·40	1·10
336		10p. on 100p. red	1·10	80

38 CAMS 53H Flying Boat, Maurice Nogues and Flight Route

1938. Air. 10th Anniv of 1st Air Service Flight between France and Syria.

No.	Type	Description	Unused	Used
337	38	10p. green	2·00	4·50

39 Pres. Atasi

41 Palmyra

1938. Unissued stamp surch **12.50** and in Arabic figures.

No.	Type	Description	Unused	Used
338	39	12p.50 on 10p. blue	1·75	25

1938.

No.	Type	Description	Unused	Used
339	39	10p. blue	2·00	65
339a		20p. brown	1·75	40

1940.

No.	Type	Description	Unused	Used
340	41	5p. pink	2·25	65

42 Damascus Museum

45 Deir-el-Zor Bridge

1940.

No.	Type	Description	Unused	Used
341	42	0p.10 red (postage)	15	65
342		0p.20 blue	10	65
343		0p.25 brown	10	1·10
344		0p.50 blue	10	15
345	–	1p. blue	20	20
346	–	1p.50 brown	40	1·00
347	–	2p.50 green	15	55
348	–	5p. violet	35	20
349	–	7p.50 red	55	60
350	–	50p. purple	3·25	3·50

DESIGNS—As Type **45**: 1p., 1p.50, 2p.50, Hotel de Bloudan; 5p., 7p.50, 50p. Kasr-el-Heir Fortress.

No.	Type	Description	Unused	Used
351	45	0p.25 black (air)	15	1·40
352		0p.50 blue	15	1·25
353		1p. blue	40	1·75
354		2p. brown	20	1·60
355		5p. green	1·00	1·75
356		10p. red	75	1·10
357		50p. violet	3·75	4·50

E. SYRIAN REPUBLIC.

46 President Taj Addin el-Husni

47 President Taj Addin el-Husni

1942. National Independence. Inscr "PROCLAMATION DE L'INDEPENDENCE 27 Septembre 1941".

No.	Type	Description	Unused	Used
358	46	0p.50 green (postage)	3·25	3·25
359		1p.50 brown	3·25	3·25
360		6p. red	3·25	3·25
361		15p. blue	3·25	3·25
362	–	10p. blue (air)	2·50	2·50
363	–	50p. purple	2·50	2·50

DESIGN: 10, 50p. As Type **46**, but President bareheaded and airplane inset.

1942. (a) Postage. Portrait in oval frame.

No.	Type	Description	Unused	Used
364	47	6p. purple and pink	1·90	1·90
365		15p. blue and light blue	1·90	1·90
		(b) Air. Portrait in rectangular frame.		
366		10p. green and emerald	3·75	3·75

48 Syria and late President's portrait

49 Pres. Shukri Bey al-Quwatli

1943. Union of Latakia and Jebel Druze with Syria. (a) President bare-headed.

No.	Type	Description	Unused	Used
367	48	1p. green (postage)	1·90	1·90
368		4p. brown	1·90	1·90
369		8p. violet	1·90	1·90
370		10p. orange	1·90	1·90
371		20p. blue	1·90	1·90
		(b) President wearing turban.		
372		2p. brown (air)	1·90	1·90
373		10p. purple	1·90	1·90
374		20p. blue	1·90	1·90
375		50p. pink	1·90	1·90

1943. Death of President Taj Addin el-Husni. Nos. 367/75 optd with narrow black border.

No.	Type	Description	Unused	Used
376	48	1p. green (postage)	1·90	1·90
377		4p. brown	1·90	1·90
378		8p. violet	1·90	1·90
379		10p. orange	1·90	1·90
380		20p. blue	1·90	1·90
381	–	2p. brown (air)	1·90	1·90
382	–	10p. purple	1·90	1·90
383	–	20p. blue	1·90	1·90
384	–	50p. pink	1·90	1·90

1944. Air.

No.	Type	Description	Unused	Used
385	49	200p. purple	7·00	7·00
386		500p. blue	12·00	12·00

(**50** Trans. "First Congress of Arab Lawyers, Damascus ")

(**51** Trans. "Aboulula-el-Maari. Commemoration of Millenary, 363–1363")

1944. Air. 1st Arab Lawyers' Congress. Optd with T **50**.

No.	Type	Description	Unused	Used
387	–	10p. brown (No. 327)	2·25	2·25
388	–	15p. red (No. 267)	2·25	2·20
389	–	25p. orange (No. 268)	2·25	2·25
390	–	100p. mauve (No. 270)	6·50	6·50
391	49	200p. purple	9·50	9·50

1945. Millenary of Aboulula-el-Maari (Arab poet and philosopher). Optd with T **51**.

No.	Type	Description	Unused	Used
392	–	2p.50 green (No. 347) (postage)	2·50	2·50
393	–	7p.50 red (No. 349)	2·50	2·50
394	–	15p. red (No. 267) (air)	2·25	2·25
395	–	25p. orange (No. 268)	2·25	2·25
396	49	500p. blue	19·00	19·00

52 Pres. Shukri Bey al-Quwatli

53 Pres. Shukri Bey al-Quwatli

1945. Resumption of Constitutional Govt.

No.	Type	Description	Unused	Used
397	52	4p. violet (postage)	30	30
398		6p. blue	30	30
399		10p. red	30	30
400		15p. brown	55	55
401		20p. green	60	60
402		40p. orange	1·10	1·10
403	53	5p. green (air)	35	40
404		10p. red	40	40
405		15p. orange	40	40
406		25p. blue	75	40
407		50p. violet	1·25	55
408		100p. brown	2·75	95
409		200p. red	6·75	3·25

(54)

(55)

1945. Fiscal stamps inscr "TIMBRE FISCAL". (a) Optd with T **54** (No. 411 surch also).

No.	Type	Description	Unused	Used
410		25p. brown	3·25	3·25
411		50p. on 75p. brown	3·75	3·75
412		75p. brown	5·50	5·50
413		100p. green	6·25	6·25
		(b) Surch as T **55**.		
414		12½p. on 15p. green	1·75	1·75
415		25p. on 25s. purple	2·10	2·10
		(c) Optd or surch (416) with T **54** and with additional Arabic inscription at top.		
416		50p. on 75p. brown	1·40	1·40
417		50p. mauve	1·75	1·75
418		100p. green	2·40	2·40

(56)

57 Ear of Wheat

58 Pres. Shukri Bey al-Quwatli

60 Arab Horse

1946. Fiscal stamp optd with T **56**.

No.	Type	Description	Unused	Used
419		200p. blue	18·00	10·00

1946.

No.	Type	Description	Unused	Used
420	57	0p.50 orange (postage)	15	10
421		1p. violet	25	10
422		2p.50 grey	30	15
423		5p. green	40	20
424	58	7p.50 brown	15	10
425		10p. blue	15	10
426		12p.50 violet	50	15
427	–	15p. red	20	20
428	–	20p. violet	40	25
429	–	25p. blue	60	25
430	60	50p. brown	3·25	60
431		100p. green	7·50	1·75
432a		200p. purple	60·00	5·50

DESIGN—As Type **58**: 15, 20, 25p. Pres. Shukri Bey al-Quwatli bareheaded.

No.	Type	Description	Unused	Used
433	–	3p. red (air)	80	25
434	–	5p. green	80	25
435	–	6p. orange	80	25
436	–	10p. grey	30	10
437	–	15p. red	30	10
438	–	25p. blue	45	20
439	–	50p. violet	65	25
440	–	100p. blue	2·10	55
441	–	200p. brown	4·00	1·10
442	–	300p. brown	12·00	2·50
443	–	500p. green	13·00	4·50

DESIGNS—HORIZ: 3, 5, 6p. Flock of sheep; 10, 15, 25p. Kattineh Dam; 50, 100, 200p. Temple ruins, Kanaouat; 300, 500p. Sultan Ibrahim Mosque.

(65)

1946. Evacuation of Foreign Troops from Syria. Optd with T **65**.

No.	Type	Description	Unused	Used
444	58	10p. blue (postage)	55	55
445		12p.50 violet	75	75
446	60	50p. brown	2·25	2·25
447	–	25p. blue (No. 438) (air)	1·50	1·10

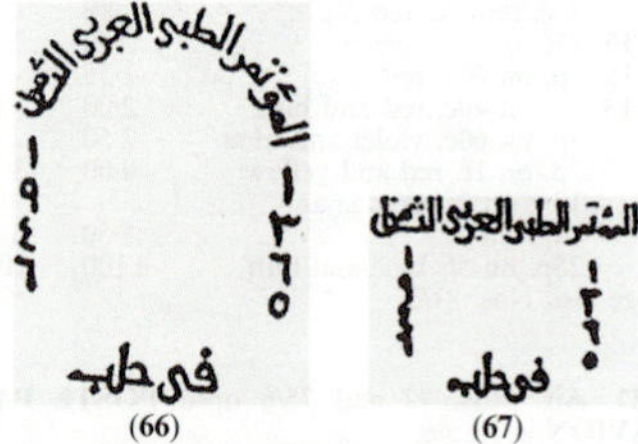

(66) (67)

1946. 8th Arab Medical Congress, Aleppo. (a) Postage. Optd with T **66**.

No.	Type	Description	Unused	Used
448		25p. blue (No. 429)	1·60	1·40
		(b) Air. Optd with T **67**.		
449		25p. blue (No. 438)	1·60	90
450		50p. violet (No. 439)	2·50	1·25
451		100p. blue (No. 440)	5·00	2·25

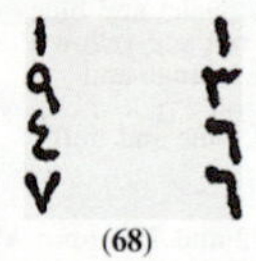

(68)

1947. 1st Anniv of Evacuation of Allied Forces. Nos. 444/7 optd as T **68** (= "1947 1366").

No.	Type	Description	Unused	Used
452	58	10p. blue (postage)	50	15
453		12p.50 violet	75	20
454	60	50p. brown	2·25	65
455	–	25p. blue (air)	1·90	1·10

69 Hercules and Lion

70 Mosaic of the Mosque of the Omayades

1947. 1st Arab Archaeological Congress, Damascus.

No.	Type	Description	Unused	Used
456	69	12p.50 green (postage)	80	65
457	70	25p. blue	1·75	95
458	–	12p.50 violet (air)	1·25	65
459	–	50p. brown	4·50	1·90

DESIGNS—As T **70**: 12p.50, Window at Kasr El-Heir El-Gharbi; 50p. King Hazael's throne.

71 Courtyard of Azem Palace

72 Congress Symbol

1947. 3rd Arab Engineers' Congress, Damascus. Inscr "3e CONGRES DES INGENIEURS ARABES 1947".

No.	Type	Description	Unused	Used
460	71	12p.50 purple (postage)	60	50
461	–	25p. blue	1·40	75
462	–	12p.50 green (air)	95	50
463	72	50p. violet	3·50	1·75

DESIGNS—HORIZ: No. 461, Telephone Exchange Building; 462, Fortress at Kasr El-Heir El-Charqui.

73 Parliament Building

74 Pres. Shukri Bey al-Quwatli

1948. Re-election of Pres. Shukri Bey al-Quwatli.

No.	Type	Description	Unused	Used
464	73	12p.50 brown and grey (postage)	50	20
465	74	25p. mauve	1·00	45
466	73	12p.50 blue and violet (air)	50	20
467	74	50p. purple and green	2·50	90

75 Syrian Arms **76** Soldier and Flag

1948. Compulsory Military Service.
468 **75** 12p.50 brown and grey (postage) 50 25
469 **76** 25p. multicoloured . . . . 1·00 40
470 **75** 12p.50 blue and light blue (air) 65 25
471 **76** 50p. green, red and black 3·25 75

1948. Surch. (a) Postage.
472 – 0p.50 on 0p.75 red (No. 247a) 20 10
472ab **60** 2p.50 on 200p. purple 40 10
472b 10p. on 100p. green . . 45 20
473 25p. on 200p. purple . . 3·25 45

(b) Air.
474 – 2p.50 on 3p. (No. 433) . . 10 10
475 – 2p.50 on 6p. (No. 435) . . 10 10
475a – 2p.50 on 100p. (No. 440) 10 10
476 – 25p. on 200p. (No. 441) . . 60 20
477 – 50p. on 300p. (No. 442) . . 15·00 75
478 – 50p. on 500p. (No. 443) . . 15·00 75

78 Palmyra **79** President Husni el-Zaim and Lockheed Super Constellation over Damascus

1949. 75th Anniv of U.P.U.
479 – 12p.50 violet (postage) . . 1·90 1·90
480 **78** 25p. blue . . . . 3·25 3·25
481 – 12p.50 purple (air) . . . . 6·25 6·25
482 **79** 50p. black . . . . 18·00 12·50
DESIGNS—HORIZ: No. 479, Ain-el-Arous; 481, Globe and mountains.

80 President Husni el-Zaim **81** Pres. Husni el-Zaim and Map

1949. Revolution of 30 March 1949.
483 **80** 25p. blue (postage) 85 45
484 50p. brown (air) . . . . . 3·50 2·10

1949. Presidential Election.
485 **81** 25p. brown & bl (postage) 2·75 1·90
486 50p. green and pink (air) 3·50 1·90

82 Tel-Chehab **83** Damascus

1949.
487 **82** 5p. grey 15 15
488 7p.50 brown 25 15
524 7p.50 green 40 15
489 **83** 12p.50 purple 50 20
490 25p. blue . . . . 1·00 45

84 Syrian Arms **85** G.P.O., Damascus

1950.
491 **84** 0p.50 brown 10 10
492 2p.50 pink 15 10
493 – 10p. violet 35 20
494 – 12p.50 green 65 40
495 **85** 25p. blue . . . . 1·25 25
496 50p. black . . . . 4·00 60
DESIGN—HORIZ: 10, 12p.50, Abous–Damascus road.

86 Port of Latakia

1950. Air.
497 **86** 2p.50 violet 45 10
526 10p. blue 50 10
499 15p. brown . . . . 3·00 25
500 25p. blue . . . . 6·25 40

87 Parliament Building

88 Book and Torch

1951. New Constitution, 1950.
501 **87** 12p.50 black (postage) . . 30 20
502 25p. blue 65 40
503 **88** 12p.50 red (air) 35 15
504 50p. purple . . . . 1·25 70

89 Hama

1952.
505 **89** 0p.50 brown (postage) . . 10 10
506 2p.50 blue 20 10
507 5p. green 20 10
508 10p. red 25 10
509 – 12p.50 black 65 10
510 – 15p. purple . . . . 4·00 25
511 – 25p. blue . . . . 1·90 35
512 – 100p. brown . . . . 7·50 1·90
513 – 2p.50 red (air) 15 10
514 – 5p. green 35 10
515 – 15p. violet 50 15
516 – 25p. blue 65 30
517 – 100p. purple . . . . 4·50 85
DESIGNS—Postage: 12p.50 to 100p. Palace of Justice, Damascus. Air: 2p.50 to 15p. Palmyra; 25, 100p. Citadel, Aleppo.

1952. Air. United Nations Social Welfare Seminar, Damascus. Optd **U. N. S. W. S. Damascus 8-20 Dec. 1952** and curved line of Arabic.
518 **86** 10p. blue . . . . 1·90 95
519 – 15p. violet (No. 515) . . . 1·90 95
520 – 25p. blue (No. 516) . . . 3·25 1·60
521 – 50p. violet (No. 439) . . . 8·25 2·25

91 Qalaat el Hasn Fortress **92** "Labour"

93 "Family" **94** "Communications"

1953.
522 **91** 0p.50 red (postage) 15 10
523 – 2p.50 brown 20 10
525 **91** 12p.50 blue . . . . 1·75 15
527 – 50p. brown (air) . . . . . 1·60 25
DESIGNS: 2p,50, Qalaat el Hasn fortress (different); 50p. G.P.O., Aleppo.

1954.
528 **92** 1p. green (postage) 10 10
529 2½p. red 10 10
530 5p. blue 10 10
531 **93** 7½p. red 20 10
532 10p. black 25 10
533 12½p. violet 40 10
534 – 20p. purple 60 20
535 – 25p. violet . . . . 1·40 40
536 – 50p. green . . . . 3·50 75
537 **94** 5p. violet (air) 20 10
538 10p. brown 25 10
539 15p. green 25 10
540 – 30p. brown 65 20
541 – 35p. blue 95 20
542 – 40p. orange . . . . 1·25 40
543 – 50p. purple . . . . 1·60 50
544 – 70p. violet . . . . 2·75 65
DESIGNS—As Type **93**. Postage: 20 to 50p. "Industry". Air: 30 to 70p. Syrian University.

95 Monument to Hejaz Railway **96a**

1954. Air. Damascus Fair. Inscr as in T **95**.
545 **95** 40p. mauve . . . . 1·75 55
546 – 50p. green . . . . 1·25 50
DESIGN—VERT: 50p. Mosque and Syrian flag.

1954. Cotton Festival, Aleppo. Optd **FESTIVAL du COTON. Alep. oct. 1954** and Arab inscription.
547 **93** 10p. black (postage) . . . 90 40
548 – 25p. violet (No. 535) . . . 1·00 50
549 – 50p. brown (No. 527) (air) 95 65
550 – 100p. purple (No. 517) . . 2·25 1·60

1955. Arab Postal Union.
551 **96a** 12½p. green (postage) . . 50 15
552 25p. violet 90 25
553 5p. brown (air) 30 15

97 **98**

1955. Air. Middle East Rotary Congress.
554 **97** 35p. red 75 40
555 65p. green . . . . 1·90 75

1955. Air. 50th Anniv of Rotary International.
556 **98** 25p. violet 50 25
557 75p. blue . . . . 2·25 95

99 "Facing the Future" **100** Mother and Child

1955. Air. 9th Anniv of Evacuation of Foreign Troops from Syria.
558 **99** 40p. mauve 65 40
559 – 60p. blue . . . . 2·00 60
DESIGN: 60p. Tank and infantry attack.
See also Nos. 847/9.

1955. Mothers' Day.
560 **100** 25p. red (postage) 45 25
561 35p. violet (air) 95 45
562 40p. black . . . . 1·60 60

101 Lockheed Super Constellation Airliner, Flag and Crowd **102** Syrian Pavilion

1955. Air. Emigrants' Congress.
563 **101** 5p. mauve 50 20
564 – 15p. blue 65 30
DESIGN: 15p. Lockheed Super Constellation over globe.

1955. Air. International Fair, Damascus.
565 **102** 25p.+5p. black 50 50
566 – 35p.+5p. blue 70 70
567 – 40p.+10p. purple 90 90
568 – 70p.+10p. green . . . . . 1·40 1·40
DESIGNS: 35, 40p. "Industry and Agriculture"; 70p. Exhibition pavilions and flags.

103 Mother and Baby **104** U.N. Emblem and Torch

1955. Air. International Children's Day.
569 **103** 25p. blue 65 35
570 50p. purple . . . . 1·25 50

1955. 10th Anniv of U.N.O.
571 **104** 7½p. red (postage) 50 25
572 12½p. green 85 35
573 – 15p. blue (air) 65 30
574 – 35p. brown . . . . 1·25 50
DESIGN: 15, 35p. Globe, dove and Scales of Justice.

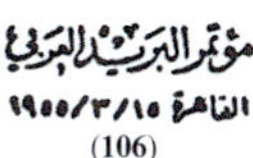

105 Saracen Gate, Aleppo Citadel **(106)**

1955. Installation of Aleppo Water Supply from River Euphrates.
575 **105** 7p.50 violet (postage) . . 25 10
576 12p.50 red 35 15
577 30p. blue (air) . . . . . 2·25 90

1955. 2nd Arab Postal Union Congress, Cairo. Nos. 551/3 optd with T **106**.
578 12½p. green (postage) 40 25
579 25p. violet . . . . 1·25 50
580 5p. brown (air) 50 15

(107) **108** Monument

1956. Visit of King Hussein of Jordan. Nos. 551/3 optd with T **107**.
581 12½p. green (postage) 50 40
582 25p. violet 90 75
583 5p. brown (air) 50 20

1956. Air. 10th Anniv of Evacuation of Foreign Troops from Syria.
584 **108** 35p. sepia 65 45
585 – 65p. red 95 65
586 – 75p. grey . . . . 1·90 95
DESIGNS: 65p. Winged female figure; 75p. Pres. Shukri Bey al-Quwatli.

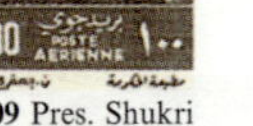

109 Pres. Shukri Bey al-Quwatli   110 Cotton

1956. Air.
587 **109** 100p. black . . . . 1·25 95
588 200p. violet . . . . . . 2·50 1·25
589 300p. red . . . . 3·75 3·00
590 500p. green . . . . . . 7·75 5·00

1956. Aleppo Cotton Festival.
591 **110** 2½p. green 50 25

1956. Air. Nos. 565/8 with premiums obliterated by bars.
592 **102** 25p. black 50 25
593 – 35p. blue 65 40
594 – 40p. purple . . . . 1·25 50
595 – 70p. green . . . . 1·50 1·10

111 Gate of Kasr al-Heir, Palmyra   112 Clay Alphabetical Tablet

1956. Air. 3rd International Fair, Damascus.
596 **111** 15p. brown 40 40
597 – 20p. blue 50 50
598 – 30p. green . . . . 1·10 1·10
599 – 35p. blue 90 90
600 – 50p. purple 90 90
DESIGNS: 20p. Cotton mill; 30p. Tractor; 35p. Phoenician galley and cogwheels; 50p. Textiles, carpets and pottery.

1956. Air. International Campaign for Museums.
601 **112** 20p. black 90 50
602 – 30p. red . . . . 1·00 50
603 – 50p. brown . . . . 1·90 1·00
DESIGNS—VERT: 30p. Syrian legionary's helmet. HORIZ: 50p. Lintel of Belshamine Temple, Palmyra.

1956. 11th Anniv of U.N.O. Nos. 571/4 optd **11eme ANNIVERSAIRE de L'ONU** in French and Arabic.
604 **104** 7½p. red (postage) 55 30
605 – 12½p. green 70 45
606 – 15p. blue (air) . . . . . 1·25 50
607 – 35p. brown . . . . 2·50 1·10

114 Oaks and Mosque

1956. Air. Afforestation Day.
608 **114** 10p. brown 40 20
609 40p. green 90 50

115 Azem Palace, Damascus

1957.
610 **115** 12½p. purple 25 10
611 15p. black 40 10

116 "Resistance"

118 Mother and Child

1957. Syrian Defence Force.
612 **116** 5p. mauve 20 10
613 20p. green 50 25

1957. Evacuation of Port Said. Optd **22.12.56 EVACUATION PORT SAID** in French and Arabic.
614 **116** 5p. mauve 25 10
615 20p. green 65 40

1957. Air. Mothers' Day.
616 – 40p. blue 65 45
617 **118** 60p. red . . . . 1·25 80
DESIGN: 40p. Mother fondling child.

119 "Sword of Liberty"   120 Freighter "Latakia" and Fair Emblem

1957. Air. 11th Anniv of Evacuation of Foreign Troops from Syria.
618 **119** 10p. brown 10 10
619 – 15p. green 25 10
620 – 25p. violet 50 15
621 – 35p. mauve 65 35
622 **119** 40p. black . . . . 1·00 55
DESIGNS: 15, 35p. Map and woman holding torch; 25p. Pres. Shukri Bey al-Quwatli.

1957. Air. 4th Damascus Fair.
623 **120** 25p. mauve 50 40
624 – 30p. brown 50 40
625 – 35p. blue 90 50
626 – 40p. green . . . . 1·10 65
627 **120** 70p. green . . . . 1·40 65
DESIGNS—VERT: 30, 40p. Girls harvesting and cotton picking. HORIZ: 35p. Interior of processing plant.

121 "Cotton"   122 Children at Work and Play

1957. Aleppo Cotton Festival.
628 **121** 12½p. black & grn (postage) 50 25
629 17½p. black & orange (air) 60 40
630 40p. black and blue . . . 1·25 50

1957. International Children's Day.
631 **122** 12½p. green (postage) . . 65 25
632 17½ blue (air) . . . . . . 1·25 50
633 20p. brown . . . . 1·25 50

123 Letter and Post-box

1957. International Correspondence Week.
634 **123** 5p. mauve (postage) . . . 50 25
635 – 5p. green (air) 50 15
DESIGN: 5p. (air) Family writing letters.

اسبوع التحصين
(124)

125 Scales of Justice, Map and Damascus Silhouette

1957. National Defence Week. Optd with T **124**.
636 **116** 5p. mauve 15 10
637 20p. green 50 25

1957. 3rd Arab Lawyers Union Congress, Damascus.
638 **125** 12½p. green (postage) . . 40 20
639 17½p. red (air) 40 25
640 40p. black 90 50

126 Glider

1957. Air. Gliding Festival.
641 **126** 25p. brown 80 35
642 35p. green . . . . 1·25 40
643 40p. blue . . . . 2·75 60

127 Torch and Map   128 Khaled Ibn el- Walid Mosque, Homs

1957. Afro-Asian Jurists' Congress, Damascus.
644 **127** 20p. brown (postage) . . 65 25
645 30p. green (air) 50 30
646 50p. violet 75 40

1957.
647 **128** 2½p. brown 20 15

UNITED ARAB REPUBLIC

129 Telecommunications Building

1958. Five Year Plan.
648 **129** 25p. blue (postage) . . . 40 25
649 10p. green (air) 25 10
650 – 15p. brown 30 20
DESIGN—VERT: 15p. Telephone, radio tower and telegraph pole.

129a Union of Egypt and Syria

1958. Birth of United Arab Republic.
651 **129a** 12½p. green and yellow (postage) 35 20
652 17½p. brown & blue (air) 50 30

130 "Eternal Flame"

1958. 12th Anniv of Evacuation of Foreign Troops from Syria.
653 **130** 5p. violet & yellow (postage) 50 25
654 15p. red and green . . . 90 40
655 – 35p. black and red (air) 95 45
656 – 45p. brown and blue . . . 1·60 60
DESIGN: 35, 45p. Broken chain, dove and olive branch.

131 Scout fixing Tent-peg

1958. Air. 3rd Pan-Arab Scout Jamboree.
657 **131** 35p. brown . . . . 2·25 2·25
658 40p. blue . . . . 2·75 2·75

132 Mosque, Chimneys and Cogwheel   133 Bronze Rattle

1958. Air. 5th Int Fair, Damascus. Inscr "1.9.58".
659 – 25p. red 80 60
660 – 30p. green . . . . 1·25 90
661 **132** 45p. violet . . . . 1·40 1·00
DESIGNS—HORIZ: 25p. View of Fair. VERT: 30p. Minaret, vase and emblem.

1958. Ancient Syrian Art.
662 **133** 10p. green 10 10
663 – 15p. brown 15 10
664 – 20p. purple 15 15
665 – 30p. brown 25 15
666 – 40p. grey 45 20
667 – 60p. green 65 25
668 – 75p. blue . . . . 1·25 40
669 – 100p. purple . . . . . . 1·50 65
670 – 150p. purple . . . . . . 3·25 90
DESIGNS: 15p. Goddess of Spring; 20p. "Lamgi Mari" (statue); 30p. Mithras fighting bull; 40p. Aspasia; 60p. Minerva; 75p. Ancient gourd; 100p. Enamelled vase; 150p. Mosaic from Omayyad Mosque, Damascus.

1958. International Children's Day. Optd **R A U** and Arabic inscription.
670a **122** 12½p. green (postage) . . 60·00 50·00
670b 17½p. blue (air) . . . . 35·00 35·00
670c 20p. brown . . . . 35·00 35·00

134 Cotton and Textiles   134a Hand holding Torch, and Iraqi Flag

1958. Air. Aleppo Cotton Festival.
671 **134** 25p. yellow and brown . . 55 50
672 35p. red and brown . . . 95 60

1958. Republic of Iraq Commemoration.
673 **134a** 12½p. red 25 15

135 Light Airplane and Children with Model Airplane   137 U.N. Emblem and Charter

136 Damascus

1958. Air. Gliding Festival.
674 **135** 7½p. green 90 50
675 12½p. green . . . . 3·00 1·75

1958. 4th N.E. Regional Conference, Damascus.
676 **136** 12½p. green (postage) . . 40 20
677 17½p. violet (air) 35 20

1958. Air. 10th Anniv of Declaration of Human Rights.
678 **137** 25p. purple 35 25
679 35p. grey 45 30
680 40p. brown 65 40

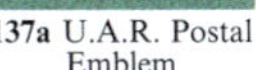
137a U.A.R. Postal Emblem
137b

1959. Post Day and Postal Employees' Social Fund.
681 **137a** 20p.+10p. red, black and green 60 60

1959. 1st Anniv of United Arab Republic.
682 **137b** 12½p. red, black and green 25 15

138 Secondary School, Damascus

1959.
683 **138** 12½p. green 25 10

138a "Telecommunications"

1959. Air. Arab Telecommunications Union Commemoration.
684 **138a** 40p. black and green . . 75 50

1959. Second Damascus Conference. No. 684 optd **2nd CONFERANCE DAMASCUS 1-3-1959** in English and Arabic.
685 **138a** 40p. black and green . . 50 25

139a U.A.R. and Yemeni Flags

1959. 1st Anniv of Proclamation of United Arab States (U.A.R. and Yemen).
686 **139a** 12½p. red and green . . 25 15

140 Mother with Children
142

1959. Arab Mothers' Day.
687 **140** 15p. red 30 20
688 25p. green 45 30

1959. Surch **U.A.R 2½p** and also in Arabic.
689 **92** 2½p. on 1p. green 20 10

1959. Air. 13th Anniv of Evacuation of Foreign Troops from Syria.
690 **142** 15p. green and yellow . . 25 10
691 – 35p. red and grey 50 30
DESIGN: 35p. Broken chain and flame.

143
144 "Emigration"

1959. Patterns as T **143**.
692 **143** 2½p. violet 10 10
693 – 5p. brown 10 10
694 – 7½p. blue 10 10
695 – 10p. green 20 10
DESIGNS: 5 to 10p. Different styles of ornamental scrollwork.

1959. Air. Emigrants' Congress.
696 **144** 80p. black, red and green 1·10 65

(145)
147

146 Oil Refinery

1959. Optd as T **145**.
697 **115** 15p. black (postage) . . . 30 15
698 – 50p. green (No. 536) . . . 75 55
690 – 5p. green (No. 635) (air) 15 15
700 – 50p. purple (No. 543) . . 60 30
701 – 70p. violet (No. 544) . . . 95 40

1959. Air. Inauguration of Oil Refinery.
702 **146** 50p. red, black and blue 1·40 65

1959. 6th Damascus Fair.
703 **147** 35p. green, violet and grey 60 25

148
149 Child and Factory

1959. Air. Aleppo Cotton Festival.
704 **148** 45p. blue 65 25
705 50p. purple 65 40

1959. Air. Children's Day.
706 **149** 25p. red, blue and lilac . . 40 15

150 Boys' College, Damascus
150a "Shield against Aggression"

1959.
707 **150** 25p. blue 45 20
708 – 35p. brown 65 25
DESIGN: 35p. Girls' College, Damascus.

1959. Army Day.
709 **150a** 50p. brown 75 40

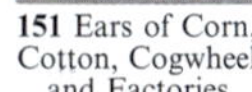
151 Ears of Corn, Cotton, Cogwheel and Factories
152 Mosque and Oaks

1959. Industrial and Agricultural Production Fair, Aleppo.
710 **151** 35p. brown, blue and grey 60 25

1959. Tree Day.
711 **152** 12½p. brown and green . . 30 20

153 A. R. Kawakbi
153a

1960. 50th Death Anniv of A. R. Kawakbi (writer).
712 **153** 15p. green 25 10

1960. 2nd Anniv of U.A.R.
713 **153a** 12½p. green and red . . 25 10

154 Diesel Train

1960. Latakia–Aleppo Railway Project.
714 **154** 12½p. brown, black & blue . . . . 1·90 1·25

154a Arab League Centre, Cairo

1960. Inaug of Arab League Centre, Cairo.
715 **154a** 12½p. black and green 25 15

1960. Mothers' Day. Optd **ARAB MOTHERS DAY 1960** in English and Arabic.
716 **140** 15p. red 30 15
717 25p. green 40 25

155a Mother, Child and Map of Palestine

1960. World Refugee Year.
718 **155a** 12½p. red 35 15
719 50p. green 65 40

156 Government Building and Inscription

1960. 14th Anniv of Evacuation of Foreign Troops from Syria.
720 **156** 12½p. multicoloured . . . 35 10

157 Hittin School

1960.
721 **157** 17½p. lilac 40 10

1960. Industrial and Agricultural Production Fair, Aleppo. Optd **1960** and in Arabic.
722 **151** 35p. brown, blue and grey 40 25

159 Mobile Crane and Compasses
(160)

1960. Air. 7th International Damascus Fair.
723 **159** 50p. black, bistre and red 60 35

1960. Air. Aleppo Cotton Festival. Optd with T **160**.
724 **148** 45p. blue 65 25
725 50p. purple 65 40

161
162 Basketball

1960. Children's Day.
726 **161** 35p. brown and green . . 60 30

1960. Air. Olympic Games.
727 **162** 15p. brown, black and blue 40 20
728 – 20p. brown, black and blue 50 20
729 – 25p. multicoloured . . . 50 20
730 – 40p. violet, pink and black 95 50
DESIGNS: 20p. Swimming; 25p. Fencing (Arab-style); 40p. Horse-jumping.

(163)
164 "UN" and Globe

1960. Tree Day. Optd with T **163**.
731 **152** 12½p. brown and green . . 40 15

1960. Air. 15th Anniv of U.N.O.
732 **164** 35p. red, green and blue 50 25
733 50p. blue, brown and red 65 40

165 Hanano
165a State Emblem

1961. Air. 25th Death Anniv (1960) of Ibrahim Hanano (patriot).
734 **165** 50p. green and brown . . 60 35

1961. 3rd Anniv of U.A.R.
735 **165a** 12½p. violet 25 15

166 St. Simeon's Monastery   167 Raising the Flag

1961.
736 **166** 12½p. blue (postage) . . . 25 15
746 – 200p. blue (air) . . . 2·50 1·50
DESIGN—VERT: 200p. Entrance to St. Simeon's Monastery.

1961. Air. 15th Anniv of Evacuation of Foreign Troops from Syria.
737 **167** 40p. green 60 30

168 Eye and Hand "reading" Braille   169 Palestinian and Map

1961. Air. U.N. Campaign for Welfare of Blind.
738 **168** 40p.+10p. black & grn . . 65 50

1961. Air. Palestine Day.
739 **169** 50p. blue and black . . . 75 40

170 Cogwheel and Corn   171 Abou Tammam (796–846)

1961. Industrial and Agricultural Production Fair, Aleppo.
740 **170** 12½p. multicoloured . . . 30 20

1961. Air. Abou Tammam (writer) Commem.
741 **171** 50p. brown 65 30

172 Damascus University, Discus-thrower and Lyre

1961. Air. 5th Universities Youth Festival.
742 **172** 15p. black and red . . . 30 10
743 35p. violet and green . . 95 30

173 Open Window on World

1961. Air. 8th International Damascus Fair.
744 **173** 17½p. violet and green . . 25 15
745 – 50p. violet and black . . 55 30
DESIGN: 50p. U.A.R. Pavilion.

SYRIAN ARAB REPUBLIC

175 Assembly Chamber   176 The Noria, Hama

177 Arch of Triumph, Latakia   178 Arab League Emblem and Headquarters, Cairo

1961. Establishment of Syrian Arab Republic.
747 **175** 15p. red 25 10
748 35p. green 65 25

1961.
749 **176** 2½p. red (postage) . . . 10 10
750 5p. blue 10 10
751 – 7½p. green 25 10
752 – 10p. orange 40 10
753 **177** 12½p. brown 60 10
754 – 12½p. green 45 10
755 – 15p. blue 50 10
756 – 17½p. brown 60 10
757 – 22½p. turquoise 65 10
758 **177** 25p. brown 85 10
759 – 45p. yellow (air) 50 30
760 – 50p. red 65 40
761 – 85p. purple . . . . . . 1·10 50
762 – 100p. purple . . . . . . 1·40 55
763 – 200p. green . . . . . . 2·50 1·00
764 – 300p. blue . . . . . . 3·25 1·10
764a – 500p. purple . . . . . . 5·00 2·50
764b – 1000p. black . . . . . . 11·00 4·50
DESIGNS: 7½, 10p. Khaled ibn-el-Walid Mosque, Homs; 12½p. (No. 754), 15, 17½, 22½, 45, 50p. "The Beauty of Palmyra" (statue); 85, 100p. Archway and columns, Palmyra; 200 to 1000p. King Zahir Bibar's tomb.
See also Nos. 799/800.

1962. Air. Arab League Week.
765 **178** 17½p. turquoise and green 20 10
766 22½p. violet and blue . . 35 20
767 50p. brown and orange 75 30

179 Campaign Emblem   180 Prancing Horse

1962. Air. Malaria Eradication.
768 **179** 12½p. violet, brown & blue 25 15
769 50p. green, brown & yell 70 40

1962. Air. 16th Anniv of Evacuation of Foreign Troops from Syria.
770 **180** 45p. orange and violet . . 50 25
771 – 55p. violet and blue . . 75 35
DESIGN: 55p. Military commander.

181 Qalb Lozah Church

1962.
772 **181** 17½p. green 35 10
773 35p. green 50 25

182 Martyrs' Memorial, Swaida   183 Jupiter Temple Gate

1962. Syrian Revolution Commemoration.
774 **182** 12½p. brown and drab . . 20 10
775 35p. green and turquoise 50 20

1962.
776 **183** 2½p. turquoise 10 10
777 5p. brown 20 10
778 7½p. brown 35 10
779 10p. purple 20 10

184 Globe, Monument to Hejaz Railway and Handclasp

1962. Air. 9th International Fair, Damascus.
780 **184** 17½p. brown and purple 40 20
781 22½p. mauve and red . . 55 30
782 – 40p. purple and brown . . 40 20
783 – 45p. blue and green . . 65 30
DESIGN: 40, 45p. Fair entrance.

185 Festival Emblem   186 Pres. Kudsi

1962. Air. Aleppo Cotton Festival.
784 **185** 12½p. multicoloured . . . 25 10
785 50p. multicoloured . . . 65 40
See also Nos. 820/1.

1962. Presidential Elections.
786 **186** 12½p. brown and blue (postage) 30 10
787 50p. blue and buff (air) 65 30

187 Zenobia   188 Saadallah el-Jabiri

1962. Air.
788 **187** 45p. violet 55 20
789 50p. red 70 25
790 85p. green 80 40
791 100p. purple . . . . . . 1·75 60
See also Nos. 801/4.

1962. Air. 15th Death Anniv of Saadallah el-Jabiri (revolutionary).
792 **188** 50p. blue 50 30

189 Moharde Woman   190 Ears of Wheat, Hand and Globe

1962. Air. Women in Regional Costumes. Mult.
793 40p. Marje Sultan 40 15
794 45p. Kalamoun 50 25
795 50p. Type **189** 65 30
796 55p. Jabal al-Arab 75 35
797 60p. Afrine 80 35
798 65p. Hauran . . . . 1·00 45

1963. As previous designs but size 20×26 mm.
799 – 2½p. violet 15 10
800 – 5p. purple 15 10
801 **187** 7½p. grey 35 10
802 10p. brown 65 10
803 12½p. blue 95 10
804 15p. brown . . . . 1·60 15
DESIGN: Nos. 799/800, "The Beauty of Palmyra" (statue).

1963. Freedom from Hunger.
805 **190** 12½p. black & bl (postage) 20 10
806 – 50p. black and red (air) 50 25
DESIGN: 50p. Bird feeding young in nest.

191 Faris el-Khouri (politician)   192 S.A.R. Emblem

1963. Air. 17th Anniv of Evacuation of Foreign Troops from Syria.
807 **191** 17½p. brown 30 15
808 **192** 22½p. green and black . . 30 15

193 Eagle   194 Ala el-Ma'ari (bust)

1963. Air. Baathist Revolution Commemoration.
809 **193** 12½p. green 10 10
810 50p. mauve 55 35

1963. Air. 990th Birth Anniv of Ala el-Ma'ari (poet).
811 **194** 50p. violet 50 35

195 Copper Water Jug

1963. Air. 10th International Fair, Damascus.
812 **195** 37½p. multicoloured . . . 55 25
813 50p. multicoloured . . . 70 40

196 Central Bank

1963. Damascus Buildings.
814 – 17½p. violet . . . . . . 2·50 45
815 – 22½p. violet 35 20
816 **196** 25p. brown 25 15
817 – 35p. purple 40 20
BUILDINGS: 17½p. Hejaz Railway Station; 22½p. Mouassat Hospital; 35p. Post Office, Al-Jalaa.

197 "Red Crescent" and Centenary Emblem   198 Child with Ball

1963. Air. Red Cross Centenary. Crescent in red.
818 **197** 15p. black and blue . . . 25 20
819 – 50p. black and green . . 65 40
DESIGN: 50p. "Red Crescent", globe and centenary emblem.

1963. Aleppo Cotton Festival. As T **185** but inscr "POSTAGE" and "1963" in place of "AIRMAIL" and "1962".
820 **185** 17½p. multicoloured . . . 25 10
821 22½p. multicoloured . . . 45 15

1963. Children's Day.
822 **198** 12½p. green and deep green 20 10
823 22½p. green and red . . . 35 10

199 Firas el-Hamadani  **200** Flame on Head

1963. Air. Death Millenary of Abou Firas el-Hamadani (poet).
824 **199** 50p. brown and bistre . . 50 40

1963. Air. 15th Anniv of Declaration of Human Rights. Flame in red.
825 **200** 17½p. black and grey . . 20 10
826 22½p. black and green . . 25 15
827 50p. black and violet . . 60 25

201 Emblem and Flag

1964. Air. 1st Anniv of Baathist Revolution of 8 March 1963. Emblem and flag in red, black and green; inscr in black.
828 **201** 15p. green 10 10
829 17½p. pink 20 10
830 22½p. grey 40 15

202 Ugharit Princess  **203** Chahba, Thalassa, Mosaic

1964.
831 **202** 2½p. grey (postage) . . . 10 10
832 5p. brown 10 10
833 7½p. purple 10 10
834 10p. green 10 10
835 12½p. violet 10 10
836 17½p. blue 20 10
837 20p. red 50 10
838 25p. orange 80 15
839 **203** 27½p. red (air) 25 10
840 45p. brown 45 15
841 50p. green 60 15
842 55p. green 65 25
843 60p. blue 75 30

204 Kaaba, Mecca, and Mosque, Damascus

1964. Air. 1st Arab Moslem Wakf Ministers' Conference.
844 **204** 12½p. black and blue . . 10 10
845 22½p. black and purple . . 25 15
846 50p. black and green . . 65 25

1964. Air. 18th Anniv of Evacuation of Foreign Troops from Syria. As T **99** but larger, 38¼ × 26 mm. Inscr "1964".
847 **99** 20p. blue 15 10
848 25p. purple 30 15
849 60p. green 55 25

205 Abou al Zahrawi 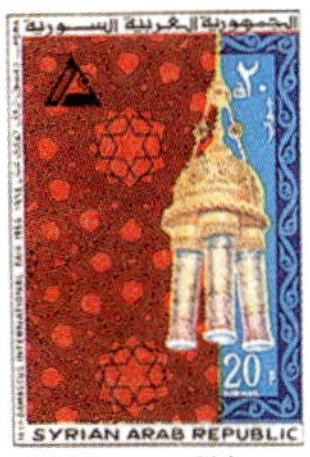 **206** Bronze Chimes

1964. Air. 4th Arab Dental and Oral Surgery Congress, Damascus.
850 **205** 60p. brown 65 40

1964. Air. 11th International Fair, Damascus.
851 **206** 20p. multicoloured . . . 50 10
852 – 25p. multicoloured . . . 55 20
DESIGN: 25p. Fair emblem.

207 Cotton Plant and Symbols 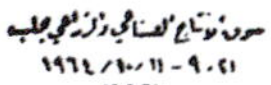 (**208**)

1964. Air. Aleppo Cotton Festival. No. 854 is optd with T **208**.
853 **207** 25p. multicoloured . . . 25 10
854 25p. multicoloured . . . 40 25

209 Aero Club Emblem

1964. Air. 10th Anniv of Syrian Aero Club.
855 **209** 12½p. black and green . . 20 10
856 17½p. black and red . . . 30 15
857 20p. black and blue . . . 65 20

210 A.P.U. Emblem  **211** Book within Hands

1964. Air. 10th Anniv of Arab Postal Union's Permanent Office, Cario.
858 **210** 12½p. black and orange 15 10
859 20p. black and green . . 20 10
860 25p. black and mauve . . 25 15

1964. Air. Burning of Algiers Library.
861 **211** 12½p. black and green . . 10 10
862 17½p. black and red . . . 20 10
863 20p. black and blue . . . 25 15

212 Tennis

1965. Air. Olympic Games, Tokyo. Multicoloured.
864 12½p. Type **212** 15 10
865 17½p. Wrestling 30 20
866 20p. Weightlifting 45 20

213 Flag, Map and Revolutionaries

1965. 2nd Anniv of Baathist Revolution of 8 March 1963.
867 **213** 12½p. multicoloured . . . 10 10
868 17½p. multicoloured . . . 20 10
869 20p. multicoloured . . . 25 10

214 Rameses II in War Chariot, Abu Simbel

1965. Air. Nubian Monuments Preservation.
870 **214** 22½p. black, blue and green 30 20
871 – 50p. black, green and blue 65 30
DESIGN: 50p. Heads of Rameses II.

215 Weather Instruments and Map

1965. World Meteorological Day.
872 **215** 12½p. black and purple . . 10 10
873 27½p. black and blue . . 40 15

216 Al-Radi  **217** Evacuation Symbol

1965. Air. 950th Death Anniv of Al-Sharif al-Radi (writer).
874 **216** 50p. black 65 40

1965. 19th Anniv of Evacuation of Foreign Troops from Syria.
875 **217** 12½p. green and blue . . 10 10
876 27½p. lilac and red . . . 25 15

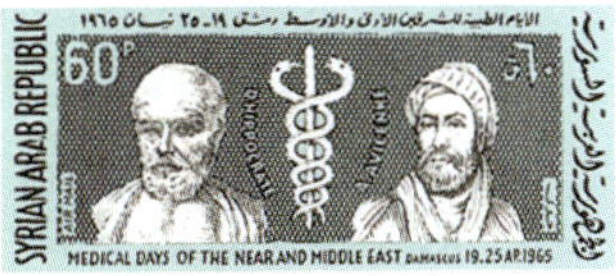

218 Hippocrates and Avicenna

1965. Air. "Medical Days of the Near and Middle East".
877 **218** 60p. black and green . . 75 50

219 Dagger on Deir Yassin, Palestine

1965. Air. Deir Yassin Massacre on 9 April 1948.
878 **219** 12½p. multicoloured . . . 20 10
879 60p. multicoloured . . . 50 30

220 I.T.U. Emblem and Symbols  **221** Arab Family, Flags and Map

1965. Air. Centenary of I.T.U.
880 **220** 12½p. multicoloured . . . 25 10
881 27½p. multicoloured . . . 40 15
882 60p. multicoloured . . . 70 45

1965. Palestine Week.
883 **221** 12½p.+5p. multicoloured 25 20
884 25p.+5p. multicoloured 25 25

222 Hands holding Hoe and Pick  **223** Welcoming Emigrant

1965. Peasants' Union.
885 **222** 2½p. green 10 10
886 12½p. violet 10 10
887 15p. purple 10 10
The above stamps are inscr "RERUBLIC" for "REPUBLIC".

1965. Air. "Welcome Arab Emigrants".
888 **223** 25p. multicoloured . . . 25 10
889 100p. multicoloured . . . 90 40

224 Fair Entrance  **226** Cotton Boll and Shuttles

1965. Air. 12th Int Fair, Damascus. Multicoloured.
890 12½p. Type **224** 10 10
891 27½p. Globe and compasses 25 10
892 60p. Syrian brassware 65 30

1965. Air. Aleppo Industrial and Agricultural Production Fair. Optd **INDUSTRIAL & AGRICULTURAL PRODUCTION FAIR-ALEPPO 1965** in English and Arabic.
893 **226** 25p. multicoloured . . . 40 10

1965. Air. Aleppo Cotton Festival.
894 **226** 25p. multicoloured . . . 40 10

227 I.C.Y. Emblem and View of Damascus

1965. Air. International Co-operation Year.
895 **227** 25p. multicoloured . . . 40 15

228 Arabs, Torch and Map  **229** Industrial Workers

1965. National Revolution Council.
896 **228** 12½p. multicoloured . . . 10 10
897 25p. multicoloured . . . 25 10

1966. Labour Unions.
898 **229** 12½p. blue 10 10
899 15p. red 10 10
900 20p. lilac 20 10
901 25p. brown 25 15

230 Radio Aerial, Globe and Flag  **231** Dove-shaped Hand holding Flower

1966. Air. Arab Information Ministers' Conf, Damascus.
902 **230** 25p. multicoloured . . . 20 10
903 60p. multicoloured . . . 50 25

1966. Air. 3rd Anniv of Baathist Revolution of 8 March 1963. Multicoloured.
904 12½p. Type **231** 10 10
905 17½p. Revolutionaries (horiz) 25 10
906 50p. Type **231** 90 25

232 Colossi, Abu Simbel

233 Roman Lamp

1966. Air. Nubian Monuments Preservation Week.
907 **232** 25p. blue 30 10
908 60p. grey 65 25

1966.
909 **233** 2½p. green 10 10
910 5p. purple 20 10
911 – 7½p. brown 10 10
912 – 10p. violet 15 10
DESIGN: 7½, 10p. 12th-century Islamic vessel.

234 U.N. Emblem and Headquarters

1966. Air. 20th Anniv of U.N.O.
913 **234** 25p. black and grey . . 15 10
914 50p. black and green . . 50 25

236 "Evacuation" (abstract)

1966. 20th Anniv of Evacuation of Foreign Troops from Syria.
916 **236** 12½p. multicoloured . . . 10 10
917 27½p. multicoloured . . . 25 15

237 Workers marching across Globe

1966. Air. Labour Day.
918 **237** 60p. multicoloured . . . 50 25

238 W.H.O. Building

1966. Air. Inauguration of W.H.O. Headquarters, Geneva.
919 **238** 60p. black, blue and yellow 50 25

239 Traffic Signals and Map on Hand

240 Astarte and Tyche (wrongly inscr "ASTRATE")

1966. Air. Traffic Day.
920 **239** 25p. multicoloured . . . 35 10

1966. Air.
921 **240** 50p. brown 50 25
922 60p. grey 75 40

241 Fair Emblem

242 Shuttle (stylized)

1966. Air. 13th International Fair, Damascus.
923 **241** 12½p. multicoloured . . . 10 10
924 60p. multicoloured . . . 55 35

1966. Air. Aleppo Cotton Festival.
925 **242** 50p. black, red and grey 50 25

243 Decade Emblem

244 Emir Abd-el-Kader

1966. Air. International Hydrological Decade.
926 **243** 12½p. black, orange & green 15 10
927 60p. black, orange and blue 65 35

1966. Air. Return of Emir Abd-el-Kader's Remains to Algiers.
928 **244** 12½p. black and green . . 30 10
929 50p. brown and green . . 45 30

245 U.N.R.W.A. Emblem

1966. Air. 21st Anniv of U.N. Day and Refugee Week.
930 **245** 12½p.+2½p. black and blue 10 10
931 50p.+5p. black and green 45 45

246 Handclasp and Map

247 Doves and Oil Pipelines

1967. Air. Solidarity Congress, Damascus.
932 **246** 20p. multicoloured . . . 20 10
933 25p. multicoloured . . . 25 15

1967. Air. 4th Anniv of Baathist Revolution of 8 March 1963.
934 **247** 17½p. multicoloured . . . 25 10
935 25p. multicoloured . . . 30 20
936 27½p. multicoloured . . . 45 20

248 Soldier and Citizens with Banner

249 Workers' Monument, Damascus

1967. Air. 21st Anniv of Evacuation of Foreign Troops from Syria.
937 **248** 17½p. green 15 10
938 25p. purple 25 15
939 27½p. blue 35 15

1967. Air. Labour Day.
940 **249** 12½p. turquoise 10 10
941 50p. mauve 55 25

250 Core Bust

251 "African Woman" (vase)

252 Head of a Young Man from Amrith

253 Flags and Fair Entrance

1967.
942 **250** 2½p. green (postage) . . . 10 10
943 5p. red 10 10
944 10p. blue 10 10
945 12½p. brown 10 10
946 **251** 15p. purple 10 10
947 20p. blue 15 10
948 25p. green 25 10
949 27½p. blue 35 10
950 **252** 45p. red (air) 40 20
951 50p. mauve 55 20
952 60p. blue 60 40
953 – 100p. green 80 50
954 – 500p. red . . . . 3·75 2·50
DESIGN—VERT: 100, 500p. Bust of Princess (2nd-century bronze).

1967. Air. 14th International Damascus Fair.
955 **253** 12½p. multicoloured . . . 10 10
956 60p. multicoloured . . . 55 30

254 Statue of Ur-Nina and Tourist Emblem

1967. Air. International Tourist Year.
957 **254** 12½p. purple, black & blue 10 10
958 25p. red, black and blue 15 10
959 27½p. blue, black & lt blue 40 20

255 Cotton Boll and Cogwheel

257 Ibn el-Naphis (scientist)

1967. Air. Aleppo Cotton Festival.
961 **255** 12½p. black, brown and yellow 10 10
962 60p. black, brown and yellow 65 25

1967. Air. Industrial and Agricultural Production Fair, Aleppo. Optd **INDUSTRIAL & AGRICULTURAL PRODUCTION FAIR ALEPPO 1967** in English and Arabic.
963 **255** 12½p. black, brown & yellow 10 10
964 60p. black, brown & yell 65 25

1967. Air. Sciences Week.
965 **257** 12½p. red and green . . . 10 10
966 27½p. mauve and blue . . 40 10

258 Acclaiming Human Rights

1968. Air. Human Rights Year.
967 **258** 12½p. black, turquoise and blue 10 10
968 60p. black, red and pink 55 35

259 Learning to Read

260 "The Arab Revolutionary" (Damascus statue)

1968. Air. Literacy Campaign.
970 **259** 12½p. multicoloured . . . 10 10
971 – 17½p. multicoloured . . . 10 10
972 **259** 25p. multicoloured . . . 25 10
973 – 45p. multicoloured . . . 45 25
DESIGN: 17½, 45p. Flaming torch and open book.

1968. 5th Anniv of Baathist Revolution of 8 March 1963.
974 **260** 12½p. brown, yellow & black 10 10
975 25p. mauve, pink and black 30 10
976 27½p. green, light green and black 30 15

261 Map of North Africa and Arabia

263 Hands holding Spanner, Rifle and Torch

262 Euphrates Dam

1968. 21st Anniv of Baath Arab Socialist Party.
977 **261** 12½p. multicoloured . . . 10 10
978 60p. multicoloured . . . 50 25

1968. Air. Euphrates Dam Project.
979 **262** 12½p. multicoloured . . . 20 10
980 17½p. multicoloured . . . 20 15
981 25p. multicoloured . . . 45 20

1968. "Mobilisation Efforts".
982 **263** 12½p. multicoloured . . . 10 10
983 17½p. multicoloured . . . 15 10
984 25p. multicoloured . . . 25 10

264 Railway Track and Sun

266 Torch, Map and Laurel

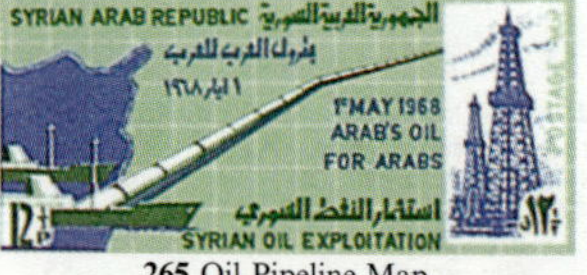

265 Oil Pipeline Map

1968. 22nd Anniv of Evacuation of Foreign Troops from Syria.
985 **264** 12½p. multicoloured . . . 60 60
986 27½p. multicoloured . . . 1·90 1·90

1968. Syrian Oil Exploration.
987 **265** 12½p. blue, green and light green 30 10
988 17½p. blue, brown and pink 65 20

1968. Palestine Day.
989 **266** 12½p. multicoloured . . . 15 10
990 25p. multicoloured . . . 20 15
991 27½p. multicoloured . . . 35 15

267 Refugee Family

1968. Red Crescent Refugees Fund.
992 **267** 12½p.+2½p. black, purple and blue 35 35
993 27½p.+7½p. black, red and violet 35 35

268 Avenzoar (physician) and W.H.O. Emblem

1968. Air. 20th Anniv of W.H.O.
994 **268** 12½p. multicoloured . . . 10 10
995 – 25p. multicoloured . . . 25 10
996 – 60p. multicoloured . . . 65 25
DESIGNS—As Type **268**, but with different portraits of Arab physicians: 25p. Razi; 60p. Jabir.

269 Ear of Corn, Cogwheel and Saracen Gate, Aleppo Citadel

1968. Industrial and Agricultural Production Fair, Aleppo.
997 **269** 12½p. multicoloured . . . 10 10
998 27½p. multicoloured . . . 20 10

270 Emblems of Fair, Agriculture and Industry

271 Gathering Cotton

1968. 15th International Damascus Fair.
999 **270** 12½p. black, green & brown 10 10
1000 – 27½p. multicoloured . . 25 10
1001 **270** 60p. black, orange & blue 45 30
DESIGN—HORIZ: 27½p. Flag, hand with torch and emblems.

1968. Aleppo Cotton Festival.
1002 **271** 12½p. multicoloured . . 10 10
1003 27½p. multicoloured . . 25 10

272 Monastery of St. Simeon the Stylite

273 Oil Derrick

1968. Air. Ancient Monuments (1st series).
1004 **272** 15p. multicoloured . . . 10 10
1005 – 17½p. deep brown, brown and chocolate 15 15
1006 – 22½p. multicoloured . . 20 20
1007 – 45p. multicoloured . . 40 20
1008 – 50p. brown, sepia and blue 45 30
DESIGNS—VERT: 17½p. El Tekkieh Mosque, Damascus; 22½p. Temple columns, Palmyra. HORIZ: 45p. Chapel of St. Paul, Bab Kisan; 50p. Amphitheatre, Bosra.
See also Nos. 1026/30.

1968.
1009 **273** 2½p. green and blue . . 10 10
1010 5p. blue and green . . . 10 10
1011 7½p. blue and green . . 10 10
1012 10p. green and yellow . . 15 10
1013 12½p. red and yellow . . 15 10
1014 15p. brown and bistre 20 10
1015 27½p. brown and orange 30 10

274 Al-Jahez (scientist)

275 Throwing the Hammer

1968. 9th Science Week.
1016 **274** 12½p. black and green 10 10
1017 27½p. black and grey . . 40 20

1968. Air. Olympic Games, Mexico.
1018 **275** 12½p. black, mauve and green 10 10
1019 – 25p. black, red and green 25 10
1020 – 27½p. black, grey and green 30 10
1021 – 60p. multicoloured . . . 45 25
DESIGNS: 25p. Throwing the discus; 27½p. Running; 60p. Basketball.

276 Aerial View of Airport

1969. Air. Construction of Damascus Int Airport.
1023 **276** 12½p. green, blue & yellow 15 10
1024 17½p. violet, red and green 30 10
1025 60p. black, mauve and yellow 95 30

277 Baal-Shamin Temple, Palmyra

1969. Air. Ancient Monuments (2nd series). Mult.
1026 25p. Type **277** 15 10
1027 45p. Omayyad Mosque, Damascus (vert) 25 10
1028 50p. Amphitheatre, Palmyra 30 15
1029 60p. Khaled ibn el-Walid Mosque, Homs (vert) . . 45 20
1030 100p. St. Simeon's Column, Jebel Samaan 75 40

278 "Sun" and Clenched Fists in Broken Handcuffs

1969. 6th Anniv of Baathist Revolution of 8 March 1963.
1031 **278** 12½p. multicoloured . . 10 10
1032 25p. multicoloured . . . 25 10
1033 27½p. multicoloured . . 30 10

279 "Sun of Freedom"

280 Symbols of Progress

1969. 5th Youth Festival, Homs.
1034 **279** 12½p. red, yellow and blue 10 10
1035 25p. red, yellow and green 20 10

1969. 23rd Anniv of Evacuation of Foreign Troops from Syria.
1036 **280** 12½p. multicoloured . . 10 10
1037 27½p. multicoloured . . 20 10

281 "Workers", Cogwheel and I.L.O. Emblem

1969. Air. 50th Anniv of I.L.O.
1038 **281** 12½p. multicoloured . . 10 10
1039 27½p. multicoloured . . 30 10

282 Russian Dancers

283 "Fortune" (statue)

1969. Air. 16th Int Damascus Fair. Mult.
1041 12½p. Type **282** 20 10
1042 27½p. Ballet dancers 35 15
1043 45p. Lebanese dancers . . . 40 25
1044 55p. Egyptian dancers . . . 45 25
1045 60p. Bulgarian dancers . . . 60 30

1969. Air. 9th International Archaeological Congress, Damascus. Multicoloured.
1046 17½p. Type **283** 25 10
1047 25p. "Lady from Palmyra" (statue) 30 10
1048 60p. "Motherhood" (statue) 60 25

284 Children dancing

285 Mahatma Gandhi

1969. Air. Children's Day.
1049 **284** 12½p. green, blue and turquoise 15 10
1050 25p. violet, blue and red 20 10
1051 27½p. grey, dp blue & blue 25 10

1969. Birth Centenary of Mahatma Gandhi.
1052 **285** 12½p. brown and buff . . 15 10
1053 27½p. green and yellow 25 15

286 Cotton

287 "Arab World" (6th Arab Science Congress)

1969. Aleppo Cotton Festival.
1054 **286** 12½p. multicoloured . . 10 10
1055 17½p. multicoloured . . 10 10
1056 25p. multicoloured . . . 25 15

1969. 10th Science Week.
1057 **287** 12½p. blue and green . . 10 10
1058 – 25p. violet and pink . . 20 15
1059 – 27½p. brown and green 25 20
DESIGNS: 25p. Arab Academy (50th anniv); 27½p. Damascus University (50th anniv of Faculty of Medicine).

288 Cockerel

1969. Air. Damascus Agricultural Museum. Mult.
1060 12½p. Type **288** 20 10
1061 17½p. Cow 25 15
1062 20p. Maize 35 15
1063 50p. Olives 50 25

289 Rising Sun, Hand and Book

1970. 7th Anniv of Baathist Revolution of 8 March 1963.
1064 **289** 17½p. black, brown & blue 10 10
1065 25p. black, blue and red 20 10
1066 27½p. black, brown & green 25 15

290 Map of Arab World, League Emblem and Flag

1970. Silver Jubilee of Arab League.
1067 **290** 12½p. multicoloured . . 10 10
1068 25p. multicoloured . . . 20 10
1069 27½p. multicoloured . . 25 15

291 Dish Aerial and Hand on Book

1970. Air. World Meteorological Day.
1070 **291** 25p. black, yellow & green 30 10
1071 60p. black, yellow & blue 60 35

292 Lenin

1970. Air. Birth Centenary of Lenin.
1072 **292** 15p. brown and red . . 20 10
1073 60p. green and red . . . 45 30

293 Battle of Hattin

1970. 24th Anniv of Evacuation of Foreign Troops from Syria.
1074 **293** 15p. brown and cream 15 10
1075 35p. violet and cream . . 40 20

294 Emblem of Workers' Syndicate

1970. Air. Labour Day.

1076	**294**	15p. brown and green . .	10	10
1077		60p. brown and orange	55	30

295 Young Syrians and Map

1970. Revolution's Youth Union, 1st Youth Week.

1078	**295**	15p. green and brown . .	10	10
1079		25p. brown and ochre	20	15

This issue is inscr "YOUTH'S FIRST WEAK" in error.

296 Refugee Family

1970. World Arab Refugee Week.

1080	**296**	15p. multicoloured . . .	10	10
1081		25p. multicoloured . . .	25	10
1082		35p. multicoloured . . .	25	10

297 Dish Aerial and Open Book

1970. Air. World Telecommunications Day.

1083	**297**	15p. black and lilac . . .	10	10
1084		60p. black and blue . .	60	35

298 New U.P.U. Headquarters Building

1970. Air. New U.P.U. Headquarters Building.

1085	**298**	15p. multicoloured . . .	10	10
1086		60p. multicoloured . . .	55	30

299 "Industry" and Graph **300** Khaled ibn el-Walid

1970.

1087	**299**	2½p. red and brown (postage)	10	10
1088		5p. blue and orange . .	10	10
1089		7½p. grey and purple . .	10	10
1090		10p. brown and light brown	10	10
1091		12½p. red and blue . . .	10	10
1092		15p. mauve and green	15	10
1093		20p. brown and blue . .	15	10
1094		22½p. green and brown	20	10
1095		25p. blue and grey . . .	20	10
1096		27½p. brown and green	25	10
1097		35p. green and red . . .	35	20
1098	**300**	45p. mauve (air)	40	20
1099		50p. green	45	25
1100		60p. brown	60	35
1101		100p. blue	85	35
1102		200p. green	1·60	85
1103		300p. violet	2·75	1·60
1104		500p. grey	3·75	3·00

301 Medieval Warriors

1970. Air. Folk Tales and Legends.

1105	**301**	5p. multicoloured . . .	10	10
1106	–	10p. multicoloured . . .	10	10
1107	–	15p. multicoloured . . .	15	15
1108	–	20p. multicoloured . . .	20	15
1109	–	60p. multicoloured . . .	70	35

Nos. 1106/9 show horsemen similar to Type **301**.

302 Cotton

1970. Aleppo Agricultural and Industrial Fair. Multicoloured.

1110		5p. Type **302**	10	10
1111		10p. Tomatoes	10	10
1112		15p. Tobacco	15	15
1113		20p. Sugar beet	20	15
1114		35p. Wheat	45	25

303 Mosque in Flames

1970. Air. 1st Anniv of Burning of Al-Aqsa Mosque, Jerusalem.

1115	**303**	15p. multicoloured . . .	15	10
1116		60p. multicoloured . . .	60	35

304 Wood-carving

1970. Air. 17th Damascus Int Fair. Mult.

1117		15p. Type **304**	10	10
1118		20p. Jewellery	20	10
1119		25p. Glass-making	20	15
1120		30p. Copper-engraving . . .	45	20
1121		60p. Shell-work	95	40

305 Scout, Encampment and Badge

1970. Pan-Arab Scout Jamboree, Damascus.

1122	**305**	15p. green	35	20

306 Olive Tree and Emblem

1970. World Year of Olive-oil Production.

1123	**306**	15p. multicoloured . . .	20	10
1124		25p. multicoloured . . .	40	15

307 I.E.Y. Emblem

1970. Air. International Education Year.

1125	**307**	15p. brown, green & black	10	10
1126		60p. brown, blue & black	55	30

308 U.N. Emblems

309 Protective Shield

1970. Air. 25th Anniv of U.N.O.

1127	**308**	15p. multicoloured . . .	10	10
1128		60p. multicoloured . . .	55	30

1971. 8th Anniv of Baathist Revolution of 8 March 1963.

1129	**309**	15p. blue, yellow & green	10	10
1130		22½p. green, yellow & brown	15	10
1131		27½p. brown, yellow & blue	25	15

310 Girl holding Garland

1971. Air. 25th Anniv of Evacuation of Foreign Troops from Syria.

1132	**310**	15p. multicoloured . . .	10	10
1133		60p. multicoloured . . .	55	35

311 Globe and World Races

1971. Air. Racial Equality Year.

1134	**311**	15p. multicoloured . . .	10	10
1135		60p. multicoloured . . .	50	25

312 Soldier, Worker and Labour Emblems

1971. Labour Day.

1136	**312**	15p. purple, blue & yell	10	10
1137		25p. deep blue, blue and yellow	25	10

313 Hailing Traffic

1971. World Traffic Day.

1138	**313**	15p. red, blue and black	10	10
1139	–	25p. multicoloured . . .	20	15
1140	**313**	45p. red, yellow and black	45	30

DESIGN—VERT: 25p. Traffic signs and signal lights.

314 Cotton, Cogwheel and Factories

1971. Aleppo Agricultural and Industrial Fair.

1141	**314**	15p. black, blue and green	10	10
1142		30p. black, scarlet and red	25	20

315 A.P.U. Emblem **317** Flag and Federation Map

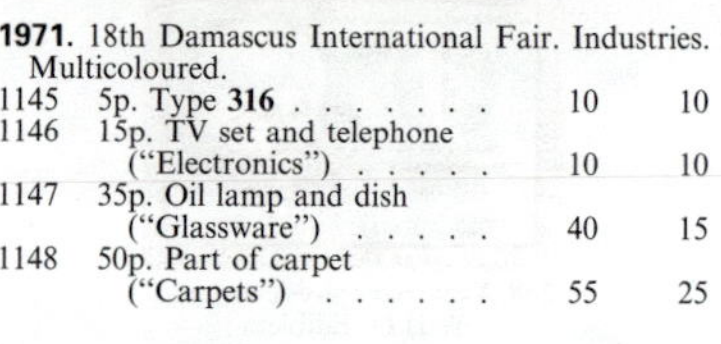

316 Peppers and Fertilizer Plant

1971. 25th Anniv of Sofar Conference and Founding of Arab Postal Union.

1143	**315**	15p. multicoloured . . .	10	10
1144		20p. multicoloured . . .	20	10

1971. 18th Damascus International Fair. Industries. Multicoloured.

1145		5p. Type **316**	10	10
1146		15p. TV set and telephone ("Electronics")	10	10
1147		35p. Oil lamp and dish ("Glassware")	40	15
1148		50p. Part of carpet ("Carpets")	55	25

1971. Arab Federation Referendum.

1149	**317**	15p. green, black and red	20	10

318 Pres. Hafez al-Assad and People's Council Chamber

1971. Air. People's Council and Presidential Election.

1150	**318**	15p. multicoloured . . .	10	10
1151		65p. multicoloured . . .	70	25

319 Pres. Nasser **320** "Telstar" and Dish Aerial

1971. Air. 1st Death Anniv of Pres. Nasser of Egypt.

1152	**319**	15p. brown and green . .	10	10
1153		20p. brown and grey . .	25	10

1971. 25th Anniv of U.N.E.S.C.O.

1154	**320**	15p. multicoloured . . .	10	10
1155		50p. multicoloured . . .	50	30

321 Flaming Torch **322** Quill-pen and Open Book

1971. "Movement of 16 November 1970".

1156	**321**	15p. multicoloured . . .	10	10
1157		20p. multicoloured . . .	20	15

1971. 8th Writers' Congress.

1158	**322**	15p. brown, orange and green	20	10

323 Children with Ball

324 Book Year Emblem

1971. 25th Anniv of U.N.I.C.E.F.
1159 **323** 15p. red, blue and deep blue 10 10
1160 25p. brown, green & blue 25 15

1972. International Book Year.
1161 **324** 15p. violet, blue & brown 10 10
1162 20p. green, light green and brown 25 10

325 Emblems of Reconstruction

326 Baath Party Emblem

1972. 9th Anniv of Baathist Revolution of 8 March 1963.
1163 **325** 15p. violet and green . . 10 10
1164 20p. red and bistre . . . 15 10

1972. 25th Anniv of Baath Party.
1165 **326** 15p. multicoloured . . . 10 10
1166 20p. multicoloured . . . 15 10

327 Eagle, Factory Chimneys and Rifles

328 Flowers and Broken Chain

1972. 1st Anniv of Arab Republics Federation.
1167 **327** 15p. gold, black and red 25 10

1972. 26th Anniv of Evacuation of Foreign Troops from Syria.
1168 **328** 15p. grey and red . . . 10 10
1169 50p. grey and green . . 50 30

329 Hand with Spanner

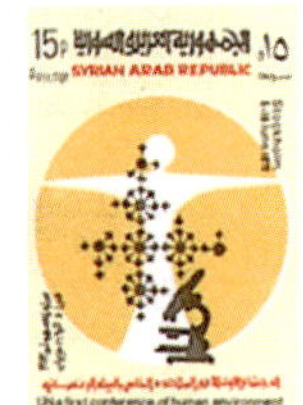

331 Environment Emblem

330 Telecommunications Emblem

1972. Labour Day.
1170 **329** 15p. multicoloured . . . 10 10
1171 50p. multicoloured . . . 50 30

1972. Air. World Telecommunications Day.
1172 **330** 15p. multicoloured . . . 10 10
1173 50p. multicoloured . . . 60 25

1972. United Nations Environmental Conservation Conference, Stockholm.
1174 **331** 15p. blue, azure and pink 10 10
1175 50p. purple, orange & yellow 60 30

332 Discus, Football and Swimming

1972. Olympic Games, Munich.
1176 **332** 15p. violet, black & bistre 10 10
1177 – 60p. orange, black & blue 50 40
DESIGN: 60p. Running, gymnastics and fencing.

334 Dove and Factory

335 President Hafez al-Assad

1972. Aleppo Agricultural and Industrial Fair.
1179 **334** 15p. multicoloured . . . 10 10
1180 20p. multicoloured . . . 15 10

1972. Air.
1181 **335** 100p. green . . . . . . 1·00 45
1182 500p. brown . . . . . . 4·50 1·90

336 Women's Dance

1972. 19th Damascus International Fair. Mult.
1183 15p. Type **336** 15 10
1184 20p. Tambourine dance . . 20 15
1185 50p. Men's drum dance . . 65 35

337 Airline Emblem

338 Emblem of Revolution

1972. Air. 25th Anniv of "Syrianair" Airline.
1186 **337** 15p. blue, light blue and black 25 10
1187 50p. blue, grey and black 70 25

1973. 10th Anniv of Baathist Revolution of 8 March 1963.
1188 **338** 15p. green, red and black 10 10
1189 20p. orange, red & black 15 10
1190 25p. blue, red and black 25 10

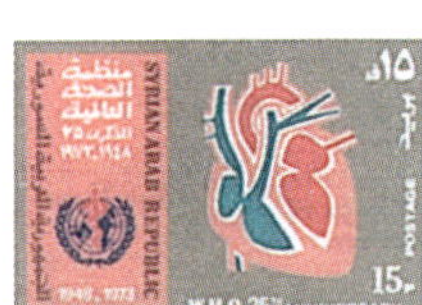

339 Human Heart

1973. 25th Anniv of W.H.O.
1191 **339** 15p. blue, purple and grey 20 10
1192 20p. blue, purple & brn 50 25

340 Emblems of Agriculture and Industry

341 Globe and Workers

1973. 27th Anniv of Evacuation of Foreign Troops from Syria.
1193 **340** 15p. multicoloured . . . 10 10
1194 20p. multicoloured . . . 15 10

1973. Labour Day.
1195 **341** 15p. black, purple and stone 15 10
1196 50p. black, blue and buff 45 25

342 Family and Emblems

343 Three Heads

1973. 10th Anniv of World Food Programme.
1197 **342** 15p. red and green . . . 10 10
1198 50p. blue and lilac . . . 40 25

1973.
1199 **343** 2½p. green 10 10
1200 5p. orange 10 10
1201 – 7½p. brown 10 10
1202 – 10p. red 10 10
1203 **343** 15p. blue 10 10
1204 – 25p. blue 15 10
1205 – 35p. blue 25 15
1206 – 55p. green 35 15
1207 – 70p. purple 50 25
DESIGNS—HORIZ: 7½, 10, 55p. As Type **343** but with one head above the other two. VERT: 25, 35, 70p. Similar to Type **343**, but with heads in vertical arrangement.

344 Stock

1973. Int Flower Show, Damascus. Mult.
1208 5p. Type **344** 15 10
1209 10p. Gardenia 15 10
1210 15p. Jasmine 20 10
1211 20p. Rose 30 10
1212 25p. Narcissus 35 10

345 Cogs and Flowers

1973. Aleppo Agricultural and Industrial Fair.
1213 **345** 15p. multicoloured . . . 20 10

346 Euphrates Dam

1973. Euphrates Dam Project. Diversion of the River.
1214 **346** 15p. multicoloured . . . 25 10
1215 50p. multicoloured . . . 45 25

347 Deir Ezzor Costume

348 Anniversary Emblem

1973. 20th Damascus International Fair. Costumes. Multicoloured.
1216 5p. Type **347** 15 10
1217 10p. Hassake 15 10
1218 20p. As Sahel 20 10
1219 25p. Zakie 30 10
1220 50p. Sarakeb 40 25

1973. 25th Anniv of Declaration of Human Rights.
1221 **348** 15p. black, red and green 10 10
1222 50p. black, red and blue 40 15

349 Citadel of Ja'abar

1973. "Save the Euphrates Monuments" Campaign. Multicoloured.
1223 10p. Type **349** 10 10
1224 15p. Meskeneh Minaret (vert) 15 10
1225 25p. Psyche, Anab al-Safinah (vert) 20 10

350 W.M.O. Emblem

1973. Centenary of W.M.O.
1226 **350** 70p. multicoloured . . . 50 25

351 Ancient City of Maalula

1973. Arab Emigrants' Congress, Buenos Aires.
1227 **351** 15p. black and blue . . 10 10
1228 – 50p. black and brown . . 35 15
DESIGN: 50p. Ruins of Afamia.

352 Soldier and Workers

1973. 3rd Anniv of Revolution of 16 November 1970.
1229 **352** 15p. blue and bistre . . 10 10
1230 25p. violet and red . . . 15 10

353 Copernicus

1973. 14th Science Week.
1231 **353** 15p. black and gold . . 10 10
1232 – 25p. black and gold . . 20 10
DESIGN: 25p. Al-Biruni.

354 National Symbols

355 U.P.U. Monument, Berne

1973. 11th Anniv of Baathist Revolution of 8 March 1963.
1233 **354** 10p. blue and green . . 10 10
1234 25p. blue and green . . 10 10

1974. Centenary of U.P.U. Multicoloured.
1235 15p. Type **355** 10 10
1236 20p. Emblem on airmail letter (horiz) 15 10
1237 70p. Type **355** 50 30

356 Postal Institute

1974. Inauguration of Higher Arab Postal Institute, Damascus.
1238 **356** 15p. multicoloured . . . 20 10

357 Sun and Monument 358 Machine Fitter

1974. 28th Anniv of Evacuation of Foreign Troops from Syria.
1239 **357** 15p. multicoloured . . . 10 10
1240 20p. multicoloured . . . 10 10

1974. Labour Day.
1241 **358** 15p. multicoloured . . . 10 10
1242 50p. multicoloured . . . 35 20

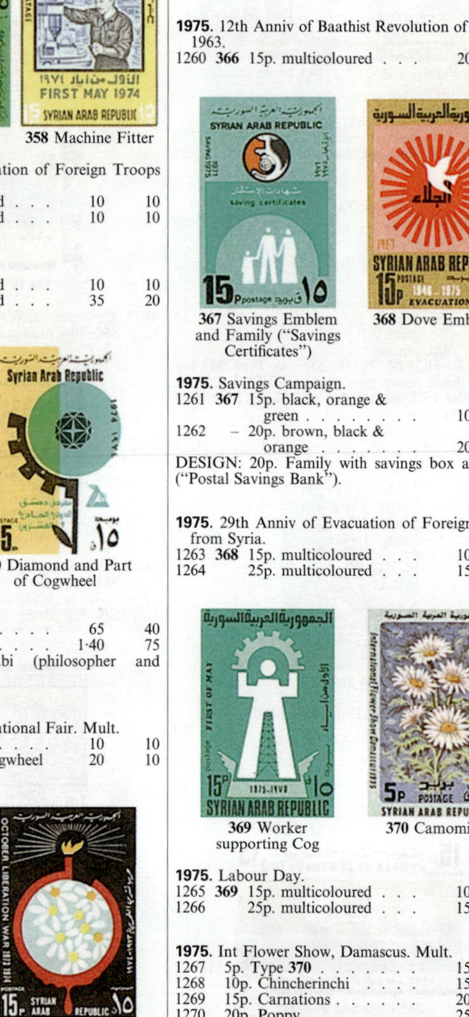

359 Abul Fida (historian) 360 Diamond and Part of Cogwheel

1974. Famous Arabs.
1243 **359** 100p. green 65 40
1244 – 200p. brown . . . . . . 1·40 75
DESIGN: 200p. Al-Farabi (philosopher and encyclopedist).

1974. 21st Damascus International Fair. Mult.
1245 15p. Type **360** 10 10
1246 25p. "Sun" within cogwheel 20 10

361 Figs 362 Flowers within Drop of Blood

1974. Aleppo Agricultural and Industrial Fair. Fruits. Multicoloured.
1247 5p. Type **361** 15 10
1248 15p. Grapes 15 10
1249 20p. Pomegranates 15 10
1250 25p. Cherries 20 15
1251 35p. Rose-hips 35 20

1974. 1st Anniv of October Liberation War. Multicoloured.
1252 15p. Type **362** 25 10
1253 20p. Flower and stars . . . 40 10

363 Knight and Rook 364 Symbolic Figure, Globe and Emblem

1974. 50th Anniv of International Chess Federation.
1254 **363** 15p. blue, lt blue & black 65 15
1255 – 50p. multicoloured . . . 2·10 1·25
DESIGN: 50p. Knight on chessboard.

1974. World Population Year.
1256 **364** 50p. multicoloured . . . 35 20

365 Ishtup-ilum 366 Oil Rig and Crowd

1974. Statuettes.
1257 **365** 20p. green 15 10
1258 – 55p. brown 30 15
1259 – 70p. blue 55 25
DESIGNS: 55p. Woman with vase; 70p. Ur-nina.

1975. 12th Anniv of Baathist Revolution of 8 March 1963.
1260 **366** 15p. multicoloured . . . 20 10

367 Savings Emblem and Family ("Savings Certificates") 368 Dove Emblem

1975. Savings Campaign.
1261 **367** 15p. black, orange & green 10 10
1262 – 20p. brown, black & orange 20 10
DESIGN: 20p. Family with savings box and letter ("Postal Savings Bank").

1975. 29th Anniv of Evacuation of Foreign Troops from Syria.
1263 **368** 15p. multicoloured . . . 10 10
1264 25p. multicoloured . . . 15 10

369 Worker supporting Cog 370 Camomile

1975. Labour Day.
1265 **369** 15p. multicoloured . . . 10 10
1266 25p. multicoloured . . . 15 10

1975. Int Flower Show, Damascus. Mult.
1267 5p. Type **370** 15 10
1268 10p. Chincherinchi 15 10
1269 15p. Carnations 20 10
1270 20p. Poppy 25 10
1271 25p. Honeysuckle 45 15

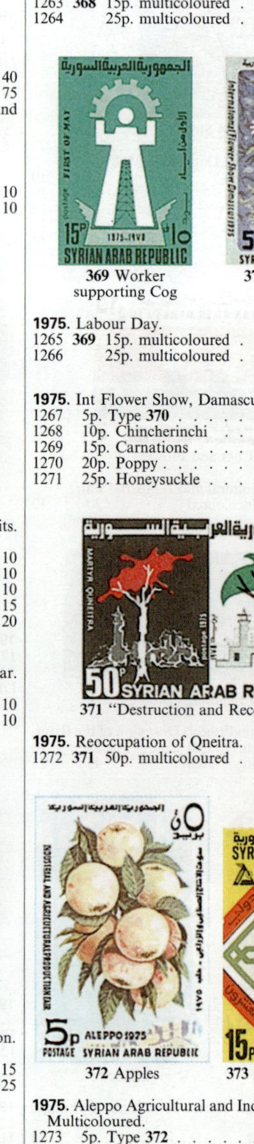

371 "Destruction and Reconstruction"

1975. Reoccupation of Qneitra.
1272 **371** 50p. multicoloured . . . 40 20

372 Apples 373 Arabesque Pattern

1975. Aleppo Agricultural and Industrial Fair. Fruits. Multicoloured.
1273 5p. Type **372** 15 10
1274 10p. Quinces 15 10
1275 15p. Apricots 20 10
1276 20p. Mulberries 25 10
1277 25p. Loquats 30 10

1975. 22nd International Damascus Fair.
1278 **373** 15p. multicoloured . . . 10 10
1279 35p. multicoloured . . . 35 15

374 Pres. Hafez al-Assad

1975. 5th Anniv of "Movement of 16 November 1970".
1280 **374** 15p. multicoloured . . . 10 10
1281 50p. multicoloured . . . 30 20

375 Symbolic Woman 376 Bronze "Horse" Lamp

1976. International Women's Year. Multicoloured.
1282 10p. Type **375** 10 10
1283 15p. "Motherhood" 10 10
1284 25p. "Education" 15 10
1285 50p. "Science" 35 25

1976.

1286 – 5p. green 10 10
1287 **376** 10p. green 10 10
1288 – 10p. blue 10 10
1289 – 15p. brown 20 10
1290 **376** 20p. red 10 10
1291 25p. blue 15 10
1292 – 30p. brown 20 10
1293 – 35p. green 20 10
1294 – 40p. orange 25 10
1295 – 50p. blue 40 20
1296 – 55p. mauve 40 10
1297 – 60p. violet 45 15
1298 – 70p. red 45 15
1299 – 75p. orange 50 30
1300 – 80p. green 60 20
1301 – 100p. mauve 65 25
1302 – 200p. blue . . . . . . 1·40 50
1303 – 300p. mauve . . . . . 2·10 85
1304 – 500p. grey . . . . . . 3·50 2·40
1305 – 1000p. green . . . . . 6·25 3·75
DESIGNS—VERT: 5p. Wall-painting showing figure of a man; 10p. (No. 1288) Flying goddess with wreath; 30, 35, 40p. Man's head inkstand; 50, 55, 60p. Statue of Nike; 70, 75, 80p. Statue of Hera; 100p. Imdugub-Mari (bird goddess); 200p. Arab astrolabe; 500p. Palmyrean coin of Valabathus; 1000p. Abraxas stone. HORIZ: 15p. Wall-painting showing figures; 300p. Herodian coin from Palmyra.

377 National Theatre, Damascus

1976. 13th Anniv of Baathist Revolution of 8 March 1963.
1306 **377** 25p. green, black & silver 15 10
1307 35p. green, black & silver 20 15

378 Nurse and Emblem 380 Eagle and Stars

379 Syrian 5m. Stamp of 1920

1976. 8th Arab Red Crescent Societies' Conf, Damascus.
1308 **378** 25p. blue, black and red 20 10
1309 100p. violet, black and red 65 50

1976. Arab Post Day.
1310 **379** 25p. multicoloured . . . 25 10
1311 35p. multicoloured . . . 40 20

1976. 30th Anniv of Evacuation of Foreign Troops from Syria.
1312 **380** 25p. multicoloured . . . 20 10
1313 35p. multicoloured . . . 25 15

381 Hand gripping Spanner 382 Cotton Boll

1976. Labour Day.
1314 **381** 25p. blue and black . . 20 10
1315 – 60p. multicoloured . . . 45 30
DESIGN: 60p. Hand supporting globe.

1976. Aleppo Agricultural and Industrial Fair.
1316 **382** 25p. multicoloured . . . 30 10
1317 35p. multicoloured . . . 25 15

383 Tulips

1976. Int Flower Show, Damascus. Multicoloured.
1318 5p. Type **383** 15 10
1319 15p. Yellow daisies . . . 15 10
1320 20p. Turk's-cap lilies . . . 20 10
1321 25p. Irises 40 10
1322 35p. Honeysuckle 50 25

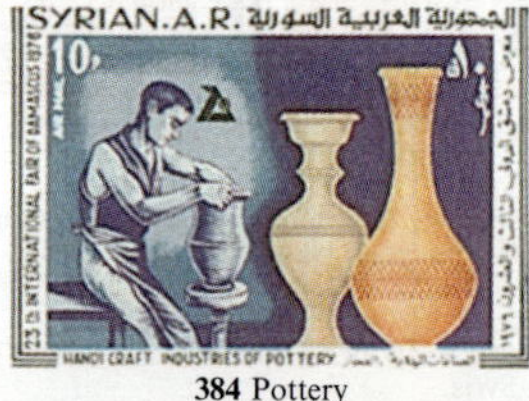

384 Pottery

1976. Air. 23rd International Damascus Fair. Handicraft Industries. Multicoloured.
1323 10p. Type **384** 15 10
1324 25p. Rug-making 25 10
1325 30p. Metalware 25 10
1326 35p. Wickerware 40 10
1327 100p. Wood-carving 95 65

385 People supporting Olive Branch

1976. Non-aligned Countries Summit Conference, Colombo. Multicoloured.
1328 40p. Type **385** 25 20
1329 60p. Symbolic arrow penetrating "grey curtain" 40 25

386 Football

387 Construction Emblems

1976. 5th Pan-Arab Games. Multicoloured.
1330 5p. Type **386** 10 10
1331 10p. Swimming 15 10
1332 25p. Running 20 10

1333 35p. Basketball 35 20
1334 50p. Throwing the javelin 50 25

1976. 6th Anniv of Movement of 16 November 1970.
1336 **387** 35p. multicoloured . . . 20 10

388 "The Fox and the Crow"

389 Muhammad Kurd-Ali (philosopher)

1976. Fairy Tales. Multicoloured.
1337 10p. Type **388** 15 10
1338 15p. "The Hare and the Tortoise" (horiz) 15 10
1339 20p. "Little Red Riding Hood" 15 10
1340 25p. "The Wolf and the Goats" (horiz) 20 10
1341 35p. "The Wolf and the Lamb" 30 15

1976. Birth Centenary of Muhammad Kurd-Ali.
1342 **389** 25p. multicoloured . . . 20 10

390 Boeing 747SP

1977. Civil Aviation Day.
1343 **390** 35p. multicoloured . . . 75 20

391 Woman hoisting Flag

392 A.P.U. Emblem

1977. 14th Anniv of Baathist Revolution of 8 March 1963.
1344 **391** 35p. multicoloured . . . 40 20

1977. 25th Anniv of Arab Postal Union.
1345 **392** 35p. multicoloured . . . 25 10

393 Mounted Horseman

1977. 31st Anniv of Evacuation of Foreign Troops from Syria.
1346 **393** 100p. multicoloured . . 75 50

394 Industrial Scene and Tools

1977. Labour Day.
1347 **394** 60p. multicoloured . . . 40 25

395 I.C.A.O. Emblem, Boeing 747SP and Globe

1977. 30th Anniv of I.C.A.O.
1348 **395** 100p. multicoloured . . 1·00 75

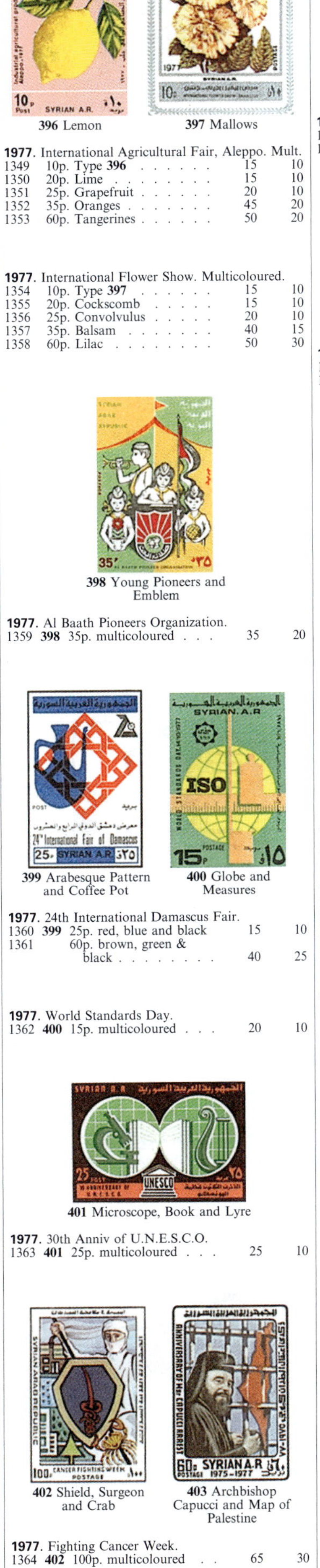

396 Lemon

397 Mallows

1977. International Agricultural Fair, Aleppo. Mult.
1349 10p. Type **396** 15 10
1350 20p. Lime 15 10
1351 25p. Grapefruit 20 10
1352 35p. Oranges 45 20
1353 60p. Tangerines 50 20

1977. International Flower Show. Multicoloured.
1354 10p. Type **397** 15 10
1355 20p. Cockscomb 15 10
1356 25p. Convolvulus 20 10
1357 35p. Balsam 40 15
1358 60p. Lilac 50 30

398 Young Pioneers and Emblem

1977. Al Baath Pioneers Organization.
1359 **398** 35p. multicoloured . . . 35 20

399 Arabesque Pattern and Coffee Pot

400 Globe and Measures

1977. 24th International Damascus Fair.
1360 **399** 25p. red, blue and black 15 10
1361 60p. brown, green & black 40 25

1977. World Standards Day.
1362 **400** 15p. multicoloured . . . 20 10

401 Microscope, Book and Lyre

1977. 30th Anniv of U.N.E.S.C.O.
1363 **401** 25p. multicoloured . . . 25 10

402 Shield, Surgeon and Crab

403 Archbishop Capucci and Map of Palestine

1977. Fighting Cancer Week.
1364 **402** 100p. multicoloured . . 65 30

1977. 3rd Anniv of Archbishop Capucci's Arrest.
1365 **403** 60p. multicoloured . . . 40 20

404 Blind Man, Eye and Globe

1977. World Blind Week.
1366 **404** 55p. multicoloured . . . 25 15
1367 70p. multicoloured . . . 40 20

405 Dome of the Rock, Jerusalem

1977. Palestinian Welfare.
1368 **405** 5p. multicoloured . . . 15 10
1369 10p. multicoloured . . . 25 10

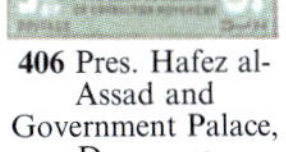

406 Pres. Hafez al-Assad and Government Palace, Damascus

408 Arrow and Blood Circulation

407 Eurasian Goldfinch

1977. 7th Anniv of Movement of 16 November 1970.
1370 **406** 50p. multicoloured . . . 25 10

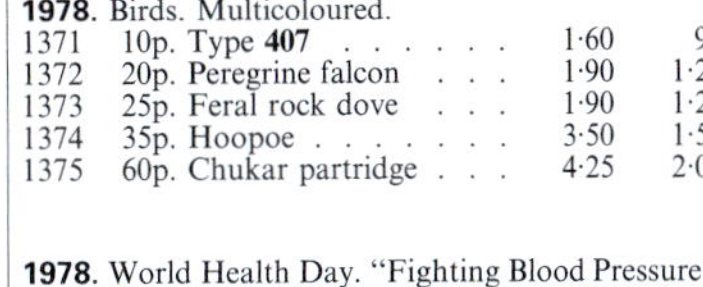

1978. Birds. Multicoloured.
1371 10p. Type **407** . . . . . . 1·60 90
1372 20p. Peregrine falcon . . . 1·90 1·25
1373 25p. Feral rock dove . . . 1·90 1·25
1374 35p. Hoopoe . . . . 3·50 1·50
1375 60p. Chukar partridge . . . 4·25 2·00

1978. World Health Day. "Fighting Blood Pressure".
1376 **408** 100p. multicoloured . . 60 30

409 Factory, Moon and Stars

410 Geometric Design

1978. 32nd Anniv of Evacuation of Foreign Troops from Syria.
1377 **409** 35p. green, orange & black 20 10

1978. 14th Arab Engineering Conf, Damascus.
1378 **410** 25p. green and black . . 25 10

411 Map of Arab Countries, Flag, Eye and Police

412 Brown Trout

1978. 6th Arab Conference of Police Commanders.
1379 **411** 35p. multicoloured . . . 30 10

1978. Fishes. Multicoloured.
1380 10p. Type **412** 40 20
1381 20p. Seabream 50 20
1382 25p. Grouper 50 20
1383 35p. Striped red mullet . . . 60 35
1384 60p. Wels 75 45

413 President Assad

1978. Air. Re-election of President Hafez al-Assad.
1385 **413** 25p. multicoloured . . . 25 15
1386 35p. multicoloured . . . 35 15
1387 60p. multicoloured . . . 45 15

414 "Lobivia sp."

415 President Hafez al-Assad

1978. International Flower Show, Damascus. Mult.
1389 25p. Type **414** 15 10
1390 30p. "Mamillaria sp." . . . 25 15
1391 35p. "Opuntia sp." 25 15
1392 50p. "Chamaecereus sp." . . 40 20
1393 60p. "Mamillaria sp." (different) 40 20

1978. 8th Anniv of Movement of 16 November 1970.
1394 **415** 60p. multicoloured . . . 30 15

416 Euphrates Dam

1978. Inauguration of Euphrates Dam.
1395 **416** 60p. multicoloured . . . 50 25

417 Fair Emblem

418 Averroes (philosopher)

1979. 25th International Damascus Fair.
1396 **417** 25p. multicoloured . . . 20 10
1397 35p. black, violet and silver 20 10

1979. Averroes Commemoration.
1399 **418** 100p. multicoloured . . 1·00 40

419 Standing Figures within Globe

420 Pyramid and Flower

1979. International Year to Combat Racism.
1400 **419** 35p. multicoloured . . . 25 10

1979. 16th Anniv of Baathist Revolution of 8 March 1963.
1401 **420** 100p. multicoloured . . 70 25

421 Hands supporting Globe

422 Helmet of Homs

1979. 30th Anniv of Declaration of Human Rights.

1402 **421** 60p. multicoloured . . . 35 15

1979. Exhibits from National Museum, Damascus.

1403 – 5p. red 10 10

1404 – 10p. green 15 10

1405 – 15p. mauve 25 10

1406 **422** 20p. green 10 10

1407 – 25p. red 20 10

1408 – 35p. brown 20 10

1409 – 75p. blue 50 20

1410 – 160p. green 90 40

1411 – 500p. brown . . . . 3·25 1·25

DESIGNS—VERT: 5, 160p. Umayyad window; 10p. Figurine; 15p. Rakka horseman (Abbcid ceramic); 25p. Head of Clipeata (Cleopatra); 35p. Seated statue of Ishtar (Astarte). HORIZ: 75p. Abdul Malik gold coin; 500p. Umar B. Abdul Aziz gold coin.

423 Geometric Design and Flame

424 Ibn Assaker

1979. 33rd Anniv of Evacuation of Foreign Troops from Syria.

1416 **423** 35p. multicoloured . . . 20 10

1979. 900th Anniv of Ibn Assaker (historian and biographer).

1417 **424** 75p. brown, blue & green 40 20

425 Tooth, Emblem and Mosque

426 Welder working on Power Pylon

1979. International Middle East Dental Congress.

1418 **425** 35p. multicoloured . . . 40 10

1979. Labour Day.

1419 **426** 50p. multicoloured . . . 25 10

1420 75p. multicoloured . . . 35 20

427 Girl holding Emblem with Flowers

428 Wright Type A

1979. International Year of the Child. Mult.

1421 10p. Type **427** 10 10

1422 15p. Boy and globe 20 10

1979. 75th Anniv of First Powered Flight. Mult.

1423 50p. Type **428** 35 10

1424 75p. Bleriot's plane crossing English Channel 50 30

1425 100p. Lindbergh's "Spirit of St. Louis" 70 45

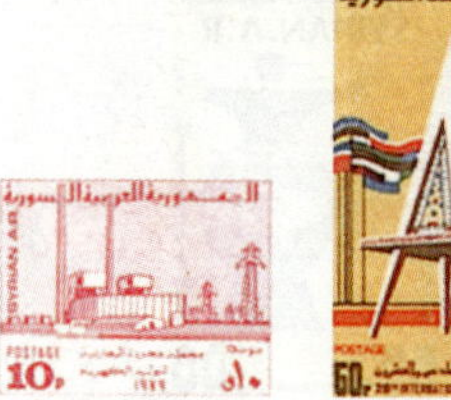

429 Power Station

430 Flags and Pavilion

1979.

1426 **429** 5p. blue 10 10

1427 10p. mauve 10 10

1428 15p. green 10 10

1979. 26th International Damascus Fair. Mult.

1429 60p. Type **430** 35 15

1430 75p. Lamp post and flags 40 20

431 Running

1979. 8th Mediterranean Games, Split. Mult.

1431 25p. Type **431** 10 10

1432 35p. Swimmer on starting-block 20 10

1433 50p. Football 25 15

432 President Assad with Symbols of Agriculture and Industry

1979. 9th Anniv of Movement of 16 November 1970.

1434 **432** 100p. multicoloured . . 75 20

433 Swallowtail

434 Astrolabe

1979. Butterflies. Multicoloured.

1435 20p. Type **433** 35 10

1436 25p. Peacock 40 15

1437 30p. White admiral 50 20

1438 35p. Blue morpho 65 25

1439 50p. Apollo 85 40

1979. International Flower Show, Damascus. Designs similar to T **414** showing various roses.

1440 5p. multicoloured 10 10

1441 10p. multicoloured 15 10

1442 15p. multicoloured 15 10

1443 50p. multicoloured 30 15

1444 75p. multicoloured 45 25

1445 100p. multicoloured 75 35

1980. 2nd International Symposium on History of Arab Science.

1446 **434** 50p. violet 25 10

1447 100p. brown 55 25

1448 1000p. green . . . . . . 5·50 2·25

435 "8" over Buildings

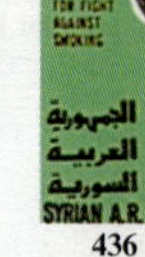

436 Smoker

1980. 17th Anniv of Baathist Revolution of 8 March 1963.

1449 **435** 40p. multicoloured . . . 25 10

1980. World Health Day. Anti-smoking Campaign.

1450 **436** 60p. brown, green & black 50 25

1451 – 100p. multicoloured . . . 80 30

DESIGN: 100p. Skull and cigarette.

437 Monument

1980. 34th Anniv of Evacuation of Foreign Troops from Syria.

1452 **437** 40p. multicoloured . . . 20 10

1453 60p. multicoloured . . . 25 15

438 Wrestling

1980. Olympic Games, Moscow. Multicoloured.

1454 15p. Type **438** 20 10

1455 25p. Fencing 25 10

1456 35p. Weightlifting 30 10

1457 50p. Judo 35 10

1458 75p. Boxing 50 20

439 "Savings"

1980. Savings Certificates.

1460 **439** 25p. violet, red and blue 20 10

440 "Aladdin and the Magic Lamp"

1980. Popular Stories. Multicoloured.

1461 15p. "Sinbad the Sailor" . . 15 10

1462 20p. "Shahrazad and Shahrayar" 20 10

1463 35p. "Ali Baba and the Forty Thieves" 30 10

1464 50p. "Hassan the Clever" 45 10

1465 100p. Type **440** 65 30

441 Kaaba and Mosque, Mecca

1980. 1400th Anniv of Hegira.

1466 **441** 35p. multicoloured . . . 35 20

442 Daffodils

443 "Industry"

1980. International Flower Show, Damascus. Mult.

1467 20p. Type **442** 20 10

1468 30p. Dahlias 25 10

1469 40p. Bergamot 30 10

1470 60p. Globe flowers 50 15

1471 100p. Cornflowers 75 25

1980. 10th Anniv of Movement of 16 November 1970.

1472 **443** 100p. multicoloured . . 65 25

444 Construction Worker

445 Children encircling Globe

1980. Labour Day.

1473 **444** 35p. multicoloured . . . 35 15

1980. International Children's Day.

1474 **445** 25p. green, black & yell 25 10

446 Steam-powered Passenger Wagon, 1830

447 Mother's Arms around Child

1980. Cars. Multicoloured.

1475 25p. Type **446** 20 15

1476 35p. Benz, 1899 . . . . . . 40 15

1477 40p. Rolls-Royce, 1903 . . 40 15

1478 50p. Mercedes, 1906 . . . . 50 20

1479 60p. Austin, 1915 . . . . . 65 20

1980. Mothers' Day. Multicoloured.

1480 40p. Type **447** 35 10

1481 100p. Faces of mother and child 70 25

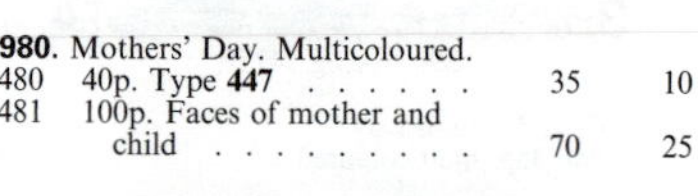

448 Fair Emblem

1980. 27th International Damascus Fair. Mult.

1482 50p. Type **448** 40 15

1483 100p. As T **448** but with different motif on right 75 25

449 Armed Forces

1980. Army Day.

1484 **449** 50p. multicoloured . . . 1·00 30

450 Arabesque Pattern

451 Geometric Design, Laurel and Hand holding Torch

1981. 18th Anniv of Baathist Revolution of 8 March 1963.

1485 **450** 50p. multicoloured . . . 35 15

1981. 35th Anniv of Evacuation of Foreign Troops from Syria.

1486 **451** 50p. multicoloured . . . 40 15

452 Mosque and Script

1981. History of Arab-Islamic Civilization World Conference, Damascus.

1487 **452** 100p. green, deep green and black 70 35

453 Marching Workers and Emblem

454 Human Figure and House on Graph

1981. May Day.
1488 **453** 100p. multicoloured . . 65 25

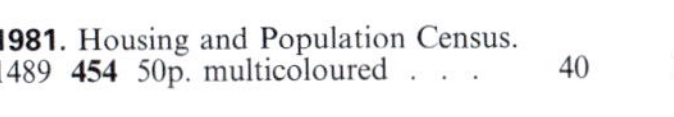

1981. Housing and Population Census.
1489 **454** 50p. multicoloured . . . 40 15

455 Family and Savings Emblem

456 Dove and Map on Globe

1981. Savings Certificates.
1490 **455** 50p. black and brown . . 40 15

1981. International Syrian and Palestinian Solidarity Conference, Damascus.
1491 **456** 160p. multicoloured . . 1·90 65

457 Avicenna

459 Festival Emblem

458 Glass Lamp

1981. Birth Millenary of Avicenna (philosopher and physician).
1492 **457** 100p. multicoloured . . 75 35

1981. Damascus Museum Exhibits.
1493 **458** 50p. red 35 15
1494 – 180p. multicoloured . . 1·60 50
1495 – 180p. multicoloured . . 1·60 50
DESIGNS: No. 1494, "Grand Mosque, Damascus" (painting); 1495, Hunting scene (tapestry).

1981. Youth Festival.
1496 **459** 60p. multicoloured . . . 45 15

460 Decorative Pattern

461 Palestinians and Dome of the Rock

1981. 28th International Damascus Fair.
1497 **460** 50p. mauve, blue & green 35 15
1498 – 160p. brown, yell & lilac 95 45
DESIGN: 160p. Globe encircled by wheat and cogwheel.

1981. Palestinian Solidarity.
1499 **461** 100p. multicoloured . . 80 30

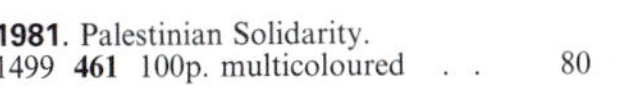

462 F.A.O. Emblem

463 Tobacco Flowers

1981. World Food Day.
1500 **462** 180p. blue, green and black . . . . 1·40 55

1981. International Flower Show, Damascus. Mult.
1501 25p. Type **463** 25 10
1502 40p. Mimosa 35 20
1503 50p. Ixias 40 20
1504 60p. Passion flower 65 25
1505 100p. Dendrobium . . . . 1·10 50

464 Hands releasing Dove and Horseman

1981. 1300th Anniv of Bulgarian State.
1506 **464** 380p. multicoloured . . 2·25 95

465 Classroom

1981. International Children's Day.
1507 **465** 180p. black, red & green 1·50 65

467 President Assad and Diesel Train

468 Symbols of Development

1981. 11th Anniv of Movement of 16 November 1970.
1509 **467** 60p. blue, black and brown . . . . 2·40 1·00

1982. 19th Anniv of Baathist Revolution of 8 March 1963.
1510 **468** 50p. grey, red and black 45 15

469 Robert Koch and Microscope

1982. Cent of Discovery of Tubercle Bacillus.
1511 **469** 180p. blue, brown and black . . . . . . 1·50 65

470 Pattern and Hand holding Rifle

471 Disabled People and Emblem

1982. 36th Anniv of Evacuation of Foreign Troops from Syria.
1512 **470** 70p. red and blue . . . 50 25

1982. International Year of Disabled Persons (1981).
1513 **471** 90p. black, blue and yellow 80 30

472 A.P.U. Emblem

473 Traffic Lights

1982. 30th Anniv of Arab Postal Union.
1514 **472** 60p. red, green and yellow 50 20

1982. World Traffic Day.
1515 **473** 180p. black, red and blue 1·50 65

474 Geometric Pattern

1982. World Telecommunications Day.
1516 **474** 180p. light yellow, brown and yellow . . . . 1·25 65

475 Oil Rig, Factory Chimneys and Hand holding Torch

476 Mother and Children

1982. Labour Day.
1517 **475** 180p. red, blue and light blue . . . . 1·25 65

1982. Mothers' Day.
1518 **476** 40p. green 30 10
1519 75p. brown 50 25

477 Olives

478 Pres. Assad

1982.
1520 **477** 50p. green 40 25
1521 60p. grey 40 25
1522 – 100p. mauve 65 30
1523 **478** 150p. blue . . . . 1·00 50
1524 – 180p. red . . . . 1·25 65
DESIGN: 100, 180p. Harbour.

479 Footballer

1982. World Cup Football Championship, Spain. Multicoloured.
1525 40p. Type **479** 35 25
1526 60p. Two footballers 50 25
1527 100p. Two footballers (different) 75 40

480 Policeman

481 Government Building

1982. Police Day.
1529 **480** 50p. black, red and green 45 20

1982.
1530 **481** 30p. brown 20 10
1531 – 70p. green 45 25
1532 – 200p. red . . . . 1·40 70
DESIGNS—HORIZ: 200p. Ruins. VERT: 70p. Arched wall.

482 Communications Emblem and Map

1982. Arab Telecommunication Day.
1533 **482** 50p. blue, ultramarine and red 45 20

483 Scout pitching Tent

1982. 75th Anniv of Boy Scout Movement.
1534 **483** 160p. green . . . . . . 1·40 65

484 Dish Aerial and World Map

1982. I.T.U. Delegates' Conference, Nairobi.
1535 **484** 180p. blue, ultramarine and red . . . . 1·60 75

485 President Assad

1982. 12th Anniv of Movement of 16 November 1970.
1536 **485** 50p. blue and grey . . . 40 20

486 Water-wheel, Hama

487 Dragonfly

1982.
1537 **486** 5p. brown 10 10
1538 10p. violet 10 10
1539 20p. red 20 10
1540 50p. turquoise 50 20

1982. Insects. Multicoloured.
1541 5p. Type **487** 25 25
1542 10p. Stag beetle 30 30
1543 20p. Seven-spotted ladybird 50 50
1544 40p. Desert locust 90 90
1545 50p. Honey bee . . . . . . 1·00 1·00

488 Honeysuckle

489 Satellites within Dove

1982. Int Flower Show, Damascus. Mult.
1546 50p. Type **488** 50 25
1547 60p. Geranium 65 40

1982. U.N. Conference on Exploration and Peaceful Uses of Outer Space, Vienna.
1548 **489** 50p. multicoloured . . . 50 20

490 Dove on Gun

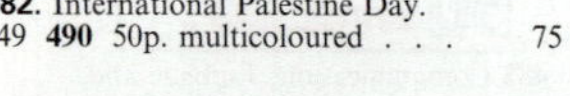

1982. International Palestine Day.
1549 **490** 50p. multicoloured . . . 75 30

491 Damascus International Airport

1983. 20th Anniv of Baathist Revolution of 8 March 1963.
1550 **491** 60p. multicoloured . . . 1·25 50

492 Communications Emblems

1983. World Communications Year.
1551 **492** 180p. multicoloured . . 1·50 70

493 Figurine

1983.
1552 **493** 380p. brown and green 3·25 1·25

494 Pharmacist

1983. Arab Pharmacists' Day.
1553 **494** 100p. multicoloured . . 1·00 40

495 Liberation Monument, Qneitra

496 Wave within Ship's Wheel

1983. 9th Anniv of Liberation of Qneitra.
1554 **495** 50p. green 95 40
1555 – 100p. brown . . . . . . 1·90 40
DESIGN: 100p. Ruined buildings.

1983. 25th Anniv of I.M.O.
1556 **496** 180p. multicoloured . . 1·75 65

497 Flame on Map

1983. Namibia Day.
1557 **497** 180p. blue, mauve and black . . . . 1·25 65

498 I.S.O. Emblem and Factory

499 Gateway, Bosra

1983. World Standards Day.
1558 **498** 50p. multicoloured . . . 45 25
1559 – 100p. violet, green & black . . . . 1·00 55
DESIGN: 100p. I.S.O. emblem and measuring equipment.

1983. 10th Anniv of World Heritage Agreement.
1560 **499** 60p. brown 55 25

500 Flowers

1983. Int Flower Show, Damascus. Mult.
1561 50p. Type **500** 55 25
1562 60p. Hibiscus 65 40

501 Farmland

502 Factory

1983. World Food Day.
1563 **501** 180p. green, cream and deep green . . . . . 1·60 75

1983.
1564 **502** 50p. green 50 10

503 Statuette

504 Aleppo

1984. International Deir Ez-Zor History and Archaeology Symposium.
1565 **503** 225p. brown . . . . . 2·25 95

1984. International Symposium for the Conservation of Aleppo.
1566 **504** 245p. multicoloured . . 2·25 95

505 Alassad Library

1984. 21st Anniv of Baathist Revolution of 8 March 1963.
1567 **505** 60p. multicoloured . . . 60 30

506 Bodies and mourning Woman with Child

1984. Sabra and Shatila (refugee camps in Lebanon) Massacres.
1568 **506** 225p. multicoloured . . 1·90 80

507 Mother and Child

509 Swimming

508 Dam, Emblem and Pioneers

1984. Mothers' Day.
1569 **507** 245p. brown and green 2·25 95

1984. 9th Regional Festival of Al Baath Pioneers. Multicoloured.
1570 50p. Type **508** 50 25
1571 60p. Pioneers, ruins and emblems 65 30

1984. Olympic Games, Los Angeles. Multicoloured.
1572 30p. Type **509** 35 10
1573 50p. Wrestling 50 20
1574 60p. Running 55 25
1575 70p. Boxing 65 30
1576 90p. Football 90 40

510 Flowers

511 Pres. Assad and Text

1984. Int Flower Show, Damascus. Mult.
1578 245p. Type **510** . . . . . . 2·50 1·25
1579 285p. Flowers (different) . . 2·75 1·60

1984. 4th Revolutionary Youth Union Congress.
1580 **511** 50p. brown, deep brown and green 45 25
1581 – 60p. multicoloured . . . 50 35
DESIGN—37 × 25 mm: 60p. Pres. Assad and saluting youth.

512 Emblem and Administration Building, Damascus

1984. Arab Postal Union Day.
1582 **512** 60p. multicoloured . . . 50 30

513 Globe, Dish Aerial and Telephone

514 Arabesque Pattern

1984. World Telecommunications Day.
1583 **513** 245p. multicoloured . . 2·25 1·00

1984. 31st International Damascus Fair. Mult.
1584 45p. Type **514** 40 20
1585 100p. Ornate gold decoration . . . . 1·25 45

515 Stylized Aircraft and Emblem

1984. 40th Anniv of I.C.A.O.
1586 **515** 45p. blue and deep blue 40 20
1587 – 245p. blue, ultramarine and deep blue . . . . 1·90 95
DESIGN: 245p. Emblem and stylized building.

516 Text, Flag and Pres. Assad

1984. 14th Anniv of Movement of 16 November 1970.
1588 **516** 65p. orange, black and brown 65 35

517 Palmyra Roman Arch and Colonnades

1984. International Tourism Day.
1589 **517** 100p. brown, black and blue 90 45

518 Wooded Landscape

1985. Woodland Conservation.
1590 **518** 45p. multicoloured . . . 60 25

519 University and Students

1985. 26th Anniv (1984) of Aleppo University.
1591 **519** 45p. black, blue and brown 45 25

520 Oil Lamp

1985. 26th Anniv (1984) of Supreme Council of Science.
1592 **520** 65p. green, red and black 65 40

521 Soldier holding Flag

1985. Army Day.
1593 **521** 65p. brown and bistre 65 40

522 Pres. Assad

524 Torch and "22"

523 Flag and Party Emblem

1985. Re-election of President Assad.
1594 **522** 200p. multicoloured . . 1·90 1·25
1595 300p. multicoloured . . 2·50 1·50
1596 500p. multicoloured . . 4·50 2·25

1985. 8th Baath Arab Socialist Party Congress.
1598 **523** 50p. multicoloured . . . 55 20

1985. 22nd Anniv of Baathist Revolution of 8 March 1963.
1599 **524** 60p. multicoloured . . . 60 25

525 Tractor and Cow

1985. Aleppo Industrial and Agricultural Fair (1984). Multicoloured.
1600 65p. Type **525** 65 25
1601 150p. Fort and carrots (vert) 1·75 50

526 Liberation Movement, Qneitra

1985. 10th Anniv (1984) of Liberation of Qneitra.
1602 **526** 70p. multicoloured . . . 1·25 40

527 Parliament Building

1985. 10th Anniv of Arab Parliamentary Union.
1603 **527** 245p. multicoloured . . 2·50 1·25

528 U.P.U. Emblem and Pigeon with Letter

529 A.P.U. Emblem

1985. World Post Day.
1604 **528** 285p. multicoloured . . 3·25 95

1985. 12th Arab Postal Union Conference, Damascus.
1605 **529** 60p. multicoloured . . . 55 20

530 Medal

1985. Labour Day.
1606 **530** 60p. multicoloured . . . 55 20

531 Steam and Diesel Locomotives

1985. 2nd Scientific Symposium.
1607 **531** 60p. blue . . . . 2·75 1·60

532 Emblem and Child with empty Bowl

1985. U.N. Child Survival Campaign.
1608 **532** 60p. black, green & pink 55 20

533 Pres. Assad and Road

1985. 15th Anniv of Movement of 16 November 1970.
1609 **533** 60p. multicoloured . . . 55 20

534 Emblem and "40"

535 Lily-flowered Tulip

1985. 40th Anniv of U.N.O.
1610 **534** 245p. multicoloured . . 1·90 75

1986. Int Flower Show, Damascus (1985). Mult.
1611 30p. Type **535** 30 15
1612 60p. Tulip 70 25

536 Flask

1986. 32nd International Damascus Fair (1985).
1613 **536** 60p. multicoloured . . . 55 20

537 Abd-er-Rahman I

538 Pres. Hafez al-Assad

1986. 1200th Anniv of Abd-er-Rahman I ad Dakhel, Emir of Cordoba.
1614 **537** 60p. brown, cinnamon and light brown . . . 60 20

1988.
1615 **538** 10p. red 10 10
1616 30p. blue 20 10
1616a 50p. lilac 10 10
1617 100p. blue 65 20
1618 150p. brown 75 40
1619 175p. violet 95 40
1620 200p. brown . . . . . 1·25 45
1621 300p. mauve . . . . . 1·90 75
1622 500p. orange . . . . . 3·50 1·25
1623 550p. pink . . . . . . 3·00 1·50
1624 600p. green . . . . . . 3·75 1·75
1625 1000p. mauve . . . . . 7·00 2·75
1626 2000p. green . . . . . 14·00 5·75
For similar design but with full-face portrait, see Nos. 1774/80.

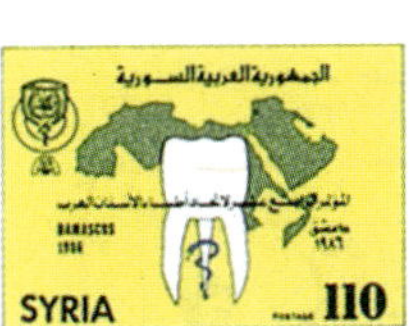

539 Tooth and Map

540 Tower Blocks, Ear of Wheat and Kangaroo

1986. 19th Arab Dentists' Union Congress, Damascus.
1627 **539** 110p. multicoloured . . 1·25 50

1986. 15th Anniv of Syrian Investment Certificates.
1628 **540** 100p. multicoloured . . 90 25

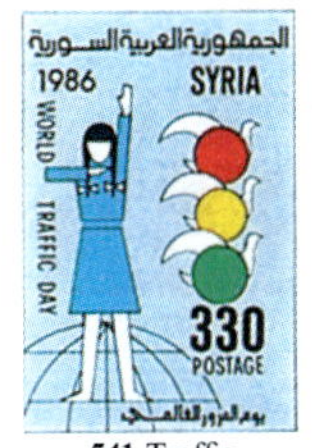

541 Traffic Policewoman, Globe and Traffic Lights

542 Policeman and Building in Laurel Wreath

1986. World Traffic Day.
1629 **541** 330p. multicoloured . . 3·00 1·25

1986. Police Day.
1630 **542** 110p. multicoloured . . 90 35

543 Industrial Symbols and Hand Holding Spanner

544 Building

1986. Labour Day.
1631 **543** 330p. red, black and blue 2·40 1·00

1986. 12th Anniv of Liberation of Qneitra.
1632 **544** 110p. multicoloured . . 85 35

545 Pictogram and Ball

546 Mother and Children

1986. World Cup Football Championship, Mexico.
1633 **545** 330p. multicoloured . . 2·25 90
1634 370p. multicoloured . . 2·75 1·00

1986. Mothers' Day.
1636 **546** 100p. multicoloured . . 80 30

547 Pres. Assad and Diesel Train

1986. 23rd Anniv of Baathist Revolution of 8 March 1963.
1637 **547** 110p. multicoloured . . 2·25 1·40

548 A.P.U. Emblem, Post Office and Box

1986. Arab Post Day.
1638 **548** 110p. multicoloured . . 80 30

549 Fists, Map and Globe

1986. International Palestine Day.
1639 **549** 110p. multicoloured . . 80 30

550 Tulips

1986. Int Flower Show, Damascus. Mult.
1640 10p. Type **550** 15 10
1641 50p. Mauve flowers 45 15
1642 100p. Yellow flowers . . . 95 30
1643 110p. Pink flowers . . . . 1·10 50
1644 330p. Yellow flowers (different) . . . . 2·75 1·40

551 Pres. Assad and Tishreen Palace

1986. 16th Anniv of Movement of 16 November 1970.
1645 **551** 110p. multicoloured . . 75 30

552 Rocket and Flags

553 Jug and Star

1986. 1st Anniv of Announcement of Syrian–Soviet Space Flight.
1646 **552** 330p. multicoloured . . 2·50 1·25

1986. 33rd International Damascus Fair.
1647 **553** 110p. multicoloured . . 85 35
1648 – 330p. black, green and brown . . . . 2·40 95
DESIGN: 330p. Coffee pot.

554 Girls and National Flag

1987. International Children's Art Exhibition.
1649 **554** 330p. multicoloured . . 1·90 75

555 U.P.U. Emblem and Airmail Envelope

556 Children in Balloon over Town

1987. World Post Day.
1650 **555** 330p. multicoloured . . 1·90 75

1987. International Children's Day.
1651 **556** 330p. multicoloured . . 1·90 75

557 Citadel, Aleppo

1987. International Tourism Day.
1652 330p. Type **557** . . . . . . 1·90 75
1653 370p. Water-wheel, Hama 2·25 85

558 Industrial Symbols

1987. 24th Anniv of Baathist Revolution of 8 March 1963.
1654 **558** 100p. multicoloured . . 65 25

559 Doves flying from Globe

560 Party Emblem

1987. International Peace Year.
1655 **559** 370p. multicoloured . . 2·25 85

1987. 40th Anniv of Baath Arab Socialist Party.
1656 **560** 100p. multicoloured . . 65 25

561 Stars

1987. 41st Anniv of Evacuation of Foreign Troops from Syria.
1657 **561** 100p. multicoloured . . 65 25

562 Draughtsman

1987. 6th Arab Ministers of Culture Conference.
1658 **562** 330p. blue, green & black . . . . 2·50 1·00

563 Map of Arab Postal Union Members

1987. Arab Post Day.
1659 **563** 110p. multicoloured . . 65 25

564 Couple within Cogwheel

565 Statue

1987. Labour Day.
1660 **564** 330p. multicoloured . . 1·90 75

1987. 13th Anniv of Liberation of Qneitra.
1661 **565** 100p. multicoloured . . 60 30

566 Pres. Assad with Children and Nurse

1987. Child Vaccination Campaign.
1662 **566** 100p. multicoloured . . 65 35
1663 330p. multicoloured . . 2·25 95

567 Dome of the Rock, Battle Scene and Saladin

1987. 800th Anniv of Battle of Hattin.
1664 **567** 110p. multicoloured . . 75 35

568 Rocket Launch and National Flags

1987. Syrian–Soviet Space Flight. Multicoloured.
1665 330p. Type **568** . . . . . . 2·00 1·00
1666 330p. Spacecraft docking with "Mir" space station (37 × 25 mm) . . . . . . 2·00 1·00
1667 330p. Space capsule re-entering Earth's atmosphere and group of cosmonauts (25 × 37 mm) 2·00 1·00

569 Flags, Cosmonauts and Pres. Assad

1987. President's Space Conversation with Lt-Col. Mohammed Faris (Syrian cosmonaut).
1669 **569** 500p. multicoloured . . 3·50 1·60

570 Stylized Flowers

571 Sports Pictograms

1987. 34th International Damascus Fair.
1670 **570** 330p. multicoloured . . 2·00 1·00

1987. 10th Mediterranean Games, Latakia.
1671 **571** 100p. purple and black 65 35
1672 – 110p. multicoloured . . 85 40
1673 – 330p. multicoloured . . 2·40 1·50
1674 – 370p. multicoloured . . 2·50 1·25
DESIGNS—As Type **571** but HORIZ: 110p. Swimming bird and emblem. 52 × 23 mm: 330p. Phoenician galley (Games emblem); 370p. Flags forming "SYRIA".

572 Soldier, Mikoyan Gurevich MiG-21D Fighter, Ship and Tank

573 Trees, Sun and Birds

1987. Army Day.
1676 **572** 100p. multicoloured . . 1·00 40

1987. Tree Day.
1677 **573** 330p. multicoloured . . 1·90 1·10

574 Poppies

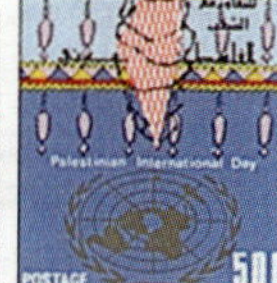
576 Barbed Wire around Map of Israel

575 Pres. Assad acknowledging Applause

1987. International Flower Show, Damascus.
1678 330p. Type **574** . . . . . 2·25 90
1679 370p. Mauve flower . . . . 2·50 1·00

1987. 17th Anniv of Corrective Movement of 16 November 1970.
1680 **575** 150p. multicoloured . . 1·00 45

1987. International Palestine Day.
1681 **576** 500p. multicoloured . . 3·25 1·50

577 U.P.U. and U.N. Emblems

1988. World Post Day.
1682 **577** 500p. multicoloured . . 3·50 1·75

578 Bosra Amphitheatre

1988. International Tourism Day. Multicoloured.
1683 500p. Type **578** . . . . . 3·25 1·40
1684 500p. Palmyra ruins . . . . 3·25 1·40

579 Children as Cosmonauts

1988. International Children's Day.
1685 **579** 500p. multicoloured . . 3·25 1·40

580 Hand holding Torch

581 Woman cradling Baby, Children and Adults

1988. 25th Anniv of Baathist Revolution of 8 March 1963.
1686 **580** 150p. multicoloured . . 85 45

1988. Mothers' Day.
1688 **581** 500p. multicoloured . . 3·25 1·40

582 Arms, Cogwheel, Laurel Branch and Book

583 Dove, Airmail Envelope and Map

1988. 42nd Anniv of Evacuation of Foreign Troops from Syria.
1689 **582** 150p. multicoloured . . 85 45

1988. Arab Post Day.
1690 **583** 150p. multicoloured . . 85 45

584 Spanner, Chimney, Cogwheel and Scroll

585 Modern Buildings

1988. Labour Day.
1691 **584** 550p. multicoloured . . 3·00 1·50

1988. Arab Engineers' Union.
1692 **585** 150p. multicoloured . . 85 45

586 Lily

1988. Int Flower Show, Damascus. Mult.
1693 550p. Type **586** . . . . . 3·25 1·60
1694 600p. Carnations . . . . . 3·75 1·90

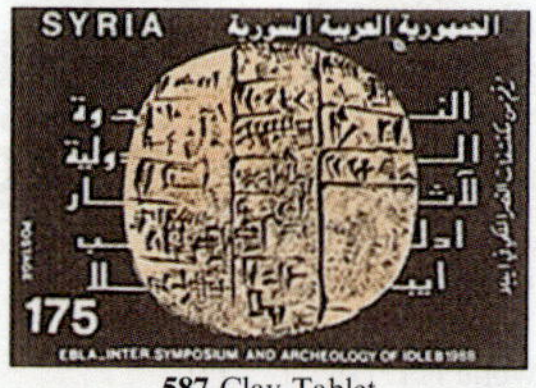
587 Clay Tablet

1988. Int Symposium on Archaeology of Ebla.
1695 **587** 175p. black and brown 1·00 50
1696 – 550p. brown, blue & black . . . . 3·25 1·60
1697 – 600p. multicoloured . . 3·50 1·75
DESIGNS: 550p. King making offering (carving from stone votive basin); 600p. Golden statue of goddess Ishtar.

588 Old City

589 Emblem

1988. Preservation of Sana'a, Yemen.
1698 **588** 550p. multicoloured . . 3·50 1·60

1988. Children's Day.
1699 **589** 600p. black, green and emerald . . . . 3·50 1·75

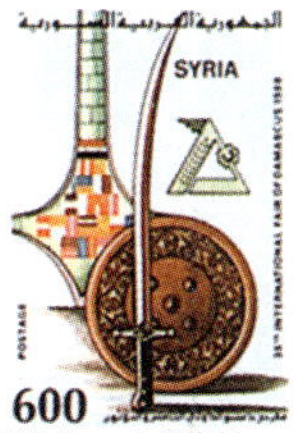

590 Sword, Shield and Emblems

591 Emblem and People

1988. 35th International Damascus Fair.
1700 **590** 600p. multicoloured . . 3·50 1·75

1988. 40th Anniv of W.H.O.
1701 **591** 600p. multicoloured . . 3·50 1·75

592 Emblems and Map

1988. 50th Anniv of Arab Scout Movement.
1702 **592** 150p. mutlicoloured . . 1·25 50

593 Cycling

1988. Olympic Games, Seoul. Multicoloured.
1703 550p. Type **593** . . . . . . 3·75 1·50
1704 600p. Football . . . . . . 3·75 1·75

594 Old Houses and Modern Flats

1988. Housing. Multicoloured.
1706 150p. Type **594** (Arab Housing Day) . . . . . 1·25 65
1707 175p. House and makeshift shelter (International Year of Shelter for the Homeless (1987)) . . . . 1·25 50
1708 550p. Types of housing (World Housing Day) . . 3·00 1·50
1709 600p. As No. 1707 but inscr for International Day for Housing the Homeless . . 3·25 1·75

595 Euphrates Bridge, Deir el Zor

596 Ear of Wheat and Globe

1988. International Tourism Day. Multicoloured.
1710 550p. Type **595** . . . . . . 3·00 1·50
1711 600p. Tetrapylon of Latakia 3·25 1·75
No. 1711 is erroneously inscribed "INTEPNATIONAL".

1988. World Food Day.
1712 **596** 550p. multicoloured . . 3·25 1·40

597 Al-Assad University Hospital

1988. 18th Anniv of Corrective Movement of 16 November 1970.
1713 **597** 150p. multicoloured . . 90 45

598 Tree and Flowers

599 Dove with Envelope over Globe

1988. Tree Day.
1714 **598** 600p. multicoloured . . 3·50 1·60

1988. World Post Day.
1715 **599** 600p. multicoloured . . 3·25 1·60

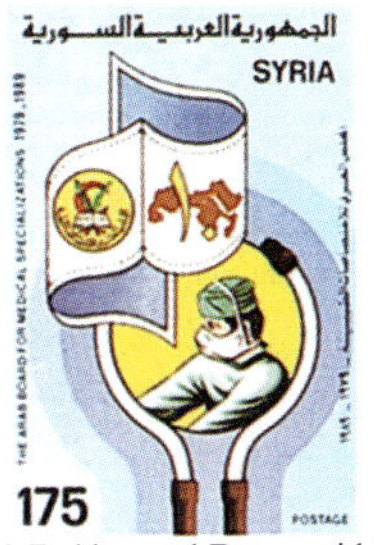

600 Emblem and Doctor within Stethoscope

1989. 10th Anniv of Arab Board for Medical Specializations.
1716 **600** 175p. multicoloured . . 1·00 45

601 Symbols of Agriculture and Industry

1989. 26th Anniv of Baathist Revolution of 8 March 1963.
1717 **601** 150p. multicoloured . . 40 20

602 Pres. Assad and Women

1989. 5th General Congress of Union of Women.
1718 **602** 150p. multicoloured . . 40 20

603 Candle and Books

1989. Arab Teachers' Day.
1719 **603** 175p. multicoloured . . 45 20

604 Nehru

1989. Birth Centenary of Jarwaharlal Nehru (Indian statesman).
1720 **604** 550p. brown & lt brown 1·40 65

605 Mother and Children

1989. Mothers' Day.
1721 **605** 550p. multicoloured . . 1·25 60

606 Eurasian Goldfinch ("Goldfinch")

1989. Birds. Multicoloured.
1722 600p. Type **606** . . . . . . 1·50 85
1723 600p. European bee eater ("Bee Eater") . . . . . . 1·50 85
1724 600p. Turtle dove . . . . . 1·50 85

607 State Arms on Map

608 Workers

1989. 43rd Anniv of Evacuation of Foreign Troops from Syria.
1725 **607** 150p. multicoloured . . 40 20

1989. Labour Day.
1726 **608** 850p. green and black 1·90 85

609 Snapdragons

610 Girl and Envelope

1989. Int Flower Show, Damascus. Mult.
1727 150p. Type **609** 40 25
1728 150p. "Canaria" 40 25
1729 450p. Cornflowers . . . . . 1·25 65
1730 850p. "Clematis sackmani" 1·90 1·00
1731 900p. "Gesneriaceae" . . . 1·90 1·00

1989. Arab Post Day.
1732 **610** 175p. multicoloured . . 45 20

611 Emblem and Map

612 Painted Lady

1989. 13th Arab Teachers' Union General Congress.
1733 **611** 175p. multicoloured . . 45 20

1989. Butterflies. Multicoloured.
1734 550p. Type **612** . . . . . . 1·25 85
1735 550p. Clouded yellow . . . 1·25 85
1736 550p. Large (inscr "small") white . . . . 1·25 85

613 Symbols of International Co-operation

1989. World Telecommunications Day.
1737 **613** 550p. multicoloured . . 1·25 65

614 Emblem and Map

615 Monument and Al-Baath Pioneers

1989. 17th Arab Lawyers' Union Congress.
1738 **614** 175p. multicoloured . . 45 20

1989. 15th Anniv of Liberation of Qneitra.
1739 **615** 450p. multicoloured . . 1·25 50

616 Globe and Envelopes

1989. World Post Day.
1740 **616** 550p. multicoloured . . 1·25 65

617 Parliament Building

1989. Centenary of Interparliamentary Union.
1741 **617** 900p. multicoloured . . 1·90 75

618 Emblem and Monument

619 Jaabar Castle, Raqqa

1989. 36th International Damascus Fair.
1742 **618** 450p. multicoloured . . 1·10 50

1989. International Tourism Day. Multicoloured.
1743 550p. Type **619** . . . . . . 1·25 75
1744 600p. Baal-Shamin Temple, Palmyra . . . . 1·25 75

620 Child's View of Intifada

621 Common Carp

1989. Palestinian "Intifada" Movement.
1745 **620** 550p. multicoloured . . 1·25 50

1989. Fishes. Multicoloured.
1746 550p. Type **621** . . . . . . 1·75 1·00
1747 600p. Brown trout . . . . 1·75 1·00

622 Omayyad Palace, Pres. Assad and Ebla Hotel

1989. 19th Anniv of Corrective Movement of 16 November 1970.
1748 **622** 150p. multicoloured . . 40 20

623 Children of Different Races taking Food from Large Bowl

624 Dove, Globe and Children of Different Races

1990. World Food Day (1989).
1749 **623** 850p. multicoloured . . 1·90 1·00

1990. International Children's Day.
1750 **624** 850p. multicoloured . . 1·90 90

625 Flag, Emblem and Ear of Wheat

626 Tree-lined Road

1990. 5th Revolutionary Youth Union Congress.
1751 **625** 150p. multicoloured . . 40 20

1990. 27th Anniv of Baathist Revolution of 8 March 1963.
1752 **626** 600p. multicoloured . . 1·25 50

627 Flag and Arab Fighters

628 Woman carrying Child

1990. 44th Anniv of Evacuation of Foreign Troops from Syria.
1753 **627** 175p. multicoloured . . 40 20

1990. Mothers' Day.
1754 **628** 550p. multicoloured . . 1·25 50

629 Globe and Couple

630 Doctor examining Boy

1990. Labour Day.
1755 **629** 550p. multicoloured . . 1·25 60

1990. World Health Day.
1756 **630** 600p. multicoloured . . 1·25 65

631 Lilies

633 Flag, Tree and City

632 Goalkeeper saving Goal

1990. Int Flower Show, Damascus. Mult.
1757 600p. Type **631** . . . . . . 1·25 75
1758 600p. Cyclamen . . . . . . 1·25 75
1759 600p. Marigolds . . . . . . 1·25 75
1760 600p. "Viburnum opulus" . . 1·25 75
1761 600p. Swan river daisies . . 1·25 75

1990. World Cup Football Championship, Italy. Multicoloured.
1762 550p. Type **632** . . . . . . 1·25 65
1763 550p. Players marking opponent . . . . . . 1·25 90
1764 600p. Map of Italy and ball (vert) . . . . 1·25 1·00

1990. 16th Anniv of Liberation of Qneitra.
1766 **633** 550p. multicoloured . . 1·25 50

634 Man and Book

635 Weather Map

1990. International Literacy Year.
1767 **634** 550p. multicoloured . . 1·25 50

1990. World Meteorology Day.
1768 **635** 450p. multicoloured . . 1·00 50

636 Emblem

637 Old and Modern Methods of Ploughing

1990. 37th International Damascus Fair.
1769 **636** 550p. multicoloured . . 1·25 50

1990. United Nations Conference on Least Developed Countries.
1770 **637** 600p. multicoloured . . 1·40 65

638 Boy watering Young Tree

639 Children with Bread and Water in Wheat Field

1990. Tree Day.
1771 **638** 550p. multicoloured . . 1·25 65

1990. World Food Day.
1772 **639** 850p. multicoloured . . 1·90 75

640 Al-Maqdisi and Map

641 Pres. Hafez al-Assad

1990. Death Millenary of Al-Maqdisi (geographer).
1773 **640** 550p. multicoloured . . 1·25 65

1990. (a) As T **538** but with full-face portrait.
1774 50p. lilac 10 10
1775 70p. grey 15 10
1776 100p. blue 20 10
1777 150p. brown ("POSTAGE" in brown) 25 10
1777a 150p. brown ("POSTAGE" in white) 25 10
1778 300p. mauve 50 25
1779 350p. grey 60 30
1780 400p. red 65 30

(b) Type **641**.
1781 175p. multicoloured 30 20
1782 300p. multicoloured 55 20
1783 550p. multicoloured 95 25
1784 600p. multicoloured . . . . 1·25 45

(c) Horiz design with portrait as T **641** within decorative frame.
1786 1000p. multicoloured . . . 1·90 65
1787 1500p. multicoloured . . . 2·75 95
1788 2000p. multicoloured . . . 3·75 1·25
1789 2500p. multicoloured . . . 4·75 1·60

643 Control Tower, Douglas DC-9-80 Super Eighty Airliner and Emblem

1990. Arab Civil Aviation Day.
1796 **643** 175p. multicoloured . . 45 25

644 Emblem, Open Book, Cogwheel and Ear of Wheat

645 U.P.U. Emblem and Girl posting Letter

1990. 40th Anniv of United Nations Development Programme.
1797 **644** 550p. multicoloured . . 1·25 65

1990. World Post Day.
1798 **645** 550p. multicoloured . . 1·25 65

646 Leapfrog

647 Emblem, Flames and Open Book

1990. World Children's Day.
1799 **646** 550p. multicoloured . . 1·25 65

1990. Arab–Spanish Cultural Symposium.
1800 **647** 550p. multicoloured . . 1·40 75

648 Paths to and away from AIDS

649 Modern Roads and Buildings

1990. World AIDS Day.
1801 **648** 550p. multicoloured . . 1·40 75

1991. 28th Anniv of Baathist Revolution of 8 March 1963.
1802 **649** 150p. multicoloured . . 40 20

650 Lesser Purple Emperor

651 Golden Orioles

1991. Butterflies. Multicoloured.
1803 550p. Type **650** (inscr "Change Ful Great Mars") . . . . 1·40 75
1804 550p. Small tortoiseshell . . 1·40 75
1805 550p. Swallowtail . . . . . 1·40 75

1991. Birds. Multicoloured.
1806 600p. Type **651** . . . . . . 1·50 75
1807 600p. House sparrows . . . 1·50 75
1808 600p. European roller . . . 1·50 75

652 Three Generations

653 Statue

1991. Mothers' Day.
1809 **652** 550p. multicoloured . . 1·40 65

1991. 45th Anniv of Evacuation of Foreign Troops from Syria.
1810 **653** 150p. multicoloured . . 40 20

654 Dividers and Spanner

655 Daffodils

1991. Labour Day.
1811 **654** 550p. multicoloured . . 1·40 65

1991. International Flower Show, Damascus. Mult.
1812 550p. Type **655** . . . . . . 1·40 65
1813 600p. Bee balm . . . . . . 1·60 65

656 City and Ruins

1991. 17th Anniv of Liberation of Qneitra.
1814 **656** 550p. multicoloured . . 1·40 65

657 Running

1991. 11th Mediterranean Games, Athens. Mult.
1815 550p. Type **657** . . . . . . 1·40 65
1816 550p. Football . . . . 1·40 65
1817 600p. Show jumping . . . . 1·50 65

658 Hall

660 People encircling Block of Flats

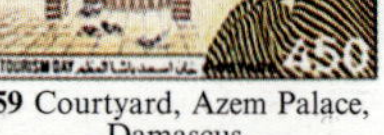

659 Courtyard, Azem Palace, Damascus

1991. 38th International Damascus Fair.
1819 **658** 550p. multicoloured . . 1·40 65

1991. International Tourism Day. Multicoloured.
1820 450p. Type **659** . . . . . . 1·10 50
1821 550p. Castle, Arwad Island 1·40 65

1991. Housing Day.
1822 **660** 175p. multicoloured . . 45 25

661 Roller Skating

1991. International Children's Day.
1823 **661** 600p. multicoloured . . 1·50 65

662 Rhazes treating Patient

1991. Science Week.
1824 **662** 550p. multicoloured . . 1·40 65

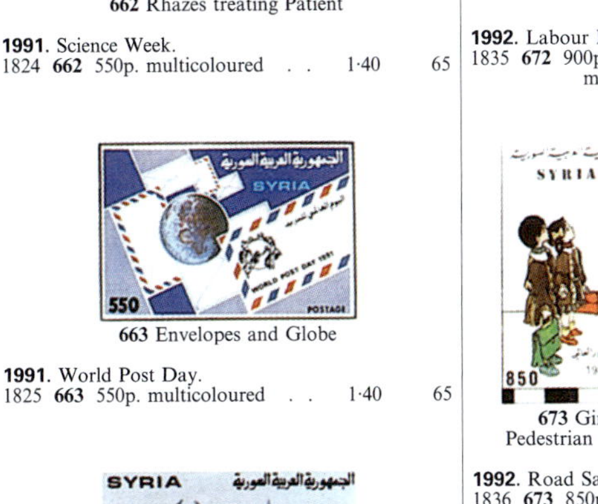

663 Envelopes and Globe

1991. World Post Day.
1825 **663** 550p. multicoloured . . 1·40 65

664 Globe, Produce and Livestock

1991. World Food Day.
1826 **664** 550p. multicoloured . . 1·40 65

665 Tomb of Unknown Soldier, Damascus

1991.
1827 **665** 600p. multicoloured . . 1·50 65

667 Polluted and Clean Environments

668 Transmission Mast, Globe and Satellite

1991. Environmental Protection.
1830 **667** 175p. multicoloured . . 50 30

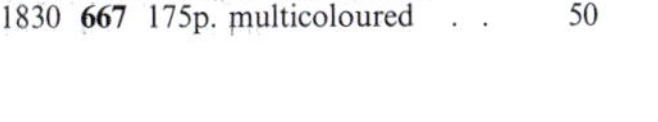

1991. International Telecommunications Fair.
1831 **668** 600p. multicoloured . . 1·50 65

669 Leaf and Port

672 Crane and Mason building Wall

671 Chimneys, Gun-barrel, Ear of Wheat, Dove and Flag

1992. 29th Anniv of Baathist Revolution of 8 March 1963.
1832 **669** 600p. multicoloured . . 1·10 55

1992. 45th Anniv of Baath Arab Socialist Party.
1834 **671** 850p. multicoloured . . 1·50 75

1992. Labour Day.
1835 **672** 900p. black, blue & mauve . . . . 1·60 80

673 Girls at Pedestrian Crossing

674 Girl listening to Mother's Stomach

1992. Road Safety Campaign.
1836 **673** 850p. multicoloured . . 1·50 75

1992. Mothers' Day.
1837 **674** 900p. multicoloured . . 1·60 80

675 Memorial

1992. 46th Anniv of Evacuation of Foreign Troops from Syria.
1838 **675** 900p. multicoloured . . 1·60 80

676 Flax

1992. International Flower Show, Damascus. Mult.
1839 300p. Type **676** 50 25
1840 800p. "Yucca filamentosa" (vert) . . . . 1·40 70
1841 900p. "Zinnia elegans" (vert) . . . . 1·60 80

677 Football

1992. Olympic Games, Barcelona. Multicoloured.
1842 150p. Type **677** 25 15
1843 150p. Running 25 15
1844 450p. Swimming 75 35
1845 750p. Wrestling . . . . . . 1·25 60

678 Smoker standing in Ashtray

679 Pendant

1992. Anti-smoking Campaign.
1847 **678** 750p. multicoloured . . 1·25 60

1992. 39th International Damascus Fair.
1848 **679** 900p. multicoloured . . 1·50 75

680 Football

1992. 7th Pan-Arab Games, Damascus. Mult.
1849 750p. Type **680** . . . . . . 1·25 60
1850 850p. Gymnastics . . . . . 1·50 75
1851 900p. Pole vaulting . . . . 1·60 80

681 Envelopes, Dove and Globe

682 Boy blowing Dandelion Clock

1992. World Post Day.
1852 **681** 600p. multicoloured . . 1·10 55

1992. International Children's Day.
1853 **682** 850p. multicoloured . . 1·50 75

683 Sebtt el-Mardini (astronomer)

684 Table Tennis

1992.
1854 **683** 850p. multicoloured . . 1·50 75

1992. Paralympic Games for Mentally Handicapped, Madrid.
1855 **684** 850p. multicoloured . . 1·50 75

685 People's Square, Damascus

686 Tree

1992. 22nd Anniv of Corrective Movement of 16 November 1970.
1856 **685** 450p. multicoloured . . 80 40

1992. Tree Day.
1857 **686** 600p. multicoloured . . 1·10 55

687 Statue of Pres. Assad, Damascus

1993. 30th Anniv of Baathist Revolution of 8 March 1963.
1858 **687** 1100p. multicoloured . . 1·10 55

688 Common Blue

689 Family

1993. Butterflies. Multicoloured.
1859 1000p. Type **688** 90 45
1860 1500p. Silver-washed fritillary . . . . 1·25 60
1861 2500p. Blue argus . . . . . 2·10 1·00

1993. Mothers' Day.
1862 **689** 1100p. multicoloured . . 1·10 55

690 Saladin Monument, Damascus

1993. 47th Anniv of Evacuation of Foreign Troops from Syria.
1863 **690** 1100p. multicoloured . . 1·10 55

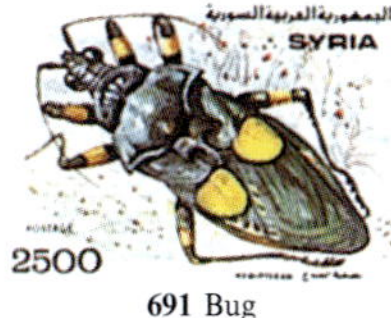

691 Bug

1993.
1864 **691** 2500p. multicoloured . . 2·10 1·00

692 Tractor in Field of Crops

1993. 25th Anniv of Arab Agrarian Union.
1865 **692** 1150p. multicoloured . . 1·10 55

693 Oil Workers

1993. Labour Day.
1866 **693** 1100p. multicoloured . . 1·10 55

694 Eye and Eye-chart

1993. 2nd Pan-Arab Ophthalmology International Council Congress.
1867 **694** 1100p. multicoloured . . 1·10 55

695 Landscapes and Eye

696 "Alcea setosa"

1993. 25th Anniv of National Ophthalmological Association.
1868 **695** 1150p. multicoloured . . 1·10 55

1993. 21st Int Flower Show, Damascus. Mult.
1869 1000p. Type **696** 95 45
1870 1100p. Primulas . . . . . 1·10 55
1871 1150p. Gesnerias . . . . . 1·10 55

697 Prism Tomb

1993. International Tourism Day.
1872 **697** 1000p. multicoloured . . 1·10 55

698 Hand posting Letter and Globe

1993. World Post Day.
1873 **698** 1000p. multicoloured . . 1·10 55

699 Boys playing Football

700 Ibn al-Bittar (chemist)

1993. International Children's Day.
1874 **699** 1150p. multicoloured . . 1·10 55

1993. Science Week.
1875 **700** 1150p. multicoloured . . 1·10 55

702 White Horse

1993. Arab Horses. Multicoloured.
1877 1000p. Type **702** 95 45
1878 1000p. Horse with white feet 95 45
1879 1500p. Black horse . . . . 1·25 60
1880 1500p. White horse with brown mane . . . . . . 1·25 60

703 Orchard in Blossom

1993. Tree Day.
1881 **703** 1100p. multicoloured . . 1·10 55

704 Flags outside Venue

1993. 40th International Damascus Fair.
1882 **704** 1100p. multicoloured . . 1·10 55

705 Basel al-Assad

1994. Basel al-Assad (President's son) Commem.
1883 **705** 2500p. multicoloured . . 2·25 1·10

706 Oranges

1994. 31st Anniv of Baathist Revolution of 8 March 1963. Multicoloured.
1884 1500p. Type **706** . . . . . 1·25 60
1885 1500p. Mandarins . . . . . 1·25 60
1886 1500p. Lemons . . . . . . 1·25 60

707 Flags, Flame, Laurel and Dates

1994. 48th Anniv of Evacuation of Foreign Troops from Syria.
1887 **707** 1800p. multicoloured . . 1·50 75

708 Mechanical Digger loading Truck

1994. Labour Day.
1888 **708** 1700p. multicoloured . . 1·50 75

709 Mother and Child at Different Ages

1994. Mothers' Day.
1889 **709** 1800p. multicoloured . . 1·50 75

710 Emblem, "50" and "75"

1994. 75th Anniv of I.L.O. and 50th Anniv of Philadelphia Declaration (social charter).
1890 **710** 1700p. multicoloured . . 1·25 60

711 Match Scene

1994. World Cup Football Championship, U.S.A. Multicoloured.
1891 1700p. Type **711** . . . . . 1·25 60
1892 1700p. Match scene (different) . . . . 1·25 60

712 Olympic Flag, Greek Temple and "100"

1994. Cent of International Olympic Committee.
1894 **712** 1700p. multicoloured . . 1·10 55

713 Flags, Lanters and Fountain

714 Camomile

1994. 41st International Damascus Fair.
1895 **713** 1800p. multicoloured . . 1·25 60

1994. Int Flower Show, Damascus. Mult.
1896 1800p. Type **714** . . . . . 1·25 60
1897 1800p. Gloxinia . . . . . . 1·25 60
1898 1800p. Mimosa . . . . . . 1·25 60

715 Apollo

1994. Butterflies. Multicoloured.
1899 1700p. Type **715** . . . . . 1·10 55
1900 1700p. Purple emperor (value at right) . . . . . 1·10 55
1901 1700p. Birdwing (value at left) . . . . 1·10 55

716 Symbols and Map

1994. 4th Population Census.
1902 **716** 1000p. multicoloured . . 65 30

717 Al-Kinsi (philosopher)

1994. Science Week.
1903 **717** £S10 multicoloured . . . 70 35

719 Airport

1994. 50th Anniv of I.C.A.O.
1905 **719** £S17 multicoloured . . . 1·10 55

720 Al-Marjeh Square

721 Child with Tennis Racquet

1994.
1906 **720** £S50 mauve . . . . . . 3·25 1·60

1994. International Children's Day.
1907 **721** £S10 multicoloured . . . 70 35

722 Girl watching Birds with Envelopes

723 Palmyra Roman Arch

1994. World Post Day.
1908 **722** £S10 multicoloured . . . 70 35

1994. International Tourism Day.
1909 **723** £S17 multicoloured . . . 1·10 55

724 Modern Building

1995. 32nd Anniv of Baathist Revolution of 8 March 1963.
1910 **724** £S18 multicoloured . . . 85 40

725 League Emblem and Map

726 Water Pump

1995. 50th Anniv of Arab League.
1911 **725** £S17 multicoloured . . . 80 40

1995. World Water Day.
1912 **726** £S17 multicoloured . . . 80 40

727 Woman sheltering Figures

1995. Mothers' Day.
1913 **727** £S17 multicoloured . . . 80 40

728 Hand holding Tree

729 Family

1995. Tree Day.
1914 **728** 1800p. multicoloured . . 85 40

1995. International Year of the Family (1994).
1915 **729** 1700p. multicoloured . . 80 40

730 Statue and Flag

731 Honey Bees on Flowers

1995. 49th Anniv of Evacuation of Foreign Troops from Syria.
1916 **730** £S17 multicoloured . . . 80 40

1995. 1st Anniv of Arab Apiculturalists Union.
1917 **731** £S17 multicoloured . . . 80 40

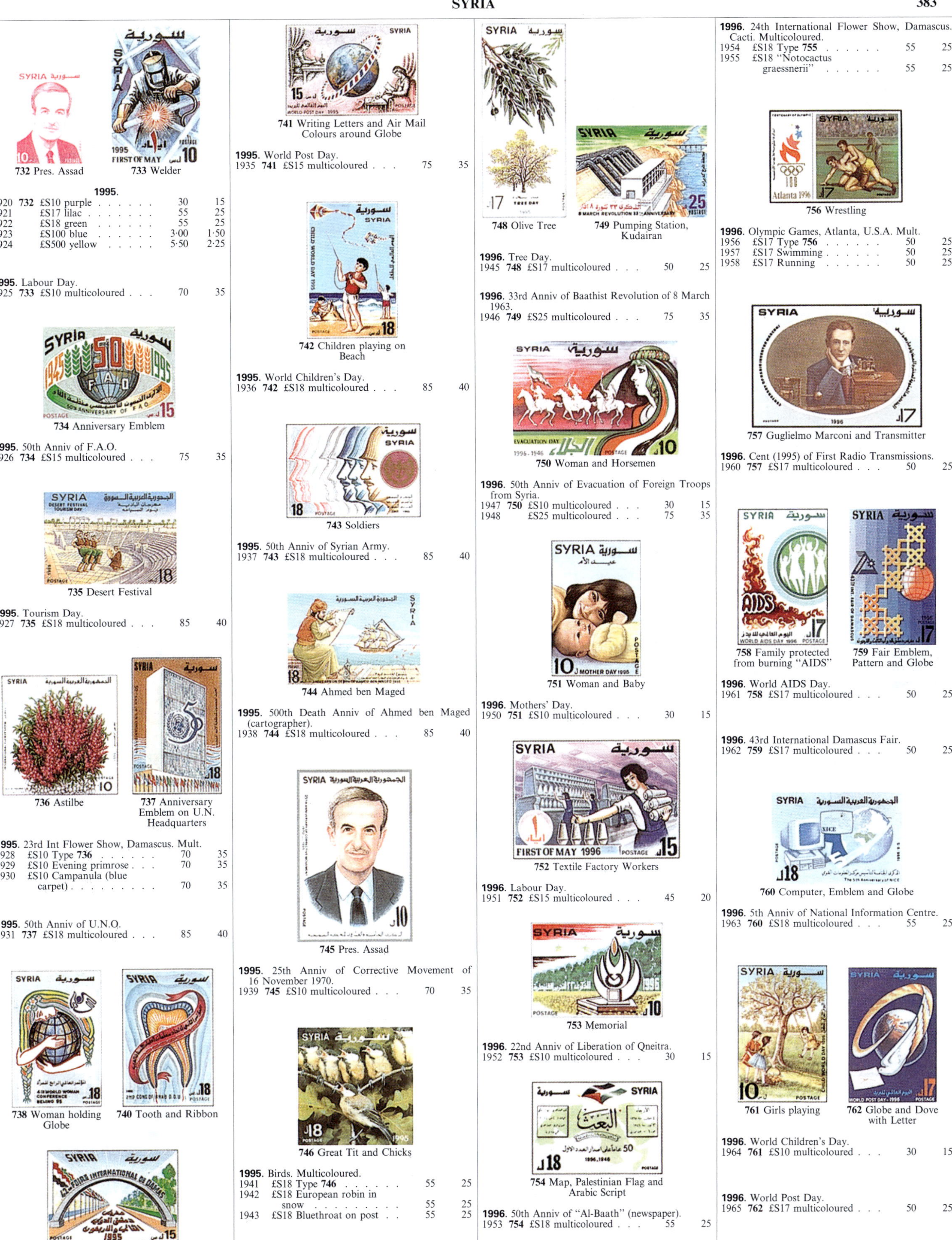

732 Pres. Assad
733 Welder

1995.
1920 **732** £S10 purple 30 15
1921 £S17 lilac 55 25
1922 £S18 green 55 25
1923 £S100 blue . . . . . . 3·00 1·50
1924 £S500 yellow . . . . . 5·50 2·25

1995. Labour Day.
1925 **733** £S10 multicoloured . . . 70 35

734 Anniversary Emblem

1995. 50th Anniv of F.A.O.
1926 **734** £S15 multicoloured . . . 75 35

735 Desert Festival

1995. Tourism Day.
1927 **735** £S18 multicoloured . . . 85 40

736 Astilbe
737 Anniversary Emblem on U.N. Headquarters

1995. 23rd Int Flower Show, Damascus. Mult.
1928 £S10 Type **736** 70 35
1929 £S10 Evening primrose . . . 70 35
1930 £S10 Campanula (blue carpet) 70 35

1995. 50th Anniv of U.N.O.
1931 **737** £S18 multicoloured . . . 85 40

738 Woman holding Globe
740 Tooth and Ribbon

739 Fair Entrance

1995. 4th World Conference on Women, Peking.
1932 **738** £S18 multicoloured . . . 85 40

1995. 42nd International Damascus Fair.
1933 **739** £S15 multicoloured . . . 75 35

1995. 2nd Congress of Arab Dentists' Association.
1934 **740** £S18 multicoloured . . . 85 40

741 Writing Letters and Air Mail Colours around Globe

1995. World Post Day.
1935 **741** £S15 multicoloured . . . 75 35

742 Children playing on Beach

1995. World Children's Day.
1936 **742** £S18 multicoloured . . . 85 40

743 Soldiers

1995. 50th Anniv of Syrian Army.
1937 **743** £S18 multicoloured . . . 85 40

744 Ahmed ben Maged

1995. 500th Death Anniv of Ahmed ben Maged (cartographer).
1938 **744** £S18 multicoloured . . . 85 40

745 Pres. Assad

1995. 25th Anniv of Corrective Movement of 16 November 1970.
1939 **745** £S10 multicoloured . . . 70 35

746 Great Tit and Chicks

1995. Birds. Multicoloured.
1941 £S18 Type **746** 55 25
1942 £S18 European robin in snow 55 25
1943 £S18 Bluethroat on post . . 55 25

747 Pasteur and Laboratory

1995. Death Centenary of Louis Pasteur (chemist).
1944 **747** £S18 multicoloured . . . 55 25

748 Olive Tree
749 Pumping Station, Kudairan

1996. Tree Day.
1945 **748** £S17 multicoloured . . . 50 25

1996. 33rd Anniv of Baathist Revolution of 8 March 1963.
1946 **749** £S25 multicoloured . . . 75 35

750 Woman and Horsemen

1996. 50th Anniv of Evacuation of Foreign Troops from Syria.
1947 **750** £S10 multicoloured . . . 30 15
1948 £S25 multicoloured . . . 75 35

751 Woman and Baby

1996. Mothers' Day.
1950 **751** £S10 multicoloured . . . 30 15

752 Textile Factory Workers

1996. Labour Day.
1951 **752** £S15 multicoloured . . . 45 20

753 Memorial

1996. 22nd Anniv of Liberation of Qneitra.
1952 **753** £S10 multicoloured . . . 30 15

754 Map, Palestinian Flag and Arabic Script

1996. 50th Anniv of "Al-Baath" (newspaper).
1953 **754** £S18 multicoloured . . . 55 25

755 "Mammilaria erythosperma"

1996. 24th International Flower Show, Damascus. Cacti. Multicoloured.
1954 £S18 Type **755** 55 25
1955 £S18 "Notocactus graessnerii" 55 25

756 Wrestling

1996. Olympic Games, Atlanta, U.S.A. Mult.
1956 £S17 Type **756** 50 25
1957 £S17 Swimming 50 25
1958 £S17 Running 50 25

757 Guglielmo Marconi and Transmitter

1996. Cent (1995) of First Radio Transmissions.
1960 **757** £S17 multicoloured . . . 50 25

758 Family protected from burning "AIDS"
759 Fair Emblem, Pattern and Globe

1996. World AIDS Day.
1961 **758** £S17 multicoloured . . . 50 25

1996. 43rd International Damascus Fair.
1962 **759** £S17 multicoloured . . . 50 25

760 Computer, Emblem and Globe

1996. 5th Anniv of National Information Centre.
1963 **760** £S18 multicoloured . . . 55 25

761 Girls playing
762 Globe and Dove with Letter

1996. World Children's Day.
1964 **761** £S10 multicoloured . . . 30 15

1996. World Post Day.
1965 **762** £S17 multicoloured . . . 50 25

763 Sons of Musa ibn Shaker

1996. Science Week.
1966 **763** £S10 multicoloured . . . 30 15

764 Pres. Assad

765 Child sitting on Globe

1996. 26th Anniv of Corrective Movement of 16 November 1970.
1967 **764** £S10 multicoloured . . . 30 15

1996. 50th Anniv of U.N.I.C.E.F.
1969 **765** £S17 multicoloured . . . 50 25

766 Hands and Map

767 Grain Silos and Wheat

1997. 25th Anniv of National Progressive Front.
1970 **766** £S3 multicoloured . . . 10 10

1997. 34th Anniv of Baathist Revolution of 8 March 1963.
1971 **767** £S15 multicoloured . . . 45 20

768 Party Emblem

769 Apple Trees

1997. 50th Anniv of Baath Arab Socialist Party.
1972 **768** £S25 multicoloured . . . 75 35

1997. Tree Day.
1974 **769** £S10 multicoloured . . . 30 15

770 Mother and Daughter feeding Doves

771 "Beautiful Woman from Palmyra" (relief)

1997. Mothers' Day.
1975 **770** £S15 multicoloured . . . 45 20

1997. World Tourism Day (1996).
1976 **771** £S17 multicoloured . . . 50 25

772 Grey Mullet

1997. Fishes. Multicoloured.
1977 £S17 Type **772** 50 25
1978 £S17 Mediterranean horse mackerel (country inscr at top) 50 25

773 Horsemen

1997. 51st Anniv of Evacuation of Foreign Troops from Syria.
1979 **773** £S15 multicoloured . . . 45 20

774 Building Pipeline

775 Library and Books

1997. Labour Day.
1980 **774** £S15 multicoloured . . . 45 20

1997. World Book Day.
1981 **775** £S10 multicoloured . . . 25 10

776 Smoker's Diseased Lungs and Cigarettes

777 "Echinoereus purporeus"

1997. World "No Smoking" Day.
1982 **776** £S18 multicoloured . . . 50 25

1997. International Flower Show, Damascus. Mult.
1983 £S18 Type **777** 50 25
1984 £S18 Irises 50 25

778 Emblem

779 Flags and Monument

1997. 4th Arab Union of Dentists' Associations Congress.
1985 **778** £S10 multicoloured . . . 25 10

1997. 44th International Damascus Fair.
1986 **779** £S17 multicoloured . . . 45 20

780 Child reaching for Landmine

1997. International Children's Day.
1987 **780** £S17 multicoloured . . . 45 20

781 Post Rider and Dove

1997. World Post Day.
1988 **781** £S17 multicoloured . . . 45 20

782 Tourists on Flying Carpet

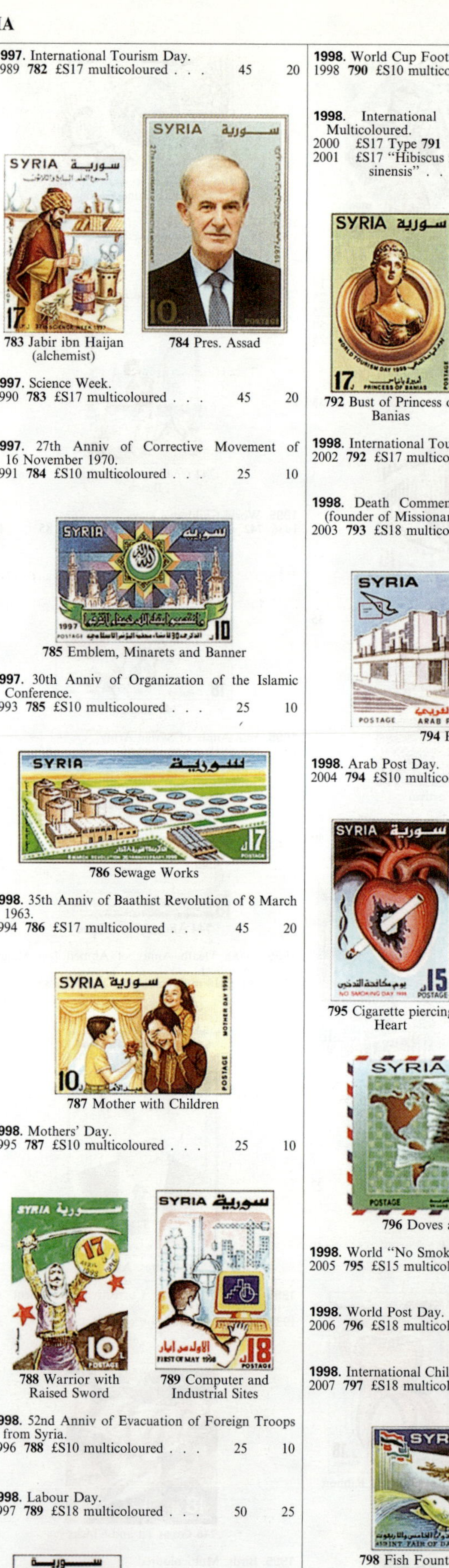

1997. International Tourism Day.
1989 **782** £S17 multicoloured . . . 45 20

783 Jabir ibn Haijan (alchemist)

784 Pres. Assad

1997. Science Week.
1990 **783** £S17 multicoloured . . . 45 20

1997. 27th Anniv of Corrective Movement of 16 November 1970.
1991 **784** £S10 multicoloured . . . 25 10

785 Emblem, Minarets and Banner

1997. 30th Anniv of Organization of the Islamic Conference.
1993 **785** £S10 multicoloured . . . 25 10

786 Sewage Works

1998. 35th Anniv of Baathist Revolution of 8 March 1963.
1994 **786** £S17 multicoloured . . . 45 20

787 Mother with Children

1998. Mothers' Day.
1995 **787** £S10 multicoloured . . . 25 10

788 Warrior with Raised Sword

789 Computer and Industrial Sites

1998. 52nd Anniv of Evacuation of Foreign Troops from Syria.
1996 **788** £S10 multicoloured . . . 25 10

1998. Labour Day.
1997 **789** £S18 multicoloured . . . 50 25

790 Players challenging for Ball

791 "Bougainvillea glabra"

1998. World Cup Football Championship, France.
1998 **790** £S10 multicoloured . . . 25 10

1998. International Flower Show, Damascus. Multicoloured.
2000 £S17 Type **791** 45 20
2001 £S17 "Hibiscus rosa-sinensis" 45 20

792 Bust of Princess of Banias

793 Mother Teresa

1998. International Tourism Day.
2002 **792** £S17 multicoloured . . . 45 20

1998. Death Commemoration of Mother Teresa (founder of Missionaries of Charity).
2003 **793** £S18 multicoloured . . . 50 25

794 Post Office

1998. Arab Post Day.
2004 **794** £S10 multicoloured . . . 25 10

795 Cigarette piercing Heart

797 Child on Globe and Dove

796 Doves and World Map

1998. World "No Smoking" Day.
2005 **795** £S15 multicoloured . . . 40 20

1998. World Post Day.
2006 **796** £S18 multicoloured . . . 50 25

1998. International Children's Day.
2007 **797** £S18 multicoloured . . . 50 25

798 Fish Fountain and Fair Venue

1998. 45th International Damascus Fair.
2008 **798** £S18 multicoloured . . . 50 25

800 Ibn ad-Durainim (mathematician)

1998. Science Week.
2010 **800** £S10 multicoloured . . . 30 15

801 Pres. Assad

1998. 28th Anniv of Corrective Movement of 16 November 1970.
2011 **801** 10p. multicoloured . . . 30 15

802 Dome of the Rock and Old City

1998. Jerusalem.
2013 **802** £S10 multicoloured . . . 30 15

803 Dromedaries

1998.
2014 **803** £S17 multicoloured . . . 50 25

804 Pres. Assad

1999. Re-election of President Hafez al-Assad to Fifth Term.
2015 **804** £S10 multicoloured . . . 30 15
2016 £S17 multicoloured . . . 50 25
2017 £S18 multicoloured . . . 50 25

805 New Communications Office Building

1999. 36th Anniv of Baathist Revolution of 8 March 1963.
2019 **805** £S25 multicoloured . . . 70 35

806 Fig Tree

807 Mother breast-feeding Baby

1999. Tree Day.
2021 **806** £S17 multicoloured . . . 50 25

1999. Mothers' Day.
2022 **807** £S17 multicoloured . . . 50 25

808 Woman in Baath Party Colours and Man with Rifle

809 16 November Workers' Further Education Institute

1999. 53rd Anniv of Evacuation of Foreign Troops from Syria.
2023 **808** £S18 multicoloured . . . 50 25

1999. Labour Day.
2024 **809** £S10 multicoloured . . . 30 15

810 Crowd with "Human Rights" Banner

1999. 50th Anniv (1998) of Universal Declaration of Human Rights.
2025 **810** £S18 multicoloured . . . 50 25

811 Jasmin

1999. International Flower Show, Damascus. Mult.
2026 £S10 Type **811** 30 15
2027 £S10 Acanthus 30 15

812 Show Jumping and Crowd with Lighted Crowns

1999. 10th Friendship Festival, Al Basel.
2028 **812** £S10 multicoloured . . . 25 10

813 Globes and Emblem

1999. 46th International Damascus Fair.
2029 **813** £S15 multicoloured . . . 40 20

814 Patient receiving Treatment and Emblem

815 Postman and Map of Arab States

1999. 7th Arab Union of Dentists' Associations Congress.
2030 **814** £S17 multicoloured . . . 45 20

1999. Arab Post Day.
2031 **815** £S10 multicoloured . . . 25 10

816 Abu Hanifah al Deilouri (botanist)

1999. Science Week.
2032 **816** £S17 multicoloured . . . 45 20

817 Postal Transport, Emblem and Headquarters, Berne

1999. 125th Anniv of Universal Postal Union.
2033 **817** £S17 multicoloured . . . 45 20

818 Ummayed Mosque and Our Lady of Saydnaya Convent, Damascus

1999. 2000 Years of Religious Co-existence.
2034 **818** £S17 multicoloured . . . 45 20

819 October 1973 Liberation War Monument and Pres. Assad (statues)

1999. 29th Anniv of Corrective Movement of 16 November 1970. Multicoloured.
2035 £S17 Type **819** 45 20
2036 £S17 Close-up detail of statue (vert) 45 20

820 Children holding Hands around Globe

821 Factories, Corn and Family

1999. International Children's Day.
2038 **820** £S18 multicoloured . . . 50 25

2000. 37th Anniv of Baathist Revolution of 8 March 1963.
2039 **821** £S18 multicoloured . . . 50 25

822 Mother holding Child

824 Rose and Cog

2000. Mothers' Day.
2040 **822** £S17 multicoloured . . . 45 20

2000. Labour Day.
2042 **824** £S10 multicoloured . . . 25 10

825 Foxy Charaxes

826 Tree and Fruit

2000. Butterflies. Multicoloured.
2043 £S17 Type **825** 45 20
2044 £S18 Apaturairis 50 25

2000. Tree Day.
2045 **826** £S18 multicoloured . . . 50 25

827 President Basher Al-Assad

828 Child with Balloons

2000. Election of President Basher Al-Assad.
2046 **827** £S3 multicoloured . . . 10 10
2047 £S10 multicoloured . . . 15 10
2048 £S17 multicoloured . . . 45 20
2049 £S18 multicoloured . . . 50 25

2000.
2051 **828** £S10 multicoloured . . . 45 20

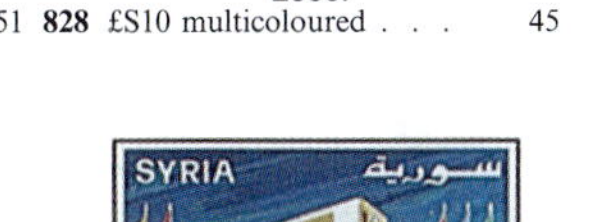

829 Flags, Exhibition Building and Crowd

2000. 47th International Damascus Fair.
2052 **829** £S15 multicoloured . . . 40 20

830 U.P.U. Emblem, Envelope and Globe

2000. World Post Day.
2053 **830** £S18 multicoloured . . . 50 25

831 Map and Emblem

2000. Arab Post Day.
2054 **831** £S18 multicoloured . . . 50 25

832 Weight Llifting

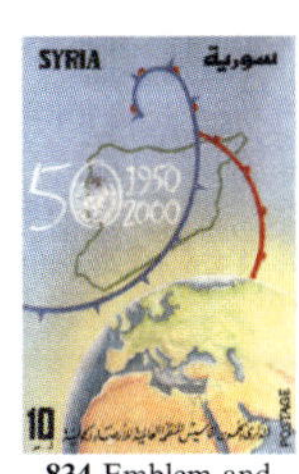

834 Emblem and Globe

833 Nasir Al-din Altusi (scientist)

2000. Olympic Games, Sydney. Multicoloured.
2055 £S17 Type **832** 45 20
2056 £S18 Shot-put 50 25
MS2057 81 × 75 mm. £S25 Javelin 70 70

2000. Science Week.
2058 **833** £S15 multicoloured . . . 40 20

2000. 50th Anniv of World Meteorological Organization.
2059 **834** £S10 multicoloured . . . 30 15

835 Cherubs in Rowing Boat and City (mosaic) (1/3-size illustration)

2000. World Tourism Day. Sheet 111 × 85 mm. Imperf.
MS2060 **835** £S50 multicoloured 1·25 1·25

OBLIGATORY TAX STAMPS

T 57 T 58

T 59 T 60

T 61

1945. Syrian Army Fund. Revenue Stamps surch or optd.
T419 **T 57** 5p. on 25p. on 40p. pink . . . . . . 65·00 3·00
T420 – 5p. on 25p. on 40p. pink . . . . . . 90·00 7·50
T421 **T 58** 5p. on 25p. on 40p. pink . . . . . . 65·00 1·50
T422 **T 59** 5p. blue £100 90
T423 **T 60** 5p. blue . . . . . . 65·00 1·10
T424 – 5p. blue . . . . . . 80·00 30
T425 **T 61** 5p. blue . . . . . . 80·00 1·00
T426 – 5p. blue . . . . . . £100 2·00

No. T420 is as Type **57** but with additional overprint as top line of Type **61**.

No. T424 has top line of overprint as Type **59** and other lines as Type **60**.

No. T426 has top line overprinted as Type **61** and other lines as Type **60**.

POSTAGE DUE STAMPS

A. FRENCH MILITARY OCCUPATION

1920. "Mouchon" and "Merson" key-types of French Post Offices in the Turkish Empire (inscr "LEVANT") surch **O. M. F. Syrie Ch. taxe** and value.
D48 **B** 1p. on 10c. red £160 £160
D49 2p. on 20c. brown £160 £160
D50 3p. on 30c. lilac £160 £160
D51 **C** 4p. on 40c. red and blue £160 £160

1920. Postage Due stamps of France surch **O. M. F. Syrie** and value.
D60 **D 11** 50c. on 10c. brown . . . 65 1·25
D52 1p. on 10c. brown . . . 2·00 3·75
D61 1p. on 20c. green . . . 95 1·25
D53 2p. on 20c. green . . . 2·25 4·00
D62 2p. on 30c. red . . . 3·25 4·50
D54 3p. on 30c. red . . . 2·00 3·75
D63 3p. on 50c. purple . . . 3·50 5·25
D55 4p. on 50c. purple . . . 4·75 8·50
D64 5p. on 1f. purple on yellow . . . . 7·25 10·00

1921. Issued at Damascus. No. KD96 of Arab Kingdom surch **O. M. F. Syrie Chiffre Taxe** and value.
D69 **K 3** 50c. on 1p. black . . . . 3·75 6·00
D70 1p. on 1p. black . . . . 3·00 4·50

1921. Issued at Damascus. No. 64a/5 of Syria optd **TAXE**.
D89 **K 4** 2p. on 5m. red . . . . . 8·00 8·75
D90 **K 3** 3p. on 1p. blue . . . . 18·00 17·00

B. ARAB KINGDOM

1920. As No. K92 but colour changed.
KD96 **K 3** 1p. black . . . . 1·25 1·25

C. FRENCH MANDATED TERRITORY

1923. Postage Due stamps of France surch **Syrie Grand Liban** and value.
D118 **D 11** 50c. on 10c. brown . . 2·50 3·50
D119 1p. on 20c. green . . . 2·50 4·00
D120 2p. on 30c. red . . . 2·25 3·50
D121 3p. on 50c. purple . . 2·25 3·75
D122 5p. on 1f. purple on yellow . . . . . . 5·00 6·50

1924. Postage Due stamps of France surch **SYRIE** and value.
D139 **D 11** 50c. on 10c. brown . . 1·25 3·00
D140 1p. on 20c. green . . . 1·75 3·00
D141 2p. on 30c. red . . . 2·00 3·50
D142 3p. on 50c. purple . . 1·25 3·50
D143 5p. on 1f. purple on yellow . . . . . . 1·75 3·75

1924. Postage Due stamps of France surch **Syrie** and value and also in Arabic.
D175 **D 11** 0p.50 on 10c. brown 65 2·00
D176 1p. on 20c. olive . . . 1·50 3·25
D177 2p. on 30c. red . . . 2·00 3·00
D178 3p. on 50c. purple . . 2·50 3·50
D179 5p. on 1f. red on yellow . . . . . . 3·00 4·25

D 20 Hama

1925.
D192 **D 20** 0p.50 brown on yellow 40 1·50
D193 – 1p. purple on pink . . 15 45
D194 – 2p. black on blue . . 70 1·10
D195 – 3p. black on red . . 1·00 1·50
D196 – 5p. black on green . . 90 1·40
D197 – 8p. black on blue . . 5·25 5·50
D198 – 15p. black on pink . . 8·25 9·75

DESIGNS—VERT: 1p. Antioch. HORIZ: 2p. Tarsus; 3p. Banias; 5p. Castle; 8p. Ornamental design; 15p. Lion.

E. SYRIAN REPUBLIC

D 221

1965.
D883 **D 221** 2½p. blue 10 10
D884 5p. brown 10 10
D885 10p. green 15 10
D886 17½p. red 40 40
D887 25p. blue 55 55

TAHITI Pt. 6

The largest of the Society Islands in the S. Pacific Ocean. Later renamed Oceanic Settlements.

100 centimes = 1 franc.

1882. Stamps of French Colonies. "Peace and Commerce" type, surch **25c.**
1 **H** 25c. on 35c. black on orange £200 £190
3a 25c. on 40c. red on yellow £2750 £3250

1884. Stamps of French Colonies, "Commerce" (perf) and "Peace and Commerce" (imperf) types, surch **TAHITI** and value.
4 **J** 5c. on 20c. red on green . . . £150 £120
5 10c. on 20c. red on green . . £200 £180
2 **H** 25c. on 35c. black on orange £3250 £3250
6 25c. on 1f. green £450 £375

1893. Stamps of French Colonies, "Commerce" type, optd **TAHITI**.
7 **J** 1c. black on blue £500 £450
8 2c. brown on buff £2250 £1700
9 4c. brown on grey £850 £650
10 5c. green on green . . . . 17·00 27·00
11 10c. black on lilac . . . . 20·00 35·00
12 15c. blue . . . . . . 25·00 30·00
13 20c. red on green . . . . . 48·00 45·00
14 25c. brown £5000 £4500
15 25c. black on pink . . . . 23·00 32·00
16 35c. black on orange . . . £1500 £1500
17 75c. red on pink . . . . . 60·00 60·00
18 1f. green . . . . 65·00 60·00

1893. Stamps of French Colonies, "Commerce" type, optd **1893 TAHITI**.
32 **J** 1c. black on blue £550 £500
33 2c. brown on buff £2500 £1800
34 4c. brown on grey £1000 £900
35 5c. green on green £650 £550
36 10c. black on lilac £200 £200
37 15c. blue . . . . . . 32·00 22·00
38 20c. red on green . . . . . 35·00 35·00
39 25c. brown £22000 £20000
40 25c. black on pink . . . . 35·00 35·00
41 35c. black on orange . . . £1500 £1200
42 75c. red on pink . . . . . 30·00 35·00
43 1f. green . . . . 35·00 35·00

1903. Stamps of Oceanic Settlements, "Tablet" key-type, surch **TAHITI 10 centimes**.
57 **D** 10c. on 15c. blue and red . . 6·00 7·50
58 10c. on 25c. black and red on pink . . . . . . 5·00 6·00
59 10c. on 40c. red and blue on yellow . . . . . . 7·00 7·00

1915. Stamps of Oceanic Settlements, "Tablet" key-type, optd **TAHITI** and red cross.
60 **D** 15c. blue and red £130 £130
61 15c. grey and red . . . . . 25·00 25·00

POSTAGE DUE STAMPS

1893. Postage Due stamps of French Colonies optd **TAHITI**.
D19 **U** 1c. black £225 £225
D20 2c. black £200 £250
D21 3c. black £225 £275
D22 4c. black £275 £275
D23 5c. black £275 £275
D24 10c. black £275 £275
D25 15c. black £275 £275
D26 20c. black £225 £225
D27 30c. black £275 £275
D28 40c. black £275 £275
D29 60c. black £300 £300
D30 1f. brown £650 £650
D31 2f. brown £650 £650

1893. Postage Due stamps of French Colonies optd **1893 TAHITI**.
D44 **U** 1c. black £1600 £1600
D45 2c. black £350 £350
D46 3c. black £350 £350
D47 4c. black £350 £350
D48 5c. black £350 £350
D49 10c. black £350 £350
D50 15c. black £350 £350
D51 20c. black £225 £225
D52 30c. black £350 £350
D53 40c. black £350 £350
D54 60c. black £350 £350
D55 1f. brown £350 £350
D56 2f. brown £350 £350

For later issues see **OCEANIC SETTLEMENTS**.

TAJIKISTAN Pt. 10

Formerly a constituent republic of the Soviet Union, Tajikistan became independent in 1991.

1992. 100 kopeks = 1 (Russian) rouble.
1995. 100 tanga = 1 (Tajik) rouble.

1 Hunter (gold relief)

2 Sheikh Muslihiddin Mosque, Khudzand

1992.
1 **1** 50k. multicoloured 15 15

1992.
2 **2** 50k. multicoloured 15 15

3 Traditional Musical Instruments

1992.
3 **3** 35k. multicoloured 15 15

4 Argali

1992.
4 **4** 30k. multicoloured 15 15

(5) (7)

1992. No. 2 surch as T **5**.
5 **2** 5r. on 50k. multicoloured . . 25 25
6 25r. on 50k. multicoloured . . 50 50

1992. No. 3 surch.
7 **3** 15r. on 35k. multicoloured . . 25 25
8 50r. on 35k. multicoloured . . 25 25

1993. No. 6072 of Russia surch as T **7**.
9 **2410** 3r. on 1k. brown 10 10
10 100r. on 1k. brown . . . 1·75 1·75

(8) (9)

1993. No. 6073 of Russia surch as T **8**.
11 10r. on 2k. brown 20 20
12 15r. on 2k. brown 50 50

1993. No. 1 surch with T **9**.
13 **1** 60r. on 50k. multicoloured 50 50

10 Mountain Landscape

1993. Multicoloured.
16 1r. Statue of Abuabdullokhi Rudaki, Dushanbe (vert) . . 10 10
17 5r. Type **10** 10 10
18 15r. Mausoleum of Sadriddin Aini (poet), Dushanbe (vert) 10 10
19 20r. State flag and map . . . 10 10
20 25r. Hissar Fort 15 10
21 50r. Aini Opera and Ballet House, Dushanbe 25 15
22 100r. State flag and map (different) 50 30

11 Brown Bear

1993. Mammals. Multicoloured.
23 3r. Type **11** 10 10
24 10r. Red deer 10 10
25 15r. Markhor 15 10
26 25r. Porcupine 25 15
27 100r. Snow leopard . . . . . 1·00 65

12 Geb and Talkhand in Battle

1993. Millenary of "Book of Kings" by Abu-I Kasim Mansur, Firdausi (Persian poet). Multicoloured.
28 5r. Type **12** 10 10
29 20r. Rustam and Sukhrov in combat 25 10
30 30r. Eagle Simurgh brings Zola to his father Som (vert) 35 20

14 Ceiling Decoration 15 Arms

1993.
33 **14** 1r.50 multicoloured 25 15

1994.
34 **15** 10r. multicoloured 10 10
35 15r. multicoloured 10 10
36 35r. multicoloured 10 10
37 50r. multicoloured 10 10
38 100r. multicoloured 10 10
39 160r. multicoloured 15 10
40 500r. mult (23 × 37 mm) . . 40 25
41 1000r. mult (23 × 37 mm) . . 85 55

16 Hamadony (after Vafo Nazarovym) 18 Post Office

1994. 680th Birth Anniv of Ali Hamadony (Persian mystic).
42 **16** 1000r. multicoloured (inscr in Roman alphabet) . . . 50 35
43 1000r. multicoloured (inscr in Cyrillic) 50 35

1994. Historic Monuments. Multicoloured.
45 10r. Statue of Firdausi (vert) 10 10
46 35r. Type **18** 10 10
47 100r. Theatre 10 10
48 160r. Ulum Academy 20 10
49 160r. "Safar" building 20 10

19 Tyrannosaurus

1994. Prehistoric Animals. Multicoloured.
50 500r. Type **19** 30 20
51 500r. Stegosaurus 30 20
52 500r. Anatosaurus 30 20
53 500r. Parasaurolophus 30 20
54 500r. Triceratops 30 20
55 500r. Diatryma 30 20
56 500r. Tyrannosaurus (different) 30 20
57 500r. Spinosaurus 30 20

1995. No. 33 surch **1995** and value.
58 **14** 100r. on 1r.50 mult 10 10
59 600r. on 1r.50 mult 30 15
60 1000r. on 1r.50 mult 50 25
61 5000r. on 1r.50 mult . . . . 1·60 90

21 Gecko ("Alsophylax loricatus")

1995. Lizards. Multicoloured.
62 500r. Type **21** 20 15
63 500r. Sunwatcher ("Phrynocephalus helioscopus") 20 15
64 500r. Toad-headed agama ("Phrynocephalus mystaceus") 20 15
65 500r. Toad agama ("Phrynocephalus sogdianus") 20 15
66 500r. Plate-tailed gecko ("Teratoscincus scineus") . . 20 15
67 500r. Transcaspian desert monitor ("Varanus griseus") 20 15

22 National Flag 25 State Arms

1995. Membership of International Organizations. Multicoloured.
69 1000r. Type **22** (Organization for Security and Co-operation in Europe) . . . 45 30
70 1000r. National flag and New York Headquarters (United Nations) (horiz) 45 30
71 1000r. Emblem and national flag (Universal Postal Union) 45 30

1995. "Beijing '95" International Stamp Exhibition, China (73) and "Singapore '95" International Stamp Exhibition (74). Nos. 64 and 67 optd with relevant exhibition emblem.
73 500r. multicoloured . . . . . 1·25 1·00
74 500r. multicoloured . . . . . 1·25 1·00

1995.
75 **25** 1r. multicoloured 10 10
76 2r. multicoloured 10 10
77 5r. multicoloured 10 10
78 12r. multicoloured 15 10
79 40r. multicoloured 40 25

26 Bar-headed Goose ("Anser indicus")

1996. Birds. Multicoloured.
80 200r. Type **26** 60 40
81 200r. Indian black-headed gull ("Larus brunnicephalus") 60 40
82 200r. Houbara bustard ("Otis undulata") 60 40
83 200r. Daurian partridge ("Perdix dauricae") 60 40
84 200r. Tibetan sandgrouse ("Syrrhaptes tibetana") . . 60 40
85 200r. Tibetan snowcock ("Tetraogallus tibetanus") 60 40

27 New York Headquarters

1996. 50th Anniv of U.N.O.
87 **27** 100r. multicoloured 35 20

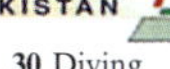

29 Pallas's Cat

1996. Wild Cats. Multicoloured. (a) With World Wildlife Fund emblem. Pallas's Cat.
90 100r. Type **29** 50 30
91 100r. Close-up 50 30
92 150r. Head 75 50
93 150r. Sitting 75 50

(b) Without W.W.F. emblem.
95 200r. Jungle cat ("Felis chaus") . . . . 1·00 75
96 200r. Lynx ("Felis lynx") . . . 1·00 75

30 Diving 31 Kamol Khujandi

1996. Olympic Games, Atlanta, U.S.A. Mult.
97 200r. Type **30** 85 50
98 200r. Football 85 50
99 200r. Throwing the hammer 85 50
100 200r. Judo 85 50
101 200r. Baron Pierre de Coubertin (founder of modern Games) 85 50

1996. Kamol Khujandi (writer) Commemoration.
102 **31** 500r. multicoloured (inscr in Roman letters) . . . 1·60 1·00
103 500r. multicoloured (inscr in Cyrillic letters) . . . . 1·60 1·00

32 Emblem

1996. 5th Anniv of Central Asian Postal Union.
104 **32** 100r. multicoloured . . . . 1·00 1·00

33 Mt. Krozhenevskoi

1997. Mountains over 7000 m. Multicoloured.
105 100r. Type **33** 45 30
106 100r. Mt. Lenin 45 30
107 100r. Mt. Communism . . . 45 30

1997. Nos. 58/61 surch **A 1997**.
109 A (12r.) on 100r. on 1r.50 multicoloured 35 20
110 A (12r.) on 600r. on 1r.50 multicoloured 35 20
111 A (12r.) on 1000r. on 1r.50 multicoloured 35 20
112 A (12r.) on 5000r. on 1r.50 multicoloured 35 20

35 Copper Vessel 36 Woman from Khujand

1998. Crafts. Multicoloured.
113 30r. Type **35** 20 10
114 100r. Cradles 60 40

1998. Traditional Costumes. Multicoloured.
116 100r. Type **36** 40 25
117 100r. Woman from Darvoz carrying pot 40 25
118 150r. Man from Khujand (blue coat) 60 40
119 150r. Man from Darvoz (striped coat) 60 40

37 "Tulipa greigii"

1998. Flowers. Multicoloured.
120 12r. Type **37** 10 10
121 30r. "Crocus korolkowi" . . 15 10
122 70r. "Iris darwasica" 40 25
123 150r. "Petilium eduardii" . . 80 50

38 "Catocala timur"

1998. Butterflies and Moths. Multicoloured.
125 12r. Type **38** 10 10
126 30r. "Celerio chamyla apocyni" 15 10
127 70r. "Colias sieversi" 40 25
128 150r. Southern swallowtail . . 80 50

39 Ruby

1998. Minerals. Multicoloured.
130 1r. Type **39** 10 10
131 1r. Sapphire 10 10
132 12r. Tourmaline 10 10
133 12r. Lapis lazuli 10 10
134 150r. Spinel 80 50
135 150r. Amethyst 80 50

40 Ghafurov

1998. Death Commemoration of Bobojon Ghafurov (politician).
137 **40** 12r. multicoloured 10 10
138 150r. multicoloured 80 50

41 Centenary Poster

1999. Birth Bicentenary of Aleksandr Sergeevich Pushkin (poet). Multicoloured.
139 100r. Type **41** 65 40
140 270r. Portrait of Pushkin . . 1·25 70

42 Diamond Design 43 Key Design

44 Pyramid Design 45 Lion shaped figurine

1999. Carpet Designs, Value expressed by Cyrillic letter
141 **42** (A) multicoloured 65 40
142 **43** (B) multicoloured 65 40
143 **44** (V) multicoloured 65 40

1999. 1100th Anniv of Samanids State. Multicoloured.
144 30r. Type **45** 20 15
145 50r. Anniversary emblem 35 20
146 100r. Animal-shaped vessel 65 40
147 270r. Clay ornaments 1·25 75

47 *Pleurotus eryngii*

1999. Fungi. Multicoloured.
150 100r. Type **47** 65 40
151 270r. Naked mushroom 1·25 75

TANGANYIKA Pt. 1

Formerly the German colony of German East Africa. After the 1914–18 War it was under British mandate until 1946 and then administered by Britain under United Nations trusteeship until 1961 when it became independent within the British Commonwealth. It had a common postal service with Kenya and Uganda from 1935 to 1961 (for these issues see under Kenya, Uganda and Tanganyika). Renamed Tanzania in 1965.

1915. 16 annas = 1 rupee.
1917. 100 cents = 1 rupee.
1922. 100 cents = 1 shilling.

1915. Stamps of the Indian Expeditionary Forces optd **G. R. POST MAFIA**.
M33 **55** 3p. grey 30·00 70·00
M34 **56** ½a. green 48·00 75·00
M35 **57** 1a. red 50·00 75·00
M36 **59** 2a. lilac 80·00 £120
M37 **61** 2½a. blue £100 £150
M38 **62** 3a. orange £100 £160
M39 **63** 4a. olive £130 £180
M40 **65** 8a. mauve £225 £300
M41 **66** 12a. red £275 £400
M42 **67** 1r. brown and green £325 £425

1916. Stamps of Nyasaland (King George V) optd **N.F.**
N1 ½d. green 1·50 8·00
N2 1d. red 1·50 3·25
N3 3d. purple on yellow 7·50 17·00
N4 4d. black and red on yellow 29·00 40·00
N5 1s. black on green 29·00 42·00

1917. Stamps of Kenya and Uganda (King George V, 1912) optd **G.E.A.**
45 1c. black 15 80
47 3c. green 15 15
48 6c. red 15 10
49 10c. orange 50 60
50 12c. grey 50 2·25
51 15c. blue 70 2·00
52 25c. black and red on yellow 80 3·50
53 50c. black and lilac 80 3·25
54 75c. black on green 1·00 4·50
55 1r. black on green 2·75 7·00
56 2r. red and black on blue 9·00 42·00
57 3r. violet and green 13·00 75·00
58 4r. red and green on yellow 17·00 90·00
59 5r. blue and purple 38·00 90·00
60 10r. red and green on green 75·00 £325
61 20r. black and purple on red £190 £375
62 50r. red and green £475 £800

4 Giraffe

5

1922.
74 **4** 5c. black and purple 2·25 20
89 5c. black and green 2·00 1·50
75 10c. black and green 2·25 85
90 10c. black and yellow 3·75 1·50
76 15c. black and red 2·00 10
77 20c. black and orange 1·75 10
78 25c. black 5·50 6·50
91 25c. black and blue 4·00 17·00
79 30c. black and blue 5·00 5·00
92 30c. black and purple 4·00 12·00
80 40c. black and brown 2·75 4·50
81 50c. black and grey 2·00 1·50
82 75c. black and yellow 3·25 18·00
83a **5** 1s. black and green 2·50 11·00
84 2s. black and purple 5·00 15·00
85 3s. black 13·00 28·00
86a 5s. black and red 13·00 75·00
87a 10s. black and blue 50·00 95·00
88a £1 black and orange £150 £300

6

7

1927.
93 **6** 5c. black and green 1·50 10
94 10c. black and yellow 2·00 10
95 15c. black and red 1·50 10
96 20c. black and orange 2·50 10
97 25c. black and blue 3·50 2·00
98 30c. black and purple 2·75 2·50
98a 30c. black and blue 24·00 30
99 40c. black and brown 2·00 4·50
100 50c. black and grey 2·25 1·00
101 75c. black and olive 2·00 12·00
102 **7** 1s. black and green 4·00 2·75
103 2s. black and purple 16·00 4·50
104 3s. black 16·00 48·00
105 5s. black and red 16·00 16·00
106 10s. black and blue 55·00 95·00
107 £1 black and orange £140 £250

8 Teacher and Pupils

15 Freedom Torch over Mt. Kilimanjaro

1961. Independence. Inscr "UHURU 1961".
108 **8** 5c. sepia and green 10 10
109 – 10c. turquoise 10 10
110 – 15c. sepia and blue 10 10
111 – 20c. brown 10 10
112 – 30c. black, green and yellow 10 10
113 – 50c. black and yellow 10 10
114 – 1s. brown, blue and yellow 15 10
115 **15** 1s.30 multicoloured 2·50 10
116 – 2s. multicoloured 60 10
117 – 5s. turquoise and red 75 50
118 – 10s. black, purple and blue 15·00 4·75
119 **15** 20s. multicoloured 4·00 8·50
DESIGNS—VERT (as Type **8**): 10c. District nurse and child; 15c. Coffee picking; 20c. Harvesting maize; 50c. Serengeti lions. HORIZ (as Type **8**): 30c. Tanganyikan flag. (As Type **15**): 1s. "Maternity" (mother with nurse holding baby); 2s. Dar-es-Salaam waterfront; 5s. Land tillage; 10s. Diamond mine.

19 Pres. Nyerere inaugurating Self-help Project

23 Map of Republic

1962. Inauguration of Republic.
120 **19** 30c. green 10 10
121 – 50c. multicoloured 10 10
122 – 1s.30 multicoloured 10 10
123 – 2s.50 black, red and blue 30 50
DESIGNS: 50c. Hoisting flag on Mt. Kilimanjaro; 1s.30, Presidential emblem; 2s.50, Independence monument.

1964. United Republic of Tanganyika and Zanzibar Commemoration.
124 **23** 20c. green and blue 10 10
125 – 30c. blue and sepia 10 10
126 – 1s.30 purple and blue 10 10
127 **23** 2s.50 purple and blue 80 50
DESIGN: 30c., 1s.30, Torch and spear emblem.
Despite the inscription on the stamps they had no validity in Zanzibar.

OFFICIAL STAMPS

1961. Independence stamps of 1961 optd **OFFICIAL**.
O1 5c. brown and green 10 10
O2 10c. turquoise 10 10
O3 15c. brown and blue 10 10
O4 20c. brown 10 10
O5 30c. black, green and yellow 10 10
O6 50c. black and yellow 10 10
O7 1s. brown, blue and yellow 10 10
O8 5s. turquoise and red 75 85

For later issues see **TANZANIA**.

TANZANIA Pt. 1

A republic within the British Commonwealth formerly known as Tanganyika and incorporating Zanzibar.

100 cents = 1 shilling.

NOTE—Stamps inscribed "UGANDA KENYA TANGANYIKA & ZANZIBAR" (or "TANZANIA UGANDA KENYA") will be found listed under Kenya, Uganda and Tanganyika (Tanzania).

For use in Tanzania. Issues to No. 176 were also valid for use in Kenya and Uganda.

25 Hale Hydro-electric Scheme

39 Black-footed Cardinalfish

33 Dar-es-Salaam Harbour

1965.
128 **25** 5c. blue and orange 10 10
129 – 10c. multicoloured 10 10
130 – 15c. multicoloured 10 10
131 – 20c. sepia, green and blue 10 10
132 – 30c. black and brown 10 10
133 – 40c. multicoloured 75 20
134 – 50c. multicoloured 30 10
135 – 65c. green, brown and blue 2·50 2·25
136 **33** 1s. multicoloured 1·25 10
137 – 1s.30 multicoloured 6·50 1·25
138 – 2s.50 blue and brown 6·50 1·25
139 – 5s. brown, green and blue 80 20
140 – 10s. yellow, green and blue 1·00 3·50
141 – 20s. multicoloured 7·00 16·00
DESIGNS—HORIZ (as Type **25**): 10c. Tanzania flag; 20c. Road-building; 50c. Common zebras, Manyara National Park; 65c. Mt. Kilimanjaro. (As Type **33**): 1s.30, Skull of "Zinjanthropus" and excavations, Olduvai Gorge; 2s.50, Fishing; 5s. Sisal industry; 10s. State House, Dar-es-Salaam. VERT (as Type **25**): 15c. National servicemen; 30c. Drum, spear, shield and stool; 40c. Giraffes, Mikumi National Park. (As Type **33**): 20s. Arms of Tanzania.

Z 39 Pres. Nyerere and First Vice-Pres. Karume within Bowl of Flame

1966. 2nd Anniv of United Republic. Mult.
Z142 30c. Type **Z 39** 20 45
Z143 50c. Hands supporting Bowl of Flame 20 45
Z144 1s.30 As 50c. 30 45
Z145 2s.50 Type **Z 39** 40 1·25
Nos. Z142/5 were on sale in Zanzibar only

1967. Fishes. Multicoloured.
142 **39** 5c. mauve, green and black 10 1·75
143 – 10c. brown and bistre 10 10
144 – 15c. grey, blue and black 10 1·25
145 – 20c. brown and green 10 10
146 – 30c. green and black 20 10
147 – 40c. yellow, brown & green 80 10
148 – 50c. multicoloured 20 10
149 – 65c. yellow, green & black 2·00 4·50
150 – 70c. multicoloured 1·00 2·50
151 – 1s. brown, blue and purple 30 10
152 – 1s.30 multicoloured 4·00 10
153a – 1s.50 multicoloured 2·25 10
154 – 2s.50 multicoloured 2·25 2·75
155a – 5s. yellow, black and green 3·25 10
156a – 10s. multicoloured 1·00 10
157a – 20s. multicoloured 5·50 15
DESIGNS—As Type **39**: 10c. Sobrinus mud-skipper; 15c. White-spotted puffer; 20c. Thorny seahorse; 30c. Dusky batfish; 40c. Black-spotted sweetlips; 50c. Blue birdwrasse; 65c. Bennett's butterflyfish; 70c. Black-tipped grouper. 42 × 25mm: 1s. Lionfish; 1s.30, Powder-blue surgeonfish; 1s.50, Yellow-finned fusilier; 2s.50, Emperor snapper; 5s. Moorish idol; 10s. Painted triggerfish; 20s. Horned squirrelfish.

53 "Papilio hornimani"

54 "Euphaedra neophron"

1973. (a) As T **53**.
158 **53** 5c. green, blue and black 60 30
159 – 10c. multicoloured 60 15
160 – 15c. lavender and black 60 30
161 – 20c. brown, yellow & black 70 15
162 – 30c. yellow, orange & black 70 10
163 – 40c. multicoloured 70 15
164 – 50c. multicoloured 1·00 15
165 – 60c. brown, yellow and lake 1·50 20
166 – 70c. green, orange and black 1·50 20

(b) As T **54**.
167 **54** 1s. multicoloured 1·50 15
168 – 1s.50 multicoloured 2·50 45
169 – 2s.50 multicoloured 2·75 80
170 – 5s. multicoloured 2·50 95
171 – 10s. multicoloured 2·75 6·00
172 – 20s. multicoloured 3·25 13·00
BUTTERFLIES: 10c. "Colotis ione"; 15c. "Amauris hyalites" (s sp. "makuyuensis"); 20c. "Libythea labdrea (s sp. "laius"); 30c. "Danaus chrysippus"; 40c. "Asterope rosa"; 50c. "Axiocerses styx"; 60c. "Terias hecabe"; 70c. "Acraea insignis"; 1s. "Euphaedra neophron"; 1s.50, "Precis octavia"; 2s.50, "Charaxes eupale"; 5s. "Charaxes pollux"; 10s. "Salamis parhassus"; 20s. "Papilio ophidicephalus".

1975. Nos. 165, 168/9 and 172 surch.
173 80c. on 60c. "Terias hecabe" 2·00 2·00
174 2s. on 1s.50 "Precis octavia" 3·75 6·00
175 3s. on 2s.50 "Charaxes eupale" 12·00 27·00
176 40s. on 20s. "Papilio ophidicephalus" 5·50 12·00

1976. Telecommunications Development. As Nos. 56/9 of Kenya.
177 50c. Microwave tower 10 10
178 1s. Cordless switchboard 15 10
179 2s. Telephones 25 30
180 3s. Message switching centre 30 40
MS181 120 × 120 mm. Nos. 177/80 1·10 1·50

1976. Olympic Games, Montreal. As Nos. 61/4 of Kenya.
182 50c. Akii Bua, Ugandan hurdler 10 10
183 1s. Filbert Bayi, Tanzanian runner 15 10
184 2s. Steve Muchoki, Kenyan boxer 25 40
185 3s. Olympic flame and East African flags 30 40
MS186 129 × 154 mm. Nos. 182/5 2·50 1·75

1976. Railway Transport. As Nos. 66/9 of Kenya.
187 50c. Diesel-hydraulic train, Tanzania–Zambia Railway 20 10
188 1s. Nile Bridge, Uganda 25 10
189 2s. Nakuru Station, Kenya 35 30
190 3s. Uganda Railway Class A locomotive, 1896 40 45
MS191 154 × 103 mm. Nos. 187/90 4·00 3·50

1977. Game Fish of East Africa. As Nos. 71/4 of Kenya.
192 50c. Nile perch 20 10
193 1s. Nile mouthbrooder 25 10
194 3s. Sailfish 70 40
195 5s. Black marlin 80 60
MS196 153 × 129 mm. Nos. 192/5 2·75 2·50

1977. Second World Black and African Festival of Arts and Culture. As Nos. 76/9 of Kenya.
197 50c. Maasai manyatta (village), Kenya 15 10
198 1s. "Heartbeat of Africa" (Ugandan dancers) 15 10
199 2s. Makonde sculpture 40 70
200 3s. "Early Man and Technology" (skinning hippopotamus) 45 1·00
MS201 132 × 190 mm. Nos. 197/200 1·10 3·00

1977. 25th Anniv of Safari Rally. As Nos. 81/4 of Kenya. Multicoloured.
202 50c. Rally-car and villagers 15 10
203 1s. Starting line 15 10
204 2s. Car fording river 30 40
205 5s. Car and elephants 1·00 1·10
MS206 126 × 93 mm. Nos. 202/5 1·40 2·00

1977. Centenary of Ugandan Church. As Nos. 86/9 of Kenya. Multicoloured.
207 50c. Canon Kivebulaya 10 10
208 1s. Modern Namirembe Cathedral 15 10
209 2s. The first Cathedral 30 40
210 5s. Early congregation Kigezi 60 1·40
MS211 126 × 89 mm. Nos. 207/10 1·00 1·75

1977. Endangered Species. As Nos. 96/100 of Kenya. Multicoloured.
212 50c. Pancake tortoise 40 10
213 1s. Nile crocodile 45 10

214 2s. Hunter's hartebeest . . . 1·40 55
215 3s. Red colobus monkey . . 1·50 75
216 5s. Dugong . . . . 1·75 1·00
MS217 127 × 101 mm. Nos. 213/16 4·75 5·50

56 Prince Philip and President Nyerere

1977. Silver Jubilee. Multicoloured.
218 50c. Type **56** 10 10
219 5s. Pres. Nyerere with Queen and Prince Philip 15 25
220 10s. Jubilee emblem and Commonwealth flags . . . 25 40
221 20s. The Crowning 40 60
MS222 128 × 102 mm. Nos. 218/21 75 1·50

57 Improvements in Rural Living Standards

1978. 1st Anniv of Chama Cha Mapinduzi (New Revolutionary Party).
223 **57** 50c. multicoloured 10 10
224 – 1s. multicoloured 10 10
225 – 3s. multicoloured 25 60
226 – 5s. black, green and yellow 35 85
MS227 142 × 106 mm. Nos. 223/6 1·00 1·40
DESIGNS: 1s. Flag-raising ceremony, Zanzibar; 3s. Handing over of TANU headquarters, Dodoma; 5s. Chairman Julius Nyerere.

1978. World Cup Football Championship. As Nos. 122/5 of Kenya. Multicoloured.
228 50c. Joe Kadenge and forwards 10 10
229 1s. Mohamed Chuma and cup presentation 10 10
230 2s. Omari Kidevu and goal mouth scene 30 70
231 3s. Polly Ouma and forwards 40 90
MS232 136 × 81 mm. Nos. 228/31 2·25 1·75

1979. 25th Anniv of Coronation. Nos. 218/21 optd **25th ANNIVERSARY CORONATION 2nd JUNE 1953.**
233A 50c. Type **56** 10 10
234A 5s. Pres. Nyerere with Queen and Prince Philip 20 30
235A 10s. Jubilee emblem and Commonwealth flags . . . 25 50
236A 20s. The Crowning . . . 40 90
MS237A 128 × 102 mm. Nos. 233A/6A . . . . 75 1·25

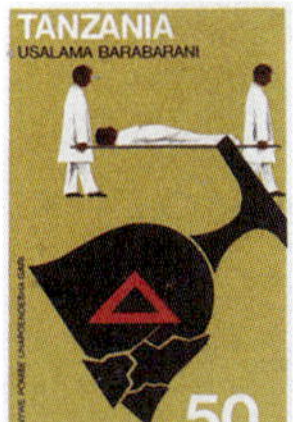

60 "Do not Drink and Drive"

61 Lake Manyara Hotel

1978. Road Safety.
238 **60** 50c. multicoloured 15 10
239 – 1s. multicoloured 20 10
240 – 3s. orange, black and brown 45 70
241 – 5s. multicoloured . . . . . 75 1·40
MS242 92 × 129 mm. Nos. 238/41 1·40 2·00
DESIGNS: 1s. "Show courtesy to young, old and crippled"; 3s. "Observe the Highway Code"; 5s. "Do not drive a faulty vehicle.

1978. Game Lodges. Multicoloured.
243 50c. Type **61** 10 10
244 1s. Lobo Wildlife Lodge . . 10 10
245 3s. Ngorongoro Crater Lodge 20 35
246 5s. Ngorongoro Wildlife Lodge 30 55
247 10s. Mafia Island Lodge . . 40 1·10
248 20s. Mikumi Wildlife Lodge 75 2·75
MS249 118 × 112 mm. Nos. 243/8 5·00 7·50

62 "Racial Suppression"

1978. International Anti-Apartheid Year.
250 **62** 50c. multicoloured 10 10
251 – 1s. black, green and yellow 10 10
252 – 2s.50 multicoloured 30 75
253 – 5s. multicoloured . . . . . 60 1·40
MS254 127 × 132 mm. Nos. 250/3 1·25 2·75
DESIGNS: 1s. "Racial division"; 2s.50, "Racial harmony"; 5s. "Fall of suppression and rise of freedom".

63 Fokker F.27 Friendship

1978. 75th Anniv of Powered Flight. Mult.
255 50c. Type **63** 20 10
256 1s. De Havilland Dragon Mk 1 on Zanzibar Island, 1930's 25 10
257 2s. Concorde . . . . 1·00 75
258 5s. Wright brothers' Flyer I, 1903 . . . . 1·25 1·25
MS259 133 × 97 mm. Nos. 255/8 2·75 3·50

64 Corporation Emblem

1979. 1st Anniv of Tanzania Posts and Telecommunications Corporation. Mult.
260 50c. Type **64** 10 10
261 5s. Headquarters buildings 50 70
MS262 82 × 97 mm. Nos. 260/1 1·00 1·50

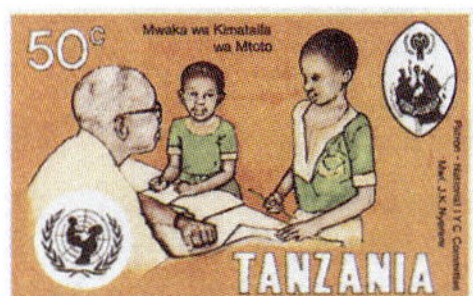

65 Pres. Nyerere (patron of National I.Y.C. Committee) with Children

1979. Int Year of the Child. Mult.
263 50c. Type **65** 10 10
264 1s. Day care centre 15 10
265 2s. "Immunisation" (child being vaccinated) 25 45
266 5s. National I.Y.C. Committee emblem . . . . 40 1·00
MS267 127 × 91 mm. Nos. 263/6 1·25 1·25

1979. Nos. 159 and 166 surch.
268 10c.+30c. multicoloured . . . 1·75 1·50
269 50c. on 70c. green, orange and black . . . . 2·75 2·25
No. 268 was used as a 40c. value.

67 Planting Young Trees

1979. Forest Preservation. Multicoloured.
270 50c. Type **67** 15 10
271 1s. Replacing dead trees with saplings 15 10
272 2s. Rainfall cycle 35 50
273 5s. Forest fire warning . . . 60 1·50

68 Mwenge Earth Satellite Station

1979. Inauguration of Mwenge Earth Satellite Station.
274 **68** 10c. multicoloured 10 10
275 40c. multicoloured 15 10
276 50c. multicoloured 15 10
277 1s. multicoloured 25 20

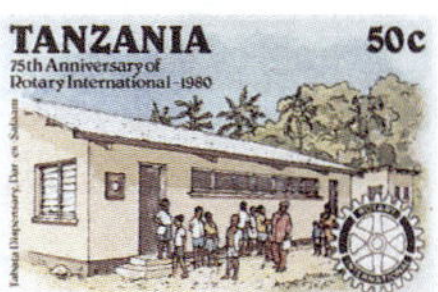

69 Tabata Dispensary, Dar-es-Salaam

1980. 75th Anniv of Rotary International. Multicoloured.
278 50c. Type **69** 10 10
279 1s. Ngomvu Village water project 10 10
280 5s. Flying Doctor service (plane donation) 35 50
281 20s. Torch and 75th anniversary emblem . . . 60 2·00
MS282 120 × 101 mm. Nos. 278/81 1·00 2·25

70 Zanzibar 1896 2r. Stamp and 1964 25c. Definitive

1980. Death Cent of Sir Rowland Hill. Mult.
283 40c. Type **70** 10 10
284 50c. Tanganyika 1962 Independence 50c. commemorative and man attaching stamp to letter (vert) 10 10
285 10s. Tanganyika 1922 25c. stamp and 1961 1s.30 definitive 35 75
286 20s. Penny Black and Sir Rowland Hill (vert) . . . 60 1·40
MS287 158 × 120 mm. Nos. 283/6 1·00 2·00

1980. "London 1980" International Stamp Exhibition. Nos. 283/6 optd **'LONDON 1980' PHILATELIC EXHIBITION.**
288 **70** 40c. multicoloured 10 10
289 – 50c. multicoloured 10 10
290 – 10s. multicoloured 35 75
291 – 20s. multicoloured . . . . 60 1·40
MS292 158 × 120 mm. Nos. 288/91 1·00 2·00

1980. Annual Conference of District 920. Rotary International, Arusha. Nos. 278/81 optd **District 920-55th Annual Conference, Arusha. Tanzania.**
293 **69** 50c. multicoloured 15 10
294 – 1s. multicoloured 15 10
295 – 5s. multicoloured 30 50
296 – 20s. multicoloured . . . . 75 2·00
MS297 120 × 101 mm. Nos. 293/6 1·25 2·25

73 Conference, Tanzanian Posts and Telecommunications Corporation and U.P.U. Emblems

1980. P.A.P.U. (Pan-African Postal Union) Plenipotentiary Conference, Arusha.
298 **73** 50c. black and violet . . . 10 10
299 1s. black and blue 10 10
300 5s. black and red 30 80
301 10s. black and green . . . 65 1·75

74 Gidamis Shahanga (marathon)

75 Spring Hare

1980. Olympic Games, Moscow. Multicoloured.
302 50c. Type **74** 10 15
303 1s. Nzael Kyomo (sprints) . . 15 15
304 10s. Zakayo Malekwa (javelin) . . . . 60 1·00
305 20s. William Lyimo (boxing) 1·00 1·75
MS306 172 × 117 mm. Nos. 302/5 1·25 2·25

1980. Wildlife. Multicoloured.
307 10c. Type **75** 10 15
308 20c. Large-spotted genet . . 10 15
309 40c. Banded mongoose . . . 10 10
310 50c. Ratel 10 10
311 75c. Large-toothed rock hyrax 10 15
312 80c. Leopard 30 15
313 1s. Impala 10 10
314 1s.50 Giraffe 30 20
315 2s. Common zebra 30 30
316 3s. Buffalo 30 30
317 5s. Lion 40 50
318 10s. Black rhinoceros . . . . 1·00 1·40
319 20s. African elephant . . . . 1·00 1·60
320 40s. Cheetah . . . . 1·00 3·25
Nos. 313/20 are larger, 40 × 24 mm.

77 Ngorongoro Conservation Area Authority Emblem

1981. 60th Anniv of Ngorongoro and Serengeti National Parks.
321 **77** 50c. multicoloured 10 10
322 – 1s. black, gold and green 10 10
323 – 5s. multicoloured 30 60
324 – 20s. multicoloured . . . . 80 2·25
DESIGNS: 1s. Tanzania National Parks emblem; 5s. Friends of the Serengeti emblem; 20s. Friends of Ngorongoro emblem.

1981. Royal Wedding. Nos. 220/1 optd **ROYAL WEDDING H.R.H. PRINCE CHARLES 29th JULY 1981.**
325 10s. Jubilee emblem and Commonwealth flags . . . 30 60
326 20s. The Crowning 40 80
MS327 88 × 97 mm. Nos. 325/6 2·00 2·00

79 Mail Runner

1981. Commonwealth Postal Administrations Conference, Arusha. Multicoloured.
328 50c. Type **79** 10 10
329 1s. Letter sorting 10 10
330 5s. Letter Post symbols . . . 30 1·00
331 10s. Flags of Commonwealth nations . . . . 70 2·50
MS332 130 × 100 mm. Nos. 328/31 1·40 3·00

80 Morris Nyunyusa (blind drummer)

1981. International Year of Disabled Persons. Multicoloured.
333 50c. Type **80** 25 10
334 1s. Mgulani Rehabilitation Centre, Dar-es-Salaam . . 30 10
335 5s. Aids for disabled persons 1·00 2·25
336 10s. Disabled children cleaning school compound 1·50 3·75

81 Pres. Mwalimu Julius K. Nyerere

1981. 20th Anniv of Independence. Mult.
337 50c. Type **81** 10 10
338 1s. Electricity plant, Mtoni 10 10
339 3s. Sisal industry 25 90
340 10s. "Universal primary education" . . . . 70 2·50
MS341 120 × 85 mm. Nos. 337/40 1·25 3·00

82 Ostrich **83** Jella Mtaga

1982. Birds. Multicoloured.

342 50c. Type **82** 80 10
343 1s. Secretary bird 85 10
344 5s. Kori bustard 3·00 2·75
345 10s. Saddle-bill stork 3·75 5·50

1982. World Cup Football Championship, Spain. Multicoloured.

346 50c. Type **83** 30 10
347 1s. Football stadium 35 10
348 10s. Diego Maradona 3·00 3·00
349 20s. FIFA emblem 4·75 5·00
MS350 130 × 100 mm. Nos. 346/9 8·00 8·00

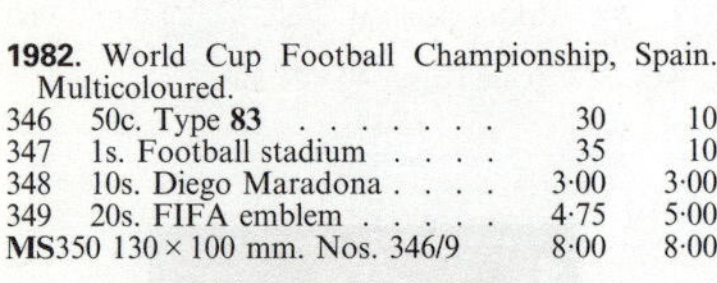

84 "Jade" of Seronera (cheetah) with Cubs

1982. Animal Personalities. Multicoloured.

351 50c. Type **84** 20 10
352 1s. Female golden jackal and cubs 30 10
353 5s. "Fiji" and two sons of "Gombe" (chimpanzees) 50 1·75
354 10s. "Bahati" of Lake Manyara with twins, "Rashidi" and "Ramadhani" (elephants) 1·00 2·75
MS355 120 × 89 mm. Nos. 351/4 1·50 5·00

85 Brick-laying

1982. 75th Anniv of Boy Scout Movement. Multicoloured.

356 50c. Type **85** 15 10
357 1s. Camping 20 10
358 10s. Tracing signs 75 1·50
359 20s. Lord Baden-Powell 1·10 2·75
MS360 130 × 100 mm. Nos. 356/9 2·00 4·00

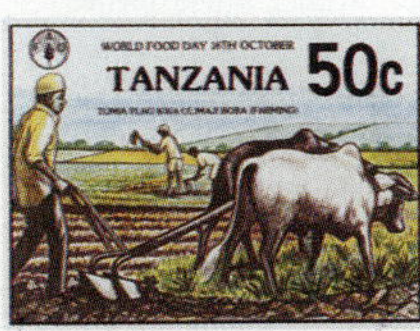

86 Ploughing Field

1982. World Food Day. Multicoloured.

361 50c. Type **86** 10 10
362 1s. Dairy farming 10 10
363 5s. Maize farming 45 60
364 10s. Grain storage 75 1·25
MS365 129 × 99 mm. Nos. 361/4 1·25 2·25

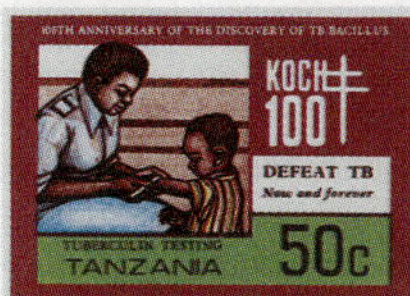

87 Immunization

1982. Centenary of Robert Koch's Discovery of Tubercle Bacillus. Multicoloured.

366 50c. Type **87** 15 10
367 1s. Dr. Robert Koch 20 10
368 5s. International Union against TB emblem 65 1·25
369 10s. World Health Organization emblem 1·25 2·75

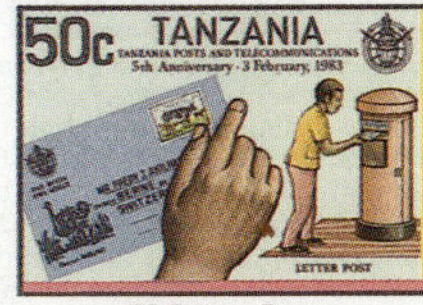

88 Letter Post

1982. 5th Anniv of Posts and Telecommunications Corporation. Multicoloured.

370 50c. Type **88** 10 10
371 1s. Training institute 10 10
372 5s. Satellite communications 35 90
373 10s. U.P.U., I.T.U. and T.P.T.C.C. (Tanzania Post and Telecommunications Corporation) emblems 60 2·00
MS374 126 × 96 mm. Nos. 370/3 1·50 3·00

89 Pres. Mwalimu Julius Nyerere

1982. Commonwealth Day. Multicoloured.

375 50c. Type **89** 10 10
376 1s. Athletics and boxing 15 10
377 5s. Flags of Commonwealth countries 40 90
378 10s. Pres. Nyerere and members of British Royal Family 70 1·90
MS379 121 × 100 mm. Nos. 375/8 1·10 2·75

90 Eastern and Southern African Management Institute, Arusha, Tanzania

1983. 25th Anniv of Economic Commission for Africa. Multicoloured.

380 50c. Type **90** 15 10
381 1s. 25th Anniversary inscription and U.N. logo 20 10
382 5s. Mineral collections 2·75 2·75
383 10s. E.C.A. Silver Jubilee logo and O.A.U. flag 2·75 3·50
MS384 132 × 102 mm. Nos. 380/3 5·75 5·75

91 Telephone Cables

1983. World Communications Year. Mult.

385 50c. Type **91** 10 10
386 1s. W.C.Y. logo 10 10
387 5s. Postal service 50 1·50
388 10s. Microwave tower 75 2·50
MS389 102 × 92 mm. Nos. 385/8 1·50 3·75

92 Bagamoyo Boma

1983. Historical Buildings of Tanzania. Multicoloured.

390 1s. Type **92** 10 10
391 1s.50 Beit el Ajaib, Zanzibar 15 25
392 5s. Anglican Cathedral, Zanzibar 40 1·00
393 10s. Original German Government House and present State House, Dar-es-Salaam 75 2·00
MS394 130 × 100 mm. Nos. 390/3 1·25 3·00

93 Sheikh Abeid Amani Karume (founder of Afro-Shirazi Party)

1984. 20th Anniv of Zanzibar Revolution. Multicoloured.

395 1s. Type **93** 10 10
396 1s.50 Clove farming 15 25
397 5s. Symbol of Industrial Development 40 1·00
398 10s. New housing schemes 75 2·00
MS399 130 × 100 mm. 15s. "Mapinduzi" (ferry) and map 1·25 2·50

94 Boxing

1984. Olympic Games, Los Angeles. Multicoloured.

400 1s. Type **94** 10 10
401 1s.50 Running 15 10
402 5s. Basketball 70 60
403 20s. Football 1·60 2·25
MS404 130 × 100 mm. Nos. 400/3 2·25 2·75

95 Icarus in Flight

1984. 40th Anniv of I.C.A.O. Mult.

405 1s. Type **95** 10 10
406 1s.50 Douglas DC-10, Boeing 737 aircraft and air traffic controller 15 20
407 5s. Boeing 737 undergoing maintenance 55 1·25
408 10s. I.C.A.O. badge 1·10 2·00
MS409 130 × 100 mm. Nos. 405/8 2·40 3·25

96 Sochi Conical House

1984. Traditional Houses. Multicoloured.

410 1s. Type **96** 10 10
411 1s.50 Isyenga circular type 15 20
412 5s. Tembe flatroofed type 40 1·25
413 10s. Banda coastal type 70 2·00
MS414 129 × 99 mm. Nos. 410/13 1·50 3·25

97 Production of Cotton Textiles

1985. 5th Anniv of Southern African Development Co-ordination Conference. Multicoloured.

415 1s.50 Type **97** 30 15
416 4s. Diamond mining 2·00 1·50
417 5s. Map of member countries and means of communication 2·00 1·50
418 20s. Flags and signatures of member countries 2·75 4·00
MS419 110 × 104 mm. Nos. 415/18 8·00 8·00

98 Tortoise

1985. Rare Animals of Zanzibar. Mult.

420 1s. Type **98** 50 10
421 4s. Leopard 1·75 1·50
422 10s. Civet cat 2·25 3·75
423 17s.50 Red colobus monkey (vert) 3·00 5·50
MS424 110 × 93 mm. 15s. Black rhinoceros; 20s. Giant ground pangolin 1·50 3·50

99 The Queen Mother

1985. Life and Times of Queen Elizabeth the Queen Mother. Multicoloured.

425 20s. Type **99** 10 15
426 20s. Queen Mother waving to crowd 10 15
427 100s. Oval portrait with flowers 30 75
428 100s. Head and shoulders portrait 30 75
MS429 Two sheets, each 125 × 63 mm. (a) Nos. 425 and 427. (b) Nos. 426 and 428 Set of 2 sheets 80 2·75

100 Steam Locomotive No. 3022

1985. Tanzanian Railway Steam Locomotives (1st series). Multicoloured.

430 5s. Type **100** 10 15
431 10s. Locomotive No. 3107 15 30
432 20s. Locomotive No. 6004 25 60
433 30s. Locomotive No. 3129 40 90
MS434 125 × 93 mm. Nos. 430/3 80 2·75

See also Nos. 445/9.

1985. Olympic Games Gold Medal Winners, Los Angeles. Nos. 400/3 optd.

435 1s. Type **94** (optd **GOLD MEDAL HENRY TILLMAN USA**) 15 10
436 1s.50 Running (optd **GOLD MEDAL USA**) 20 20
437 5s. Basketball (optd **GOLD MEDAL USA**) 1·75 1·50
438 20s. Football (optd **GOLD MEDAL FRANCE**) 2·25 4·00
MS439 130 × 100 mm. Nos. 435/8 8·00 10·00

102 Cooking and Water Pots

1985. Pottery. Multicoloured.

440 1s.50 Type **102** 20 10
441 2s. Large pot and frying pot with cover 25 15
442 5s. Trader selling pots 60 35
443 40s. Beer pot 2·25 4·50
MS444 129 × 98 mm. 30s. Water pots 4·00 4·00

103 Class 64 Diesel Locomotive

1985. Tanzanian Railway Locomotives (2nd series).

445 **103** 1s.50 multicoloured 50 20
446 – 2s. multicoloured 50 30
447 – 5s. multicoloured 75 75
448 – 10s. multicoloured 1·00 1·75
449 – 30s. black, brown and red 2·25 3·75
MS450 130 × 100 mm. 15s. black, brown and pink; 20s. black, brown and pink 9·00 8·00

DESIGNS: 2s. Class 36 diesel locomotive; 5s. DFH1013 diesel shunter; 10s. DE1001 diesel-electric locomotive; 15s. Class 30 steam locomotive; 20s. Class II steam locomotive; 30s. Steam locomotive, Zanzibar, 1906.

104 Young Pioneers

1986. International Youth Year.

451 **104** 1s.50 multicoloured 15 15
452 – 4s. brown, light brown and black 20 50
453 – 10s. multicoloured 50 1·25
454 – 20s. brown, light brown and black 1·10 2·50
MS455 130 × 100 mm. 30s. brown, light brown and black 2·25 3·50

DESIGNS: 4s. Child health care; 10s. Uhuru Torch Race; 20s. Young workers and globe; 30s. Young people farming.

105 Rolls-Royce "20/25" (1936)

1986. Centenary of Motoring. Multicoloured.

456 1s.50 Type **105** 10 10
457 5s. Rolls-Royce "Phantom II" (1933) 15 25
458 10s. Rolls-Royce "Phantom I" (1926) 25 60
459 30s. Rolls-Royce "Silver Ghost" (1907) 40 2·00
MS460 125 × 93 mm. Nos. 456/9 80 2·50

106 Rotary Logo and Staunton Queen Chess Piece

1986. World Chess Championships, London and Leningrad.
461 **106** 20s. blue and mauve . . . 35 50
462 – 100s. multicoloured . . . 50 2·50
MS463 124 × 64 mm. Nos. 461/2 1·10 3·25
DESIGN: 100s. Hand moving rook on board.
No. 461 also commemorates Rotary International.

107 Mallard

1986. Birth Bicentenary (1985) of John J. Audubon (ornithologist). Multicoloured.
464 5s. Type **107** 15 35
465 10s. Eider ("American Eider") 25 60
466 20s. Scarlet ibis . . . . . . 30 1·25
467 30s. Roseate spoonbill . . . 40 1·40
MS468 122 × 91 mm. Nos. 464/7 1·00 3·50

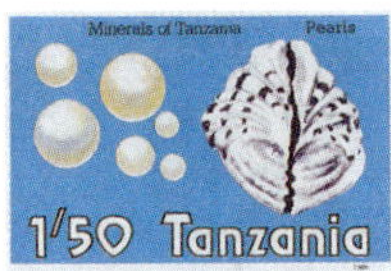

108 Pearls

1986. Tanzanian Minerals. Multicoloured.
469 1s.50 Type **108** 80 15
470 2s. Sapphire . . . . 1·10 65
471 5s. Tanzanite . . . . 2·00 1·25
472 40s. Diamonds . . . . 7·25 10·00
MS473 130 × 100 mm. 30s. Rubies 13·00 13·00

110 "Hibiscus calyphyllus" **111** Oryx

1986. Flowers of Tanzania. Multicoloured.
474 1s.50 Type **110** 10 10
475 5s. "Aloe graminicola" . . . 15 25
476 10s. "Nersium oleander" . . 20 45
477 30s. "Nymphaea caerulea" . . 40 2·00
MS478 90 × 119 mm. Nos. 474/7 75 2·50

1986. Endangered Animals of Tanzania. Multicoloured.
479 5s. Type **111** 15 15
480 10s. Giraffe 20 35
481 20s. Rhinoceros 25 85
482 30s. Cheetah . . . . 25 1·40
MS483 91 × 121 mm. Nos. 479/82 75 3·25

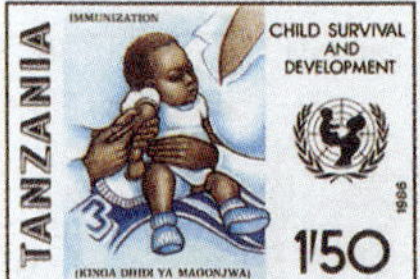

112 Immunization

1986. U.N.I.C.E.F. Child Survival Campaign. Multicoloured.
484 1s.50 Type **112** 25 10
485 2s. Growth monitoring . . . 35 15
486 5s. Oral rehydration therapy 60 40
487 40s. Breast-feeding . . . . . 2·75 4·50
MS488 110 × 101 mm. 30s. Healthy baby . . . . 1·00 1·75

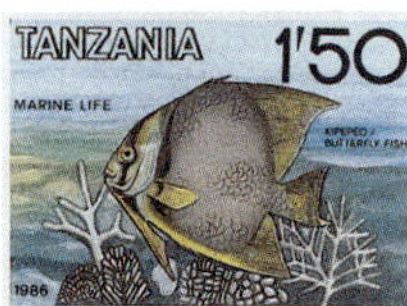

113 Angelfish

1986. Marine Life. Multicoloured.
489 1s.50 Type **113** 70 10
490 4s. Parrotfish . . . . 1·50 85
491 10s. Turtle . . . . 2·25 2·75
492 20s. Octopus . . . . 3·50 5·50
MS493 131 × 101 mm. 30s. Corals 2·50 2·50

114 Team Captains shaking Hands

1986. World Cup Football Championship, Mexico. Multicoloured.
494 1s.50 Type **114** 15 10
495 2s. Referee sending player off 15 10
496 10s. Goalkeeper and ball in net . . . . 60 1·00
497 20s. Goalkeeper saving ball 1·00 2·25
MS498 95 × 72 mm. 30s. Winning Argentine team . . . . 1·10 1·25

115 Pres. Nyerere receiving Beyond War Award

1986. International Peace Year. Mult.
499 1s.50 Type **115** 30 10
500 2s. Children of many races 50 20
501 10s. African cosmonaut and rocket launch . . . . . . 1·25 1·75
502 20s. United Nations Headquarters, New York 1·75 3·50
MS503 109 × 86 mm. 30s. International Peace Year symbols 2·75 4·25

116 Mobile Bank Service

1987. 20th Anniv of National Bank of Commerce. Multicoloured.
504 1s.50 Type **116** 30 10
505 2s. National Bank of Commerce Head Office . . 50 20
506 5s. Pres. Mwinyi laying foundation stone 80 90
507 20s. Cotton harvesting . . . 2·00 3·25

117 Parade of Young Party Members

1987. 10th Anniv of Chama Cha Mapinduzi Party and 20th Anniv of Arusha Declaration. Mult.
508 2s. Type **117** 15 10
509 3s. Harvesting coffee 15 10
510 10s. Pres. Nyerere addressing Second Peace Initiative Reunion 20 30
511 30s. Presidents Julius Nyerere and Ali Hassan Mwinyi . . 35 1·25

118 Nungu Nungu Hair Style **121** "Apis mellifera" (bee)

120 Royal Family on Buckingham Palace Balcony after Trooping the Colour

1987. Traditional Hair Styles. Multicoloured.
512 1s.50 Type **118** 30 10
513 2s. Upanga wa jogoo style . . 45 20
514 10s. Morani style . . . . . . 80 1·25
515 20s. Twende kilioni style . . 1·50 2·50
MS516 110 × 99 mm. 30s. Hair plaiting . . . . 2·75 3·50

1987. 60th Birthday (1986) of Queen Elizabeth II. Multicoloured.
517 5s. Type **120** 15 20
518 10s. Queen and Prince Philip at Royal Ascot 20 25
519 40s. Queen Elizabeth II . . . 60 1·10
520 60s. Queen Elizabeth with crowd . . . . 80 1·60
MS521 125 × 90 mm. Nos. 517/20 1·50 3·50

1987. Insects. Multicoloured.
522 1s.50 Type **121** 60 15
523 2s. "Prostephanus truncatus" (grain borer) 80 25
524 10s. "Glossina palpalis" (tsetse fly) . . . . 1·50 2·00
525 20s. "Polistes sp." (wasp) . . 2·25 4·25
MS526 110 × 101 mm. 30s. "Anopheles" sp (mosquito) . . 3·75 5·00

122 Crocodile

1987. Reptiles. Multicoloured.
527 2s. Type **122** 75 25
528 3s. Black-striped grass-snake 80 30
529 10s. Adder . . . . 1·60 1·60
530 20s. Green mamba . . . . . 2·25 3·25
MS531 101 × 101 mm. 30s. Tortoise 1·00 1·00

123 Emblems of Posts/ Telecommunications and Railways

1987. 10th Anniv of Tanzania Communications and Transport Corporations. Multicoloured.
532 2s. Type **123** 50 30
533 8s. Emblems of Air Tanzania and Harbours Authority 75 95
MS534 100 × 66 mm. 20s. Methods of transport and communication 2·50 1·75

124 Basketry

1987. Traditional Handicrafts. Multicoloured.
535 2s. Type **124** 15 10
536 3s. Decorated gourds 15 15
537 10s. Stools 30 30
538 20s. Makonde carvings . . . 50 55
MS539 89 × 89 mm. 40s. Makonde carver at work 65 75

1987. 10th Anniv of Tanzania–Zambia Railway (1986). Nos. 445/9 optd **10th Anniversary of TANZANIA ZAMBIA RAILWAY AUTHORITY 1976-1986**.
540 **103** 1s.50 multicoloured . . . 70 30
541 – 2s. multicoloured 75 30
542 – 5s. multicoloured . . . . 1·10 90
543 – 10s. multicoloured . . . . 1·60 1·75
544 – 30s. black, brown and red 2·75 5·00

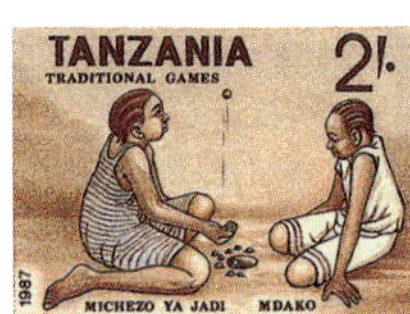

126 Mdako (pebble game)

1988. Traditional Pastimes. Multicoloured.
545 2s. Type **126** 10 10
546 3s. Wrestling 10 10
547 8s. Bull fighting, Zanzibar . . 15 15
548 20s. Bao (board game) . . . 35 35
MS549 100 × 90 mm. 30s. Archery 70 80

127 Plateosaurus

1988. Prehistoric and Modern Animals. Mult.
550 2s. Type **127** 50 65
551 3s. Pteranodon 50 65
552 5s. Apatosaurus ("Brontosaurus") 60 65
553 7s. Lion 60 75
554 8s. Tiger 75 80
555 12s. Orang-utan 75 85
556 20s. Elephant . . . . 1·10 1·50
557 100s. Stegosaurus . . . . . 1·75 3·25

128 Marchers with Party Flag

1988. National Solidarity Walk. Mult.
558 2s.+1s. Type **128** 25 25
559 3s.+1s. Pres. Mwinyi leading Walk 25 25
MS560 121 × 121 mm. 50s.+1s. Pres. Ali Hassan Mwinyi (35 × 25 mm) 75 85

129 Population Symbols on Map

1988. 3rd National Population Census. Mult.
561 2s. Type **129** 10 10
562 3s. Census official at work . . 10 10
563 10s. Community health care 15 15
564 20s. Population growth 1967–88 . . . . 30 30
MS565 96 × 91 mm. 40s. Development of modern Tanzania 65 65

130 Javelin

1988. Olympic Games, Seoul (1st issue). Mult.
566 2s. Type **130** 70 15
567 3s. Hurdling 70 15
568 7s. Long distance running . . 1·25 40
569 12s. Relay racing . . . . . . 1·40 70
MS570 100 × 70 mm. 40s. Badminton . . . . 3·50 1·50

131 Football **132** Goat

1988. Olympic Games, Seoul (2nd issue). Mult.
571 10s. Type **131** 25 10
572 20s. Cycling 60 25
573 50s. Fencing 70 50
574 70s. Volleyball 80 65
MS575 77 × 92 mm. 100s. Gymnastics . . . . 1·50 2·00

1988. Winter Olympic Games, Calgary. As T **131**. Multicoloured.
576 5s. Cross-country skiing . . . 50 20
577 25s. Figure skating . . . . . 1·00 30
578 50s. Downhill skiing . . . . 1·60 80
579 75s. Bobsleighing . . . . . . 1·90 1·50
MS580 77 × 92 mm. 100s. Ice hockey sticks wrapped in Olympic and Canadian colours . . . . 2·25 1·25

1988. Domestic Animals. Multicoloured.
581 4s. Type **132** 30 30
582 5s. Rabbit (horiz) 30 30
583 8s. Cows (horiz) 40 40
584 10s. Kitten (horiz) 80 70
585 12s. Pony . . . . 1·10 85
586 20s. Puppy . . . . 1·50 1·25
MS587 102 × 73 mm. 100s. Chicken (horiz) . . . . 1·75 1·75

133 "Love You, Dad" (Pinocchio)

1988. Greetings Stamps. Walt Disney cartoon characters. Multicoloured.
588 4s. Type **133** 10 10
589 5s. "Happy Birthday" (Brer Rabbit and Chip n' Dale) 10 10
590 10s. "Trick or Treat" (Daisy and Donald Duck) 15 15
591 12s. "Be Kind to Animals" (Ferdie and Mordie with Pluto) 15 15
592 15s. "Love" (Daisy and Donald Duck) 20 20
593 20s. "Let's Celebrate" (Mickey Mouse and Goofy) 30 30
594 30s. "Keep in Touch" (Daisy and Donald Duck) 65 65
595 50s. "Love you, Mom" (Minnie Mouse with Ferdie and Mordie) . . . . 1·25 1·25
MS596 Two sheets, each 127×101 mm. (a) 150s. "Let's work together" (Goofy dressed as a fireman). (b) 150s. "Have a super Sunday" (Goofy dressed as American footballer) Set of 2 sheets . . . . 4·75 4·50

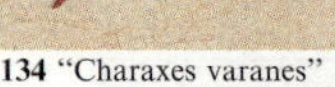

134 "Charaxes varanes" 135 Independence Torch and Mt. Kilimanjaro

1988. Butterflies. Multicoloured.
597 8s. Type **134** 50 10
598 30s. "Neptis melicerta" . . . 90 30
599 40s. "Mylothris chloris" . . . 1·00 40
600 50s. "Charaxes bohemani" . . 1·25 50
601 60s. "Myrina silenus" . . . . 1·40 70
602 75s. "Papilio phorcas" . . . 1·90 90
603 90s. "Cyrestis camillus" . . . 2·25 1·10
604 100s. "Salamis temora" . . . 2·25 1·25
MS605 Two sheets, each 80×50 mm. (a) 200s. "Asterope rosa". (b) 250s. "Kallima rumia" Set of 2 sheets . . . . 8·00 6·00

1988. National Monuments. Multicoloured.
606 5s. Type **135** 10 10
607 12s. Arusha Declaration Monument 10 10
608 30s. Askari Monument . . . 25 30
609 60s. Independence Monument 55 60
MS610 100×89 mm. 100s. Askari Monument statue . . . . . . 1·25 1·40

136 Eye Clinic

1988. 25th Anniv of Dar-es-Salaam Lions Club. Multicoloured.
611 2s. Type **136** 20 20
612 3s. Family at shallow water well 20 20
613 7s. Rhinoceros and outline map of Tanzania . . . . . 2·00 30
614 12s. Club presenting school desks 30 45
MS615 100×65 mm. 40s. Lions International logo . . . . . . 1·00 1·00

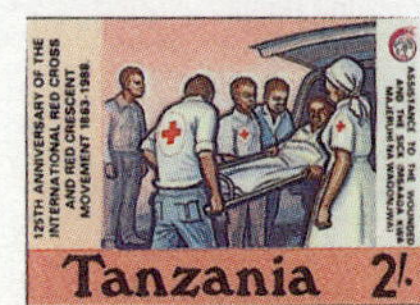

137 Loading Patient into Ambulance

1988. 125th Anniv of International Red Cross and Red Crescent. Multicoloured.
616 2s. Type **137** 20 20
617 3s. Mother and baby health clinic 20 20
618 7s. Red Cross flag 40 30
619 12s. Henri Dunant (founder) 45 45
MS620 90×90 mm. 40s. Members of Red Cross International Committee, 1863 . . . . . . 1·00 1·00

138 Paradise Whydah 139 Bushbaby

1989. Birds. Multicoloured.
621 20s. Type **138** 90 85
622 20s. Black-collared barbet . . 90 85
623 20s. Bateleur 90 85
624 20s. Lilac-breasted roller and African open-bill storks in flight 90 85
625 20s. Red-tufted malachite sunbird and African open-bill stork in flight . . . 90 85
626 20s. Dark chanting goshawk 90 85
627 20s. White-fronted bee eater, carmine bee eater and little bee eaters 90 85
628 20s. Narina's trogon and marabou stork in flight . . 90 85
629 20s. Grey parrot 90 85
630 20s. Hoopoe 90 85
631 20s. Masked lovebird ("Yellow-collared lovebird") 90 85
632 20s. Yellow-billed hornbill . . 90 85
633 20s. Hammerkop 90 85
634 20s. Violet-crested turaco and flamingos in flight . . . 90 85
635 20s. Malachite kingfisher . . 90 85
636 20s. Greater flamingos . . . 90 85
637 20s. Yellow-billed storks . . 90 85
638 20s. Whale-headed stork ("Shoebill stork") 90 85
639 20s. Saddle-bill stork and blacksmith plover 90 85
640 20s. South African crowned crane 90 85
MS641 Two sheets, each 105×75 mm. (a) 350s. Helmeted guineafowl (28×42 mm). (b) 350s. Ostrich (28×42 mm) Set of 2 sheets . . . . 11·00 6·00
Nos. 622/40 were printed together, se-tenant, forming a composite design of birds at a waterhole.

1989. Fauna and Flora. Multicoloured.
642 5s. Type **139** 15 15
643 10s. Bushbaby holding insect (horiz) 20 20
644 20s. Bushbaby on forked branch 30 30
645 30s. Black cobra on umbrella acacia 60 60
646 45s. Bushbaby at night (horiz) 60 60
647 70s. Red-billed tropic bird and tree ferns . . . . . . 3·50 3·25
648 100s. African tree frog on cocoa tree . . . . 3·50 3·50
649 150s. Black-headed heron and Egyptian papyrus . . . . . 6·50 7·00
MS650 Two sheets. (a) 115×85 mm. 350s. African palm civet (horiz). (b) 65×65 mm. 350s. Pink-backed pelican and baobab Tree (horiz) Set of 2 sheets . . . . 10·00 6·00
Nos. 646, 648/9 and **MS**650 are without the World Wildlife Fund logo.

140 Juma Ikangaa (marathon runner) 142 Chama Cha Mapinduzi Party Flag

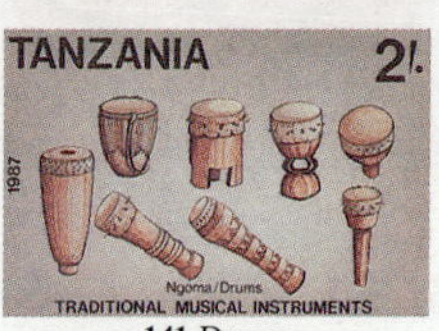

141 Drums

1989. International Sporting Personalities. Mult.
651 4s. Type **140** 15 15
652 8s.50 Steffi Graf (tennis player) . . . . 1·00 30
653 12s. Yannick Noah (tennis player) 80 40
654 40s. Pele (footballer) 90 65
655 100s. Erhard Keller (speed skater) . . . . 1·00 80
656 125s. Sadanoyama (sumo wrestler) . . . . 1·25 1·00
657 200s. Taino (sumo wrestler) 1·75 1·75
658 250s. T. Nakajima (golfer) . . 5·50 2·75
MS659 Two sheets. (a) 100×71 mm. 350s. Joe Louis (boxer). (b) 100×76 mm. 350s. I. Aoki (golfer) Set of 2 sheets . . . . . . 11·00 6·00
The captions on Nos. 658 and **MS**659b are transposed.

1989. Musical Instruments. Multicoloured.
660 2s. Type **141** 65 25
661 3s. Xylophones 65 25
662 10s. Thumbpiano . . . . . 1·00 1·00
663 20s. Fiddles . . . . 1·60 3·50
MS664 91×80 mm. 40s. Violins with calebash resonators . . . . . 1·00 1·00

1989. National Solidarity Walk. Mult.
665 5s.+1s. Type **142** 25 25
666 10s.+1s. Marchers with party flag and President Mwinyi 25 25
MS667 122×122 mm. 50s.+1s. President Mwinyi (vert) 60 60

143 Class P36 Locomotive, Russia, 1953

1989. Steam Locomotives. Multicoloured.
668 10s. Type **143** 75 35
669 25s. Class 12 streamlined locomotive, Belgium, 1939 85 45
670 60s. Class C62 locomotive, Japan, 1948 . . . . 1·25 1·00
671 75s. Pennsylvania Railroad Class T1 streamlined locomotive, U.S.A., 1942 1·40 1·25
672 80s. Class WP locomotive, India, 1946 . . . . 1·50 1·25
673 90s. East African Railways Class 59 Garratt locomotive No. 5919 . . . 1·60 1·50
674 150s. Class "People" locomotive No. 1206, China . . . . 2·00 2·50
675 200s. Southern Pacific "Daylight" express, U.S.A 2·00 2·50
MS676 Two sheets, each 114×85 mm. (a) 350s. Stephenson's "Planet", Great Britain, 1830 (vert). (b) 350s. L.M.S. "Coronation Scot", Great Britain, 1937 (vert) Set of 2 sheets 6·00 7·50

1989. "World Stamp Expo '89" International Stamp Exhibition, Washington. Landmarks of Washington. sheet 78×62 mm, containing design as T **201b** of St. Vincent, but vert.
MS677 500s. Union Station . . . 4·00 5·50

144 "Luna 3" Satellite orbiting Moon, 1959

1989. History of Space Exploration and 20th Anniv of First Manned Landing on Moon. Multicoloured.
678 20s. Type **144** 65 40
679 30s. "Gemini 6" and "7", 1965 . . . . 75 45
680 40s. Astronaut Edward White in space, 1965 . . . . . . 85 55
681 60s. Astronaut Aldrin on Moon, 1969 . . . . . . 1·25 90
682 70s. Aldrin performing experiment, 1969 . . . . . 1·40 1·00
683 100s. "Apollo 15" astronaut and lunar rover, 1971 . . . 1·60 1·40
684 150s. "Apollo 18" and "Soyuz 19" docking in space, 1975 . . . . 1·90 2·25
685 200s. Spacelab, 1983 . . . . 2·00 2·50
MS686 Two sheets, each 110×90 mm. (a) 250s. Lunar module "Eagle" and "Apollo 11" emblem. (b) 250s. Projected U.S. space station Set of 2 sheets . . 6·50 7·00

1989. Olympic Medal Winners, Calgary and Seoul. Various stamps optd. (a) Nos. 571/4.
687 10s. Type **131** (optd **Gold-USSR Silver-Brazil Bronze-W. Germany**) 70 40
688 20s. Cycling (optd **Men's Match Sprint, Lutz Hesslich, DDR**) . . . . . 2·75 1·00
689 50s. Fencing (optd **Epee, Schmitt, W. Germany**) . . 1·75 1·40
690 70s. Volleyball (optd **Men's Team, USA**) . . . . . . 2·50 2·50
MS691 77×92 mm. 100s. Gymnastics (optd **Women's Team, Gold — USSR**) . . . . . . 3·00 3·75

(b) Nos. 576/9.
692 5s. Cross-country skiing (optd **Biathlon, Peter-Roetsch, DDR**) 60 40
693 25s. Figure skating (optd **Pairs, Gordeeva & Grinkov, USSR**) . . . . 1·25 75
694 50s. Downhill skiing (optd **Zurbriggen, Switzerland**) . . 2·00 1·60
695 75s. Bobsleighing (optd **Gold-USSR Silver-DDR Bronze-DDR**) . . . . 2·50 2·25
MS696 77×92 mm. 100s. Ice hockey sticks wrapped in Olympic and Canadian colours (optd **Ice Hockey: Gold — USSR**) . . . 7·00 7·00

146 Spotted Tilapia

1989. Reef and Freshwater Fishes of Tanzania. Multicoloured.
697 9s. Type **146** 70 40
698 13s. Painted triggerfish . . . 70 40
699 20s. Powder-blue surgeonfish 90 50
700 40s. Red-tailed butterflyfish 1·40 75
701 70s. Red-tailed notho . . . 1·75 1·25
702 100s. Ansorge's neolebias . . 2·25 1·75
703 150s. Blue panchax . . . . . 2·50 2·75
704 200s. Regal angelfish . . . . 2·50 2·75
MS705 Two sheets, each 112×83 mm. (a) 350s. Jewel cichlid (50×38 mm). (b) 350s. Dusky batfish (38×50 mm) Set of 2 sheets . . . . 12·00 12·00

147 Rural Polling Station

1989. Centenary of Inter-Parliamentary Union.
706 **147** 9s. multicoloured 10 10
707 – 13s. multicoloured 10 10
708 – 80s. multicoloured 40 55
709 – 100s. black, ultram & bl 50 75
MS710 90×90 mm. 40s. multicoloured . . . . 70 1·25
DESIGNS: 13s. Parliament Building, Dar-es-Salaam; 40s. Sir William Randal Cremer and Frederic Passy (founders); 80s. Tanzania Parliament in session; 100s. Logo.

148 Logo

1990. 10th Anniv of Pan-African Postal Union.
711 **148** 9s. yellow, green and black 15 15
712 – 13s. multicoloured 15 15
713 – 70s. multicoloured . . . . 1·25 90
714 – 100s. multicoloured . . . 2·25 2·00
MS715 90×90 mm. 40s. multicoloured . . . . 1·50 2·25
DESIGNS: 13s. Collecting mail from post office box; 40s. Logos of Tanzania Posts and Telecommunications Corporation, P.A.P.U. and U.P.U.; 70s. Taking mail to post office; 100s. Mail transport.

149 Admiral's Flag and "Nina"

1990. 500th Anniv (1992) of Discovery of America by Columbus (50, 60, 75, 200s.) and Modern Scientific Discoveries (others). Multicoloured.
716 9s. Bell XS-1 aircraft (first supersonic flight, 1947) . . 60 50
717 13s. "Trieste" (bathyscaphe) (first dive to depth of 35,000 ft, 1960) 60 50
718 50s. Type **149** . . . . 1·25 90
719 60s. Fleet flag and "Pinta" 1·25 1·10
720 75s. Standard of Castile and Leon and "Santa Maria" 1·50 1·25
721 150s. Transistor technology 1·25 2·00
722 200s. Arms of Columbus and map of First Voyage . . . 2·50 2·75
723 250s. DNA molecule . . . . 2·75 2·75
MS724 Two sheets, each 106×78 mm. (a) 350s. Caravels in the Caribbean. (b) 350s. "Voyager II" and Neptune Set of 2 sheets 5·50 7·00

150 Tecopa Pupfish

1990. Extinct Species. Multicoloured.
725 25s. Type **150** 80 60
726 40s. Thylacine 1·25 1·00
727 50s. Quagga 1·50 1·10
728 60s. Passenger pigeon 2·25 1·75
729 75s. Rodriguez saddleback tortoise 2·00 1·75
730 100s. Toolache wallaby 2·25 2·00
731 150s. Texas red wolf 2·25 2·50
732 200s. Utah lake sculpin 2·25 2·50
MS733 Two sheets. (a) 102 × 74 mm. 350s. South Island Whekau. (b) 71 × 99 mm. 350s. Hawaii O-o (vert) Set of 2 sheets 11·00 11·00

151 Camping

1990. 60th Anniv of Girl Guides Movement in Tanzania. Multicoloured.
734 9s. Type **151** 15 20
735 13s. Guides planting sapling 15 20
736 50s. Guide teaching woman to write 40 65
737 100s. Guide helping at child-care clinic 65 1·10
MS738 89 × 89 mm. 40s. Guide teaching child to read (vert) 1·00 1·25

152 Fishing

1990. 25th Anniv of Union of Tanganyika and Zanzibar. Multicoloured.
739 9s. Type **152** 35 30
740 13s. Vineyard 35 30
741 50s. Cloves 1·25 1·25
742 100s. Presidents Nyerere and Karume exchanging Union instruments (vert) 2·25 3·25
MS743 90 × 90 mm. 40s. Arms (vert) 2·25 2·50

153 Footballer

154 Miriam Makeba

1990. World Cup Football Championship, Italy (1st issue). Multicoloured.
744 25s. Type **153** 1·50 30
745 60s. Player passing ball 2·00 90
746 75s. Player turning 2·25 1·25
747 200s. Player kicking ball 4·50 5·50
MS748 Two sheets, each 105 × 76 mm. (a) 350s. Two players fighting for possession. (b) 350s. Player kicking ball Set of 2 sheets 11·00 10·00
See also Nos. 789/92 and 794/7.

1990. Famous Black Entertainers. Mult.
749 9s. Type **154** 15 10
750 13s. Manu Dibango 15 10
751 25s. Fela 20 15
752 70s. Smokey Robinson 1·00 40
753 100s. Gladys Knight 1·10 55
754 150s. Eddie Murphy 2·25 2·25
755 200s. Sammy Davis Jnr. 2·50 2·75
756 250s. Stevie Wonder 2·50 3·00
MS757 Two sheets, each 69 × 88 mm. (a) 350s. Bill Cosby (30 × 39 mm). (b) 350s. Michael Jackson (30 × 39 mm) Set of 2 sheets 4·25 5·00

155 Ring of People round Party Flag

1990. Solidarity Walk, 1990. Multicoloured.
758 9s.+1s. Type **155** 80 90
759 13s.+1s. President Mwinyi 80 90
MS760 90 × 90 mm. 50s.+1s. Handclasp on map (vert) 1·50 2·00

156 Diesel Train

157 Pope John Paul II

1990. 10th Anniv of Southern African Development Co-ordination Conference. Multicoloured.
761 8s. Type **156** 1·00 40
762 11s.50 Paper-making plant 25 20
763 25s. Tractor factory and ploughing 30 20
764 100s. Map and national flags 3·00 3·25
MS765 89 × 89 mm. 50s. Map of Southern Africa 2·75 3·00

1990. Papal Visit to Tanzania. Multicoloured.
766 10s. Type **157** 20 15
767 15s. Pope in ceremonial robes 25 15
768 20s. Pope giving blessing 30 15
769 100s. Papal coat of arms 80 1·10
MS770 172 × 143 mm. 50s. Pope John Paul II (horiz); 50s. St. Joseph's Cathedral, Dar-es-Salaam (horiz); 50s. Christ the King Cathedral, Moshi (horiz); 50s. Saint Theresa's Cathedral, Tabora (horiz); 50s. Cathedral of the Epiphany, Bugando Mwanza (horiz); 50s. St. Mathias Mulumba Kalemba Cathedral, Songea (horiz) 3·50 3·75

158 Mickey and Minnie Mouse in Herby the Love Bug

1990. Motor Cars from Disney Films. Mult.
771 20s. Type **158** 30 30
772 30s. The Absent-minded Professor's car 35 35
773 45s. Chitty-Chitty Bang-Bang 45 45
774 60s. Mr. Toad's car 65 65
775 75s. Scrooge's limousine 75 75
776 100s. The Shaggy Dog's car 1·00 1·00
777 150s. Donald Duck's nephews cleaning car 1·60 1·60
778 200s. Fire engine from "Dumbo" 1·75 1·75
MS779 Two sheets, each 127 × 112 mm. (a) 350s. The Mickeymobile. (b) 350s. Cruella De Vil and dog wagon from "101 Dalmations" Set of 2 sheets 8·50 8·50

159 "St. Mary Magdalen in Penitence" (detail)

160 Klinsmann of West Germany

1990. Paintings by Titian. Multicoloured.
780 5s. Type **159** 10 10
781 10s. "Averoldi Polyptych" (detail) 10 10
782 15s. "Saint Margaret" (detail) 15 15
783 50s. "Venus and Adonis" (detail) 40 40
784 75s. "Venus and the Lutenist" (detail) 55 55
785 100s. "Tarquin and Lucretia" (detail) 70 70
786 125s. "Saint Jerome" (detail) 90 90
787 150s. "Madonna and Child in Glory with Saints" (detail) 1·00 1·00
MS788 Three sheets. (a) 95 × 110 mm. 300s. "Adoration of the Holy Trinity" (detail). (b) 95 × 110 mm. 300s. "St. Catherine of Alexandria at Prayer" (detail). (c) 110 × 95 mm. 300s. "The Supper at Emmaus" (detail) Set of 3 sheets 9·00 10·00

1990. World Cup Football Championship, Italy (2nd issue). Multicoloured.
789 10s. Type **160** 50 30
790 60s. Serena of Italy 90 60
791 100s. Nicol of Scotland 1·75 1·75
792 300s. Susic of Yugoslavia 3·25 4·00
MS793 Two sheets, each 85 × 95 mm. (a) 400s. Montero of Costa Rica. (b) 400s. Seifo of Belgium Set of 2 sheets 10·00 10·00

161 Throw-in

1990. World Cup Football Championship, Italy (3rd issue). Multicoloured.
794 9s. Type **161** 50 20
795 13s. Penalty kick 50 20
796 25s. Dribbling 70 25
797 100s. Corner kick 2·00 2·50
MS798 82 × 82 mm. 50s. World Cup and world map 2·75 3·00

162 Canoe

163 Lesser Masked Weaver

164 Lesser Flamingo

1990. Marine Transport. Multicoloured.
799 9s. Type **162** 15 20
800 13s. Sailing canoe 20 20
801 25s. Dhow 70 25
802 100s. Freighter 2·75 2·75
MS803 90 × 90 mm. 40s. Mashua dhow 2·50 3·00

1990. Birds. Designs as T **163** (5s. to 30s.) or T **164** (40s. to 500s.). Multicoloured.
804 5s. Type **163** 15 40
805 9s. African emerald cuckoo 20 10
806 13s. Little bee eater 30 10
807 15s. Red bishop 30 10
808 20s. Bateleur 40 10
809 25s. Scarlet-chested sunbird 40 10
809a 30s. African wood pigeon 40 15
810 40s. Type **164** 40 15
811 70s. Helmeted guineafowl 45 30
812 100s. Eastern white pelican 55 30
813 170s. Saddle-bill stork 70 85
814 200s. South African crowned crane 80 90
814a 300s. Pied crow 90 1·25
814b 400s. White-headed vulture 1·00 1·60
815 500s. Ostrich 1·10 1·60
MS816 100 × 102 mm. 40s. Superb starling; 60s. Lilac-breasted roller 3·25 3·75

165 Athletics

1990. 14th Commonwealth Games, Auckland, New Zealand. Multicoloured.
817 9s. Type **165** 45 20
818 13s. Netball (vert) 70 20
819 25s. Pole vaulting 1·00 25
820 100s. Long jumping (vert) 2·25 2·75
MS821 100 × 100 mm. 40s. Boxing (vert) 1·75 2·25

166 Former German Post Office, Dar-es-Salaam

1991. 150th Anniv of the Penny Black and "Stamp World London 90" International Stamp Exhibition. Multicoloured.
822 50s. Type **166** 75 75
823 50s. "Reichstag" (German mail steamer), 1890 75 75
824 75s. Dhows, Zanzibar 1·10 1·10
825 75s. Cobham's Short S.5 Singapore I flying boat, Mwanza, Lake Victoria, 1928 1·10 1·10
826 100s. Air Tanzania Fokker F.27 Friendship over Livingstone's house, Zanzibar 1·50 1·50
827 100s. Mail train at Moshi station 1·50 1·50
828 100s. English mail coach, 1840 1·50 1·50
829 150s. Stephenson's "Rocket" and mail coach, 1838 1·90 1·90
830 200s. Imperial Airways Handley Page H.P.42 at Croydon 2·00 2·00
MS831 Two sheets, each 85 × 65 mm. (a) 350s. Sir Rowland Hill and Penny Black. (b) 350s. Thurn and Taxis letter of 1860 Set of 2 sheets 8·50 10·00

167 Petersberg Railway, Konigswinter, Germany

1991. Cog Railways. Multicoloured.
832 8s. Type **167** 50 30
833 25s. "Waumbek" (locomotive), Mt. Washington Railway, U.S.A. 70 60
834 50s. Sarajevo–Dubrovnik line, Yugoslavia 85 75
835 100s. Budapest Rack Railway, Hungary 1·25 1·00
836 150s. Steam locomotive No. 97218, Vordenberg–Eisenerz line, Austria 1·75 1·75
837 200s. Last train on Rimutaka Incline, New Zealand, 1955 1·90 1·90
838 250s. "John Stevens" rack and pinion drive locomotive, U.S.A., 1825 1·90 2·00
839 300s. Mt. Pilatus Rack Railway steam railcar, Switzerland 2·00 2·00
MS840 Two sheets, each 117 × 87 mm. (a) 400s. Sylvester Marsh and Presidential excursion train, Mt. Washington Cog Railway, U.S.A., 1869 (51 × 38 mm). (b) 400s. Steam locomotive, Schneeberg Railway, Austria (51 × 38 mm) Set of 2 sheets 8·50 9·00

1991. International Literacy Year (1st issue). As T **226a** of St. Vincent, showing Walt Disney cartoon characters illustrating the Alphabet. Multicoloured.
841/67 1, 2, 3, 5, 10, 15, 18, 20, 25, 30, 35, 40, 45, 50, 55, 60, 75, 80, 90, 100, 120, 125, 145, 150, 160, 175, 200s. Set of 27 14·00 16·00
MS868 Two sheets, each 128 × 112 mm. (a) 600s. Tiger Lily and Lost Boys. (b) 600s. Mickey Mouse driving miniature railway locomotive (vert) Set of 2 sheets 9·50 11·00
See also Nos. 905/8.

1991. Olympic Games, Barcelona (1st issue). As T **239a** of Sierra Leone. Multicoloured.
869 5s. Archery 40 30
870 10s. Women's gymnastics 40 30
871 25s. Boxing 50 30
872 50s. Canoeing 75 55
873 100s. Volleyball 1·40 1·25
874 150s. Men's gymnastics 1·60 1·75
875 200s. 4 × 100 metres relay 2·00 2·25
876 300s. Judo 2·25 2·50
MS877 Two sheets, each 102 × 71 mm. (a) 400s. Cycling. (b) 400s. 400 metres men's hurdles Set of 2 sheets 9·00 9·00
See also Nos. 1309/12 and 1404/11.

167a "Phalaenopsis Lipperose"

1991. "EXPO 90" International Garden and Greenery Exhibition, Osaka. Orchids. Multicoloured.

878 10s. Type **167a** 20 15
879 25s. "Lycoste Aquila" 30 20
880 30s. "Vuylstekeara Cambria Plush" 30 20
881 50s. "Vuylstekeara Monica Burnham" 45 35
882 90s. "Odontocidium Crowborough Plush" . . . 85 85
883 100s. "Oncidioda Crowborough Chelsea" . . 85 85
884 250s. "Sophrolaeliocattleya Phena Saturn" . . . . . . 1·40 1·60
885 300s. "Laeliocattleya Lykas" 1·50 1·75
MS886 Two sheets, each 100 × 69 mm. (a) 400s. "Cymbidium Baldoyle Melbury". (b) 400s. "Cymbidium Tapestry Long Beach" Set of 2 sheets 5·50 6·50

168 Olympic "Sailing" Class Yacht Racing

1991. Record-breaking Sports Events. Mult.

887 5s. Type **168** 40 30
888 20s. Olympic downhill skiing 70 35
889 30s. "Tour de France" cycle race . . . . 1·75 70
890 40s. Le Mans 24-hour endurance motor race . . . 1·50 75
891 75s. Olympic two man bob-sleighing . . . . 1·75 1·10
892 100s. Belgian Grand Prix motor cycle race . . . 2·50 1·75
893 250s. Indianapolis 500 motor race . . . . 2·50 3·00
894 300s. Gold Cup power boat championship . . . . . . 2·50 3·25
MS895 Two sheets, each 85 × 64 mm. (a) 400s. Colorado 500 motor cycle race (vert). (b) 400s. Schneider Trophy air race (vert) Set of 2 sheets . . . . . 9·50 11·00

169 Mickey Mouse as Cowboy

1991. Mickey Mouse in Hollywood. Walt Disney cartoon characters as actors. Mult.

896 5s. Type **169** 30 30
897 10s. Mickey as boxer 30 30
898 15s. Mickey as astronaut . . 30 30
899 20s. Mickey and Minnie as lovers 30 30
900 100s. Mickey as pirate rescuing Minnie . . . . . 1·25 1·25
901 200s. Mickey and Donald Duck as policemen arresting Big Pete . . . . 2·50 2·50
902 350s. Mickey and Donald with Goofy in historical drama . . . . 2·75 2·75
903 450s. Mickey, Donald and Goofy as sailors . . . . . 2·75 2·75
MS904 Two sheets, each 127 × 96 mm. (a) 600s. Mickey, Minnie and Donald in the mummy's tomb. (b) 600s. Mickey as Canadian Mountie rescuing Minnie from Big Pete Set of 2 sheets . . . . 10·00 10·00

170 Women learning to Read

1991. International Literacy Year (2nd issue). Multicoloured.

905 9s. Type **170** 20 20
906 13s. Teacher with blackboard 25 20
907 25s. Literacy aids 35 25
908 100s. Reading newspaper . . 2·25 3·00
MS909 104 × 73 mm. 50s. Adult education class . . . . 1·50 2·00

171 Ngorongoro Crater

1991. Historical Craters and Caves. Mult.

910 3s. Type **171** . . . . 1·75 1·25
911 5s. Prehistoric rock painting, Kondoa Caves . . . . 1·75 1·25
912 9s. Inner crater, Mt. Kilimanjaro . . . . 2·00 1·50
913 12s. Olduvai Gorge . . . . . 2·75 2·00
MS914 91 × 92 mm. 10s. Discarded bottles, Amboni Caves; 10s. Rock paintings, Amboni Caves; 10s. Entrance to Amboni Caves; 10s. Rock formation, Amboni Caves 11·00 9·50

1991. 350th Death Anniv of Rubens. Cartoons for Decius Mus Tapestries. As T **242a** of Sierra Leone. Multicoloured.

915 85s. "Proclamation of the Vision" . . . . 1·50 1·50
916 85s. "Divining of the Entrails" . . . . 1·50 1·50
917 85s. "Dispatch of the Lictors" . . . . 1·50 1·50
918 85s. "Dedication to Death" 1·50 1·50
919 85s. "Victory and Death of Decius Mus" . . . . . . 1·50 1·50
920 85s. "Funeral Rites" . . . . 1·50 1·50
MS921 70 × 100 mm. 500s. "Trophy of War" (detail) (vert) . . . . 8·50 9·00

172 Stegosaurus

1991. Prehistoric Creatures. Multicoloured.

922 10s. Type **172** 25 25
923 15s. Triceratops 25 25
924 25s. Edmontosaurus 40 40
925 30s. Plateosaurus 40 40
926 35s. Diplodocus 45 45
927 100s. Iguanodon . . . . . . 1·40 1·40
928 200s. Silviasaurus . . . . . 2·00 2·00
MS929 90 × 90 mm. 150s. Rhamphorhynchus . . . . 2·50 3·00

173 Dairy Farming

1991. 20th Anniv of Tanzania Investment Bank. Multicoloured.

930 10s. Type **173** 25 20
931 13s. Industrial development 30 20
932 25s. Engineering 35 20
933 100s. Tea picking . . . . . 2·00 2·50
MS934 93 × 91 mm. Nos. 930/3 2·50 3·00

174 Pres. Mwinyi leading Walk

1991. National Solidarity Walk. Multicoloured.

935 4s.+1s. Type **174** 50 75
936 30s.+1s. Pres. Mwinyi planting sapling . . . . . 1·25 1·50
MS937 91 × 91 mm. 50s.+1s. Pres. Mwinyi sorting cloves . . . . 2·00 2·50

174a Class 150 Steam Locomotive, 1872 (first locomotive in Japan)

1991. "Phila Nippon '91" International Stamp Exhibition, Tokyo. Japanese Railway Locomotives. Multicoloured.

938 10s. Type **174a** . . . . . . 1·00 65
939 25s. Class 4500 steam locomotive, 1902 . . . . 1·40 90
940 35s. Class C 62 steam locomotive, 1948 . . . . 1·50 1·00
941 50s. Mikado steam locomotive . . . . 1·60 1·25
942 75s. Class 6250 steam locomotive, 1915 . . . . 2·00 1·50
943 100s. Class C 11 steam locomotive, 1932 . . . . 2·25 1·75
944 200s. Class E 10 steam locomotive, 1948 . . . . . 2·75 3·00
945 300s. Class 8550 steam locomotive, 1899 . . . . . 3·25 3·75
MS946 Four sheets, each 102 × 71 mm. (a) 400s. Series 400 electric train. (b) 400s. Class EH10 electric locomotive, 1954. (c) 400s. Class DD51 diesel-hydraulic locomotive, 1962. (d) 400s. Class EF58 electric locomotive Set of 4 sheets . . . . 11·00 12·00

175 Zebra and Golden-winged Sunbird, Ngorongoro Crater

1991. National Game Parks. Multicoloured.

947 10s. Type **175** 80 70
948 25s. Greater kudu and elephant, Ruaha Park . . . 1·25 1·00
949 30s. Sable antelope and red and yellow barbet, Mikumi Park . . . . 1·25 1·00
950 50s. Leopard and wildebeest, Serengeti Park . . . . . 1·25 1·25
951 90s. Giraffe and white starred robin, Ngurdoto Park . . 2·50 2·25
952 100s. Eland and Abbot's duiker, Kilimanjaro Park 1·75 1·75
953 250s. Lion and impala, Lake Manyara Park . . . . . . 3·00 3·50
954 300s. Black rhinoceros and ostrich, Tarangire Park . . 4·25 4·25
MS955 Two sheets, each 99 × 68 mm. (a) 400s. Blue-breasted kingfisher and defassa waterbuck, Selous Game Reserve. (b) 400s. Paradise whydah and oryx, Mkomazi Game Reserve Set of 2 sheets . . . . 14·00 12·00

176 "Eronia cleodora"

1991. Butterflies. Multicoloured.

956 10s. Type **176** 55 45
957 15s. "Precis westermanni" . . 70 60
958 35s. "Antanartia delius" . . 1·00 90
959 75s. "Bematistes aganice" . . 1·75 1·60
960 100s. "Kallima jacksoni" . . 1·90 1·75
961 150s. "Apaturopsis cleocharis" . . . . 2·75 2·75
962 200s. "Colotis aurigineus" . . 3·00 3·00
963 300s. "Iolaus crawshayi" . . 3·25 3·50
MS964 Four sheets, each 117 × 76 mm. (a) 400s. "Charaxes zoolina". (b) 400s. "Papilio phorcas". (c) 400s. "Charaxes ethalion". (d) 400s. "Papilio nobilis" Set of 4 sheets . . . . 14·00 15·00

177 Microwave Tower and Dish Aerial

1991. 25th Anniv of Intelsat Satellite System. Multicoloured.

965 10s. Type **177** 40 20
966 25s. Satellite picture of Earth 55 30
967 100s. Mwenge "B" Earth station . . . . 1·75 1·50
968 500s. Mwenge "A" Earth station . . . . 6·50 7·50
MS969 90 × 86 mm. 50s. Satellite links on world map . . . . . 2·50 2·50

178 Rice Cultivation

1991. 40th Anniv of United Nations Development Programme. Multicoloured (except No. **MS**974).

970 10s. Type **178** 10 10
971 15s. Vocational and Civil Service training 15 10
972 100s. Terrace farming . . . . 1·25 1·60
973 500s. Renovated Arab door (vert) . . . . 4·75 7·50
MS974 90 × 90 mm. 40s. UNDP anniversary emblem (blue and black) . . . . 1·10 1·50

179 Netball

180 "TELECOM 91" Logo

1991. All-Africa Games, Cairo. Mult.

975 10s. Type **179** 40 30
976 15s. Football (horiz) 40 30
977 100s. Tennis . . . . 2·00 1·50
978 200s. Athletics . . . . 2·25 2·50
979 500s. Baseball (horiz) . . . . 5·50 7·50
MS980 80 × 60 mm. 500s. Basketball 8·00 8·00

1991. "TELECOM 91" International Telecommunication Exhibition, Geneva (10, 15s.) and World Telecommunications Day (others). Mult.

981 10s. Type **180** 10 10
982 15s. "TELECOM '91" logo and address on envelope (horiz) 15 10
983 35s. Symbolic telecommunication signals 25 20
984 100s. Symbolic telecommunication signals (horiz) . . . . 70 1·00

181 Japanese Bobtail Cat

1991. Cats. Multicoloured.

985 50s. Type **181** 80 80
986 50s. Cornish rex 80 80
987 50s. Malayan 80 80
988 50s. Tonkinese 80 80
989 50s. Abyssinian 80 80
990 50s. Russian blue 80 80
991 50s. Cymric 80 80
992 50s. Somali 80 80
993 50s. Siamese 80 80
994 50s. Himalayan 80 80
995 50s. Singapura 80 80
996 50s. Manx 80 80
997 50s. Oriental shorthair . . . 80 80
998 50s. Maine coon 80 80
999 50s. Persian 80 80
1000 50s. Birman 80 80

182 Shire Horse

1991. Horses and Ponies. Multicoloured.

1001 50s. Type **182** 80 80
1002 50s. Thoroughbred 80 80
1003 50s. Kladruber 80 80
1004 50s. Appaloosa 80 80
1005 50s. Hanoverian 80 80
1006 50s. Arab 80 80
1007 50s. Breton 80 80
1008 50s. Exmoor 80 80
1009 50s. Connemara 80 80
1010 50s. Lipizzaner 80 80
1011 50s. Shetland 80 80
1012 50s. Percheron 80 80
1013 50s. Pinto 80 80
1014 50s. Orlov 80 80
1015 50s. Palomino 80 80
1016 50s. Welsh cob 80 80

Nos. 1001/16 were printed together, se-tenant, as a sheetlet of 16 with the backgrounds of each horizontal strip of 4 forming a composite design.

183 Yellow Tetra

1991. Aquarium Fish. Multicoloured.

1017 75s. Type **183** 70 70
1018 75s. Five-banded barb . . . 70 70
1019 75s. Simpson platy 70 70
1020 75s. Guppy 70 70
1021 75s. Zebra danio 70 70
1022 75s. Neon tetra 70 70
1023 75s. Siamese fighting fish . . 70 70

1024 75s. Tiger barb 70 70
1025 75s. Two-striped lyretail . . 70 70
1026 75s. Fan-tailed goldfish . . 70 70
1027 75s. Pearl gourami 70 70
1028 75s. Freshwater angelfish . . 70 70
1029 75s. Clown loach 70 70
1030 75s. Red swordtail 70 70
1031 75s. Blue discus 70 70
1032 75s. Rosy barb 70 70
Nos. 1017/32 were printed together, se-tenant, with the backgrounds of each stamp forming a composite design.

184 African Elephant 186 Indian Elephant

185 Budgerigar

1991. African Elephants. Multicoloured.
1033 75s. Type **184** . . . . . . 1·10 1·10
1034 75s. Two elephants fighting 1·10 1·10
1035 75s. Elephant facing forward and tree . . . . 1·10 1·10
1036 75s. Elephant facing left and tree . . . . 1·10 1·10
1037 75s. Cow elephant and calf facing right standing in water . . . . 1·10 1·10
1038 75s. Cow watching over calf in water . . . . 1·10 1·10
1039 75s. Two adults and calf in water . . . . 1·10 1·10
1040 75s. Cow and calf facing left standing in water . . . . 1·10 1·10
1041 75s. Elephant facing right 1·10 1·10
1042 75s. Elephants feeding . . . 1·10 1·10
1043 75s. Elephant feeding . . . 1·10 1·10
1044 75s. Elephant and zebra . . 1·10 1·10
1045 75s. Cow and calf drinking 1·10 1·10
1046 75s. Calf suckling . . . . . 1·10 1·10
1047 75s. Bull elephant . . . . . 1·10 1·10
1048 75s. Cow with small calf . . 1·10 1·10
Nos. 1033/48 were printed together, se-tenant, as a sheetlet of 16 with each horizontal strip of 4 forming a composite design.

1991. Pet Birds. Multicoloured.
1049 75s. Type **185** 80 80
1050 75s. Orange-breasted bunting ("Rainbow Bunting") 80 80
1051 75s. Golden-fronted leafbird 80 80
1052 75s. Black-headed caique . . 80 80
1053 75s. Java sparrow 80 80
1054 75s. Diamond firetail finch 80 80
1055 75s. Peach-faced lovebird . . 80 80
1056 75s. Golden conure 80 80
1057 75s. Military macaw 80 80
1058 75s. Yellow-faced parrotlet 80 80
1059 75s. Sulphur-crested cockatoo 80 80
1060 75s. White-fronted amazon ("Spectacled Amazon Parrot") 80 80
1061 75s. Paradise tanager . . . 80 80
1062 75s. Gouldian finch 80 80
1063 75s. Masked lovebird . . . 80 80
1064 75s. Southern grackle ("Hill Mynah") 80 80
Nos. 1049/64 were printed together, se-tenant, forming a composite design.

1991. Death Centenary (1990) of Vincent van Gogh (artist). As T **215a** of St. Vincent. Multicoloured.
1065 10s. "Peasant Woman Sewing" 60 30
1066 15s. "Head of Peasant Woman with Greenish Lace Cap" 70 35
1067 35s. "Flowering Orchard" 1·00 60
1068 75s. "Portrait of a Girl" . . 1·75 1·00
1069 100s. "Portrait of a Woman with Red Ribbon" . . . 2·00 1·25
1070 150s. "Vase with Flowers" 2·75 2·75
1071 200s. "Houses in Antwerp" 3·00 3·25
1072 400s. "Seated Peasant Woman with White Cap" 5·50 7·00
MS1073 Two sheets, each 127 × 112 mm. (a) 400s. "Bulb Fields" (horiz). (b) 400s. "The Parsonage Garden at Nuenen in the Snow" (horiz). Imperf Set of 2 sheets . . . . 14·00 15·00

1991. Elephants. Multicoloured.
1074 10s. Type **186** 80 50
1075 15s. Indian elephant uprooting tree 95 65
1076 25s. Indian elephant with calf . . . . 1·25 80
1077 30s. African elephant . . . 1·25 80
1078 35s. Head of African elephant (horiz) . . . . . 1·25 85
1079 100s. African elephant and calf bathing (horiz) . . . 2·50 2·25
1080 200s. Two African elephants (horiz) . . . . 4·00 5·00
MS1081 90 × 90 mm. 400s. Mammoth (horiz) . . . . . . 4·00 4·50

187 Class Em Steam Locomotive, Russia, 1930

1991. Locomotives of the World. Mult.
1082 10s. Type **187** 25 25
1083 15s. "Hikari" express train, Japan, 1964 . . . . . . 35 35
1084 25s. Russian steam locomotive, 1834 (vert) . . 45 45
1085 35s. TGV express train, France, 1979 . . . . . . 55 55
1086 60s. Diesel railcar No. R16-01, France, 1972 . . 80 80
1987 100s. High Speed Train 125, Great Britain, 1972 . . . 1·40 1·40
1088 300s. Russian steam locomotive, 1833 (vert) . . 3·00 3·00
MS1089 91 × 91 mm. French electric locomotive, 1952 (vert) . . . . 1·60 2·00
No. 1088 is inscribed "1837" in error.

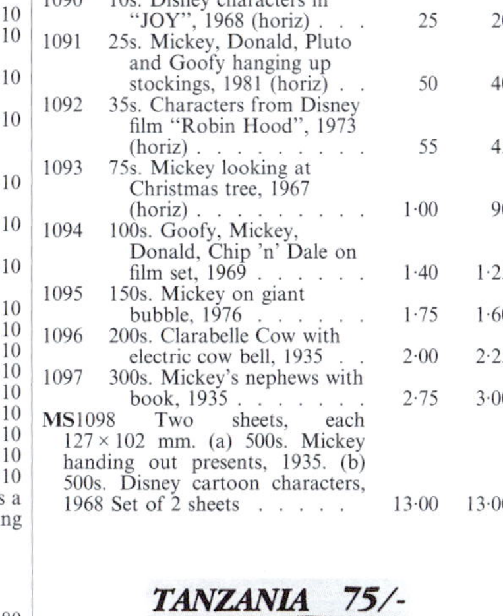

1991. Christmas. Walt Disney Christmas Cards. As T **228** of St. Vincent. Multicoloured.
1090 10s. Disney characters in "JOY", 1968 (horiz) . . . 25 20
1091 25s. Mickey, Donald, Pluto and Goofy hanging up stockings, 1981 (horiz) . . 50 40
1092 35s. Characters from Disney film "Robin Hood", 1973 (horiz) 55 45
1093 75s. Mickey looking at Christmas tree, 1967 (horiz) . . . . 1·00 90
1094 100s. Goofy, Mickey, Donald, Chip 'n' Dale on film set, 1969 . . . . . . 1·40 1·25
1095 150s. Mickey on giant bubble, 1976 . . . . . . 1·75 1·60
1096 200s. Clarabelle Cow with electric cow bell, 1935 . . 2·00 2·25
1097 300s. Mickey's nephews with book, 1935 . . . . . . 2·75 3·00
MS1098 Two sheets, each 127 × 102 mm. (a) 500s. Mickey handing out presents, 1935. (b) 500s. Disney cartoon characters, 1968 Set of 2 sheets . . . . . 13·00 13·00

188 Bruce Lee

1992. Entertainers.
1099 75s. × 36 multicoloured Set of 36 . . . . 25·00 25·00
MS1135 Four sheets, each 78 × 108 mm. 500s. × 4 multicoloured (Bruce Lee, Marilyn Monroe, Elvis Presley, Kouyate & Kouyate, each 28 × 42 mm) Set of 4 sheets . . . . 21·00 24·00
Nos. 1099/1134 were issued as four sheetlets each of nine different designs, as Type **188**, depicting Bruce Lee, Marilyn Monroe, Elvis Presley and black entertainers (Scott Joplin, Sammy Davis Jnr, Joan Armatrading, Louis Armstrong, Miriam Makeba, Lionel Ritchie, Whitney Houston, Bob Marley, Tina Turner).

189 Sand Tilefish

1992. Fishes. Multicoloured.
1136 10s. Type **189** 40 40
1137 15s. Five-banded cichlid . . 45 45
1138 25s. Pearly lamprologus . . 60 60
1139 35s. Jewel cichlid 70 70
1140 60s. Two-striped lyretail . . 1·00 1·00
1141 100s. Reef stonefish . . . . 1·50 1·50
1142 300s. Ahl's lyretail . . . . 3·75 3·75
MS1143 90 × 90 mm. 100s. Oarfish 1·60 2·00

190 Chimpanzee in Tree

191 Pope John Paul II in Dominican Republic, 1979

1992. Common Chimpanzee. Multicoloured.
1144 10s. Type **190** 60 50
1145 15s. Feeding 65 55
1146 35s. Two chimpanzees . . . 1·00 85
1147 75s. Adult male with arms folded . . . . 1·50 1·25
1148 100s. Breaking branch . . . 1·75 1·50
1149 150s. Young chimpanzee in tree . . . . 2·50 2·50
1150 200s. Female holding young 3·00 3·25
1151 300s. Chimpanzee sitting in tree . . . . 4·00 4·25
MS1152 Two sheets, each 99 × 68 mm. (a) 400s. Eating termites. (b) 400s. Swinging through trees Set of 2 sheets 7·00 7·00

1992. Papal Visits.
1153/1272 100s. × 120 multicoloured Set of 120 . . . . . 90·00 75·00
DESIGNS: Nos. 1154/1272 Various scenes on Papal visits as Type **191**.

192 Balcony

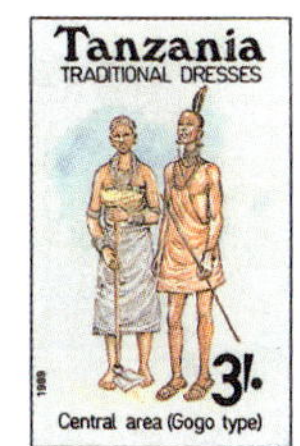

193 Gogo Costume

1992. Zanzibar Stone Town. Multicoloured.
1273 10s. Type **192** 30 25
1274 20s. Bahlnara Mosque . . . 55 35
1275 30s. High Court Building . . 65 40
1276 200s. National Museum (horiz) . . . . 4·25 5·50
MS1277 91 × 91 mm. 150s. Old Fort (horiz); 300s. Maruhubi ruins (horiz) . . . . 4·25 6·00

1992. Traditional Costumes. Multicoloured.
1278 3s. Type **193** 70 60
1279 5s. Swahili 70 60
1280 9s. Hehe and Makonde . . 80 70
1281 12s. Maasai . . . . 1·00 85
MS1282 91 × 91 mm. 40s. Mwarusha 2·25 2·50

194 Melisa and Mike (chimpanzees)

1992. Chimpanzees of the Gombe. Multicoloured.
(a) Horiz designs as T **194**.
1283 10s. Type **194** 70 40
1284 15s. Leakey and David Greybeard 80 50
1285 30s. Fifi termiting . . . . . 1·00 70
1286 35s. Galahad . . . . 1·10 75
MS1287 90 × 90 mm. 100s. Fifi, Flo and Faben . . . . 2·50 2·75

(b) Vert design showing individual chimpanzees.
1288 10s. Leakey 90 90
1289 15s. Fifi 90 90
1290 20s. Faben 90 90
1291 30s. David Greybeard . . . 90 90
1292 35s. Mike 90 90
1293 65s. Galahad 90 90
1294 100s. Melisa . . . . 1·10 1·10
1295 200s. Flo . . . . 1·50 1·50

195 Sorghum Farming, Serena

1992. 25th Anniv of National Bank of Commerce. Multicoloured.
1296 10s. Type **195** 55 15
1297 15s. Samora Avenue branch and computer operator (vert) 60 25
1298 35s. Training centre 85 65
1299 40s. Women dyeing textiles 90 90
MS1300 111 × 117 mm. 30s. Bank head office . . . . 1·25 1·75

196 Giant Spider Conch

197 Basketball

1992. Shells. Multicoloured.
1301 10s. Type **196** 30 30
1302 15s. Bull-mouth helmet . . 35 35
1303 25s. Rugose mitre 50 50
1304 30s. Lettered cone 50 50
1305 35s. True heart cockle . . . 50 50
1306 50s. Ramose murex 60 70
1307 250s. Indian volute . . . . 1·75 3·25
MS1308 91 × 91 mm. 300s. Giant clam . . . . 3·50 4·00

1992. Olympic Games, Barcelona (2nd issue). Multicoloured.
1309 40s. Type **197** 45 30
1310 100s. Billiards 75 60
1311 200s. Table tennis . . . . . 1·25 1·40
1312 400s. Darts . . . . 2·75 3·50
MS1313 90 × 85 mm. 500s. Weightlifting . . . . 3·00 4·25

198 British-designed Radar, Pearl Harbor

1992. 50th Anniv of Japanese Attack on Pearl Harbor. Multicoloured.
1314 75s. Type **198** . . . . . . 1·50 1·40
1315 75s. Winston Churchill . . . 1·50 1·40
1316 75s. Sinking of H.M.S. "Repulse" (battle cruiser) 1·50 1·40
1317 75s. Sinking of H.M.S. "Prince of Wales" (battleship) . . . . 1·50 1·40
1318 75s. Surrender of Singapore 1·50 1·40
1319 75s. Sinking of H.M.S. "Hermes" (aircraft carrier) . . . . 1·50 1·40
1320 75s. Japanese attack on Malayan airfield . . . . 1·50 1·40
1321 75s. Japanese gun crew, Hong Kong . . . . . . 1·50 1·40
1322 75s. Japanese landing craft 1·50 1·40
1323 75s. "Haguro" (Japanese cruiser) . . . . 1·50 1·40

199 French Resistance Monument and Medal

1992. Birth Centenary (1990) of Charles de Gaulle (French statesman). Multicoloured.
1324 25s. Type **199** 50 40
1325 30s. Free French tank on Omaha beach, D-Day . . 50 40
1326 150s. Concorde at Charles de Gaulle Airport . . . . 6·00 5·50
MS1327 115 × 92 mm. 500s. Free French local Cross of Lorraine opt on Petain 1f.50 and De Gaulle label postmarked 25 August 1944 (39 × 51 mm) . . . . 7·50 8·50

200 Scout Bridge, Giraffe and Elephant

1992. 50th Death Anniv (1991) of Lord Baden-Powell (founder of Boy Scout movement). Multicoloured.
1328 10s. Type **200** 70 30
1329 15s. Scouts in boat 70 30
1330 400s. John Glenn's space capsule . . . . 5·50 6·00
MS1331 90 × 117 mm. 500s. Tanzanian scout (39 × 51 mm) 4·25 6·50

201 Marcella Sembrich as Zerlina in "Don Giovanni"

1992. Death Bicentenary of Mozart.
1332 **201** 10s. black and mauve . . 1·00 40
1333 – 50s. multicoloured . . . 2·50 1·10
1334 – 300s. black and mauve . . 6·00 6·50
MS1335 115 × 87 mm. 500s. brown, stone and black . . . . 8·00 8·50
DESIGNS—HORIZ: 50s. Planet Jupiter (Symphony No. 41); 300s. Luciano Pavarotti as Idamente in "Idomeneo". VERT (35 × 47 mm): Wolfgang Amadeus Mozart.

1992. "Granada '92" International Stamp Exhibition, Spain. Paintings. As T **250b** of Sierra Leone.
1336 25s. red and black 50 40
1337 35s. multicoloured 60 50
1338 50s. multicoloured 75 60
1339 75s. multicoloured . . . . . 1·10 1·00
1340 100s. black, brown and pink 1·50 1·25
1341 150s. red and black . . . . 2·00 2·00
1342 200s. red and black . . . . 2·25 2·25
1343 300s. multicoloured . . . . 2·75 3·00
MS1344 Two sheets, each 121 × 95 mm. (a) 400s. multicoloured. (b) 400s. multicoloured. Imperf Set of 2 sheets . . . . 7·50 8·50
DESIGNS—HORIZ (49½ × 36 mm): 25s. "A Picador, mounted on a Chulo's Shoulders, spears a Bull" (Goya); 150s. "Another Madness (of Martincho) in the Plaza de Zaragoza" (Goya); 200s. "Recklessness of Martincho in the Plaza de Zaragoza" (Goya). (111 × 86 mm): 400s. (**MS**1344a) "Two Men at Table" (Velasquez); 400s. (**MS**1344b) "Seascape" (Mariana Salvador Maella). VERT: 35s. "Philip IV at Fraga" (Velazquez); 50s. "Head of a Stag" (Velazquez); 75s. "The Cardinal-Infante Ferdinand as a Hunter" (Velazquez); 100s. "The Dream of Reason brings forth Monsters" (Goya); 300s. "Pablo de Valladolid" (Velazquez).

202 Lucky Omens

203 Superb Starling

1992. 500th Anniv of Discovery of America by Columbus. Multicoloured.
1345 10s. Type **202** 20 20
1346 15s. Map and compass . . . 25 25
1347 25s. Look-out in crow's nest 35 35
1348 30s. Amerindians sighting ships (horiz) 40 40
1349 35s. "Pinta" and "Nina" (horiz) 55 45
1350 75s. "Santa Maria" (horiz) 90 80
1351 250s. Wreck of "Santa Maria" . . . . 1·75 2·50
MS1352 93 × 93 mm. 200s. Columbus . . . . 1·75 2·50

1992. Birds. Multicoloured.
1353 5s. Type **203** 55 50
1354 10s. Golden Bishop ("Canary") 65 50
1355 15s. Four-coloured bush shrike 75 55
1356 25s. Grey-headed kingfisher 80 55
1357 30s. River kingfisher (Common Kingfisher") . . 80 55
1358 35s. Yellow-billed oxpecker 80 55
1359 150s. Black-throated honeyguide . . . . 2·00 2·25
MS1360 93 × 92 mm. 300s. European cuckoo (horiz) . . . 2·75 3·50

1992. 15th Death Anniv of Elvis Presley. Nos. 1117/25 optd **15th Anniversary**.
1361 75s. Looking pensive . . . 85 85
1362 75s. Wearing black and yellow striped shirt . . . 85 85
1363 75s. Singing into microphone 85 85
1364 75s. Wearing wide-brimmed hat 85 85
1365 75s. With microphone in right hand 85 85
1366 75s. In Army uniform . . . 85 85
1367 75s. Wearing pink shirt . . 85 85
1368 75s. In yellow shirt 85 85
1369 75s. In jacket and bow tie 85 85

205 Iguanodon

1992. African Dinosaurs. Multicoloured.
1370 100s. Type **205** 95 90
1371 100s. Saltasaurus 95 90
1372 100s. Cetiosaurus 95 90
1373 100s. Camarasaurus 95 90
1374 100s. Spinosaurus 95 90
1375 100s. Stegosaurus 95 90
1376 100s. Allosaurus 95 90
1377 100s. Ceratosaurus 95 90
1378 100s. Lesothosaurus 95 90
1379 100s. Anchisaurus 95 90
1380 100s. Ornithomimus 95 90
1381 100s. Baronyx 95 90
1382 100s. Pachycephalosaurus 95 90
1383 100s. Heterodontosaurus . . 95 90
1384 100s. Dryosaurus 95 90
1385 100s. Coelophysis 95 90
Nos. 1370/85 were printed together, se-tenant, forming a composite design.

206 Spotted Tilapia

1992. Fishes. Multicoloured.
1386 100s. Type **206** 85 85
1387 100s. Butterfly barb 85 85
1388 100s. Blunthead Molino cichlid 85 85
1389 100s. Angel squeaker . . . 85 85
1390 100s. Dickfield's Julie . . . 85 85
1391 100s. Nile mouthbrooder . . 85 85
1392 100s. Blue-finned notho . . 85 85
1393 100s. Crabro mbuna 85 85
1394 100s. Pearl-scaled lamprologus 85 85
1395 100s. Zebra mbuna 85 85
1396 100s. Marlier's Julie 85 85
1397 100s. Brichard's chalinochromis 85 85
MS1398 Three sheets, each 71 × 55 mm. (a) 500s. Palmqvist's notho. (b) 500s. Electric blue haplochromis. (c) 500s. Short lamprologus Set of 3 sheets . . 11·00 12·00
Nos. 1386/97 were printed together, se-tenant, forming a composite design.

207 Hunting Birds with Catapults

1992. Traditional Hunting. Multicoloured.
1399 20s. Type **207** 75 30
1400 70s. Hunting antelope with bow and arrow . . . . . . 1·00 55
1401 100s. Hunting antelopes with dogs . . . . 1·50 1·00
1402 150s. Hunting lion with spears and shields . . . . 2·25 2·75
MS1403 100 × 100 mm. 40s. Traditional hunting weapons 2·25 2·50

1992. Olympic Games, Albertville and Barcelona (3rd issue). As T **251a** of Sierra Leone. Multicoloured.
1404 20s. Men's 4000 m pursuit cycling 90 50
1405 40s. Men's double sculls rowing (horiz) 40 20
1406 50s. Water polo (horiz) . . 50 20
1407 70s. Women's single luge (horiz) 60 30
1408 100s. Marathon (horiz) . . 65 50
1409 150s. Women's asymmetrical bars gymnastics (horiz) . . 1·50 1·50
1410 200s. Ice hockey . . . . . 2·75 2·00
1411 400s. Men's rings gymnastics 3·00 4·00
MS1412 Two sheets, each 100 × 71 mm. (a) 500s. Tennis. (b) 500s. Football Set of 2 sheets 12·00 12·00

207a Donald Duck in "Sea Scout", 1939

1992. Mickey's Portrait Gallery. Walt Disney cartoon characters. Multicoloured.
1413 25s. Type **207a** 30 30
1414 25s. Minnie Mouse in "Hawaiian Holiday", 1937 . . . . 30 30
1415 25s. Pluto in "Society Dog Show", 1939 . . . . 30 30
1416 35s. Donald in "Fire Chief", 1940 . . . . 40 40
1417 50s. Donald in "Truant Officer Donald", 1941 . . 50 50
1418 75s. Goofy in "Clock Cleaners", 1937 . . . . 60 60
1419 100s. Goofy in "Goofy and Wilbur", 1939 . . . . . 70 70
1420 100s. Mickey Mouse in "Magician Mickey", 1937 70 70
1421 200s. Minnie in "The Nifty Nineties", 1941 . . . . . 1·25 1·25
1422 300s. Mickey and Pluto in "Society Dog Show", 1939 . . . . 1·50 1·50
1423 400s. Pluto and pups in "Pluto's Quin-Puplets", 1937 . . . . 1·60 1·60
1424 500s. Daisy and Donald in "Mr. Duck Steps Out", 1940 . . . . 1·75 1·75
MS1425 Three sheets. (a) 127 × 102 mm. 600s. Goofy in "Forever Goofy". (b) 127 × 102 mm. 600s. Daisy in "Don Donald", 1937. (c) 112 × 104 mm. 600s. Mickey and Minnie in "Brave Little Tailor", 1938 (horiz) Set of 3 sheets . . 9·50 11·00

208 "Couroupita guinensis"

209 Abyssinian Cat

1993. Botanical Gardens of the World. Rio de Janeiro. African Plants. Vert designs as T **208**.
1426/45 70s. × 20 multicoloured Set of 20 . . . . 13·00 15·00
MS1446 110 × 74 mm. 500s. Avenue of royal palms . . . . 3·25 4·00

1992. Cats. Multicoloured.
1447 20s. Type **209** 45 45
1448 30s. Havana cat 45 45
1449 50s. Persian black cat . . . 55 55
1450 70s. Persian blue cat . . . 65 65
1451 100s. European silver tabby cat 85 85
1452 150s. Persian silver tabby cat . . . . 1·00 1·00
1453 200s. Maine coon cat . . . 1·25 1·25
MS1454 90 × 90 mm. 300s. European cat . . . . 2·75 3·00

209a Baltimore Ohio Tunnel Locomotive No. 5, 1904

1992. "Genova '92" International Stamp Exhibition. Toy Trains manufactured by Lionel. Multicoloured.
1455 10s. Type **209a** 50 25
1456 20s. "Liberty Bell" locomotive No. 385E, 1930 . . . . 60 35
1457 30s. Armoured rail car No. 203, 1917 . . . . . 65 40
1458 50s. Open trolley No. 202, 1910–14 . . . . 90 60
1459 70s. "Macy Special" electric locomotive No. 405 . . . 1·00 70
1460 100s. "Milwaukee Road" bi-polar electric locomotive, 1929 . . . . 1·10 80
1461 200s. New York Central Type S locomotive, 1912 1·50 1·75
1462 300s. Locomotive No. 7, 1914 . . . . 1·75 2·75
MS1463 Two sheets. (a) 91 × 75 mm. 500s. Display model locomotive in clear plastic, 1947. (b) 71 × 89 mm. 500s. Mickey and Minnie Mouse on clockwork handcar, 1936 Set of 2 sheets . . . . 6·00 7·00

210 Count Ferdinand von Zeppelin

1992. Anniversaries and Events. Mult.
1464 30s. Type **210** 40 30
1465 70s. "Santa Maria" 70 70
1466 70s. "Apollo–Soyuz" link-up, 1975 . . . . 70 70
1467 150s. African elephant . . . 1·50 1·00
1468 150s. Child being offered apple . . . . 1·00 1·00
1469 200s. Zebra . . . . 1·10 1·10
1470 200s. Trying on glasses . . 1·10 1·10
1471 300s. Airship "Graf Zeppelin", 1929 . . . . . 1·75 1·75
1472 300s. Christopher Columbus 1·75 1·75
1473 400s. Space shuttle . . . . 2·25 2·25
1474 400s. Wolfgang Amadeus Mozart (vert) . . . . . . 2·50 2·50
MS1475 Five sheets. (a) 110 × 82 mm. 500s. LZ-5 Zeppelin airship. (b) 114 × 81 mm. 500s. Head of Columbus. (c) 110 × 82 mm. 500s. "Voyager 2" space probe. (d) 114 × 81 mm. 500s. African elephant (different). (e) 110 × 68 mm. 500s. Queen of the Night from "The Magic Flute" (vert) Set of 5 sheets . . . . . 15·00 16·00
ANNIVERSARIES AND EVENTS: Nos. 1464, 1471, **MS**1475a, 75th death anniv of Count Ferdinand von Zeppelin; 1465, 1472, **MS**1475b, 500th anniv of discovery of America by Columbus; 1466, 1473, **MS**1475c, International Space Year; 1467, 1469, **MS**1475d, Earth Summit '92, Rio; 1468, International Conference on Nutrition, Rome; 1470, 75th anniv of International Association of Lions Clubs; 1474, **MS**1475e, Death bicentenary of Mozart.

1992. Bicentenary of the Louvre, Paris. Paintings by Jean Chardin. As T **254a** of St Vincent. Multicoloured.
1476 100s. "Young Draughtsman sharpening Pencil" . . . 85 85
1477 100s. "The Buffet" 85 85
1478 100s. "Return from the Market" 85 85
1479 100s. "The Hard-working Mother" 85 85
1480 100s. "Grace" 85 85
1481 100s. "The Copper Water Urn" 85 85
1482 100s. "The House of Cards" 85 85
1483 100s. "Boy with a Top" . . 85 85
MS1484 100 × 70 mm. 500s. "The Ray" (85 × 52 mm) . . . . . 3·50 4·00

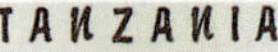

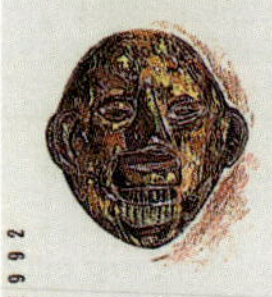

211 Carved Head

1992. Makonde Art.
1485 **211** 20s. multicoloured . . . 15 15
1486 – 30s. multicoloured . . . 15 15
1487 – 50s. multicoloured . . . 20 20
1488 – 70s. multicoloured . . . 30 30
1489 – 100s. multicoloured . . . 40 40
1490 – 150s. multicoloured . . . 70 70
1491 – 200s. multicoloured . . . 80 80
MS1492 91 × 91 mm. 350s. multicoloured . . . . 1·75 2·25
DESIGNS: 30s. to 200s. Various carvings.

212 Russian Cycle, 1813

1992. Bicycles of the World. Multicoloured.
1493 20s. Type **212** 20 20
1494 30s. German, 1840 . . . . 20 20
1495 50s. German, 1818 . . . . 30 30
1496 70s. German, 1850 . . . . 30 40
1497 100s. Italian, 1988 . . . . . 35 50
1498 150s. Swedish, 1982 . . . . 50 80
1499 300s. Italian, 1989 . . . . . 70 1·25
MS1500 90 × 90 mm. 350s. British pennyfarthing, 1887 . . . . . 1·00 2·50

213 Seal

1993. Large Sea Creatures. Multicoloured.
1501 20s. Type **213** 65 50
1502 30s. Whale . . . . 1·50 80
1503 70s. Shark . . . . 1·00 1·00
1504 100s. Walrus . . . . 1·25 1·50
MS1505 99 × 91 mm. 500s. Sea turtle 6·00 6·00

214 Boxing

215 "Macrolepiota rhacodes"

1993. Sports. Multicoloured.
1506 20s. Type **214** 15 15
1507 50s. Hockey 75 30
1508 70s. Show jumping 40 40
1509 100s. Marathon running 45 45
1510 150s. Football 60 70
1511 200s. Diving 70 90
1512 400s. Basketball 1·75 2·25
MS1513 91 × 91 mm. 300s. High jumping (horiz) 1·75 2·25

1993. 40th Anniv of Coronation. As T **256a** of St. Vincent.
1514 100s. multicoloured 65 65
1515 150s. multicoloured 85 85
1516 200s. lilac and black 1·10 1·10
1517 300s. multicoloured 1·25 1·25
MS1518 102 × 70 mm. 500s. multicoloured 3·75 3·75
DESIGNS: 100s. Queen Elizabeth II at Coronation (photograph by Cecil Beaton); 150s. Gold salt-cellar; 200s. Prince Philip at Coronation; 300s. Queen Elizabeth II and Prince Andrew. (28½ × 42½ mm): 500s. "Princess Elizabeth opening the New Broadgate, Coventry" (detail) (Dame Laura Knight).

1993. Fungi. Multicoloured.
1519 20s. Type **215** 60 35
1520 40s. "Mycena pura" 80 50
1521 50s. "Chlorophyllum molybdites" 80 50
1522 70s. "Agaricus campestris" 90 60
1523 100s. "Volvariella volvacea" 1·00 70
1524 150s. "Leucoagaricus naucinus" 1·40 1·25
1525 200s. "Oudemansiella radicata" 1·60 1·50
1526 300s. "Clitocybe nebularis" 1·75 2·00
MS1527 Two sheets, each 100 × 70 mm. (a) 500s. "Omphalotus olearius". (b) 500s. "Lepista nuda" Set of 2 sheets 6·50 7·50

216 "Geochelone elephantopus" (tortoise) **217** Pancake Tortoise on Rock

1993. Reptiles. Multicoloured.
1528 20s. Type **216** 20 20
1529 50s. "Iguana iguana" 30 30
1530 70s. "Varanus salvator" (lizard) (horiz) 70 70
1531 100s. "Naja oxiana" (cobra) 45 45
1532 150s. "Chamaeleo jacksoni" (horiz) 70 70
1533 200s. "Eunectes murinus" (snake) (horiz) 80 80
1534 250s. "Alligator mississippensis" (horiz) 90 90
MS1535 90 × 90 mm. 500s. "Vipera berus" (snake) 3·00 3·50

1993. Endangered Species. Pancake Tortoise. Multicoloured.
1536 20s. Type **217** 35 35
1537 30s. Drinking 40 40
1538 50s. Under rock 60 60
1539 70s. Tortoise hatching 75 75

218 Elephant

1993. Wildlife.
1540/87 100s. × 48 multicoloured Set of 48 26·00 27·00
MS1588 Two sheets, each 100 × 71 mm. (a) 500s. Lion cub (horiz). (b) 500s. Elephant calf (horiz) Set of 2 sheets 5·25 5·75
Nos. 1540/87 were issued together, se-tenant, as four sheetlets each of twelve different vertical designs. The species depicted are, in addition to Type **218**, Gazelle, Hartebeest, Duiker, Genet, Civet, Eastern white pelican, Waterbuck, Blacksmith plover, Lesser pied kingfisher, Black-winged stilt, Bush pig, Brown-hooded kingfisher, Sable antelope, Impala, Buffalo, Leopard, Aardvark, Hippopotamus, Spotted hyena, South African crowned crane, Crocodile, Greater flamingo, Baboon, Potto, Lesser flamingo, Grey-headed kingfisher, Red colobus monkey, Dik-dik, Aardwolf (incorrectly inscribed "ARDWOLF"), Black-backed jackal, Tree pangolilin, Serval, Yellow-billed hornbill, Pygmy mongoose, Bat-eared fox, Bushbaby, Egyptian vulture, Ostrich, Greater kudu, Diana monkey, Giraffe, Cheetah, Wildebeest, Chimpanzee, Warthog, Zebra and Rhinoceros.

219 Grant's Zebra galloping

1992. Wild Animals. Multicoloured.
1589 100s. Type **219** 85 85
1590 100s. Grant's zebra standing 85 85
1591 100s. Grant's gazelle doe 85 85
1592 100s. Grant's gazelle buck 85 85
1593 100s. Thomson's gazelle 85 85
1594 100s. White-bearded gnu with calf 85 85
1595 100s. Female cheetah with cubs 85 85
1596 100s. Young cheetah drinking 85 85
1597 100s. Lioness carrying cub in mouth 85 85
1598 100s. Pair of hunting dogs 85 85
1599 100s. Three hunting dogs 85 85
1600 100s. Four hunting dogs 85 85
MS1601 Two sheets, each 106 × 76 mm. (a) 500s. African elephant. (b) 500s. Rhinoceros Set of 2 sheets 10·00 9·00

220 Valentina Tereshkova (first woman in space) **222** Arthur Ashe (tennis)

221 "Iolaus aphnaeoides"

1993. Famous 20th-century Women. Mult.
1602 20s. Type **220** 65 65
1603 40s. Marie Curie (physicist) 1·25 1·00
1604 50s. Indira Gandhi (Prime Minister of India) 1·25 1·00
1605 70s. Wilma Rudolph (Olympic athlete) 1·00 1·00
1606 100s. Margaret Mead (anthropologist) 1·00 1·00
1607 150s. Golda Meir (Prime Minister of Israel) 1·50 1·50
1608 200s. Dr. Elizabeth Blackwell (first female medical doctor) 1·50 1·50
1609 400s. Margaret Thatcher (Prime Minister of Great Britain) 2·25 2·50
MS1610 116 × 80 mm. 500s. Mother Teresa (humanitarian) 3·50 3·50

1993. Butterflies.
1611/54 100s. × 44 multicoloured Set of 44 35·00 30·00
MS1655 Four sheets, each 69 × 58 mm. (a) 500s. "Cymothoe sangaris". (b) 500s. "Precis octavia". (c) 500s. "Charaxes violetta". (d) 500s. "Papilio nobilis" Set of 4 sheets 13·00 13·00
Nos. 1611/54 were printed se-tenant in two sheetlets of 12 (Nos. 1611/34) and one of 20 (Nos. 1635/54). The species depicted, in addition to Type **221**, are "Charaxes eupale", "Danaus formosa", "Antanartia hippomene", "Mylothris sagala", "Charaxes anticlea", "Salamis temora", "Nepheronia argia", "Acraea pseudolycia", "Hypolimnas antevorta", "Colotis hildebrandti", "Acraea bonasia", "Eurema desjardinsi", "Myrina silenus", "Iolaus ismenias", "Charaxes candiope", "Precis artaxia", "Danaus chrysippus", "Axiocerses bambana", "Precis orithya", "Pinacopteryx eriphia", "Iolaus coecolus", "Precis hierta", "Colotis regina", "Euphaedra neophron", "Mylothris poppea", "Aphaneus flavescens", "Eronia leda", "Charaxes zoolina", "Papilio bromius", "Cyrestis camillus", "Hypolycaena buxtoni", "Charaxes achaemenes", "Asterope rosa", "Graphium antheus", "Charaxes acuminatus", "Kallima rumia", "Leptosia alcesta", "Pseudacraea boisduvali", "Iolaus sidus", "Salamis parhassus", "Charaxes protoclea azota", "Charaxes bohemani" and "Papilio ophidicephalus".

1993. Black Sporting Personalities. Multicoloured.
1656 20s. Type **222** 50 40
1657 40s. Michael Jordan (basketball) 60 40
1658 50s. Daley Thompson (decathlon) 60 40
1659 70s. Jackie Robinson (baseball) 50 40
1660 100s. Kareem Abdul-Jabbar (basketball) 80 60
1661 150s. Florence Joyner (athletics) 85 80
1662 200s. Jesse Owens (athletics) 90 1·00
1663 400s. Jack Johnson (boxing) 1·50 1·75
MS1664 72 × 101 mm. 500s. Muhammed Ali (boxing) (horiz) 2·50 2·75

223 Short-finned Mako

1993. Sharks. Multicoloured.
1665 20s. Type **223** 15 15
1666 30s. Lantern shark 20 20
1667 50s. Tiger shark 25 25
1668 70s. African angelshark 35 35
1669 100s. "Pristiophorus cirratus" 45 45
1670 150s. White-tipped reef shark 65 65
1671 200s. Scalloped hammerhead 75 75
MS1672 91 × 91 mm. 350s. Six-gilled shark (vert) 1·75 2·00

224 Alpha Jet

1993. Military Aircraft. Multicoloured.
1673 20s. Type **224** 20 20
1674 30s. Northrop F-5E 20 25
1675 50s. Dassault Mirage 3NG 25 30
1676 70s. MB 339C 35 45
1677 100s. MiG-31 35 50
1678 150s. C-101 Aviojet 40 70
1679 200s. General Dynamics F-16 Fighting Falcon 45 80
MS1680 91 × 91 mm. 500s. EAP fighter (vert) 1·40 2·00

225 Gordon Setter **227** "Ansellia africana"

226 Rhinoceros, Ngorongoro Crater

1993. Dogs. Multicoloured.
1681 20s. Type **225** 20 20
1682 30s. Zwergschnauzer 25 25
1683 50s. Labrador retriever 30 30
1684 70s. Wire fox terrier 45 45
1685 100s. English springer spaniel 50 50
1686 150s. Newfoundlander 70 70
1687 200s. Moscow toy terrier 80 80
MS1688 91 × 91 mm. 350s. Dobermann Pinscher 1·75 2·00

1993. National Parks. Multicoloured.
1689 20s. Type **226** 20 20
1690 50s. Buffalo, Ngurdoto Crater 20 20
1691 70s. Leopard, Kilimanjaro 30 30
1692 100s. Baboon, Gombe 35 35
1693 150s. Lion, Selous 45 45
1694 200s. Giraffe, Mikumi 65 65
1695 250s. Zebra, Serengeti 70 70
MS1696 91 × 91 mm. 500s. Elephant, Lake Manyara (vert) 1·75 2·00

1993. Flowers. Multicoloured.
1697 20s. Type **227** 35 20
1698 30s. "Saintpaulia ionantha" 40 25
1699 40s. "Stapelia semota lutea" 45 30
1700 50s. "Impatiens walleriana" 45 30
1701 60s. "Senecio petraeus" 50 35
1702 70s. "Kalanchoe velutina" 60 40
1703 100s. "Kaempferia brachystemon" 75 60
1704 150s. "Nymphaea colorata" 1·10 1·10
1705 200s. "Thunbergia battiscombei" 1·25 1·25
1706 250s. "Crossandra nilotica" 1·25 1·40
1707 300s. "Spathodea campanulata" 1·40 1·60
1708 350s. "Ruttya fruticosa" 1·40 1·60
MS1709 Two sheets, each 100 × 70 mm. (a) 500s. "Streptocarpus saxorum". (b) 500s. "Glorioso verschurii" Set of 2 sheets 5·25 7·00

228 Norman-Arab

1993. Horses. Multicoloured.
1710 20s. Type **228** 30 30
1711 40s. Nonius 40 40
1712 50s. Boulonnais 40 40
1713 70s. Arab 50 50
1714 100s. Anglo-Arab 55 55
1715 150s. Tarpon 70 70
1716 200s. Thoroughbred 80 80
MS1717 91 × 91 mm. 400s. Anglo-Norman (vert) 1·75 2·00
No. 1716 is inscribed "THOROUGBLED" in error.

229 Berts Warrior **230** Downhill Skiing

1993. Traditional African Costumes. Multicoloured.
1718 20s. Type **229** 10 10
1719 40s. Galla 15 15
1720 50s. Guinean 15 15
1721 70s. Goloff 20 25
1722 100s. Peul 30 30
1723 150s. Abyssinian 45 45
1724 200s. Pahuin 55 55
MS1725 91 × 91 mm. 350s. Zulu 1·10 1·25

1994. Hummel Figurines. As T **251b** of St. Vincent. Multicoloured.
1726 20s. Boy playing accordion 30 25
1727 40s. Girl with guitar and boy with lute 35 30
1728 50s. Boy playing euphonium 35 30
1729 70s. Boy playing mouth organ 40 35
1730 100s. Boy with trumpet on fence 50 45
1731 150s. Boy playing recorder 80 80
1732 200s. Boy with trumpet and bird on feet 90 90
1733 300s. Girl playing banjo 1·25 1·40
1734 350s. Boy carrying double bass on back 1·40 1·60
1735 400s. Girls with banjo and song sheet 1·40 1·60
MS1736 Two sheets, each 70 × 101 mm. (a) 500s. Carol singers. (b) 500s. Angels with trumpets in bell tower Set of 2 sheets 8·00 8·50

1994. Winter Olympic Games, Lillehammer, Norway. Multicoloured.
1737 40s. Type **230** 20 20
1738 50s. Ice hockey 20 20
1739 70s. Speed skating 30 30
1740 100s. Bobsleighing 35 35
1741 120s. Figure skating 40 40
1742 170s. Free style skiing 55 55
1743 250s. Biathlon 75 75
MS1744 93 × 91 mm. 500s Cross-country skiing 1·50 2·00

231 Ruud Gullit (Netherlands) **233** African Hawk Eagle

232 Mickey Mouse, Goofy, Pluto and Donald Duck boarding Airliner

1994. World Cup Football Championship, U.S.A. (1st issue). Multicoloured.
1745 20s. Type **231** 40 30
1746 30s. Kevin Sheedy (Ireland) 40 30
1747 50s. Giuseppe Giannini (Italy) 50 40
1748 70s. Julio Cesar (Brazil) . . 55 45
1749 250s. John Barnes (England) and Grun (Belgium) . . . 1·50 1·50
1750 300s. Chendo (Spain) . . . 1·50 1·50
1751 350s. Frank Rijkaard (Netherlands) . . . . . . 1·60 1·75
1752 400s. Lothar Matthaeus (Germany) . . . . 1·60 1·75
MS1753 Two sheets. (a) 76 × 106 mm. 500s. Nicola Berti (Italy). (b) 106 × 76 mm. 500s. Des Walker (England) Set of 2 sheets 7·50 7·50
See also Nos. 1838/45 and 1892/8.

1994. "Hong Kong '94" International Stamp Exhibition. As T **271a** of St. Vincent. Multicoloured
1754 350s. Blue-barred orange parrotfish and red cap white pearl-scale goldfish at right . . . . 1·40 1·40
1755 350s. Regal angelfish and red cap white pearl-scale goldfish at left . . . . . 1·40 1·40
Nos. 1754/5 were printed together, se-tenant, forming a composite design.

1994. 65th Anniv of Mickey Mouse. Walt Disney Cartoon Characters on World Tour. Mult.
1756 10s. Type **232** 50 25
1757 20s. Daisy Duck and Minnie Mouse dancing, Tonga . . 60 30
1758 30s. Mickey and Goofy playing bowls, Australia 65 35
1759 40s. Mickey, Donald and Goofy building igloo, Arctic Circle 70 40
1760 50s. Pluto, Goofy, Mickey and Donald on guard at Buckingham Palace, London 70 40
1761 60s. Pluto at Esna Bazaar, Egypt 75 55
1762 70s. Donald being chased by Zsambox herders, Hungary (vert) 75 55
1763 100s. Donald and Daisy on Grand Canal, Venice (vert) 90 70
1764 150s. Goofy dancing, Bali (vert) . . . . 1·40 1·50
1765 200s. Donald with monks, Thailand (vert) . . . . . 1·60 1·60
1766 300s. Goofy water skiing at Taj Mahal, India (vert) 1·75 2·25
1767 400s. Mickey, Minnie, Goofy and Donald being carried by Sherpas, Nepal 2·00 2·50
MS1768 Three sheets. (a) 127 × 102 mm. 500s. Mickey at Livingstone's memorial, Ujiji (vert). (b) 127 × 102 mm. 500s. Mickey at Kigoma railway station, Tanzania (vert). (c) 102 × 127 mm. 500s. Mickey climbing Mt. Kilimanjaro (vert) Set of 3 sheets 8·50 9·50

1994. Birds. Multicoloured.
1769 20s. Type **233** 85 85
1770 30s. Whale-headed stork ("Shoe-bill Stork") . . . 85 85
1771 50s. Brown snake eagle ("Harrier Eagle") . . . . 1·00 1·00
1772 70s. Black-casqued hornbill ("Casqued Horn-Bill") . . 1·10 1·10
1773 100s. Crowned cranes . . . 1·10 1·10
1774 150s. Greater flamingos . . 1·40 1·40
1775 200s. Pair of eastern white pelicans ("Pelicans") (horiz) . . . . 1·10 1·10
1776 250s. African jacana and African black crake (horiz) . . . . 1·10 1·10
1777 300s. Pair of ostriches (horiz) . . . . 1·25 1·25
1778 350s. Pair of helmeted guineafowl (horiz) . . . . 1·25 1·25
1779 400s. Malachite kingfisher (horiz) . . . . 1·25 1·25
1780 500s. Pair of saddle-billed storks ("Saddle-billed Stork") (horiz) . . . . . 1·40 1·40

234 Henry Ford and Model "T"

1994. Centenaries of Henry Ford's First Petrol Engine (Nos. 1781 and 1783) and Karl Benz's First Four-wheeled Car (others). Multicoloured.
1781 200s. Type **234** . . . . . . 1·40 1·40
1782 200s. Benz, 1893, and "500 SEL", 1993 . . . . 1·40 1·40
1783 400s. Ford, 1893, Mustang Cobra and emblem . . . 2·25 2·25
1784 400s. Karl Benz and emblem 2·25 2·25
MS1785 Two sheets, each 106 × 71 mm. (a) 500s. Henry Ford outside first factory. (b) 500s. Benz emblem and bonnet of 1937 "540k" Set of 2 sheets . . . . 5·00 6·00

235 Sopwith Pup Biplane

1994. Aviation Anniversaries. Multicoloured.
1786 200s. Type **235** . . . . . . 1·75 1·75
1787 200s. Inflating hot-air balloons . . . . 1·75 1·75
1788 400s. Hawker Siddeley Harrier and design drawing . . . . 2·75 2·75
1789 400s. Jean-Pierre Blanchard and his balloon . . . . . 2·75 2·75
MS1790 Two sheets, each 105 × 71 mm. (a) 500s. Supermarine Spitfire. (b) 500s. Hot-air balloons in flight (vert) Set of 2 sheets . . . . . . 6·50 6·50
ANNIVERSARIES: Nos. 1786, 1788, 75th anniv of Royal Air Force; Nos. 1787, 1789, Bicentenary of first balloon flight in the U.S.A.

236 Jahazi (sailing canoe)

237 Diatryma

1994. Sailing Ships. Multicoloured.
1791 40s. Type **236** 15 15
1792 50s. Caravel 15 15
1793 70s. Pirate carrack 25 25
1794 100s. Baltic galeass 25 30
1795 170s. Frigate (inscr "Battle-ship") 35 55
1796 200s. British ship of the line (inscr "Frigate") 40 65
1797 250s. Brig 40 75
MS1798 91 × 91 mm. 500s. Clipper 1·25 2·00

1994. Prehistoric Animals. Multicoloured.
1799 40s. Type **237** 50 30
1800 50s. Tyrannosaurus rex . . 50 30
1801 100s. Uintaterius 70 50
1802 120s. Stiracosaurus 80 70
1803 170s. Diplodocus . . . . . 1·00 1·10
1804 250s. Archaeopteryx . . . . 1·25 1·40
1805 300s. Sordes . . . . 1·40 1·75
MS1806 91 × 91 mm. 500s. Dimetrodon . . . . 1·90 2·25
No. 1799 is inscribed "DIATRUMA" in error.

238 Koala Bear with Cub

1994. Endangered Species. Multicoloured.
1807 40s. Type **238** 25 25
1808 70s. Giant panda with cub 40 40
1809 100s. Golden eagles 55 55
1810 120s. African elephant with calf 70 70
1811 250s. Carribean monk seals 90 90
1812 400s. Dolphins . . . . . . 1·00 1·00
1813 500s. Whales . . . . 1·50 1·50
MS1814 90 × 90 mm. 500s. Tiger (vert) . . . . 2·00 2·50

239 Pres. Salmin Amour of Zanzibar

241 Tanzanian Family

240 Lorry at Customs Post

1994. 30th Anniv of Zanzibar Revolution. Multicoloured.
1815 40s. Type **239** 30 10
1816 70s. Amani Karume (first President of Zanzibar) . . 50 20
1817 120s. Harvesting cloves (horiz) 85 80
1818 250s. Carved door . . . . . 1·40 2·25
MS1819 91 × 91 mm. 500s. Hands clasped over map . . . . . . 2·00 2·50

1994. 81st/82nd Customs Co-Operation Council Meeting, Arusha. Multicoloured.
1820 20s. Type **240** 45 20
1821 50s. Container ship 75 30
1822 100s. Passengers and airliner 1·10 65
1823 150s. Customs and U.P.U. logos . . . . 1·10 1·50
MS1824 99 × 99 mm. 500s. Customs arms (30 × 40 mm) . . . . . . 3·50 3·25

1994. Int Year of the Family. Mult.
1825 40s. Type **241** 20 10
1826 120s. Father playing with children 45 40
1827 170s. Family clinic (horiz) 60 80
1828 250s. Woman harvesting tobacco . . . . 75 1·25
MS1829 91 × 91 mm. 300s. Emblem 1·60 2·00

242 "Trombidium sp."

1994. Arachnids. Multicoloured.
1830 40s. Type **242** 20 20
1831 50s. "Eurypelma sp." . . . 20 20
1832 100s. "Salticus sp." 30 30
1833 120s. "Micrommata rosea" (vert) 35 35
1834 170s. "Araneus sp." (vert) 50 50
1835 250s. "Micrathena sp." (vert) 70 70
1836 300s. "Araneus diadematus" (vert) 80 80
MS1837 92 × 92 mm. 500s. Claw of "Hadogenes" sp (vert) . . . . 1·75 2·00

243 Giuseppe Signori (Italy)

244 Bateleur

1994. World Cup Football Championship, U.S.A. (2nd issue). Multicoloured.
1838 300s. Type **243** . . . . . 1·00 1·00
1839 300s. Ruud Gullit (Netherlands) . . . . . . 1·00 1·00
1840 300s. Roberto Mancini (Italy) . . . . 1·00 1·00
1841 300s. Marco van Basten (Netherlands) . . . . . . 1·00 1·00
1842 300s. Dennis Bergkamp (Netherlands) . . . . . . 1·00 1·00
1843 300s. Oscar Ruggeri (Argentina) . . . . 1·00 1·00
1844 300s. Frank Rijkaard (Netherlands) . . . . . . 1·00 1·00
1845 300s. Peter Schmeichel (Denmark) . . . . 1·00 1·00
MS1846 100 × 70 mm. 1000s. World Cup trophy . . . . 4·00 4·50
See also Nos. 1892/8.

1994. Birds of Prey. Multicoloured.
1847 40s. Type **244** 40 40
1848 50s. Ornate hawk eagle . . 40 40
1849 100s. Osprey 60 60
1850 120s. Andean condor . . . 60 60
1851 170s. African fish eagle (horiz) 70 70
1852 250s. King vulture 80 80
1853 400s. Peregrine falcon (horiz) . . . . 1·25 1·25
MS1854 90 × 90 mm. 500s. African white-backed vulture . . . . 1·75 2·25

245 Afghan Hound

1994. Dogs of the World. Multicoloured.
1855/63 120s. × 9 (Type **245**; Basenji; Siberian husky; Irish setter; Norwegian elkhound; Bracco Italiano; Australian cattle dog; German short-haired pointer; Rhodesian ridgeback)
1864/72 120s. × 9 (Alsatian; Japanese chin; Shetland sheepdog; Italian spinone; Great dane; English setter; Welsh corgi; St. Bernard; Irish wolfhound) . . . . . .
1873/81 120s. × 9 (Doberman pinscher; Chihuahua; Bloodhound; Keeshond; Tibetan spaniel; Japanese akita; Tervueren; Chow; Pharaoh hound) . . .
1882/90 120s. × 9 (Alaskan malamute; Scottish cairn terrier; American foxhound; British bulldog; Boston terrier; Borzoi; Shar pei; Saluki; Bernese mountain dog) . . . .
1855/90 Set of 36 . . . . 16·00 17·00
MS1891 Two sheets, each 76 × 106 mm. (a) 1000s. As No. 1856. (b) 1000s. As No. 1868 Set of 2 sheets . . . . 8·00 9·00

246 Players and Flags from Group B

1994. World Cup Football Championship, U.S.A. (3rd issue). Multicoloured.
1892 40s. Type **246** 45 45
1893 50s. Players and flags from Group C 50 50
1894 70s. Players and flags from Group D 60 60
1895 100s. Players and flags from Group E 65 65
1896 170s. Players and flags from Group A 90 90
1897 200s. Players and World Cup . . . . 1·10 1·10
1898 250s. Players and flags from Group F . . . . 1·40 1·40
MS1899 92 × 92 mm. 500s. Player heading ball . . . . 3·25 3·75

247 "Rangaeris amaniensis"

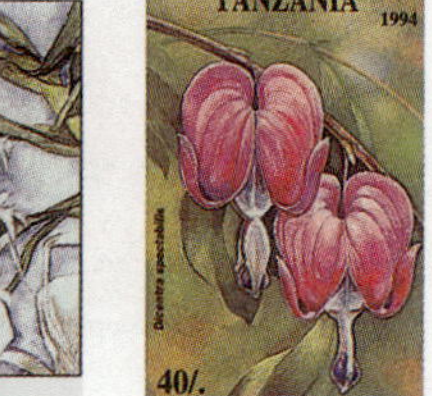

248 "Dicentra spectabilis"

1994. Orchids. Multicoloured.
1900 200s. Type **247** 65 65
1901 200s. "Eulophia macowanii" 65 65
1902 200s. "Cytorchis arcuata" 65 65
1903 200s. "Centrostigma occultans" 65 65
1904 200s. "Cirrhopetalum umbellatum" 65 65
1905 200s. "Ansellia gigantea" . . 65 65
1906 200s. "Angraecum ramosum" 65 65
1907 200s. "Disa englerana" . . . 65 65
1908 200s. "Nervilia stolziana" . . 65 65
1909 200s. "Satyrium orbiculare" 65 65
1910 200s. "Schizochilus sulphureus" 65 65
1911 200s. "Disa stolzii" 65 65
1912 200s. "Platycornye mediocris" 65 65
1913 200s. "Satyrium breve" . . . 65 65

1914 200s. "Eulophia nuttii" . . 65 65
1915 200s. "Disa ornithantha" . . 65 65
MS1916 Two sheets, each 106×76 mm. (a) 1000s. "Phaius tankervilliae" (horiz). (b) 1000s. "Eulophia thomsonii" (horiz) Set of 2 sheets . . . . 7·50 8·00

1994. Flowers. Multicoloured.
1917 40s. Type **248** 30 30
1918 100s. "Thunbergia alata" . . 40 45
1919 120s. "Cyrtanthus minimiflorus" 40 50
1920 170s. "Nepenthes hybrida" 45 70
1921 250s. "Allamanda cathartica" 50 80
1922 300s. "Encyclia pentotis" . . 50 85
1923 400s. "Protea lacticolor" . . 55 90
MS1924 91×92 mm. 500s. Tradescantia . . . . 1·25 1·75

249 "Limenitis sydyi"

1994. Butterflies. Multicoloured.
1925 120s. Type **249** 55 55
1926 120s. "Agraulis vanillae" . . 55 55
1927 120s. "Danaus chrysippus" 55 55
1928 120s. "Eurytides marcellus" 55 55
1929 120s. "Artopoetes pryeri" 55 55
1930 120s. "Heliconius charitonius" 55 55
1931 120s. "Limenitis weidemeyerii" 55 55
1932 120s. "Phoebis sennae" . . 55 55
1933 120s. "Timelaea albescens" 55 55
1934 120s. "Papilio glaucus" . . 55 55
1935 120s. "Danaus plexippus" 55 55
1936 120s. "Papilio troilus" . . . 55 55
1937 120s. "Hypolimnas antevorta" 55 55
1938 120s. "Cirrochroa imperatrix" 55 55
1939 120s. "Vanessa atalanta" . . 55 55
1940 120s. "Limenitis archippus" 55 55
1941 120s. "Hypolimnas pandarus" 55 55
1942 120s. "Anthocharis belia" 55 55
MS1943 Two sheets, each 101×70 mm. (a) 1000s. "Papilio polyxenes". (b) 1000s. "Vanessa cardui" Set of 2 sheets . . . . 7·50 8·00

250 Donald Duck and Goofy with Safari Equipment

1994. Mickey Mouse Safari Club. Walt Disney Cartoon Characters on Safari. Multicoloured.
1944 70s. Type **250** 45 45
1945 70s. Donald and Mickey Mouse with leopard cubs 45 45
1946 100s. Donald photographing antelope 55 55
1947 100s. Donald between elephant's legs 55 55
1948 120s. Mickey with monkeys 60 60
1949 120s. Donald with hippopotamuses 60 60
1950 150s. Goofy carrying equipment 70 70
1951 150s. Mickey, Donald and Goofy sheltering under elephant's ears 70 70
1952 200s. Goofy with zebras . . 80 80
1953 200s. Donald, Goofy and Mickey with lion 80 80
1954 250s. Donald filming monkeys 90 90
1955 250s. Giraffe licking Mickey 90 90
MS1956 Three sheets, each 101×121 mm. (a) 1000s. Goofy in tree with camera (vert). (b) 1000s. Donald and Goofy with camera (vert). (c) 1000s. Donald and Mickey with camera (vert) Set of 3 sheets . . . . 11·00 12·00

251 Plan indicating Moon Landing Point

1994. 25th Anniv of First Moon Landing. Multicoloured.
1957 150s. Type **251** 75 75
1958 150s. Photograph showing Sea of Tranquility 75 75
1959 150s. Lunar surface 75 75
1960 150s. Lift-off 75 75
1961 150s. Jettisoning first stage rocket 75 75
1962 150s. Jettisoning second stage rocket 75 75
1963 150s. Lunar module "Eagle" leaving command module 75 75
1964 150s. "Eagle" descending towards lunar surface . . 75 75
1965 150s. Armstrong and Aldrin (astronauts) inside "Eagle" 75 75
1966 150s. "Apollo 11" crew in space suits 75 75
1967 150s. "Eagle" on lunar surface 75 75
1968 150s. Armstrong descending to lunar surface 75 75
1969 150s. Astronaut, "Eagle" and experiment 75 75
1970 150s. Astronaut setting-up equipment 75 75
1971 150s. Reflection in astronaut's visor 75 75
1972 150s. Astronaut and U.S.A. flag 75 75
1973 150s. Astronaut carrying equipment 75 75
1974 150s. "Eagle" blasting off from Moon 75 75
1975 150s. Command module . . 75 75
1976 150s. "Eagle" leaving Moon 75 75
1977 150s. Capsule leaving Moon orbit 75 75
1978 150s. Capsule heading for Earth 75 75
1979 150s. Capsule re-entering Earth's atmosphere . . . 75 75
1980 150s. Capsule in sea 75 75
1981 150s. Recovery crew opening hatch 75 75
1982 150s. Transferring astronauts by helicopter 75 75
1983 150s. Armstrong, Collins and Aldrin (astronauts) after recovery 75 75

252 "Astacus leptodactytus"

1994. Crabs. Multicoloured.
1984 40s. Type **252** 30 30
1985 100s. "Eriocheir sinensis" (vert) 50 50
1986 120s. "Caneer opillo" (vert) 55 55
1987 170s. "Cardisoma quanhumi" 70 70
1988 250s. "Birgus latro" (vert) 85 85
1989 300s. "Menippe mercenaria" 90 90
1990 400s. "Dromia vulgaris" (vert) 95 95
MS1991 92×92 mm. 500s. Coral and crab's claw . . . . 1·60 2·00

1994. Centenary of International Olympic Committee. Gold Medal Winners. As T **285a** of St. Vincent. Multicoloured.
1992 350s. Kristin Otto (Germany) (50 metres freestyle swimming), 1988 1·00 1·00
1993 500s. Carl Lewis (U.S.A.) (various track and field events), 1984 and 1988 . . 1·40 1·40
MS1994 74×104 mm. 1000s. Oksana Baiul (Ukraine) (figure skating), 1994 . . . . 3·00 3·50

1994. 50th Anniv of D-Day (1st issue). As T **284b** of St. Vincent. Multicoloured.
1995 350s. Troops leaving landing craft . . . . 1·25 1·25
1996 600s. Amphibious tank and troops, Omaha Beach . . 1·75 1·75
MS1997 104×74 mm. 1000s. Loading landing craft in England 3·25 3·75
See also Nos. 1998/2016.

253 Supermarine Spitfire over Beaches

1994. 50th Anniv of D-Day (2nd issue). Multicoloured.
1998 200s. Type **253** 80 80
1999 200s. D.U.K.W.s landing on Gold Beach 80 80
2000 200s. Canadian troops landing on Juno Beach . . 80 80
2001 200s. Canadian cyclists disembarking, Juno Beach 80 80
2002 200s. Amphibious Sherman tank on beach 80 80
2003 200s. German gun emplacement 80 80
2004 200s. General Montgomery and British troops on beach 80 80
2005 200s. British engineers with AVRE Churchill tank, Gold Beach 80 80
2006 200s. U.S.S. "Thompson" (destroyer) being refuelled 80 80
2007 200s. H.M.S. "Warspite" (battleship) 80 80
2008 200s. Royal Marines on Juno Beach 80 80
2009 200s. Sherman Mark 1 flail tank leaving landing craft 80 80
2010 200s. General Eisenhower and U.S. troops on Omaha Beach 80 80
2011 200s. North American P-51 Mustang escorting ships 80 80
2012 200s. U.S. coastguard cutter alongside landing craft . . 80 80
2013 200s. U.S. troops in landing craft 80 80
2014 200s. U.S. troops landing on Omaha Beach 80 80
2015 200s. U.S. troops on Omaha Beach 80 80
MS2016 Two sheets, each 99×70 mm. (a) 1000s. U.S. marines amongst beach obstacles. (b) 1000s. U.S. troops landing on Utah Beach Set of 2 sheets . . 7·00 8·00
No. 2004 is inscribed "COMMANDER-IN-CHIEF" and No. 2010 "OPERATION OVERLOAD", both in error.

254 "Deinonychus"

1994. Prehistoric Animals.
2017/48 120s. × 32 multicoloured 21·00 22·00
MS2049 80×110 mm. 1000s. multicoloured . . . . 4·25 4·75
DESIGNS—VERT: No. 2018, Styracosaurus; 2019, Anatosaurus; 2020, Plateosaurus; 2021, Iguanodon; 2022, Oviraptor; 2023, Dimorphodons; 2024, Ornithomimus; 2025, Lambeosaurus; 2026, Megalosaurus; 2027, Cetiosaurus; 2028, Hypsilophodon; 2029, Rhamphorynchus; 2030, Scelidosaurus; 2031, Antrodemus; 2032, Dimetrodon; **MS**2049, Brachiosaurus. HORIZ: No. 2033, Brontosaurus; 2034, Albertosaurus; 2035, Parasaurolophus; 2036, Pteranodons; 2037, Stegosaurus; 2038, Tyrannosaurus rex; 2039, Triceratops; 2040, Ornitholestes; 2041, Camarasaurus; 2042, Ankylosaurus; 2043, Trachodon; 2044, Allosaurus; 2045, Corythosaurus; 2046, Struthiomimus; 2047, Camptosaurus; 2048, Heterodontosaurus.
Nos. 2017/32 and 2033/48 respectively were printed together, se-tenant, Nos. 2033/48 forming a composite design.

255 "Hubble" Space Telescope

1994. Space Research. Multicoloured.
2050 40s. Type **255** 30 30
2051 100s. "Mariner" 50 50
2052 120s. "Voyager 2" 55 55
2053 170s. "Work Package-03" 70 70
2054 250s. Orbiting solar observer 85 85
2055 300s. "Magellan" 90 90
2056 400s. "Galilei" 95 95
MS2057 91×91 mm. 500s. "Fobos" 1·90 2·25

It is understood that the following issues were freely available for postal purposes from Tanzanian post offices. Further issues, for which evidence of normal postal use cannot be found, could be obtained from the Philatelic Bureau in Dar-es-Salaam. Such issues will be found in the Appendix.

1995. No. 906 surch **70/-**.
2058 70s. on 13s. Teacher with blackboard 10 10

257 Coconuts

1995. Fruit. Multicoloured.
2059 70s. Type **257** 10 10
2060 100s. Pineapple 10 15
2061 150s. Pawpaw 20 25
2062 200s. Tomatoes 25 30
MS2063 91×91 mm. 500s. Type **257** 60 65

258 Farmer and Maize Crop

261 *Plumeria rubra acutifolia*

260 Presidents Mwinyi (Tanzania), Moi (Kenya) and Museveni (Uganda)

1995. 50th Anniv of United Nations and Food and Agriculture Organization. Multicoloured designs (except No. **MS**2068).
2064 70s. Type **258** 10 10
2065 100s. Ploughing with ox team (horiz) 10 15
2066 150s. Women in spinning mill (horiz) 20 25
2067 200s. Child drawing 25 30
MS2068 101×97 mm. 500s. U.N. 50th anniv logo (horiz) (black and blue) 60 65

1995. No. 810 surch **100/-**.
2069 100s. on 40s. Lesser flamingo 10 15

1995. 2nd Anniversary of East African Treaty. Multicoloured.
2070 100s. Type **260** 10 15
2071 150s. Map of East Africa and national flags (vert) 20 25
2072 180s. Cotton boll (vert) . . 20 25
2073 200s. Fishermen on Lake Victoria 25 30
MS2074 100×102 mm. 500s. Type **260** 60 65

1996. Flowers. Multicoloured. (a) Without imprint date.
2075 100s. Type **261** 10 15
2076 140s. *Lilaceae* 20 25
2077 180s. *Alamanda* 20 25
2078 200s. *Lilaceae* 25 30
2079 210s. *Zinnia* 25 30
2080 260s. *Malvaviscus penduliflorus* 30 35
2081 300s. *Cannai* 35 40
2082 380s. *Nerium oleander carneum* 50 55
2083 400s. *Hibiscus rosa sinensis* 50 55
2084 600s. *Catharanthus roseus* 70 75
2085 700s. *Bougainvillea formosa* 80 85
2086 750s. *Acalypha* 90 95
MS2087 88×112 mm. 125s.× 4 in designs of 210, 300, 380 and 700s. (each 31×36 mm) 60 65

(b) With 1997 imprint date.
2088 150s. As 140s. 20 25
Nos. 2081 and **MS**2087 are inscribed "Carna", both in error.

262 Pineapple

1996. East African Fruit. Multicoloured.
2089 140s. Type **262** 20 25
2090 180s. Orange and limes . . . 20 25
2091 200s. Pear and apples . . . 25 30
2092 300s. Bananas 35 40
MS2093 92×92 mm. 300s. No. 2092 35 40

263 Children's Clinic

264 Couple and setting Sun

1996. 25th Anniv of U.N. Volunteers. Mult.
2094 140s. Type **263** 20 25
2095 200s. Food distribution . . 25 30

2096 260s. Clean water supply 30 35
2097 300s. Public education 35 40
MS2098 95 × 95 mm. 500s. Refugee camp 60 65

1996. World Aids Day. Multicoloured.
2099 140s. Type **264** 20 25
2100 310s. People from various occupations (horiz) 35 40
2101 370s. Discussion group (horiz) 45 50
2102 410s. Orphans with foster mother (horiz) 50 55
MS2103 95 × 95 mm. 500s. Type **264** 60 65

265 Game Reserve

1996. 2nd Anniv of Common Market for Eastern and Southern Africa (COMESA). Multicoloured.
2104 140s. Type **265** 20 25
2105 180s. Fishermen in canoe 20 25
2106 200s. Container ship at Dar-es-Salaam docks 25 30
2107 300s. Goods train on Tazara railway 35 40
MS2108 90 × 90 mm. 500s. Cotton bolls 60 65

266 *Bukoba* (ferry) sinking

1997. 1st Anniv of Sinking of *Bukoba* (ferry). Multicoloured.
2109 140s. Type **266** 20 25
2110 350s. Recovering bodies from wreck 30 45
2111 370s. Identifying victims 40 45
2112 410s. Religious service for victims 50 55
MS2113 90 × 90 mm. 500s. *Bukoba* (ferry) 60 65

267 Mount Kilimanjaro and Animals

1997. Tourist Attractions. Multicoloured.
2114 140s. Type **267** 20 25
2115 310s. Members of the Masai tribe 35 40
2116 370s. Old Stone Town, Zanzibar 40 45
2117 410s. Buffalo on Ruaha Plains 50 55
MS2118 87 × 87 mm. 500s. Mount Kilimanjaro and elephant 60 65

268 Red Hornbill

269 Mount Kilimanjaro and Elephant

1997. Coastal Birds. Multicoloured.
2119 140s. Type **268** 20 25
2120 350s. Sacred ibis (horiz) 40 45
2121 370s. Gulls (horiz) 40 45
2122 410s. Ring-necked dove (horiz) 50 55
MS2123 90 × 90 mm. 500s. Red hornbill, sacred ibis, gulls and ring-necked dove 60 65

1997.
2124 **269** 410s. multicoloured 50 55

1998. Nos. 805/6 and 808 surch **150/-**.
2125 150s. on 9s. African emerald cuckoo 20 25
2126 150s. on 13s. Little bee eater 20 25
2127 150s. on 20s. Bateleur 20 25

271 Tanzania and P.A.P.U. Flags

1998. 18th Anniv of Pan African Postal Union. Multicoloured.
2128 150s. Type **271** 20 25
2129 250s. P.A.P.U. logo 30 35
2130 400s. Postman making E.M.S. delivery 50 55
2131 500s. Two giraffes 60 65

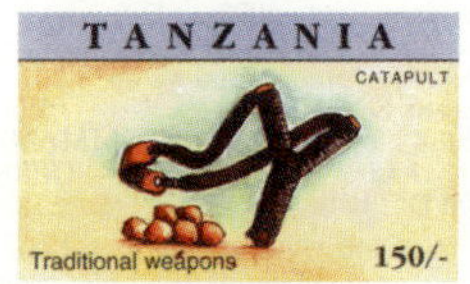

272 Catapult

1998. Traditional Weapons. Multicoloured.
2132 150s. Type **272** 20 25
2133 250s. Cutlass and club 30 35
2134 400s. Rifle and ammunition 50 55
2135 500s. Bow and arrows 60 65

273 Children carrying Banner

1998. Children's Rights in Tanzania. Multicoloured.
2136 150s. Type **273** 20 25
2137 250s. Teacher with children 30 35
2138 400s. Adult with stick and child (vert) 50 55
2139 500s. Child hugging adult (vert) 60 65
MS2140 90 × 90 mm. 500s. As 250s 60 65

274 U.P.U. Emblem

275 The Dhow Harbour

1998. World Stamp Day. Multicoloured.
2141 150s. Type **274** 20 25
2142 250s. Cancelling mail 30 35
2143 400s. Dove carrying air mail letter 50 55
2144 500s. Woman posting letter 60 65
MS2145 90 × 90 mm. 500s. Woman posting letter, dove and U.P.U. emblem 60 65

1998. Tourist Attractions of Zanzibar. Mult.
2146 100s. Type **275** 10 15
2147 150s. Girl on giant tortoise in countryside 20 25
2148 250s. Children with giant tortoise (horiz) 30 35
2149 300s. Stone Town street 35 40
2150 400s. The Old Fort (horiz) 50 55
2151 500s. Red colobus monkeys (horiz) 60 65
MS2152 70 × 100 mm. 600s. Girl on giant tortoise in Stone Town street 70 75

OFFICIAL STAMPS

1965. Nos. 128 etc, optd **OFFICIAL**.
O 9 **25** 5c. blue and orange 10 1·00
O10 – 10c. multicoloured 10 1·00
O11 – 15c. multicoloured 10 1·00
O12 – 20c. sepia, green and blue 10 1·00
O13 – 30c. black and brown 10 40
O14 – 50c. multicoloured 15 1·00
O15 **33** 1s. multicoloured 30 40
O16 – 5s. brown, green and blue 1·75 7·00

1967. Nos. 142, etc, optd **OFFICIAL**.
O20 5c. mauve, green and black 10 2·50
O21 10c. brown and bistre 10 50
O22 15c. grey, blue and black 10 2·50
O23 20c. brown and green 10 30
O24 30c. green and black 10 30
O36 40c. yellow, brown and green — 2·50
O25 50c. multicoloured 15 1·25
O26 1s. brown, blue and purple 30 2·50
O27 5s. yellow, black and green 2·50 14·00

1973. Nos. 158 etc, optd **OFFICIAL**.
O40 **53** 5c. green, blue and black 50 2·50
O41 – 10c. multicoloured 65 30
O42 – 20c. brown, yellow & black 80 30
O43 – 40c. multicoloured 1·25 30
O44 – 50c. multicoloured 1·25 30
O45 – 70c. green, orange & black 1·25 65
O46 **54** 1s. multicoloured 1·25 30
O47 – 1s.50 multicoloured 2·50 3·50
O48 – 2s.50 multicoloured 3·00 8·00
O49 – 5s. multicoloured 3·25 11·00

1980. Nos. 307/13 and 315/17 optd **OFFICIAL**.
O54 10c. Type **75** 20 1·00
O55 20c. Large-spotted genet 25 80
O56 40c. Banded mongoose 30 80
O57 50c. Ratel 30 30
O58 75c. Large-toothed rock hyrax 40 50
O59 80c. Leopard 55 1·25
O60 1s. Impala 55 30
O66 1s.50 Giraffe 4·00 4·00
O61 2s. Common zebra 85 2·50
O62 3s. African buffalo 1·00 2·75
O63 5s. Lion 1·50 3·75

1990. Nos. 804/12 optd **OFFICIAL**.
O70 5s. Type **163** 20 1·00
O71 9s. African emerald cuckoo 25 80
O72 13s. Little bee eater 25 80
O73 15s. Red bishop 25 1·00
O74 20s. Bateleur 35 1·00
O75 25s. Scarlet-chested sunbird 35 1·00
O76 30s. African wood pigeon 35 1·00
O77 40s. Type **164** 50 1·00
O78 70s. Helmeted guineafowl 70 1·25
O79 100s. Eastern white pelican 1·00 1·75

POSTAGE DUE STAMPS

The Postage Due stamps of Kenya, Uganda and Tanganyika were used in Tanganyika until 2 January 1967.

D 1

D 2

1967.
D19 **D 1** 5c. red 15 2·25
D20 10c. green 20 2·25
D21 20c. blue 30 2·50
D22 30c. brown 45 3·25
D23 40c. purple 50 4·50
D24 1s. orange 70 4·75

1990.
D30 **D 2** 50c. green 10 30
D31 80c. blue 10 30
D32 1s. brown 10 30
D33 2s. green 10 40
D34 3s. purple 10 40
D35 5s. brown 15 45
D36 10s. brown 25 60
D37 20s. brown 40 75

APPENDIX

The following stamps have either been issued in excess of postal needs, or have not been made available to the public in reasonable quantities at face value.

1985.

Life and Times of Queen Elizabeth the Queen Mother. As Nos. 425/8 but embossed on gold foil. 20s. × 2, 100s. × 2.

Tanzanian Railway Locomotives (1st series). As Nos. 430/3 but embossed on gold foil. 5, 10, 20, 30s.

1986.

Caribbean Royal Visit. Optd on previous issues. (a) On Nos. 425/8. 20s. × 2, 100s. × 2. (b) On Nos. 430/3. 5, 10, 20, 30s.

"Ameripex" International Stamp Exhibition, Chicago. Optd on Nos. 425/8. 20s. × 2, 100s. × 2.

1988.

Cent of Statue of Liberty (1986). 1, 2, 3, 4, 5, 6, 7, 8, 10, 12, 15, 18, 20, 25, 30, 35, 40, 45, 50, 60s.

Royal Ruby Wedding. Optd on No. 378. 10s.

125th Anniv of Red Cross. Optd on Nos. 486/7. 5, 40s.

63rd Anniv of Rotary International in Africa. Optd on Nos. 422/3. 10s., 17s.50.

1995.

The Beatles. 100s. × 18.

Hoofed Animals. 70, 100, 150, 180, 200, 260, 380s.

Fauna of Coral Reefs. 70, 100, 150, 180, 200, 260, 380s.

"Singapore '95" International Stamp Exhibition. Trains of the World. 200s. × 18.

Centof Sierra Club. 150s. × 18.

Bats. 70, 100, 150, 180, 200, 260, 380s.

History of Rock and Roll. 250s. × 9.

90th Anniv of Rotary International. 600s.

Winter Olympic Games, Lillehammer, Norway. 300, 400s.

Picasso Paintings. 30, 200, 300s.

450th Death Anniv of Copernicus (astronomer) (1993). 100, 300s.

"Polska'93" International Stamp Exhibition, Poznan. 200, 300s.

95th Birthday of Queen Elizabeth the Queen Mother. 250s. × 4.

Olympic Games, Atlanta, 1996. Olympic History. 200s. × 18.

50th Anniv of End of Second World War in the Pacific. 250s. × 6.

50th Anniv of End of Second World War. 250s. × 8.

Cacti. 70, 100, 150, 180, 200, 260, 380s.

African Reptiles. 200s. × 12.

Predatory Animals. 70, 100, 150, 200, 250, 280, 300s.

50th Anniv of United Nations. 250s. × 3.

50th Anniv of U.N. Food and Agriculture Organization. 250s. × 3.

Cent of Cinema. Biblical Epics. 250s. × 9.

20th Anniv of World Tourism Organization. 100, 300, 400s.

Gerry Garcia (rock musician) Commemoration. 200s.

Frogs. 100, 140, 180, 200, 210, 260, 300s.

Fauna of Kilimanjaro. 100s. × 16, 250s. × 4.

Butterflies. 200s. × 19, 250, 370, 410s.

1996.

Moths and Butterflies. 70, 100, 150, 200, 250, 260, 300s.

Chinese New Year ("Year of the Rat"). 200s. × 4.

Horses. 250s. × 9.

Cats. 100, 150, 200, 250s. × 9, 300s. × 4.

Dogs. 70s, 250s. × 10, 300s. × 4, 600s.

Crocodiles. 100, 150, 200, 250, 260, 300, 380s.

125th Anniv of the Metropolitan Museum, New York. Paintings. 200s. × 18.

Elvis Presley Commemoration. 200s. × 9.

Snakes. 100, 140, 180, 200, 260, 300, 400s.

"China 96", International Stamp Exhibition. Deng Xiaoping. 250s. × 6.

70th Birthday of Queen Elizabeth II. 300s. × 3.

Famous People. 70, 100, 150, 200, 250s. × 6.

Olympic Games, Atlanta. 100, 150, 200, 300s.

Birds. 300s. × 16.

Cent of Radio. Famous People. 70, 100, 150, 200s.

Flowers. 300s. × 16.

Fish. 100, 150, 200s. × 9, 250, 500s.

Mercedes and Ferrari Cars. 250s. × 12.

50th Anniv of UNESCO. 200, 250, 600s.

50th Anniv of UNICEF. 200, 250, 500s.

90th Anniv of Rotary. Nos. 985/1000 and 1589/600 optd **90th ANNIVERSARY OF ROTARY 1905–1995** and emblem. 50s. × 16, 100s. × 12.International Scout Camp, Thailand and 34th World Scout Conf, Norway. Nos. 1001/16 and 1564/75 optd either **34th WORLD SCOUT CONFERENCE NORWAY JULY 8–12 1996** or **INTERNATIONAL SCOUT CAMP THAILAND MARCH 25–31 1996**, both with Scout emblem. 50s. × 16, 100s. × 12

Fungi. 300s. × 16.

1997.

"Hong Kong 97" International Stamp Exhibition. Portraits of Sun Yat-sen. 300s. × 6.

Horses. 250s. × 12.

Chernobyl's Children. 700s. × 2.

Birds. 140s. × 6, 150, 200, 370s. × 6, 410, 500s.

Flowers. 200s. × 6, 300s. × 6.

175th Anniv of Brothers Grimm's Third Collection of Fairy Tales *Rumpelstiltskin*. 400s. × 3.

Birth Bicent of Hiroshige (Japanese painter). 250s. × 6.

Golden Wedding of Queen Elizabeth and Prince Philip. 370s. × 6.

Return of Hong Kong to China. 1000s. × 5.

Winter Olympic Games, Nagano (1998). 100, 200, 250s. × 4, 500, 600s.

World Cup Football Championship, France (1998). 100, 150, 200, 250s. × 17, 500, 600s.

African Safari. 250s. × 9.

Northern Wilderness (Arctic). 250s. × 9.

Endangered Species. 250s. × 24.

Seven Wonders of the Ancient World. 370s. × 6.

Seven Wonders of the Modern World. 140s. × 6.

Aviation. 100, 150s. × 18, 200, 250s. × 8, 300, 400, 500s.

1998.

Diana, Princess of Wales Commemoration. 150, 250s.

Marine Life. 200s. × 12, 250s. × 18.

Chinese New Year ("Year of the Tiger"). 370s. × 4.

Classic Cars. 370s. × 12.

Aircraft. 300s. × 18.

Exotic Flowers. 250s. × 26.

Endangered Species. 200s. × 12, 370s. × 12.

Eagles. 370s. × 6.

Fauna and Flora. 250, 370s. × 12, 410, 500, 600s.

International Year of the Ocean (1st issue). 150, 200s. × 12, 250, 300s. × 9, 400, 500s.

International Year of the Ocean (2nd issue). 1998 Marine Life overprinted with emblem. 200s. × 12, 250s. × 18.

Fungi and Insects. 140, 150, 200, 250s. × 19, 370, 410, 500, 600s.

Rudolph the Red-nosed Reindeer (cartoon film). 200s. × 12.

25th Death Anniv of Pablo Picasso (painter). 400s. × 2, 500s.

50th Death Anniv of Mahatma Gandhi. 370s.

1st Death Anniv of Diana, Princess of Wales. 600s.

19th World Scout Jamboree, Chile. 600s. × 3.

80th Anniv of Royal Air Force 500s. × 4.

TASMANIA Pt. 1

An island south of Australia, one of the States of the Australian Commonwealth, whose stamps it now uses.

12 pence = 1 shilling;
20 shillings = 1 pound.

1

2

1853. Imperf.
3 **1** 1d. blue £3500 £850
8 **2** 4d. orange £2000 £400

3

7

8

1855. Imperf.
28 **3** 1d. red . . . . . 90·00 20·00
34 2d. green . . . . . £170 65·00
36 4d. blue . . . . . £130 17·00
46 **7** 6d. purple . . . . . £180 55·00
41 **8** 1s. orange . . . . . £500 70·00

1864. Perf.
82 **3** 1d. red . . . . . 38·00 10·00
71 2d. green . . . . . £150 48·00
72 4d. blue . . . . . 90·00 14·00
143 **7** 6d. purple . . . . . 25·00 12·00
141 **8** 1s. orange . . . . . 90·00 40·00

11 20

1870.
159 **11** ½d. orange . . . . . 3·00 2·75
156 1d. red . . . . . 3·00 75
157 2d. green . . . . . 4·00 75
165 3d. brown . . . . . 8·00 3·75
130 4d. blue £700 £400
226 4d. yellow . . . . . 12·00 6·00
158 8d. purple . . . . . 14·00 4·75
256 9d. blue . . . . . 7·00 3·50
131 10d. black . . . . . 23·00 23·00
149b 5s. mauve . . . . . £140 55·00

1889. Surch **Halfpenny**.
167 **11** 2½d. on 9d. blue . . . . . 9·50 13·00

1889. Surch **d. 2½**.
169 **11** 2½d. on 9d. blue . . . . . 5·00 3·25

1892. Various frames.
216 **20** ½d. orange and mauve . . 1·50 70
217 2½d. purple . . . . . 2·50 1·00
218 5d. blue and brown . . . . 5·00 2·00
219 6d. violet and black . . . 7·50 2·50
220 10d. lake and green . . . . 9·00 9·00
221 1s. red and green . . . . 7·50 2·25
222 2s.6d. brown and blue . . 22·00 13·00
223 5s. purple and red . . . 45·00 18·00
224 10s. mauve and brown . . . 80·00 55·00
225 £1 green and yellow . . . £250 £200

22 Lake Marion
23 Mount Wellington

1899.
249 **22** ½d. green . . . . . 1·50 30
250 **23** 1d. red . . . . . 1·50 20
251b – 2d. violet . . . . . 2·75 20
232 – 2½d. blue . . . . . 14·00 3·75
253 – 3d. brown . . . . . 8·00 4·00
247 – 4d. orange . . . . . 13·00 3·75
235 – 5d. blue . . . . . 21·00 10·00
236 – 6d. lake . . . . . 23·00 16·00
DESIGNS—HORIZ: 2d. Hobart; 3d. Spring River, Port Davey; 5d. Mt. Gould, Lake St. Clair; 6d. Dilston Falls. VERT: 2½d. Tasman's Arch; 4d. Russell Falls.

1904. No. 218 surch **1½d.**
244 **20** 1½d. on 5d. blue and brown . . . . . 1·25 60

1912. No. 251b surch **ONE PENNY**.
260 1d. on 2d. violet 90 70

TCHONGKING (CHUNGKING) Pt. 17

An Indo-Chinese Post Office was opened at Chungking in February 1902 and operated until it closed in December 1922.

1903. 100 centimes = 1 franc.
1919. 100 cents = 1 piastre.

Stamps of Indo-China surch.

1903. "Tablet" key-type surch with value in Chinese and **TCHONGKING**.
1 D 1c. black and red on blue . . 4·25 4·50
2 2c. brown and blue on buff 3·25 3·75
3 4c. brown and blue on grey 3·25 3·75
4 5c. green and red . . . . 3·25 3·50
5 10c. red and blue . . . . 3·25 4·00
6 15c. grey and red . . . . 2·75 4·50
7 20c. red and blue on green 3·75 4·25
8 25c. blue and red . . . . 30·00 45·00
9 25c. black and red on pink 5·00 8·00
10 30c. brown and blue on drab 9·75 12·00
11 40c. red and blue on yellow 42·00 48·00
12 50c. red and blue on pink £170 £170
13 50c. brown and red on blue 95·00 £120
14 75c. brown and red on orange . . . . . 45·00 48·00
15 1f. green and red . . . . 50·00 60·00
16 5f. mauve and blue on lilac 85·00 £100

1906. Surch with value in Chinese and **Tch'ong K'ing**.
17 **8** 1c. green . . . . . 2·25 3·50
18 2c. purple on yellow . . . 2·00 2·75
19 4c. mauve on blue . . . . 2·50 2·75
20 5c. green . . . . . 2·75 2·75
21 10c. pink . . . . . 2·75 3·00
22 15c. brown on blue . . . 7·50 8·00
23 20c. red on green . . . . 3·25 3·50
24 25c. blue . . . . . 4·00 4·25
25 30c. brown on cream . . . 3·75 4·25
26 35c. black on yellow . . . 3·50 3·75
27 40c. black on grey . . . . 6·25 6·50
28 50c. brown on cream . . . 6·25 9·25
29 D 75c. brown and red on orange . . . . . 35·00 40·00
30 **8** 1f. green . . . . . 24·00 32·00
31 2f. brown on yellow . . . 20·00 32·00
32 D 5f. mauve and blue on lilac £100 £110
33 **8** 10f. red on green £110 £120

1908. Native types surch with value in Chinese and **TCHONGKING**.
34 **10** 1c. black and brown . . . 1·00 75
35 2c. black and brown . . . 1·10 90
36 4c. black and blue . . . 1·40 1·60
37 5c. black and green . . . 2·25 2·00
38 10c. black and red . . . 1·90 2·50
39 15c. black and violet . . . 2·75 3·50
40 **11** 20c. black and violet . . . 4·00 4·25
41 25c. black and blue . . . 3·50 3·75
42 30c. black and brown . . . 3·50 4·50
43 35c. black and green . . . 5·50 7·50
44 40c. black and brown . . . 10·00 16·00
45 50c. black and red . . . 10·00 11·50
46 **12** 75c. black and orange . . . 9·00 11·50
47 – 1f. black and red . . . 11·00 15·00
48 – 2f. black and green . . . 85·00 £100
49 – 5f. black and blue . . . 35·00 35·00
50 – 10f. black and violet . . . £170 £200

1919. As last, but surch in addition in figures and words.
51 **10** ⅖c. on 1c. black and brown 1·40 30
52 ⅘c. on 2c. black and brown 80 3·00
53 1⅗c. on 4c. black and blue 85 3·00
54 2c. on 5c. black and green 2·50 2·75
55 4c. on 10c. black and red 1·40 1·75
56 6c. on 15c. black and violet 2·75 2·50
57 **11** 8c. on 20c. black and violet 2·25 2·00
58 10c. on 25c. black and blue 3·00 2·25
59 12c. on 30c. black & brown 3·00 95
60 14c. on 35c. black and green 3·50 3·00
61 16c. on 40c. black and brown . . . . . 3·50 3·50
62 20c. on 50c. black and red 13·00 12·50
63 **12** 30c. on 75c. black & orange 3·75 4·25
64 – 40c. on 1f. black and red . . 4·25 4·00
65 – 80c. on 2f. black and green 6·25 5·50
66 – 2p. on 5f. black and blue . . 9·00 8·75
67 – 4p. on 10f. black and violet 12·00 11·00

TETE Pt. 9

Formerly using the stamps of Mozambique, this district of Mozambique was permitted to issue its own stamps from 1913 until 1920 when Mozambique stamps were again used.

100 centavos = 1 escudo.

1913. Surch **REPUBLICA TETE** and new value on "Vasco da Gama" issues of (a) Portugese Colonies.
1 ¼c. on 2½r. green 40 35
2 ½c. on 5r. red 40 35
3 1c. on 10r. purple 40 35
4 2½c. on 25r. green 40 35
5 5c. on 50r. blue 40 35
6 7½c. on 75r. brown 75 55
7 10c. on 100r. brown 45 40
8 15c. on 150r. brown 45 40

(b) Macao.
9 ¼c. on ½a. green 40 35
10 ½c. on 1a. red 40 35
11 1c. on 2a. purple 40 35
12 2½c. on 4a. green 40 35
13 5c. on 8a. blue 40 35
14 7½c. on 12a. brown 75 60
15 10c. on 16a. brown 45 40
16 15c. on 24a. brown 45 40

(c) Timor.
17 ¼c. on ½c. green 40 35
18 ½c. on 1a. red 40 35
19 1c. on 2a. purple 40 35
20 2½c. on 4a. green 40 35
21 5c. on 8a. blue 40 35
22 7½c. on 12a. brown 75 60
23 10c. on 16a. brown 45 40
24 15c. on 24a. brown 45 40

1914. "Ceres" key-type inscr "TETE".
25 U ¼c. green 35 25
26 ½c. black 35 25
27 1c. green 35 20
28 1½c. brown 35 20
29 2c. red 35 25
30 2½c. violet 35 20
31 5c. blue 35 25
32 7½c. brown 50 50
33 8c. grey 50 50
34 10c. red 60 60
35 15c. purple 75 60
36 20c. green 75 60
37 30c. brown on green 75 60
38 40c. brown on pink 90 65
39 50c. orange on orange . . . 90 85
40 1e. green on blue . . . . . 1·25 1·00

THAILAND Pt. 21

An independent kingdom in S.E. Asia, previously known as Siam.

1883. 32 solot = 16 atts = 8 peinung (sio)
= 4 songpy (sik) = 2 fuang
= 1 salung; 4 salungs = 1 tical.
1909. 100 satangs = 1 tical.
1912. 100 satangs = 1 baht.

1 King Chulalongkorn

2

3 King Chulalongkorn

9

1883.
1 **1** 1solot (⅛a.) blue . . . . . 5·25 5·25
2 1att red . . . . . 7·00 6·25
3 1sio (2a.) red . . . . . 15·00 15·00
4 **2** 1sik (4a.) yellow . . . . . 6·00 7·00
5 **3** 1salung (16a.) orange . . . . 22·00 22·00

1885. Surch. (a) **1 TICAL**.
6 **1** 1t. on 1solot blue £2250 £1500

(b) **1 Tical**.
7 **1** 1t. on 1solot blue £225 £200

1887.
11 **9** 1a. green . . . . . 1·90 60
12 2a. green and red . . . . . 3·00 60
13 3a. green and blue . . . . . 5·50 2·25
14 4a. green and brown . . . . 5·75 2·75
15 8a. green and yellow . . . . 5·75 1·90
16 12a. purple and red . . . . 9·50 85
17 24a. purple and blue . . . . 13·50 1·10
18 64a. purple and brown . . . 50·00 14·50

อัฐ (11) ๓ อัฐ 1 (12)

1889. Surch with T **11**.
19 **1** 1a. on 1sio red . . . . . 8·00 8·00

1889. (a) Surch as T **12**.
20 **9** 1a. on 2a. green and red . . 1·75 1·40
24 1a. on 3a. green and blue . . 3·50 3·25
26 2a. on 3a. green and blue . . 16·00 15·00

(b) No. 24 further surch as T **12**.
28 **9** 2a. on 1a. on 3a. green & blue £1000 £750

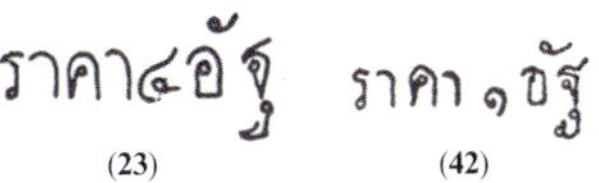

(23) (42)

1892. Surch with T **23**.
32 **9** 4a. on 24a. purple and blue 18·00 15·00

1892. No. 32 further surch **4 atts** in English (with or without full point).
33 **9** 4a. on 24a. purple and blue 4·75 3·25

1892. Surch as T **42**.
63 **9** 1Att. on 12a. purple and red 7·25 2·50
54 1Att. on 12a. purple and red £160 £160
37 1Att. on 64a. purple and brown . . . . . 1·75 1·75
46 1Att. on 64a. purple & brown 85 85
44 2a. on 64a. purple and brown 1·10 1·10
58 3a. on 12a. purple and red 5·75 1·75
60 4a. on 12a. purple and red 6·75 1·75
50 10a. on 24a. purple and blue 3·75 85

49

50

53 Wat Cheng "Temple of Light"

1899.
67 **49** 1a. green 85 45
68 2a. green . . . . . 1·10 45
69 2a. red and blue . . . . 1·40 55
70 3a. red and blue . . . . 3·25 1·10
71 3a. green . . . . . 9·50 5·50
72 4a. red . . . . . 1·40 55
73 4a. brown and pink . . . . 4·50 1·10
74 6a. red . . . . . 15·00 6·25
75 8a. green and orange . . . 3·50 60
76 10a. blue . . . . . 4·25 1·10
77 12a. purple and red . . . . 19·00 90
78 14a. blue . . . . . 11·00 8·00
79 24a. purple and blue . . . . £120 9·00
80 28a. brown and blue . . . . 12·50 11·50
81 64a. purple and brown . . . 32·00 3·50

1899.
82 **50** 1a. green . . . . . £120 65·00
83 2a. green and red £170 £100
84 3a. red and blue £250 £140
85 4a. black and green £1800 £500
86 10a. pink and green £2000 £700

1905. Surch in English and Siamese.
90 **49** 1a. on 14a. blue . . . . . 4·25 3·25
91 2a. on 28a. brown and blue 4·75 3·75

1905.
92 **53** 1a. green and yellow . . . 70 30
93 2a. grey and violet . . . . 1·00 55
94 2a. green . . . . . 3·75 2·50
95 3a. green . . . . . 1·90 90
96 3a. grey and violet . . . . 7·00 3·00
97 4a. red and brown . . . . 2·75 60
98 4a. red . . . . . 3·50 60
99 5a. red . . . . . 3·75 1·00
100 8a. bistre and black . . . 4·25 55
101 9a. blue . . . . . 11·50 4·25
102 12a. blue . . . . . 8·50 1·25
103 18a. brown . . . . . 35·00 8·75
104 24a. brown . . . . . 15·00 3·00
105 1t. bistre and blue . . . . 24·00 2·25

54

๒ อัฐ

2 Atts.

(57)

1907. Fiscal stamps optd **Siam. Postage** and new value.

106 **54** 10t. green . . . . £400 65·00
107 20t. green £4000 £200
108 40t. green £3250 £400

1907. Surch **1 att.** and thin line.

109 **9** 1a. on 24a. purple and blue 85 55

1908. Surch in English and Siamese as T **57**.

110 **9** 2a. on 24a. purple and blue 85 55
111 **53** 4a. on 5a. red . . . . . 5·00 2·25
112 **49** 9a. on 10a. blue . . . . . 5·75 2·75

1908. 40th Anniv of Reign of King Chulalongkorn. Optd **Jubilee 1868-1908** in English and Siamese.

113 **53** 1a. green and yellow . . . 85 60
114 3a. green . . . . 1·40 1·25
115 4a. on 5a. (No. 111) . . . 2·25 1·75
116 8a. bistre and black . . . 13·00 13·00
117 18a. brown . . . . 18·00 11·50

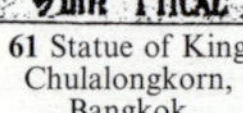

61 Statue of King Chulalongkorn, Bangkok

64 King Chulalongkorn

1908.

118 **61** 1t. violet and green . . . . 20·00 1·40
119 2t. orange and purple . . . 40·00 6·00
120 3t. blue and green . . . . 55·00 8·25
121 5t. green and lilac . . . . 75·00 16·00
122 10t. red and green . . . . £900 55·00
123 20t. brown and grey . . . £190 50·00
124 40t. brown and blue . . . £300 £150

1909. Surch in satangs in English and Siamese.

125 **53** 2s. on 1a. green & yellow 55 30
127a 2s. on 2a. green 60 30
164 2s. on 2a. grey and violet 2·40 1·50
129 3s. on 3a. green . . . . . 1·40 1·10
130 3s. on 3a. grey and violet 1·25 30
131 6s. on 4a. red and brown 32·00 29·00
132a 6s. on 4a. red . . . . . . 1·50 55
134 6s. on 5a. red . . . . . . 1·40 1·40
138 **49** 6s. on 6a. red . . . . . . 1·10 1·10
135 **53** 12s. on 8a. bistre & black 3·00 55
136 14s. on 9a. blue . . . . . 4·25 85
137 14s. on 12a. blue . . . . . 11·00 11·00
139 **9** 14s. on 12a. purple & red 50·00 50·00
140 **49** 14s. on 14a. blue . . . . 9·00 9·00

1910.

141 **64** 2s. green and orange . . . 60 30
142 3s. green 90 30
143 6s. red . . . . 1·40 30
144 12s. brown and black . . . 4·00 60
145 14s. blue . . . . 9·75 85
146 28s. brown . . . . 20·00 4·00

65 King Vajiravudh

66

1912.

166 **65** 2s. brown 45 15
167 3s. green 70 30
168 5s. red . . . . 1·00 15
149 6s. red . . . . 1·25 30
169 10s. brown and black . . . 85 20
150 12s. brown and black . . . 1·90 35
151 14s. blue . . . . 2·50 45
170 15s. blue . . . . 2·00 45
152 28s. brown . . . . 10·50 3·75
153 **66** 1b. brown and blue . . . . 11·00 75
154 2b. brown and red . . . . 16·00 1·40
155 3b. black and green . . . 20·00 2·00
156 5b. black and violet . . . 27·00 2·50
157 10b. purple and green . . . £160 35·00
158 20b. brown and blue . . . £275 35·00

1914. Surch in **Satang** in English and Siamese.

165 **64** 2s. on 14s. blue . . . . . 1·10 45
159 **65** 2s. on 14s. blue 60 15
160 5s. on 6s. red . . . . . . 1·50 15
161 10s. on 12s. brown & black 1·40 30
162 15s. on 28s. brown . . . . 3·00 45

1918. Red Cross Fund. Optd with small cross in circle.

177 **65** 2s.(+3s.) brown 60 60
178 3s.(+2s.) green 60 60
179 5s.(+5s.) red . . . . . . 1·50 1·25
180 10s.(+5s.) brown and black 2·75 2·50
181 15s.(+5s.) blue . . . . . 3·00 2·50
182 **66** 1b.(+25s.) brown & blue 14·00 8·25
183 2b.(+30s.) brown and red 22·00 12·00
184 3b.(+35s.) black and green 30·00 20·00
185 5b.(+40s.) black and violet 90·00 50·00
186 10b.(+1b.) purple & green £275 £140
187 20b.(+1b.) brown & grn . . £1400 £850

1918. Optd **VICTORY** in English and Siamese.

188 **65** 2s. brown 55 50
189 3s. green 75 50
190 5s. red . . . . 1·25 1·10
191 10s. brown and black . . . 1·40 1·25
192 15s. blue . . . . 2·50 2·00
193 **66** 1b. brown and blue . . . . 18·00 15·00
194 2b. brown and red . . . . 35·00 30·00
195 3b. black and green . . . 80·00 45·00
196 5b. black and violet . . . £200 £150

1919. Surch in English and Siamese with figures only.

197 **65** 5s. on 6s. red 75 15
198 10s. on 12s. brown & black 1·75 15

(72a)

(72b)

1920. Scouts' Fund. Various stamps handstamped.

(a) With Type **72a**.

199 **65** 2s.(+3s.) brown . . . . . 25·00 25·00
200 3s.(+2s.) green . . . . . 25·00 25·00
201 5s. on 6s. (+5s.) red (No. 160) . . . . 35·00 35·00
202 10s. on 12s. (+5s.) brown and black (No. 161) . . . 35·00 35·00
203 15s.(+5s.) blue . . . . . 70·00 70·00
204 **53** 1t.(+25s.) bistre and blue £250 £250

(b) With Type **72b**.

205 **65** 2s.(+3s.) brown . . . . . 9·00 9·00
206 3s.(+2s.) green . . . . . 9·00 9·00
207 **73** 5s.(+5s.) red on pink . . 60·00 60·00
208 **65** 10s. on 12s. (+5s.) brown and black (No. 161) . . 13·00 13·00
209 15s.(+5s.) blue . . . . . 13·00 13·00
210 **53** 1t.(+25s.) bistre and blue £200 £200

These stamps were sold in aid of the "Wild Tiger" Scouts organization at the premium stated.

73

บำรุงเสือป่า

SCOUT'S FUND

(73a)

1920.

211 **73** 2s. brown on yellow . . . 75 15
212 3s. green on green . . . . 1·00 25
213 3s. brown . . . . 1·00 15
214 5s. red on pink . . . . . 1·25 15
215 5s. green . . . . 12·00 1·60
216 5s. violet on mauve . . . . 2·50 25
217 10s. brown and black . . . 2·50 15
218 15s. blue on blue . . . . . 3·75 20
219 15s. red . . . . 20·00 2·25
220 25s. brown . . . . 10·00 1·25
221 25s. blue . . . . 16·00 45
222 50s. black and brown . . . 24·00 75

1920. Scouts' Fund. Optd with T **73a**.

223 **73** 2s.(+3s.) brown on yellow 7·00 7·00
224 3s.(+2s.) green on green . 7·00 7·00
225 5s.(+5s.) red on pink . . . 7·00 7·00
226 10s.(+5s.) brown and black 7·00 7·00
227 15s.(+5s.) blue on blue . . 14·00 14·00
228 25s.(+25s.) brown . . . . 38·00 38·00
229 50s.(+30s.) black & brn . . £180 £180

74 "Garuda" Bird

75 Coronation Stone

1925. Air.

230 **74** 2s. brown on yellow . . . 60 15
231 3s. brown 60 15
239 5s. green 60 15
240 10s. orange and black . . . 60 15
234 15s. red . . . . 2·50 50
242 25s. blue . . . . 1·25 75
243 50s. black and brown . . . 1·25 75
237 1b. brown and blue . . . . 23·00 6·50

1926.

244 **75** 1t. green and lilac . . . . 7·50 1·25
245 2t. red and carmine . . . . 18·00 3·75
246 3t. blue and green . . . . 28·00 16·00
247 5t. green and violet . . . . 38·00 12·00
248 10t. brown and red . . . . £120 15·00
249 20t. brown and blue . . . £150 48·00

1928. Surch in English and Siamese.

250 **73** 5s. on 15s. red . . . . . . 2·25 1·25
251 **65** 10s. on 28s. brown . . . . 6·50 60

76 King Prajadhipok

77

1928.

252 **76** 2s. brown 50 15
253 3s. green 50 25
254 5s. violet 50 15
255 10s. red 50 15
256 15s. blue 55 25
257 25s. orange and black . . . 2·50 50
258 50s. black and orange . . . 1·25 75
259 80s. black and blue . . . . 2·50 50
260 **77** 1b. black and blue . . . . 3·75 75
261 2b. brown and red . . . . 5·00 1·50
262 3b. black and green . . . 7·50 2·00
263 5b. brown and violet . . . 12·00 3·00
264 10b. purple and green . . . 25·00 5·00
265 20b. brown and green . . . 50·00 10·00
266 40b. brown and green . . . 90·00 38·00

1930. Surch in English and Siamese.

267 **64** 10s. on 12s. brown & black 3·00 50
268 25s. on 28s. brown . . . . 13·00 1·00

79 Kings Prajadhipok and Chao Phya Chakri

81 Chao Phya Chakri (Rama I)

80 Kings Prajadhipok and Chao Phya Chakri

1932. 150th Anniv of Chakri Dynasty and of Bangkok as Capital and Opening of Memorial Bridge over Menam.

269 **79** 2s. red . . . . 1·00 15
270 3s. green . . . . 1·50 25
271 5s. violet . . . . 1·00 15
272 **80** 10s. black and red . . . . 1·50 15
273 15s. black and blue . . . . 5·00 50
274 25s. black and mauve . . . 7·50 75
275 50s. black and purple . . . 32·00 1·90
276 **81** 1b. blue . . . . 50·00 8·50

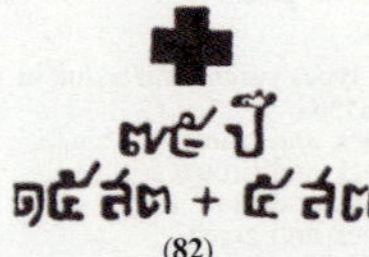

(82)

1939. Red Cross Fund. 75th Anniv of Membership of the International Red Cross. Surch as T **82**.

277 **66** 5+5s. on 1b. (153) . . . . 8·50 8·50
278 10+5s. on 2b. (154) . . . . 20·00 20·00
279 15+5s. on 3b. (155) . . . . 16·00 16·00

83 National Assembly Hall

1939. 7th Anniv of Constitution and National Day (1st issue).

280 **83** 2s. brown . . . . 2·50 35
281 3s. green . . . . 5·00 1·25
282 5s. purple . . . . 2·50 15
283 10s. red . . . . 7·50 15
284 15s. blue . . . . 20·00 65

84 Chakri Palace and "Garuda" Bird

1940. National Day (2nd issue).

285 **84** 2s. brown . . . . 1·25 35
286 3s. green . . . . 3·75 1·25
287 5s. purple . . . . 2·50 15
288 10s. red . . . . 12·00 15
289 15s. blue . . . . 25·00 65

85 King Ananda Mahidol

86 Ploughing Rice Field

87 Ban Pa'im Palace, Ayuthia

88 Monument of Democracy, Bangkok

1941.

290 **85** 2s. brown 50 15
291 3s. green 75 25
292 5s. violet 50 15
293 10s. red 75 15
294 **86** 15s. grey and blue 75 25
295 25s. orange and grey . . . 75 25
296 50s. grey and orange . . . 1·00 25
297 **87** 1b. grey and blue . . . . 2·75 65
298 2b. grey and red . . . . . 5·00 1·25
299 3b. grey and green . . . . 13·00 4·00
300 5b. red and black . . . . 35·00 12·00
301 10b. yellow and green . . . 50·00 30·00

1942. Air. With or without gum.

302 **88** 2s. brown . . . . 1·25 1·00
303 3s. green . . . . 20·00 22·00
304 5s. purple . . . . 1·25 50
305 10s. red . . . . 12·00 75
306 15s. blue . . . . 2·75 1·40

89 King Ananda Mahidol

90 Indo-China War Monument, Bangkok

91 Bangkaen Monument and Ears of Rice

1943.

307 **89** 1b. blue . . . . 10·00 1·00

1943.

310 **90** 3s. green . . . . 1·60 75

1943. 10th Anniv of Failure of 1933 Revolt.

311 **91** 2s. orange . . . . 1·25 1·00
312 10s. red . . . . 2·50 25

92 King Bhumibol

93

1947.

313 **92** 5s. violet 50 15
314 10s. red 75 15
315 20s. brown 50 15
316 50s. green 75 15
317 1b. blue and violet . . . . 5·00 15
318 2b. green and blue . . . . 13·00 90
319 3b. black and red . . . . 20·00 2·00
320 5b. red and green . . . . 45·00 3·00
321 10b. violet and brown . . £180 1·00
322 20b. purple and black . . . £225 3·75

The baht values are larger, size $21\frac{1}{2} \times 27$ mm.

1947. Coming of Age of King Bhumibol. With gum (10, 50s.) or without gum (others).

323 **93** 5s. orange . . . . 1·00 1·00
324 10s. brown . . . . 42·00 40·00
325 10s. green . . . . 1·00 1·00
326 20s. blue . . . . 3·00 1·00
327 50s. green . . . . 7·50 2·00

94 King and Palace

95 King Bhumibol

1950. King's Coronation.
328 **94** 5s. purple 25 15
329 10s. red 50 15
330 15s. violet 1·75 1·75
331 20s. brown 50 15
332 80s. green 5·50 2·50
333 1b. blue 3·00 15
334 2b. yellow 10·00 1·00
335 3b. grey 45·00 6·00

1951.
336 **95** 5s. purple 25 10
337 10s. green 25 10
338 15s. brown 75 15
339 20s. brown 75 10
340 25s. red 25 10
341 50s. green 75 10
342 1b. blue 1·00 15
343 1b.15 blue 25 15
344 1b.25 red 3·75 25
345 2b. green 4·50 25
346 3b. grey 7·50 40
347 5b. red and blue 30·00 50
348 10b. violet and brown £180 90
349 20b. green and black £160 9·00

96 U.N. Emblem

97 "Garuda" Bird

1951. United Nations Day.
350 **96** 25s. blue 2·50 2·50

1952. Air.
351 **97** 1b.50 purple 2·50 25
352 2b. blue 7·50 1·50
353 3b. grey 10·00 75

1952. United Nations Day. Optd **1952**.
354 **96** 25s. blue 1·50 1·50

1952. 20th Anniv of Constitution. Surch with Vase emblem and **+ 20** in English and Siamese.
355 **76** 80s.+20s. black and blue 12·00 11·00

99 Dancer over Cross

103 Processional Elephant

1953. 60th Anniv of Thai Red Cross Society. Cross in red, figures in blue and red.
356 **99** 25s.+25s. cream & green 3·75 3·75
357 50s.+50s. cream and pink 13·00 13·00
358 1b.+1b. cream and blue 15·00 15·00

1953. United Nations Day. Optd **1953**.
359 **96** 25s. blue 1·00 1·00

1954. United Nations Day. Optd **1954** vert.
360 **96** 25s. blue 2·50 2·50

1955. Optd **THAILAND** in English and Siamese.
361 **76** 5s. violet 4·00 5·00
362 10s. red 4·00 5·00

1955. Surch.
363 **92** 5s. on 20s. brown 1·00 35
364 10s. on 20s. brown 1·50 35

1955. 400th Birth Anniv of King Naresuan.
365 **103** 25s. red 75 15
366 80s. purple 13·00 4·00
367 1b.25 green 30·00 75
368 2b. blue 7·00 1·10
369 3b. brown 26·00 60

1955. Red Cross Fair. Optd **24 98**.
370 **99** 25s.+25s. multicoloured 13·00 13·00
371 50s.+50s. multicoloured 75·00 75·00
372 1b.+1b. red, cream and blue £100 £100

105 Tao Suranari

106 Equestrian Statue

1955. Tao Suranari Commemoration.
373 **105** 10s. lilac 75 25
374 25s. green 50 15
375 1b. brown 21·00 1·60

1955. King Taksin Commemoration.
376 **106** 5s. blue 75 25
377 25s. green 5·50 10
378 1b.25 red 18·00 1·75

1955. U.N. Day. Optd **1955** vert.
379 **96** 25s. blue 2·50 2·50

107 Don Chedi Pagoda

108 Dharmachakra and Sambar

1956.
380 **107** 10s. green 1·25 1·10
381 50s. brown 11·00 1·00
382 75s. violet 3·75 75
383 1b.50 brown 11·00 75

1956. United Nations Day. Optd **1956** vert.
384 **96** 25s. blue 1·25 1·25

1957. 2500th Anniv of Buddhist Era.
385 **108** 5s. brown 50 15
386 10s. purple 50 15
387 15s. green 1·25 1·00
388 – 20s. orange 1·25 1·00
389 – 25s. brown 25 10
390 – 50s. mauve 1·00 30
391 – 1b. brown 1·50 40
392 – 1b.25 blue 17·00 2·75
393 – 2b. purple 3·25 50
DESIGNS: 20s. to 50s. Hand of Peace and Dharmachakra; 1b. to 2b. Nakon Phatom pagoda.

110 U.N. Emblem and Laurel Sprays

111 Gateway to Grand Palace

1957. United Nations Day.
394 **110** 25s. green 60 25
395 25s. brown (1958) 60 25
400 25s. blue (1959) 75 25

1959. 1st South-East Asia Peninsula Games.
396 **111** 10s. orange 25 15
397 – 25s. red 40 15
398 – 1b.25 green 1·90 1·00
399 – 2b. blue 2·00 50
DESIGNS: 25s. Royal parasols; 1b.25, Bowman; 2b. Wat Arun (temple) and prow of royal barge.

112 Pagoda

113 Wat Arun Temple

1960. World Refugee Year.
401 **112** 50s. brown 25 10
402 2b. green 75 40

1960. Leprosy Relief Campaign.
403 **113** 50s. red 25 10
404 2b. blue 1·75 45

114 Indian Elephant

115 S.E.A.T.O. Emblem

1960. 5th World Forestry Congress, Seattle.
405 **114** 25s. green 50 15

1960. S.E.A.T.O. Day.
406 **115** 50s. brown 60 15

116 Siamese Child

117 Letter-writing

1960. Children's Day.
407 **116** 50s. mauve 25 10
408 1b. brown 2·25 45

1960. International Correspondence Week.
409 **117** 50s. mauve 35 10
410 2b. blue 2·10 55

118 U.N. Emblem and Globe

119 King Bhumibol

1960. United Nations Day.
411 **118** 50s. violet 50 15
446 50s. red (1961) 35 15
467 50s. red (1962) 35 15

1961.
422 **119** 5s. purple 15 10
423 10s. green 15 10
424 15s. brown 25 10
425 20s. brown 15 10
426 25s. red 25 10
427 50s. green 25 10
428 80s. orange 1·25 65
429 1b. brown and blue 90 15
430 1b.25 green and red 2·50 50
431 1b.50 green and violet 80 15
432 2b. violet and red 1·10 10
433 3b. blue and brown 2·75 25
434 4b. black and bistre 3·00 1·00
435 5b. green and blue 9·00 30
436 10b. black and red 45·00 40
437 20b. blue and green 40·00 2·00
438 25b. blue and green 15·00 1·25
439 40b. black and yellow 32·00 3·00

120 Children in Garden

1961. Children's Day.
440 **120** 20s. blue 50 15
441 2b. violet 1·75 50

121 Pen, Letters and Globe

122 Thai Scout Badge and Saluting Hand

1961. International Correspondence Week.
442 – 25s. myrtle 25 15
443 – 50s. purple 15 10
444 **121** 1b. red 80 35
445 2b. blue 1·25 40
DESIGN: 25s., 50s. Pen, and world map on envelope.

1961. 50th Anniv of Thai Scout Movement.
447 **122** 50s. red 25 15
448 – 1b. green 75 40
449 – 2b. blue 1·00 50
DESIGNS—VERT: 1b. Scout camp and scout saluting flag; 2b. King Vajiravudh in uniform, and scout, cub and guide marching.

123 Campaign Emblem and Temple

124 Bangkok

1962. Malaria Eradication.
450 **123** 5s. brown 15 10
451 10s. brown 15 10
452 20s. blue 15 10
453 50s. red 15 10
454 – 1b. green 75 15
455 – 1b.50 purple 1·75 50
456 – 2b. blue 1·00 25
457 – 3b. violet 3·25 1·75
DESIGN: 1b. to 3b. Hanuman fighting mosquitoes.

1962. "Century 21" Exhibition, Seattle.
458 **124** 50s. purple 50 15
459 2b. blue 3·25 50

125 Thai Child with Doll

126 Corres-pondence Symbols

127 Exhibition Emblem

1962. Children's Day.
460 **125** 25s. green 40 15
461 50s. brown 50 10
462 2b. mauve 3·25 55

1962. International Correspondence Week.
463 **126** 25s. violet 25 15
464 50s. red 25 10
465 – 1b. bistre 2·00 30
466 – 2b. green 3·25 50
DESIGN: 1, 2b. Quill pen.

1962. Students' Exhibition, Bangkok.
468 **127** 50s. bistre 60 15

128 Harvesting

1963. Freedom from Hunger.
469 **128** 20s. green 60 25
470 50s. brown 50 15

129 "Temple Guardian"

130 Centenary Emblem

1963. 1st Anniv of Asian–Oceanic Postal Union.
471 **129** 50s. green and brown 50 10

1963. Red Cross Centenary.
472 **130** 50s.+10s. red and grey 20 15
473 – 50s.+10s. red and grey 20 15
DESIGN: No. 473, As Type **130**, but with positions of emblem and inscriptions reversed.

131 G.P.O. Bangkok and (inset) old P.O.

1963. 80th Anniv of Post and Telegraph Department.
474 **131** 50s. green, orange and violet 75 15
475 3b. brown, green and red 3·50 1·10

132 King Bhumibol

133 Children with Dolls

1963.
476 **132** 5s. mauve 10 10
477 10s. green 10 10
478 15s. brown 10 10
479 20s. brown 10 10
480 25s. red 10 10
481 50s. green 15 10
482 75s. lilac 25 10
483 80s. orange 75 30
484 1b. brown and blue 75 15
485 1b.25 bistre and brown 3·00 75
486 1b.50 green and violet 75 15
487 2b. violet and red 60 10
488 3b. blue and brown 1·25 20
489 4b. black and bistre 1·50 25
490 5b. green and blue 6·50 25
491 10b. black and red 12·00 55
492 20b. blue and green 65·00 2·75
493 25b. blue and green 3·50 50
494 40b. black and yellow 70·00 3·25

1963. Children's Day.

505	133	50s. red	25	10
506		2b. blue	3·25	45

134 "Garuda" Bird with Scroll in Beak

1963. International Correspondence Week.

507	134	50s. purple and turquoise	50	15
508		1b. purple and green	3·00	40
509	–	2b. blue and brown	17·00	50
510	–	3b. green and brown	6·25	1·60

DESIGN: 2b., 3b. Thai women writing letters.

135 U.N. Emblem

137 Mother and Child

136 King Bhumibol

1963. United Nations Day.

511	135	50s. blue	35	10

1963. King Bhumibol's 36th Birthday.

512	136	1b.50 indigo, yellow & bl	1·50	25
513		5b. blue, yellow & mauve	10·50	1·50

1964. 17th Anniv of U.N.I.C.E.F.

514	137	50s. blue	25	10
515		2b. green	2·50	35

138 "Hand" of Flags, Pigeon and Globe

1964. International Correspondence Week.

516	138	50s. mauve and green	25	10
517	–	1b. brown and green	3·00	30
518	–	2b. violet and yellow	7·50	35
519	–	3b. brown and blue	3·75	1·25

DESIGNS: 1b. Thai girls and map; 2b. Map, pen and pencil; 3b. Hand with quill pen, and globe.

139 Globe and U.N. Emblem

140 King Bhumibol and Queen Sirikit

1964. United Nations Day.

520	139	50s. grey	75	10

1965. 15th Royal Wedding Anniv.

521	140	2b. multicoloured	5·25	25
522		5b. multicoloured	11·50	1·50

141 I.T.U. Emblem and Symbols

1965. I.T.U. Centenary.

523	141	1b. green	2·50	35

142 Goddess, Letters and Globes

1965. International Correspondence Week. Mult.

524		50s. Type **142**	25	10
525		1b. Type **142**	1·75	30
526		2b. Handclasp, letters and world map	7·00	40
527		3b. As 2b.	11·00	1·75

143 Grand Palace, Bangkok

145 U.P.U. Monument, Berne, and Map of Thailand

1965. International Co-operation Year and 20th Anniv of United Nations.

528	143	50s. lt blue, yellow & blue	70	10

1965. 80th Anniv of Thailand's Admission to Universal Postal Union.

529	145	20s. blue and mauve	25	10
530		50s. black and blue	50	15
531		1b. brown and blue	3·00	30
532		3b. green and brown	7·00	1·50

146 Child and Lotus

1965. Children's Day.

533	146	50s. brown and black	35	10
534	–	1b. green and black	1·90	15

DESIGN: 1b. Child mounting stairs.

147 Cycling

1966. Publicity for 5th Asian Games, Bangkok.

535		20s. red (Type **147**)	25	10
536		25s. violet (Tennis)	50	15
537		50s. red (Running)	25	10
538		1b. blue (Weightlifting)	1·50	25
539		1b.25 black (Boxing)	2·50	1·50
540		2b. blue (Swimming)	5·00	25
541		3b. brown (Basketball)	11·00	2·40
542		5b. purple (Football)	32·00	8·00

See also Nos. 553/6.

148 Emblem and Fair Buildings

1966. 1st International Trade Fair, Bangkok.

543	148	50s. purple	75	25
544		1b. brown	1·25	50

149 "Reading and Writing"

1966. International Correspondence Week.

545	–	50s. red	25	10
546	–	1b. brown	1·00	20
547	149	2b. violet	7·50	25
548		3b. green	3·50	1·50

DESIGN: 50s., 1b. "Map" envelope representing the five continents and pen.

150 U.N. Emblem

151 Pra Buddha Bata (monastery)

1966. United Nations Day.

549	150	50s. blue	50	10

1966. 20th Anniv of U.N.E.S.C.O.

550	151	50s. green and black	35	10

152 "Goddess of Rice"

1966. International Rice Year.

551	152	50s. blue and green	1·25	25
552		3b. red and purple	8·50	2·75

153 Thai Boxing

1966. 5th Asian Games, Bangkok. Each black, red and brown.

553		50s. Type **153**	50	15
554		1b. Takraw (ball game)	2·00	90
555		2b. "Kite fighting"	16·00	1·50
556		3b. "Cudgel play"	12·50	6·50

154 Chevron Snakehead

1967. Fishes. Multicoloured.

557		1b. Type **154**	2·50	75
558		2b. Short mackerel	17·00	1·25
559		3b. Siamese barb	7·50	3·00
560		5b. Siamese fighting fish	10·00	3·75

The 2 and 3b. are size 45 × 26 mm.

155 Djarmachakra and Globe

1967. Establishment of Buddhist World Fellowship Headquarters in Thailand.

561	155	2b. black and yellow	2·50	50

156 Great Indian Hornbill

157 "Vandopsis parishii"

1967. Birds. Multicoloured.

562		20s. Type **156**	1·00	40
563		25s. Southern grackle ("Talking Myna")	1·50	75
564		50s. White-rumped shama	2·50	25
565		1b. Siamese fireback pheasant ("Diard's Fireback Pheasant")	5·50	1·25
566		1b.50 Spotted-necked dove	5·50	1·50
567		2b. Sarus crane	32·00	2·25
568		3b. White-throated kingfisher ("White-breasted Kingfisher")	16·00	6·50
569		5b. Asian open-bill stork ("Open-billed Storks")	35·00	8·50

1967. Thai Orchids. Multicoloured.

570		20s. Type **157**	50	25
571		50s. "Ascocentrum curvifolium"	75	15
572		80s. "Rhynchostylis retusa"	1·25	85
573		1b. "Rhynchostylis gigantea"	2·50	75
574		1b.50 "Dendrobium alconeri"	2·50	75
575		2b. "Paphiopedilum callosum"	12·50	1·00
576		3b. "Dendrobium formosum"	7·50	3·75
577		5b. "Dendrobium primulinum"	14·50	5·00

158 Thai House

1967. Thai Architecture.

578	158	50s. violet and blue	80	25
579	–	1b.50 chestnut and brown	2·50	1·00
580	–	2b. blue and turquoise	12·00	1·25
581	–	3b. brown and yellow	8·00	5·00

BUILDINGS: 1b.50, Pagodas; 2b. Temple bell-tower; 3b. Temple.

159 "Sri Suphanahong" (royal barge) and Palace

1967. International Tourist Year.

582	159	2b. brown and blue	3·00	50

160 Dove, Globe, People and Letters

1967. International Correspondence Week.

583	160	50s. multicoloured	25	10
584		1b. multicoloured	1·00	30
585	–	2b. black and green	4·00	40
586	–	3b. black and brown	5·75	1·75

DESIGNS: 2, 3b. Handclasp, globe and doves.

161 U.N. Emblem

1967. United Nations Day.

587	161	50s. multicoloured	35	10

162 National Flag

1967. 50th Anniv of Thai National Flag.

588	162	50s. red, blue & turquoise	35	10
589		2b. red, blue and green	3·75	90

163 Elephant carrying Teak Log

1968. Export Promotion.

590	163	2b. brown and red	2·75	25

See also Nos. 630, 655 and 673.

164 Satellite and Thai Tracking Station

1968. "Satellite Communications".

591	164	50s. multicoloured	25	10
592		3b. multicoloured	2·25	80

165 "Goddess of the Earth"

1968. International Hydrological Decade.
593 **165** 50s. multicoloured 40 10

166 Snakeskin Gourami

1968. Thai Fishes. Multicoloured.

594	10s. Type **166**	25	10
595	20s. Red-tailed black shark	25	15
596	25s. Thai mahseer	50	15
597	50s. Giant pangasius	75	15
598	80s. Bumblebee catfish . . .	1·25	1·00
599	1b.25 Rambaia goby	3·75	2·00
600	1b.50 Giant carp	11·50	1·50
601	4b. Clown knifefish	28·00	8·75

167 Blue Peacock

1968. Thai Butterflies. Multicoloured.

602	50s. Type **167**	70	15
603	1b. Golden birdwing	3·75	60
604	3b. Great mormon	12·00	3·00
605	4b. "Papilio palinurus" . . .	19·00	6·50

168 Queen Sirikit

1968. Queen Sirikit's "Third Cycle" Anniversary. Designs showing Queen Sirikit in different Thai costumes.

606	**168**	50s. multicoloured	30	10
607	–	2b. multicoloured	1·60	45
608	–	3b. multicoloured	3·50	1·75
609	–	5b. multicoloured	8·00	1·75

169 W.H.O. Emblem and Medical Equipment

1968. 20th Anniv of W.H.O.
610 **169** 50s. black and green . . . 40 10

170 Globe, Letter and Pen

1968. International Correspondence Week. Mult.

611	50s. Type **170**	25	10
612	1b. Globe on pen nib	80	20
613	2b. Type **170**	1·50	30
614	3b. Globe on pen nib	4·00	1·40

171 U.N. Emblem and Flags

173 King Rama II

172 Human Rights Emblem and Sculpture

1968. United Nations Day.
615 **171** 50s. multicoloured 40 10

1968. 20th Anniv of Human Rights Year.
616 **172** 50s. violet, red and green 50 10

1968. Birth Bicentenary of King Rama II.
617 **173** 50s. yellow and brown . . 25 10

174 National Assembly Building

1969. First Election Day under New Constitution.

618	**174**	50s. multicoloured	25	10
619		2b. multicoloured	2·25	45

175 I.L.O. Emblem within Cogwheels

1969. 50th Anniv of I.L.O.
620 **175** 50s. blue, black and violet 25 10

176 Ramwong Dance

1969. Thai Classical Dances. Multicoloured.

621	50s. Type **176**	25	10
622	1b. Candle dance	80	30
623	2b. Krathop Mai dance . . .	1·60	25
624	3b. Nohra dance	2·75	1·60

177 "Letters by Post"

1969. International Correspondence Week. Mult.

625	50s. Type **177**	15	10
626	1b. Type **177**	40	20
627	2b. Writing and posting a letter	1·00	30
628	3b. As 2b.	1·60	80

178 Globe in Hand

1969. United Nations Day.
629 **178** 50s. multicoloured 25 10

179 Tin Mine

1969. Export Promotion and 2nd Technical Conf of the International Tin Council, Bangkok.
630 **179** 2b. blue, brown and light blue . . . . 2·00 25

180 Loy Krathong Festival

1969. Thai Ceremonies and Festivals. Multicoloured.

631	50s. Type **180**	15	10
632	1b. Marriage ceremony . . .	65	20
633	2b. Khwan ceremony	80	25
634	5b. Songkran festival	2·40	90

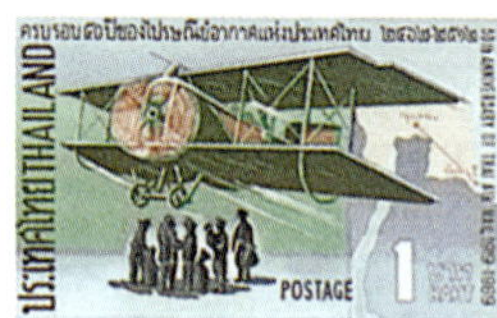

181 Breguet 14 Mail Plane

1969. 50th Anniv of Thai Airmail Services.
635 **181** 1b. brown, green and blue 65 15

182 "Phra Rama"

1969. Nang Yai Shadow Theatre. Multicoloured.

636	50s. Type **182**	25	10
637	2b. "Ramasura"	2·00	20
638	3b. "Mekhala"	1·60	75
639	5b. "Ongkhot"	2·75	75

183 "Improvement of Productivity"

1969. Productivity Year.
640 **183** 50s. multicoloured 25 10

184 Thai Temples within I.C.W. Emblem

1970. 19th Triennial Conference of International Council of Women, Bangkok.
641 **184** 50s. black and blue . . . 40 10

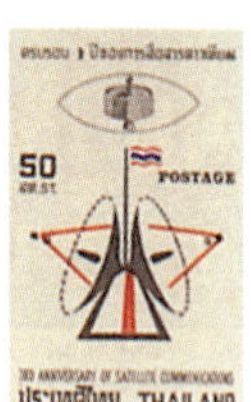

185 Dish Aerials

1970. 3rd Anniv of Thai Satellite Communications.
642 **185** 50s. multicoloured 25 10

186 Households and Data

1970. 7th Population Census.
643 **186** 1b. multicoloured 25 10

187 New Headquarters Building

1970. Inauguration of New U.P.U. Headquarters Building, Berne.
644 **187** 50s. black, green and blue 25 10

188 Khun Ram Kamhang as Teacher

1970. International Education Year.
645 **188** 50s. multicoloured 25 10

189 Swimming Stadium

1970. 6th Asian Games, Bangkok.

646	**189**	50s. lilac, red and yellow	25	15
647	–	1b.50 green, red and blue	55	20
648	–	3b. black, red and bronze	1·25	30
649	–	5b. blue, red and green	1·90	80

STADIUMS: 1b.50, Velodrome; 3b. Subhajala-saya Stadium; 5b. Kittikachorn Indoor Stadium.
See also No. 660.

190 Boy and Girl writing Letter

1970. International Correspondence Week. Mult.

650	50s. Type **190**	15	10
651	1b. Woman writing letter . .	55	20
652	2b. Women reading letters . .	1·25	30
653	3b. Man reading letter . . .	1·40	80

See also Nos. 683/6.

191 U.N. Emblem and Royal Palace, Bangkok

194 King Bhumibol lighting Flame

193 The Heroes of Bangrachan

1970. 25th Anniv of United Nations.
654 **191** 50s. multicoloured 55 10

1970. Export Promotion. As T **163**.
655 2b. brown, red and green . . 1·25 20
DESIGN: 2b. Rubber plantation.

1970. Heroes and Heroines of Thai History.
656 **193** 50s. violet and red 25 10
657 – 1b. purple and violet . . 65 30
658 – 2b. brown and mauve . . 1·90 50
659 – 3b. green and blue . . . 1·40 65
DESIGNS: 1b. Heroines Thao Thepkrasatri and Thao Srisunthorn on ramparts; 2b. Queen Suriyothai riding elephant; 3b. Phraya Phichaidaphak and battle scene.

1970. Inaug of 6th Asian Games, Bangkok.
660 **194** 1b. multicoloured 25 10

195 Woman playing So Sam Sai

1970. Classical Thai Musical Instruments. Mult.
661 50s. Type **195** 25 10
662 2b. Khlui phiang-o (flute) . . 80 20
663 3b. Krachappi (guitar) . . . 1·60 40
664 5b. Thon rammana (drums) 2·75 80

196 Chocolate-point Siamese

1971. Siamese Cats. Multicoloured.
665 50s. Type **196** 15 10
666 1b. Blue-point cat . . . . . . 1·25 35
667 2b. Seal-point cat . . . . . 2·40 30
668 3b. Pure white cat and kittens 3·50 1·40

197 Pagoda, Nakhon Si Thammarat

1971. Buddhist Holy Places in Thailand. Pagodas.
669 **197** 50s. black, brown and mauve 25 10
670 – 1b. brown, violet and green 50 20
671 – 3b. sepia, brown & orange 1·40 30
672 – 4b. brown, sepia and blue 1·90 1·60
DESIGNS: 1b. Nakhon Phanom; 3b. Nakhon Pathom; 4b. Chiang Mai.

1971. Export Promotion. As T **163**.
673 2b. multicoloured . . . . . 1·00 20
DESIGN: 2b. Corncob and field.

199 Buddha's Birthplace, Lumbini, Nepal

1971. 20th Anniv of World Fellowship of Buddhists.
674 **199** 50s. black and blue . . . 15 10
675 – 1b. black and green . . . 55 20
676 – 2b. black and brown . . . 1·60 25
677 – 3b. black and red . . . 1·60 80
DESIGNS: 1b. "Place of Enlightenment", Buddha Gaya, Bihar; 2b. "Place of First Sermon", Sarnath, Banaras; 3b. "Place of Final Passing Away", Kusinara.

200 King Bhumibol and Thai People
201 Floating Market, Wat Sai

1971. 25th Anniv of Coronation.
678 **200** 50s. multicoloured 45 10

1971. Visit ASEAN Year.
679 **201** 4b. multicoloured . . . . 1·40 30
ASEAN = Association of South East Asian Nations.

202 King and Queen in Scout Uniform

1971. 60th Anniv of Thai Boy Scout Movement.
680 **202** 50c. black, red and yellow 50 10

1971. "THAILANDPEX 71" National Stamp Exhibition, Bangkok. Optd **4-8 AUGUST 1971 THAILANDPEX'71** in English and Thai and map within "perforations", covering four stamps.
681 **119** 80s. orange . . . . 2·50 2·00
682 **132** 80s. orange . . . . 2·50 2·00
Prices are for blocks of four stamps showing the entire overprint.

1971. International Correspondence Week. As T **190**. Multicoloured.
683 50s. Two girls writing a letter 15 10
684 1b. Two girls reading letters 40 20
685 2b. Women with letter on veranda . . . . 1·10 25
686 3b. Man handing letter to woman . . . . 1·60 60

205 Marble Temple, Bangkok

1971. United Nations Day.
687 **205** 50s. multicoloured 25 10

206 Raising Ducks

1971. Rural Life. Multicoloured.
688 50s. Type **206** 15 10
689 1b. Growing tobacco seedlings 40 30
690 2b. Cooping fish . . . . . . 1·10 20
691 3b. Cleaning rice-seed . . . . 1·75 65

207 Mother and Child

1971. 25th Anniv of U.N.I.C.E.F.
692 **207** 50s. multicoloured 25 10

208 Costumes from Chiang Saen Period (17th-century)

1972. Historical Costumes. Multicoloured.
693 50s. Type **208** 15 10
694 1b. Sukhothai period (13th–14th centuries) 40 20
695 1b.50 Ayudhya period (14th–17th centuries) . . . . . . 1·10 25
696 2b. Bangkok period (18th–19th centuries) . . . . . . 1·90 50

209 Globe and A.O.P.U. Emblem

1972. 10th Anniv of Asian–Oceanic Postal Union.
697 **209** 75s. blue 25 10

210 King Bhumibol

1972.
698 **210** 10s. green 10 10
699 20s. blue 15 10
700 25s. red 15 10
701 50s. green 20 10
702 75s. lilac 15 10
703 1b.25 pink and green . . 55 15
704 2b. violet and red . . . 25 10
705 2b.75 turquoise and purple 55 10
706 3b. blue and brown . . 1·50 15
707 4b. red and blue 80 15
708 5b. brown and violet . . 80 10
709 6b. violet and green . . 1·50 20
710 10b. black and red . . . 90 15
711 20b. green and orange 2·00 40
898d 40b. violet and brown 2·75 65
712a 50b. green and purple 15·00 1·00
713 100b. blue and orange 32·00 1·75

211 Two Women, Iko Tribe

1972. Hill Tribes of Thailand. Multicoloured.
714 50s. Type **211** 15 10
715 2b. Musician and children, Musoe tribe 90 20
716 4b. Woman embroidering, Yao tribe . . . . 3·50 2·00
717 5b. Woman with chickens, Maeo tribe . . . . 4·25 60

212 Ruby

1972. Precious Stones.
718 **212** 75s. multicoloured 25 10
719 – 2b. multicoloured . . . . 3·75 35
720 – 4b. black and green . . . 5·25 2·00
721 – 6b. brown, black and red 5·75 1·75
DESIGNS: 2b. Yellow sapphire; 4b. Zircon; 6b. Star sapphire.

213 Prince Vajiralongkorn
214 Thai Ruan-ton Costume

1972. Prince Vajiralongkorn's 20th Birthday.
722 **213** 75s. multicoloured 25 10

1972. Thai Women's National Costumes. Mult.
723 75s. Type **214** 15 10
724 2b. Thai Chitrlada 65 20
725 4b. Thai Chakri . . . . . . 1·90 1·25
726 5b. Thai Borompimarn . . . 2·75 55

215 Rambutan

1972. Thai Fruits. Multicoloured.
728 75s. Type **215** 15 10
729 1b. Mangosteen 90 30
730 3b. Durian . . . . 2·00 75
731 5b. Mango . . . . 7·50 1·40

216 Princess-Mother with Old People

1972. Princess-Mother Sisangwan's 72nd Birthday.
732 **216** 75s. green and orange . . 1·00 10

217 Lod Cave, Phangnga

1972. International Correspondence Week. Mult.
733 75s. Type **217** 15 10
734 1b.25 Kang Kracharn Reservoir, Phetchaburi . . 40 20
735 2b.75 Erawan Waterfall, Kanchanaburi . . . . . . 3·25 15
736 3b. Nok-kaw Mountain, Loei 2·10 90

218 Globe on U.N. Emblem
220 Crown Prince Vajiralongkorn

219 Watphrajetubon Vimolmanklaram Rajvaramahaviharn (ancient university)

1972. 25th Anniv of E.C.A.F.E.
737 **218** 75s. multicoloured 25 10

1972. International Book Year.
738 **219** 75s. multicoloured 25 10

1972. Investiture of Crown Prince.
739 **220** 2b. multicoloured 50 15

221 Servicemen and Flag

1973. 25th Anniv of Veterans' Day.
740 **221** 75s. multicoloured 25 10

1973. Red Cross Fair (1972). Nos. 472/3 surch **75+25 2515 1972.**
741 **130** 75s.+25s. on 50s.+10s. 50 50
742 – 75s.+25s. on 50s.+10s. 50 50

223 Emblem, Bank and Coin-box

1973. 60th Anniv of Government Savings Bank.
743 **223** 75s. multicoloured 25 10

224 "Celestial Being" and Emblem

1973. 25th Anniv of W.H.O.
744 **224** 75s. multicoloured 25 10

225 "Nymphaea pubescens"

1973. Lotus Flowers. Multicoloured.
745 75s. Type **225** 25 10
746 1b.50 "Nymphaea pubescens" (different) 50 30
747 2b. "Nelumbo nucifera" . . . 1·75 25
748 4b. "Nelumbo nucifera" (different) . . . . 4·75 1·25

227 King Bhumibol

1973.
749 **227** 5s. purple 15 10
1031 20s. blue 15 10
1031a 25s. red 15 10
1032 50s. green 75 10
1032a 75s. violet 15 10
753 5b. brown and violet 3·00 50
754 6b. violet and green . . 1·75 50
755 10b. brown and red . . 5·50 75
755a 20b. green and orange 55·00 5·00

228 Silverware

1973. Thai Handicrafts. Multicoloured.
756 75s. Type **228** 25 10
757 2b.75 Lacquerware . . . . . 1·00 20
758 4b. Pottery . . . . 3·25 1·50
759 5b. Paper umbrellas . . . . 3·00 50

229 King Janaka's Procession

1973. "Ramayana" Mural, Temple of Emerald Buddha, Bangkok. Multicoloured.
760 25s. Type **229** 25 15
761 75s. Contest for Sita's hand 15 10
762 1b.50 Monkey prince toppling portico . . . . . 1·50 1·00
763 2b. Monkey king breaking umbrella . . . . 2·75 90
764 2b.75 Maleenarj as Court chief . . . . 1·25 20
765 3b. Sprinkling holy water . . 5·50 1·40
766 5b. Tapansura fighting Rama 6·75 3·00
767 6b. Bharata on march . . . 2·25 1·10

230 "Postal Services"

1973. 90th Anniv of Thai Post and Telegraph Department. Multicoloured.
768 75s. Type **230** 30 10
769 2b. "Telecommunication Services" 90 40

231 1 Solot Stamp of 1883

1973. "THAIPEX 73" National Stamp Exn.
770 **231** 75s. blue and red 25 10
771 – 1b.25 red and blue . . . 1·00 30
772 – 1b.50 purple and green . . 1·50 50
773 – 2b. green and orange . . 1·75 70
DESIGNS: 1b.25, 6s. stamp of 1912; 1b.50, 5s. stamp of 1928; 2b. 3s. stamp of 1941.

232 Interpol Emblem

1973. 50th Anniv of International Criminal Police Organization (Interpol).
775 **232** 75s. multicoloured 25 10

233 "Lilid Pralaw"

1973. Int Correspondence Week. Characters from Thai Literature. Multicoloured.
776 75s. Type **233** 15 10
777 1b.50 "Khun Chang Khun Phan" 65 30
778 2b. "Sang Thong" . . . . 1·90 55
779 5b. "Pha Apai Manee" . . . 3·75 90

234 Wat Suan Dok Temple, Chiangmai

1973. United Nations Day.
781 **234** 75s. multicoloured 25 10

235 Schomburgk's Deer

1973. Protected Wild Animals. Multicoloured.
782 20s. Type **235** 25 10
783 25s. Kouprey 25 10
784 75r. Common gorals 50 10
785 1b.25 Water buffaloes . . . 50 25
786 1b.50 Javan rhinoceros . . . 2·75 1·50
787 2b. Thamin . . . . 6·00 1·60
788 2b.75 Sumatran rhinoceros 3·25 40
789 4b. Mainland serows . . . . 4·25 3·75

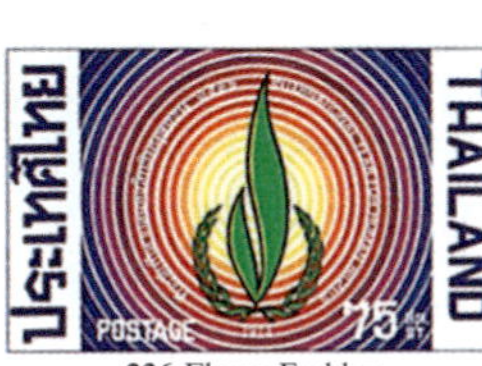

236 Flame Emblem

1973. 25th Anniv of Declaration of Human Rights.
790 **236** 75s. multicoloured 50 10

238 Children within Flowers

241 "Pha la Phiang Lai"

240 Statue of Krom Luang Songkia Nakarin

1973. Children's Day.
791 **238** 75s. multicoloured 40 10

1974. Red Cross Fair. Nos. 472/3 surch **75+25 1973** in English and Thai.
792 **130** 75s.+25s. on 50s.+10s. 30 30
793 – 75s.+25s. on 50s.+10s. 30 30

1974. 84th Anniv of Siriraj Hospital.
794 **240** 75s. multicoloured 25 10

1974. Thai Classical Dance. Multicoloured.
795 75s. Type **241** 25 10
796 2b.75 "Phra Lak Phlaeng Rit" . . . . 1·00 20
797 4b. "Chin Sao Sai" . . . . 2·50 1·40
798 5b. "Charot Phra Sumen" . . 2·50 50

242 World's Largest Teak, Amphur Nam-Pad

1974. 15th Anniv of Arbor Day.
799 **242** 75s. multicoloured 25 10

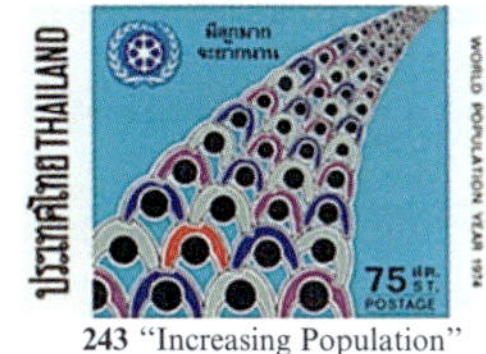

243 "Increasing Population"

1974. World Population Year.
800 **243** 75s. multicoloured 25 10

244 Royal Chariot

1974. Centenary of National Museum. Mult.
801 75s. Type **244** 15 10
802 2b. Ban Chiang painted pottery vase 50 30
803 2b.75 Avalokitesavara Bodhisattva statue . . . . 1·40 25
804 3b. King Mongkut Rama IV 1·90 50
Nos. 802/4 have the face values incorrectly shown as "BATH".

245 "Cassia fistula"

1974. International Correspondence Week. Tropical Plants. Multicoloured.
805 75s. Type **245** 15 10
806 2b.75 "Butea superba" . . . 65 20
807 3b. "Jasminum sambac" . . 1·75 25
808 4b. "Lagerstroemia speciosa" 1·40 1·10

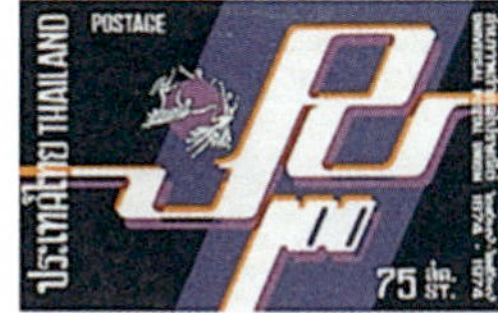

246 "UPU 100"

1974. Centenary of U.P.U.
810 **246** 75s. multicoloured 25 10

247 Wat Suthat Thepvararam

1974. United Nations Day.
811 **247** 75s. multicoloured 25 10

248 Elephant Round-up

1974. Tourism.
812 **248** 4b. multicoloured . . . . 1·50 75

249 "Vanda coerulea"

1974. Thai Orchids (1st series). Multicoloured.
813 75s. Type **249** 15 10
814 2b.75 "Dendrobium aggregatum" 65 20
815 3b. "Dendrobium scabrilingue" . . . . . . 1·75 40
816 4b. "Aerides falcata" var "houlletiana" . . . . . . 1·25 90
See also Nos. 847/50.

250 Boy riding Toy Horse

1974. Children's Day.
818 **250** 75c. multicoloured 40 10

252 Democracy Monument

1975. Democratic Institutions Campaign. Mult.
819 75s. Type **252** 15 10
820 2b. "Rights and Liberties" 65 25
821 2b.75 "Freedom to choose work" . . . . 1·40 20
822 5b. Top of monument and text . . . . 1·75 65

1975. Red Cross Fair 1974. Nos. 472/3 surch **1974 75+25** in English and Thai.
823 **130** 75s.+25s. on 50s.+10s. red and grey 50 50
824 – 75s.+25s. on 50s.+10s. red and grey 50 50

254 Marbled Cat

1975. Protected Wild Animals (1st series). Mult.
825 20s. Type **254** 25 15
826 75s. Gaur 50 10

827 2b.75 Indian elephant . . . . 4·25 55
828 3b. Clouded leopard . . . . 2·75 1·25
See Nos. 913/16.

255 White-eyed River Martin

1975. Thailand Birds. Multicoloured.
829 75s. Type **255** . . . . 1·00 45
830 2b. Asiatic paradise fly catcher . . . . 4·25 2·25
831 2b.75 Long-tailed broadbill 5·00 1·40
832 5b. Sultan tit . . . . 8·50 4·25

256 King Bhumibol and Queen Sirikit

1975. Silver Wedding of King Bhumibol and Queen Sirikit. Multicoloured.
833 75s. Type **256** 25 10
834 3b. As Type **256**, but different background . . . 80 20

257 "Roundhouse Kick"

1975. Thai Boxing. Multicoloured.
835 75s. Type **257** 25 15
836 2b.75 "Reverse elbow" . . . 1·00 25
837 3b. "Flying knee" . . . . 1·75 90
838 5b. "Ritual homage" . . . 5·25 1·40

258 Toskanth

1975. Thai Culture. Masks. Multicoloured.
839 75s. Type **258** 25 10
840 2b. Kumbhakarn . . . . . . 1·50 20
841 3b. Rama . . . . 2·00 55
842 4b. Hanuman . . . . 5·75 2·40

259 "Thaipex 75" Emblem

1975. "Thaipex 75" National Stamp Exhibition, Bangkok. Multicoloured.
843 75s. Type **259** 25 10
844 2b.75 Stamp designer . . . 75 20
845 4b. Stamp printing works . . 1·40 90
846 5b. "Stamp collecting" . . . 1·50 40

1975. Thai Orchids (2nd series). As T **249**. Multicoloured.
847 75s. "Dendrobium cruentum" 25 10
848 2b. "Dendrobium parishii" 80 30
849 2b.75 "Vanda teres" . . . . 1·10 25
850 5b. "Vanda denisoniana" . . 2·75 80

260 Green Mussel

1975. Sea Shells. Multicoloured.
852 75s. Type **260** 75 50
853 1b. Great green turban . . . 50 15
854 2b.75 "Oliva mustelina" . . 2·25 25
855 5b. Money cowrie . . . . . 5·75 1·75

261 Yachting

1975. 8th South-East Asian Peninsula Games, Bangkok (1st issue).
856 **261** 75s. black and blue . . . 15 10
857 – 1b.25 black and mauve 40 20
858 – 1b.50 black and red . . . 1·40 65
859 – 2b. black and green . . 2·00 65
DESIGNS: 1b.25, Badminton; 1b.50, Volleyball; 2b. Rifle and pistol shooting.
See also Nos. 878/81.

262 Pataya Beach

1975. International Correspondence Week. Mult.
861 75s. Type **262** 25 10
862 2b. Samila Beach 80 30
863 3b. Prachuap Bay . . . . 1·50 25
864 5b. Laem Singha Bay . . . . 2·25 90

263 Children within Letters "U N"

1975. United Nations Day.
865 **263** 75s. multicoloured 25 10

264 Early Telegraphs

1975. Centenary of Telegraph Service. Mult.
866 75s. Type **264** 40 25
867 2b.75 Teleprinter and dish aerial 75 25

265 "Sukhrip Khrong Muang"

1975. Thai Ceremonial Barges. Multicoloured.
868 75s. Type **265** 50 10
869 1b. Royal barge "Anekchat Phuchong" . . . . 1·25 40
870 2b. Royal barge "Anantanakarat" . . . . 1·75 50
871 2b.75 "Krabi Ran Ron Rap 2·00 50
872 3b. "Asura Wayuphak" . . . 3·00 80
873 4b. "Asura Paksi" . . . . 2·40 1·50
874 5b. Royal barge "Sri Suphanahong" . . . . . 5·50 3·00
875 6b. "Phali Rang Thawip" . . 3·50 2·00

266 King's Cipher and Thai Crown

1975. King Bhumibol's 48th Birthday. Multicoloured.
876 75s. Type **266** 15 10
877 5b. King Bhumibol in uniform . . . . 1·25 30

267 Putting the Shot

1975. 8th South-East Asian Peninsula Games, Bangkok (2nd issue).
878 **267** 1b. black and orange . . 25 10
879 – 2b. black and green . . . 75 50
880 – 3b. black and yellow . . . 1·25 35
881 – 4b. black and violet . . . 1·60 65
DESIGNS: 2b. Table tennis; 3b. Cycling; 4b. Relay-running.

268 I.W.Y. Emblem on Globe

1975. International Women's Year.
883 **268** 75s. blue, orange and black 25 10

269 Children writing

1976. Children's Day.
884 **269** 75s. multicoloured 50 10

270 "Macrobrachium rosenbergii"

1976. Thai Lobsters and Shrimps. Multicoloured.
885 75s. Type **270** 25 10
886 2b. "Penaeus merguiensis" . . 2·25 55
887 2b.75 "Panulirus ornatus" . . 2·00 25
888 5b. "Penaeus monodon" . . 5·00 1·60

1976. Red Cross Fair 1975. Nos. 472/3 surch **75+25 2518 1975**.
889 **130** 75s.+25s. on 50s.+10s. red and grey 25 25
890 – 75s.+25s. on 50s.+10s. red and grey 25 25

271 Common Gold-backed Woodpecker

272 Ben Chiang Pot

1976. Thailand Birds. Multicoloured.
891 1b. Type **271** . . . . 1·50 35
892 1b.50 Greater green-billed malcoha 85 70
893 3b. Long-billed scimitar babbler . . . . 5·50 1·75
894 4b. Green magpie . . . . . 2·75 85

1976. Ben Chiang Pottery.
895 **272** 1b. multicoloured 25 10
896 – 2b. miticoloured . . . . 2·75 30
897 – 3b. multicoloured . . . . 1·75 25
898 – 4b. multicoloured . . . . 2·25 1·25
DESIGNS: 2b. to 4b. Various items of pottery.

273 Postman of 1883

275 "Drug Addictions"

274 Kinnari

1976. Postmen's Uniforms. Multicoloured.
899 1b. Type **273** 25 10
900 3b. Postman of 1935 . . . . 1·00 20
901 4b. Postman of 1950 . . . . 1·75 1·25
902 5b. Postman of 1974 . . . . 3·00 50

1976. Int Correspondence Week. Deities. Mult.
903 1b. Type **274** . . . . 2·75 65
904 2b. Suphan-Mat-Cha 25 15
905 4b. Garuda 75 25
906 5b. Naga . . . . 1·40 20

1976. United Nations Day.
907 **275** 1b. multicoloured 25 10

276 Early and Modern Telephones

1976. Telephone Centenary.
908 **276** 1b. multicoloured 25 10

277 Sivalaya

1976. Thai Royal Halls. Multicoloured.
909 1b. Type **277** 15 10
910 2b. Cakri . . . . 3·75 30
911 4b. Mahisra . . . . 1·75 1·00
912 5b. Dusit . . . . 2·00 65

1976. Protected Wild Animals (2nd series). As T **254**. Multicoloured.
913 1b. Bangteng . . . . 1·90 50
914 2b. Malayan tapir . . . . . 2·40 75
915 4b. Sambar 65 25
916 5b. Hog-deer 90 25

278 "From Child to Adult"

1977. Children's Day.
917 **278** 1b. multicoloured 25 10

279 Alsthom Diesel-electric Locomotive No. 4101

1977. 80th Anniv of Thai State Railway. Multicoloured.
918 1b. Type **279** 55 10
919 2b. Davenport diesel locomotive No. 577 . . . 2·50 35
920 4b. Pacific steam locomotive No. 825, Japan . . . . . 6·00 2·50
921 5b. George Egestoff's steam locomotive . . . . 10·00 1·90

280 University Building

1977. 60th Anniv of Chulalongkorn University.
922 **280** 1b. multicoloured 40 10

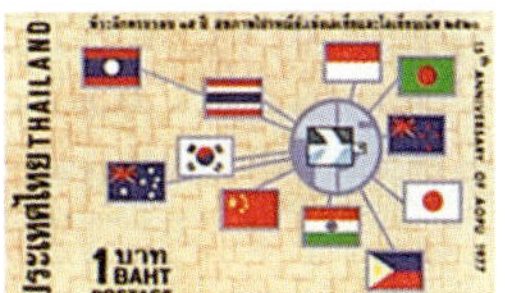
281 Flags of A.O.P.U. Countries

1977. 15th Anniv of Asian–Oceanic Postal Union.
923 **281** 1b. multicoloured 40 10

282 Crippled Ex-Serviceman

1977. Sai-Jai-Thai Foundation Day.
924 **282** 5b. multicoloured 75 15

1977. Red Cross Fair. Nos. 472/3 surch **75+25 2520-1977.**
925 **130** 75s.+25s. on 50s.+10s. red and grey 25 25
926 – 75s.+25s. on 50s.+10s. red and grey 25 25

284 Phra Aphai Mani and Phisua Samut

1977. Puppet Shows. Multicoloured.
927 2b. Type **284** 25 10
928 3b. Rusi and Sutsakhon . . . 1·00 20
929 4b. Nang Vali and Usren . . 50 25
930 5b. Phra Aphai Mani and Nang Laweng's portrait . . 1·00 40

285 Drum Dance

1977. Thai Folk Dances. Multicoloured.
931 2b. Type **285** 25 10
932 3b. Dance of Dip-nets . . . 1·00 15
933 4b. Harvesting dance 40 20
934 5b. Kan dance 65 25

286 1b. Stamp of 1972

1977. "THAIPEX 77" National Stamp Exhibition.
935 **286** 75s. multicoloured 40 10

287 "Pla Bu Thong"

1977. International Correspondence Week. Scenes from Thai Literature. Multicoloured.
936 75s. Type **287** 50 10
937 2b. "Krai Thong" 75 40
938 5b. "Nang Kaew Na Ma" . . 1·60 25
939 6b. "Pra Rot Mali" . . . . 1·90 30

288 U.N. Building, Bangkok

1977. United Nations Day.
940 **288** 75s. multicoloured 50 10

289 King Bhumibol in Scout Uniform, and Camp Fire

1977. 9th National Scout Jamboree.
941 **289** 75s. multicoloured 75 10

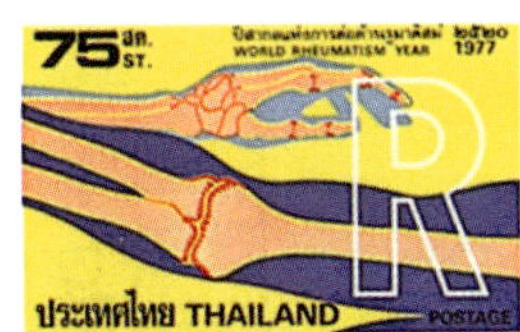
290 Map of A.S.E.A.N. Countries

1977. 10th Anniv of Association of South East Asian Nations.
942 **290** 5b. multicoloured . . . . 1·00 20

291 Elbow and Wrist Joints

1977. World Rheumatism Year.
943 **291** 75s. multicoloured 40 10

292 Children with Thai Flag

1978. Children's Day.
944 **292** 75s. multicoloured 50 10

293 "Dendrobium heterocarpum"

1978. 9th World Orchid Conference. Mult.
945 75s. Type **293** 50 25
946 1b. "Dendrobium pulchellum" . . . . 1·00 25
947 1b.50 "Doritis pulcherrima var buyssoniana" . . . . 1·50 75
948 2b. "Dendrobium hercoglossum" 25 15
949 2b.75 "Aerides odorata" . . 3·00 10
950 3b. "Trichoglottis fasciata" 25 10
951 5b. "Dendrobium wardianum" 65 20
952 6b. "Dendrobium senile" . . 65 35

294 Agricultural Scenes and Rice Production Graph

1978. Agricultural Census.
953 **294** 75s. multicoloured 20 10

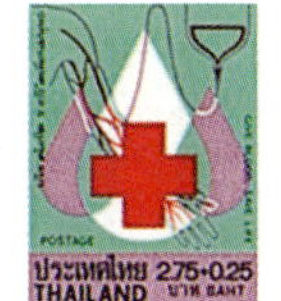
295 Blood Donation and Red Cross

1978. Red Cross.
954 **295** 2b.75+25s. multicoloured 75 75

296 Climbing Perch

1978. Fishes. Multicoloured.
955 1b. Type **296** . . . . 1·50 90
956 2b. Siamese tigerfish 20 15
957 3b. Glass catfish 50 20
958 4b. Esok 60 40

297 "Birth of Prince Siddhartha"

1978. "Buddha's Story" Mural; Puthi Savan Hall, National Museum. Multicoloured.
959 2b. Type **297** 50 15
960 3b. "Prince Siddhartha cuts his hair" . . . . 1·00 25
961 5b. "Buddha descends from Tavatimsa Heaven" . . . 4·75 90
962 6b. "Buddha enters Nirvana" 2·25 1·00

298 Bhumibol Dam

1978. Dams. Multicoloured.
963 75s. Type **298** 50 10
964 2b. Sirikit Dam 50 15
965 2b.75 Vajiralongkorn Dam 1·25 20
966 6b. Ubolratana Dam . . . . 1·50 1·25

299 "Idea lynceus"

1978. Butterflies.
967 **299** 2b. black, violet and red 50 15
968 – 3b. multicoloured . . . . 1·00 15
969 – 5b. multicoloured . . . . 3·25 15
970 – 6b. multicoloured . . . . 1·90 1·00
DESIGNS: 3b. Eastern courtier; 5b. "Charaxes durnfordi"; 6b. "Cethosia penthesilea".

300 Phra Chedi Chai Mongkhon, Ayutthaya
301 Mother and Children

1978. International Correspondence Week. Mult.
971 75s. Type **300** 25 10
972 2b. Phra That Hariphunchai, Lamphun 40 15
973 2b.75 Phra Borom That Chaiya, Surat Thani . . . 2·40 20
974 5b. Phra That Choeng Chum, Sakon Nakhon 90 65

1978. United Nations Day.
975 **301** 75s. multicoloured 25 10

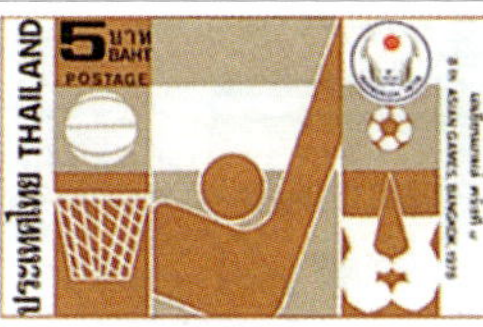
302 Basketball, Hockey and Boxing

1978. 8th Asian Games, Bangkok. Multicoloured.
976 25s. Silhouettes of boxers, footballer and pole-vaulter 15 10
977 2b. Silhouettes of javelin-thrower, weightlifter and runner 25 15
978 3b. Football, shuttlecock, yacht and table-tennis bat and ball 65 20
979 5b. Type **302** . . . . 1·75 75

303 World Map and Different Races holding Hands

1978. International Anti-Apartheid Year.
980 **303** 75s. multicoloured 25 10

304 Children and S.O.S. Village, Tambol Bangpu

1979. International Year of the Child. Mult.
981 75s. Children painting Thai flag (horiz) 75 20
982 75s. Type **304** 25 10

305 "Matuta lunaris"

1979. Crabs. Multicoloured.
983 2b. Type **305** 40 15
984 2b.75 "Matuta planipes" . . 2·25 15
985 3b. "Portunus pelagicus" . . 95 40
986 5b. "Scylla serrata" . . . . 2·75 75

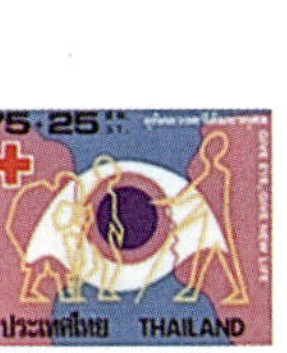

306 Eye and Blind People
307 Sugar Apples

1979. Red Cross.
987 **306** 75s.+25s. multicoloured 40 30

1979. Fruits. Multicoloured.
988 1b. Type **307** 75 15
989 2b. Pineapple 50 15
990 5b. Bananas . . . . 1·90 65
991 6b. Longans . . . . 1·60 90

308 Planting Sapling

1979. 20th Arbor Day.
992 **308** 75s. multicoloured 25 10

309 Pencil, Brush and Colours

1979. "Thaipex '79" National Stamp Exhibition, Bangkok. Multicoloured.

993 75s. Type **309** 15 10
994 2b. Envelopes 25 15
995 2b.75 Stamp stockbook . . . 50 15
996 5b. Tweezers, stamps and magnifying glass . . . . . 1·90 70

310 Baisi Pak Cham

311 U.N.O. Emblem, Farmer, Cattle and Wheat

1979. International Correspondence Week. Traditional Flower Arrangements. Mult.

997 75s. Kruai upatcha (used at Buddhist ordination ceremony) 15 10
998 2b. Type **310** (used at Braminical ceremonies) . . 25 15
999 2b.75 Krathong dokmai (for paying respects to elders or superiors) 50 15
1000 5b. Phum dokmai (altar decoration) . . . . 1·90 70

1979. United Nations Day.

1001 **311** 75s. multicoloured . . . 25 10

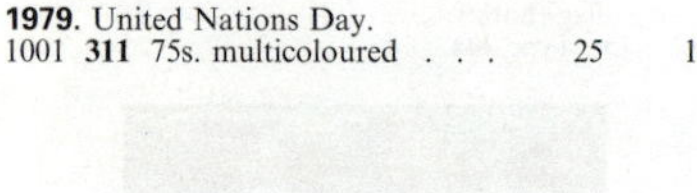

312 "Makutrajakumarn" (frigate)

1979. Ships of the Royal Thai Navy. Mult.

1002 2b. Type **312** 40 15
1003 3b. "Tapi" (frigate) 60 15
1004 5b. "Prabparapak" (missile craft) . . . . 3·00 75
1005 6b. T 91 (patrol boat) . . . 3·50 1·00

313 Order of the Rajamitrabhorn

314 Transplanting Rice

1979. Royal Orders and Decorations. Mult.

1006 1b. Type **313** 50 25
1007 1b. Rajamitrabhorn ribbon 50 25
1008 2b. Order of the Royal House of Chakri 50 15
1009 2b. Royal House of Chakri ribbon 50 15
1010 5b. Order of the Nine Gems 1·00 40
1011 5b. Nine Gems ribbon . . . 1·00 40
1012 6b. Knight Grand Cross of the Order of Chula Chom Klao . . . . 1·50 50
1013 6b. Chula Chom Klao ribbon . . . . 1·50 50

1980. Children's Day. Multicoloured.

1014 75s. Type **314** 40 15
1015 75s. Harvesting rice 40 15

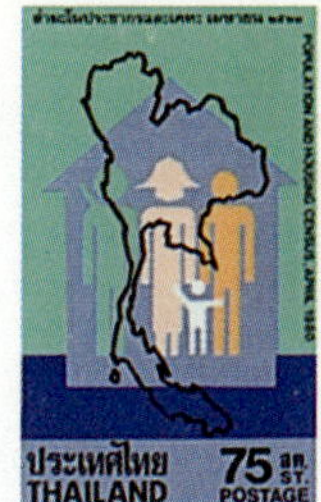
315 Family House and Map of Thailand

316 Golden-fronted Leafbird

1980. Population and Housing Census.

1016 **315** 75s. multicoloured . . . 20 10

1980. 9th Conference of Int Commission for Bird Preservation (Asian Section), Chiang Mai. Mult.

1017 75s. Type **316** 45 25
1018 2b. Chinese yellow tit . . . 80 30
1019 3b. Chestnut-tailed minla . . 2·10 40
1020 5b. Scarlet minivet . . . . 3·25 1·40

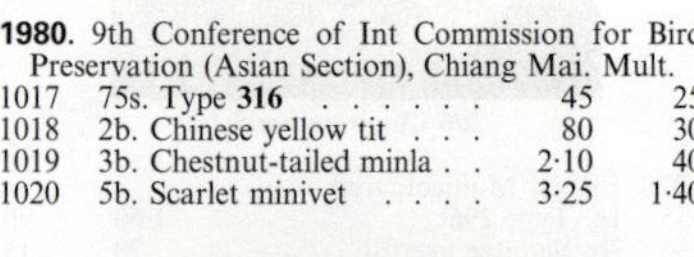

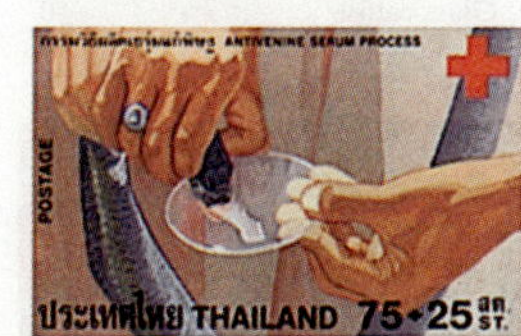
317 Extracting Snake Venom

1980. Red Cross.

1021 **317** 75s.+25s. mult 40 30

318 Smokers and Diagram of Lungs

1980. World Health Day. Anti-smoking Campaign.

1022 **318** 75s. multicoloured . . . 20 10

319 Garuda and Rotary Emblem

1980. 75th Anniv of Rotary International.

1023 **319** 5b. multicoloured . . . 75 20

320 Sai Yok Falls, Kanchanaburi

1980. Waterfalls. Multicoloured.

1024 1b. Type **320** 15 10
1025 2b. Punyaban Falls, Ranong 25 15
1026 5b. Heo Suwat Falls, Nakhon Ratchasima . . . 1·00 45
1027 6b. Siriphum Falls, Chiang Mai 90 65

321 Family and Reverse of F.A.O. Medal

1980. Queen Sirikit's "Fourth Cycle" Anniv (48th Birthday). Multicoloured.

1028 75s. Queen Sirikit (vert) . . 15 10
1029 5b. Type **321** 75 25
1030 5b. Thai family and obverse of F.A.O. medal 75 25

322 Khao Phanomrung Temple, Buri Ram

1980. Int Correspondence Week. Temples. Mult.

1033 75s. Type **322** 15 10
1034 2b. Prang Ku Temple, Chaiyaphum 25 15
1035 2b.75 Phimai Temple, Nakhon Ratchasima . . . 40 15
1036 5b. Srikhoraphum Temple, Surin . . . . 1·00 55

323 Princess Mother

324 Golden Mount Temple, Bangkok

1980. The Princess Mother's 80th Birthday.

1037 **323** 75s. multicoloured . . . 60 10

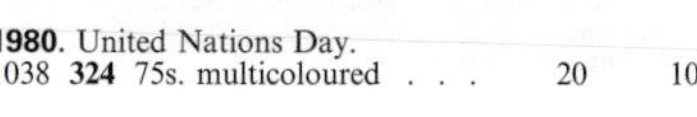

1980. United Nations Day.

1038 **324** 75s. multicoloured . . . 20 10

325 King Bhumibol

326 "King Rama VII signing Constitutional Document"

1980.

1039 **325** 25s. red 50 10
1179 50s. green . . . . . . 1·25 10
1040 75s. violet 15 10
1041 1b. blue 10 10
1040a 1b.25 green 15 10
1180a 1b.50 orange . . . . . 1·00 85
1041a 2b. purple and red . . 2·75 15
1235b 2b. brown 25 10
1042a 3b. blue and brown . . 15 10
1042b 4b. brown and blue . . 25 10
1043a 5b. brown and lilac . . 25 10
1044a 6b. lilac and green . . 25 10
1044b 6b.50 olive and green 50 15
1044c 7b. dp brown & brown 50 10
1044d 7b.50 blue and red . . 40 20
1044e 8b. green and brown 40 15
1045 8b.50 brown and green 50 20
1045a 9b. brown and blue . . 45 15
1046 9b.50 green and olive 50 20
1047 10b. green and red . . 50 10
1048 20b. green and orange 1·00 20
1049 50b. green and lilac . . 3·00 40
1050 100b. blue and orange 4·50 50

1980. Monument to King Prajadhipok (Rama VII).

1051 **326** 75s. multicoloured . . . 20 10

327 Bowl

1980. Bencharong Ware. Multicoloured.

1052 2b. Type **327** 40 15
1053 2b.75 Covered bowls . . . 40 15
1054 3b. Jar 75 25
1055 5b. Stem-plates 75 50

328 King Vajiravudh

329 "Youth in Electronics Age" (Veth Maichun)

1981. Birth Centenary of King Vajiravudh.

1056 **328** 75s. multicoloured . . . 20 10

1981. Children's Day.

1057 **329** 75s. multicoloured . . . 40 20

330 Mosque, Pattani Province

1981. 1400th Anniv of Hegira.

1058 **330** 5b. multicoloured . . . 1·00 40

331 Palm Leaf Fish Mobile

1981. Int Handicraft Exhibition. Mult.

1059 75s. Type **331** 15 10
1060 75s. Carved teakwood elephant 15 10
1061 2b.75 Basketwork 50 30
1062 2b.75 Thai folk dolls . . . 50 30

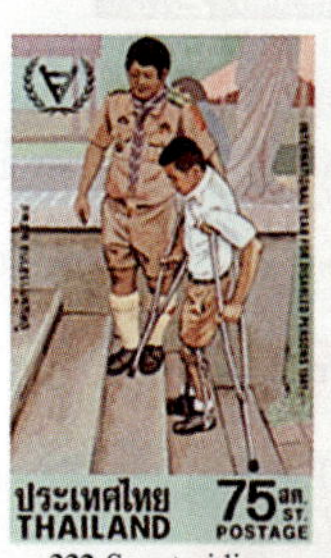
332 Scout aiding Cripple

334 Ongkhot

333 Red Cross Volunteer aiding Refugee

1981. Int Year of Disabled Persons. Mult.

1063 75s. Type **332** 15 10
1064 5b. Disabled person cutting gem-stones 65 20

1981. Red Cross.

1065 **333** 75s.+25s. green and red 75 75

1981. Khon (Thai classical dance) Masks. Mult.

1066 75s. Type **334** 15 10
1067 2b. Maiyarab 25 15
1068 3b. Sukrip 65 20
1069 5b. Indrajit 75 50

336 8a. Stamp, 1899

1981. "Thaipex '81" National Stamp Exn. Mult.

1070 75s. Type **336** 15 10
1071 75s. 28s. stamp, 1910 . . . 15 10
1072 2b.75 50s. stamp, 1919 . . . 50 25
1073 2b.75 3s. stamp, 1932 . . . 50 25

337 Luang Praditphairo

338 Mai Hok-Hian

1981. Birth Centenary of Luang Praditphairo (musician).
1074 **337** 1b.25 multicoloured . . 25 10

1981. International Correspondence Week. Dwarf Trees. Multicoloured.
1075 75s. Type **338** 15 10
1076 2b. Mai Kam-Mao-Lo . . . 25 15
1077 2b.75 Mai Khen 50 15
1078 5b. Mai Khabuan . . . . . 1·25 55

339 Food Produce

1981. World Food Day.
1079 **339** 75s. multicoloured . . . 25 10

340 Samran Mukhamat Pavilion, Bangkok

1981. United Nations Day.
1080 **340** 1b.25 multicoloured . . 25 10

341 Expressway at Klongtoey

1981. Inaug of First Thai Expressway. Mult.
1081 1b. Type **341** 15 10
1082 5b. Expressway interchange 1·00 30

342 King Cobra

1981. Snakes. Multicoloured.
1083 75s. Type **342** 15 10
1084 2b. Banded krait 50 30
1085 2b.75 Thai cobra 50 15
1086 5b. Malayan pit viper . . . 1·25 50

343 Girl carrying Child

344 Scouts reaching for Peace

1982. Children's Day.
1087 **343** 1b.25 multicoloured . . 25 10

1982. 75th Anniv of Boy Scout Movement.
1088 **344** 1b.25 multicoloured . . 25 10

345 King Buddha Yod-Fa (Rama I)

1982. Bicentenary of Chakri Dynasty and of Bangkok. Multicoloured.
1089 1b. Type **345** 15 10
1090 1b.25 Aerial view of Bangkok 15 10
1091 2b. King Buddha Lert La Naphalai (Rama II) . . . 50 10
1092 3b. King Nang Klao (Rama III) . . . . 1·00 15
1093 4b. King Mongkut (Rama IV) 80 15
1094 5b. King Chulalongkorn (Rama V) . . . . 2·00
1095 6b. King Vajiravudh (Rama VI) . . . . 1·60 30
1096 7b. King Prajadhipok (Rama VII) . . . . . . 1·75 75
1097 8b. King Ananda Mahidol (Rama VIII) 90 50
1098 9b. King Bhumipol Adulyadej (Rama IX) . . 90 30

346 Dr. Robert Koch and Cross of Lorraine

1982. Cent of Discovery of Tubercle Bacillus.
1100 **346** 1b.25 multicoloured . . 20 10

347 "Quisqualis indica"

1982. Flowers. Multicoloured.
1101 1b.25 Type **347** 15 10
1102 1b.50 "Murraya paniculata" 25 15
1103 6b.50 "Mesua ferrea" . . . 75 40
1104 7b. "Desmos chinensis" . . 65 30

348 Wat Bowon Sathan Sutthawat

1982. "Bangkok 1983" International Stamp Exhibition (1st issue). Multicoloured.
1105 1b.25 Type **348** 15 10
1106 4b.25 Wat Phra Chetuphon Wimon Mangkhalaram 40 20
1107 6b.50 Wat Mahathat Yuwarat Rangsarit . . . 65 40
1108 7b. Wat Phra Sri Rattana Satsadaram 90 25
See also Nos. 1133/4 and 1142/5.

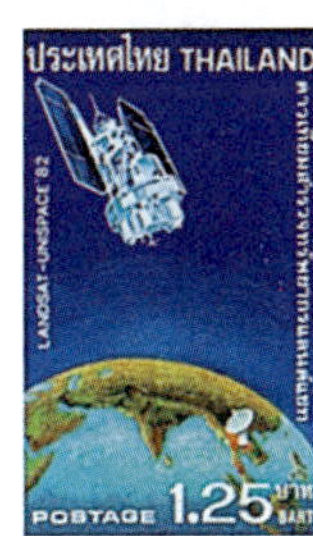
349 "Landsat" Satellite

350 Prince Purachatra

1982. 2nd U.N. Conference on the Exploration and Peaceful Uses of Outer Space, Vienna.
1110 **349** 1b.25 multicoloured . . 20 10

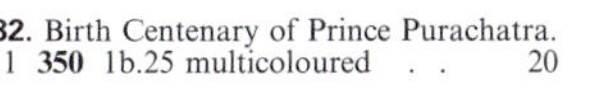
1982. Birth Centenary of Prince Purachatra.
1111 **350** 1b.25 multicoloured . . 20 10

351 Covered Jar

1982. International Correspondence Week. Sangalok Pottery. Multicoloured.
1112 1b.25 Type **351** 15 10
1113 3b. Small jar 65 15
1114 4b.25 Celadon plate 50 30
1115 7b. Plate with fish design . . 75 50

352 Loha Prasat, Bangkok

1982. United Nations Day.
1116 **352** 1b.25 multicoloured . . 20 10

353 Chap and Ching

1982. Thai Musical Instruments. Multicoloured.
1117 50s. Type **353** 10 10
1118 1b. Pi nok and pi nai (pipes) 30 10
1119 1b.25 Klong that and taphon (drums) 15 10
1120 1b.50 Khong mong (gong) and krap (wooden sticks) 15 15
1121 6b. Khong wong yai (glockenspiel) . . . . . . 2·00 65
1122 7b. Khong wong lek (glockenspiel) 90 25
1123 8b. Ranat ek (xylophone) 75 40
1124 9b. Ranat thum (xylophone) 75 40

354 Pileated Gibbon

355 Emblem and Flags of Member Countries

1982. National Wild Animal Preservation Day. Monkeys. Multicoloured.
1125 1b.25 Type **354** 15 10
1126 3b. Pigtail macaque 90 20
1127 5b. Slow loris 50 40
1128 7b. Silvered leaf monkey . . 75 40

1982. 15th Anniv of Association of South-East Asian Nations.
1129 **355** 6b.50 multicoloured . . 75 25

356 Child sweeping

1983. Children's Day.
1130 **356** 1b.25 multicoloured . . 20 10

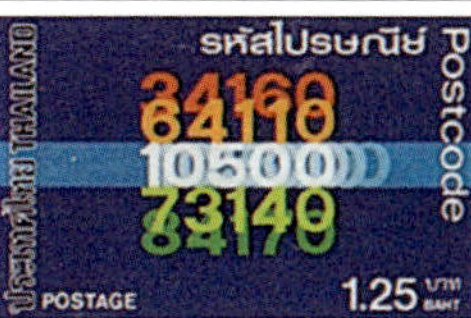
357 Postcodes

1983. 1st Anniv of Postcodes. Multicoloured.
1131 1b.25 Type **357** 25 10
1132 1b.25 Postcoded envelope 25 10

358 Old General Post Office

1983. "Bangkok 1983" International Stamp Exhibition (2nd issue).
1133 **358** 7b. multicoloured . . . 75 20
1134 10b. multicoloured . . . 1·25 30

359 Junks

1983. 25th Anniv of International Maritime Organization.
1136 **359** 1b.25 multicoloured . . 20 10

360 Civil Servant's Shoulder Strap
362 Prince Sithiporn Kridakara

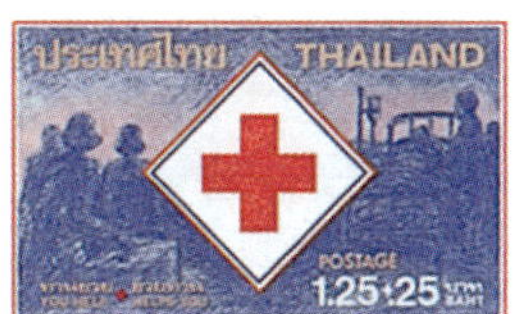
361 Giving and receiving Aid and Red Cross

1983. Civil Servants' Day.
1137 **360** 1b.25 multicoloured . . 20 10

1983. Red Cross.
1138 **361** 1b.25+25s. multicoloured 50 50

1983. Birth Centenary of Prince Sithiporn Kridakara (agriculturalist).
1139 **362** 1b.25 multicoloured . . 20 10

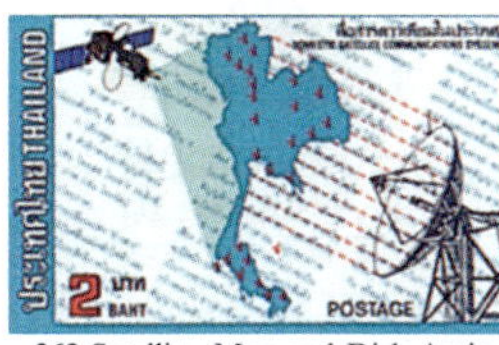
363 Satellite, Map and Dish Aeria

1983. Domestic Satellite Communications System.
1140 **363** 2b. multicoloured . . . 25 10

364 Prince Bhanurangsi

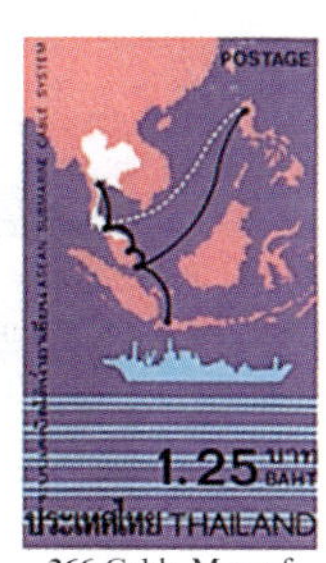
366 Cable Map of A.S.E.A.N. Countries and "Long Lines" (cable ship)

365 Post Box Clearance

1983. Prince Bhanurangsi (founder of Thai postal service) Commemoration.
1141 **364** 1b.25 multicoloured . . 25 10

1983. "Bangkok 1983" International Stamp Exhibition (3rd issue). Multicoloured.
1142 1b.25 Type **365** 15 10
1143 7b.50 Post office counter . . 75 30
1144 8b.50 Mail transportation 75 65
1145 9b.50 Mail delivery . . . 50 25

1983. Inauguration of Malaysia–Singapore–Thailand Submarine Cable. Multicoloured.
1147 1b.25 Type **366** 40 15
1148 7b. Map of new cable . . . 65 30

367 Flower Coral

1983. Int Correspondence Week. Corals. Mult.
1149 2b. Type **367** 25 15
1150 3b. Lesser valley coral . . . 75 15
1151 4b. Mushroom coral 25 25
1152 7b. Common lettuce coral 1·00 50

368 Satellite and Submarine Cable Communications Equipment

1983. World Communications Year. Mult.
1153 2b. Type **368** 60 15
1154 3b. Telephone and telegraph service equipment 25 15

369 Fishing for Tuna

1983. United Nations Day.
1155 **369** 1b.25 multicoloured . . 40 10

370 Buddha (sculpture)

1983. 700th Anniv of Thai Alphabet.
1156 **370** 3b. multicoloured . . . 50 15
1157 – 7b. black and brown . . 75 25
1158 – 8b. multicoloured . . . 40 25
1159 – 9b. multicoloured . . . 40 25
DESIGNS—HORIZ: 3b. Sangkhalok pottery; 7b. Thai characters. VERT: 9b. Mahathat Temple.

371 Prince Mahidol of Songkhla

1983. 60th Anniv of Co-operation between Siriraj Hospital and Rockefeller Foundation.
1160 **371** 9b.50 multicoloured . . 75 50

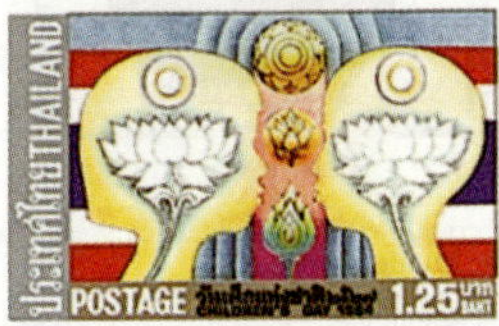

372 Lotus Blossoms within Heads

1984. Children's Day.
1161 **372** 1b.25 multicoloured . . 20 10

373 Running

1984. 17th National Games, Phitsanulok Province. Multicoloured.
1162 1b.25 Type **373** 30 10
1163 3b. Football 25 15

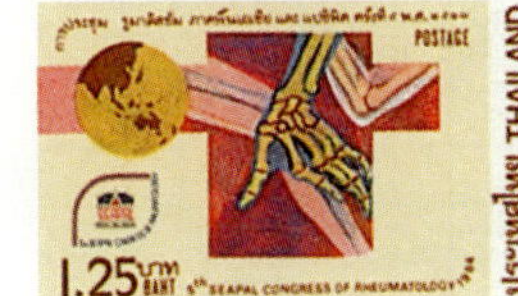

374 Skeletal Joints, Globe and Emblem

1984. 5th South East Asia and Pacific Area League against Rheumatism Congress.
1164 **374** 1b.25 multicoloured . . 20 10

375 Statue of King Naresuan and Modern Armed Forces
376 Royal Institute Emblem in Door Arch

1984. Armed Forces Day.
1165 **375** 1b.25 multicoloured . . 30 10

1984. 50th Anniv of Royal Institute.
1166 **376** 1b.25 multicoloured . . 20 10

1984. Red Cross. No. 954 surch **3.25 + 0.25** in English and Thai.
1167 **295** 3b.25+25s. on 2b.75+25s. mult . . . . 1·00 60

378 King and Queen examining Land Development Project

1984. Royal Initiated Projects. Multicoloured.
1168 1b.25 Type **378** 25 10
1169 1b.25 Improving barren area 25 10
1170 1b.25 Dam, terrace farming and rain-making aircraft 25 10
1171 1b.25 Crops, fish and farm animals 40 20
1172 1b.25 King and Queen of Thailand 25 10

379 Dome Building and University Emblem

1984. 50th Anniv of Thammasat University.
1173 **379** 1b.25 multicoloured . . 20 10

381 A.B.U. Emblem and Map

1984. 20th Anniv of Asia-Pacific Broadcasting Union.
1174 **381** 4b. multicoloured . . . 50 20

382 Chiang Saen Style Buddha
384 "Alocasia indica var. metallica"

1984. Thai Sculptures of Buddhas. Multicoloured
1175 1b.25 Type **382** 15 10
1176 7b. Sukhothai style 75 30
1177 8b.50 Thong style 40 40
1178 9b.50 Ayutthaya style . . . 40 40

1984. International Correspondence Week. Medicinal Plants. Multicoloured.
1181 1b.50 Type **384** 15 10
1182 2b. "Aloe barbadensis" . . 20 10
1183 4b. "Gynura pseudo-china" 35 15
1184 10b. "Rhoeo spathacea" . . 1·25 70

385 Princess Mother
386 Threshing Rice

1984. 84th Birthday of Princess Mother.
1185 **385** 1b.50 multicoloured . . 15 10

1984. United Nations Day.
1186 **386** 1b.50 multicoloured . . 15 10

387 Bhutan Glory

1984. Butterflies. Multicoloured.
1187 2b. Type **387** 40 20
1188 3b. "Stichophthalma louisa" 60 25
1189 5b. Clipper 75 35
1190 7b. "Stichophthalma godfreyi" . . . . 1·00 40

388 "Crossing the Road by Flyover" (U-Tai Raksorn)
390 Monument to Tao-Thep-Krasattri and Tao-Sri-Sundhorn

389 Bangkok Mail Centre

1985. Children's Day. Multicoloured.
1191 1b.50 Type **388** 15 10
1192 1b.50 "Crossing the Road by Flyover" (Sravudh Charoennawee) (horiz) . . 15 10

1985. Inauguration of Bangkok Mail-sorting Centre.
1193 **389** 1b.50 multicoloured . . 25 10

1985. Heroines of Phuket. Bicentennial Ceremony.
1194 **390** 2b. multicoloured . . . 20 10

1985. Red Cross. No. 987 surch **2 + .25 BAHT**.
1195 **306** 2b.+25s. on 75s.+25s. multicoloured 75 75

392 Bank Headquarters, Bangkok, and King Vajiravudh (Rama VI)

1985. 72nd Anniv of Government Savings Bank.
1196 **392** 1b.50 multicoloured . . 15 10

393 Satellite over Thai Buildings

1985. 20th Anniv of International Telecommunications Satellite Organization.
1197 **393** 2b. multicoloured . . . 25 10

394 Douglas DC-6 and DC-8 and Loi-Krathong Festival

1985. 25th Anniv of Thai Airways. Mult.
1198 2b. Type **394** 15 10
1199 7b.50 Douglas DC-10-30 and Thai classical dancing 1·00 55
1200 8b.50 Airbus Industrie A-300 and Thai buildings 1·10 80
1201 9b.50 Boeing 747-200 and world landmarks . . . . 1·10 80

395 U.P.U.Emblem
397 Aisvarya Pavilion

396 Pigeon

1985. Centenary of Membership of U.P.U. and I.T.U. Multicoloured.
1202 2b. Type **395** 15 10
1203 10b. I.T.U. Emblem 55 20

1985. National Communications Day.
1204 **396** 2b. blue, red & ultram 20 10

1985. "Thaipex '85" Stamp Exhibition. Multicoloured.
1205 2b. Type **397** 15 10
1206 3b. Varopas Piman Pavilion (horiz) 25 15
1207 7b. Vehas Camrun Pavilion (horiz) 50 20
1208 10b. Vitoon Tassana Tower 60 50

398 King Mongkut, Eclipsed Sun and Telescope

1985. National Science Day.
1210 **398** 2b. multicoloured . . . 20 10

399 Department Seals, 1885 and 1985

1985. Centenary of Royal Thai Survey Department.
1211 **399** 2b. multicoloured . . . 20 10

400 Boxing

1985. 13th South-East Asia Games, Bangkok (1st issue). Multicoloured.
1212 2b. Type **400** 20 10
1213 2b. Putting the shot 20 10
1214 2b. Badminton 20 10
1215 2b. Throwing the javelin . . 20 10
1216 2b. Weightlifting 20 10
See also Nos. 1229/32.

401 Golden Trumpet

402 Mothers and Children at Clinic

1985. International Correspondence Week. Climbing Plants. Multicoloured.
1218 2b. Type **401** 25 15
1219 3b. "Jasminum auriculatum" 35 15
1220 7b. Passion flower 50 25
1221 10b. Coral-vine 60 35

1985. United Nations Day.
1222 **402** 2b. multicoloured . . . 20 10

403 Prince Dhani Nivat

404 Prince of Jainad

1985. Birth Centenary of Prince Dhani Nivat, Kromamun Bidyalabh Bridhyakorn.
1223 **403** 2b. multicoloured . . . 15 10

1985. Birth Centenary of Rangsit, Prince of Jainad (Minister of Health).
1224 **404** 1b.50 multicoloured . . 15 10

405 Emblem and Buildings

1985. 5th Asian–Pacific Postal Union Congress.
1225 **405** 2b. multicoloured . . . 15 10
1226 – 10b. multicoloured . . . 55 25
DESIGN: 10b. As Type **405** but different buildings.

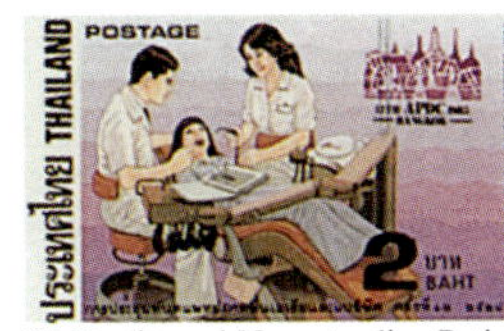

406 Emblem

1985. International Youth Year.
1227 **406** 2b. multicoloured . . . 25 10

407 Dentist and Nurse tending Patient

1985. 12th Asian–Pacific Dental Congress.
1228 **407** 2b. multicoloured . . . 20 10

408 Volleyball

409 Chevalier de Chaumont presenting Message from Louis XIV to King Narai the Great, 1685

1985. 12th South-East Asia Games, Bangkok (2nd issue). Multicoloured.
1229 1b. Type **408** 20 15
1230 2b. Sepak-takraw (kick-ball) 20 10
1231 3b. Gymnastics 25 15
1232 4b. Bowls 25 20

1985. 300th Anniv of Franco–Thai Relations. Multicoloured.
1234 2b. Type **409** 15 10
1235 8b.50 Siamese emissaries carrying reply from King Narai to Louis XIV (horiz) 50 40

410 Emblem

1986. 3rd Anniv of International and Inauguration of Domestic Express Mail Services.
1236 **410** 2b. multicoloured . . . 15 10

411 Green Turtle

1986. Turtles. Multicoloured.
1237 1b.50 Type **411** 15 10
1238 3b. Hawksbill turtle 35 10
1239 5b. Leatherback turtle . . . 1·25 20
1240 10b. Olive turtle . . . . . 1·00 25

412 "Family picking Lotus" (Areeya Makarabhundhu)

414 Statue of Sunthon Phu (Sukij Laidej), Amphoe Klaeng

1986. Children's Day.
1241 **412** 2b. multicoloured . . . 20 10

1986. Red Cross. No. 1021 surch. **1986 2 + .25 BAHT** in English and Thai.
1242 **317** 2b.+25s. on 75s.+25s. multicoloured 75 75

1986. Birth Bicentenary of Sunthon Phu (poet).
1243 **414** 2b. multicoloured . . . 20 10

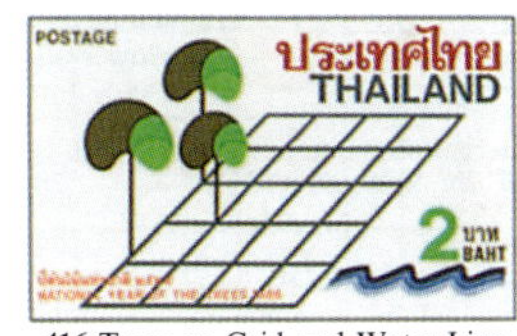

415 Watermelon

1986. Fruit. Multicoloured.
1244 2b. Type **415** 50 15
1245 2b. Malay apple ("Eugenia malaccensis") 50 15
1246 6b. Pomelo ("Citrus maxima") 75 15
1247 6b. Papaya ("Carica papaya") 75 15

416 Trees on Grid and Water Line

1986. National Tree Year.
1248 **416** 2b. multicoloured . . . 15 10

417 Pigeon flying from Man's Head to Transmission Masts

1986. National Communications Day.
1249 **417** 2b. multicoloured . . . 15 10

418 Chalom

1986. International Correspondence Week. Bamboo Baskets. Multicoloured.
1250 2b. Type **418** 15 10
1251 2b. Krabung 15 10
1252 6b. Kratib 35 15
1253 6b. Kaleb 35 15

1986. No. 1031 surch **1 BAHT**.
1254 **227** 1b. on 20s. blue 20 10

420 Emblem and War Scenes

1986. International Peace Year.
1255 **420** 2b. light blue, blue & red 20 10

421 Industrial and Agricultural Scenes within Emblem

1986. Productivity Year.
1256 **421** 2b. multicoloured . . . 20 10

422 Scouts saluting and Scout helping Blind Man across Road

1986. 75th Anniv of Thai Scouting. Mult.
1257 2b.+50s. Type **422** 15 15
1258 2b.+50s. Scouting activities 15 15
1259 2b.+50s. King and Queen making presentations to scouts 15 15
1260 2b.+50s. 15th Asia–Pacific Scout Conference, Thailand 15 15

423 Vanda "Varavuth"

1986. 6th ASEAN Orchid Congress, Thailand. Multicoloured.
1261 2b. Type **423** 20 10
1262 3b. Ascocenda "Emma" . . 20 15
1263 4b. Dendrobium "Sri-Siam" (horiz) 35 30
1264 5b. Dendrobium "Ekapol Panda" (horiz) 35 25

424 Chinese Mushroom

1986. Edible Fungi. Multicoloured.
1266 2b. Type **424** 50 15
1267 2b. Oyster fungus ("Pleurotus ostreatus") . . 50 15
1268 6b. Ear mushroom ("Auricularia polytricha") 1·25 30
1269 6b. Abalone mushroom ("Pleurotus cystidiosus") 1·25 30

425 Black Sharkminnow

1986. 60th Anniv of Fisheries Department. Multicoloured.
1270 2b. Type **425** 20 15
1271 2b. Blanc's knifefish ("Notopterus blanci") . . 20 15
1272 7b. Asian bonytongue ("Scleropages formosus") 55 20
1273 7b. Giant catfish ("Pangasianodon gigas") 55 20

426 Children in Playground

1987. Children's Day. Multicoloured.
1274 2b. Type **426** 20 10
1275 2b. Children in and around swimming pool 20 10
Nos. 1274/5 were printed together, se-tenant, forming a composite design showing "Our School" by Lawan Maneenetr.

427 Northrop F-5 Tiger II and General Dynamics F-16 Fighting Falcon Fighters and Pilot

1987. 72nd Anniv of Royal Thai Air Force.
1276 **427** 2b. multicoloured . . . 25 10

428 King Rama III and Temples

1987. Birth Bicentenary of King Rama III.
1277 **428** 2b. multicoloured . . . 20 10

429 Communications and Transport Systems

1987. 75th Anniv of Ministry of Communications.
1278 **429** 2b. multicoloured . . . 30 20

1987. Red Cross. No. 1065 surch **2 + 0.50 BAHT**.
1279 **333** 2b.+50s. on 75s.+25s. green and red 75 75

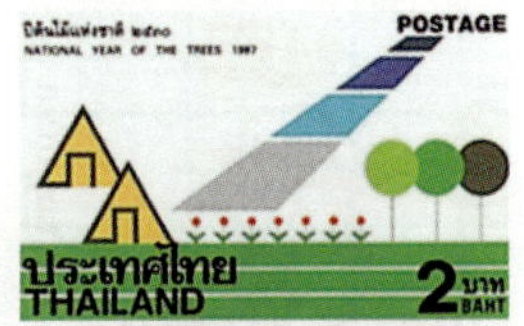

431 Tree-lined Street

1987. National Tree Year.
1280 **431** 2b. multicoloured . . . 15 10

432 Gold Peacock

1987. "Thaipex'87" National Stamp Exhibition. Handicrafts. Multicoloured.
1281 2b. Type **432** 15 10
1282 2b. Gold hand-mirrors . . . 15 10
1283 6b. Gold lustre water urn and finger bowls with trays (horiz) 30 15
1284 6b. Gold swan vase (horiz) 30 15

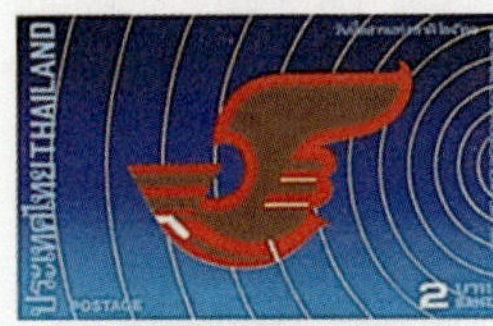

433 Flying Bird and Animal Horn (Somsak Junthavorn)

1987. National Communications Day.
1286 **433** 2b. multicoloured . . . 15 10

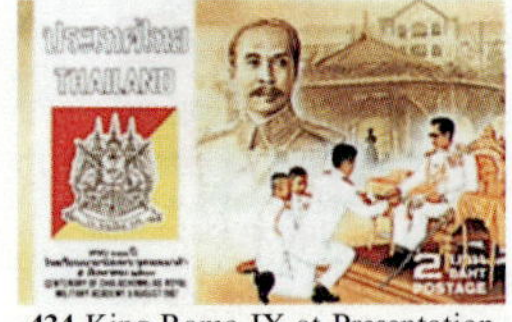

434 King Rama IX at Presentation Ceremony, King Rama V and Emblem

1987. Centenary of Chulachomklao Royal Military Academy, Khao Cha-Ngok.
1287 **434** 2b. multicoloured . . . 40 10

435 Spiral Ropes leading to Member Countries' Flags

1987. 20th Anniv of Association of South-East Asian Nations.
1288 **435** 2b. multicoloured . . . 10 10
1289 3b. multicoloured . . . 20 10
1290 4b. multicoloured . . . 30 15
1291 5b. multicoloured . . . 50 20

436 People and Open Book
437 Flower-offering Ceremony, Saraburi

1987. International Literacy Day.
1292 **436** 2b. multicoloured . . . 10 10

1987. Visit Thailand Year.
1293 2b. Type **437** 15 10
1294 3b. Duan Sib Festival (honouring ancestors), Nakhon Si Thammarat 20 10
1295 5b. Bang Fai (rain) Festival, Yasothon 30 20
1296 7b. Loi Krathong, Sukhothai 55 20

438 Ministry Building

1987. 72nd Anniv of Auditor General's Office.
1297 **438** 2b. multicoloured . . . 15 10

439 Temple of Dawn, "Sri Suphanahong" (royal barge) and Mt Fuji within "100"

1987. Centenary of Japan–Thailand Friendship Treaty.
1298 **439** 2b. multicoloured . . . 30 10

440 Tasselled Garland

1987. International Correspondence Week. Ceremonial Floral Garlands. Multicoloured.
1299 2b. Floral tassle 15 10
1300 3b. Type **440** 25 10
1301 5b. Wrist garland 30 20
1302 7b. Double-ended garland 35 25

1987. No. 1180a surch **2 BAHT**.
1303 **325** 2b. on 1b.50 orange . . 15 10

442 Thai Pavilion

1987. Inauguration of Social Education and Cultural Centre.
1304 **442** 2b. multicoloured . . . 15 10

443 King Bhumibol Adulyadej as a Boy

1987. King Bhumibol Adulyadej's 60th Birthday. Multicoloured (except 1320).
1305 2b. Type **443** 15 10
1306 2b. Wedding photograph of King Bhumibol Adulyadej and Queen Sirikit, 1950 15 10
1307 2b. King on throne during Accession ceremony at Paisan Hall, 1950 . . . . 15 10
1308 2b. King as monk on alms round 15 10
1309 2b. Elderly woman greeting King 15 10
1310 2b. King demonstrating to hill tribes how to take medicine 15 10
1311 2b. King and Queen presenting gift bag to wounded serviceman . . . 15 10
1312 2b. King examining new system for small farms . . 15 10
1314 2b. Princess Mother Somdej Phra Sri Nakarindra Boromrajjonnani 15 10
1315 2b. Crown Prince Maha Vajiralongkorn 15 10
1316 2b. Princess Maha Chakri Sirindhorn 15 10
1317 2b. Princess Chulabhorn . . 15 10
1318 2b. King Bhumibol Adulyadej and Queen Sirikit 15 10
1319 2b. King and family (48 × 33 mm) 15 10
1320 100b. gold and blue (King Bhumibol Adulyadej) (48 × 33 mm) . . . . . . 32·00 32·00

444 "Teacher's Day" (Nutchaliya Suddhiprasit)
445 Prince Kromamun Bridhyalongkorn (founder)

1988. Children's Day.
1321 **444** 2b. multicoloured . . . 15 10

1988. 72nd Anniv of Thai Co-operatives.
1322 **445** 2b. multicoloured . . . 15 10

446 Society Building

1988. 84th Anniv of Siam Society (for promotion of arts and sciences).
1323 **446** 2b. multicoloured . . . 15 10

447 Phra Phai Luang Monastery

1988. Sukhothai Historical Park. Multicoloured.
1324 2b. Type **447** 15 10
1325 3b. Traphang Thonglang Monastery 20 10
1326 4b. Maha That Monastery 30 15
1327 6b. Thewalai Maha Kaset 45 25

1988. No. 1040a surch **1 BAHT**.
1557 **325** 1b. on 1b.25 green . . . 10 10

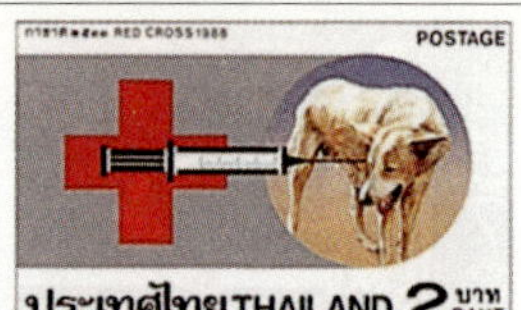

449 Syringe between Red Cross and Dog

1988. Red Cross Anti-rabies Campaign.
1329 **449** 2b. multicoloured . . . 15 10

450 King Rama V (founder)
452 Hand holding Coloured Ribbons

451 Crested Fireback Pheasant

1988. Centenary of Siriraj Hospital.
1330 **450** 5b. multicoloured . . . 50 15

1988. Pheasants. Multicoloured.
1331 2b. Type **451** 70 20
1332 3b. Kalij pheasant 80 35
1333 6b. Silver pheasant . . . . 1·40 55
1334 7b. Mrs. Hume's pheasant 1·50 65

1988. Centenary of International Women's Council.
1335 **452** 2b. multicoloured . . . 15 10

453 King Rama IX in King's Own Bodyguard Uniform
454 King Rama IX in Full Robes

1988.
1631 **453** 25s. brown 10 10
1336 50s. green 10 10
1337 1b. blue 10 10
1753 2b. red 10 10
1339 3b. blue and brown . . . 15 10
1340 4b. red and blue 20 10
1341 5b. brown and lilac . . . 25 10
1342 6b. purple and green . . 30 10
1343 7b. deep brown & brown 35 15
1344 8b. green and brown . . 40 20
1345 9b. brown and blue . . . 45 15
1346 10b. green and red . . . 50 15
1348 20b. green and orange 75 40
1350 25b. blue and green . . 90 50
1352 50b. green and lilac . . . 1·50 70
1354 100b. blue and orange 3·00 3·75

1988. 42nd Anniv of Accession to Throne of King Rama IX. Multicoloured. (a) T **454**.
1356 2b. Type **454** 75 10

(b) Royal Regalia. Size 33 × 48 mm (1357) or 48 × 33 mm (others).
1357 2b. Great Crown of Victory 15 10
1358 2b. Sword of Victory and scabbard (horiz) 15 10
1359 2b. Sceptre (horiz) 15 10
1360 2b. Royal Fan and Fly Whisk (horiz) 15 10
1361 2b. Slippers (horiz) 15 10

(c) Thrones.
1362 2b. Atthathit Uthumphon Ratchaat throne (octagonal base) 15 10
1363 2b. Phatthrabit throne (rectangular base) 15 10
1364 2b. Phuttan Kanchanasinghat throne (gold throne on angular steps) 15 10
1365 2b. Butsabokmala Mahachakkraphatphiman throne (ship shape) . . . 15 10

1366 2b. Throne inlaid with mother-of-pearl (blue throne on angular steps) 15 10
1367 2b. Peony design niello throne (circular steps) 15 10

455 Bridge, Building and Trees

1988. National Tree Year.
1369 **455** 2b. multicoloured 15 10

456 Globe and Dish Aerials

1988. National Communications Day.
1370 **456** 2b. multicoloured 15 10

458 Grasshopper

1988. International Correspondence Week. Woven Coconut-leaf Folk Toys. Multicoloured.
1371 2b. Type **458** 15 10
1372 2b. Carp 15 10
1373 6b. Bird 30 15
1374 6b. Takro 30 15

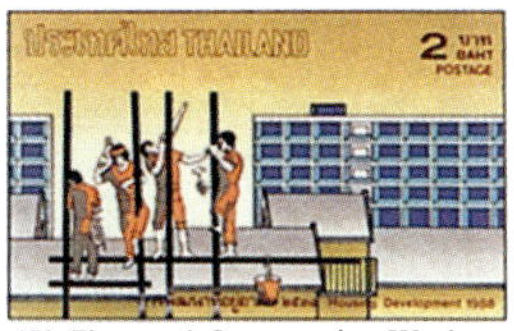

459 Flats and Construction Workers

1988. Housing Development.
1375 **459** 2b. multicoloured 15 10

460 King Rama V in Full Uniform

461 Road Signs

1988. 120th Anniv of King's Own Bodyguard.
1376 **460** 2b. multicoloured 1·10 10

1988. Road Safety Campaign.
1377 **461** 2b. multicoloured 15 10

462 "Crotalaria sessiliflora"

464 Knight Grand Commander of Honourable Order of Rama

463 Buddha's Birthplace

1988. New Year. Multicoloured.
1378 1b. Type **462** 10 10
1379 1b. "Uvaria grandiflora" 10 10
1380 1b. "Reinwardtia trigyna" 10 10
1381 1b. "Impatiens griffithii" 10 10

1988. Buddha Monthon Celebrations. Mult.
1382 2b. Type **463** 15 10
1383 3b. Buddha's place of enlightenment 15 10
1384 4b. Site of Buddha's first sermon 20 15
1385 5b. Buddha's Place of Nirvana 30 15
1386 6b. Statue of Buddha (vert) 35 20

1988. Insignia of Orders. Multicoloured.
1387 2b. Type **464** 15 10
1388 2b. Close-up of badge 15 10
1389 3b. Knight Grand Cordon (Special Class) of Most Exalted Order of the White Elephant 20 15
1390 3b. Close-up of badge 20 15
1391 5b. Knight Grand Cordon of Most Noble Order of Crown of Thailand 25 15
1392 5b. Close-up of badge 25 15
1393 7b. Close-up of Rarana Varabhorn Order of Merit 35 20
1394 7b. Badge on chain of office 35 20
Stamps of the same value were issued together, se-tenant, each pair forming a composite design.

465 "Floating Market" (Thongbai Siyam)

1989. National Children's Day. Plasticine Paintings by Blind People. Multicoloured.
1395 2b. Type **465** 30 10
1396 2b. "Flying Birds" (Kwanchai Kerd-Daeng) 20 10
1397 2b. "Little Mermaid" (Chalermpol Jiengmai) 20 10
1398 2b. "Golden Fish" (Natetip Korsantirak) 20 10

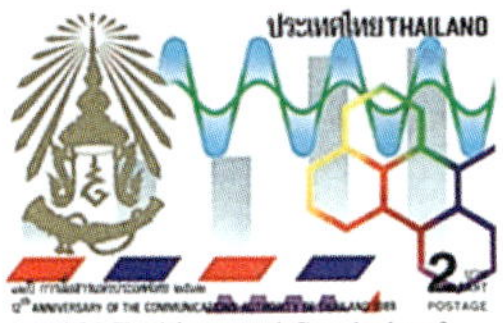

466 Emblem and Symbols of Communication

1989. 12th Anniv of Thai Communications Authority.
1399 **466** 2b. multicoloured 15 10

467 Statue of Kings Rama V and VI and Auditorium

1989. 72nd Anniv of Chulalongkorn University.
1400 **467** 2b. multicoloured 15 10

468 Red Cross Worker

469 Phra Kaeo Monastery

1989. 96th Anniv of Thai Red Cross (1401) and 125th Anniv of Int Red Cross (1402). Mult.
1401 2b. Type **468** 15 10
1402 10b. Red Cross and pillar 50 30

1989. Phra Nakhon Khiri Historical Park. Multicoloured.
1403 2b. Type **469** 15 10
1404 3b. Chatchawan Wiangchai Observatory 25 15
1405 5b. Phra That Chom Phet stupa 35 25
1406 6b. Wetchayan Wichian Phrasat Throne Hall 50 35

470 Lottery Office Building and Profit Recipients

1989. 50th Anniv of Government Lottery Office.
1407 **470** 2b. multicoloured 15 10

471 Campaign Emblem and Figures

472 Gold Nielloware Figures

1989. International Anti-drugs Day.
1408 **471** 2b. multicoloured 15 10

1989. National Arts and Crafts Year. Mult.
1409 2b. Type **472** 15 10
1410 2b. Ceramics 15 10
1411 6b. Ornament inlaid with gemstones (horiz) 30 15
1412 6b. Triangular cushion (horiz) 30 15

473 Thailand Cone

1989. Shells. Multicoloured.
1413 2b. Type **473** 15 10
1414 3b. Thorny oyster 25 15
1415 6b. Great spotted cowrie 35 20
1416 10b. Chambered nautilus 75 60

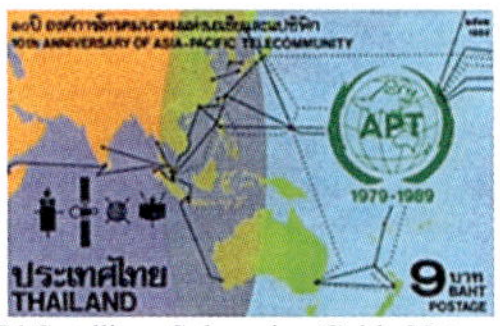

474 Satellites, Submarine Cable Network and Emblem

1989. 10th Anniv of Asia–Pacific Telecommunity.
1417 **474** 9b. multicoloured 45 20

475 Phya Anuman Rajadhon

1989. Birth Centenary (1988) of Phya Anuman Rajadhon (writer).
1418 **475** 2b. multicoloured 15 10

476 Emblem and School

1989. Centenary of Post and Telecommunications School.
1419 **476** 2b. multicoloured 15 10

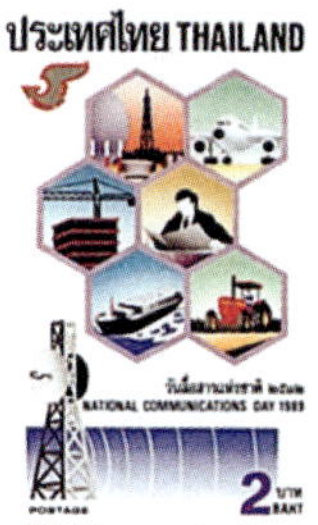

477 Communications Symbols

478 Post Box

1989. National Communications Day.
1420 **477** 2b. multicoloured 30 10

1989. "Thaipex '89" National Stamp Exhibition. Post Boxes. Multicoloured.
1421 2b. Type **478** 15 10
1422 3b. Provincial box 20 10
1423 4b. City box 25 15
1424 5b. Imported English box 30 15
1425 6b. West German box sent as gift on introduction of Thai Postal Service 30 15

479 Dragonfly

1989. Int Correspondence Week. Mult.
1426 2b. Type **479** 20 10
1427 5b. Dragonfly (different) 30 15
1428 6b. Dragonfly (different) 45 20
1429 10b. Damselfly 60 40

480 Means of Transport and Communications

1989. Asia–Pacific Transport and Communications Decade.
1431 **480** 2b. multicoloured 30 10

481 Figure and "Thoughts"

482 "Hypericum uralum"

1989. Centenary of Mental Health Care.
1432 **481** 2b. multicoloured 15 10

1989. New Year. Flowers. Multicoloured.
1433 1b. Type **482** 10 10
1434 1b. "Uraria rufescens" 10 10
1435 1b. "Manglietia garrettii" 10 10
1436 1b. "Aeschynanthus macranthus" 10 10

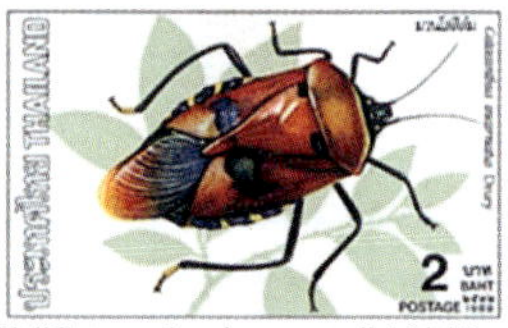

483 "Catacanthus incarnatus" (shieldbug)

1989. Beetles. Multicoloured.
1438 2b. Type **483** 20 10
1439 3b. "Aristobia approximator" 25 10
1440 6b. "Chrysochroa chinensis" 60 20
1441 10b. "Enoplotrupes sharpi" 60 50

484 Medallists on Rostrum

1989. Sports Welfare Fund. Multicoloured.
1442 2b.+1b. Type **484** 15 15
1443 2b.+1b. Nurse attending fallen cyclist 15 15
1444 2b.+1b. Boxing 15 15
1445 2b.+1b. Football 15 15

485 Official, Family and Graph

1990. Population and Housing Census.
1446 **485** 2b. multicoloured . . . 15 10

486 Skipping (Phethai Setharangsi)

1990. National Children's Day. Multicoloured.
1447 2b. Type **486** 15 10
1448 2b. Various sports activities (Chalermpol Wongpim) (vert) 15 10

487 Skull splitting Heart

488 Tiap

1990. Red Cross. Anti-AIDS Campaign.
1449 **487** 2b. blue, red and black 15 10

1990. Heritage Conservation Day. Mother-of-Pearl Inlaid Containers. Multicoloured.
1450 2b. Type **488** 15 10
1451 2b. Phan waenfa 15 10
1452 8b. Lung (horiz) 40 25
1453 8b. Chiat klom (horiz) . . . 40 25

489 Dental Students and Old Chair

490 Tin

1990. 50th Anniv of Chulalongkorn University Dentistry Faculty.
1454 **489** 2b. multicoloured . . . 15 10

1990. Minerals. Multicoloured.
1460 2b. Type **490** 15 10
1461 3b. Zinc 15 10
1462 5b. Lead 25 15
1463 6b. Fluorite 30 20

491 Pigeon

1990. National Communications Day.
1465 **491** 2b. blue, violet and purple 15 10

492 Pigeons and Envelopes

1990. 20th Anniv of Asian–Pacific Postal Training Centre, Bangkok.
1466 **492** 2b. green, blue and black 15 10
1467 8b. blue, green and black 40 30

493 Jaipur Foot Project

1990. 60th Anniv of Rotary International in Thailand. Multicoloured.
1468 2b. Type **493** 15 10
1469 3b. Child anti-polio vaccination campaign . . 15 10
1470 6b. Literacy campaign . . . 30 15
1471 8b. King Chulalongkorn and his engraved cypher (Thai Museum, Nordkapp, Norway) . . . 60 30

494 Account and Staff at Computer Terminals

1990. Centenary of Comptroller-General's Department.
1472 **494** 2b. multicoloured . . . 15 10

495 Flowers in Dish (Cho Muang)

1990. Int Correspondence Week. Mult.
1473 2b. Type **495** 15 10
1474 3b. Flowers on tray (Cha Mongkut) 20 15
1475 5b. Sweetmeats on tray with leaf design (Sane Chan) 25 20
1476 6b. Fruit in bowl (Luk Chup) 35 25

496 Princess Mother with Flower

497 "Cyrtandromoea grandiflora"

1990. 90th Birthday of Princess Mother.
1478 **496** 2b. multicoloured . . . 60 10

1990. New Year. Flowers. Multicoloured.
1479 1b. Type **497** 15 10
1480 1b. "Rhododendron arboreum sp. delavayi" 15 10
1481 1b. "Merremia vitifolia" . . 15 10
1482 1b. "Afgekia mahidolae" . . 15 10

498 Wiman Mek Royal Hall

1990. Dusit Palace. Multicoloured.
1484 2b. Type **498** 15 10
1485 3b. Ratcharit Rungrot Royal House 15 10
1486 4b. Aphisek Dusit Royal Hall 20 15
1487 5b. Amphon Sathan Palace 25 15
1488 6b. Udon Phak Royal Hall 30 20
1489 8b. Anantasamakhom Throne Hall 40 30

499 Phrachetuphon Wimolmangkalaram Temple and Supreme Patriarch

1990. Birth Bicentenary of Supreme Patriarch Somdet Phra Maha Samanachao Kromphra Paramanuchitchinorot (formerly Prince Wasukri).
1490 **499** 2b. multicoloured . . . 15 10

500 Judo

1990. Sports Welfare Fund. Multicoloured.
1491 2b.+1b. Type **500** 20 20
1492 2b.+1b. Archery 20 20
1493 2b.+1b. High jumping . . . 20 20
1494 2b.+1b. Windsurfing 20 20

501 Aspects of Petroleum Industry

1990. 12th Anniv of Thai Petroleum Authority.
1495 **501** 2b. multicoloured . . . 15 10

502 Mae Klong Railway Locomotive No. 6

1990. Steam Locomotives. Multicoloured.
1496 2b. Type **502** 25 20
1497 3b. "Sung Noen" locomotive No. 32 . . . 55 30
1498 5b. Class C 56 locomotive No. 715, Japan 75 40
1499 6b. Mikado locomotive No. 953, Japan 75 40

503 Luk Khang (tops)

1991. Children's Day. Games. Multicoloured.
1501 2b. Type **503** 15 10
1502 3b. Pid Ta Ti Mo (blindfolded child smashing vase) 15 10
1503 5b. Doen Kala (walking on stones) 25 20
1504 6b. Phong Phang (blind man's buff) 30 20

504 Map, Surveyor and Cartographer

505 Princess (patron) wearing Red Cross Uniform

1991. Land Deeds Project.
1505 **504** 2b. multicoloured 15 10

1991. Red Cross. Princess Maha Chaki Sirindhorn's "Third Cycle" (36th) Birthday.
1506 **505** 2b. multicoloured . . . 40 10

506 "Indra's Heavenly Abode"

507 Goddess riding Goat

1991. Heritage Conservation Day. Floral Hanging Decorations. Multicoloured.
1508 2b. Type **506** 15 10
1509 3b. "Celestial Couch" . . . 15 10
1510 4b. "Crystal Ladder" . . . 20 15
1511 5b. "Crocodile" 25 20

1991. Songkran (New Year) Day. Year of the Goat.
1513 **507** 2b. multicoloured . . . 90 35

508 Prince Narisranuvattivongs

1991. 44th Death Anniv of Prince Narisranuvattivongs.
1515 **508** 2b. brown, deep brown and yellow 15 10

509 Pink Lotus (Sutthiporn Wiset)

511 Yok

510 World Map, Communication Systems and Healthy Tree

1991. Runners-up in International Correspondence Week Competition. Multicoloured.
1516 2b. Type **509** 10 10
1517 3b. Pink lotuses (Mathayom Suksa group, Khonkaen-vityayon School) 15 10

1518 5b. White lotus (Rattanaporn Sukhasem) (horiz) 25 20
1519 6b. Red lotuses (Phanupongs Sayasombat and Kanokwan Cholaphum) (horiz) . . . 30 20

1991. National Communications Day. "Communications and Preservation of the Environment".
1520 **510** 2b. multicoloured . . . 10 10

1991. "Thaipex '91" National Stamp Exhibition. Textile Patterns. Multicoloured.
1521 2b. Type **511** 10 10
1522 4b. Mudmee 20 10
1523 6b. Khit 30 15
1524 8b. Chok 40 30

512 Workers and Productivity Arrow

1991. International Productivity Congress.
1526 **512** 2b. multicoloured . . . 15 10

513 "Co-operation of Women around the World"

1991. 26th Int Council of Women Triennial.
1527 **513** 2b. multicoloured . . . 15 10

514 Black

1991. International Correspondence Week. Japanese Bantams. Multicoloured.
1528 2b. Type **514** 10 10
1529 3b. Black-tailed buff 20 10
1530 6b. Buff 30 15
1531 8b. White 40 30

515 Silver Coin of King Rama IV and Wat Phra Sri Rattana Satsadaram

1991. World Bank and International Monetary Fund Annual Meetings. Multicoloured.
1533 2b. Type **515** 10 10
1534 4b. Pod Duang money, Wat Mahathat Sukhothai and Wat Aroonrachawararam 20 10
1535 8b. Chieng and Hoi money and Wat Phrathat Doi Suthep 40 25
1536 10b. Funan, Dvaravati and Srivijaya money, Phra Pathom Chedi and Phra Borommathat Chaiya . . 50 35

516 1908 1t. Stamp

518 "Dillenia obovata"

517 Adult and Calves

1991. "Bangkok 1993" International Stamp Exhibition (1st series). Stamps from the 1908 King Chulalongkorn Issue. Multicoloured.
1538 2b. Type **516** 10 10
1539 3b. 2t. stamp 15 10
1540 4b. 3t. stamp 20 15
1541 5b. 5t. stamp 25 15
1542 6b. 10t. stamp 30 15
1543 7b. 20t. stamp 35 20
1544 8b. 40t. stamp 40 25
See also Nos. 1618/22, 1666/9 and 1700/3.

1991. The Indian Elephant. Multicoloured.
1546 2b. Type **517** 10 10
1547 4b. Elephants pulling log . . 20 15
1548 6b. Adult male resting . . . 30 15
1549 8b. Adults bathing 40 25

1991. New Year. Flowers. Multicoloured.
1551 1b. Type **518** 10 10
1552 1b. "Melastoma sanguineum" 10 10
1553 1b. "Commelina diffusa" . . 10 10
1554 1b. "Plumbago indica" . . . 10 10

520 Jogging

522 Prince Mahidol

521 Large Indian Civet

1991. Sports Welfare Fund. Multicoloured.
1558 2b.+1b. Type **520** 15 15
1559 2b.+1b. Cycling 15 15
1560 2b.+1b. Skipping 15 15
1561 2b.+1b. Swimming 15 15

1991. Mammals. Multicoloured.
1562 2b. Type **521** 10 10
1563 3b. Banded linsang 15 10
1564 6b. Asiatic golden cat . . . 30 15
1565 8b. Black giant squirrel . . 40 30

1992. Birth Centenary (1991) of Prince Mahidol of Songkla (pioneer of modern medicine in Thailand).
1567 **522** 2b. brown, gold & yellow 15 10

523 Archaeologists and Dinosaur Skeletons

1992. Centenary of Department of Mineral Resources. Multicoloured.
1568 2b. Type **523** 10 10
1569 2b. Mining excavation . . . 10 10
1570 2b. Extracting natural gas and oil 30 10
1571 2b. Digging artesian wells 10 10

524 Drawing by Nachadong Bunprasoet

1992. Children's Day. "World under the Sea". Children's Drawings. Multicoloured.
1572 2b. Type **524** 15 10
1573 3b. Fishes and seaweed (Varaporn Phadkhan) . . 15 10
1574 5b. Mermaid (Phannipha Ngoenkon) (vert) 35 20

525 Battle Scene (mural, Chan Chittrakon)

1992. 400th Anniv of Duel between King Naresuan the Great of Thailand and Phra Maha Upparacha of Burma.
1575 **525** 2b. multicoloured . . . 15 10

526 "Paphiopedilum bellatulum"

1992. 4th Asia–Pacific Orchid Conf. Mult.
1576 2b. Type **526** 10 10
1577 2b. "Paphiopedilum exul" 10 10
1578 3b. "Paphiopedilum godefroyae" 15 10
1579 3b. "Paphiopedilum concolor" 15 10
1580 6b. "Paphiopedilum niveum" 30 15
1581 6b. "Paphiopedilum villosum" 30 15
1582 10b. "Paphiopedilum parishii" 50 35
1583 10b. "Paphiopedilum sukhahulii" 50 35

527 Sugar Cane

528 Prince Rabi Badhanasakdi (founder of School of Law)

1992. 21st International Sugar Cane Technologists Society Congress.
1585 **527** 2b. multicoloured . . . 15 10

1992. Centenary of Ministry of Justice. Legal Reformers. Multicoloured.
1586 3b. Type **528** 15 10
1587 5b. King Rama V (reformer of Courts system) 25 15

529 "Innocent" (Kamolporn Tapsuang)

1992. Red Cross.
1588 **529** 2b. multicoloured . . . 15 10

530 Container Ships and Lorry

531 Prince Damrong Rajanubharb (first Minister)

1992. 80th Anniv of Ministry of Transport and Communications. Multicoloured.
1589 2b. Type **530** 20 10
1590 3b. Diesel train and bus . . 25 15
1591 5b. Boeing 747-200 airliner and control tower 25 15
1592 6b. Lorry, satellites and aerials 30 20

1992. Cent of Ministry of the Interior. Mult.
1593 2b. Type **531** 10 10
1594 2b. Polling station 10 10
1595 2b. Emergency services and army 10 10
1596 2b. Child fetching water . . 10 10

532 Royal Ceremony of First Ploughing

1992. Centenary of Ministry of Agriculture and Co-operatives.
1597 **532** 2b. multicoloured . . . 10 10
1598 3b. multicoloured . . . 15 10
1599 4b. multicoloured . . . 20 15
1600 5b. multicoloured . . . 25 20

533 Ministry

535 Demon riding Monkey

534 Western Region

1992. Centenary of Ministry of Education.
1601 **533** 2b. multicoloured . . . 10 10

1992. Thai Heritage Conservation Day. Traditional Carts. Multicoloured.
1602 2b. Type **534** 10 10
1603 3b. Northern region 15 10
1604 5b. North-eastern region . . 25 15
1605 10b. Eastern region 50 35

1992. Songkran (New Year) Day. Year of the Monkey.
1607 **535** 2b. multicoloured . . . 10 10

536 American Brahman and Livestock

1992. 50th Anniv of Department of Livestock Development.
1609 **536** 2b. multicoloured . . . 10 10

537 Birth of Buddha (mural, Wat Angkaeo, Bangkok)

538 Weather Balloon, Dish Aerial, Satellite and Map

1992. Wisakhabucha Day. Multicoloured.
1610 2b. Type **537** 10 10
1611 3b. "Enlightenment of Buddha" (illustration by Phraya Thewaphinimmit from biography) 20 15
1612 5b. Death of Buddha (mural, Wat Kanmatuyaram, Bangkok) 25 20

1992. 50th Anniv of Meteorological Department.
1613 **538** 2b. multicoloured . . . 10 10

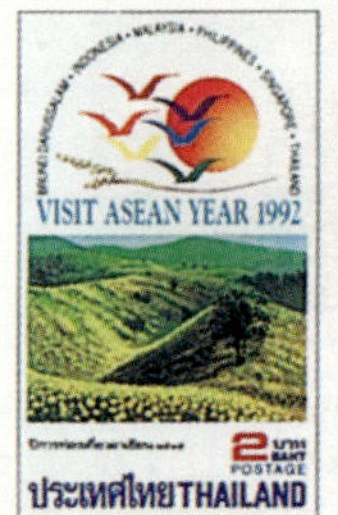

539 Bua Tong Field, Mae Hong Son Province

540 1887 64a. stamp

1992. Association of South-East Asian Nations Tourism Year. Multicoloured.

1614	2b. Type **539**	10	10
1615	3b. Klong Larn Waterfall, Kamphaeng Phet Province	15	10
1616	4b. Coral, Chumphon Province	20	15
1617	5b. Khao Ta-Poo, Phangnga Province	30	20

1992. "Bangkok 1993" International Stamp Exhibition (2nd series). Multicoloured.

1618	2b. Type **540**	10	10
1619	3b. 1916 20b. stamp	15	10
1620	5b. 1928 40b. stamp	25	15
1621	7b. 1943 1b. stamp	35	20
1622	8b. 1947 20b. stamp	40	25

541 Prince Chudadhuj Dharadilok

543 Culture and Sports

542 "Communications"

1992. Birth Centenary of Prince Chudadhuj Dharadilok of Bejraburna.

1624	**541** 2b. multicoloured	10	10

1992. National Communications Day.

1625	**542** 2b. multicoloured	10	10

1992. 25th Anniv of Association of South-East Asian Nations. Multicoloured.

1626	2b. Type **543**	10	10
1627	3b. Tourist sites	15	10
1628	5b. Transport and communications	35	15
1629	7b. Agriculture	35	20

544 Sirikit Medical Centre

1992. Inauguration of Sirikit Medical Centre.

1630	**544** 2b. multicoloured	10	10

545 Wedding Ceremony

546 Queen Sirikit and Cipher

1992. 60th Birthday of Queen Sirikit. (a) As T **545**. Multicoloured.

1635	2b. Type **545**	10	10
1636	2b. Royal couple seated at Coronation ceremony	10	10
1637	2b. Anointment as Queen	10	10
1638	2b. Seated on chair	10	10
1639	2b. Visiting hospital patient	10	10
1640	2b. Talking to subjects	10	10

(b) Royal Regalia. Enamelled gold objects. As T **546**. Multicoloured.

1642	2b. Bowls on footed tray (betel and areca nut set)	10	10
1643	2b. Kettle	10	10
1644	2b. Water holder within bowl	10	10
1645	2b. Box on footed tray (betel and areca nut set)	10	10
1646	2b. Vase	10	10

(c) Type **546**.

1647	100b. blue and gold	4·00	4·00

547 Prince Wan Waithayakon

548 Bhirasri

1992. Birth Centenary (1991) of Prince Wan Waithayakon, Krommun Naradhip Bongsprabandh (diplomat).

1648	**547** 2b. multicoloured	10	10

1992. Birth Centenary of Silpa Bhirasri (sculptor).

1649	**548** 2b. multicoloured	10	10

549 "Catalaphyllia jardinei"

1992. Int Correspondence Week. Corals. Mult.

1650	2b. Type **549**	10	10
1651	3b. "Porites lutea"	15	10
1652	6b. "Tubastraea coccinea"	30	20
1653	8b. "Favia pallida"	40	30

550 "Rhododendron simsii"

551 Figures of Man and Woman

1992. New Year. Flowers. Multicoloured.

1655	1b. Type **550**	10	10
1656	1b. "Cynoglossum lanceolatum"	10	10
1657	1b. "Tithonia diversifolia"	10	10
1658	1b. "Agapetes parishii"	10	10

1992. 1st Asian–Pacific Allergy and Immunology Congress, Bangkok.

1660	**551** 2b. multicoloured	10	10

552 Anantasamakhom Throne Hall, National Assembly Building and King Prajadhipok's Monument

1992. 60th Anniv of National Assembly.

1661	**552** 2b. multicoloured	10	10

553 Bank's Emblem and Bang Khun Phrom Palace (old headquarters)

1992. 50th Anniv of Bank of Thailand.

1662	**553** 2b. multicoloured	10	10

554 "River and Life" (Prathinthip Mensin)

1993. Children's Day. Drawings. Mult.

1663	2b. Type **554**	15	10
1664	2b. "Lovely Wild Animals and Beautiful Forest" (Pratsani Thammaprasert)	15	10
1665	2b. "Communications in the Next Decade" (Natchaliya Sutiprasit)	45	15

555 Kendi, Water Dropper and Bottle

1993. "Bangkok 1993" International Stamp Exn (3rd series). Traditional Pottery. Multicoloured.

1666	3b. Type **555**	15	10
1667	6b. Vase and bottles	30	20
1668	7b. Bowls	35	20
1669	8b. Jars	40	25

556 Anniversary Emblem

1993. Centenary of Thai Teacher Training Institute.

1671	**556** 2b. multicoloured	10	10

557 Agricultural Produce

1993. 50th Anniv of Kasetsart University.

1672	**557** 2b. multicoloured	10	10

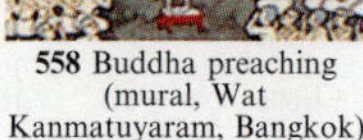

558 Buddha preaching (mural, Wat Kanmatuyaram, Bangkok)

559 Queen Sri Bajarindra (first royal patron)

1993. Maghapuja Day.

1673	**558** 2b. multicoloured	10	10

1993. Centenary of Thai Red Cross.

1674	**559** 2b. multicoloured	10	10

560 Clock, Emblem and Attorney General

1993. Centenary of Attorney General's Office.

1675	**560** 2b. multicoloured	15	10

561 Wat Chedi Chet Thaeo

1993. Thai Heritage Conservation Day. Si Satchanalai Historical Park, Sukhothai Province. Mult.

1676	3b. Type **561**	15	10
1677	4b. Wat Chang Lom	20	15
1678	6b. Wat Phra Si Rattanamahathat	30	20
1679	7b. Wat Suan Kaeo Utthayan Noi	40	20

562 Demon riding Cock

1993. Songkran (New Year) Day. Year of the Cock.

1681	**562** 2b. multicoloured	10	10

563 "Marasmius sp."

1993. Fungi. Multicoloured.

1683	2b. Type **563**	15	10
1684	4b. "Coprinus sp."	30	20
1685	6b. "Mycena sp."	45	25
1686	8b. "Cyathus sp."	65	30

564 "Communications in the Next Decade"

1993. National Communications Day.

1688	**564** 2b. multicoloured	30	10

565 Emblem, Morse Key and Satellite

1993. 110th Anniv of Post and Telegraph Department.

1689	**565** 2b. multicoloured	10	10

566 Monument, Park and Reservoir

1993. Unveiling of Queen Suriyothai's Monument.

1690	**566** 2b. multicoloured	10	10

567 Fawn Ridgeback

1993. International Correspondence Week. The Thai Ridgeback. Multicoloured.

1691	2b. Type **567**	10	10
1692	3b. Black	15	10
1693	5b. Tan	25	15
1694	10b. Grey	50	30

568 Tangerine

569 Bencharong Cosmetic Jar

1993. Fruits. Multicoloured.

1696	2b. Type **568**	10	10
1697	3b. Bananas	15	10
1698	6b. Star gooseberry	30	15
1699	8b. Marian plum	40	25

1993. "Bangkok 1993" International Stamp Exhibition (4th issue). Multicoloured.

1700	3b. Type **569**	15	10
1701	5b. Bencharong round cosmetic jar	25	15
1702	6b. Lai Nam Thong tall cosmetic jar	30	20
1703	7b. Lai Nam Thong cosmetic jar	35	20

570 Emblem and Oil Rigs

1993. 5th Association of South East Asian Nations Council on Petroleum Conference and Exhibition.

1706	**570** 2b. multicoloured	10	10

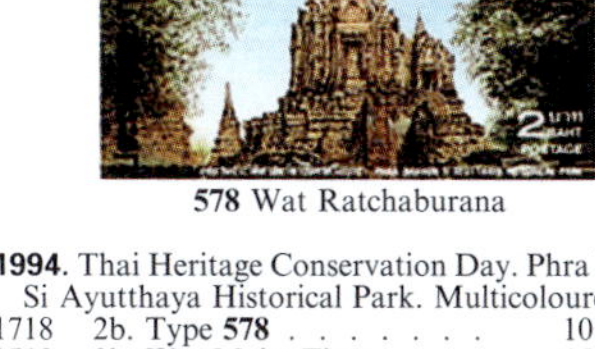

571 King Prajadhipok

572 "Ipomea cairica"

1993. Birth Centenary of King Prajadhipok (Rama VII).

1707	**571** 2b. brown and gold	15	10

1993. New Year. Flowers. Multicoloured.

1708	1b. Type **572**	10	10
1709	1b. "Decaschistia parviflora"	10	10
1710	1b. "Hibiscus tiliaceus"	10	10
1711	1b. "Passiflora foetida"	10	10

1993. No. 1031a surch **1 BAHT**.

1713	**227** 1b. on 25s. red	10	10

574 "Thaicom-1" Satellite, "Ariane 4" Rocket and Map of Thailand

1993. Launch of "Thaicom-1" (1st Thai communications satellite).

1714	**574** 2b. multicoloured	10	10

575 "Play Land" (Piyathida Chapirom)

1994. Children's Day.

1715	**575** 2b. multicoloured	10	10

576 Hospital Administrative Building

1994. Red Cross. 80th Anniv of Chulalongkorn Hospital.

1716	**576** 2b. multicoloured	10	10

577 Emblem and Book

1994. 60th Anniv of Royal Institute.

1717	**577** 2b. multicoloured	10	10

578 Wat Ratchaburana

1994. Thai Heritage Conservation Day. Phra Nakhon Si Ayutthaya Historical Park. Multicoloured.

1718	2b. Type **578**	10	10
1719	3b. Wat Maha That	15	10
1720	6b. Wat Maheyong	30	20
1721	9b. Wat Phra Si Sanphet	45	30

579 Friendship Bridge

1994. Inauguration of Friendship Bridge (between Thailand and Laos).

1723	**579** 9b. multicoloured	45	30

580 Demon riding Dog

1994. Songkran (New Year) Day. Year of the Dog.

1724	**580** 2b. multicoloured	10	10

582 Football

1994. Centenary of Int Olympic Committee. Mult.

1727	2b. Type **582**	10	10
1728	3b. Running	15	10
1729	5b. Swimming	25	15
1730	6b. Weightlifting	30	20
1731	9b. Boxing	45	30

583 Dome Building

1994. 60th Anniv of Thammasat University.

1732	**583** 2b. multicoloured	10	10

584 "Buddha giving First Sermon" (mural from Wat Thong Thammachat)

1994. Asalhapuja Day.

1733	**584** 2b. multicoloured	10	10

585 Communications orbiting Thailand

1994. National Communications Day.

1734	**585** 2b. multicoloured	10	10

586 "Phricotelphusa limula"

1994. Crabs. Multicoloured.

1735	3b. Type **586**	15	10
1736	5b. "Thaipotamon chulabhorn"	25	15
1737	6b. "Phricotelphusa sirindhorn"	30	20
1738	10b. "Thaiphusa sirikit"	50	30

587 Gold Niello Betel Nut Set

1994. International Correspondence Week. Betel Nut Sets.

1740	2b. Type **587**	10	10
1741	6b. Gold-plated silver niello set	30	20
1742	8b. Silver niello set	40	25
1743	9b. Gold niello set	45	25

588 Emblem and Workers

1994. 75th Anniv of I.L.O.

1745	**588** 2b. multicoloured	10	10

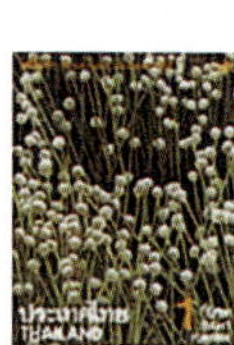

589 "Eriocaulon odoratum"

1994. New Year. Flowers. Multicoloured.

1746	1b. Type **589**	10	10
1747	1b. "Utricularia bifida"	10	10
1748	1b. "Utricularia delphinioides"	10	10
1749	1b. "Utricularia minutissima"	10	10

590 Making Garland

1994. 60th Anniv of Suan Dusit Teachers' College.

1751	**590** 2b. multicoloured	10	10

591 Chakri Mahaprasart Throne Hall and Kings Chulalongkorn and Bhumibol

1994. 120th Anniv of Council of State.

1754	**591** 2b. stone, blue and green	10	10

592 Emblem and Airplane

1994. 50th Anniv of I.C.A.O.

1755	**592** 2b. multicoloured	10	10

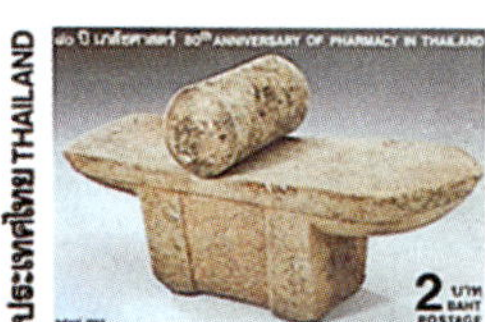

593 Dvaravati Grinding Stone (7–11th century)

1994. 80th Anniv of Pharmacy in Thailand.

1756	2b. Type **593**	10	10
1757	6b. Lopburi grinding stone (11–13th century)	30	20
1758	9b. Bangkok period grinding stone (18–20th century)	45	30

594 Water Polo

1994. 18th South-East Asian Games, Chiang Mai. Multicoloured.

1759	2b.+1b. Type **594**	15	10
1760	2b.+1b. Tennis	15	10
1761	2b.+1b. Hurdling	15	10
1762	2b.+1b. Gymnastics	15	10

595 First Bar Building and Kings Vajiravudh and Bhumibol

1995. 80th Anniv of the Bar.

1764	**595** 2b. multicoloured	10	10

596 "Kites decorate the Summer Sky" (Kontorn Taechoran)

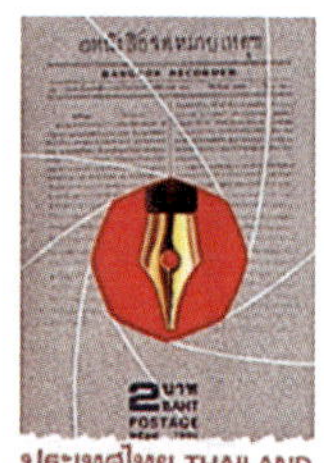

597 Front Page of First Edition and Pen Nib in Camera Shutter

1995. Children's Day. Multicoloured.

1765	2b. Type **596**	10	10
1766	2b. "Trees and Streams" (Yuvadee Samutpong) (horiz)	10	10
1767	2b. "Youths and Religion" (Yutdanai Polyium) (horiz)	10	10

1995. 150th Anniv of "Bangkok Recorder" (newspaper).

1768 **597** 2b. multicoloured . . . 10 10

598 Breguet Biplane and General Dynamics Fighting Falcon Jet Fighter

1995. 80th Anniv of Royal Thai Airforce.

1769 **598** 2b. multicoloured . . . 10 10

599 "Wetchapha"

1995. Red Cross. 40th Anniv of "Wetchapha" (hospital ship).

1770 **599** 2b. multicoloured . . . 10 10

600 Naga Bridge

1995. Thai Heritage Conservation Day. Phimai Historical Park. Multicoloured.

1771	3b. Type **600**	15	10
1772	5b. Brahmin Hall	25	15
1773	6b. Gateway in inner wall	30	20
1774	9b. Main pagoda	45	30

601 Administration Hall

1995. 108th Anniv of Ministry of Defence.

1776 **601** 2b. multicoloured . . . 10 10

602 Woman riding Boar

1995. Songkran (New Year) Day.

1777 **602** 2b. multicoloured . . . 10 10

603 King Rama V and Saranrom Palace

1995. 120th Anniv of Ministry of Foreign Affairs.

1779 **603** 2b. multicoloured . . . 10 10

604 Emerald Buddha

605 Emblem forming Flower and Globe

1995. Visakhapuja Day. Statues of Buddha. Multicoloured.

1780	2b. Type **604**	10	10
1781	6b. Phra Phuttha Chinnarat	30	20
1782	8b. Phra Phuttha Sihing	40	25
1783	9b. Phra Sukhothai Traimit	45	30

1995. Association of South East Asian Nations Environment Year.

1785 **605** 2b. multicoloured . . . 10 10

606 Emblem

1995. Thailand Information Technology Year.

1786 **606** 2b. multicoloured . . . 10 10

607 Asian Elephants and Young

1995. 20th Anniv of Thailand–China Diplomatic Relations. Multicoloured.

1787	2b. Type **607**	10	10
1788	2b. Asian elephants at river (face value at left)	10	10

Nos. 1787/8 were issued together, se-tenant, forming a composite design.

608 Optical Fibre Cables

1995. National Communications Day.

1790 **608** 2b. multicoloured . . . 10 10

609 Khoa Manee

610 Headquarters

1995. "Thaipex'95" National Stamp Exhibition. Cats. Multicoloured.

1791	3b. Type **609**	15	10
1792	6b. Korat	30	20
1793	7b. Sealpoint Siamese	35	20
1794	9b. Burmese	45	30

1995. 80th Anniv of Revenue Department.

1796 **610** 2b. multicoloured . . . 10 10

611 Money and Industry

1995. 120th Anniv of National Auditing.

1797 **611** 2b. multicoloured . . . 10 10

612 Khong

1995. International Correspondence Week. Wicker Aquatic Animal Baskets.

1798	2b. Type **612**	10	10
1799	2b. Krachangklom (round basket)	10	10
1800	9b. Sum (open-ended basket)	45	30
1801	9b. Ichu (jar)	45	30

613 Foodstuffs and Anniversary Emblem

1995. 50th Anniv of F.A.O.

1803 **613** 2b. multicoloured . . . 10 10

614 Telescope and Eclipse

1995. Total Solar Eclipse.

1804 **614** 2b. multicoloured . . . 10 10

615 U.N. Building, Thailand

1995. 50th Anniv of U.N.O.

1805 **615** 2b. multicoloured . . . 10 10

616 Tower

617 "Adenium obesum"

1995. "WORLDTECH'95" International Agricultural and Industrial Exhibition, Suranaree. Multicoloured.

1806	2b. Type **616**	10	10
1807	5b. Agriculture	25	15
1808	6b. Modern technology (horiz)	30	15
1809	9b. Reservoirs and coastline (horiz)	45	30

1996. New Year. Flowers. Multicoloured.

1810	2b. Type **617**	10	10
1811	2b. "Bauhinia acuminata"	10	10
1812	2b. "Cananga odorata"	10	10
1813	2b. "Thunbergia erecta"	10	10

618 Vaccinating Cattle

1995. 60th Anniv of Veterinary Science in Thailand.

1815 **618** 2b. multicoloured . . . 10 10

619 Fencing

620 Queen Somdej Phra Sri Patcharin (founder)

1996. 18th South-East Asian Games, Chiang Mai. Multicoloured.

1816	2b.+1b. Type **619**	15	10
1817	2b.+1b. Snooker	15	10
1818	2b.+1b. Diving	15	10
1819	2b.+1b. Pole vaulting	15	10

Nos. 1815/18 were issued together, se-tenant, forming a composite design.

1996. Centenary of Siriraj School of Nursing and Midwifery.

1821 **620** 2b. multicoloured . . . 10 10

621 Breguet Biplane and Emblem

1996. National Aviation Day.

1822 **621** 2b. multicoloured . . . 10 10

622 "Visakhapuja Day" (Malinee Sanaewong)

1996. Children's Day. Children's Drawings. Multicoloured.

1823	2b. Type **622**	10	10
1824	2b. "Maghapuja Day" (Thirapon Deephlub) (tree in centre) (vert)	10	10
1825	2b. "Asalhapuja Day" (Voraphat Pankian) (tree at left) (vert)	10	10

623 Handshake and Map of Asia and Europe

1996. Asia–Europe Summit Meeting, Thailand.

1826 **623** 2b. multicoloured . . . 10 10

624 Temiyajataka

1996. Maghapuja Day. Multicoloured.

1827	2b. Type **624**	10	10
1828	6b. Mahajanakajataka	30	15
1829	8b. Suvannasamjataka	40	25
1830	9b. Nemijataka	45	30

625 Princess Mother and Golden Crematorium

1996. Princess Mother's Cremation.

1832 **625** 2b. multicoloured . . . 10 10

626 Wat Phra Kaeo

1996. Thai Heritage Conservation Day. Kamphaeng Phet Historical Park. Multicoloured.
1833 2b. Type **626** 10 10
1834 3b. Wat Phra Non 15 10
1835 6b. Wat Chang Rop 30 15
1836 9b. Wat Pgra Si Iriyabot . . 45 30

627 Buddhist Pagoda, Wat Chiang Man

1996. 700th Anniv of Chiang Mai. Multicoloured.
1838 2b. Type **627** 10 10
1839 6b. Angel sculpture, Wat Chet Yot's Pagoda . . . 30 15
1840 8b. Insignia of Wat Phan Tao monastery 40 25
1841 9b. Sattaphanta 45 30

628 Rufous-necked Hornbills

629 Angel riding Rat

1996. 2nd International Asian Hornbill Workshop. Multicoloured.
1843 3b. Type **628** 15 10
1844 3b. Long-crested hornbill ("White-crowned Hornbill") 15 10
1845 9b. Blyth's hornbill ("Plain-pouched Hornbill") . . . 45 30
1846 9b. Rhinoceros hornbill . . 45 30

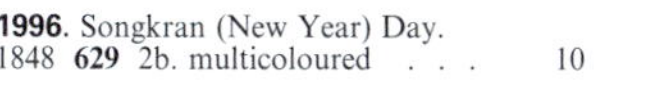

1996. Songkran (New Year) Day.
1848 **629** 2b. multicoloured . . . 10 10

630 Royal Ablutions Ceremony

631 King Bhumibol

1996. 50th Anniv of King Bhumibol's Accession to Throne as Rama IX (1st issue). Multicoloured.
(a) Coronation Ceremony. Multicoloured.
1851 3b. Type **630** 15 10
1852 3b. Pouring of the Libation 15 10
1853 3b. Grand Audience 15 10
1854 3b. Royal Progress by land 15 10
1855 3b. Making speech from balcony 15 10

(b) Royal Regalia. As T **630**.
1857 3b. Betal and areca-nut set 15 10
1858 3b. Water urn 15 10
1859 3b. Gold-enamelled cuspidor and golden spittoon (horiz) 15 10

(c) National Development. As T **630** but horiz.
1861 3b. Cultivation of vetiver grass (prevention of soil erosion) 15 10
1862 3b. Chai Pattana aerator (improvement of water quality) 15 10
1863 3b. Airplane (rain-making project) 15 10
1864 3b. Dam (water resources development) 15 10
1865 3b. Sapling (Golden Jubilee Reforestation Campaign) 15 10

(d) Type **631**.
1867 100b. multicoloured . . . . 3·75 3·25
See also No. 1885.

632 Baron Pierre de Coubertin (founder) and Grave

633 King Bhumibol using Short-wave Radio

1996. Centenary of Modern Olympic Games. Multicoloured.
1868 2b. Type **632** 10 10
1869 3b. Lighting Olympic flame at Olympia, Greece . . . 15 10
1870 5b. First modern Games and Olympic flag 25 15
1871 9b. Athlete and medal from 1896 Games 45 30

1996. National Communications Day.
1872 **633** 2b. multicoloured . . . 10 10

634 Tropical Rain Forest

1996. Centenary of Royal Forest Department. Multicoloured.
1873 3b. Type **634** 15 10
1874 6b. Evergreen mountain forest 30 15
1875 7b. Swamp forest 35 20
1876 9b. Mangrove forest 45 30

635 "Ramayana"

1996. International Correspondence Week. Thai Novels. Multicoloured.
1878 3b. Type **635** 15 10
1879 3b. Inao and Budsaba in cave ("Inao") 15 10
1880 9b. Lunhap being shown round forest ("Ngao Pa") 45 30
1881 9b. The cursing of Nang Mathanal ("Mathanapatha") . . . 45 30

636 Youth Activities

1996. Asia Regional Conference of Rotary International, Thailand.
1883 **636** 2b. multicoloured . . . 10 10

637 Huoy Kha Khang National Park

1996. 50th Anniv of U.N.E.S.C.O.
1884 **637** 2b. multicoloured . . . 10 10

638 "Narai Song Suban H.M. King Rama IX" (new royal barge) (½-size illustration)

1996. 50th Anniv of King Bhumibol's Accession to Throne as Rama IX (2nd issue). Multicoloured.
1885 **638** 9b. multicoloured . . . 40 25

639 "Limnocharis flava"

640 Indian Whistling Duck ("Dendrocygna javanica")

1996. New Year. Flowers. Multicoloured.
1887 2b. Type **639** 10 10
1888 2b. "Crinum thaianum" (vert) 10 10
1889 2b. "Monochoria hastata" (vert) 10 10
1890 2b. "Nymphoides indicum" 10 10

1996. Water Birds. Multicoloured.
1892 3b. Type **640** 15 10
1893 3b. Comb duck ("Sarkidiornis melanotos") (horiz) . . . 15 10
1894 7b. Cotton teal ("Nettapus coromandelianus") (horiz) 35 20
1895 7b. White-winged wood duck ("Cairina scutulata") 35 20

641 King Rama IX in Admiral's Uniform

1996.
2005 **641** 50s. green 10 10
1897 2b. red 10 10
2077 2b. red 10 10
2078 4b. red and blue . . . 20 10
1900 5b. red and lilac . . . 25 15
2079 5b. brown and violet . . 25 15
1901 6b. lilac and green . . 30 20
1902 7b. green and pink . . 35 20
1902a 9b. orange and blue . . 40 25
1903 10b. black and orange . . 45 30
1903a 12b. blue and green . . 55 25
1903b 15b. green and brown . . 65 30
1904 20b. red and violet . . 75 50
1905 25b. olive and green . . 80 40
1905a 30b. brown and pink . . 90 30
1906 50b. green and violet . . 1·60 55
1907 100b. blue and yellow . . 3·25 55
1908 200b. purple and mauve . 6·50 1·00
1909 500b. mauve and orange (26 × 31mm) . . 14·00 2·50

642 Children at Zoo (Ruangchai Khot-Tha)

1996. 50th Anniv of U.N.I.C.E.F.
1910 **642** 2b. multicoloured . . . 10 10

643 Medal, Flag and Boxers

1996. 1st Thai Olympic Gold Medal (won by Somluck Khamsingh for boxing at Atlanta, U.S.A.).
1911 **643** 6b. multicoloured . . . 30 20

644 School, King Rama V and Crown Prince Vajiravudh (Rama VI)

645 "Good Things in my Province" (Natamol Thongsai)

1997. Centenary of Mahavajiravudh School, Songkhla.
1912 **644** 62b. multicoloured . . . 10 10

1997. Children's Day. Children's Drawings. Multicoloured.
1913 2b. Type **645** (dried fish, Samut Prakan) 10 10
1914 2b. "Tourist Sites in my Province", Chanthaburi (Somkiat Thongchomphu) 10 10

646 Old and New Buildings

1997. 20th Anniv of Communications Authority.
1915 **646** 2b. multicoloured . . . 10 10

647 Statue

1997. Unveiling of Statue of Prince Bhanurangsi (founder of postal service) outside Communications Authority, Laksi (Bangkok).
1916 **647** 2b. multicoloured . . . 10 10

648 Building

1997. Laksi Mail Centre. Multicoloured.
1917 2b. Type **648** 10 10
1918 2b. Letter sorting equipment 10 10
Nos. 1917/18 were issued together, se-tenant, forming a composite design.

649 Windsor Palace (University building)

1997. 80th Anniv of Chulalongkorn University. Multicoloured.
1919 2b. Type **649** 10 10
1920 2b. Faculty of Arts building 10 10

650 Early Steam Locomotive

1997. Cent of Thai State Railway. Mult.
1921 3b. Type **650** 15 10
1922 4b. Garratt steam locomotive 20 10
1923 6b. Sulzer diesel-mechanic locomotive 30 20
1924 7b. Hitachi diesel-electric locomotive 35 20

651 Rajakarun Museum

1997. Red Cross.
1926 **651** 3b. multicoloured . . . 15 10

652 First Headquarters

1997. 84th Anniv of Government Savings Bank.
1927 **652** 2b. multicoloured . . . 10 10

653 Outer Staircase

1997. Thai Heritage Conservation Day. Phanomrung Historical Park. Multicoloured.
1928 3b. Type **653** 15 10
1929 3b. Pavilion 15 10
1930 7b. Pathway and stairs to Sanctuary 35 20
1931 7b. Naga balustrade and Eastern Gallery central gate 35 20

654 Man riding Bull

1997. Songkran (New Year) Day. Year of the Bull.
1933 **654** 2b. multicoloured . . . 10 10

655 Pheasant-tailed Jacana

1997. Water Birds. Multicoloured.
1935 3b. Type **655** 15 10
1936 3b. Bronze-winged jacana 15 10
1937 7b. Painted stork 35 20
1938 7b. Black-winged stilt . . . 35 20

656 Suthee Aerial and King Bhumibol using Radio

1997. Telecommunications. Multicoloured.
1940 2b. Type **656** 10 10
1941 3b. King using hand-held radio and various radios 15 10
1942 6b. King using computer . . 25 15
1943 9b. King, schoolchildren and "Thaicom" satellite (expanding secondary education to rural areas using satellite technology) 35 20

657 First Thai Cinema Advertisement, Equipment and Prince Sanbassatra

1997. Cent of Cinema in Thailand. Mult.
1945 3b. King Prajadhipok filming and King Chulalongkorn's state visit to Europe, 1897 (first film documenting Thai history) 15 10
1946 3b. Type **657** 15 10
1947 7b. Poster for "Double Luck" (first movie with Thai producer) and band outside cinema 30 20
1948 7b. Open-air cinema and poster for "Going Astray" (first Thai sound film) . . 30 20

658 King Ananda Mahidol (Rama VIII) (founder), Building and Operation

1997. 50th Anniv of Faculty of Medicine, Chulalongkorn University.
1949 **658** 2b. multicoloured . . . 10 10

659 Peterhof Palace and King Chulalongkorn

1997. Centenary of Thailand–Russia Diplomatic Relations and State Visit of King Chulalongkorn (Rama V) to Russia.
1950 **659** 2b. multicoloured . . . 10 10

660 Mahosathajataka

1997. Asalhapuja Day. Designs illustrating ten Jataka stories. Multicoloured.
1951 3b. Type **660** 15 10
1952 4b. Bhuridattajataka 15 10
1953 6b. Candakumarajataka . . 25 15
1954 7b. Naradajataka 30 20

661 Northern Region

1997. "Thaipex 97" Stamp Exhibition. Traditional Houses. Multicoloured.
1956 2b. Type **661** 10 10
1957 5b. Central region 20 10
1958 6b. North-eastern region . . 25 15
1959 9b. Southern region 35 20

662 Cape Blue Water-lily ("Nymphaea capensis")

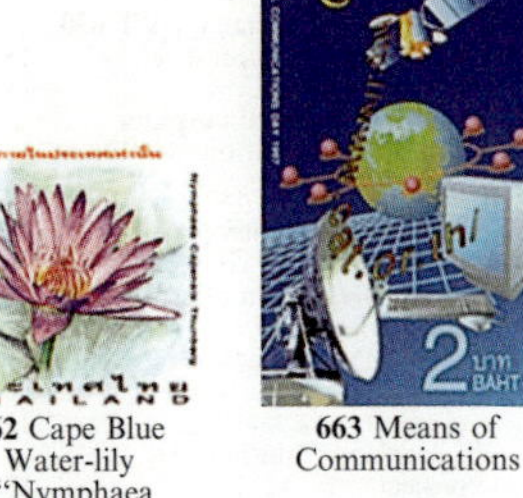
663 Means of Communications

1997. Greetings booklet stamps. No value indicated. Multicoloured.
1961 (2b.) Type **662** 10 10
1962 (2b.) Indian lotus ("Nymphaea stellata") . . 10 10

1997. National Communications Day.
1963 **663** 2b. multicoloured . . . 10 10

664 Luang Chiang Dao Mountain, Chiang Mai

1997. 30th Anniv of Association of South-East Asian Nations. Tourist Sights. Multicoloured.
1964 2b. Type **664** 10 10
1965 2b. Thi Lo Su Falls, Tak . . 10 10
1966 9b. Thalu Island, Chumphon 35 20
1967 9b. Phromthep Cape, Phuket 35 20

665 "Phuwiangosaurus sirindhornae"

1997. Dinosaurs. Multicoloured.
1968 2b. Type **665** 10 10
1969 3b. "Siamotyrannus isanensis" 15 10
1970 6b. "Siamosaurus suteethorni" 25 15
1971 9b. "Psittacosaurus sattayaraki" 35 20

666 King Chulalongkorn

1997. Centenary of Visit to Switzerland of King Chulalongkorn (Rama V).
1973 **666** 2b. multicoloured . . . 10 10

667 Rickshaw and Bicycle Hybrid

1997. International Correspondence Week. Tricycles. Multicoloured.
1974 3b. Type **667** 10 10
1975 3b. Bicycle with attached side-seat and wheel . . 10 10
1976 9b. Motor tricycle No. 345 30 20
1977 9b. Tuk-tuk (open-sided three-wheel motor) . . . 30 20

668 Purple Pacific Drupe

1997. World Post Day. Shells. Multicoloured.
1979 2b. Type **668** 10 10
1980 2b. "Nerita chamaeleon" . . 10 10
1981 9b. "Littoraria melanostoma" 30 20
1982 9b. "Cryptospira elegans" 30 20

669 Chalerm Prakiat (energy efficient building), Khlong Har

1997. Energy Conservation.
1984 **669** 2b. multicoloured . . . 10 10

670 "Suphannahong" (Royal Barge, 1911) (⅓-size illustration)

1997.
1985 **670** 9b. multicoloured . . . 30 20

671 "Cassia alata"

1997. New Year. Flowers. Multicoloured.
1987 2b. Type **671** 10 10
1988 2b. "Strophanthus caudatus" 10 10
1989 2b. "Clinacanthus nutans" 10 10
1990 2b. "Acanthus ilicifolius" . . 10 10

672 Playing Saxophone and Score of his "Falling Rain"

1997. 70th Birthday of King Bhumibol. Multicoloured.
1992 2b. Type **672** 10 10
1993 2b. At easel and one of his paintings 10 10
1994 2b. Model airplane, "OK" class dinghy and bust and Bhumibol building boat 10 10
1995 2b. Sailing "OK" class dinghy and wearing team blazer with gold medal from South-East Asian Games 10 10
1996 6b. With camera and his photograph of Royal Water Development Project 20 10
1997 7b. Writing and his books "Nai In", "Tito" and "The Story of Mahajanaka" 25 15
1998 9b. Using computer, map from "The Story of Mahajanaka" and his New Year card 30 20

673 "Sport-minded in Maimed Bodies" (Sumonmarl Chaneiam)

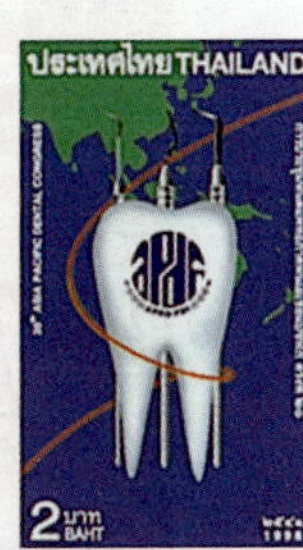
674 Dental Tools and Emblem on Tooth

1998. Children's Day. Children's Drawings. Multicoloured.
1999 2b. Type **673** 10 10
2000 2b. "Kite-flying Contest" (Pavinee Rodsawat) . . . 10 10
2001 2b. "Gymnastics" (Kejsarin Nilwong) 10 10
2002 2b. "Windsurf Racing" (Voraphat Phankhian) . . 10 10

1998. 20th Asia Pacific Dental Congress, Bangkok.
2003 **674** 2b. multicoloured . . . 10 10

675 Victory Monument and Military and Civilian Representatives

676 Queen Sirikit (Red Cross president)

1998. 50th Anniv of Veterans' Day.
2004 **675** 2b. multicoloured . . . 10 10

1998. Red Cross.
2015 **676** 2b. multicoloured . . . 10 10

677 Shooting

1998. 13th Asian Games, Bangkok. Multicoloured.
2016 2b.+1b. Type **677** 10 10
2017 3b.+1b. Gymnastics 15 10
2018 4b.+1b. Swimming 15 10
2019 7b.+1b. Windsurfing 25 15

678 Main Tower

1998. Thai Heritage Conservation Day. Phanomrung Historical Park. Multicoloured.
2020 3b. Type **678** 10 10
2021 4b. Minor Tower 10 10
2022 6b. Scripture repository . . 20 10
2023 7b. Lintel depicting Vishnu sleeping in ocean (eastern doorway, Main Tower) 25 15

679 Woman riding Tiger

1998. Songkran (New Year) Day. Year of the Tiger.
2025 **679** 2b. multicoloured . . . 10 10

680 Fishing Cat

1998. Wild Cats. Multicoloured.
2027 2b. Type **680** 10 10
2028 4b. Tiger 15 10
2029 6b. Leopard 20 10
2030 8b. Jungle cat 25 15

681 Airliner and Radar Grid

1998. 50th Anniv of Aerothai (air-traffic control).
2032 **681** 2b. multicoloured . . . 10 10

682 "Vidhurajataka" (Kritsana Moka-siri)

1998. Visakhapuja Day. Prize-winning Drawings of Ten Jataka Stories. Multicoloured.
2033 3b. Type **682** 10 10
2034 4b. "Vessantarajataka: Dana Kanda" (Chuttumrong Chalow-thorn-phises) . . 15 10
2035 6b. "Vessantarajataka: Kumara Kanda" (Surasin Chinna-wong) 20 10
2036 7b. "Vessantarajataka: Sakkapabba Kanda" (Chuttumrong Chalow-thorn-phises) 25 10

683 Kiartiwongse and "Phra Ruang" (destroyer)

1998. 75th Death Anniv of Admiral Prince Abhakara Kiartiwongse, Prince of Jumborn.
2038 **683** 2b. multicoloured . . . 10 10

684 Modern Technology (Porntiva Prasert)

1998. "Education Develops People and thus Nation". Under-9 Years Prize-winning Drawings.
2039 **684** 2b. multicoloured . . . 10 10

685 Commemorative Coin and Map and Flags of Europe

1998. Centenary (1997) of First State Visit to Europe of King Chulalongkorn (Rama V).
2040 **685** 6b. multicoloured . . . 20 10
2041 20b. multicoloured . . . 65 40

686 Irrawaddy Dolphin

1998. International Year of the Ocean. Marine Mammals. Multicoloured.
2042 2b. Type **686** 10 10
2043 3b. Bottle-nosed dolphin . . 10 10
2044 6b. Sperm whale 20 10
2045 9b. Dugong 30 20

687 Dams

1998. 60th Anniv of Irrigation Engineering.
2047 **687** 2b. multicoloured . . . 10 10

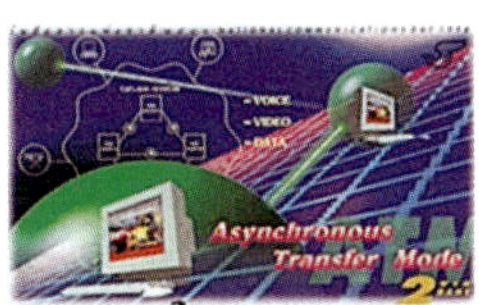
688 Model of Asynchronous Transfer Mode

1998. National Communications Day.
2048 **688** 2b. multicoloured . . . 10 10

689 Faculty Building and Emblems

1998. 50th Anniv of Faculty of Political Science, Chulalongkorn University.
2049 **689** 2b. multicoloured . . . 10 10

690 Correspondence Students

1998. 20th Anniv of Sukhothai Thammathirat Open University.
2050 **690** 2b. multicoloured . . . 10 10

691 Warrior

1998. Chinese Stone Statues. Multicoloured.
2051 2b. Type **691** 10 10
2052 2b. Warrior holding barbed spear 10 10
2053 10b. Warrior holding mace 30 20
2054 10b. Warrior holding spear with jagged blade 30 20

692 Archer

1998. "Amazing Thailand" Year. Perforated Hides. Multicoloured.
2056 3b. Type **692** 10 10
2057 3b. Warriors on elephants 10 10
2058 7b. Warrior seizing opponent 25 15
2059 7b. Deity hovering in sky 25 15

693 Kraisara Rajasiha (king lion)

1998. International Correspondence Week. Himavanta Mythical Animals of the Singha (lion) Family. Multicoloured.
2060 2b. Type **693** 10 10
2061 2b. Gajasiha (tusked lions) 10 10
2062 12b. Kesara Singha (hoofed lions) 40 25
2063 12b. Singhas 40 25

694 International Headquarters, Illinois

1998. Thai Presidency of International Association of Lions Clubs.
2065 **694** 2b. multicoloured . . . 10 10

695 "Barleria lupulina"

696 Knight Grand Cross (First Class)

1998. New Year. Flowers. Multcoloured.
2066 2b. Type **695** 10 10
2067 2b. Glory lily ("Gloriosa superba") 10 10
2068 2b. "Asclepias curassavica" 10 10
2069 2b. "Sesamum indicum" . . 10 10

1998. Most Admirable Order of the Direkgunabhorn. Multicoloured.
2071 15b. Type **696** 50 30
2072 15b. Close-up of badge . . 50 30

697 Hockey

1998. 13th Asian Games, Bangkok. Multicoloured.
2073 2b.+1b. Type **697** 10 10
2074 3b.+1b. Wrestling 15 10
2075 4b.+1b. Rowing 15 10
2076 7b.+1b. Show jumping . . . 25 15

698 "Gymkhana" (Khontorn Taechoran)

1999. Children's Day. Children's Paintings. Multicoloured.
2081 2b. Type **698** 10 10
2082 2b. "Swimming" (Sunhapong Phitukburapa) 10 10
2083 2b. "Volleyball" (Vipharat Sae Lim) 10 10
2084 2b. "Sepak Takraw" (three-aside net game) (Phanot Ratanawongkae) 10 10

699 Wheel-chair Athletes

1999. Asian and Pacific Decade of Disabled Persons.
2085 **699** 2b. multicoloured . . . 10 10

700 Paddy Sprouts and Workers planting Rice

1999. Rice Cultivation. Multicoloured.
2086 6b. Type **700** 20 10
2087 6b. Workers harvesting rice and ear of paddy 20 10
2088 12b. Paddy-threshing machine 40 25
2089 12b. Golden paddy field and bowl of cooked rice . . . 40 25

701 Birth of Mahajanaka

1999. Maghapuja Day. Showing murals from Wat Tha Sutthawat illustrating the story of Mahajanaka.

2091 3b. Type **701** 10 10
2092 6b. Mani Mekkhala carrying Mahajanaka to Mithila City 20 10
2093 9b. Two mango trees . . . 30 20
2094 15b. Mahajanaka founding educational institute . . . 50 30

702 Queen Somdetch the Queen Grandmother

1999. Red Cross.

2096 **702** 2b. multicoloured . . . 10 10

703 Kite Flying

1999. "BANGKOK 2000" World Youth Stamp Exhibition and 13th Asian International Stamp Exhibition, Bangkok. Children's Games (1st issue). Multicoloured.

2097 2b. Type **703** 10 10
2098 2b. Hoop rolling 10 10
2099 15b. Catching the last one in the line (children passing under arched arms) . . . 50 30
2100 15b. Snatching a baby from Mother Snake 50 30

See also Nos. 2119/22 and 2195/8.

704 "Hooks and Squids" Motif

705 Woman riding Rabbit

1999. Thai Heritage Conservation Day. Silk Mudmee Textiles. Multicoloured.

2102 2b. Type **704** 10 10
2103 4b. "Royal Umbrella" motif 15 10
2104 12b. "Naga upholding the Baisi" motif 40 25
2105 15b. "Naga upholding a flower pot" motif 50 30

1999. Songkran (New Year) Day. Year of the Rabbit.

2107 **705** 2b. multicoloured . . . 10 10

706 Hands encircling Emblem

1999. Consumer Protection Years, 1998–1999.

2109 **706** 2b. multicoloured . . . 10 10

707 Chitralada Villa, Dusit Palace, Bangkok

1999. Sixth Cycle (72nd Birthday) of King Bhumibol. Royal Palaces (1st issue). Multicoloured.

2110 6b. Type **707** 20 10
2111 6b. Phu Phing Ratchaniwet Palace, Chieng Mai Province (red and green roofs) 20 10
2112 6b. Phu Phan Ratchaniwet Palace, Sakon Nakhon province (with large green lawn) 20 10
2113 6b. Thaksin Ratchaniwet Palace, Narathiwat Province (two-storey building with drive and ornamental trees) 20 10

See also Nos. 2130/8, 2146/54 and 2161/3.

708 Administrative Building and Faculty Emblem

1999. 50th Anniv of Political Science Faculty, Thammasat University.

2115 **708** 3b. multicoloured . . . 10 10

709 Float, Candle Festival, Ubon Ratchathani

1999. 125th Anniv of Universal Postal Union. Multicoloured.

2116 2b. Floating vessel, Light Festival 10 10
2117 15b. Type **709** 50 30

710 King Chulalongkorn and Customs Building

1999. 125th Anniv of the Customs Department.

2118 **710** 6b. multicoloured . . . 20 10

711 Sut Sakhon riding Dragon

1999. "BANGKOK 2000" World Youth Stamp Exhibition and 13th Asian International Stamp Exhibition, Bangkok (2nd issue). Folk Tales. Multicoloured.

2119 2b. Type **711** (Tale of Phra Aphai Mani) 50 30
2120 2b. Rishi transforming tiger cub and cow calf into children (Tale of Honwichai-Khawi) . . . 50 30
2121 15b. Phra Sang climbing out of conch shell (Tale of Sang Thong) 50 30
2122 15b. Khun Chang, Khun Phaen and Nang Phim playing (Tale of Khun Chang and Khun Phaen) 50 30

712 Communication by Eye, Ear, Mouth and Hand

1999. National Communications Day.

2124 **712** 4b. multicoloured . . . 15 10

713 Rabbits

1999. "THAIPEX'99" 13th Thailand Stamp Exhibition, Bangkok. Domestic Rabbits. Multicoloured.

2125 6b. Type **713** 20 10
2126 6b. One golden and one brown rabbit 20 10
2127 12b. One grey and one grey and white rabbit 40 25
2128 12b. Two white rabbits . . 40 25

714 Prince Mahidol with Bhumibol as Baby

1999. Sixth Cycle (72nd Birthday) of King Bhumibol (2nd issue). Portraits of the King. Multicoloured.

2130 3b. Type **714** 10 10
2131 3b. Princess Mother and her children 10 10
2132 3b. With his brother King Ananda Mahidol 10 10
2133 6b. Bhumibol and King Ananda Mahidol in military uniform 20 10
2134 6b. On wedding day 20 10
2135 6b. Coronation ceremony 20 10
2136 12b. As a monk 40 25
2137 12b. King and Queen with their children 40 25
2138 12b. In royal robes 40 25

715 Older Person with Children

1999. International Year of the Elderly.

2140 **715** 2b. multicoloured . . . 10 10

716 Orchid Tree

718 "Thunbergia laurifolia"

717 In Open-top Car on Returning to School in Switzerland

1999. International Correspondence Week. Flowers. Multicoloured.

2141 2b. Type **716** 10 10
2142 2b. "Bombax ceiba" (red flower) 10 10
2143 12b. "Radermachera ignea" (tubular yellow flowers) 40 25
2144 12b. "Bretschneidera sinensis" (pink bell flowers) 40 25

1999. Sixth Cycle (72nd Birthday) of King Bhumibol (3rd issue). The King and his Subjects. Multicoloured.

2146 3b. Type **717** 10 10
2147 3b. With Buddhist monks 10 10
2148 3b. King and Queen with students 10 10
2149 6b. With soldiers 10 10
2150 6b. With children prostrate at his feet 20 10
2151 6b. With boy on crutches 20 10
2152 12b. Visiting a hilltribe home 40 25
2153 12b. Drawing plan on ground 40 25
2154 12b. Talking to crowds . . 40 25

1999. New Year. Flowers. Multicoloured.

2156 2b. Type **718** 10 10
2157 2b. "Gmelina arborea" . . 10 10
2158 2b. "Prunus cerasoides" . . 10 10
2159 2b. "Fagraea fragans" . . . 10 10

719 King Bhumibol

1999. Sixth Cycle (72nd Birthday) of King Bhumibol (4th issue).

2161 **719** 100b. gold and blue . . 3·00 2·00
2162 100b. silver and blue . . 3·00 2·00
2163 100b. bronze and blue 3·00 2·00

720 King Bhumibol and Prince Vajiralongkorn

1999. Investiture of Crown Prince Maha Vajiralongkorn.

2165 **720** 3b. multicoloured . . . 10 10

721 Lilies, Thale Noi

2000. Lake of Lilies, Phatthalung Province. Mult.

2166 3b. Type **721** 10 10
2167 3b. Forest and lilies 10 10
2168 3b. Forest, buildings and lilies 10 10
2169 3b. Birds flying over lilies 10 10
2170 3b.15 lily flowers 10 10
2171 3b. Seven lily flowers . . . 10 10
2172 3b. Six lily flowers 10 10
2173 3b. Eight lily flowers and three buds 10 10
2174 3b. Four lily flowers and two buds 10 10
2175 3b. Two lily flowers and eight lily pads 10 10
2176 3b. Two lily flowers 10 10
2177 3b. Three lily flowers . . . 10 10

Nos. 2166/77 were issued together, se-tenant, forming a composite design of the lake.

The stamps are identified by the number of complete flowers shown.

722 Flowers

2000. Kulap Khao Meadow, Chiang Mai Province. Multicoloured.

2178 3b. Type **722** 10 10
2179 3b. Flowers and two peaks 10 10
2180 3b. Flowers, four buds and mountains 10 10
2181 3b. Flowers, three buds and mountains 10 10
2182 3b. Three open flowers . . . 10 10
2183 3b. Open flowers and seven buds 10 10
2184 3b. Open flowers and six buds 10 10
2185 3b. Open flowers and one bud 10 10
2186 3b. One open flower and five buds 10 10
2187 3b. Open flowers and four buds 10 10
2188 3b. Four open flowers . . . 10 10
2189 3b. Four partially open flowers 10 10

Nos. 2178/89 were issued together, se-tenant, forming a composite design of the Kulap Khao meadow.

The stamps are identified by the number of complete flowers and buds shown.

723 Small Dwarf Honey Bee

2000. Bees. Multicoloured.
2190 3b. Type **723** 10 10
2191 3b. Dwarf bee (*Apis florea*) 10 10
2192 3b. Asian honey bee (*Apis cerana*) 10 10
2193 3b. Giant bee (*Apis dorsata*) 10 10

724 Child being Blessed

2000. "BANGKOK 2000" International Youth Stamp Exhibition and 13th Asian International Stamp Exhibition, Bangkok (3rd issue). Ceremonies. Multicoloured.
2195 2b. Type **724** 10 10
2196 2b. Woman cutting child's hair (Tonsure ceremony) 10 10
2197 15b. Pupils paying respects to teacher 50 35
2198 15b. Boy being carried aloft during ordination of novice 50 35

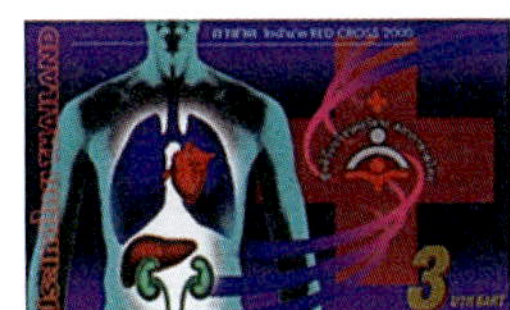

725 Human Body and Emblem

2000. Thai Red Cross Organ Donation Campaign.
2200 **725** 3b. multicoloured . . . 10 10

726 Sukhothai Province

2000. Thai Heritage Conservation. Chok Cloth Designs. Multicoloured.
2201 3b. Type **726** 10 10
2202 6b. Chiang Mai Province . . 20 10
2203 8b. Uthai Thani Province 25 15
2204 12b. Ratchaburi Province 40 25

727 Angel riding Snake

2000. Songkran (New Year) Day. Year of the Snake.
2206 **727** 2b. multicoloured . . . 10 10

728 Engagement Photograph (½-size illustration)

2000. Golden Wedding Anniv of King Bhumibol and Queen Sirikit. Multicoloured.
2208 10b. Type **728** 35 25
2209 10b. Signing marriage register, 1950 . . . . . . 35 25
2210 10b. Sitting on thrones during Coronation ceremony 35 25
2211 10b. With family 35 25
2212 10b. King Bhumibol and Queen Sirikit, 2000 . . . 35 25

729 Buddha

730 Flowers and Trees, Krachieo

2000. Asalhapuja Day.
2213 **729** 3b. multicoloured . . . 10 10

2000. Krachieo Meadow, Pa Hin Ngam, Chaiyaphum Province. Multicoloured.
2214 3b. Type **730** 10 10
2215 3b. Flowers and sparse trees in distance 10 10
2216 3b. Flowers, two close trees and dense trees in distance 10 10
2217 3b. Flowers, four close trees and dense trees in distance 10 10
2218 3b. Six complete flowers . . 10 10
2219 3b. Eleven complete flowers 10 10
2220 3b. Seven complete flowers and half a flower at right-hand side 10 10
2221 3b. Six complete flowers and two incomplete flowers at bottom 10 10
2222 3b. Two flowers 10 10
2223 3b. Three flowers close together 10 10
2224 3b. One open and two partially open flowers . . 10 10
2225 3b. Two complete and three incomplete flowers 10 10

Nos. 2214/25 were issued together, se-tenant, forming a composite design of the meadow.

The stamps are identified by the number of trees or flowers shown.

731 Crown Prince and Rice Seeds Sowing Ceremony

2000. Fourth Cycle (48th Birthday) of Crown Prince Maha Vajiralongkorn.
2226 **731** 2b. multicoloured . . . 10 10

732 Sun, Emblem, Envelope and Moon

2000. National Communications Day.
2228 **732** 3b. multicoloured . . . 10 10

733 Cabbage Design Tea Set

2000. International Correspondence Week. Rattanakosin Period Tea Sets. Multicoloured.
2229 6b. Type **733** 20 10
2230 6b. Duck and animals in lotus pond design 20 10
2231 12b. Lotus bud design . . . 40 20
2232 12b. Butterflies and bees design 40 20

734 Princess Srinagarindra

2000. Birth Centenary of Princess Srinagarindra the Princess Mother.
2234 **734** 2b. multicoloured . . . 10 10

735 Glory Bower (*Clerodendrum philippinum*)

736 Flowers

2000. New Year. Flowers. Multicoloured.
2236 2b. Type **735** 10 10
2237 2b. *Capparis micracantha* . . 10 10
2238 2b. Leopard lily (*Belamcanda chinensis*) . . 10 10
2239 2b. *Memecylon caeruleum* 10 10

2000. Bua Tong Meadow, Mae Hong Son Province. Multicoloured.
2241 3b. Type **736** 10 10
2242 3b. Meadow and trees (top left) 10 10
2243 3b. Meadow 10 10
2244 3b. Meadow and trees (top right) 10 10
2245 3b. Four flowers 10 10
2246 3b. Eleven flowers 10 10
2247 3b. Fifteen flowers 10 10
2248 3b. Twelve flowers 10 10
2249 3b. Three large flowers, two smaller flowers and one dead flower 10 10
2250 3b. Three large flowers . . . 10 10
2251 3b. One large flower 10 10
2252 3b. Five flowers and one dead flower 10 10

Nos. 2241/52 were issued together, se-tenant, forming a composite design.

The stamps are identified by the number of complete flowers shown.

737 Anantanakkharat (Royal Barge, 1914) (¼-size illustration)

2000.
2253 **737** 9b. multicoloured . . . 30 15

738 Moustached Parakeet (*Psittacula alexandri*)

739 King Rama V and First Title Deed

2001. Parrots. Multicoloured.
2255 2b. Type **738** 10 10
2256 5b. Alexandrine parakeet (*Psittacula eupatria*) . . . 15 10
2257 8b. *Psittacula cyanurus* . . . 25 10
2258 10b. Blossom-headed parakeet (*Psittacula roseata*) 30 15

2001. Centenary of Department of Lands.
2260 **739** 5b. multicoloured . . .

740 Manta Ray

2001. Marine Life. Multicoloured.
2261 3b. Type **740** 10 10
2262 3b. Fishes and jellyfish . . . 10 10
2263 3b. Turtle 10 10
2264 3b. Coral and lionfish . . . 10 10
2265 3b. Black and white fish and coral 10 10
2266 3b. Head of eel and yellow coral 10 10
2267 6b. Fishes and coral(28 × 47 mm) 20 10
2268 6b. Pufferfish and other fishes (28 × 47 mm) . . . 20 10
2269 6b. Yellow and blue fish and coral (45 × 23 mm) . . . 20 10

Nos. 2261/9 were issued together, se-tenant, forming a composite design.

741 Diamond and Ring

2001. Precious Stones. Multicoloured.
2270 3b. Type **741** 10 10
2271 4b. Green sapphire and necklace 15 10
2272 6b. Pearl and necklace . . . 20 10
2273 12b. Blue sapphire and necklace 40 20

742 Women and Orphans

2001. Red Cross. 20th Anniv of Thai Red Cross Children's Homes.
2275 **742** 4b. multicoloured . . . 15 10

743 Gold and Red Brocade

744 Woman riding Snake

2001. Thai Heritage Conservation Day. Showing different brocade designs. Multicoloured.
2276 2b. Type **743** 10 10
2277 3b. Green and gold design 10 10
2278 10b. Orange and gold design 30 15
2279 10b. Pink and gold design 30 15

2001. Songkran (New Year) Day. Year of the Snake.
2281 **744** 2b. multicoloured . . . 10 10

745 Buddha

746 Maiyarap, Emerald Buddha Temple

2001. Visakhapuja Day.
2283 **745** 3b. multicoloured . . . 10 10

2001. Demon Statues. Multicoloured.
2284 2b. Type **746** 10 10
2285 5b. Wirunchambang, Emerald Buddha Temple 15 10
2286 10b. Thotsakan, Temple of Dawn 30 15
2287 12b. Sahatsadecha, Temple of Dawn 40 20
MS2288 145 × 110 mm. Nos. 2284/7 (sold at 33b.) . . . . 1·00 50

747 Prince Purachatra Jayakara (first governor)

2001. 66th Anniv of Rotary International in Thailand.
2289 **747** 3b. multicoloured . . . 10 10

748 Split Gill (*Schizophyllum commune*)

2001. Fungi. Multicoloured.
2290 2b. Type **748** 10 10
2291 3b. *Lentinus giganteus* . . . 10 10

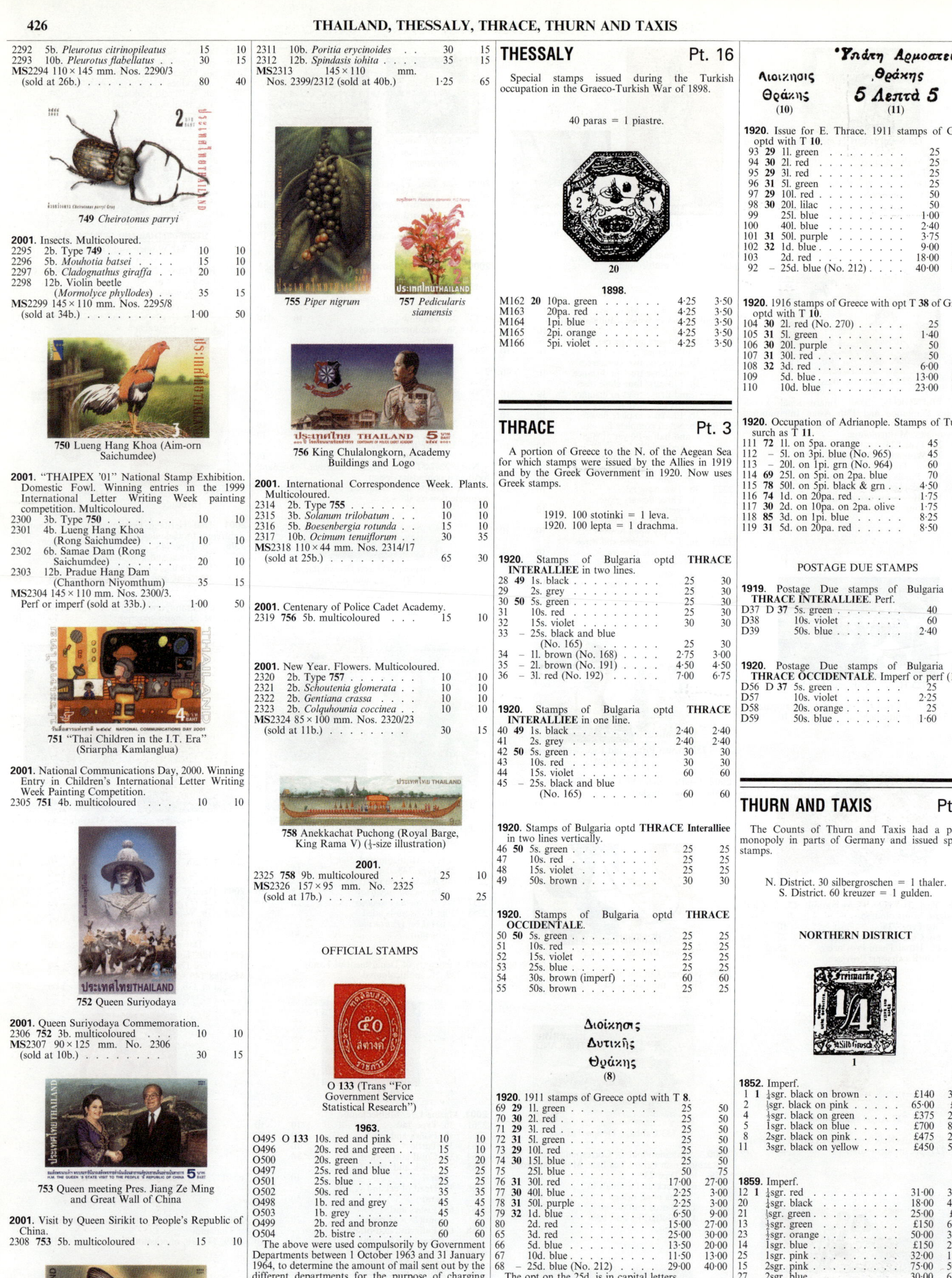

2292 5b. *Pleurotus citrinopileatus* . . 15 10
2293 10b. *Pleurotus flabellatus* . . 30 15
MS2294 110 × 145 mm. Nos. 2290/3 (sold at 26b.) 80 40

749 *Cheirotonus parryi*

2001. Insects. Multicoloured.
2295 2b. Type **749** 10 10
2296 5b. *Mouhotia batsei* 15 10
2297 6b. *Cladognathus giraffa* . . 20 10
2298 12b. Violin beetle (*Mormolyce phyllodes*) . . 35 15
MS2299 145 × 110 mm. Nos. 2295/8 (sold at 34b.) . . . . 1·00 50

750 Lueng Hang Khoa (Aim-orn Saichumdee)

2001. "THAIPEX '01" National Stamp Exhibition. Domestic Fowl. Winning entries in the 1999 International Letter Writing Week painting competition. Multicoloured.
2300 3b. Type **750** 10 10
2301 4b. Lueng Hang Khoa (Rong Saichumdee) . . . 10 10
2302 6b. Samae Dam (Rong Saichumdee) 20 10
2303 12b. Pradue Hang Dam (Chanthorn Niyomthum) . . 35 15
MS2304 145 × 110 mm. Nos. 2300/3. Perf or imperf (sold at 33b.) . . 1·00 50

751 "Thai Children in the I.T. Era" (Sriarpha Kamlanglua)

2001. National Communications Day, 2000. Winning Entry in Children's International Letter Writing Week Painting Competition.
2305 **751** 4b. multicoloured . . . 10 10

752 Queen Suriyodaya

2001. Queen Suriyodaya Commemoration.
2306 **752** 3b. multicoloured . . . 10 10
MS2307 90 × 125 mm. No. 2306 (sold at 10b.) 30 15

753 Queen meeting Pres. Jiang Ze Ming and Great Wall of China

2001. Visit by Queen Sirikit to People's Republic of China.
2308 **753** 5b. multicoloured . . . 15 10

754 *Pachliopta aristolochiae goniopeltis*

2001. Butterflies. Multicoloured.
2309 2b. Type **754** 10 10
2310 4b. *Rhinopalpa polynice* . . 10 10
2311 10b. *Poritia erycinoides* . . 30 15
2312 12b. *Spindasis iohita* 35 15
MS2313 145 × 110 mm. Nos. 2399/2312 (sold at 40b.) 1·25 65

755 *Piper nigrum*

757 *Pedicularis siamensis*

756 King Chulalongkorn, Academy Buildings and Logo

2001. International Correspondence Week. Plants. Multicoloured.
2314 2b. Type **755** 10 10
2315 3b. *Solanum trilobatum* . . . 10 10
2316 5b. *Boesenbergia rotunda* . . 15 10
2317 10b. *Ocimum tenuiflorum* . . 30 35
MS2318 110 × 44 mm. Nos. 2314/17 (sold at 25b.) 65 30

2001. Centenary of Police Cadet Academy.
2319 **756** 5b. multicoloured . . . 15 10

2001. New Year. Flowers. Multicoloured.
2320 2b. Type **757** 10 10
2321 2b. *Schoutenia glomerata* . . 10 10
2322 2b. *Gentiana crassa* 10 10
2323 2b. *Colquhounia coccinea* . . 10 10
MS2324 85 × 100 mm. Nos. 2320/23 (sold at 11b.) 30 15

758 Anekkachat Puchong (Royal Barge, King Rama V) ($\frac{1}{2}$-size illustration)

2001.
2325 **758** 9b. multicoloured . . . 25 10
MS2326 157 × 95 mm. No. 2325 (sold at 17b.) 50 25

OFFICIAL STAMPS

O 133 (Trans "For Government Service Statistical Research")

1963.
O495 **O 133** 10s. red and pink . . 10 10
O496 20s. red and green . . 15 10
O500 20s. green 25 20
O497 25s. red and blue . . 25 25
O501 25s. blue 25 25
O502 50s. red 35 35
O498 1b. red and grey . . 45 45
O503 1b. grey 45 45
O499 2b. red and bronze . . 60 60
O504 2b. bistre 60 60

The above were used compulsorily by Government Departments between 1 October 1963 and 31 January 1964, to determine the amount of mail sent out by the different departments for the purpose of charging them in the future. They were postmarked in the usual way.

THESSALY Pt. 16

Special stamps issued during the Turkish occupation in the Graeco-Turkish War of 1898.

40 paras = 1 piastre.

20

1898.
M162 **20** 10pa. green . . . . . . 4·25 3·50
M163 20pa. red . . . . 4·25 3·50
M164 1pi. blue . . . . 4·25 3·50
M165 2pi. orange . . . . . . 4·25 3·50
M166 5pi. violet . . . . 4·25 3·50

THRACE Pt. 3

A portion of Greece to the N. of the Aegean Sea for which stamps were issued by the Allies in 1919 and by the Greek Government in 1920. Now uses Greek stamps.

1919. 100 stotinki = 1 leva.
1920. 100 lepta = 1 drachma.

1920. Stamps of Bulgaria optd **THRACE INTERALLIEE** in two lines.
28 **49** 1s. black 25 30
29 2s. grey 25 30
30 **50** 5s. green 25 30
31 10s. red 25 30
32 15s. violet 30 30
33 – 25s. black and blue (No. 165) 25 30
34 – 1l. brown (No. 168) . . . . 2·75 3·00
35 – 2l. brown (No. 191) . . . . 4·50 4·50
36 – 3l. red (No. 192) . . . . . 7·00 6·75

1920. Stamps of Bulgaria optd **THRACE INTERALLIEE** in one line.
40 **49** 1s. black . . . . 2·40 2·40
41 2s. grey . . . . 2·40 2·40
42 **50** 5s. green 30 30
43 10s. red 30 30
44 15s. violet 60 60
45 – 25s. black and blue (No. 165) 60 60

1920. Stamps of Bulgaria optd **THRACE Interalliee** in two lines vertically.
46 **50** 5s. green 25 25
47 10s. red 25 25
48 15s. violet 25 25
49 50s. brown 30 30

1920. Stamps of Bulgaria optd **THRACE OCCIDENTALE.**
50 **50** 5s. green 25 25
51 10s. red 25 25
52 15s. violet 25 25
53 25s. blue 25 25
54 30s. brown (imperf) 60 60
55 50s. brown 25 25

Διοίκησις
Δυτικῆς
Θράκης
(8)

1920. 1911 stamps of Greece optd with T **8**.
69 **29** 1l. green 25 50
70 **30** 2l. red 25 50
71 **29** 3l. red 25 50
72 **31** 5l. green 25 50
73 **29** 10l. red 25 50
74 **30** 15l. blue 25 50
75 25l. blue 50 75
76 **31** 30l. red . . . . 17·00 27·00
77 **30** 40l. blue . . . . 2·25 3·00
78 **31** 50l. purple . . . . 2·25 3·00
79 **32** 1d. blue . . . . 6·50 9·00
80 2d. red . . . . 15·00 27·00
65 3d. red . . . . 25·00 30·00
66 5d. blue . . . . 13·50 20·00
67 10d. blue . . . . 11·50 13·00
68 – 25d. blue (No. 212) . . . . 29·00 40·00

The opt on the 25d. is in capital letters.

1920. 1916 stamps of Greece, with opt Greece T **38**, optd with T **8**.
81 **29** 1l. green (No. 269) 75 75
82 **30** 2l. red 25 25
83 **29** 10l. red 50 50
84 **30** 20l. purple 50 50
85 **31** 30l. red 70 70
86 **32** 2d. red . . . . 17·00 25·00
87 3d. red . . . . 8·50 15·00
88 5d. blue . . . . 21·00 30·00
89 10d. blue . . . . 15·00 28·00

Διοίκησις
Θράκης
(10)

Ὑπάτη Ἁρμοστεία
Θράκης
5 Λεπτὰ 5
(11)

1920. Issue for E. Thrace. 1911 stamps of Greece optd with T **10**.
93 **29** 1l. green 25 25
94 **30** 2l. red 25 25
95 **29** 3l. red 25 25
96 **31** 5l. green 25 25
97 **29** 10l. red . . . . 50 1·00
98 **30** 20l. lilac . . . . 50 1·00
99 25l. blue . . . . 1·00 1·50
100 40l. blue . . . . 2·40 3·75
101 **31** 50l. purple . . . . 3·75 6·50
102 **32** 1d. blue . . . . 9·00 17·00
103 2d. red . . . . 18·00 26·00
92 – 25d. blue (No. 212) . . . . 40·00 60·00

1920. 1916 stamps of Greece with opt T **38** of Greece, optd with T **10**.
104 **30** 2l. red (No. 270) 25 75
105 **31** 5l. green . . . . 1·40 3·25
106 **30** 20l. purple . . . . 50 1·40
107 **31** 30l. red . . . . 50 1·40
108 **32** 3d. red . . . . 6·00 11·00
109 5d. blue . . . . 13·00 23·00
110 10d. blue . . . . 23·00 35·00

1920. Occupation of Adrianople. Stamps of Turkey surch as T **11**.
111 **72** 1l. on 5pa. orange 45 60
112 – 5l. on 3pi. blue (No. 965) 45 55
113 – 20l. on 1pi. grn (No. 964) 60 60
114 **69** 25l. on 5pi. on 2pa. blue 70 70
115 **78** 50l. on 5pi. black & grn . . 4·50 4·50
116 **74** 1d. on 20pa. red . . . . . 1·75 1·75
117 **30** 2d. on 10pa. on 2pa. olive 1·75 1·75
118 **85** 3d. on 1pi. blue . . . . . 8·25 8·25
119 **31** 5d. on 20pa. red . . . . . 8·50 8·50

POSTAGE DUE STAMPS

1919. Postage Due stamps of Bulgaria optd **THRACE INTERALLIEE.** Perf.
D37 **D 37** 5s. green 40 40
D38 10s. violet 60 60
D39 50s. blue . . . . 2·40 2·40

1920. Postage Due stamps of Bulgaria optd **THRACE OCCIDENTALE.** Imperf or perf (10s.).
D56 **D 37** 5s. green 25 25
D57 10s. violet . . . . 2·25 2·25
D58 20s. orange 25 25
D59 50s. blue . . . . 1·60 1·60

THURN AND TAXIS Pt. 7

The Counts of Thurn and Taxis had a postal monopoly in parts of Germany and issued special stamps.

N. District. 30 silbergroschen = 1 thaler.
S. District. 60 kreuzer = 1 gulden.

NORTHERN DISTRICT

1

1852. Imperf.
1 **1** $\frac{1}{4}$sgr. black on brown . . . . £140 32·00
2 $\frac{1}{3}$sgr. black on pink . . . . . 65·00 £150
4 $\frac{1}{2}$sgr. black on green . . . . £375 22·00
5 1sgr. black on blue . . . . . £700 85·00
8 2sgr. black on pink . . . . . £475 20·00
11 3sgr. black on yellow . . . . £450 50·00

1859. Imperf.
12 **1** $\frac{1}{4}$sgr. red . . . . 31·00 38·00
20 $\frac{1}{4}$sgr. black . . . . 18·00 40·00
21 $\frac{1}{3}$sgr. green . . . . 25·00 £150
13 $\frac{1}{2}$sgr. green . . . . £150 65·00
23 $\frac{1}{2}$sgr. orange . . . . 50·00 30·00
14 1sgr. blue . . . . £150 27·00
25 1sgr. pink . . . . 32·00 18·00
15 2sgr. pink . . . . 75·00 50·00
27 2sgr. blue . . . . 30·00 65·00
17 3sgr. red . . . . 75·00 70·00
29 3sgr. brown . . . . 15·00 30·00
18 5sgr. mauve . . . . 1·20 £225
19 10sgr. orange . . . . 1·50 £500

1865. Rouletted.
31 **1** $\frac{1}{4}$sgr. black . . . . 7·25 £450
32 $\frac{1}{3}$sgr. green . . . . 11·00 £300
33 $\frac{1}{2}$sgr. yellow . . . . 22·00 32·00
34 1sgr. pink . . . . 22·00 22·00
35 2sgr. blue . . . . 1·50 48·00
36 3sgr. brown . . . . 2·50 30·00

SOUTHERN DISTRICT

3

1852. Imperf.

No.	Type	Description	Unused	Used
51	**3**	1k. black on green	£130	11·00
53		3k. black on blue	£500	32·00
57		6k. black on pink	£425	5·75
58		9k. black on yellow	£400	25·00

1859. Imperf.

No.	Type	Description	Unused	Used
60	**3**	1k. green	12·50	8·25
62		3k. blue	£300	17·00
68		3k. pink	7·25	22·00
63		6k. pink	£300	36·00
70		6k. blue	7·25	22·00
65		9k. yellow	£300	60·00
73		9k. brown	7·25	22·00
66		15k. purple	1·50	£110
67		30k. orange	1·50	£300

1865. Roul.

No.	Type	Description	Unused	Used
74	**3**	1k. green	9·50	15·00
81		3k. pink	1·30	22·00
76		6k. blue	1·50	22·00
77		9k. brown	2·20	25·00

TIBET Pt. 17

Former independent state in the Himalayas, now part of China.

A. CHINESE POST OFFICES

12 pies = 1 anna;
16 annas = 1 Indian rupee.

分 貳

One Anna

སྐར་གཅིག།

(C 1)

1911. Stamps of China of 1898 surch as Type C **1**.

No.	Type	Description	Unused	Used
C 1	**32**	3p. on 1c. brown	3·00	6·00
C 2		½a. on 2c. green	4·00	6·50
C 3		1a. on 4c. red	5·00	6·50
C 4		2a. on 7c. red	5·00	8·00
C 5		2½a. on 10c. blue	5·00	8·00
C 6	**33**	3a. on 16c. green	15·00	14·00
C 7		4a. on 20c. red	14·00	15·00
C 8		6a. on 30c. red	20·00	22·00
C 9		12a. on 50c. green	40·00	35·00
C 10	**34**	1r. on $1 red and pink	£400	£450
C 11		2r. on $2 red and yellow	£750	£900

These stamps were used in Post Offices set up by the Chinese army sent to Tibet in 1910. Following a revolt by the Tibetans these troops were withdrawn during 1912.

B. INDEPENDENT STATE

6⅔ trangka = 1 sang.

1 (⅙ t.)

⅓t. ½t. ⅔t. 1t. 1s.

1912. Imperf.

No.	Type	Description	Unused	Used
1	**1**	⅙t. green	15·00	15·00
2		⅓t. blue	18·00	15·00
3b		½t. purple	18·00	18·00
4		⅔t. red	22·00	18·00
5		1t. red	30·00	40·00
6		1s. green	45·00	45·00

2 (4t.)

1914. Imperf.

No.	Type	Description	Unused	Used
7b	**2**	4t. blue	£250	£225
8b		8t. red	£140	£140

In the 8t. the rays from the circles in the corners of the stamp point outwards towards the corner.

3 (1t.) Tibetan Lion ½t. ⅔t. 2t. 4t.

1933. Perf or imperf.

No.	Type	Description	Unused	Used
9a	**3**	½t. yellow to orange	9·00	15·00
10b		⅔t. blue	10·00	12·00
11a		1t. red	8·00	8·50
11b		1t. orange	8·00	9·00
12a		2t. red	9·00	8·00
12c		2t. orange	9·50	9·00
13d		4t. green	8·50	5·50

TIERRA DEL FUEGO Pt. 20

An island at the extreme S. of S. America. Stamp issued for use on correspondence to the mainland. Currency is expressed in centigrammes of gold dust.

1 Gold-digger's Pick and Hammer

1891.

No.	Type	Description	Unused	Used
1	**1**	10c. red	12·00	

TOBAGO Pt. 1

An island in the British West Indies, north-east of Trinidad. From 1896 to 1913 it used the stamps of Trinidad; from 1913 there were combined issues for Trinidad and Tobago.

12 pence = 1 shilling;
20 shillings = 1 pound.

1

2

1879.

No.	Type	Description	Unused	Used
1	**1**	1d. red	80·00	65·00
2		3d. blue	80·00	50·00
3		6d. orange	38·00	50·00
4		1s. green	£375	65·00
5		5s. grey	£650	£600
6		£1 mauve	£4000	

In the above issue only stamps watermarked Crown CC were issued for postal use and our prices are for stamps bearing this watermark. Stamps with watermark Crown CA are fiscals and were never admitted to postal use.

1880. No. 3 divided vertically down the centre and surch with pen and ink.

No.	Type	Description	Unused	Used
7	**1**	1d. on half of 6d. orange	£4500	£750

1880. "POSTAGE" added in design.

No.	Type	Description	Unused	Used
14	**2**	½d. lilac	1·00	12·00
20		½d. green	1·75	65
21		1d. red	2·25	80
16a		2½d. blue	4·50	75
10		4d. green	£200	27·00
22		4d. grey	2·25	1·00
11		6d. buff	£300	£100
23		6d. brown	2·00	4·00
24		1s. yellow	2·25	15·00

1883. Surch in figures and words.

No.	Type	Description	Unused	Used
26	**2**	½d. on 2½d. blue	4·25	11·00
30		½d. on 4d. grey	13·00	48·00
27		½d. on 6d. buff	2·50	19·00
28		½d. on 6d. brown	£100	£130
29		1d. on 2½d. blue	60·00	16·00
31		2½d. on 4d. grey	6·00	6·50
13		2½d. on 6d. buff	48·00	48·00

1896. Surch ½**d POSTAGE**.

No.	Type	Description	Unused	Used
33	**1**	½d. on 4d. lilac and red	55·00	30·00

TOGO Pt. 7; Pt. 1; Pt. 6; Pt. 14

A territory in W. Africa, formerly a German Colony. Divided between France and Gt. Britain in 1919, the British portion being attached to the Gold Coast for administration and using the stamps of that country. In 1956 the French portion became an autonomous republic within the French Union. Full independence was achieved in April 1960.

GERMAN ISSUES

100 pfennig = 1 mark.

1897. Stamps of Germany optd **TOGO**.

No.	Type	Description	Unused	Used
G1	**8**	3pf. brown	4·50	5·50
G2		5pf. green	3·75	2·10
G3	**9**	10pf. red	4·50	2·10
G4		20pf. blue	5·00	9·00
G5		25pf. orange	35·00	42·00
G6		50pf. brown	35·00	48·00

1900. "Yacht" key-types inscr "TOGO".

No.	Type	Description	Unused	Used
G 7	N	3pf. brown	55	1·00
G21		5pf. green	90	1·25
G 9		10pf. red	23·00	1·00
G10		20pf. blue	1·10	1·25
G11		25pf. black & red on yell	1·00	7·25
G12		30pf. black & orge on buff	1·10	7·25
G13		40pf. black and red	90	7·00
G14		50pf. black & pur on buff	1·40	7·00
G15		80pf. black & red on pink	2·40	13·50
G16	O	1m. red	3·00	48·00
G17		2m. blue	6·75	60·00
G18		3m. black	6·00	£120
G19		5m. red and black	£120	£400

ANGLO-FRENCH OCCUPATION

BRITISH ISSUES

1914. Nos. 7/21 (German Colonial Types) optd **TOGO Anglo-French Occupation**.

No.	Type	Description	Unused	Used
H 1	N	3pf. brown	£110	95·00
H 2		5pf. green	£100	95·00
H 3		10pf. red	£120	£100
H17		20pf. blue	17·00	12·00
H18		25pf. black & red on yell	23·00	30·00
H19		30pf. blk & orge on buff	19·00	29·00
H 7		40pf. black and red	£225	£250
H 8		50pf. black & pur on buff	£9000	£7000
H 9		80pf. black & red on rose	£225	£275
H10	O	1m. red	£5000	£2500
H11		2m. blue	£8000	£8500
H25		3m. black	†	£38000
H26		5m. lake and black	†	£38000

1914. Nos. 1/2 surch in words.

No.	Type	Description	Unused	Used
H27	N	½d. on 3pf. brown	35·00	26·00
H28		1d. on 5pf. green	4·25	4·25

1915. Stamps of Gold Coast (King George V) optd **TOGO ANGLO-FRENCH OCCUPATION**.

No.	Type	Description	Unused	Used
H34		½d. green	30	1·00
H35		1d. red	30	50
H49		2d. grey	50	60
H50		2½d. blue	80	1·50
H38		3d. purple on yellow	80	1·40
H52		6d. purple	1·25	1·00
H53		1s. black on green	2·00	4·50
H54		2s. purple and blue on blue	4·50	8·50
H55		2s.6d. black and red on blue	4·50	7·00
H44		5s. green and red on yellow	8·00	15·00
H57a		10s. green and red on green	16·00	55·00
H58		20s. purple and black on red	£140	£160

FRENCH ISSUES

1914. Stamps of German Colonies, "Yacht" key-type, optd **Togo Occupation franco-anglaise** or surch also.

No.	Type	Description	Unused	Used
1	N	05 on 3pf. brown	50·00	60·00
9		5pf. green	£900	£350
2		10 on 5pf. green	25·00	16·00
10		10pf. red	£1000	£375
3		20pf. blue	55·00	48·00
4		25pf. black & red on yellow	65·00	60·00
5		30pf. black & orge on orange	90·00	90·00
6		40pf. black and red	£450	£400
15		50pf. black & purple on buff	£15000	£10000
7		80pf. black and red on pink	£450	£400
16	O	1m. red		
17		2m. blue	—	£15000
18		3m. black	—	£18000
19		5m. red and black		

1916. Stamps of Dahomey optd **TOGO Occupation franco-anglaise**.

No.	Type	Description	Unused	Used
20	**6**	1c. black and violet	15	2·00
21		2c. pink and brown	20	1·60
22		4c. brown and black	20	2·00
23		5c. green and light green	80	2·50
24		10c. pink and orange	20	1·90
25		15c. purple and red	95	1·60
26		20c. brown and grey	85	2·75
27		25c. blue and ultramarine	80	2·75
28		30c. violet and brown	1·25	3·00
29		35c. black and brown	80	3·00
30		40c. orange and black	80	3·00
31		45c. blue and grey	1·00	3·00
32		50c. brown and chocolate	1·25	2·75
33		75c. violet and blue	6·25	9·00
34		1f. black and green	8·50	12·00
35		2f. brown and yellow	11·50	16·00
36		5f. blue and violet	13·50	20·00

FRENCH MANDATE

1921. Stamps of Dahomey optd **TOGO**.

No.	Type	Description	Unused	Used
37	**6**	1c. green and grey	20	2·75
38		2c. orange and blue	10	2·25
39		4c. orange and green	20	2·75
40		5c. black and red	20	2·25
41		10c. green and turquoise	20	2·25
42		15c. red and brown	30	2·50
43		20c. orange and green	2·25	3·00
44		25c. orange and grey	1·60	2·00
45		30c. red and carmine	1·75	3·00
46		35c. green and purple	2·50	3·25
47		40c. grey and green	2·50	4·00
48		45c. grey and purple	1·25	4·00
49		50c. blue	2·00	3·00
50		75c. blue and brown	1·25	4·00
51		1f. blue and grey	3·00	4·00
52		2f. red and green	7·00	9·00
53		5f. black and yellow	10·00	12·50

1922. Stamps of 1921 (No. 57 colour changed) surch.

No.	Type	Description	Unused	Used
54	**6**	25c. on 15c. red and brown	90	3·00
55		25c. on 2f. red and green	2·00	3·00
56		25c. on 5f. black and orange	2·00	3·00
57		60 on 75c. violet on pink	85	3·25
58		65 on 45c. grey and purple	3·00	3·75
59		85 on 75c. blue and brown	2·50	4·00

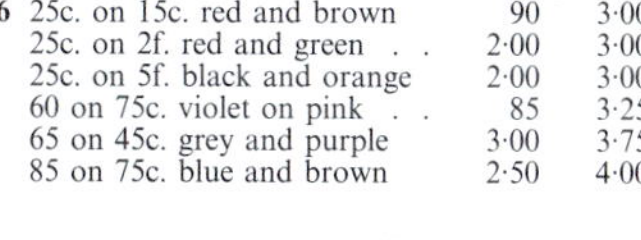

5 Coconut Palms

1924.

No.	Type	Description	Unused	Used
60	**5**	1c. black and yellow	20	2·75
61		2c. black and red	25	2·00
62		4c. black and blue	1·00	2·50
63		5c. black and orange	30	55
64		10c. black and mauve	10	15
65		15c. black and green	10	55
66	–	20c. black and grey	45	45
67	–	25c. black and green on yellow	45	30
68	–	30c. black and green	35	1·25
69	–	30c. green and olive	75	80
70	–	35c. black and brown	1·90	3·00
71	–	35c. green and turquoise	55	2·75
72	–	40c. black and red	20	50
73	–	45c. black and red	40	1·50
74	–	50c. black and orange on blue	95	2·00
75	–	55c. red and blue	1·50	3·00
76	–	60c. black and purple on pink	2·00	2·75
77	–	60c. red	60	3·00
78	–	65c. brown and lilac	40	60
79	–	75c. black and blue	1·75	1·75
80	–	80c. lilac and blue	1·90	3·25
81	–	85c. brown and orange	1·60	2·75
82	–	90c. pink and red	2·50	3·00
83	–	1f. black and purple on blue	2·25	1·50
84	–	1f. blue	2·50	2·25
85	–	1f. green and lilac	3·00	2·50
86	–	1f. orange and red	90	2·00
87	–	1f.10 brown and mauve	6·00	3·25
88	–	1f.25 red and mauve	1·90	2·50
89	–	1f.50 blue	1·10	2·25
90	–	1f.75 pink and brown	10·50	3·50
91	–	1f.75 blue and ultramarine	1·75	3·50
92	–	2f. grey and black on blue	45	65
93	–	3f. red and green	1·40	2·00
94	–	5f. black and orange on blue	2·00	1·75
95	–	10f. pink and brown	1·75	2·75
96	–	20f. black and red on yellow	2·25	1·50

DESIGNS: 20c. to 90c. Cocoa trees; 1f. to 20f. Palm trees.

1926. No. 84 surch.

No.	Type	Description	Unused	Used
98		1f.25 on 1f. blue	1·60	2·25

1931. "Colonial Exhibition" key-types inscr "TOGO".

No.	Type	Description	Unused	Used
99	E	40c. green and black	5·75	7·75
100	F	50c. mauve and black	5·75	7·75
101	G	90c. red and black	5·00	8·25
102	H	1f.50 blue and black	7·25	8·25

1937. International Exhibition, Paris. As Nos. 168/73 of St.-Pierre et Miquelon.

No.	Type	Description	Unused	Used
103		20c. violet	1·40	3·75
104		30c. green	2·00	4·00
105		40c. red	70	4·00
106		50c. brown	75	4·00
107		90c. red	80	3·75
108		1f.50 blue	75	3·25

1938. International Anti-cancer Fund. As T **38** of St. Pierre et Miquelon.

No.	Type	Description	Unused	Used
109		1f.75+50c. blue	11·50	26·00

1939. Centenary of Death of R. Caillie. As T **40** of Senegal.

No.	Type	Description	Unused	Used
110		90c. orange	30	35
111		2f. violet	65	2·75
112		2f.25 blue	60	2·75

1939. New York World's Fair. As T **41** of St. Pierre et Miquelon.

No.	Type	Description	Unused	Used
113		1f.25 red	1·75	3·00
114		2f.25 blue	30	3·00

1939. 150th Anniv of French Revolution. As T **42** of St. Pierre et Miquelon.

No.	Type	Description	Unused	Used
115		45c.+25c. green and black	5·00	12·00
116		70c.+30c. brown and black	5·00	12·00
117		90c.+35c. orange and black	5·00	12·00
118		1f.25+1f. red and black	5·00	12·00
119		2f.25+2f. blue and black	5·75	12·00

1940. Air. As T **48** of St. Pierre et Miquelon.

120		1f.90 blue	60	2·75
121		2f.90 red	50	2·50
122		4f.50 green	1·10	2·75
123		4f.90 olive	80	3·00
124		6f.90 orange	1·10	3·25

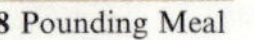
8 Pounding Meal

9 Riverside Village

10 Hunting

11 Young Girl

1940.

125	**8**	2c. violet	10	2·75
126		3c. green	10	2·75
127		4c. black	45	2·75
128		5c. red	70	2·75
129		10c. blue	70	2·75
130		15c. brown	35	2·75
131	**9**	20c. plum	40	1·25
132		25c. blue	65	2·75
133		30c. black	15	2·50
134		40c. red	25	2·75
135		45c. green	20	2·75
136		50c. brown	25	3·00
137		60c. violet	35	2·50
138	**10**	70c. black	1·25	3·00
139		90c. violet	1·40	3·25
140		1f. green	1·90	3·00
141		1f.25 red	1·00	2·50
142		1f.40 brown	1·90	3·25
143		1f.60 orange	95	2·25
144		2f. blue	80	1·90
145	**11**	2f.25 blue	1·75	3·50
146		2f.50 red	80	1·60
147		3f. violet	90	2·00
148		5f. red	1·25	1·60
149		10f. violet	55	2·50
150		20f. black	1·00	2·75

1941. National Defence Fund. Surch **SECOURS NATIONAL** and value.

151	+1f. on 50c. (No. 136)	4·25	5·00
152	+2f. on 80c. (No. 80)	6·25	7·50
153	+2f. on 1f.50 (No. 89)	6·50	7·50
154	+3f. on 2f. (No. 144)	7·00	7·50

1942. Air. As T **40d** of Senegal.

154a	50f. violet and yellow	1·75	3·25

1944. Nos. 75 and 82 surch **1 fr. 50**.

155	1f.50 on 55c. red and blue	85	1·75
156	1f.50 on 90c. pink and red	55	90

1944. No. 139 surch in figures and ornament.

157	**10**	3f.50 on 90c. violet	1·75	2·25
158		4f. on 90c. violet	80	2·50
159		5f. on 90c. violet	2·00	3·50
160		5f.50 on 90c. violet	2·00	3·75
161		10f. on 90c. violet	2·75	4·00
162		20f. on 90c. violet	3·00	3·75

18 Oil Extraction Process

19 Archer

20 Postal Runner and Lockheed Constellation

1947.

163	**18**	10c. red (postage)	15	2·25
164		30c. blue	15	2·75
165		50c. green	15	1·50
166	**19**	60c. pink	15	2·75
167		1f. brown	20	20
168		1f.20 green	20	3·00
169	–	1f.50 orange	85	3·00
170	–	2f. bistre	35	2·00
171	–	2f.50 black	85	3·75
172	–	3f. blue	95	40
173	–	3f.60 red	1·00	3·25
174	–	4f. blue	95	25
175	–	5f. brown	95	35
176	–	6f. blue	1·10	70
177	–	10f. red	1·25	20
178	–	15f. green	1·00	45
179	–	20f. green	1·25	55
180	–	25f. pink	85	65
181	–	40f. blue (air)	8·50	4·00
182	–	50f. mauve and violet	3·50	95
183	–	100f. brown and green	3·25	1·90
184	**20**	200f. pink	7·75	9·00

DESIGNS—As Type **18**: VERT: 1f.50 to 2f.50, Women hand-spinning cotton. HORIZ: 3f. to 4f. Drummer and village; 5f. to 10f. Red-fronted gazelles; 15f. to 25f. Trees and village. As Type **20**: 40f. African elephants and Sud Ouest SO.95 Corse II airplane; 50f. Airplane; 100f. Lockheed Constellation.

1949. Air. 75th Anniv of U.P.U. As T **58** of St. Pierre et Miquelon.

185	25f. multicoloured	3·00	9·25

1950. Colonial Welfare Fund. As T **59** of St. Pierre et Miquelon.

186	10f.+2f. blue and indigo	3·75	5·25

1952. Centenary of Military Medal. As T **60** of St. Pierre et Miquelon.

187	15f. brown, yellow and green	5·50	5·75

1954. Air. 10th Anniv of Liberation. As T **66** of St. Pierre et Miquelon.

188	15f. violet and blue	5·00	2·50

22 Gathering Palm Nuts

23 Roadway through Forest

1954.

189	**22**	8f. purple, lake and violet (postage)	3·00	2·50
190		15f. brown, grey and blue	3·00	20
191	**23**	500f. blue and green (air)	55·00	50·00

AUTONOMOUS REPUBLIC

24 Goliath Beetle

25 Rural School

1955. Nature Protection.

192	**24**	8f. black and green	2·25	3·75

1956. Economic and Social Fund Development Fund.

193	**25**	15f. brown and chestnut	1·60	75

26 Togolese Woman and Flag

1957. New National Flag.

194	**26**	15f. brown, red & turquoise	55	35

27 Togolese Woman and "Liberty" releasing Dove

1957. Air. 1st Anniv of Autonomous Republic.

195	**27**	25f. sepia, red and blue	60	2·25

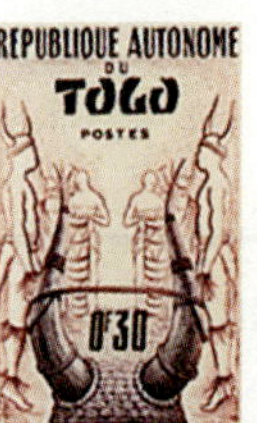
28 Konkomba Helmet

29 Kob

30 Torch and Flags

1957. Inscr "REPUBLIQUE AUTONOME DU TOGO".

196	**28**	30c. lilac and red (postage)	10	1·50
197		50c. indigo and blue	10	75
198		1f. lilac and purple	10	1·50
199		2f. brown and green	10	2·75
200		3f. black and green	15	1·60
201	**29**	4f. black and blue	50	2·50
202		5f. purple and grey	50	60
203		6f. grey and red	60	3·00
204		8f. violet and grey	65	3·00
205		10f. brown and green	2·25	45
206	–	15f. multicoloured	2·00	1·25
207	–	20f. multicoloured	2·50	40
208	–	25f. multicoloured	2·25	1·00
209	–	40f. multicoloured	2·50	1·60
210	**30**	50f. multicoloured (air)	85	1·10
211		100f. multicoloured	1·10	1·40
212		200f. multicoloured	2·50	3·75
213	–	500f. indigo, green and blue	14·00	9·50

DESIGNS—HORIZ: 15f. to 40f. Teak forest. 48 × 27 mm: 500f. Great egret.

See also Nos. 217/35.

31 "Human Rights"

32 "Bombax"

1958. 10th Anniv of Human Rights Declaration.

214	**31**	20f. red and green	50	35

1959. Tropical Flora.

215	**32**	5f. multicoloured	90	1·50
216	–	20f. yellow, green and black	1·25	1·60

DESIGN—HORIZ: 20f. "Tectona".

1959. As Nos. 196/213 but colours changed and inscr "REPUBLIQUE DU TOGO".

217	**28**	30c. blue & black (postage)	10	2·25
218		50c. green and green	15	2·75
219		1f. purple and green	20	10
220		2f. brown and green	25	10
221		3f. violet and purple	25	75
222	**29**	4f. violet and purple	1·90	1·10
223		5f. brown and green	1·90	85
224		6f. blue and ultramarine	2·00	1·25
225		8f. bistre and green	2·00	1·75
226		10f. brown and violet	1·60	85
227	–	15f. multicoloured	90	1·25
228	–	20f. multicoloured	1·10	20
229	–	25f. multicoloured	1·25	1·25
230	–	40f. multicoloured	1·00	30
231	–	25f. brown, grn & bl (air)	1·10	1·90
232	**30**	50f. multicoloured	85	1·10
233		100f. multicoloured	1·10	1·40
234		200f. multicoloured	2·50	4·00
235	–	500f. sepia, green & purple	12·00	4·50

DESIGN—VERT: 25f. (No. 231) Togo flag and shadow of airliner over Africa.

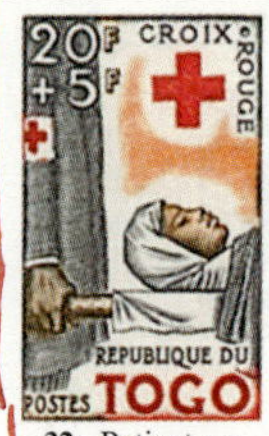
32a Patient on Stretcher

33 "The Five Continents"

1959. Red Cross Commemoration.

236	**32a**	20f.+5f. red, orge & slate	3·00	2·75
237	–	30f.+5f. red, brown & bl	3·00	3·50
238	–	50f.+10f. red, brn & grn	3·00	3·50

DESIGNS: 30f. Mother feeding child; 50f. Nurse superintending blood transfusion.

1959. United Nations Day.

239	**33**	15f. blue and brown	2·00	2·75
240		20f. blue and violet	2·00	2·75
241		25f. blue and brown	2·25	2·50
242		40f. blue and green	2·25	2·75
243		60f. blue and red	2·50	3·00

34 Skiing

35 "Uprooted Tree"

1960. Olympic Games, California and Rome.

244	**34**	30c. turquoise, red & green	10	65
245	–	50c. purple, red and black	40	2·25
246	–	1f. green, red and black	50	2·25
247	–	10f. brown, blue and indigo	2·50	2·75
248	–	15f. purple and green	2·25	3·00
249	–	20f. chocolate, green & brown	2·50	3·00
250	–	25f. brown, red and orange	2·75	2·75

DESIGNS—HORIZ: 50c. Ice hockey; 1f. Tobogganing; 10f. Cycling; 25f. Running. VERT: 125f. Throwing the discus; 20f. Boxing.

1960. World Refugee Year.

251	**35**	25f.+5f. green, brown & bl	40	3·25
252	–	45f.+5f. olive, black & bl	40	3·25

DESIGN: 45f. As Type **35** but "TOGO" at foot.

INDEPENDENT REPUBLIC

36 Prime Minister S. Olympio and Flag

37 Benin Hotel

1960. Independence Commemoration. (a) Postage. Centres multicoloured; backgrounds cream; inscription and frame colours given.

253	**36**	30c. sepia	10	10
254		50c. brown	10	10
255		1f. purple	10	10
256		10f. blue	15	10
257		20f. red	40	15
258		25f. green	50	20

(b) Air.

259	**37**	100f. red, yellow and green	1·60	50
260		200f. multicoloured	2·75	90
261	–	500f. brown and green	9·50	3·25

DESIGN—As Type **37**: VERT: 500f. Palm-nut vulture and map of Togo.

38 Union Jack and Flags

1960. Four-Power "Summit" Conference, Paris. Flags and inscr in red and blue.

262	**38**	50c. buff	10	10
263	–	1f. turquoise	10	10
264	–	20f. grey	35	20
265	–	25f. blue	40	20

DESIGNS—As Type **38** but flags of: 1f. Soviet Union; 20f. France; 25f. U.S.A. The Conference did not take place.

39 Togo Flag

40 South African Crowned Cranes

1961. Admission of Togo into U.N.O. Flag in red, yellow and green.
266 **39** 30c. red 10 10
267 50c. brown 10 10
268 1f. blue 10 10
269 10f. purple 20 10
270 25f. black 40 15
271 30f. violet 45 20

1961.
272 **40** 1f. multicoloured 50 10
273 10f. multicoloured 70 15
274 25f. multicoloured . . . . 1·10 40
275 30f. multicoloured . . . . 1·25 50

41 Augustino de Souza (statesman)

42 Daniel Beard (founder of American Boy Scout Movement) and Scout Badge

1961. 1st Anniv of Independence.
276 **41** 50c. black, red and yellow 10 10
277 1f. black, brown and green 10 10
278 10f. black, violet and blue 20 15
279 25f. black, green & salmon 40 10
280 30f. black, blue and mauve 50 20

1961. Boy Scout Movement Commemoration.
281 **42** 50c. lake, green and red . . 10 10
282 – 1f. violet and red 10 10
283 – 10f. black and brown . . . 20 10
284 – 25f. multicoloured 55 15
285 – 30f. red, brown and green 65 20
286 – 100f. mauve and blue . . . 1·60 60
DESIGNS—HORIZ: 1f. Lord Baden-Powell; 10f. Daniel Mensah ("Rover" Scout Chief); 100f. Scout salute. VERT: 25f. Chief Daniel Wilson (Togolese Scout); 30f. Campfire on triangular emblem.

43 Jet Airliner and Motor Launch

44 UNICEF Emblem

1961. U.N. Economic Commission on Africa. Mult.
287 20f. Type **43** 30 15
288 25f. Electric train and gantry 95 15
289 30f. Excavator and pylons . . 65 30
290 85f. Microscope and atomic symbol . . . . 1·25 50
The designs are superimposed on a map of Africa spread over the four stamps when the 30 and 85f. are mounted below the 20 and 25f.

1961. 15th Anniv of UNICEF.
291 **44** 1f. blue, green and black 10 10
292 – 10f. multicoloured 15 10
293 – 20f. multicoloured 20 10
294 – 25f. multicoloured 45 20
295 – 30f. multicoloured 80 20
296 – 85f. multicoloured . . . . 1·25 60
DESIGNS: 10f. to 85f. Children dancing round the globe. The six stamps, arranged in the following order, form a composite picture: Upper row, 1, 25 and 20f. Lower row, 10, 85 and 30f.

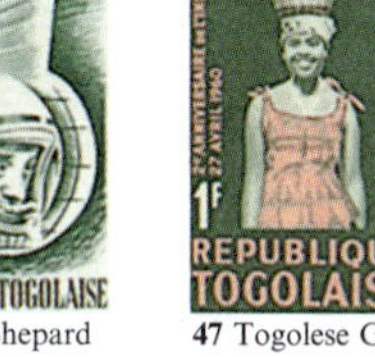

45 Alan Shepard

47 Togolese Girl

1962. Space Flights Commemoration.
297 **45** 50c. green 10 10
298 – 1f. mauve 15 10
299 **45** 25f. blue 35 20
300 – 30f. violet 50 30
DESIGN: 1, 30f. As Type **45** but portrait of Yuri Gagarin.

1962. Col. Glenn's Space Flight. Surch **100F COL. JOHN H. GLENN U S A VOL ORBITAL 20 FEVRIER 1962.**
301 **45** 100f. on 50c. green . . . . 2·00 2·00

1962. 2nd Anniv of Independence.
303 – 50c. multicoloured 10 10
304 **47** 1f. green and pink 10 10
305 – 5f. multicoloured 20 15
306 **47** 20f. violet and yellow . . . 30 15
307 – 25f. multicoloured 35 15
308 **47** 30f. red and yellow 35 15
DESIGN: 50c., 5, 25f. Independence Monument.

48 Arrows piercing Mosquito

1962. Malaria Eradication.
309 **48** 10f. multicoloured 30 10
310 25f. multicoloured 45 20
311 30f. multicoloured 50 35
312 85f. multicoloured . . . . 1·00 55

49 Presidents Kennedy and Olympio, and Capitol, Washington

1962. Visit of President Olympio to U.S.A.
313 **49** 50c. slate and ochre . . . 10 10
314 1f. slate and blue 10 10
315 2f. slate and red 10 10
316 5f. slate and mauve 10 10
317 25f. slate and lilac 40 15
318 100f. slate and green . . . 1·60 70

50 Stamps of 1897 and Mail-coach

1963. 65th Anniv of Togolese Postal Services.
319 **50** 30c. multicoloured (postage) 10 10
320 – 50c. multicoloured 10 10
321 – 1f. multicoloured 35 10
322 – 10f. multicoloured 45 15
323 – 25f. multicoloured 60 20
324 – 30f. multicoloured 85 40
325 – 100f. multicoloured (air) 2·40 1·00
DESIGNS (Togo stamps of): 50c. 1900 and German imperial yacht "Hohenzollern"; 1f. 1915 and steam mail train; 10f. 1924 and motor-cycle mail carrier; 25f. 1940 and mail-van; 30f. 1947 and Douglas DC-3 airplane; 100f. 1960 and Boeing 707 airplane.

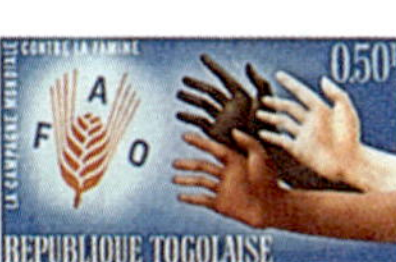

51 Hands reaching for F.A.O. Emblem

53 Centenary Emblem

52 Lome Port and Togolese Flag

1963. Freedom from Hunger.
326 **51** 50c. multicoloured 10 10
327 1f. multicoloured 10 10
328 25f. multicoloured 60 20
329 30f. multicoloured 85 30

1963. 3rd Anniv of Independence. Flag in red, yellow and green.
330 **52** 50c. black and brown . . . 10 10
331 1f. black and red 15 10
332 25f. black and blue 35 20
333 50f. black and ochre . . . 70 35

1963. Red Cross Centenary. Flag in red, yellow and green; cross red.
334 **53** 25f. blue and black 85 30
335 30f. green and black . . . 1·10 40

54 Broken Shackles and Abraham Lincoln

55 Flame and U.N. Emblem

1963. Cent of American Slaves' Emancipation. Centre in grey and green.
336 **54** 50c. black & brn (postage) 10 10
337 1f. black and blue 10 10
338 25f. black and red 45 15
339 100f. black and orange (air) . . . . 1·40 60

1963. 15th Anniv of Declaration of Human Rights. Flame in red.
340 **55** 50c. blue and ultramarine 10 10
341 1f. green and black 15 10
342 25f. lilac and blue 40 15
343 85f. gold and blue . . . . 1·10 60

56 Hibiscus

58 Temple and Isis

1964. Multicoloured.
344 50c. "Odontoglossum grande" (orchid) (postage) 10 10
345 1f. Type **56** 10 10
346 2f. "Papilio dardanus" (butterfly) 35 10
347 3f. "Morpho aega" (butterfly) 55 10
348 4f. "Pandinus imperator" (scorpion) 40 10
349 5f. Tortoise 20 15
350 6f. Strelitzia (flower) 55 15
351 8f. Python 45 15
352 10f. "Bunaea alcinde" (butterfly) 85 15
353 15f. Chameleon . . . . . . 1·25 15
354 20f. Common octopus . . . 1·50 20
355 25f. John Dory (fish) . . . . 1·60 20
356 30f. French angelfish . . . . 2·00 35
357 40f. Pygmy hippopotamus . . 2·00 35
358 45f. African palm civet . . . 3·25 60
359 60f. Bohar reedbuck . . . . 4·50 90
360 85f. Olive baboon . . . . . 5·50 1·00
361 50f. Black-bellied seedcracker (air) . . . . 3·50 50
362 100f. Black and white mannikin . . . . 8·25 90
363 200f. Red-faced lovebird . . 12·00 1·90
364 250f. Grey parrot . . . . . 28·00 4·25
365 500f. Yellow-breasted barbet 38·00 1·10

1964. President Kennedy Memorial Issue. Optd **En Memoire de JOHN F. KENNEDY 1917-1963.** Centre in grey and green.
366 **54** 50c. black & brn (postage) 15 10
367 1f. black and blue 15 10
368 25f. black and red 50 20
369 100f. black and orange (air) . . . . 1·60 80

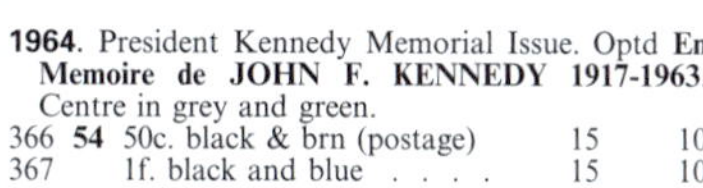

1964. Nubian Monuments Preservation.
370 **58** 20f. multicoloured 30 10
371 – 25f. mauve and black . . . 35 20
372 – 30f. olive, black and yellow 50 30
DESIGNS: 25f. Head of Rameses II, Abu Simbel; 30f. Temple of Philae.

59 Phosphate Mine, Kpeme

1964. 4th Anniv of Independence.
373 **59** 5f. ochre, bistre and brown 35 10
374 – 25f. lake, brown and violet 35 15
375 – 60f. yellow, olive and green 1·25 50
376 – 85f. blue, slate and violet 1·50 50
DESIGNS: 25f. Mine installations; 60f. Diesel phosphate train; 85f. Loading phosphate onto "Panama Maru" bulk carrier.

60 Togolese breaking Chain

61 Pres. Grunitzky and "Papilio memnon"

1964. 1st Anniv of African Heads of State Conference, Addis Ababa.
377 **60** 5f. sepia & orange (postage) 15 10
378 25f. sepia and green . . . 35 15
379 85f. sepia and red 95 45
380 100f. sepia & turquoise (air) . . . . 1·25 65

1964. "National Union and Reconciliation".
381 **61** 1f. violet and mauve . . . 20 10
382 – 5f. sepia and ochre 10 10
383 – 25f. violet and blue 45 15
384 **61** 45f. purple and red . . . . 1·75 50
385 – 85f. bronze and green . . . 1·90 60
DESIGNS—President and: 5f. Dove; 25, 85f. Flowers.

62 Football

1964. Olympic Games, Tokyo.
386 **62** 1f. green (postage) 10 10
387 – 5f. blue (Running) 25 15
388 – 25f. red (Throwing the discus) 75 15
389 **62** 45f. turquoise . . . . . . 1·00 40
390 – 100f. brown (Tennis) (air) 1·75 55

1964. French, African and Malagasy Co-operation. As T **60a** of Senegal.
391 25f. brown, bistre and purple 40 20

63 Charles's Hydrogen Balloon, Giffard's Steam-powered Dirigible Airship and Airship LZ-5

1964. Inaug of "Air Togo" (National Airline).
392 **63** 5f. multicoloured (postage) 10 10
393 10f. blue, lake and green 30 10
394 – 25f. ultramarine, orge & blue 50 15
395 – 45f. mauve, green and bl 1·10 35
396 – 100f. multicoloured (air) 1·90 80
DESIGNS: 25, 45f. Farman H.F. III biplane, Lilienthal biplane glider and Boeing 707; 100f. Boeing 707 and Togolese flag.

64 Sun, Globe and Satellites "Ogo" and "Mariner"

1964. International Quiet Sun Years. Sun yellow.
397 **64** 10f. blue and red 15 10
398 – 15f. blue, brown and mauve 20 10
399 – 20f. green and violet . . . 30 10
400 – 25f. purple, green and blue 35 15
401 **64** 45f. blue and green 70 35
402 – 50f. green and red 80 40
SATELLITES: 15, 25f. "Tiros", "Telstar" and orbiting solar observatory; 20, 50f. "Nimbus", "Syncom" and "Relay".

65 Pres. Grunitzky and the Mount of the Beatitudes Church

1965. Israel–Togo Friendship. Inscr "AMITIE ISRAEL–TOGO 1964".
403 – 5f. purple 10 10
404 **65** 20f. blue and purple 20 10
405 – 25f. turquoise and red 35 15
406 – 45f. olive, bistre and purple 70 35
407 – 85f. turquoise and purple 1·10 50
DESIGNS—VERT: 5f. Togolese stamps being printed on Israel press. HORIZ: 25, 85f. Arms of Israel and Togo; 45f. As Type **65** but showing old synagogue, Capernaum.

66 "Syncom 3", Dish Aerial and I.T.U. Emblem

1965. I.T.U. Centenary.
408 **66** 10f. turquoise and green 15 10
409 20f. olive and black 35 15
410 25f. blue and ultramarine 40 15
411 45f. rose and red 70 35
412 50f. green and black 90 45

67 Abraham Lincoln **68** Throwing the Discus

1965. Death Centenary of Lincoln.
413 **67** 1f. purple (postage) 10 10
414 5f. greeen 10 10
415 20f. brown 35 10
416 25f. blue 45 20
417 100f. olive (air) 1·60 70

1965. 1st African Games, Brazzaville. Flags in red, yellow and green.
418 **68** 5f. purple (postage) 10 10
419 – 10f. blue 15 10
420 – 15f. brown 35 10
421 – 25f. purple 90 20
422 – 100f. green (air) 1·50 65
SPORTS: 10f. Throwing the javelin; 15f. Hand-ball; 25f. Running; 100f. Football.

69 Sir Winston Churchill

1965. Churchill Commemoration.
423 **69** 5f. green (postage) 10 10
424 – 10f. violet and blue 15 10
425 **69** 20f. brown 40 15
426 – 45f. blue 65 35
427 **69** 85f. red (air) 1·50 65
DESIGNS—HORIZ: 10, 45f. Stalin, Roosevelt and Churchill at Teheran Conference, 1943.

70 Unisphere

1965. New York World's Fair.
428 **70** 5f. plum and blue 15 10
429 – 10f. sepia and green 20 10
430 **70** 25f. myrtle and brown 35 20
431 – 50f. myrtle and violet 65 40
432 **70** 85f. brown and red 1·10 50
DESIGNS: 10f. Native dancers and drummer; 50f. Michelangelo's "Pieta".

71 "Laying Bricks of Peace"

1965. International Co-operation Year.
433 **71** 5f. multicoloured 10 10
434 15f. multicoloured 15 15
435 – 25f. multicoloured 30 15
436 – 40f. multicoloured 60 30
437 – 85f. multicoloured 1·00 50
DESIGNS: 25, 40f. Hands suppporting globe; 85f. I.C.Y. emblem.

72 Leonov with Camera

1965. Astronauts in Space.
438 **72** 25f. mauve and blue 50 20
439 – 50f. brown and green 90 40
DESIGN: 50f. White with rocket-gun.

73 "ONU" and Doves

1966. 20th Anniv of U.N.O.
440 **73** 5f. brown, yellow and blue (postage) 10 10
441 – 10f. blue, turquoise and orange 20 10
442 – 20f. orange, green and light green 35 15
443 – 25f. blue, turquoise & yell 45 20
444 – 100f. ochre, blue and light blue (air) 1·60 55
DESIGNS: 10f. U.N. Headquarters and emblem; 20f. "ONU" and orchids; 25f. U.N. Headquarters and Adlai Stevenson; 100f. "ONU", fruit and ears of wheat.

74 Pope Paul, Boeing 707 and U.N. Emblem

1966. Pope Paul's Visit to U.N. Organization. Multicoloured.
445 5f. Type **74** (postage) 10 10
446 15f. Pope before microphones at U.N. (vert) 20 10
447 20f. Pope and U.N. Headquarters 35 15
448 30f. As 15f. 45 20
449 45f. Pope before microphones at U.N., and map (air) 80 30
450 90f. Type **74** 1·60 80

75 W.H.O. Building and Roses

1966. Inaug of W.H.O. Headquarters, Geneva. Multicoloured designs showing W.H.O. Building and flower as given.
451 5f. Type **75** (postage) 20 10
452 10f. Alstroemerias 35 10
453 15f. Asters 45 20
454 20f. Freesias 55 35
455 30f. Geraniums 65 35
456 50f. Asters (air) 95 35
457 50f. Type **75** 1·50 55

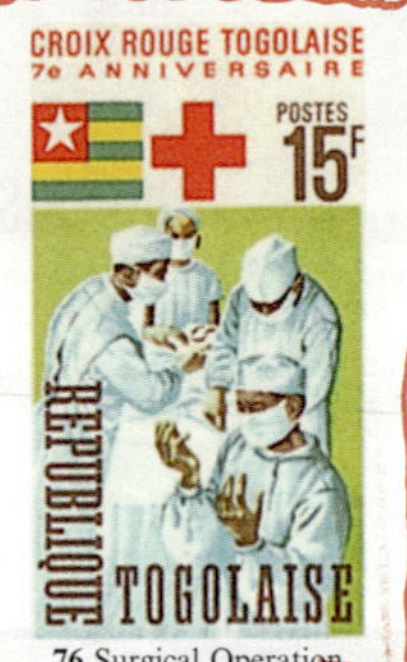

76 Surgical Operation

1966. 7th Anniv of Togolese Red Cross. Mult.
459 5f. Type **76** (postage) 10 10
460 10f. Blood transfusion 15 10
461 15f. Type **76** 30 15
462 30f. Blood transfusion 40 15
463 45f. African man and woman 70 45
464 100f. J. H. Dunant (air) 1·75 90

1966. Space Achievements. Nos. 438/9 optd as below or surch also.
465 50f. (**ENVOLEE SURVEYOR 1**) 85 40
466 50f. (**ENVOLEE GEMINI 9**) 85 40
467 100f. on 25f. (**ENVOLEE LUNA 9**) 1·60 70
468 100f. on 25f. (**ENVOLEE VENUS 3**) 1·60 70

78 Wood-carving **79** Togolese Man

1966. Togolese Arts and Crafts.
469 **78** 5f. brn, yell & bl (postage) 10 10
470 – 10f. brown, salmon & green 15 10
471 – 15f. brown, yellow and red 30 15
472 – 30f. brown, bistre and violet 55 20
473 – 60f. brown, salmon and blue (air) 1·40 60
474 **78** 90f. brown, yellow and red 1·40 60
DESIGNS: 10, 60f. Basket-making; 15f. Weaving; 30f. Pottery.

1966. Air. Inauguration of Douglas DC-8F Air Services. As T **76a** of Senegal.
475 30f. black, green and yellow 65 25

1966. Togolese Costumes and Dances. Mult.
476 5f. Type **79** (postage) 10 10
477 10f. Togolese woman 10 10
478 20f. Female dancer 40 10
479 25f. Male dancer 50 15
480 30f. Dancer in horned helmet 65 20
481 45f. Drummer 1·00 50
482 50f. Female dancer (air) 85 45
483 60f. Dancer in horned helmet 1·40 60

80 Footballers and Jules Rimet Cup

1966. World Cup Football Championship, England. Showing football scenes and Jules Rimet Cup.
484 **80** 5f. multicoloured (postage) 20 10
485 – 10f. multicoloured 30 10
486 – 20f. multicoloured 50 10
487 – 25f. multicoloured 50 15
488 – 30f. multicoloured 65 20
489 – 45f. multicoloured 1·00 40
490 – 50f. multicoloured (air) 1·00 30
491 – 60f. multicoloured 1·50 40

81 African Mouthbrooder

1967. Fishes. Multicoloured designs showing fishes with fishing craft in the background.
493 5f. Type **81** (postage) 30 10
494 10f. Golden trevally 50 15
495 15f. Six banded distichodus 60 25
496 25f. Jewel cichlid 85 30
497 30f. Type **81** 1·25 55
498 45f. As 10f. (air) 2·00 70
499 90f. As 15f. 2·75 1·00

82 African Boy and Greyhound

1967. 20th Anniv (1966) of UNICEF.
500 **82** 5f. multicoloured (postage) 20 10
501 – 10f. brown, green & lt grn 40 15
502 **82** 15f. black, brown & mauve 60 20
503 – 20f. black, ultramarine & blue 75 30
504 **82** 30f. black, blue and olive 1·10 35
505 – 45f. bronze, brown and yellow (air) 1·25 40
506 **82** 90c. black, bronze and blue 1·75 55
DESIGNS: 10f. Boy and Irish setter; 20f. Girl and doberman; 45f. Girl and miniature poodle.

83 Launching "Diamant" Rocket

1967. French Space Achievements. Multicoloured.
508 5f. Type **83** (postage) 10 10
509 10f. Satellite "A-1" (horiz) 20 10
510 15f. Satellite "FR-1" 30 10
511 20f. Satellite "D-1" (horiz) 40 15
512 25f. As 10f. 50 30
513 40f. As 20f. 70 35
514 50f. Type **83** (air) 95 40
515 90f. As 15f. 1·50 55

84 Bach and Organ

1967. 20th Anniv (1966) of UNESCO.
517 **84** 5f. multicoloured (postage) 10 10
518 – 10f. multicoloured 20 10
519 – 15f. multicoloured 45 20
520 – 20f. multicoloured 55 20
521 – 30f. multicoloured 90 45
522 **84** 45f. multicoloured (air) 1·10 40
523 – 90f. multicoloured 1·60 55
DESIGNS: 10, 90f. Beethoven, violin and clarinet; 15, 30f. Duke Ellington, saxophone, trumpet and drums; 20f. Debussy, grand piano and harp.

85 British Pavilion and Lilies

1967. World Fair, Montreal. Multicoloured.
525 5f. Type **85** (postage) 15 10
526 10f. French Pavilion and roses 30 10
527 30f. "Africa Place" and strelitzia 75 15
528 45f. As 10f. (air) 1·00 35
529 60f. Type **85** 1·10 45
530 90f. As 30f. 1·75 60
531 105f. U.S. Pavilion and daisies 2·25 65

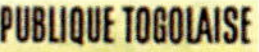
86 "Peace"

1967. Air. Disarmament. Designs showing sections of the "Peace" mural by J. Zanetti at the U.N. Headquarters Building Conference Room.
533 **86** 5f. multicoloured 15 10
534 A 15f. multicoloured 20 10
535 B 30f. multicoloured 40 10
536 **86** 45f. multicoloured 70 35
537 A 60f. multicoloured 1·25 45
538 B 90f. multicoloured 1·60 55

87 Lions Emblem with Supporters

1967. 50th Anniv of Lions International. Mult.
540 10f. Type **87** 20 10
541 20f. Flowers and Lions emblem 35 15
542 30f. Type **87** 45 20
543 45f. As 20f. 1·25 45

88 Bohar Reedbuck

1967. Wildlife.
544 **88** 5f. brown & pur (postage) 10 10
545 – 10f. blue, red and yellow 25 10
546 – 15f. black, lilac and green 45 15
547 – 20f. blue, sepia and yellow 55 25
548 – 25f. brown, yellow and olive 85 35
549 – 30f. blue, violet and yellow 1·75 50
550 – 45f. brown and blue (air) 90 35
551 – 60f. black, brown and green 1·25 50
DESIGNS: 10, 20, 30f. Montagu's harriers (birds of prey); 15f. Common zebra; 25f. Leopard; 45f. Lion; 60f. African elephants.

1967. Air. 5th Anniv of U.A.M.P.T. As T **86a** of Senegal.
552 100f. brown, blue and green 1·60 1·10

89 Stamp Auction and Togo Stamps—1m. (German) of 1900 and 100f. Conference of 1964

1967. 70th Anniv of 1st Togolese Stamps. Mult.
553 5f. Type **89** (postage) 15 10
554 10f. Exhibition and 1d. (British) of 1915 and 50f. I.T.U. of 1965 15 10
555 15f. Stamp shop and 50c. (French) of 1924 40 10
556 20f. Stamp-packet vending machine and 5f. U.N. of 1965 40 10
557 30f. As 15f. 60 30
558 45f. As 10f. 85 40
559 90f. Type **89** (air) 1·50 60
560 105f. Father and son with album and 1f. Kennedy of 1964 1·75 80

89a Currency Tokens

1967. 5th Anniv of West African Monetary Union.
562 **89a** 30f. blue and green 55 30

90 Long Jumping

1967. Olympic Games, Mexico and Grenoble (1968). Multicoloured.
563 5f. Type **90** (postage) 10 10
564 15f. Ski-jumping 20 10
565 30f. Relay runners 55 20
566 45f. Bob-sleighing 90 35
567 60f. As 30f. (air) 1·10 40
568 90f. Type **90** 1·00 55

1967. National Day (29 Sept). Nos. 525/31 optd **JOURNEE NATIONALE DU TOGO 29 SEPTEMBRE 1967**.
570 5f. multicoloured (postage) 35 20
571 10f. multicoloured 35 20
572 30f. multicoloured 1·00 40
573 45f. multicoloured (air) 40 20
574 60f. multicoloured 80 35
575 90f. multicoloured 1·25 45
576 105f. multicoloured 2·25 65

92 "The Gleaners" (Millet) and Benin Phosphate Mine

1968. Paintings and Local Industries.
577 **92** 10f. multicoloured 20 10
578 – 20f. multicoloured 30 10
579 **92** 30f. multicoloured 60 15
580 – 45f. multicoloured 70 20
581 **92** 60f. multicoloured 1·25 45
582 – 90f. multicoloured 1·40 70
DESIGN: 20, 45, 90f. "The Weaver at the Loom" (Van Gogh) and textile plant, Dadja.

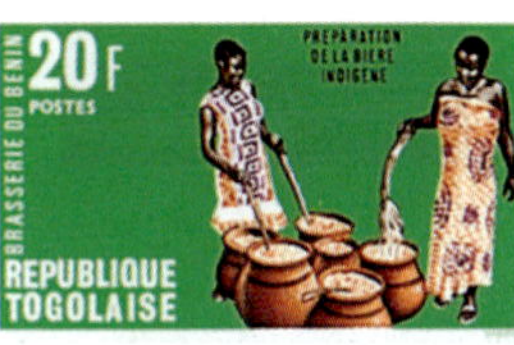

93 Brewing Beer

1968. Benin Brewery. Multicoloured.
583 20f. Type **93** 35 10
584 30f. "Drinking at a Bar" (detail from painting by Manet) (vert) 1·00 30
585 45f. Bottling-washing machine and bottle of Benin beer 70 40

94 Decade Emblem and Sunflowers

96 Dr. Adenauer and Europa "Key"

95 Viking Longship and Portuguese Galleon

1968. International Hydrological Decade.
586 **94** 30f. multicoloured (postage) 60 30
587 60f. multicoloured (air) 85 40

1968. Inaug of Lome Port. Multicoloured.
588 5f. Type **95** (postage) 15 10
589 10f. Paddle-steamer "Clermont" and Liner "Athlone Castle" 20 10
590 20f. Quayside, Lome Port 65 20
591 30f. Type **95** 90 35
592 45f. As 10f. (air) 1·10 40
593 90f. Nuclear-powered freighter "Savannah" 2·00 60

1968. Adenauer (German statesman) Commem.
595 **96** 90f. multicoloured 1·60 80

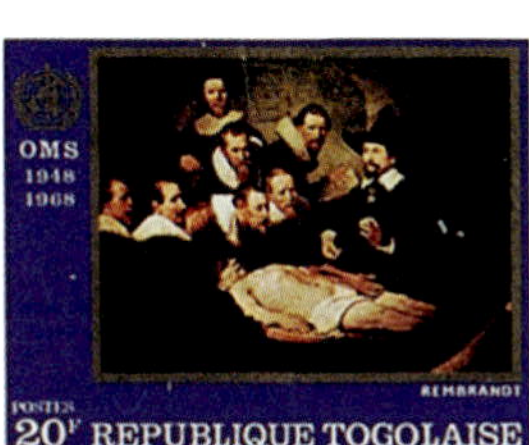

97 "Dr. Turp's Anatomy Lesson" (Rembrandt)

1968. 20th Anniv of World Health Organization. Paintings. Multicoloured.
596 15f. "Expulsion from the Garden of Eden" (Michelangelo) (postage) 30 10
597 20f. Type **97** 40 15
598 30f. "Johann Deyman's Anatomy Lesson" (Rembrandt) 55 20
599 45f. "Christ healing the sick" (Raphael) 85 35
600 60f. As 30f. (air) 85 40
601 90f. As 45f. 1·10 55

98 Wrestling

1968. Olympic Games, Mexico. Multicoloured.
603 15f. Type **98** (postage) 20 15
604 20f. Boxing 45 15
605 30f. Judo 65 20
606 45f. Running 80 35
607 60f. Type **98** (air) 90 40
608 90f. As 45f. 1·25 55

99 "Try Your Luck"

100 Scout and Tent

1968. 2nd Anniv of National Lottery. Mult.
610 30f. Type **99** 55 25
611 45f. Lottery ticket, horse-shoe and cloverleaf 80 30

1968. Air. "Philexafrique" Stamp Exhibition, Abidjan (Ivory Coast, 1969) (1st issue). As T **98a** of Senegal. Multicoloured.
612 100f. "The Letter" (J. A. Franquelin) 2·75 1·90

1968. Togolese Scouts. Multicoloured.
613 5f. Type **100** (postage) 10 10
614 10f. Scoutmaster with cubs 30 10
615 20f. Giving first aid 40 15
616 30f. Scout game 50 20
617 45f. As 10f. 65 35
618 60f. As 20f. (air) 90 45
619 90f. As 30f. 1·25 65
The 10, 20, 45 and 60f. are horiz.

101 "The Adoration of the Shepherds" (Giorgione)

1968. Christmas. Paintings. Multicoloured.
621 15f. Type **101** (postage) 35 10
622 20f. "The Adoration of the Kings" (Brueghel) 45 10
623 30f. "The Adoration" (Botticelli) 55 15
624 45f. "The Adoration" (Durer) 90 35
625 60f. As 20f. (air) 1·00 40
626 90f. As 45f. 1·50 55

102 Martin Luther King

1969. Human Rights Year.
628 **102** 15f. green & brown (postage) 20 10
629 – 20f. violet and turquoise 35 15
630 **102** 30f. blue and red 55 20
631 – 45f. red and olive 1·10 45
632 – 60f. blue and purple (air) 90 45
633 **102** 90f. brown and green 1·25 55
PORTRAITS: 20f. Prof. Rene Cassin (Nobel Peace Prize-winner); 45f. Pope John XXIII; 60f. Robert E. Kennedy.

1969. Air. "Philexafrique" Stamp Exn, Abidjan, Ivory Coast (2nd issue). As T **101a** of Senegal.
635 50f. red, brown and green 80 80
DESIGN: 50f. Aledjo Rock and stamp of 1900.

103 Football

1969. Inaug of Sports Stadium, Lome.
636 **103** 10f. brown, red and green (postage) 10 10
637 – 15f. brown, blue and orange 30 10
638 – 20f. brown, green and yellow 40 15

639 – 30f. brown, blue and green 50 20
640 – 45f. brown, violet and orange 65 30
641 – 60f. brown, red and blue (air) 90 35
642 – 90f. brown, mauve and blue . . . . 1·25 55
DESIGNS: 15f. Handball; 20f. Volleyball; 30f. Basketball; 45f. Tennis; 60f. Boxing; 90f. Cycling.

104 Module landing on Moon

1969. 1st Man on the Moon. Multicoloured.
644 1f. Type **104** (postage) . . . 10 10
645 20f. Astronaut and module on Moon 20 10
646 30f. As Type **104** 40 15
647 45f. As 20f. 65 35
648 60f. Astronaut exploring lunar surface (air) 85 40
649 100f. Astronaut gathering Moon rock . . . . 1·40 70

105 "The Last Supper" (Tintoretto)

1969. Religious Paintings. Multicoloured.
651 5f. Type **105** (postage) . . . 15 10
652 10f. "Christ's Vision at Emmaus" (Velazquez) . . 30 10
653 20f. "Pentecost" (El Greco) 50 20
654 30f. "The Annunciation" (Botticelli) 70 20
655 45f. As 10f. . . . . 1·10 45
656 90f. As 20f. (air) . . . . . . 1·90 65

1969. Eisenhower Commem. Nos. 628/33 optd with Eisenhower's silhouette and **EN MEMOIRE DWIGHT D. EISENHOWER 1890-1968**.
658 **102** 15f. green & brown (postage) 25 15
659 – 20f. violet and turquoise 45 15
660 **102** 30f. blue and red 55 20
661 – 45f. red and olive 95 30
662 – 60f. blue and purple (air) 90 45
663 **102** 90f. brown and green . . 1·25 65

107 Bank in Hand and Emblem

1969. 5th Anniv of African Development Bank. Multicoloured.
665 30f. Type **107** (postage) . . . 85 20
666 45f. Diesel locomotive in hand, and emblem . . . . 2·75 75
667 100f. Farmer and cattle in hand, and emblem (air) . . 1·25 55

108 Dunant and Red Cross Workers

1969. 50th Anniv of League of Red Cross Societies. Multicoloured.
668 15f. Type **108** (postage) . . . 35 10
669 20f. Pasteur and help for flood victims 40 10
670 30f. Fleming and flood control 75 20
671 45f. Rontgen and Red Cross post 95 30
672 60f. As 45f. (air) 90 45
673 90f. Type **108** . . . . 1·25 65

109 Weeding Corn

1969. Young Pioneers Agricultural Organization. Multicoloured.
675 1f. Type **109** (postage) . . . 10 10
676 2f. Glidji Agricultural Centre 10 10
677 3f. Founding meeting 10 10
678 4f. Glidji class 15 10
679 5f. Student "pyramid" . . . 15 10
680 7f. Students threshing . . . 15 10
681 8f. Gardening instruction . . 15 10
682 10f. Co-op village 15 10
683 15f. Students gardening . . . 30 15
684 20f. Cattle-breeding 35 15
685 25f. Poultry-farming 45 15
686 30f. Independence parade . . 45 20
687 40f. Boys on high-wire . . . 65 35
688 45f. Tractor and trailer . . . 80 35
689 50f. Co-op village 85 35
690 60f. Tractor-driving tuition 90 45
691 90f. Harvesting manioc (air) 1·10 45
692 100f. Gardening instruction 1·40 55
693 200f. Thinning-out corn . . . 2·25 1·10
694 250f. Drummers marching . . 4·25 1·50
695 500f. Young pioneers marching . . . . 9·50 3·00

111 Books and Map

1969. 12th Anniv of International African Library Development Association.
700 **111** 30f. multicoloured 45 30

1969. Christmas. No. 644/5 and 647/9 optd **JOYEUX NOEL**.
701 1f. Type **104** (postage) . . . 35 20
702 20f. Astronaut and module on Moon . . . . 1·10 45
703 45f. As 20f. . . . . 1·50 1·00
704 60f. Astronaut exploring lunar surface (air) . . . . 1·90 65
705 100f. Astronaut gathering Moon rock . . . . 3·00 1·00

113 George Washington

114 "Ploughing" (Klodt)

1969. "Leaders of World Peace". Multicoloured.
707 15f. Type **113** (postage) . . . 30 10
708 20f. Albert Luthule 35 10
709 30f. Mahatma Gandhi . . . 55 15
710 45f. Simon Boliver 70 20
711 60f. Friedrich Ebert (air) . . 90 35
712 90f. As 30f. . . . . 1·25 50

1970. 50th Anniv of I.L.O. Paintings. Mult.
713 5f. Type **114** (postage) . . . 10 10
714 10f. "Gardening" (Pissarro) 20 10
715 20f. "Harvesting Fruit" (Rivera) 35 10
716 30f. "Seeds of Spring" (Van Gogh) 80 35
717 45f. "Workers of the Fields" (Rivera) 80 35
718 60f. As 30f. (air) . . . . . . 1·00 35
719 90f. As 45f. . . . . 1·50 50

115 Model Coiffures

1970. Togolese Hair-styles. Multicoloured.
721 5f. Type **115** (postage) . . . 15 10
722 10f. As T **115**, but different styles 35 10
723 20f. Fefe style 50 15
724 30f. Danmlongbedji style . . 1·25 20
725 45f. Blom style (air) 90 30
726 90f. Aklui and Danmlongbedji styles . . . 1·60 65
Nos. 723/5 are vert.

116 Togo Stamp and Independence Monument, Lome

1970. 10th Anniv of Independence. Multicoloured.
727 20f. Type **116** (postage) . . . 45 15
728 30f. Pres. Eyademe and Palace 65 20
729 50f. Map, dove and monument (vert) . . . . . 1·10 35
730 60f. Togo stamp and monument (air) 80 40

117 New U.P.U. Headquarters Building

1970. New U.P.U. Headquarters Building.
731 **117** 30f. violet and orange (postage) . . . . 1·00 35
732 50f. red and blue (air) . . 80 35

118 Italy and Uruguay

1970. World Cup Football Championships, Mexico. Multicoloured.
733 5f. Type **118** (postage) . . . 10 10
734 10f. England and Brazil . . . 20 10
735 15f. Russia and Mexico . . . 35 10
736 20f. Germany and Morocco 45 10
737 30f. Rumania and Czechoslovakia 85 20
738 50f. Sweden and Israel (air) 55 30
739 60f. Bulgaria and Peru . . . 65 35
740 90f. Belgium and El Salvador 1·25 50

119 Lenin

1970. Birth Centenary of Lenin. Multicoloured.
742 30f. Type **119** (postage) . . . 1·00 45
743 50f. "Peasant messengers with Lenin" (Serov) (air) . . . 1·10 35

120 British Pavilion

1970. "Expo 70", Osaka, Japan. Multicoloured.
744 2f. Pennants, Sanyo Pavilion (57 × 36 mm) 15 10
745 20f. Type **120** 20 10
746 30f. French Pavilion 45 15
747 50f. Soviet Pavilion 85 30
748 60f. Japanese Pavilion . . . 1·10 45

121 Armstrong, Collins and Aldrin

1970. "Apollo" Moon Flights. Multicoloured.
750 1f. Type **121** (postage) . . . 10 10
751 2f. U.S. flag and moon-rock 10 10
752 20f. Astronaut and module on Moon 35 10
753 30f. Conrad, Gordon and Bean 65 20
754 50f. As 2f. . . . . 1·00 35
755 200f. Lovell, Haise and Swigert ("Apollo 13") (air) 2·50 1·40

1970. Safe Return of "Apollo 13". As Nos. 750/5, but additionally inscr "FELICITATIONS BON RETOUR APOLLO XIII".
757 **121** 1f. multicoloured (postage) 10 10
758 – 2f. multicoloured 10 10
759 – 20f. multicoloured 35 10
760 – 30f. multicoloured 65 20
761 – 50f. multicoloured . . . . 1·00 35
762 – 200f. multicoloured (air) 2·50 1·60

123 "Euchloron megaera"

1970. Butterflies and Moths. Multicoloured.
764 1f. Type **123** (postage) . . . 15 10
765 2f. "Cymothoe sangaris" . . . 30 10
766 30f. "Danaus chrysippus" . . 1·50 35
767 50f. "Morpho sp." . . . . . 2·75 65
768 60f. Type **123** (air) . . . . . 3·00 70
769 90f. "Pseudacraea boisiduvali" . . . . 4·25 95

124 Painting by Velasquez (I.L.O.)

1970. 25th Anniv of U.N.O. Multicoloured.
770 1f. Type **124** (postage) . . . 10 10
771 15f. Painting by Delacroix (F.A.O.) 10 10
772 20f. Painting by Holbein (UNESCO) 20 15
773 30f. Painting of U.N. H.Q., New York 60 15
774 50f. Painting by Renoir (UNICEF 90 35
775 60f. Painting by Van Gogh (U.P.U.) (air) . . . . . 1·00 35
776 90f. Painting by Carpaccio (W.H.O./O.M.S.) . . . . . 1·50 50

125 "The Nativity" (Botticelli)

1970. Christmas. "Nativity" Paintings by Old Masters. Multicoloured.
778 15f. Type **125** (postage) . . . 15 10
779 20f. Veronese 15 10
780 30f. El Greco 55 15
781 50f. Fra Angelico . . . . . 1·00 30
782 60f. Botticelli (different) (air) 1·25 30
783 90f. Tiepolo . . . . 1·75 45

1971. De Gaulle Commemoration (1st issue). Nos. 708/9 and 711/12 optd **EN MEMOIRE Charles De Gaulle 1890-1970** or surch in addition.
785 30f. multicoloured (postage) 1·10 35
786 30f. on 90f. multicoloured . . 1·10 35
787 150f. on 20f. multicoloured 6·75 1·75
788 200f. on 60f. mult (air) . . . 5·25 2·50

127 De Gaulle and Churchill

1971. De Gaulle Commemoration (2nd issue).
789 **127** 20f. blue & black (postage) 55 15
790 – 30f. red and black 65 20
791 – 40f. green and black . . . 1·00 40
792 – 50f. brown and black . . 1·25 50
793 – 60f. violet and black (air) 2·25 55
794 – 90f. blue and black . . . 3·25 80
DESIGNS: 30f. De Gaulle with Eisenhower; 40f. With Pres. Kennedy; 50f. With Adenauer; 60f. With Pope Paul VI; 90f. General De Gaulle.

128 Shepard and Moon Exploration

1971. Moon Mission of "Apollo 14". Mult.
796 1f. Type **128** (postage) . . . 10 10
797 10f. Mitchell and rock-gathering 15 10
798 30f. Roosa and module approaching Moon 50 15
799 40f. Launch from Moon . . . 90 30
800 50f. "Apollo 14" emblem (air) 60 20
801 100f. As 40f. . . . . 1·25 40
802 200f. As 50f. . . . . 2·10 80

129 "The Resurrection" (after Raphael)

131 Sud Aviation Caravelle over Control Tower

130 Cocoa Tree and Pods

1971. Easter. Paintings of "The Resurrection" by various artists. Multicoloured.
804 1f. Type **129** (postage) . . . 15 10
805 30f. Master of Trebon . . . 55 15
806 40f. Type **129** 95 30
807 50f. M. Grunewald (air) . . . 80 30
808 60f. As 30f. . . . . 1·00 40
809 90f. El Greco . . . . 1·50 55

1971. International Cocoa Day. Multicoloured.
811 30f. Type **130** (postage) . . . 55 15
812 40f. Sorting beans 85 20
813 50f. Drying beans . . . . . 1·10 35
814 60f. Agricultural Ministry, Lome (air) 60 30
815 90f. Type **130** . . . . 1·10 50
816 100f. As 40f. . . . . 1·25 60

1971. 10th Anniv of A.S.E.C.N.A. (Aerial Navigation Security Agency).
817 **131** 30f. multicoloured (postage) 90 35
818 100f. multicoloured (air) 1·50 65

132 Napoleon

1971. 150th Death Anniv of Napoleon. Embossed on gold foil.
819 **132** 1000f. gold . . . . 22·00

133 Great Market, Lome

1971. Tourism. Multicoloured.
821 20f. Type **133** (postage) . . . 35 10
822 30f. Wooden sculpture and protea 55 15
823 40f. Aledjo Gorge and olive baboon 80 20
824 50f. Vale Castle and red-fronted gazelle (air) 65 20
825 60f. Lake Togo and alligator 90 30
826 100f. Furnace, Tokpli, and hippopotamus . . . . . . 1·25 40

134 Gbatchoume Image

1971. Togolese Religions. Multicoloured.
827 20f. Type **134** (postage) . . . 35 15
828 30f. High priest, Temple of Atta Sakuma 50 20
829 40f. "Holy Stone" ceremony 85 30
830 50f. Moslem worshippers, Lome Mosque (air) 55 20
831 60f. Protestants 70 30
832 90f. Catholic ceremony, Djogbegan Monastery . . 95 40

1971. Memorial Issue for "Soyuz 11" Astronauts. Nos. 799/802 optd **EN MEMOIRE DOBROVOLSKY - VOLKOV - PATSAYEV SOYUZ 11** or surch also.
834 40f. multicoloured (postage) 1·00 35
835 90f. on 50f. multicoloured (air) 90 35
836 100f. multicoloured . . . . . 1·10 40
837 200f. multicoloured . . . . . 2·00 65

136 Speed-skating

1971. Winter Games, Sapporo, Japan (1972). Mult.
839 1f. Type **136** (postage) . . . 10 10
840 10f. Slalom skiing 10 10
841 20f. Figure-skating 35 10
842 30f. Bob-sleighing 55 20
843 50f. Ice-hockey . . . . . . 1·10 35
844 200f. Ski-jumping (air) . . . 2·25 95

1971. Air. 10th Anniv of African and Malagasy Posts and Telecommunications Union. As T **141** of Senegal. Multicoloured.
846 100f. U.A.M.P.T. H.Q. and Adjogobo dancers . . . . 1·10 55

137 Togolese Child and Mask

1971. Air. "Children of the World". Embossed on gold foil.
847 **137** 1500f. gold . . . . 15·00

138 Wooden Crocodile

1971. 25th Anniv of UNICEF. Multicoloured.
848 20f. Type **138** (postage) . . . 20 10
849 30f. Toy "Bambi" and butterfly 45 15
850 50f. Toy monkey 80 30
851 50f. Wooden elephant on wheels . . . . 1·00 30
852 60f. Toy turtle (air) 55 20
853 90f. Toy parrot 85 35

139 "Virgin and Child" (Botticelli)

1971. Christmas. "Virgin and Child" Paintings by Old Masters. Multicoloured.
855 10f. Type **139** (postage) . . . 10 10
856 30f. (Maitre de la Vie de Marie) 65 20
857 40f. (Durer) . . . . 1·10 35
858 50f. (Veronese) . . . . 1·40 45
859 60f. (Giorgione) (air) . . . . 1·00 35
860 100f. (Raphael) . . . . . . 1·75 55

140 St. Mark's Basilica, Venice

1972. UNESCO "Save Venice" Campaign. Mult.
862 30f. Type **140** (postage) . . . 90 30
863 40f. Rialto Bridge . . . . . 1·25 40
864 100f. Doge's Palace (air) . . 1·40 65

141 "The Crucifixion" (unknown artist)

1972. Easter. Religious Paintings. Multicoloured.
866 25f. Type **141** (postage) . . . 45 15
867 30f. "The Deposition" (Botticelli) 70 15
868 40f. Type **141** 90 30
869 50f. "The Resurrection" (Thomas de Coloswar) (air) 85 20
870 100f. "The Ascension" (Mantegna) . . . . 1·60 40

142 Heart Emblem and Blacksmith

145 Woman preparing Cassava

143 Hotel de la Paix, Lome

1972. World Heart Month. Multicoloured.
872 30f. Type **142** (postage) . . . 45 15
873 40f. Typist 55 20
874 60f. Javelin-thrower 85 35
875 100f. Type **142** (air) . . . . 1·25 45

1972. O.C.A.M. Summit Conference, Lome. Embossed on gold foil.
877 **143** 1000f. gold, red and green 10·00

1972. Pres. Nixon's Visit to China. Nos. 823/4 optd **VISITE DU PRESIDENT NIXON EN CHINE FEVRIER 1972** and additionally surch (No. 879).
878 300f. on 40f. mult (postage) 4·00 1·90
879 50f. multicoloured (air) . . . 1·00 35

1972. Cassava Industries. Multicoloured.
880 25f. Collecting cassava (horiz) (postage) 45 15
881 40f. Type **145** 65 20
882 60f. Cassava truck and factory (horiz) (air) 90 20
883 80f. Mother with Benin tapioca cake . . . . 1·25 45

146 Video-telephone

148 Basketball

1972. World Telecommunications Day. Mult.
884 40f. Type **146** (postage) . . . 1·00 35
885 100f. "Intelsat 4" and map of Africa (air) . . . . 1·50 45

1972. Air. Pres. Nixon's Visit to Russia. No. 743 surch **VISITE DU PRESIDENT NIXON EN RUSSIE MAI 1972** and value.
886 300f. on 50f. multicoloured 5·00 2·75

1972. Olympic Games, Munich. Multicoloured.
887 30f. Type **148** (postage) . . . 50 15
888 40f. Running 65 20
889 50f. Throwing the discus . . 90 30
890 90f. Gymnastics (air) 65 35
891 200f. Type **148** . . . . 1·75 80

149 Pin-tailed Whydah 150 Paul Harris (founder)

1973. Exotic Birds. Multicoloured.
893 25f. Type **149** (postage) . . . 75 25
894 30f. Broad-tailed paradise whydah . . . . 1·00 35
895 40f. Yellow-mantled whydah 1·40 55
896 60f. Long-tailed whydah . . 2·75 90
897 90f. Rose-ringed parakeet (air) . . . . 3·75 1·25

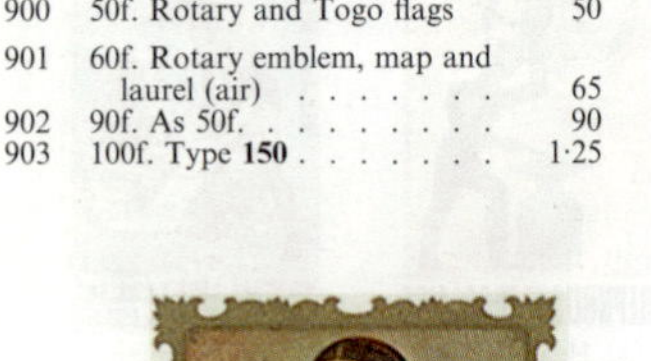

1972. Rotary International. Multicoloured.
899 40f. Type **150** (postage) . . . 40 20
900 50f. Rotary and Togo flags 50 30
901 60f. Rotary emblem, map and laurel (air) 65 20
902 90f. As 50f. 90 35
903 100f. Type **150** . . . . 1·25 45

151 "Mona Lisa" (L. da Vinci)

1972. Famous Paintings. Multicoloured.
905 25f. Type **151** (postage) . . . 1·10 30
906 40f. "Virgin and Child" (Bellini) . . . . 1·25 30
907 60f. "Mystical Marriage of St. Catherine" (Master P.N.'s assistant) (air) . . . 1·00 30
908 80f. "Self-portrait" (L. da Vinci) . . . . 1·25 35
909 100f. "St. Marie and Angels" (Botticelli) . . . . 1·60 50

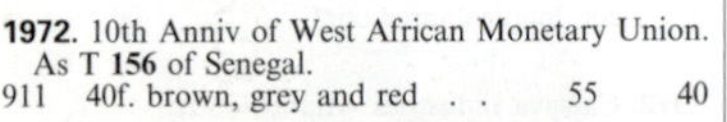

1972. 10th Anniv of West African Monetary Union. As T **156** of Senegal.
911 40f. brown, grey and red . . 55 40

152 Party H.Q. of R.P.T. and Presidents Pompidou and Eyadama

1972. Visit of President Pompidou to Togo. Multicoloured.
912 40f. Type **152** (postage) . . . 1·10 45
913 100f. Party H.Q. rear view and portraits as T **152** (air) 1·75 55

153 Goethe

1972. Air. 140th Death Anniv of Goethe (poet).
914 **153** 100f. multicoloured . . . 1·50 65

154 "The Annunciation" (unknown artist)

1972. Christmas. Religious Paintings. Mult.
915 25f. Type **154** (postage) . . . 35 20
916 30f. "The Nativity" (Master Theodor of Prague) . . . 55 20
917 40f. Type **154** 80 20
918 60f. As 30f. (air) 80 20
919 80f. "The Adoration of the Magi" (unknown artist) . . 1·00 30
920 100f. "The Flight into Egypt" (Giotto) . . . . 1·25 45

155 R. Follerau and Allegory

1973. "World Day of the Leper". (a) Postage. 20th Anniv of Follereau Foundation.
922 **155** 40f. violet and green . . . 1·60 55

(b) Air. Cent of Hansen's Bacillus Discovery.
923 – 100f. blue and red . . . . . 2·50 85
DESIGN: 100f. Dr. Hansen, microscope and bacillus slide.

156 W.H.O. Emblem 157 "The Crucifixion"

1973. 25th Anniv of W.H.O.
924 **156** 30f. multicoloured 45 15
925 40f. multicoloured 55 20

1973. Easter. Multicoloured.
926 25f. Type **157** (postage) . . . 35 15
927 30f. "The Deposition" . . . 55 20
928 40f. "The Resurrection" . . . 80 20
929 90f. "Christ in Majesty" (air) 1·25 45

158 Astronauts Cernan, Evans and Schmitt

1973. "Apollo 17" Moon Flight. Multicoloured.
931 30f. Type **158** (postage) . . . 80 15
932 40f. Moon rover . . . . . . 1·00 30
933 100f. Discovery of "orange" rock (air) . . . . 1·10 40
934 200f. Pres. Kennedy and lift-off . . . . 2·25 85

159 Erecting Tent 160 Heliocentric System

1973. International Scout Congress. Nairobi/Addis Ababa. Multicoloured.
936 10f. Type **159** (postage) . . . 20 10
937 20f. Cooking meal (horiz) . . 45 10
938 30f. Rope-climbing 75 15
939 40f. Type **159** . . . . 1·00 20
940 100f. Canoeing (horiz) (air) 1·50 40
941 200f. As 20f. . . . . 2·75 85

1973. 500th Birth Anniv of Copernicus. Mult.
943 10f. Type **160** (postage) . . . 15 10
944 20f. Copernicus 30 10
945 30f. "Astronomy" and "Astronautics" 65 15
946 40f. Astrolabe 85 20
947 90f. Type **160** (air) . . . . . 1·25 35
948 100f. As 20f. . . . . 1·40 45

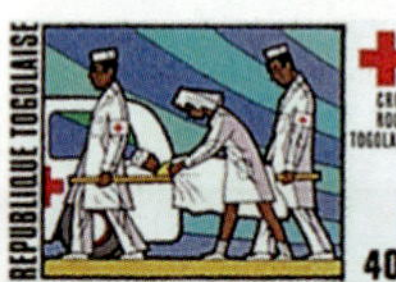

161 Ambulance Team

1973. Togolese Red Cross. Multicoloured.
950 40f. Type **161** (postage) . . . 90 35
951 100f. Dove of peace, sun and map (air) . . . . 1·90 65

1973. "Drought Relief". African Solidarity. No. 766 surch **SECHERESSE SOLIDARITE AFRICAINE 100F.**
952 100f. on 30f. multicoloured 1·25 85

163 Classroom

1973. Literacy Campaign. Multicoloured.
953 30f. Type **163** (postage) . . . 35 15
954 40f. African reading book (vert) 85 30
955 90f. Classroom (different) (air) 85 45

1973. African and Malagasy Posts and Telecommunications Union. As T **170** of Senegal.
956 100f. red, yellow and purple 1·10 65

164 Interpol Emblem and H.Q. Paris 165 W.M.O. Emblem in Weather-vane

1973. 50th Anniv of Interpol.
957 **164** 30f. green, brown & yellow 45 15
958 40f. blue, mauve and green 65 20

1973. Centenary of W.M.O.
959 **165** 40f. grn, brn & yell (post) 90 35
960 200f. brown, vio & bl (air) 1·90 85

166 Togo Stamp and Steam and Diesel Locomotives

1973. 75th Anniv of Togolese Postal Services. Mult.
961 25f. Type **166** (postage) . . . 65 20
962 30f. Togo stamp and mail coaches 60 20
963 90f. Togo stamps and mail boats . . . . 1·75 45
964 100f. Togo stamps and mail-planes (air) . . . . 2·40 80

167 Kennedy and A. Schaerf 168 Flame Emblem and "People"

1973. 10th Death Anniv of Pres. Kennedy.
966 **167** 20f. violet and black on blue (postage) 35 10
967 – 30f. brown and black on brown 50 20
968 – 40f. green & black on green 85 30
969 – 90f. purple and black on mauve (air) . . . . 1·60 45
970 – 100f. blue & black on blue . . . . 1·60 45
971 – 200f. brown & blk on brown . . . . 2·75 80
DESIGNS: 30f. Kennedy and Harold Macmillan; 40f. Kennedy and Konrad Adenauer; 90f. Kennedy and Charles de Gaulle; 100f. Kennedy and Nikita Kruschev; 200f. Kennedy and "Apollo" spacecraft.

1973. Air. 25th Anniv of Declaration of Human Rights.
973 **168** 250f. multicoloured . . . 2·75 1·40

169 "Virgin and Child" (anon) 173 "Girl Before Mirror" (Picasso)

171 Footballers

1973. Christmas. Multicoloured.
974 25f. Type **169** (postage) . . . 50 15
975 30f. "Adoration of the Magi" (Vivarini) 60 20
976 90f. "Virgin and Child" (S. di Pietro) (air) . . . . . . 1·00 35
977 100f. "Adoration of the Magi" (anon) . . . . . . 1·40 40

1974. Lome District Rotary International Convention. Nos. 899, 901 and 903 optd **PREMIERE CONVENTION 210eme DISTRICT FEVRIER 1974 LOME.**
979 **150** 40f. mult (postage) . . . 55 35
980 – 60f. multicoloured (air) 45 20
981 **150** 100f. multicoloured . . . 90 35

1974. World Cup Football Championship, West Germany.
982 **171** 20f. mult (postage) . . . 35 15
983 – 30f. multicoloured 45 15
984 – 40f. multicoloured 55 20
985 – 90f. multicoloured (air) 90 35
986 – 100f. multicoloured . . . 1·00 40
987 – 200f. multicoloured . . . 2·00 70
DESIGNS: Nos. 983/7, similar designs to Type **171**, showing footballers in action.

1974. 10th Anniv of World Food Programme. Nos. 880/1 optd **10e ANNIVERSAIRE DU P. A. M.** or surch also.
989 **145** 40f. multicoloured 55 35
990 – 100f. on 25f. . . . . . . 1·25 80

1974. Picasso Commemoration. Multicoloured.
991 20f. Type **173** (postage) . . . 55 20
992 30f. "The Turkish Shawl" . . 80 35
993 40f. "Mandoline and Guitar" 1·10 35
994 90f. "The Muse" (air) . . . 1·00 35
995 100f. "Les Demoiselles d'Avignon" . . . . 1·25 40
996 200f. "Sitting Nude" . . . . 2·50 85

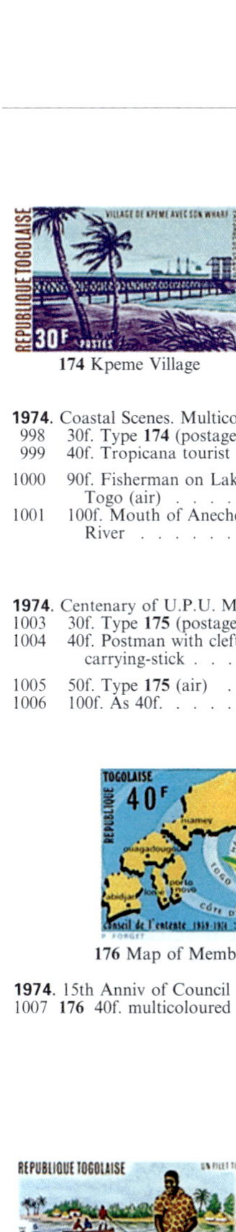

174 Kpeme Village   175 Togolese Postman

1974. Coastal Scenes. Multicoloured.
998 30f. Type **174** (postage) . . 45 20
999 40f. Tropicana tourist village 65 40
1000 90f. Fisherman on Lake Togo (air) . . . . 1·00 35
1001 100f. Mouth of Aneche River . . . . 1·25 40

1974. Centenary of U.P.U. Multicoloured.
1003 30f. Type **175** (postage) . . 40 20
1004 40f. Postman with cleft carrying-stick 50 30
1005 50f. Type **175** (air) 60 30
1006 100f. As 40f. . . . . 1·25 45

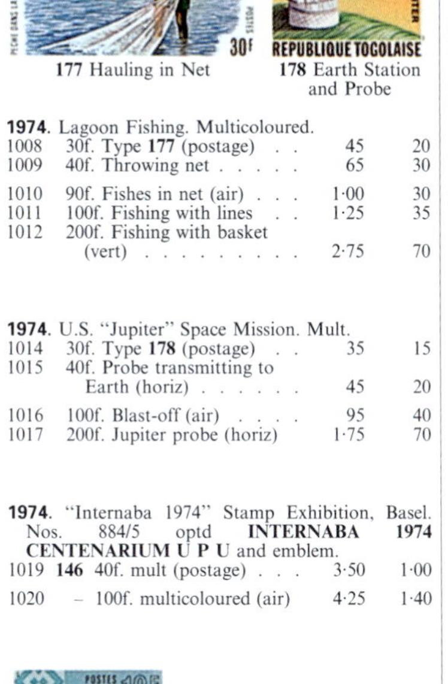

176 Map of Member Countries

1974. 15th Anniv of Council of Accord.
1007 **176** 40f. multicoloured . . . 50 30

177 Hauling in Net   178 Earth Station and Probe

1974. Lagoon Fishing. Multicoloured.
1008 30f. Type **177** (postage) . . 45 20
1009 40f. Throwing net 65 30
1010 90f. Fishes in net (air) . . . 1·00 30
1011 100f. Fishing with lines . . 1·25 35
1012 200f. Fishing with basket (vert) . . . . 2·75 70

1974. U.S. "Jupiter" Space Mission. Mult.
1014 30f. Type **178** (postage) . . 35 15
1015 40f. Probe transmitting to Earth (horiz) 45 20
1016 100f. Blast-off (air) 95 40
1017 200f. Jupiter probe (horiz) 1·75 70

1974. "Internaba 1974" Stamp Exhibition, Basel. Nos. 884/5 optd **INTERNABA 1974 CENTENARIUM U P U** and emblem.
1019 **146** 40f. mult (postage) . . . 3·50 1·00
1020 – 100f. multicoloured (air) 4·25 1·40

180 "Tympanotomus radula"   181 Groom with Horses

1974. Sea Shells. Multicoloured.
1021 10f. Type **180** (postage) . . 25 20
1022 20f. Giant tun 35 20
1023 30f. Trader cone 55 20
1024 40f. Great ribbed cockle . . 85 20
1025 90f. Ponsonbyi's volute (air) 1·40 40
1026 100f. Iredale's bonnet . . . 1·90 40

1974. Horse-racing. Multicoloured.
1028 30f. Type **181** (postage) . . 45 20
1029 40f. Exercising horses . . . 65 30
1030 90f. Steeple-chaser taking fence (air) . . . . 1·00 35
1031 100f. Horses racing . . . . 1·50 45

1974. Air. West Germany's Victory in World Cup Football Championship. Nos. 890/1 optd **COUPE DU MONDE DE FOOTBALL MUNICH 1974 VAINQUERS REPUBLIQUE FEDERALE ALLEMAGNE**.
1033 – 90f. multicoloured . . . 90 35
1034 **148** 200f. multicoloured . . . 1·75 80

183 Leopard

1974. Wild Animals. Multicoloured.
1036 20f. Type **183** (postage) . . 50 15
1037 30f. Giraffes 75 20
1038 40f. Two African elephants 1·00 35
1039 90f. Lion and lioness (air) 1·50 45
1040 100f. Black rhinoceros and calf . . . . 2·00 45

184 Herd of Cows

1974. Pastoral Economy. Multicoloured.
1042 30f. Type **184** (postage) . . 45 20
1043 40f. Milking 65 30
1044 90f. Cattle at water-hole (air) 85 45
1045 100f. Village cattle-pen . . . 1·10 55

185 Churchill and Frigate H.M.S. "Loch Fada"

1974. Birth Centenary of Sir Winston Churchill. Multicoloured.
1047 30f. Type **185** (postage) . . 50 15
1048 40f. Churchill and Supermarine Spitfires . . 60 20
1049 100f. Type **185** (air) . . . . 1·40 35
1050 200f. As 40f. . . . . 2·25 80

1975. Opening of Hotel de la Paix, Lome. Optd **Inauguration de la l'hotel Paix 9-1-75**.
1051a **143** 1000f. gold, red and green . . . . 9·50

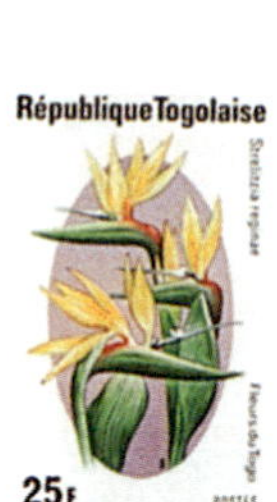

186 "Strelitzia reginae"   189 "Jesus Mocked" (El Greco)

188 Radio Station, Kamina

1975. Flowers of Togo. Multicoloured.
1052 25f. Type **186** (postage) . . 35 15
1053 30f. "Strophanthus sarmentosus" 45 15
1054 40f. "Chlamydocarya macrocarpa" (horiz) . . . 55 20
1055 60f. "Clerodendrum scandens" (horiz) 90 35
1056 100f. "Clerodendrum thosonae" (horiz) (air) . . 1·40 45
1057 200f. "Gloriosa superba" (horiz) . . . . 2·50 65

1975. 70th Anniv of Rotary International. Optd **70e ANNIVERSAIRE 23 FEVRIER 1975**.
1059 **150** 40f. mult (postage) . . . 30 25
1060 – 90f. multicoloured (No. 902) (air) 85 35
1061 **150** 100f. multicoloured . . . 1·00 40

1975. Tourism. Multicoloured.
1062 25f. Type **188** 20 10
1063 30f. Benedictine Monastery, Zogbegan 35 20
1064 40f. Causeway, Atchinedji 45 30
1065 60f. Ayome Waterfalls . . . 80 40

1975. Easter. Multicoloured.
1066 25f. Type **189** (postage) . . 20 10
1067 30f. "The Crucifixion" (Master Janoslen) 35 10
1068 40f. "The Descent from the Cross" (Bellini) 55 20
1069 90f. "Pieta" (anon) 95 40
1070 100f. "Christ rising from the Grave" (Master MS) (air) 1·10 35
1071 200f. "The Holy Trinity" (detail) (Durer) . . . . . 1·90 80

190 Stilt-walking

1975. 15th Anniv of Independence. Mult.
1073 25f. Type **190** (postage) . . 30 10
1074 30f. Dancers 35 15
1075 50f. Independence parade (vert) (air) 40 15
1076 60f. Dancer 60 35

191 Hunting Bush Hare with Club

1975. Hunting. Multicoloured.
1078 30f. Type **191** (postage) . . 45 20
1079 40f. Hunting Eurasian beavers with bow 55 35
1080 90f. Hunting red deer with snare (air) . . . . 1·25 45
1081 100f. Hunting wild boar with gun . . . . 1·40 55

192 Pounding Palm Nuts

1975. Palm-oil Production. Multicoloured.
1082 30f. Type **192** (postage) . . 35 15
1083 40f. Extracting palm-oil (vert) 40 20
1084 85f. Selling palm-oil (vert) (air) 80 45
1085 100f. Oil-processing plant, Aloknegbe 90 55

193 "Apollo" and "Soyuz" in Docking Procedure

1975. "Apollo–Soyuz" Space Link. Mult.
1087 30f. Type **193** (postage) . . 45 15
1088 50f. "Soyuz" spacecraft (vert) (air) 40 15
1089 60f. Slaton, Brand and Stafford ("Apollo" astronauts) 55 20
1090 90f. Leonov and Kubasov ("Soyuz" cosmonauts) . . 70 30
1091 100f. U.S. and Soviet flags and "Apollo" and "Soyuz" linked . . . . . 1·10 50
1092 200f. Emblem and globe . . 2·25 65

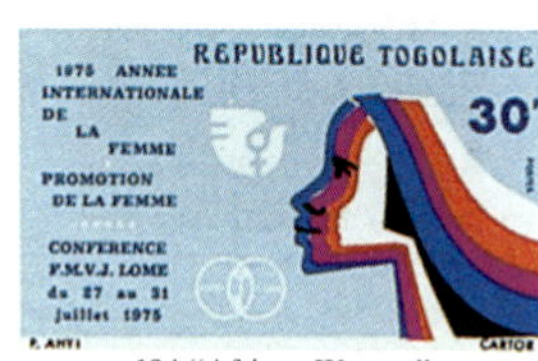

194 "African Women"

1975. International Women's Year.
1094 **194** 30f. multicoloured . . . 40 15
1095 40f. multicoloured . . . 45 20

195 Dr. Schweitzer, and Children drinking Milk

1975. Birth Centenary of Dr. Albert Schweitzer. Multicoloured.
1096 40f. Type **195** (postage) . . 55 30
1097 80f. Schweitzer playing organ (vert) (air) 90 30
1098 90f. Schweitzer feeding Eastern white pelican (vert) . . . . 1·40 40
1099 100f. Schweitzer and Lambarene Hospital . . . 1·25 35

196 "Merchant writing Letter" (V. Carpaccio)   199 "Virgin and Child" (Mantegna)

1975. International Letter-writing Week. Mult.
1101 40f. Type **196** (postage) . . 55 30
1102 80f. "Erasmus writing Letter" (Holbein) (air) . . 90 35

1975. 30th Anniv of United Nations. Nos. 851/3 optd **30eme Anniversaire des Nations-Unies**.
1103 50f. multicoloured (postage) 55 30
1104 60f. multicoloured (air) . . 50 20
1105 90f. multicoloured 60 30

1975. Air. World Scout Jamboree, Norway. Nos. 940/1 optd **14eme JAMBOREE MONDIAL DES ECLAIREURS**.
1107 100f. multicoloured 95 45
1108 200f. multicoloured . . . . 1·75 80

1975. Christmas. "Virgin and Child" paintings by artists named. Multicoloured.
1110 20f. Type **199** (postage) . . 30 20
1111 30f. El Greco 40 20
1112 40f. Barend van Orley . . . 45 20
1113 90f. Federigo Barocci (air) 80 30
1114 100f. Bellini 90 35
1115 200f. Correggio . . . . . . 1·60 55

200 Crashed Airplane

1975. Pres. Eyadema's Escape in Air Crash at Sarakawa.
1117 **200** 50f. multicoloured . . . 7·25 5·00
1118 60f. multicoloured . . . 7·25 5·00

200a Pole Vault

1976. Olympic Games, Montreal. Multicoloured.
1118a 1000f. Type **200a** . . . . . 10·00
1118b 1000f. Diving . . . . . . 10·00
1118c 1000f. Running . . . . . 10·00
1118d 1000f. Show-jumping . . . 10·00
1118e 1000f. Cycling . . . . . . 10·00

201 "Frigates forcing the Hudson Passage"

1976. Bicentenary of American Revolution. Mult.
1119 35f. Type **201** (postage) . . 40 20
1120 50f. "George Washington" (G. Stuart) (vert) 55 30
1121 60f. "Surrender of Burgoyne" (Trumbull) (air) 65 20
1122 70f. "Surrender at Trenton" (Trumbull) (vert) 85 30
1123 100f. "Signing of Declaration of Independence" (Trumbull) 90 35
1124 200f. "Washington crossing the Delaware" (E. Leutze) 1·75 60

202 "Salerum" (cable ship) **203** Blind Man and Mosquito

1976. Telephone Centenary. Multicoloured.
1126 25f. Type **202** (postage) . . 30 15
1127 30f. Automatic telephone and tape-recording equipment 40 30
1128 70f. Edison and communications equipment (air) 55 30
1129 105f. Alexander Graham Bell, early and modern telephones 85 40

1976. World Health Day. Multicoloured.
1131 50f. Type **203** (postage) . . 65 30
1132 60f. Eye examination (air) 55 20

204 A.C.P. and C.E.E. Emblems **205** Exhibition Hall

1976. 1st Anniv of A.C.P./C.E.E. Treaty (between Togo and European Common Market). Mult.
1133 10f. Type **204** (postage) . . 15 10
1134 50f. Map of Africa, Europe and Asia 40 30
1135 60f. Type **204** (air) 45 20
1136 70f. As 50f. 55 30

1976. Anniversaries. Multicoloured.
1136a 5f. Type **205** (postage) . . 10 10
1136b 10f. Electricity pylon and flags 15 10
1137 50f. Type **205** 50 30
1138 60f. As 10f. (air) 50 30

The 5f. and 50f. commemorate the 10th anniv of the Marine Exhibition and the 10f. and 60f. the 1st anniv of the Ghana–Togo–Dahomey Electricity Link.

1976. Air. "Interphil '76" International Stamp Exhibition, Philadelphia. Nos. 1121/4 optd **INTERPHIL MAI 29 - JUIN 6**.
1139 60f. multicoloured 40 15
1140 70f. multicoloured 60 20
1141 100f. multicoloured 90 30
1142 200f. multicoloured . . . . 1·40 55

207 Running

1976. Olympic Games, Montreal. Multicoloured.
1144 25f. Type **207** (postage) . . 20 10
1145 30f. Canoeing 35 15
1146 50f. High-jumping 45 20
1147 70f. Sailing (air) 55 20
1148 105f. Motorcycling 85 35
1149 200f. Fencing . . . . 1·60 55

208 "Titan 3" and "Viking" Emblem

1976. "Viking" Space Mission. Multicoloured.
1151 30f. Type **208** (postage) . . 15 10
1152 50f. "Viking" en route between Earth and Mars 40 20
1153 60f. "Viking landing on Mars" (air) 55 20
1154 70f. Nodus Gordii, Mars . . 65 20
1155 100f. "Viking" over Mare Tyrrhenum 85 40
1156 200f. "Viking" landing on Mars (different) . . . . . 1·50 55

209 "Young Routy"

212 Quaid-i-Azam

211 "Adoration of the Shepherds" (Pontormo)

1976. 75th Death Anniv of Toulouse-Lautrec (painter). Multicoloured.
1158 10f. Type **209** (postage) . . 15 10
1159 20f. "Helene Vary" 50 15
1160 35f. "Louis Pascal" 75 15
1161 60f. "Carmen" (air) . . . . 1·00 20
1162 70f. "Maurice at the Somme" . . . . 1·00 30
1163 200f. "Messalina" . . . . . 2·50 60

1976. International Children's Day. Nos. 950/1 optd **Journee Internationale de l'Enfance**.
1165 **161** 40f. mult (postage) . . . 45 15
1166 – 100f. multicoloured (air) 80 45

1976. Christmas. Nativity scenes by artists named. Multicoloured.
1167 25f. Type **211** (postage) . . 35 15
1168 30f. Crivelli 45 15
1169 50f. Pontormo 80 20
1170 70f. Lotto (air) 65 20
1171 105f. Pontormo (different) 1·90 35
1172 200f. Lotto (different) . . . 1·60 55

1976. Birth Centenary of Mohammad Ali Jinnah, "Quaid-i-Azam".
1174 **212** 50f. multicoloured . . . 55 30

1977. Gold Medal Winners, Montreal Olympic Games. Nos. 1146/7 and 1149 optd **CHAMPIONS OLYMPIQUES** with events and countries.
1175 50f. multicoloured (postage) 60 20
1176 70f. multicoloured (air) . . 75 35
1177 200f. multicoloured . . . . 1·75 80

OPTD: 50f. **SAUT EN HAUTEUR POLOGNE**; 70f. **YACHTING - FLYING DUTCHMAN REPUBLIQUE FEDERALE ALLEMAGNE**; 200f. **ESCRIME-FLEURET PAR EQUIPES REPUBLIQUE FEDERALE ALLEMAGNE.**

214 Queen Elizabeth II

1977. Silver Jubilee of Queen Elizabeth II.
1179 **214** 1000f. multicoloured . . 7·75

215 Phosphate Complex, Kpeme

1977. 10th Anniv of Eyadema Regime. Mult.
1181 50f. Type **215** (postage) . . 1·25 35
1182 60f. Parliament Building, Lome (air) 55 30
1183 100f. Crowd greeting Pres. Eyadema 80 40

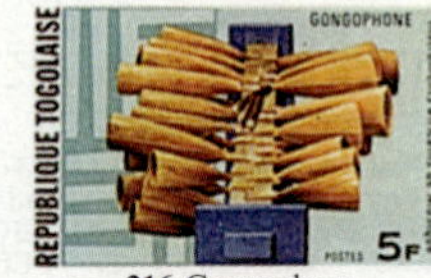

216 Gongophone

1977. Musical Instruments. Multicoloured.
1185 5f. Type **216** (postage) . . . 15 10
1186 10f. Tamtam (vert) 20 10
1187 25f. Dondon 65 15
1188 60f. Atopani (air) 75 20
1189 80f. One-string fiddle (vert) 1·25 30
1190 105f. African flutes (vert) . . 1·75 35

217 Victor Hugo and Guernsey Scene

1977. 175th Birth Anniv of Victor Hugo (writer). Multicoloured.
1192 50f. Victor Hugo as a young man, and residence (postage) 55 15
1193 60f. Type **217** (air) 60 30

218 Beethoven and Birthplace, Bonn

1977. 150th Death Anniv of Ludwig van Beethoven. Multicoloured.
1195 30f. Type **218** (postage) . . 70 15
1196 50f. Beethoven's bust and Heiligenstadt residence . . 75 20
1197 100f. Young Beethoven and grand piano (air) . . . . 1·25 35
1198 200f. Beethoven on death-bed and Trinity Church, Vienna . . . . 2·25 65

219 Benz, 1894

1977. Early Motor Cars. Multicoloured.
1200 35f. Type **219** (postage) . . 65 20
1201 50f. De Dion Bouton, 1903 1·00 30
1202 60f. Cannstatt-Daimler, 1899 (air) 80 20
1203 70f. Sunbeam, 1904 . . . . 90 20
1204 100f. Renault, 1908 . . . . 1·10 35
1205 200f. Rolls-Royce, 1909 . . 1·90 65

220 Lindbergh, Ground Crew and "Spirit of St. Louis"

1977. 50th Anniv of Lindbergh's Transatlantic Flight. Multicoloured.
1207 25f. Type **220** (postage) . . 35 15
1208 50f. Lindbergh before take-off 65 20
1209 60f. Lindbergh with son (air) 50 15
1210 85f. Lindbergh's home, Kent (England) 80 20
1211 90f. "Spirit of St. Louis" over Atlantic 80 30
1212 100f. Concorde over New York City . . . . 1·25 50

1977. 10th Anniv of International French Language Council. Nos. 1192/3 optd **10eme ANNIVERSAIRE DU CONSEIL INTERNATIONAL DE LA LANGUE FRANCAISE.**
1214 **217** 50f. mult (postage) . . . 60 40
1215 60f. multicoloured (air) . . 55 35

222 Nile Crocodile

1977. Endangered Wildlife. Multicoloured.
1216 5f. African crocodile (postage) 15 15
1217 15f. Type **222** 50 20
1218 60f. Western black-and-white colobus (air) . . . 90 15
1219 90f. Chimpanzee (vert) . . . 1·00 20
1220 100f. Leopard . . . . . . 1·25 30
1221 200f. African manatee . . . 2·25 55

223 Agricultural School, Tove

1977. Agricultural Development. Multicoloured.
1223 50f. Type **223** (postage) . . 50 20
1224 60f. Corn silo (air) 55 15
1225 100f. Hoeing and planting 70 30
1226 200f. Tractor . . . . 1·50 55

224 "Landscape at Sunset" (Rubens)

1977. 400th Birth Anniv of Rubens. Multicoloured.
1228 15f. Type **224** (postage) . . 35 10
1229 35f. "Exchange of the Princesses at Hendaye" 80 15
1230 60f. "Four Negro Heads" (air) 85 15
1231 100f. "Anne of Austria" . . 1·10 40

225 Shuttle after Landing

1977. Space Shuttle. Multicoloured.
1233 20f. Type **225** (postage) . . 20 10
1234 30f. Launching 35 15
1235 50f. Ejecting propellant tanks 55 15
1236 90f. Retrieving a satellite (air) 70 20
1237 100f. Ejecting repaired satellite 85 30
1238 200f. Shuttle landing . . . . 1·50 60

226 Lafayette at 19 (after Le Mire)

227 Lenin and Cruiser "Aurora"

1977. Bicent of Lafayette's Arrival in America.
1240 **226** 25f. brown, yellow and purple (postage) . . . 30 10
1241 – 50f. red, violet and pink 55 15
1242 – 60f. turquoise, green and deep green (air) . . . 50 15
1243 – 105f. blue, light blue and purple 90 35

DESIGNS—HORIZ: 50f. Lafayette at Montpelier; 60f. Lafayette's arrival in New York; 105f. Lafayette with Washington at Valley Forge.

1977. 60th Anniv of Russian Revolution.
1245 **227** 50f. multicoloured . . . 80 30

228 "Madonna and Child" (Lotto) **229** Edward Jenner

1977. Christmas. "Madonna and Child" by artists named. Multicoloured.
1246 20f. Type **228** (postage) . . 20 15
1247 30f. Crivelli 35 15
1248 50f. C. Tura 55 15
1249 90f. Crivelli (different) (air) 65 30
1250 100f. Bellini 90 35
1251 200f. Crivelli (different) . . 1·50 55

1978. World Eradication of Smallpox.
1253 **229** 5f. ochre, black and lilac (postage) 10 10
1254 – 20f. multicoloured . . . 20 10
1255 **229** 50f. ochre, black and green (air) 35 15
1256 – 60f. multicoloured . . . 40 15
DESIGN—HORIZ: 20, 60f. Patients queuing for vaccination.

230 Wright Brothers

1978. 75th Anniv of 1st Flight by Wright Brothers. Multicoloured.
1258 35f. Type **230** (postage) . . 45 20
1259 50f. Wilbur Wright flying Glider No. III 85 35
1260 60f. Orville Wright Flight of 7 min 31 sec (air) . . . . 1·00 40
1261 70f. Wreckage of Wright Type A . . . . 1·10 40
1262 200f. Wright Brothers' cycle workshop, Dearborn, Michigan . . . . . . 1·40 55
1263 300f. Wright Flyer I (1st motorized flight) . . . . 2·00 85

231 "Apollo 8" (10th anniv of first mission) **232** St. John

1978. Anniversaries and Events. Multicoloured.
1265 1000f. Type **231** . . . . . 8·25
1266 1000f. High-jumping (Olympic Games, 1980) 8·25
1267 1000f. Westminster Abbey (25th anniv of Queen Elizabeth II's Coronation) 8·25
1268 1000f. "Duke of Wellington" (150th death anniv of Goya) . . . . 8·25
1269 1000f. Footballers and Cup (World Cup Football Championship) . . . . . 8·25

1978. The Evangelists. Multicoloured.
1271 5f. Type **232** 10 10
1272 10f. St. Luke 10 10
1273 25f. St. Mark 20 10
1274 30f. St. Mathew 30 10

233 Fishing Harbour

1978. Autonomous Port of Lome. Multicoloured.
1276 25f. Type **233** (postage) . . 45 15
1277 60f. Industrial port (air) . . 80 25
1278 100f. Merchant port . . . . 1·25 40
1279 200f. General view . . . . 1·25 55

234 "Venera 1" Probe **235** Goalkeeper catching Ball

1978. Space Mission—Venus. Multicoloured.
1281 20f. Type **234** (postage) . . 15 10
1282 30f. "Pioneer" (horiz) . . . 20 15
1283 50f. Soviet fuel base and antenna 40 15
1284 90f. "Venera" blast jets (horiz) (air) 40 20
1285 100f. "Venera" antennae . . 55 30
1286 200f. "Pioneer" in orbit . . 1·00 55

1978. World Cup Football Championship, Argentina. Multicoloured.
1288 30f. Type **235** (postage) . . 30 10
1289 50f. Two players with ball 40 15
1290 60f. Heading the ball (air) 60 15
1291 80f. High kick 70 20
1292 200f. Chest stop . . . . . 1·50 55
1293 300f. Player with ball . . . 2·25 85

236 Thomas Edison (inventor) **237** "Celerifere" 1818

1878. Centenary of Invention of the Phonograph. Multicoloured.
1295 30f. Type **236** (postage) . . 20 10
1296 50f. Couple dancing to H.M.V. "Victor", phonograph, 1905 . . . . 45 15
1297 60f. Edison's original phonograph (horiz) (air) 40 15
1298 80f. Berliner's first phono-graph, 1888 . . . . . . 50 20
1299 200f. Berliner's improved phonograph, 1894 (horiz) 1·25 55
1300 300f. "His Master's Voice" phonograph, c. 1900 (horiz) . . . . 2·00 85

1978. Early Bicycles. Multicoloured.
1302 25f. Type **237** (postage) . . 35 15
1303 50f. First bicycle side-car (vert) 65 20
1304 60f. Bantam bicycle (vert) (air) 55 15
1305 85f. Military folding bicycle 65 20
1306 90f. "La Draisienne" (vert) 90 35
1307 100f. Penny-farthing (vert) 95 40

238 Dunant's Birthplace, Geneva **240** Eiffel Tower

239 "Threshing" (Raoul Dufy)

1978. 150th Birth Anniv of Henri Dunant (founder of Red Cross).
1309 **238** 5f. blue and red (postage) 10 10
1310 – 10f. brown and red . . . 15 10
1311 – 25f. green and red . . . 30 10
1312 – 60f. purple and red (air) 55 20

DESIGNS: 10f. Dunant at 35; 25f. Tending battle casualties, 1864; 60f. Red Cross pavilions, Paris Exhibition, 1867.

1978. Air. "Philexafrique" Stamp Exhibition, Libreville (Gabon), and Int Stamp Fair, Essen, West Germany. As T **237a** of Senegal. Mult.
1314 100f. Jay and Thurn and Taxis ½sgr. stamp of 1854 2·75 2·25
1315 100f. Warthog and Togo 50f. stamp, 1964 . . . . 2·75 2·25

1978. Artists' Anniversaries. Multicoloured.
1316 25f. Type **239** (25th death anniv) (postage) 50 15
1317 50f. "Horsemen on the Seashore" (Gauguin, 75th death anniv) . . . . . . 1·00 15
1318 60f. "Langlois Bridge" (Van Gogh, 125th birth anniv) (air) 60 15
1319 70f. "Sabbath of the Witches" (Goya, 150th death anniv) 75 20
1320 90f. "Christ Among the Doctors" (Durer, 450th death anniv) 85 20
1321 200f. "View of Arco" (Durer) . . . . 1·75 55

1978. Centenary of Paris U.P.U. Congress. Mult.
1323 50f. Type **240** (postage) . . 80 20
1324 60f. Full-rigged ship "Slieve Roe" (air) 85 25
1325 105f. Congress medallion . . 70 30
1326 200f. Steam locomotive, 1870 . . . . 1·60 55

241 "Madonna and Child" (Antonello) **242** H.M.S. "Endeavour" and Route round New Zealand

1978. Christmas. Paintings of the Virgin and Child by artists shown below. Multicoloured.
1328 20f. Type **241** (postage) . . 20 15
1329 30f. Crivelli 35 15
1330 50f. Tura 55 15
1331 90f. Crivelli (different) (air) 65 30
1332 100f. Tura (different) . . . 90 30
1333 200f. Crivelli (different) . . 1·50 55

1979. Death Bicentenary of Captain James Cook. Multicoloured.
1335 25f. Type **242** (postage) . . 80 25
1336 50f. Careening H.M.S. "Endeavour" (horiz) . . . 1·00 35
1337 60f. "Freelove" at Whitby (horiz) (air) . . . . . . 1·25 35
1338 70f. Antarctic voyage of H.M.S. "Resolution" (horiz) . . . . 1·75 60
1339 90f. Capt. Cook . . . . . 2·00 75
1340 200f. Sail plan of H.M.S. "Endeavour" . . . . . . 2·75 1·75

243 Christ entering Jerusalem

1979. Easter. Multicoloured.
1342 30f. Type **243** (postage) . . 20 10
1343 40f. The Last Supper (horiz) 30 15
1344 50f. Descent from the Cross (horiz) 40 15
1345 60f. Resurrection (air) . . . 45 15
1346 100f. Ascension 65 30
1347 200f. Jesus appearing to Mary Magdalene . . . . 1·25 55

244 Statuette of Drummer

1979. Air. "Philexafrique 2" Stamp Exhibition, Libreville. Multicoloured.
1349 60f. Type **244** . . . . 1·10 55
1350 100f. Hands with letter . . . 1·60 1·10

245 Einstein Observatory, Potsdam

1979. Birth Centenary of Albert Einstein (physicist).
1351 **245** 35f. red, yellow and black (postage) . . . 20 10
1352 – 50f. green, mauve & black 35 10
1353 – 60f. multicoloured (air) 40 10
1354 – 85f. lilac, brown and black 60 15
1355 – 100f. multicoloured . . . 65 20
1356 – 200f. green, brown & black . . . . 1·40 40
DESIGNS—HORIZ: 50f. Einstein and J. R. Macdonald in Berlin, 1931; 60f. Sight and actuality diagram. VERT: 85f. Einstein playing violin; 100f. Atomic symbol and relativity formula; 200f. Albert Einstein.

246 Children with Flag **247** Planting Sapling

1979. International Year of the Child. Mult.
1358 5f. Type **246** 10 10
1359 10f. Mother with children 10 10
1360 15f. Children's Village symbol on map of Africa (horiz) 15 10
1361 20f. Woman taking children to Children's Village (horiz) 15 10
1362 25f. Children sitting round Fan palm 30 10
1363 30f. Map of Togo showing Children's Villages . . . 35 10

1979. Tree Day.
1365 **247** 50f. green and violet (postage) 50 15
1366 – 60f. brown & green (air) 55 20
DESIGN: 60f. Watering sapling.

248 Sir Rowland Hill **249** Stephenson's "Rocket", 1829

1979. Death Centenary of Sir Rowland Hill. Multicoloured.
1367 20f. Type **248** (postage) . . 15 10
1368 30f. French mail sorting office in the reign of Louis XV (horiz) 20 10
1369 50f. Parisian postbox, 1850 40 15
1370 90f. Bellman collecting letters, 1820 (air) 60 20

1371 100f. "Centre-cycles" used for mail delivery, 1880 (horiz) 65 20

1372 200f. French Post Office railway carriage, 1848 (horiz) 1·25 40

1979. Railway Locomotives. Multicoloured.

1374 35f. Type **249** (postage) 35 10

1375 50f. William Norris's "Austria", 1843 (horiz) 45 15

1376 60f. William Hudson's "General", 1855 (horiz) (air) 55 15

1377 85f. Stephenson locomotive, 1843 (horiz) 75 35

1378 100f. John Jarvis's "De Witt Clinton", 1831 (horiz) 85 35

1379 200f. David Joy's "Jenny Lind", 1847 (horiz) 1·75 55

250 Skiing

251 Native praying

1979. Olympic Games, Lake Placid and Moscow. Multicoloured.

1381 20f. Type **250** (postage) 15 10

1382 30f. Olympic dinghies 20 15

1383 50f. Throwing the discus 40 10

1384 90f. Ski-jumping (air) 65 20

1385 100f. Canoeing 70 20

1386 200f. Gymnastics (rings exercise) 1·40 40

1979. Togo Religions.

1388 **251** 30f. brown, green and yellow (postage) 20 10

1389 – 50f. blue, brown and red 35 10

1390 – 60f. purple, blue and buff (air) 45 15

1391 – 70f. lilac, orange & green 50 20

DESIGNS—HORIZ: 50f. Catholic priests; 60f. Muslims at prayer; 70f. Protestant preachers.

252 Astronaut on Moon

253 Dish Aerial

1979. 10th Anniv of First Moon Landing. Mult.

1393 35f. Type **252** (postage) 30 10

1394 50f. Capsule orbiting Moon 40 10

1395 60f. Armstrong descending to Moon 45 10

1396 70f. Astronaut and flag (air) 50 15

1397 200f. Astronaut performing experiment 1·25 35

1398 300f. Module leaving Moon 2·00 50

1979. 3rd World Telecommunications Exposition, Geneva.

1400 – 50f. light brown, brown and green (postage) 35 10

1401 **253** 60f. green, blue and deep blue (air) 50 20

DESIGN—HORIZ: 50f. Television screen.

254 Pres. Eyadema

1979. Air. 10th Anniv of R.P.T. Multicoloured.

1402 1000f. Pres. Eyadema and Party badge 6·75

1403 1000f. Type **254** 6·75

255 Holy Family

256 Rotary Emblem

1979. Christmas. Multicoloured.

1404 20f. Type **255** (postage) 15 10

1405 30f. Madonna and Child and angels playing musical instruments 20 10

1406 50f. Adoration of the shepherds 40 10

1407 90f. Adoration of the Magi (air) 55 20

1408 100f. Mother presenting Child 70 20

1409 200f. The Flight into Egypt 1·50 40

1980. 75th Anniv of Rotary International. Mult.

1411 25f. Type **256** (postage) 15 10

1412 30f. Anniversary emblem 30 10

1413 40f. Paul Harris (founder) 35 10

1414 90f. Figure exercising and sun (health) (air) 65 20

1415 100f. Fish and grain (food) 70 20

1416 200f. Family group (humanity) 1·40 40

257 Shooting (Biathlon)

1980. Winter Olympic Games, Lake Placid. Mult.

1418 50f. Type **257** (postage) 50 10

1419 60f. Downhill skiing 40 10

1420 100f. Speed skating (air) 70 20

1421 200f. Cross-country skiing 1·40 40

258 Swimming

1980. Olympic Games, Moscow. Multicoloured.

1423 20f. Type **258** (postage) 15 10

1424 30f. Gymnastics 20 10

1425 50f. Running 40 10

1426 100f. Fencing (air) 65 20

1427 200f. Pole vaulting 1·25 45

1428 300f. Hurdles 2·00 55

259 Truck going to Market

1980. Market Scenes. Multicoloured.

1430 1f. Grinding savo (postage) 10 10

1431 2f. Women preparing meat 10 10

1432 3f. Type **259** 10 10

1433 4f. Unloading produce 10 10

1434 5f. Sugar-cane seller 10 10

1435 6f. Barber doing child's hair 10 10

1436 7f. Vegetable seller 10 10

1437 7f. Mangoes (vert) 10 10

1438 9f. Grain seller 10 10

1439 10f. Fish seller 10 10

1440 15f. Clay pot seller 10 10

1441 20f. Straw baskets 15 10

1442 25f. Lemon and onion seller (vert) 15 10

1443 30f. Straw baskets (different) 20 10

1444 40f. Shore market 30 15

1445 45f. Selling cooked food 35 15

1446 50f. Women carrying produce (vert) 35 15

1447 60f. Selling oil 45 15

1448 90f. Linen seller (air) 55 15

1449 100f. Bananas 65 20

1450 200f. Pottery 1·25 45

1451 250f. Setting-up stalls 1·60 55

1452 500f. Vegetable seller (different) 3·00 1·10

1453 1000f. Drink seller 6·00 2·25

See also Nos. D1454/7.

260 Concorde and Map of Africa

1980. 20th Anniv of African Air Safety Organization.

1458 **260** 50f. mult (postage) 55 20

1459 60f. multicoloured (air) 55 25

261 "Christ with Angels" (Mantegna)

263 Radio Waves

1980. Easter. Multicoloured.

1460 30f. Type **261** (postage) 30 15

1461 40f. "Christ with Disciples" (Crivelli) 40 15

1462 50f. "Christ borne by His Followers" (Pontormo) 45 15

1463 60f. "The Deposition" (Lotto) (air) 50 10

1464 100f. "The Crucifixion" (El Greco) 70 20

1465 200f. "Christ with Angels" (Crivelli) 1·40 45

1980. "London 1980" International Stamp Exhibition. No. 1267 optd **Londres 1980**.

1467 1000f. Westminster Abbey 7·25

1980. World Telecommuncations Day.

1469 – 50f. violet and green (postage) 45 10

1470 **263** 60f. pink, brown and blue (air) 50 15

DESIGN—HORIZ: 50f. Satellite.

264 Red Cross and Globe

265 Jules Verne

1980. Togo Red Cross. Multicoloured.

1471 50f. Type **264** (postage) 55 10

1472 60f. Nurses and patient (air) 45 15

1980. 75th Death Anniv of Jules Verne (writer). Multicoloured.

1473 30f. Type **265** (postage) 30 10

1474 50f. "20,000 Leagues under the Sea" 55 10

1475 60f. "From the Earth to the Moon" (air) 40 15

1476 80f. "Around the World in Eighty Days" 55 20

1477 100f. "From the Earth to the Moon" (different) 3·50 1·25

1478 200f. "20,000 Leagues under the Sea" (different) 1·75 60

266 "Baroness James de Rothschild"

1980. Birth Bicentenary of Jean Ingres (painter). Multicoloured.

1480 25f. Type **266** (postage) 35 10

1481 30f. "Napoleon I on the Imperial Throne" 55 10

1482 40f. "Don Pedro of Toledo putting down the Sword of Henry IV" 50 10

1483 90f. "Jupiter and Thetis" (air) 65 20

1484 100f. "The Countess of Hassonville" 85 20

1485 200f. "Tu Marcellus Eris" 1·50 35

267 Minnie holding Mirror for Leopard

1980. Walt Disney Characters and Wildlife.

1487 1f. Type **267** 10 10

1488 2f. Goofy cleaning hippo's teeth 10 10

1489 3f. Donald clinging to crocodile 10 10

1490 4f. Donald hanging over cliff edge from rhino's horn 10 10

1491 5f. Goofy riding a water buffalo 10 10

1492 10f. Monkey photographing Mickey 10 10

1493 100f. Doctor Mickey examining giraffe 1·00 20

1494 300f. Elephant showering Goofy 2·00 40

1980. 50th Anniv of Pluto. As T **267**.

1496 200f. Pluto in party mood 1·60 40

268 Wreath

1980. Famous Men of the Decade.

1498 **268** 25f. orange and green (postage) 15 10

1499 – 40f. deep green and green 65 20

1500 – 90f. dp blue & blue (air) 60 20

1501 – 100f. lilac and pink 1·10 20

DESIGNS: 40f. Mao Tse Tung; 90f. Pres. Allende; 100f. Pope Paul VI; 200f. Pres. Kenyatta.

269 Tourist Hotel Emblem

270 Human Rights Emblem and Map of Australia

1980. World Tourism Conference, Manila. Mult.

1504 50f. Type **269** 35 10

1505 150f. Conference emblem 1·00 35

1980. 30th Anniv of Human Rights Convention.

1506 **270** 30f. violet, purple and black (postage) 30 10

1507 – 50f. green, light green and black 40 10

1508 – 60f. deep blue, blue and black (air) 40 15

1509 – 150f. brown, orange & black 1·00 35

DESIGNS: 50f. Map of Eurasia; 60f. Map of the Americas; 250f. Map of Africa.

271 Emblem

1980. Air. General Conclave of French-speaking Countries of the American Order of Rosicrucians, Lome.
1511 **271** 60f. multicoloured . . . 50 15

272 Church at Melk, Austria

272a U.A.P.T. Emblem

1980. Christmas. Multicoloured.
1512 20f. Type **272** (postage) . . 15 10
1513 30f. Tarragona Cathedral, Spain 20 10
1514 50f. Church of St. John the Baptist, Florence 35 10
1515 100f. Cologne Cathedral (air) . . . . 1·75 65
1516 150f. Notre-Dame, Paris . . 1·00 30
1517 200f. Canterbury Cathedral 1·40 35

1980. 5th Anniv of African Posts and Telecommunications Union.
1519 **272a** 100f. multicoloured . . 65 40

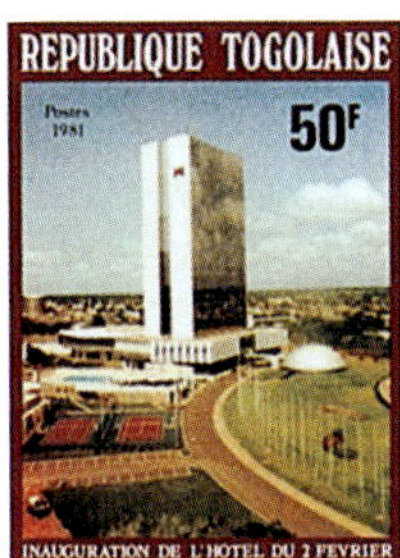

273 "February 2nd" Hotel

1981. Inauguration of "February 2nd" Hotel.
1520 **273** 50f. mult (postage) . . . 45 15
1521 60f. multicoloured (air) 45 15

274 "Rembrandt's Father"

1981. Easter. Rembrandt Paintings. Multicoloured.
1522 30f. Type **274** (postage) . . 30 10
1523 40f. "Self-portrait" 35 10
1524 50f. "Rembrandt's Father as an Old Man" 40 10
1525 60f. "Rider on Horseback" 50 15
1526 100f. "Rembrandt's Mother" (air) 70 20
1527 200f. "Man in a Ruff" . . 1·50 45

275 Grey-necked Bald Crow

1981. Birds. Multicoloured.
1529 30f. Type **275** (postage) . . 40 10
1530 40f. Splendid sunbird . . . 50 10
1531 60f. Violet starling 65 15
1532 90f. Red-collard whydah . . 1·10 20
1533 50f. Violet-backed sunbird (air) 65 15
1534 100f. Red bishop . . . . . 1·40 25

276 Dish Aerial

1981. 6th African Postal Union Council Meeting. Multicoloured.
1536 70f. Type **276** 50 15
1537 90f. Telecommunications control room 60 20
1538 105f. Map of Togo and Africa (vert) 70 30

277 Blind Man with Guide Dog

1981. International Year of Disabled People. Mult.
1539 70f. Type **277** (postage) . . 85 30
1540 90f. One-legged carpenter (air) 60 15
1541 200f. Wheelchair basket-ball 1·60 55

278 "Woman with Hat"

1981. Birth Centenary of Pablo Picasso. Mult.
1543 25f. Type **278** (postage) . . 35 10
1544 50f. "She-goat" 45 10
1545 60f. "Violin" 55 15
1546 90f. "Violin and Bottle on Table" (air) 80 20
1547 100f. "Baboon with Young" 90 30
1548 200f. "Mandolin and Clarinet" . . . . 1·90 55

279 Aachen Cathedral, West Germany

1981. World Heritage Convention. Multicoloured.
1550 30f. Type **279** (postage) . . 20 10
1551 40f. Yellowstone National Park, U.S.A. 30 10
1552 50f. Nahanni National Park, Canada 35 10
1553 60f. Cruciform rock churches, Lalibela, Ethiopia 40 15
1554 100f. Old city centre, Cracow, Poland (air) . . 65 20
1555 200f. Goree Island, Senegal 1·25 35

280 "Vostok I" (20th anniv of first Manned Space Flight)

1981. Space Anniversaries. Multicoloured.
1557 25f. Type **280** (postage) . . 15 10
1558 50f. "Freedom 7", first American in space (20th anniv) 35 10
1559 60f. "Lunar Orbiter I" (15th anniv) 40 15
1560 90f. "Soyuz 10" (10th anniv) (air) 60 15
1561 100f. Astronauts on Moon ("Apollo XIV", 10th anniv) 65 20

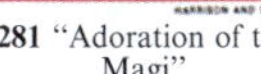

281 "Adoration of the Magi"

282 Association Emblem and Togo Flag

1981. Christmas. Paintings by Rubens. Mult.
1563 20f. Type **281** (postage) . . 15 10
1564 30f. "Adoration of the Shepherds" 20 10
1565 50f. "Coronation of St. Catherine" 40 10
1566 100f. "Adoration of the Magi" (different) (air) . . 60 20
1567 200f. "Madonna and Child" 1·40 45
1568 300f. "The Madonna giving the Robe to St. Idefonse" 2·25 65

1981. West African Rice Development Association.
1570 **282** 70f. mult (postage) . . . 60 20
1571 105f. multicoloured (air) 65 30

283 Peace Dove and National Flag

1982. 15th Anniv of National Liberation. Mult.
1572 70f. Type **283** (postage) . . 55 20
1573 90f. Pres. Eyadema and citizens (vert) 60 20
1574 105f. Pres. Eyadema and citizens holding hands (vert) (air) 65 35
1575 130f. Hotel complex 90 45

284 Scouts

1982. 75th Anniv of Boy Scout Movement. Mult.
1576 70f. Type **284** (postage) . . 50 15
1577 90f. Signalling (air) 65 20
1578 120f. Constructing a tower 85 30
1579 130f. Scouts with canoe . . 90 50
1580 135f. Scouts and tent . . . 95 35

285 Moses and the Burning Bush

286 Togo and Italy Olympic Stamps

1982. Easter. The Ten Commandments. Mult.
1582 10f. Type **285** (postage) . . 10 10
1583 25f. Jephtha's daughter . . 15 10
1584 30f. St. Vincent Ferrer preaching in Verona . . . 20 10
1585 45f. The denouncing of Noah 30 10
1586 50f. Cain and Abel 35 10
1587 70f. Potiphar's wife 50 20
1588 90f. Isaac blessing Jacob . . 60 35
1589 105f. Susannah and the elders (air) 65 30
1590 120f. Bathsheba 85 35

1982. Air. "Romolymphil" Stamp Exhibition.
1592 **286** 105f. multicoloured . . . 70 30

287 First Stamps of France and Togo

1982. Air. "Philexfrance '82" International Stamp Exhibition.
1593 **287** 90f. multicoloured . . . 65 40

288 Goalkeeper

1982. World Cup Football Championship, Spain. Multicoloured.
1594 25f. Type **288** (postage) . . 15 10
1595 45f. Tackle 35 10
1596 105f. Heading ball (air) . . . 65 20
1597 200f. Fighting for possession 1·25 45
1598 300f. Dribble . . . . 2·00 55

289 "Papilio dardanus"

1982. Butterflies. Multicoloured.
1600 15f. Type **289** (postage) . . 20 10
1601 20f. "Belenois calypso" . . 35 10
1602 25f. "Palla decius" 50 10
1603 90f. "Euxanthe eurinome" (air) . . . . 1·60 90
1604 105f. "Mylothris rhodope" 1·75 1·00

290 Infant Jesus

1982. Christmas. Details of Raphael's "Madonna del Baldacchino". Multicoloured.
1606 45f. Type **290** 40 10
1607 70f. Madonna 55 15
1608 105f. Angel 70 20
1609 130f. Angel (different) . . . 1·00 30
1610 150f. Putti . . . . 1·10 35

291 Building, Sokode

1983. Visit of President Mitterrand of France. Mult.
1612 35f. Type **291** (postage) 20 10
1613 45f. Children of different races and world map 35 15
1614 70f. French and Togolese soldiers (vert) 55 20
1615 90f. President Mitterrand (air) (vert) 70 30
1616 105f. Presidents Mitterrand and Eyadema shaking hands (vert) 80 35
1617 130f. Presidents Mitterrand and Eyadema and crowds 1·00 40

1983. World Cup Football Championship Results. Nos. 1594/8 optd **VAINQUER COUPE DU MONDE FOOTBALL 82 "ITALIE"**.
1618 25f. Type **288** (postage) 15 10
1619 45f. Tackle 35 15
1620 105f. Heading ball (air) 65 35
1621 200f. Fighting for possession 1·25 55
1622 300f. Dribble 2·00 80

293 Map of Africa showing W.A.M.U. Members

294 Drummer

1983. 20th Anniv of West African Monetary Union. Multicoloured.
1624 70f. Type **293** 50 15
1625 90f. West African coin 60 20

1983. World Communications Year. Multicoloured.
1626 70f. Type **294** (postage) 55 15
1627 90f. Modern post office and telecommunications system (air) 65 20

295 Boxing

1983. Air. Pre-Olympic Year. Multicoloured.
1628 70f. Type **295** 50 15
1629 90f. Hurdles 60 20
1630 105f. Pole vault 65 20
1631 130f. Sprinting 1·00 30

296 Kondona Dance

1983. Traditional Dances. Multicoloured.
1633 70f. Type **296** (postage) 60 20
1634 90f. Kondona dance (different) (air) 80 20
1635 105f. Toubole dance 90 20
1636 130f. Adjogbo dance 1·10 20

297 Painting by Bellini

1983. Easter. Multicoloured.
1637 35f. Type **297** (postage) 30 10
1638 70f. Raphael (vert) 50 15
1639 90f. Carracci (air) 65 20

298 Catholic Church, Kante

1983. Christmas. Multicoloured.
1641 70f. Type **298** (postage) 50 15
1642 90f. Altar, Dapaong Cathedral (air) 60 20
1643 105f. Protestant church, Dapaong 70 20

299 Wrecked Airplane

1984. 10th Anniv of Sarakawa Assassination Attempt. Multicoloured.
1645 70f. Type **299** (postage) 50 25
1646 90f. Wrecked airplane (different) 60 30
1647 120f. Memorial Hall (air) 85 40
1648 270f. Statue of President Eyadema (vert) 1·90 70

300 Picking Coffee Beans

1984. World Food Programme Day. Multicoloured.
1649 35f. Type **300** 20 10
1650 70f. Harvesting cocoa pods 50 15
1651 90f. Planting rice 65 20

301 Flags, Agriculture and Symbols of Unity Growth

1984. 25th Anniv of Council of Unity.
1653 **301** 70f. multicoloured 50 15
1654 90f. multicoloured 60 20

1984. Air. 19th Universal Postal Union Congress, Hamburg. Nos 1451/2 optd **19E CONGRES UPU HAMBOURG 1984**.
1655 250f. multicoloured 1·60 85
1656 500f. multicoloured 3·25 1·60

303 Tim Thorpe (gold, pentathlon and decathlon, 1912)

304 Thief on right-hand Cross

1984. Air. Olympic Games Medal Winners (1st series). Multicoloured.
1657 500f. Type **303** 4·50 85
1658 500f. Mathias Behr (silver, fencing, 1984) 4·50 85
1659 500f. Fredy Schmidtke (gold, cycling, 1984) 4·50 85
1660 500f. Dietmar Mogenburg (gold, high jumping, 1984) 4·50 85
1661 500f. Sabine Everts (bronze, heptathlon, 1984) 4·50 85
1662 500f. Jesse Owens (gold, 200 m, 1936) 4·50 85
1663 500f. Bob Beamon (gold, long jumping, 1968) 4·50 85
1664 500f. Muhammad Ali (gold, boxing, 1960) 22·00 85
See also Nos. 1825/32.

1984. Easter. Details from stained glass window in Norwich Cathedral. Multicoloured.
1665 70f. Roman guard (postage) 50 15
1666 90f. Mary Magdalene (air) 55 15
1667 120f. The Apostles comforting Mary 80 20
1668 270f. Type **304** 1·60 45
1669 300f. Thief on left-hand Cross 2·00 55

305 Baguida (site of Protectorate Treaty signature, 1884)

1984. Centenary of Proclamation of German Protectorate. Multicoloured.
1671 35f. Type **305** 20 20
1672 35f. Degbenou School, 1893 (horiz) 20 20
1673 35f. Degbenou Catholic Mission, 1893 (horiz) 20 20
1674 35f. Kara suspension bridge, 1911 (horiz) 20 20
1675 35f. Adjido state school (horiz) 20 20
1676 35f. Administration post, Sansane Mango, 1908 (horiz) 20 20
1677 35f. Sokode cotton market, 1910 (horiz) 20 20
1678 45f. Main street, Lome, 1895, and 5m. "Yacht" stamp (horiz) 35 35
1679 45f. Governor's Palace, Lome, 1905 (horiz) 35 35
1680 45f. Drilling police squad, 1905 (horiz) 35 35
1681 45f. Guillaume fountain, Atakpame, 1906 35 35
1682 45f. Constructing Lome–Atakpame railway (horiz) 85 85
1683 45f. Rue de Commerce, Lome, and 10pf. "Yacht" stamp (horiz) 85 85
1684 70f. 20pf. and 2m. "Yacht" stamps, 1900 (horiz) 50 45
1685 70f. Lome wharf, 1903 (horiz) 1·10 1·10
1686 90f. Farming, Sansane Mango, 1908 (horiz) 60 55
1687 90f. Chancellor Otto von Bismark 60 55
1688 90f. Emperor Wilhelm II 60 55
1689 90f. Commissioner J. von Puttkamer, 1891–3 60 55
1690 90f. Consul-General G. Nachtigal, 1884 60 55
1691 90f. Governor A. Koehler, 1895–1902 60 55
1692 90f. Governor W. Horn, 1902–5 60 55
1693 90f. Governor J. G. von Zech, 1905–10 60 55
1694 90f. Governor E. Bruckner, 1911–12 60 55
1695 90f. Governor A. F. von Mecklenberg, 1912–14 60 55
1696 90f. Governor H. G. von Doering, 1914 60 55
1697 120f. Signing of Protectorate Treaty, 1885 (horiz) 90 85
1698 120f. Postmen, 1885 90 85
1699 150f. Children dancing around maps and flags 1·10 95
1700 270f. German gunboat "Mowe", 1884 (horiz) 2·00 1·75
1701 270f. German sail corvette "Sophie", 1884 2·00 1·75
1702 270f. Steam train, Anecho railway, 1905 (horiz) 3·50 2·75
1703 270f. Mallet steam locomotive, Kpalime Railway, 1905 (dated "1907") (horiz) 3·50 2·75
1704 270f. Flags and Presidents of Togo and Germany (horiz) 2·25 1·90

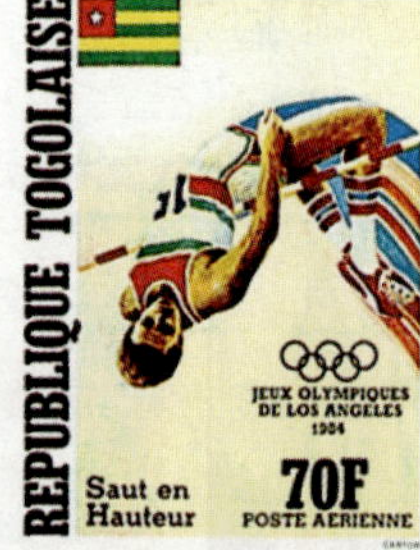

306 High Jumping

1984. Air. Olympic Games, Los Angeles. Mult.
1705 70f. Type **306** 45 25
1706 90f. Cycling 55 20
1707 120f. Football 80 30
1708 250f. Boxing (horiz) 1·60 50
1709 400f. Running (horiz) 2·75 80

307 Donald with Presents and Chip

1984. 50th Anniv of Donald Duck (cartoon character). Multicoloured.
1711 1f. Type **307** (postage) 10 10
1712 2f. Donald and Chip'n'Dale 10 10
1713 3f. Huey, Chip and Dale blowing up balloons 10 10
1714 5f. Donald and Chip holding birthday cake 10 10
1715 10f. Daisy kissing Donald 30 10
1716 15f. Goofy giving Donald his present 40 10
1717 105f. Huey, Dewey and Louie decorating cake (air) 85 15
1718 500f. Huey, Dewey, Louie and Donald with birthday cake 4·50 95
1719 1000f. Huey, Duey and Louie startling Donald 7·50 1·60

308 West African Manatee

1984. Endangered Wildlife. Multicoloured.
1722 45f. Type **308** (postage) 1·50 20
1723 70f. Manatee (close up) 1·25 20
1724 90f. Manatees in water (air) 1·75 35
1725 105f. Manatee with cub 1·75 35

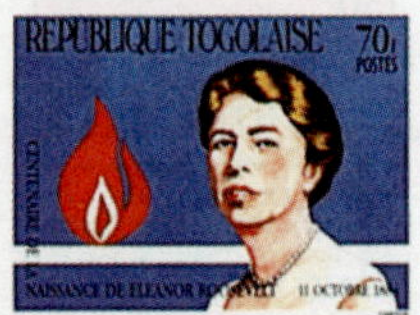

309 Flame and Eleanor Roosevelt

1984. Birth Cent of Eleanor Roosevelt. Mult.
1727 70f. Type **309** (postage) 55 15
1728 90f. Eleanor Roosevelt and Statue of Liberty (air) 65 15

310 Lockheed Constellation, 1944

1984. 40th Anniv of International Civil Aviation Organization. Multicoloured.

1729 70f. Type **310** (postage) . . 55 30
1730 105f. Boeing 707, 1954 (air) 60 40
1731 200f. Douglas DC-8-61, 1966 . . . . 1·25 80
1732 500f. Concorde, 1966 . . . 3·25 1·75

311 Bristol "400", 1947

1984. Classic Cars. Multicoloured.

1734 1f. Type **311** (postage) . . . 10 10
1735 2f. Frazer Nash "Standard", 1925 . . . . 10 10
1736 3f. Healey "Silverstone", 1950 . . . . 10 10
1737 4f. Kissell "Gold Bug Speedstar", 1925 . . . . 10 10
1738 50f. La Salle 5 litre, 1927 . . 80 15
1739 90f. Minerva 30 h.p., 1921 (air) 70 15
1740 500f. Morgan "Plus 4", 1950 . . . . 4·25 95
1741 1000f. Napier "40/50 T75 Six", 1921 . . . . 7·75 2·25

313 "Connestabile Madonna"

1984. Christmas. Paintings by Raphael. Mult.

1744 70f. Type **313** (postage) . . 55 15
1745 290f. "The Cowper Madonna" (air) . . . . . 1·90 65
1746 300f. "The Alba Madonna" 2·00 65
1747 500f. "Madonna of the Curtain" . . . . 3·25 1·10

314 Rack Railway Steam Train, Madeira

1984. Railway Locomotives. Multicoloured.

1749 1f. Type **314** (postage) . . . 10 10
1750 2f. British-built steam locomotive, Egypt 10 10
1751 3f. Garratt steam locomotive, Algeria 10 10
1752 4f. Diesel train, Congo-Ocean Railway 10 10
1753 50f. Italian-built steam locomotive, Libya 40 10
1754 90f. Northern Railway steam locomotive No. 49 (air) 70 15
1755 105f. Mallet steam locomotive, Togo 80 15
1756 500f. Steam locomotive, Rhodesia . . . . 3·75 70
1757 1000f. Beyer-Garratt steam locomotive, East African Railway . . . . 7·50 1·40

315 Map of Americas and Flags

316 St. Paul

1984. 3rd E.E.C.–African States Convention, Lome. Multicoloured.

1759 100f. Type **315** 80 20
1760 130f. Map of Europe and Africa and flags . . . . 1·10 30
1761 270f. Map of Asia and Australasia and flags . . 2·00 60

Nos. 1759/61 were printed in se-tenant strips of three, forming a composite design showing map of the world.

1984. The Twelve Apostles. Multicoloured.

1763 1f. Type **316** (postage) . . . 10 10
1764 2f. St. Thomas 10 10
1765 3f. St. Matthew 10 10
1766 4f. St. James, the Less . . . 10 10
1767 5f. St. Simon, the Zealot . . 10 10
1768 70f. St. Thaddeus 85 15
1769 90f. St. Bartholomew (air) 55 15
1770 105f. St. Philip 65 15
1771 200f. St. John . . . . . . 1·25 35
1772 270f. St. James, son of Zebedee . . . . 1·60 45
1773 400f. St. Andrew . . . . . . 2·50 80
1774 500f. St. Peter . . . . . . 3·25 90

317 Allez France

1985. Racehorses. Multicoloured.

1776 1f. Type **317** (postage) . . . 10 10
1777 2f. Arkle (vert) 10 10
1778 3f. Tingle Creek (vert) . . . 10 10
1779 4f. Interco 10 10
1780 50f. Dawn Run 95 15
1781 90f. Seattle Slew (vert) (air) 85 20
1782 500f. Nijinsky . . . . . . 4·75 90
1783 1000f. Politician . . . . . . 7·75 2·25

318 Map, Globe and Doves

1985. Air. Peace and Human Rights. Multicoloured.

1785 230f. Type **318** . . . . . . 1·50 55
1786 270f. Palm tree by shore and emblem . . . . 1·75 55
1787 500f. Mining and emblem 3·25 1·10
1788 1000f. Human Rights monument . . . . 6·75 2·50

319 "Christ and the Fisherman"

1985. Easter. Paintings by Raphael. Multicoloured.

1789 70f. "Christ and the Apostles" (postage) . . . 55 15
1790 90f. Type **319** 60 20
1791 135f. "Christ making Benediction" (vert) (air) 1·00 20
1792 150f. "The Entombment" (vert) . . . . 1·10 30
1793 250f. "The Resurrection" (vert) . . . . 1·75 50

320 Profiles and Emblem

1985. 15th Anniv of Cultural and Technical Co-operation Agency.

1795 **320** 70f. multicoloured . . . 50 20
1796 90f. multicoloured . . . 60 30

321 Adifo Dance

1985. Air. Traditional Dances. Multicoloured.

1797 120f. Type **321** 80 30
1798 125f. Whip dance 90 35
1799 290f. Idjombi dance . . . . 1·90 65
1800 500f. Moba dance . . . . . 3·25 95

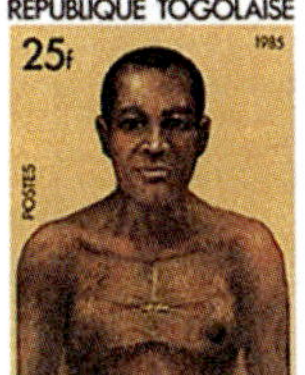

322 Kabye Man

1985. Tribal Markings. Multicoloured.

1801 25f. Type **322** (postage) . . 15 10
1802 70f. Mollah woman 50 20
1803 90f. Moba man (air) 60 20
1804 105f. Kabye woman 80 20
1805 270f. Peda woman . . . . . 1·90 65

323 Woman carrying Basket on Head and Workers on Map

1985. "Philexafrique" Stamp Exhibition, Lome. "Youth and Development". Multicoloured.

1806 200f. Type **323** . . . . . . 1·60 90
1807 200f. Man ploughing field with oxen . . . . 1·60 90

324 Muricate Turrid

1985. Sea Shells. Multicoloured.

1808 70f. Type **324** (postage) . . 95 20
1809 90f. Desjardin's marginalla (air) . . . . 1·00 25
1810 120f. Nifat turrid . . . . . 1·25 25
1811 135f. Rat cowrie . . . . . 1·50 25
1812 270f. Garter cone . . . . . 3·00 60

1985. "Expo '85" World's Fair, Tsukuba, Japan. Nos. 1738 and 1741 optd **EXPOSITION MONDIALE 1985 TSUKUBA, JAPON**.

1814 50f. La Salle 5 litre, 1927 (postage) 85 20
1815 1000f. Napier "40/50 T75 Six", 1921 (air) . . . . . 9·50 2·75

326 Pope giving Blessing

327 Brown Pelican

1985. Air. Visit of Pope John Paul II. Mult.

1817 90f. Pope and children . . . 85 20
1818 130f. Type **326** . . . . . . 1·10 35
1819 500f. Pres. Eyadema greeting Pope . . . . 4·25 2·25

1985. Birth Bicentenary of John J. Audubon (ornithologist). Multicoloured.

1820 120f. Type **327** (postage) . . 1·40 30
1821 270f. Golden eagle . . . . 3·50 70
1822 90f. Bonaparte's gulls (air) 1·10 20
1823 135f. Great-tailed grackle . . 1·75 30
1824 500f. Red-headed woodpecker . . . . . . 7·75 1·50

1985. Air. Olympic Games Medal Winners (2nd series). Nos. 1657/64 optd.

1826 500f. **"ITALIE MEDAILLE D'OR"** . . . . 4·00 85
1827 500f. **"PHILIPPE BOISSE FRANCE MEDAILLE D'OR"** . . . . 4·00 85
1828 500f. **"ROLF GOLZ R.F.A. MEDAILLE D'ARGENT"** . . . . . 4·00 85
1829 500f. **"PATRIK SJOBERG SUEDE MEDAILLE D'ARGENT"** . . . . . 4·00 85
1830 500f. **"GLYNIS NUNN AUSTRALIE MEDAILLE D'OR"** . . . 4·00 85

1831 500f. **"KIRK BAPTISTE ETATS UNIS MEDAILLE D'ARGENT"** . . . . . . 4·00 85
1832 500f. **"CARL LEWIS ETATS UNIS MEDAILLE D'OR"** . . . 4·00 85
1833 500f. **"KEVIN BARRY NLE ZELANDE MEDAILLE D'ARGENT"** . . . . . . 4·00 85

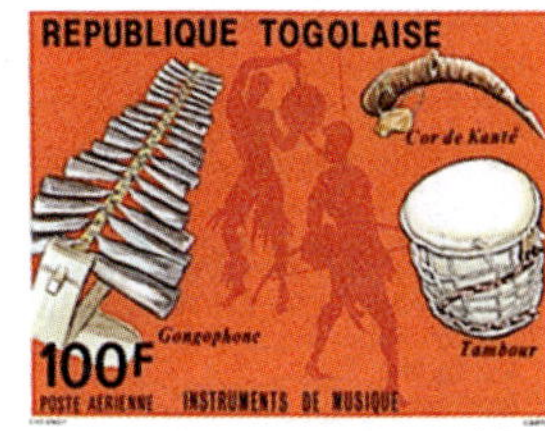

330 Gongophone, Kante Horn and Drum

1985. Air. "Philexafrique" Stamp Exhibition, Lome (2nd issue). Musical Instruments. Mult.

1835 100f. Type **330** . . . . . . 1·40 65
1836 100f. Twin drums, Bassar horn and castanets . . . 1·40 65

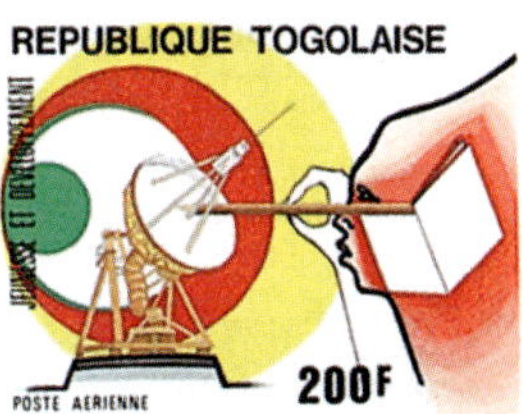

331 Open Book, Profile, Hand holding Pencil and Dish Aerial

1985. Air. "Philexafrique" Stamp Exhibition, Lome (3rd issue). "Youth and Development". Multicoloured.

1837 200f. Type **331** . . . . . . 1·90 1·10
1838 200f. Profiles, factory, cogwheel and maize . . . 1·90 1·10

332 Dove, Sun and U.N. Emblem

1985. 40th Anniv of U.N.O. Multicoloured.

1839 90f. Type **332** (postage) . . 60 20
1840 115f. Hands reaching up to Emblem 90 20
1841 150f. Building new bridge on river Kara (air) . . . 1·10 35
1842 250f. Preparing experimental field of millet at Atalote, Keran . . . . 1·60 50
1843 500f. Pres. Eyadema, U.N. Secretary-General, U.N. and national flags . . . . 3·25 85

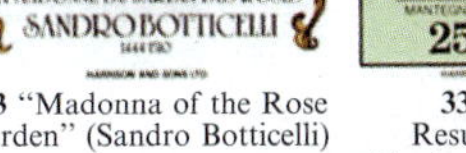

333 "Madonna of the Rose Garden" (Sandro Botticelli)

335 "The Resurrection" (Andrea Mantegna)

1985. Christmas. Multicoloured.

1844 90f. Type **333** (postage) . . 65 20
1845 115f. "Madonna and Child" (11th-century Byzantine painting) (air) 90 20
1846 150f. "Rest during the flight into Egypt" (Gerard David) . . . . 1·00 30

1847 160f. "African Madonna" (16th-century statue) 1·10 30
1848 250f. "African Madonna" (statue, 1900) 2·00 45

1985. Various stamps optd. (a) Nos. 1739/40 optd **10e ANNIVERSAIRE DE APOLLO-SOYUZ.**
1850 90f. Minerva 30 h.p., 1921 85 30
1851 500f. Morgan "Plus 4", 1950 4·75 1·40

(b) Nos. 1752, 1755 and 1757 optd **80e ANNIVERSAIRE du ROTARY INTERNATIONAL.**
1853 4f. Diesel train, Congo-Ocean Railway (postage) 55 35
1854 105f. Mallet steam locomotive, Togo (air) 1·10 1·00
1855 1000f. Beyer-Garratt steam locomotive, East African Railway 11·00 5·75

(c) 150th Anniv of German Railways. Nos. 1753/4 and 1756 optd **150e ANNIVERSAIRE DE CHEMIN FER "LUDWIG".**
1857 50f. Italian-built steam locomotive, Libya (postage) 1·00 35
1858 90f. Northern Railway steam locomotive No. 49 (air) 1·00 50
1859 500f. Steam locomotive, Rhodesia 6·25 2·75

(d) Nos. 1773/4 optd **"75e ANNIVERSAIRE DE LA MORT DE HENRI DUNANT FONDATEUR DE LA CROIX ROUGE".**
1861 400f. St. Andrew 3·25 1·10
1862 500f. St. Peter 4·00 1·40

(e) Nos. 1780 and 1783 optd **"75e ANNIVERSAIRE DU SCOUTISME FEMININ".**
1864 50f. Dawn Run 85 20
1865 1000f. Politician 8·25 2·25

1986. Easter. Multicoloured.
1867 25f. Type **335** (postage) 20 10
1868 70f. "Calvary" (Paul Veronese) 55 15
1869 90f. "The Last Supper" (Jacopo Robusti Tintoretto) (horiz) (air) 65 30
1870 200f. "Christ in the Tomb" (Berruguette) (horiz) 1·50 55

336 "Suisie" Space Probe and Kohoutek's Comet

1986. Appearance of Halley's Comet (1st issue). Multicoloured.
1872 70f. Type **336** (postage) 55 15
1873 90f. "Vega I" space probe and people pointing at comet (air) 55 20
1874 150f. Comet and observation equipment 90 30
1875 200f. "Giotto" space probe and comet over town 1·25 40
See also Nos. 1917/20.

337 New York, Statue and Eiffel Tower

338 Cashew Nut

1986. Air. Centenary of Statue of Liberty. Mult.
1877 70f. Type **337** 50 15
1878 90f. Statue, Arc de Triomphe and Brooklyn Bridge 1·25 45
1879 500f. Statue, Pantheon and Empire State Building 3·25 1·10

1986. Fruit. Multicoloured.
1880 70f. Type **338** (postage) 55 15
1881 90f. Pineapple 80 20
1882 120f. Avocado (air) 90 20
1883 135f. Papaw 1·10 20
1884 290f. Mango (vert) 2·25 65

339 Footballers

341 "Ramaria moelleriana"

1986. World Cup Football Championship, Mexico.
1885 **339** 70f. mult (postage) 55 15
1886 – 90f. multicoloured (air) 55 30
1887 – 130f. multicoloured 85 35
1888 – 300f. multicoloured 1·90 70
DESIGNS: 90f. to 300f. Various footballing scenes.

1986. Air. "Ameripex '86" International Stamp Exhibition, Chicago. Nos. 1718/19 optd **AMERIPEX 86.**
1890 500f. Huey, Dewey, Louie and Donald with birthday cake 4·50 1·10
1891 1000f. Huey, Dewey and Louie startling Donald 8·25 2·25

1986. Fungi. Multicoloured.
1893 70f. Type **341** 1·25 50
1894 90f. "Hygrocybe firma" 1·50 70
1895 150f. "Kalchbrennera corallocephala" 2·50 1·25
1896 200f. "Cookeina tricholoma" 3·50 1·75

342 Hand framing Huts and Child

1986. International Youth Year (1985). Mult.
1897 25f. Type **342** 30 15
1898 90f. Children feeding birds 1·10 40

343 Wrestlers

344 Miss Sarah Ferguson

1986. Evala Wrestling Contest.
1899 **343** 15f. mult (postage) 15 10
1900 – 20f. multicoloured 30 10
1901 – 70f. multicoloured 65 15
1902 – 90f. multicoloured (air) 40 35
DESIGNS: 20 to 90f. Wrestling scenes.

1986. Wedding of Prince Andrew. Multicoloured.
1903 10f. Type **344** (postage) 55 10
1904 1000f. Prince Andrew (air) 6·75 2·25

1986. World Cup Winners. Nos. 1886/9 optd.
1906 70f. **DEMI-FINALE ARGENTINE 2 BELGIQUE 0** (postage) 55 35
1907 90f. **DEMI-FINALE ALLEMAGNE DE L'OUEST 2 FRANCE 0** (air) 55 20
1908 130f. **3 eme et 4 eme PLACE FRANCE 4 BELGIQUE 2** 85 35
1909 300f. **FINALE ARGENTINE 3 ALLEMAGNE DE L'OUEST 2** 1·90 80

346 Fazao Hotel

1986. Hotels. Multicoloured.
1910 70f. Type **346** (postage) 55 15
1911 90f. Sarakawa Hotel (air) 65 30
1912 120f. The Lake Hotel 90 40

347 Spur-winged Geese

1986. Keran National Park. Multicoloured.
1913 70f. Type **347** (postage) 80 40
1914 90f. Antelope (air) 65 30
1915 100f. African elephant 80 35
1916 130f. Kob 1·00 45

1986. Appearance of Halley's Comet (2nd issue). Nos. 1872/5 optd as T **198a** of Sierra Leone.
1917 **336** 70f. mult (postage) 1·25 35
1918 – 90f. multicoloured (air) 1·00 30
1919 – 150f. multicoloured 1·50 40
1920 – 200f. multicoloured 1·90 70

349 "The Annunciation"

1986. Christmas. Multicoloured.
1922 45f. Type **349** (postage) 45 15
1923 120f. "Nativity" (air) 90 35
1924 130f. "Adoration of the Magi" 1·10 45
1925 200f. "Flight into Egypt" 1·50 65

350 Rainbow and Douglas DC-10

1986. Air. 25th Anniv of Air Afrique.
1927 **350** 90f. multicoloured 75 45

351 Pres. Eyadema and Phosphate Mine

1987. 20th Anniv of National Liberation. Mult.
1928 35f. Type **351** (postage) 20 10
1929 50f. Anie sugar refinery 35 15
1930 70f. Nangbeto Dam 50 20
1931 90f. February 2 Hotel and Posts and Telecommunications building, Lome 60 20
1932 100f. Post and Telecommunications building, Kara (air) 55 15
1933 120f. Peace monument 80 30
1934 130f. Baby being vaccinated 90 35

352 "The Last Supper"

1987. Easter. Paintings from Nadoba Church, Keran. Multicoloured.
1936 90f. Type **352** (postage) 65 30
1937 130f. "Christ on the Cross" (air) 90 30
1938 300f. "The Resurrection" 2·00 65

353 Adenauer speaking in the Bundestag

1987. Air. 20th Death Anniv of Konrad Adenauer (German Chancellor). Multicoloured.
1940 120f. Type **353** 85 30
1941 500f. Adenauer with John F. Kennedy 3·25 1·10

354 Player falling with Ball

1987. World Rugby Football Cup. Multicoloured.
1943 70f. Type **354** (postage) 80 30
1944 130f. Player running with ball (air) 1·25 35
1945 300f. Scrum 2·75 1·25

355 "Adenium obesum"

1987. Flowers. Multicoloured.
1947 70f. Type **355** (postage) 70 20
1948 90f. "Amorphophallus abyssinicus" (vert) (air) 85 30
1949 100f. "Ipomoea mauritiana" 1·00 30
1950 120f. "Salacia togoica" (vert) 1·25 35

356 Wilhelm I Coin and Victory Statue

1987. Air. 750th Anniv of Berlin. Multicoloured.
1951 90f. Type **356** 65 30
1952 150f. Friedrich III coin and Brandenburg Gate 1·00 35
1953 300f. Wilhelm II coin and Place de la Republique 2·00 65

357 Hoefler's Butterflyfish

1987. Fishes. Multicoloured.
1955 70f. Type **357** 1·00 35
1956 90f. Nile pufferfish 1·25 40
1957 120f. Goree spadefish 1·50 60
1958 130f. Dwarf labeo 1·75 60

358 Long Jumping

1987. Olympic Games, Seoul (1988). Mult.
1959 70f. Type **358** (postage) 60 20
1960 90f. Relay race (air) 60 20
1961 200f. Cycling 1·25 45
1962 250f. Javelin throwing 1·60 55

1987. Endangered Wildlife. As Nos. 1722/5 but values changed and size 37 × 24 mm.
1964 60f. Type **308** (postage) 1·00 20
1965 75f. Manatee (close up) 1·10 35
1966 80f. Manatee in water 1·50 35
1967 100f. Manatee with cub (air) 1·75 40

359 Doctor vaccinating Child

1987. "Health for All by Year 2000". Anti-tuberculosis Campaign. Multicoloured.
1968 80f. Type **359** (postage) 55 30
1969 90f. Family under umbrella (vert) (air) 60 30
1970 115f. Faculty of Medicine building, Lome University 80 35

360 "Spring or the Earthly Paradise"

1987. Christmas. Multicoloured.
1971 40f. Type **360** (postage) . . 35 10
1972 45f. "The Creation of Adam" (Michelangelo) . . 35 10
1973 105f. "Presentation in the Temple" (vert) (air) . . . 65 20
1974 270f. "The Original Sin" (vert) . . . . 1·75 65

361 Men ploughing and Women collecting Water

1988. 10th Anniv of Agricultural Development Fund.
1976 **361** 90f. multicoloured . . . 65 20

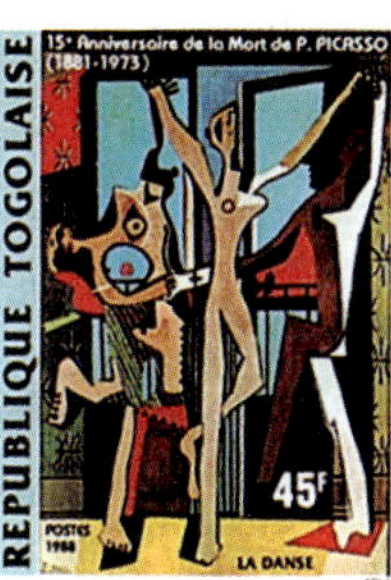

363 "The Dance"

1988. 15th Death Anniv of Pablo Picasso (painter). Multicoloured.
1978 45f. Type **363** (postage) . . 45 10
1979 160f. "Portrait of a Young Girl" . . . . 1·50 35
1980 300f. "Gueridon" (air) . . . 2·75 85

364 Cement

365 "Jesus and the Disciples at Emmaus"

1988. Industries. Multicoloured.
1982 125f. Type **364** 85 30
1983 165f. Brewery . . . . 1·10 40
1984 195f. Phosphates . . . . . 1·25 45
1985 200f. Plastics . . . . 1·25 45
1986 300f. Milling (vert) . . . . 2·10 65

1988. Easter. Stained Glass Windows. Mult.
1987 70f. Type **365** (postage) . . 60 15
1988 90f. "Mary at the Foot of the Cross" 80 20
1989 120f. "Crucifixion" (air) . . 85 30
1990 200f. "St. Thomas and Resurrected Jesus" . . . 1·40 45

366 Paris Crowd welcoming Kennedy, 1961

367 Watchi Chief

1988. 25th Death Anniv of John F. Kennedy (U.S. President). Multicoloured.
1992 125f. Type **366** . . . . . . 1·00 20
1993 155f. Kennedy at Paris Town Hall (vert) . . . . 1·10 20
1994 165f. Kennedy and De Gaulle at Elysee Palace (vert) . . . . 1·25 40
1995 180f. John and Jacqueline Kennedy at Orly Airport 1·40 75

1988. Traditional Tribal Costumes. Multicoloured.
1997 80f. Type **367** 55 20
1998 125f. Watchi woman 85 20
1999 165f. Kotokoli man . . . . 1·10 35
2000 175f. Ewe man . . . . . . 1·10 35

368 Basketball

369 People with Candles

1988. Olympic Games, Seoul. Multicoloured.
2002 70f. Type **368** (postage) . . 50 15
2003 90f. Tennis 60 20
2004 120f. Archery (air) 85 30
2005 200f. Throwing the discus 1·40 45

1988. 40th Anniv of W.H.O. Multicoloured.
2007 80f. Type **369** 55 15
2008 125f. Maps, emblem and "40" 85 20

370 Plaited Style

1988. Hairstyles. Multicoloured.
2009 80f. Type **370** 55 20
2010 125f. Knotted style 85 20
2011 170f. Plaited style with bow 1·00 40
2012 180f. Style with plaits all over head (vert) . . . . . 1·25 40

371 Collecting Water (B. Gossner)

372 "Adoration of the Magi" (Pieter Brueghel the Elder)

1988. "Philtogo" National Stamp Exhibition. Designs depicting winning entries of a schools drawing competition. Multicoloured.
2014 10f. Type **371** 10 10
2015 35f. Villagers working on farm (K. Ekoue-Kouvahey) 20 10
2016 70f. Family (A. Abbey) . . 65 15
2017 90f. Village women preparing food (T. D. Lawson) 85 30
2018 120f. Fishermen and boats on shore (A. Tazzar) . . 1·10 30

1988. Christmas. Multicoloured.
2019 80f. Type **372** (postage) . . 55 20
2020 150f. "The Virgin, The Infant Jesus, Saints Jerome and Dominic" (Fra. Filippo Lippi) (air) 1·00 20
2021 175f. "The Madonna, The Infant Jesus, St. Joseph and the Infant St. John the Baptist" (Federico Barocci) . . . . 1·25 35
2022 195f. "The Virgin and Child" (Gentile Bellini) 1·40 45

373 Wreckage of Airplane

1989. 15th Anniv of Sarakawa Assassination Attempt. Multicoloured.
2024 10f. Type **373** 10 10
2025 80f. Tail section (vert) . . . 55 25
2026 125f. Soldiers and wreckage 85 50

374 Anniversary Emblem

1989. 20th Anniv of Benin Electricity Community.
2027 **374** 80f. multicoloured . . . 60 20
2028 125f. multicoloured . . . 95 20

375 Boxing

1989. Prince Emanuel of Liechtenstein Foundation. Multicoloured.
2029 80f. Type **375** 55 20
2030 125f. Long jumping 55 30
2031 165f. Running . . . . . . 1·10 40

376 Table Tennis

1989. Olympic Games, Barcelona (1992). Mult.
2032 80f. Type **376** (postage) . . 65 20
2033 125f. Running (horiz) . . . 90 20
2034 165f. Putting the shot . . . 1·00 35
2035 175f. Basketball . . . . . . 1·25 35
2036 380f. High jumping (horiz) (air) . . . . 2·50 55
2037 425f. Boxing (horiz) . . . . 3·00 55

377 Footballers and St. Janvier's Cathedral, Naples

1989. World Cup Football Championship, Italy. Multicoloured.
2039 80f. Type **377** (postage) . . 55 20
2040 125f. Milan Cathedral . . . 85 20
2041 165f. Bevilacqua Palace, Verona . . . . 1·10 35
2042 175f. Baptistry, Florence . . 1·10 35
2043 380f. Madama Palace, Turin (air) . . . . 2·75 55
2044 425f. St. Laurent's Cathedral, Genoa . . . . 2·75 55

378 Bundestag

1989. 40th Anniv of Federal Republic of Germany. Multicoloured.
2046 90f. Type **378** 65 20
2047 125f. Konrad Adenauer (Chancellor, 1949–63) and Theodor Heuss (President, 1949–59) (vert) 95 30
2048 180f. West German flag and emblem . . . . 1·25 40

379 Tractor, Map and Woman at Water-pump

1989. 30th Anniv of Council of Unity.
2049 **379** 75f. multicoloured . . . 55 20

380 Boys learning First Aid

1989. 125th Anniv of International Red Cross. Multicoloured.
2050 90f. Type **380** 50 20
2051 125f. Founding meeting . . 85 35

381 Storming the Bastille

383 People with Banners and Pres. Eyadema

382 Jacques Necker (statesman) and The Three Orders

1989. Bicentenary of French Revolution (1st issue). Multicoloured.
2052 90f. Type **381** 65 20
2053 125f. Oath of the Tennis Court (horiz) . . . . . . 1·00 35
2054 180f. Abolition of Privileges (horiz) . . . . 1·40 45
See also Nos. 2056/9.

1989. Bicentenary of French Revolution (2nd issue). Multicoloured.
2056 90f. Type **382** (postage) . . 65 20
2057 190f. Guy le Chapelier and abolition of seigneurial rights . . . . 1·50 45
2058 425f. Talleyrand-Perigord (statesman) and La Fayette's oath (air) . . . 2·75 55
2059 480f. Paul Barras (revolutionary) and overthrow of Robespierre 3·25 55

1989. 20th Anniv of Kpalime Appeal. Mult.
2061 90f. Type **383** 60 20
2062 125f. Pres. Eyadema addressing gathering . . . 90 35

384 "Apollo II" Launch

386 Emblem

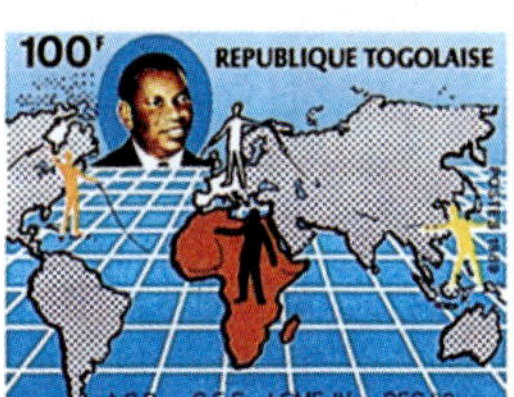

385 Figures on Map (dated "DEC.89")

1989. 20th Anniv of First Manned Landing on Moon. Multicoloured.
2063 40f. Type **384** 30 10
2064 90f. Space capsule in orbit 55 20
2065 150f. Landing capsule . . . 1·10 35
2066 250f. Splashdown . . . . . 1·60 45

1989. 4th Lome Convention (on relations between European Community and African, Caribbean and Pacific countries). Multicoloured.

2068 100f. Type **385** 80 30
2069 100f. As T **385** but dated "15 DEC.89" 80 30

1990. 10th Anniv of Pan-African Postal Union.

2070 **386** 125f. gold, blue & brown 90 30

387 Party Headquarters, Kara

1990. 20th Anniv (1989) of Rally of Togolese People Party. Multicoloured.

2071 45f. Type **387** 35 15
2072 90f. Pres. Eyadema and anniversary emblem . . . 60 20

388 "Myrina silenus" and Scout

389 "Danaus chrysippus"

1990. Scouts, Butterflies and Fungi. Mult.

2073 80f. Type **388** (postage) . . 65 15
2074 90f. "Phlebobus silvaticus" (fungus) 65 15
2075 125f. "Volvariella esculenta" (fungus) 90 20
2076 165f. "Hypolycaena antifaunus" (butterfly) . . 1·10 35
2077 380f. "Termitomyces striatus" (fungus) (air) . . 3·00 55
2078 425f. "Axiocerces harpax" (butterfly) . . . . . . 3·00 55

1990. Butterflies. Multicoloured.

2080 5f. Type **389** 50 10
2081 10f. "Morpho aega" 50 10
2082 15f. "Papilio demodocus" 50 10
2083 90f. "Papilio dardanus" . . 1·50 35

390 Emblem

391 Nile Monitor

1990. 9th Convention of Lions Club Internationals District 403, Lome.

2085 **390** 90f. multicoloured . . . 60 35
2086 125f. multicoloured . . . 85 55
2087 165f. multicoloured . . . 1·10 80

1990. Reptiles. Multicoloured.

2088 1f. Type **391** 50 10
2089 25f. Puff adder 75 10
2090 60f. Black-lipped cobra . . 1·00 15
2091 90f. African rock python . . 1·25 20

392 Pile of Cowrie Shells

393 Maps, Cogwheel and Arrows

1990. Money Cowrie Shells. Multicoloured.

2092 90f. Type **392** . . . . . . 1·00 20
2093 125f. Cowrie and bead ornament . . . . . . 1·50 25
2094 180f. Headdress with cowries and animal horns 2·00 55

1990. United States–Togo Friendship. Mult.

2095 125f. Type **393** 90 35
2096 180f. Presidents Bush and Eyadema shaking hands (horiz) . . . . 1·25 35

394 Cinkasse Post Office

1990. Stamp Day.

2098 **394** 90f. multicoloured . . . 60 35

395 Addressing Crowd, Brazzaville, 1944

1990. 20th Death Anniv of Charles de Gaulle (statesman).

2099 **395** 125f. multicoloured . . . 85 45

396 Thatched Houses

1990. Traditional Housing. Multicoloured.

2100 90f. Type **396** 60 35
2101 125f. Village 85 45
2102 190f. Tamberma house . . . 1·25 65

397 Airport, Airliners and Airline Emblems

1990. New Lome Airport.

2103 **397** 90f. multicoloured . . . 1·00 35

398 Woman carrying Basket on Head (Sikou Dapau)

1990.

2104 **398** 90f. multicoloured . . . 60 35

399 Chimpanzee, Missahoue Kloto

1991. Forests. Multicoloured.

2105 90f. Type **399** 60 35
2106 170f. Jardine's parrot, Aledjo Forest . . . . . 1·25 75
2107 185f. Grey parrot, Chateau Vial Kloto Forest . . . . 1·40 75

400 Dancers

1992. Spirit Dances.

2108 **400** 90f. multicoloured . . . 75 35
2109 – 125f. multicoloured . . . 1·00 55
2110 – 190f. multicoloured . . . 1·50 80

DESIGNS: 125, 190f. Various dances.

401 Royal Python hatching

1992. The Royal Python. Multicoloured.

2111 90f. Type **401** 75 35
2112 125f. Hatchlings emerging from shells . . . . . . 1·00 35
2113 190f. Hatchlings and empty shells . . . . 1·50 65
2114 300f. Close-up of hatchling and empty shell . . . . . 2·25 90

402 Emblem

403 Postal Sorter

1994. 120th Anniv of U.P.U.

2115 **402** 180f. multicoloured . . . 45 20

1994. World Post Day.

2117 **403** 90f. multicoloured . . . 20 10
2118 120f. multicoloured . . . 30 10

404 Footballers

1994. World Cup Football Championship, U.S.A.

2119 **404** 5f. multicoloured . . . 10 10
2120 – 10f. multicoloured . . . 10 10
2121 – 25f. multicoloured . . . 10 10
2122 – 60f. multicoloured . . . 15 10
2123 – 90f. multicoloured . . . 20 10
2124 – 100f. multicoloured . . . 25 10
2125 – 200f. multicoloured . . . 50 20
2126 – 1000f. multicoloured . . 2·40 95

DESIGNS: 10f. to 1000f. Various footballing scenes.

405 Northern Pike

1995. Fishes. Multicoloured.

2128 10f. Type **405** 10 10
2129 90f. Derbio 35 20
2130 180f. Common carp 75 40

406 "The Resurrection" (detail) (Andrea Mantegna)

407 Hill

1995. Easter. Multicoloured.

2131 90f. Type **406** 20 10
2132 180f. "Calvary" (Paolo Veronese) 45 20
2133 190f. "The Last Supper" (Jacopo Tintoretto) (horiz) 45 20

1995. Birth Bicentenary of Sir Rowland Hill (instigator of postage stamp).

2134 **407** 125f. multicoloured . . . 30 10

408 Secretary Bird

409 Madagascan Belvache

1995. Birds. Multicoloured.

2135 5f. Type **408** 10 10
2136 10f. African paradise flycatcher ("Paradise Flycatcher") 10 10
2137 25f. African spoonbill (horiz) 10 10
2138 60f. Red-cheeked cordon-bleu ("Cordon Bleu") (horiz) 15 10
2139 90f. Orange-breasted sunbird 20 10
2140 100f. Yellow-billed hornbill 25 10
2141 180f. Barn owl (horiz) . . . 45 20
2142 200f. Hoopoe feeding chick (horiz) 50 20
2143 300f. Red-crowned bishop ("Fire-crowned Bishop") 75 30
2144 1000f. Red-throated bee eater . . . . 2·40 95

1995. Plants. Multicoloured.

2146 15f. Type **409** 10 10
2147 90f. Marigolds 20 10
2148 125f. Agave (horiz) 30 10

410 Anniversary Emblem

411 Globe and Doves

1995. 50th Anniv of U.N.O. (1st issue).

2149 **410** 180f. multicoloured . . . 45 20

See also Nos. 2150/2.

1995. 50th Anniversaries. Multicoloured. (a) U.N.O. (2nd issue).

2150 25f. Type **411** 10 10
2151 90f. Doves and Headquarters building, New York 20 10
2152 400f. Globe and doves (different) 95 40

Nos. 2150/2 were issued together, se-tenant, forming a composite design.

(b) Food and Agriculture Organization.

2154 45f. Cattle 10 10
2155 125f. Cow 30 10
2156 125f. Mother and child collecting water (horiz) . . 30 10
2157 200f. Herdsmen 50 20

Nos. 2154/5 and 2157 were issued together, se-tenant, forming a composite design.

412 Montecassino, Italy

1995. 50th Anniv of End of Second World War (1st issue). Victory in Europe. Multicoloured.

2159 45f. Type **412** 10 10
2160 90f. Warsaw in ruins . . . 20 10
2161 125f. Russian tanks in Berlin 30 10
2162 200f. German fighter planes 50 20
2163 200f. American cruiser in north Atlantic 50 20
2164 200f. Capture of Ludendorf Bridge 50 20
2165 200f. Russian "Katyusha" rockets 50 20
2166 500f. United Nations flag 2·50 90

See also Nos. 2191/6.

413 National Flag and Scout Badge

414 Manfred Eigen (Chemistry, 1967)

1995. 18th World Scout Jamboree, Dronten, Netherlands. Multicoloured.
2168 90f. Type **413** 20 10
2169 190f. Saluting scout and camp 45 20
2170 300f. Lord Baden-Powell (founder of Boy Scout Movement) 75 30

1995. Centenary of Nobel Prize Trust Fund. Mult.
2172 200f. Type **414** 50 20
2173 200f. Donald J. Cram (Chemistry, 1987 . . . . 50 20
2174 200f. Paul J. Flory (Chemistry, 1974) 50 20
2175 200f. Johann Deisenhofer (Chemistry, 1988) 50 20
2176 200f. Percy Williams Bridgman (Physics, 1946) 50 20
2177 200f. Otto Stern (Physics, 1943) 50 20
2178 200f. Arne Tiselius (Chemistry, 1948) 50 20
2179 200f. J. Georg Bednorz (Physics, 1987) 50 20
2180 200f. Albert Claude (Medicine, 1974) 50 20
2181 200f. Elihu Root (Peace, 1912) 50 20
2182 200f. Alfred Fried (Peace, 1911) 50 20
2183 200f. Henri Moissan (Chemistry, 1906) 50 20
2184 200f. Charles Barkla (Physics, 1917) 50 20
2185 200f. Rudolf Eucken (Literature, 1908) 50 20
2186 200f. Carl von Ossietzky (Peace, 1935) 50 20
2187 200f. Sir Edward Appleton (Physics, 1947) 50 20
2188 200f. Camillo Golgi (Medicine, 1906) 50 20
2189 200f. Wilhelm Rontgen (Physics, 1901) 50 20

415 Admiral Isoroko Yamamoto

1995. 50th Anniv of End of Second World War (2nd issue). Victory in the Pacific. Japanese commanders. Multicoloured.
2191 200f. Type **415** 50 20
2192 200f. General Hideki Tojo (Minister of War, 1940–41 and Premier, 1941–44) . . 50 20
2193 200f. Vice-admiral Shigeru Fukudome 50 20
2194 200f. Admiral Shigetaro Shimada 50 20
2195 200f. Rear-admiral Chuichi Nagumo 50 20
2196 200f. General Shizu Ichi Tanaka 50 20

416 Drawing
417 Original and Current Emblems

1995. 95th Birthday of Queen Elizabeth the Queen Mother. Multicoloured.
2198 250f. Type **416** 60 25
2199 250f. Carrying umbrella . . 60 25
2200 250f. Seated at writing table (face value white) . . . 60 25
2201 250f. As young woman . . 60 25
2202 250f. As No. 2200 but face value black 60 25
2203 250f. Cutting cake 60 25
2204 250f. Waving from car . . . 60 25

1995. 90th Anniv of Rotary International.
2206 **417** 1000f. multicoloured . . 2·40 95

418 Woman buying Stamps

1995. World Post Day. Multicoloured.
2208 220f. Type **418** 55 20
2209 315f. Clerk arranging stamps on page 75 30
2210 335f. Sorting office 80 30

419 Nativity

1995. Christmas. Paintings. Multicoloured.
2211 90f. Type **419** 20 10
2212 325f. Adoration of the Wise Men 80 30
2213 340f. Adoration of the shepherds (horiz) 80 30

POSTAGE DUE STAMPS

1921. Postage Due stamps of Dahomy, "figure" key-type, optd **TOGO**.
D54 M 5c. green . . . . 45 3·25
D55 10c. red . . . . 30 3·25
D56 15c. grey . . . . 40 3·50
D57 20c. brown . . . . 2·25 4·25
D58 30c. blue . . . . 1·75 5·00
D59 50c. black . . . . 2·00 3·75
D60 60c. orange . . . . 2·50 4·25
D61 1f. violet . . . . 4·25 8·25

D **8** Cotton Growing

1925. Centres and inscr in black.
D 97 D **8** 2c. blue . . . . 10 2·75
D 98 4c. red . . . . 10 2·75
D 99 5c. greeen . . . . . . 10 2·75
D100 10c. red . . . . 20 3·00
D101 15c. yellow . . . . . . 20 3·00
D102 20c. mauve . . . . . . 1·75 3·00
D103 25c. grey . . . . 1·75 3·25
D104 30c. yellow on blue . . 75 3·00
D105 50c. brown . . . . . . 2·25 3·25
D106 60c. green . . . . . . 1·75 3·00
D107 1f. violet . . . . . . 1·50 2·75

1927. Surch.
D108 D **8** 2f. on 1f. mauve and red . . . . 2·00 5·50
D109 3f. on 1f. blue and brown . . . . 2·25 6·25

D **12** Native Mask
D **21**
D **31** Konkomba Helmet

1940.
D151 D **12** 5c. black . . . . . . 1·60 2·75
D152 10c. green . . . . . . 1·00 3·00
D153 15c. red . . . . 30 2·75
D154 20c. blue . . . . . . 45 3·00
D155 30c. brown . . . . . 25 3·00
D156 50c. olive . . . . . . 1·10 4·50
D157 60c. violet . . . . . 65 3·00
D158 1f. blue . . . . 1·25 3·50
D159 2f. red . . . . 1·25 3·25
D160 3f. violet . . . . . . 1·75 3·50

1947.
D185 D **21** 10c. blue . . . . . . 10 1·40
D186 30c. red . . . . 10 2·75
D187 50c. green . . . . . . 10 2·75
D188 1f. brown . . . . . . 20 2·75
D189 2f. red . . . . 85 3·00
D190 3f. black . . . . . . 1·10 3·00
D191 4f. blue . . . . 1·10 3·25
D192 5f. brown . . . . . . 80 3·25
D193 10f. orange . . . . . 1·00 3·50
D194 20f. blue . . . . . . 1·40 3·75

1957.
D214 D **31** 1f. violet . . . . . . 1·00 1·75
D215 2f. orange . . . . . . 95 2·50
D216 3f. grey . . . . 1·25 2·75
D217 4f. red . . . . 1·25 2·75
D218 5f. blue . . . . 1·25 2·75
D219 10f. green . . . . . . 1·40 3·00
D220 20f. purple . . . . . 1·60 3·25

1959. As Nos. D214/20 but colours changed and inscr "REPUBLIQUE DU TOGO".
D244 D **31** 1f. brown . . . . . . 10 1·10
D245 2f. turquoise . . . . . 10 1·10
D246 3f. orange . . . . . . 10 1·75
D247 4f. blue . . . . 15 1·25
D248 5f. purple . . . . . . 15 2·50
D249 10f. violet . . . . . . 25 2·25
D250 20f. black . . . . . . 35 2·25

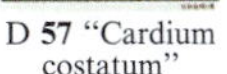

D **57** "Cardium costatum"
D **110** Tomatoes

1964. Sea Shells. Multicoloured.
D366 1f. Butterfly cone 20 20
D367 2f. Ermine marginella . . . 20 20
D368 3f. Rat cowrie 20 20
D369 4f. Bubonian conch 30 30
D370 5f. Type D **57** 75 75
D371 10f. "Cancellaria cancellata" . . . . . . 1·00 1·00
D372 15f. African Neptue volute 2·00 2·00
D373 20f. "Tympanotomus radula" . . . . 2·50 2·50

1969. Young Pioneers Agricultural Organization. Multicoloured.
D696 5f. Type D **110** 10 10
D697 10f. Corn on the cob . . . 30 30
D698 19f. Red pepper 40 40
D699 20f. Peanuts 55 55

1980. As T **259**. Multicoloured.
D1454 5f. Women examining produce (vert) 10 10
D1455 10f. Market stall 10 10
D1456 25f. Poultry seller 15 10
D1457 50f. Carvings and ornaments 35 15

APPENDIX

The following stamps have either been issued in excess of postal needs or have not been available to the public in reasonable quantities at face value. Such stamps may later be given full listing if there is evidence of regular postal use.

All embossed on gold foil.

1989.

Prince Emanuel of Liechtenstein Foundation. Air 1500f. × 2.

Bicentenary of French Revolution (2nd issue). Air 1500f.

Scouts, Butterflies and Fungi. Air 1500f.

TOKELAU Pt. 1

Three islands situated north of Samoa. Formerly known as the Union Islands, they were administered as part of the Gilbert and Ellice Islands until transferred to New Zealand in 1925. Administered by Western Samoa (using stamps of Samoa) until they became a dependency of New Zealand in 1949. Adopted name of Tokelau in 1946.

1948. 12 pence = 1 shilling;
20 shillings = 1 pound.
1967. 100 cents or sene = 1 New Zealand dollar.

1 Atafu Village and Map
1a Queen Elizabeth II

1948.
1 **1** ½d. brown and purple 15 50
2 – 1d. red and green 15 30
3 – 2d. green and blue 15 30
DESIGNS: 1d. Nukunonu hut and map; 2d. Fakaofo village and map.

1953. Coronation.
4 **1a** 3d. brown . . . . 1·50 1·50

1956. Surch **ONE SHILLING**.
5 **1** 1s. on ½d. brown and purple 75 1·25

1966. Arms types of New Zealand without value, surch **TOKELAU ISLANDS** and value in sterling.
6 F **6** 6d. blue 25 80
7 8d. green 25 80
8 2s. pink 30 80

1967. Decimal currency. Nos. 1/3 surch.
9 – 1c. on 1d. (No. 2) 20 60
10 – 2c. on 2d. (No. 3) . . . . . 30 1·00
11 **1** 10c. on ½d. (No. 1) . . . . . 70 2·00

1968. Arms types of New Zealand without value, surch **TOKELAU ISLANDS** and value in decimal currency.
12 F **6** 3c. lilac 30 20
13 5c. blue 30 20
14 7c. green 30 20
15 20c. pink 30 30

8 British Protectorate (1877)
8a "The Nativity" (Federico Fiori (Barocci))

1969. History of Tokelau Islands.
16 **8** 5c. blue, yellow and black . . 15 10
17 – 10c. red, yellow and black . . 15 10
18 – 15c. green, yellow and black 20 15
19 – 20c. brown, yellow and black 25 15
DESIGNS: 10c. Annexed to Gilbert and Ellice Islands (1916); 15c. New Zealand Administration (1925); 20c. New Zealand Territory (1948).

1969. Christmas.
20 **8a** 2c. multicoloured 10 15

8b "The Virgin adoring the Child" (Correggio)

1970. Christmas.
21 **8b** 2c. multicoloured 10 20

12 H.M.S. "Dolphin", 1765
13 Fan

1970. Discovery of Tokelau Islands. Mult.
22 5c. Type **12** . . . . 1·00 35
23 10c. H.M.S. "Pandora", 1791 1·00 35
24 25c. "General Jackson" (American whaling ship), 1835 (horiz) . . . . 1·75 70

1971. Handicrafts. Multicoloured.
25 1c. Type **13** 15 20
26 2c. Hand-bag 20 30
27 3c. Basket 20 40
28 5c. Hand-bag 20 50
29 10c. Shopping-bag 20 55
30 15c. Hand-bag . . . . 25 1·10
31 20c. Canoe . . . . 25 1·40
32 25c. Fishing hooks . . . . . 25 1·40

14 Windmill Pump
15 Horny Coral

1972. 25th Anniv of South Pacific Commission. Multicoloured.
33 5c. Type **14** 45 70
34 10c. Community well 55 80
35 15c. Pest eradication . . . . . 80 1·40
36 20c. Flags of member nations 85 1·40
On No. 35 "PACIFIC" is spelt "PACFIC".

1973. Coral. Multicoloured.
37 3c. Type **15** 60 80
38 5c. Soft coral 60 90
39 15c. Mushroom coral . . . . 1·00 1·25
40 25c. Staghorn coral . . . . . 1·10 1·50

16 Hump-back Cowrie

17 Moorish Idol

1975. "Shells of the Coral Reef". Multicoloured.

41	3c. Type **16**	70	1·25
42	5c. Tiger cowrie	70	1·25
43	15c. Mole cowrie	1·00	2·00
44	25c. Eyed cowrie	1·10	2·25

1975. Fishes. Multicoloured.

45	5c. Type **17**	20	50
46	10c. Long-nosed butterflyfish	20	60
47	15c. Lined butterflyfish	30	80
48	25c. Lionfish ("Red-Fire Fish")	30	90

18 Canoe Building

1976. Multicoloured.

49a	1c. Type **18**	10	15
50	2c. Reef fishing	30	1·90
51a	3c. Weaving preparation	10	15
52a	5c. Uma (kitchen)	10	15
53a	9c. Carving (vert)	15	15
54a	20c. Husking coconuts (vert)	15	20
55a	50c. Wash day (vert)	20	20
56a	$1 Meal time (vert)	30	30

19 White Tern

20 Westminster Abbey

1977. Birds of Tokelau. Multicoloured.

57	8c. Type **19**	30	40
58	10c. Ruddy turnstone	35	45
59	15c. White-capped noddy	45	70
60	30c. Common noddy	50	90

1978. 25th Anniv of Coronation. Multicoloured.

61	8c. Type **20**	20	20
62	10c. King Edward's Chair	20	20
63	15c. Coronation regalia	30	35
64	30c. Queen Elizabeth II	50	60

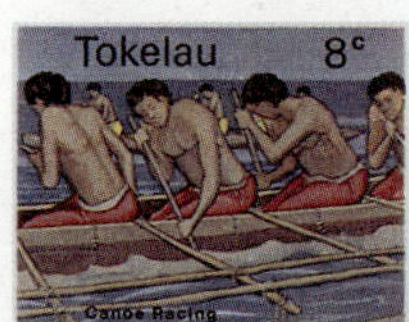

21 Canoe Race

1978. Canoe Racing.

65	**21** 8c. multicoloured	20	30
66	– 12c. multicoloured	20	35
67	– 15c. multicoloured	20	40
68	– 30c. multicoloured	30	70

DESIGNS: 12c. to 30c. Different scenes of canoe racing.

22 Rugby

1979. Local Sports. Multicoloured.

69	10c. Type **22**	20	30
70	15c. Cricket	1·00	85
71	20c. Rugby (different)	55	90
72	30c. Cricket (different)	1·00	1·10

23 Surfing

24 Pole Vaulting

1980. Water Sports. Multicoloured.

73	10c. Type **23**	10	15
74	20c. Surfing (different)	15	20
75	30c. Swimming	20	25
76	50c. Swimming (different)	25	35

1981. Sports. Multicoloured.

77	10c. Type **24**	10	10
78	20c. Volleyball	20	20
79	30c. Athletics (different)	25	30
80	50c. Volleyball (different)	30	35

25 Wood Carving

26 Octopus Lure

1982. Handicrafts. Multicoloured.

81	10s. Type **25**	10	20
82	22s. Bow drilling sea shell	10	35
83	34s. Bowl finishing	15	45
84	60s. Basket weaving	25	80

1982. Fishing Methods. Multicoloured.

85	5s. Type **26**	15	10
86	18s. Multiple-hook fishing	25	20
87	23s. Ruvettus fishing	30	25
88	34s. Netting flying fish	35	30
89	63s. Noose fishing	40	40
90	75s. Bonito fishing	50	45

27 Outrigger Canoe

1983. Transport. Multicoloured.

91	5s. Type **27**	10	10
92	18s. Wooden whaleboat	10	15
93	23s. Aluminium whaleboat	10	20
94	34s. "Alia" (fishing catamaran)	15	25
95	63s. "Frysna" (freighter)	25	40
96	75s. Grumman MacKinnon Goose flying boat	30	50

28 Javelin Throwing

1983. Traditional Pastimes. Multicoloured.

97	5s. Type **28**	10	10
98	18s. String game	10	15
99	23s. Fire making	10	20
100	34s. Shell throwing	15	25
101	63s. Hand-ball game	20	40
102	75s. Mass wrestling	25	50

29 Planting and Harvesting

30 Convict Tang ("Manini")

1984. Copra Industry. Multicoloured.

103	48s. Type **29**	30	40
104	48s. Husking and splitting	30	40
105	48s. Drying	30	40
106	48s. Bagging	30	40
107	48s. Shipping	30	40

1984. Fishes. Multicoloured.

108	1s. Type **30**	15	10
109	2s. Flyingfish ("Hahave")	15	10
110	5s. Surge wrasse ("Uloulo")	20	10
111	9s. Unicornfish ("Ume ihu")	20	10
112	23s. Wrasse ("Lafilafi")	50	20
113	34s. Red snapper ("Fagamea")	60	25
114	50s. Yellow-finned tuna ("Kakahi")	80	40
115	75s. Oilfish ("Palu po")	1·10	55
116	$1 Grey shark ("Mokoha")	1·50	70
117	$2 Black marlin ("Hakula")	2·00	1·40

31 "Ficus tinctoria" ("Mati")

1985. Native Trees. Multicoloured.

118	5c. Type **31**	10	10
119	18c. "Morinda citrifolia" ("Nonu")	10	15
120	32c. Breadfruit tree ("Ulu")	15	25
121	48c. "Pandanus tectorius" ("Fala")	25	40
122	60c. "Cordia subcordata" ("Kanava")	30	45
123	75s. Coconut palm ("Niu")	35	55

32 Administration Centre, Atafu

1985. Tokelau Architecture (1st series). Public Buildings. Multicoloured.

124	5c. Type **32**	10	10
125	18c. Administration Centre, Nukunonu	15	15
126	32c. Administration Centre, Fakaofo	15	25
127	48c. Congregational Church, Atafu	20	40
128	60c. Catholic Church, Nukunonu	25	45
129	75c. Congregational Church, Fakaofo	25	55

See also Nos. 130/5.

33 Atafu Hospital

1986. Tokelau Architecture (2nd series). Hospitals and Schools. Multicoloured.

130	5c. Type **33**	10	15
131	18c. St. Joseph's Hospital, Nukunonu	15	15
132	32c. Fenuafala Hospital, Fakaofo	15	30
133	48c. Matauala School, Atafu	20	45
134	60c. Matiti School, Nukunonu	25	60
135	75c. Fenuafala School, Fakaofo	25	90

34 Coconut Crab

1986. Agricultural Livestock. Multicoloured.

136	5c. Type **34**	10	10
137	18c. Pigs	10	15
138	32c. Chickens	20	25
139	48c. Reef hawksbill turtle	25	40
140	60c. Goats	30	45
141	75c. Ducks	35	60

35 "Scaevola taccada" ("Gahu")

1987. Tokelau Flora. Multicoloured.

142	5c. Type **35**	45	50
143	18c. "Hernandia nymphaeifolia" ("Puka")	60	80
144	32c. "Pandanus tectorius" ("Higano")	80	1·10
145	48c. "Gardenia taitensis" ("Tialetiale")	1·00	1·40
146	60c. "Pemphis acidula" ("Gagie")	1·25	1·75
147	75c. "Guettarda speciosa" ("Puapua")	1·40	1·90

36 Javelin Throwing

1987. Tokelau Olympic Sports. Multicoloured.

148	5c. Type **36**	25	30
149	18c. Shot-putting	45	50
150	32c. Long jumping	60	90
151	48c. Hurdling	70	1·10
152	60c. Sprinting	80	1·75
153	75c. Wrestling	1·10	1·90

37 Small Boat Flotilla in Sydney Harbour

1988. Bicentenary of Australian Settlement and "Sydpex '88" National Stamp Exhibition, Sydney. Multicoloured.

154	50c. Type **37**	1·75	2·00
155	50c. Sailing ships and liners	1·75	2·00
156	50c. Sydney skyline and Opera House	1·75	2·00
157	50c. Sydney Harbour Bridge	1·75	2·00
158	50c. Sydney waterfront	1·75	2·00

Nos. 154/8 were printed together, se-tenant, forming a composite aerial view of the re-enactment of First Fleet's arrival.

38 Island Maps and Ministerial Representatives

1988. Political Development. Multicoloured.

159	5c. Type **38** (administration transferred to N.Z. Foreign Affairs Ministry, 1975)	40	50
160	18c. General Fono (island assembly) meeting, 1977	45	55
161	32c. Arms of New Zealand (first visit by New Zealand Prime Minister, 1985)	70	80
162	48c. U.N. logo (first visit by U.N. representative, 1976)	80	1·00
163	60c. Canoe and U.N. logo (first Tokelau delegation to U.N., 1987)	1·00	1·40
164	75c. Secretary and N.Z. flag (first islander appointed as Official Secretary, 1987)	1·50	1·50

39 Three Wise Men in Canoe and Star

1988. Christmas. Designs showing Christmas in Tokelau. Multicoloured.

165	5c. Type **39**	30	35
166	20c. Tokelau Nativity	35	40
167	40c. Flight to Egypt by canoe	70	70
168	60c. Children's presents	80	1·00
169	70c. Christ Child in Tokelauan basket	90	1·10
170	$1 Christmas parade	1·10	1·40

40 Launching Outrigger Canoe

1989. Food Gathering. Multicoloured.

171	50c. Type **40**	1·50	1·75
172	50c. Paddling canoe away from shore	1·50	1·75
173	50c. Fishing punt and sailing canoe	1·50	1·75
174	50c. Canoe on beach	1·50	1·75
175	50c. Loading coconuts into canoe	1·50	1·75
176	50c. Tokelauans with produce	1·50	1·75

Nos. 171/3 and 174/6 were each printed together, se-tenant, forming composite designs.

41 Basketwork

1990. Women's Handicrafts. Multicoloured.
177 5c. Type **41** 65 65
178 20c. Preparing cloth 1·10 1·10
179 40c. Tokelau fabrics 1·50 1·50
180 60c. Mat weaving 2·00 2·25
181 80c. Weaving palm fronds 2·75 3·25
182 $1 Basket making 3·00 3·50

42 Man with Adze and Wood Blocks

1990. Men's Handicrafts. Multicoloured.
183 50c. Type **42** 1·75 2·00
184 50c. Making fishing boxes 1·75 2·00
185 50c. Fixing handles to fishing boxes 1·75 2·00
186 50c. Two men decorating fishing boxes 1·75 2·00
187 50c. Canoe building (two men) 1·75 2·00
188 50c. Canoe building (three men) 1·75 2·00

43 Swimming

45 Queen Elizabeth II in 1953

44 "Santa Maria"

1992. Olympic Games, Barcelona. Mult.
189 40c. Type **43** 60 60
190 60c. Long jumping 80 90
191 $1 Volleyball 1·60 1·75
192 $1.80 Running 2·25 3·25

1992. 500th Anniv of Discovery of America by Columbus. Multicoloured.
193 40c. Type **44** 80 80
194 60c. Christopher Columbus 1·10 1·25
195 $1.20 Fleet of Columbus 2·50 2·75
196 $1.80 Columbus landing in the New World 3·50 3·75

1993. 40th Anniv of Coronation. Mult.
197 25c. Type **45** 80 80
198 40c. Prince Philip 1·00 1·00
199 $1 Queen Elizabeth II in 1993 1·75 1·90
200 $2 Queen Elizabeth II and Prince Philip 3·00 3·25

46 Bristle-thighed Curlew

1993. Birds of Tokelau. Multicoloured.
201 25c. Type **46** 75 75
202 40c. Red-tailed tropic bird 1·10 1·10
203 $1 Reef heron 1·75 1·75
204 $2 Pacific golden plover 2·50 3·25

1994. "Hong Kong '94" International Stamp Exhibition. Multicoloured.
MS205 125 × 100 mm. As Nos. 201/4 (sold at $5) 5·00 6·00

47 Great Egret ("White Heron")

1994. "Philakorea '94" International Stamp Exhibition, Seoul.
206 **47** $2 multicoloured 2·50 3·25
MS207 110 × 76 mm. No. 206 3·75 4·00

48 Model Outrigger Canoe

1994. Handicrafts. Multicoloured.
208 5c. Type **48** 10 10
209 25c. Plaited fan 15 20
210 40c. Plaited baskets 25 30
211 50c. Fishing box 30 35
212 80c. Water bottle 50 55
213 $1 Fishing hook 65 70
214 $2 Coconut gourds 1·25 1·40
215 $5 Shell necklace 3·25 3·50

49 Fishing Pigs

1995. Chinese New Year ("Year of the Pig"). Sheet 100 × 75 mm.
MS218 **49** $5 multicoloured 6·50 7·00

1995. "PostX '95" National Stamp Exhibition, Auckland. No. **MS**218 optd with "PostX '95" emblem on sheet margin in red.
MS219 **49** $5 multicoloured 8·50 9·50

50 Pacific Pigeon on Branch

1995. Endangered Species. Pacific Pigeon. Mult.
220 25c. Type **50** 60 65
221 40c. On branch (different) 85 90
222 $1 On branch with berries 1·40 1·75
223 $2 Chick in nest 2·40 3·25

51 Long Nosed Butterflyfish

52 "Danaus plexippus"

1995. Reef Fishes. Multicoloured.
224 25c. Type **51** 45 55
225 40c. Emperor angelfish 70 75
226 $1 Moorish idol 1·40 1·60
227 $2 Lined butterflyfish 2·40 3·00
MS228 130 × 90 mm. Lionfish (39 × 34 mm) 3·25 4·00

1995. "Singapore '95" International Stamp Exhibition. No. **MS**218 optd with exhibition emblem on sheet margin.
MS229 **49** $5 multicoloured 5·50 7·00

1995. Butterflies and Moths. Multicoloured.
230 25c. Type **52** 65 65
231 40c. "Precis villida samoensis" 90 90
232 $1 "Hypolimnas bolina" 2·00 2·25
233 $2 "Euploea lewenii" 3·00 3·50

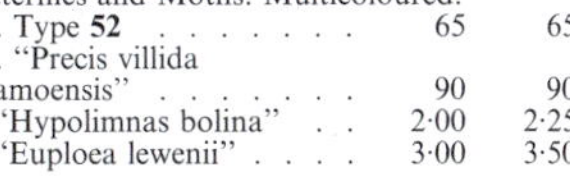

53 Hawksbill Turtle

1995. Year of the Sea Turtle. Multicoloured.
234 25c. Type **53** 65 65
235 40c. Leatherback turtle 90 90
236 $1 Green turtle 2·00 2·25
237 $2 Loggerhead turtle 3·00 3·50
MS238 130 × 90 mm. $3 As $2 (50 × 40 mm) 4·00 5·50

54 Pacific Rat

1996. Chinese New Year ("Year of the Rat"). Sheet 128 × 97 mm.
MS239 **54** $3 multicoloured 3·25 4·25

55 Queen Elizabeth II and Nukunonu

1996. 70th Birthday of Queen Elizabeth II. Each incorporating a different photograph of the Queen. Multicoloured.
240 40c. Type **55** 50 50
241 $1 Atafu at night 1·40 1·50
242 $1.25 Atafu 1·60 1·75
243 $2 Atafu village 2·00 2·50
MS244 64 × 66 mm. $3 Queen Elizabeth II 3·25 4·00

1996. "CHINA '96" 9th Asian International Stamp Exhibition, Peking. No. **MS**239 optd with exhibition emblem on sheet margin in red.
MS245 128 × 97 mm. $3 Type **54** 3·75 4·75

56 Fraser's Dolphin

1996. Dolphins. Multicoloured.
246 40c. Type **56** 1·00 1·00
247 $1 Common dolphin 2·50 2·50
248 $1.25 Striped dolphin 2·50 2·50
249 $2 Spotted dolphin 3·50 3·50

57 Mole Cowrie

1996. Sea Shells. Multicoloured.
250 40c. Type **57** 60 60
251 $1 Humpback cowrie 1·50 1·50
252 $1.25 Eyed cowrie 1·60 1·75
253 $2 Tiger cowrie 2·25 2·75
MS254 123 × 83 mm. $3 Humpback cowrie (different) (50 × 40 mm) 3·50 4·50

1996. "TAIPEI '96" 10th Asian International Stamp Exhibition, Taiwan. No. **MS**239 optd with exhibition emblem on sheet margin.
MS255 128 × 97 mm. $3 Type **54** 3·25 4·00

1997. Chinese New Year ("Year of the Ox"). Sheet 120 × 78 mm.
MS256 **58** $2 multicoloured 2·25 3·00

1997. "HONG KONG '97" International Stamp Exhibition. No. **MS**256 optd with **HONG KONG '97 STAMP EXHIBITION** in gold on sheet margin.
MS257 120 × 78 mm. **58** $2 multicoloured 2·25 3·00

1997. "Pacific '97" International Stamp Exhibition, San Francisco. No. **MS**256 optd with exhibition emblem on sheet margin.
MS258 120 × 78 mm. **58** $2 multicoloured 2·25 3·00

59 Humpback Whale

1997. Humpback Whales. Multicoloured.
259 40c. Type **59** 60 55
260 $1 Family of humpback whales 1·10 1·10
261 $1.25 Humpback whale feeding 1·40 1·75
262 $2 Humpback whale and calf 2·25 2·75

60 Church by Lagoon

1997. 50th Anniv of South Pacific Commission. Multicoloured.
264 40c. Type **60** 45 45
265 $1 Boy looking across lagoon 90 90
266 $1.25 Bungalow on small island 1·25 1·50
267 $2 Tokelau from the air 1·90 2·50

61 Gorgonian Coral and Emperor Angelfish

1997. Pacific Year of the Coral Reef. Mult.
268 $1 Type **61** 1·00 1·25
269 $1 Soft coral 1·00 1·25
270 $1 Mushroom coral 1·00 1·25
271 $1 Staghorn coral 1·00 1·25
272 $1 Staghorn coral and moorish idols 1·00 1·25

Nos. 268/72 were printed together, se-tenant, with the backgrounds forming a composite design.

1997. "Aupex '97" National Stamp Exhibition, Auckland. No. **MS**263 optd **AUPEX '97, 13–16 NOVEMBER NZ NATIONAL STAMP EXHIBITION** on sheet margin in black.
MS273 135 × 87 mm. $3 Head of humpback whale 2·75 3·50

1998. Chinese New Year ("Year of the Tiger"). Sheet 130 × 95 mm.
MS274 **62** $2 multicoloured 1·75 2·50

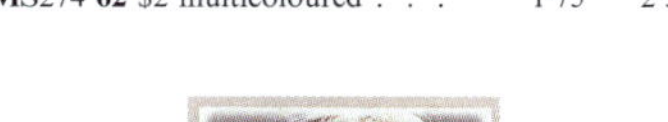

62a Carrying Yellow Bouquet

1998. Diana, Princess of Wales Commemoration. Multicoloured.
275 **62a** $1 Carrying yellow bouquet 80 90
MS276 145 × 70 mm. $1 Wearing red polka-dot dress; $1 Wearing matching pink hat and jacket; $1 No. 275; $1 In pink and yellow jacket with flowers (sold at $4+50c. charity premium) . . . 3·50 4·25

63 1948 ½d. Atafu Village Stamp

1998. 50th Anniv of Tokelau Postage Stamps. Sheet 105 × 80 mm, containing T **63** and similar horiz designs. Multicoloured.
MS277 $1 Type **63**; $1 1948 1d. Nukunono hut stamp; $1 1948 2d. Fakaofo village stamp . . . . 2·50 3·25

64 "Oryctes rhinoceros"

1998. Beetles. Multicoloured.
278 40c. Type **64** 55 55
279 $1 "Tribolium castaneum" . . . 1·10 1·10
280 $1.25 "Coccinella repanda" . . 1·25 1·25
281 $2 "Amarygmus hydrophiloides" . . . . . 1·90 2·25
MS282 125 × 86 mm. $3 Coccinella repanda (different) . . . . . . 2·25 3·00

65 "Ipomoea pes-caprae"

1998. Tropical Flowers. Multicoloured.
283 40c. Type **65** 40 50
284 $1 "Ipomoea littoralis" . . . 85 95
285 $1.25 "Scaevola taccada" . . 1·00 1·40
286 $2 "Thespesia populnea" . . 1·60 2·25

66 Rabbit

1999. Chinese New Year ("Year of the Rabbit"). Sheet 105 × 70 mm.
MS287 **66** $3 multicoloured . . . 2·25 3·00

67 H.M.S. *Pandora* (frigate)

1999. "Australia '99" International Stamp Exhibition, Melbourne. Sheet 119 × 80 mm.
MS288 **67** $3 multicoloured . . . 2·75 3·25

1999. "iBRA '99" International Stamp Exhibition, Nuremberg. No. **MS**287 optd with the **iBRA** logo on the sheet margin.
MS289 105 × 70 mm. **66** $3 multicoloured . . . . 2·50 2·75

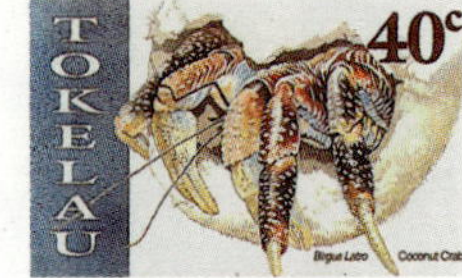

68 Coconut Crab

1999. Pacific Crabs. Multicoloured.
290 40c. Type **68** 40 40
291 $1 Ghost crab 85 85
292 $1.25 Land hermit crab . . . 1·00 1·25
293 $2 Purple hermit crab . . . . 1·60 2·00
MS294 127 × 89 mm. $3 Ghost crab (different) . . . . 2·25 2·75

69 Lift-off **71** Dragon

70 Black-naped Tern Chick and Egg

1999. 30th Anniv of First Manned Landing on Moon. Multicoloured.
295 25c. Type **69** 40 40
296 50c. Rocket stage separation 60 60
297 75c. Aldrin deploying experiment 70 70
298 $1 Planting the flag 85 85
299 $1.25 Separation of command module . . . . 1·00 1·25
300 $2 Recovery of astronauts . . 1·50 2·00
MS301 90 × 65 mm. $3 Lunar module, Earth and Jupiter . . 2·25 2·75

1999. Black-naped Tern. Multicoloured.
302 40c. Type **70** 45 45
303 $1 Black-naped tern perched on pebbles 90 90
304 $1.25 Two black-naped terns 1·10 1·10
305 $2 Two black-naped terns in flight . . . . 1·75 2·00

2000. Chinese New Year ("Year of the Dragon"). Sheet 105 × 70 mm.
MS306 **71** $3 multicoloured . . . 2·00 2·50

2000. "Bangkok 2000" World Youth Stamp Exhibition. No. **MS**306 optd on the margin with **WORLD YOUTH STAMP EXHIBITION BANGKOK 2000** in English and Thai.
MS307 105 × 70 mm. $3 Type **71** 2·00 2·50

72 Nukunonu

2000. "The Stamp Show 2000" International Stamp Exhibition, London. Sheet 105 × 85 mm.
MS308 **72** $6 multicoloured . . . 3·50 4·25

2000. "EXPO 2000" World Stamp Exhibition, Anaheim, U.S.A. No. **MS**301 optd **WORLD STAMP EXPO 2000 7–16 JULY ANAHEIM – U.S.A.** on sheet margin.
MS309 90 × 65 mm. $3 Lunar module, Earth and Jupiter . . 2·00 2·50

73 Queen Elizabeth the Queen Mother

2000. Queen Elizabeth the Queen Mother's 100th Birthday. Multicoloured.
310 40c. Type **73** 45 35
311 $1.20 Queen Mother waving 85 85
312 $1.80 Wearing diamond earrings and pearl necklace 1·40 1·60
313 $3 Wearing blue hat and tartan scarf . . . . 2·00 2·25

74 *Gehyra oceanica*

2001. Lizards. Multicoloured.
314 40c. Type **74** 45 45
315 $1 *Lepidodactylus lugubris* . . 85 95
316 $1.25 *Gehyra mutilata* . . . . 1·10 1·25
317 $2 *Emoia cyanura* . . . . . 1·75 2·00

75 Snake

2001. Chinese New Year ("Year of the Snake"). Sheet 105 × 73 mm.
MS318 **75** $3 multicoloured . . . 2·00 2·50

2001. "Hong Kong 2001" Stamp Exhibition. No. **MS**318 optd **HONG KONG 2001** in English and Chinese on the sheet margin.
MS319 105 × 73 mm. $3 Type **75** 2·00 2·50

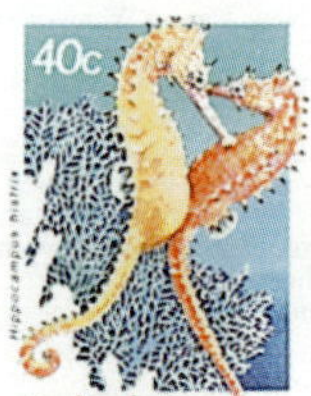

76 Yellow and Orange Seahorses

2001. Seahorses. Multicoloured.
320 40c. Type **76** 40 40
321 $1 Baby seahorses 70 70
322 $1.25 Pink seahorse 90 90
323 $2 Yellow seahorse . . . . . 1·40 1·60
MS324 104 × 73 mm. $3 No. 320 2·25 2·75

77 Atafu Island

2001. Island Views. Multicoloured.
325 40c. Type **77** 40 40
326 $1 Fakaofo 70 70
327 $2 Sunrise over Nukunonu village . . . . 1·40 1·60
328 $2.50 Nukunonu beach . . . 1·60 1·75

78 Princess Elizabeth and Lieutenant Philip Mountbatten, 1947

2002. Golden Jubilee.
329 **78** 40c. brown, red and gold 40 40
330 – $1 multicoloured 70 70
331 – $1.25 black, red and gold 85 85
332 – $2 multicoloured . . . . . 1·40 1·60
MS333 162 × 95 mm. Nos. 329/2 and $3 multicoloured . . . . . . 5·50 5·50
DESIGNS—HORIZ: $1 Queen Elizabeth in mauve hat; $1.25, Princess Elizabeth holding Prince Charles, 1948; $2 Queen Elizabeth in Poland, 1996. VERT:—(38 × 51 mm): $3 Queen Elizabeth after Annigoni.

79 Horse

2002. Chinese New Year ("Year of the Horse"). Sheet 105 × 70 mm.
MS334 multicoloured . . . . . 2·50 2·75

2002. "Stampex 2002" Stamp Exhibition, Hong Kong. No. **MS**334 optd **STAMPEX 2002 HONG KONG 22–24 FEBRUARY 2002** in gold on the sheet margin.
MS335 105 × 70 mm. $4 Type **79** 2·50 2·75

80 Pelagic Thresher Sharks

2002. Endangered Species. Pelagic Thresher Shark.
336 **80** 40c. multicoloured 25 30
337 – $1 multicoloured 65 70
338 – $2 multicoloured . . . . . 1·25 1·40
339 – $2.50 multicoloured . . . 1·60 1·75
DESIGNS: $1 to $2.25, Show sharks.

2002. Queen Elizabeth the Queen Mother Commemoration. As T **215** of St. Helena.
340 40c. black, gold and purple 25 40
341 $2 multicoloured . . . . . . 1·25 1·40
MS342 145 × 70 mm. $2.50 black and gold; $4 multicoloured . . 4·00 4·25
DESIGNS: 40c. Queen Elizabeth wearing wide-brimmed hat; $2 Queen Mother wearing mauve hat and coat; $2.50, Wearing feathered hat and pearls; $4 Queen Mother smiling. Designs in No. **MS**342 omit the "1900–2002" inscription and the coloured frame.

81 H.M.N.Z.S. *Kaniere* (frigate), 1958–59

2002. Royal New Zealand Navy Ships which have visited Tokelau. Multicoloured.
343 40c. Type **81** 25 40
344 $1 H.M.N.Z.S. *Endeavour* (supply ship), 1990 . . . . 65 70
345 $2 H.M.N.Z.S. *Wellington* (frigate), 1987, 1988, 1990 1·25 1·40
346 $2.50 H.M.N.Z.S. *Monowai* (survey ship), 1979, 1985, 1994 . . . . 1·60 1·75

82 Ram

2003. Chinese New Year ("Year of the Sheep"). Sheet 105 × 70 mm.
MS347 multicoloured . . . . . 2·50 2·40

TOLIMA Pt. 20

One of the states of the Granadine Confederation. A department of Colombia from 1886, now uses Colombian stamps.

100 centavos = 1 peso.

1 2 3

1870. On white or coloured paper. Imperf.

6	**1**	5c. black	25·00	20·00
13		10c. black	30·00	18·00

1871. Various frames. Imperf.

14	**2**	5c. brown	75	75
15	**3**	10c. blue	2·00	2·00
16		50c. green	3·00	3·00
17		1p. red	6·00	6·00

6 7 8

9 10 11

1879. Imperf.

18a	**6**	5c. brown	20	20
19	**7**	10c. blue	25	25
20a	**8**	50c. green	25	30
21a	**9**	1p. red	90	1·00

1883. Imperf.

22	**6**	5c. orange	20	20
23	**7**	10c. red	35	35
24	**10**	20c. violet	50	50

1884. Imperf.

25	**11**	1c. grey	10	10
26		2c. red	10	10
27		2½c. orange	10	10
28		5c. brown	10	10
29a		10c. blue	15	15
30		20c. yellow	30	30
31		25c. black	15	15
32		50c. green	20	20
33		1p. red	25	25
34		2p. violet	40	35
35		5p. orange	25	25
36		10p. red	60	60

12 16

1886. Condor's wings touch Arms. Perf.

37	**12**	5c. brown	50	50
38		10c. blue	1·75	1·75
39		50c. green	60	60
40		1p. red	1·25	1·25

1886. Condor's wings do not touch Arms. Perf or imperf.

45	**16**	1c. grey	2·50	2·50
46		2c. red	3·25	3·25
47		2½c. pink	12·00	12·00
48		5c. brown	4·50	4·50
49		10c. blue	6·00	6·00
50		20c. yellow	3·25	3·25
51		25c. black	3·00	3·00
52		50c. green	1·40	1·10
53		1p. red	2·25	2·25
54		2p. violet	4·00	4·00
55		5p. orange	7·50	7·50
56		10p. red	3·50	3·50

20 21

1888. Perf.

67	**20**	1c. blue on red	15	15
68		2c. green on green	15	15
69		5c. red	10	10
70		10c. green	20	25
71		20c. blue on yellow	30	30
65		50c. blue	45	45
72		1p. brown	75	75

1903. Imperf or perf.

85	**21**	4c. black on green	10	10
78		10c. green	10	10
87		20c. orange	20	20
88		50c. black on red	15	15
81		1p. brown	10	10
82		2p. grey	10	10
91		5p. red	10	10
92		10p. black on blue	15	15
92a		10p. black on green	15	15

TONGA Pt. 1

(Or Friendly Is.). A group of islands in the S. Pacific Ocean. An independent Polynesian kingdom formerly under British protection, Tonga became a member of the Commonwealth in June 1970.

1886. 12 pence = 1 shilling;
20 shillings = 1 pound.
1967. 100 seniti = 1 pa'anga.

1 King George I

1886.

1b	**1**	1d. red	10·00	3·25
2b		2d. violet	29·00	2·75
3ab		6d. blue	27·00	2·25
9		6d. orange	16·00	26·00
4ba		1s. green	55·00	3·25

1891. Surch with value in words.

5	**1**	4d. on 1d. red	3·00	11·00
6		8d. on 2d. violet	35·00	90·00

1891. Optd with stars in upper right and lower left corners.

7	**1**	1d. red	45·00	50·00
8		2d. violet	70·00	38·00

5 Arms of Tonga 6 King George I

1892.

10	**5**	1d. red	12·00	17·00
11	**6**	2d. olive	16·00	16·00
12	**5**	4d. brown	48·00	70·00
13	**6**	8d. mauve	55·00	£170
14		1s. brown	80·00	£110

1893. Surch in figures.

15	**5**	½d. on 1d. blue	23·00	27·00
16	**6**	2½d. on 2d. green	14·00	12·00
18		7½d. on 6d. red	24·00	75·00

1893. Surch **FIVE PENCE.**

17	**5**	5d. on 4d. orange	4·00	6·50

1894. Surch vert **SURCHARGE.** and value in words.

21	**5**	½d. on 4d. brown	2·00	7·00
22	**6**	½d. on 1s. brown	2·50	11·00
25		1d. on 2d. blue	45·00	22·00

1894. Surch vert **SURCHARGE.** and value in figures.

26b	**6**	1½d. on 2d. blue	48·00	28·00
27		2½d. on 2d. blue	40·00	45·00
23		2½d. on 8d. mauve	5·00	8·00
24b	**1**	2½d. on 1s. green	15·00	42·00
28b	**6**	7½d. on 2d. blue	60·00	45·00

13 King George II 15 Arms

16 Ovava Tree, Kana-Kubolu

21 View of Haapai

1895. Surch **SURCHARGE** and new value.

29	**13**	½d. on 2½d. red	30·00	32·00
30		1d. on 2½d. red	60·00	40·00
31		7½d. on 2½d. red	55·00	60·00

1895.

32	**13**	1d. green	20·00	26·00
33		2½d. red	20·00	13·00
34		5d. blue	22·00	50·00
35		7½d. yellow	30·00	48·00

1896. Nos. 26a and 28a surch with typewritten **Half-Penny-** and Tongan inscription.

36Aa	**6**	½d. on 1½d. on 2d. blue	£425	£425
37A		½d. on 7½d. on 2d. blue	85·00	£110

1897.

38a	**15**	½d. blue	70	3·00
55		½d. green	1·00	1·25
39	**16**	1d. black and red	80	80
40a	–	2d. sepia and bistre	13·00	3·50
43b	–	2½d. black and blue	3·50	1·60
78	–	3d. black and green	65	3·50
45	–	4d. green and purple	3·75	4·00
46	–	5d. black and orange	32·00	14·00
79	–	6d. red	3·50	2·00
48	–	7½d. black and green	16·00	23·00
49	–	10d. black and red	45·00	48·00
50	–	1s. black and brown	14·00	7·50
51a	**21**	2s. black and blue	20·00	28·00
81	–	2s.6d. purple	29·00	21·00
82	–	5s. black and red	16·00	45·00

DESIGNS—VERT (as Type **26**): 2, 2½, 5, 7½, 10d., 1s. King George II. (As Type **16**): 6d. Coral. (As Type **21**): 2s.6d. Red shining parrot. HORIZ (as Type **16**): 3d. Prehistoric trilith at Haamonga; 4d. Breadfruit. (As Type **21**): 5s. Vavau Harbour.

1899. Royal Wedding. Optd **T - L 1 June, 1899.**

54	**16**	1d. black and red	28·00	55·00

26 Queen Salote 29 Queen Salote

1920.

56	**26**	1½d. black	50	3·00
57		2d. purple and violet	8·50	13·00
76		2d. black and purple	5·00	2·75
58		2½d. black and blue	4·75	40·00
77		2½d. blue	1·50	1·50
60		5d. black and orange	3·25	4·75
61		7½d. black and green	1·75	1·75
62		10d. black and red	2·50	4·75
63		1s. black and brown	1·25	2·50

1923. Nos. 46 and 48/82 surch **TWO PENCE PENI-E-UA.**

64		2d. on 5d. black and orange	1·00	85
65		2d. on 7½d. black and green	18·00	28·00
66		2d. on 10d. black and red	11·00	50·00
67		2d. on 1s. black and brown	48·00	22·00
68a		2d. on 2s. black and blue	11·00	5·00
69		2d. on 2s.6d. purple	32·00	6·50
70a		2d. on 5s. black and red	3·25	2·50

1938. 20th Anniv of Queen Salote's Accession. Dated "1918–1938" at foot.

71	**29**	1d. black and red	1·00	3·50
72		2d. black and purple	8·50	2·75
73		2½d. black and blue	8·50	3·25

1944. Silver Jubilee of Queen Salote's Accession. Tablet at foot dated "1918–1943".

83	**29**	1d. black and red	15	1·00
84		2d. black and violet	15	1·00
85		3d. black and green	15	1·00
86		6d. black and orange	85	1·75
87		1s. black and brown	60	1·75

1949. 75th Anniv of U.P.U. As T **33d/g** of St. Helena.

88		2½d. blue	20	80
89		3d. olive	1·60	3·00
90		6d. red	20	50
91		1s. brown	25	50

31 Queen Salote 32 Queen Salote

1950. 50th Birthday of Queen Salote.

92	**31**	1d. red	60	2·00
93	**32**	5d. green	60	2·25
94	–	1s. violet	60	2·50

DESIGN—VERT: 1s. Half-length portrait of Queen.

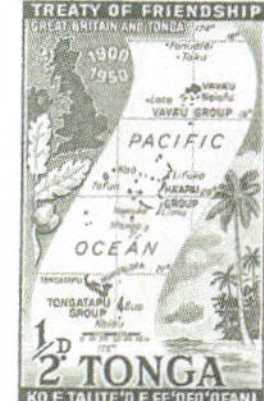

34 Map 35 Palace, Nuku'alofa

1951. 50th Anniv of Treaty of Friendship with Great Britain.

95	**34**	½d. green	15	2·75
96	**35**	1d. black and red	15	2·75
97	–	2½d. green and brown	30	2·75
98	–	3d. yellow and blue	2·25	2·75
99	–	5d. red and green	1·50	1·00
100	–	1s. orange and violet	1·25	1·00

DESIGNS—HORIZ: 2½d. Beach scene; 5d. Flag and island; 1s. Arms of Tonga and Great Britain. VERT: 3d. H.M.N.Z.S. "Bellona".

40 Royal Palace, Nuku'alofa

1953.

101	**40**	1d. black and brown	10	10
102	–	1½d. blue and green	20	10
103	–	2d. turquoise and black	1·00	20
104	–	3d. blue and green	1·50	20
105	–	3½d. yellow and red	75	70
106	–	4d. yellow and red	2·25	10
107	–	5d. blue and brown	50	10
108	–	6d. black and blue	75	30
109	–	8d. green and violet	1·50	40
110	–	1s. blue and black	1·00	10
111	–	2s. olive and brown	7·00	60
112	–	5s. yellow and lilac	24·00	9·00
113	–	10s. yellow and black	8·00	9·00
114	–	£1 yellow, red and blue	8·00	6·50

DESIGNS—HORIZ: 1½d. Shore fishing with throw-net; 2d. "Hifofua" and "Aoniu" (ketches); 3½d. Map of Tongatapu; 4d. Vava'u Harbour; 5d. Post Office, Nuku'alofa; 6d. Aerodrome, Fua'amotu; 8d. "Matua" (inter-island freighter) at Nuku'alofa Wharf; 2s. Lifuka, Ha'apai; 5s. Mutiny on the "Bounty". VERT: 3d. Swallows' Cave, Vava'u; 1s. Map of Tonga Islands; 10s. Queen Salote; £1 Arms of Tonga.

54 Stamp of 1886

1961. 75th Anniv of Tongan Postal Service.

115	**54**	1d. red and orange	10	10
116	–	2d. blue	1·25	45
117	–	4d. turquoise	20	45
118	–	5d. violet	1·25	45
119	–	1s. brown	1·25	45

DESIGNS: 2d. Whaling ship and whaleboat; 4d. Queen Salote and Post Office, Nuku'alofa; 5d. "Aoniu II" (inter-island freighter); 1s. Douglas DC-4 mail plane over Tongatapu.

1962. Centenary of Emancipation. Stamps of 1953 and No. 117 optd **1862 TAU'ATAINA EMANCIPATION 1962** or surch also.

120		1d. black and brown	10	75
121		4d. turquoise (No. 117)	10	80
122		5d. blue and brown	15	80
123		6d. black and blue	20	1·00
124		8d. green and violet	40	1·60
125		1s. blue and black	20	90
126		2s. on 3d. blue and green	40	3·75
127		5s. yellow and lilac	5·50	3·75

60 "Protein Foods"

1963. Freedom from Hunger.

128	**60**	11d. blue	50	15

61 Coat of Arms

1963. First Polynesian Gold Coinage Commem. Circular designs backed with paper, inscr overall "TONGA THE FRIENDLY ISLANDS". Imperf.
(a) Postage ¼ koula coin. Diameter 1⅝ in.

129	**61**	1d. red on gold	10	10
130	A	2d. blue on gold	10	10
131	**61**	6d. green on gold	15	15
132	A	9d. purple on gold	15	15

133 **61** 1s.6d. violet on gold . . . 30 30
134 A 2s. green on gold 40 40

(b) Air (i) $\frac{1}{2}$ koula coin. Diameter $2\frac{1}{8}$ in.
135 B 10d. red on gold 20 20
136 **61** 2s.4d. green on gold . . . 30 30
137 B 1s.1d. blue on gold 30 30

(ii) 1 koula coin. Diameter $3\frac{1}{8}$ in.
138 B 2s.1d. purple on gold . . . 45 45
139 **61** 2s.4d. green on gold . . . 50 50
140 B 2s.9d. violet on gold . . . 50 50
DESIGNS: A, Queen Salote (head); B. Queen Salote (full length).

64 Red Cross Emblem

1963. Centenary of Red Cross.
141 **64** 2d. red and black 15 10
142 11d. red and blue . . . . 35 1·50

65 Queen Salote

66 Map of Tongatapu ($\frac{3}{5}$-size illustration)

1964. Pan-Pacific South-East Asia Women's Assn Meeting, Nuku'alofa. T **65/66** backed with paper inscr overall "TONGA THE FRIENDLY ISLANDS". Imperf.
143 **65** 3d. pink (postage) 15 20
144 9d. blue 20 25
145 2s. green 35 40
146 3s. lilac 65 85

147 **66** 10d. turquoise (air) 20 20
148 1s.2d. black 30 40
149 3s.6d. red 50 75
150 6s.6d. violet . . . . . . 85 1·60

1965. "Gold Coin" stamps of 1963 surch and with star over old value.
151 **61** 1s.3d. on 1s.6d. (postage) 25 25
152 A 1s.9d. on 9d. 25 25
153 **61** 2s.6d. on 6d. 30 50
154 5s. on 1d. . . . . . . 16·00 18·00
155 A 5s. on 2d. . . . . . . 2·75 3·75
156 5s. on 2s. . . . . 70 1·00

157 B 2s.3d. on 10d. (air) 25 40
158 **61** 2s.9d. on 11d. 30 55
159 B 4s.6d. on 2s.1d. . . . . 13·00 14·00
160 **61** 4s.6d. on 2s.4d. . . . . 13·00 14·00
161 B 4s.6d. on 2s.9d. . . . . 7·50 8·50

1966. Centenary of Tupou College and Secondary Education. Nos. 115/16 and 118/19 optd or surch **1866-1966 TUPOU COLLEGE & SECONDARY EDUCATION**.
162 **54** 1d. red and orange (postage) 10 10
163 3d. on 1d. red and orange 10 10
164 – 6d. on 2d. blue 10 10
165 – 1s.2d. on 2d. blue 20 10
166 – 2s. on 2d. blue 40 10
167 – 3s. on 2d. blue 40 15

As above opt but with additional **AIRMAIL** and **CENTENARY**.

168 – 5d. violet (air) 10 10
169 **54** 10d. on 1d. red and brown 10 10
170 – 1s. brown 30 10
171 – 2s.9d. on 2d. blue 40 15
172 – 3s.6d. on 5d. violet 45 15
173 – 4s.6d. on 1s. brown . . . 75 15

1966. Queen Salote Commemoration. Nos. 143/4 and 147/8 optd. **IN MEMORIAM QUEEN SALOTE 1900+1965** (postage) or **1900 1965+** and laurel spray (air) or surch also. Inscr and new figures of value in first colour and obliterating shapes in second colour given.
174 **65** 3d. (silver & blue) (postage) 20 10
175 5d. on 9d. (silver and black) 25 10
176 9d. (silver and black) . . . 35 10
177 1s.7d. on 3d. (silver and blue) 80 65
178 3s.6d. on 9d. (silver & blk) 1·10 85
179 6s.6d. on 3d. (silver and blue) . . . . 1·60 1·90

180 **66** 10d. (silver and black) (air) 30 10
181 1s.2d. (black and gold) . . 35 25
182 4s. on 10d. (silver and black) . . . . 1·25 85
183 5s.6d. on 1s.2d. (black and gold) . . . . 1·50 1·75
184 10s.6d. on 1s.2d. (gold and black) . . . . 2·00 2·25

1967. Various stamps surch **SENITI** or **Seniti** and value. (a) Postage.
185 1s. on 1d. (No. 101) 10 10
229 2s. on 4d. (No. 106) 10 10
230 3s. on 3d. (No. 104) 10 10
187 3s. on 5d. (No. 107) 10 10
231 4s. on 5d. (No. 107) 10 10
232 5s. on 2d. (No. 108) 10 10
189 5s. on $3\frac{1}{2}$d. (No. 105) . . . 10 10
233 6s. on 6d. (No. 108) 10 10
190 6s. on 8d. (No. 109) 30 10
191 7s. on $1\frac{1}{2}$d. (No. 102) . . . 10 10
192 8s. on 6d. (No. 108) 30 10
235 8s. on 8d. (No. 109) 10 15
193 9s. on 3d. (No. 104) 15 15
236 9s. on $3\frac{1}{2}$d. (No. 105) . . . 20 20
194 10s. on 1s. (No. 110) 15 15
195 11s. on 3d. on 1d. (No. 163) 30 20
238 20s. on 5s. (No. 112) . . . 1·50 50
196 21s. on 3s. on 2d. (No. 167) 25 35
197 23s. on 1d. (No. 101) . . . 25 35
198 30s. on 2s. (No. 111)* . . . 2·25 2·50
199 30s. on 2s. (No. 111)* . . . 2·50 3·00
200 50s. on 6d. (No. 108) . . . 1·25 1·75
201 60s. on 2d. (No. 103) . . . 1·50 2·00
239 2p. on 2s. (No. 111) . . . . 1·50 2·50
*No. 198 has the surcharged value expressed horizontally; No. 199 has the figures "30" above and below "SENITI".

(b) Air. Surch with **AIRMAIL** added.
240 11s. on 10s. (No. 113) . . . 25 25
241 21s. on 10s. (No. 113) . . . 40 40
242 23s. on 10s. (No. 113) . . . 40 40

74 Coat of Arms (reverse)

1967. Coronation of King Taufa'ahau IV. Circular designs backed with paper inscr overall "TONGA, THE FRIENDLY ISLANDS" etc. Imperf.
202 **74** 1s. orange & bl (b) (post) 10 10
203 A 2s. blue and mauve (c) . . 10 10
204 **74** 4s. green and purple (d) . . 10 10
205 A 15s. turquoise & vio (e) . . 30 25
206 **74** 28s. black and purple (a) 80 60
207 A 50s. red and blue (c) . . . 1·50 1·50
208 **74** 1p. blue and red (f) . . . 2·25 2·75

209 A 7s. red and black (b) (air) 15 10
210 **74** 9s. purple and green (c) . . 20 10
211 A 11s. blue and orange (d) 25 15
212 **74** 21s. black and green (e) . . 50 30
213 A 23s. purple and green (a) 65 45
214 **74** 29s. blue and green (c) . . 80 60
215 A 2p. purple and orange (f) 3·25 3·75
DESIGN: A, King Taufa'ahau IV (obverse).
Sizes: (a) Diameter $1\frac{1}{2}$in.; (b) Diameter $1\frac{7}{10}$ in.; (c) Diameter 2in.; (d) Diameter $2\frac{3}{10}$ in.; (e) Diameter $2\frac{7}{10}$ in.; (f) Diameter $2\frac{9}{10}$ in.
The commemorative coins depicted in reverse (Type **74**) are inscribed in various denominations as follows: 1s. "20 SENTIT"; 4s. "PA'ANGA"; 9s. "50 SENITI"; 21s. "TWO PA'ANGA"; 28s. "QUARTER HAU"; 29s. "HALF HAU"; 1p. "HAU".

1967. Arrival of U.S. Peace Corps in Tonga. As Nos. 101/13 but imperf in different colours and surch **The Friendly Islands welcome the United States Peace Corps** and new value (or S only).
216 1s. on 1d. black and yellow (postage) 10 10
217 2s. on 2d. blue and red . . . 10 10
218 3s. on 3d. brown and yellow 10 10
219 4s. on 4d. violet and yellow 10 10
220 5s. on 5d. green and yellow 10 10
221 10s. on 1s. red and yellow . . 10 10
222 20s. on 2s. red and blue . . . 30 15
223 50s. on 5s. sepia and yellow 2·50 1·00
224 1p. on 10s. yellow . . . . . 70 1·25

225 11s. on $3\frac{1}{2}$d. blue (air) . . . 15 10
226 21s. on $1\frac{1}{2}$d. green 30 20
227 23s. on $3\frac{1}{2}$d. blue 30 20

1968. 50th Birthday of King Taufa'ahua IV. Nos. 202/15 optd **H.M'S BIRTHDAY 4 JULY 1968.**
243 **74** 1s. orange and blue (postage) 10 20
244 A 2s. blue and mauve . . . 15 20
245 **74** 4s. green and purple . . . 20 20
246 A 15s. turquoise and violet 85 25
247 **74** 28s. black and purple . . . 1·50 30
248 A 50s. red and blue . . . . 2·25 1·25
249 **74** 1p. blue and red . . . . 4·50 4·00

250 A 7s. red and black (air) . . 35 20
251 **74** 9s. purple and green . . . 40 20
252 A 11s. blue and orange . . . 60 20
253 **74** 21s. black and green . . . 1·25 25
254 A 23s. purple and green . . . 1·25 25
255 **74** 29s. blue and green . . . . 1·50 35
256 A 2p. purple and orange . . 8·00 7·50

1968. South Pacific Games Field and Track Trials, Port Moresby, New Guinea. As Nos. 101/13 surch **Friendly Islands Field & Track Trials South Pacific Games Port Moresby 1969** and value.
257 5s. on 5d. green & yell (post) 10 15
258 10s. on 1s. red and yellow . . 10 15
259 15s. on 2s. red and blue . . . 15 20
260 25s. on 2d. blue and red . . 20 20
261 50s. on 1d. black and yellow 35 45
262 75s. on 10s. orange and yellow 60 85

263 6s. on 6d. black & yellow (air) 10 15
264 7s. on 4d. violet and yellow 10 15
265 8s. on 8d. black and yellow 10 15
266 9s. on $1\frac{1}{2}$d. green 10 15
267 11s. on 3d. brown and yellow 15 15
268 21s. on $3\frac{1}{2}$d. blue 20 20
269 38s. on 5s. sepia and yellow 2·00 70
270 1p. on 10s. yellow . . . . . 70 1·25

1969. Emergency Provisionals. Various stamps (Nos. 273/6 are imperf and in different colours) surch. (a) Postage.
271 1s. on 1s.2d. blue (No. 165) 1·75 2·50
272 1s. on 2s. on 3d. blue (No. 166) . . . . 1·75 2·50
273 1s. on 6d. blk & yell (No. 108) 60 60
274 2s. on $3\frac{1}{2}$d. blue (No. 105) . . 65 60
275 3s. on $1\frac{1}{2}$d. green (No. 102) 65 60
276 4s. on 8d. blk & yell (No. 109) 90 90

(b) Air. Nos. 171/3 surch.
277 1s. on 2s.9d. on 2d. blue . . 1·75 2·50
278 1s. on 3s.6d. on 5d. violet . . 1·75 2·50
279 1s. on 4s.6d. on 1s. brown . . 1·75 2·50

83 Banana

1969. Coil stamps. Self-adhesive.
280 **83** 1s. red, black and yellow 1·00 1·25
281 2s. green, black and yellow 1·10 1·40
282 3s. violet, black and yellow 1·40 1·60
283 4s. blue, black and yellow 1·50 1·75
284 5s. green, black and yellow 1·60 1·75
See also Nos. 325/9, 413/17, 657/89, O45/9, O82/6 and O169/83.

84 Putting the Shot

1969. 3rd South Pacific Games, Port Moresby. Imperf. Self-adhesive.
285 **84** 1s. black, red & buff (postage) 10 10
286 3s. green, red and buff . . 10 10
287 6s. blue, red and buff . . . 10 10
288 10s. violet, red and buff . . 15 10
289 30s. blue, red and buff . . 30 20

290 – 9s. black, vio & orge (air) 15 10
291 – 11s. black, blue and orange 15 10
292 – 20s. black, green and orange 25 20
293 – 60s. black, red and orange 75 1·00
294 – 1p. black, green and orange . . . . 1·10 1·75
DESIGN: Nos. 290/4, Boxing.

86 Oil Derrick and Map

1969. 1st Oil Search in Tonga. Imperf. Self-adhesive.
295 **86** 3s. multicoloured (postage) 15 10
296 7s. multicoloured 20 15
297 20s. multicoloured 50 40
298 25s. multicoloured 55 45
299 35s. multicoloured 80 80

300 – 9s. multicoloured (air) . . . 30 20
301 – 10s. multicoloured 30 20
302 – 24s. multicoloured 60 45
303 – 29s. multicoloured 70 70
304 – 38s. multicoloured 80 80
DESIGN: Nos. 300/4, Oil derrick and island of Tongatapu.

87 Members of the British and Tongan Royal Families

1970. Royal Visit. Imperf. Self-adhesive.
305 **87** 3s. multicoloured (postage) 25 15
306 5s. multicoloured 30 15
307 10s. multicoloured 45 30
308 25s. multicoloured . . . . 1·25 65
309 50s. multicoloured . . . . 2·25 1·75

310 – 7s. multicoloured (air) . . 40 20
311 – 9s. multicoloured 45 30
312 – 24s. multicoloured . . . . 1·25 65
313 – 29s. multicoloured . . . . 1·50 70
314 – 38s. multicoloured . . . . 1·75 90
DESIGN: Nos. 310/14, Queen Elizabeth II and King Taufu'aha Tupou IV.

89 Book, Tongan Rulers and Flag ($\frac{3}{5}$-size illustration)

1970. Entry into British Commonwealth. Imperf. Self-adhesive.
315 **89** 3s. multicoloured (postage) 20 15
316 7s. multicoloured 30 20
317 15s. multicoloured 55 30
318 25s. multicoloured 70 40
319 50s. multicoloured . . . . 1·25 1·25

320 – 9s. blue, gold and red (air) 20 20
321 – 10s. purple, gold and blue 20 20
322 – 24s. yellow, gold and green 50 30
323 – 29s. blue, gold and red . . 55 30
324 – 38s. yellow, gold and green 70 55
DESIGN—"Star" shaped (size 44×51 mm): Nos. 320/4, Star and King Taufa'ahua Tupou IV.

90 Coconut

1970. Coil stamps. Imperf. Self-adhesive. (a) As T **83** but colours changed.
325 **83** 1s. yellow, purple and black 55 75
326 2s. yellow, blue and black 65 85
327 3s. yellow, brown and black 65 85
328 4s. yellow, green and black 65 85
329 5s. yellow, red and black 70 85

(b) Multicoloured; colour of face values given.
330 **90** 6s. red . . . . 80 1·00
331 7s. purple . . . . 85 1·10
332 8s. violet . . . . 95 1·10
333 9s. green . . . . 1·10 1·25
334 10s. orange . . . . . . 1·10 1·25

91 "Red Cross"

1970. Centenary of British Red Cross. Imperf. Self-adhesive.
335 **91** 3s. red, black and green (postage) 10 10
336 7s. red, black and blue . . 15 15

337 15s. red, black and purple 40 40
338 25s. red, black and blue . . 70 70
339 75s. red, black and brown 4·50 4·50

340 – 9s. red and turquoise (air) 20 20
341 – 10s. red and purple 20 20
342 – 18s. red and green 50 50
343 – 38s. red and blue . . . . . 2·25 2·25
344 – 1p. red and silver . . . . 5·50 6·50
DESIGN—As Type **91**: Nos. 340/4, As Nos. 335/9 but with inscription rearranged and coat of arms omitted.

1971. 5th Death Anniv of Queen Salote. Nos. 174/80, 182/4 with part of old surch obliterated and further surch **1965 1970** and value. On air values the surch includes two laurel leaves.
345 **65** 2s. on 5d. on 9d. (postage) 20 20
346 3s. on 9d. 20 20
347 5s. on 3d. 30 20
348 15s. on 3s.6d. on 9d. . . . 1·00 35
349 25s. on 6s.6d. on 3d. . . . 1·75 80
350 50s. on 1s.7d. on 3d. . . . 2·75 2·00

351 **66** 9s. on 10d. (air) 75 20
352 24s. on 4s. on 10d . . . . 1·75 75
353 29s. on 5s.6d. on 1s.2d. 2·00 1·00
354 38s. on 10s.6d. on 1s.2d. 2·50 1·50

1971. "Philatokyo '71" Stamp Exhibition, Japan. As Nos. 101 etc but imperf with colours changed and surch **PHILATOKYO '71**, emblem and value or **HONOURING JAPANESE POSTAL CENTENARY 1871-1971** (Nos. 357, 362, 364). Nos. 360/4 also surch **AIRMAIL**.
355 3s. on 8d. blk & yell (postage) 10 10
356 7s. on 4d. violet and yellow 15 10
357 15s. on 1s. red and yellow . . 30 20
358 25s. on 1d. black and yellow 40 30
359 75s. on 2s. red and blue . . . 1·75 1·75

360 9s. on 1½d. green (air) . . . 15 10
361 10s. on 4d. violet and yellow 15 10
362 18s. on 1s. red and yellow . . 35 25
363 38s. on 1d. black and yellow 70 50
364 1p. on 2s. red and blue . . . 1·75 2·00

96 Wristwatch

1971. Air. Imperf. Self-adhesive.
365 **96** 14s. multicoloured . . . . 2·00 2·25
365a 17s. multicoloured . . . . 2·25 2·50
366 21s. multicoloured . . . . 2·25 2·50
366a 38s. multicoloured . . . . 3·25 3·50
See also Nos. O65/6a.

97 Pole-vaulter

98 Medal of Merit (reverse)

1971. 4th South Pacific Games, Tahiti. Imperf. Self-adhesive.
367 **97** 3s. multicoloured (postage) 10 10
368 7s. multicoloured 10 10
369 15s. multicoloured 20 20
370 25s. multicoloured 30 35
371 50s. multicoloured 60 90

372 – 9s. multicoloured (air) . . 10 10
373 – 10s. multicoloured 10 10
374 – 24s. multicoloured 30 35
375 – 29s. multicoloured 40 50
376 – 38s. multicoloured 55 70
DESIGN—HORIZ: Nos. 372/6, High-jumper.

1971. Investiture of Royal Tongan Medal of Merit. Multicoloured, colour of medal given. Imperf. Self-adhesive.
377 **98** 3s. gold (postage) 10 10
378 24s. silver 35 25
379 – 38s. brown 60 50

380 – 10s. gold (air) 20 15
381 – 75s. silver . . . . 1·10 1·25
382 **98** 1p. brown . . . . 1·40 1·60
DESIGN—As Type **98**: Nos. 379/81, Obverse of the Medal of Merit.

99 Child

1971. 25th Anniv of UNICEF. Imperf. Self-adhesive.
383 **99** 2s. multicoloured (postage) 10 10
384 4s. multicoloured 10 10
385 8s. multicoloured 10 10
386 16s. multicoloured 25 25
387 30s. multicoloured 45 45

388 – 10s. multicoloured (air) . . 15 15
389 – 15s. multicoloured 25 25
390 – 25s. multicoloured 40 40
391 – 50s. multicoloured . . . . 85 1·00
392 – 1p. multicoloured . . . . 1·75 2·00
DESIGN—VERT (21 × 42 mm): Nos. 388/92, Woman.

100 Map of South Pacific, and "Olovaha"

1972. Merchant Marine Routes. Imperf. Self-adhesive.
393 **100** 2s. multicoloured (postage) 30 40
394 10s. multicoloured 60 30
395 17s. multicoloured 90 30
396 21s. multicoloured . . . . 1·00 40
397 60s. multicoloured . . . . 4·25 3·50

398 – 9s. multicoloured (air) . . 60 30
399 – 12s. multicoloured 75 30
400 – 14s. multicoloured 85 30
401 – 75s. multicoloured . . . . 4·50 4·00
402 – 90s. multicoloured . . . . 4·75 5·50
DESIGN: Nos. 398/402, Map of South Pacific, and "Niuvakai".

101 ¼ Hau Coronation Coin

1972. 5th Anniv of Coronation. Imperf. Self-adhesive.
403 **101** 5s. multicoloured (postage) 10 10
404 7s. multicoloured 10 10
405 10s. multicoloured 15 15
406 17s. multicoloured 30 20
407 60s. multicoloured . . . . 1·00 85

408 – 9s. multicoloured (air) . . 15 15
409 – 12s. multicoloured 20 15
410 – 14s. multicoloured 25 20
411 – 21s. multicoloured 35 20
412 – 75s. multicoloured . . . . 1·25 85
DESIGNS—(47 × 41 mm): Nos. 408/12, As T **101** but with coins above inscription instead of beneath it.

102 Water Melon

1972. Imperf. Self-adhesive. (a) As T **83** but inscription altered omitting "Best in the Pacific", and colours changed.
413 **83** 1s. yellow, red and black 50 30
414 2s. yellow, blue and black 55 30
415 3s. yellow, green and black 60 30
416 4s. yellow, blue and black 60 30
417 5s. yellow, brown and black 60 30

(b) As T **90** but colours changed. Multicoloured. Colour of face value given.
418 **90** 6s. orange 70 35
419 7s. blue 75 35
420 8s. purple 75 35
421 9s. orange 75 35
422 10s. blue 80 35

(c) Type **102**. Multicoloured. Colour of face value given.
423 **102** 15s. blue . . . . 1·60 55
424 20s. orange . . . . 1·75 75
425 25s. brown . . . . 2·00 85
426 40s. orange . . . . 3·25 1·75
427 50s. lemon . . . . 3·25 2·00

1972. Inauguration of Internal Airmail. No. 398 surch **7s NOVEMBER 1972 INAUGURAL Internal Airmail Nuku'alofa – Vava'u**.
428 7s. on 9s. multicoloured . . . 1·00 2·25

104 Hoisting Tongan Flag

1972. Proclamation of Sovereignty over Minerva Reefs. Imperf. Self-adhesive.
429 **104** 5s. multicoloured (postage) 10 10
430 7s. multicoloured 10 10
431 10s. multicoloured 15 15
432 15s. multicoloured 25 20
433 40s. multicoloured 80 55

434 – 9s. multicoloured (air) . . 15 15
435 – 12s. multicoloured 20 15
436 – 14s. multicoloured 25 15
437 – 38s. multicoloured 75 55
438 – 1p. multicoloured . . . . 2·00 2·50
DESIGN—SPHERICAL (52 mm diameter): Nos. 434/8, Proclamation in Govt Gazette.

105 Coins around Bank

1973. Foundation of Bank of Tonga. Imperf. Self-adhesive.
439 **105** 5s. multicoloured (postage) 15 10
440 7s. multicoloured 15 10
441 10s. multicoloured 20 10
442 20s. multicoloured 50 20
443 30s. multicoloured 75 30

444 – 9s. multicoloured (air) . . 25 10
445 – 12s. multicoloured 25 10
446 – 17s. multicoloured 45 15
447 – 50s. multicoloured . . . . 1·50 1·25
448 – 90s. multicoloured . . . . 2·75 3·00
DESIGN—HORIZ (64 × 52 mm): Nos. 444/8, Bank and banknotes.

106 Handshake and Scout in Outrigger Canoe

1973. Silver Jubilee of Scouting in Tonga. Imperf. Self-adhesive.
449 **106** 5s. multicoloured (postage) 20 10
450 7s. multicoloured 30 15
451 15s. multicoloured 95 40
452 21s. multicoloured . . . . 1·25 50
453 50s. multicoloured . . . . 4·50 2·25

454 – 9s. multicoloured (air) . . 50 20
455 – 12s. multicoloured 60 30
456 – 14s. multicoloured 85 50
457 – 17s. multicoloured 95 60
458 – 1p. multicoloured . . . . 10·00 6·50
DESIGN—SQUARE (53 × 53 mm): Nos. 454/8, Scout badge.

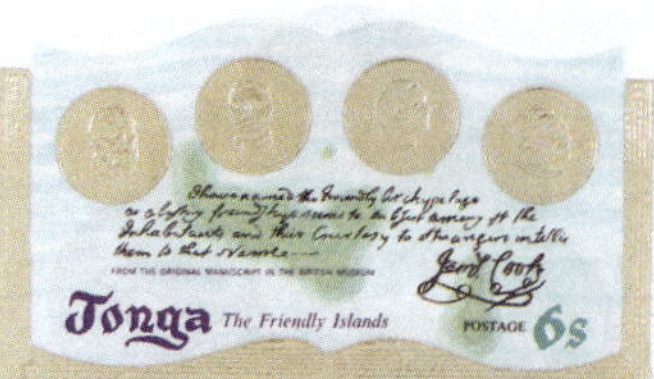

107 Excerpt from Cook's Log-book (⅔-size illustration)

1973. Bicentenary of Capt. Cook's Visit to Tonga. Imperf. Self-adhesive.
459 **107** 6s. multicoloured (postage) 40 30
460 8s. multicoloured 40 35
461 11s. multicoloured 60 40
462 35s. multicoloured . . . . 4·00 2·25
463 40s. multicoloured . . . . 4·00 2·50

464 – 9s. multicoloured (air) . . 70 30
465 – 14s. multicoloured . . . . 1·25 50
466 – 29s. multicoloured . . . . 4·00 2·00
467 – 38s. multicoloured . . . . 4·50 2·50
468 – 75s. multicoloured . . . . 8·50 4·50
DESIGN—VERT: Nos. 464/8, H.M.S. "Resolution".

1973. Commonwealth Games, Christchurch. Various stamps surch **Commonwealth Games CHRISTCHURCH 1974** and No. 474 optd **AIRMAIL** in addition.
469 **97** 5s. on 50s. multicoloured (No. 371) (postage) . . . 15 10
470 – 12s. on 38s. mult (No. 379) 30 15
471 – 14s. on 75s. mult (No. 381) 30 15
472 **98** 20s. on 1p. mult (No. 382) 50 30
473 50s. on 24s. mult (No. 378) 1·00 1·00

474 **97** 7s. on 25s. mult (No. 370) (air) 15 10
475 – 9s. on 38s. mult (No. 376) 20 10
476 – 24s. mult (No. 374) 60 30
477 – 29s. on 9s. mult (No. 374) 70 40
478 – 40s. on 14s. mult (No. 456) 85 90

109 Red Shining Parrot

1974. Air. Imperf. Self-adhesive.
479 **109** 7s. multicoloured 95 65
480 9s. multicoloured . . . . 1·10 75
481 12s. multicoloured . . . . 1·25 75
482 14s. multicoloured . . . . 1·40 75
483 17s. multicoloured . . . . 1·50 1·00
484 29s. multicoloured . . . . 2·50 1·40
485 38s. multicoloured . . . . 3·00 1·50
486 50s. multicoloured . . . . 3·50 4·75
487 75s. multicoloured . . . . 4·75 7·00
For 25s. value in smaller design, 27 × 36 mm, see No. 1284.

110 "Stamped Letter"

1974. Centenary of U.P.U. Imperf. Self-adhesive.
488 **110** 5s. multicoloured (postage) 10 20
489 10s. multicoloured 15 20
490 15s. multicoloured 25 30
491 20s. multicoloured 30 30
492 50s. multicoloured . . . . 1·00 1·50

493 – 14s. multicoloured (air) 25 25
494 – 21s. multicoloured 35 35
495 – 60s. multicoloured . . . . 1·10 1·60
496 – 75s. multicoloured . . . . 1·25 1·90
497 – 1p. multicoloured . . . . 1·50 2·25
DESIGN—HORIZ: Nos. 493/7, Carrier pigeon scattering letters over Tonga.

111 Girl Guides Badges

1974. Tongan Girl Guides. Imperf. Self-adhesive.

498	**111**	5s. multicoloured (postage)	40	30
499		10s. multicoloured	60	30
500		20s. multicoloured	1·50	65
501		40s. multicoloured	3·25	1·75
502		60s. multicoloured	4·00	2·75
503	–	14s. multicoloured (air)	1·00	45
504	–	16s. multicoloured	1·00	45
505	–	29s. multicoloured	2·00	1·00
506	–	31s. multicoloured	2·25	1·25
507	–	75s. multicoloured	5·50	3·50

DESIGN—VERT: Nos. 503/7, Girl Guide leaders.

112 H.M.S. "Resolution"

1974. Establishment of Royal Marine Institute. Imperf. Self-adhesive.

508	**112**	5s. multicoloured (postage)	1·25	50
509		10s. multicoloured	1·40	50
510		25s. multicoloured	2·75	80
511		50s. multicoloured	4·00	3·00
512		75s. multicoloured	5·50	4·50
513	–	9s. multicoloured (air)	1·25	30
514	–	14s. multicoloured	1·75	55
515	–	17s. multicoloured	2·00	60
516	–	60s. multicoloured	4·25	3·75
517	–	90s. multicoloured	6·00	5·50

DESIGN—HORIZ (53×47 mm): Nos. 513/17, "James Cook" (bulk carrier).

113 Dateline Hotel, Nuku'alofa

1975. South Pacific Forum and Tourism. Imperf. Self-adhesive.

518	**113**	5s. multicoloured (postage)	10	10
519		10s. multicoloured	10	10
520		15s. multicoloured	20	20
521		30s. multicoloured	45	45
522		1p. multicoloured	1·60	2·00
523	**113**	9s. multicoloured (air)	10	10
524	–	12s. multicoloured	15	15
525	–	14s. multicoloured	20	20
526	–	17s. multicoloured	20	20
527	–	38s. multicoloured	55	65

DESIGNS—(46×60 mm): 9, 12, 14s. Beach; 17, 38s. Surf and sea.

114 Boxing

1975. 5th South Pacific Games, Guam. Imperf. Self-adhesive.

528	**114**	5s. multicoloured (postage)	15	15
529		10s. multicoloured	20	15
530		20s. multicoloured	30	25
531		25s. multicoloured	35	35
532		65s. multicoloured	80	1·40
533	–	9s. multicoloured (air)	20	15
534	–	12s. multicoloured	25	15
535	–	14s. multicoloured	25	15
536	–	17s. multicoloured	30	20
537	–	90s. multicoloured	1·10	1·75

DESIGN—(37×43 mm): Nos. 533/7, Throwing the discus.

115 Commemorative Coin

1975. F.A.O. Commemoration. Imperf. Self-adhesive.

538	**115**	5s. multicoloured (postage)	15	10
539	–	20s. multicoloured	35	15
540	–	50s. blue, black and silver	75	35
541	–	1p. blue, black and silver	1·50	1·25
542	–	2p. black and silver	2·50	2·25
543	–	12s. multicoloured (air)	30	15
544	–	14s. multicoloured	30	15
545	–	25s. red, black and silver	45	20
546	–	50s. purple, black & silver	70	50
547	–	1p. black and silver	1·50	1·25

DESIGNS: Nos. 539/47 are as T **52** but showing different coins. Nos. 542 and 544 are horiz, size 75×42 mm.

116 Commemorative Coin

1975. Centenary of Tongan Constitution. Mult. Imperf. Self-adhesive.

548	5s. Type **116** (postage)	20	15
549	10s. King George I	30	20
550	20s. King Taufa'ahau IV	55	30
551	50s. King George II	1·25	1·25
552	75s. Tongan arms	2·00	2·25
553	9s. King Taufa'ahau IV (air)	30	20
554	12s. Queen Salote	35	25
555	14s. Tongan arms	35	25
556	38s. King Taufa'ahau IV	80	40
557	1p. Four monarchs	2·25	2·75

SIZES: 60×40 mm, Nos. 549 and 551; 76×76 mm, Nos. 552 and 557; 57×56 mm, others.

117 Montreal Logo

1976. 1st Participation in Olympic Games. Imperf. Self-adhesive. (a) Type **117**.

558		5s. red, black & blue (postage)	60	35
559		10s. red, black and green	70	35
560		25s. red, black and brown	1·60	70
561		35s. red, black and mauve	2·00	75
562		70s. red, black and green	4·00	2·75

(b) Montreal logo optd on Nos. 500/1, 504 and 507.

563	**111**	12s. on 20s. mult (air)	1·25	45
564	–	14s. on 16s. multicoloured	1·25	45
565	–	16s. multicoloured	1·40	45
566	**111**	38s. on 40s. multicoloured	2·75	60
567	–	75s. multicoloured	4·75	3·25

118 Signatories of Declaration of Independence

1976. Bicentenary of American Revolution. Imperf. Self-adhesive.

568	**118**	9s. multicoloured (postage)	30	15
569	–	10s. multicoloured	30	15
570	–	15s. multicoloured	45	45
571	–	25s. multicoloured	60	70
572	–	75s. multicoloured	1·50	2·50
573	–	12s. multicoloured (air)	40	15
574	–	14s. multicoloured	40	20
575	–	17s. multicoloured	50	35
576	–	38s. multicoloured	70	75
577	–	1p. multicoloured	1·75	3·50

DESIGNS: Nos. 569/77 show the signatories to the Declaration of Independence.

119 Nathaniel Turner and John Thomas (Methodist missionaries)

1976. 150th Anniv of Christianity in Tonga. Imperf. Self-adhesive.

578	**119**	5s. multicoloured (postage)	35	25
579		10s. multicoloured	50	25
580		20s. multicoloured	70	40
581		25s. multicoloured	75	45
582		85s. multicoloured	2·75	3·50
583	–	9s. multicoloured (air)	65	40
584	–	12s. multicoloured	70	45
585	–	14s. multicoloured	80	55
586	–	17s. multicoloured	1·00	60
587	–	38s. multicoloured	2·25	1·10

DESIGN: Nos. 583/7 show missionary ship "Triton".

120 Emperor Wilhelm I and King George Tupou I

1976. Centenary of Treaty of Friendship with Germany. Imperf. Self-adhesive.

588	**120**	9s. multicoloured (postage)	20	20
589		15s. multicoloured	30	30
590		22s. multicoloured	40	45
591		50s. multicoloured	90	1·25
592		73s. multicoloured	1·40	1·90
593	–	11s. multicoloured (air)	25	25
594	–	17s. multicoloured	40	45
595	–	18s. multicoloured	40	45
596	–	31s. multicoloured	60	80
597	–	39s. multicoloured	70	90

DESIGNS—CIRCULAR (52 mm diameter): Nos. 593/7, Treaty signing.

121 Queen Salote and Coronation Procession

1977. Silver Jubilee. Imperf. Self-adhesive.

598	**121**	11s. mult (postage)	40	30
599		20s. multicoloured	30	30
600		30s. multicoloured	30	30
601		50s. multicoloured	50	65
602		75s. multicoloured	65	85
603	–	15s. multicoloured (air)	30	25
604	–	17s. multicoloured	30	30
605	–	22s. multicoloured	3·00	1·25
606	–	31s. multicoloured	30	40
607	–	39s. multicoloured	30	40

DESIGN—SQUARE (59×59 mm): Nos. 603/7, Queen Elizabeth and King Taufa'ahau.

122 Tongan Coins

1977. 10th Anniv of King's Coronation. Imperf. Self-adhesive.

608	**122**	10s. mult (postage)	20	20
609		15s. multicoloured	25	25
610		25s. multicoloured	35	45
611		50s. multicoloured	75	90
612		75s. multicoloured	1·00	1·50
613	–	11s. multicoloured (air)	25	20
614	–	17s. multicoloured	30	30
615	–	18s. multicoloured	30	30
616	–	39s. multicoloured	45	60
617	–	1p. multicoloured	1·50	2·25

DESIGN—OVAL (64×46 mm): Nos. 613/17, 1967 Coronation coin.

123 H.M.S. "Resolution"

1977. Bicentenary of Capt. Cook's Last Voyage. Imperf. Self-adhesive.

618	**123**	10s. mult (postage)	1·75	75
619		17s. multicoloured	2·25	1·10
620		25s. multicoloured	3·75	2·00
621		30s. multicoloured	3·75	2·75
622		40s. multicoloured	4·50	4·50
623	–	15s. multicoloured (air)	1·75	1·25
624	–	22s. multicoloured	2·75	2·25
625	–	31s. multicoloured	3·25	2·75
626	–	50s. multicoloured	4·50	4·50
627	–	1p. multicoloured	8·00	8·50

DESIGN—52×46 mm: Nos. 623/7, Medal and extract from Cook's journal.

124 Humpback Whale

1977. Whale Conservation. Imperf. Self-adhesive.
628 **124** 15s. black, grey and blue (postage) . . . . . 3·00 80
629 22s. black, grey and green 3·25 1·25
630 31s. black, grey and orange . . . . 3·75 1·75
631 38s. black, grey and lilac 4·00 2·25
632 64s. black, grey and brown . . . . 6·50 5·50
633 – 11s. multicoloured (air) 3·00 75
634 – 17s. multicoloured . . . . 3·25 90
635 – 18s. multicoloured . . . . 3·25 1·00
636 – 39s. multicoloured . . . . 4·50 2·25
637 – 50s. multicoloured . . . . 5·50 3·25
DESIGN—HEXAGONAL (66 × 51 mm): Nos. 633/7, Sei and fin whales.
For 60s. value as Type **124**, see No. 1282.

1978. Various stamps surch.
638 **115** 15s. on 5s. mult (postage) 1·50 1·75
639 **119** 15s. on 5s. multicoloured 1·50 1·75
640 **117** 15s. on 10s. red, blk & grn . . . . 1·50 1·75
641 **119** 15s. on 10s. multicoloured 1·50 1·75
642 **121** 15s. on 11s. multicoloured 1·50 2·75
643 **114** 15s. on 20s. multicoloured 1·50 1·75
644 – 15s. on 38s. multicoloured (No. O133) . . . . . . 1·50 1·75
645 – 17s. on 9s. multicoloured (No. 533) (air) . . . . 1·75 2·00
646 – 17s. on 9s. mult (No. 583) 1·75 2·00
647 – 17s. on 12s. mult (No. 534) . . . . . . 1·75 2·00
648 – 17s. on 12s. mult (No. 573) . . . . . . 1·75 2·00
649 – 17s. on 18s. mult (No. 595) . . . . . . 1·75 2·00
650 – 17s. on 38s. mult (No. 527) . . . . . . 1·75 2·00
651 – 17s. on 38s. mult (No. 556) . . . . . . 1·75 2·00
652 – 1p. on 35s. mult (No. O151) . . . . 20·00 27·00
653 – 1p. on 38s. mult (No. 576) 8·50 9·00
654 – 1p. on 75s. mult (No. 572) 8·50 9·00
The surcharges on Nos. 638/9 are formed by adding a "1" to the existing face value.

126 Flags of Canada and Tonga

1978. 11th Commonwealth Games, Edmonton. Imperf. Self-adhesive.
655 **126** 10s. blue, red and black (postage) 20 20
656 15s. multicoloured 30 30
657 20s. green, black and red 40 40
658 25s. red, blue and black 45 45
659 45s. black and red . . . . 1·10 1·25
660 – 17s. black and red (air) 40 30
661 – 35s. black, red and blue 70 65
662 – 38s. black, red and green 85 85
663 – 40s. black, red and green 90 90
664 – 65s. black, red and brown 1·60 2·00
DESIGN—LEAF-SHAPED (39 × 40 mm): Nos. 660/4, Maple leaf.

127 King Taufa'ahau Tupou IV

1978. 60th Birthday of King Taufa'ahau Tupou IV. Imperf. Self-adhesive.
665 **127** 2s. black, deep blue and blue (postage) 15 30
666 5s. black, blue and pink 15 30
667 10s. black, blue & mauve 25 25
668 25s. black, blue and grey 55 40
669 75s. black, blue and yellow . . . . 1·40 1·50
670 – 11s. black, bl & yell (air) 25 20
671 – 15s. black, blue and brown 35 25
672 – 17s. black, blue and lilac 40 25
673 – 39s. black, blue and green 80 55
674 – 1p. black, blue and pink 2·00 2·25
DESIGN—STAR SHAPED (44 × 51 mm): Nos. 670/4, Portrait of King.

128 Banana

1978. Coil stamps. Imperf. Self-adhesive.
675 **128** 1s. black and yellow . . 20 50
676 – 2s. blue and yellow . . . 20 50
677 – 3s. brown and yellow . . 30 50
678 – 4s. blue and yellow . . . 30 50
679 – 5s. red and yellow . . . 30 50
680 – 6s. purple, green & brown 40 50
681 – 7s. blue, green and brown 40 50
682 – 8s. red, green and brown 40 50
683 – 9s. mauve, green & brown 40 50
684 – 10s. green and brown . . 40 50
684a – 13s. mauve, green & brown . . . . 8·50 5·00
685 – 15s. green and brown . . 1·25 1·25
686 – 20s. brown and green . . 1·40 1·40
687 – 30s. mauve, brown & green . . . . 1·60 1·60
688 – 50s. black, brown & grn 2·00 2·00
689 – 1p. purple, brown & grn 2·50 3·00
689a – 2p. multicoloured . . . 12·00 13·00
689b – 3p. multicoloured . . . 13·00 14·00
DESIGNS—As Type **128**: 2s. to 5s. Bananas, the number shown coinciding with the face value. 18 × 26 mm: 6s. to 10s. Coconuts. 17 × 30 mm: 13s. to 1p. Pineapple. 55 × 29 mm: 2, 3p. Mixed fruit.
For 10s. value as Type **128** but in smaller size (21 × 9 mm), see No. 1281.

129 Humpback Whale

1978. Endangered Wildlife. Multicoloured. Self-adhesive.
690 15s. Type **129** (postage) . . . 3·00 1·75
691 18s. Insular flying fox . . . . 2·75 1·75
692 25s. Turtle . . . . 2·75 1·75
693 28s. Red shining parrot . . . 5·00 2·25
694 60s. Type **129** . . . . 7·50 6·50
695 17s. Type **129** (air) . . . . . 3·00 1·75
696 22s. As 18s. . . . . 2·75 1·75
697 31s. As 25s. . . . . 2·75 2·00
698 39s. As 28s. . . . . 6·00 3·00
699 45s. As Type **129** . . . . . . 6·50 3·50

130 Metrication Symbol

1979. Decade of Progress. Self-adhesive.
700 **130** 5s. multicoloured (postage) 15 30
701 – 11s. multicoloured 40 30
702 – 18s. multicoloured 35 35
703 – 22s. multicoloured 40 30
704 – 50s. multicoloured . . . . 1·25 1·00
705 – 15s. multicoloured (air) 50 30
706 – 17s. multicoloured 50 30
707 – 31s. gold and blue 60 60
708 – 39s. multicoloured 70 65
709 – 1p. multicoloured . . . . 2·25 2·25
DESIGNS—VERT (58 × 55 mm): 11, 17s. Map of South Pacific Islands; 22s. New churches; 50, 15s. Air routes; 39s. Government offices; 1p. Communications. TEAR DROP (35 × 52 mm): 18s. Building wall of progress with the assistance of United States Peace Corps. As Type **130**: 31s. Rotary International emblem.

131 Various Envelopes bearing Self-adhesive Stamps

1979. Death Centenary of Sir Rowland Hill and 10th Anniv of Tongan Self-adhesive Stamps. Self-adhesive.
710 **131** 5s. multicoloured (postage) 20 10
711 10s. multicoloured 30 15
712 25s. multicoloured 50 35
713 50s. multicoloured 85 60
714 1p. multicoloured . . . . 1·50 1·25
715 – 15s. multicoloured (air) 40 20
716 – 17s. multicoloured 45 25
717 – 18s. multicoloured 45 25
718 – 31s. multicoloured 60 40
719 – 39s. multicoloured 70 45
DESIGN—MULTI-ANGULAR (53 × 53 mm): 15s. to 39s. Self-adhesive stamps.

132

1979. Air. Coil stamps. Self-adhesive.
720 **132** 5s. black and blue . . . 40 50
721 11s. black and blue . . . 50 50
722 14s. black and violet . . 50 50
723 15s. black and mauve . . 55 50
724 17s. black and mauve . . 55 50
725 18s. black and red . . . 55 50
726 22s. black and red . . . 65 50
726a 29s. black and red . . . 11·00 5·00
727 31s. black and yellow . . 85 1·00
727a 32s. black and brown . . 12·00 5·50
728 39s. black and green . . 1·00 1·00
728a 47s. black and brown . . 12·00 6·50
729 75s. black and green . . 1·50 3·00
730 1p. black and green . . 2·00 4·00

133 Rain Forest, Island of 'Eua

1979. Views as seen through the Lens of a Camera. Self-adhesive.
731 **133** 10s. mult (postage) . . . 30 40
732 18s. multicoloured 30 40
733 31s. multicoloured 50 40
734 50s. multicoloured . . . . 70 1·25
735 60s. multicoloured . . . . 70 2·00
736 – 5s. multicoloured (air) . . 20 30
737 – 15s. multicoloured 30 30
738 – 17s. multicoloured 30 30
739 – 39s. multicoloured 60 60
740 – 75s. multicoloured . . . . 80 2·00
DESIGN: 5s. to 75s. Isle of Kao.

134 King Tupou I, Admiral Du Bouzet and Map of Tonga

1979. 125th Anniv of France–Tonga Treaty of Friendship. Self-adhesive.
741 **134** 7s. multicoloured (postage) 15 15
742 10s. multicoloured 20 20
743 14s. multicoloured 30 30
744 50s. multicoloured . . . . 1·00 1·25
745 75s. multicoloured . . . . 1·50 2·00
746 – 15s. multicoloured (air) 30 30
747 – 17s. multicoloured 35 35
748 – 22s. multicoloured 55 55
749 – 31s. multicoloured 70 90
750 – 39s. multicoloured . . . . 75 1·00
DESIGN: 15s. to 39s. King Tupou II, Napoleon III and "L'Aventure" (French warship).

1980. Olympic Games, Moscow. Nos. 710/19 surch or optd only (Nos. 753 and 755) **1980 OLYMPIC GAMES**, Olympic mascot and symbol.
751 **131** 13s. on 5s. multicoloured (postage) 35 35
752 – 20s. on 10s. multicoloured 55 55
753 – 25s. multicoloured 70 70
754 – 33s. on 50s. multicoloured 85 85
755 – 1p. multicoloured . . . . 3·25 3·50
756 – 9s. on 15s. multicoloured (air) 30 30
757 – 16s. on 17s. multicoloured 50 50
758 – 29s. on 18s. multicoloured 80 80
759 – 32s. on 31s. multicoloured 90 90
760 – 47s. on 39s. multicoloured 1·50 1·75

136 Scout at Campfire

1980. South Pacific Scout Jamboree, Tonga, and 75th Anniv of Rotary International. Self-adhesive.
761 **136** 9s. multicoloured (postage) 30 30
762 13s. multicoloured 40 30
763 15s. multicoloured 40 30
764 30s. multicoloured 75 60
765 – 29s. multicoloured (air) 75 45
766 – 32s. multicoloured 80 45
767 – 47s. multicoloured . . . . 1·10 70
768 – 1p. multicoloured . . . . 2·00 3·50
DESIGN: 29s. to 1p. Scout activities and Rotary emblem.

1980. Various stamps surch.
769 **117** 9s. on 35s. red, black and mauve (postage) 40 50
770 **119** 13s. on 20s. mult 55 80
771 13s. on 25s. mult 55 80
772 – 19s. on 25s. mult (No. 571) . . . . . . 75 1·25
773 **114** 1p. on 65s. mult . . . . 3·00 4·50
773a – 5p. on 25s. mult (No. O214) . . . . 12·00 15·00
773b – 5p. on 2p. mult (No. O215) . . . . 12·00 15·00
774 – 29s. on 14s. mult (No. 585) (air) . . . . 90 1·25
775 – 29s. on 39s. mult (No. 597) . . . . 90 1·25
776 – 32s. on 12s. mult (No. 554) . . . . . . 1·10 1·50
777 – 32s. on 14s. mult (No. 574) . . . . . . 1·10 1·50
778 – 47s. on 12s. mult (No. 524) . . . . . . 1·60 2·00
779 – 47s. on 12s. mult (No. 584) . . . . . . 1·60 2·00

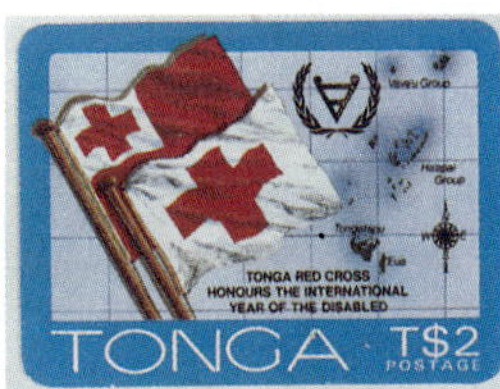

138 Red Cross and Tongan Flags, with Map of Tonga

1981. International Year of Disabled Persons. Self-adhesive.
780 **138** 2p. multicoloured (postage) . . . . 2·00 1·25
781 3p. multicoloured . . . . 2·25 1·50
782 – 29s. multicoloured (air) 50 20
783 – 32s. multicoloured 60 25
784 – 47s. multicoloured 70 30
DESIGN: Nos. 782/4, Red Cross flag and map depicting Tongatapu and Eua.

139 Prince Charles and King Taufa'ahau Tupou IV

141 Landing Scene

140 Report of Printing in "Missionary Notices"

1981. Royal Wedding and Centenary of Treaty of Friendship between Tonga and Great Britain. Multicoloured. Self-adhesive.

785	13s. Type **139**	30	30
786	47s. Prince Charles and Lady Diana Spencer	60	30
787	1p.50 Prince Charles and Lady Diana (different)	1·00	1·50
788	3p. Prince and Princess of Wales after wedding ceremony	1·40	2·25

1981. Christmas. 150th Anniv of First Books Printed in Tonga. Multicoloured. Self-adhesive.

789	9s. Type **140**	25	35
790	13s. "Missionary Notice" report (different)	30	40
791	32s. Type in chase	85	1·00
792	47s. Bible class	1·40	1·50

1981. Bicentenary of Maurelle's Discovery of Vava'u. Multicoloured. Self-adhesive.

793	9s. Type **141**	40	40
794	13s. Map of Vava'u	60	50
795	47s. "La Princesa"	2·75	1·50
796	1p. "La Princesa" (different)	5·00	6·50
MS797	100 × 78 mm. As No. 796. Imperf	8·50	12·00

The stamp from No. **MS**797 is as No. 796 but without inscription at foot of design.

142 Battle Scene

1981. 175th Anniv of Capture of "Port au Prince" (ship). Each black and blue. Self-adhesive.

798	29s. Type **142**	1·25	50
799	32s. Battle scene (different)	1·25	55
800	47s. Map of the Ha'apali Group	1·75	1·40
801	47s. Native canoes preparing to attack	1·75	1·40
802	1p. "Port au Prince"	2·75	2·25

143 Baden-Powell at Brownsea Island, 1907

145 Ball Control

1982. 75th Anniv of Boy Scout Movement and 125th Birth Anniv of Lord Baden-Powell (founder). Multicoloured. Self-adhesive.

803	29s. Type **143**	75	30
804	32s. Baden-Powell on his charger "Black Prince"	80	35
805	47s. Baden-Powell at Imperial Jamboree, 1924	1·00	45
806	1p.50 Cover of first "Scouting for Boys" journal	2·25	1·75
807	2p.50 Newsboy, 1900, and Mafeking Siege 3d. stamp	3·50	4·00

1982. Cyclone Relief. No. 788 optd **CYCLONE RELIEF T$1+50s POSTAGE & RELIEF**.

808	1p.+50s. on 3p. Prince and Princess of Wales after wedding ceremony	80	2·00

1982. World Cup Football Championship, Spain. Multicoloured. Self-adhesive.

809	32s. Type **145**	75	45
810	47s. Goalkeeping	95	60
811	75s. Heading	1·40	95
812	1p.50 Shooting	2·50	1·75

146 "Olovaha II" (inter-island freighter)

147 Mail Canoe

1982. Inter-Island Transport. Multicoloured. Self-adhesive.

813	9s. Type **146**	55	15
814	13s. Type **146**	60	25
815	47s. SPIA De Havilland Twin Otter 300	1·50	1·00
816	1p. As 47s.	2·40	3·00

1982. Centenary of Tin Can Mail. Self-adhesive.

817 **147**	13s. multicoloured	15	25
818 –	32s. multicoloured	25	30
819 –	47s. multicoloured	35	35
820 –	2p. black and green	1·40	2·00
MS821	135 × 90 mm. Nos. 817/19. Imperf	1·25	2·25
MS822	135 × 89 mm. As No. 820 but with gold inscriptions. Imperf	3·00	4·50

DESIGNS: 32s. Mail canoe and ship; 47s. Collecting Tin Can mail; 2p. Map of Niuafo'ou.

148 Decathlon

1982. Commonwealth Games, Brisbane. Mult. Self-adhesive.

823	32s. Type **148**	50	50
824	$1.50 Tongan Police band at opening ceremony (horiz)	4·50	6·00

149 Pupils

1982. Cent of Tonga College. Mult. Self-adhesive.

825	5s. Type **149** (Tongan inscription)	60	1·00
826	5s. Type **149** (English inscription)	60	1·00
827	29s. School crest and monument (Tongan inscr) (29 × 22 mm)	2·25	2·75
828	29s. As No. 827 but inscr in English	2·25	2·75
829	29s. King George Tupou I (founder) and school (Tongan inscr) (29 × 22 mm)	2·25	2·75
830	29s. As No. 829 but inscr in English	2·25	2·75

1982. Christmas. Nos. 817/9 optd **Christmas Greetings 1982**.

831	13s. Type **147**	25	50
832	32s. Mail boat and ship	60	75
833	47s. Collecting Tin Can mail	70	85

151 H.M.S. "Resolution" and S.S. "Canberra"

1983. Sea and Air Transport. Mult. Self-adhesive.

834	29s. Type **151**	3·00	1·75
835	32s. Type **151**	3·00	1·75
836	47s. Montgolfier's balloon and Concorde	4·25	3·00
837	1p.50 As No. 836	6·50	10·00
MS838	120 × 165 mm. 2p.50 "Canberra" (liner) and Concorde	4·00	7·00

152 Globe and Inset of Tonga

1983. Commonwealth Day. Multicoloured. Self-adhesive.

839	29s. Type **152**	35	45
840	32s. Tongan dancers	6·00	4·25
841	47s. Trawler	50	80
842	1p.50 King Taufa'ahau Tupou IV and flag	1·75	5·00

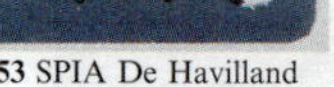

153 SPIA De Havilland Twin Otter 300

154 "Intelsat IV" Satellite

1983. Inauguration of Niuafo'ou Airport. Mult. Self-adhesive.

843	32s. Type **153**	1·00	30
844	47s. Type **153**	1·10	35
845	1p. SPIA Boeing 707	1·75	1·25
846	1p.50 As No. 845	2·75	1·75

1983. World Communications Year. Multicoloured. Self-adhesive.

847	29s. Type **154**	40	20
848	32s. "Intelsat IVA" satellite	50	25
849	75s. "Intelsat V" satellite	1·00	70
850	2p. Moon post cover (45 × 32 mm)	1·50	2·00

155 Obverse and Reverse of Pa'anga Banknote

1983. 10th Anniv of Bank of Tonga. Self-adhesive.

851 **155**	1p. multicoloured	1·25	1·75
852	2p. multicoloured	2·25	3·00

156 Early Printing Press

157 Yacht off Coast

1983. Printing in Tonga. Multicoloured. Self-adhesive.

853	13s. Type **156**	20	15
854	32s. Arrival of W. Woon	40	30
855	1p. Early Tongan print	95	95
856	2p. "The Tonga Chronicle"	1·50	2·00

1983. Christmas. Yachting off Vava'u. Mult. Self-adhesive.

857	29s. Type **157**	60	35
858	32s. View of yacht from cave	60	35
859	1p.50 Anchored yacht	2·00	2·25
860	2p.50 Yacht off coast (different)	2·75	3·50

158 Abel Tasman and "Zeehan"

1984. Navigators and Explorers of the Pacific (1st series). Self-adhesive.

861 **158**	32s. green and black	1·50	1·50
862 –	47s. violet and black	2·00	2·00
863 –	90s. brown and black	3·75	3·75
864 –	1p.50 blue and black	5·00	5·00

DESIGNS: 47s. Capt. Samuel Wallis and H.M.S. "Dolphin"; 90s. Capt. William Bligh and H.M.S. "Bounty"; 1p.50, Capt. James Cook and H.M.S. "Resolution".

See also Nos. 896/9.

159 Chaste Mitre

160 Printer checking Newspaper

1984. Marine Life. Multicoloured. Self-adhesive.

865	1s. Type **159**	40	1·50
866	2s. "Porites sp"	1·00	1·50
867	3s. Red squirrelfish	1·25	1·75
868	5s. Green map cowrie	50	1·50
869	6s. "Dardanus megistos" (crab)	1·25	1·75
870	9s. Variegated shark	1·25	70
871	10s. Bubble cone	1·00	1·50
872	13s. Lionfish	1·50	75
873	15s. Textile or cloth of gold cone	1·00	1·75
874	20s. White-tailed damselfish	2·25	2·25
875	29s. Princely cone	1·75	1·00
876	32s. Powder-blue surgeonfish	3·00	1·00
877	47s. Giant spider conch	3·00	1·60
878	1p. "Millepora dichotama"	10·00	9·50
879	2p. "Birgus latro" (crab)	14·00	15·00
880	3p. Rose-branch murex	9·00	16·00
881	5p. Yellow-finned tuna	11·00	18·00

Nos. 865/77 are 25 × 28 mm in size and Nos. 878/81 38 × 23 mm.

For these designs with normal gum but redrawn see Nos. 999/1017a and 1087/95. For similar designs but with face value at foot see Nos. 1218/34 and 1346/7.

1984. 20th Anniv of "Tonga Chronicle" (newspaper). Self-adhesive.

882 **160**	3s. brown and blue	15	20
883	32s. brown and red	60	65

161 U.S.A. Flag and Running

1984. Olympic Games, Los Angeles. Each in black, red and blue. Self-adhesive.

884	29s. Type **161**	25	25
885	47s. Javelin-throwing	30	30
886	1p.50 Shot-putting	1·00	1·00
887	3p. Olympic torch	1·90	1·90

162 Sir George Airy and Dateline on World Map

1984. Centenary of International Dateline. Mult. Self-adhesive.

888	47s. Type **162**	1·25	1·00
889	2p. Sir Sandford Fleming and Map of Pacific time zones	4·25	4·50

163 Australia 1914 Laughing Kookaburra 6d. Stamp

164 Beach at Sunset ("Silent Night")

1984. "Ausipex" International Stamp Exhibition, Melbourne. Multicoloured. Self-adhesive.
890 32s. Type **163** . . . . 1·50 75
891 1p.50 Tonga 1897 Red shining parrot 2s.6d. . . . 3·25 3·00
MS892 90 × 100 mm. As Nos. 890/1, but without exhibition logo and with "TONGA" and face values in gold. . . . . 4·00 4·00

1984. Christmas. Carols. Mult. Self-adhesive.
893 32s. Type **164** 60 45
894 47s. Hut and palm trees ("Away in a Manger") . . 85 65
895 1p. Sailing boats ("I Saw Three Ships") . . . . . . 1·75 3·00

1985. Navigators and Explorers of the Pacific (2nd series). As T **158**. Self-adhesive.
896 32s. black and blue . . . . . 3·00 1·25
897 47s. black and green . . . . 3·25 1·50
898 90s. black and red . . . . . 7·00 4·00
899 1p.50 black and brown . . . 7·50 6·50
DESIGNS: 32s. Willem Schouten and "Eendracht"; 47s. Jacob Le Maire and "Hoorn"; 90s. Fletcher Christian and "Bounty"; 1p.50, Francisco Maurelle and "La Princessa".

165 Section of Tonga Trench

1985. Geological Survey of the Tonga Trench. Multicoloured. Self-adhesive.
900 29s. Type **165** . . . . 1·25 1·00
901 32s. Diagram of marine seismic survey . . . . . . 1·25 1·00
902 47s. Diagram of aerial oil survey (vert) . . . . 1·50 1·50
903 1p.50 Diagram of sea bed survey (vert) . . . . 4·75 6·00
MS904 100 × 100 mm. 1p.50 Bearded angler (fish) . . . . . 7·50 5·00

166 "Port au Prince" at Gravesend, 1805

1985. 175th Anniv of Will Mariner's Departure for England. Multicoloured. Self-adhesive.
905B 29s. Type **166** 60 50
906B 32s. Capture of "Port au Prince", Tonga, 1806 . . 60 50
907B 47s. Will Mariner on Tongan canoe, 1807 . . . 80 70
908B 1p.50 Mariner boarding brig "Favourite", 1810 2·25 2·75
909B 2p.50 "Cuffnells" in English Channel, 1811 . . . . . 3·50 4·25

167 Quintal (Byron Russell) and Captain Bligh (Charles Laughton)

1985. 50th Anniv of Film "Mutiny on the Bounty". Multicoloured. Self-adhesive.
910 47s. Type **167** . . . . 8·00 8·00
911 47s. Captain Bligh and prisoners . . . . 8·00 8·00
912 47s. Fletcher Christian (Clark Gable) . . . . 8·00 8·00
913 47s. Mutineers threatening Bligh . . . . 8·00 8·00
914 47s. Bligh and Roger Byam (Franchot Tone) in boat 8·00 8·00

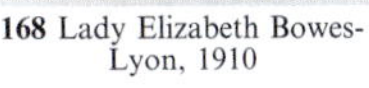
168 Lady Elizabeth Bowes-Lyon, 1910

169 Mary and Joseph arriving at Inn

1985. Life and Times of Queen Elizabeth the Queen Mother and 75th Anniv of Girl Guide Movement. Self-adhesive.
915A **168** 32s. black, pink and brown . . . . 1·50 1·25
916A – 47s. black, lilac and brown . . . . 1·75 1·50
917A – 1p.50 black, yellow and brown . . . . 5·00 5·50
918A – 2p.50 multicoloured . . . . 8·00 9·50
DESIGNS: 47s. Duchess of York at Hadfield Girl Guides' Rally, 1931; 1p.50, Duchess of York in Girl Guide uniform; 2p.50, Queen Mother in 1985 (from photo by Norman Parkinson).

1985. Christmas. Multicoloured. Self-adhesive.
919 32s. Type **169** 55 30
920 42s. The Shepherds 60 40
921 1p.50 The Three Wise Men 2·25 3·00
922 2p.50 The Holy Family . . . 3·25 4·50

170 Comet and Slogan "Maybe Twice in a Lifetime"

1986. Appearance of Halley's Comet. Mult.
923 42s. Type **170** . . . . 3·25 3·25
924 42s. Edmond Halley . . . . 3·25 3·25
925 42s. Solar System . . . . . 3·25 3·25
926 42s. Telescope . . . . 3·25 3·25
927 42s. "Giotto" spacecraft . . 3·25 3·25
928 57s. Type **170** . . . . 3·25 3·25
929 57s. As No. 924 . . . . . . 3·25 3·25
930 57s. As No. 925 . . . . . . 3·25 3·25
931 57s. As No. 926 . . . . . . 3·25 3·25
932 57s. As No. 927 . . . . . . 3·25 3·25
Nos. 923/7 and 928/32 were each printed together, se-tenant, forming composite designs.

1986. Nos. 866/7, 869/70, 872, 874, 879 and 881 surch.
933 4s. on 2s. "Porites sp" . . . 90 2·00
934 4s. on 13s. Lionfish . . . . 90 2·00
935 42s. on 3s. Red squirrelfish 2·25 1·50
936 42s. on 9s. Variegated shark 2·25 1·50
937 57s. on 6s. "Dardanus megistos" . . . . 2·75 2·00
938 57s. on 20s. White-tailed damselfish . . . . 2·75 2·00
939 2p.50 on 2p. "Birgus latro" 8·50 10·00
940 2p.50 on 5p. Yellow-finned tuna . . . . 8·50 10·00

172 King Taufa'ahau Tupou IV of Tonga

1986. Royal Links with Great Britain and 60th Birthday of Queen Elizabeth II.
941 **172** 57s. multicoloured . . . . 75 1·00
942 – 57s. multicoloured . . . . 75 1·00
943 – 2p.50 brown, black and blue . . . . 3·25 4·00
DESIGNS—HORIZ (as Type **172**): No. 942, Queen Elizabeth II. SQUARE (40 × 40 mm): No. 943, Queen Elizabeth II and King Taufa'ahau Tupou IV, Tonga, 1970.

173 Peace Corps Nurse giving Injection

1986. "Ameripex '86" International Stamp Exhibition, Chicago. 25th Anniv of United States Peace Corps. Multicoloured.
944 57s. Type **173** . . . . 1·25 1·00
945 1p.50 Peace Corps teacher and pupil . . . . 2·25 3·25
MS946 90 × 90 mm. Nos. 944/5, magnifying glass and tweezers 3·00 4·50

174 Hockey

1986. Sporting Events. Multicoloured.
947 42s. Type **174** (World Hockey Cup for Men, London) . . 1·75 1·00
948 57s. Handball (13th Commonwealth Games, Edinburgh) . . . . 1·50 1·00
949 1p. Boxing (13th Commonwealth Games, Edinburgh) . . . . 2·00 2·75
950 2p.50 Football (World Cup Football Championship, Mexico) . . . . 4·75 6·00

175 1886 1d. King George I Definitive

1986. Centenary of First Tonga Stamps. Mult.
951 32s. Type **175** . . . . 1·75 1·10
952 42s. 1897 7½d. King George II inverted centre error . . . . 2·00 1·25
953 57s. 1950 Queen Salote's 50th Birthday 1d. . . . . 2·50 1·40
954 2p.50 1986 Royal Links with Great Britain 2p.50 . . . . 4·25 7·00
MS955 132 × 104 mm. 50s. × 8 Vert designs forming a montage of Tonga stamps . . . . 11·00 10·00

176 Girls wearing Shell Jewellery

1986. Christmas. Multicoloured.
956 32s. Type **176** . . . . 2·00 70
957 42s. Boy with wood carvings (vert) . . . . 2·25 75
958 57s. Children performing traditional dance (vert) . . 2·50 1·10
959 2p. Children in dugout canoe 5·50 9·00

1986. Scout Jamboree, Tongatapu. Nos. 957/8 optd **BOY SCOUT JAMBOREE 5TH-10TH DEC'86**.
960 42s. Boy with wood carvings (vert) . . . . 2·75 2·75
961 57s. Children performing traditional dance (vert) . . 3·25 3·25

178 Dumont D'Urville and "L'Astrolabe"

1987. 150th Anniv of Dumont D'Urville's Second Voyage. Multicoloured.
962 32s. Type **178** . . . . 3·50 1·75
963 42s. Tongan girls (from "Voyage au Pole et dans l'Oceanie") . . . . 3·50 1·75
964 1p. Contemporary chart . . . 8·00 6·00
965 2p.50 Wreck of "L'Astrolabe" . . . . . . 13·00 13·00

179 Noah's Ark

1987. World Wildlife Fund. Sheet 115 × 110 mm containing T **179** and similar vert designs. Multicoloured.
MS966 42s. Type **179**; 42s. American Bald Eagles; 42s. Giraffes and birds; 42s. Gulls; 42s. Ostriches and elephants; 42s. Elephant; 42s. Lions, zebras, antelopes and giraffes; 42s. Chimpanzees; 42s. Frogs and antelopes; 42s. Lizard and tigers; 42s. Snake and tiger; 42s. "Papilio machaon" (butterfly) 40·00 40·00
The stamps within No. **MS**966 show a composite design of animals entering Noah's Ark.

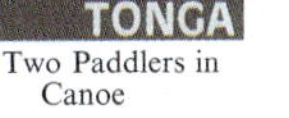

180 Two Paddlers in Canoe

181 King Taufa'ahau Tupou IV

1987. "Siv'a'alo (Tonga-Fiji-Samoa) Canoe Race. Multicoloured.
967 32s. Type **180** 55 40
968 42s. Five paddlers 65 50
969 57s. Paddlers and canoe bow 80 65
970 1p.50 Two paddlers (different) . . . . 2·10 2·75
MS971 153 × 159 mm. Nos. 967/70 3·50 4·25
The stamps within **MS**971 show a composite design of two canoes racing.

1987. 20th Anniv of Coronation of King Taufa'ahau Tupou IV. Self-adhesive.
972 **181** 1s. black and green . . . 20 60
972d 2s. black and orange . . 2·25 3·00
973 5s. black and mauve . . 20 60
974 10s. black and lilac . . . 25 60
975 15s. black and red . . . 35 70
976 32s. black and blue . . . 45 80

182 Arms and Tongan Citizens

1987. 125th Anniv of First Parliament.
977 **182** 32s. multicoloured 40 30
978 42s. multicoloured 50 40
979 75s. multicoloured . . . . 90 1·00
980 2p. multicoloured . . . . 2·25 3·00

183 Father Christmas Octopus and Rat with Sack of Presents

1987. Christmas. Cartoons. Multicoloured.
981 42s. Type **183** . . . . 1·00 50
982 57s. Delivering presents by outrigger canoe . . . . . . 1·25 65
983 1p. Delivering presents by motorized tricycle . . . . 2·25 2·50
984 3p. Drinking cocktails . . . 5·50 7·00

184 King Taufa'ahau Tupou IV, "Olovaha II" (inter-island freighter), Oil Rig and Pole Vaulting

1988. 70th Birthday of King Taufa'ahau Tupou IV. Designs each show portrait. Multicoloured.
985 32s. Type **184** . . . . 2·00 80
986 42s. Banknote, coins, Ha'amonga Trilithon and woodcarver . . . . 1·50 80
987 57s. Rowing, communications satellite and Red Cross worker . . . . 1·75 90
988 2p.50 Scout emblem, 1982 47s. Scout stamp and Friendly Islands Airways De Havilland Twin Otter 200/300 aircraft . . . . . 7·50 8·50
See also Nos. 1082/5.

185 Capt. Cook and Journal

186 Athletics

1988. Bicentenary of Australian Settlement. Sheet 115×110 mm containing T **185** and similar vert designs. Multicoloured.
MS989 42s. Type **185**; 42s. Ships in Sydney Harbour and Governor Philip; 42s. Australia 1952 2s.6d. aborigine definitive and early settlement; 42s. Burke and Wills (explorers); 42s. Emu, opals and gold prospector's licence; 42s. ANZAC cap badge and soldier; 42s. Cover from first overland mail by Trans Continental; 42s. Ross Smith, England–Australia flown cover and G.B. 1969 1s.9d. commemorative stamp; 42s. Don Bradman and Harold Larwood (cricketers); 42s. World War II campaign medals; 42s. Australia 1978 18c. Flying Doctor Service stamp and sheep station; 42s. Sydney Opera House . . . . . 26·00 27·00

1988. Olympic Games, Seoul. Multicoloured.
990 57s. Type **186** 65 65
991 75s. Sailing 95 95
992 2p. Cycling . . . . 5·00 3·50
993 3p. Tennis . . . . 6·00 4·75

187 Traditional Tongan Fale

1988. Music in Tonga. Multicoloured.
994 32s. Type **187** 30 35
995 42s. Church choir 40 45
996 57s. Tonga Police Band outside Royal Palace . . . 1·00 80
997 2p.50 "The Jets" pop group 2·40 3·25

188 Olympic Flame

1988. "Sport Aid '88". Sheet 105×75 mm, containing T **188** and design as No. 997. Multicoloured.
MS998 57s. Type **188**; 57s. As No. 997 . . . . 1·40 2·00

1988. Redrawn designs (each showing wider gap between upper and lower lines) as Nos. 865/6, 868/9, 871/6 and 879/81 and new values, all normal gum. Multicoloured.
999 1s. Type **159** . . . . . . 30 1·25
1000 2s. "Porites sp" . . . . . 40 1·50
1001 4s. Lionfish . . . . 1·50 1·75
1002 5s. Green map cowrie . . . 50 1·50
1003 6s. "Dardanus megistos" (crab) . . . . 1·00 2·25
1004 7s. Wandering albatross . . 3·50 2·50
1005 10s. Bubble cone 60 80
1006 15s. Textile or cloth of gold cone . . . . . . 60 1·00
1007 20s. White-tailed damselfish 90 1·75
1008 32s. Powder-blue surgeonfish . . . . . . 1·00 70
1009 35s. Seahorse . . . . . . 3·00 2·75
1010 42s. Lesser frigate bird . . 3·75 70
1011 50s. Princely cone . . . . 3·50 1·75
1012 57s. Brown booby . . . . 4·50 1·00
1013 1p. "Chelonia mydas" (turtle) . . . . 5·50 4·50
1014 1p.50 Humpback whale . . 11·00 7·00
1015 2p. "Birgus latro" (crab) 8·00 8·00
1016 3p. Rose-branch murex . . 2·75 8·00
1017 5p. Yellow-finned tuna . . 13·00 16·00
1017a 10p. Variegated shark . . 18·00 22·00
Nos. 1013/17 are 41×22 mm and No. 1017a 26×41.
For smaller designs, 19×22 mm, see Nos. 1087/95.

189 Capt. Cook's H.M.S. "Resolution"

1988. Centenary of Tonga–U.S.A. Treaty of Friendship. Multicoloured.
1018 42s. Type **189** 80 70
1019 57s. "Santa Maria" . . . . 1·00 80
1020 2p. Capt. Cook and Christopher Columbus . . 3·25 4·50
MS1021 140×115 mm. Nos. 1018/20 4·50 6·00

190 Girl in Hospital Bed

1988. Christmas. 125th Anniv of International Red Cross and 25th Anniv of Tongan Red Cross. Multicoloured.
1022 15s. Type **190** (A) 15 20
1023 15s. Type **190** (B) 15 20
1024 32s. Red Cross nurse reading to young boy (A) 30 35
1025 32s. Red Cross nurse reading to young boy (B) 30 35
1026 42s. Red Cross nurse taking pulse (A) 40 45
1027 42s. Red Cross nurse taking pulse (B) 40 45
1028 57s. Red Cross nurse with sleeping child (A) 55 60
1029 57s. Red Cross nurse with sleeping child (B) 55 60
1030 1p.50 Boy in wheelchair (A) 1·40 2·00
1031 1p.50 Boy in wheelchair (B) 1·40 2·00
Nos. 1022/3, 1024/5, 1026/7, 1028/9 and 1030/1 were printed together, se-tenant, in horizontal pairs throughout the sheets with the first stamp in each pair inscribed "INTERNATIONAL RED CROSS 125TH ANNIVERSARY" (A) and the second "SILVER JUBILEE OF TONGAN RED CROSS" (B).

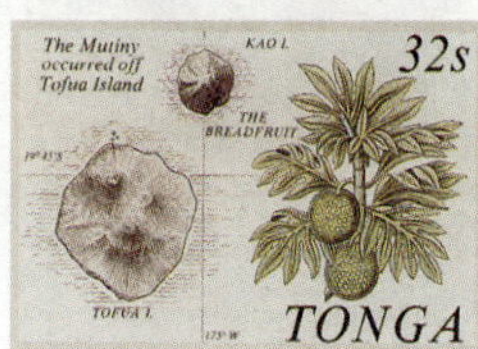

191 Map of Tofua Island and Breadfruit

1989. Bicentenary of Mutiny on the "Bounty". Multicoloured.
1032 32s. Type **191** . . . . . . 2·75 1·75
1033 42s. H.M.S. "Bounty" and chronometer . . . . . . 4·50 2·00
1034 57s. Captain Bligh and "Bounty's" launch cast adrift . . . . 6·00 3·00
MS1035 106×80 mm. 2p. Fletcher Christian on H.M.S. "Bounty" (vert); 3p. Bligh cast adrift. . . 8·00 10·00

192 "Hypolimnas bolina"

1989. Butterflies. Multicoloured.
1036 42s. Type **192** . . . . . . 1·00 80
1037 57s. "Jamides bochus" . . . 1·25 90
1038 1p.20 "Melanitis leda" . . . 2·25 2·75
1039 2p.50 "Danaus plexippus" . . 3·75 5·50

193 Football at Rugby School, 1870

1989. Inauguration of National Sports Stadium and South Pacific Mini Games, Tonga. Designs showing development of rugby, tennis and cricket. Multicoloured.
1040 32s. Type **193** . . . . . . 1·00 1·00
1041 32s. D. Gallaher (All Blacks' captain, 1905) and Springboks rugby match, 1906 . . . . 1·00 1·00
1042 32s. King George V with Cambridge team, 1922, and W. Wakefield (England captain, 1926) 1·00 1·00
1043 32s. E. Crawford (Ireland captain, 1926) and players on cigarette cards . . . . 1·00 1·00
1044 32s. S. Mafi (Tonga captain, 1970s) and modern rugby match . . . . 1·00 1·00
1045 42s. Royal tennis, 1659 . . 1·50 1·50
1046 42s. Major Wingfield and lawn tennis, 1873 . . . . 1·50 1·50
1047 42s. Oxford and Cambridge tennis teams, 1884 . . . 1·50 1·50
1048 42s. Bunny Ryan, 1910, and players on cigarette cards 1·50 1·50
1049 42s. Boris Becker and modern tennis match . . 1·50 1·50
1050 57s. Cricket match, 1743, and F. Pilch memorial . . 2·25 2·25
1051 57s. W. G. Grace (19th-century cricketer) . . 2·25 2·25
1052 57s. "Boys Own Paper" cricket article, 1909 . . . 2·25 2·25
1053 57s. Australian cricket team, 1909, and players on cigarette cards . . . . . 2·25 2·25
1054 57s. The Ashes urn, and modern cricket match . . 2·25 2·25

194 Short S.30 Modified "G" Class Flying Boat "Aotearoa", 1939 (50th anniv of first flight)

195 CASA C-212 Aviocar landing

1989. Aviation in Tonga. Multicoloured.
1055 42s. Type **194** . . . . . . 2·25 1·10
1056 57s. Chance Vought F4U Corsair, 1943 . . . . . . 2·75 1·50
1057 90s. Boeing 737 at Fua'amotu Airport . . . 4·75 4·50
1058 3p. Montgolfier balloon, Wright Flyer I biplane, Concorde and space shuttle (97×26 mm) . . . 11·00 11·00

1989. Christmas. "Flying Home".
1059 **195** 32s. green, brown & orange . . . . 1·50 80
1060 – 42s. green, brown & lt green . . . . 1·75 80
1061 – 57s. green, brown and red . . . . 2·00 90
1062 – 3p. green, brown & mve 6·00 8·00
DESIGNS: 42s. Villagers waving to CASA C-212 Aviocar aircraft; 57s. Outrigger canoe and CASA C-212 Aviocar aircraft; 3p. CASA C-212 Aviocar over headland.

196 Rowland Hill, Mulready Cover and Penny Blacks

198 Boxing

197 1989 U.P.U. Congress Stamps

1989. 20th Universal Postal Union Congress, Washington. Sheet 115×110 mm containing T **196** and similar vert designs. Multicoloured.
MS1063 57s. Type **196**; 57s. Early train and steam ship; 57s. Stage coach, Pony Express poster and rider; 57s. French hot-air balloon and flown cover; 57s. Samuel Morse and telegraph key; 57s. Early British mail van and pillar box; 57s. Unloading De Havilland D.H.4.M mail biplane; 57s. "Queen Mary" (liner) and Airship LZ-127 "Graf Zeppelin" flown cover; 57s. Westland Dragonfly helicopter and mail van; 57s. Computer and fax machine; 57s. "Apollo 11" emblem and space cover; 57s. U.P.U. Monument and space shuttle . . . . 27·00 28·00

1989. "World Stamp Expo '89" International Stamp Exhibition, Washington.
1064 **197** 57s. multicoloured . . . 2·50 1·75

1990. 14th Commonwealth Games, Auckland. Mult.
1065 42s. Type **198** 90 70
1066 57s. Archery . . . . 1·50 1·10
1067 1p. Bowls . . . . 2·00 2·50
1068 2p. Swimming . . . . . . 3·50 5·00

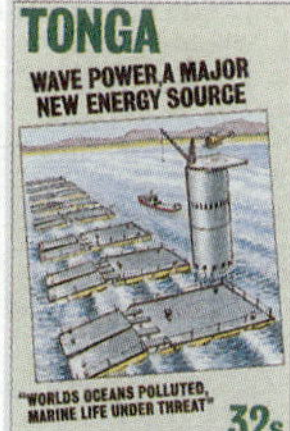

199 Wave Power Installation

201 Departure of Canoe

200 Penny Black

1990. Alternative Sources of Electricity. Mult.
1069 32s. Type **199** . . . . . . 1·00 65
1070 57s. Wind farm . . . . . . 1·50 1·10
1071 1p.20 Experimental solar cell vehicle . . . . 3·00 4·75
MS1072 110×90 mm. 2p.50 Planet Earth . . . . 7·00 8·00

1990. 150th Anniv of the Penny Black.
1073 **200** 42s. multicoloured . . . 1·25 1·25
1074 – 42s. multicoloured . . . 1·25 1·25
1075 – 57s. red and black . . . 1·50 1·25
1076 – 1p.50 multicoloured . . 3·50 4·00
1077 – 2p.50 multicoloured . . 5·00 5·50
DESIGNS: 42s. (1074) Great Britain 1840 Twopence Blue; 57s. Tonga 1886 1d.; 1p.50, 1980 South Pacific Scout Jamboree and Rotary 75th anniv 2p. official stamp; 2p.50, 1990 Alternative Sources of Electricity 57s.

1990. Polynesian Voyages of Discovery.
1078 **201** 32s. green 75 65
1079 – 42s. blue . . . . 1·00 80
1080 – 1p.20 brown . . . . . . 2·75 3·00
1081 – 3p. violet . . . . 5·50 8·00
DESIGNS: 42s. Navigating by night; 1p.20, Canoe and sea birds; 3p. Landfall.

1990. Silver Jubilee of King Taufa'ahau Tupou IV. As Nos. 985/8 but inscr "Silver Jubilee of His Majesty King Taufa'ahau Tupou IV. 1965–1990" and with "TONGA" and values in silver.
1082 32s. Type **184** . . . . . . 1·10 75
1083 42s. Banknote, coins Ha'amonga Trilithon and woodcarver . . . . . . 1·10 75
1084 57s. Rowing, communications satellite and Red Cross worker . . 1·40 85
1085 2p.50 Scout emblem, 1982 47s. Scout stamp and Friendly Island Airways De Havilland Twin Otter aircraft . . . . 5·00 7·00

1990. As Nos. 1000, 1002, 1003 (value changed), 1005 and 1008 redrawn smaller, 19×22 mm. Multicoloured.
1087 2s. "Porites sp." 40 65
1089 5s. Green map cowrie . . . 40 65
1092 10s. Bubble cone 40 65
1093 15s. "Dardanus megistos" (crab) . . . . 1·50 80
1095 32s. Powder-blue surgeonfish 65 65

202 Iguana searching for Food

1990. Endangered Species. Banded Iguana. Mult.
1105 32s. Type **202** . . . . . . 1·50 75
1106 42s. Head of male . . . . . 1·75 85
1107 57s. Pair of iguanas during courtship . . . . 2·25 1·25
1108 1p.20 Iguana basking . . . 5·00 6·50

203 Tourism

1990. 40th Anniv of United Nations Development Programme. Multicoloured.
1109 57s. Type **203** . . . . . . 1·25 1·50
1110 57s. Agriculture and Fisheries . . . . 1·25 1·50
1111 3p. Education . . . . . . 6·00 7·50
1112 3p. Healthcare . . . . . . 6·00 7·50

204 Boy **205** Safety at Work

1990. Christmas. Rotary International Interact Project. Multicoloured.

1113 32s. Type **204** 70 40
1114 42s. Young boys 90 55
1115 2p. Girls in western clothes 3·50 4·25
1116 3p. Girls in traditional costumes . . . . 4·50 5·50

1991. Accident Prevention. Multicoloured.

1117 32s. Type **205** (English inscription) 80 80
1118 32s. Safety at home (English inscription) . . 80 80
1119 32s. As No. 1118 (Tongan inscription) 80 80
1120 32s. As Type **205** (incorrectly inscr "Ngauo tokanga") 80 80
1120a 32s. As Type **205** (inscr corrected to "Ngaue tokanga") . . . . 18·00 18·00
1121 42s. Safety in cars (English inscription) . . . . . 1·25 1·25
1122 42s. Safety on bikes (English inscription) . . 1·25 1·25
1123 42s. As No. 1122 (Tongan inscription) . . . . . . 1·25 1·25
1124 42s. As No. 1121 (Tongan inscription) . . . . . . 1·25 1·25
1125 57s. Safety at sea (English inscription) . . . . . . 1·50 1·50
1126 57s. Safety on the beach (English inscription) . . 1·50 1·50
1127 57s. As No. 1126 (Tongan inscription) . . . . . . 1·50 1·50
1128 57s. As No. 1125 (Tongan inscription) . . . . . . 1·50 1·50

206 Yacht at Dawn

1991. Around the World Yacht Race. Sheet 120 × 103 mm containing T **206** and similar vert designs. Multicoloured.

MS1129 1p. Type **206**; 1p. Yacht in the morning; 1p. Yacht at midday; 1p. Yacht in the evening; 1p. Yacht at night . . . . 6·75 7·50

207 Fishes in the Sea **208** Tonga Temple

1991. Heilala Week. Multicoloured.

1130 42s. Type **207** 70 55
1131 57s. Island and yacht . . . 90 65
1132 2p. Pile of fruit . . . . . . 2·75 3·50
1133 3p. Turtle on beach . . . . 3·50 4·00

1991. Centenary of Church of Latter Day Saints in Tonga. Multicoloured.

1134 42s. Type **208** . . . . . . 1·10 1·10
1135 57s. Temple at night . . . . 1·40 1·40

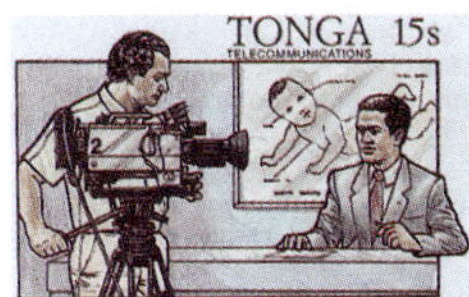

209 Making T.V. Childcare Programme

1991. Telecommunications in Tonga. Mult.

1136 15s. Type **209** 35 45
1137 15s. T.V. satellite 35 45
1138 15s. Mothers watching programme 35 45
1139 32s. Man on telephone and woman with computer . . 65 75
1140 32s. Telecommunications satellite 65 75
1141 32s. Overseas customer on telephone 65 75
1142 42s. Sinking coaster . . . . 1·10 1·25
1143 42s. Coastguard controller 1·10 1·25
1144 42s. Maritime rescue . . . . 1·10 1·25
1145 57s. Weather satellite above Southern Hemisphere . . 1·25 1·40
1146 57s. Meteorologists collecting data . . . . . 1·25 1·40
1147 57s. T.V. weather map and storm . . . . 1·25 1·40

210 Women's Rowing Eight

1991. "Siu'a'alo" Rowing Festival. Mult.

1148 42s. Type **210** 85 45
1149 57s. Longboat . . . . . . 1·00 55
1150 1p. Outrigger canoe . . . . 2·00 2·00
1151 2p. Stern of fautasi (large canoe) . . . . 3·25 4·25
1152 2p. Bow of fautasi . . . . 3·25 4·25

Nos. 1151/2 were printed together, se-tenant, forming a composite design.

211 Turtles pulling Santa's Sledge

1991. Christmas. Multicoloured.

1153 32s. Type **211** 85 35
1154 42s. Santa Claus on roof of fala (Tongan house) . . . 95 45
1155 57s. Family opening presents 1·10 60
1156 3p.50 Family waving goodbye to Santa . . . . 6·50 8·50

212 "Pangai" (patrol boat) **214** Columbus and Signature

1991. Royal Tongan Defence Force. Mult.

1157 42s. Type **212** . . . . . . 1·00 1·00
1158 42s. Marine in battle dress 1·00 1·00
1159 57s. Tonga Royal Guards 1·25 1·25
1160 57s. Raising the ensign on "Neiafu" (patrol boat) . . 1·25 1·25
1161 2p. "Savea" (patrol boat) (horiz) . . . . 3·00 3·75
1162 2p. King Taufa'ahau Tupou IV inspecting parade (horiz) . . . . 3·00 3·75

1992. No. 1007 surch **1s**.

1163 1s. on 20s. White-tailed damselfish 65 85

1992. 500th Anniv of Discovery of America by Columbus. Sheet 119 × 109 mm containing T **214**; and similar vert designs. Multicoloured.

MS1164 57s. Type **214**; 57s. Monastery of Santa Maria de la Chevas; 57s. Obverse and reverse of coin of Ferdinand and Isabella; 57s. Spain commemorative stamps of 1930; 57s. Compass and astrolabe; 57s. Model of "Santa Maria"; 57s. Sketch map and signature; 57s. 15th-century woodcut of Columbus arriving in New World; 57s. Lucayan artefacts and parrot; 57s. Pineapple, bird pendant and Indian nose ring; 57s. Columbus reporting to Spanish Court; 57s. Medal showing Columbus and signature . . . . 24·00 26·00

215 U.S.S. "Arizona" under attack, Pearl Harbor, 1941

1992. 50th Anniv of Outbreak of Pacific War. Multicoloured.

1165 42s. Type **215** . . . . . . 1·60 1·60
1166 42s. Japanese invasion of the Philippines . . . . . 1·60 1·60
1167 42s. U.S. landings in the Gilbert Islands . . . . . 1·60 1·60
1168 42s. Landing on Iwo Jima 1·60 1·60
1169 42s. Admiral Nimitz and Battle of Midway map . . 1·60 1·60
1170 42s. General MacArthur and liberation of Philippines map . . . . 1·60 1·60
1171 42s. Lt-Gen. Holland Smith and map of landings on Saipan and Tinian . . . . 1·60 1·60
1172 42s. Major-Gen. Curtis Lemay and bombing of Japan map . . . . 1·60 1·60
1173 42s. Japanese Mitsubishi A6M Zero-Sen . . . . . 1·60 1·60
1174 42s. Douglas SBD Dauntless 1·60 1·60
1175 42s. Grumman FM-2 Wildcat . . . . 1·60 1·60
1176 42s. Supermarine Seafire Mk III . . . . 1·60 1·60

Nos. 1165/76 were printed togther, se-tenant, forming a composite design.

216 Boxing **217** King Taufa'ahau Taupou IV and Queen Halaevalu

1992. Olympic Games, Barcelona. Mult.

1177 42s. Type **216** 75 50
1178 57s. Diving 95 55
1179 1p.50 Tennis . . . . 4·00 4·25
1180 3p. Cycling . . . . 6·00 6·50

1992. 25th Anniv of the Coronation of King Tupou IV.

1181 **217** 45s. multicoloured . . . 75 45
1182 – 80s. multicoloured . . . 1·50 1·75
1183 – 80s. black and brown . . 1·50 1·75
1184 – 80s. multicoloured . . . 1·50 1·75
1185 – 2p. multicoloured . . . 3·50 4·00

DESIGNS—48 × 35 mm: No. 1182, King Tupou IV and Crown; 1183, Extract from Investiture ceremony; 1184, King Tupou IV and 1967 Coronation 2p. commemorative; 1185, As Type **217** but larger.

Nos. 1181/5 show the King's first name incorrectly spelt as "Tauf'ahau".

1992. No. 1095 surch **45s 45s**.

1186 45s. on 32s. Powder-blue surgeonfish . . . . 3·75 1·50

1992. Nos. 1121/4 surch **60**.

1187 60s. on 42s. Safety in cars (English inscr) . . . . . 3·50 3·50
1188 60s. on 42s. Safety on bikes (English inscr) . . . . . 3·50 3·50
1189 60s. on 42s. As No. 1187 (Tongan inscr) . . . . . 3·50 3·50
1190 60s. on 42s. As No. 1188 (Tongan inscr) . . . . . 3·50 3·50

220 Bats flying Home **222** Tonga Flag and Rotary Emblem (25th anniv of Rotary International in Tonga)

221 Tongan Pearls

1992. Sacred Bats of Kolovai. Multicoloured.

1191 60s. Type **220** . . . . . . 1·60 1·75
1192 60s. Tongan fruit bat . . . 1·60 1·75
1193 60s. Bats alighting on branches . . . . 1·60 1·75
1194 60s. Bats hanging from tree 1·60 1·75
1195 60s. Tongan fruit bat in tree 1·60 1·75

Nos. 1191/5 were printed together, se-tenant, forming a composite design.

1992. Christmas. Multicoloured.

1197 60s. Type **221** 70 65
1198 80s. Reef fish 90 80
1199 2p. Pacific orchids . . . . . 4·25 5·00
1200 3p. Red shining parrots from Eua . . . . 5·50 7·00

1992. Anniversaries and Events.

1201 **222** 60s. multicoloured . . . 1·00 65
1202 – 80s. multicoloured . . . 1·25 90
1203 – 1p.50 violet, lilac & black . . . . 2·75 3·75
1204 – 3p.50 multicoloured . . 5·50 7·00

DESIGNS: 80s. Pres. Kennedy and Peace Corps emblem (25th anniv of Peace Corps in Tonga); 1p.50, F.A.O. and W.H.O. emblems (International Conference); 3p.50, Globe and Rotary Foundation emblem (75th anniv of Rotary Foundation).

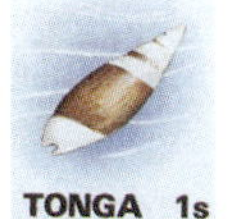

223 Mother and Child **226** Chaste Mitre

224 Anti-smoking and Anti-drugs Symbols with Healthy Food (½-size illustration)

1993. Family Planning.

1205 **223** 15s. black, blue and mauve (English inscr) 40 70
1206 – 15s. black, blue and mauve (Tongan inscr) 40 70
1207 – 45s. black, yellow and green (English inscr) 90 1·00
1208 – 45s. black, yellow and green (Tongan inscr) 90 1·00
1209 – 60s. black, red and yellow (English inscr) 1·90 2·25
1210 – 60s. black, red and yellow (Tongan inscr) 1·90 2·25
1211 – 2p. black, yellow & orange (English inscr) 4·25 4·75
1212 – 2p. black, yellow & orange (Tongan inscr) 4·25 4·75

DESIGNS: 45s. Child on bike; 60s. Girl with cats; 2p. Old man and boy playing chess.

1993. Health and Fitness Campaign. Mult.

1213 60s. Type **224** . . . . . . 1·25 90
1214 80s. Anti-smoking symbol and weight training . . . 1·60 1·10
1215 1p.50 Anti-drugs symbol and water sports . . . . 2·75 3·50
1216 2p.50 Healthy food with cyclist and jogger . . . . 5·00 6·50

1993. Nos. 1001 and 1087 surch.

1217 10s. on 2s. "Porites sp." . . 60·00 15·00
1217a 20s. on 4s. Lionfish £400

1993. As Nos. 867, 872, 875, 877, 999, 1002, 1005, 1007, 1013/16 and 1017a, some with new face values, redrawn as in T **226** with species inscr at foot. Multicoloured.

1218 1s. Type **226** 25 80
1219 3s. Red squirrelfish . . . . 40 1·00
1220 5s. Green map cowrie . . . 40 80
1221a 10s. Bubble cone 40 60
1223a 20s. White-tailed damselfish 60 70
1225a 45s. Giant spider conch (as No. 877) 70 70
1227a 60s. Princely cone (as No. 875) . . . . 1·00 1·00
1229a 80s. Lionfish (as No. 872) 1·00 1·00
1230 1p. "Chelonia mydas" (turtle) . . . . 1·00 1·40
1231 2p. "Birgus latro" (crab) 1·75 2·75
1232 3p. Rose-branch murex . . 2·50 4·00
1233 5p. Humpback whale (as No. 1014) . . . . . . 5·00 7·50
1234 10p. Variegated shark . . . 22·00 23·00

Nos. 1218/29 are 19 × 22 mm, Nos. 1230/3 are 40 × 28 mm and No. 1234, 28 × 40 mm.

For 1 to 10p. with species inscription at top left, see Nos. 1345/9.

227 Fire Brigade Badge

1993. 25th Annivs of Police Training College and Fire Service. Multicoloured.

1235 45s. Type **227** . . . . . . 1·50 1·75
1236 45s. Police badge and van 1·50 1·75
1237 60s. Police band . . . . . 1·75 2·00
1238 60s. Fire engine at fire . . . 1·75 2·00
1239 2p. Fire engine at station . . 4·00 5·00
1240 2p. Policeman and dog handler . . . . 4·00 5·00

228 Old Map of Islands

229 King Taufa'ahau Tupou IV and Musical Instruments

1993. 300th Anniv of Abel Tasman's Discovery of Eua. Multicoloured.

1241 30s. Type **228** 80 55
1242 60s. "Heemskirk" and "Zeehaan" at sea . . . . 1·25 85
1243 80s. Tongan canoes welcoming ships . . . . 1·60 1·25
1244 3p.50 Tasman landing on Eua . . . . 6·00 8·00

1993. 75th Birthday of King Taufa'ahau Tupou IV. Multicoloured.

1245 45s. Type **229** 60 45
1246 80s. King Tupou IV and sporting events . . . . . 1·00 1·40
1247 80s. King Tupou IV and ancient landmarks . . . . 1·00 1·40
1248 80s. King Tupou IV and Royal Palace . . . . . . 1·00 1·40
1249 2p. As Type **229** but larger 2·50 3·25

Nos. 1246/9 are larger, 38½ × 51 mm.

230 Christmas Feast

231 "Land of Sun, Sea and Sand" (Kiley and Peter Moala)

1993. Christmas. Multicoloured.

1250 60s. Type **230** 90 60
1251 80s. Firing home-made cannon . . . . 1·25 80
1252 1p.50 Band playing carols 2·50 3·25
1253 3p. Going to church . . . . 5·00 6·00

1993. Winners of Children's Painting Competition.

1254 **231** 10s. multicoloured . . . 30 50
1255 – 10s. multicoloured . . . 30 50
1256 – 10s. multicoloured . . . 30 50
1257 – 10s. multicoloured . . . 30 50
1258 – 10s. black and grey . . . 30 50
1259 – 10s. black and grey . . . 30 50
1260 **231** 80s. multicoloured . . . 1·40 1·60
1261 – 80s. multicoloured . . . 1·40 1·60
1262 – 80s. multicoloured . . . 1·40 1·60
1263 – 80s. multicoloured . . . 1·40 1·60
1264 – 80s. multicoloured . . . 1·40 1·60
1265 – 80s. multicoloured . . . 1·40 1·60

DESIGNS: Nos. 1255 and 1261, "Maui, Fisher God of Tonga" (Kiley and Peter Moala); 1256 and 1262, "Traditional Island Transport" (Kiley and Peter Moala); 1257 and 1263, "Young Girl making Kava" (Pulotu Pole'o); 1258 and 1264, "Maui and his Hook" (Salome Tapou); 1259 and 1265, "Communications in the South Pacific" (Fe'ofa'aki Taufa).

232 Boy holding Cockerel

1994. Animal Welfare. Sheet 122 × 100 mm, containing T **232** and similar vert designs. Multicoloured.

MS1266 60s. Type **232**; 60s. Girl with butterfly; 60s. Dog and puppies; 60s. Boy with puppy; 80s. Boy holding puppy; 80s. Girl holding cat . . . . 6·00 7·00

233 Tiger Shark

1994. Game Fishing. Multicoloured.

1267 60s. Type **233** . . . . . . 1·10 85
1268 80s. Dolphin (fish) . . . . 1·50 1·10
1269 1p.50 Yellow-finned tuna . . 2·75 3·50
1270 2p.50 Blue marlin . . . . . 3·50 4·50

234 Hands holding World Cup

1994. World Cup Football Championship, U.S.A. Multicoloured.

1271 80s. Type **234** . . . . . . 1·50 1·50
1272 80s. Player's legs . . . . . 1·50 1·50
1273 2p. German player (black shorts) . . . . 3·25 4·00
1274 2p. American player . . . . 3·25 4·00

235 Policewoman

1994. Pan Pacific and South East Asia Women's Association Conference, Tonga. Multicoloured.

1275 45s. Type **235** . . . . . . 1·50 1·50
1276 45s. Woman barrister . . . 1·50 1·50
1277 2p.50 Nurse . . . . 4·25 4·75
1278 2p.50 Woman doctor . . . 4·25 4·75

1994. Christmas. No. **MS**1266 optd **MERRY CHRISTMAS** or equivalent in Tongan.

MS1279 60s. Type **232**; 60s. Girl with butterfly; 60s. Dog and puppies; 60s. Boy with puppy; 80s. Boy holding puppy; 80s. Girl holding cat . . . . 5·00 6·00

The 60s. in the centre of the bottom row (dog and puppies) is overprinted "KILISIMASI FIEFIA".

1994. Visit South Pacific Year '95 (1st issue). No. 1204 surch **VISIT SOUTH PACIFIC YEAR '95 60** and emblem.

1280 60s. on 3p.50 multicoloured 1·25 1·25

See also Nos. 1297/1308.

1994. 25th Anniv of Tongan Self-adhesive Stamps.

(a) Various previous self-adhesive designs, some in smaller size, with new values.

1281 **128** 10s. black and yellow (21 × 9 mm) (postage) 25 40
1282 **124** 60s. black, grey and brown . . . . 1·50 2·00
1283 – 60s. multicoloured (as Nos. O214/15) . . . . 1·50 2·00
1284 **109** 25s. multicoloured (27 × 36 mm) (air) . . . 1·50 2·00

(b) As Nos. 915/18, but new face value and inscr "SELF-ADHESIVE ANNIVERSARY 1969–1994".

1285 **168** 45s. black, pink and brown 75 85
1286 – 45s. black, lilac and brown (as No. 916) . . 75 85
1287 – 45s. black, yellow and brown (as No. 917) . . 1·25 1·50
1288 – 45s. mult (as No. 918) . . 3·00 4·00

(c) Hologram design, 39 × 29 mm, showing "Tongastar 1" satellite.

1289 – 2p. multicoloured . . . . 6·50 7·50

238 Farmer, Produce and Emblem

1995. 50th Anniv of F.A.O.

1290 **238** 5p. multicoloured . . . 11·00 11·00

239 Polynesian Girl with Bicycle on Beach

1995. 25th Anniv of Tonga's Entry into Commonwealth. Children with Bicycles. Mult.

1291 45s. Type **239** 75 55
1292 60s. Children and skyscrapers, Hong Kong 90 60
1293 80s. Boy in African village 1·25 80
1294 2p. Indian boy and palace 2·75 3·75
1295 2p.50 English children and village church . . . . . . 3·25 4·00

240 Three Players running with Ball

242 Soldier on Scrambling Net

1995. World Cup Rugby Championship, South Africa. Two sheets, each 84 × 117 mm, containing T **240** and similar vert designs.

MS1296 (a) 80s. × 2 Type **240**; 80s. × 2 Two players running with ball. (b) 2p. × 2 Player making pass; 2p. × 2 Player receiving pass.
Set of 2 sheets . . . . 15·00 16·00

The miniature sheets contain two of each design.

1995. Visit South Pacific Year '95 (2nd issue). (a) Nos. 1149/52, but inscr "VISIT SOUTH PACIFIC YEAR '95", optd or surch **WHERE TIME BEGINS** and emblem.

1297 60s. on 57s. Longboat . . . 75 60
1298 80s. on 2p. Stern of fautasi (large canoe) . . . . . . 1·00 1·50
1299 80s. on 2p. Bow of fautasi 1·00 1·50
1300 1p. Outrigger canoe . . . . 1·40 1·75

(b) Nos. 1197/1200 inscr either (A) "WHERE TIME BEGINS" or (B) "THE 21st CENTURY STARTS HERE" and surch **WHERE TIME BEGINS 60** and emblem.

1301 60s. on 60s. Type **221** (A) 75 1·00
1302 60s. on 60s. Type **221** (B) 75 1·00
1303 60s. on 80s. Reef fish (A) . . 75 1·00
1304 60s. on 80s. Reef fish (B) . . 75 1·00
1305 60s. on 2p. Pacific orchids (A) . . . . 75 1·00
1306 60s. on 2p. Pacific orchids (B) . . . . 75 1·00
1307 60s. on 3p. Red shining parrots from Eua (A) . . 75 1·00
1308 60s. on 3p. Red shining parrots from Eua (B) . . 75 1·00

1995. 50th Anniv of End of Second World War in the Pacific.

1309 **242** 60s. yellow, black & blue 1·25 1·50
1310 – 60s. yellow, black & blue 1·25 1·50
1311 – 60s. yellow, black & blue 1·25 1·50
1312 – 60s. multicoloured . . . 1·25 1·50
1313 – 60s. multicoloured . . . 1·25 1·50
1314 **242** 80s. yellow, black and red . . . . 1·25 1·50
1315 – 80s. yellow, black and red . . . . 1·25 1·50
1316 – 80s. yellow, black and red . . . . 1·25 1·50
1317 – 80s. multicoloured . . . 1·25 1·50
1318 – 80s. multicoloured . . . 1·25 1·50

DESIGNS: Nos. 1310 and 1315, U.S.S. "Nevada" (battleship) with troops in foreground; 1311 and 1316, U.S.S. "West Virginia" (battleship) and rear of landing craft; 1312 and 1317, U.S.S. "Idaho" (battleship) and front of landing craft; 1313 and 1318, Map of South-east Asia and Pacific.

Nos. 1309/18 were printed together, se-tenant, in sheetlets of 10 with the horizontal strips of 5 forming the same composite design.

243 1995 Commonwealth 45s. Stamp and Exhibition Emblem

1995. "Singapore '95" International Stamp Exhibition. Multicoloured.

1319 45s. Type **243** . . . . . . 1·00 1·25
1320 60s. 1995 Commonwealth 60s. stamp and emblem 1·00 1·25

245 Holocaust Victims

1995. 50th Anniv of United Nations and End of Second World War.

1323 **245** 60s. multicoloured . . . 1·00 1·25
1324 – 60s. black and blue . . . 1·00 1·25
1325 – 60s. multicoloured . . . 1·00 1·25
1326 – 80s. multicoloured . . . 1·00 1·25
1327 – 80s. blue and black . . . 1·00 1·25
1328 – 80s. multicoloured . . . 1·00 1·25

DESIGNS—As T **245**: No. 1325, Children of Holocaust survivors with balloons; 1326, Atomic explosion, Hiroshima; 1328, U.S. Space Shuttle. 23 × 35 mm: Nos. 1324 and 1327, U.N. anniversary emblem.

246 "Calanthe triplicata"

249 Running

247 Humpback Whale

1995. Greetings Stamps. Orchids. Inscribed either "MERRY CHRISTMAS" (A) or "A HAPPY 1996" (B). Multicoloured.

1329 20s. Type **246** (A) 50 50
1330 45s. "Spathoglottis plicata" (A) 75 75
1331 45s. As No. 1330 (B) . . . 75 75
1332 60s. "Dendrobium platygastrium" (A) . . . 90 90
1333 60s. As No. 1332 (B) . . . 90 90
1334 80s. "Goodyera rubicunda" (B) . . . . 1·25 1·25
1335 2p. "Dendrobium toki" (B) 2·75 3·25
1336 2p.50 "Phaius tankervillae" (A) . . . . 3·50 4·00

1996. Endangered Species. Humpback Whale. Multicoloured.

1337 45s. Type **247** . . . . . . 1·40 75
1338 60s. Whale and calf . . . . 1·75 80
1339 1p.50 Whale's tail and white-throated storm petrels . . . . 3·25 3·75
1340 2p.50 Whale breaking surface . . . . 4·75 6·00

248 Rats and Top Left Quarter of Clock Face

1996. Chinese New Year ("Year of the Rat"). Sheets, 127 × 85 mm, containing T **248** and similar horiz designs showing rats and quarter segments of clock face. Multicoloured.

MS1341 10s. Type **248**; 10s. Top right quarter; 10s. Bottom left quarter; 10s. Bottom right quarter 75 1·00
MS1342 20s. Type **248**; 20s. Top right quarter; 20s. Bottom left quarter; 20s. Bottom right quarter 1·50 1·75
MS1343 45s. Type **248**; 45s. Top right quarter; 45s. Bottom left quarter; 45s. Bottom right quarter 3·00 3·50
MS1344 60s. Type **248**; 60s. Top right quarter; 60s. Bottom left quarter; 60s. Bottom right quarter 4·00 4·50

1996. Multicoloured designs as Nos. 1230/4, but redrawn with species inscriptions at top left.

1345 1p. "Chelonia mydas" (turtle) . . . . 3·25 2·50
1346 2p. "Birgus latro" (crab) . . 4·75 4·50
1347 3p. Rose branch murex . . 5·50 6·00
1348 5p. Humpback whale . . . 12·00 12·00
1349 10p. Variegated shark (vert) 20·00 22·00

1996. Centennial Olympic Games, Atlanta. Ancient Greek and Modern Athletes. Multicoloured.

1350 45s. Type **249** 90 65
1351 80s. Throwing the discus . . 1·50 1·25
1352 2p. Throwing the javelin . . 4·00 4·50
1353 3p. Equestrian dressage . . 5·50 6·50

250 Aspects of Prehistoric Life

1996. 13th Congress of International Union of Prehistoric and Protohistoric Sciences, Forli, Italy. Multicoloured.

1354 1p. Type **250** . . . . 1·75 2·25
1355 1p. Aspects of Egyptian, Greek and Roman civilisations . . . . 1·75 2·25

251 "Virgin and Child" (Sassoferrato)

1996. Christmas. Religious Paintings. Mult.

1356 20s. Type **251** 45 45
1357 60s. "Adoration of the Shepherds" (Murillo) . . 1·10 75
1358 80s. "Virgin and Child" (Delaroche) . . . . . . 1·40 1·10
1359 3p. "Adoration of the Shepherds" (Champaigne) 4·50 6·00

252 Athletics and Rugby

1996. 50th Anniv of UNICEF Children's Sports. Multicoloured.

1360 80s. Type **252** . . . . . . 1·40 1·75
1361 80s. Tennis . . . . 1·40 1·75
1362 80s. Cycling . . . . 1·40 1·75

Nos. 1360/2 were printed together, se-tenant, forming a composite design.

253 Queen Halaevalu Mata'aho and Flag

1996. 70th Birthday of Queen Halaevalu Mata'aho. Multicoloured.

1363 60s. Type **253** . . . . . . 1·00 65
1364 2p. Queen and obverse (portrait) of commemorative coin . . . 3·25 4·00
1365 2p. Queen and reverse (arms) of commemorative coin . . . . 3·25 4·00

254 Globe, the Haamonga and Kao Island

1996. "Towards the Millennium". Multicoloured.

1366 80s. Type **254** . . . . . . 1·50 1·75
1367 80s. Mount Talau, Royal Palace and satellite . . . 1·50 1·75
1368 2p. Type **254** . . . . 3·25 3·75
1369 2p. As No. 1367 . . . . . 3·25 3·75

1997. Chinese New Year ("Year of the Ox"). Sheet 126×85 mm, containing horiz designs as T **248**, showing ox and quarter segments of clock face. Multicoloured.

MS1370 60s. Top left quarter; 60s. Top right quarter; 80s. Bottom left quarter; 2p. Bottom right quarter 5·50 6·50

1997. Nos. 1235/40 surch.

1371 10s. on 45s. Type **227** . . . 2·75 2·50
1372 10s. on 45s. Police badge and van . . . . 2·75 2·50
1373 10s. on 60s. Police band . . 2·75 2·50
1374 10s. on 60s. Fire engine at fire . . . . 2·75 2·50
1375 20s. on 2p. Fire engine at station . . . . 3·25 3·00
1376 20s. on 2p. Policeman and dog handler . . . . . . 3·25 3·00

1997. Tongan Medal Winner at Atlanta Olympic Games. Nos. 1350/3 surch **A SILVER FOR TONGA**.

1378 10s. on 45s. Type **249** . . . 50 60
1379 10s. on 80s. Throwing the discus 50 60
1380 10s. on 2p. Throwing the javelin 50 60
1381 3p. Equestrian dressage . . 5·50 6·00

258 Captain James Wilson and "Duff" (full-rigged missionary ship)

1997. Birth Bicentenary of King George I and Bicentenary of Christianity in Tonga (1st issue). Multicoloured.

1382 10s. Type **258** . . . . . . 2·75 2·75
1383 10s. King George Tupou I 85 85
1384 10s. Missionaries landing at Tongatapu . . . . 1·50 1·50
1385 10s. Missionaries and Tongans . . . . 1·50 1·50
1386 60s. Type **258** . . . . . . 1·50 1·50
1387 60s. As No. 1384 . . . . . 1·50 1·50
1388 60s. As No. 1385 . . . . . 1·50 1·50
1389 80s. Type **258** . . . . . . 1·50 1·50
1390 80s. As No. 1384 . . . . . 1·50 1·50
1391 80s. As No. 1385 . . . . . 1·50 1·50

For 10s. (value as Nos. 1382/5, but smaller, 28×18 mm), see Nos. 1405/8.

259 Pacific Swallow

1997. "Pacific '97" International Stamp Exhibition, San Francisco. Sheet 84×110 mm.

MS1392 **259** 2p. multicoloured 3·00 4·00

260 Children and School Building

1997. 50th Anniv of Tonga High School. Mult.

1393 20s. Type **260** 55 55
1394 60s. Athletic team . . . . . 1·10 75
1395 80s. School band . . . . . 1·50 1·00
1396 3p.50 Athletics meeting . . 4·25 6·50

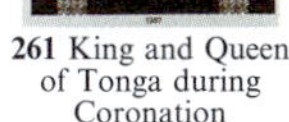

261 King and Queen of Tonga during Coronation

262 "Lenzites elegans"

1997. King and Queen of Tonga's Golden Wedding and 30th Anniv of the Coronation. Multicoloured. (a) Size 23×34 mm.

1397 10s. Type **261** . . . . . . 1·25 1·25
1398 10s. Moment of Crowning and procession . . . . . 1·25 1·25
1399 10s. King and Queen of Tonga . . . . 1·25 1·25
1400 45s. Royal Crown . . . . . 1·50 1·50

(b) Size 50×37 mm.

1401 60s. As T **261** . . . . . . 1·75 1·75
1402 60s. As No. 1398 . . . . . 1·75 1·75
1403 60s. As No. 1399 . . . . . 1·75 1·75
1404 2p. As No. 1400 . . . . . 3·50 4·25

1997. Birth Bicentenary of King George I and Bicentenary of Christianity in Tonga (2nd issue). As Nos. 1382/5, but smaller, 28×18 mm.

1405 10s. Type **258** 80 80
1406 10s. As No. 1384 . . . . . 80 80
1407 10s. As No. 1385 . . . . . 80 80
1408 10s. As No. 1383 . . . . . 50 50

1997. Fungi. Multicoloured. (a) Size 18×28 mm.

1409 10s. Type **262** . . . . . . 1·25 1·25
1410 10s. "Marasmiellus semiustus" . . . . 1·25 1·25
1411 10s. "Aseroe rubra" . . . . 1·25 1·25
1412 10s. "Podoscypha involuta" 1·25 1·25
1413 10s. "Microporus xanthopus" . . . . 1·25 1·25
1414 10s. "Lentinus tuber-regium" . . . . 1·25 1·25

(b) Size 28×42 mm.

1415 20s. Type **262** . . . . . . 1·75 1·75
1416 20s. As No. 1410 . . . . . 1·75 1·75
1417 60s. As No. 1411 . . . . . 2·00 2·00
1418 60s. As No. 1412 . . . . . 2·00 2·00
1419 2p. As No. 1413 . . . . . 3·00 3·00
1420 2p. As No. 1414 . . . . . 3·00 3·00

Nos. 1409/14 were printed together, se-tenant, with the backgrounds forming a composite design.

1998. Diana, Princess of Wales Commemoration. Sheet, 145×170 mm, containing vert designs as T **194** of St. Helena. Multicoloured.

MS1421 10s. Princess Diana, 1992; 80s. Wearing white jacket, 1992; 1p. Wearing black jacket, 1991; 2p.50, Wearing white top, 1993 (sold at 4p.40+50s. charity premium) . . . . 4·50 4·75

263 King Taufa'ahua Tupou IV

264 White Tern ("Fairy Tern")

1998. 80th Birthday of King Taufa'ahua Tupou IV.

1422 **263** 2p.70 multicoloured . . 5·00 5·50

MS1423 80×90 mm. 2p.70, No. 1422 2p.70, No. 276 of Niuafo'ou . . . . 6·00 7·00

1998. Chinese New Year ("Year of the Tiger"). Sheet, 126×85 mm, containing horiz designs as T **248**, each showing a tiger and quarter segment of clock face. Multicoloured.

MS1424 55s. Top left quarter; 80s. Top right quarter; 1p. Bottom left quarter; 1p. Bottom right quarter 3·50 4·00

1998. Birds. Multicoloured.

1425 5s. Type **264** 10 10
1426 10s. Tongan whistler 10 10
1427 15s. Barn owl 10 15
1428 20s. Purple swamphen . . . 15 20
1429 30s. Red-footed booby . . . 20 25
1430 40s. Buff-banded rail ("Banded Rail") (horiz) 30 35
1431 50s. Pacific marsh harrier ("Swamp Harrier") (horiz) 35 40
1432 55s. Blue-crowned lorikeet 40 45
1433 60s. Great frigate bird . . . 45 50
1434 70s. Friendly quail dover ("Friendly Ground Dove") (horiz) 50 55
1435 80s. Red-tailed tropic bird 60 65
1436 1p. Red shining parrot . . . 70 75
1437 2p. Pacific pigeon . . . . . 1·40 1·50
1438 3p. Pacific golden plover (horiz) . . . . 2·10 2·25
1439 5p. Polynesian scrub hen ("Tongan Megapode") (horiz) . . . . 3·50 3·75

265 "Chaetodon pelewensis"

1998. International Year of the Ocean. Mult.

1440 10s. Type **265** 40 50
1441 55s. "Chaetodon lunula" . . 1·00 1·10
1442 1p. "Chaetodon ephippium" 1·40 2·00

266 Angel (inscr in Tongan)

1998. Christmas. Multicoloured.

1443 10s. Type **266** 50 40
1444 80s. Angel (inscr in English) 2·00 1·00
1445 1p. Boy with candle (inscr in Tongan) . . . . 2·25 1·75
1446 1p.60 Girl holding candle (inscr in English) . . . . 3·00 3·50

267 Rabbit and Segment of Flower

1999. Chinese New Year ("Year of the Rabbit"). Sheet 126×85 mm, containing horiz designs as T **267**, showing rabbits and segments of flower. Multicoloured.

MS1447 10s. Three rabbits; 55s. Rabbit eating leaf; 80s. Type **267**; 1p. Rabbit running . . . . . 2·00 2·50

268 "Heemskerk" (Tasman), 1643

1999. Early Explorers. Multicoloured.

1448 55s. Type **268** . . . . . . 1·10 60
1449 80s. "L'Astrolabe" (La Perouse), 1788 . . . . . 1·60 1·00
1450 1p. H.M.S. "Bounty" (Bligh), 1789 . . . . . . 2·00 1·75
1451 2p.50 H.M.S. "Resolution" (Cook), 1777 . . . . . . 3·50 4·00

MS1452 118×60 mm. No. 1451 3·50 4·00

269 Neiafu

1999. Scenic Views of Vava'u. Multicoloured.

1453 10s. Type **269** 45 40
1454 55s. Yachts at Port of Refuge 85 50
1455 80s. Port of Refuge from the air . . . . 1·40 80
1456 1p. Sunset at Neiafu . . . . 1·50 1·25
1457 2p.50 Mounu Island . . . . 3·00 4·25

270 "Fagraea berteroana"

1999. Fragrant Flowers. Multicoloured.

1458 10s. Type **270** 25 25
1459 80s. "Garcinia pseudoguttifera" 80 65
1460 1p. "Phaleria disperma" (vert) . . . . 1·00 1·25
1461 2p.50 "Gardenia taitensis" (vert) . . . . 2·40 3·25

271 Crowd and Trilith at Haamonga

1999. New Millennium (1st issue). Multicoloured.
1462 55s. Type **271** . . . . . . 80 1·10
1463 80s. Crowd and doves . . . 1·10 1·40
1464 1p. Tongans watching sunrise . . . . 1·25 1·60
1465 2p.50 King Taufa'ahau Tupou IV, dove and Millennium emblem . . . 1·90 2·25
Nos. 1462/5 were printed together, se-tenant, with the backgrounds forming a composite design.

272 Dove and Heilala (flowers)

2000. New Millennium (2nd issue). Circular designs incorporating a clock face and inscribed "FIRST TO SEE THE MILLENNIUM". Multicoloured.
1466 10s. Type **272** 35 35
1467 1p. Haamonga Arch . . . . 1·40 1·40
1468 2p.50 Kalia (traditional canoe) . . . . 3·00 3·25
1469 2p.70 Royal Crown . . . . 3·00 3·25
MS1470 130 × 90 mm. Nos. 1468/9 6·00 6·50

273 Dragon

2000. Chinese New Year ("Year of the Dragon"). Sheet, 126 × 85 mm, containing T **273** and similar horiz designs. Multicoloured.
MS1471 10s. Type **273**; 55s. Dragon blowing on sphere; 80s. Dragon on hills; 1p. Sea dragon . . . . . 2·25 2·50

274 Queen Elizabeth the Queen Mother

2000. "The Stamp Show 2000" International Stamp Exhibition, London. Queen Elizabeth the Queen Mother's 100th Birthday. Sheet, 106 × 71 mm, containing T **274** and similar vert design. Multicoloured.
MS1472 1p. Type **274**; 2p.50, Queen Salote Tupou III of Tonga . . 3·50 4·00

275 Launch of Proton RU500 **276** Siulolo Liku (hurdling)

2000. "EXPO 2000" World Stamp Exhibition, Anaheim, U.S.A. Geostationary Orbital Slot Space Programme. Multicoloured.
1473 10s. Type **275** 35 35
1474 1p. LM3 rocket for "Apstar 1" satellite (horiz) . . . . 1·25 1·25
1475 2p.50 "Apstar 1" satellite in orbit (horiz) . . . . . 2·50 3·00
1476 2p.70 "Gorizont" satellite over Tonga (horiz) . . . 2·50 3·00
MS1477 134 × 80 mm. (trapezium). Nos. 1475/6 . . . . 5·00 6·00

2000. Olympic Games, Sydney. Multicoloured.
1478 80s. Type **276** . . . . . . 80 1·00
1479 80s. Paea Wolfgramm (boxing) . . . . 80 1·00
1480 80s. Olympic Torch passing through Tonga (60 × 45 mm) . . . . . . 80 1·00
1481 80s. Mele Hifo Uhi (discus) 80 1·00
1482 80s. Viliami Toutai (weightlifting) . . . . . . 80 1·00
Nos. 1478/82 were printed together, se-tenant, with a composite series of Australian landmarks running along the bottom of each strip.

277 "Education"

2000. 30th Anniv of Tonga's Membership of the Commonwealth. Multicoloured.
1483 10s. Type **277** 25 25
1484 55s. "The Arts" 60 45
1485 80s. "Health" 85 65
1486 2p.70 "Agriculture" . . . . 2·50 3·25

278 Snake

2001. Chinese New Year ("Year of the Snake") and "Hong Kong 2001" Stamp Exhibition. Sheet 125 × 87 mm, containing T **278** and similar horiz designs showing different snakes.
MS1487 10s. multicoloured; 55s. multicoloured; 80s. multicoloured; 1p. multicoloured . . . . . . 2·00 2·50

279 Ma'ulu'ulu Dance

2001. Traditional Tongan Dances. Multicoloured.
1488 10s. Type **279** 20 20
1489 55s. Me'etupaki dance . . . 55 45
1490 80s. Tau'olunga dance . . . 75 65
1491 2p.70 Faha'iula dance . . . 2·25 3·00

280 Fiddler Crab

2001. International Mangrove Environment Day. Multicoloured.
1492 10s. Type **280** 25 25
1493 55s. Spotbill duck ("Black Ducks") and grey mullet (vert) 65 45
1494 80s. Red mangrove and emperor fish (vert) . . . 85 65
1495 1p. Mangrove flowers and reef heron . . . . 1·00 90
1496 2p.70 Mangrove crab . . . 2·50 3·00
MS1497 165 × 75 mm. Nos. 1492/6 4·50 5·00

281 Fisherman catching Sailfish **282** Banana

2001. Game Fishing in Tonga. Multicoloured.
1498 45s. Type **281** 30 35
1499 80s. Blue marlin and fishing launch 60 65
1500 2p.40 Wahoo . . . . 1·75 1·90
1501 2p.60 Dorado . . . . 1·90 2·00

2001. Fruits. Multicoloured. Self-adhesive.
1502 10s. Type **282** 10 10
1503 45s. Coconut 30 35
1504 60s. Pineapple 45 50
1505 80s. Watermelon 60 65
1506 2p.40 Passion fruit . . . . 1·75 1·90
Nos. 1502/6 were printed together, se-tenant, with the surplus self-adhesive paper around each stamp showing a composite design of foliage.

283 *Haliotis ovina* Shell

2001. Shells. Multicoloured.
1507 10s. Type **283** 10 10
1508 80s. *Turbo petholatus* . . . 60 65
1509 1p. *Trochus niloticus* 70 75
1510 2p.70 *Turbo marmoratus* . . 1·90 2·00

2002. Golden Jubilee. Sheet, 162 × 95 mm, containing designs as T **211** of St. Helena.
MS1511 15s. brownish black, rosine and gold; 90s. multicoloured; 1p.20, grey-black, rosine and gold; 1p.40, multicoloured; 2p.25, multicoloured . . . . 4·25 4·50
DESIGNS—HORIZ (as Type **211** of St. Helena)—15s. Princess Elizabeth as a young girl; 90s. Queen Elizabeth in yellow outfit; 1p.20, Queen Elizabeth with Prince Charles and Princess Anne; 1p.40, Queen Elizabeth in evening dress. VERT: (38 × 51 mm)—2p.25, Queen Elizabeth after Annigoni.

284 Horses galloping

2002. Chinese New Year ("Year of the Horse"). Sheet 126 × 89 mm, containing T **284** and similar vert designs. Multicoloured.
MS1512 65s. Type **284**; 80s. Palomino and grey horses; 1p. Chestnut horse rearing; 2p.50 Piebald and bay horses . . . . . 3·50 3·75

285 Surfer and Whale

2002. U.N. Year of Eco Tourism. Multicoloured.
1513 5s. Type **285** 10 10
1514 15s. Tongan girl and rocky coastline 10 15
1515 70s. Tropical fish and tourist beach 50 55
1516 1p.40 Island dancer and Haamonga trilith . . . . 1·00 1·10
1517 2p.25 Tongan man and canoes at sunset . . . . . 1·60 1·75

286 Oyster Farm

2002. Development of Tonga Pearl Industry. Multicoloured.
1518 90s. Type **286** 65 70
1519 1p. Oysters on underwater frame 70 75
1520 1p.20 Tongan girl and pearls 85 90
1521 2p.50 Pearls and island scene . . . . 1·75 1·90
MS1522 Circular (97 mm diameter). Nos. 1520/1. . . . . 4·00 4·25

287 Leaping for Ball

2002. 17th Commonwealth Games, Manchester. Rugby Sevens. Multicoloured.
1523 15s. Type **287** 10 15
1524 30s. Players in a ruck 20 25
1525 90s. Running with ball . . . 65 70
1526 4p. Scoring a try . . . . . 3·00 3·25

288 Woman slitting Pandanus Leaves **289** Red Shining Parrots in Tree Trunk Nest

2002. Weaving. Multicoloured.
1527 30s. Type **288** 20 25
1528 90s. Leaves drying and boy with large baskets 65 70
1529 1p.40 Women weaving baskets . . . . 1·00 1·10
1530 2p.50 Girl weaving basket lid . . . . 1·75 1·90

2002. 10th Anniv of Eua National Park. Red Shining Parrots. Multicoloured.
1531 45s. Type **289** 30 35
1532 1p. Eating fruit 70 75
1533 1p.50 Two parrots on branch . . . . 1·10 1·25
1534 2p.50 Red shining parrot with wings spread . . . . 1·75 1·90

EXPRESS STAMP

E 1 Short-eared Owl in Flight

1990. Air.
E1 **E 1** 10p. black, red and blue 7·00 7·25

OFFICIAL STAMPS

1893. Optd **G.F.B.**
O1 **5** 1d. blue . . . . 10·00 48·00
O2 **6** 2d. blue . . . . 27·00 55·00
O3 **5** 4d. blue . . . . 48·00 95·00
O4 **6** 8d. blue . . . . 90·00 £170
O5 1s. blue £100 £190

1893. Nos. O1/5 variously surch.
O 6 **5** ½d. on 1d. blue . . . . . . 18·00 50·00
O 7 **6** 2½d. on 2d. blue . . . . . 24·00 45·00
O 8 **5** 5d. on 4d. blue . . . . . . 24·00 45·00
O 9 **6** 7½d. on 8d. blue . . . . . 24·00 80·00
O10 10d. on 1s. blue . . . . . 28·00 85·00

1962. Air. Stamps of 1953 and 1961 optd as Nos. 120/7 but with **OFFICIAL AIRMAIL** in addition.
O11 2d. blue . . . . 14·00 6·00
O12 5d. violet . . . . 15·00 6·50
O13 1s. brown . . . . 10·00 3·75
O14 5s. yellow and lilac . . . . £100 60·00
O15 10s. yellow and black . . . 42·00 22·00
O16 £1 yellow, red and blue . . . 70·00 35·00

1963. Air. 1st Polynesian Gold Coinage Commemoration. As No. 138 but additionally inscr "OFFICIAL". 1 koula coin. Diameter 3⅛ in. Imperf.
O17 **B** 15s. black on gold . . . . 7·00 8·00

1965. Air. Surch as Nos. 151/61.
O18 **B** 30s. on 15s. (No. O17) . . 3·25 4·25

1966. Air. Tupou College and Secondary Education Centenary. No. 117 surch **OFFICIAL AIRMAIL** and new value, with commemoration inscr as Nos. 168/73.
O19 10s. on 4d. green 80 35
O20 20s. on 4d. green . . . . . 1·00 50

1967. Air. No. 112 surch **OFFICIAL AIRMAIL ONE PA'ANGA**.
O21 1p. on 5s. yellow and lilac 6·00 2·50

1967. Air. No. 114 surch **OFFICIAL AIRMAIL** and new value.
O22 40s. on £1 yellow, red & blue 60 75
O23 60s. on £1 yellow, red & blue 80 1·00

O24 1p. on £1 yellow, red and blue . . . . 1·10 2·00
O25 2p. on £1 yellow, red and blue . . . . 1·75 2·50

1967. Air. Arrival of U.S. Peace Corps in Tonga. As No. 114, but inperf and background colour changed, surch as Nos. 216/27 but with **Official Airmail** in addition.
O26 30s. on £1 multicoloured . . 50 30
O27 70s. on £1 multicoloured . . 70 90
O28 1p.50 on £1 multicoloured 1·00 1·50

1968. Air. 50th Birthday of King Taufa'ahua IV. No. 207 surch **HIS MAJESTY'S 50th BIRTHDAY OFFICIAL AIRMAIL** and new value.
O29 40s. on 50s. red and blue . . 2·25 70
O30 60s. on 50s. red and blue . . 2·75 1·50
O31 1p. on 50s. red and blue . . 3·75 3·75
O32 2p. on 50s. red and blue . . 7·00 7·50

1968. Air. South Pacific Games Field and Track Trials, Port Moresby, New Guinea. As No. 114 but imperf, background colour changed, surch **Friendly Islands Trials Field & Track South Pacific Games Port Moresby 1969 OFFICIAL AIRMAIL** and value.
O33 20s. on £1 multicoloured . . 20 20
O34 1p. on £1 multicoloured . . 70 1·25

1969. Air. 3rd South Pacific Games, Port Moresby. As Nos. 290/4 surch **OFFICIAL AIRMAIL**.
O35 70s. red, green and turquoise 75 1·40
O36 80s. red, orange and turquoise . . . . 85 1·40

1969. Air. Oil Search. As No. 114 but imperf, background colour changed and optd **1969 OIL SEARCH** and new value.
O37 90s. on £1 multicoloured . . 3·50 4·50
O38 1p.10 on £1 multicoloured 3·50 4·50
No. O37 is additionally optd **OFFICIAL AIRMAIL**.

1969. Air. Royal Visit. As No. 110, but imperf, colour changed, and surch **Royal Visit MARCH 1970 OFFICIAL AIRMAIL** and new value.
O39 75s. on 1s. red and yellow 4·00 3·25
O40 1p. on 1s. red and yellow . . 4·50 3·75
O41 1p.25 on 1s. red and yellow 5·50 5·00

1970. Air. Entry into British Commonwealth. As No. 112, but imperf and surch **Commonwealth Member JUNE 1970 OFFICIAL AIRMAIL** and value.
O42 50s. on 5s. yellow and brown 2·50 1·50
O43 90s. on 5s. yellow and brown 3·50 2·25
O44 1p.50 on 5s. yellow & brown 4·50 4·00

1970. Imperf. Self-adhesive. Colour of "TONGA" given for 6s. to 10s.
O45 **83** 1s. yellow, purple & black 55 75
O46 2s. yellow, blue and black 65 85
O47 3s. yellow, brown & black 65 85
O48 4s. yellow, green and black 65 85
O49 5s. yellow, red and black 70 85
O50 **90** 6s. blue . . . . 80 1·00
O51 7s. mauve . . . . 85 1·10
O52 8s. gold . . . . 95 1·10
O53 9s. red . . . . 1·10 1·25
O54 10s. silver . . . . 1·10 1·25
On the official issues Nos. O45 to O54, the value tablet is black (banana issue) or green (coconut issue). On the postage issues the colour is white.
See also Nos. O82/91.

1970. Air. Centenary of British Red Cross. As No. 102 and 112 but imperf in different colours and surch **Centenary British Red Cross 1870-1970 OFFICIAL AIRMAIL** and value.
O55 30s. on 1½d. green . . . . . 1·75 2·00
O56 80s. on 5s. yellow and brown 4·75 4·50
O57 90s. on 5s. yellow and brown 4·75 4·50

1971. Air. 5th Death Anniv of Queen Salote. As No. 113, but imperf and colour changed surch **OFFICIAL AIRMAIL 1965 IN MEMORIAM 1970** and value.
O58 20s. on 10s. orange . . . . 1·25 80
O59 30s. on 10s. orange . . . . 1·50 1·00
O60 50s. on 10s. orange . . . . 2·75 2·00
O61 2p. on 10s. orange . . . . . 9·00 10·00

1971. Air. Philatokyo '71 Stamp Exhibition, Japan. Nos. O55/7 optd **PHILATOKYO '71** and emblem.
O62 30s. on 5d. green and yellow 90 65
O63 80s. on 5d. green and yellow 1·75 1·75
O64 90s. on 5d. green and yellow 2·00 2·00

1971. Air. As T **96** but inscr "OFFICIAL AIRMAIL".
O65 14s. multicoloured . . . . 2·00 2·25
O65a 17s. multicoloured . . . . 2·25 2·50
O66 21s. multicoloured . . . . 2·25 2·50
O66a 38s. multicoloured . . . . 3·25 3·50

O **13**

1971. Air. 4th South Pacific Games, Tahiti. Imperf. Self-adhesive.
O67 O **13** 50s. multicoloured . . . 60 90
O68 90s. multicoloured . . . 85 1·50
O69 1p.50 multicoloured . . 1·25 1·75

1971. Air. Investiture of Royal Tongan Medal of Merit surch **INVESTITURE 1971 OFFICIAL AIRMAIL**.
O70 **89** 60s. on 3s. multicoloured 80 1·10
O71 80s. on 25s. multicoloured 1·10 1·40
O72 1p.10 on 7s. multicoloured 1·25 1·75

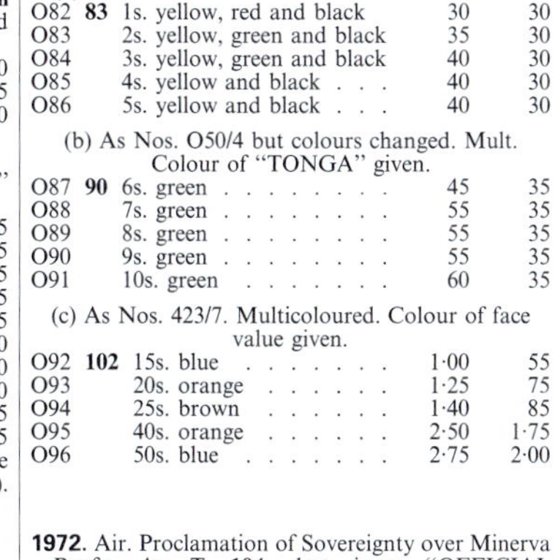

O **15** "UNICEF" and Emblem

1971. Air. 25th Anniv of UNICEF. Imperf. Self-adhesive.
O73 O **15** 70s. multicoloured . . . 1·60 1·75
O74 80s. multicoloured . . . 1·75 2·00
O75 90s. multicoloured . . . 1·90 2·25

1972. Air. Merchant Marine Routes. As T **100** but inscr "OFFICIAL AIRMAIL". Imperf. Self-adhesive.
O76 20s. multicoloured . . . . . 1·25 80
O77 50s. multicoloured . . . . . 2·75 2·50
O78 1p.20 multicoloured . . . . 5·50 7·00
DESIGN: Nos. O76/8, Map of South Pacific and "Aoniu".

1972. Air. 5th Anniv of Coronation. Design similar to T **101**, but inscr "OFFICIAL AIRMAIL".
O79 50s. multicoloured . . . . . 1·00 85
O80 70s. multicoloured . . . . . 1·40 1·25
O81 1p.50 multicoloured . . . . 2·75 3·00
DESIGN—(47 × 57 mm): Nos. O79/81, As Type **101** but with different background.

1972. As Nos. 413/27 but inscr "OFFICIAL POST".
(a) As Nos. 413/17.
O82 **83** 1s. yellow, red and black 30 30
O83 2s. yellow, green and black 35 30
O84 3s. yellow, green and black 40 30
O85 4s. yellow and black . . . 40 30
O86 5s. yellow and black . . . 40 30

(b) As Nos. O50/4 but colours changed. Mult. Colour of "TONGA" given.
O87 **90** 6s. green 45 35
O88 7s. green 55 35
O89 8s. green 55 35
O90 9s. green 55 35
O91 10s. green 60 35

(c) As Nos. 423/7. Multicoloured. Colour of face value given.
O92 **102** 15s. blue . . . . 1·00 55
O93 20s. orange . . . . . . 1·25 75
O94 25s. brown . . . . . . 1·40 85
O95 40s. orange . . . . . . 2·50 1·75
O96 50s. blue . . . . 2·75 2·00

1972. Air. Proclamation of Sovereignty over Minerva Reefs. As T **104**, but inscr "OFFICIAL AIRMAIL".
O97 25s. multicoloured 40 35
O98 75s. multicoloured . . . . . 1·25 1·50
O99 1p.50 multicoloured . . . . 2·50 3·00

1973. Air. Foundation of Bank of Tonga. No. 396 surch **TONGA 1973 ESTABLISHMENT BANK OF TONGA OFFICIAL AIRMAIL**, star and value.
O100 **100** 40s. on 21s. mult . . . 1·50 1·25
O101 85s. on 21s. mult . . . 3·00 3·25
O102 1p.25 on 21s. mult . . . 3·75 5·00

1973. Silver Jubilee of Scouting in Tonga. Nos. O76, O74 and 319 surch or optd.
O103 – 30s. on 20s. mult . . . 10·00 2·75
O104 O **15** 80s. multicoloured . . 25·00 10·00
O105 **89** 1p.40 on 50s. mult . . 35·00 25·00
OVERPRINT AND SURCHARGES: 30s. **SILVER JUBILEE TONGAN SCOUTING 1948-1973**, scout badge and value; 80c. **SILVER JUBILEE 1948-1973** and scout badge; 1p.40, **OFFICIAL AIRMAIL 1948-1973 SILVER JUBILEE TONGAN SCOUTING** and value.

1973. Air. Bicentenary of Capt. Cook's Visit. Design similar to T **107** but inscr "OFFICIAL AIRMAIL".
O106 25s. multicoloured . . . . 3·25 1·50
O107 80s. multicoloured . . . . 8·50 4·50
O108 1p.30 multicoloured . . . . 10·00 7·50
DESIGN—HORIZ (52 × 45 mm): Nos. O106/8, "James Cook" (bulk carrier).

1973. Air. Commonwealth Games, Christchurch. Nos. O67/9 optd **1974 Commonwealth Games Christchurch OFFICIAL AIRMAIL**.
O109 O **13** 50s. multicoloured . . 80 1·10
O110 90s. multicoloured . . 1·40 1·75
O111 1p.50 multicoloured . . 2·00 2·50

O **19** Dove of Peace

1974. Air.
O112 O **19** 7s. green, violet and red 70 30
O113 9s. green, violet & brn 75 35
O114 12s. green, violet & brown 80 85
O115 14s. green, violet & yellow 85 50
O116 17s. multicoloured . . 95 70
O117 29s. multicoloured . . 1·75 1·00
O118 38s. multicoloured . . 2·25 1·25
O119 50s. multicoloured . . 2·75 2·75
O120 75s. multicoloured . . 4·00 4·50

1974. Air. Centenary of U.P.U. As Nos. 488/97 but inscr "OFFICIAL AIRMAIL".
O121 25s. orange, green and black 50 60
O122 35s. yellow, red and black 60 75
O123 70s. orange, blue and black 1·25 2·00
DESIGNS—HORIZ (43 × 40 mm): Nos. O121/3, Letters "UPU".

1974. Air. Tongan Girl Guides. As Nos. 498/507 inscr "OFFICIAL AIRMAIL".
O124 45s. multicoloured . . . . 4·00 2·00
O125 55s. multicoloured . . . . 4·25 2·25
O126 1p. multicoloured . . . . 7·50 5·50
DESIGNS—OVAL (36 × 52 mm): Nos. O124/6, Lady Baden-Powell.

1974. Air. Establishment of Royal Marine Institute. No. 446 surch **OFFICIAL AIRMAIL 80s** and RMI emblem and No. 451 surch **Establishment Royal Marine Institute Official Airmail TONGA TONGA**, RMI emblem and value.
O127 **106** 30s. on 15s. multicoloured . . . . 2·50 1·75
O128 – 35s. on 15s. multicoloured . . . . 2·75 2·00
O129 – 80s. on 17s. multicoloured . . . . 4·25 4·50

1975. Air. South Pacific Forum and Tourism. As T **113**. Imperf. Self-adhesive.
O130 50s. multicoloured . . . . 1·10 1·00
O131 75s. multicoloured . . . . 1·75 1·50
O132 1p.25 multicoloured . . . . 2·50 2·25
DESIGNS—(49 × 43 mm): 50s. Jungle arch; 75s., 1p.25, Sunset scene.

1975. Air. 5th South Pacific Games. As T **114**. Imperf. Self-adhesive.
O133 38s. multicoloured 55 50
O134 75s. multicoloured . . . . 90 1·50
O135 1p.20 multicoloured . . . . 1·60 2·50
DESIGN—OVAL (51 × 27 mm): Nos. O133/5, Runners on track.

O **21** Tongan Monarchs
(⅗-size illustration)

1975. Air. Centenary of Tongan Constitution. Imperf. Self-adhesive.
O136 O **21** 17s. multicoloured . . 65 50
O137 60s. multicoloured . . 1·40 1·75
O138 90s. multicoloured . . 2·00 2·50

1976. Air. First Participation in Olympic Games. As Nos. 558/67 but inscr "OFFICIAL AIRMAIL".
O139 45s. multicoloured . . . . 4·00 1·50
O140 55s. multicoloured . . . . 4·00 1·60
O141 1p. multicoloured . . . . 7·50 7·50
DESIGN—OVAL (36 × 53 mm): Montreal logo.

1976. Air. Bicentenary of American Revolution. As Nos. 568/77 but inscr "OFFICIAL AIRMAIL".
O142 20s. multicoloured 75 50
O143 50s. multicoloured . . . . 1·00 1·50
O144 1p.15 multicoloured . . . . 2·00 3·50

1976. Air. 150th Anniv of Christianity in Tonga.
O145 65s. multicoloured . . . . 2·50 2·75
O146 85s. multicoloured . . . . 2·75 3·50
O147 1p.15 multicoloured . . . . 3·25 4·25
DESIGN—HEXAGONAL (65 × 52 mm): Lifuka Chapel.

1976. Air. Centenary of Treaty of Friendship with Germany.
O148 30s. multicoloured 60 70
O149 60s. multicoloured . . . . 1·40 1·75
O150 1p.25 multicoloured . . . . 2·75 3·50
DESIGN—RECTANGULAR (51 × 47 mm): Text.

1977. Air. Silver Jubilee.
O151 35s. multicoloured 70 40
O152 45s. multicoloured 30 30
O153 1p.10 multicoloured 45 50
DESIGN—57 × 66 mm: Flags of Tonga and the U.K.

1977. Air. 10th Anniv of King's Coronation.
O154 20s. multicoloured 40 45
O155 40s. multicoloured . . . . 80 1·00
O156 80s. multicoloured . . . . 1·75 2·25
DESIGN—SQUARE (50 × 50 mm): 1967 Coronation coin.

1977. Air. Bicent of Capt. Cook's Last Voyage.
O157 20s. multicoloured . . . . 2·75 2·50
O158 55s. on 20s. multicoloured 6·00 6·50
O159 85s. on 20s. multicoloured 8·50 9·00
DESIGN—RECTANGULAR (52 × 46 mm): Text.

1977. Air. Whale Conservation.
O160 45s. multicoloured . . . . 5·50 3·00
O161 65s. multicoloured . . . . 7·50 5·00
O162 85s. multicoloured . . . . 9·00 6·00
DESIGN—HEXAGONAL (66 × 51 mm): Blue whale.

1978. Air. Commonwealth Games, Edmonton.
O163 30s. black, blue and red . . 60 60
O164 60s. black, red and blue . . 1·40 1·75
O165 1p. black, red and blue . . 1·75 2·00
DESIGN—TEAR-DROP (35 × 52 mm): Games emblem.

1978. Air. 60th Birthday of King Taufa'ahau Tupou IV.
O166 26s. black, red and yellow 50 30
O167 85s. black, brown and yellow . . . . 1·40 1·60
O168 90s. black, violet and yellow 1·50 1·60
DESIGN—MEDAL-SHAPED (21 × 45 mm): Portrait of King.

1978. Coil stamps. As Nos. 675/89 but inscr "OFFICIAL POST".
O169 1s. purple and yellow . . . 20 20
O170 2s. brown and yellow . . . 20 20
O171 3s. red and yellow 30 30
O172 4s. brown and yellow . . . 30 30
O173 5s. green and yellow . . . 30 30
O174 6s. brown and green . . . 40 40
O175 7s. black, green and brown 40 40
O176 8s. red, green and brown 40 40
O177 9s. brown and green . . . 40 40
O178 10s. green and brown . . . 40 40
O179 15s. black, brown and green 1·00 1·00
O180 20s. red, brown and green 1·10 1·10
O181 30s. green and brown . . . 1·25 1·50
O182 50s. blue, brown and green 1·50 1·75
O183 1p. violet, brown and green 2·25 2·75

1978. Air. Endangered Wildlife. Multicoloured.
O184 40s. Type **129** . . . . . . 6·00 3·50
O185 50s. Insular flying fox . . . 5·50 3·50
O186 1p.10 Turtle . . . . 7·50 9·00

1979. Air. Decade of Progress. As Nos. 700/9, but inscr "OFFICIAL AIRMAIL".
O187 G 38s. multicoloured . . . 1·00 65
O188 E 74s. multicoloured . . . 1·40 1·50
O189 A 80s. multicoloured . . . 2·00 2·00

1979. Air. Death Centenary of Sir Rowland Hill and 10th Anniv of Tongan Self-adhesive Stamps.
O190 45s. multicoloured 75 60
O191 65s. multicoloured . . . . 1·10 85
O192 80s. multicoloured . . . . 1·25 1·10
DESIGN—HAND SHAPED (45 × 53 mm): 45s. to 80s. Removing self-adhesive stamp from backing paper.

O **22** Blue-crowned Lory (with foliage)

O **23** Blue-crowned Lory (without foliage)

1979. Air. Coil Stamps.
O193 O **22** 5s. multicoloured . . . 50 50
O194 11s. multicoloured . . 55 50
O195 14s. multicoloured . . 55 50
O196 15s. multicoloured . . 60 50
O197 17s. multicoloured . . 60 50
O198 18s. multicoloured . . 60 50
O199 22s. multicoloured . . 70 50
O200 31s. multicoloured . . 75 65
O201 39s. multicoloured . . 90 80
O202 75s. multicoloured . . 1·75 2·75
O203 1p. multicoloured . . . 2·25 3·50

1979. Air. Views as seen through the Lens of a Camera.
O204 35s. multicoloured 55 75
O205 45s. multicoloured 65 85
O206 1p. multicoloured 1·25 2·75
DESIGN: 35s. to 1p. Niuatoputapu and Tafahi.

1980. Air. 125th Anniv of France–Tonga Friendship Treaty.
O207 40s. multicoloured 75 1·00
O208 55s. multicoloured 1·00 1·25
O209 1p.25 multicoloured 2·00 2·75
DESIGN: 40s. to 1p.25, Establishment of the Principle of Religious Freedom in the Pacific Islands.

1980. Air. Olympic Games, Moscow. Nos. O190/2 surch mascot, **1980 OLYMPIC GAMES**, value and emblem.
O210 26s. on 45s. multicoloured 85 85
O211 40s. on 65s. multicoloured 1·40 1·40
O212 1p.10 on 1p. multicoloured 3·50 3·75

1980. No. O193 redrawn without foliage as Type O **23**.
O213 O **23** 5s. multicoloured £100 80·00

1980. Air. South Pacific Scout Jamboree, Tonga and 75th Anniv of Rotary International.
O214 25s. multicoloured 75 65
O215 2p. multicoloured 3·50 5·50
DESIGN: 25s., 2p. Scout camp and Rotary emblem. Nos. O214/15 show maps of Tonga on the reverse.

1980. Air. Nos. O145 surch **T$2**.
O216 2p. on 65s. multicoloured 4·50 6·50

1983. Nos. 834/6 optd **OFFICIAL**.
O217 29s. Type **151** 4·50 4·50
O218 32s. Type **151** 4·50 4·50
O219 47s. Montgolfier's balloon and Concorde 9·00 7·50

1984. Nos. 865/79 and 881 optd **OFFICIAL**.
O220 1s. Type **159** 50 1·40
O221 2s. "Porites sp" 50 1·40
O222 3s. Red squirrelfish 50 1·50
O223 5s. Green map cowrie 50 1·25
O224 6s. "Dardanus megistos" 50 1·50
O225 9s. Variegated shark 75 80
O226 10s. Bubble cone 80 1·25
O227 13s. Lionfish 1·25 80
O228 15s. Textile or cloth of gold cone 1·25 1·75
O229 20s. White-tailed damselfish 1·50 2·00
O230 29s. Princely cone 1·75 85
O231 32s. Powder-blue surgeonfish 1·75 85
O232 47s. Giant spider conch 2·00 90
O233 1p. "Millepora dichotama" 3·75 3·75
O234 2p. "Birgus latro" 7·00 7·00
O235 5p. Yellow-finned tuna 12·00 13·00

1986. Nos. 933/9 optd **OFFICIAL**.
O236 4s. on 2s. "Porites sp" 90 2·00
O237 4s. on 13s. Lionfish 90 2·00
O238 42s. on 3s. Red squirrelfish 2·75 2·50
O239 42s. on 9s. Variegated shark 2·75 2·50
O240 57s. on 6s. "Dardanus megistos" 3·00 2·75
O241 57s. on 20s. White-tailed damselfish 3·00 2·75
O242 2p.50 on 2p. "Birgus latro" 10·00 11·00

1994. Air. 25th Anniv of Tongan Self-adhesive Stamps. Design as No. O192, but inscr "25th ANNIVERSARY OF THE INTRODUCTION OF SELFADHESIVE STAMPS 1969–1994 BERNARD MECHANICK: 1915–80 INVENTOR FREEFORM SELFADHESIVE STAMPS" at centre foot.
O243 80s. multicoloured 5·50 6·00

O **30** Bubble Cone

1995. Designs as Nos. 1221a, 1223a, 1225a, 1227a and 1229a, but inscr as Type O **30**.
O247 10s. Type O **30** 50 1·00
O249 20s. White-tailed dascyllus 75 1·00
O251 45s. Giant spider conch 1·00 60
O253 60s. Princely cone 1·25 75
O255 80s. Lionfish 1·50 1·00
O256 1p. "Chelonia mydas" (turtle) 2·00 1·75
O257 2p. "Birgus latro" (crab) 3·50 3·75
O258 3p. Rose branch murex 4·50 5·00
O259 5p. Humpback whale 8·50 8·50
O260 10p. Variegated shark (vert) 12·00 13·00

TRANSCAUCASIAN FEDERATION Pt. 10

A Federation of Armenia, Azerbaijan and Georgia, which was absorbed into the U.S.S.R. in 1923.

100 kopeks = 1 rouble.

1 Mt. Ararat and Oilfield

2 Mts. Ararat and Elbruz and Oil-derricks

1923.
1 **1** 40,000r. purple 2·00 4·00
2 75,000r. green 2·00 4·00
3 100,000r. grey 1·25 2·00
4 150,000r. red 2·25 1·25
5 **2** 200,000r. green 1·25 1·75
6 300,000r. blue 90 1·75
7 350,000r. brown 90 1·75
8 500,000r. red 1·75 3·00

1923. Surch **700000 RYb.**
9 **1** 700,000r. on 40,000r. purple 2·00 4·00
10 700,000r. on 75,000r. green 2·00 4·00

1923. Values in gold kopeks.
11 **2** 1k. orange 1·00 1·50
12 2k. green 1·00 1·50
13 3k. red 1·00 1·50
14 4k. brown 1·00 1·50
15 **1** 5k. purple 1·00 1·50
16 9k. blue 1·00 1·50
17 18k. grey 1·00 1·50

TRANSKEI Pt. 1

The Republic of Transkei was established on 26 October 1976, as the first of the independent "black homelands" constructed from the territory of the Republic of South Africa.

This independence did not receive international political recognition, but the stamps were accepted as valid on international mail.

Transkei was reincorporated with the Republic of South Africa on 27 April 1994.

100 cents = 1 rand.

1 Lubisi Dam

1976. Transkei Scenes and Occupations. Mult.
1 1c. Type **1** 10 10
2 2c. Soil cultivation 10 10
3 3c. Threshing sorghum 15 10
4a 4c. Transkei matron 15 10
5a 5c. Grinding maize 15 10
6 6c. Cutting "Phormium tenax" 15 10
7 7c. Herd-boy 40 10
8 8c. Felling timber 20 10
9 9c. Agricultural schooling 15 15
10a 10c. Tea picking 20 15
11a 15c. Carrying wood 30 15
12a 20c. Weaving industry 35 15
13 25c. Cattle 45 25
14a 30c. Sledge transportation 60 45
15 50c. Coat of arms and map 85 50
16 1r. Administration building, Umtata 50 1·25
17 2r. The Bunga (Parliamentary building), Umtata 75 2·25

2 K. D. Matanzima

4 "Artemisia afra"

3 Beech 100 King Air of Transkei Airways

1976. Independence. Multicoloured.
18 4c. Type **2** 20 20
19 10c. Flag and mace 45 45
20 15c. K. D. Matanzima, Paramount Chief (different) 55 75
21 20c. Coat of arms 60 80

1977. Transkei Airways' Inaugural Flight. Mult.
22 4c. Type **3** 25 15
23 15c. Beech King Air landing at Matanzima Airport 75 85

1977. Medicinal Plants (1st series). Mult.
24 4c. Type **4** 15 10
25 10c. "Bulbine natalensis" 45 45
26 15c. "Melianthus major" 55 65
27 20c. "Cotyledon orbiculata" 65 90
See also Nos. 88/91.

5 Disc Jockey

6 Blind Basket Weaver

1977. 1st Anniv of Transkei Radio. Mult.
28 4c. Type **5** 15 10
29 15c. Announcer 60 60

1977. Help for the Blind.
30 **6** 4c. black, lilac and gold 15 10
31 – 15c. black, drab and gold 35 35
32 – 20c. black, brown and gold 75 80
DESIGNS: 15c. Hands reading braille; 20c. Blind woman spinning.

7 Men's Carved Pipes

1978. Carved Pipes. Multicoloured.
33 4c. Type **7** 10 10
34 10c. Two men's pipes 15 15
35 15c. Multi-bowled men's pipes 35 55
36 20c. Woman's and witch-doctor's pipes 40 70

8 Angora Goat

9 "Carissa bispinosa"

1978. Weaving Industry. Multicoloured.
37 4c. Type **8** 10 10
38 10c. Spinning mohair 15 15
39 15c. Dyeing mohair 20 25
40 20c. Weaving a mohair rug 30 40

1978. Edible Wild Fruits. Multicoloured.
41 4c. Type **9** 15 10
42 10c. "Dovyalis caffra" 20 25
43 15c. "Harpephyllum caffrum" 35 55
44 20c. "Syzygium cordatum" 40 70

10 Calipers

12 President K. D. Matanzima

11 Chi Cha Youth

1978. Care of Cripples.
45 **10** 4c. black, brown and gold 10 10
46 – 10c. black, grey and gold 25 25
47 – 15c. black, yellow and gold 40 50

DESIGNS: 10c. Child in wheelchair; 15c. Nurse examining child's leg.

1979. Abakwetha (coming-of-age ceremony of Xhosa males). Multicoloured.
48 4c. Type **11** 10 10
49 10c. Youths in three-month seclusion 20 20
50 15c. Umtshilo dance 35 35
51 20c. Burning of seclusion hut at end of final ceremony 45 45

1979. Inaug of Second State President.
52 **12** 4c. red and gold 15 10
53 15c. green and gold 50 45

13 Windpump

14 Magwa Falls

1979. Water Resources. Multicoloured.
54 4c. Type **13** 15 10
55 10c. Woman ladling water into jar 20 25
56 15c. Indwe River Dam (horiz) 35 55
57 20c. Ncora Dam (horiz) 40 70

1979. Waterfalls. Multicoloured.
58 4c. Type **14** 15 10
59 10c. Bawa Falls 20 25
60 15c. Waterfall Bluff (horiz) 35 55
61 20c. Tsitsa Falls (horiz) 40 70

15 Expectant Mother pouring Milk

16 Black Gnat (dry fly)

1979. Child Health. Multicoloured.
62 5c. Type **15** 15 10
63 15c. Mother breast-feeding baby 45 45
64 20c. Immunizing child 60 65

1980. Fishing Flies (1st series). Multicoloured.
65 5c. Type **16** 25 35
66 5c. Zug Bug (nymph) 25 35
67 5c. March Brown (wet fly) 25 35
68 5c. Durham Ranger (salmon fly) 25 35
69 5c. Colonel Bates (streamer) 25 35
See also Nos. 83/7, 99/103, 116/20 and 133/7.

17 Rotary Emblem

18 "Encephalartos altensteinii"

1980. 75th Anniv of Rotary International.
70 **17** 15c. blue and gold 35 30

1980. Cycads. Multicoloured.
71 5c. Type **18** 15 10
72 10c. "Encephalartos princeps" 25 25
73 15c. "Encephalartos villosus" 40 40
74 20c. "Encephalartos friderici-guilielmi" 50 55

19 Red-chested Cuckoo

1980. Birds. Multicoloured.
75 5c. Type **19** 20 10
76 10c. Cape puff-back fly-catcher 45 25

77 15c. South African crowned crane 65 60
78 20c. Spectacled Weaver 70 70

20 Hole in the Wall

1980. Tourism. Multicoloured.
79 5c. Type **20** 15 10
80 10c. Port St. Johns 25 25
81 15c. The Citadel (rock) 40 40
82 20c. The Archway (rock) 50 55

1981. Fishing Flies (2nd series). As T **16**. Mult.
83 10c. Kent's Lightning (streamer) 25 25
84 10c. Wickham's Fancy (dry fly) 25 25
85 10c. Jock Scott (wet fly) 25 25
86 10c. Green Highlander (salmon fly) 25 25
87 10c. Tan Nymph 25 25

1981. Medicinal Plants (2nd series). As T **4**. Mult.
88 5c. "Leonotis leonurus" 15 10
89 15c. "Euphorbia bupleurifolia" 30 30
90 20c. "Pelargonium reniforme" 35 35
91 25c. "Hibiscus trionum" 35 40

21 Eyamakhwenkwe

1981. Xhosa Women's Headdresses. Multicoloured.
92 5c. Type **21** 10 10
93 15c. Eyabafana 20 35
94 20c. Umfazana 25 45
95 25c. Ixhegokazi 30 55
MS96 126 × 91 mm. Nos. 92/5 1·00 1·25

22 State House, Umtata

1981. 5th Anniv of Independence.
97 **22** 5c. black, brown and green 15 10
98 – 15c. black, brown and green 45 30
DESIGN: 15c. University of Transkei.

1982. Fishing Flies (3rd series). As T **16**. Mult.
99 10c. Blue Charm 30 30
100 10c. Royal Coachman 30 30
101 10c. Light Spruce 30 30
102 10c. Montana Nymph 30 30
103 10c. Butcher 30 30

23 Cub Scout

24 Hippocrates

1982. 75th Anniv of Boy Scout Movement. Mult.
104 8c. Type **23** 15 10
105 10c. Scout planting tree 15 10
106 20c. Scout on raft 25 30
107 25c. Scout with dog 25 30

1982. Celebrities of Medicine (1st series). Mult.
108 15c. Type **24** 20 20
109 20c. Antonie van Leeuwenhoek 25 30
110 25c. William Harvey 30 40
111 30c. Joseph Lister 35 45
See also Nos. 125/8, 160/3, 176/9, 249/52, 273/6, 281/4 and 305/8.

25 City Hall

1982. Centenary of Umtata. Multicoloured.
112 8c. Type **25** 10 10
113 15c. The Bunga 15 15
114 20c. Botha Sigcau Building 20 20
115 25c. Palace of Justice and K. D. Matanzima Building 25 30

1983. Fishing Flies (4th series). As T **16**. Mult.
116 20c. Alexandra 25 25
117 20c. Kent's Marbled Sedge 25 25
118 20c. White Marabou 25 25
119 20c. Mayfly Nymph 25 25
120 20c. Silver Wilkinson 25 25

26 Hotel Complex, Mzamba

1983. Wildcoast Holiday Complex, Mzamba. Mult.
121 10c. Type **26** 15 15
122 20c. Beach scene 25 25
123 25c. Casino 35 35
124 40c. Carousel 50 50

1983. Celebrities of Medicine (2nd series). As T **24**. Multicoloured.
125 10c. Edward Jenner 15 15
126 20c. Gregor Mendel 25 30
127 25c. Louis Pasteur 30 35
128 40c. Florence Nightingale 40 55

27 Lady Frere Post Office

1983. Transkei Post Offices (1st series). Mult.
129 10c. Type **27** 15 15
130 20c. Idutywa 20 30
131 25c. Lusikisiki 20 35
132 40c. Cala 30 55
See also Nos. 156/9.

1984. Fishing Flies (5th series). As T **16**. Mult.
133 20c. Silver Grey 45 45
134 20c. Ginger Quill 45 45
135 20c. Hardy's Favourite 45 45
136 20c. March Brown 45 45
137 20c. Kent's Spectrum Mohawk 45 45

28 Amagqira

1984. Xhosa Culture. Multicoloured.
138 1c. Type **28** 20 10
139 2c. Horseman 20 10
140 3c. Mat making 20 10
141 4c. Xhosa dancers 20 10
142 5c. Shopping with donkeys 20 10
143 6c. Young musicians 30 15
144 7c. Fingo brides 30 20
145 8c. Tasting the beer 30 20
146 9c. Thinning the maize 30 30
147 10c. Dancing demonstration 30 15
148 11c. Water from the river 30 15
148a 12c. Preparing a meal 30 15
148b 14c. Weeding mealies 30 20
149 15c. National sport: stick fighting 20 20
149a 16c. Morning pasture 30 20
150 20c. Abakhwetha dance 30 25
150a 21c. Building of initiation hut 1·50 20
151 25c. Tribesman singing 30 25
152 30c. Jovial matrons 50 35
153 50c. Pipe making 50 60
154 1r. Intonjane 60 1·10
155 2r. Abakhwetha 75 2·00

1984. Transkei Post Offices (2nd series). As T **27**. Multicoloured.
156 11c. Umzimkulu 15 15
157 20c. Mount Fletcher 20 25
158 25c. Qumbu 20 25
159 50c. Umtata 30 50

1984. Celebrities of Medicine (3rd series). As T **24**. Multicoloured.
160 11c. Nicholas of Cusa 15 15
161 25c. William Morton 25 25
162 30c. Wilhelm Rontgen 30 40
163 45c. Karl Landsteiner 40 60

29 Soil Erosion by Overgrazing

1985. Soil Conservation. Multicoloured.
164 11c. Type **29** 15 15
165 25c. Removal of stock and construction of walls as sediment collectors 25 25
166 30c. Regeneration of vegetation 30 40
167 50c. Cattle grazing in lush landscape 40 60

30 Tsitsa Bridge

1985. Bridges. Multicoloured.
168 12c. Type **30** 20 15
169 25c. White Kei Railway Bridge 25 25
170 30c. Mitchell Bridge 35 35
171 50c. Umzimvubu Bridge 55 60

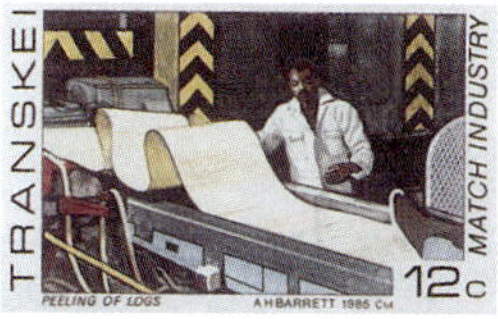

31 Veneer-peeling Machine

1985. Match Industry, Butterworth. Mult.
172 12c. Type **31** 15 15
173 25c. Cutting wood to match-size 20 25
174 30c. Dipping splints in chemical to form match heads 25 35
175 50c. Boxing matches 40 65

1985. Celebrities of Medicine (4th series). As T **24**. Multicoloured.
176 12c. Andreas Vesalius 20 15
177 25c. Marcello Malpighi 30 40
178 30c. Francois Magendie 35 45
179 50c. William Stewart Halsted 50 70

32 Early Street Scene

1986. Historic Port St. Johns. Multicoloured.
180 12c. Type **32** 20 15
181 20c. "Umzimvubu" (coaster) anchored at old jetty 45 45
182 25c. Wagons off-loading maize at jetty 50 50
183 30c. View of town at end of 19th century 50 55
MS184 130 × 94 mm. Nos. 180/3 1·50 1·50

33 "Aloe ferox"

34 First Falls Station, Umtata River

1986. Aloes. Multicoloured.
185 14c. Type **33** 20 15
186 20c. "Aloe arborescens" 30 30
187 25c. "Aloe maculata" 35 35
188 30c. "Aloe ecklonis" 45 45

1986. Hydro-electric Power Stations. Mult.
189 14c. Type **34** 20 15
190 20c. Second Falls, Umtata River 25 25
191 25c. Ncora, Qumanco River 40 40
192 30c. Collywobbles, Mbashe River 50 50

35 Prime Minister George Matanzima

1986. 10th Anniv of Independence. Mult.
193 14c. Type **35** 15 15
194 20c. Technical College, Umtata 25 30
195 25c. University of Transkei, Umtata 30 40
196 30c. Palace of Justice, Umtata 40 50

36 Piper Apache 235 "Ulundi" flying through Clouds

1987. 10th Anniv of Transkei Airways Corporation. Multicoloured.
197 14c. Type **36** 20 15
198 20c. Tail fin of "Ulundi" 30 30
199 25c. Beech 100 King Air 40 40
200 30c. Control tower, K. D. Matanzima Airport 55 60

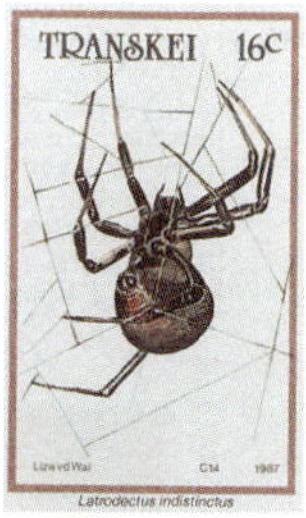

37 Pondo Girl

38 "Latrodectus indistinctus"

1987. Transkei Beadwork. Multicoloured.
201 16c. Type **37** 15 15
202 20c. Bomvana woman 25 30
203 25c. Xessibe woman 35 40
204 30c. Xhosa man 40 60

1987. Spiders. Multicoloured.
205 16c. Type **38** 20 15
206 20c. "Naephila pilipes" 30 30
207 25c. "Lycosidue sp" 40 40
208 30c. "Argiope nigrovittata" 50 55

39 Common Black Pigs

1987. Domestic Animals. Multicoloured.
209 16c. Type **39** 15 15
210 30c. Goats 20 30
211 40c. Merino sheep 30 50
212 50c. Cattle 45 65

40 "Plocamium corallorhiza"

41 Spinning

1988. Seaweed. Multicoloured.
213 16c. Type **40** 15 15
214 30c. "Gelidium amanzii" 25 30
215 40c. "Ecklonia biruncinata" 30 40
216 50c. "Halimeda cuneata" 40 55

1988. Blanket Factory, Butterworth. Mult.
217 16c. Type **41** 15 15
218 30c. Warping 25 30
219 40c. Weaving 30 40
220 50c. Raising the nap 40 55

42 Map showing Wreck Site

1988. 206th Anniv of Shipwreck of "Grosvenor" (East Indiaman). Multicoloured.
221 16c. Type **42** 40 20
222 30c. "The Wreck of the 'Grosvenor'" (R. Smirke) 50 50
223 40c. Dirk hilt, dividers and coins from wreck 55 55
224 50c. "African Hospitality" (G. Morland) 60 70

43 Small-spotted Cat

1988. Endangered Animals. Multicoloured.
225 16c. Type **43** 60 30
226 30c. Blue duiker 70 60
227 40c. Oribi 85 75
228 50c. Hunting dog . . . . . 1·25 1·00

44 Class 14 CRB Steam Locomotives

1989. Trains. Multicoloured.
229 16c. Type **44** 20 20
230 30c. Class 14 CRB locomotive and passenger train at Toleni Halt . . . 40 40
231 40c. Double-headed steam train on Great Kei River Bridge (vert) 60 70
232 50c. Double-headed steam train in Kei Valley (vert) 65 80

45 Mat, Baskets and Jar

1989. Basketry. Multicoloured.
233 18c. Type **45** 20 15
234 30c. Basket and jar 30 30
235 40c. Jars and bag 40 50
236 50c. Dish and jars 55 75

46 Chub Mackerel

1989. Seafood. Multicoloured.
237 18c. Type **46** 55 15
238 30c. Squid 70 50
239 40c. Perna or brown mussels 85 70
240 50c. Rock lobster . . . . . 1·00 1·00

47 Broom Cluster Fig

1989. Trees. Multicoloured.
241 18c. Type **47** 50 20
242 30c. Natal fig 75 55
243 40c. Broad-leaved coral . . . 85 85
244 50c. Cabbage tree . . . . . 1·10 1·25

48 "Ginkgo koningensis"

49 Aretaeus (discoverer of diabetes)

1990. Plant Fossils. Multicoloured.
245 18c. Type **48** 80 25
246 30c. "Pseudoctenis spatulata" 1·10 80
247 40c. "Rissikia media" . . . . 1·25 1·10
248 50c. "Taeniopteris anavolans" . . . . 1·40 1·50

1990. Celebrities of Medicine (5th series). Diabetes Research. Multicoloured.
249 18c. Type **49** 70 20
250 30c. Claude Bernard (discovered sugar formation by liver) . . . . 1·10 70
251 40c. Oscar Minkowski (discovered pancreas removal caused diabetes) 1·25 90
252 50c. Frederick Banting (discoverer of insulin) . . . 1·40 1·25

50 Diviner dancing to Drum

51 Soldier Lily

1990. Diviners. Multicoloured.
253 21c. Type **50** 60 20
254 35c. Lecturing Imichetywa (novitiates) 90 70
255 40c. Neophyte initiation . . . 1·00 90
256 50c. Diviner's induction ceremony . . . . 1·25 1·40

1990. Flowers. Multicoloured.
257 21c. Type **51** 55 20
258 35c. "Disa crassicornis" . . . 80 65
259 40c. Christmas bells 90 90
260 50c. Port St. John's creeper 1·00 1·40

52 Pink Ink Plant

53 Common Dolphin

1991. Parasitic Plants. Multicoloured.
261 21c. Type **52** 60 20
262 35c. White harveya 90 70
263 40c. "Alectra sessiliflora" . . 1·00 1·10
264 50c. "Hydnora africana" . . 1·25 1·50

1991. Dolphins. Multicoloured.
265 25c. Type **53** . . . . 1·00 25
266 40c. Bottle-nosed dolphin . . 1·40 85
267 50c. Humpbacked dolphin . . 1·60 1·25
268 60c. Risso's dolphin . . . . 1·60 1·60

54 South African Crowned Cranes ("Crowned Cranes")

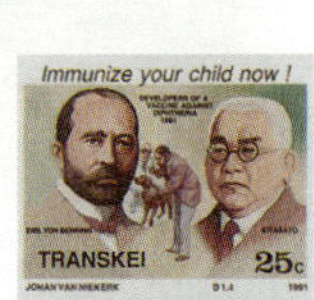

55 Emil von Behring and Shibasaburo Kitasao (diphtheria)

1991. Endangered Birds. Multicoloured.
269 25c. Type **54** 65 30
270 40c. Cape vulture . . . . . 1·00 85
271 50c. Wattled crane . . . . . 1·10 1·10
272 60c. Egyptian vulture . . . . 1·25 1·40

1991. Celebrities of Medicine (6th series). Vaccine Development. Multicoloured.
273 25c. Type **55** 90 25
274 40c. Camile Guerin and Albert Calmette (tuberculosis) . . . . . . 1·40 90
275 50c. Jonas Salk (poliomyelitis) . . . . . . 1·60 1·25
276 60c. John Enders (measles) 1·75 1·50

56 "Eulophia speciosa"

57 Thomas Weller (researcher into infectious viruses)

1992. Orchids. Multicoloured.
277 27c. Type **56** 25 20
278 45c. "Satyrium sphaerocarpum" 40 40
279 65c. "Disa scullyi" 60 70
280 85c. "Disa tysonii" . . . . . 80 1·00

1992. Celebrities of Medicine (7th series). Mult.
281 27c. Type **57** 75 25
282 45c. Ignaz Semmelweis . . . 1·10 80
283 65c. Sir James Simpson . . . 1·50 1·25
284 85c. Rene Laennec . . . . . 1·75 1·60

58 Red-billed Pintail

59 "Pseudomelania sutherlandi" (gastropod)

1992. Waterfowl. Multicoloured.
285 35c. Type **58** 60 60
286 35c. Hottentot teal 60 60
287 70c. Maccoa duck 90 90
288 70c. White-backed duck . . . 90 90
289 90c. African black duck . . . 1·10 1·10
290 90c. Egyptian goose . . . . 1·10 1·10
291 1r.05 Cape shoveler . . . . 1·40 1·40
292 1r.05 Cape teal . . . . . . 1·40 1·40

1992. Marine Fossils. Multicoloured.
293 35c. Type **59** . . . . 1·10 35
294 70c. "Gaudryceras denseplicatum" (ammonite) 1·50 1·10
295 90c. "Neithea quinquecostata" (bivalve) 1·60 1·50
296 1r.05 "Pugilina acuticarinatus" (gastropod) 1·75 1·60

60 Papillon

1993. Dogs. Multicoloured.
297 35c. Type **60** 60 30
298 70c. Pekingese 90 90
299 90c. Chihuahua . . . . . . 1·10 1·25
300 1r.05 Dachshund . . . . . . 1·40 1·60

61 Fab[illegible]

1993. P[illegible]
301 45[illegible] 10 40
302 65[illegible] 50 1·10
303 85[illegible] 75 1·60
304 1r.0[illegible] 75 1·75

62 Sir Alexander Fleming and Howard Florey (discoverer and refiner of penicillin)

63 Laughing Doves

1993. Celebrities of Medicine (8th series). Mult.
305 45c. Type **62** 70 40
306 65c. Alexis Carrel . . . . . 1·10 1·10
307 85c. James Lind . . . . . . 1·25 1·50
308 1r.05 Santiago Ramon y Cajal . . . . 1·40 1·60

1993. Doves. Multicoloured.
309 45c. Type **63** 60 40
310 65c. Tambourine doves . . . 90 90
311 85c. Emerald-spotted wood doves . . . . 1·25 1·25
312 1r.05 Namaqua doves . . . . 1·50 1·60
MS313 98 × 83 mm. Nos. 309/12 3·75 3·75

64 "Clan Lindsay" (steamer) on Rocks, Mazeppa Bay, 1898

1994. Shipwrecks. Multicoloured.
314 45c. Type **64** . . . . 1·10 60
315 65c. "Horizon" (freighter) on rocks near River Mngazi, 1967 . . . . 1·50 1·25
316 85c. "Oceanos" (pleasure cruiser) sinking near Coffee Bay, 1991 . . . . 1·75 1·60
317 1r.05 "Forresbank" (freighter) on fire near River Mtakatye, 1958 . . . 1·75 1·90

TRANSVAAL Pt. 1

Formerly South African Republic under Boer rule, annexed by Gt. Britain in 1877, restored to the Boers in 1881 and again annexed in 1900 and since 1919 a province of the Union of S. Africa.

12 pence = 1 shilling;
20 shillings = 1 pound.

1

1870. Imperf or roul.
61 **1** 1d. red . . . . 22·00 16·00
22 1d. black . . . . 17·00 25·00
53 3d. lilac . . . . 45·00 38·00
54a 6d. blue . . . . 45·00 38·00
32 1s. green . . . . 70·00 38·00

1874. Perf.
38a **1** 1d. red . . . . 75·00 35·00
171 1d. grey . . . . 4·25 1·50
172 3d. black on red . . . . . 21·00 4·00
173 3d. red . . . . 8·00 2·00
173b 3d. brown . . . . 22·00 3·50
41 6d. blue . . . . £100 45·00
174 1s. green . . . . 45·00 3·00

1877. Optd **V. R. TRANSVAAL.** Imperf or roul.
101 **1** 1d. red . . . . 21·00 21·00
102 3d. lilac . . . . 70·00 38·00
103 6d. blue . . . . 85·00 32·00
113 6d. blue on red . . . . . . 70·00 45·00
104 1s. green . . . . 90·00 45·00

1877. Optd **V. R. Transvaal.** Imperf or roul.
116 **1** 1d. red on blue . . . . . 48·00 26·00
117 1d. red on orange . . . . 17·00 16·00
118 3d. lilac on brown . . . . 38·00 24·00
119e 3d. lilac on green . . . . . 95·00 35·00
149 3d. lilac on blue . . . . . 42·00 25·00
126 6d. blue on green . . . . . 70·00 25·00
121 6d. blue on blue . . . . . 48·00 24·00

9

18

1878. Perf.
133 **9** $\frac{1}{2}$d. red . . . . 18·00 70·00
134a 1d. brown . . . . 9·00 2·75
135 3d. red . . . . 12·00 3·50
136 4d. olive . . . . 17·00 4·25
137 6d. black . . . . 8·50 3·25
138 1s. green . . . . £100 32·00
139 2s. blue . . . . £140 65·00

1879. Surch **1 Penny**.
145 **9** 1d. on 6d. black . . . . . 38·00 22·00

1882. Surch **EEN PENNY**.
170 **9** 1d. on 4d. green . . . . . 11·00 4·00

1885.
175 **18** $\frac{1}{2}$d. grey 30 10
176 1d. red 30 10
177 2d. purple . . . . 1·75 2·00
178 2d. brown 70 10
179 2$\frac{1}{2}$d. mauve . . . . 1·50 50
180 3d. mauve . . . . 1·50 80
181 4d. olive . . . . 2·75 70
182 6d. blue . . . . 3·75 2·25
183 1s. green . . . . 2·50 50
184 2s.6d. yellow . . . . 4·00 1·75
185 5s. grey . . . . 6·00 3·00
186 10s. brown . . . . 30·00 6·50
187 £5 green £3250 £180

1885. Surch **HALVE PENNY** vert, reading up or down.
188 **1** $\frac{1}{2}$d. on 3d. red (No. 173) 3·50 8·50
192 **18** $\frac{1}{2}$d. on 3d. mauve . . . . 3·25 3·25
189 **1** $\frac{1}{2}$d. on 1s. green (No. 174) 18·00 45·00

1885. Surch with value in words and **Z. A. R.** both vert.
190 **9** $\frac{1}{2}$d. on 6d. black . . . . . 48·00 75·00
191 2d. on 6d. black . . . . . 4·00 9·00

1887. Surch **2d** and thick bar.
194 **18** 2d. on 3d. mauve . . . . 1·25 2·50

1893. Surch **Halve Penny** and bars.
196 **18** $\frac{1}{2}$d. on 2d. pale brown . . 85 85

1893. Surch in figures and words between bars. (A) in one line, (B) in two.
197 **18** 1d. on 6d. blue (A) 50 50
198 2$\frac{1}{2}$d. on 1s. green (A) . . . 1·00 2·50
199 2$\frac{1}{2}$d. on 1s. green (B) . . . 3·50 3·50

29 (Wagon with shafts) 30 (Wagon with pole)

1894.

200	**29**	½d. grey	60	20
201		1d. red	80	10
202		2d. brown	80	10
203		6d. blue	1·50	40
204		1s. green	9·00	11·00

1895.

205	**30**	½d. grey	50	10
206		1d. red	50	10
207		2d. brown	50	10
208		3d. mauve	1·00	30
209		4d. black	1·75	80
210		6d. blue	1·75	60
211		1s. green	2·25	1·00
212		5s. grey	12·00	20·00
212a		10s. brown	12·00	4·00

1895. Surch **Halve Penny** and bar.

213	**30**	½d. on 1s. green	60	10

1895. Surch **1d.** and thick bar.

214	**18**	1d. on 2½d. mauve	50	10

33 34

1895. Fiscal stamp optd **POSTZEGEL**.

215	**33**	6d. red	75	1·75

1895. Introduction of Penny Postage.

215c	**34**	1d. red	1·50	1·75

1896.

216	**30**	½d. green	50	10
217		1d. red and green	50	10
218		2d. brown and green	50	10
219		2½d. blue and green	70	10
220		3d. purple and green	1·25	1·50
221		4d. olive and green	1·25	1·50
222		6d. lilac and green	70	1·00
223		1s. pale brown and green	1·00	20
224		2s.6d. violet and green	1·50	1·75

1900. Optd **V.R.I.**

226	**30**	½d. green	30	15
227		1d. red and green	30	15
228		2d. brown and green	2·00	1·25
229		2½d. blue and green	1·00	1·25
230		3d. purple and green	1·00	1·00
231		4d. olive and green	2·00	65
232		6d. lilac and green	2·00	1·00
233		1s. brown and green	2·00	2·00
234		2s.6d. violet and green	3·00	7·00
235		5s. grey	5·00	9·00
236		10s. brown	7·00	11·00
237	**18**	£5 green	£1800	£750

The majority of the £5 stamps, No. 237 on the market, are forgeries.

1901. Optd **E.R.I.**

238	**30**	½d. green	50	70
239		1d. red and green	50	10
240		3d. purple and green	2·25	2·75
241		4d. olive and green	2·25	2·75
242		2s.6d. violet and green	6·50	12·00

1901. Surch **E.R.I. Half Penny**.

243	**30**	½d. on 2d. brown and green	65	65

38

1902.

244	**38**	½d. black and green	1·50	20
273		½d. green	1·75	10
245		1d. black and red	1·25	15
274		1d. red	1·25	10
246		2d. black and purple	3·00	50
275		2d. purple	3·50	50
247		2½d. black and blue	5·00	1·25
276		2½d. blue	12·00	4·25
264		3d. black and green	3·50	30
265		4d. black and brown	4·75	70
266a		6d. black and orange	2·75	50
251		1s. black and green	10·00	8·00
267		1s. grey and brown	6·50	50
252		2s. black and brown	32·00	35·00
268		2s. grey and yellow	20·00	5·00
253		2s.6d. mauve and black	14·00	9·00
270		5s. black & purple on yellow	17·00	1·50
271		10s. black & purple on red	42·00	2·75
272		£1 green and violet	£180	25·00
259		£5 brown and violet	£1200	£475

Nos. 267, 268 and all values of 2s.6d. and above have the inscription "POSTAGE" on both sides. The rest are inscribed "POSTAGE" at left and "REVENUE" at right.

POSTAGE DUE STAMPS

D 1

1907.

D1	**D 1**	½d. black and green	3·25	1·25
D2		1d. black and red	4·00	85
D3		2d. brown	4·00	1·25
D4		3d. black and blue	7·50	4·00
D5		5d. black and violet	2·00	12·00
D6		6d. black and brown	4·25	12·00
D7		1s. red and black	8·50	8·50

TRAVANCORE Pt. 1

A state of south-east India. In 1949 formed part of Travancore-Cochin.

16 cash = 1 chuckram;
28 chuckrams = 1 rupee.

1 Conch or Chank Shell 3 Conch or Chank Shell

1888. Various frames.

9	**3**	4cash pink	30	10
24	–	5cash olive	80	20
34	–	5cash brown	2·75	20
10	**1**	6cash brown	30	10
11a		½ch. purple	1·00	10
27	–	10cash pink	40	10
13	–	ch. black	1·50	25
39	–	ch. mauve	35	10
14c	**1**	1ch. blue	75	10
15		1¼ch. purple	55	55
42		1½ch. red	2·75	10
16a		2ch. red	60	10
17	–	3ch. violet	2·75	20
18a	**1**	4ch. green	2·00	35
19	–	7ch. purple	2·00	50
20	–	14ch. orange	2·75	1·60

1906. Surch in figures.

21a	**1**	¼ on ½ch. purple	30	20
22		⅜ on ½ch. purple	20	35

1921. Surch in figures.

31	**3**	1c. on 4cash pink	15	20
57	–	1c. on 5cash brown	15	15
58	–	1c. on 5cash purple	1·25	20
50	**1**	1c. on 1¼ch. purple	15	50
59	–	2c. on 10cash pink	15	15
51	**1**	2c. on 1¼ch. purple	15	20
32		5c. on 1ch. blue	1·00	10

11 Sri Padmanabha Shrine 13 Maharaja Bala Rama Varma XI

1931. Coronation.

47	**11**	6cash black and green	1·50	1·50
48	–	10cash black and blue	1·25	70
49	**13**	3ch. black and purple	2·50	2·50

DESIGN—As Type **11**: 10cash, State chariot.

16 Maharaja Bala Rama Varma XI and Subramania Shrine

1937. Temple Entry Proclamation.

60	**16**	6cash red	1·25	1·25
61	–	12cash blue	2·25	30
62	–	1½ch. green	1·50	1·25
63	–	3ch. violet	3·25	2·00

DESIGNS: Portraits of the Maharaja and the temples of Sri Padmanabha (12cash), Mahadeva (1½ch.) and Kanyakumari (3ch.).

17 Lake Ashtamudi 18 Maharaja Bala Rama Varma XI

1939. 27th Birthday of Maharaja.

64	**17**	1ch. green	4·25	10
65	–	1½ch. red	3·00	2·75
66	**18**	2ch. orange	4·75	1·25
67	–	3ch. brown	5·50	10
68	–	4ch. red	5·00	40
69	–	7ch. blue	8·50	15·00
70	–	14ch. green	7·00	48·00

DESIGNS—As Type **18**: 1½, 3ch. Portraits of Maharaja. As Type **17**: 4ch. Sri Padmanabha Shrine; 7ch. Cape Comorin; 14ch. Pachipari Reservoir.

19 Maharaja and Aruvikara Falls 21 Maharaja Bala Rama Varma XI

1941. 29th Birthday of Maharaja.

71	**19**	6cash violet	6·00	10
72	–	ch. brown	6·50	20

DESIGN: ch. Maharaja and Marthanda Varma Bridge, Alwaye.

1943. Stamps of 1939 and 1941 surch in figures and capital letters.

73e	–	2cash on 1½ch. red (No. 65)	40	20
74a	–	4cash on ch. brown (No. 72)	3·75	30
75a	**19**	8cash on 6cash red (as No. 7)	3·25	10

1946. 34th Birthday of Maharaja.

76a	**21**	8cash red	65	1·25

1946. No. O103 optd **SPECIAL**.

77	**19**	6cash violet	6·00	2·25

OFFICIAL STAMPS

1911. Optd **On S S.**

O 1	**3**	4cash pink	20	10
O14	–	5cash olive	60	10
O29	–	5cash brown	25	40
O15	**1**	6cash brown	30	10
O54		½ch. purple	20	10
O18	–	10cash pink	65	10
O39	–	ch. black	35	15
O56	–	ch. mauve	30	15
O 5	**1**	1ch. blue	65	10
O21		1¼ch. purple	40	10
O59		1½ch. red	40	10
O 6		2ch. red	35	10
O 8	–	3ch. violet	35	10
O10	**1**	4ch. green	55	10
O64	–	7ch. purple	1·25	30
O65	–	14ch. orange	1·75	40

1932. Official stamps surch in figures.

O74	–	6c. on 5cash olive	1·60	1·25
O75	–	6c. on 5cash brown	20	25
O83	–	12c. on 10cash pink	20	15
O84	**1**	1ch.8ch. on 1¼ch. red	35	25

1939. Optd **SERVICE**.

O 85b	**1**	6cash brown	70	30
O 94	–	ch. mauve (No. 39)	12·00	20
O 96	**17**	1ch. green	1·00	10
O 97b	–	1½ch. red (No. 65)	1·50	15
O 95a	**1**	1¼ch. red	4·50	1·00
O 98	**17**	2ch. orange	1·50	30
O 99	–	3ch. brown (No. 67)	1·00	10
O100	–	4ch. red (No. 68)	2·50	75
O101	–	7ch. blue (No. 69)	7·00	35
O102	–	14ch. green (No. 70)	12·00	70

1942. Optd **SERVICE**.

O103	**19**	6cash violet	40	50
O104	–	ch. brown (No. 72)	4·00	10

1942. Nos. 73/5 optd **SERVICE**.

O106a	–	2cash on 1½ch. red	50	15
O107a	–	4cash on ch. brown	1·75	20
O105a	**19**	8cash on 6cash red	1·25	10

1947. Optd **SERVICE**.

O108	**21**	8cash red	2·25	70

TRAVANCORE-COCHIN Pt. 1

In 1949 the states of Cochin and Travancore in south-east India were united under the name of the United States of Travancore and Cochin. Now uses stamps of India.

12 pies = 1 anna; 16 annas = 1 rupee.

1949. Stamps of Travancore surch in **PIES** or **ANNAS** in English and native characters.

1e	**19**	2p. on 6cash violet	40	20
2d	**21**	2p. on 8cash red	75	30
3e	**17**	½a. on 1ch. green	65	40
4a	**18**	1a. on 2ch. orange	55	30
5d	**11**	2a. on 4ch. brown	2·50	55
6a	–	3a. on 7ch. blue (No. 69)	5·00	2·75
7b	–	6a. on 14ch. green (No. 70)	12·00	20·00

1949. No. 106 of Cochin optd **U.S.T.C.**

8	**21**	1a. orange	4·50	50·00

1950. No. 106 of Cochin optd **T.-C.**

9	**21**	1a. orange	5·50	48·00

1950. No. 9 surch with new value.

10	**21**	6p. on 1a. orange	3·25	42·00
11		9p. on 1a. orange	2·75	38·00

5 Conch or Chank Shell 6 Palm Trees

1950.

12	**5**	2p. red	2·25	2·25
13	**6**	4p. blue	3·00	14·00

OFFICIAL STAMPS

1949. Stamps of Travancore surch **SERVICE** and value in **PIES** or **ANNAS** in English and native characters.

O 1f	**19**	2p. on 6cash (No. 71)	35	35
O10	**21**	4p. on 8cash (No. 76a)	50	20
O11b	**17**	½a. on 1ch. (No. 64)	30	20
O12c	**18**	1a. on 2ch. (No. 66)	40	20
O 9a	–	2a. on 4ch. (No. 68)	60	65
O14e	–	3a. on 7ch. (No. 69)	1·50	1·10
O15	–	6a. on 14ch. (No. 70)	1·50	3·50

TRENGGANU Pt. 1

A state of the Federation of Malaya, incorporated in Malaysia in 1963.

100 cents = 1 dollar (Straits or Malayan).

1 Sultan Zain ul ab din 2 Sultan Zain ul ab din

1910.

1	**1**	1c. green	1·50	1·00
2		2c. brown and purple	80	90
3		3c. red	2·25	2·25
4		4c. orange	3·50	5·50
5		4c. brown and green	2·00	3·75
5a		4c. red	1·25	1·75
6		5c. grey	1·25	3·25
7		5c. grey and brown	2·25	2·00
8		8c. blue	1·25	9·00
9a		10c. purple on yellow	3·25	5·00
10		10c. green and red on yellow	1·25	2·25
11		20c. mauve and purple	3·50	4·25
12		25c. green and purple	7·00	30·00
13		30c. purple and black	6·50	50·00
14		50c. black on green	4·50	8·00
15		$1 black and red on blue	16·00	22·00
16		$3 green and red on green	£140	£300
17	**2**	$5 green and purple	£150	£425
18		$25 red and green	£900	£950

1917. Surch **RED CROSS 2c.**

19	**1**	2c. on 3c. red	50	6·50
20		2c. on 4c. orange	1·50	14·00
21		2c. on 4c. brown and green	3·00	35·00
22		2c. on 8c. blue	1·00	27·00

4 Sultan Suleiman 7 Sultan Ismail

1921. (a) T **4**.
26 **4** 1c. black . . . . 1·50 1·25
27 2c. green . . . . 1·25 1·75
28 3c. green . . . . 2·00 1·00
29 3c. brown . . . . 23·00 13·00
30 4c. red . . . . 1·50 1·00
31 5c. grey and brown . . . . . 2·00 5·00
32 5c. purple on yellow . . . . 1·75 1·25
33 6c. orange . . . . 3·50 50
34 8c. grey . . . . 26·00 5·50
35 10c. blue . . . . 2·00 1·00
36 12c. blue . . . . 4·25 4·50
37 20c. purple and orange . . . 2·25 1·50
38 25c. green and purple . . . . 2·25 3·00
39 30c. purple and black . . . . 3·25 3·50
40 35c. red on yellow . . . . . 4·75 8·00
41 50c. green and red . . . . . 6·50 3·00
42 $1 purple and blue on blue 9·00 3·75
43 $3 green and red on green . . 60·00 £150

(b) Larger type, as T **2**, but portrait of Sultan Suleiman.
25 $5 green and red on yellow . . £100 £300
45 $25 purple and blue £650 £1100
46 $50 green and yellow £1600 £2750
47 $100 green and red £5000 £6000

1922. Optd **MALAYA-BORNEO EXHIBITION.**
48 **4** 2c. green . . . . 4·25 27·00
49 4c. red . . . . 6·50 32·00
50 5c. grey and brown . . . . . 3·25 38·00
51 **1** 10c. green and red on yellow 4·75 32·00
52 20c. mauve and purple . . . 4·75 35·00
53 25c. green and purple . . . . 4·50 35·00
54 30c. purple and black . . . . 4·75 35·00
55 50c. black on green . . . . . 4·75 35·00
56 $1 black and red on blue . . 13·00 70·00
57 $3 green and red on green . . £140 £375
58 **2** $5 green and purple £250 £650

1941. Surch.
59 **4** 2c. on 5c. purple on yellow 6·50 3·50
60 8c. on 10c. blue . . . . . . 7·00 3·75

1948. Silver Wedding. As T **33b/c** of St. Helena.
61 10c. violet . . . . 15 1·40
62 $5 red . . . . 23·00 38·00

1949. 75th Anniv of U.P.U. As T **33d/g** of St. Helena.
63 10c. purple 30 60
64 15c. blue . . . . 1·60 2·75
65 25c. orange . . . . 40 2·25
66 50c. black . . . . 1·00 3·25

1949.
67 **7** 1c. black 15 50
68 2c. orange 20 50
69 3c. green . . . . 1·00 3·00
70 4c. brown 20 50
71 5c. purple . . . . 30 1·50
72 6c. grey . . . . 1·00 50
73 8c. red . . . . 30 2·25
74 8c. green . . . . 65 1·25
75 10c. purple 30 20
76 12c. red . . . . 65 2·50
77 15c. blue . . . . 2·00 30
78 20c. black and green . . . . 2·25 3·25
79 20c. blue 80 30
80 25c. purple and orange . . . 1·75 1·75
81 30c. red and purple . . . . . 1·25 1·75
82 35c. red and purple . . . . . 80 2·00
83 40c. red and purple . . . . . 5·00 14·00
84 50c. black and blue . . . . . 2·00 2·00
85 $1 blue and green . . . . . 7·00 7·50
86 $2 green and red . . . . . 26·00 23·00
87 $3 green and brown . . . . 50·00 50·00

1953. Coronation. As T **33h** of St. Helena.
88 10c. black and purple . . . . 1·25 1·00

1957. As Nos. 92/102 of Kedah but inset portrait of Sultan Ismail.
89 1c. black 10 20
90 2c. red . . . . 1·25 30
91 4c. brown 10 10
92 5c. red 10 10
93 8c. green . . . . 4·00 60
94 10c. brown 80 10
94a 10c. purple . . . . 4·25 25
95 20c. blue . . . . 1·00 1·40
96a 50c. black and blue . . . . . 45 1·40
97 $1 blue and purple . . . . . 6·50 6·50
98 $2 green and red . . . . . 16·00 6·50
99 $5 brown and green . . . . 16·00 20·00

8 "Vanda hookeriana"

9 Sultan of Trengganu

1965. As Nos. 115/21 of Kedah, but inset portrait of Sultan Ismail as in T **8**.
100 **8** 1c. multicoloured . . . . . 10 1·75
101 – 2c. multicoloured . . . . . 10 1·75
102 – 5c. multicoloured 15 60
103 – 6c. multicoloured . . . . . 15 1·75
104 – 10c. multicoloured 20 20
105 – 15c. multicoloured . . . . . 1·50 10
106 – 20c. multicoloured . . . . . 1·50 1·00

The higher values used in Trengganu were Nos. 20/7 of Malaysia (National Issues).

1970. 25th Anniv of Installation of H.R.H. Tuanku Ismail Nasiruddin Shah as Sultan of Trengganu.
107 **9** 10c. multicoloured . . . . . 1·00 2·00
108 15c. multicoloured . . . . . 60 1·25
109 50c. multicoloured . . . . . 1·00 2·50

10 "Papilio demoleus"

1971. Butterflies. As Nos. 124/30 of Kedah but with portrait of Sultan Ismail Nasiruddin Shah as in T **10**.
110 – 1c. multicoloured . . . . . 40 2·25
111 – 2c. multicoloured . . . . . 80 2·25
112 – 5c. multicoloured . . . . . 1·00 1·00
113 **10** 6c. multicoloured . . . . . 1·50 2·50
114 – 10c. multicoloured . . . . 1·50 70
115 – 15c. multicoloured . . . . 1·50 20
116 – 20c. multicoloured . . . . 1·75 1·50

The high values in use with this issue were Nos. 64/71 of Malaysia (National Issues).

11 "Durio zibethinus"

1979. Flowers. As Nos. 135/41 of Kedah, but with portrait of Sultan Ismail Nasiruddin Shah as in T **11**.
118 1c. "Rafflesia hasseltii" . . . 10 1·00
119 2c. "Pterocarpus indicus" . . 10 1·00
120 5c. "Largerstoemia speciosa" 10 50
121 10c. Type **11** 15 10
122 15c. "Hibiscus rosa-sinensis" 15 10
123 20c. "Rhododendron scortechinii" 20 10
124 25c. "Etlingera elatior" (inscr "Phaeomeria speciosa") . . 40 50

12 Sultan Mahmud

13 Rubber

1981. Installation of Sultan Mahmud.
125 **12** 10c. black, blue and gold 35 1·25
126 15c. black, yellow and gold 45 50
127 50c. black, purple and gold 1·00 2·75

1986. As Nos. 152/8 of Kedah but with portrait of Sultan Mahmud and inscr "TERENGGANU" as in T **13**.
135 1c. Coffee 10 10
136 2c. Coconuts 10 10
137 5c. Cocoa 15 10
138 10c. Black pepper 15 10
139 15c. Type **13** 20 10
140 20c. Oil palm 25 15
141 30c. Rice 30 15

14 Sultan Mizan Zainal Abidin and Maziah Palace in 1999

1999. Installation of Sultan Mizan Zainal Abidin as Sultan of Trengganu. Multicoloured.
142 30c. Type **14** 30 10
143 50c. Maziah Palace, 1903 . . . 50 50
144 $1 Tengku Tengah Zahara Mosque at night . . . . . 80 1·50

1999. As Nos. 137/8 and 140/1, but with portrait of Sultan Mizan.
147 5c. Cocoa . . . . 3·25
148 10c. Black pepper . . . . . 3·25
150 20c. Oil palm . . . . 3·25
151 30c. Rice 80 85

POSTAGE DUE STAMPS

D 1

1937.
D1 **D 1** 1c. red . . . . 7·50 55·00
D2 4c. green . . . . 9·50 60·00
D3 8c. yellow . . . . 55·00 £325
D4 10c. brown . . . . £110 95·00

TRIESTE Pt. 8

The Free Territory of Trieste situated on the Adriatic Coast between the frontiers of Italy and Yugoslavia. In 1954, when the Territory was divided between Italy and Yugoslavia, the overprinted issues were superseded by the ordinary issues of these countries in their respective zones.

For stamps of Italy surcharged **1.V.1945. TRIESTE TRST**, five-pointed star and value, see Venezia Giulia Nos. 20/32.

ZONE A

ALLIED MILITARY GOVERNMENT

100 centesimi = 1 lira.

Stamps of Italy variously overprinted **A.M.G. F.T.T.** or **AMG-FTT** (Allied Military Government – Free Territory of Trieste) except where otherwise stated.

1947. Postage stamps of 1945, Nos. 647, etc.
1 25c. blue 20 10
2 50c. violet 20 10
3 1l. green 20 10
4 2l. brown 20 10
5 3l. red 20 10
6 4l. red 20 10
7 5l. blue 20 10
8 6l. violet 20 10
9 8l. green . . . . 1·40 85
10 10l. grey 20 10
11 10l. red . . . . 5·75 10
12 15l. blue 25 10
13 20l. violet 65 10
14 25l. green . . . . 1·75 1·75
15 30l. blue . . . . £130 2·75
16 50l. purple . . . . 3·00 1·75
17 100l. red (No. 669) . . . . . 19·00 13·00

1947. Air stamps of 1945, Nos. 670, etc.
18 1l. grey 25 20
19 2l. blue 25 20
20 5l. green . . . . 1·10 40
21 10l. red . . . . 1·25 40
22 25l. brown . . . . 2·25 1·10
23 50l. violet . . . . 21·00 2·00
24 100l. green . . . . 80·00 3·50
25 300l. mauve . . . . 9·00 11·00
26 500l. blue . . . . 12·00 10·00
27 1000l. brown . . . . £110 85·00

1947. Air. 50th Anniv of Radio (Nos. 688/93).
59 6l. violet 70 70
60 10l. red 70 70
61 20l. orange . . . . 5·25 1·40
62 25l. blue 75 70
63 35l. blue 75 70
64 50l. purple . . . . 4·50 5·25

1948. Cent of 1848 Revolution (Nos. 706, etc).
65 3l. brown 15 20
66 4l. purple 15 20
67 5l. blue 15 20
68 6l. green 20 20
69 8l. brown 15 20
70 10l. red 15 20
71 12l. green . . . . 1·10 70
72 15l. black . . . . 6·00 4·00
73 20l. red . . . . 7·50 4·50
74 30l. blue . . . . 45 1·25
75 50l. violet . . . . 3·25 8·50
76 100l. blue . . . . 13·50 20·00

1948. Trieste Philatelic Congress stamps of 1945 optd **A.M.G. F.T.T. 1948 TRIESTE** and posthorn.
77 8l. green (postage) 20 20
78 10l. red 20 20
79 30l. blue . . . . 1·10 30
80 10l. red (air) 30 20
81 25l. brown 40 55
82 50l. violet 40 55

1948. Rebuilding of Bassano Bridge.
84 **209** 15l. green 85 70

1948. Donizetti.
85 **210** 15l. brown . . . . 4·75 70

1949. 25th Biennial Art Exhibition, Venice.
86 **212** 5l. red and flesh 70 20
87 – 15l. green and cream . . . . 5·75 3·00
88 – 20l. brown and buff . . . . 2·75 1·00
89 – 50l. blue and yellow . . . . 7·50 4·75

1949. 27th Milan Fair.
90 **211** 20l. brown . . . . 4·25 1·00

1949. 75th Anniv of U.P.U.
91 **213** 50l. blue . . . . 2·00 1·75

1949. Centenary of Roman Republic.
92 **214** 100l. brown . . . . 28·00 28·00

1949. 1st Trieste Free Election.
93 **218** 20l. red . . . . 2·10 1·25

1949. European Recovery Plan.
94 **215** 5l. green . . . . 4·50 3·50
95 15l. violet . . . . 6·75 6·50
96 20l. brown . . . . 6·75 6·50

1949. 2nd World Health Congress, Rome.
97 **219** 20l. violet . . . . 7·50 2·75

1949. Giuseppe Mazzini.
98 **216** 20l. black . . . . 4·75 1·75

1949. Bicentenary of Vittorio Alfieri.
99 **217** 20l. brown . . . . 4·75 1·75

1949. 400th Anniv of Palladio's Basilica at Vicenza.
100 **220** 20l. violet . . . . 9·25 6·50

1949. 500th Birth Anniv of Lorenzo de Medici.
101 **221** 20l. blue . . . . 4·75 1·75

1949. 13th Bari Fair.
102 **222** 20l. red . . . . 4·75 2·25

1949. (a) Postage.
103 **195** 1l. green 15 20
104 – 2l. brown (No. 656) . . . 15 20
105 – 3l. red (No. 657) 15 20
106 **193** 5l. blue 15 20
107 **195** 6l. violet 15 20
108 – 8l. green (No. 661) . . . 9·00 4·75
109 **193** 10l. red 15 20
110 **195** 15l. blue . . . . 1·25 20
111 – 20l. purple (No. 665) . . . 65 20
112 **196** 25l. green . . . . 18·00 1·75
113 50l. purple . . . . 25·00 1·10
114 **197** 100l. red . . . . 55·00 4·75

(b) Air.
115 **198** 10l. red 15 10
116 – 25l. brown (No. 676) . . . 25 10
117 **198** 50l. violet 20 10
118 – 100l. green (No. 911) . . . 80 10
119 – 300l. mauve (No. 912) . . 9·75 3·50
120 – 500l. blue (No. 913) . . . 11·00 7·25
121 – 1000l. purple (No. 914) . . 16·00 12·00

1949. 150th Anniv of Volta's Discovery of the Electric Cell.
135 **223** 20l. red 2·75 1·75
136 **224** 50l. blue 7·25 6·50

1949. Rebuilding of Holy Trinity Bridge, Florence.
137 **225** 20l. green 2·40 1·40

1949. Death Bimillenary of Catullus (poet).
138 **226** 20l. blue 1·90 1·40

1949. Birth Bicentenary of Domenico Cimarosa (composer).
153 **227** 20l. violet 2·40 1·40

1950. 28th Milan Fair.
154 **228** 20l. brown 2·40 1·00

1950. 32nd Int Automobile Exn, Turin.
155 **229** 20l. violet 90 70

1950. 5th General U.N.E.S.C.O. Conference.
156 – 20l. green 1·10 55
157 **230** 55l. blue 7·50 5·50

1950. Holy Year.
158 **231** 20l. violet 1·75 35
159 55l. blue 8·00 4·00

1950. Honouring Gaudenzio Ferrari (painter).
160 **232** 20l. green 1·50 1·25

1950. International Radio Conference.
161 **233** 20l. violet 3·25 3·50
162 55l. blue 12·50 13·00

1950. Death Bicentenary of Ludovico Murator (historian).
163 **234** 20l. brown 2·40 1·00

1950. 900th Death Anniv of D'Arezzo.
164 **235** 20l. green 2·40 1·00

1950. 14th Levant Fair, Bari.
165 **236** 20l. brown 1·60 1·00

1950. 2nd Trieste Fair. Optd **AMG FTT Fiera di Trieste 1950**.
166 **195** 15l. blue 90 1·00
167 – 20l. purple (No. 665) 1·90 35

1950. Wool Industry Pioneers.
168 **237** 20l. blue 80 35

1950. European Tobacco Conf (Nos. 755/7).
169 5l. green and mauve 35 20
170 20l. green and brown 2·25 85
171 55l. brown and blue 14·00 13·00

1950. Bicentenary of Fine Arts Academy.
172 **239** 20l. red and deep brown 1·75 1·00

1950. Birth Centenary of Augusto Righi.
173 **240** 20l. black and buff 2·25 1·00

1950. Provincial Occupations (Nos. 760/78).
176 50c. blue 10 15
177 1l. violet 10 10
178 2l. brown 10 10
179 5l. black 10 10
180 6l. brown 10 10
181 10l. green 10 10
182 12l. green 40 30
183 15l. blue 75 10
184 20l. violet 40 10
185 25l. brown 75 10
186 30l. purple 25 20
187 35l. red 95 65
188 40l. brown 65 30
189 50l. violet 15 10
190 55l. blue 15 30
191 60l. red 2·40 1·60
192 65l. green 15 30
193 100l. brown 1·90 10
194 200l. brown 1·25 2·00

1951. Centenary of 1st Tuscan Stamp.
195 **249** 20l. red and purple 2·25 1·00
196 55l. blue and ultramarine 20·00 21·00

1951. 33rd International Motor Show, Turin.
197 **243** 20l. green 90 1·00

1951. Consecration of Hall of Peace, Rome.
198 **244** 20l. violet 1·10 80

1951. 29th Milan Fair.
199 **245** 20l. brown 1·40 65
200 **246** 55l. blue 1·60 1·40

1951. 10th International Textiles Exn, Turin.
201 **247** 20l. violet 1·10 1·00

1951. 500th Birth Anniv of Columbus.
202 **248** 20l. green 1·60 1·40

1951. International Gymnastic Festival, Florence.
203 **249** 5l. red and brown 3·50 4·00
204 10l. red and green 3·50 4·00
205 15l. red and blue 3·50 4·00

1951. Restoration of Montecassino Abbey.
206 **250** 20l. violet 60 35
207 – 55l. blue (No. 791) 90 50

1951. 3rd Trieste Fair. Optd **AMG-FTT FIERA di TRIESTE 1951** and shield.
208 6l. brown (No. 764) 25 10
209 20l. violet (No. 768) 30 10
210 55l. blue (No. 774) 85 50

1951. 500th Birth Anniv of Perugino.
211 **251** 20l. brown and sepia 55 35

1951. Triennial Art Exhibition, Milan.
212 **252** 20l. black and green 90 1·00
213 – 55l. pink and blue (No. 794) 95 1·00

1951. World Cycling Championship.
214 **253** 25l. black 3·25 1·40

1951. 15th Levant Fair, Bari.
215 **254** 25l. blue 60 35

1951. Birth Centenary of F. P. Michetti.
216 **255** 25l. brown 60 35

1951. Sardinian Stamp Centenary.
217 **256** 10l. black and brown 30 45
218 – 25l. green and red (No. 799) 40 20
219 – 60l. red and blue (No. 800) 80 65

1951. 3rd Industrial and Commercial Census.
220 **257** 10l. green 45 40

1951. 9th National Census.
221 **258** 25l. black 45 20

1951. Forestry Festival.
222 **260** 10l. green and olive 35 20
223 25l. green (No. 807) 55 40

1951. Verdi.
224 – 10l. green and purple (No. 803) 45 20
225 **259** 25l. sepia and brown 40 20
226 – 60l. blue and green (No. 805) 85 85

1952. Bellini.
227 **261** 25l. black 55 35

1952. Caserta Palace.
228 **262** 25l. bistre and green 55 35

1952. 1st International Sports Stamps Exn, Rome.
229 **263** 25l. brown and black 40 35

1952. 30th Milan Fair.
230 **264** 60l. blue 1·10 1·00

1952. Leonardo da Vinci.
231 **265** 25l. orange 15 15
232 – 60l. blue (No. 813) 75 65
233 **265** 80l. red 85 15

1952. Overseas Fair, Naples.
234 **268** 25l. blue 50 35

1952. Modena and Parma Stamp Centenaries.
235 **267** 25l. black and brown 30 15
236 60l. indigo and blue 70 65

1952. Art Exhibition, Venice.
237 **269** 25l. black and cream 55 35

1952. 30th Padua Fair.
238 **270** 25l. red and blue 40 35

1952. 4th Trieste Fair.
239 **271** 25l. green, red and brown 40 35

1952. 16th Levant Fair, Bari.
240 **272** 25l. green 40 35

1952. Savonarola.
241 **273** 25l. violet 40 35

1952. 1st Private Aeronautics Conf, Rome.
242 **274** 60l. blue and ultramarine 90 1·00

1952. Alpine Troops National Exhibition.
243 **275** 25l. black 45 35

1952. Armed Forces Day.
244 **276** 10l. green 10 10
245 **277** 25l. brown & light brown 20 10
246 – 60l. black and blue (No. 827) 50 20

1952. Mission to Ethiopia.
247 **278** 25l. deep brown and brown 60 35

1952. Birth Centenary of Gemito (sculptor).
248 **279** 25l. brown 45 35

1952. Birth Centenary of Mancini (painter).
249 **280** 25l. green 45 35

1952. Centenary of Martyrdom of Belfiore.
250 **281** 25l. blue and black 45 35

1953. Antonello Exhibition, Messina.
251 **282** 25l. red 40 35

1953. 20th "Mille Miglia" Car Race.
252 **283** 25l. violet 40 35

1953. Labour Orders of Merit.
253 **284** 25l. violet 40 35

1953. 300th Birth Anniv of Corelli.
254 **285** 25l. brown 40 35

1953. Coin type.
255 **286** 5l. grey 10 10
256 10l. red 10 10
257 12l. green 10 10
258 13l. purple 10 10
259 20l. brown 10 10
260 25l. violet 10 10
261 35l. red 25 25
262 60l. blue 50 25
263 80l. brown 55 25

1953. 7th Death Centenary of St. Clare.
264 **287** 25l. red and brown 50 35

1953. 5th Trieste Fair. Optd **V FIERA DI TRIESTE AMG FTT 1953**.
265 10l. green (No. 765) 25 20
266 25l. orange (No. 769) 25 20
267 60l. red (No. 775) 30 30

1953. Mountains Festival.
272 **288** 25l. green 60 35

1953. International Agricultural Exn, Rome.
273 **289** 25l. brown 20 10
274 60l. blue 40 30

1953. 4th Anniv of Atlantic Pact.
275 **290** 25l. turquoise and orange 50 35
276 60l. blue and mauve 1·10 1·75

1953. 5th Birth Centenary of Signorelli.
277 **291** 25l. green and brown 45 35

1953. 6th Int Microbiological Congress, Rome.
278 **292** 25l. brown and black 55 35

1953. Tourist series (Nos. 855/60).
279 10l. brown and sepia 10 10
280 12l. black and blue 10 10
281 20l. brown and orange 10 10
282 25l. green and blue 10 10
283 35l. brown and buff 20 20
284 60l. blue and green 25 20

1954. 25th Anniv of Lateran Treaty.
285 **294** 25l. sepia and brown 15 10
286 60l. blue and light blue 35 25

1954. Introduction of Television in Italy.
287 **295** 25l. violet 25 10
288 60l. green 40 30

1954. Encouragement to Taxpayers.
289 **296** 25l. violet 55 20

1954. Milan–Turin Helicopter Mail Flight.
290 **297** 25l. green 50 35

1954. 10th Anniv of Resistance Movement.
291 **298** 25l. black and brown 50 35

1954. 6th Trieste Fair. Nos. 282 and 284 of Trieste additionally optd **FIERA DI TRIESTE 1954**.
292 – 25l. green and blue 30 10
293 **293** 60l. blue and green 50 35

1954. Birth Centenary of Catalani.
294 **299** 25l. green 45 35

1954. 7th Birth Centenary of Marco Polo.
295 **300** 25l. brown 20 20
296 60l. green 40 50

1954. 60th Anniv of Italian Touring Club.
297 **301** 25l. green and red 45 30

1954. International Police Congress, Rome.
298 **302** 25l. red 20 10
299 60l. blue 30 25

CONCESSIONAL LETTER POST

1947. Optd **A.M.G. F.T.T.** in two lines.
CL44 – 1l. brn (No. CL649) 15 10
CL45 CL **201** 8l. red 4·00 1·00
CL46 CL **220** 15l. violet 25·00 3·50

1949. Optd **AMG-FTT**.
CL122 CL **220** 15l. violet 1·00 20
CL123 20l. violet 3·75 20

CONCESSIONAL PARCEL POST

1953.
CP268 CP **288** 40l. orange 3·50 1·40
CP269 50l. blue 3·50 1·40
CP270 75l. brown 9·75 1·40
CP271 110l. pink 11·50 1·40
Unused prices are for the complete stamp, used prices for the left half of the stamp.

EXPRESS LETTER STAMPS

1947. Express Letter stamps optd **A.M.G. F.T.T.** in two lines.
E28 – 15l. red (No. E681) 20 20
E29 **200** 25l. orange 16·00 3·75
E30 30l. violet 40 55
E31 – 60l. red (No. E685) 11·50 6·50

1948. Centenary of 1848 Revolution. Express Letter stamp optd **A.M.G.-F.T.T.**
E83 E **209** 35l. violet 1·25 1·00

1950. Express Letter stamps optd **AMG-FTT** in one line.
E174 E **209** 50l. purple 1·75 75
E175 – 60l. red (No. E685) 1·75 85

PARCEL POST STAMPS

Unused prices are for complete stamps, used prices for a half-stamp.

1947. Parcel Post stamps optd **A.M.G. F.T.T.** in two lines on each half of stamp.
P32 P **201** 1l. brown 25 10
P33 2l. blue 25 10
P34 3l. orange 25 10
P35 4l. grey 35 10
P36 5l. purple 1·40 10
P37 10l. violet 1·90 10
P38 20l. purple 2·75 10
P39 50l. red 3·75 10
P40 100l. blue 8·00 10
P41 200l. green £150 2·00
P42 300l. purple 95·00 85
P43 500l. brown 50·00 45

1949. Parcel Post stamps optd **AMG-FTT** in one line on each half of stamp.
P139 P **201** 1l. brown 1·10 15
P140 2l. blue 30 10
P141 3l. orange 30 10
P142 4l. grey 30 10
P143 5l. purple 30 10
P144 10l. violet 60 10
P145 20l. purple 60 10
P146 30l. purple 60 10
P147 50l. red 65 10
P148 100l. blue 1·25 10
P149 200l. green 12·00 25
P150 300l. purple 40·00 30
P151 500l. brown 20·00 90
P152 P **928** 1000l. blue £120 4·00

POSTAGE DUE STAMPS

1947. Postage Due stamps optd **A.M.G. F.T.T.** in two lines.
D44 **D 192** 1l. orange 55 35
D48 **D 201** 1l. orange 35 20
D49 2l. green 35 20
D50 3l. red . . . . . . 75 5·00
D51 4l. brown . . . . . . 3·00 5·50
D45 **D 192** 5l. violet . . . . . . 2·50 20
D52 **D 201** 5l. violet . . . . . . 65·00 7·25
D53 6l. blue . . . . . . 13·50 11·50
D54 8l. mauve . . . . . . 19·00 22·00
D46 **D 192** 10l. blue . . . . . . 4·50 20
D55 **D 201** 10l. blue . . . . . . 75·00 5·00
D56 12l. brown . . . . . . 16·00 13·00
D47 **D 192** 20l. red . . . . . . 16·00 65
D57 **D 201** 20l. purple . . . . . . 12·00 1·00
D58 50l. green . . . . . . 1·25 35

1949. Postage Due stamps optd **AMG-FTT** in one line.
D122 **D 201** 1l. orange 20 10
D123 2l. green 20 10
D124 3l. red 20 10
D125 5l. violet 45 20
D126 6l. blue 25 20
D127 8l. mauve 25 20
D128 10l. blue 45 20
D129 12l. brown . . . . . 1·10 20
D130 20l. purple . . . . . 2·75 20
D131 25l. red . . . . . 4·00 1·00
D132 50l. green . . . . . 1·60 20
D133 100l. orange . . . . . 6·00 20
D134 500l. purple and blue 21·00 11·50

ZONE B
YUGOSLAV MILITARY GOVERNMENT

1948. 100 centesimi = 1 lira.
1949. 100 paras = 1 dinar.

Apart from the definitive issues illustrated below the following are stamps of Yugoslavia (sometimes in new colours), variously overprinted **STT VUJA** or **VUJA-STT** or (Nos. B65 onwards) **STT VUJNA** unless otherwise stated.

B 1 B 2

1948. Labour Day.
B1 **B 1** 100l. red and stone (A) . . 6·50 4·50
B2 100l. red and stone (B) . . 7·00 4·50
B3 100l. red and stone (C) . . 6·50 4·50
Inscr in Slovene (A) "I. MAJ 1948 V STO"; Italian (B) "I. MAGGIO 1948 NEL TLT"; or Croat (C) "I. SVIBANJ 1948 U STT".

1948. Red Cross. No. 545 optd and surch.
B3a **131** 2l. on 50p. brown and red . . . . 9·25 8·00

1948. Air. Economic Exhibition, Capodistria.
B4 **B 2** 25l. grey 50 40
B5 50l. orange 50 40

B 3 Clasped Hands, Hammer and Sickle

B 4 Fishermen and Flying Boat

B 5 Man with Donkey
B 6 Mediterranean Gull over Chimneys

1949. Labour Day.
B6 **B 3** 10l. green 35 25

1949. Air.
B 7 **B 4** 1l. turquoise 20 10
B 8 **B 5** 2l. brown 20 10
B 9 **B 4** 5l. blue 20 10
B10 **B 5** 10l. violet . . . . . . 1·25 40
B11 **B 4** 25l. brown . . . . . . 1·40 2·00
B12 **B 5** 50l. green . . . . . . 1·60 1·60
B13 **B 6** 100l. brown . . . . . . 3·50 3·00

1949. Partisans issue.
B14 **119** 50p. grey 25 10
B15 1d. green 25 10
B16 **120** 2d. red 25 10
B17 – 3d. red (No. 508) . . . 45 10
B18 **120** 4d. blue 45 10
B19 – 5d. blue (No. 511) . . . 45 10
B20 – 9d. mauve (No. 514) . . . 90 80
B21 – 12d. blue (No. 515) . . . 2·75 1·25
B22 **119** 16d. blue . . . . 5·25 5·50
B23 – 20d. red (No. 517) . . . 5·50 6·00

1949. 75th Anniv of U.P.U.
B24 – 5d. blue (No. 612) . . . 5·75 6·00
B25 **158** 12d. brown . . . . . . 5·75 6·00

1949. Air. Optd **DIN** or surch also.
B26 **B 4** 1d. turquoise 15 10
B27 **B 5** 2d. brown 15 10
B28 **B 4** 5d. blue 20 10
B29 **B 5** 10d. violet 40 10
B30 **B 4** 15d. on 25l. brown . . . 6·25 7·00
B31 **B 5** 20d. on 50l. green . . . 1·40 3·00
B32 **B 6** 30d. on 100l. purple . . . 2·25 3·00

1950. Centenary of Yugoslav Railways.
B33 **116** 2d. green 90 65
B34 – 3d. red (No. 632) . . . 2·00 65
B35 – 5d. blue (No. 633) . . . 1·75 65
B36 – 10d. orange (No. 633a) . . . 7·75 3·00

B 10 Girl on Donkey
B 11 Workers

1950.
B37 **B 10** 50p. grey 20 20
B38 – 1d. red (Cockerel) . . . 20 20
B38a – 1d. brown (Cockerel) . . . 45 20
B39 – 2d. blue (Geese) . . . 20 20
B40 – 3d. brown (Bees) . . . 20 20
B40a – 3d. red (Bees) . . . 60 20
B41 – 5d. green (Oxen) . . . 75 20
B42 – 10d. brown (Turkey) . . . 1·40 80
B43 – 15d. violet (Kids) . . . 9·75 4·00
B44 – 20d. green (Silkworms) . . . 3·25 1·60

1950. May Day.
B45 **B 11** 3d. violet 50 35
B46 10d. red 60 45

1950. Red Cross.
B47 **160** 50p. brown and red . . . 70 50

B 12 Worker
B 13 P. P. Vergerio Jr.

1951. May Day.
B48 **B 12** 3d. red 75 65
B49 10d. green . . . . 1·60 95

1951. Red Cross
B49a **191** 0d.50 blue and red . . . 9·25 8·25

1951. Festival of Italian Culture.
B50 **B 13** 5d. blue 65 65
B51 10d. purple 65 65
B52 20d. brown . . . . 65 1·00

1951. Cultural Anniversaries.
B53 **189** 10d. orange 75 80
B54 – 12d. black (As No. 699) . . . 75 80

B 14a Koper Square
B 15 Cyclists

1952. Air. 75th Anniv of U.P.U.
B54a **B 14a** 5d. brown . . . . . 4·00 4·00
B54b – 15d. blue . . . . . 7·25 4·00
B54c – 25d. green . . . . . 6·25 3·50
DESIGNS—VERT: 15d. Lighthouse, Piran. HORIZ: 25d. Hotel, Portoroz.

1952. Physical Culture Propaganda.
B55 **B 15** 5d. brown 15 10
B56 – 10d. green 20 10
B57 – 15d. red 20 10
B58 – 28d. blue 55 20
B59 – 50d. red . . . . . . 1·10 1·00
B60 – 100d. blue . . . . . . 5·75 6·50
DESIGNS: 10d. Footballers; 15d. Rowing four; 28d. Yachting; 50d. Netball players; 100d. Diver.

1952. Marshal Tito's 60th Birthday. As Nos. 727/9 of Yugoslavia additionally inscr "STT VUJA".
B61 **196** 15d. brown . . . . . . 1·60 1·25
B62 **197** 28d. red . . . . . . 1·50 80
B63 – 50d. green (No. 729) . . 2·10 2·00

1952. Children's Week.
B64 **198** 15d. pink 80 80

1952. 15th Olympic Games, Helsinki. As Nos. 731/6.
B65 **199** 5d. brown on flesh . . . 45 20
B66 – 10d. green on cream . . . 45 20
B67 – 15d. violet on mauve . . 45 20
B68 – 28d. brown on buff . . . 95 20
B69 – 50d. brown on yellow . . 5·50 2·00
B70 – 100d. blue on pink . . . 4·50 10·00

1952. Navy Day (Nos. 737/9).
B71 – 15d. purple . . . . . . 1·40 1·10
B72 **200** 28d. brown . . . . . . 1·40 1·10
B73 – 50d. black . . . . . . 2·40 2·40

1952. Red Cross.
B74 **201** 50p. red, grey and black 30 20

1952. 6th Yugoslav Communist Party Congress.
B75 **202** 15d. brown 55 65
B76 15d. turquoise 55 65
B77 15d. brown 55 65
B78 15d. blue 55 65

B 17 European Anchovy and Starfish

1952. Philatelic Exhibition, Koper.
B78a **B 17** 15d. brown . . . . . 1·90 1·25

1953. 10th Death Anniv of Tesla (inventor).
B79 **203** 15d. red 30 10
B80 30d. blue 70 25

1953. Pictorials of 1950.
B81 1d. grey (No. 705) . . . . 4·00 2·50
B86 2d. red (No. 718) 20 20
B82 3d. red (No. 655) 30 20
B87 5d. orange (No. 719) 15 10
B83 10d. green (No. 721) 30 10
B88 15d. red (No. 723) 30 10
B84 30d. blue (No. 712) . . . . 3·00 5·25
B85 50d. turquoise (No. 714) . . 8·50 6·00

1953. United Nations (Nos. 747/9).
B89 **204** 15d. green 20 15
B90 – 30d. blue 25 15
B91 – 50d. red 65 40

1953. Adriatic Car Rally. As Nos. 750/3.
B92 **205** 15d. brown and yellow 30 10
B93 – 30d. green and emerald 30 10
B94 – 50d. mauve and orange 30 10
B95 – 70d. deep blue and blue 80 40

1953. Marshal Tito.
B96 **206** 50d. green . . . . 1·60 1·60

1953. 38th Esperanto Congress, Zagreb.
B97 **207** 15d. grn & turq (postage) 1·00 1·25
B98 300d. green and violet (air) £140 £140

1953. 10th Anniv of Liberation of Istria and Slovene Coast.
B99 **209** 15d. blue . . . . 1·75 1·25

1953. Death Centenary of Radicevic (poet).
B100 **210** 15d. black . . . . . . 1·10 80

1953. Red Cross.
B101 **211** 2d. red and bistre . . . 35 15

1953. 10th Anniv of 1st Republican Legislative Assembly. As Nos. 762/4.
B102 **212** 15d. violet 45 40
B103 – 30d. red 75 40
B104 – 50d. green 75 80

1954. Air. As Nos. 675 etc.
B108 1d. lilac 20 10
B109 2d. green 20 10
B110 3d. purple 20 10
B111 5d. brown 20 10
B112 10d. turquoise 20 10
B113 20d. brown 30 10
B114 30d. blue 30 40
B115 50d. black 50 40
B116 100d. red . . . . 1·60 65
B117 200d. violet . . . . 2·50 80
B118 500d. orange . . . . 12·00 6·00

1954. Animals. As Nos. 765/76.
B119 2d. grey, buff and red . . . 25 20
B120 5d. slate, buff and grey . . 25 20
B121 10d. brown and green . . . 25 20
B122 15d. brown and blue . . . 30 25
B123 17d. sepia and brown . . . 30 25
B124 25d. yellow, blue and brown 35 25
B125 30d. brown and violet . . . 45 25
B126 35d. black and purple . . . 55 40
B127 50d. brown and green . . . 90 65
B128 65d. black and brown . . . 2·25 2·25
B129 70d. brown and blue . . . 3·25 2·40
B130 100d. black and blue . . . 10·50 9·00

1954. Serbian Insurrection. As Nos. 778/81.
B131 – 15d. multicoloured . . . 40 20
B132 **214** 30d. multicoloured . . . 40 20
B133 – 50d. multicoloured . . . 40 20
B134 – 70d. multicoloured . . . 65 65

POSTAGE DUE STAMPS

1948. Red Cross. No. D546 surch **VUJA STT** and new value.
BD4 **131** 2l. on 50p. green and red £100 90·00

1949. On 1946 issue.
BD26 **D 126** 50p. orange 60 15
BD27 1d. orange 40 15
BD74 1d. brown 15 10
BD28 2d. blue 50 15
BD75 2d. green 15 10
BD29 3d. green 60 15
BD30 5d. violet 70 80
BD76 5d. blue 15 10
BD77 10d. red 10 10
BD78 20d. violet 25 10
BD79 30d. orange 40 20
BD80 50d. blue . . . . 3·25 1·10
BD81 100d. purple . . . . 3·50 1·60
Nos. BD26/30 optd **STT VUJA** and the rest **STT VUJNA**.

1950. Red Cross. No. D617 optd **VUJA STT**.
BD48 **160** 50p. purple and red . . 80 40

BD 12 European Anchovy

1950. Fishes.
BD49 – 50p. brown 55 20
BD50 – 1d. green . . . . 1·25 40
BD51 **BD 12** 2d. blue . . . . 1·90 1·25
BD52 3d. blue . . . . 1·90 1·25
BD53 5d. purple . . . . 4·25 2·75
DESIGN: 50p., 1d. Two meagres.

1951. Red Cross. No. D703 optd **STT VUJA**.
BD54 **191** 0d.50 green and red . . 95·00 90·00

The following are optd **STT VUJNA.**

1952. Red Cross. No. D741.
BD82 **D 202** 50p. red and grey . . 1·10 65

1953. Red Cross. As No. D762.
BD102 **211** 2d. red and purple . . 50 70

TRINIDAD Pt. 1

An island in the West Indies off the coast of Venezuela. Now uses stamps of Trinidad and Tobago.

12 pence = 1 shilling;
20 shillings = 1 pound.

2 Britannia
4 Britannia

1851. Imperf.
2 **2** (1d.) purple . . . . 11·00 70·00
3 (1d.) blue . . . . 11·00 55·00
5 (1d.) grey . . . . 65·00 60·00
8 (1d.) red . . . . £150 65·00
25 **4** 4d. lilac . . . . 90·00 £325
28 6d. green . . . . – £425
29 1s. blue . . . . 90·00 £325

3

1852.
18 **3** (1d.) blue £4000 £650
19 (1d.) grey £4000 £400
20 (1d.) red . . . . 13·00 £600

1859. Perf.
75 **2** (1d.) red . . . . 22·00 1·00
70 **4** 4d. lilac . . . . £100 13·00
76 4d. grey . . . . 95·00 70
72c 6d. green . . . . 65·00 4·75
63 1s. blue . . . . £2000 90·00
73b 1s. purple . . . . 90·00 4·25
78 1s. yellow . . . . £100 2·50

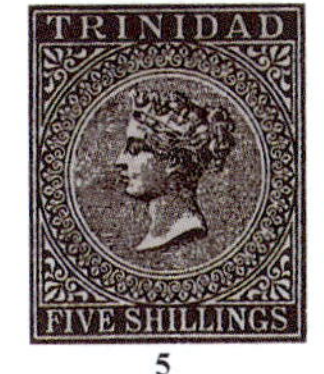

5 10

1869.

113	5	5s. red	50·00	80·00

1879. Surch in words.

98	2	½d. lilac	10·00	7·00
101		1d. red	27·00	80

1882. No. 95 surch **1d** with pen.

104	4	1d. on 6d. green	7·00	4·50

1883.

106	10	½d. green	4·00	1·25
107		1d. red	10·00	50
108		2½d. blue	11·00	60
110		4d. grey	2·50	60
111		6d. black	3·25	4·25
112		1s. orange	3·75	2·25

11 Britannia

12 Britannia

1896.

114	11	½d. purple and green	3·25	30
126		½d. green	65	2·00
115		1d. purple and red	3·50	10
127		1d. black on red	1·25	10
135		1d. red	1·25	10
117		2½d. purple and blue	4·75	20
128		2½d. purple and blue on blue	15·00	25
137		2½d. blue	2·50	15
118		4d. purple and orange	6·50	17·00
129		4d. green and blue on buff	1·75	14·00
138		4d. grey and red on yellow	1·50	8·00
119		5d. purple and mauve	6·50	14·00
120		6d. purple and black	7·50	5·50
140		6d. purple and mauve	7·00	9·00
121		1s. green and brown	7·00	6·50
130		1s. black and blue on yellow	18·00	5·50
142		1s. purple & blue on yellow	10·00	13·00
143		1s. black on green	1·75	1·25
122	12	5s. green and brown	42·00	75·00
131		5s. purple and mauve	42·00	65·00
123		10s. green and blue	£150	£275
124		£1 green and red	£130	£190

13 Landing of Columbus

14

1898. 400th Anniv of Discovery of Trinidad.

125	13	2d. brown and violet	2·50	1·25

1909. Figures in corners.

146	14	½d. green	3·50	10
147	–	1d. red	3·00	10
148	–	2½d. blue	10·00	3·25

On the 1d. figures are in lower corners only.

POSTAGE DUE STAMPS

D 1

1885.

D 1	D 1	½d. black	15·00	45·00
D18		1d. black	1·00	1·75
D19		2d. black	2·00	1·50
D20		3d. black	2·00	2·50
D21		4d. black	2·75	21·00
D14		5d. black	11·00	11·00
D15		6d. black	6·00	10·00
D16		8d. black	12·00	14·00
D17		1s. black	12·00	35·00

For stamps in Type D 1 but with value in cents see under Trinidad and Tobago.

OFFICIAL STAMPS

1894. Optd **O S.**

O1	10	½d. green	35·00	55·00
O2		1d. red	38·00	60·00
O3		2½d. blue	45·00	90·00
O4		4d. grey	48·00	95·00
O5		6d. black	48·00	95·00
O6		1s. orange	65·00	£130
O7	5	5s. red	£160	£475

1909. Optd **OFFICIAL.**

O8	11	½d. green	90	6·00
O9		1d. red	90	6·00

1910. Optd **OFFICIAL.**

O10	14	½d. green	4·25	6·00

TRINIDAD AND TOBAGO Pt. 1

Combined issues for Trinidad and Tobago, administratively one colony. Part of the British Caribbean Federation from 1958 until 31 August 1962, when it became independent within the British Commonwealth.

1913. 12 pence = 1 shilling; 20 shillings = 1 pound.
1935. 100 cents = 1 West Indian dollar.

17

18

1913.

149	17	½d. green	3·00	10
207		1d. red	60	30
208		1d. brown	60	1·50
209		2d. grey	1·00	1·25
151		2½d. blue	6·00	50
211		3d. blue	3·00	3·00
152a		4d. black and red on yellow	70	6·00
153a		6d. purple and mauve	9·50	4·00
154c		1s. black on green	1·50	3·00
155d	18	5s. purple and mauve	48·00	90·00
156a		£1 green and red	£120	£170

1915. Optd cross over **21. 10. 15.**

174	17	1d. red	1·50	1·50

1916. Optd **19.10.16.** over cross.

175	17	1d. red	50	2·00

1917. Optd **WAR TAX** in one line (No. 176) or two lines (others).

177	17	½d. green	10	20
176		1d. red	2·25	2·75
180		1d. red	10	75

1918. Optd **War Tax** in two lines.

187	17	½d. green	10	1·75
188b		1d. red	10	60

27

28 First Boca

1922.

218	27	½d. green	50	10
219		1d. brown	50	10
220b		1½d. red	1·75	30
222		2d. grey	50	1·25
223		3d. blue	50	1·25
224		4d. black and red on yellow	3·25	3·25
225		6d. purple and mauve	2·25	25·00
226		6d. green and red on green	1·25	60
227		1s. black on green	5·50	1·75
228		5s. purple and mauve	22·00	38·00
229		£1 green and red	95·00	£200

1935.

230a	28	1c. blue and green	30	10
231a	–	2c. blue and brown	1·00	10
232	–	3c. black and red	1·00	30
233	–	6c. brown and blue	4·25	2·50
234	–	8c. green and red	3·75	3·50
235	–	12c. black and violet	3·25	1·75
236	–	24c. black and green	2·75	1·50
237	–	48c. green	8·50	15·00
238	–	72c. green and red	28·00	30·00

DESIGNS: 2c. Imperial College of Tropical Agriculture; 3c. Mt. Irvine Bay, Tobago; 6c. Discovery of Lake Asphalt; 8c. Queen's Park, Savannah; 12c. Town Hall, San Fernando; 24c. Govt. House; 48c. Memorial Park; 72c. Blue Basin.

1935. Silver Jubilee. As T **32a** of St. Helena.

239	2c. blue and black	30	75
240	3c. blue and red	30	1·25
241	6c. brown and blue	1·50	2·50
242	24c. grey and purple	5·50	16·00

1937. Coronation. As T **32b** of St. Helena.

243	1c. green	15	20
244	2c. brown	35	15
245	8c. orange	90	1·75

37 First Boca

47 King George VI

1938. Designs as 1935 issue but with portrait of King George VI as in T **37** and without "POSTAGE & REVENUE", and T **47**.

246	37	1c. blue and green	1·00	30
247	–	2c. blue and brown	1·25	20
248	–	3c. black and red	11·00	1·00
248a	–	3c. green and purple	30	20
249	–	4c. brown	25·00	1·50
249a	–	4c. red	50	1·00
249b	–	5c. mauve	50	15
250	–	6c. brown and blue	2·75	80
251	–	8c. green and red	2·75	1·00
252a	–	12c. black and purple	2·75	10
253	–	24c. black and olive	2·00	10
254	–	60c. green and red	8·50	1·50
255	47	$1.20 green	10·00	1·50
256		$4.80 red	21·00	30·00

NEW DESIGNS: 4c. Memorial Park; 5c. G.P.O. and Treasury; 60c. As No. 238.

1946. Victory. As T **33a** of St. Helena.

257	3c. brown	10	10
258	6c. blue	10	1·00

1948. Silver Wedding. As T **33b/c** of St. Helena.

259	3c. brown	10	10
260	$4.80 red	19·00	25·00

1949. 75th Anniv of U.P.U. As T **33d/g** of St. Helena.

261	5c. purple	30	70
262	6c. blue	1·50	75
263	12c. violet	30	1·00
264	24c. green	40	85

1951. B.W.I. University College. As T **10a/b** of St. Kitts-Nevis.

265	3c. green and brown	20	75
266	12c. black and violet	30	75

48 First Boca

51 Cipriani Memorial

53 Copper-rumped Hummingbird ("Humming Bird")

1953. Designs as 1938 and 1940 issues but with portrait of Queen Elizabeth in place of King George VI as in T **48** (1c., 2c., 12c.) or facing left (others).

267	48	1c. blue and green	20	40
268	–	2c. blue and brown	20	40
269	–	3c. green and purple	20	10
270	–	4c. red	20	40
271	–	5c. mauve	30	30
272	–	6c. brown and blue	50	30
273	–	8c. olive and red	1·75	30
274	–	12c. black and purple	30	10
275	–	24c. black and olive	1·75	30
276	–	60c. green and red	20·00	1·25
277a	–	$1.20 green	1·25	30
278a	–	$4.80 red	8·50	14·00

1953. Coronation. As T **33h** of St. Helena.

279	3c. black and green	20	10

1956. No. 268 surch **ONE CENT.**

280	1c. on 2c. blue and brown	1·25	1·75

1958. Inaug of British Caribbean Federation. As T **27a** of St. Kitts-Nevis.

281	5c. green	20	10
282	6c. blue	25	1·50
283	12c. red	25	10

1960.

284	51	1c. stone and black	10	10
285	–	2c. blue	10	10
286	–	5c. blue	10	10
287	–	6c. brown	10	50
288	–	8c. green	10	1·00
289	–	10c. lilac	10	10
290	–	12c. red	10	75
291	–	15c. orange (A)	1·00	50
291a	–	15c. orange (B)	4·00	10
292	–	25c. red and blue	80	10
293	–	35c. green and black	3·25	10
294	–	50c. yellow, grey and blue	35	75
295	–	60c. red, green and blue	55	30
296	53	$1.20 multicoloured	15·00	2·50
297	–	$4.80 green and blue	15·00	10·00

DESIGNS—HORIZ (as Type **51**): 2c. Queen's Hall; 5c. Whitehall; 6c. Treasury Building; 8c. Governor-General's House; 10c. General Hospital, San Fernando; 12c. Oil refinery; 15c. (A) Crest, (B) Coat of arms; 25c. Scarlet ibis; 35c. Pitch Lake; 50c. Mohammed Jinnah Mosque. VERT (as Type **51**): 60c. Anthurium lilies. (As Type **53**): $4.80, Map of Trinidad and Tobago.

65 Scouts and Gold Wolf Badge

1961. 2nd Caribbean Scout Jamboree. Design multicoloured. Background colours given.

298	65	8c. green	15	10
299		25c. blue	15	10

66 "Buccoo Reef" (painting by Carlisle Chang)

1962. Independence.

300	66	5c. turquoise	10	10
301	–	8c. grey	40	60
302	–	25c. violet	15	10
303	–	35c. multicoloured	2·25	15
304	–	60c. red, black and blue	2·75	3·50

DESIGNS: 8c. Piarco Air Terminal; 25c. Hilton Hotel, Port-of-Spain; 35c. Greater bird of paradise ("Bird of Paradise") and map; 60c. Scarlet ibis and map.

71 "Protein Foods"

1963. Freedom from Hunger.

305	71	5c. red	15	10
306		8c. bistre	15	45
307		25c. blue	25	20

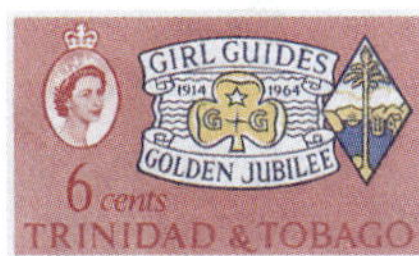
72 Jubilee Emblem

1964. Golden Jubilee of Trinidad and Tobago Girl Guides' Association.

308	72	6c. yellow, blue and red	10	70
309		25c. yellow, ultram & blue	15	20
310		35c. yellow, blue and green	15	20

73 I.C.Y. Emblem

1965. International Co-operation Year.

311	73	35c. brown, green & yellow	65	20

74 Eleanor Roosevelt, Flag and U.N. Emblem

1965. Eleanor Roosevelt Memorial Foundation.

312	74	25c. black, red and blue	15	10

75 Parliament Building

1966. Royal Visit. Multicoloured.
313 5c. Type **75** 15 10
314 8c. Map, Royal Yacht "Britannia" and arms . . . 1·25 70
315 25c. Map and flag . . . . . 1·25 55
316 35c. Flag and panorama . . 1·25 70

1967. 5th Year of Independence. Nos. 289, 291a and 295 optd **FIFTH YEAR OF INDEPENDENCE 31st AUGUST 1967**.
318 8c. green 10 10
319 10c. lilac 10 10
320 15c. orange 10 10
321 60c. blue, green and red . . . 25 15

80 Musical Instruments

1968. Trinidad Carnival. Multicoloured.
322 5c. Type **80** 10 10
323 10c. Calypso King (vert) . . 10 10
324 15c. Steel band 10 10
325 25c. Carnival procession . . 15 10
326 35c. Carnival King (vert) . . 15 10
327 60c. Carnival Queen (vert) . . 20 1·00

86 Doctor giving Eye-test

87 Peoples of the World and Emblem

1968. 20th Anniv of World Health Organization.
328 **86** 5c. red, brown and gold . . 15 10
329 25c. orange, brown and gold 35 10
330 35c. blue, black and gold 40 15

1968. Human Rights Year.
331 **87** 5c. red, black and yellow 10 10
332 10c. blue, black and yellow 15 10
333 25c. green, black and yellow 30 15

88 Cycling

1968. Olympic Games, Mexico. Multicoloured.
334 5c. Type **88** 50 10
335 15c. Weightlifting 20 10
336 25c. Relay-racing 20 10
337 35c. Sprinting 20 10
338 $1.20 Maps of Mexico and Trinidad . . . . 1·00 45

93 Cocoa Beans

1969. Multicoloured.
339c 1c. Type **93** 10 20
340 3c. Sugar refinery 10 10
341a 5c. Rufous-vented chachalaca ("Cocrico") 2·00 10
342 6c. Oil refinery 10 10
343 8c. Fertiliser plant . . . . 1·50 2·25
344 10c. Green hermit . . . . . 2·50 10
345 12c. Citrus fruit . . . . . . 15 2·25
346 15c. Arms of Trinidad and Tobago 10 10
347 20c. Flag and outline of Trinidad and Tobago . . 30 10
348 25c. As 20c. 30 50
349 30c. Chaconia plant 30 10
350 40c. Scarlet ibis . . . . . . 5·50 10
351 50c. Maracas Bay . . . . . 30 2·50
352 $1 Poui tree 60 15
353 $2.50 Fishing . . . . 1·00 4·00
354 $5 Red house . . . . 1·25 4·00
Nos. 344/9 and 352 are vert.

108 Captain A. A. Cipriani (labour leader) and Entrance to Woodford Square

1969. 50th Anniv of Int Labour Organization.
355 **108** 6c. black, gold and red . . 15 25
356 – 15c. black, gold and blue 15 25
DESIGN: 15c. Arms of Industrial Court and entrance to Woodford Square.

110 Cornucopia and Fruit

117 Parliamentary Chamber, Flags and Emblem

114 Space Module landing on Moon

1969. 1st Anniv of C.A.R.I.F.T.A. Mult.
357 6c. Type **110** 10 10
358 10c. Flags of Britain and member nations (horiz) . . 10 10
359 30c. Map showing C.A.R.I.F.T.A. countries 20 20
360 40c. Boeing 727-100 "Sunjet" in flight (horiz) 40 90

1969. 1st Man on the Moon. Multicoloured.
361 6c. Type **114** 20 10
362 40c. Space module and astronauts on Moon (vert) 30 10
363 $1 Astronauts seen from inside space module . . . 60 35

1969. 15th Commonwealth Parliamentary Association Conference, Port-of-Spain. Mult.
364 10c. Type **117** 10 10
365 15c. J.F. Kennedy College . . 10 10
366 30c. Parliamentary maces . . 25 50
367 40c. Cannon and emblem . . 25 50

121 Congress Emblem

124 "Man in the Moon"

1969. International Congress of the Junior Chamber of Commerce.
368 **121** 6c. black, red and gold . . 10 10
369 – 30c. gold, lake and blue 25 40
370 – 40c. black, gold and blue 25 40
DESIGNS: (both incorporating the Congress emblem). HORIZ: 30c. Islands at daybreak. VERT: 40c. Palm trees and ruin.

1970. Carnival Winners. Multicoloured.
371 5c. Type **124** 10 10
372 6c. "City beneath the Sea" 10 10
373 15c. "Antelope" God Bamibara 15 10
374 30c. "Chanticleer" Pheasant Queen of Malaya 25 10
375 40c. Steel Band of the Year 25 30

129 Statue of Gandhi

131 Symbols of Culture, Science, Arts and Technology

1970. Gandhi Centenary Year (1969). Mult.
376 10c. Type **129** 25 10
377 30c. Head of Gandhi and flag of India (horiz) 45 20

1970. 25th Anniv of U.N.
378 **131** 5c. multicoloured 10 10
379 – 10c. multicoloured 20 10
380 – 20c. multicoloured 20 45
381 – 30c. multicoloured 25 30
DESIGNS AND SIZES: 10c. Children of different races, map and flag (34 × 25 mm); 20c. Noah's Ark, rainbow and dove (34 × 23 mm); 30c. New U.P.U. H.Q. Building (46 × 27½ mm).

1970. Inauguration of National Commercial Bank. No. 341 optd **NATIONAL COMMERCIAL BANK ESTABLISHED 1.7.70.**
382 5c. multicoloured 30 10

134 "East Indian Immigrants" (J. Cazabon)

1970. 125th Anniv of San Fernando. Paintings by Cazabon.
383 **134** 3c. multicoloured 10 90
384 – 5c. black, blue and ochre 10 10
385 – 40c. black, blue and ochre 60 20
DESIGNS—HORIZ: 5c. "San Fernando Town Hall"; 40c. "San Fernando Harbour, 1860".

135 "The Adoration of the Shepherds" (detail, School of Seville)

1970. Christmas. Multicoloured.
386 3c. Type **135** 10 10
387 5c. "Madonna and Child with Saints" (detail, Titian) 10 10
388 30c. "The Adoration of the Shepherds" (detail, Le Nain) 15 20
389 40c. "The Virgin and Child, St. John and an Angel" (Morando) 15 10
390 $1 "The Adoration of the Kings" (detail, Veronese) 35 2·25
MS391 114 × 153 mm. Nos. 386/9 1·00 1·25

136 Red Brocket

1971. Trinidad Wildlife. Multicoloured.
392 3c. Type **136** 15 30
393 5c. Collared peccary 20 15
394 6c. Paca 20 50
395 30c. Brazilian agouti . . . . 60 3·50
396 40c. Ocelot . . . . 60 2·75

137 A. A. Cipriani

138 "Virgin and Child with St. John" (detail, Bartolommeo)

1971. 9th Anniv of Independence. Mult.
397 5c. Type **137** 10 10
398 30c. Chaconia medal 30 70

1971. Christmas.
399 **138** 3c. multicoloured 15 15
400 – 5c. multicoloured 20 10
401 – 10c. multicoloured 25 10
402 – 15c. multicoloured 30 20
DESIGNS: 5c. Local creche; 10c. "Virgin and Child with Saints Jerome and Dominic" (detail, Lippi); 15c. "Virgin and Child with St. Anne" (detail, Gerolamo dai Libri).

139 Satellite Earth Station, Matura

1971. Satellite Earth Station. Multicoloured.
403 10c. Type **139** 10 10
404 30c. Dish antennae 25 90
405 40c. Satellite and the Earth 35 90
MS406 140 × 76 mm. Nos. 403/5 65 2·25

140 "Morpho peleides x achilleana"

1972. Butterflies. Multicoloured.
407 3c. Type **140** 75 75
408 5c. "Eryphanis polyxena" . . 80 10
409 6c. "Phoebis philea" 85 75
410 10c. "Prepona laertes" . . . 1·00 15
411 20c. "Eurytides telesilaus" . . 1·75 2·25
412 30c. "Eurema proterpia" . . 2·00 2·75

141 "Lady McLeod" (paddle-steamer) and McLeod Stamp

1972. 125th Anniv of First Trinidad Postage Stamp.
413 **141** 5c. multicoloured 15 10
414 – 10c. multicoloured 25 10
415 – 30c. blue, brown and black 70 45
MS416 83 × 140 mm. Nos. 413/15 1·00 1·25
DESIGNS: 10c. Lady McLeod stamp and map; 30c. Lady McLeod and inscription.

142 Trinity Cross

144 "Adoration of the Kings" (detail, Dosso)

143 Bronze Medal, 1964 Relay

1972. 10th Anniv of Independence. Mult.
417 5c. Type **142** 10 10
418 10c. Chaconia Medal 10 10
419 20c. Humming-bird Medal . 15 15
420 30c. Medal of Merit 15 20
MS421 93 × 121 mm. Nos. 417/20 60 1·00
See also Nos. 440/4.

1972. Olympic Games, Munich. Multicoloured.
422 10c. Type **143** 15 10
423 20c. Bronze, 1964 200 m . . 25 25
424 30c. Silver, 1952 weightlifting 35 25
425 40c. Silver, 1964 400 m . . 35 25
426 50c. Silver, 1948 weightlifting 35 1·75
MS427 153 × 82 mm. Nos. 422/6 1·75 2·25

1972. Christmas. Multicoloured.
431 3c. Type **144** 10 10
432 5c. "The Holy Family and a Shepherd" (Titian) 10 10
433 30c. As 5c. 70 55
MS434 73 × 99 mm. Nos. 431/3 1·00 1·50

145 E.C.L.A. Building, Chile

1973. Anniversaries. Events described on stamps. Multicoloured.

435	10c. Type **145**	10	10
436	20c. Interpol emblem	45	30
437	30c. W.M.O. emblem	45	30
438	40c. University of the West Indies	45	80
MS439	155 × 92 mm. Nos. 435/8	1·25	1·25

1973. 11th Anniv of Independence. Medals as T **142**. Multicoloured.

440	10c. Trinity Cross	10	10
441	20c. Medal of Merit	20	35
442	30c. Chaconia Medal	20	40
443	40c. Hummingbird Medal	30	40
MS444	75 × 122 mm. Nos. 440/3	70	1·25

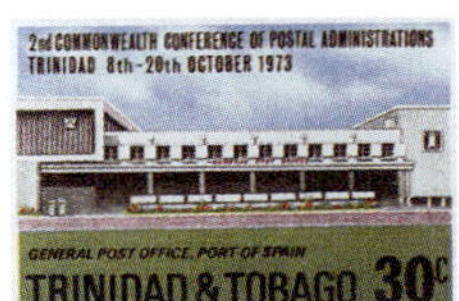

146 G.P.O., Port-of-Spain

1973. 2nd Commonwealth Conference of Postal Administrations, Trinidad. Multicoloured.

445	30c. Type **146**	20	65
446	40c. Conference Hall, Chaguaramas (wrongly inscr "Chagaramas")	30	65
MS447	115 × 115 mm. Nos. 445/6	60	1·00

147 "Madonna with Child" (Murillo)

1973. Christmas.

448 **147**	5c. multicoloured	10	10
449	$1 multicoloured	60	1·25
MS450	94 × 88 mm. Nos. 448/9	85	1·40

148 Berne H.Q. within U.P.U. Emblem

1974. Centenary of U.P.U. Multicoloured.

451	40c. Type **148**	30	15
452	50c. Map within emblem	30	85
MS453	117 × 104 mm. Nos. 451/2	10·00	20·00

149 "Humming Bird I" (ketch) crossing Atlantic Ocean (1960)

1974. 1st Anniv of World Voyage by H. and K. La Borde. Multicoloured.

454	40c. Type **149**	50	15
455	50c. "Humming Bird II" (ketch) crossing globe	60	1·10
MS456	109 × 84 mm. Nos. 454/5	1·50	4·00

150 "Sex Equality"

1975. International Women's Year.

457 **150**	15c. multicoloured	15	30
458	30c. multicoloured	35	70

151 Common Vampire Bat, Microscope and Syringe

1975. Isolation of Rabies Virus. Multicoloured.

459	25c. Type **151**	45	1·00
460	30c. Dr. Pawan, instruments and book	55	55

152 Route-map and Tail of Boeing 707

1975. 35th Anniv of British West Indian Airways. Multicoloured.

461	20c. Type **152**	40	80
462	30c. 707 on ground	60	90
463	40c. 707 in flight	70	1·00
MS464	119 × 110 mm. Nos. 461/3	1·50	2·25

153 "From the Land of the Humming Bird"

1975. Carnival. 1974 Prize-winning Costumes. Multicoloured.

465	30c. Type **153**	10	10
466	$1 "The Little Carib"	40	50
MS467	83 × 108 mm. Nos. 465/6	1·10	1·10

154 Angostura Building, Port-of-Spain

1976. 150th Anniv of Angostura Bitters. Mult.

468	5c. Type **154**	10	40
469	35c. Medal, New Orleans, 1885/6	20	35
470	45c. Medal, Sydney, 1879	25	40
471	50c. Medal, Brussels, 1897	25	1·10
MS472	119 × 112 mm. Nos. 468/71	65	1·50

1976. West Indian Victory in World Cricket Cup. As T **126** of Barbados.

474	35c. Caribbean map	45	65
475	45c. Prudential Cup	55	65
MS476	80 × 80 mm. Nos. 474/5	1·75	3·00

155 "Columbus sailing Through the Bocas" (Campins)

1976. Paintings, Hotels and Orchids. Mult.

479	5c. Type **155**	2·25	30
480	6c. Robinson Crusoe Hotel, Tobago	20	2·50
482	10c. "San Fernando Hill" (J. Cazabon)	20	10
483	12c. "Paphinia cristata"	2·00	3·50
484	15c. Turtle Beach Hotel	50	2·50
485	20c. "East Indians in a Landscape" (J. Cazabon)	70	10
486	25c. Mt. Irvine Hotel	60	10
487	30c. "Caularthron bicornutum"	2·00	2·25
488	35c. "Los Gallos Point" (J. Cazabon)	1·50	10
489	40c. "Miltassia"	2·50	10
490	45c. "Corbeaux Town" (J. Cazabon)	1·00	10
491	50c. "Oncidium ampliatum"	2·25	20
492	70c. Beach facilities, Mt. Irvine Hotel	70	1·25
494	$2.50 "Oncidium papilio"	2·25	2·25
495	$5 Trinidad Holiday Inn	1·25	6·50
MS497	171 × 100 mm. Nos. 479, 482, 485, 488 and 490	2·50	1·50
MS498	171 × 88 mm. Nos. 480, 484, 486, 492 and 495	2·25	6·50
MS499	170 × 90 mm. Nos. 483, 487, 489, 491 and 494	3·75	4·00

156 Hasely Crawford and Olympic Gold Medal

1977. Hasely Crawford Commemoration.

501 **156**	25c. mulicoloured	30	50
MS502	93 × 70 mm. No. 501	60	1·25

157 Lindbergh's Sikorsky S-38, 1929

1977. 50th Anniv of Airmail Service. Mult.

503	20c. Type **157**	40	20
504	35c. Arrival of Charles and Anne Lindbergh	50	35
505	45c. Boeing 707, c. 1960	60	60
506	50c. Boeing 747-200, 1969	1·00	3·50
MS507	130 × 100 mm. Nos. 503/6	3·00	4·25

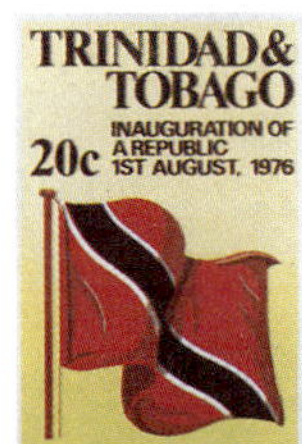

158 National Flag

159 White Poinsettia

1977. Inauguration of Republic. Multicoloured.

508	20c. Type **158**	40	15
509	35c. Coat of arms	60	65
510	45c. Government House	70	85
MS511	125 × 84 mm. Nos. 508/10	1·00	1·25

1977. Christmas. Multicoloured.

512	10c. Type **159**	20	10
513	35c. Type **159**	25	10
514	45c. Red poinsettia	30	30
515	50c. As 45c.	35	2·25
MS516	112 × 142 mm. Nos. 512/15	1·00	2·75

160 Miss Janelle (Penny) Commissioning with Trophy

162 "Burst of Beauty"

1978. "Miss Universe 1977" Commemoration. Mult.

517	10c. Type **160**	25	10
518	35c. Portrait	40	60
519	45c. In evening dress	45	75
MS520	186 × 120 mm. Nos. 517/19	1·00	1·25

161 Tayra

1978. Wildlife. Multicoloured.

521	15c. Type **161**	20	20
522	25c. Ocelot	30	30
523	40c. Brazilian tree porcupine	50	30
524	70c. Tamandua	65	2·75
MS525	128 × 101 mm. Nos. 521/4	1·50	3·25

1979. Carnival 1978.

526 **162**	5c. multicoloured	10	10
527	– 10c. multicoloured	10	10
528	– 35c. multicoloured	10	10
529	– 45c. multicoloured	10	10
530	– 50c. brown, red and lilac	10	15
531	– $1 multicoloured	20	65

DESIGNS: 10c. Rain worshipper; 35c. "Zodiac"; 45c. Praying mantis; 50c. "Eye of the Hurricane"; $1 Steel orchestra.

163 Day Care

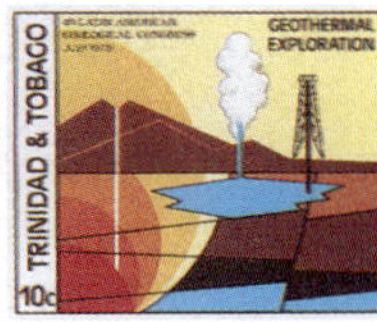

164 Geothermal Exploration

1979. International Year of the Child. Mult.

532	5c. Type **163**	10	10
533	10c. School feeding programme	10	10
534	35c. Dental care	30	15
535	45c. Nursery school	30	20
536	50c. Free bus transport	30	65
537	$1 Medical care	65	2·25
MS538	114 × 132 mm. Nos. 532/7	1·60	2·25

1979. 4th Latin American Geological Congress. Multicoloured.

539	10c. Type **164**	20	10
540	35c. Hydrogeology	35	40
541	45c. Petroleum exploration	40	40
542	70c. Environmental preservation	55	1·60
MS543	185 × 89 mm. Nos. 539/42	1·50	2·00

165 1879 1d. Stamp and Map of Tobago

1979. Tobago Stamp Centenary.

544 **165**	10c. multicoloured	10	10
545	– 15c. multicoloured	15	10
546	– 35c. multicoloured	20	20
547	– 45c. multicoloured	20	20
548	– 70c. multicoloured	25	1·50
549	– $1 black, lilac and orange	25	1·75
MS550	165 × 155 mm. Nos. 544/9	1·25	4·00

DESIGNS: 15c. 1879 3d. and 1880 ½d. surcharged on half of 6d; 35c. 1879 6d. and 1886 ½d. surcharged on 6d; 45c. 1879 1s. and 1886 ½d. surcharged on 2½d; 70c. 1879 5s. and Great Britain 1856 1s. with "A14" (Scarborough, Tobago) postmark; $1 1879 £1 and General Post Office, Scarborough, Tobago.

166 1962 60c. Independence Commemorative Stamp and Sir Rowland Hill

1979. Death Cent of Sir Rowland Hill. Mult.

551	25c. Type **166**	30	15
552	45c. 1977 35c. Inauguration of Republic commemorative	35	20
553	$1 1879 Trinidad ½d. surcharge and Tobago, 1880 4d.	45	1·25
MS554	115 × 125 mm. No. 551/3	1·00	1·50

167 Poui Tree in Churchyard

1980. Centenary of Princes Town. Mult.

555	5c. Type **167**	10	10
556	10c. Princes Town Court House	10	10
557	50c. Locomotive of the Royal Train, 1880	60	90
558	$1.50 H.M.S. "Bacchante" (screw corvette)	1·00	2·00
MS559	177 × 102 mm. Nos. 555/8	1·60	2·75

1980. Population Census. Nos. 479/80 and 482 optd **1844–1980 POPULATION CENSUS 12th MAY 1980**.

560	5c. Type **155**	20	20
561	6c. Robinson Crusoe Hotel, Tobago	20	80
562	10c. "San Fernando Hill" (J. Cazabon)	20	20

169 Scarlet Ibis (male)

1980. Scarlet Ibis. Multicoloured.

563	50c. Type **169**	50	1·40
564	50c. Male and female	50	1·40
565	50c. Hen and nest	50	1·40
566	50c. Nest and eggs	50	1·40
567	50c. Chick in nest	50	1·40

170 Silver and Bronze Medals for Weightlifting, 1948 and 1952

1980. Olympic Games, Moscow.

568	**170** 10c. multicoloured	10	10
569	– 15c. multicoloured	10	10
570	– 70c. multicoloured	45	65
MS571	110×149 mm. $2.50 black, silver and red	1·75	3·00

DESIGNS—HORIZ: 15c. Hasely Crawford (100 metres sprint winner, 1976) and gold medal; 70c. Silver medal for 400 metres and bronze medal for 4×400 metres relay, 1964. VERT: $2.50, Olympic Games emblems for Moscow, 1980, Olympia 776 B.C. and Athens, 1896.

171 Charcoal Production

1980. 11th Commonwealth Forestry Conf. Mult.

572	10c. Type **171**	10	10
573	55c. Logging	20	25
574	70c. Teak plantation	30	60
575	$2.50 Watershed management	60	2·25
MS576	135×87 mm. Nos. 572/5	1·50	2·75

172 Beryl McBurnie (dance and culture) and Audrey Jeffers (social worker)

1980. Decade for Women (1st issue). Mult.

577	$1 Type **172**	35	55
578	$1 Elizabeth Bourne (judiciary) and Isabella Teshier (government)	35	55
579	$1 Dr. Stella Abidh (public health) and Louise Horne (nutrition)	35	55

See also Nos. 680/2.

173 Netball Stadium

1980. World Netball Tournament

580	**173** 70c. multicoloured	30	50

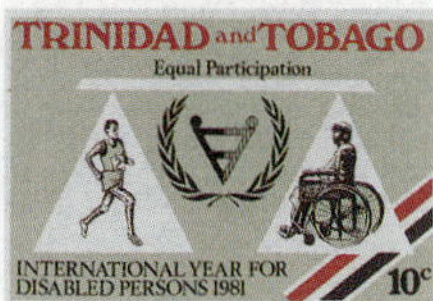

174 I.Y.D.P. Emblem, Athlete and Disabled Person

1981. International Year of Disabled Persons.

581	**174** 10c. green, black and red	15	10
582	– 70c. orange, black and red	30	70
583	– $1.50 blue, black and red	40	1·40
584	– $2 flesh, black and red	40	1·75

DESIGNS: 70c. I.Y.D.P. emblem and doctor with disabled person; $1.50, Emblem and blind man and woman; $2, Emblem and inscription.

175 "Our Land Must Live"

1981. Environmental Preservation. Mult.

585	10c. Type **175**	15	10
586	55c. "Our seas must live"	45	30
587	$3 "Our skies must live"	1·60	1·60
MS588	142×89 mm. Nos. 555/7	2·50	4·50

176 "Food For Famine"

1981. World Food Day. Multicoloured.

589	10c. Type **176**	10	10
590	15c. "Produce more" (threshing and milling rice)	10	10
591	45c. "Fish for food" (Bigeye)	30	20
592	55c. "Prevent hunger"	35	25
593	$1.50 "Fight malnutrition"	85	90
594	$2 "Fish for food" (Small-mouthed grunt)	1·10	1·25
MS595	164×98 mm. Nos. 589/94	2·75	4·50

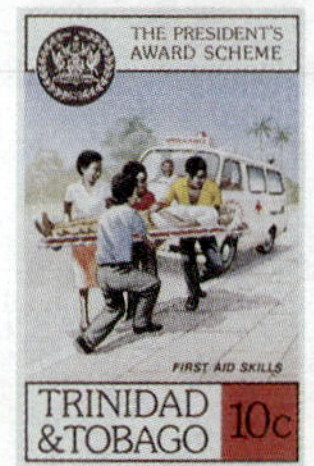

177 "First Aid Skills" 178 Pharmacist at Work

1981. President's Award Scheme. Mult.

596	10c. Type **177**	20	10
597	70c. "Motor mechanics"	40	45
598	$1 "Expedition"	50	55
599	$2 Presenting an award	60	1·40

1982. Commonwealth Pharmaceutical Conference. Multicoloured.

600	10c. Type **178**	15	10
601	$1 Gerritoute (plant)	1·75	2·25
602	$2 Rachette (plant)	2·75	4·25

179 "Production" 180 Charlotteville

1982. 75th Anniv of Boy Scout Movement. Mult.

603	15c. Type **179**	60	10
604	55c. "Tolerance"	1·50	30
605	$5 "Discipline"	5·50	7·00

1982. 25th Anniv of Tourist Board. Mult.

606	55c. Type **180**	30	25
607	$1 Boating	40	55
608	$3 Fort George	1·25	2·25

181 "Pa Pa Bois"

1982. Folklore. Local Spirits and Demons. Mult.

609	10c. Type **181**	10	10
610	15c. "La Diablesse"	10	10
611	65c. "Lugarhoo", "Phantom" and "Soucouyant"	35	30
612	$5 "Bois de Soleil", "Davens" and "Mamma de l'Eau"	2·50	3·25
MS613	133×100 mm. Nos. 609/12	4·25	6·00

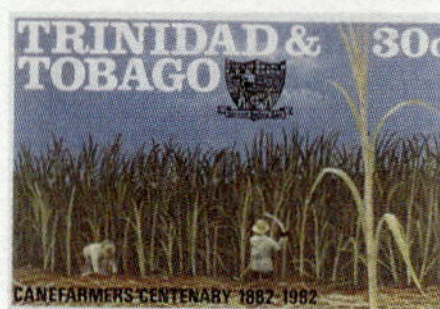

182 Cane Harvesting

1982. Cent of Canefarmers' Association. Mult.

614	30c. Type **182**	30	15
615	70c. Farmers loading bullock cart	60	85
616	$1.50 Cane field in bloom	1·10	2·75
MS617	72×117 mm. Nos. 614/16	1·40	1·50

183 National Stadium

1982. 20th Anniv of Independence. Mult.

618	10c. Type **183**	30	10
619	35c. Caroni water treatment plant	45	15
620	50c. Mount Hope Maternity Hospital	1·25	25
621	$2 National Insurance Board Mall, Tobago	1·40	2·00

184 Commonwealth Flags

1983. Commonwealth Day. Multicoloured.

622	10c. Type **184**	10	10
623	55c. Satellite view of Trinidad and Tobago	25	20
624	$1 "Nodding donkey" oil pump (vert)	40	70
625	$2 Map of Trinidad and Tobago (vert)	85	1·50

185 Lockheed Tristar 500 "Flamingo"

1983. 10th Anniv of CARICOM.

626	**185** 35c. multicoloured	1·50	1·75

186 V.D.U. Operator

1983. World Communications Year. Mult.

627	15c. Type **186**	20	10
628	55c. Scarborough Post Office, Tobago	30	20
629	$1 Textel building	60	70
630	$3 Morne Blue E.C.M.S. station	1·10	2·50

187 Financial Complex

1983. Conference of Commonwealth Finance Ministers.

631	**187** $2 multicoloured	60	1·25

188 King Mackerel

1983. World Food Day. Multicoloured.

632	10c. Type **188**	20	10
633	55c. Four-winged flyingfish	1·00	40
634	70c. Queen or pink conch	1·25	1·40
635	$4 Red shrimp	4·50	7·50

189 Bois Pois 190 Rooks in Staunton and 17th-century Styles

1983. Flowers. Multicoloured.

636A	5c. Type **189**	1·00	1·50
687	10c. Maraval lily	30	30
638A	15c. Star grass	90	50
639A	20c. Bois caco	30	30
640A	25c. Strangling fig	1·10	1·75
641A	30c. "Cassia moschata"	50	30
642A	50c. Chalice flower	50	40
643A	65c. Black stick	55	50
644A	80c. "Columnea scandens"	65	1·25
695	95c. Cat's claw	50	70
696	$1 Bois l'agli	65	30
647A	$1.50 "Eustoma exaltatum"	1·25	2·00
648A	$2 Chaconia (39×29 mm)	1·50	2·50
649A	$2.50 "Chrysothemis pulchella" (39×29 mm)	1·25	3·50
700	$5 "Centratherum punctatum" (39×29 mm)	1·75	2·00
701	$10 Savanna flower (39×29 mm)	3·50	4·50

1984. 60th Anniv of Int Chess Federation. Mult.

652	50c. Type **190**	3·00	50
653	70c. Bishops in Staunton and 12th-century Lewis styles	3·25	2·00
654	$1.50 Queens in Staunton and 13th-century Swedish styles	4·25	5·50
655	$2 Kings in Staunton and 19th-century Chinese styles	5·50	7·00

191 Swimming 192 Slave Schooner and Shackles

1984. Olympic Games, Los Angeles. Multicoloured.

656	15c. Type **191**	10	10
657	55c. Track and field events	30	20
658	$1.50 Sailing	1·00	1·75
659	$4 Cycling	5·50	7·00
MS660	132×85 mm. Nos. 656/9	6·50	7·50

1984. 150th Anniv of Abolition of Slavery. Mult.

661	35c. Type **192**	1·25	40
662	55c. Slave and "Slave Triangle" map	2·25	60
663	$1 "Capitalism and Slavery" (book by Dr. Eric Williams)	2·25	2·25
664	$2 Toussaint l'Ouverture (Haitian revolutionary)	3·00	6·00
MS665	95×100 mm. Nos. 661/4	8·00	10·00

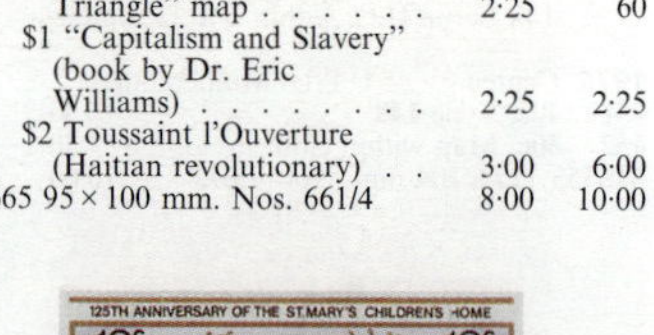

193 Children's Band

1984. 125th Anniv of St. Mary's Children's Home. Multicoloured.

666	10c. Type **193**	15	10
667	70c. St. Mary's Children's Home	50	50
668	$3 Group of children	2·25	4·00

194 Parang Band

1984. Parang Festival. Multicoloured.

669	10c. Type **194**	20	10
670	30c. Music and poinsettia	50	15

671 $1 Bandola, bandolin and cuatro (musical instruments) . . . . 1·50 1·10
672 $3 Double bass, fiddle and guitar (musical instruments) 2·50 5·00

195 Capt. A. A. Cipriani and T. U. B. Butler

1985. Labour Day. Labour Leaders.
673 **195** 55c. black and red . . . . 1·25 1·25
674 – 55c. black and yellow . . 1·25 1·25
675 – 55c. black and green . . . 1·25 1·25
DESIGNS: No. 674, C. P. Alexander and Q. O'Connor; 675, A. Cola Rienzi and C. T. W. E. Worrell.

196 "Lady Nelson" (1928)

1985. Ships. Multicoloured.
676 30c. Type **196** 70 25
677 95c. "Lady Drake", (1928) 1·50 1·75
678 $1.50 "Federal Palm" (1961) 1·50 3·00
679 $2 "Federal Maple" (1961) 1·75 3·50

197 Marjorie Padmore (music) and Sybil Atteck (art)

1985. Decade for Women (2nd issue). Mult.
680 $1.50 Type **197** . . . . . . 1·75 2·25
681 $1.50 May Cherrie (medical social worker) and Evelyn Tracey (social worker) . . 1·75 2·25
682 $1.50 Umilta McShine (education) and Jessica Smith-Phillips (public service) . . . . 1·75 2·25

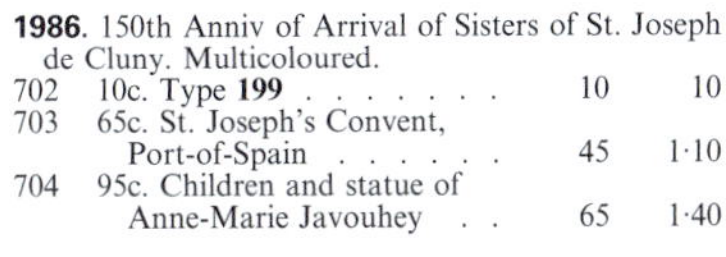
198 Badge of Trinidad and Tobago Cadet Force (75th Anniv)
199 Anne-Marie Javouhey (foundress)

1985. International Youth Year. Multicoloured.
683 10c. Type **198** 45 10
684 65c. Guide badges (75th anniv of Girl Guide movement) . . . . 2·00 2·50
685 95c. Young people of Trinidad . . . . 2·50 3·00

1986. 150th Anniv of Arrival of Sisters of St. Joseph de Cluny. Multicoloured.
702 10c. Type **199** 10 10
703 65c. St. Joseph's Convent, Port-of-Spain . . . . . . 45 1·10
704 95c. Children and statue of Anne-Marie Javouhey . . 65 1·40

200 Tank Locomotive "Arima"

1986. "Ameripex 86" International Stamp Exhibition, Chicago. Trinidad Railway Locomotives. Multicoloured.
705 65c. Type **200** 25 35
706 95c. Canadian-built steam locomotive No. 22 . . . . 35 60
707 $1.10 Steam tender engine . . 40 1·10
708 $1.50 Saddle tank locomotive 60 1·50
MS709 105 × 80 mm. Nos. 705/8 1·40 3·00

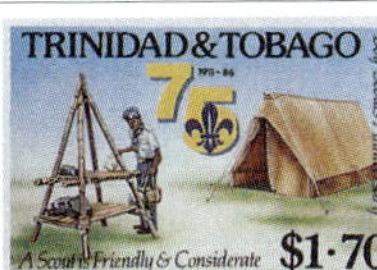
201 Scout Camp

1986. 75th Anniv of Trinidad and Tobago Boy Scouts. Multicoloured.
710 $1.70 Type **201** . . . . . . 1·00 1·75
711 $2 Scouts of 1911 and 1986 1·25 2·00

202 Queen and Duke of Edinburgh laying Wreath at War Memorial
203 Eric Williams at Graduation, 1935

1986. 60th Birthday of Queen Elizabeth II. Mult.
712 10c. Type **202** 35 10
713 15c. Queen with Trinidadian dignitaries aboard "Britannia" . . . . 1·00 30
714 30c. With President Ellis Clarke 65 30
715 $5 Receiving bouquet . . . . 3·00 6·50

1986. 75th Birth Anniv of Dr. Eric Williams. Multicoloured.
716 10c. Type **203** 55 10
717 30c. Premier Eric Williams (wearing red tie) 85 30
718 30c. As No. 717 but wearing black and orange tie 85 30
719 95c. Arms of University of West Indies and Dr. Williams as Pro-Chancellor (horiz) . . . . 1·60 1·25
720 $5 Prime Minister Williams and Whitehall (horiz) . . . 2·25 7·00
MS721 105 × 100 mm. Nos. 716/17 and 719/20 . . . . 5·00 9·00

204 "PEACE" Slogan and Outline map of Trinidad and Tobago
205 Miss Giselle La Ronde and BWIA Airliner

1986. International Peace Year. Multicoloured.
722 95c. Type **204** 40 50
723 $3 Peace dove with olive branch . . . . 1·25 2·50

1987. Miss World 1986. Multicoloured.
724 10c. Type **205** . . . . 1·00 20
725 30c. In swimsuit on beach . . 1·75 30
726 95c. Miss Giselle La Ronde 3·25 2·50
727 $1.65 Wearing Miss World sash . . . . 4·25 6·50

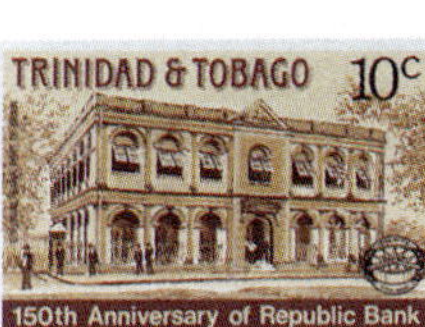
206 Colonial Bank, Port-of-Spain

1987. 150th Anniv of Republic Bank. Mult.
728 10c. Type **206** 10 10
729 65c. Cocoa plantation . . . 55 75
730 95c. Oil field . . . . 2·25 2·25
731 $1.10 Belmont Tramway Company tramcar . . . . 2·25 3·25

207 Sergeant in Parade Order and Soldiers in Work Dress and Battle Dress
208 Uriah Butler (labour leader)

207a George John

1988. 25th Anniv of Defence Force. Mult.
732 10c. Type **207** 85 15
733 30c. Women soldiers . . . . 2·00 30
734 $1.10 Defence Force officers 3·00 2·75
735 $1.50 Naval ratings and patrol boat . . . . 4·25 3·50

1988. West Indian Cricket. Showing portrait, cricket equipment and early belt buckle. Mult.
736 30c. Type **207a** . . . . . . 1·50 40
737 65c. Learie Constantine . . . 2·50 1·00
738 95c. Sonny Ramadhin . . . 2·75 1·75
739 $1.50 Gerry Gomez . . . . 3·25 3·75
740 $2.50 Jeffrey Stollmeyer . . . 4·25 6·50

1988. 50th Anniv (1987) of Oilfield Workers Trade Union. Multicoloured.
741 10c. Type **208** 10 10
742 30c. Adrian Rienzi (O.W.T.U. president, 1937–42) 10 10
743 65c. John Rojas (O.W.T.U. president, 1943–62) 15 25
744 $5 George Weekes (O.W.T.U. president, 1962–87) . . . . 1·25 2·25

209 Mary Werges and Santa Rosa Church

1988. Centenary of Borough of Arima. Mult.
745 20c. Type **209** 15 10
746 30c. Governor W. Robinson and Royal Charter 15 10
747 $1.10 Arrival of Governor Robinson at railway station . . . . 1·75 1·50
748 $1.50 Mayor J. F. Wallen and Centenary logo . . . 1·00 2·00

1988. 300th Anniv of Lloyd's of London. As T **152a** of St. Helena. Multicoloured.
749 30c. Queen Mother at topping out of new building, 1984 . . . . . . 75 20
750 $1.10 BWIA Lockheed Tristar 500 airliner "Flamingo" (horiz) . . . . 2·00 1·40
751 $1.55 Steel works, Trinidad (horiz) . . . . 1·75 1·75
752 $2 "Atlantic Empress" (tanker) on fire off Tobago, 1979 . . . . 3·75 2·75

210 Colonial Arms of Trinidad & Tobago and 1913 1d. Stamp

1989. Centenary of Union of Trinidad and Tobago. Multicoloured.
753 40c. Type **210** 90 10
754 $1 Pre-1889 Tobago emblem and Tobago 1896 ½d. on 4d. stamp . . . . 2·25 1·00
755 $1.50 Pre-1889 Trinidad emblem and Trinidad 1883 4d. stamp . . . . 2·50 3·50
756 $2.25 Current Arms of Trinidad and Tobago and 1977 45c. Republic commemorative . . . . . 3·00 5·00

211 Blue-throated Piping Guan

1989. Rare Fauna of Trinidad and Tobago. Mult.
757 $1 Type **211** . . . . 3·25 3·50
758 $1 "Phyllodytes auratus" (frog) . . . . 3·25 3·50
759 $1 "Cebus albifrons trinitatis" (monkey) . . . 3·25 3·50
760 $1 Tamandua . . . . 3·25 3·50
761 $1 "Lutra longicaudis" (otter) 3·25 3·50
Nos. 757/61 were printed together, se-tenant, forming a composite background design.

212 Blind Welfare
213 Tenor Pan

1989. Anniveraries. Multicoloured.
762 10c. Type **212** (75th anniv) 70 15
763 40c. Port-of-Spain City Hall (75th anniv) 40 20
764 $1 Guides and Brownies (75th anniv) . . . . 2·50 60
765 $2.25 Red Cross members (50th anniv) . . . . 3·25 2·75

1990. Steel Pans (1st series). Multicoloured.
766 10c. Type **213** 10 10
767 40c. Guitar pans 15 15
768 $1 Cello pans 45 70
769 $2.25 Bass pans . . . . . . 85 2·50
See also Nos. 828/31.

214 "Xeromphalina tenuipes"

1990. "Stamp World London 90" International Stamp Exhibition. Fungi. Multicoloured.
770 10c. Type **214** 35 20
771 40c. "Phallus indusiatus" ("Dictyophora indusiata") 65 25
772 $1 "Leucocoprinus birnbaumii" . . . . 1·25 1·00
773 $2.25 "Crinipellis perniciosa" 2·00 4·00

215 Scarlet Ibis in Immature Plumage

1990. Scarlet Ibis. Multicoloured.
774 40c. Type **215** . . . . 1·50 30
775 80c. Pair in pre-nuptial display . . . . 1·75 1·40
776 $1 Male in breeding plumage 1·75 1·40
777 $2.25 Adult on nest with chick . . . . 2·75 4·25

216 Princess Alice and Administration Building

1990. 40th Anniv of University of West Indies. Multicoloured.
778 40c. Type **216** 60 15
779 80c. Sir Hugh Wooding and Library 80 80
780 $1 Sir Allen Lewis and Faculty of Engineering . . 1·00 1·00
781 $2.25 Sir Shridath Ramphal and Faculty of Medical Sciences . . . . 2·75 5·00

217 Lockheed Lodestar

1990. 50th Anniv of British West Indies Airways. Multicoloured.

782 40c. Type **217** . . . . . . 1·50 30
783 80c. Vickers Viking 1A . . . 2·00 1·25
784 $1 Vickers Viscount 702 . . . 2·25 1·25
785 $2.25 Boeing 707 . . . . . . 3·25 6·00
MS786 77 × 52 mm. $5 Lockheed L-1011 TriStar 500 . . . . . 4·50 6·00

218 Yellow Oriole 219 "Lygodium volubile"

1990. Birds. Multicoloured.

787 20c. Type **218** 40 30
837 25c. Green-rumped parrotlet 60 30
789 40c. Fork-tailed flycatcher . . 50 20
839 50c. Copper-rumped hummingbird 40 20
840 $1 Bananaquit . . . . 1·25 30
841 $2 Violaceous euphonia ("Semp") . . . . 1·75 1·00
793 $2.25 Channel-billed toucan 1·50 1·50
843 $2.50 Bay-headed tanager . . 1·00 1·50
844 $5 Green honeycreeper . . . 1·40 2·50
845 $10 Cattle egret . . . . . . 2·25 3·50
846 $20 Golden-olive woodpecker 4·00 6·50
798 $50 Peregrine falcon . . . . 10·00 13·00

1991. Ferns. Multicoloured.

799 40c. Type **219** 40 15
800 80c. "Blechnum occidentale" 75 70
801 $1 "Gleichenia bifida" . . . 85 85
802 $2.25 "Polypodium lycopodioides" . . . . . . 2·00 3·50

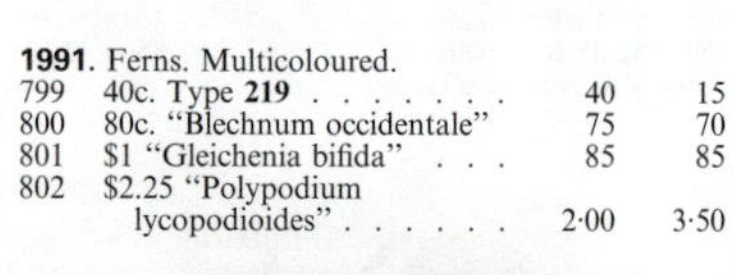

220 Trinidad and Tobago Regiment Anti-aircraft Battery

1991. 50th Anniv of Second World War. Mult.

803 40c. Type **220** . . . . . . 1·00 30
804 80c. Fairey Barracuda Mk III attacking U-boat . . . . . 1·50 1·00
805 $1 Avro Type 683 Lancaster 1·75 1·00
806 $2.25 H.M.S. "Wye" (frigate) escorting convoy . . . . . 2·75 5·00
MS807 117 × 85 mm. $2.50, Presentation Supermarine Spitfire; $2.50, Presentation Vickers-Armstrong Wellington bomber 7·50 8·50

221 H. E. Rapsey (founder) 222 Baptism (Baptist)

1992. Anniversaries. Multicoloured.

808 40c. Type **221** (centenary of Trinidad Building and Loan Association.) 30 15
809 80c. "Inca clathrata quesneli" (beetle) (Trinidad & Tobago Field Naturalists' Club) . . . . 1·00 1·10
810 $1 Holy Name Convent (centenary) . . . . 1·10 1·25

1992. Religions of Trinidad and Tobago. Mult.

811 40c. Type **222** 80 90
812 40c. Minaret with star and crescent (Islam) 80 90
813 40c. Logo (Hinduism) 80 90
814 40c. Cross (Christian) 80 90
815 40c. Logo (Baha'i) 80 90

223 McDonnell Douglas MD-83

1992. Aircraft. Multicoloured.

816 $2.25 Type **223** . . . . . . 2·25 2·50
817 $2.25 Lockheed L-1011 TriStar aircraft . . . . . 2·25 2·50

224 "Trinidad Guardian" Title (75th anniv of newspaper)

1992. Anniversaries. Multicoloured.

818 40c. Type **224** 10 10
819 40c. Nativity scene (Christmas) (vert) 10 10
820 $1 National Museum and Art Gallery (centenary) 35 50
821 $2.25 Cover to St. James Internment Camp, 1942 (50th anniv of Trinidad and Tobago Philatelic Society) . . . . 80 1·60

225 Derek Walcott, Sir Shridath Ramphal and William Demas with Caribbean Maps (⅔-size illustration)

1994. 20th Anniv of CARICOM (Caribbean Economic Community). Recipients of Order of the Caribbean Community.

822 **225** 50c. multicoloured 20 20
823 $1.50 multicoloured . . . 45 75
824 $2.75 multicoloured . . . 85 1·50
825 $3 multicoloured . . . 1·00 1·75
MS826 90 × 90 mm. $6 multicoloured (Insignia of the Order (34½ × 51½ mm)) . . . . 2·00 3·25

226 Aldwyn Roberts Kitchener (bass player)

1994. "Land of Calypso".

827 **226** 50c. multicoloured . . . . 1·50 1·00

227 Quadrophonic Pans

1994. Steel Pans (2nd series). Multicoloured.

828 50c. Type **227** 20 20
829 $1 Tenor base pans 35 30
830 $2.25 Six pans . . . . 80 1·40
831 $2.50 Rocket pans . . . . . 90 1·40

1994. "Hong Kong '94" International Stamp Exhibition. Nos. 837, 789, 841 and 796 optd **HONG KONG '94** and emblem.

832 25c. Green-rumped parrotlet 30 20
833 40c. Fork-tailed flycatcher . . 35 20
834 $2 Violaceous euphonia . . . 95 1·25
835 $10 Cattle egret . . . . . . 3·25 5·50

228 Trinidad Hilton 230 "Snowballman" (painting, Mahmoud Alladin)

229 Boa Constrictor

1994. Hotels and Lodgings. Multicoloured.

848 $3 Type **228** . . . . 90 1·25
849 $3 Sandy Point Village, Tobago . . . . 90 1·25
850 $3 Asa Wright Nature Centre and Lodge . . . . 90 1·25
851 $3 M.L.'s Bed and Breakfast 90 1·25

1994. Snakes. Multicoloured.

852 50c. Type **229** 20 20
853 $1.25 Vine snake 45 55
854 $2.50 Bushmaster . . . . . 80 1·10
855 $3 Large coral snake . . . . 95 1·25

1995. 50th Anniv of Trinidad Art Society. Mult.

856 50c. Type **230** 40 60
857 50c. "Fishermen" (painting, Sybil Atteck) 40 60
858 50c. Copper sculpture (Ken Morris) 40 60

231 Loggerhead Turtle

1995. Conservation. Multicoloured.

859 $1.25 Type **231** 60 60
860 $2.50 Port-of-Spain Lighthouse (vert) . . . . . . 1·25 1·25
861 $3 "Knowsley" (location of Ministry of Foreign Affairs) . . . . 1·00 1·50

232 Brian Lara 234 Wendy Fitzwilliam

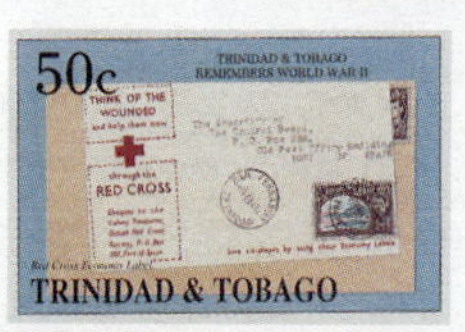

233 Red Cross Economy Label on Envelope

1996. Brian Lara (cricketer) Commemoration.

862 **232** 50c. multicoloured 20 10
863 – $1.25 multicoloured . . . 45 35
864 – $2.50 multicoloured . . . 75 1·25
865 – $3 multicoloured . . . 90 1·40
MS866 62 × 75 mm. $3.75 multicoloured; $5.01 multicoloured . . . . 3·25 3·50

DESIGNS: $1.25 to $5.01, Cricket scenes.

1996. 50th Anniv of End of Second World War (1995). Multicoloured.

867 50c. Type **233** 30 10
868 $1.25 U.S.S. "Missouri" (battleship), 1944 . . . . 80 50
869 $2.50 U.S. servicemen playing baseball, 1942 . . . . . . 90 1·60
870 $3 Fleet Air Arm Fulmar 1 (fighter) . . . . 1·25 1·75
MS871 116 × 85 mm. $3 Fleet Air Arm Grumman Mackinnon G-21C Goose flying boat; $3 U.S. Navy airship . . . . 2·25 3·00

1997. "HONG KONG '97" International Stamp Exhibition. Sheet 130 × 90 mm, containing design as No. 795. Multicoloured.

MS872 $5 Green honeycreeper 1·50 2·00

1999. Wendy Fitzwilliam ("Miss Universe 1998"). Multicoloured.

873 50c. Type **234** 35 15
874 $1.25 Lying on beach 75 40
875 $2.50 In national costume . . 1·40 1·50
876 $3 In white evening gown . . 1·50 1·75
MS877 70 × 100 mm. $5 Wearing "Miss Universe" sash . . . . 2·50 2·50

235 Bottle of Angostura Bitters

2000. 175th Anniv of Angostura Bitters. Mult. Self-adhesive.

878 75c. Type **235** 25 15
879 $3 Angostura Building inside bottle . . . . 1·10 1·40
880 $4.50 Cocktails and Angostura inside bottle (horiz) . . . . 1·60 1·90
MS881 120 × 80 mm. Nos. 878/80. Imperf . . . . 2·50 3·00

2000. Nos. 789 surch **75c.**

883 75c. on 40c. Fork-tailed flycatcher . . . . 2·50 40

237 Maracas Bay

2000. Beaches of Trinidad and Tobago. Mult.

884 75c. Type **237** 30 20
885 $1 Pirate's Bay 40 25
886 $3.75 Pigeon Point . . . . . 1·25 1·60
887 $5 Toco, North Coast . . . 1·75 2·25

238 Moon over Caroni Landscape

2000. Christmas. Multicoloured.

888 75c. Type **238** 30 20
889 $3.75 Traditional food and drink . . . . 1·25 1·25
890 $4.50 Parang singers on beach . . . . 1·50 1·75
891 $5.25 Angels playing steel pans . . . . 2·00 2·50

239 National Mail Centre

2000. New National Mail Centre. Multicoloured.

892 $3 Type **239** . . . . 1·25 1·00
893 $10 Side view of Centre . . . 3·50 4·00

2001. No. 793 surch **75c.**

894 75c. on $2.25 Channel-billed toucan . . . . 5·50 3·75

241 Pacca

2001. Endangered Wildlife. Multicoloured.

895	25c. Type **241**	10	10
896	50c. Prehensile-tailed porcupine	10	15
897	75c. Iguana	15	20
898	$1 Leatherback turtle	20	25
899	$2 Golden tegu	40	45
900	$3 Red howler monkey	60	65
901	$4 Weeping capuchin monkey (vert)	80	85
902	$5 River otter	1·00	1·10
903	$10 Ocelot	2·00	2·10
904	$20 Blue-throated piping guan ("Trinidad Piping Guan") (vert)	4·00	4·25

242 Port of Spain Public Library and Carnegie Library, San Fernando

2001. Anniversaries. Multicoloured.

905	75c. Type **242**	30	25
906	75c. National flag and Salvation Army emblem (vert)	30	25
907	$2 William Booth Memorial Hall (vert)	80	90
908	$3.25 New National Library	1·25	1·50
MS909	Two sheets each 125 × 85 mm. (a) Nos. 905 and 908. (b) Nos. 906/7	2·50	2·75

ANNIVERSARIES: Nos. 905 and 908, 150th anniv of public libraries; 906/7, centenary of Salvation Army in Trinidad and Tobago.

243 National Football Team Logo

2001. FIFA Under 17 World Football Championships. Multicoloured.

910	$2 Type **243**	80	90
911	$3.25 National flag and team slogan	1·25	1·40
912	$4.50 Stryka (team mascot) with national flag	1·50	1·75
913	$5.25 Four new football grounds	1·75	2·00
MS914	110 × 99 mm. Nos. 910/13	4·75	5·50

244 *Pachystachys coccinea*

2001. Flowers. Multicoloured designs.

915	$1 Type **244**	20	25
916	$2.50 *Heliconia psittacorum*	50	55
917	$3.25 *Brownea latifolia* (horiz)	70	75
918	$3.75 *Oncidium papilio*	75	80

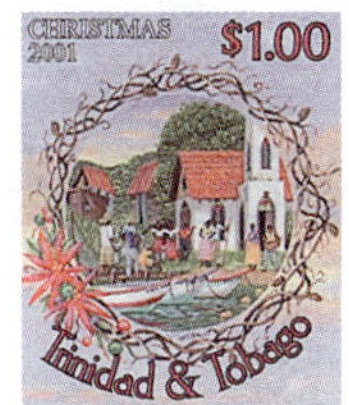

245 Congregation and Church inside Wreath

2001. Christmas. Multicoloured.

919	$1 Type **245**	20	25
920	$3.75 Musicians and dancers within Christmas tree	75	80
921	$4.50 Family and house inside wreath	90	95
922	$5.25 Church and choir within Christmas tree	1·10	1·25
MS923	118 × 157 mm. Nos. 919/22	2·00	2·25

246 Rufous-breasted Hermit

2002. Hummingbirds. Multicoloured.

924	$1 Type **246**	20	25
925	$2.50 Black-throated mango	50	55
926	$3.25 Tufted coquette	70	75
927	$3.75 White-chested emerald	75	80

247 Cracker Butterfly

2002. Butterflies. Multicoloured.

928	$1 Type **247**	20	25
929	$3.75 Tiger butterfly	75	80
930	$4.50 Four continent butterfly	90	95
931	$5.25 89 butterfly	1·10	1·25

248 Fort Picton

2002. Forts. Multicoloured.

932	$1 Type **248**	20	25
933	$3.75 Fort George	75	80
934	$4.50 Fort King George	90	95
935	$5.25 Fort James	1·10	1·25
MS936	152 × 120 mm. Nos. 932/5	2·00	2·25

249 Dr. Eric Williams addressing Public Meeting, Woodford Square, Port of Spain

2002. 40th Anniv of Independence ($1) and Golden Jubilee (others). Showing the 1966 Royal Visit. Multicoloured.

937	$1 Type **249**	20	25
938	$3.75 Queen Elizabeth and Duke of Edinburgh with Dr. Williams and Governor-General	75	80
939	$4.50 Queen and Duke of Edinburgh with Mayor Taylor, Port of Spain	90	95
940	$5.25 Queen Elizabeth addressing Parliament	1·10	1·25
MS941	148 × 111 mm. $10 Queen Elizabeth in open car	2·00	2·25

250 Child playing on a Pan

252 Ian Bishop (bowler)

2002. Christmas. Multicoloured.

942	$1 Type **250**	20	25
943	$2.50 Parranderos singers (horiz)	50	55
944	$3.75 Decorated hillside homes (horiz)	75	80
945	$5.25 Father Christmas in donkey cart	1·10	1·25

2003. Trinidad Cricketers. Multicoloured.

950	$1 Type **252**	20	25
951	$2.50 Deryck Murray (wicket-keeper)	50	55
952	$4.50 Augustine Logie (batsman)	90	95
953	$5.25 Ann John (female cricketer)	1·10	1·25

253 Children dressed as Flowers

2003. Carnival. Multicoloured.

954	$1 Type **253**	20	25
955	$2.50 Group of minstrels	50	55
956	$3.75 Reveller in fly costume (vert)	75	80
957	$4.50 Buddha float (vert)	90	95
958	$5.25 Carnival dancers (vert)	1·10	1·25
MS959	90 × 90 mm. No. 958	1·10	1·25

254 President Robinson of Trinidad & Tobago with U.N. Secretary-General Kofi Annan

2003. Inauguration of International Criminal Court. Multicoloured.

960	$1 Type **254**	20	25
961	$2.50 Pres. Robinson with group of international lawyers	50	55
962	$3.75 Pres. Robinson with Ambassador Philippe Kirsch of Canada	75	80
963	$4.50 Pres. Robinson with Pres. Ciampi of Italy and Emma Bonino M.E.P.	90	95
MS964	90 × 90 mm. $6 President Arthur Robinson (vert)	1·25	1·40

OFFICIAL STAMP

1913. Optd **OFFICIAL**.

O14	**17** $\frac{1}{2}$d. green	1·00	2·50

POSTAGE DUE STAMPS

1947. As Type D **1** of Trinidad but value in cents.

D26a	2c. black	20	3·75
D27	4c. black	85	3·00
D28	6c. black	1·60	6·00
D29a	8c. black	35	22·00
D30	10c. black	1·10	4·00
D31a	12c. black	40	17·00
D32	16c. black	2·00	42·00
D33	24c. black	7·00	7·50

D 2

1969. Size 19 × 24 mm.

D34	D **2** 2c. green	15	2·50
D35	4c. red	25	4·00
D36	6c. brown	50	4·50
D37	8c. violet	65	4·75
D38	10c. red	1·00	5·00
D39	12c. yellow	80	4·75
D40	16c. green	1·00	5·00
D41	24c. grey	1·00	5·50
D42	50c. blue	1·00	4·50
D43	60c. green	1·00	4·00

1976. Smaller design, 17 × 21 mm.

D44	D **2** 2c. green	20	1·50
D45	4c. red	25	1·25
D46	6c. brown	25	1·75
D47	8c. lilac	30	1·75
D48	10c. red	30	1·25
D49	12c. orange	50	1·50

TRIPOLITANIA Pt. 8

One of the provinces into which the Italian colony of Libya was divided.

100 centesimi = 1 lira.

Stamps optd **Tripoli di Barberia**, formerly listed here, will be found under Italian P.O.s in the Levant Nos. 171/81.

Nos. 1/138, except where otherwise described, are Italian stamps, sometimes in new colours, overprinted **TRIPOLITANIA**.

1923. Propagation of the Faith.
1 **66** 20c. orange and green . . . 2·00 6·00
2 30c. orange and red . . . 2·00 6·00
3 50c. orange and violet . . . 2·00 6·00
4 1l. orange and blue . . . . 2·00 6·00

1923. Fascist March on Rome.
5 **73** 10c. green . . . . 1·40 6·00
6 30c. violet . . . . 1·40 6·00
7 50c. red . . . . 1·40 6·00
8 **74** 1l. blue . . . . 1·40 6·00
9 2l. brown . . . . 1·40 6·00
10 **75** 5l. black and blue . . . . . 1·40 7·50

1924. Manzoni.
11 **77** 10c. black and purple . . . 75 12·00
12 – 15c. black and green . . . . 75 12·00
13 – 30c. black . . . . 75 12·00
14 – 50c. black and brown . . . 75 12·00
15 – 1l. black and blue . . . . 18·00 90·00
16 – 5l. black and purple £250 £1000

1925. Holy Year.
17 – 20c.+10c. brown & green . . 1·00 4·25
18 **81** 30c.+15c. brown & choc . . 1·00 4·25
19 – 50c.+25c. brown & violet . . 1·00 4·25
20 – 60c.+30c. brown and red . . 1·00 4·25
21 – 1l.+50c. purple and blue . . 1·00 4·25
22 – 5l.+2l.50 purple and red . . 1·00 4·25

1925. Royal Jubilee.
23 **82** 60c. red . . . . 25 2·75
24 1l. blue . . . . 30 2·75
24c 1l.25 blue . . . . 60 9·00

1926. St. Francis of Assisi.
25 **83** 20c. green . . . . 1·00 4·25
26 – 40c. violet . . . . 1·00 4·25
27 – 60c. red . . . . 1·00 4·25
28 – 1l.25 blue . . . . 1·00 4·25
29 – 5l.+2l.50 green . . . . . 2·00 5·50

1926. As Colonial Propaganda stamps of Somalia, T **21**, but inscr "TRIPOLITANIA".
30 5c.+5c. brown . . . . . . 20 2·25
31 10c.+5c. green . . . . . . 20 2·25
32 20c.+5c. green . . . . . . 20 2·25
33 40c.+5c. red . . . . . . 20 2·25
34 60c.+5c. orange . . . . . 20 2·25
35 1l.+5c. blue . . . . . . 20 2·25

6 Port of Tripoli

9 Palm Tree

1927. 1st Tripoli Trade Fair.
36 **6** 20c.+05c. black and purple . . 2·00 3·00
37 25c.+05c. black and green . . 2·00 3·00
38 – 40c.+10c. black and brown . . 2·00 3·00
39 – 60c.+10c. black and brown . . 2·00 3·00
40 – 75c.+20c. black and red . . . 2·00 3·00
41 – 1l.25+20c. black and blue . . 7·50 9·50
DESIGNS: 40, 60c. Arch of Marcus Aurelius; 75c., 1l.25, View of Tripoli.

1927. 1st National Defence issue.
42 **88** 40+20c. black and brown . . 1·00 4·25
43 60+30c. brown and red . . 1·00 4·25
44 1l.25+60c. black and blue . . 1·00 4·25
45 5l.+2l.50 black and green . . 1·50 6·50

1927. Death Centenary of Volta.
46 **91** 20c. violet . . . . 3·00 10·00
47 50c. orange . . . . 3·00 7·00
48 1l.25 blue . . . . 4·00 10·00

1928. 2nd Tripoli Trade Fair.
49 – 30c.+20c. brown & purple . . 1·60 4·25
50 **9** 50c.+20c. brown and green . . 1·60 4·25
51 – 1l.25+20c. brown and red . . 1·60 4·25
52 – 1l.75+20c. brown and blue . . 1·60 4·25
53 – 2l.55+50c. sepia & brown . . 2·25 6·00
54 – 5l.+1l. brown and violet . . 3·00 9·00
DESIGNS: As T **9**: 30c. Tripoli; 1l.25, Camel riders. 38 × 22½ mm: 1l.75, Arab citadel; 2l.55, Tripoli; 5l. Desert outpost.

1928. 45th Anniv of Italian-African Society. As T **25** of Somalia.
55 20c.+5c. green . . . . . . 75 3·50
56 30c.+5c. red . . . . 75 3·50
57 50c.+10c. violet . . . . . 75 3·50
58 1l.25+20c. blue . . . . . 75 3·50

1929. 2nd National Defence issue.
59 **89** 30c.+10c. black and red . . 1·40 4·75
60 – 50c.+20c. grey . . . . . 1·40 4·75
61 – 1l.25+50c. blue & brown . . 1·75 6·00
62 – 5l.+2l. black and olive . . . 1·75 6·00

1929. 3rd Tripoli Trade Fair. Inscr "1929".
63 30c.+20c. black and purple . . 5·00 12·00
64 50c.+20c. black and green . . 5·00 12·00
65 1l.25+20c. black and red . . 5·00 12·00
66 1l.75+20c. black and blue . . 5·00 12·00
67 2l.55+50c. black and brown . 5·00 12·00
68 5l.+1l. black and violet . . . 90·00 £170
DESIGNS—As T **9**: 30c., 1l.25, Different trees; 50c. Dorcas gazelle. 38 × 22½ mm: 1l.75, Goats; 2l.55, Camel caravan; 5l. Trees.

1929. Abbey of Montecassino.
69 **104** 20c. green . . . . 1·75 4·25
70 – 25c. red . . . . 1·75 4·25
71 – 50c.+10c. red . . . . . 1·75 8·50
72 – 75c.+15c. brown . . . . . 1·75 8·50
73 **104** 1l.25+25c. purple . . . . 3·25 8·50
74 – 5l.+1l. blue . . . . . . 3·25 8·50
75 – 10l.+2l. brown . . . . . 3·25 10·00

1930. 4th Tripoli Trade Fair. Inscr "1930".
76 30c. brown . . . . 1·40 4·75
77 50c. violet . . . . 1·40 4·75
78 1l.25 blue . . . . 1·40 4·75
79 1l.75+20c. red . . . . . . 1·40 7·00
80 2l.55+45c. green . . . . . 8·00 12·00
81 5l.+1l. orange . . . . . . 8·00 15·00
82 10l.+2l. purple . . . . . . 8·00 17·00
DESIGNS—As T **9**: 30c. Gathering bananas; 50c. Tobacco plant; 1l.25, Venus of Cyrene. 38 × 22½ mm: 5l. Motor and camel transport; 10l. Rome pavilion, at exhibition entrance.

1930. Marriage of Prince Humbert and Princess Marie José.
83 **109** 20c. green . . . . 45 1·90
84 50c.+10c. red . . . . . 45 2·50
85 1l.25+25c. red . . . . . 45 2·75

1930. Ferrucci.
86 **114** 20c. violet (postage) . . . 50 1·60
87 – 25c. green (No. 283) . . . 50 1·60
88 – 50c. black (as No. 284) . . 50 1·60
89 – 1l.25 blue (No. 285) . . . 50 1·60
90 – 5l.+2l. red (as No. 286) . . 1·75 2·75

91 **117** 50c. purple (air) . . . . . 80 2·25
92 1l. blue . . . . 80 2·25
93 5l.+2l. red . . . . 4·50 10·00

1930. 3rd National Defence issue.
94 **89** 30c.+10c. green and deep green . . . . 5·00 15·00
95 – 50c.+10c. violet and green . 5·00 15·00
96 – 1l.25+30c. brown and deep brown . . . . 5·00 15·00
97 – 5l.+1l.50 green and blue . . 14·00 42·00

17 Roman Arch

18 Columns of Leptis

19

1930. 25th Anniv (1929) of Italian Colonial Agricultural Institute.
98 **17** 50c.+20c. brown . . . . . 1·00 5·00
99 1l.25+20c. blue . . . . . 1·00 5·00
100 1l.75+20c. green . . . . . 1·00 5·00
101 2l.55+50c. violet . . . . . 1·75 5·00
102 5l.+1l. red . . . . 1·75 5·00

1930. Virgil.
103 – 15c. grey (postage) . . . 40 1·40
104 – 20c. brown . . . . 40 1·40
105 – 25c. green . . . . 40 1·10
106 – 30c. brown . . . . 40 1·40
107 – 50c. purple . . . . 40 1·10
108 – 75c. red . . . . 40 1·40
109 – 1l.25 blue . . . . 40 1·40
110 – 5l.+1l.50 purple . . . . . 2·00 7·00
111 – 10l.+2l.50 brown . . . . 2·00 7·00

112 **119** 50c. green (air) . . . . . 1·00 2·25
113 1l. red . . . . 1·00 2·25
114 7l.70+1l.30 brown . . . . 2·75 10·00
115 9l.+2l. blue . . . . 2·75 10·00

1931. Air.
116 **18** 50c. red 20 10
117 60c. red . . . . 1·60 6·00
117a 75c. blue . . . . 1·60 6·00
118 80c. purple . . . . 3·00 6·50
119 **19** 1l. blue 45 10
120 1l.20 brown . . . . 6·50 10·00
121 1l.50 red . . . . 3·00 6·00
122 5l. green . . . . 7·00 7·00

20 Statue of Youth

22 Savoia Marchetti S-55A Flying Boat over Ruins

1931. 5th Tripoli Trade Fair.
123 **20** 10c. black (postage) . . . 2·00 5·00
124 – 25c. green . . . . 2·00 5·00
125 – 50c. violet . . . . 2·00 5·00
126 – 1l.25 blue . . . . 2·00 5·00
127 – 1l.75+25c. red . . . . . 2·40 7·00
128 – 2l.75+45c. orange . . . . 2·40 10·00
129 – 5l.+1l. purple . . . . . . 8·00 17·00
130 – 10l.+2l. brown . . . . . 30·00 45·00

131 – 50c. blue (air) . . . . . 2·00 5·00
DESIGNS—As Type **20**: 25c. Arab musician; 50c. (postage) View of Zeughet; 1l.25, Snake charmer; 1l.75, House and windmill; 2l.75, Libyan "Zaptie"; 5l. Arab horseman. As Type E **21**: 10l. Exhibition Pavilion; 50c. (air) Airplane over desert.

1931. St. Antony of Padua.
132 **121** 20c. brown . . . . 55 2·50
133 – 25c. green . . . . 55 2·50
134 – 30c. black . . . . 55 2·50
135 – 50c. purple . . . . 55 1·40
136 – 75c. grey . . . . 55 2·50
137 – 1l.25 blue . . . . 55 2·50
138 – 5l.+2l.50 brown . . . . . 2·00 11·00

1931. Air. 25th Anniv (1929) of Italian Colonial Agricultural Institute.
139 **22** 50c. blue . . . . 1·50 6·00
140 80c. violet . . . . 1·50 6·00
141 1l. black . . . . 1·50 6·00
142 2l. green . . . . 3·00 7·00
143 5l.+2l. red . . . . 5·00 15·00

23 Paw-paw Tree

24 Incense Plant

1932. 6th Tripoli Trade Fair. Inscr "1932".
144 **23** 10c. brown (postage) . . . 3·00 6·00
145 – 20c. brown . . . . 3·00 6·00
146 – 25c. green . . . . 3·00 6·00
147 – 30c. green . . . . 3·00 6·00
148 – 50c. violet . . . . 3·00 6·00
149 – 75c. red . . . . 4·00 10·00
150 – 1l.25 blue . . . . 4·00 10·00
151 – 1l.75+25c. brown . . . . 18·00 32·00
152 – 5l.+1l. blue . . . . . . 20·00 45·00
153 – 10l.+2l. purple . . . . . 50·00 90·00

154 – 50c. blue (air) . . . . . 5·50 12·00
155 – 1l. brown . . . . 5·50 12·00
156 – 2l.+1l. black . . . . . . 16·00 45·00
157 – 5l.+2l. red . . . . 50·00 90·00
DESIGNS—POSTAGE. VERT: 10c. to 50c. Various trees; 75c. Roman mausoleum at Ghirza; 10l. Dorcas gazelle. HORIZ: 1l.25, Mogadiscio aerodrome; 1l.75, Lioness; 5l. Arab and camel. AIR. HORIZ: 50c., 1l. Marina Fiat MF.5 flying boat over Bedouin camp; 2, 5l. Marina Fiat MF.5 flying boat over Tripoli.

1933. 7th Tripoli Trade Fair. Inscr "1933".
158 – 10c. purple (postage) . . . 24·00 15·00
159 **24** 25c. green . . . . 12·00 11·00
160 – 30c. brown . . . . 12·00 15·00
161 – 50c. violet . . . . 12·00 9·00
162 – 1l.25 blue . . . . 22·00 38·00
163 – 5l.+1l. brown . . . . . . 35·00 85·00
164 – 10l.+2l.50 red . . . . . 35·00 85·00

165 – 50c. green (air) . . . . . 6·00 12·00
166 – 75c. red . . . . 6·00 12·00
167 – 1l. blue . . . . 6·00 12·00
168 – 2l.+50c. violet . . . . . 12·00 24·00
169 – 5l.+1l. brown . . . . . . 15·00 32·00
170 – 10l.+2l.50 black . . . . . 15·00 32·00
DESIGNS—POSTAGE. VERT: 10c. Ostrich; 50c. Arch of Marcus Aurelius; 1l.25, Golden eagle; 10l. Tripoli and Fascist emblem. HORIZ: 30c. Arab drummer; 5l. Leopard. AIR. HORIZ: 50c., 2l. Seaplane over Tripoli; 75c., 10l. Caproni Ca 101 airplane over Tagiura; 1, 5l. Seaplane leaving Tripoli.

25 Mercury

1933. Airship "Graf Zeppelin".
171 **25** 3l. brown . . . . 5·00 35·00
172 – 5l. violet . . . . 5·00 35·00
173 – 10l. green . . . . 5·00 55·00
174 **25** 12l. blue . . . . 5·00 85·00
175 – 15l. red . . . . 5·00 70·00
176 – 20l. black . . . . 5·00 95·00
DESIGNS: 5, 15l. "Graf Zeppelin" and Arch of Marcus Aurelius; 10, 20l. "Graf Zeppelin" and allegory of "dawn".

26 "Flight"

1933. Air. Balbo Transatlantic Mass Formation Flight.
177 **26** 19l.75 brown and black . . 10·00 £225
178 44l.75 green and blue . . . 10·00 £225

1934. Air. Rome–Buenos Aires Flight. Optd with Savoia Marchetti S-71 airplane and **1934-XII PRIMO VOLO DIRETTO ROMA = BUENOS-AYRES TRIMOTORE LOMBARDI-MAZZOTTI** or surch also in Italian.
179 **19** 2l. on 5l. brown . . . . . 1·50 27·00
180 3l. on 5l. green . . . . . 1·50 27·00
181 5l. brown . . . . 1·50 27·00
182 10l. on 5l. red . . . . . . 1·50 27·00

27 Water Carriers

1934. 8th Tripoli Trade Fair.
183 **27** 10c. brown (postage) . . . 2·00 5·00
184 – 20c. red . . . . 2·00 5·00
185 – 25c. green . . . . 2·00 5·00
186 – 30c. brown . . . . 2·00 5·00
187 – 50c. violet . . . . 2·00 5·00
188 – 75c. red . . . . 2·00 5·00
189 – 1l.25 blue . . . . 24·00 38·00
DESIGNS—VERT: 20c. Arab; 25c. Minaret; 50c. Statue of Emperor Claudius. HORIZ: 30c., 1l.25, Moslem shrine; 75c. Ruins of Ghadames.

190 50c. blue (air) . . . . . . 4·50 12·00
191 75c. red . . . . 4·50 12·00
192 5l.+1l. green . . . . 38·00 95·00
193 10l.+2l. purple . . . . . . 38·00 95·00
194 25l.+3l. brown . . . . . . 42·00 95·00
DESIGNS—HORIZ: 50c., 5l. Marina Fiat MF.5 flying boat off Tripoli; 75c., 10l. Airplane over mosque. VERT: 25l. Caproni Ca 101 airplane and camel.

See also Nos. E195/6.

1934. Air. Oasis Flight. As Nos. 190/4 optd **CIRCUITO DELLE OASI TRIPOLI MAGGIO 1934-XII.**
197 50c. red . . . . 4·50 10·00
198 75c. bistre . . . . 4·50 10·00
199 5l.+1l. brown . . . . . . 4·50 10·00
200 10l.+2l. blue £140 £200
201 25l.+3l. violet £140 £200

See also Nos. E202/3.

29 Village

1934. 2nd International Colonial Exn, Naples.
204 **29** 5c. brown and green (postage) . . . . 1·75 7·50
205 10c. black and brown . . . 1·75 7·50
206 20c. blue and red . . . . 1·75 7·50
207 50c. brown and violet . . . 1·75 7·50
208 60c. blue and brown . . . 1·75 7·50
209 1l.25 green and blue . . . 1·75 7·50

210 – 25c. orange and blue (air) . 1·75 7·50
211 – 50c. blue and green . . . . 1·75 7·50
212 – 75c. orange and brown . . 1·75 7·50
213 – 80c. green and brown . . . 1·75 7·50
214 – 1l. green and red . . . . 1·75 7·50
215 – 2l. brown and blue . . . . 1·75 7·50
DESIGNS: 25c. to 75c. Shadow of airplane over desert; 80c. to 2l. Arab camel corps and Caproni Ca 101 airplane.

30

1934. Air. Rome–Mogadiscio Flight.
216 **30** 25c.+10c. green . . . . . 1·75 5·00
217 50c.+10c. brown . . . . . 1·75 5·00
218 75c.+15c. red . . . . . . 1·75 5·00
219 80c.+15c. black . . . . . 1·75 5·00
220 1l.+20c. brown . . . . . . 1·75 5·00
221 2l.+20c. blue . . . . 1·75 5·00
222 3l.+25c. violet . . . . . . 14·00 40·00
223 5l.+25c. orange . . . . . . 14·00 40·00
224 10l.+30c. purple . . . . . 14·00 40·00
225 25l.+2l. green . . . . . . 14·00 40·00

32 Camel Transport

1935. 9th Tripoli Exhibition.

226	–	10c.+10c. brown (post)	50	2·50
227	–	20c.+10c. red	50	2·50
228	–	50c.+10c. violet	50	2·50
229	–	75c.+15c. red	50	2·50
230	–	1l.25+25c. blue	50	2·50
231	–	2l.+50c. green	50	2·50
232	–	25c.+10c. green (air)	70	3·00
233	32	50c.+10c. blue	70	3·00
234	–	1l.+25c. blue	70	3·00
235	–	2l.+30c. red	70	3·50
236	–	3l.+1l.50 brown	70	3·75
237	–	10l.+5l. purple	6·00	15·00

DESIGNS—POSTAGE. VERT: 10, 20c. Pomegranate tree; 50c., 2l. Arab flautist; 75c., 1l.25, Arab in burnous. AIR. VERT: 25c., 3l. Watch-tower. HORIZ: 1, 10l. Arab girl and Caproni Ca 101 airplane.

For issue inscr "XII FIERA CAMPIONARIA TRIPOLI" and dated "1938", see Libya Nos. 88/95.

CONCESSIONAL LETTER POST

1931. Optd **TRIPOLITANIA**.

CL123	CL 109	10c. brown	4·00	5·00

EXPRESS LETTER STAMPS

Express stamps optd **TRIPOLI DI BARBERIA**, formerly listed here, will be found under Italian P.O.s in the Levant Nos. E6/7.

1927. 1st Tripoli Exhibition. Inscr "EXPRES".

E42	1l.25+30c. black and violet	8·00	8·00
E43	2l.50+1l. black and yellow	8·00	8·00

DESIGN—As T **6**: 1l.25, 2l.50, Camels and palm trees.

E 21 War Memorial

1931. 5th Tripoli Trade Fair.

E132	E 21	1l.25+20c. red	4·50	10·00

1934. Air. 8th Tripoli Trade Fair.

E195	2l.25 black	14·00	38·00
E196	4l.50+1l. blue	14·00	38·00

DESIGN—As T **27**: Nos. E195/6, Caproni Ca 101 airplane over Bedouins in desert.

1934. Air. Oasis Flight. As Nos. E195/6 optd **CIRCUITO DELLE OASI TRIPOLI MAGGIO 1934-XII**.

E202	2l.25 red	4·50	10·00
E203	4l.50+1l. red	4·50	10·00

OFFICIAL STAMP

1934. No. 225 (colour changed) optd **SERVIZIO DI STATO** and Crown.

O226	30	25l.+2l. red	£1300	£2750

From 1943 to 1951 Tripolitania was under British administration; stamps issued during this period are listed under British Occupation of Italian Colonies. From 1952 it was part of independent Libya.

TRISTAN DA CUNHA Pt. 1

An island in the south Atlantic Ocean west of S. Africa. Following a volcanic eruption the island was evacuated on 10 October 1961, but resettled in 1963.

1952. 12 pence = 1 shilling;
20 shilling = 1 pound.
1961. 100 cents = 1 rand.
1963. Reverted to sterling currency.

1952. Stamps of St. Helena optd **TRISTAN DA CUNHA**.

1	33	½d. violet	15	1·75
2		1d. black and green	70	1·50
3		1½d. black and red	70	1·50
4		2d. black and red	70	1·50
5		3d. grey	1·00	1·50
6		4d. blue	3·75	2·00
7		6d. blue	4·25	2·50
8		8d. green	4·00	5·00
9		1s. brown	4·25	2·00
10		2s.6d. purple	19·00	13·00
11		5s. brown	21·00	20·00
12		10s. purple	40·00	30·00

1953. Coronation. As T **33h** of St. Helena.

13	3d. black and green	50	1·25

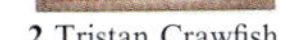

2 Tristan Crawfish

16 Starfish

1954.

14	2	½d. red and brown	10	10
15	–	1d. sepia and green	10	50
16	–	1½d. black and purple	1·75	1·50
17	–	2d. violet and orange	30	20
18	–	2½d. black and red	1·50	60
19	–	3d. blue and olive	60	1·50
20	–	4d. turquoise and blue	60	70
21	–	5d. green and black	60	70
22	–	6d. green and violet	60	75
23	–	9d. lilac and red	60	45
24	–	1s. green and sepia	60	45
25	–	2s.6d. sepia and blue	17·00	8·00
26	–	5s. black and red	50·00	11·00
27	–	10s. orange and purple	21·00	12·00

DESIGNS—HORIZ: 1d. Carting flax; 2d. Big Beach factory; 2½d. Yellow-nosed albatross (sea birds); 4d. Tristan from S.W.; 5d. Girls on donkeys; 6d. Inaccessible Is. from Tristan; 9d. Nightingale Is; 1s. St. Mary's Church; 2s.6d. Southern elephant seal at Gough Is; 5s. Inaccessible Island rail (bird); 10s. Spinning wheel. VERT: 1½d. Rockhopper penguin; 3d. Island longboat.

1960. Marine Life. Value, fish and inscriptions in black.

28	16	½d. orange	15	40
29	–	1d. purple	15	20
30	–	1½d. turquoise	20	70
31	–	2d. green	30	90
32	–	2½d. sepia	55	60
33	–	3d. red	1·25	70
34	–	4d. olive	1·25	60
35	–	5d. yellow	1·50	60
36	–	6d. blue	1·50	60
37	–	9d. red	1·75	60
38	–	1s. brown	1·75	50
39	–	2s.6d. blue	11·00	12·00
40	–	5s. green	12·00	15·00
41	–	10s. violet	38·00	32·00

FISH: 1d. Concha wrasse; 1½d. Two-spined thornfish; 2d. Atlantic saury; 2½d. Bristle snipefish; 3d. Tristan crawfish; 4d. False jacopever; 5d. Five-fringed morwong; 6d. Long-finned scad; 9d. Christophersen's medusafish; 1s. Blue medusafish; 2s.6d. Snoek; 5s. Blue shark; 10s. Black right whale.

1961. As 1960 issue but values in new currency. Value, fish and inscriptions in black.

42	16	½c. orange	10	1·25
43	–	1c. purple (as 1d.)	15	1·25
44	–	1½c. turquoise (as 1½d.)	35	1·25
45	–	2c. sepia (as 2½d.)	65	1·25
46	–	2½c. red (as 3d.)	1·00	1·25
47	–	3c. olive (as 4d.)	1·00	1·25
48	–	4c. yellow (as 5d.)	1·25	1·25
49	–	5c. blue (as 6d.)	1·25	1·25
50	–	7½c. red (as 9d.)	1·25	1·25
51	–	10c. brown (as 1s.)	2·00	1·25
52	–	25c. blue (as 2s.6d.)	7·00	9·00
53	–	50c. green (as 5s.)	14·00	15·00
54	–	1r. violet (as 10s.)	38·00	35·00

1963. Tristan Resettlement. Nos. 176/88 of St. Helena optd **TRISTAN DA CUNHA RESETTLEMENT 1963**.

55	50	1d. multicoloured	15	80
56	–	1½d. multicoloured	20	70
57	–	2d. red and grey	25	80
58	–	3d. multicoloured	30	80
59	–	4½d. multicoloured	50	60
60	–	6d. red, sepia and olive	85	30
61	–	7d. brown, black and violet	50	30
62	–	10d. purple and blue	50	30
63	–	1s. yellow, green and brown	50	30
64	–	1s.6d. grey, black and blue	4·25	80
65	–	2s.6d. red, yellow & turquoise	1·00	45
66	–	5s. yellow, brown and green	6·00	1·25
67	–	10s. red, black and blue	6·50	1·25

1963. Freedom from Hunger. As T **63a** of St. Helena.

68	1s.6d. red	50	30

1964. Cent of Red Cross. As T **63b** of St. Helena.

69	3d. red and black	20	15
70	1s.6d. red and blue	30	20

31 South Atlantic Map

1965.

71	31	½d. black and blue	15	15
72	–	1d. black and green	50	15
73	–	1½d. black and blue	50	15
74	–	2d. black and purple	50	15
75	–	3d. black and turquoise	50	15
75a	–	4d. black and orange	4·00	4·00
76	–	4½d. black and brown	50	15
77	–	6d. black and green	50	15
78	–	7d. black and red	50	30
79	–	10d. black and brown	50	55
80	–	1s. black and red	50	30
81	–	1s.6d. black and olive	3·50	2·50
82	31	2s.6d. black and brown	2·75	2·75
83	–	5s. black and violet	5·00	3·50
84	–	10s. blue and red	1·75	1·25
84a	–	10s. black and blue	13·00	11·00
84b	–	£1 blue and brown	13·00	14·00

DESIGNS—HORIZ: 1d. Flagship of Tristao da Cunha, 1506; 1½d. "Heemstede" (Dutch East Indiaman), 1643; 2d. "Edward" (American whaling ship), 1864; 3d. "Shenandoah" (Confederate warship), 1862; 4d. H.M.S. "Challenger" (survey ship), 1873; 4½d. H.M.S. "Galatea" (screw frigate), 1867; 6d. H.M.S. "Cilicia" (transport), 1942; 7d. Royal Yacht "Britannia"; 10d. H.M.S. "Leopard" (frigate); 1s. "Tjisadane" (liner); 1s.6d. "Tristania" (crayfish trawler); 2s.6d. "Boissevain" (cargo liner); 5s. "Bornholm" (liner); 10s. (No. 84a), "R.S.A." (research vessel). VERT: 10s. (No. 84), £1 Queen Elizabeth II (portrait as in T **31** but larger).

1965. Cent of I.T.U. As T **64a** of St. Helena.

85	3d. red and grey	20	15
86	6d. violet and orange	30	15

1965. I.C.Y. As T **64b** of St. Helena.

87	1d. purple and turquoise	20	15
88	6d. green and lavender	50	25

1966. Churchill Commemoration. As T **64c** of St. Helena.

89	1d. blue	35	40
90	3d. green	75	50
91	6d. brown	1·00	65
92	1s.6d. violet	1·25	70

45 H.M.S. "Falmouth" (frigate) at Tristan and Soldier of 1816

1966. 150th Anniv of Tristan Garrison.

93	45	3d. multicoloured	15	10
94		6d. multicoloured	15	15
95		1s.6d. multicoloured	20	25
96		2s.6d. multicoloured	25	25

1966. World Cup Football Championship. As T **64d** of St. Helena.

97	3d. multicoloured	20	10
98	2s.6d. multicoloured	50	20

1966. Inauguration of W.H.O. Headquarters, Geneva. As T **64e** of St. Helena.

99	6d. black, green and blue	60	30
100	5s. black, purple and ochre	90	70

1966. 20th Anniv of U.N.E.S.C.O. As T **64f/h** of St. Helena.

101	10d. multicoloured	25	15
102	1s.6d. yellow, violet and olive	35	20
103	2s.6d. black, purple and orange	40	25

46 Calshot Harbour

1967. Opening of Calshot Harbour.

104	46	6d. multicoloured	10	10
105		10d. multicoloured	10	10
106		1s.6d. multicoloured	10	15
107		2s.6d. multicoloured	15	20

1967. No. 76 surch **4d** and bars.

108	4d. on 4½d. black and brown	10	10

48 Prince Alfred, First Duke of Edinburgh

1967. Centenary of First Duke of Edinburgh's Visit to Tristan.

109	48	3d. multicoloured	10	10
110		6d. multicoloured	10	10
111		1s.6d. multicoloured	10	10
112		2s.6d. multicoloured	15	15

49 Wandering Albatross

1968. Birds. Multicoloured.

113	4d. Type **49**	40	30
114	1s. Wilkins's finch	45	30
115	1s.6d. Tristan thrush	50	55
116	2s.6d. Greater shearwater	90	65

53 Union Jack and Dependency Flag

1968. 30th Anniv of Tristan da Cunha as a Dependency of St. Helena.

117	53	6d. multicoloured	10	30
118	–	9d. sepia and blue	10	35
119	53	1s.6d. multicoloured	15	40
120	–	2s.6d. red and blue	20	40

DESIGN: 9d. and 2s.6d. St. Helena and Tristan on chart.

55 Frigate

1969. Clipper Ships.

121	55	4d. blue	40	35
122	–	1s. red	40	40
123	–	1s.6d. green	45	80
124	–	2s.6d. brown	50	85

DESIGNS: 1s. Full-rigged ship; 1s.6d. Barque; 2s.6d. Full-rigged clipper.

59 Sailing Ship off Tristan da Cunha

1969. United Society for the Propagation of the Gospel. Multicoloured.

125	4d. Type **59**	40	30
126	9d. Islanders going to first gospel service	15	30
127	1s.6d. Landing of the first minister	15	40
128	2s.6d. Procession outside St. Mary's Church	20	40

63 Globe and Red Cross Emblem

1970. Centenary of British Red Cross.

129	63	4d. deep green, red and green	10	25
130		9d. bistre, red and green	15	30
131	–	1s.9d. drab, red and blue	25	45
132	–	2s.6d. purple, red and blue	30	55

DESIGN—VERT: Nos. 131/2, "Union Jack" and Red Cross flag.

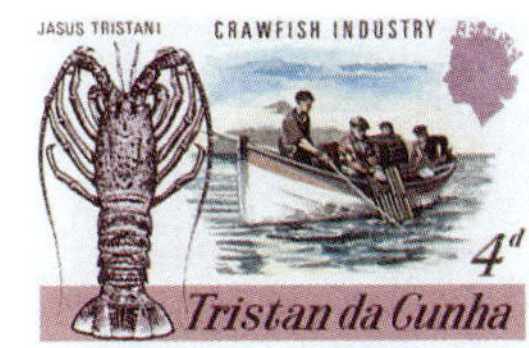

64 Crawfish and Longboat

1970. Crawfish Industry. Multicoloured.

133	4d. Type **64**	25	30
134	10d. Packing and storing crawfish	30	35
135	1s.6d. Type **64**	50	60
136	2s.6d. As 10d.	50	70

1971. Decimal Currency. Nos. 72, etc surch.

137	31	½p. on 1d. black and green	15	15
138	–	1p. on 2d. black and purple	15	15
139	–	1½p. on 4d. black and orange	30	15
140	–	2½p. on 6d. black and green	30	15
141	–	3p. on 7d. black and red	30	15
142	–	4p. on 10d. black and brown	30	20
143	–	5p. on 1s. black and red	30	20
144	–	7½p. on 1s.6d. black & olive	1·75	1·75
145	–	12½p. on 2s.6d. black & brown	2·50	2·50
146	–	15p. on 1½d. black and blue	2·50	3·00

147 – 25p. on 5s. black and violet 2·50 5·50
148 – 50p. on 10s. black and blue (No. 84a) 2·50 11·00

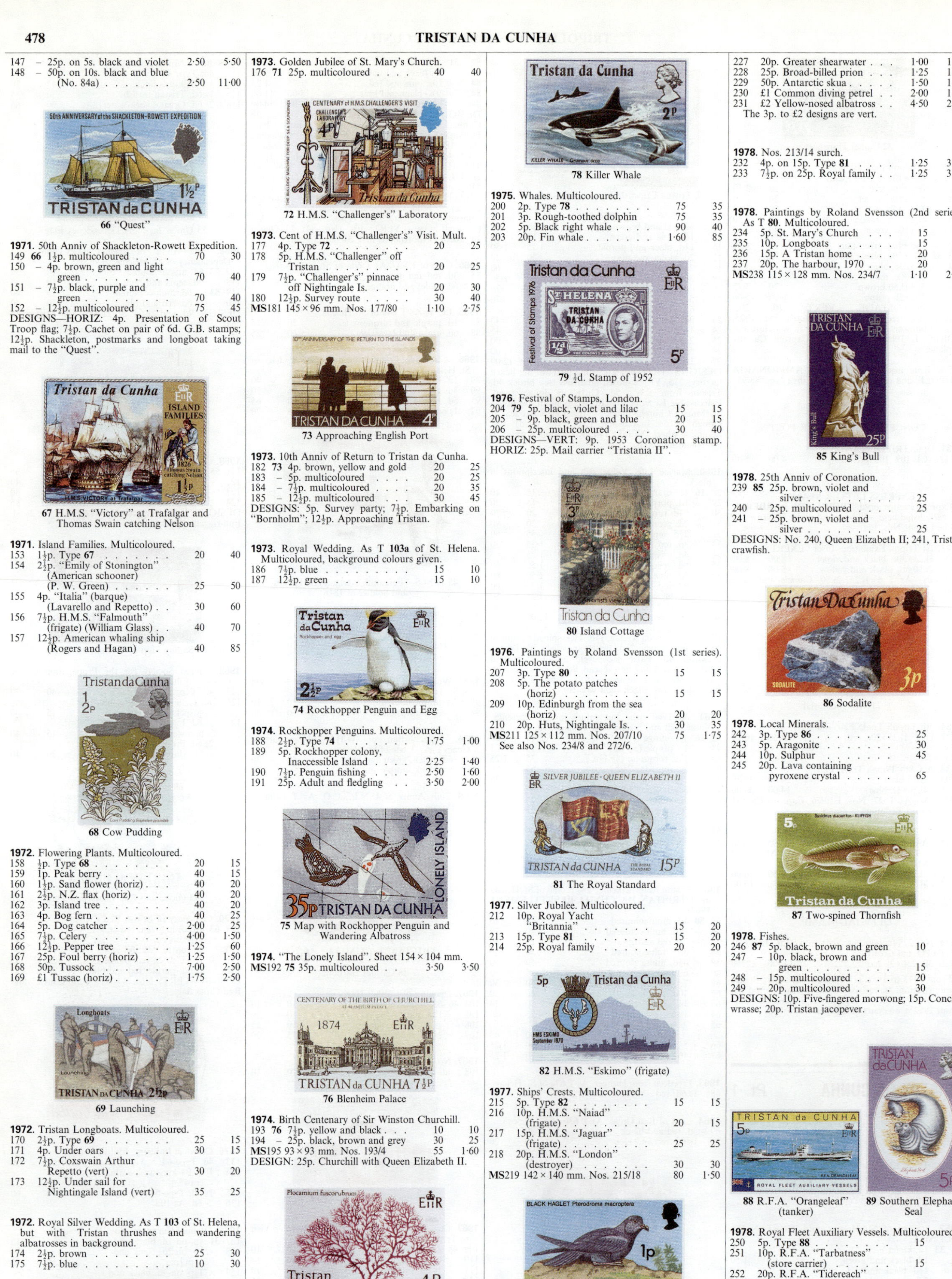

66 "Quest"

1971. 50th Anniv of Shackleton-Rowett Expedition.
149 66 1½p. multicoloured 70 30
150 – 4p. brown, green and light green 70 40
151 – 7½p. black, purple and green 70 40
152 – 12½p. multicoloured 75 45
DESIGNS—HORIZ: 4p. Presentation of Scout Troop flag; 7½p. Cachet on pair of 6d. G.B. stamps; 12½p. Shackleton, postmarks and longboat taking mail to the "Quest".

67 H.M.S. "Victory" at Trafalgar and Thomas Swain catching Nelson

1971. Island Families. Multicoloured.
153 1½p. Type 67 20 40
154 2½p. "Emily of Stonington" (American schooner) (P. W. Green) 25 50
155 4p. "Italia" (barque) (Lavarello and Repetto) 30 60
156 7½p. H.M.S. "Falmouth" (frigate) (William Glass) 40 70
157 12½p. American whaling ship (Rogers and Hagan) 40 85

68 Cow Pudding

1972. Flowering Plants. Multicoloured.
158 ½p. Type 68 20 15
159 1p. Peak berry 40 15
160 1½p. Sand flower (horiz) 40 20
161 2½p. N.Z. flax (horiz) 40 20
162 3p. Island tree 40 20
163 4p. Bog fern 40 25
164 5p. Dog catcher 2·00 25
165 7½p. Celery 4·00 1·50
166 12½p. Pepper tree 1·25 60
167 25p. Foul berry (horiz) 1·25 1·50
168 50p. Tussock 7·00 2·50
169 £1 Tussac (horiz) 1·75 2·50

69 Launching

1972. Tristan Longboats. Multicoloured.
170 2½p. Type 69 25 15
171 4p. Under oars 30 15
172 7½p. Coxswain Arthur Repetto (vert) 30 20
173 12½p. Under sail for Nightingale Island (vert) 35 25

1972. Royal Silver Wedding. As T 103 of St. Helena, but with Tristan thrushes and wandering albatrosses in background.
174 2½p. brown 25 30
175 7½p. blue 10 30

71 Church Altar

1973. Golden Jubilee of St. Mary's Church.
176 71 25p. multicoloured 40 40

72 H.M.S. "Challenger's" Laboratory

1973. Cent of H.M.S. "Challenger's" Visit. Mult.
177 4p. Type 72 20 25
178 5p. H.M.S. "Challenger" off Tristan 20 25
179 7½p. "Challenger's" pinnace off Nightingale Is. 20 30
180 12½p. Survey route 30 40
MS181 145×96 mm. Nos. 177/80 1·10 2·75

73 Approaching English Port

1973. 10th Anniv of Return to Tristan da Cunha.
182 73 4p. brown, yellow and gold 20 25
183 – 5p. multicoloured 20 25
184 – 7½p. multicoloured 20 35
185 – 12½p. multicoloured 30 45
DESIGNS: 5p. Survey party; 7½p. Embarking on "Bornholm"; 12½p. Approaching Tristan.

1973. Royal Wedding. As T 103a of St. Helena. Multicoloured, background colours given.
186 7½p. blue 15 10
187 12½p. green 15 10

74 Rockhopper Penguin and Egg

1974. Rockhopper Penguins. Multicoloured.
188 2½p. Type 74 1·75 1·00
189 5p. Rockhopper colony, Inaccessible Island 2·25 1·40
190 7½p. Penguin fishing 2·50 1·60
191 25p. Adult and fledgling 3·50 2·00

75 Map with Rockhopper Penguin and Wandering Albatross

1974. "The Lonely Island". Sheet 154×104 mm.
MS192 75 35p. multicoloured 3·50 3·50

76 Blenheim Palace

1974. Birth Centenary of Sir Winston Churchill.
193 76 7½p. yellow and black 10 10
194 – 25p. black, brown and grey 30 25
MS195 93×93 mm. Nos. 193/4 55 1·60
DESIGN: 25p. Churchill with Queen Elizabeth II.

77 "Plocamium fuscorubrum"

1975. Sea Plants.
196 77 4p. red, lilac and black 15 10
197 – 5p. green, blue and turquoise 15 15
198 – 10p. orange, brown & purple 20 15
199 – 20p. multicoloured 30 25
DESIGNS: 5p. "Ulva lactua"; 10p. "Epymenia flabellata"; 20p. "Macrocystis pyrifera".

78 Killer Whale

1975. Whales. Multicoloured.
200 2p. Type 78 75 35
201 3p. Rough-toothed dolphin 75 35
202 5p. Black right whale 90 40
203 20p. Fin whale 1·60 85

79 ½d. Stamp of 1952

1976. Festival of Stamps, London.
204 79 5p. black, violet and lilac 15 15
205 – 9p. black, green and blue 20 15
206 – 25p. multicoloured 30 40
DESIGNS—VERT: 9p. 1953 Coronation stamp. HORIZ: 25p. Mail carrier "Tristania II".

80 Island Cottage

1976. Paintings by Roland Svensson (1st series). Multicoloured.
207 3p. Type 80 15 15
208 5p. The potato patches (horiz) 15 15
209 10p. Edinburgh from the sea (horiz) 20 20
210 20p. Huts, Nightingale Is. 30 35
MS211 125×112 mm. Nos. 207/10 75 1·75
See also Nos. 234/8 and 272/6.

81 The Royal Standard

1977. Silver Jubilee. Multicoloured.
212 10p. Royal Yacht "Britannia" 15 20
213 15p. Type 81 15 20
214 25p. Royal family 20 20

82 H.M.S. "Eskimo" (frigate)

1977. Ships' Crests. Multicoloured.
215 5p. Type 82 15 15
216 10p. H.M.S. "Naiad" (frigate) 20 15
217 15p. H.M.S. "Jaguar" (frigate) 25 25
218 20p. H.M.S. "London" (destroyer) 30 30
MS219 142×140 mm. Nos. 215/18 80 1·50

83 Great-winged Petrel

1977. Birds. Multicoloured.
220 1p. Type 83 15 60
221 2p. White-faced storm petrel 20 90
222 3p. Hall's giant petrel 20 90
223 4p. Soft-plumaged petrel 60 1·00
224 5p. Wandering albatross 60 1·00
225 10p. Kerguelen petrel 60 1·00
226 15p. Antarctic tern 60 1·25
227 20p. Greater shearwater 1·00 1·25
228 25p. Broad-billed prion 1·25 1·25
229 50p. Antarctic skua 1·50 1·25
230 £1 Common diving petrel 2·00 1·50
231 £2 Yellow-nosed albatross 4·50 2·50
The 3p. to £2 designs are vert.

1978. Nos. 213/14 surch.
232 4p. on 15p. Type 81 1·25 3·50
233 7½p. on 25p. Royal family 1·25 3·50

1978. Paintings by Roland Svensson (2nd series). As T 80. Multicoloured.
234 5p. St. Mary's Church 15 15
235 10p. Longboats 15 15
236 15p. A Tristan home 20 25
237 20p. The harbour, 1970 20 25
MS238 115×128 mm. Nos. 234/7 1·10 2·00

85 King's Bull

1978. 25th Anniv of Coronation.
239 85 25p. brown, violet and silver 25 30
240 – 25p. multicoloured 25 30
241 – 25p. brown, violet and silver 25 30
DESIGNS: No. 240, Queen Elizabeth II; 241, Tristan crawfish.

86 Sodalite

1978. Local Minerals.
242 3p. Type 86 25 25
243 5p. Aragonite 30 30
244 10p. Sulphur 45 45
245 20p. Lava containing pyroxene crystal 65 65

87 Two-spined Thornfish

1978. Fishes.
246 87 5p. black, brown and green 10 10
247 – 10p. black, brown and green 15 15
248 – 15p. multicoloured 20 20
249 – 20p. multicoloured 30 25
DESIGNS: 10p. Five-fingered morwong; 15p. Concha wrasse; 20p. Tristan jacopever.

88 R.F.A. "Orangeleaf" (tanker) 89 Southern Elephant Seal

1978. Royal Fleet Auxiliary Vessels. Multicoloured.
250 5p. Type 88 15 10
251 10p. R.F.A. "Tarbatness" (store carrier) 15 10
252 20p. R.F.A. "Tidereach" (tanker) 20 25
253 25p. R.F.A. "Reliant" (store carrier) 25 30
MS254 136×140 mm. Nos. 250/3 65 2·75

1978. Wildlife Conservation. Multicoloured.
255 5p. Type 89 10 10
256 10p. Afro-Australian fur seal 15 15
257 15p. Tristan thrush 25 20
258 20p. Nightingale finch ("Tristan Bunting") 35 25

90 Tristan Longboat

1978. Visit of "Queen Elizabeth 2". Mult.
259 5p. Type **90** 15 15
260 10p. "Queen Mary" (liner) 15 15
261 15p. "Queen Elizabeth" (liner) 20 25
262 20p. "Queen Elizabeth 2" (liner) 20 25
MS263 148 × 96 mm. 25p. Queen Elizabeth 2 (liner) (131 × 27 mm) 75 1·50

91 1952 "TRISTAN DA CUNHA" overprint on St. Helena 10s. Definitive

1979. Death Centenary of Sir Rowland Hill.
264 **91** 5p. black, lilac and yellow 10 15
265 – 10p. black, red and green 15 20
266 – 25p. multicoloured 30 30
MS267 83 × 103 mm. 50p. black and red 60 70
DESIGNS—HORIZ: 10p. 1954 5s. definitive. VERT: 25p. "TRISTAN DA CUNHA RESETTLEMENT 1963" overprint on St. Helena 3d. definitive; 50p. 1946 1d. 4 Potatoes local label.

92 "The Padre's House"

1979. International Year of the Child. Children's Drawings. Multicoloured.
268 5p. Type **92** 10 10
269 10p. "Houses in the Village" 15 15
270 15p. "St. Mary's Church" 15 15
271 20p. "Rockhopper Penguins" 20 25

1980. Paintings by Roland Svensson (3rd series). As T **80**. Multicoloured.
272 5p. "Stoltenhoff Island" (horiz) 10 10
273 10p. "Nightingale from the East" (horiz) 15 20
274 15p. "The Administrator's Abode" 15 25
275 20p. "Ridge where the Goat jump off" 20 30
MS276 126 × 109 mm. Nos. 272/6 70 1·25

93 "Tristania II" (crayfish trawler)

95 "Golden Hind"

94 Queen Elizabeth the Queen Mother at Royal Opera House, 1976

1980. "London 1980" Int Stamp Exhibition. Mult.
277 5p. Type **93** 10 10
278 10p. Mail being unloaded at Calshot Harbour 15 15
279 15p. Tractor transporting mail to Post Office 15 20
280 20p. Ringing the "dong" to summon people to Post Office 20 20
281 25p. Distributing mail 25 25

1980. 80th Birthday of The Queen Mother.
282 **94** 14p. multicoloured 25 25

1980. 400th Anniv of Sir Francis Drake's Circumnavigation of the World. Multicoloured.
283 5p. Type **95** 10 10
284 10p. Drake's route 15 15
285 20p. Sir Francis Drake 20 20
286 25p. Queen Elizabeth I 25 25

96 "Humpty Dumpty"

1980. Christmas. Scenes from Nursery Rhymes. Multicoloured.
287 15p. Type **96** 15 25
288 15p. "Mary had a little Lamb" 15 25
289 15p. "Little Jack Horner" 15 25
290 15p. "Hey Diddle Diddle" 15 25
291 15p. "London Bridge" 15 25
292 15p. "Old King Cole" 15 25
293 15p. "Sing a Song of Sixpence" 15 25
294 15p. "Tom, Tom the Piper's Son" 15 25
295 15p. "The Owl and the Pussy Cat" 15 25

97 South Atlantic Ocean showing Islands on Mid-Atlantic Ridge

98 Revd. Dodgson as Young Man

1980. 150th Anniv of Royal Geographical Society. Maps. Multicoloured.
296 5p. Type **97** 15 20
297 10p. Tristan da Cunha group (Beauforts Survey, 1806) 15 25
298 15p. Tristan Island (Crawford, 1937–38) 20 30
299 20p. Gough Island (1955–56) 25 40

1981. Centenary of Revd. Edwin Dodgson's Arrival on Tristan da Cunha. Multicoloured.
300 10p. Type **98** 10 15
301 20p. Dodgson and view of Tristan da Cunha (horiz) 20 30
302 30p. Dodgson with people of Tristan da Cunha 25 45
MS303 140 × 134 mm. Nos. 300/2 75 1·40

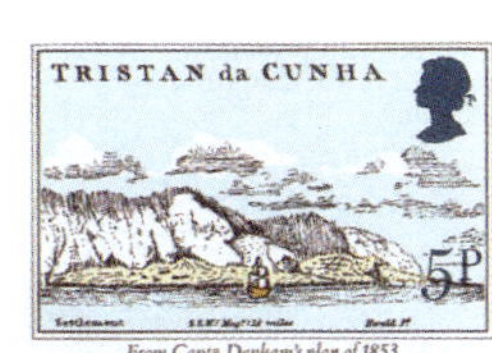

99 Detail from Captain Denham's Plan, 1853

1981. Early Maps. Multicoloured.
304 5p. Type **99** 15 10
305 14p. Detail from map by A. Dalrymple, 17 March 1781 20 20
306 21p. Detail from Captain Denham's plan, 1853 (different) 25 30
MS307 110 × 70 mm. 35p. Detail from map by J. van Keulen, circa 1700 50 60

100 Wedding Bouquet from Tristan da Cunha

101 Explorer with Rucksack

1981. Royal Wedding. Multicoloured.
308 5p. Type **100** 10 10
309 20p. Investiture of Prince of Wales 15 15
310 50p. Prince Charles and Lady Diana Spencer 45 45

1981. 25th Anniv of Duke of Edinburgh Award Scheme. Multicoloured.
311 5p. Type **101** 10 10
312 10p. Explorer at campsite 10 10
313 20p. Explorer map reading 20 20
314 25p. Duke of Edinburgh 25 25

102 Inaccessible Island Rail on Nest

1981. Inaccessible Island Rail. Multicoloured.
315 10p. Type **102** 20 30
316 10p. Inaccessible Island rail eggs 20 30
317 10p. Rail chicks 20 30
318 10p. Adult rail 20 30

103 Six-gilled Shark

1982. Sharks. Multicoloured.
319 5p. Type **103** 25 10
320 14p. Porbeagle 25 20
321 21p. Blue shark 25 35
322 35p. Golden hammerhead 35 50

104 "Marcella" (barque)

1982. Sailing Ships (1st series). Multicoloured.
323 5p. Type **104** 20 25
324 15p. "Eliza Adams" (full-rigged ship) 20 35
325 30p. "Corinthian" (American whaling ship) 25 45
326 50p. "Samuel and Thomas" (American whaling ship) 40 65
See also Nos. 341/4.

105 Lady Diana Spencer at Windsor, July 1981

106 Lord Baden-Powell

1982. 21st Birthday of Princess of Wales. Mult.
327 5p. Tristan da Cunha coat of arms 10 10
328 15p. Type **105** 40 20
329 30p. Prince and Princess of Wales in wedding portrait 45 40
330 50p. Formal portrait 1·25 60

1982. 75th Anniv of Boy Scout Movement. Mult.
331 5p. Type **106** 15 15
332 20p. First Scout camp, Brownsea, 1907 20 35
333 50p. Local Scouts on parade (horiz) 45 75
MS334 88 × 104 mm. 50p. Moral of the Acorn and the Oak 75 1·40

1982. Commonwealth Games, Brisbane. Nos. 224 and 228 optd **1ST PARTICIPATION COMMONWEALTH GAMES 1982.**
335 5p. Wandering albatross 15 10
336 25p. Broad-billed prion 40 30

108 Formation of Island

1982. Volcanoes. Multicoloured.
337 5p. Type **108** 15 15
338 15p. Plan showing surface cinder cones and cross-section of volcano showing feeders 25 35
339 25p. Eruption 35 50
340 35p. 1961 Tristan eruption 40 70

1983. Sailing Ships (2nd series). As T **104**. Mult.
341 5p. "Islander" (barque) (vert) 15 15
342 20p. "Roscoe" (full-rigged ship) 25 25
343 35p. "Columbia" (whaling ship) 35 40
344 50p. "Emeline" (schooner) (vert) 50 60

109 Tractor pulling Trailer

1983. Land Transport. Multicoloured.
345 5p. Type **109** 10 15
346 15p. Pack donkeys 15 25
347 30p. Bullock cart 20 40
348 50p. Landrover 30 60

110 Early Chart of South Atlantic

1983. Island History. Multicoloured.
349 1p. Type **110** 30 50
350 3p. Tristao da Cunha's caravel 40 50
351 4p. Notice left by Dutch on first landing, 1643 40 50
352 5p. 17th-century views of the island 40 50
353 10p. British army landing party, 1815 45 50
354 15p. 19th-century view of the settlement 55 70
355 18p. Governor Glass's house 55 70
356 20p. The Revd. W. F. Taylor and Peter Green 65 75
357 25p. "John and Elizabeth" (American whaling ship) 85 75
358 50p. Letters Patent declaring Tristan da Cunha a dependency of St. Helena 1·10 1·50
359 £1 Commissioning of H.M.S. "Atlantic Isle", 1944 1·25 2·50
360 £2 Evacuation, 1961 2·00 4·00

111 "Christ's Charge to St. Peter" (detail)

113 "Agrocybe praecox var. cutefracta"

112 1952 6d. Stamp

1983. 500th Birth Anniv of Raphael.
361 **111** 10p. multicoloured 15 20
362 – 25p. multicoloured 25 35
363 – 40p. multicoloured 45 60
MS364 115 × 90 mm. 50p. multicoloured (horiz) 70 80
On No. **MS**364 the Queen's head has been replaced by the Royal Cypher.
DESIGNS: 25, 40p. Different details of "Christ's Charge to St. Peter" (Raphael).

1984. 150th Anniv of St. Helena as British Colony. Multicoloured.
365 10p. Type **112** 20 35
366 15p. 1952 1s. stamp 25 45
367 25p. 1952 2s.6d. stamp 30 70
368 60p. 1952 10s. stamp 60 1·25

1984. Fungi. Multicoloured.
369 10p. Type **113** 35 70
370 20p. "Laccaria tetraspora" 45 1·00
371 30p. "Agrocybe cylindracea" (horiz) 55 1·10
372 50p. "Sacoscypha coccinea" (horiz) 65 1·40

114 Constellation of "Orion" **115** Sheep-shearing

1984. The Night Sky. Multicoloured.
373 10p. Type **114** 35 80
374 20p. "Scorpius" 40 90
375 25p. "Canis Major" 45 95
376 50p. "Crux" . . . . 60 1·10

1984. Tristan Woollens Industry. Multicoloured.
377 9p. Type **115** 15 45
378 17p. Carding wool 20 50
379 29p. Spinning 30 80
380 45p. Knitting 45 90
MS381 120 × 85 mm. As Nos. 377/80, but without white borders around the designs . . 1·00 3·00

116 "Christmas Dinner-table"

1984. Christmas. Children's Drawings. Mult.
382 10p. Type **116** 20 35
383 20p. "Santa Claus in ox cart" 25 40
384 30p. "Santa Claus in longboat" 30 70
385 50p. "The Nativity" 50 80

117 "H.M.S. 'Julia' Ashore, 1817" (Midshipman C. W. Browne) **118** The Queen Mother at Ascot with Princess Margaret

1985. Shipwrecks (1st series).
386 **117** 10p. blue and light blue 40 80
387 – 25p. brown and green . . 50 1·40
388 – 35p. brown and yellow . . 65 1·60
MS389 142 × 101 mm. 60p. multicoloured . . . . 75 2·25

DESIGNS—VERT: 25p. Bell from "Mabel Clark", St. Mary's Church. HORIZ: 35p. "Barque 'Glenhuntley' foundering, 1898" (John Hagan); 60p. Map of Tristan da Cunha showing site of shipwrecks.

See also Nos. 411/14 and 426/9.

1985. Life and Times of Queen Elizabeth the Queen Mother. Multicoloured.
390 10p. The Queen Mother and Prince Charles, 1954 . . . 20 30
391 20p. Type **118** 30 60
392 30p. Queen Elizabeth the Queen Mother 40 85
393 50p. With Prince Henry at his christening . . . . . . 70 1·25
MS394 91 × 73 mm. 80p. The Queen Mother and the young Princess Anne at Trooping the Colour. 2·25 3·00

119 Jonathan Lambert and "Isles of Refreshment" Flag, 1811

1985. Flags. Multicoloured.
395 10p. Type **119** 70 90
396 15p. 21st Light Dragoons guidon and cannon from Fort Malcolm (1816–17) (vert) . . . . 80 1·00
397 25p. White Ensign and H.M.S. "Falmouth" (frigate) offshore, 1816 (vert) . . . . 1·00 1·40
398 60p. Union Jack and Tristan da Cunha (vert) . . . . . 2·00 2·75

120 Lifeboat heading for Barque "West Riding"

1985. Cent of Loss of Island Lifeboat. Mult.
399 10p. Type **120** 20 60
400 30p. Map of Tristan da Cunha . . . . 30 1·00
401 50p. Memorial plaque to lifeboat crew . . . . . . 40 1·50

121 Halley's Comet, 1066, from Bayeux Tapestry

1986. Appearance of Halley's Comet. Mult.
402 10p. Type **121** 40 75
403 20p. Path of Comet . . . . 50 1·25
404 30p. Comet over Inaccessible Island . . . . 60 1·50
405 50p. H.M.S. "Paramour" (pink) and map of South Atlantic . . . . 1·00 2·00

1986. 60th Birthday of Queen Elizabeth II. As T **145a** of St. Helena. Multicoloured.
406 10p. With Prince Charles, 1950 . . . . 15 35
407 15p. Queen at Trooping the Colour 20 45
408 25p. In robes of Order of the Bath, Westminster Abbey, 1972 . . . . 25 70
409 45p. In Canada, 1977 . . . . 40 1·25
410 65p. At Crown Agents Head Office, London, 1983 . . . 55 1·50

122 " 'Allanshaw' wrecked on East Beach, 1893" (drawing by John Hagan)

1986. Shipwrecks (2nd series).
411 **122** 9p. blue, deep blue and black 30 90
412 – 20p. green, yellow and black . . . . 60 1·50
413 – 40p. blue, violet and black 1·10 2·25
MS414 142 × 80 mm. 65p. brown and black . . . . 1·75 3·25

DESIGNS—VERT: 20p. Church font from wreck of "Edward Vittery", 1881; 40p. Ship's figurehead. HORIZ: 65p. Gaetano Lavarello and Andrea Repetto, survivors from "Ilatia", 1892.

1986. Royal Wedding. As T **146a** of St. Helena. Multicoloured.
415 10p. Prince Andrew and Miss Sarah Ferguson 20 65
416 40p. Prince Andrew piloting helicopter, Digby, Canada, 1985 . . . . 80 1·60

123 Wandering Albatross **124** "Dimorphinoctua cunhaensis" (flightless moth) and Edinburgh

1986. Flora and Fauna of Inaccessible Island. Multicoloured.
417 5p. Type **123** 50 80
418 10p. "Lagenophora nudicaulis" (daisy) 50 90
419 20p. "Cynthia virginiensis" (butterfly) . . . . 75 1·60
420 25p. Wilkins's finch ("Wilkins' Bunting") . . . 80 1·60
421 50p. White-chinned petrel ("Ring-eye") . . . . 1·00 2·25

1987. Island Flightless Insects and Birds. Mult.
422 10p. Type **124** 25 70
423 25p. "Tristanomyia frustilifera" (fly) and Crater Lake . . . . 45 1·40
424 35p. Inaccessible Island rail ("Flightless Rail") and Inaccessible Island . . . . 1·00 2·25
425 50p. Gough Island coot ("Gough Island Moorhen") and Gough Island . . . . 1·40 2·50

125 Castaways from "Blenden Hall" attacking Sea Elephant, 1821

1987. Shipwrecks (3rd series).
426 **125** 11p. black and brown . . 70 1·25
427 – 17p. black and lilac . . . 80 1·60
428 – 45p. black and green . . 1·10 2·00
MS429 131 × 70 mm. blue, green and light blue . . . . 2·75 3·00

DESIGNS—HORIZ: 17p. Barquentine "Henry A. Paull" stranded at Sandy Point, 1879; 70p. Map of Inaccessible Island showing sites of shipwrecks. VERT: 45p. Gustav Stoltenhoff, 1871, and Stoltenhoff Island.

126 Rockhopper Penguin swimming

1987. Rockhopper Penguins. Multicoloured.
430 10p. Type **126** 85 95
431 20p. Adult with egg . . . . 1·25 1·50
432 30p. Adult with juvenile . . . 1·60 1·90
433 50p. Head of rockhopper penguin . . . . 1·90 2·25

127 Microscope and Published Report **128** Nightingale Finch ("Tristan Bunting")

1987. 50th Anniv of Norwegian Scientific Expedition. Multicoloured.
434 10p. Type **127** . . . . 90 1·00
435 20p. Scientists ringing yellow-nosed albatross ("Mollymawk") . . . . . 1·90 2·00
436 30p. Expedition hut, Little Beach Point . . . . 2·25 2·50
437 50p. S.S. "Thorshammer" (whale factory ship) . . . 3·25 3·50

1988. Royal Ruby Wedding. Nos. 406/10 optd **40TH WEDDING ANNIVERSARY**.
438 10p. Princess Elizabeth with Prince Charles, 1950 . . . 20 25
439 15p. Queen Elizabeth II at Trooping the Colour . . . 25 35
440 25p. In robes of Order of the Bath, Westminster Abbey, 1972 . . . . 35 55
441 45p. In Canada, 1977 . . . . 60 95
442 65p. At Crown Agents Head Office, London, 1983 . . . 75 1·40

1988. Fauna of Nightingale Island. Mult.
443 5p. Type **128** 50 65
444 10p. Tristan thrush (immature) 65 75
445 20p. Yellow-nosed albatross (chick) . . . . 85 1·10
446 25p. Greater shearwater ("Great Shearwater") . . . 85 1·25
447 50p. Elephant seal . . . . . 1·40 2·25

129 Painted Penguin Eggs

1988. Tristan da Cunha Handicrafts. Mult.
448 10p. Type **129** 25 45
449 15p. Moccasins 35 60
450 35p. Knitwear . . . . 75 1·25
451 50p. Model longboat . . . . 1·10 1·60

130 Processing Blubber

1988. 19th-century Whaling. Multicoloured.
452 10p. Type **130** 75 65
453 20p. Harpoon guns 95 85
454 30p. Scrimshaw (carved whale bone) . . . . 1·25 1·00
455 50p. Whaling ships . . . . . 2·00 2·00
MS456 76 × 56 mm. £1 Right whale 3·00 2·75

1988. 300th Anniv of Lloyd's of London. As T **152a** of St. Helena.
457 10p. multicoloured 30 40
458 25p. multicoloured . . . . . 1·10 1·10
459 35p. black and green . . . . 1·50 1·50
460 50p. black and red . . . . . 1·90 1·90

DESIGNS—VERT: 10p. New Lloyd's Building, 1988; 50p. "Kobenhavn" (cadet barque). HORIZ: 25p. "Tristania II" (crayfish trawler); 35p. "St. Helena" (mail ship).

131 "Government House"

1988. Augustus Earle's Paintings, 1824. Mult.
461 1p. Type **131** 30 75
462 3p. "Squall off Tristan" . . . 45 75
463 4p. "Rafting Blubber" . . . 50 75
464 5p. "View near Little Beach" . 50 75
465 10p. "Man killing Albatross" 70 75
466 15p. "View on The Summit" 90 1·25
467 20p. "Nightingale Island" . . 1·00 1·40
468 25p. "Earle on Tristan" . . . 1·25 1·60
469 35p. "Solitude–Watching the Horizon" . . . . 1·40 1·75
470 50p. "Northeaster" . . . . . 1·50 2·25
471 £1 "Tristan Village" . . . . 2·25 3·25
472 £2 "Governor Glass at Dinner" . . . . 2·75 4·50

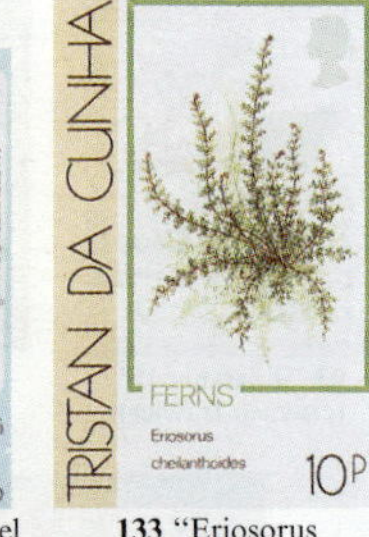

132 Hall's Giant Petrel **133** "Eriosorus cheilanthoides"

1989. Fauna of Gough Island. Multicoloured.
473 5p. Type **132** . . . . 75 1·00
474 10p. Gough Island coot ("Gough Island Moorhen") 85 1·00
475 20p. Gough Island finch ("Gough Bunting") . . . . 1·10 1·40
476 25p. Sooty albatross . . . . 1·25 1·60
477 50p. Amsterdam fur seal . . 1·60 2·50

1989. Ferns. Multicoloured.
478 10p. Type **133** 65 65
479 25p. "Asplenium alvarezense" 1·10 1·10
480 35p. "Elaphoglossum hybridum" . . . . 1·40 1·40
481 50p. "Ophioglossum opacum" . . . . 1·60 1·60

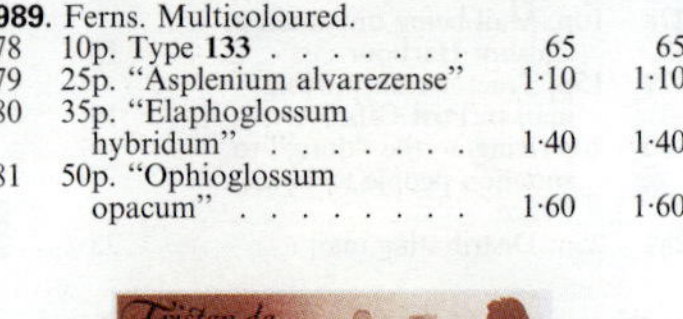

134 Surgeon's Mortar

1989. Nautical Museum Exhibits. Mult.
482 10p. Type **134** 65 65
483 20p. Parts of darting-gun harpoon . . . . 1·10 1·10
484 30p. Ship's compass with binnacle-hood . . . . . . 1·40 1·40
485 60p. Rope-twisting device . . 1·75 1·75

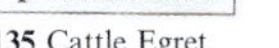

135 Cattle Egret

137 Sea Urchin

136 "Peridroma saucia"

1989. Vagrant Birds. Multicoloured.
486 10p. Type **135** . . . . 1·50 1·50
487 25p. Spotted sandpiper . . . 2·25 2·50
488 35p. American purple gallinule ("Purple Gallinule") . . . . 2·50 2·75
489 50p. Barn swallow . . . . . 2·75 3·25

1990. Moths. Multicoloured.
490 10p. Type **136** . . . . 90 1·00
491 15p. "Ascalapha odorata" . . 1·25 1·60
492 35p. "Agrius cingulata" . . . 2·00 2·50
493 60p. "Eumorpha labruscae" 2·75 3·25

1990. Echinoderms.
494 **137** 10p. multicoloured . . . 90 1·00
495 – 20p. multicoloured . . . 1·50 2·00
496 – 30p. multicoloured . . . 1·90 2·50
497 – 60p. multicoloured . . . 2·50 3·25
DESIGNS: 20p. to 60p. Different starfish.

1990. 90th Birthday of Queen Elizabeth the Queen Mother. As T **161a** of St. Helena.
498 25p. multicoloured . . . . . 1·25 1·50
499 £1 brown and blue . . . . . 3·25 3·75
DESIGNS—21 × 36 mm: 25p. Queen Mother at the London Coliseum. 29 × 37 mm: £1 Queen Elizabeth broadcasting to women of the Empire, 1939.

1990. Maiden Voyage of "St. Helena II". As T **162** of St. Helena. Multicoloured.
500 10p. "Dunnottar Castle" (liner), 1942 . . . . 1·00 1·00
501 15p. "St. Helena I" (mail ship) at Tristan . . . . . 1·60 1·60
502 35p. Launch of "St. Helena II" (mail ship) . . . . . . 2·25 2·50
503 60p. Duke of York launching "St. Helena II" . . . . . 3·00 3·50
MS504 100 × 100 mm. £1 "St. Helena II" and outline map of Tristan da Cunha . . . . . . 3·75 6·00
No. **MS**504 also contains two imperforate designs of similar stamps from Ascension and St. Helena without face values.

138 H.M.S. "Pyramus" (frigate), 1829

1990. Ships of the Royal Navy (1st series). Mult.
505 10p. Type **138** . . . . 1·50 1·25
506 25p. H.M.S. "Penguin" (sloop), 1815 . . . . 2·50 2·50
507 35p. H.M.S. "Thalia" (screw corvette), 1886 . . . . 2·75 2·75
508 50p. H.M.S. "Sidon" (paddle frigate), 1858 . . . . 3·25 3·50
See also Nos. 509/12 and 565/8.

1991. Ships of the Royal Navy (2nd series). As T **138**. Multicoloured.
509 10p. H.M.S. "Milford" (sloop), 1938 . . . . 1·50 1·25
510 25p. H.M.S. "Dublin" (cruiser), 1923 . . . . 2·50 2·50
511 35p. H.M.S. "Yarmouth" (cruiser), 1919 . . . . 2·75 2·75
512 50p. H.M.S. "Carlisle" (cruiser), 1938 . . . . 3·25 3·50

139 "Royal Viking sun" (cruise liner)

1991. Visit of "Royal Viking Sun". Sheet 62 × 47 mm.
MS513 **139** £1 multicoloured . . 5·50 7·00

140 Prince Alfred and H.M.S. "Galatea" (screw frigate), 1867

1991. 70th Birthday of Prince Philip, Duke of Edinburgh.
514 **140** 10p. black, lt blue & blue 1·75 1·75
515 – 25p. black, lt green & green . . . . 2·25 2·50
516 – 30p. black, brown & yellow . . . . 3·00 3·25
517 – 50p. multicoloured . . . . 3·50 3·75
DESIGNS: 25p. Prince Philip meeting local inhabitants, 1957; 30p. Prince Philip and Royal Yacht "Britannia", 1957; 50p. Prince Philip and Edinburgh settlement.

141 Pair of Gough Island coots ("Gough Island Moorhens")

1991. Endangered Species. Birds. Mult.
518 8p. Type **141** . . . . 1·75 1·75
519 10p. Gough Island finch ("Gough Bunting") . . . . 1·75 1·75
520 12p. Gough Island coot ("Gough Island Moorhen") on nest . . . . 1·90 1·90
521 15p. Gough Island finch ("Gough Bunting") feeding chicks . . . . 1·90 1·90

1992. 500th Anniv of Discovery of America by Columbus and Re-enactment Voyages. As T **168** of St. Helena. Multicoloured.
522 10p. Map of re-enactment voyages and "Eye of the Wind" (cadet brig) . . . . 1·00 1·50
523 15p. Compass rose and "Soren Larsen" (cadet brigantine) . . . . 1·50 2·00
524 35p. Ships of Columbus . . . 2·50 3·00
525 60p. Columbus and "Santa Maria" . . . . 2·75 3·25

1992. 40th Anniv of Queen Elizabeth II's Accession. As T **168a** of St. Helena. Mult.
526 10p. Tristan from the sea . . 60 60
527 20p. Longboat under sail . . 90 90
528 25p. Aerial view of Edinburgh . . . . 1·00 1·00
529 35p. Three portraits of Queen Elizabeth . . . . 1·25 1·25
530 65p. Queen Elizabeth II . . . 2·25 2·25

142 Coats' Perch

1992. Fishes. Multicoloured.
531 10p. Type **142** 80 80
532 15p. Lined trumpeter . . . . 1·25 1·25
533 35p. Karrer's morid cod . . . 2·25 2·50
534 60p. Long-finned scad . . . 2·75 3·00

143 "Italia" leaving Greenock

1992. Cent of the Wreck of Barque "Italia". Mult.
535 10p. Type **143** . . . . 1·00 1·00
536 45p. In mid-Atlantic . . . . 2·50 3·00
537 65p. Driving ashore on Stony Beach . . . . 3·00 3·50
MS538 101 × 75 mm. £1 "Italia" becalmed . . . . 6·00 7·00

144 "Stenoscelis hylastoides"

1993. Insects. Multicoloured.
539 15p. Type **144** . . . . 1·25 1·25
540 45p. "Trogloscaptomyza brevilamellata" . . . . . 2·50 2·75
541 60p. "Senilites tristanicola" 3·00 3·50

145 Ampulla and Anointing Spoon

147 "Madonna with Child" (School of Botticelli)

146 "Tristania" and "Frances Repetto" (crayfish trawlers)

1993. 40th Anniv of Coronation.
542 **145** 10p. green and black . . 90 90
543 – 15p. mauve and black . . 1·40 1·50
544 – 35p. violet and black . . 1·90 2·25
545 – 60p. blue and black . . . 2·50 3·00
DESIGNS: 15p. Orb; 35p. Imperial State Crown; 60p. St. Edward's Crown.

1993. 30th Anniv of Resettlement of Tristan. Mult.
546 35p. Type **146** . . . . 2·25 2·50
547 35p. "Boissevain" (cargo liner) . . . . 2·25 2·50
548 50p. "Bornholm" (liner) and longboat . . . . 2·75 3·50

1993. Christmas. Religious Paintings. Mult.
549 5p. Type **147** 80 80
550 15p. "The Holy Family" (Daniel Gran) . . . . . . 1·75 2·00
551 35p. "The Holy Virgin and Child" (Rubens) . . . . . 2·75 3·25
552 65p. "The Mystical Marriage of St. Catherine with the Holy Child" (Jan van Balen) . . . . 3·50 4·50

148 "Duchess of Atholl" (liner)

1994. Ships. Multicoloured.
553 1p. Type **148** 50 60
554 3p. "Empress of Australia" (liner) 60 70
555 5p. "Anatolia" (freighter) . . 60 70
556 8p. "Viceroy of India" (liner) 70 80
557 10p. "Rangitata" (transport) 70 80
558 15p. "Caronia" (liner) . . . 80 1·00
559 20p. "Rotterdam" (liner) . . 90 1·10
560 25p. "Leonardo da Vinci" (liner) . . . . 95 1·10
561 35p. "Vistafjord" (liner) . . . 1·25 1·40
562 £1 "World Discoverer" (liner) 2·50 3·00
563 £2 "Astor" (liner) . . . . . 4·50 6·00
564 £5 "St. Helena II" (mail ship) 10·00 11·00

1994. Ships of the Royal Navy (3rd series). As T **138**. Multicoloured.
565 10p. H.M.S. "Nigeria" (cruiser), 1948 . . . . . . 1·25 1·50
566 25p. H.M.S. "Phoebe" (cruiser), 1949 . . . . . . 2·25 2·50
567 35p. H.M.S. "Liverpool" (cruiser), 1949 . . . . . . 2·25 2·50
568 50p. H.M.S. "Magpie" (frigate), 1955 . . . . . . 3·00 3·25

149 Blue Shark

1994. Sharks. Multicoloured.
569 10p. Type **149** . . . . . . 90 1·25
570 45p. Seven-gilled shark . . . 2·50 3·25
571 65p. Short-finned mako . . . 3·25 4·00

150 Pair of Donkeys

1994. Island Livestock (1st series). Multicoloured.
572 10p. Type **150** . . . . 1·10 1·25
573 20p. Cattle . . . . 1·40 1·50
574 35p. Ducks and geese . . . . 2·50 3·00
575 60p. Girl bottle-feeding lamb 3·25 4·00
See also Nos. 620/3.

151 Pick-up Truck

1995. Local Transport. Multicoloured.
576 15p. Type **151** . . . . 1·10 1·25
577 20p. Sherpa van . . . . . . 1·50 1·50
578 45p. Scooter and Yamaha motorcycle . . . . 2·50 3·00
579 60p. Administrator's Land Rover . . . . 3·00 3·75

1995. 50th Anniv of End of Second World War. As T **182a** of St. Helena. Multicoloured.
580 15p. Sailors training on Lewis guns . . . . 1·25 1·50
581 20p. Tristan Defence Volunteers . . . . 1·50 1·60
582 45p. Wireless and meteorological station . . 2·25 2·75
583 60p. H.M.S. "Birmingham" (cruiser) . . . . 3·00 3·50
MS584 75 × 85 mm. £1 Reverse of 1939–45 War Medal (vert) . . 2·00 2·50

152 Queen Elizabeth the Queen Mother

1995. 95th Birthday of Queen Elizabeth the Queen Mother. Sheet 75 × 103 mm.
MS585 **152** $1.50 multicoloured 6·50 6·50

153 Sub-Antarctic Fur Seal on Rock

1995. Seals. Multicoloured.
586 10p. Type **153** . . . . 90 1·25
587 35p. Sub-Antarctic fur seals with pups . . . . 2·00 2·50
588 45p. Southern elephant seal asleep with pups . . . . . 2·50 3·00
589 50p. Southern elephant seals in water . . . . 2·50 3·00

1996. 50th Anniv of United Nations. As T **201a** of St. Helena. Multicoloured.
590 20p. Bedford 4-ton lorry . . 1·25 1·50
591 30p. Saxon armoured personnel carrier . . . . . 1·50 1·75
592 45p. Mi26 heavy lift helicopter . . . . 3·00 3·25
593 50p. R.F.A. "Sir Tristram" (landing ship) . . . . . . 3·00 3·25

1996. 70th Birthday of Queen Elizabeth II. As T **55** of Tokelau, each incorporating a different photograph of the Queen.
594 15p. Tristan from the sea . . 70 1·00
595 20p. Traditional cottage . . . 80 1·25

596 45p. The Residency . . . . . 1·75 2·50
597 60p. The Queen and Prince Philip . . . . 2·25 3·00

154 Old Harbour and "St. Helena I" (mail ship)

1996. Construction of New Harbour. Multicoloured.
598 15p. Type **154** . . . . 1·25 1·50
599 20p. Excavator and dump truck (44 × 27 mm) . . . . 1·25 1·50
600 45p. Construction of new mole (44 × 27 mm) . . . . 2·00 2·50
601 60p. New harbour and "St. Helena II" (mail ship) 3·25 3·75

155 Gough Island coot ("Gough Island Moorhen")

156 19th-century Map

1996. Declaration of Gough Island as World Heritage Site. Birds. Multicoloured.
602 15p. Type **155** . . . . 85 1·00
603 20p. Wandering albatross . . 95 1·10
604 45p. Sooty albatross . . . . 1·75 2·25
605 60p. Gough Island finch ("Gough Bunting") . . . . 2·25 3·00

1996. Centenary of the Presentation of the Queen Victoria Portrait to Tristan. Multicoloured.
606 20p. Type **156** . . . . 1·25 1·25
607 30p. H.M.S. "Magpie" (gunboat) . . . . 1·75 2·00
608 45p. Governor Peter Green 1·90 2·25
609 50p. "Queen Victoria" (H. von Angeli) (detail) . . . . 2·00 2·50

157 Archelon (turtle)

1997. Atlantic Marine Fauna (1st series). Cretaceous Period. Sheet 92 × 100 mm, containing T **157** and similar horiz designs. Multicoloured.
MS610 35p. Type **157**; 35p. Trinacromerum; 35p. Platecarpus; 35p. Clidastes . . . . 4·50 4·75
See also No. **MS**638.

158 Smoke Signals

1997. Visual Communications. Multicoloured.
611 10p. Type **158** 30 60
612 10p. H.M.S. "Eurydice" (frigate) 30 60
613 15p. H.M.S. "Challenger" (survey ship) 50 90
614 15p. Flag hoists 50 90
615 20p. Semaphore 65 90
616 20p. H.M.S. "Carlisle" (cruiser) 65 90
617 35p. Aldis lamp . . . . . . 80 1·10
618 35p. H.M.S. "Cilicia" (transport) . . . . 80 1·10
Nos. 611/12, 613/14, 615/16 and 617/18 respectively were printed together, se-tenant, forming composite designs.

1997. Return of Hong Kong to China. Sheet 130 × 90 mm, containing designs as No. 605, but with "1997" imprint date.
MS619 60p. Gough Island finch ("Gough Bunting") . . . 1·50 2·00

1997. Island Livestock (2nd series). As T **192** of St. Helena. Multicoloured.
620 20p. Chickens 70 90
621 30p. Bull . . . . 90 1·40
622 45p. Sheep . . . . 1·40 2·00
623 50p. Collie dogs . . . . . . 1·75 2·25

1997. Golden Wedding of Queen Elizabeth and Prince Philip. As T **192a** of St. Helena. Mult.
624 15p. Queen Elizabeth 45 80
625 15p. Prince Philip playing polo 45 80
626 20p. Queen Elizabeth with horse 55 90
627 20p. Prince Philip 55 90
628 45p. Queen Elizabeth with Prince Philip in R.A.F. uniform . . . . 1·25 1·60
629 45p. Princess Anne on horseback . . . . 1·25 1·60
MS630 110 × 70 mm. £1.50, Queen Elizabeth and Prince Philip in landau (horiz) . . . . 6·50 7·50
Nos. 624/5, 626/7 and 628/9 respectively were printed together, se-tenant, with the backgrounds forming composite designs.

159 "Hilary" and "Melodie"

1998. 50th Anniv of First Lobster Survey. Lobster Trawlers. Multicoloured.
631 15p. Type **159** 55 80
632 20p. "Tristania II" and "Hekla" 65 90
633 30p. "Pequena" and "Frances Repetto" . . . . 85 1·25
634 45p. "Tristania" and "Gillian Gaggins" . . . . 1·40 1·75
635 50p. "Kelso" and "Edinburgh" . . . . 1·40 1·75
MS636 100 × 80 mm. £1.20, Revd. C. P. Lawrence and lobster . . 4·00 5·00

1998. Diana, Princess of Wales Commemoration. Sheet 145 × 70 mm, containing vert designs as T **149** of St. Helena. Multicoloured
MS637 35p. Wearing pink jacket, 1993; 35p. Wearing white jacket, 1990; 35p. Laughing, in striped dress, 1991; 35p. Wearing blue and white dress, 1989 (sold at £1.40 + 20p. charity premium) . . . . 3·25 3·75

1998. Atlantic Marine Fauna (2nd series). Miocene Epoch. Sheet 92 × 100 mm, containing horiz designs as T **157**. Multicoloured.
MS638 45p. Carcharodon (shark); 45p. Orycterocetus (sperm whale); 45p. Eurhinodelphis (dolphin); 45p. Hexanchus (shark) and Myliobatis (ray) . . . . 5·50 6·50

160 "Livonia"

1998. Cruise Ships. Multicoloured.
639 15p. Type **160** . . . . 1·25 1·25
640 20p. "Professor Molchanov" 1·40 1·40
641 45p. "Explorer" . . . . . . 2·00 2·25
642 60p. "Hanseatic" . . . . . . 2·25 2·50

161 "H. G. Johnson" (barque)

1998. Maritime Heritage (1st series). Mult.
643 15p. Type **161** . . . . 1·00 1·25
644 35p. "Theodore" (full-rigged ship) . . . . 1·75 2·00
645 45p. "Hesperides" (full-rigged ship) . . . . 1·90 2·00
646 50p. "Bessfield" (barque) . . 2·00 2·25

1999. Maritime Heritage (2nd series). As T **161**. Multicoloured.
647 20p. "Derwent" (full-rigged ship) . . . . 1·00 1·25
648 30p. "Strathgryfe" (full-rigged ship) . . . . 1·60 1·75
649 50p. "Celestial Empire" (full-rigged ship) . . . . . . 1·90 2·25
650 60p. "Lamorna" (full-rigged ship) . . . . 1·90 2·25

162 Wandering Albatross Courtship Dance

1999. Endangered Species. Wandering Albatross. Multicoloured.
651 5p. Type **162** 40 60
652 8p. Adult and chick 40 60
653 12p. Adult with spread wings 40 60
654 15p. Two adults in flight . . 40 60

1999. Royal Wedding. As T **197a** of St. Helena. Multicoloured.
655 45p. Photographs of Prince Edward and Miss Sophie Rhys-Jones . . . . 1·10 1·25
656 £1.20 Engagement photograph . . . . 2·75 3·00

1999. "Queen Elizabeth the Queen Mother's Century". As T **199** of St. Helena. Multicoloured (except £1.50).
657 20p. With King George VI and Princess Elizabeth, 1944 . . . . 70 70
658 30p. King George and Queen Elizabeth at Balmoral, 1951 . . . . 90 90
659 50p. Family group outside Clarence House, 1994 . . . 1·40 1·50
660 60p. Inspecting The Black Watch parade . . . . . . 1·60 1·75
MS661 145 × 70 mm. £1.50, Lady Elizabeth Bowes-Lyon, 1905, and Hurricane squadron, Battle of Britain, 1940 (black) . . . . . 3·75 4·50

163 Winter Sunrise

2000. New Millennium. Multicoloured.
662 20p. Type **163** . . . . 1·00 1·00
663 30p. Spring sunrise . . . . . 1·25 1·25
664 50p. Summer sunrise . . . . 1·90 1·90
665 60p. Autumn sunrise . . . . 2·00 2·00

164 King Manuel I of Portugal

2000. Monarchs connected with Tristan da Cunha. Multicoloured (except 1p. and 5p.).
666 1p. Type **164** (black, stone and brown) 10 10
667 3p. Frederick Henry, Prince of Orange 10 10
668 5p. Empress Maria Theresa of Austria (green, stone and black) 10 10
669 8p. King George III 15 20
670 10p. King George IV 20 25
671 15p. King William IV 30 35
672 20p. Queen Victoria 40 45
673 25p. King Edward VII 50 55
674 35p. King George V 70 75
675 £1 King Edward VIII . . . . 2·00 2·10
676 £2 King George VI . . . . . 4·00 4·25
677 £5 Queen Elizabeth II . . . 10·00 10·50

165 Longboat under Oars

2000. "The Stamp Show 2000" International Stamp Exhibition. Visit of *Cutty Sark* (clipper), 1876 Multicoloured.
678 15p. Type **165** 60 70
679 45p. Longboat under sail . . 1·50 1·75
680 50p. *Cutty Sark* at sea . . . 1·75 1·75
681 60p. *Cutty Sark* on display at Greenwich . . . . 1·75 2·00
MS682 102 × 65 mm. £1.50, "Cutty Sark" off Tristan da Cunha . . 5·50 5·50

2000. 18th Birthday of Prince William. As T **48** of South Georgia and South Sandwich Islands. Multicoloured.
683 45p. Prince Charles with sons, 1985 . . . . 1·40 1·75
684 45p. Prince William in 1995 1·40 1·75
685 45p. Prince William in 1999 (horiz) . . . . 1·40 1·75
686 45p. Prince William in overcoat and scarf (horiz) 1·40 1·75
MS687 175 × 95 mm. 45p. With Shetland pony, 1995 (horiz) and Nos. 683/6. . . . . 6·50 6·50

166 *Agulhas* (South African Antarctic research ship)

2000. Helicopters and Ships. Multicoloured.
688 10p. Type **166** 60 70
689 10p. S.A. 330J Puma helicopter, 1999 . . . . . 60 70
690 15p. H.M.S. *London* (destroyer) 70 85
691 15p. Westland Wessex HAS1 helicopter, 1964 . . . . . 70 85
692 20p. H.M.S. *Endurance II* (ice patrol ship) 80 95
693 20p. Westland Lynx HAS3 helicopter, 1996 . . . . . 80 95
694 50p. U.S.S. *Spiegel Grove* (landing ship) . . . . . . 1·25 1·50
695 50p. Sikorsky UH-19F helicopter, 1963 . . . . . 1·25 1·50
Nos. 688/9, 690/1, 692/3 and 694/5 were each printed together, se-tenant, with the backgrounds forming composite designs.

167 Winston Churchill as Home Secretary and Siege of Sidney Street, 1911

2000. Centenary of Sir Winston Churchill's Election to Parliament. Multicoloured.
696 20p. Type **167** . . . . 1·00 1·00
697 30p. As Chancellor of the Exchequer, 1925, and with Pres. Roosevelt at signing of Atlantic Treaty, 1941 . . 1·40 1·40
698 50p. Showing Victory sign and making V.E. Day broadcast, 1945 . . . . . 1·75 1·75
699 60p. In retirement and greeting Queen Elizabeth II at 10 Downing Street, 1955 1·90 1·90

168 Inaccessible Island Rail

2001. "HONG KONG 2001" Stamp Exhibition. Sheet 150 × 90 mm, containing T **168** and similar horiz design showing island bird. Multicoloured.
MS700 30p. Type **168**; 45p. Black-faced spoonbill . . . . 2·75 2·75

169 Letter from Tristan da Cunha, 1846

2001. Death Centenary of Queen Victoria. Mult.
701 15p. Type **169** 55 55
702 20p. Prince Alfred, Duke of Edinburgh (vert) 65 65
703 30p. H.M.S. *Galatea* (screw frigate) 80 85
704 35p. Queen Victoria (vert) . . 85 90
705 50p. Charles Dickens (vert) . 1·25 1·40
706 60p. Longboats re-supplying warship . . . . 1·40 1·50
MS707 104 × 80 mm. £1.50, Queen Victoria outside St. Paul's during Diamond Jubilee celebrations 3·50 4·00

170 Longboat under Sail

2001. Tristan Longboats. Multicoloured.
708 30p. Type **170** 65 70
709 30p. Two longboats at sea (face value at bottom right) 65 70
710 30p. Two longboats at sea (face value at bottom left) 65 70
711 30p. Longboat with multicoloured mainsail near island 65 70
712 30p. Longboat with blue and white striped sail near island 65 70
713 30p. Longboat with white mainsail near island . . . 65 70
714 30p. Longboat with blue mainsail near island . . . 65 70
715 30p. Longboat in harbour . . 65 70

2001. Hurricane Relief. Nos. 688/95 optd **HURRICANE RELIEF 2001**. Multicoloured.
716 10p. Type **166** 45 50
717 10p. S.A. 330J Puma helicopter, 1999 . . . . . 45 50
718 15p. H.M.S. *London* (destroyer) 65 70
719 15p. Westland Wessex HAS1 helicopter, 1964 . . . . . 65 70
720 20p. H.M.S. *Endurance II* (ice patrol ship) 75 80
721 20p. Westland Lynx HAS3 helicopter, 1996 . . . . . 75 80
722 50p. U.S.S. *Spiegel Grove* (landing ship) . . . . . . 1·25 1·50
723 50p. Sikorsky UH-19F helicopter, 1963 . . . . . 1·25 1·50

172 Head of White-chinned Petrel ("Spectacled Petrel")

2001. Birdlife World Bird Festival. White-chinned Petrel. Sheet 175 × 80 mm, containing T **172** and similar multicoloured designs.
MS724 35p. Type **172**; 35p. Petrel in front of cliffs (*vert*); 35p. Petrel, descending to sea (*vert*); 35p. Petrel flying; 35p. Petrel chick 4·75 5·00

173 H.M.S. *Julia* (sloop), 1817

2001. Royal Navy Connections with Tristan da Cunha. Multicoloured.
725 20p. Type **173** 75 80
726 20p. H.M.S. *Penguin* (sloop), 1815 . . . . 75 80
727 35p. H.M.S. *Beagle* (screw sloop), 1901 . . . . 1·10 1·25
728 35p. H.M.S. *Puma* (frigate), 1962 . . . . 1·10 1·25
729 60p. H.M.S. *Monmouth* (frigate), 1997 . . . . . . 1·60 1·75
730 60p. H.M.S. *Somerset* (frigate), 1999 . . . . . . 1·60 1·75

174 Procession at St. Mary's Anglican Church

2001. 150th Anniv of Arrival of First U.S.P.G. Missionary on Tristan da Cunha. Multicoloured (except No. 731).
731 35p. Type **174** (brown, black and yellow) . . . . 1·10 1·25
732 35p. St. Joseph's Catholic Church . . . . 1·10 1·25
733 60p. Altar, St. Mary's Church (vert) . . . . 1·75 1·90
734 60p. Stained glass, St. Joseph's Church (vert) 1·75 1·90

175 1952 Overprints on St. Helena 3d., 4d., 1s. and 2s.6d.

2002. 50th Anniv of First Stamp Issue. Mult (except 60p.).
735 15p. Type **175** 70 75
736 20p. 1952 6d., 8d., 5s. and 10s. overprinted stamps . . 80 85
737 50p. 1952 ½d., 1d., 1½d. and 2d. overprinted stamps . . 1·75 1·90
738 60p. Buying stamps, 1952 (black, sepia and bistre) . . 1·75 1·90
MS739 146 × 90 mm. 45p. × 4 As Nos. 735/8, but each inscr "Tristan da Cunha" in mock manuscript 5·50 6·00

2002. Golden Jubilee. As T **211** of St. Helena.
740 15p. black, red and gold . . 60 65
741 30p. multicoloured 90 95
742 45p. multicoloured . . . . . 1·40 1·60
743 50p. multicoloured . . . . . 1·50 1·75
MS744 162 × 95 mm. Nos. 740/3 and 60p. multicoloured . . . . . . 6·00 6·50
DESIGNS—HORIZ: 15p. Princess Elizabeth, 1947; 30p. Queen Elizabeth in evening dress, Buckingham Palace, 1991; 45p. Queen Elizabeth in multicoloured turban; 50p. Queen Elizabeth at Newmarket, 1997. VERT: (38 × 51 mm)—50p. Queen Elizabeth after Annigoni.
DESIGNS as Nos. 740/3 in No. **MS**744 omit the gold frame around each stamp and the "Golden Jubilee 1952-2002" inscription.

176 Pelagic Armourhead (fish)

2002. Extension of Fishing Industry to New Species. Multicoloured.
745 20p. Type **176** 70 75
746 35p. Yellowtail . . . . . . 1·10 1·25
747 50p. Splendid alfonsino . . . 1·50 1·75
MS748 140 × 75 mm. 60p. *San Liberatore* (stern trawler) and Nos. 745/7 . . . . 4·00 4·25

2002. Queen Elizabeth the Queen Mother Commemoration. As T **215** of St. Helena.
749 20p. black, gold and purple 40 45
750 £1.50 multicoloured . . . . 3·00 3·25
MS751 145 × 70 mm. 75p. black and gold; 75p. multicoloured . . . 3·00 3·25
DESIGNS: 20p. Queen Elizabeth visiting a shipyard, 1942; 75p. black and gold (No. **MS**751) Duchess of York with Princess Margaret, 1930; 75p. multicoloured (No. **MS**751) Queen Mother at Cheltenham Races; £1.50, Queen Mother on her birthday, 1995.
Designs in No. **MS**751 omit the "1900–2002" inscription and the coloured frame.

177 Gray's Beaked Whale

2002. Marine Mammals. Multicoloured.
752 30p. Type **177** 60 65
753 30p. Dusky dolphin 60 65
754 30p. False killer whale . . . 60 65
755 30p. Long-finned pilot whale 60 65
756 30p. Sperm whale 60 65
757 30p. Shepherd's beaked whale 60 65
MS758 81 × 92 mm. £2 Humpback whale . . . . 4·00 4·25
Nos. 752/7 were printed together, se-tenant, forming a composite design.

178 Captain Denham and Officers of H.M.S. *Herald* (survey ship)

2002. 150th Anniv of Survey by H.M.S. *Herald*. Multicoloured (except 20p.).
759 20p. Type **178** (ochre and agate) 40 45
760 35p. H.M.S. *Herald* in Bay of Biscay 70 75
761 50p. H.M.S. *Herald* off Tristan da Cunha, 1852 . . 1·00 1·10
762 60p. H.M.S. *Herald* and H.M.S. *Torch* (paddle steamer) at sunset . . . . 1·25 1·40

179 Great Barrier Reef, Australia (longest reef)

2003. World Geographical Records. Multicoloured.
763 30p. Type **179** 60 65
764 30p. Greenland (biggest island) 60 65
765 30p. Sahara (biggest desert) 60 65
766 30p. River Amazon (longest river) 60 65
767 30p. Mt Everest (highest mountain) 60 65
768 30p. Edinburgh, Tristan da Cunha (most remote inhabited island) 60 65
MS769 90 × 68 mm £2 Closer view of Edinburgh . . . . 4·00 4·25

POSTAGE DUE STAMPS

1957. As Type D **1** of Barbados.
D1 1d. red . . . . 1·75 11·00
D2 2d. yellow . . . . 2·50 4·75
D3 3d. green . . . . 2·50 5·50
D4 4d. blue . . . . 4·50 7·00
D5 5d. lake . . . . 2·50 23·00

D **2**

D **3** Outline Map of Tristan da Cunha

1976.
D11 D **2** 1p. purple 10 30
D12 2p. green 15 30
D13 4p. violet 20 35
D14 5p. blue 20 40
D15 10p. brown 20 45

1986.
D16 D **3** 1p. brown & light brown 10 50
D17 2p. brown and orange 10 50
D18 5p. brown and red . . . 15 50
D19 7p. black and violet . . 20 60
D20 10p. black and blue . . 30 60
D21 25p. black and green . . 60 1·10

TRUCIAL STATES Pt. 1

Seven Arab shaikhdoms on the Persian Gulf and Gulf of Oman, in treaty relations with Great Britain. The following stamps were issued at the British Postal Agency at Dubai until it closed on 14 June 1963.
Individual issues were later made by Abu Dhabi, Ajman, Dubai, Fujeira, Ras al Khaima, Sharjah and Umm al Qiwain.

100 naye paise = 1 rupee.

1 Palms

2 Dhow

1961.
1 **1** 5n.p. green . . . . 1·00 10
2 15n.p. brown 50 10
3 20n.p. blue . . . . 1·00 10
4 30n.p. orange 50 10
5 40n.p. violet 50 10
6 50n.p. bistre 50 10
7 75n.p. grey 60 10
8 **2** 1r. green . . . . 5·00 2·25
9 2r. black . . . . 4·00 17·00
10 5r. red . . . . 6·50 21·00
11 10r. blue . . . . 12·00 21·00

TUNISIA Pt. 6; Pt. 14

Formerly a French Protectorate in N. Africa, Tunisia became an independent kingdom in 1956 and a republic in 1957.

1888. 100 centimes = 1 franc.
1959. 1000 milliemes = 1 dinar.

1

2

1888. Arms on plain background.
1 **1** 1c. black on blue . . . . . . 1·75 2·25
2 2c. brown on buff 75 75
3 5c. green on green . . . . . 12·50 12·50
4 15c. blue on blue . . . . . . 35·00 4·75
5 25c. black on pink . . . . . 80·00 20·00
6 40c. red on yellow . . . . . 48·00 32·00
7 75c. pink on pink . . . . . . 60·00 75·00
8 5f. mauve on lilac £375 £250

1888. Arms on shaded background.
9 **2** 1c. black on blue 30 15
10 2c. brown on buff 30 15
22 5c. green . . . . 4·25 10
12 10c. black on lilac . . . . . 9·25 15
23 10c. red . . . . 3·75 10
14 15c. blue . . . . 60·00 35
24 15c. grey . . . . 6·00 15
15 20c. red on green . . . . . 18·00 35
16 25c. black on pink . . . . . 20·00 45
25 25c. blue . . . . 17·00 20
26 35c. brown . . . . 50·00 95
17 40c. red on yellow . . . . . 10·00 25
18 75c. pink on pink . . . . . £130 55·00
19 75c. violet on yellow . . . . 20·00 2·25
20 1f. green . . . . 20·00 4·25
27 2f. lilac £110 £110
21 5f. mauve on lilac . . . . . £160 60·00

1902. Surch **25** and bars.
28 **2** 25 on 15c. blue . . . . . . 2·50 2·00

4 Mosque at Kairouan

6 Ruins of Hadrian's Aqueduct

5 Agriculture

7 Carthaginian Galley

1906.
30 **4** 1c. black on yellow 10 10
31 2c. brown 10 10
32 3c. red . . . . 10 1·00
33 5c. green on green 15 10
34 **5** 10c. red 25 10
35 15c. violet . . . . 1·50 15
36 20c. brown 15 10
37 25c. blue . . . . 1·40 20
38 **6** 35c. brown and green . . . . 10·00 85
39 40c. red and brown . . . . . 4·75 60
40 75c. red and purple 50 45
41 **7** 1f. brown and red . . . . . 1·75 60
42 2f. green and brown . . . . 5·75 1·75
43 5f. blue and violet . . . . . 15·00 5·00
See also Nos. 72/8, 105 and 107/13.

1908. Surch.
44 **2** 10 on 15c. grey 55 25
45 35 on 1f. green . . . . . . 2·00 2·75
46 40 on 2f. lilac . . . . . . 3·25 7·25
47 75 on 5f. mauve on lilac . . 2·25 7·00

1911. Surch in figures and bar.
48 **5** 10 on 15c. violet . . . . . . 3·25 20
60 15c. on 10c. red . . . . . . 1·50 10
79 20c. on 15c. violet . . . . . 1·75 15

1915. Red Cross Fund. Optd with red cross.
49 **5** 15c. violet 60 45

1916. Red Cross Fund. Optd with red cross and bars.
50 **4** 5c. green on green . . . . . 45 2·25

1916. Prisoners-of-War Fund. Surch with red cross and **10c.**
51 **5** 10c. on 15c. brown on blue 1·25 2·25
52 10c. on 20c. brown on yellow 1·75 3·00
53 10c. on 25c. blue on green . . 1·90 4·25
54 **6** 10c. on 35c. violet and green 4·00 8·25
55 10c. on 40c. black and brown 2·50 4·50
56 10c. on 75c. green and red 4·25 12·50
57 **7** 10c. on 1f. green and red . . 5·25 5·75
58 10c. on 2f. blue and brown 80·00 £100
59 10c. on 5f. red and violet . . £100 £110

1918. Prisoners-of-War Fund. Surch **15c** and red cross.
61 **5** 15c. on 20c. black on green 1·75 3·50
62 15c. on 25c. blue . . . . . . 1·75 3·50
63 **6** 15c. on 35c. red and olive . . 2·75 5·00

64 15c. on 40c. blue and brown 2·75 6·00
65 15c. on 75c. black and red 7·00 11·00
66 7 15c. on 1f. violet and red 13·50 32·00
67 15c. on 2f. red and brown 75·00 85·00
68 15c. on 5f. black and violet £120 £130

1919. Air. Optd **Poste Aerienne** and wings or surch **30c** and bars also.
69 6 30c. on 35c. brown and green 1·60 2·00
70 30c. blue and olive 30 1·10

1920. New values and colours changed.
72 4 5c. orange 10 20
73 5 10c. green 20 20
74 25c. violet 20 10
75 6 30c. violet and purple 1·60 80
76 5 30c. red 1·60 2·25
77 50c. blue 1·50 60
78 6 60c. violet and green 1·25 85

18 Ruin at Dougga

1922.
80 18 10c. green 15 20
81 30c. red 1·90 1·90
82 50c. blue 75 40
See also Nos. 104 and 106.

1923. War Wounded Fund. Surch **AFFt**, medal and new value.
83 4 0c. on 1c. blue 40 2·50
84 0c. on 2c. brown 30 3·00
85 1c. on 3c. green 80 3·00
86 2c. on 5c. mauve 80 2·75
87 18 3c. on 10c. mauve on blue 90 2·50
88 5 5c. on 15c. green 1·50 3·00
89 5c. on 20c. blue on red 2·50 4·50
90 5c. on 25c. mauve on blue 3·50 4·50
91 18 5c. on 30c. orange 2·50 4·50
92 6 5c. on 35c. mauve and blue 3·00 4·25
93 5c. on 40c. brown and blue 3·00 3·50
94 18 10c. on 50c. black on blue 3·00 3·75
95 6 10c. on 60c. blue and brown 3·00 3·25
96 10c. on 75c. green & mauve 3·75 6·75
97 7 25c. on 1f. mauve and lake 4·75 6·75
98 25c. on 2f. red and blue 15·00 27·00
99 25c. on 5f. brown and green 40·00 80·00

1923. Surch.
100 4 10 on 5c. green on green 1·00 15
101 5 20 on 15c. violet 2·00 2·00
102 30 on 20c. brown 10 25
103 50 on 25c. blue 1·25 10

1923. New values and colours.
104 18 10c. pink 30 10
105 5 15c. brown on orange 60 10
106 18 30c. mauve 10 10
107 5 40c. black on pink 65 65
108 40c. green 10 10
109 6 60c. carmine and red 1·50 2·25
110 75c. scarlet and red 1·00 85
111 7 1f. light blue and blue 35 20
112 2f. red and green on pink 2·00 2·25
113 5f. green and lilac 2·00 2·75

1925. Parcel Post stamps surch **PROTECTION DE L'ENFANCE POSTES** and value in figures.
114 P 8 1c. on 5c. red and brown on rose 10 1·40
115 2c. on 10c. blue and brown on yellow 10 1·25
116 3c. on 20c. red and purple on mauve 75 3·25
117 5c. on 25c. red and green on green 55 3·25
118 5c. on 40c. green and red on yellow 1·00 3·00
119 10c. on 50c. green and violet on mauve 1·75 4·50
120 10c. on 75c. brown and green on green 1·90 3·75
121 25c. on 1f. green and blue on blue 1·60 3·75
122 25c. on 2f. purple and red on rose 2·50 8·75
123 25c. on 5f. brown and red on green 23·00 55·00

21 Arab Woman
22 Grand Mosque, Tunis
23 Mosque, Place Halfaouine, Tunis
24 Amphitheatre, El Djem

1926.
124 21 1c. red 10 50
125 2c. green 10 55
126 3c. blue 10 1·60
127 5c. green 25 10
128 10c. mauve 1·25 15
129 22 15c. lilac 30 10
130 20c. red 10 15
131 25c. green 70 15
131a 25c. mauve 1·10 20
132 30c. mauve 15 15
133 30c. green 95 15
134 40c. brown 20 20
134a 45c. green 2·00 3·25
135 23 50c. black 1·00 10
135a 50c. blue 1·40 10
135b 50c. green 60 20
135c 60c. red 15 25
135d 65c. blue 2·25 20
135e 70c. red 20 45
136 75c. red 2·00 15
136a 75c. mauve 1·40 10
137 80c. blue 75 1·75
137a 80c. brown 30 75
138 80c. red 15 10
138a 90c. blue 13·00 14·00
139 1f. purple 25 10
139a 1f. red 10 10
140 24 1f.05 pink and blue 35 1·00
141 1f.25 blue and light blue 65 1·25
141a 1f.25 red 1·90 2·75
141b 1f.30 violet and blue 70 70
141c 1f.40 purple 3·00 3·00
142 1f.50 blue and light blue 1·25 1·40
142a 1f.50 orange and red 1·25 60
143 2f. brown and red 50 20
143a 2f. red 40 15
143b 2f.25 blue 70 2·25
143c 2f.50 green 60 45
144 3f. orange and blue 1·25 20
144a 3f. violet 30 15
145 5f. green and red on green 1·50 80
145a 5f. brown 1·50 3·00
146 10f. grey and red on blue 6·25 3·50
146a 10f. pink 2·00 2·75
146b 20f. red and mauve on pink 2·00 55
For similar designs see Nos. 172/91, 220/31 and 257/286.

1927. Surch **1f 50**.
147 24 1f.50 on 1f.25 blue and ultramarine 30 95

1927. Air. Optd **Poste Aerienne** and airplane or surch in figures and bars also.
148 7 1f. light blue and blue 1·00 1·40
152 24 1f.30 mauve and orange 1·75 1·60
169 1f.50 on 1f.30 mve & orge 1·90 40
170 1f.50 on 1f.80 red and green 2·25 40
171 1f.50 on 2f.55 brn & mve 3·50 1·00
149 6 1f.75 on 75c. scarlet and red 1·25 2·00
150 7 1f.75 on 5f. green and lilac 2·75 4·00
153 24 1f.80 red and green 2·00 3·75
151 7 2f. red and green on pink 3·00 2·50
154 24 2f.55 brown and mauve 1·40 2·50

26 First Tunis–Chad Motor Service

1928. Child Welfare.
155 26 40c.+40c. brown 1·10 3·00
156 50c.+50c. purple 65 3·25
157 75c.+75c. blue 60 3·00
158 1f.+1f. red 1·50 3·50
159 1f.50+1f.50 blue 1·10 3·25
160 2f.+2f. green 70 3·50
161 5f.+5f. brown 1·10 3·50

1928. Surch.
162 4 3c. on 5c. orange 10 1·40
163 5 10c. on 15c. brown on orange 15 20
164 18 25c. on 30c. mauve 15 20
165 23 40c. on 80c. blue 15 1·00
166 22 50c. on 40c. brown 4·00 20
167 23 50c. on 75c. red 15 60

1929. Precancelled **AFFRANCHts POSTES** and surch **10**.
168 22 10 on 30c. mauve 1·25 3·00

28
29
30
31

1931.
172 28 1c. blue 10 1·40
173 2c. brown 10 1·25
174 3c. black 15 2·25
175 5c. green 10 95
176 10c. red 10 95
177 29 15c. purple 70 70
178 20c. brown 10 15
179 25c. red 10 15
180 30c. green 20 15
181 40c. orange 10 15
182 30 50c. blue 20 10
183 75c. yellow 1·10 45
184 90c. red 1·00 1·40
185 1f. olive 40 20
186 31 1f.50 blue 15 25
187 2f. brown 1·10 20
188 3f. green 10·50 13·00
189 5f. red 23·00 22·00
190 10f. black 38·00 29·00
191 20f. brown 32·00 40·00

1937. Surch.
191a 23 25c. on 65c. blue 10 10
192 0.65 on 50c. blue 95 10
193 65 on 50c. blue 1·60 10
193b 1FR on 90c. blue 1·40 15
193c 24 1F. on 1f.25 red 30 2·25
193d 1F. on 1f.40 purple 20 80
193e 1F. on 2f.25 blue 15 65
194 1f.75 on 1f.50 blue and light blue 3·25 85

1938. 50th Anniv of Tunisian Postal Service. Surch **1888 1938** and value.
196 28 1c.+1c. blue 2·25 4·00
197 2c.+2c. brown 2·00 3·75
198 3c.+3c. black 1·50 3·75
199 5c.+5c. green 2·25 3·75
200 10c.+10c. red 2·25 3·75
201 29 15c.+15c. purple 2·00 3·75
202 20c.+20c. brown 2·25 4·00
203 25c.+25c. red 1·75 3·75
204 30c.+30c. green 1·75 3·75
205 40c.+40c. orange 1·75 3·75
206 30 50c.+50c. blue 2·25 3·75
207 75c.+75c. yellow 1·75 3·75
208 90c.+90c. red 1·75 3·75
209 1f.+1f. olive 1·60 4·00
210 31 1f.50+1f. blue 2·25 3·75
211 2f.+1f.50 brown 2·50 4·50
212 3f.+2f. green 2·25 5·50
213 5f.+3f. red 9·75 29·00
214 10f.+5f. black 22·00 50·00
215 20f.+10f. brown 75·00 75·00

1941. National Relief. Surch **SECOURS NATIONAL1941** and value.
216 22 1f. on 45c. green 1·25 4·75
217 24 1f.30 on 1f.25 red 1·50 4·75
218 1f.50 on 1f.40 purple 1·60 4·25
219 2f. on 2f.25 blue 1·25 4·75

1941. As stamps of 1926 but without monogram "RF".
220 22 30c. red 40 3·25
221 23 1f.20 grey 15 80
222 1f.50 brown 25 20
223 24 2f.40 pink and red 1·10 2·75
224 2f.50 light blue and blue 20 30
225 3f. violet 1·25 2·50
226 4f. blue and black 85 1·25
227 4f.50 brown and green 1·40 1·50
228 5f. black 15 15
229 10f. violet and purple 20 15
230 15f. red 5·00 6·00
231 20f. red and lilac 3·25 3·50

41a "Victory"
42 Allied Soldiers

1943.
232 41a 1f.50 red 85 40

1943. Charity. Tunisian Liberation.
233 42 1f.50+8f.50 red 15 1·25

43 Mosque and Olive Trees
44 Sidi Mahrez Mosque
45 Ramparts of Sfax

1944.
234 43 30c. yellow 20 2·75
235 40c. brown 25 2·50
236 60c. orange 25 1·25
237 70c. red 25 2·25
238 80c. green 35 2·50
239 90c. violet 25 2·50
240 1f. red 25 15
241 1f.50 blue 20 15
242 2f.40 red 25 2·75
243 2f.50 brown 25 20
244 3f. violet 25 25
245 4f. blue 40 25
246 4f.50 green 35 30
247 5f. grey 25 15
248 6f. brown 20 30
249 10f. lake 25 50
250 15f. brown 30 70
251 20f. lilac 40 70
Nos. 234/41 are smaller, 15½ × 19 mm.

1944. Forces Welfare Fund. Surch **+ 48 frcs pour nos Combattants**.
252 43 2f.+48f. red (21¼ × 26½ mm) 65 3·25

1945. Forces Welfare Fund. Surch **POUR NOS COMBATTANTS** and value.
253 44 1f.50+8f.50 brown 95 3·00
254 45 3f.+12f. green 1·10 3·25
255 – 4f.+21f. brown 1·00 3·00
256 – 10f.+40f. red 80 3·25
DESIGNS—HORIZ: 4f. Camel patrol at Fort Saint; 10f. Mosque at Sidi-bou-Said.

1945. New values and colours.
257 23 10c. brown 10 50
258 30c. olive 10 45
259 40c. red 15 15
260 50c. turquoise 10 15
261 60c. blue 15 25
262 80c. green 15 95
263 1f.20 brown 20 2·25
264 1f.50 lilac 15 15
265 2f. green 10 15
267 24 2f.40 red 50 3·00
268 23 2f.50 brown 1·50 20
269 24 3f. brown 10 10
270 23 3f. red 15 15
271 24 4f. blue 1·90 1·40
272 23 4f. violet 1·40 15
273 24 4f. violet 1·75 55
273a 23 4f. orange 95 25
274 4f.50 blue 90 20
275 24 5f. green 60 20
275a 23 5f. blue 65 30
275b 5f. green 25 10
276 24 6f. blue 1·25 65
277 6f. red 1·50 85
278 23 6f. red 20 15
279 24 10f. orange 80 35
280 10f. blue 1·25 30
281 15f. mauve 50 20
281a 23 15f. red 1·00 15
282 24 20f. green 25 10
283 25f. violet 1·25 75
284 25f. orange 75 50
285 50f. red 45 25
286 100f. red 65 35

1945. Anti-tuberculosis Fund. Type of France optd **TUNISIE**.
287 222 2f.+1f. orange 15 1·50

1945. Postal Employees' War Victims' Fund. Type of France optd **TUNISIE**.
288 223 4f.+6f. brown 1·25 2·75

1945. Stamp Day. Type of France (Louis XI) optd **TUNISIE**.
289 228 2f.+3f. green 20 1·90

1945. War Veterans' Fund. Surch **ANCIENS COMBATTANTS R F** and value.
290 21 4f.+6f. on 10c. blue 1·00 2·50
291 23 10f.+30f. on 80c. green 1·40 2·75

49 Legionary

1946. Welfare Fund for French Troops in Indo-China.
292 49 20f.+30f. black, red and green 1·60 3·50

1946. Red Cross Fund. Surch with cross **1946** and new values.
293 23 80c.+50c. green 35 3·00
294 1f.50+1f.50 lilac 50 3·00
295 2f.+2f. green 45 2·75
296 24 2f.40+2f. red 80 3·25
297 4f.+4f. blue 90 3·50

1946. Stamp Day. La Varane Type of France optd **TUNISIE**.
298 241 3f.+2f. blue 35 1·90

1947. Stamp Day. Louvois Type of France optd **TUNISIE**.
299 253 4f.50+5f.50 brown 1·75 3·00

1947. Naval Charities. Type of France surch **TUNISIE** and new value.
300 234 10+15 on 2f.+3f. blue 1·00 3·25

1947. Welfare Fund. Surch **SOLIDARITE 1947 +40 F**.
301 24 10f.+40f. black 3·00 3·00

53 Arabesque Ornamentation from Great Mosque at Kairouan

54 Neptune

1947.
302 **53** 3f. green and turquoise . . . 85 1·25
303 4f. red and purple . . . . 3·00 1·90
304 **54** 5f. black and green . . . 70 1·10
305 **53** 6f. red and brown 55 10
306 **54** 10f. black and brown . . 40 20
306a **53** 10f. violet . . . . 1·75 10
306b 12f. brown . . . . 2·00 1·60
306c 12f. orange and brown . . 1·50 15
306d 15f. red and brown . . . 2·00 2·25
307 **54** 18f. blue and green . . . 1·40 3·00
307a 25f. turquoise and blue . . 2·25 20
307b **53** 30f. blue and deep blue . . 1·60 65

55 Feeding a Fledgling 57 Triumphal Arch, Sbeitla

1947. Infant Welfare Fund.
308 **55** 4f.50+5f.50 green . . . . . 50 1·90
309 6f.+9f. blue . . . . 45 1·90
310 8f.+17f. red . . . . 20 2·00
311 10f.+40f. violet . . . . . 45 2·00

1948. Stamp Day. Type of France (Arago) optd **TUNISIE**.
312 **253** 6f.+4f. red . . . . 1·25 3·50

1948. Anti-tuberculosis Fund. Surch **AIDEZ LES TUBERCULEUX +10f**.
313 **53** 4f.+10f. orange and green 25 3·00

1948. Army Welfare Fund.
315 **57** 10f.+40f. green and bistre 1·25 3·50
316 18f.+42f. dp blue & blue 1·25 3·50

1949. Stamp Day. Type of France (Choiseul), optd **TUNISIE**.
317 **278** 15f.+5f. black . . . . . 2·25 2·75

58 Child in Cot

1949. Child Welfare Fund.
318 **58** 25f.+50f. green . . . . . 3·25 4·25

59 Oued Mellegue Barrage

1949. Tunisian Development.
319 **59** 15f. black 65 60

60 Bird from Antique Mosaic 61 Globe, Mounted Postman and Sud Est Languedoc Airliner

1949. Air.
320 **60** 100f. brown and green . . 1·90 1·40
321 200f. black and blue (A) . . 2·75 1·50
322 200f. black and blue (B) . . 4·50 3·75

In A the Arabic inscription is in two lines and in B it is in one line.

1949. 75th Anniv of U.P.U.
323 **61** 5f. green on blue (postage) 1·40 3·25
324 15f. brown on blue . . . . 1·90 3·50
325 15f. blue on blue (air) . . . 1·00 1·75

1949. Free French Association Fund. Surch Lorraine Cross and **FFL +15F**.
326 **54** 10f.+15f. red and blue . . 1·60 2·25

1950. Stamp Day. Type of France (Postman) optd **TUNISIE**.
327 **292** 12f.+3f. green . . . . . 2·00 3·25

62 "Tunisia Thanks France" 63 Old Soldier

1950. Franco–Tunisian Relief Fund.
328 **62** 15f.+35f. red . . . . . . 2·00 3·75
329 25f.+45f. blue . . . . . . 2·00 3·75

1950. Veterans' Relief Fund.
330 **63** 25f.+25f. blue . . . . . . 3·25 4·25

64 Horse (bas-relief) 65 Hermes of Berbera

1950. (a) Size $21\frac{1}{2} \times 17\frac{1}{2}$ mm.
331 **64** 10c. blue . . . . 15 1·75
332 50c. brown . . . . 10 2·25
333 1f. violet 15 30
334 2f. grey 75 15
335 3f. brown 55 30
336 4f. orange . . . . 1·00 1·25
337 5f. green 95 10
338 8f. blue . . . . 1·25 50
340 12f. red 75 20
341 15f. red 30 25
342 15f. blue . . . . 2·40 25

(b) Size $22\frac{1}{4} \times 18\frac{1}{4}$ mm.
343 **64** 15f. red . . . . 2·40 1·60
344 15f. blue . . . . 2·00 1·75
345 30f. blue . . . . 3·00 50

1950.
346 **65** 15f. red . . . . 1·50 2·50
347 25f. blue 45 15
348 50f. green 95 25

1951. Stamp Day. Type of France (Sorting Van), but colour changed, optd **TUNISIE**.
349 **300** 12f.+3f. grey . . . . . . 2·25 3·00

66 Sleeping Child

1951. Child Welfare Fund.
350 **66** 30f.+15f. blue . . . . . 3·00 3·00

67 Gammarth National Cemetery 68 Panel from Great Mosque at Kairouan

1951. War Orphans' Fund.
351 **67** 30f.+10f. blue . . . . . . 1·75 2·25

1952. Stamp Day. Type of France (Mail Coach), optd **TUNISIE**.
352 **319** 12f.+3f. violet . . . . . 2·00 2·50

1952. Army Welfare Fund. Inscr "OEUVRES SOCIALES DE L'ARMEE".
353 – 15f.+1f. indigo and blue (postage) . . . . 1·75 1·60
354 **68** 50f.+10f. green and black (air) . . . . 4·25 4·75
DESIGN: 15f. Ornamental stucco, Bardo Palace.

69 Schoolboys clasping Hands 70 Charles Nicolle

1952. Holiday Camp Fund.
355 **69** 30f.+10f. green . . . . . 2·75 3·00

1952. Golden Jubilee of Tunisian Medical Sciences Society.
356 **70** 15f. brown . . . . 45 1·25
357 30f. blue . . . . 1·10 1·75

1952. Centenary of Military Medal. Type of France surch **Tunisie +5F**.
358 **327** 15f.+5f. green . . . . . 95 4·00

1953. Stamp Day. Type of France (Count D'Argenson), optd **TUNISIE**.
359 **334** 12f.+3f. red . . . . . . 50 3·50

71 Tower and Flags 72 Tozeur Mosque

1953. 1st International Fair, Tunis.
360 **71** 8f. brown and deep brown 50 2·75
361 12f. green and emerald . . 40 3·25
362 15f. indigo and blue . . . 30 1·50
363 18f. deep violet and violet 35 3·25
364 30f. red and carmine . . . 55 3·25

1953. Air.
365 – 100f. blue, turquoise & green . . . . 4·25 2·50
366 – 200f. sepia, purple & brown . . . . 5·50 3·25
367 – 500f. brown and blue . . . 21·00 22·00
368 **72** 1000f. green . . . . 25·00 50·00
DESIGNS: 100, 200f. Monastir; 500f. View of Korbous.
For similar stamps but without "R F" see Nos. 423/6.

1954. Stamp Day. Type of France (Lavallette), optd **TUNISIE**.
369 **346** 12f.+3f. blue . . . . . . 2·00 3·25

73 Courtyard, Sousse 74 Sidi Bou Maklouf Mosque, Le Kef

1954.
370 **73** 50c. green . . . . 10 2·25
371 1f. red 10 20
372 – 2f. purple 30 30
373 – 4f. turquoise . . . . . . 1·75 35
374 – 5f. violet . . . . 1·60 20
375 – 8f. brown . . . . 1·00 70
376 – 10f. green . . . . 2·25 1·10
377 – 12f. brown . . . . 2·00 40
378 – 15f. blue (18 × 22 mm) . . 2·75 1·10
386 – 15f. blue ($17 \times 21\frac{1}{2}$ mm) . . 1·00 10
379 **74** 18f. brown . . . . 3·00 3·25
380 – 20f. blue . . . . 2·25 20
381 – 25f. blue . . . . 2·50 30
382 – 30f. purple . . . . 1·90 2·75
383 – 40f. green . . . . 2·25 1·60
384 – 50f. lilac . . . . 2·75 20
385 – 75f. red . . . . 5·50 4·75
DESIGNS—As Type **73**: 2, 4f. Takrouna ramparts; 5, 8f. Dwellings and Mosque, Tatahouine; 10, 12f. Cave dwellings, Matmata; 15f. Street, Sidi-bou-said. As Type **74**: 20, 25f. Genoese Fort, Tabarka; 30, 40f. Bab-el-Khadra Gate, Tunis; 50, 75f. Four-storey dwellings, Medenine.
For similar stamps but without "R F" see Nos. 406/22.

76 Bey of Tunisia 76a Paris Balloon Post, 1870

1954.
387 **76** 8f. deep blue and blue . . 2·25 3·25
388 12f. indigo and blue . . . 2·25 2·75
389 15f. red and carmine . . . 2·25 3·00
390 18f. deep brown and brown 2·25 2·75
391 30f. deep green and green 2·50 3·75

1955. Stamp Day.
392 **76a** 12f.+3f. brown . . . . . 3·25 1·40

77

1955. 50th Anniv of "L'Essor" (Tunisian Amateur Dramatic Society).
393 **77** 15f. blue, red and orange 2·50 2·75

78 Tunisian Buildings and Rotary Emblem 79 Bey of Tunisia

1955. 50th Anniv of Rotary International.
394 **78** 12f. deep brown and brown 35 3·00
395 15f. brown and grey . . . 35 3·00
396 18f. lilac and violet . . . 30 3·25
397 25f. deep blue and blue . . 35 3·25
398 30f. indigo and blue . . . 60 3·50

1955.
399 **79** 15f. blue . . . . 2·00 10

80 "Embroidery" 81 Bey of Tunisia

80a Francis of Taxis

1955. 3rd International Fair, Tunis.
400 **80** 5f. lake . . . . 1·50 2·75
401 12f. blue . . . . 1·40 2·75
402 – 15f. green . . . . 1·75 2·50
403 – 18f. red . . . . 1·75 3·00
404 – 20f. violet . . . . 2·00 3·25
405 – 30f. purple . . . . 75 2·00
DESIGNS: 15, 18f. "Pottery"; 20, 30f. "Jasmin sellers".

1956. Nos. 365/6 and 368/86 re-engraved without "R F".
406 50c. green (postage) 10 95
407 1f. red 10 10
408 2f. purple 15 20
409 4f. blue 15 20
410 5f. violet 15 15
411 8f. brown 15 30
412 10f. green 15 10
413 12f. brown 15 20
414 15f. blue (18 × 22 mm) . . . 2·50 2·00
415 15f. blue ($17 \times 21\frac{1}{2}$ mm) . . . 15 15
416 18f. brown 15 35
417 20f. blue 25 15
418 25f. blue . . . . 1·40 10
419 30f. purple 45 15
420 40f. green 45 25
421 50f. lilac . . . . 2·00 25
422 75f. red 65 65
423 100f. blue, turquoise and green (air) . . . . 2·50 30
424 200f. sepia, purple and brown 3·50 1·60
425 500f. brown and blue . . . . 8·00 9·00
426 1000f. green . . . . 12·50 16·00

1956. Stamp Day.
427 **80a** 12f.+3f. green . . . . . 1·90 1·90

INDEPENDENT KINGDOM

1956. Autonomous Government.
428 **81** 5f. blue . . . 35 35
429 – 12f. purple . . . 35 35
430 **81** 15f. red . . . 35 35
431 – 18f. grey . . . 45 35
432 **81** 20f. green . . . 45 35
433 – 30f. brown . . . 90 40
DESIGN: 12, 18, 30f. Tunisian girl releasing dove.

82 Farhat Hached  **83** Market Scene

1956. Labour Day.
434 **82** 15f. lake . . . 30 30
435 30f. blue . . . 35 35

1956. Tunisian Products.
436 – 12f. violet, purple & mauve 60 20
437 – 15f. green, brown and blue 60 20
438 – 18f. blue . . . 90 35
439 – 20f. brown . . . 90 35
440 **83** 25f. brown . . . 1·25 55
441 30f. blue . . . 1·40 55
DESIGNS—VERT: 12f. Bunch of grapes; 15f. Sprig of olives; 18f. Harvesting; 20f. Man with basket containing wedding offering.

84 Pres. Habib Bourguiba  **85** Pres. Bourguiba and Agricultural Workers

1957. 1st Anniv of Independence.
442 **84** 5f. blue . . . 20 20
443 **85** 12f. pink . . . 20 20
444 **84** 20f. blue . . . 30 20
445 **85** 25f. green . . . 35 20
446 **84** 30f. brown . . . 40 30
447 **85** 50f. red . . . 80 50

86 Dove and Handclasp

1957. 5th International Confederation of Free Trade Unions Congress.
448 **86** 18f. purple . . . 35 35
449 – 20f. red . . . 40 40
450 **86** 25f. green . . . 40 40
451 – 30f. blue . . . 45 45
DESIGN—VERT: 20, 30f. Handclasp and Labour Exchange.

INDEPENDENT REPUBLIC

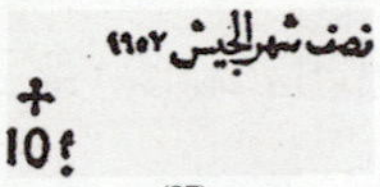

(87)

1957. Tunisian Army Fortnight. No. 417 optd with T **87**.
452 20f.+10f. blue . . . 55 55

88 Tunisian Soldiers and Flag

1957. Proclamation of Republic.
453 **88** 20f. red . . . 16·00 16·00
454 25f. violet . . . 16·00 16·00
455 30f. brown . . . 16·00 16·00

1957. 5th International Fair, Tunis. As No. 404 but additionally inscr "5e FOIRE INTERNATIONALE" and Arabic inscriptions at sides, surch **+ 10F.**
456 20f.+10f. violet . . . 45 45

90 Pres Bourguiba on Ile de la Galite  **91** Tunisian Emblems and Map

1958. 6th Anniv of Exile of Pres. Bourguiba.
457 **90** 20f. blue and brown . . . 55 35
458 25f. blue and violet . . . 55 35

1958. 2nd Anniv of Independence.
459 **91** 20f. green and brown . . . 35 15
460 – 25f. brown and blue . . . 35 15
461 – 30f. brown, deep brown and red . . . 45 20
DESIGNS: 25f. Mother and child; 30f. Clenched fist holding Tunisian flag.
For 20f. brown and blue see No. 464.

92 Andreas Vesalius (scientist) and A. ibn Khaldoun  **93** Planting Olives

1958. Brussels International Exhibition.
462 **92** 30f. green and bistre . . . 45 20

1958. Labour Day.
463 **93** 20f. multicoloured . . . 45 45

1958. 3rd Anniv of Return of Pres. Bourguiba. As T **91** but with inscr altered.
464 **91** 20f. brown and blue . . . 40 20

94  **95** Pres. Bourguiba

1958. 1st Anniv of Proclamation of Tunisian Republic.
465 **94** 5f. purple and bistre . . . 45 20
466 10f. deep green & lt green 45 20
467 15f. brown and orange . . . 45 20
468 20f. violet, olive and yellow 45 20
469 25f. purple . . . 45 20

1958. Pres. Bourguiba's 55th Birthday.
470 **95** 20f. purple and violet . . . 35 20

96 Fishermen with Catch  **97** UNESCO Headquarters, Paris

1958. 6th International Fair.
471 **96** 25f. purple, red and green 70 35

1958. Inaug of UNESCO Building.
472 **97** 25f. myrtle . . . 60 35

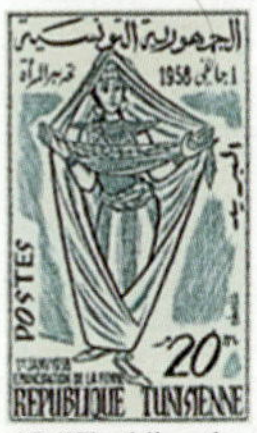

98 "Shedding the veil"  **99** Hand holding plant

1959. Emancipation of Tunisian Women.
473 **98** 20m. turquoise . . . 45 30

1959. 25th Anniv of Neo-Destour (Nationalist Party) and Victory Congress.
474 **99** 5m. red, brown and purple 30 10
475 – 10m. multicoloured . . . 35 15
476 – 20m. blue . . . 40 20
477 – 30m. blue, turquoise & brown . . . 65 40
DESIGNS—VERT: 10m. Tunisians with flaming torch and flag on shield; 20m. Pres. Bourguiba in exile at Borj le Boeuf, 1954. HORIZ: 30m. Pres. Bourguiba and Borj le Boeuf, 1934.

100 "Tunisia"

1959. 3rd Anniv of Independence.
478 **100** 50m. multicoloured . . . 65 35

101 Tunisian Horseman  **102** "Freedom"

1959. Designs as T **101**.
479 ½m. brown, green and emerald . . . 35 10
480 1m. bistre and blue . . . 10 10
481 2m. brown, yellow and blue 15 10
482 3m. myrtle . . . 10 10
483 4m. brown . . . 30 15
484 5m. myrtle . . . 20 10
485 6m. violet . . . 20 15
486 8m. purple . . . 65 30
487 10m. red, green and bistre 20 10
487a 12m. violet and bistre . . . 65 20
488 15m. blue . . . 60 10
489 16m. green . . . 30 20
490 20m. turquoise . . . 1·00 30
491 20m. purple, olive and myrtle . . . 2·25 30
492 25m. blue, brown & turquoise . . . 30 20
493 30m. brown, green & turq 45 10
494 40m. green . . . 1·60 20
495 45m. green . . . 70 30
496 50m. multicoloured . . . 90 20
497 60m. brown and green . . . 1·25 35
498 70m. multicoloured . . . 1·40 50
499 75m. brown . . . 1·25 55
500 90m. brown, green and blue 1·60 55
501 95m. multicoloured . . . 1·90 1·00
502 100m. multicoloured . . . 2·00 90
503 200m. red, bistre and blue 5·00 2·50
504 ½d. brown . . . 16·00 6·75
505 1d. ochre and green . . . 25·00 13·50
DESIGNS—VERT: ½m. Ain Draham; 2m. Camel-driver; 3m. Saddler's shop; 5m. Type **101**; 6m. Weavers; 8m. Gafsa; 10m. Woman holding pomegranates; 12m. Turner; 20m. (No. 491), Gabes; 40m. Kairouan; 70m. Carpet weaver; 75m. Nabeul vase; 95m. Olive-gatherer; ½d. Sbeitla. HORIZ: 1m. Kairouan environs; 4m. Medenine; 15m. Monastir; 16m. Tunis; 20m. (No. 490), Room in Arab house, Sidi-Bou-Said; 25m. Sfax; 30m. Aqueduct, Medjerda Valley; 45m. Bizerta; 50m. Djerba; 60m. Le Jerid; 90m. Le Kef; 100m. Sidi-bou-Said highway; 200m. Old port of Sfax; 1d. Beja ploughman.

1959. Africa Freedom Day.
506 **102** 40m. brown and blue . . . 50 35

103 Postman  **104** Clenched Hands

1959. Stamp Day.
507 **103** 20m.+5m. brown & orge 45 45

1959. U.N. Day.
508 **104** 80m. brown, blue & purple . . . 65 45

105  **106** Dancer and Coin

1959. Red Crescent Day.
509 **105** 10m.+5m. multicoloured 35 35

1959. 1st Anniv of Tunisian Central Bank.
510 **106** 50m. black and blue . . . 50 50

107 "Uprooted Tree"  **108** Camel Rider telephoning

1960. World Refugee Year. Inscr "ANNEE MONDIALE DES REFUGIES 1959–1960".
511 **107** 20m. blue . . . 40 20
512 – 40m. black and purple . . . 50 35
DESIGN—HORIZ: 40m. Doves.

1960. Stamp Day.
513 **108** 60m.+5m. orange, blue and olive . . . 80 80

109 Pres. Bourguiba signing Promulgation  **110** Fair Emblems

1960. Promulgation of Constitution.
514 **109** 20m. red, brown and green . . . 40 35

1960. 5th Sousse National Fair.
515 **110** 100m. black and green . . . 65 45

111 President Bourguiba  **112** Jamboree Emblems

1960.
516 **111** 20m. black . . . 20 10
517 30m. black, red and blue 35 10
518 40m. black, red and green 45 20

1960. 4th Arab Scout Jamboree, Tunis.
519 **112** 10m. turquoise . . . 35 35
520 – 25m. purple, red and green . . . 40 35
521 – 30m. lake, violet and green . . . 60 35
522 – 40m. black, blue and red 65 40
523 – 60m. violet, purple & sepia . . . 1·25 55
DESIGNS: 25m. Saluting hand with scouts as fingers; 30m. Camp bugler; 40m. Scout peacock badge; 60m. Scout by camp fire.

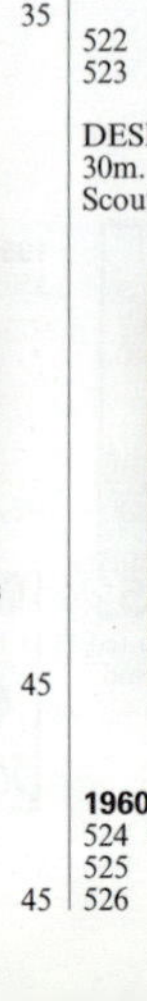
113 Cyclist in Stadium

114

1960. Olympic Games.
524 **113** 5m. brown and olive . . . 30 25
525 – 10m. purple, green & blue 35 30
526 – 15m. carmine and red . . . 35 30

527 – 25m. slate and blue . . . 45 40
528 – 50m. blue and green . . . 85 65
DESIGNS: 10m. Flowers composed of Olympic rings; 15m. Girl with racquet; 25m. Runner; 50m. Handball player.

1960. 5th World Forestry Congress, Seattle.
529 **114** 8m. lake, green and blue 35 15
530 – 15m. green 40 20
531 – 25m. red, green and violet 65 30
532 – 50m. turquoise, brown & green . . . . 1·10 50
DESIGNS: 15m. Removing bark from tree; 25m. Tree within leaf; 50m. Diamond pattern featuring palm.

115 U.N. Emblem and People's Arms
116 Dove of Peace 

1960. U.N. Day.
533 **115** 40m. blue, red and black 65 45

1961. 5th Anniv of Independence.
534 **116** 20m. blue, bistre & purple 30 20
535 30m. brown, violet & blue 35 20
536 40m. ultramarine, blue & green 55 40
537 – 75m. blue, mauve and olive 80 45
DESIGN: 75m. Globe and Arms of Tunisia.

117 Tunisian Animals and Map of Africa
118 Stamps and Magnifier 

1961. Africa Day and 3rd Anniv of Accra Conference. Inscr "JOURNEE DE L'AFRIQUE 15.4.1961".
538 **117** 40m. green, brown and bistre 35 20
539 – 60m. black, brown & turquoise 40 30
540 – 100m. violet, emerald and grey 70 45
541 – 200m. brown and orange 1·40 1·00
DESIGNS (all showing outline of Africa): 50m. Profiles of Negress and Arab woman; 100m. Masks and "Africa Day" in Arabic; 200m. Clasped hands.

1961. Stamp Day. Inscr "JOURNEE DU TIMBRE 1961". Multicoloured.
542 12m.+4m. Kerkennah dancer and costume of stamps (vert) 45 45
543 15m.+5m. Mobile postal delivery (vert) 60 60
544 20m.+6m. Type **118** 65 65
545 50m.+5m. Postman in shirt depicting stamps (vert) . . 80 80

119 "Celebration"
120 Dag Hammarskjoeld 

1961. National Day.
546 **119** 25m. brown, red and violet 45 15
547 – 50m. brown, choc & grn 45 20
548 – 95m. mauve, brown & blue 65 40
DESIGNS: 50m. Family celebrating in street; 95m. Girl astride crescent moon.

1961. U.N. Day.
549 **120** 40m. blue 60 35

121 Arms of Tunisia
122 Mosquito in Web 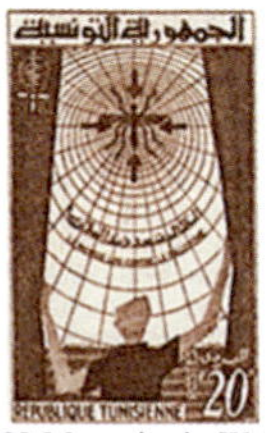

1962. 10th Anniv of Independence Campaign. Arms in red, yellow, blue and black.
550 **121** 1m. yellow and black . . 10 10
551 2m. pink and black . . . 15 15
552 3m. blue and black . . . 15 15
553 6m. grey and black . . . 20 20

1962. Malaria Eradication. Inscr "LE MONDE UNI CONTRE LE PALUDISME".
554 **122** 20m. brown 45 30
555 – 30m. brown, green & chocolate 45 30
556 – 40m. red, green and brown 80 35
DESIGNS—VERT: 30m. "Horseman" attacking mosquito; 40m. Hands destroying mosquito.

123 African

1962. Africa Day. Inscr "JOURNEE DE L'AFRIQUE 1962".
557 **123** 50m. brown and buff . . 55 35
558 – 10m. multicoloured . . . 80 45
DESIGN: 100m. Symbolic figure clasping "Africa".

124 Dancer
125 Rejoicing Tunisians 

1962. May Day. Inscr "FETE DU TRAVAIL 1962".
559 **124** 40m. multicoloured . . . 40 20
560 – 60m. brown 45 30
DESIGN: 60m. Worker with pneumatic drill.

1962. National Day.
561 **125** 20m. black and salmon 50 35

126 Gabes Costume
127 U.N. Emblem and Tunisian Flag 

1962. Republic Festival. Regional Costumes. Mult.
562 5m. Type **126** 55 20
563 10m. Mahdia 65 35
564 15m. Kairouan 90 45
565 20m. Hammamet . . . . . 1·10 55
566 25m. Djerba . . . . 1·25 55
567 30m. As 10m. . . . . . . 1·25 65
568 40m. As 20m. . . . . . . 1·40 65
569 50m. Type **126** . . . . . . 1·40 85
570 55m. Ksar Hellal . . . . . 2·50 1·00
571 60m. Tunis . . . . 3·00 1·40

1962. U.N. Day.
572 **127** 20m. red, black and grey 35 30
573 – 30m. multicoloured . . . 40 30
574 – 40m. blue, black & brown 65 35
DESIGNS—HORIZ: 30m. "Plant" with three leaves and globe. VERT: 40m. Globe and dove.

128 A. Q. Chabbi (poet)
129 Pres. Bourguiba 

1962. Aboul Qasim Chabbi Commemoration.
575 **128** 15m. violet 35 20

1962.
576 **129** 20m. blue 15 15
577 30m. red 15 10
578 40m. green 20 15

130 Hached Telephone Exchange
131 Runners 

1962. Modernization of Telephone System.
579 **130** 5m. multicoloured 30 20
580 – 10m. multicoloured . . . 35 20
581 – 15m. multicoloured . . . 50 35
582 – 50m. flesh, brown & black 80 50
583 – 100m. blue, purple & black . . . . 2·00 90
584 – 200m. multicoloured . . . 2·75 1·40
DESIGNS: 10m. Carthage Telephone Exchange; 15m. Aerial equipment; 50m. Telephone switchboard operators; 100m. Telephone equipment as human figure; 200m. Belvedere Telephone Exchange.

1963. 13th International Military Sports Council Cross-country Championships.
585 **131** 30m. brown, green & black 60 45

132 Dove with Wheatear and Globe
133 Centenary Emblem 

1963. Freedom from Hunger.
586 **132** 20m. blue and brown . . 30 20
587 – 40m. purple and brown 40 20
DESIGN: 40m. Child taking nourishment.

1963. Red Cross Centenary.
588 **133** 20m. red, grey and brown 45 20

1963. U.N. Day. Nos. 542/5 optd **1963 O.N.U.** in English and Arabic.
589 12m.+4m. multicoloured . . 30 30
590 15m.+5m. multicoloured . . 35 35
591 20m.+6m. multicoloured . . 40 40
592 50m.+5m. multicoloured . . 65 65

135 "Miss World"
136 "Out of Reach" 

1963. 15th Anniv of Declaration of Human Rights.
593 **135** 30m. brown and green . . 45 30

1964. Nubian Monuments Preservation.
594 **136** 50m. ochre, brown & blue 45 30

137 "Unsettled Forecast"
138 Mohamed Ali (trade union leader) 

1964. World Meteorological Day.
595 **137** 40m. mauve, blue & brown 45 20

1964. 70th Birth Anniv of Mohamed Ali.
596 **138** 50m. purple 45 35

139 Africa within Flower
140 Pres. Bourguiba 

1964. 1st Anniv of Addis Ababa Conference of the Organization of African Unity.
597 **139** 60m. multicoloured . . . 50 30

1964. National Day.
598 **140** 20m. blue 15 10
599 30m. brown 20 10

141 "Bizerte" ("ship")
142 Fulvous Babbler 

1964. Neo-Destour Congress, Bizerta.
600 **141** 50m. green and black . . 40 30

1965. Air. Tunisian Birds. Multicoloured.
601 25m. Type **142** . . . . 1·50 50
602 55m. Great grey strike . . . 2·25 75
603 55m. Cream-coloured courser 2·50 95
604 100m. Chaffinch . . . . . . 3·00 1·10
605 150m. Greater flamingoes . . 5·25 2·40
606 200m. Barbary partridge . . 8·00 2·75
607 300m. European roller . . . 12·50 5·25
608 500m. Houbara bustard . . . 18·00 6·25
SIZES—As Type **142**: 55m. (both). Others, 23 × 32½ mm.

143 Early Telegraphist and Aerial Mast
144 Carthaginian Coin 

1965. I.T.U. Centenary.
609 **143** 55m. blue and black . . . 50 30

1965. Festival of Popular Arts, Carthage.
610 **144** 5m. purple and green . . 15 10
611 10m. purple and yellow 30 20
612 75m. purple and blue . . 65 20

145 Girl reading Book
146 Joined Hooks

1965. Opening of Students' Home, Tunis.
613 **145** 25m. blue, black and red 30 20
614 40m. black, blue and red 40 20
615 50m. red, black and blue 45 30

1965. International Co-operation Year.
617 **146** 40m. blue, purple & black 45 25

147 Women bathing

149 Independence

148 Pres. Bourguiba and Hands

1966. Mineral Springs. Inscr "EAUX MINERALES".
618 **147** 10m. red, ochre and grey 30 20
619 – 20m. multicoloured 40 30
620 – 30m. red, blue and yellow 45 35
621 – 100m. olive, yellow & blue 1·10 55
DESIGNS: 20m. Man pouring water; 30m. Woman pouring water; 100m. Mountain and fronds of tree.

1966. 10th Anniv of Independence.
622 **148** 5m. lilac and blue 15 10
623 10m. green and blue 20 15
624 **149** 25m. multicoloured 20 15
625 – 40m. multicoloured 55 20
626 – 60m. multicoloured 80 35
DESIGNS—As Type **149**—HORIZ: 40m. "Development". VERT: 60m. "Promotion of Culture" ("man" draped in books, palette, musical instruments, etc).

150 Sectional Map of Africa

152 "Athletics"

151 UNESCO Emblem of the Muses

1966. 2nd U.N. African Regional Cartographic Conference, Tunisia.
627 **150** 15m. multicoloured 30 20
628 35m. multicoloured 35 20
629 40m. multicoloured 50 35

1966. 20th Anniv of UNESCO.
631 **151** 100m. brown and black 85 35

1967. Publicity for Mediterranean Games (September, 1967).
632 **152** 20m. brown, blue and red 20 15
633 30m. black and blue 40 30

153 Gabes Costume and Fair Emblem

154 Emblems of Civilization

1967. "Expo 67" World Fair, Montreal. T **154** and earlier designs redrawn as T **153**.
634 – 50m. mult (As No. 566) 35 15
635 **153** 75m. multicoloured 50 30
636 **154** 100m. green, black & turquoise 80 30
637 110m. red, sepia and blue 95 40
638 – 155m. mult (As No. 605) 1·60 60

155 Tunisian Pavilion, Pres. Bourguiba and Map

1967. "National Day at World Fair, Montreal".
639 **155** 65m. purple and red 40 35
640 – 105m. brown, red and blue 50 35
641 – 120m. blue 60 40
642 – 200m. black, red & purple 1·25 50
DESIGNS: 105m. As Type **155**, but with profile bust of Pres. Bourguiba. Tunisian pavilion (different view) with: 120m. Silhouette and 200m. Bust of Pres. Bourguiba.

156 "Tunisia" holding Clover

158 Bas-relief from Statue of Apollo

157 Tennis Club

1967. 10th Anniv of Republic. Multicoloured.
643 25m. Type **156** 20 15
644 40m. Woman releasing doves (vert) 35 15

1967. Mediterranean Games, Tunis.
645 **157** 5m. red and green 20 20
646 – 10m. multicoloured 20 15
647 – 15m. black 35 20
648 – 35m. turquoise, purple & black 45 20
649 – 75m. green, violet and red 80 40
DESIGNS—VERT: 10m. "Spring Triumphs" (squared panel). HORIZ: 15m. Olympic swimming pool; 35m. Sports Palace; 75m. Olympic stadium.

1967. Tunisian History. Punic period.
650 **158** 15m. red, black and green 30 20
651 – 20m. flesh, red and blue 35 20
652 – 25m. brown and olive 45 20
653 – 30m. red and grey 45 20
654 – 40m. lemon, yellow & purple 50 20
655 – 60m. multicoloured 75 30
DESIGNS: 20m. Sea horseman (Kerkouane medallion); 25m. Hannibal (bronze bust); 30m. "The Sacrifice" (votive stele); 40m. Hamilcar (coin); 60m. Glass funeral pendant mask.

159 "Human Rights"

160 "Electronic Man"

1968. Human Rights Year.
656 **159** 25m. red 40 35
657 60m. blue 45 20

1968. Electronics in Postal Service.
658 **160** 25m. blue, brown & purple 35 30
659 40m. black, brown & green 35 30
660 60m. purple, slate and blue 45 35

161 "Doctor and Patient"

162 Arabian Jasmine

1968. 20th Anniv of W.H.O.
661 **161** 25m. green and turquoise 40 35
662 60m. red and lake 45 35

1968. Tunisian Flowers. Multicoloured.
663 5m. Flax 20 15
664 6m. Indian shot 20 15
665 10m. Pomegranate 30 15
666 12m. Type **162** 30 15
667 15m. Raponticum 35 15
668 20m. Geranium 40 20
669 25m. Madonna lily 40 30
670 40m. Almond 60 30
671 50m. Capers 80 45
672 60m. Ariana rose 1·25 70
673 100m. Jasmine 1·90 1·10

163 Globe on "Sunflower"

164 Flautist

1968. Red Crescent Day.
674 **163** 15m. red, green and blue 35 30
675 – 25m. red and purple 40 30
DESIGN: 25m. Red crescent on wings of dove.

1968. Stamp Day.
676 **164** 20m. multicoloured 35 20
677 50m. multicoloured 40 35

165 Golden Jackal

166 Worker

1968. Fauna. Multicoloured.
678 5m. Type **165** 20 15
679 8m. North African crested porcupine 30 20
680 10m. Dromedary 40 20
681 15m. Dorcas gazelle 75 20
682 20m. Fennec fox 1·25 45
683 25m. Algerian hedgehog 1·50 55
684 40m. Horse 1·90 80
685 60m. Wild boar 2·50 1·25

1969. 50th Anniv of I.L.O. Multicoloured.
686 25m. Type **166** 35 30
687 60m. Youth and girl holding "May 1" banner 50 35

167 Musicians and Veiled Dancers

168 Tunisian Arms

1969. Stamp Day.
688 **167** 100m. multicoloured 70 35

1969.
689 **168** 15m. multicoloured 20 20
690 25m. multicoloured 30 20
691 40m. multicoloured 35 20
692 60m. multicoloured 40 20

169 "Industrial Development"

170 Lute

1969. 5th Anniv of African Development Bank.
693 **169** 60m. multicoloured 40 30

1970. Musical Instruments. Multicoloured.
694 25m. Type **170** 45 35
695 50m. Zither 55 35
696 70m. Rehab 80 35
697 90m. Naghrat (drums) 1·00 35
Nos. 695 and 697 are horiz, size 33 × 22 mm.

171 Nurse, Caduceus and Flags

172 New U.P.U. Headquarters Building

1970. 6th North-African Maghreb Medical Seminar, Tunis.
698 **171** 25m. multicoloured 35 20

1970. New U.P.U. Headquarters Building, Berne.
699 **172** 25m. brown and red 40 20

173 Mounted Postman

1970. Stamp Day. Multicoloured.
700 25m. Type **173** 20 20
701 35m. "Postmen of yesterday and today" (23 × 38 mm) 35 20

174 U.N. Emblem, "N" and Dove forming "O.N.U."

175 "The Flower-seller"

1970. 25th Anniv of United Nations.
702 **174** 40m. multicoloured 40 20

1970. "Tunisian Life" (1st series). Multicoloured.
703 20m. Type **175** 20 15
704 25m. "The husband's third day of marriage" 30 20
705 35m. "The Perfumer" 45 35
706 40m. "The Fish-seller" 50 35
707 85m. "The Coffee-house keeper" 80 35
See also Nos. 715/18, 757/62 and 819/23.

176 Lenin

177 Dish Aerial and Flags

1970. Birth Centenary of Lenin.
709 **176** 60m. lake 1·25 35

1971. Maghreban Posts and Telecommunciations Co-ordination.
710 **177** 25m. multicoloured 40 35

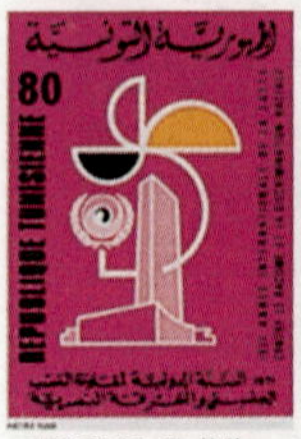

178 U.N. Building and Symbol

179 Globe and Satellites

1971. Racial Equality Year.
711 **178** 80m. multicoloured 45 30

1971. World Telecommunications Day.
712 **179** 70m. multicoloured 40 20

180 Moon, Earth and Satellites

1971. "Conquest of Space".
713 **180** 15m. black and blue . . . 35 20
714 – 90m. black and red . . . 60 30
DESIGN: 90m. Space allegory.

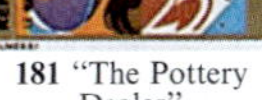

181 "The Pottery Dealer" **182** Pres. Bourguiba

1971. "Tunisian Life" (2nd series). Multicoloured.
715 25m. Type **181** 35 20
716 30m. "The Esparto dealer" . . 35 20
717 40m. "The Poulterer" 45 20
718 50m. "The Dyer" 55 30

1971. 8th P.S.D. Destourian Socialist Party Congress, Tunis. Multicoloured.
720 25m. Type **182** 20 20
721 30m. Bourguiba in bed, 1938 (horiz) 20 20
722 50m. Bourguiba acclaimed . . . 35 30
723 80m. Bourguiba—"Builder of the Nation" (horiz) 45 30
SIZES: 30m., 80m. 13½ × 14; 50m. As Type **182**.

183 Shah Mohammed Riza Pahlavi and Achaemenidian Effigy **184** Pimento

1971. 2500th Anniv of Persian Empire. Mult.
724 25m. Type **183** 30 20
725 50m. "King Bahram-Gur hunting" (14th-century) . . 35 20
726 100m. "Coronation of Louhrasap" (Persian 11th-century miniature) . . 60 30

1971. "Flowers, Fruits and Folklore". Mult.
728 1m. Type **184** 10 10
729 2m. Mint 20 15
730 5m. Pear 35 20
731 25m. Laurel rose 40 30
732 60m. Quince 80 20
733 100m. Grapefruit . . . . . . 1·50 35
Each design includes a scene from Tunisian folklore.

185 "The Musicians of Kerkena" **186** Telephone

1971. Stamp Day.
735 **185** 50m. multicoloured . . . 40 20

1971. Pan-African Telecommunications Network.
736 **186** 95m. multicoloured . . . 50 45

187 UNICEF Emblem **189** Olive-tree Emblem

188 Rialto Bridge, Venice

1971. 25th Anniv of UNICEF.
737 **187** 110m. multicoloured . . . 50 35

1971. UNESCO "Save Venice" Campaign. Multicoloured.
738 25m. Gondolier (vert) 35 20
739 30m. De Medici and Palace (vert) 40 20
740 50m. Prow of gondola (vert) 45 35
741 80m. Type **188** 80 35

1972. World Olive-oil Year.
742 **189** 60m. multicoloured . . . 40 20

190 Tunisian reading Book **191** Heart Emblem

1972. International Book Year.
743 **190** 90m. multicoloured . . . 50 40

1972. World Health Day. Multicoloured.
744 25m. Type **191** 35 20
745 60m. Heart within "hour-glass" 55 35

192 "Old Age" **193** "Only One Earth"

1972. Tunisian Red Crescent.
746 **192** 10m.+10m. violet & red 35 30
747 – 75m.+10m. brown & red 50 35
DESIGN: 75m. Mother and Child ("Child Care").

1972. U.N. Environmental Conservation Conf, Stockholm.
748 **193** 60m. green and brown . . 50 20

194 Hurdling **195** Chessboard

1972. Olympic Games, Munich.
749 – 5m. multicoloured 10 10
750 **194** 15m. multicoloured . . . 15 10
751 – 20m. black, green and gold 15 10
752 – 25m. multicoloured . . . 15 15
753 – 60m. multicoloured . . . 35 20
754 – 80m. multicoloured . . . 45 30
DESIGNS—VERT: 5m. Handball; 20m. Athletes saluting. HORIZ: 25m. Football; 60m. Swimming; 80m. Running.

1972. 20th Chess Olympiad, Skopje, Yugoslavia.
756 **195** 60m. multicoloured . . . 1·25 55

196 "The Fisherman"

1972. "Tunisian Life" (3rd series). Multicoloured.
757 5m. Type **196** 20 15
758 10m. "The Basket-maker" . . 20 15
759 25m. "The Musician" 30 15
760 50m. "The Berber Bride" . . 55 20
761 60m. "The Flower-seller" . . 80 20
762 80m. "The Mystic" . . . . . 1·10 40

197 New P.T.T. H.Q., Tunis

1972. Stamp Day.
764 **197** 25m. multicoloured . . . 30 20

198 Dome of the Rock, Jerusalem

1973. Dome of the Rock Commemoration.
765 **198** 25m. multicoloured . . . 40 30

199 Globe and Beribboned Pen

1973. 9th Writers' Congress and 11th Poetry Festival. Multicoloured.
766 25m. Type **199** 20 20
767 60m. Lyre emblem 35 20

200 Heads of Family **201** Figures "10" and Bird feeding Young

1973. Family Planning. Multicoloured.
768 20m. Type **200** 20 20
769 25m. Family profiles and bird 35 30

1973. 10th Anniv of World Food Programme. Multicoloured.
770 25m. Type **201** 60 20
771 60m. Symbolic "10" 60 20

202 Sculptured Roman Head **203** Red Crescent Nurse

1973. UNESCO "Save Carthage" Campaign. Multicoloured.
772 5m. Type **202** 30 20
773 25m. Carthagian mosaics . . 45 35
774 30m. "Cycle of mosaics" . . 45 35
775 40m. "Goodwill" stele (vert) 60 35
776 60m. Preacher's hand (from Korba statue) 70 35
777 75m. "Malga" (17th-century potsherd) (vert) 85 40

1973. Tunisian Red Crescent.
779 **203** 25m.+10m. multicoloured 45 35
780 – 60m.+10m. red and grey 65 35
DESIGN—HORIZ: 60m. Arms of blood donors.

204 "World Telecommunications" **205** Smiling Youth

1973. 5th World Telecommunications Day. Mult.
781 60m. Type **204** 35 20
782 75m. "The Universe" 40 20

1973. 1st Pan-African Festival of Youth. Mult.
783 25m. Festival Map 35 30
784 40m. Type **205** 40 30

206 Scout Badge

1973. International Scouting.
785 **206** 25m. multicoloured . . . 35 30

207 "Rover" in Car

1973. 2nd Pan-Arab Rover Rally.
786 **207** 60m. multicoloured . . . 40 35

208 Traffic Lights **209** Winged Camel

1973. Road Safety. Multicoloured.
787 25m. Motorway junction (horiz) 35 30
788 30m. Type **208** 40 30

1973. Stamp Day. Multicoloured.
789 10m. Peacock ("collectors pride") (horiz) 35 20
790 65m. Type **209** 40 35

210 Copernicus **211** O.A.U. Emblems within Arms

1973. 500th Birth Anniv of Copernicus.
791 **210** 60m. multicoloured . . . 1·25 35

1973. 10th Anniv of Organization of African Unity.
792 **211** 25m. multicoloured . . . 40 20

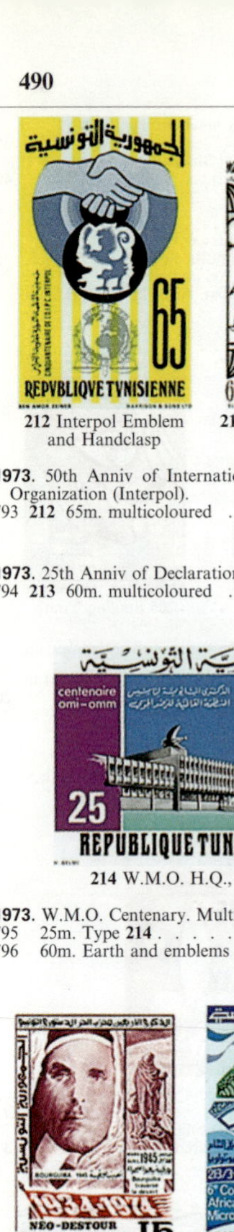

212 Interpol Emblem and Handclasp

213 Flower Offering

1973. 50th Anniv of International Criminal Police Organization (Interpol).
793 **212** 65m. multicoloured . . . 45 35

1973. 25th Anniv of Declaration of Human Rights.
794 **213** 60m. multicoloured . . . 55 35

214 W.M.O. H.Q., Geneva

1973. W.M.O. Centenary. Multicoloured.
795 25m. Type **214** 40 20
796 60m. Earth and emblems . . 45 30

215 President Bourguiba, 1934

216 Scientist using Microscope

1974. 40th Anniv of Neo-Destour Party.
797 **215** 15m. purple, red and black 20 20
798 – 25m. brown, orange & black 20 20
799 – 60m. blue, red and black 30 20
800 – 75m. brown, mauve & black 35 20
801 – 100m. green, orange & black 45 35
DESIGNS: Nos. 798/801, Various portraits of Pres. Bourguiba (founder), similar to Type **215**.

1974. 6th African Micro-Palaeontological Conf, Tunis.
803 **216** 60m. multicoloured . . . 1·40 60

217 "Blood Donation"

218 Telephonist holding Globe

1974. Tunisian Red Crescent. Multicoloured.
804 25m.+10m. Type **217** 35 35
805 75m.+10m. "Blood Transfusion" 45 45

1974. Inauguration of International Automatic Telephone Service. Multicoloured.
806 15m. Type **218** 20 20
807 60m. Telephone dial 45 35

219 Population Emblems

1974. World Population Year.
808 **219** 110m. multicoloured . . . 55 35

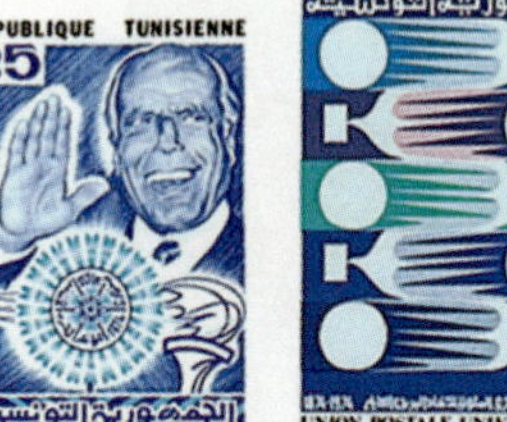

220 Pres. Bourguiba and Emblem

222 "Carrier-pigeons"

221 Aircraft crossing Globe

1974. Destourian Socialist Party Congress.
809 **220** 25m. blue, turquoise & black 20 20
810 – 60m. red, yellow and black 30 25
811 – 200m. purple, green & black 90 50
DESIGNS—HORIZ: 60m. Pres. Bourguiba and sunflower; 200m. Pres. Bourguiba and sunflower.

1974. 25th Anniv of Tunisian Aviation.
813 **221** 60m. multicoloured . . . 45 35

1974. Centenary of U.P.U. Multicoloured.
814 25m. Type **222** 35 25
815 60m. Handclasp 45 30

223 Bardo Palace as "Ballot Box"

224 Postman with Parcels on Head

1974. Legislative and Presidential Elections.
816 **223** 25m. blue, green and black 35 30
817 – 100m. black and orange 50 35
DESIGN: 100m. Pres. Bourguiba on poll card.

1974. Stamp Day.
818 **224** 75m. multicoloured . . . 45 20

225 "The Water-carrier"

226 Stylized Bird

1975. "Scenes from Tunisian Life" (4th series). Multicoloured.
819 5m. Type **225** 15 15
820 15m. "The Scent Sprinkler" 20 20
821 25m. "The Washer-women" 20 20
822 60m. "The Potter" 35 20
823 110m. "The Fruit-seller" . . 85 50

1975. 13th Arab Engineers' Union Conference, Tunis. Multicoloured.
825 25m. Skyscraper and scaffolding (vert) 20 20
826 65m. Type **226** 75 30

227 Gold Coffee-pot and Tray

1975. Handicrafts. Multicoloured.
827 10m. Type **227** 20 20
828 15m. Horseman and saddlery (embroidery) 20 20
829 25m. Still life (painting) . . . 30 20
830 30m. Bird-cage (fine-crafts) (vert) 35 20
831 40m. Silver head-dress (jewellery) (vert) 35 20
832 60m. Textile patterns 55 30

228 Man and Scales

229 "Telecommunications"

1975. Tunisian Red Crescent Campaign against Malnutrition.
833 **228** 50m.+10m. mult 40 35

1975. 7th World Telecommunications Day.
834 **229** 50m. multicoloured . . . 30 20

230 Allegory of Victory

231 Tunisian Woman

1975. 20th Anniv of "Victory" (Return of Bourguiba). Multicoloured.
835 25m. Type **230** 20 20
836 65m. Return of President Bourguiba (horiz) 35 20

1975. International Women's Year.
837 **231** 110m. multicoloured . . . 55 30

232 Children on Road Crossing

1975. Road Safety Campaign.
838 **232** 25m. multicoloured 20 20

233 Djerba

1975. "Tunisia, Yesterday and Today" (1st series). Multicoloured.
839 10m. Type **233** 20 20
840 15m. Tunis 20 20
841 20m. Monastir 20 20
842 65m. Sousse 45 30
843 500m. Tozeur . . . . . . 3·75 35
844 1d. Kairouan . . . . . . 6·25 2·50
See also Nos. 864/7.

234 Figures representing Sport

235 Bouquet of Flowers

1975. 7th Mediterranean Games, Algiers. Mult.
845 25m. Type **234** 20 20
846 50m. "Ship of sport" (horiz) 35 20

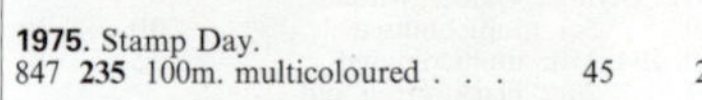

1975. Stamp Day.
847 **235** 100m. multicoloured . . . 45 20

236 College Building

1975. Centenary of Sadiki College.
848 **236** 25m. multicoloured . . . 30 20

237 "Duck"

238 Early and Modern Telephones

1976. Tunisian Mosaics. Multicoloured.
849 5m. Type **237** 30 20
850 10m. Fish 30 20
851 25m. Lioness (40 × 27 mm) 55 45
852 60m. Gorgon (40 × 27 mm) 60 45
853 75m. Circus spectators (27 × 40 mm) 65 45
854 100m. Virgil (27 × 40 mm) . . 1·25 45

1976. Telephone Centenary.
856 **238** 150m. multicoloured . . . 55 30

239 Figures "20" and Banners

240 Blind Man with Stick

1976. 20th Anniv of Independence. Mult.
857 40m. Type **239** 20 20
858 100m. Figures "20" and flag emblem 40 20
859 150m. Floral allegory of "Tunisia" 60 30

1976. World Health Day.
861 **240** 100m. black and red . . . 45 20

241 Blood Donation

242 "Urban Development"

1976. Tunisian Red Crescent.
862 **241** 40m.+10m. mult 40 30

1976. "Habitat" Human Settlements Conference, Vancouver.
863 **242** 40m. multicoloured . . . 30 20

243 Henna Tradition

1976. "Tunisia, Yesterday and Today" (2nd series). Multicoloured.
864 40m. Type **243** 20 20
865 50m. Diving for sponges . . 55 20
866 65m. Weaving 35 20
867 110m. Pottery 50 35

244 "Spirit of 1776" (Willard)

1976. Bicentenary of American Revolution.
868 **244** 200m. multicoloured . . . 1·40 65

245 Running

246 Girl reading Book

1976. Olympic Games, Montreal. Multicoloured.
870 50m. Type **245** 20 20
871 75m. Olympic flags and rings 35 20
872 120m. Olympic "dove" . . . 55 30

1976. Literature for Children.
873 **246** 100m. multicoloured . . . 45 20

247 Bird and Faces Emblem

248 Mausoleum, Tunis

1976. 15th Anniv of 1st Non-aligned Countries' Conference, Belgrade.
874 **247** 150m. multicoloured . . . 60 20

1976. Cultural Heritage. Multicoloured.
875 85m. Type **248** 35 20
876 100m. Great Mosque, Kairouan 40 20
877 150m. Ribat Monastery, Monastir 60 20
878 200m. Barber's Mosque, Kairouan 90 35

249 Emblem and Globe

1976. 25th Anniv of U.N. Postal Administration.
879 **249** 150m. multicoloured . . . 65 30

250 Red Crescent on Litter

1977. Tunisian Red Crescent.
880 **250** 50m.+10m. mult 40 35

251 Circuit Diagram

252 "Dialogue"

1977. World Telecommunications Day.
881 **251** 150m. multicoloured . . . 65 40

1977. 10th Anniv of International French Language Council.
882 **252** 100m. multicoloured . . . 80 35

253 Footballers

254 Gold Coin

1977. 1st World Junior Football Tournament.
883 **253** 150m. multicoloured . . . 90 45

1977. Cultural Patrimony. Multicoloured.
884 10m. Type **254** 10 10
885 15m. 13th-century stele . . . 15 15
886 20m. 17th-century illuminated manuscript 20 15
887 30m. Glass painting 35 20
888 40m. Ceramic pot decor . . . 40 20
889 50m. Gate, Sidi-Bou-Said . . 45 20

255 "The Young Republic"

257 Globe and Cogwheels

256 A.P.U. Emblem within Postmark

1977. 20th Anniv of Republic. Multicoloured.
890 40m. Type **255** 35 20
891 100m. "The Confident Republic" 40 20
892 150m. "The Determined Republic" 65 30

1977. 25th Anniv of Arab Postal Union.
894 **256** 40m. multicoloured . . . 20 20

1977. World Rheumatism Year.
895 **257** 120m. brown, red & black 65 35

258 Harvester and Rural Cameos

1977. Rural Development.
896 **258** 40m. multicoloured . . . 35 20

259 Factory Workers

260 Pres. Bourguiba and Flaming Torch within "9"

1978. Employment Priority Plan. Multicoloured.
897 20m. Forms of transport and driver (horiz) 85 55
898 40m. Tractor driver and farm workers (horiz) 20 20
899 100m. Type **259** 45 30

1978. 40th Anniv of 9 April Revolution.
900 **260** 40m. green, brown & olive 20 20
901 – 60m. red, brown and black 20 20
DESIGN: 60m. Pres. Bourguiba within figure "9".

261 Policeman in Safety Helmet

262 "Blood Donors"

1978. 6th African Regional Interpol Conference.
902 **261** 150m. multicoloured . . . 80 35

1978. Tunisian Red Crescent.
903 **262** 50m.+10m. mult 45 30

263 Goalkeeper catching World Cup Emblem

264 Hammer and Chisel chipping away Apartheid

1978. World Cup Football Championship, Argentina. Multicoloured.
904 40m. Type **263** 30 20
905 150m. Footballer, map and flags 85 35

1978. International Anti-Apartheid Year. Mult.
906 50m. Type **264** 20 20
907 100m. Black and white doves 45 30

265 Flora, Fauna and Polluting Factory

266 Crane removing Smallpox from Globe

1978. Protection of Nature and the Environment. Multicoloured.
908 10m. Type **265** 15 15
909 50m. "Pollution of the oceans" 40 20
910 120m. "Making the deserts green" 95 20

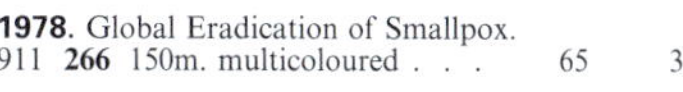

1978. Global Eradication of Smallpox.
911 **266** 150m. multicoloured . . . 65 35

267 Zlass Horseman

268 Lenin Banner

1978. Calligraphy, Art and Traditions. Mult.
912 5m. Type **267** 10 10
913 60m. Djerba wedding 30 15
914 75m. Women potters from the Mogods 40 15
915 100m. Dove over cupolas of Marabout Sidi Mahrez . . 45 20
916 500m. Opening of the ploughing season, Jenduba 3·25 1·00
917 1d. Man on swing between palm trees (Spring Festival, Tozeur) . . . . 5·50 2·25

1978. 60th Anniv of Russian Revolution.
918 **268** 150m. multicoloured . . . 1·10 45

269 Farhat Hached
270 Family Group

1978. Farhat Hached (Trade Union leader). Commemoration.
919 **269** 50m. multicoloured . . . 35 10

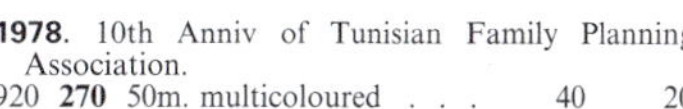

1978. 10th Anniv of Tunisian Family Planning Association.
920 **270** 50m. multicoloured . . . 40 20

271 "The Sun"

273 Hand holding Bird

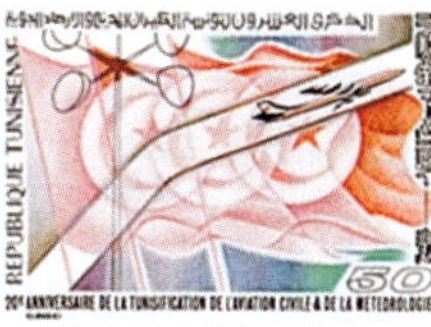
272 Boeing 747 and Flags

1978. Solar Energy.
921 **271** 100m. multicoloured . . . 60 20

1978. 20th Anniv of Tunisian Civil Aeronautics and Meteorology.
922 **272** 50m. multicoloured . . . 30 20

1979. Tunisian Red Crescent.
923 **273** 50m.+10m. mult 40 30

274 Pres. Bourguiba

275 Sun, Yacht and Golfer

1979. 20th Anniv of Constitution.
924 **274** 50m. brown, yellow & black 20 20

1979. Inauguration of El Kantaoui Port.
925 **275** 150m. multicoloured . . . 65 30

276 Korbous

277 Bow-net Making

1979. Tunisian Landscapes. Multicoloured.
926 50m. Type **276** 15 10
927 100m. Mides 35 15

1979. Crafts. Multicoloured.
928 10m. Type **277** 15 10
929 50m. Bee-keeping 35 10

278 Pres. Bourguiba and "10"

279 Dish Aerial and Satellite

1979. 10th Congress of Socialist Destourian Party.
930 **278** 50m. multicoloured . . . 30 10

1979. 3rd World Telecommunications Exhibition, Geneva.
931 **279** 150m. multicoloured . . . 65 35

280 World Map, Koran and Symbols of Arab Achievements

281 Children crossing Road

1979. The Arabs.
932 **280** 50m. multicoloured . . . 20 15

1979. International Year of the Child. Mult.
933 50m. Type **281** 20 15
934 100m. Child, fruit and birds 50 20

282 Dove and Olive Tree

283 Symbolic Figure

1979. 2nd World Olive-oil Year.
935 **282** 150m. multicoloured . . . 80 35

1979. 20th Anniv of Central Bank of Tunisia.
936 **283** 50m. multicolourd 20 20

284 Children and Jujube Tree

1979. Animals and Plants. Multicoloured.
937 20m. Type **284** 20 10
938 30m. Common peafowl . . . 40 25
939 70m. Goat 65 20
940 85m. Girl and date palm . . 70 20

285 Coded Letter

1980. Introduction of Postal Coding.
941 **285** 50m. multicoloured . . . 30 20

286 Smoker

1980. World Health Day. Anti-smoking Campaign.
942 **286** 150m. multicoloured . . . 65 30

287 Red Crescent and Globe forming an Eye

288 President Bourguiba, Flower and Open Book

1980. Tunisian Red Crescent.
943 **287** 50m.+10m. mult 40 30

1980. 25th Anniv of Victory and Return of President Bourguiba. Multicoloured.
944 50m. Type **288** 20 20
945 100m. Pres. Bourguiba, dove and mosque 85 35

289 Gymnast as Butterfly

290 Tools

1980. Turin Gymnastic Games.
946 **289** 100m. multicoloured . . . 45 20

1980. Handicrafts. Multicoloured.
947 30m. Type **290** 30 20
948 75m. Woman embroidering 40 20

291 Ibn Khaldoun (philosopher)

292 Avicenna

1980. Ibn Khaldoun Commemoration.
949 **291** 50m. multicoloured . . . 20 20

1980. Birth Millenary of Avicenna (philosopher).
950 **292** 100m. sepia and brown 65 35

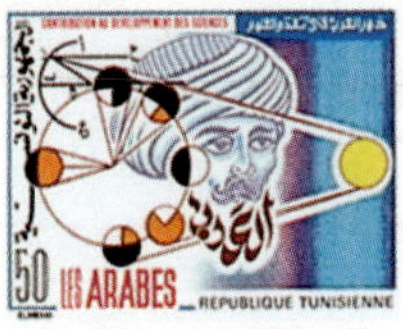

293 Al-Biruni and Scientific Diagram

1980. The Arabs' Contribution to Science.
951 **293** 50m. multicoloured . . . 35 20

294 Yachts at Sidi Bou Said

1980. Sidi Bou Said.
952 **294** 100m. multicoloured . . . 65 35

295 "Tourists"

1980. World Tourism Conference, Manila.
953 **295** 150m. multicoloured . . . 55 20

296 "Wedding at Djerba"

1980. Yahia (painter) Commemoration.
954 **296** 50m. multicoloured . . . 40 30

297 Aircraft over Tozeur

299 Spider's Web

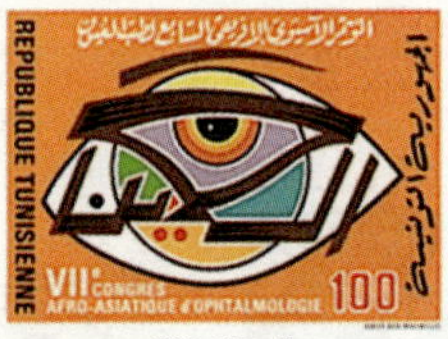

298 "Eye"

1980. Opening of Tozeur International Airport.
955 **297** 85m. multicoloured . . . 35 20

1980. 7th Afro-Asian Congress on Ophthalmology.
956 **298** 100m. multicoloured . . . 55 35

1980. 1400th Anniv of Hegira. Multicoloured.
957 50m. Type **299** 20 20
958 80m. Minarets 35 20

300 Face as Camera

1980. Carthage Cinematographic Days.
959 **300** 100m. multicoloured . . . 45 30

301 "Ophrys scolopax scolopax"

1980. Flora and Fauna. Multicoloured.
960 20m. Type **301** 20 20
961 25m. "Cyclamen europaeum" 20 20
962 50m. Mouflon 20 20
963 100m. Golden eagle 90 40

302 Kairouan Mosque

1980. Conservation of Kairouan.
964 **302** 85m. multicoloured . . . 35 20

303 H. von Stephan

304 Hands holding Bottle containing Blood Drop

1981. 150th Birth Anniv of Heinrich von Stephan (founder of U.P.U.).
965 **303** 150m. multicoloured . . . 65 35

1981. 20th Anniv of Tunisian Blood Donors Association.
966 **304** 75m. multicoloured . . . 65 45

305 Flags and Pres. Bourguiba

1981. 25th Anniv of Independence. Multicoloured.
967 50m. Type **305** 20 20
968 60m. Stork and ribbons forming "25" 35 20
969 85m. Stylized birds 55 35
970 120m. Victory riding a winged horse 55 35

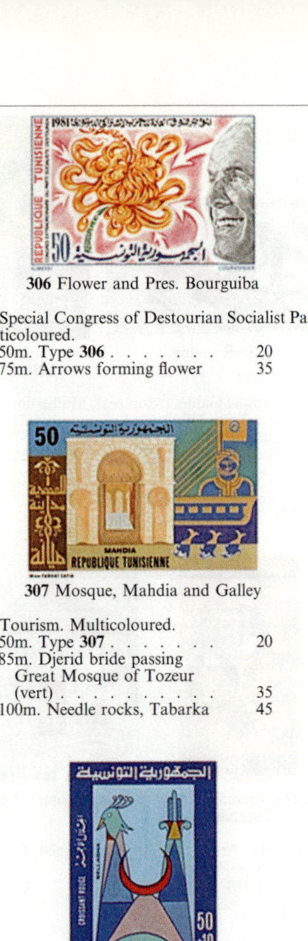

306 Flower and Pres. Bourguiba

1981. Special Congress of Destourian Socialist Party. Multicoloured.
972 50m. Type **306** 20 15
973 75m. Arrows forming flower 35 20

307 Mosque, Mahdia and Galley

1981. Tourism. Multicoloured.
974 50m. Type **307** 20 20
975 85m. Djerid bride passing Great Mosque of Tozeur (vert) 35 30
976 100m. Needle rocks, Tabarka 45 30

308 Stylized Peacock hatching Egg

1981. Red Crescent.
977 **308** 50m.+10m. mult 35 35

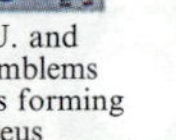

309 I.T.U. and W.H.O. Emblems and Ribbons forming Caduceus

310 Flowers and Youths

1981. World Telecommunications Day.
978 **309** 150m. multicoloured . . . 60 30

1981. Youth Festival.
979 **310** 100m. multicoloured . . . 45 20

311 Kemal Ataturk

312 Skifa Khala, Mahdia

1981. Birth Centenary of Kemal Ataturk.
980 **311** 150m. multicoloured . . . 65 35

1981. Tunisian Monuments.
981 **312** 150m. multicoloured . . . 65 35

313 Cheikh Mohamed Tahar ben Achour and Minaret

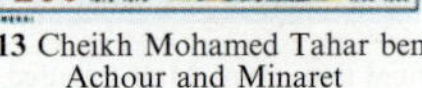

1981. Cheikh Mohamed Tahar ben Achour (scholar and teacher) Commemoration.
982 **313** 200m. multicoloured . . . 1·00 45

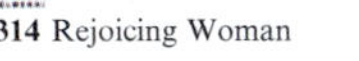

314 Rejoicing Woman **315** Tree with Broken Branch

1981. 25th Anniv of Personal Status Code. Multicoloured.
983 50m. Type **314** 20 20
984 100m. Dove and head of woman 40 30

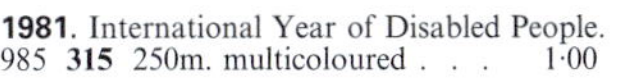

1981. International Year of Disabled People.
985 **315** 250m. multicoloured . . . 1·00 65

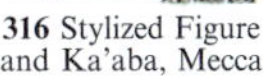

316 Stylized Figure and Ka'aba, Mecca **317** Food Sources

1981. Pilgrimage to Mecca.
986 **316** 50m. multicoloured . . . 30 20

1981. World Food Day.
987 **317** 200m. multicoloured . . . 90 50

318 Dome of the Rock

1981. Palestinian Welfare.
988 **318** 50m.+5m. mult 35 20
989 150m.+5m. mult 60 35
990 200m.+5m. mult 90 50

319 Mnaguech (earring) **321** Chemist (detail from 13th-century manuscript)

320 Ship passing under Bridge

1981. Jewellery. Multicoloured.
991 150m. Type **319** 60 30
992 180m. Mahfdha (pendant) (horiz) 70 35
993 200m. Essalta (hairnet) . . . 90 40

1981. Bizerta Drawbridge.
994 **320** 230m. multicoloured . . . 80 40

1982. Arab Pharmacists' Union.
995 **321** 80m. multicoloured . . . 55 35

322 Ring of People around Red Crescent

1982. Red Crescent.
996 **322** 80m.+10m. mult 40 30

323 "Ocean Research" **324** "Productive Family"

1982. International Symposium "Ocean Venture", Tunis.
997 **323** 150m. multicoloured . . . 80 45

1982. The Productive Family.
998 **324** 80m. multicoloured . . . 35 20

325 Pres. Bourguiba and Woman's Head **326** Scout within "50"

1982. 25th Anniv of Republic.
999 **325** 80m. blue and black . . 30 20
1000 – 100m. multicoloured . . 40 30
1001 – 200m. multicoloured . . 65 35
DESIGNS: 100m. President and woman with "XXV" headband; 200m. President and woman with "25" in hair.

1982. 75th Anniv of Scout Movement and 50th Anniv of Tunisian Scout Movement. Multicoloured.
1003 80m. Type **326** 35 20
1004 200m. Scout camp (vert) . . 65 20

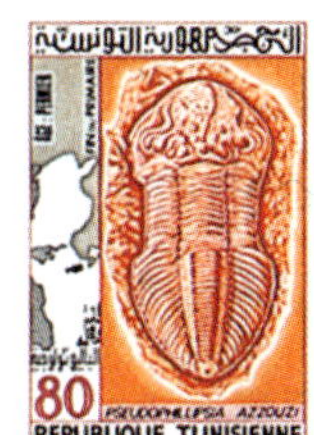

327 "Pseudophillipsia azzouzi" **328** Tunisian Woman

1982. Fossils. Multicoloured.
1005 80m. Type **327** 45 35
1006 200m. "Mediterraneo-trigonia cherahilensis" . . 1·40 65
1007 280m. "Numidiopleura enigmatica" (fish) (horiz) 2·50 1·40
1008 300m. "Micreschara tunisiensis" . . . . 2·00 1·40
1009 500m. "Mantelliceras pervinquieri" . . . . . . 3·75 2·00
1010 1000m. "Elephas africanavus" (horiz) . . . 6·25 3·00

1982. 30th Anniv of Arab Postal Union.
1011 **328** 80m. multicoloured . . . 40 20

329 I.T.U. Emblem **330** Tunisian Buildings and Congress Centre

1982. I.T.U. Delegates' Conference, Nairobi.
1012 **329** 200m. multicoloured . . 65 45

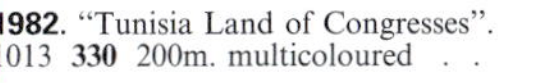

1982. "Tunisia Land of Congresses".
1013 **330** 200m. multicoloured . . 65 30

331 "Feeding the World" **332** Tahar Haddad

1982. World Food Day.
1014 **331** 200m. multicoloured . . 65 30

1982. Tahar Haddad (social reformer) Commem.
1015 **332** 200m. brown 80 35

333 Microscope **334** Figure dancing in Rain

1982. Cent of Discovery of Tubercle Bacillus.
1016 **333** 100m. multicoloured . . 55 30

1982. Stories and Songs from Tunisia. Multicoloured.
1017 20m. Type **334** 15 15
1018 30m. Woman with broom 15 15
1019 70m. Boy and fisherman . . 20 15
1020 80m. Chicken (horiz) . . . 30 20
1021 100m. Woman admiring herself in mirror (horiz) 40 20
1022 120m. Two girls 45 30

335 Clasped Hands and Palestine Flag

1982. Palestinian Solidarity Day.
1023 **335** 80m. multicoloured . . . 30 20

336 Farhat Hached **337** Bourguiba Sidi Saad Dam

1982. 30th Death Anniv of Farhat Hached.
1024 **336** 80m. red 35 20

1982. Inauguration of Bourguiba Sidi Saad Dam.
1025 **337** 80m. multicoloured . . . 45 20

338 Environment Emblem on Blackboard **339** Giving Blood

1982. Opening of Environment Training Work School.
1026 **338** 80m. multicoloured . . . 35 15

1983. Red Crescent.
1027 **339** 80m.+10m. mult 50 30

340 "Communications"

1983. World Communications Year.
1028 **340** 200m. multicoloured . . 55 30

341 Dove and Map of Africa

1983. 20th Anniv of Organization of African Unity.
1029 **341** 230m. blue and deep blue 65 40

342 Customs Officer, Globes and Suitcases

1983. 20th Anniv of Customs Co-operation Council.
1030 **342** 100m. multicoloured . . 35 20

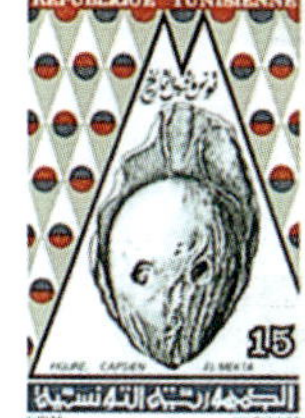

343 Aly Ben Ayed **344** Carved Face, El Mekta

1983. Aly Ben Ayed (actor) Commemoration.
1031 **343** 80m. red, black and deep red 30 30

1983. Pre-historic Artefacts. Multicoloured.
1032 15m. Type **344** 20 20
1033 20m. Neolithic necklace, Kef el Agab (horiz) 30 20
1034 30m. Neolithic grindstone, Redeyef (horiz) 30 20
1035 40m. Animal petroglyph, Gafsa 35 20
1036 80m. Dolmen, Mactar (horiz) 40 30
1037 100m. Bi-face flint, El Mekta 55 30

345 Dove, Barbed Wire and Dome of the Rock

1983. Palestinian Welfare.
1038 **345** 80m.+5m. mult 40 40

346 Sporting Activities

1983. Sport for All.
1039 **346** 40m. multicoloured . . . 15 10

347 Tunisian with Flag and "Destour" (French freighter)

1983. 20th Anniv of Evacuation of Foreign Troops.
1040 **347** 80m. multicoloured . . . 30 20

348 Fishing Boats and Fishes

1983. World Fishing Day.
1041 **348** 200m. multicoloured . . 1·00 25

349 "The Weaver" (Hedi Khayachi)

1983. Hedi Khayachi (painter) Commem.
1042 **349** 80m. multicoloured . . . 45 35

350 Saluting the Flag

351 Air Hostess and Airliner

1983. Salute to the Flag.
1043 **350** 100m. multicoloured . . 35 20

1983. 25th Anniv of Tunisian Civil Aviation and Meteorology.
1044 **351** 150m. multicoloured . . 55 20

352 Pres. Bourguiba and Archway

353 Map of Africa

1984. 50th Anniv of Neo-Destour Party. Mult.
1045 40m. Type **352** 15 10
1046 70m. Bourguiba and torch 20 10
1047 80m. Bourguiba and flag . . 30 15
1048 150m. Bourguiba and wall 50 30
1049 200m. Bourguiba and dove (horiz) 60 35
1050 230m. Pres. Bourguiba (horiz) 70 45

1984. 4th School of Molecular Biology.
1052 **353** 100m. multicoloured . . 55 30

354 First Aid

1984. Red Crescent.
1053 **354** 80m.+10m. mult 40 30

355 Ibn el Jazzar

356 "Co-operation"

1984. Ibn el Jazzar (doctor) Commem.
1054 **355** 80m. multicoloured . . . 40 30

1984. Economic Co-operation among Developing Countries.
1055 **356** 230m. multicoloured . . 80 35

357 Witch, Maiden and Coquette

1984. Stories and Songs from Tunisia. Mult.
1056 20m. Type **357** 10 10
1057 80m. Puppet, hands and mouse 30 20
1058 100m. Boy and horse (vert) 35 15

358 Family facing the Future

1984. 20th Anniv of Tunisian Education and Family Organization.
1059 **358** 80m. multicoloured . . . 30 20

359 Medina, Tunis

360 Aboul Qasim Chabbi

1984. National Heritage Protection.
1060 **359** 100m. multicoloured . . 35 30

1984. 50th Death Anniv of Aboul Qasim Chabbi (poet).
1061 **360** 100m. sepia, light brown and brown 35 20

361 Emblem, Stylized Bird and Airplane

1984. 40th Anniv of International Civil Aviation Organization.
1062 **361** 200m. multicoloured . . 65 20

362 Band and Singers

1984. Sahara Festival.
1063 **362** 20m. multicoloured . . . 45 20

363 Telephonist, Satellite and Dish Aerial

1984. 20th Anniv of "Intelsat" Communication Satellite.
1064 **363** 100m. multicoloured . . 35 15

364 "Mediterranean Countryside"

1984. Jilani Abdulwahelb (artist) Commem.
1065 **364** 100m. multicoloured . . 55 35

365 Profile and Exterior of House

366 Crescents and Stars within Circle

1985. "Expo 85" World's Fair, Tsukuba.
1066 **365** 200m. multicoloured . . 65 35

1985. Red Crescent.
1067 **366** 100m.+10m. mult . . . 35 30

367 Hands reaching from Sea and Flames

368 Pres. Bourguiba on Horseback

1985. 3rd Civil Protection Week.
1068 **367** 100m. multicoloured . . 30 15

1985. 30th Anniv of Independence. Mult.
1069 75m. Type **368** 20 10
1070 100m. Pres. Bourguiba in boat and crowd on quay (horiz) 30 10
1071 200m. Pres. Bourguiba in sombrero 55 20
1072 230m. Pres. Bourguiba waving to crowd from balcony (horiz) 60 20

369 Pres. Bourguiba and Ancient Sculpture

1985. Tunisian Day at "Expo '85" World's Fair, Tsukuba.
1074 **369** 250m. multicoloured . . 80 30

370 Images within Film

372 Heart as Dove and I.Y.Y. Emblem

371 Dark Clouds, Sun and Flowers

1985. International Amateur Film Festival, Kelibia.
1075 **370** 250m. multicoloured . . 1·50 1·10

1985. Stories and Songs from Tunisia. Multicoloured.
1076 25m. Type **371** 10 10
1077 50m. Man's profile and hand holding women . . 15 10
1078 100m. Man and cooking pot over fire 35 15

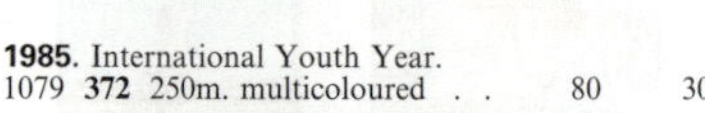

1985. International Youth Year.
1079 **372** 250m. multicoloured . . 80 30

373 "The Perfumiers Hall"

1985. Painting by Hedi Larnaout.
1080 **373** 100m. multicoloured . . 45 20

374 Matmata Wedding Dress

375 Stylized People and U.N. Emblem

1985. Wedding Dresses (1st series). Mult.
1081 20m. Type **374** 10 10
1082 50m. Moknine dress 15 10
1083 100m. Tunis dress 35 15
See also Nos. 1099/1101.

1985. 40th Anniv of U.N.O.
1084 **375** 250m. multicoloured . . 80 30

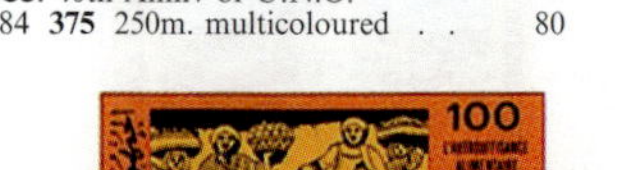

376 Harvest (Makthar stele)

1985. Food Self-sufficiency.
1085 **376** 100m. multicoloured . . 35 20

377 Emblem illuminating Globe and Flags

378 Aziza Othmana

1985. 40th Anniv of Arab League.
1086 **377** 100m. multicoloured . . 30 15

1985. Aziza Othmana (founder of hospitals) Commemoration.
1087 **378** 100m. brown, green and red 45 20

379 Surveying Instruments and Books forming Face

380 Dove and Pres. Bourguiba

1985. Centenary of Land Law.
1088 **379** 100m. multicoloured . . 30 10

1986. 30th Anniv of Independence.
1089 **380** 100m. multicoloured . . 30 10
1090 – 120m. black, blue and deep blue 35 15
1091 – 280m. blue, violet and black 80 35
1092 – 300m. multicoloured . . 85 40
DESIGNS—HORIZ: 120m. Rocket; 280m. Horse and rider. VERT: 300m. Balloons.

381 Hulusi Behcet (dermatologist) **382** Map and Red Crescent

1986. 3rd Mediterranean Rheumatology Days, Tunis, and Ninth International Society of Geographical Ophthalmology Congress, Monastir. Multicoloured.

1094 300m. Type **381** . . . . . . 1·25 35
1095 380m. Behcet and sun and eye emblems . . . . . . 1·60 45

1986. World Red Crescent and Red Cross Day.

1096 **382** 120m.+10m. mult . . . 40 30

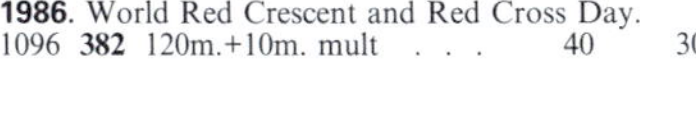

383 Pres. Bourguiba, Symbols and "12"

1986. 12th Destourian Socialist Party Congress, Tunis. Multicoloured.

1097 120m. Type **383** 30 10
1098 300m. Flaming torch, Pres. Bourguiba and "12" . . . 85 30

384 Homt Souk Dress **385** Hassen Husni Abdulwaheb

1986. Wedding Dresses (2nd series). Mult.

1099 40m. Type **384** 10 10
1100 280m. Mahdia dress 80 30
1101 300m. Nabeul dress 90 35

1986. Hassen Husni Abdulwaheb (historian) Commemoration.

1102 **385** 160m. red 55 20

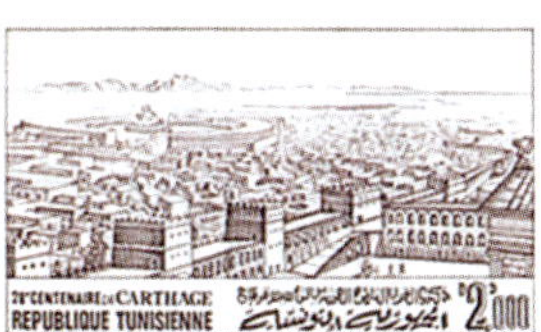

386 Reconstructed View of Carthage

1986. 2800th Anniv of Foundation of Carthage.

1103 **386** 2d. purple . . . . 6·75 2·50

387 Arrow Head, El Borma, 3000 B.C. **388** "Bedouins"

1986. Prehistoric Artefacts. Multicoloured.

1104 10m. Type **387** 20 20
1105 20m. Tomb, Sejnane, 1000 B.C. 20 20
1106 50m. Bas-relief, Zaghouan, 1000 B.C. (horiz) 35 20
1107 120m. Neolithic vase, Kesra (horiz) 55 20
1108 160m. Painting of Phoenician ship, Kef el Blida, 800 B.C. (horiz) . . 65 20
1109 250m. 7th-century decorated pottery, Sejnane . . . . . 1·40 35

1986. Painting by Ammar Farhat.

1110 **388** 250m. multicoloured . . 1·25 35

389 Doves and Globe

1986. International Peace Year.

1111 **389** 300m. multicoloured . . 85 35

390 Emblem **391** Computer Terminal

1986. 40th Anniv of F.A.O.

1112 **390** 280m. multicoloured . . 80 30

1986. Introduction of Computers into Education.

1113 **391** 2d. multicoloured . . . 6·75 2·50

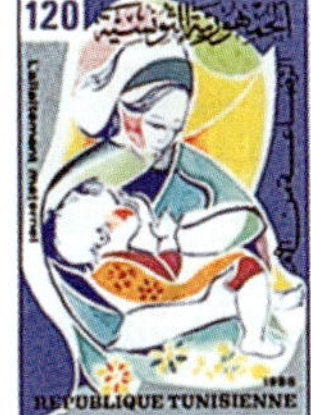

392 Mother and Child **393** Mountain Gazelle (Chambi National Park)

1986. Child Survival.

1114 **392** 120m. multicoloured . . 35 10

1986. National Parks. Multicoloured.

1115 60m. Type **393** 15 10
1116 120m. Addax (Bou Hedma National Park) 30 10
1117 350m. Monk seal (Zembra and Zembretta National Park) 85 30
1118 380m. Greylag goose (Ichkeul National Park) 1·25 40

394 Pres. Bourguiba and Arms

1987. Centenary of Monastir Municipality.

1119 **394** 120m. multicoloured . . 35 15

395 Radiation and Red Crescent Symbols in Face

1987. Radiation Protection and Red Crescent.

1120 **395** 150m.+10m. mult . . . 55 45

396 Samuel Morse (inventor) and Morse Key

1987. 150th Anniv of Morse Telegrarph.

1121 **396** 500m. multicoloured . . 1·40 55

397 Pres. Bourguiba and Woman's Head

1987. 30th Anniv of Republic. Designs each show Pres. Bourguiba and a different woman's head.

1122 **397** 150m. mve, brn and yell 35 25
1123 – 250m. brown, red & yell 55 25
1124 – 350m. blue, brn & grn 80 20
1125 – 500m. multicoloured . . 1·10 35

398 Hand injecting Baby in Globe and Dove holding Syringe **399** "The Road"

1987. Universal Vaccination for Everyone by 1990. 40th Anniv of United Nations Children's Fund.

1127 **398** 250m. multicoloured . . 65 45

1987. 25th Death Anniv of Azouz Ben Rais (painter).

1128 **399** 250m. multicoloured . . 90 45

400 Couple's Faces in House

1987. Arab Housing Day.

1129 **400** 150m. multicoloured . . 40 30

401 Dove carrying Parcel **402** Ibn Mandhour

1987. 30th Anniv of Consultative Postal Studies Council. Multicoloured.

1130 150m. Type **401** 35 10
1131 350m. Postman and electronically sorted letters 80 30

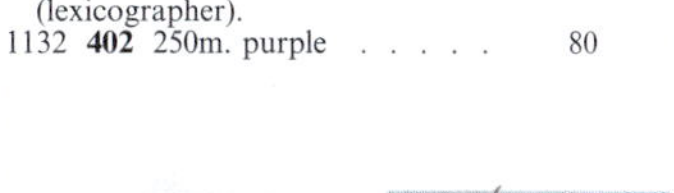

1987. 675th Death Anniv of Ibn Mandhour (lexicographer).

1132 **402** 250m. purple 80 45

403 Bunches of Grapes **404** Player with Ball

1987. International Vine Year.

1133 **403** 250m. multicoloured . . 80 35

1987. 6th African Nations Volleyball Championship, Tunis.

1134 **404** 350m. multicoloured . . 1·10 45

405 Players and Ball **406** Tunis Institute and Adrien Loir (first director)

1987. African Basketball Championships.

1135 **405** 350m. multicoloured . . 1·40 45

1987. Centenary of Pasteur Institute, Paris.

1136 **406** 250m. green, brown and black 80 35

407 Midoun **408** Narcissi

1987. Costumes. Multicoloured.

1137 20m. Type **407** 10 10
1138 30m. Tozeur 10 10
1139 150m. Sfax 40 15

1987. Flowers. Multicoloured.

1140 30m. Type **408** 10 10
1141 150m. Gladioli 40 15
1142 400m. Iris . . . . 1·00 35
1143 500m. Tulips . . . . 1·50 55

409 Hand holding Scales of Justice

1988. Declaration of 7 November 1987. Mult.

1144 150m. Type **409** (Justice for all) 35 20
1145 200m. Girl with party badges as flowers in hair (Multi-party system) (vert) 45 20
1146 350m. Girl in cornfield wearing coat of arms (International co-operation and friendship) 80 35
1147 370m. Maghreb states emblem (vert) 90 35

410 Couple

1988. Youth and Change. Multicoloured.

1149 75m. Type **410** 20 15
1150 150m. Young people 35 15

411 Crowd with Banners

1988. 50th Anniv of Martyrs' Day.

1151 **411** 150m. orange and brown 35 15
1152 – 500m. multicoloured . . 1·40 40

DESIGN: 500m. Martyrs monument.

412 Roses and Banners

1988. 125th Anniv of Red Cross.

1153 **412** 150m.+10m. mult . . . 45 35

413 Hand saving drowning Country

1988. 1st Democratic Constitutional Assembly Congress.
1154 **413** 150m. multicoloured . . 35 15

414 Sportsmen

1988. Olympic Games, Seoul. Multicoloured.
1155 150m. Type **414** 40 20
1156 430m. Sportsman (different) 1·00 45

415 Beit Hussein Sari and Eye

416 "7" and Flowers

1988. Restoration of Sana'a, Yemen.
1157 **415** 200m. multicoloured . . 45 20

1988. 1st Anniv of Presidency of Zine el Abidine.
1158 **416** 150m. multicoloured . . 35 15

417 "Amilcar Beach, 1942"

1988. 70th Birth Anniv of Amara Debbeche (painter).
1159 **417** 100m. multicoloured . . 35 20

418 Boeing 747 and Globe forming "40"

419 Man holding Book

1988. 40th Anniv of Tunis Air.
1160 **418** 500m. multicoloured . . 1·50 70

1988. 40th Anniv of Declaration of Human Rights.
1161 **419** 370m. black 85 45

420 Tweezers and Magnifying Glasses forming "100"

1988. Cent of First Tunisian Postage Stamps.
1162 **420** 150m. multicoloured . . 55 30

421 18th-century Door, Rue du Tresor

422 Ali Douagi

1988. Tunis Doorways and Fountains. Mult.
1163 50m. Type **421** 10 10
1164 70m. 19th-century door, Rue el Mbazaa 15 10
1165 100m. 15th-16th century door, Rue des Fabricants de Tamis 20 10
1166 150m. 19th-century door, Rue Bach Hamba 30 15
1167 370m. 16th-17th century door, Rue el Ariane . . . 70 30
1168 400m. Fountain, Manouba, 1793 . . . . 80 35

1989. 40th Death Anniv of Ali Douagi (writer).
1169 **422** 1d. blue . . . . 2·50 65

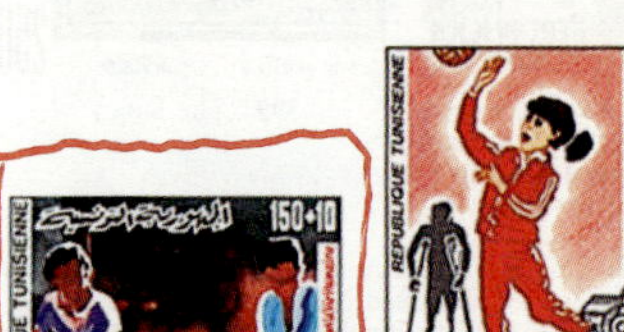

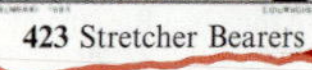

423 Stretcher Bearers

424 Crippled Person and Healthy Girl

1989. Red Crescent.
1170 **423** 150m.+10m. mult . . . 40 30

1989. National Day for Disabled People.
1171 **424** 150m. multicoloured . . 45 20

425 Children using Computer and Microscope

1989. Knowledge Day.
1172 **425** 180m. multicoloured . . 40 20

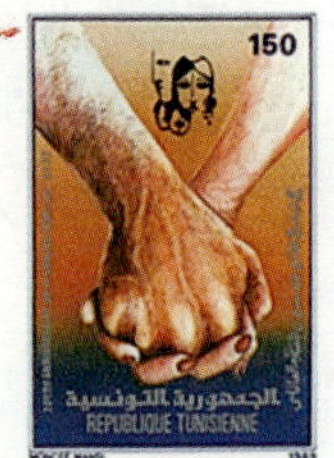

426 Clasped Hands

1989. 20th Anniv of Tunisian Family Planning Association.
1173 **426** 150m. multicoloured . . 35 15

427 Family

1989. Family Welfare.
1174 **427** 150m. multicoloured . . 35 15

428 Tortoise

1989. Endangered Animals. Multicoloured.
1175 250m. Type **428** 65 35
1176 350m. Oryx . . . . 1·00 45

429 Flags and Emblem

430 Beyram

1989. Tunis International Fair (1990). Mult.
1177 150m. Type **429** 35 15
1178 370m. Fair Pavilion 80 35

1989. Death Centenary of Mohamed Beyram (writer).
1179 **430** 150m. purple and black 35 15

431 Actors wearing Comedy Masks

432 Monument, Tunis

1989. Carthage Theatre Festival.
1180 **431** 300m. multicoloured . . 65 35

1989. 2nd Anniv of Declaration of 7 November 1987.
1181 **432** 150m. multicoloured . . 35 20

433 Nehru

434 Members' Flags

1989. Birth Centenary of Jawaharlal Nehru (Indian statesman).
1182 **433** 300m. brown 65 35

1990. Maghreb Union Presidential Summit.
1183 **434** 200m. multicoloured . . 45 30

435 Museum and Sculptures

1990. Centenary of Bardo Museum.
1184 **435** 300m. multicoloured . . 80 45

436 Ceramic Tiles, Vases and Crockery

1990. Arts and Crafts. Multicoloured.
1185 75m. Type **436** 15 10
1186 100m. Copper pots and grinder 20 15

437 Ram and Ewes

1990. Ram Museum. Multicoloured.
1187 400m. Type **437** 90 35
1188 450m. Ram's head . . . . 1·25 45

438 Houses within Crescent

440 Child's Drawing

439 Olympic Rings and Athlete

1990. Red Crescent.
1190 **438** 150m.+10m. mult . . . 35 20

1990. Tunisian Olympic Movement.
1191 **439** 150m. multicoloured . . 35 15

1990. The Child and the Environment.
1192 **440** 150m. multicoloured . . 35 15

441 Sbiba Horseman

442 Dougga

1990. Costumes. Multicoloured.
1193 150m. Type **441** 45 35
1194 500m. Bou Omrane man . . 1·40 65

1990. Tourism.
1195 **442** 300m. multicoloured . . 65 35

443 Adults learning to Read and Write

1990. International Literacy Year.
1196 **443** 120m. multicoloured . . 30 15

444 Figures, Tree and Fishes in Water

445 Fireworks and Date

1990. Water.
1197 **444** 150m. multicoloured . . 45 30

1990. 3rd Anniv of Declaration of 7 November 1987. Multicoloured.
1198 150m. Type **445** 35 15
1199 150m. Clock tower 35 15

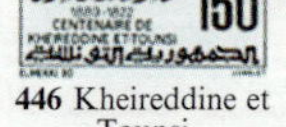

446 Kheireddine et Tounsi

447 Red Deer

1990. Death Centenary of Kheireddine et Tounsi (political reformer).
1200 **446** 150m. green 45 20

1990. Flora and Fauna. Multicoloured.
1201 150m. Type **447** 35 15
1202 200m. Thistle 45 15
1203 300m. Water buffalo 65 20
1204 600m. Orchid . . . . 1·40 55

448 Members' Flags forming Stars
449 Montazah Tabarka

1991. 2nd Anniv of Maghreb Union.
1205 **448** 180m. multicoloured . . 45 20

1991. Tourism.
1206 **449** 450m. multicoloured . . 1·00 45

450 Doves and Emblem
451 Common Seabream

1991. Red Crescent. Help for War Victims.
1207 **450** 180m.+10m. mult . . . 45 35

1991. Fishes. Multicoloured.
1208 180m. Type **451** 65 30
1209 350m. Striped red mullet . . 1·25 55
1210 450m. Atlantic mackerel . . 1·60 65
1211 550m. Common pandora . . 2·00 1·00

452 Vase of Flowers (Taieb Khlif)

1991. Children's Rights.
1212 **452** 450m. multicoloured . . 1·25 35

453 "Plein-Sud" (anon.)

1991.
1213 **453** 400m. multicoloured . . 90 35

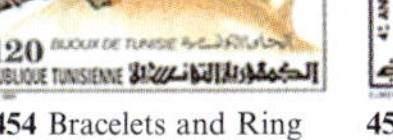
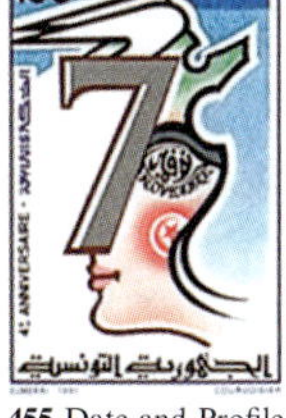

454 Bracelets and Ring
455 Date and Profile of Woman

1991. Jewellery. Multicoloured.
1214 120m. Type **454** 30 15
1215 180m. Headdress and necklace (vert) 40 15
1216 220m. Headdress, earrings and collar (vert) 45 20
1217 730m. Key-ring (vert) . . . 2·25 80

1991. 4th Anniv of Declaration of 7 November 1987.
1218 **455** 180m. multicoloured . . 45 20

456 Sorting Office

1991. Tunis-Carthage Sorting Office.
1219 **456** 80m. blue, red and green 20 10

457 Dove and Globe
458 Bayram Ettounsi

1991. World Human Rights Day.
1220 **457** 450m. blue . . . . . . 1·25 35

1991. 31st Death Anniv of Bayram Ettounsi.
1221 **458** 200m. blue 45 15

459 Emblem on Microchip
460 G.P.O.

1992. "Expo '92" World's Fair, Seville.
1222 **459** 180m. multicoloured . . 45 20

1992. Centenary of General Post Office, Tunis.
1223 **460** 180m. brown 45 20
1224 – 450m. brown . . . . . 1·25 35
DESIGN—VERT: 450m. Different view of G.P.O.

461 "When the Subconscious Awakes" (Moncef ben Amor)

1992.
1225 **461** 500m. multicoloured . . 1·40 45

462 Running
463 European Bee Eater

1992. Olympic Games, Barcelona. Multicoloured.
1226 180m. Type **462** 65 30
1227 450m. Judo (vert) . . . . . 1·60 55

1992. Birds. Multicoloured.
1228 100m. Type **463** 55 20
1229 180m. Eurasian goldfinch 80 40
1230 200m. European serin . . . 1·10 40
1231 500m. Western greenfinch 2·50 95

464 President and Children
465 Women and Open Book

1992. United Nations Convention on Rights of the Child.
1233 **464** 180m. multicoloured . . 45 30

1992. African Regional Human Rights Conference, Tunis.
1234 **465** 480m. multicoloured . . 1·50 65

466 Ribbon forming "7"
467 "Acacia tortilis"

1992. 5th Anniv of Declaration of 7 November 1987. Multicoloured.
1235 180m. Type **466** 45 20
1236 730m. President with people and doves . . . . 2·10 90

1992. National Tree Day.
1237 **467** 180m. multicoloured . . 45 30

468 Stylized Figure and Emblems

1992. International Nutrition Conference, Rome.
1238 **468** 450m. multicoloured . . 1·50 55

469 Chemesse
470 "Billy Goat between Two Bushes" (El Jem)

1992. Traditional Costumes. Multicoloured.
1239 100m. Type **469** 30 20
1240 350m. Hanifites 85 45

1992. Mosaics. Multicoloured.
1241 100m. Type **470** 30 15
1242 180m. "Wild Duck" (El Jem) 75 35
1243 350m. "Racehorse" (Sidi Abdallah) . . . . 1·25 45
1244 450m. "Gazelle in the Grass" (El Jem) . . . . . 1·40 70

471 Wolf

1992. Flora and Fauna. Multicoloured.
1245 20m. Type **471** 10 10
1246 60m. "Hoya carnosa" (plant) (vert) 10 10

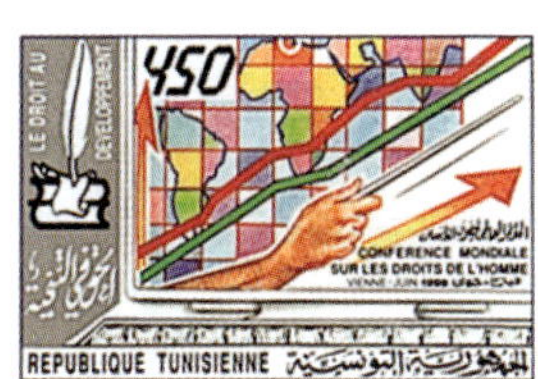

472 Line Graph on World Map

1993. United Nations World Conference on Human Rights, Vienna.
1247 **472** 450m. multicoloured . . 1·40 60

473 Publicity Poster inside Open Brief-case
474 "Relaxing on the Patio" (Ali Guermassi)

1993. Arab-African Fair, Tunis.
1248 **473** 450m. multicoloured . . 1·25 30

1993.
1249 **474** 450m. multicoloured . . 1·25 30

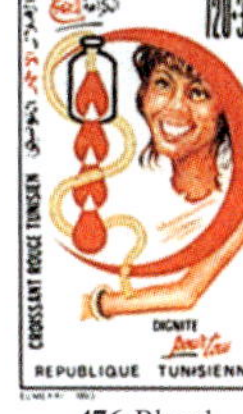

475 Conference Emblem
476 Blood Transfusion

1993. Constitutional Democratic Assembly Party Conference.
1250 **475** 180m. red and black . . 50 15

1993. Red Crescent. "Dignity for All".
1251 **476** 120m.+30m. mult . . . 60 35

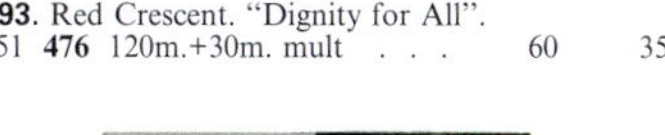

477 Louis Pasteur and Charles Nicolle (former director)

1993. Centenary of Pasteur Institute, Tunis.
1252 **477** 450m. multicoloured . . 1·40 60

478 "7"
479 Carpet

1993. 6th Anniv of Declaration of 7 November 1987. Multicoloured.
1253 180m. Type **478** 50 15
1254 450m. "7"s and waves . . . 1·25 50

1993. Kairouan Carpets.
1255 **479** 100m. multicoloured . . 15 10
1256 – 120m. multicoloured . . 15 10
1257 – 180m. multicoloured . . 50 15
1258 – 350m. multicoloured . . 1·10 60
DESIGNS: 120m. to 350m. Different carpets.

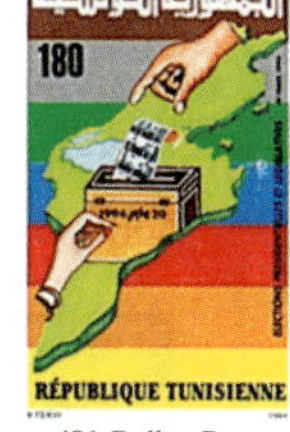

480 Boy with Guitar (Donia Haik)
481 Ballot Box, Hands and Map

1993. School Cultural Activities. Children's drawings. Multicoloured.
1259 180m. Type **480** 50 15
1260 180m. Painting and reading (Anissa Chatbouri) (horiz) 50 15

1994. Presidential and Legislative Elections.
1261 **481** 180m. multicoloured . . 50 15

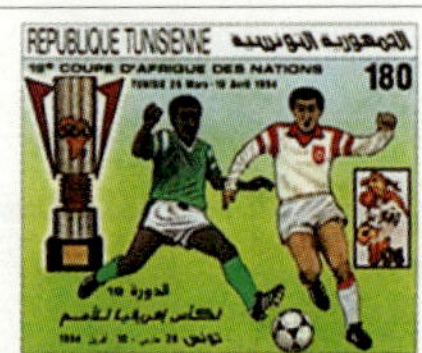
482 Players, Trophy and Mascot

1994. African Nations Cup Football Championship. Multicoloured.
1262 180m. Type **482** 50 15
1263 350m. Trophy, goalkeeper making save and mascot 1·00 25
1264 450m. Map of Africa, Olympic Rings, player, trophy and mascot . . . 1·25 60

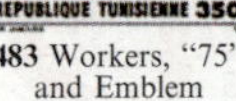

483 Workers, "75" and Emblem **484** Family within House

1994. 75th Anniv of I.L.O.
1265 **483** 350m. multicoloured . . 1·10 25

1994. International Year of the Family.
1266 **484** 180m. multicoloured . . 50 15

485 President Ben Ali **486** Blackthorn

1994. Re-election of President Zine el Abidine Ben Ali.
1267 **485** 180m. multicoloured . . 50 15
1268 350m. multicoloured . . 1·00 75

1994. Plants. Multicoloured.
1270 50m. Type **486** 10 10
1271 100m. "Xeranthemum inapertum" 15 10
1272 200m. "Orchis simia" . . . 60 15
1273 1d. "Scilla peruviana" . . . 2·75 1·50

487 Dove and Emblem

1994. 30th Organization of African Unity Summit Meeting, Tunis.
1274 **487** 480m. multicoloured . . 1·40 60

488 Torch with Map as Flame and Centenary Emblem

1994. Centenary of International Olympic Committee.
1275 **488** 450m. multicoloured . . 1·50 60

489 Pencil and Postal and Tourism Motifs

1994. "Philakorea 1994" International Stamp Exhibition, Seoul.
1276 **489** 450m. multicoloured . . 1·50 60

490 Clouded Yellow

1994. Butterflies. Multicoloured.
1277 100m. Type **490** 15 10
1278 180m. Red admiral 50 15
1279 300m. Scarce swallowtail (vert) 75 20
1280 350m. African monarch . . 1·00 50
1281 450m. Painted lady (vert) . . 1·25 60
1282 500m. Swallowtail (vert) . . 1·50 60

491 President Ben Ali and Anniversary Emblem **492** Boxers and Globe

1994. 7th Anniv of Declaration of 7 November 1987. Multicoloured.
1283 350m. Type **491** . . . . . . 1·00 25
1284 730m. "7", fireworks and state crest (vert) . . . . . 1·90 50

1994. 41st Military Boxing Championships, Tunis.
1285 **492** 450m. multicoloured . . 1·40 60

493 Tailfins **494** Greylag Geese

1994. 50th Anniv of I.C.A.O.
1286 **493** 450m. multicoloured . . 1·00 30

1994. Wildlife. Multicoloured.
1287 180m. Type **494** 25 15
1288 350m. Tufted duck and European pochard (horiz) 75 25
1289 500m. Water buffaloes . . . 1·10 60
1290 1000m. European otters (horiz) . . . . 2·10 1·25

495 "Composition" (Ridha Bettaieb)

1994.
1291 **495** 500m. multicoloured . . 1·10 35

496 "50", Map and Emblem **497** Oil Lamp

1995. 50th Anniv of League of Arab States.
1292 **496** 180m. multicoloured . . 25 15

1995. Glassware. Multicoloured.
1293 450m. Type **497** 60 30
1294 730m. Oil lamp with handle 95 50

498 Chebbi

1995. 60th Death Anniv (1994) of Aboulkacem Chebbi (poet).
1295 **498** 180m. multicoloured . . 25 15

499 Earring

1995. 4th World Conference on Women, Peking.
1296 **499** 180m. multicoloured . . 25 15

500 Farming

1995. 50th Anniv of F.A.O.
1297 **500** 350m. multicoloured . . 45 25

501 U.N. Workers and Anniversary Emblem over World Map

1995. 50th Anniv of U.N.O.
1298 **501** 350m. multicoloured . . 45 25

502 Crops

1995. Anti-desertification Campaign.
1299 **502** 180m. multicoloured . . 25 15

503 President Ben Ali visiting Village **504** Hannibal (Carthaginian general)

1995. 8th Anniv of Declaration of 7 November 1987. Multicoloured.
1300 180m. Type **503** 25 15
1301 350m. President Ben Ali meeting children 45 25

1995.
1302 **504** 180m. purple 25 15

505 Human Rights Award

1995. World Human Rights Day.
1304 **505** 350m. multicoloured . . 45 25

506 Bird carrying Olive Branch and People crossing Road

1995. Safety of Pedestrians.
1305 **506** 350m. multicoloured . . 45 25

507 "Ophrys lapethica" **508** Modern and Traditional Work

1995. Flora and Fauna. Multicoloured.
1306 50m. Type **507** 10 10
1307 180m. Dorcas gazelle . . . 25 15
1308 300m. "Scupellaria cypria" 40 20
1309 350m. Houbara bustard . . 45 25

1996. 50th Anniv of Tunisian General Workers' Union.
1310 **508** 440m. multicoloured . . 55 30

509 Man's Jebba, Khamri **510** "March 20 1996 1956"

1996. National Traditional Costume Day. Mult.
1311 170m. Type **509** 20 10
1312 200m. Woman's embroidered kaftan, Hammamet 25 15

1996. 40th Anniv of Independence. Multicoloured.
1313 200m. Type **510** 25 15
1314 390m. "20", "40", dove and rainbow 50 25

511 "Hannana" (Noureddine Khayachi)

1996.
1315 **511** 810m. multicoloured . . 1·00 50

512 Seven-spotted Ladybirds

1996. Insects. Multicoloured.
1316 200m. Type **512** 25 15
1317 810m. Honey bee . . . . . 1·00 50

513 Mascot **514** Magnifying Glass on "Stamp"

1996. World Environment Day.
1318 **513** 390m. multicoloured . . 50 25

1996. "Capex'96" International Stamp Exhibition, Toronto, Canada.
1319 **514** 200m. multicoloured . . 25 15

515 Flags over Stadium **516** Woman's Hands holding Dove

1996. Centenary of Olympic Games and Olympic Games, Atlanta. Multicoloured.
1320 20m. Type **515** 10 10
1321 200m. Runner, fireworks and "100" (vert) 25 15
1322 390m. Mosaic of ancient Greek wrestlers 50 25

1996. 40th Anniv of Code of Personal Status.
1323 **516** 200m. multicoloured . . 25 15

517 Ramparts of Sousse **518** Hammer breaking Chain on Anvil

1996. Ancient Buildings. Multicoloured.
1324 20m. Type **517** 10 10
1325 200m. Numide de Dougga mausoleum (vert) 25 15
1326 390m. Arch of Trajan, Makthar 50 25

1996. International Year against Poverty.
1327 **518** 390m. multicoloured . . 50 25

519 Candles on "7" and Map

1996. 9th Anniv of Declaration of 7 November 1987. Multicoloured.
1328 200m. Type **519** 25 15
1329 390m. Girl with doves . . . 50 25

520 Camels outside Traditional Dwellings

1996. National Saharan Tourism Day. Mult.
1330 200m. Type **520** 25 15
1331 200m. Traditional pattern 25 15
Nos. 1330/1 were issued together, se-tenant, forming a composite design.

521 Facade

1996. 1300th Anniv of Ezzitouna Mosque.
1332 **521** 250m. multicoloured . . 25 15

522 Campaign Symbols **523** United Nations Emblem, Trophy and Open Book

1996. National Solidarity Day. Multicoloured.
1333 500m. Type **522** 55 30
1334 500m. Jigsaw showing public services 55 30

1996. World Human Rights Day.
1335 **523** 500m. multicoloured . . 55 30

524 Schoolchildren

1996. 50th Anniv of UNICEF.
1336 **524** 810m. multicoloured . . 85 45

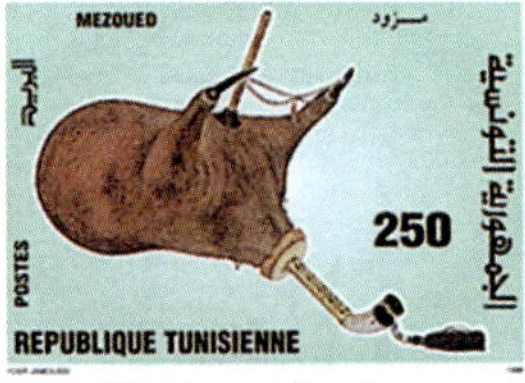

525 Mezoued (bagpipes)

1996. Musical Instruments. Multicoloured.
1337 250m. Type **525** 25 15
1338 300m. Gombri (stringed instrument) 30 15
1339 350m. Tabla (drum) 35 20
1340 500m. Tar tounsi (tambourine) 55 30

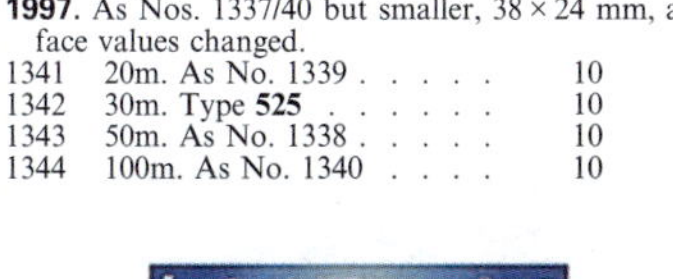
1997. As Nos. 1337/40 but smaller, 38 × 24 mm, and face values changed.
1341 20m. As No. 1339 . . . . . 10 10
1342 30m. Type **525** 10 10
1343 50m. As No. 1338 . . . . . 10 10
1344 100m. As No. 1340 . . . . 10 10

526 Writing Implements and Open Book

1997. World Book and Authors' Rights Day.
1345 **526** 1d. multicoloured . . . 1·00 50

527 Mediterranean Blue Mussels

1997. Molluscs. Multicoloured.
1346 50m. Type **527** 10 10
1347 70m. Clams 10 10
1348 350m. Common octopus . . 35 20
1349 500m. Common cuttlefish 55 30

528 San Francisco–Oakland Bay Bridge **529** Tennis Player and Runner

1997. "Pacific 97" International Stamp Exhibition, San Francisco.
1350 **528** 250m. multicoloured . . 25 15

1997. Mediterranean Games, Bari, Italy.
1351 **529** 350m. multicoloured . . 35 20

530 Emblems **531** State Arms

1997. Tunis, Cultural Capital.
1352 **530** 250m. multicoloured . . 25 15

1997. 40th Anniv of Republic. Multicoloured.
1353 130m. Type **531** 15 10
1354 500m. Airplane and flowers (horiz) 55 30

532 African Spiny-tailed Lizard

1997. Reptiles. Multicoloured.
1355 100m. Type **532** 10 10
1356 350m. Chameleon (vert) . . 40 20
1357 500m. Desert monitor . . . 55 30

533 Ariana Rose

1997.
1358 **533** 350m. multicoloured . . 40 20

534 Pres. Ben Ali with Elderly Woman

1997. World Day for Protection of the Elderly.
1359 **534** 250m. multicoloured . . 25 15

535 "Autumn" (Ammar Farhat)

1997. Art. Multicoloured.
1360 250m. Type **535** 25 15
1361 250m. "In Cafe Maure" (Farhat) 25 15
1362 250m. "Old Man" (Farhat) 25 15
1363 250m. "Fisher of Men" (sculpture, Hedi Selmi) . . 25 15
1364 500m. "Cafe des Nattes" (Sidi Bou Said) (horiz) . . 55 30
1365 500m. "Lesson" (Yahia Turki) (horiz) 55 30
1366 1000m. "Hand-spinner" (Farhat) . . . . 1·10 55

536 Pres. Ben Ali with Child, Flag and Doves forming "7"

1997. 10th Anniv of Declaration of 7 November 1987.
1367 – 250m. violet and gold . . 25 15
1368 **536** 500m. multicoloured . . 50 25
DESIGN—VERT: 250m. "7", globe and laurel leaves.

537 Sandrose (mineral)

1997.
1369 **537** 250m. multicoloured . . 25 15

538 Scales, Emblem and World Map

1997. International Day of Human Rights.
1370 **538** 500m. multicoloured . . 50 25

539 Arab

1997. Horses. Multicoloured.
1371 50m. Type **539** 10 10
1372 70m. Barbary 10 10
1373 250m. Arab-Barbary (vert) 25 15
1374 500m. Head of Arab (vert) 50 25

540 Memorial and Flowers

1998. 40th Anniv of Bombing of Sakiet Sidi Youssef.
1375 **540** 250m. multicoloured . . 25 15

541 Children and Flowers

1998. 5th School Health Week.
1376 **541** 250m. multicoloured . . 25 15

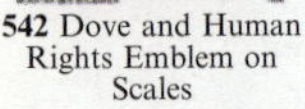

542 Dove and Human Rights Emblem on Scales

543 Monument

1998. Centenary of Tunisian Bar.
1377 **542** 250m. multicoloured . . 25 15

1998. Martyrs' Day. Multicoloured.
1378 250m. Type **543** 25 15
1379 520m. Roses and "9" . . . 55 30

544 Okba Ibn Nafaa Mosque, Kairouan

1998.
1380 **544** 500m. multicoloured . . 50 25

545 National Team

1998. World Cup Football Championship, France. Multicoloured.
1381 250m. Type **545** 25 15
1382 500m. Player, ball and trophy (vert) 50 25

546 Crab

1998. Marine Life. Multicoloured.
1383 110m. Type **546** 10 10
1384 250m. King prawn 25 15
1385 1000m. Lobster . . . . . . 1·00 50

547 Dove, Flag and Torch Bearers

1998. Constitutional Democratic Assembly Party Congress. Multicoloured.
1386 250m. Type **547** 25 15
1387 250m. President Ben Ali, flag, torch bearers and banners (horiz) 25 15

548 Isaac ibn Soleimane, Ahmed ibn el Jazzar and Constantin the African (physicians)

1998. 36th International History of Medicine Congress.
1388 **548** 500m. multicoloured . . 50 25

549 "Weaver" (Ali Guermassi)

1998. Paintings. Multicoloured.
1389 250m. Type **549** 25 15
1390 250m. "Musician" (Noureddine Khayachi) (vert) 25 15
1391 500m. "Still Life" (Ali Khouja) (vert) 50 25

550 Bank and Anniversary Emblem

551 Symbols of Industry and Agriculture

1998. 40th Anniv of Central Bank of Tunisia.
1392 **550** 250m. multicoloured . . 25 15

1998. 11th Anniv of Declaration of 7 November 1987.
1393 **551** 250m. multicoloured . . 25 15

552 "Tunisia" in Arabic and Anniversary Emblem

1998. 50th Anniv of Universal Declaration of Human Rights.
1394 **552** 250m. multicoloured . . 25 15

553 Ibn Rushd

554 Saliha (singer)

1998. 800th Death Anniv of Ibn Rushd (Averroes) (philosopher and physician).
1395 **553** 500m. multicoloured . . 50 25

1998. Musicians. Multicoloured.
1396 250m. Type **554** 25 15
1397 250m. Kaddour Srarfi (composer and violinist) (horiz) 25 15
1398 500m. Ali Riahi (singer and composer) 50 25

555 Mountain Gazelles

1998. Boukornine National Park. Multicoloured.
1399 70m. Type **555** 10 10
1400 110m. Brown hare 10 10
1401 250m. Bonelli's eagles . . . 25 15
1402 500m. Persian cyclamen . . 50 25

556 Orange Tree

1999. Trees. Multicoloured.
1403 250m. Type **556** 25 15
1404 250m. Date palm (vert) . . 25 15
1405 500m. Olive tree 50 20

557 Thuburbo Majus

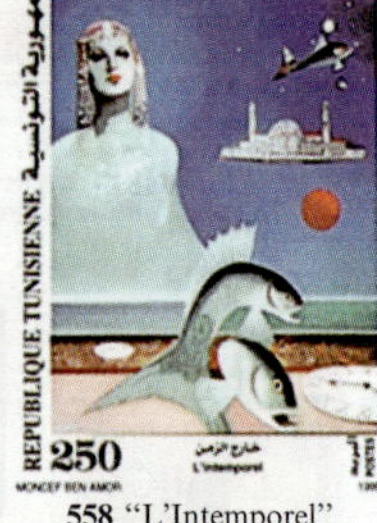

558 "L'Intemporel" (Moncef ben Amor)

1999. Archaeological Sites. Multicoloured.
1406 50m. Type **557** 10 10
1407 250m. Baths at Bulla Regia (horiz) 25 15
1408 500m. Zaghouan aqueduct (horiz) 50 20

1999. Paintings. Multicoloured.
1409 250m. Type **558** 25 15
1410 250m. "Betrothal" (Ali Guermassi) 25 15
1411 250m. "Pottery" (Ammar Farhat) 25 15
1412 250m. "Hat and Fan Seller" (Yahia Turki) 25 15

559 Arms, Columns and Legislative Chamber

1999. 40th Anniv of Constitution.
1413 **559** 250m. multicoloured . . 25 15

560 Acacia

1999. Flowers. Multicoloured.
1414 70m. Type **560** 10 10
1415 250m. Bougainvillea ("Bouganvillea spectabilis") 25 15
1416 250m. Common poppy ("Papaver rhoeas") . . . 25 15
1417 500m. Carnation 50 25

561 Stamps, Globe as Eye and Emblem

1999. "Philexfrance 99" International Stamp Exhibition, Paris.
1419 **561** 500m. multicoloured . . 50 25

562 Haddad and Women

1999. Birth Centenary of Tahar Haddad.
1420 **562** 500m. multicoloured . . 50 25

563 Loggerhead Turtle

1999. Marine Life. Multicoloured.
1421 250m. Type **563** 25 15
1422 500m. Grouper 50 25

564 Body Parts as Jigsaw Puzzle of Dove

1999. National Organ Donation Awareness Day.
1423 **564** 250m. multicoloured . . 25 15

565 U.P.U. Emblem

566 Ballot Box, Ear of Wheat and Sailing Boat

1999. 125th Anniv of Universal Postal Union.
1424 **565** 500m. multicoloured . . 50 25

1999. Presidential and Legislative Elections.
1425 **566** 500m. multicoloured . . 50 25

567 Tamarisk

568 Computer, Pencil and rising Sun

1999. Flora and Fauna. Multicoloured.
1426 250m. Type **567** 25 15
1427 500m. Dromedary 50 25

1999. 12th Anniv of Declaration of 7th November 1987.
1428 **568** 250m. multicoloured . . 25 15

569 Emblem and Scales of Justice

570 Ahmed Ibn Abi Dhiaf

1999. World Human Rights Day.
1429 **569** 250m. multicoloured . . 25 15

1999. Death Anniversaries. Multicoloured.

No.	Type	Description		
1430		250m. Type **570** (125th anniv)	25	15
1431		250m. Abdelaziz Thaalbi (55th anniv)	25	15
1432		500m. Khemaies Tarnane (35th anniv) (horiz)	50	25

571 "2000" and 20th-Century Symbols

1999. New Millennium.

No.	Type	Description		
1433	**571**	250m. multicoloured	25	15

572 17th-Century Ceramic Dish, Tunis

2000. Archaeological Sites and Artefacts. Mult.

No.	Type	Description		
1434		100m. Type **572**	10	10
1435		110m. 9th-century plate, Raqqada (triangular)	10	10
1436		250m. Water Temple, Zaghouan (35 × 35 mm)	20	10
1437		500m. "Ulysses and the Sirens" (mosaic), Dougga (35 × 35 mm)	45	25

573 *Carthage* (car ferry)

2000.

No.	Type	Description		
1438	**573**	500m. multicoloured	45	25

574 Archway and Palm Tree

2000. "EXPO 2000" World's Fair, Hanover, Germany.

No.	Type	Description		
1439	**574**	1000m. multicoloured	95	50

575 Carob Tree

2000. Trees. Multicoloured.

No.	Type	Description		
1440		50m. Type **575**	10	10
1441		100m. Apricot	10	10
1442		250m. Avocado (vert)	25	10
1443		400m. Apple	35	15

576 Emblem

577 Emblem and Sydney Opera House

2000. Mediterranean Games, Tunis (1st series).

No.	Type	Description		
1444	**576**	500m. multicoloured	45	20

See also Nos. 1473/4.

2000. Olympic Games, Sydney.

No.	Type	Description		
1445	**577**	500m. multicoloured	45	20

578 Freesias

579 Dove, Sun and Symbols

2000. Flowers. Multicoloured.

No.	Type	Description		
1446		110m. Type **578**	10	10
1447		200m. Chrysanthemums	20	10
1448		250m. Rose "Golden Times"	25	10
1449		250m. Vase of flowers (33 × 49 mm)	25	10
1450		500m. Rose "Calibra"	45	20

2000. 13th Anniv of Declaration of 7 November 1987.

No.	Type	Description		
1451	**579**	250m. multicoloured	25	10

580 "Still life" (Hedi Khayachi)

2000. Paintings. Multicoloured.

No.	Type	Description		
1452		100m. Type **580**	10	10
1453		250m. "Landscape" (Abdelaziz Berraies)	25	10
1454		250m. "The Sharpener" (Ali Guermassi)	25	10
1455		400m. "The Seller of Dates and Milk" (Yahia Turki) (vert)	35	15

581 Monument

583 Imam Sahnoun

582 *Neverita josephinia*

2000. International Year of Human Rights.

No.	Type	Description		
1456	**581**	500m. multicoloured	45	20

2000. Shells. Multicoloured.

No.	Type	Description		
1457		50m. Type **582**	10	10
1458		250m. Trunculus murex (*Phyllonotus trunculus*)	25	10
1459		250m. *Columbella rustica*	25	10
1460		1d. *Arca noe*	95	45

2000. Personalities. Multicoloured.

No.	Type	Description		
1461		250m. Type **583**	25	10
1462		250m. Ibn Arafa	25	10
1463		250m. Ali Belhaouane	25	10
1464		1d. Mohamed Jamoussi (musician)	95	45

584 Map and Flags

2001. Tunisia's Presidency of NATO. Security Council.

No.	Type	Description		
1465	**584**	250m. multicoloured	25	10

585 Globe, Clasped Hands and Dove

586 Symbols of Communications

2001. World Solidarity Fund.

No.	Type	Description		
1466	**585**	500m. multicoloured	50	25

2001. Digital Culture Year.

No.	Type	Description		
1467	**586**	250m. multicoloured	25	10

587 Flag, Father and Child

2001. Mohamed Dohra Commemoration.

No.	Type	Description		
1468	**587**	600m. multicoloured	60	30

588 Tunis Town Hall

2001. Tourism. Multicoloured.

No.	Type	Description		
1469		250m. Type **588**	25	10
1470		250m. Gighis (Roman ruins), Djerba Island	25	10
1471		250m. 19th-century tile, Tunis (vert)	25	10
1472		500m. "The Needles", Tabarka (vert)	50	25

589 Emblem, Stadium and Running Track

2001. Mediterranean Games, Tunis (2nd series). Multicoloured.

No.	Type	Description		
1473		250m. Type **589**	15	10
1474		500m. Runners and gold medal	50	25

590 "Sidi Bou Said" (Pierre Boucherle)

2001. Paintings. Multicoloured.

No.	Type	Description		
1475		250m. Type **590**	25	10
1476		250m. "Still Life" (Pierre Boucherle)	25	10
1477		250m. "Dream" (Aly Ben Salem) (vert)	25	10
1478		500m. "Traditional Outdoor Marriage" (Aly Ben Salem)	50	25

591 Stylized Faces and Arrows

2001. United Nations Year of Dialogue among Civilizations.

No.	Type	Description		
1479	**591**	500m. multicoloured	50	25

592 Emblem and Symbols of Employment

2001. National Employment Fund.

No.	Type	Description		
1480	**592**	250m. multicoloured	20	10

PARCEL POST STAMPS

P 8 Mail Carrier

P 25 Date Gathering

1906.

No.	Type	Description		
P44	**P 8**	5c. purple and green	60	15
P45		10c. pink and red	15	55
P46		20c. red and brown	1·60	20
P47		25c. brown and blue	2·00	20
P48		40c. red and grey	2·25	70
P49		50c. violet and brown	2·50	15
P50		75c. blue and brown	3·75	20
P51		1f. red and brown	2·50	10
P52		2f. blue and red	6·00	30
P53		5f. brown and violet	4·50	75

1926.

No.	Type	Description		
P147	**P 25**	5c. blue and brown	15	20
P148		10c. mauve and red	35	40
P149		20c. black and green	1·40	15
P150		25c. black and brown	55	45
P151		40c. green and red	1·00	1·25
P152		50c. black and violet	1·25	55
P153		60c. red and brown	1·40	1·40
P154		75c. green and lilac	1·75	45
P155		80c. brown and red	2·25	25
P156		1f. pink and blue	2·00	20
P157		2f. red and mauve	1·75	20
P158		4f. black and red	2·25	20
P159		5f. violet and brown	1·90	15
P160		10f. grn & red on grn	1·75	35
P161		20f. vio & grn on pink	11·50	1·75

POSTAGE DUE STAMPS

D 3

D 20 Carthaginian Statue

D 86 Agricultural Produce

1901.

No.	Type	Description		
D28	**D 3**	1c. black	15	15
D29		2c. orange	10	15
D30		5c. blue	10	10
D31		10c. brown	15	10
D32		20c. green	2·75	20
D33		30c. red	2·50	20
D34		50c. lake	1·00	30
D35		1f. olive	1·00	1·25
D36		2f. red on green	2·25	2·50
D37		5f. black on yellow	40·00	48·00

1914. Surch **2 FRANCS.**

No.	Type	Description		
D49	**D 3**	2f. on 5f. black on yell	85	30

1923.

No.	Type	Description		
D100	**D 20**	1c. black	10	2·50
D101		2c. black on yellow	10	95
D102		5c. purple	10	2·00
D103		10c. blue	20	2·25
D104		20c. orange on yellow	20	20
D105		30c. brown	35	20
D106		50c. red	90	1·00
D107		60c. mauve	1·25	25
D108		80c. brown	15	2·50
D109		90c. red	20	65
D110		1f. green	15	20
D111		2f. green	65	90
D112		3f. violet on pink	1·50	2·50
D113		5f. violet	50	50

1945.

No.	Type	Description		
D287	**D 20**	10c. green	10	2·75
D288		50c. violet	10	2·75
D289		2f. pink	15	60
D290		4f. blue	25	2·25
D291		10f. mauve	40	2·00
D292		20f. brown	1·50	80
D293		30f. blue	2·75	2·75

Nos. D293 is inscribed "TIMBRE TAXE".

1957.

No.	Type	Description		
D448	**D 86**	1f. green	20	20
D449		2f. brown	20	20
D450		3f. green	40	40
D451		4f. blue	45	45
D452		5f. mauve	45	45
D453		10f. red	45	45
D454		20f. sepia	1·75	1·75
D455		30f. blue	1·90	1·90

1960. Inscr "REPUBLIQUE TUNISIENNE" and new currency.
D534 D **86** 1m. green 10 10
D535 2m. brown 10 10
D536 3m. green 15 15
D537 4m. blue 15 15
D538 5m. violet 20 20
D539 10m. red 40 40
D540 20m. brown 60 60
D541 30m. blue 70 70
D542 40m. brown 15 15
D543 100m. green 40 30

TURKEY Pt. 16

Formerly an empire, this country is now a republic, the greater part of its territory lying in Asia Minor.

1863. 40 paras = 1 piastre or grush.
1942. 100 paras = 1 kurus.
1947. 100 kurus = 1 lira.

For designs as Types **1**, **2**, **9**, **15**, **21**, **23**, **25**, **28** and **30** but in black or brown, see Postage Due stamps.

1 2

1863. Imperf.
1 **1** 20pa. black on yellow 60·00 12·50
2 1pi. black on purple 85·00 30·00
3 2pi. black on blue 85·00 35·00
4 5pi. black on red £150 55·00

1865. Perf.
11 **2** 10pa. green 5·25 38·00
64 10pa. mauve 40 45
35a 10pa. brown 85·00 2·10
12 20pa. yellow 2·10 3·25
65 20pa. green 40 70
94 20pa. grey 1·50 3·00
13 1pi. lilac 3·75 4·00
66 1pi. yellow 40 1·25
14 2pi. blue 2·00 2·25
95 2pi. red to brown 60 70
15 5pi. red 2·25 3·75
46 5pi. blue 50 7·50
39c 5pi. grey 22·00 23·00
16 25pi. orange £300 £300
48 25pi. red 28·00 75·00

1876. Surch with value in figures and **Pres**.
77 **2** ¼pre. on 10pa. mauve 1·40 3·50
78 ½pre. on 20pa. green 4·75 6·50
79 1¼pre. on 50pa. red 40 1·25
80 2pre. on 2pi. brown 22·00 9·75
81 5pre. on 5pi. blue 2·50 42·00

9 15

1876.
89 **9** 5pa. black and yellow 90 1·25
96 5pa. lilac £150 £150
109 5pa. black 65 1·10
113 5pa. green and yellow 1·10 3·75
82 10pa. black and mauve 95 1·90
90 10pa. black and green 1·40 1·25
97 10pa. green 75 1·10
83 20pa. purple and green 42·00 8·00
91 20pa. black and pink 45 80
103 20pa. pink 65 75
84 50pa. blue and yellow 40 3·25
92 1pi. black and grey (A) 19·00 4·25
93 1pi. black and blue (B) 75·00 3·25
99 1pi. blue 75 95
85 2pi. black and flesh 40 95
126a 2pi. yellow 1·90 3·75
110 2pi. orange and blue 65 1·10
114 2pi. mauve and grey 75 75
86 5pi. pink and blue 1·60 5·00
115 5pi. brown 2·75 7·00
111 5pi. green 1·90 3·75
87 25pi. purple and mauve 9·50 38·00
107 25pi. black £225 £225
112 25pi. brown 15·00 60·00
116 25pi. red and yellow 18·00 50·00

1892. Various frames.
141 **15** 10pa. green 70 70
142a 20pa. red 50 30
143 1pi. blue 1·50 30
144 2pi. brown 75 30
145 5pi. purple 1·50 4·00

1897. Surch **5 5 Cinq Paras**.
160 **15** 5pa. on 10pa. green 1·75 25

21 22 23

1901. For Internal Mail.
167 **21** 5pa. violet 35 20
168 10pa. green 35 20
169 20pa. red 35 20
170 1pi. blue 35 20
171 2pi. orange 35 20
203 5pi. mauve 2·25 60
173 25pi. brown 5·00 1·25
174 50pi. brown 22·00 3·00

1901. For Foreign Mail.
175 **22** 5pa. brown 80 30
176 10pa. green 35 30
177 20pa. mauve 35 30
178 1pi. blue 80 30
179 2pi. blue 1·50 50
180 5pi. brown 1·50 50
181 25pi. green 60·00 22·00
182 50pi. yellow £130 65·00

1905.
212 **23** 5pa. brown 40 30
213 10pa. green 40 30
214 20pa. pink 40 30
215 1pi. blue 40 30
216 2pi. blue 45 30
217 2½pi. purple 1·00 30
218 5pi. brown 1·25 65
219 10pi. orange 1·10 65
220 25pi. green 7·50 4·50
221 50pi. purple 38·00 13·00

(24)

Type **24** is the Turkish letter "B" which stands for Behie = discount.

1906. Optd with T **24**.
230 **23** 10pa. green 2·25 95
231 20pa. pink 2·25 95
232 1pi. blue 2·25 95
233 2pi. blue 7·50 3·00

25 27 28

1908.
234 **25** 5pa. brown 70 30
235 10pa. green 1·50 30
236 20pa. red 26·00 30
237 1pi. blue 8·00 30
238 2pi. black 6·00 30
239 2½pi. brown 2·10 30
240 5pi. purple 20·00 55
241 10pi. red 60·00 1·40
242 25pi. green 8·00 3·50
243 50pi. brown 45·00 32·00

1908. Optd as T **24** but smaller.
252 **25** 10pa. green 4·25 2·25
253 20pa. red 5·00 2·75
254 1pi. blue 9·00 3·00
255 2pi. black 23·00 7·75

1908. Granting of Constitution.
256 **27** 5pa. brown 30 55
257 10pa. green 30 55
258 20pa. red 1·25 70
259 1pi. blue 1·25 80
260 2pi. black 9·75 13·00

1909.
271 **28** 2pa. green 40 35
261 5pa. brown 40 30
262 10pa. green 40 30
263 20pa. red 40 30
264 1pi. blue 1·00 30
265 2pi. black 1·10 30
266 2½pi. brown 48·00 15·00
267 5pi. purple 80 85
268 10pi. red 22·00 65
269 25pi. green £275 75·00
270 50pi. brown 65·00 75·00

1909. Optd as T **24** but smaller.
289 **28** 10pa. green 1·60 50
290 20pa. red 1·60 50
291 1pi. blue 3·25 1·75
292 2pi. black 48·00 19·00

1910. No. 261 surch **2** and Turkish inscr.
296 **28** 2pa. on 5pa. brown 30 20

30 G.P.O., Constantinople **31** Mosque of Selim

1913.
333 **30** 2pa. green 35 25
334 5pa. bistre 35 25
335 10pa. green 35 25
336 20pa. pink 35 25
337 1pi. blue 35 25
338 2pi. grey 35 25
339 5pi. purple 2·25 30
340 10pi. red 4·50 90
341 25pi. green 15·00 20·00
342 50pi. brown 55·00 75·00

1913. Optd as T **24** but smaller.
343 **30** 10pa. green 30 30
344 20pa. pink 30 30
345 1pi. blue 40 55
346 2pi. grey 9·50 4·50

1913. Recapture of Adrianople.
353 **31** 10pa. green 65 30
963 20pa. red 1·60 1·25
355 40pa. blue 1·60 1·25

For Type **31** surcharged, see Postage Due stamps.

32 Obelisk of Theodosius **34** Leander's Tower

1914.
499 **32** 2pa. purple 15 15
500 – 4pa. brown 15 15
501 **34** 5pa. purple 20 20
961 5pa. brown 40 15
502 – 6pa. blue 20 20
503 – 10pa. green 20 20
504 – 20pa. red 35 25
505 – 1pi. blue 30 25
964 – 1pi. green 2·10 20
506 – 1½pi. grey and red 35 20
507 – 1pi. brown and grey 35 20
508 – 2pi. black and green 1·25 50
509 – 2½pi. green and orange 45 20
965 – 3pi. blue 45 20
510 – 5pi. lilac 1·90 90
966 – 5pi. grey 21·00 30
511 – 10pi. brown 3·75 40
967 – 10pi. lilac 1·10 25
512 – 25pi. green 48·00 3·50
968 – 25pi. purple 2·25 1·25
513 – 50pi. pink 3·50 2·00
969 – 50pi. brown 3·00 6·00
514 – 100pi. blue 55·00 18·00
515 – 200pi. black and green £275 £275

DESIGNS—VERT: 4pa. Column of Constantine; 6pa. Seven Towers Castle, Yedikule. HORIZ: 10pa. Lighthouse-Garden, Constantinople; 20pa. Castle of Europe; 1pi. Mosque of Sultan Ahmed; 1½pi. Monument to Martyrs of Liberty; 1, 3pi. Fountains of Suleiman; 2pi. Cruiser "Hamidiye"; 2½, 5 (966) pi. Candilli, Bosphorus; 5pi. (510) Former Ministry of War; 10pi. Sweet Waters of Europe; 25pi. Suleiman Mosque; 50pi. Bosphorus at Rumeli Hisar; 100pi. Sultan Ahmed's Fountain; 200pi. Sultan Mohamed V. SIZES—As Type **32**: 4, 6pa; 31½ × 20 mm: 10pa. to 1pi; 26 × 21 mm: 1½pi. to 2½ pi; 38 × 24 mm: 5pi. to 50pi; 40 × 25½ mm: 100, 200pi.

1914. Stamps of 1914 optd with small star.
516 10pa. green 55 60
517 20pa. red 7·25 60
518 1pi. blue 1·25 60
519 1pi. brown and grey 90 1·25
520 2pi. black and green 35·00 1·90

(49)

1914. 7th Anniv of Constitution No. 506 surch with T **49**.
521 1pi. on 1½pi. grey and red 1·25 1·50

(50)

1914. Abrogation of the Capitulations. Nos. 501/11 optd with T **50**.
524 5pa. purple 1·25 50
526 10pa. green 2·00 50
527 20pa. red 2·00 50
528 1pi. blue 4·75 1·25
530 2pi. black and green 7·25 1·25
532 5pi. lilac 18·00 2·50
533 10pi. brown £110 35·00

(51)

1915. Nos. 514/15 surch as T **51**.
534 10pi. on 100pi. blue 32·00 19·00
535 25pi. on 200pi. black & green 11·50 6·00

(53) ("1331" = 1915)

1915. Various issues optd with T **53**. I. On postage stamps. (a) 1892 and 1897 issues.
536 **15** 5pa. on 10pa. green 45 20
537 10pa. green 45 20
538 2pi. brown 45 20
539 5pi. purple 1·90 20

(b) 1901 issues. (i) For Internal mail.
540 **21** 5pa. violet 45 20
541 10pa. green 75 20
542 20pa. red 75 20
543 1pi. blue 75 20
544 2pi. orange 1·90 20
545 5pi. mauve 1·00 50
546 25pi. brown 5·75 1·00

(ii) For Foreign mail.
547 **22** 5pa. brown 45 20
548 1pi. blue 2·10 20
549 2pi. blue 1·10 20
550 5pi. brown 7·75 50
551 25pi. green 30·00 10·50

(c) 1905 and 1906 issues.
552 **23** 5pa. buff 45 20
553b 10pa. green 45 20
561 10pa. green (230) 75 20
554a 20pa. pink 45 20
555a 1pi. blue 1·00 20
556b 2pi. grey 1·50 20
562 2pi. grey (233) 2·10 20
557 2½pi. purple 1·50 20
558a 5pi. brown 50 20
559 10pi. orange 7·75 20
560 25pi. green 55·00 2·10

(d) 1908 issues.
563 **25** 5pa. brown
564 2pi. black 60·00 22·00
569a 2pi. black (255) 7·75 75
565 2½pi. brown 1·50 20
566a 5pi. purple 60·00 16·00
567 10pi. red 7·75 3·00
568 25pi. green 20·00 3·00

(e) 1909 issues.
570 **28** 5pa. brown 45 20
572 20pa. red 45 20
579 20pa. red (290) 75 20
573 1pi. blue 75 20
581 1pi. blue (291) 75 20
574 2pi. black 75 20
582 2pi. black (292) 1·00 20
575 2½pi. brown 38·00 12·00
576 5pi. purple 45 20
577 10pi. red 5·00 20
578 25pi. green £1200 £650

(f) 1913 issues.
583 **30** 5pa. bistre 45 20
584 10pa. green 45 20
591 10pa. green (343) 45 20
585 20pa. pink 45 20
592 20pa. pink (344) 45 20
586 1pi. blue 45 20
593 1pi. blue (345) 1·10 20
587 2pi. grey 1·00 20
594 2pi. grey (346) 3·75 1·00
588 5pi. purple 1·10 20
589 10pi. red 5·75 50
590 25pi. green 16·00 4·50

II. On printed matter stamps (for use as postage stamps). (a) 1894 issue.
595 **15** 10pa. green 11·50 20
596 2pi. brown 50 75

(b) 1901 issues.
597 **21** 5pa. violet 50 20
600 **22** 10pa. green 1·50 75
598 **21** 20pa. red 1·50 75
599 5pi. mauve 11·50 3·75

(c) 1905 issues.
601b **23** 5pa. buff 45 20
602 2pi. grey 7·75 3·00
603 5pi. brown 5·75 45

(d) 1908 issues.
604 **25** 2pi. black £750 £300
605a 5pi. purple 4·50 75

(e) 1909 issues.
606 **28** 5pa. brown 45 20
608 5pi. purple 45·00 16·00

(54)

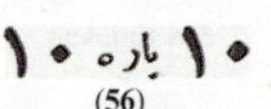
(56)

1915. Various issues optd with T **54** (star varies). I. On postage stamps. (a) 1892 issue, also surch with T **56**.
630 **15** 10pa. on 20pa. red 60 20

(b) 1901 issues.
631 **21** 1pi. blue 45 20
632a 5pi. mauve . . . . 5·00 75

(c) 1905 and 1906 issues, Nos. 633 and 636 also surch with T **56**.
609a **23** 10pa. green 45 45
611b 10pa. green (230) . . . . 25·00 4·50
633 10pa. on 20pa. pink . . . 45 25
636 10pa. on 20pa. pink (231) 45 45
634 1pi. blue . . . . 5·75 75
637 1pi. blue (232) 45 45
610 10pi. orange . . . . 9·00 45

(d) 1908 issues.
612 **25** 10pa. green 90 45
614a 10pa. green (252) £180 £110
638 20pa. red . . . .
640a 20pa. red (253) 60 45
641 1pi. blue (254) 60 45
613 5pi. purple . . . . 35·00 4·50
639 10pi. red £375 £160

(e) 1909 issues.
616 **28** 10pa. green 45 45
620 10pa. green (289) 45 45
643 20pa. red 45 45
647 20pa. red (290) . . . . . 1·00 45
645 1pi. blue 45 45
649 1pi. blue (291) . . . . . 1·50 45
619 5pi. purple . . . . 4·75 45
646 10pi. red . . . . £130 75·00

(f) 1913 issues.
623 **30** 10pa. green 60 60
625 10pa. green (343) 60 60
650 20pa. pink 45 35
653 20pa. pink (344) 60 35
624 1pi. blue 60 35
652 10pi. red . . . . 16·00 10·00

(g) 1916 Postal Jubilee issue.
654 **60** 10pa. red 60 45
655 20pa. blue 60 45
656 1pi. black and violet . . . 65 45
657 5pi. black and brown . . . 65 45

II. On printed matter stamps (for use as postage stamps). (a) 1894 issue, also surch with T **56**.
658 **15** 10pa. on 20pa. red 45 25

(b) 1901 issue.
659 **22** 5pi. brown . . . . 5·75 75

(c) 1908 issue.
626 **25** 10pa. green £275 £140
627 5pi. purple . . . . 35·00 4·75

(d) 1909 issue.
629 **28** 10pa. green 45 45

(57) ("1332" = 1916) (58) (59)

1916. Various issues optd with T **57**, some also surch in piastres as T **58**. I. On postage stamps. (a) 1892 and 1897 issues.
660 **15** 5pa. on 10pa. green (160) 45 45
661 10pa. green 45 40
662 20pa. red 45 40
663 1pi. blue . . . . 38·00 38·00
664 2pi. brown . . . . 4·00 1·10
665 5pi. purple . . . . 38·00 38·00

(b) 1901 issues. (i) Internal mail.
666 **21** 5pa. violet . . . . 38·00 38·00
667 10pa. green . . . . 1·10 1·00
668 20pa. red 45 45
669 1pi. blue 60 45
670 2pi. orange . . . . 1·10 45
671a 10pi. on 25pi. brown . . 3·75 1·00
672 10pi. on 50pi. brown . . 5·75 2·10
673a 25pi. brown . . . . . . 5·75 1·10
674 50pi. brown . . . . . . 7·75 1·10

(ii) Foreign mail.
675 **22** 5pa. brown 45 20
676 10pa. green 75 20
677 20pa. mauve 45 20
678 1pi. blue 60 20
679 2pi. blue . . . . 3·75 60
680 5pi. on 25pi. green . . . . 38·00 38·00
681 10pi. on 25pi. green . . . 38·00 38·00
682 25pi. green . . . . 38·00 38·00

(c) 1905 and 1906 issues.
683 **23** 5pa. buff 45 45
692a 10pa. green (230) 75 60
684 20pa. pink 45 45
693 20pa. pink (231) 75 60
685a 1pi. blue 45 45
694a 1pi. blue (232) 75 45
686a 2pi. grey 75 75
687 2½pi. purple . . . . 5·75 1·10
688 10pi. on 25pi. green . . . 5·75 1·10
689 10pi. on 50pi. purple . . 5·75 1·10
690 25pi. green . . . . 5·75 1·00
691 50pi. purple . . . . 3·75 75

(d) 1908 issues.
701 **25** 2pi. black (255) . . . . 38·00 38·00
695 2½pi. brown . . . . 38·00 38·00
696 10pi. on 25pi. green . . . 13·00 7·75
697a 10pi. on 50pi. brown . . 38·00 38·00
698 25pi. on 50pi. brown . . 38·00 38·00
699 25pi. green . . . . 5·75 75
700 50pi. brown . . . . 38·00 38·00

(e) 1908 Constitution issue.
702 **27** 5pa. brown . . . . 38·00 38·00

(f) 1909 issues.
703 **28** 5pa. brown . . . . 50 2·40
704 10pa. green . . . . 38·00 38·00
705 20pa. red . . . . 38·00 38·00
707 1pi. blue 80 50
711 1pi. blue (291) . . . . . 38·00 38·00
708 2pi. black . . . . 2·10 1·10
712 2pi. black (292) . . . . . 38·00 38·00
709 2½pi. brown . . . . 38·00 38·00
710 5pi. purple . . . . 38·00 38·00

(g) 1913 issues.
713 **30** 5pa. bistre 45 45
714 20pa. pink . . . . 1·10 45
715 1pi. blue . . . . 1·10 45
720 1pi. blue (345) 80 80
716 2pi. grey . . . . 2·10 80
717 10pi. on 50pi. brown . . . 7·75 2·10
718 25pi. green . . . . 4·50 1·50
719 50pi. brown . . . . 10·50 2·10

(h) 1913 Adrianople issue.
721 **31** 10pa. green 50 30
722 20pa. red 80 40
723 40pa. blue . . . . 1·90 70

(i) 1914 Constitution issue with further surch.
724 60pa. on 1pi.on 1½pi. grey and red . . . . 2·50 75

(j) 1916 Postal Jubilee issues.
725 **60** 5pi. black and brown . . . 1·50 1·00

II. On printed matter stamps (for use as postage stamps). (a) 1894 issues.
726 **15** 5pa. on 10pa. green . . . 45 45
727 10pa. green 75 20
728 20pa. red 40 20
729 5pi. purple . . . . 38·00 38·00

(b) 1901 issues. (i) Internal mail.
730 **21** 5pa. violet . . . . 26·00 38·00
731 10pa. green . . . . 26·00 38·00
732 20pa. red 50 45
733 1pi. blue 50 45
734 2pi. orange 80 45

(ii) Foreign mail.
735 **22** 5pa. brown 15 10
736 10pa. green 25 10
737 20pa. mauve 20 10
738 1pi. blue 35 15

(c) 1905 issue.
739 **23** 5pa. buff 45 45
740 10pa. green . . . . 38·00 19·00
741 20pa. pink . . . . 38·00 19·00
742a 1pi. blue . . . . 1·10 45

(d) 1908 issue.
743a **25** 5pa. brown . . . . 38·00 38·00

(e) 1909 issue.
744 **28** 5pa. brown . . . . 38·00 38·00

III. On 1913 Adrianople postage due issues (for use as postage stamps).
745 **31** 10 on 2pa. on 10pa. green 42·00 38·00
746 20 on 5pa. on 20pa. red . . 42·00 38·00
747 40 on 10pa. on 40pa. blue 42·00 38·00

1916. Occupation of Sinai Peninsula. Optd with T **59**.
749 **21** 5pa. violet 60 30
750 10pa. green 65 30
751 **28** 20pa. red . . . . 1·60 35
752 1pi. blue . . . . 3·00 60
753 **30** 5pi. purple . . . . 9·50 1·50

60 Old G.P.O., Constantinople (61)

1916. Jubilee of Constantinople City Post.
754 **60** 5pa. green . . . . 1·10 15
755 10pa. red . . . . 1·10 15
756 20pa. blue . . . . 1·10 15
757 1pi. black and violet . . . 1·10 15
758 5pi. black and brown . . . 14·50 85

1916. National Fete. Optd with T **61**.
759 **15** 10pa. green . . . . 1·25 1·50
760b **23** 20pa. red . . . . 2·25 75
761a 1pi. blue . . . . 7·00 1·90
762b 2pi. grey . . . . 8·25 1·00
763 2½pi. purple . . . . 14·00 1·10

62 Dolmabahce Palace

63 Sentry **64** Sultan Mohamed V

1916.
764 **62** 10pi. violet . . . . 18·00 2·40
765 10pi. green on grey . . . . 7·25 2·40
766 10pi. brown . . . . 11·00 65
767 **63** 25pi. red on buff . . . . 1·90 65
768 **64** 50pi. red . . . . 3·50 2·10
769 50pi. green on yellow . . . 2·00 10·00
770 50pi. blue . . . . 1·10 1·00

65 Off to the Front (66)

1917. Charity.
771 **65** 10pa. purple 80 30

1917. Various issues optd with T **66** or surch in addition. A. On postage stamp issue of 1865.
782 **2** 10pa. mauve . . . . . . 32·00 32·00
772a 20pa. yellow . . . . 32·00 32·00
783 20pa. green . . . . 32·00 32·00
785 20pa. grey . . . . 32·00 32·00
773b 1pi. lilac . . . . 32·00 32·00
784 1pi. yellow . . . . 32·00 32·00
774 2pi. blue . . . . 32·00 32·00
780 2pi. red to brown . . . . 32·00 32·00
775 5pi. red . . . . 32·00 32·00
778 5pi. blue . . . . 32·00 32·00
779 25pi. red . . . . 32·00 32·00

B. On surcharged postage stamp issue of 1876.
787 **2** ¼pre. on 10pa. mauve . . . 32·00 32·00
788 ½pre. on 20pa. green . . . 32·00 32·00
789 1¼pre. on 50pa. red . . . 32·00 32·00

C. On postage stamp issue of 1876.
790 **9** 5pa. black and yellow . . . 32·00 32·00
791 5pa. black 50 50
792 10pa. black and green . . . 32·00 32·00
793 10pa. green . . . . 32·00 32·00
794 50pa. black and yellow . . 32·00 32·00
795 2pi. black and flesh . . . 32·00 32·00
796 2pi. ochre . . . . 32·00 32·00
797 2pi. orange and blue . . . 1·25 25
798 5pi. brown . . . . 32·00 32·00
799 5pi. green . . . . 32·00 32·00
801 25pi. purple and mauve . . 32·00 32·00
802 25pi. brown . . . . 32·00 32·00

D. On postage stamp issue of 1892.
803 **15** 20pa. purple 75 75
804 2pi. brown . . . . 1·50 1·00

E. On postage stamp issue of 1901.
805 **21** 5pa. violet . . . . 23·00 23·00
806 10pa. green . . . . 2·25 2·25
807 20pa. red 50 50
808 1pi. blue 50 50
809 2pi. orange . . . . 1·50 3·00
810 5pi. mauve . . . . 23·00 23·00
811 10pi. on 50pi. brown . . . 23·00 23·00
812 25pi. brown . . . . 3·00 2·25

F. On postage stamp issue of 1901.
813 **22** 5pa. brown . . . . 1·50 1·90
814 20pa. mauve 50 50
815 1pi. blue . . . . 1·25 1·25
816 2pi. blue . . . . 3·00 3·00
817 5pi. brown . . . . 23·00 23·00
818 10pi. on 50pi. yellow . . . £110 £110
819 25pi. green . . . . 55·00 23·00

G. On postage stamp issues of 1905 and 1906.
820 **23** 5pa. buff 45 45
821 10pa. green . . . . 23·00 23·00
830 10pa. green (No. 230) . . . 1·00 1·25
822 20pa. pink 45 45
831 20pa. pink (No. 231) . . . 45 45
823 1pi. blue 45 45
832 1pi. blue (No. 232) 45 45
824 2pi. grey . . . . 3·00 3·00
833 2pi. grey (No. 233) . . . 23·00 23·00
825 2½pi. purple . . . . 3·00 3·00
826 5pi. brown . . . . 23·00 23·00
827 10pi. orange . . . . 23·00 23·00
828 10pi. on 50pi. purple . . 23·00 23·00
829 25pi. green . . . . 23·00 23·00

H. On postage stamp issues of 1908.
834a **25** 5pa. brown . . . . 2·25 2·25
835 10pa. green 50 50
840 10pa. green (No. 252) . . 60·00 60·00
841 1pi. blue (No. 254) . . . 23·00 23·00
836 2pi. black . . . . 23·00 23·00
842 2pi. black (No. 255) . . . 23·00 23·00
837a 2½pi. brown . . . . 2·25 2·25
838 10pi. on 50pi. brown . . 23·00 23·00
839 25pi. green . . . . 23·00 23·00

I. On Constitution issue of 1908.
843 **27** 5pa. brown . . . . 1·25 1·25

J. On postage stamp issues of 1909.
844 **28** 5pa. brown 50 50
846 10pa. green 50 50
854 10pa. green (No. 289) . . 60·00 60·00
847 20pa. red 50 50
849 1pi. blue 50 50
856 1pi. blue (No. 291) . . . 13·00 13·00
850 2pi. black . . . . 2·25 2·25
857 2pi. black (No. 292) . . . 12·00 12·00
851 2½pi. brown . . . . 23·00 23·00
852a 5pi. purple . . . . 23·00 23·00
853 10pi. red . . . . 23·00 23·00

K. On postage stamp issues of 1913.
858 **30** 5pa. bistre . . . . 75 1·25
859 10pa. green . . . . 23·00 23·00
865 10pa. green (No. 343) . . . 1·00 1·00
860 20pa. pink . . . . 1·00 1·00
861 1pi. blue . . . . 1·00 1·00
866 1pi. blue (No. 345) . . . . 2·10 2·10
862 2pi. grey . . . . 2·10 2·10
867 2pi. grey (No. 346) . . . 23·00 23·00
863 5pi. purple . . . . 23·00 23·00
864 10pi. red . . . . 23·00 23·00

L. On Adrianople Commem stamps of 1913.
868 **31** 10pa. green . . . . 1·50 1·50
869 40pa. blue . . . . 2·10 2·10

M. On Constitution Commem of 1914 with additional surch in Turkish.
870 60pa. on 1pi. on 1½pi. grey and red (No. 521) . . . . 1·00 1·00

N. On postage stamp issues of 1916.
871 **63** 25pi. red on buff . . . . . 3·00 3·00
872 **64** 50pi. red . . . . 12·00 12·00
873 50pi. green on yellow . . . 10·00 10·00
874 50pi. blue . . . . 23·00 23·00

O. On stamps of Eastern Roumelia of 1881 (T **9** of Turkey, but inscr "ROUMELIE ORIENTALE" at left).
876 5pa. lilac . . . . 23·00 23·00
877 10pa. green . . . . 23·00 23·00
875 20pa. black and red . . . 23·00 23·00
878 20pa. red . . . . 23·00 23·00

P. On printed matter stamps of 1893 optd with Type N **16**.
879 **15** 20pa. red (No. N 156a) . . 2·50 2·50
880 1pi. blue (No. N 157) . . . 45 65

Q. On printed matter stamps of 1901 optd with Type N **23**.
881 **21** 5pa. violet (No. N183) . . 1·50 1·50
882 10pa. green (No. N184) . . 15·00 12·50
883 20pa. red (No. N185) . . . 1·00 45
884 1pi. blue (No. N186) . . . 2·10 2·10
885 **21** 2pi. orange (No. N187) . . 1·50 1·90
886 5pi. mauve (No. N188) . . 23·00 23·00

R. On printed matter stamps of 1901 optd with Type N **23**.
887 **22** 5pa. brown (No. N189) . . 2·50 2·50
888 10pa. green (No. N190) . . 2·50 2·50
889 20pa. mauve (No. N191) 2·50 2·50
890 2pi. blue (No. N193) . . . 30·00 30·00

S. On printed matter stamps of 1905 optd with Type N **23**.
891d **23** 5pa. brown (No. N222) 45 45
892 10pa. green (No. N223) 1·00 1·25
893 20pa. pink (No. N224) . . 45 45
894 1pi. blue (No. N225) . . 45 45
895 2pi. grey (No. N226) . . 23·00 23·00
896 5pi. brown (No. N227) 23·00 23·00

T. On printed matter stamp of 1908 optd with Type N **27**.
897 **25** 5pa. brown (No. N244) . . 23·00 23·00

U. On postage due stamps of 1865.
898 **D 4** 20pa. brown . . . . . . 30·00 30·00
899 1pi. brown . . . . 30·00 30·00
900 2pi. brown . . . . 30·00 30·00
901 5pi. brown . . . . 30·00 30·00
902 25pi. brown . . . . 30·00 30·00

V. On postage due stamps of 1888.
904 **9** 1pi. black (D118) . . . . . 30·00 30·00
905 2pi. black (D119) . . . . . 30·00 30·00

W. On postage due stamps of 1892.
906 **15** 20pa. black (D146) . . . . 1·00 1·25
907 1pi. black (D148) . . . . 1·00 1·25
908 2pi. black (D149) . . . . 1·00 1·25

X. On Adrianople commemoration issue of 1913 (postage due stamps surch in Arabic further surch).
909 **31** 10 on 2pa. on 10pa. green (D356) 60 60
910 20 on 5pa. on 20pa. red (D357) 60 60
911 40 on 10pa. on 40pa. blue (D358) . . . . 1·00 1·00
912 40 on 20pa. on 40pa. blue (D359) . . . . 2·10 2·50

The overprints on printed matter and postage due stamps were used for ordinary postage.

67 In the Trenches **69** Howitzer at Sedd el Bahr

1917. Surch variously in Turkish.
913 **67** 5pa. on 1pi. red 50 45
915 **65** 10pa. on 20pa. red . . . . 1·75 45
914 **69** 5pi. on 2pa. blue . . . . . 7·50 70

72 Mosque at Ortakoy **73** Lighthouse, Achir Kapu

74 Martyrs' Column **77** Seraglio Point

75 Map of Gallipoli

76 Map of Gallipoli

1917.

916	**69**	2pa. violet	55	20
917	**72**	5pa. orange	55	20
918	**73**	10pa. green	55	20
919	**74**	20pa. red	55	20
920	**75**	1pi. blue	1·10	20
921	**76**	50pa. blue	1·25	70
921b	**77**	2pi. blue and brown	1·50	25
922	–	5pi. brown and blue	14·00	1·00

DESIGNS—As T **77**. 5pi. Pyramids.

1918. Surch **5 Piastres 5** and in Turkish.

923	**69**	5pi. on 2pa. blue	7·50	80

1918. No. 913 with additional surch.

924	**67**	2pa. on 5pa. on 1pi. red	80	70

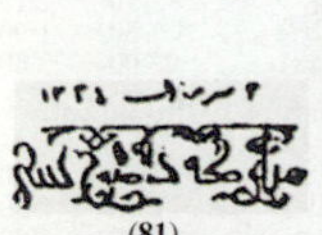
(81)

84 Wells at Beersheba

85 Sentry at Beersheba

87 Turkish Column in Sinai

1918. Armistice. Optd as T **81**.

925	**84**	20pa. purple	20	25
926	**75**	1pi. blue	4·00	4·00
927	**85**	1pi. blue	75·00	75·00
937	D **51**	1pi. blue (No. D518)	75·00	75·00
928	**76**	50pa. blue	25	30
929	**77**	2pi. blue and brown	25	30
930	–	2½pi. green and orange (No. 509)	75·00	80·00
931	–	5pi. brown and blue (No. 922)	25	25
932	**62**	10pi. green on grey	3·00	3·00
933	**63**	25pi. red on buff	3·00	3·00
934	**87**	25pi. blue	75·00	75·00
935	–	50pi. pink (No. 513)	75·00	75·00
936	**64**	50pi. green on yellow	4·00	4·00

1918. Stamp of 1909 optd with Sultan's toughra and surch in Turkish.

938	**28**	5pa. on 2pa. green	75	75

86 Dome of the Rock, Jerusalem

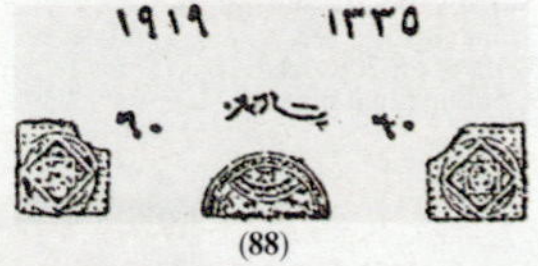
(88)

1919. Accession of Sultan Mohamed VI. Optd with date as in T **88** and ornaments or inscription.

939	**84**	20pa. purple	1·75	1·75
940	**85**	1pi. blue	2·50	10·50
941	**86**	60pa. on 10pa. green	1·10	4·50
942	**87**	25pi. blue	5·00	23·00

The illustrations Type **85** (optd with date and inscription at foot) and **86** (surch with T **88**) illustrate Nos. 940/1. Nos. 939 and 942 are overprinted with the date and the central motif only at bottom of Type **88**.

(89)

(91)

(90)

1919. 1st Anniv of Sultan's Accession. Optd or surch as T **89**, **90** or **91**.

943	**69**	2pa. violet	55	2·10
944	**72**	5pa. orange	25	35
945	**28**	5pa. on 2pa. green	25	35
946	**30**	10pa. on 2pa. green	25	35
960a	D **49**	10pa. on 5pa. brown	13·50	13·00
947	**73**	10pa. green	55	60
948	**74**	20pa. red	25	35
960b	D **50**	20pa. red	13·50	13·00
949	**75**	1pi. blue	40	75
960c	D **51**	1pi. blue	13·50	13·00
950	**76**	60pa. on 50pa. blue	80	75
951	**77**	60pa. on 2pi. blue and brown	25	35
952		2pi. blue and brown	35	35
960d	D **52**	2pi. blue	13·50	13·00
952a	–	2½pi. green and orange (No. 509)	13·50	13·00
953	–	5pi. brown and blue (No. 922)	25	35
954	**62**	10pi. brown	1·10	1·00
955	**84**	10pi. on 20pa. purple	35	35
956	**63**	25pi. red and buff	1·25	1·25
957	**85**	35pi. on 1pi. blue	2·00	1·25
958	**64**	50pi. green on yellow	2·25	2·10
958a		50pi. red	12·50	12·50
959	**86**	100pi. on 60pa. on 10pa. green	3·25	3·00
960	**87**	250pi. on 25pi. blue	3·25	3·00

Types **84** and **87** illustrate Nos. 955 and 960.

1921. Surch in figures and words and in Turkish characters.

970	**65**	30pa. on 10pa. purple	55	35
971	–	60pa. on 10pa. green (No. 503)	55	35
972	**67**	4½pi. on 1pi. red	1·25	40
973	–	7½ on 3pi. blue (No. 965)	8·50	85

Numerous fiscal and other stamps were surcharged or overprinted by the Turkish Nationalist Government at Angora during 1921, but as they are not often met with by general collectors we omit them. A full listing will be found in Part 16 (Central Asia) of the Stanley Gibbons catalogue.Nos. A79/90 and A119/24 were the only definitive issue of the Angora Government at this period.

A 24 National Pact

A 25 Parliament House, Sivas

1921.

A79	A **24**	10pa. purple	20	10
A80	–	20pa. green	25	10
A81	–	1pi. blue	45	15
A82	–	2pi. purple	1·75	15
A83	–	5pi. blue	1·40	15
A84	–	10pi. brown	3·75	25
A85	–	25pi. red	9·25	15
A86	A **25**	50pi. blue (A)	45	45
A87		50pi. blue (B)	40	85
A88	–	100pi. violet	60·00	2·75
A89	–	200pi. violet	£170	35·00
A90	–	500pi. green	90·00	17·00

DESIGNS—HORIZ: 20pa. Izmir Harbour; 1pi. Mosque, Adrianople; 10pi. Legendary grey wolf, Boz Kurt; 25pi. Castle Adana; 200pi. Map of Anatolia. VERT: 2pi. Mosque, Konya; 5pi. Soldier taking oath; 100pi. Mosque, Ourfa; 500pi. Declaration of faith from Koran.

Type (B) of the 50pi. as illustrated. In Type (A) the inscription at the top is similar to that of Type A **30** and the figures in the value tablets are above instead of below the Turkish inscription.

A 30 First Parliament House, Angora

1922.

A119	A **30**	5pa. mauve	25	30
A120		10pa. green	65	35
A121		20pa. red	90	55
A122		1pi. orange	5·25	85
A123		2pi. brown	10·00	3·00
A124		3pi. red	1·00	35

(94a)

1923. Izmir (Smyrna) Economic Congress. Nos. 918 and A80/4 optd with T **94a**.

973b	**73**	10pa. green	3·00	2·10
973c	–	20pa. green	3·00	3·25
973d	–	1pi. blue	5·75	4·50
973e	–	2pi. purple	5·75	6·75
973f	–	5pi. blue	8·50	10·00
973g	–	10pi. brown	13·00	18·00

95

96 Kemal Ataturk and Sakarya Bridge

1923.

974	**95**	10pa. grey	15	10
975		20pa. yellow	15	10
976		1pi. mauve	15	10
977		1½pi. green	15	10
978		2pi. green	1·00	10
979		3pi. brown	45	10
980		3½pi. brown	1·25	30
1001		4½pi. red	65	10
1002		5pi. violet	1·60	10
1003		7½pi. blue	1·60	10
1004		10pi. grey	4·75	1·10
1012a		10pi. blue	50·00	70
986	**95**	11½pi. pink	1·75	40
1006		15pi. brown	4·75	1·10
988		18pi. green	2·75	65
989		22½pi. orange	4·00	85
990		25pi. brown	15·00	80
991		50pi. grey	45·00	1·10
992		100pi. purple	£150	1·90
993		500pi. green	£325	80·00

1924. Treaty of Lausanne.

1013	**96**	1½pi. green	85	60
1014		3pi. violet	1·25	60
1015		4½pi. pink	1·75	1·75
1016		5pi. brown	2·10	2·50
1017		7½pi. blue	1·75	1·75
1018		50pi. orange	12·50	11·50
1019		100pi. purple	42·00	19·00
1020		200pi. olive	60·00	25·00

97 Legendary Blacksmith and Grey Wolf, Boz Kurt

98 Gorge and River Sakarya

99 Fortress of Ankara

100 Kemal Ataturk

1926.

1021	**97**	10pa. grey	10	10
1022		20pa. orange	10	10
1023		1gr. red	15	10
1024	**98**	2gr. green	1·25	45
1025		2½gr. black	1·75	10
1026		3gr. red	2·10	10
1027	**99**	5gr. violet	3·25	10
1028		6gr. red	90	10
1029		10gr. blue	8·75	10
1030		15gr. orange	10·50	10
1031	**100**	25gr. black and green	11·50	25
1032		50gr. black and red	14·50	30
1033		100gr. black and olive	30·00	85
1034		200gr. black and brown	75·00	65

(101 "1927 Izmir Exhibition")

(102 "Izmir, 9 Sept, 1928")

1927. Izmir (Smyrna) Exhibition. Optd with T **101**.

1035	**97**	1gr. red	20	10
1036	**98**	2gr. green	25	15
1037		2½gr. black	85	45
1038		3gr. red	1·10	45
1039	**99**	5gr. violet	2·40	45
1040		6gr. red	85	10
1041		10gr. blue	2·25	1·25
1042		15gr. orange	3·50	1·50
1043	**100**	25gr. black and green	11·50	5·00
1044		50gr. black and red	23·00	15·00
1045		100gr. black and olive	42·00	38·00

1928. 2nd Izmir Exhibition. T **97/9** optd with T **102** and T **100** optd **928** and 2 lines of Turkish.

1053	**97**	10pa. grey	15	10
1054		20pa. orange	15	10
1055		1gr. red	50	10
1056	**98**	2gr. green	65	45
1057		2½gr. black	65	45
1058		3gr. red	65	45
1059	**99**	5gr. violet	80	1·10
1060		6gr. red	50	10
1061		10gr. blue	2·25	75
1062		15gr. orange	2·40	45
1063	**100**	25gr. black and green	8·75	7·50
1064		50gr. black and red	11·00	7·50
1065		100gr. black and olive	25·00	17·00
1066		200gr. black and brown	35·00	17·00

1929. Surch with value in "Paradir" or "Kurustur".

1067	**97**	20par. on 1gr. red	35	15
1068	**99**	2½kur. on 5gr. violet	50	25
1069		6kur. on 10gr. blue	5·00	45

106 Bridge over Kizil-Irmak

107 Gorge and River Sakarya

1929. T **106/7** and 1926 stamps but inscr "TURKIYE CUMHURIYETI".

1076	**97**	10pa. green	10	10
1077	**106**	20pa. violet	10	10
1078		1k. green	25	35
1079	**97**	1½k. green	30	25
1070	**106**	2k. black	3·25	30
1080		2k. violet	2·40	45
1081		2½k. green	1·50	45
1072		3k. purple	3·00	35
1082		3k. red	15·00	45
1083	**97**	4k. red	6·75	15
1084	**99**	5k. purple	9·50	15
1085	**97**	6k. blue	6·00	15
1086	**107**	7½k. red	20	15
1088	**99**	12½k. blue	35	15
1089		15k. orange	45	15
1090	**107**	17½k. black	50	55
1091	**99**	20k. brown	35·00	60
1092	**107**	25k. brown	60	40
1093	**99**	30k. brown	1·25	40
1094	**107**	40k. purple	1·25	40
1075	**100**	50k. black and red	38·00	2·00

109

112 Kemal Ataturk

113

1930.

1095	**109**	50k. black and red	2·50	35
1096		100k. black and olive	2·50	45
1097		200k. black and green	2·50	95
1098		500k. black and brown	17·00	4·75

1930. Opening of Ankara–Sivas Railway. Surch **Sivas D. Y. 30ag. 930** and value.

1099	**97**	10pa. on 10pa. green	15	10
1100	**106**	10pa. on 20pa. violet	20	25
1101		20pa. on 1k. green	35	25
1102	**97**	1k. on 1½k. green	25	10
1103	**106**	1½k. on 2k. violet	45	45
1104		2k. on 2½k. green	1·10	65
1105		2½k. on 3k. red	85	65
1106	**97**	3k. on 4k. red	85	35
1107	**99**	4k. on 5k. purple	85	35
1108	**97**	5k. on 6k. blue	1·60	60
1109	**107**	6k. on 7½k. red	25	35
1110	**99**	7½k. on 12½k. blue	55	35
1111		12½k. on 15k. orange	40	35
1112	**107**	15k. on 17½k. black	2·25	1·25
1113	**99**	17½k. on 20k. brown	1·90	60
1114	**107**	20k. on 25k. brown	3·00	95
1115	**99**	25k. on 30k. brown	1·90	1·90
1116	**107**	30k. on 40k. purple	3·00	1·90

1117	109	40k. on 50k. black and red	6·00	1·90
1118		50k. on 100k. black and green	42·00	3·25
1119		100k. on 200k. black and green	55·00	6·00
1120		250k. on 500k. black and brown	45·00	4·75

1931. Surch **1 Kurus**.

1121	97	1k. on 1½k. green	2·10	15

1931.

1122	112	10pa. green	10	10
1444		10pa. brown	10	10
1444a		10pa. red	10	10
1123		20pa. orange	10	10
1445		20pa. green	10	10
1453b		20pa. yellow	10	10
1123a		30pa. violet	10	10
1124	113	1k. green	10	10
1453c		1k. orange	10	10
1124a	112	1½k. lilac	10	10
1125	113	2k. violet	15	10
1125a		2k. green	15	10
1447		2k. mauve	10	10
1447a		2k. yellow	45	10
1453d		2k. pink	10	10
1126	112	2½k. green	15	10
1126a	113	3k. brown	10	10
1448		3k. orange	10	10
1448a		3k. blue	20	10
1127		4k. black	90	10
1453f		4k. green	10	10
1128		5k. red	15	10
1128a		5k. black	55	10
1453g		5k. blue	1·60	10
1449a		5k. purple	2·40	10
1129		6k. blue	2·25	10
1129a		6k. red	30	10
1130	112	7½k. red	20	10
1130a	113	8k. blue	10	10
1453h		8k. violet	10	10
1131	112	10k. black	2·00	10
1131a		10k. blue	2·75	15
1450		10k. brown	55	10
1453i		10k. green	10	10
1132		12k. brown	35	10
1453j		12k. red	40	10
1133		12½k. blue	30	10
1134		15k. yellow	30	10
1451		15k. violet	55	10
1453k		15k. red	10	10
1135		20k. green	35	10
1452		20k. blue	9·25	10
1453la		20k. purple	3·00	10
1136		25k. blue	1·45	10
1137		30k. purple	6·75	10
1453		30k. pink	15·00	10
1453m		30k. green	20	10
1138		100k. brown	1·25	15
1139		200k. violet	45	15
1453a		200k. brown	5·00	35
1140		250k. brown	4·50	10

114 Tree with Roots in Six Balkan Capitals

115 "Rebirth of Turkey"

1931. 2nd Balkan Conference.

1141	114	2½k. green	10	10
1142		4k. red	15	10
1143		6k. blue	15	10
1144		7½k. red	20	10
1145		12k. orange	20	10
1146		12½k. blue	30	10
1147		30k. violet	45	10
1148		50k. brown	75	10
1149		100k. purple	1·10	10

1933. 10th Anniv of Turkish Republic.

1150	115	1½k. green	50	15
1151		2k. bistre	50	15
1152	–	3k. red	50	35
1153	–	6k. blue	50	25
1154	115	12½k. blue	90	65
1155		25k. brown	2·00	1·25
1156	–	50k. brown	4·50	1·50

DESIGNS—HORIZ: 3, 6, 50k. Wheat, cogwheels, factory, "X" and Kemal Ataturk.

1934. Air. Optd **1934** and airplane or surch also.

1157	107	7½k. lake	10	15
1158	99	12½k. on 15k. orange	10	15
1159	107	20k. on 25k. brown	10	20
1160		25k. brown	10	30
1161		40k. purple	35	50

1934. Izmir International Fair. Optd **Izmir 9 Eylul 934 Sergisi** or surch also.

1162	97	10pa. green	20	10
1163		1k. on 1½k. green	25	10
1164	107	2k. on 25k. brown	40	15
1165		5k. on 7½k. red	4·00	2·10
1166		6k. on 17½k. black	2·00	85
1167	99	12½k. blue	4·00	2·50
1168		15k. on 20k. brown	35·00	20·00
1169	107	20k. on 25k. brown	26·00	15·00
1170	109	50k. on 100k. black and green	48·00	15·00

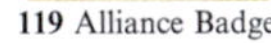

119 Alliance Badge

120 Mrs. C. Chapman Catt

1935. 12th Congress of the International Women's Alliance, Istanbul.

1171	119	20pa.+20pa. bistre	35	40
1172	–	1k.+1k. red	40	40
1173	–	2k.+2k. blue	50	75
1174	–	2½k.+2½k. green	50	75
1175	–	4k.+4k. blue	1·00	1·40
1176	–	5k.+5k. purple	1·50	2·00
1177	–	7½k.+7½k. red	2·25	3·00
1178	120	10k.+10k. orange	2·25	3·00
1179	–	12½k.+12½k. blue	4·25	5·75
1180	–	15k.+15k. violet	5·25	7·00
1181	–	20k.+20k. red	8·75	12·00
1182	–	25k.+25k. green	11·00	15·00
1183	–	30k.+30k. blue	55·00	70·00
1184	–	50k.+50k. green	£110	£140
1185	–	100k.+100k. red	75·00	£100

DESIGNS: 1k. Woman teacher; 2k. Woman farmer; 2½k. Typist; 4k. Woman pilot and policewoman; 5k. Women voters; 7½k. Yildiz Palace, Istanbul; 12½k. Jane Addams; 15k. Grazia Deledda; 20k. Selma Lagerlof; 25k. Bertha von Suttner; 30k. Sigrid Undset; 50k. Mme. Curie-Sklodowska; 100k. Kemal Ataturk.

1936. Remilitarization of Dardanelles. Surch **BOGAZLAR MUKAVELESININ IMZASI 20/7/1936** and value in figures.

1186	107	4k. on 17½k. black	50	50
1187		5k. on 25k. brown	55	50
1188	100	6k. on 50k. black and red	35	30
1189	109	10k. on 100k. black and olive	95	40
1190		20k. on 200k. black and green	3·25	50
1191		50k. on 500k. black and brown	3·25	95

122 Stag

124 Arms of Turkey, Greece, Rumania and Yugoslavia

1937. 2nd Turkish Historical Congress.

1192	122	3k. violet	30	65
1193	–	6k. blue	40	70
1194	122	7½k. red	60	30
1195	–	12½k. blue	1·90	1·60

DESIGN: 6, 12½k. Bust of Ataturk.

1937. Balkan Entente.

1196	124	8k. red	6·25	2·10
1197		12½k. blue	8·00	3·25

1938. Air. Surch **1937** with airplane above and value.

1198	107	4½k. on 7½k. lake	25	70
1199	99	9k. on 15k. orange	15·00	15·00
1200	107	35k. on 40k. purple	2·40	3·25

127 Fig Tree

129 Railway Bridge

1938. Izmir International Fair.

1201	–	10pa. brown	20	10
1202	–	30pa. violet	25	15
1203	127	2½k. green	45	45
1204	–	3k. orange	35	15
1205	–	5k. green	85	35
1206	–	6k. brown	2·25	1·40
1207	–	7½k. red	2·25	1·10
1208	–	8k. red	2·25	75
1209	–	12k. purple	2·50	1·40
1210	–	12½k. blue	7·50	5·25

DESIGNS—HORIZ: 10pa. An Izmir boulevard; 30pa. Izmir Fair; 6k. Woman gathering grapes. VERT: 3k. Clock Tower, Hukunet Square; 5k. Olive branch; 7½k. Woman gathering grapes; 8k. Izmir Harbour; 12k. Equestrian statue of Ataturk; 12½k. Ataturk.

1938. 15th Anniv of Proclamation of Turkish Republic.

1211	–	2½k. green	30	15
1212	–	3k. red	20	15
1213	–	6k. bistre	45	20
1214	129	7½k. red	1·00	60
1215	–	8k. purple	2·40	3·50
1216	–	12½k. blue	85	2·00

DESIGNS—HORIZ: 2½k. Military display; 3k. Aerial view of Kayseri; 8k. Scout buglers. VERT: 6k. Ataturk driving a tractor; 12½k. Ataturk.

130 Kemal Ataturk teaching Alphabet

1938. 10th Anniv of Introduction of Latin Alphabet into Turkey.

1217	130	2½k. green	25	25
1218		3k. orange	20	25
1219		6k. purple	25	35
1220		7½k. red	35	50
1221		8k. red	90	65
1222		12½k. blue	80	1·75

1938. Death of Kemal Ataturk. Mourning Issue. Optd **21-11-1938** and bar.

1223	113	3k. brown	10	25
1224		5k. red	10	25
1225		6k. blue	15	70
1226	112	7½k. red	10	25
1227	113	8k. blue	85	90
1228	112	12½k. blue	1·75	2·75

133 Presidents Inonu and Roosevelt and Map of North America

1939. 150th Anniv of U.S. Constitution.

1229	–	2½k. green, red and blue	20	20
1230	133	3k. brown and blue	20	20
1231	–	6k. violet, red and blue	20	20
1232	–	7½k. red and blue	30	15
1233	133	8k. purple and blue	45	45
1234	–	12½k. ultramarine & blue	1·25	95

DESIGNS—VERT: 2½, 6k. Turkish and U.S. flags. HORIZ: 7½, 12½k. Ataturk and George Washington.

1939. Cession of Hatay to Turkey. Surch **Hatayin Anavatana Kavusmasi 23/7/1939** and new values.

1235	107	3k. on 25k. brown	25	30
1236	109	6k. on 200k. black and green	15	25
1237	107	7½k. on 25k. brown	35	55
1238	109	12k. on 100k. (1096)	35	30
1239		12½k. on 200k. (1097)	60	55
1240		17½k. on 500k. (1098)	1·25	1·10

135 Railway Bridge over River Firat

136 Kemal Ataturk

1939. Opening of Ankara–Erzurum Railway.

1241	135	3k. red	1·25	2·40
1242	–	6k. brown	1·25	4·25
1243	–	7½k. red	1·60	4·50
1244	–	12½k. blue	2·75	7·00

DESIGNS—VERT: 6k. Steam locomotive. HORIZ: 7½k. Railway in Firat gorge; 12½k. Tunnel entrance at Atma-Bogazi.

1939. 1st Death Anniv of Kemal Ataturk.

1245	–	2½k. green	15	20
1246	–	3k. blue	20	25
1247	–	5k. brown	25	25
1248	136	6k. brown	25	25
1249	–	7½k. red	95	40
1250	–	8k. olive	30	65
1251	–	12½k. blue	40	65
1252	–	17½k. red	1·25	1·00

DESIGN: 2½k. Ataturk's residence; 3k. to 17½k. Portraits of Kemal Ataturk as Type **136**.

1940. Balkan Entente. As T **103** of Yugoslavia, but with the torch and Arms of Turkey, Greece, Rumania and Yugoslavia rearranged.

1253		8k. blue	85	45
1254		10k. blue	1·75	30

137 Namik Kemal

139 Map and Census Figures

1940. Birth Centenary of Namik Kemal (poet).

1255	137	6k. brown	30	30
1256		8k. olive	1·10	90
1257		12k. red	1·10	1·10
1258		12½k. blue	2·10	1·25

1940. Izmir International Fair. Surch **IZMIR ENTERNASYONAL FUARI 1940** and value.

1259	109	6k. on 200k. black and green	25	25
1260		10k. on 200k. black and green	25	25
1261		12k. on 500k. black and brown	30	30

1940. National Census.

1262	139	10pa. green	15	10
1263		3k. orange	25	20
1264		6k. red	45	35
1265		10k. blue	80	60

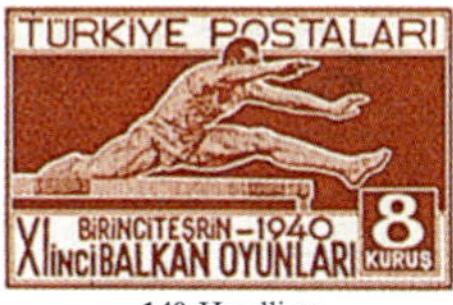

140 Hurdling

1940. 11th Balkan Games.

1266	–	3k. olive	65	1·75
1267	–	6k. red	2·75	3·25
1268	140	8k. brown	1·10	1·10
1269	–	10k. blue	2·00	85

DESIGNS—VERT: 3k. Running; 6k. Pole vaulting; 10k. Throwing the discus.

141 Postmen of 1840 and 1940

1940. Centenary of First Adhesive Postage Stamps.

1270	–	3k. green	15	10
1271	141	6k. red	30	25
1272	–	10k. blue	60	60
1273	–	12k. brown	75	55

DESIGNS—HORIZ: 3k. Mail carriers on horseback. VERT: 10k. Early paddle-steamer and modern mail launch; 12k. G.P.O., Istanbul.

142 Exhibition Building

1941. Izmir International Fair.

1274	–	30pa. green	15	10
1275	142	3k. grey	10	10
1276	–	6k. red	10	10
1277	–	10k. blue	10	10
1278	–	12k. purple	15	15
1279	–	17½k. brown	65	30

DESIGNS—HORIZ: 30pa. Freighter "Etrusk" in Izmir harbour; 6, 17½k. Exhibition pavilions; 12k. Girl in field. VERT: 10k. Equestrian statue.

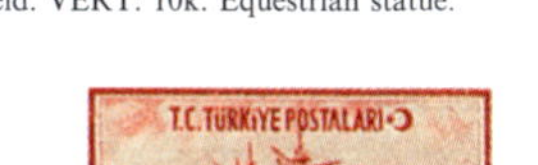

143 Barbarossa's Corsair Fleet

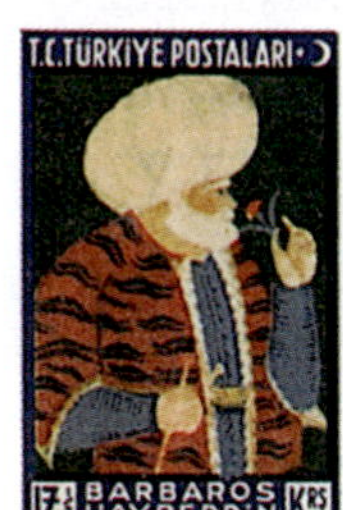

144 Barbarossa

1941. 400th Death Anniv of Barbarossa (Khair-ed-Din).

1280	–	20pa. violet	10	10
1281	143	3k. blue	35	25
1282		6k. red	55	60
1283		10k. blue	65	60

1284 12k. brown 80 60
1285 144 17½k. multicoloured 95 1·10
DESIGN—24 × 37 mm: 20pa. Barbarossa's tomb.

1941. Air. Surch with airplane and new value.
1286 107 4½k. on 25k. brown 1·60 1·25
1287 109 9k. on 200k. black & grn 4·00 7·25
1288 35k. on 500k. blk & brn 2·50 4·00

146 Pres. Inonu
147

1942.
1289 146 0.25k. bistre 10 10
1290 0.50k. green 10 10
1291 1k. grey 10 10
1292 1½k. mauve 10 10
1293 2k. green 10 10
1294 4k. brown 10 15
1295 4½k. black 10 10
1296 5k. blue 10 10
1297 6k. red 10 10
1298 6k. blue 20 15
1299 9k. violet 35 15
1300 10k. blue 10 10
1301 13½k. purple 10 10
1302 16k. green 10 10
1303 17½k. red 10 10
1304 20k. purple 15 20
1305 27½k. orange 15 20
1306 37k. brown 10 15
1307 50k. violet 20 1·10
1308 100k. brown 1·10 1·10
1309 147 200k. brown 4·25 1·00

148 Ankara
150 Pres. Inonu
149 Tile-decorating

1943. Inscr "TURKIYE POSTALARI" between two crescents and stars.
1310 148 0.25k. yellow 10 10
1311 – 0.50k. green 20 10
1312 – 1k. olive 10 10
1313 – 1½k. violet 10 10
1314 – 2k. green 15 10
1315 – 4k. red 65 15
1316 – 4½k. black 65 30
1317 149 5k. blue 35 15
1318 – 6k. red 10 10
1319 – 6k. blue 10 10
1320 – 10k. blue 10 10
1321 – 13½k. mauve 15 10
1322 – 16k. green 85 15
1323 – 17½k. brown 30 10
1324 – 20k. brown 35 10
1325 – 27½k. orange 40 30
1326 – 37k. brown 30 10
1327 – 50k. purple 2·50 15
1328 – 100k. olive 3·75 75
1329 150 200k. brown 3·75 65
DESIGNS—VERT: 0.50k. Mohair goats; 2k. Oranges; 4k. Merino sheep; 4½k. Steam train entering tunnel; 6k. Statue of Kemal Ataturk, Ankara, 6, 10k. Full face portrait of Pres. Inonu; 17½k. Republic Monument, Istanbul; 20k. National Defence Monument, Ankara; 27½k. P.O., Istanbul; 37k. Monument at Afyon; 100k. Ataturk and Inonu. HORIZ: 1k. Antioch; 1½k. Ankara Reservoir; 13½k. National Assembly building; 16k. View of Arnavutkoy; 50k. People's House, Ankara.

152 Fair Entrance

1943. Izmir International Fair.
1330 – 4½k. grey 10 10
1331 152 6k. red 10 10
1332 – 6k. blue 10 10
1333 152 10k. blue 20 10
1334 – 13½k. brown 35 25
1335 – 27½k. grey 45 35
DESIGNS—VERT: 4½, 13½k. Girl eating grapes. HORIZ: 6, 27½k. Fair Pavilion.

153 Marching Athletes
154 Soldier guarding Flag

1943. 20th Anniv of Republic.
1336 153 4½k. olive 35 40
1337 154 6k. red 10 10
1338 – 6k. blue 30 10
1339 – 10k. blue 10 10
1340 – 13½k. olive 20 15
1341 – 27½k. brown 20 25
DESIGNS—HORIZ: 6k. Railway bridge over River Firat; 10k. Hospital; 13½k. Ankara. VERT: 27½k. President Inonu.

155 Filling Census Form
157 Pres. Inonu

1945. National Census.
1342 155 4½k. olive 25 10
1343 9k. violet 30 10
1344 10k. blue 30 30
1345 18k. red 1·25 65

1945. Surch 4½ KURUS.
1346 4½k. on 6k. blue (No. 1319) 15 10

1946.
1347 157 0.25k. red 10 10
1348 1k. green 15 10
1349 1½k. purple 15 10
1350 9k. violet 40 10
1351 10k. blue 40 10
1352 50k. brown 3·25 10

158 U.S.S. "Missouri"
159 Sower

1946. Visit of U.S. Battleship "Missouri" to Istanbul.
1353 158 9k. violet 10 10
1354 10k. blue 15 10
1355 27½k. grey 20 10

1946. Agrarian Reform.
1356 159 9k. violet 10 10
1357 10k. blue 10 10
1358 18k. olive 20 10
1359 27½k. orange 35 25

160 Dove of Peace
161 Monument at Afyon

1947. Izmir International Fair.
1360 160 15k. purple and violet 10 10
1361 20k. blue and deep blue 10 10
1362 30k. brown and black 20 10
1363 1l. olive and green 60 10

1947. 25th Anniv of Battle of Dumlupinar.
1364 161 10k. brown & lt brown 15 10
1365 – 15k. violet and grey 15 10
1366 – 20k. blue and grey 20 10
1367 161 30k. green and grey 35 10
1368 – 60k. green and bistre 55 25
1369 – 1l. green and grey 1·10 65
DESIGN: 15, 60k. Ismet Inonu; 20k., 1l. Kemal Ataturk.

163 Istanbul, Grapes and Ribbon

1947. International Vintners' Congress.
1370 163 15k. purple 10 10
1371 20k. blue 10 10
1372 60k. brown 20 10

164 Steam Express Train
165 Pres. Inonu

1947. International Railway Congress, Istanbul.
1373 164 15k. purple 15 10
1374 20k. blue 20 10
1375 60k. olive 40 15

1948.
1376 165 0.25k. red 10 10
1377 1k. black 10 10
1378 2k. purple 10 10
1379 3k. orange 10 10
1380 4k. green 10 10
1381 5k. blue 10 10
1382 10k. brown 10 10
1383 12k. red 50 30
1384 15k. violet 15 10
1385 20k. blue 25 10
1386 30k. brown 1·25 30
1387 60k. black 2·50 35
1388 1l. olive 5·00 1·10
1389 2l. brown 19·00 4·25
1390 5l. purple 12·00 17·00
The lira values are larger.

167 Signing the Treaty
168 Statue of Kemal Ataturk

1948. 25th Anniv of Treaty of Lausanne.
1391 167 15k. purple 10 10
1392 – 20k. blue 15 10
1393 – 40k. green 25 10
1394 167 1l. brown 35 25
DESIGN: 20, 40k. Lausanne Palace.

1948. 25th Anniv of Proclamation of Republic.
1395 168 15k. violet 10 10
1396 20k. blue 15 10
1397 40k. green 20 10
1398 1l. brown 55 25

170 Douglas DC-6 over Izmir

1949. Air.
1399 170 5k. violet and lilac 20 10
1400 – 20k. brown and lilac 15 10
1401 – 30k. green and grey 50 10
1402 170 40k. blue and light blue 85 15
1403 – 50k. brown and mauve 60 10
1404 – 1l. green and blue 1·90 25
AIRCRAFT: 20, 50k. Vickers Viking 1B; 30k., 1l. Light monoplane.

172 Wrestlers

1949. 5th European Wrestling Championships. Designs depicting wrestling holds and inscr as in T **172**.
1405 – 15k. mauve (vert) 40 20
1406 – 20k. blue (vert) 1·00 35
1407 172 30k. brown 40 30
1408 – 60k. green (horiz) 95 65

173 Galley

1949. Navy Day.
1409 173 5k. violet 15 10
1410 – 10k. brown 20 10
1411 – 15k. red 20 10
1412 – 20k. blue 25 10
1413 – 30k. slate 40 15
1414 – 40k. olive 60 25
DESIGNS—HORIZ: 15k. Cruiser "Hamidiye"; 20k. Submarine "Sakarya"; 30k. Battlecruiser "Yavuz". VERT: 10k. Ship of the line "Mahmudiye"; 40k. Statue of Barbarossa.

175 Exhibition Building

1949. Istanbul Fair.
1415 175 15k. brown 10 10
1416 20k. blue 10 10
1417 30k. olive 20 10

176 U.P.U. Monument, Berne

1949. 75th Anniv of U.P.U.
1418 – 15k. violet 10 10
1419 – 20k. blue 10 10
1420 176 30k. red 10 10
1421 40k. green 20 10
DESIGN: 15, 20k. as Type **176** but vert.

177 Sud Est Languedoc over Bogazia

1950. Air.
1422 177 2l.50 green and blue 7·50 4·50

178 Youth, Istanbul and Ankara
180 Voting

1950. 2nd World Youth Union Meeting.
1423 178 15k. violet 10 10
1424 20k. blue 15 10

1950. General Election.
1425 180 15k. brown 10 10
1426 20k. blue 10 10
1427 – 30k. blue and green 20 10
DESIGNS—HORIZ: 30k. Kemal Ataturk and map of Turkey.

181 Hazel Nut
182 Map and Statistics

1950. Izmir Fair.
1428 181 8k. green and yellow 25 15
1429 – 12k. mauve 35 20
1430 – 15k. brown 45 20
1431 – 20k. blue and light blue 55 25
1432 – 30k. brown 70 35
DESIGN: 12k. Acorns; 15k. Cotton; 20k. Fair symbol; 30k. Tobacco.

1950. National Census.
1433 182 15k. brown 10 10
1434 20k. blue 15 10

183 Hezarfen Celebi's "Bird Flight" and Tower

184 Farabi (philosopher)

1950. Air. International Civil Aviation Congress, Istanbul.
1435 **183** 20k. blue and green . . 10 10
1436 – 40k. blue and brown . . 10 10
1437 – 60k. blue and violet . . 40 10
DESIGNS—VERT: 40k. Biplane over Taurus Mountains. HORIZ: 60k. Douglas DC-3 airplane over Istanbul.

1950. 1000th Death Anniv of Farabi.
1438 **184** 15k. multicoloured . . . 25 10
1439 20k. multicoloured . . . 50 20
1440 60k. multicoloured . . . 95 40
1441 1l. multicoloured . . . . 1·40 75

185 Mithat Pasha and Deposit Bank

1950. 3rd Co-operative Congress, Istanbul.
1442 **185** 15k. violet 45 25
1443 – 20k. blue 45 25
DESIGN: 20k. Agricultural Bank.

1951. Air. Industrial Congress, Ankara. Nos. 1399, 1401 and 1403 optd **SANAYI KONGRESI 9-NISAN-1951**.
1454 **170** 5k. violet and lilac . . . 20 10
1455 – 30k. green and grey . . 40 15
1456 – 50k. brown and mauve 55 35

187 "Iskendrun" (liner)

1951. 25th Anniv of Coastal Trading Rights.
1457 – 15k. blue 30 10
1458 **187** 20k. blue 30 10
1459 – 30k. grey 55 10
1460 – 1l. green 65 40
DESIGNS—HORIZ: 15k. Tug "Hora" and liner "Providence"; 30k. Diver and launch. VERT: 1l. Lighthouse.

188 Mosque of Sultan Ahmed **189** Count Carton de Wiart

1951. 40th Interparliamentary Conference, Istanbul.
1461 **188** 15k. green 10 10
1462 – 20k. blue 10 10
1463 **189** 30k. brown 20 10
1464 – 60k. purple 40 40
DESIGNS—As Type **188**: 20k. Dolmabahce Palace; 60k. Rumeli Tower.

190 F.A.O. Emblem and Silo

191 A. H. Tarhan

1952. U.N. Economic Conf, Ankara. Inscr "Ankara 1951".
1465 **190** 15k. green 15 10
1466 – 20k. violet 15 10
1467 – 30k. blue 35 20
1468 – 60k. red 70 30
DESIGNS: 20k. Int Bank emblem and hydro-electric station; 30k. U.N. emblem and New York headquarters; 60k. Ankara University.

1952. Birth Centenary of Tarhan (writer).
1469 **191** 15k. purple 15 10
1470 20k. blue 15 10
1471 30k. brown 35 20
1472 60k. green 70 30

192 Bergama

193 Kemal Ataturk

1952. Views. Imperf or perf.
1473 **192** 1k. orange 10 10
1474 – 2k. green 10 10
1475 – 3k. brown 10 10
1476 – 4k. green 10 10
1477 – 5k. brown 10 10
1478 **193** 10k. brown 15 10
1479 12k. red 20 20
1480 15k. violet (medallion) 20 10
1481 20k. blue (medallion) . . 35 10
1482 – 30k. green 30 10
1483 – 40k. blue . . . . 1·60 10
1484 – 50k. green 35 10
1485 – 75k. black . . . . . . 1·50 10
1486 – 1l. violet 35 10
1487 – 2l. blue . . . . 1·25 10
1488 – 5l. brown . . . . 14·00 4·25
DESIGNS—VERT: 2k. Ruins at Milas; 3k. Karatay Gate, Konya; 4k. Trees on Kozak Plateau; 5k. Urgup; 30k. Emirsultan Mosque, Bursa; 40k. Yenicami (New Mosque), Istanbul. HORIZ: 50k. Waterfall, Tarsus; 75k. Rocks at Urgup; 1l. Dolmabahce Palace, Istanbul; 2l. Pavilion, Istanbul; 5l. Interior of Istanbul Museum.

1952. Surch **0.50 Kurus**.
1489 **192** 0.50k. on 1k. orange . . 20 15

196 Congress Building

197 Turkish Sentry

1952. 8th Int Mechanics Congress, Istanbul.
1490 **196** 15k. violet 25 10
1491 20k. blue 25 15
1492 60k. brown 55 25

1952. Turkish Participation in Korean War.
1493 **197** 15k. slate 20 10
1494 – 20k. blue 20 10
1495 – 30k. brown 25 15
1496 – 60k. red and green . . . 70 35
DESIGNS: 20k. Turkish soldier and flag; 30k. Soldier and Korean child reading comic paper; 60k. Soldiers planting Turkish flag.

198 Doves, Hand and Red Crescent

199 Bas-relief on Monument

1952. 75th Anniv of Red Crescent Society.
1497 **198** 15k. red and green . . . 20 10
1498 – 20k. red and blue . . . 30 15
DESIGN: 20k. Red Crescent flag.

1952. 75th Anniv of Battle of Erzurum.
1499 **199** 15k. violet 15 10
1500 – 20k. blue 20 15
1501 – 40k. grey 45 20
DESIGNS—HORIZ: 20k. Azizye Monument, Erzurum; 40k. View of Erzurum.

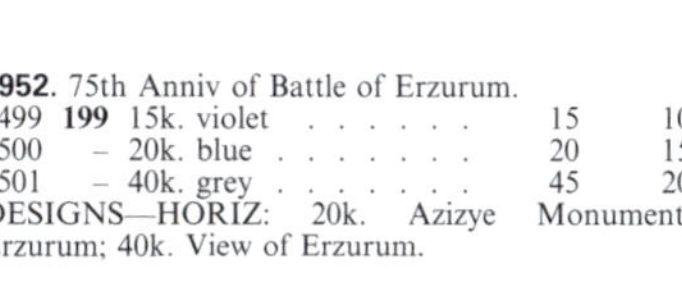

200 Pigeon carrying Newspaper

202 Sultan Mohammed II (after Gentile Bellini)

201 Rumeli Fort

1952.
1502 **200** 0.50k. green 10 10
1503 0.50k. violet 10 10
1503a 0.50k. orange 10 10
1503b 0.50k. brown 10 10

1953. 500th Anniv of Fall of Constantinople.
1504 **201** 5k. blue and ultramarine 50 20
1505 – 8k. grey 85 20
1506 – 10k. blue 55 20
1507 – 12k. purple 65 20
1508 – 15k. brown 65 10
1509 – 20k. red 65 10
1510 – 30k. green . . . . . . 1·40 55
1511 – 40k. violet . . . . . . 2·40 60
1512 – 60k. brown . . . . . . 1·40 85
1513 – 1l. green . . . . 4·00 1·10
1514 – 2l. multicoloured . . . 7·50 3·75
1515 **202** 2½l. lt brn, yell & brn . 5·50 3·75
DESIGNS—As Type **201**: HORIZ: 8k. Turkish army at Edirne; 10k. Horsemen and fleet; 12k. Landing of Turkish Army; 15k. Topkapi ramparts; 40k. Sultan Mohammed II and Patriarch Yenadios; 60k.15th-century map of Constantinople; 1l. Mausoleum of Mohammed II. VERT: 20k. Turkish army entering Constantinople; 30k. Sultan Mohammed II Mosque. As Type **202**: 2l. Sultan Mohammed II (after miniature by Sinan).

203 Odeon Theatre, Ephesus

1953. Views of Ephesus. Inscr "EFES". Multicoloured centres.
1516 **203** 12k. green 15 10
1517 – 15k. violet 10 10
1518 – 20k. slate 20 10
1519 – 40k. turquoise 35 20
1520 – 60k. blue 60 20
1521 – 1l. red . . . . 2·10 1·00
DESIGNS: 15k. St. John's Church and Acropolis; 20k. Statue of Blessed Virgin, Panaya Kapulu; 40k. Council Church ruins; 60k. Grotto of the Seven Sleepers; 1l. House of the Blessed Virgin, Panaya Kapulu.

204 Pres. Bayar, Mithat Pasha, Dr. Delitsch and Ankara Bank

1953. 5th International Public Credit Congress.
1522 **204** 15k. brown 20 10
1523 – 20k. turquoise 30 15
DESIGN: 20k. Pres. Bayar, Mithat Pasha and Ankara University.

205 Berdan Barrage

1953. 30th Anniv of Republic.
1524 – 10k. bistre 10 10
1525 **205** 15k. slate 10 10
1526 – 20k. red 10 10
1527 – 30k. olive 65 35
1528 – 35k. blue 20 15
1529 – 55k. lilac 25 30
DESIGNS—HORIZ: 10k. Combine-harvester; 20k. Soldiers on parade; 30k. Diesel train; 35k. Yesilkoy airport. VERT: 55k. Kemal Ataturk.

206 Kemal Ataturk and Mausoleum

1953. Transfer of Ashes of Kemal Ataturk to Mausoleum.
1530 **206** 15k. black 10 10
1531 20k. purple 15 10

207 Map of World and Compass

1954. 5th Anniv of N.A.T.O.
1532 **207** 15k. brown 40 25
1533 – 20k. blue 40 25
1534 – 40k. green . . . . . . 5·25 2·00
DESIGNS: 20k. Globe and stars; 40k. Allegory of growth of N.A.T.O.

208 "Industry, Agriculture and Construction"

209 Flying Exercise

1954. 5th Anniv of Council of Europe.
1535 **208** 10k. brown . . . . . . 3·00 1·25
1536 – 15k. green . . . . 1·60 35
1537 – 20k. blue . . . . 1·60 35
1538 **208** 30k. violet . . . . . . 6·00 2·50
DESIGN: 15, 20k. Flag and figure of "Peace and Justice".

1954. 47th Conference of International Aeronautical Federation. Inscr "20.IX.1954".
1539 **209** 20k. black 10 10
1540 – 35k. lilac 10 10
1541 – 45k. blue 20 10
DESIGNS: 35k. Baron Delagrange and glider; 45k. Ataturk and formation of De Havilland Tiger Moth biplanes.

210 Z. Gokalp

211 Yesilkoy Airport

1954. 30th Death Anniv of Gokalp (sociologist).
1542 **210** 15k. violet 10 10
1543 20k. green 20 10
1544 30k. red 30 15

1954. Air.
1545 **211** 5k. blue and brown . . . 65 10
1546 – 20k. blue and brown . . 30 10
1547 – 35k. blue and green . . 50 10
1548 **211** 40k. blue and red . . . 50 10
1549 – 45k. blue and violet . . 1·00 10
1550 – 55k. blue and black . . 3·25 20
DESIGNS: 20, 45k. Frontal view of Yesilkoy Airport; 35, 55k. Ankara Airport.

212 Kemal Ataturk

213 Relief Map of the Dardanelles

1955.
1551 **212** 15k. red 10 10
1552 20k. blue 15 10
1553 40k. slate 20 10
1554 50k. green 25 10
1555 75k. brown 60 10

1955. 40th Anniv of Battle of Canakkale (Dardanelles).
1556 **213** 15k. green 10 10
1557 – 20k. brown 10 10
1558 – 30k. blue 20 10
1559 – 60k. drab 45 20
DESIGNS—VERT: 20k. Gunner Seyid loading gun; 60k. Ataturk in uniform. HORIZ: 30k. Minelayer "Nusret".

214 "Reconstruction" 215 Lilies

1955. Town Planning Congress.
1560 **214** 15k. grey 10 10
1561 20k. blue 15 10
1562 50k. brown 20 10
1563 1l. violet 45 10

1955. Spring Flower Festival. Inscr "ISTANBUL 1955".
1564 – 10k. red and green . . . 25 10
1565 – 15k. yellow and green . . 25 10
1566 – 20k. red and green . . . 35 10
1567 **215** 50k. green and yellow . . 90 25
FLOWERS: 10k. Carnations; 15k. Tulips; 20k. Roses.

216 First-aid Centre

1955. 18th Congress of International Documentation Office of Military Medicine.
1568 **216** 20k. red and grey . . . 10 10
1569 – 30k. green and light green 10 10
DESIGN: 30k. Gulhane Military Hospital, Ankara.

217 Footballers

1955. Int Military Football Championships.
1570 **217** 15k. blue 20 10
1571 – 20k. red 35 10
1572 – 1l. green 75 30
DESIGNS—VERT: 20k. Footballers' badge. HORIZ: 1l. Championship plaque.

218 Police Monument, Ankara

1955. International Police Commission Meeting, Istanbul.
1573 **218** 15k. green and turquoise 15 10
1574 – 20k. violet and lilac . . 15 10
1575 – 30k. black and grey . . 20 10
1576 – 45k. brown & light brown 15 10
DESIGNS: 20k. Dolmabahce Palace, Istanbul; 30k. Police College, Ankara; 45k. Police Martyrs' Monument, Istanbul.

219 Radio Mast 220 Istanbul University

1955. Cent of Telecommunications in Turkey.
1577 – 15k. olive 10 10
1578 **219** 20k. red 10 10
1579 – 45k. brown 15 10
1580 **219** 60k. blue 25 15
DESIGNS—HORIZ: 15, 45k. Telegraph table and pole.

1955. 10th Meeting of Governors of Int Reconstruction and Development Bank and Int Monetary Fund.
1581 – 15k. orange 10 10
1582 **220** 20k. red 15 10
1583 – 60k. purple 20 10
1584 – 1l. blue 35 20
DESIGNS: 15k. Faculty of Letters, Istanbul; 60k. Hilton Hotel; 1l. Kiz Kulesi.

221 Ruins, Istanbul 222

1955. 10th International Congress of Byzantine Research.
1585 **221** 15k. green and blue . . 15 10
1586 – 20k. red and orange . . 15 10
1587 – 30k. brown and pink . . 20 10
1588 – 75k. blue and lilac . . 35 10
DESIGNS—VERT: 20k. Obelisk and Sultan Ahmed Mosque; 75k. Map of Istanbul in 1422. HORIZ: 30k. Church of St. Sophia.

1955. 10th International Road Planning Congress.
1589 – 20k. mauve 10 10
1590 **222** 30k. green 15 10
1591 – 55k. blue 25 10
DESIGNS: 20k. Congress emblem; 55k. Bridges.

223 Population Pictograph

1955. National Census.
1592 **223** 15k. grey and red . . . 15 10
1593 20k. lilac and red . . . 15 10
1594 30k. blue and red . . . 15 10
1595 60k. green and red . . . 30 10

224 Santa Claus Church, Demre 225 Kemal Ataturk

1955. Tourism.
1596 – 18k. green and blue . . 20 10
1597 – 20k. brown and blue . . 20 10
1598 – 30k. brown and green . . 20 10
1599 – 45k. green and brown . . 55 35
1600 – 50k. brown and green . . 25 10
1601 **224** 65k. black and red . . . 30 10
DESIGNS—VERT: 18k. Waterfall near Antalya; 45k. Theatre doorway ruins, Side; 50k. Countryside, Antalya. HORIZ: 20k. Alanya; 30k. Amphitheatre, Aspendos.

1955.
1602 **225** 0.50k. pink 10 10
1603 1k. yellow 10 10
1604 2k. blue 10 10
1605 3k. red 10 10
1606 5k. brown 10 10
1606a 6k. green 10 10
1607 10k. green 10 10
1607a 18k. purple 15 10
1608 20k. blue 10 10
1609 25k. olive 15 10
1610 30k. violet 15 10
1611 40k. brown 20 10
1612 75k. slate 45 15

226 Mausoleum of Hudavent Hatum 227 Zubeyde

1956. 25th Anniv of Turkish Historical Association.
1613 **226** 40k. deep blue and blue 15 10

1956. Mothers' Day.
1614 **227** 20k. brown & buff (perf) 10 10
1615 20k. olive and green (imperf) 30 25

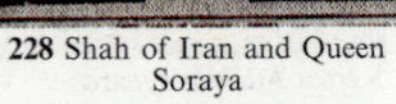

228 Shah of Iran and Queen Soraya 229 Kemal Ataturk

1956. Visit of Shah of Iran to Turkey.
1616 **228** 100k. green and light green (perf) 35 25
1617 100k. red and green (imperf) . . . . 3·25 2·00

1956.
1618 **229** ½k. green 10 10
1619 1k. orange 10 10
1620 3k. green 10 10
1621 5k. violet 10 10
1622 6k. mauve 10 10
1623 10k. purple 10 10
1624 12k. brown 10 10
1625 15k. blue 10 10
1626 18k. pink 10 10
1627 20k. brown 10 10
1628 25k. green 10 10
1629 30k. slate 10 10
1630 40k. olive 10 10
1631 50k. orange 15 10
1632 60k. blue 30 10
1633 70k. turquoise 60 10
1634 75k. brown 50 10
See also Nos. 1659/78.

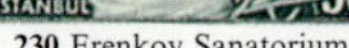

230 Erenkoy Sanatorium 231

1956. Turkish Post Office Health Service.
1635 **230** 50k. turquoise and pink 20 10

1956. 25th Izmir International Fair.
1636 **231** 45k. green (postage) . . 10 10
1637 25k. brown (air) 10 10

232 Serpent in Bottle 233 Medical Clinic, Kayseri

1956. International Anti-Alcoholism Congress.
1638 **232** 25k. multicoloured . . . 10 10

1956. 750th Anniv of Medical Clinic, Kayseri.
1639 **233** 60k. violet and yellow 10 10

234 Sariyar Barrage 235 Wrestling

1956. Inauguration of Sariyar Dam.
1640 **234** 20k. red 10 10
1641 20k. blue 10 10

1956. Olympic Games. Inscr as in T **235**.
1642 **235** 40k. sepia on green . . . 15 10
1643 – 65k. red on grey 20 10
DESIGN: 65k. Another wrestling match.

236 Mehmet Akif Ersoy 237 Vase of Troy

1956. 20th Death Anniv of Ersoy (poet).
1644 **236** 20k. brown and green . . 10 10
1645 20k. red and grey . . . 10 10
1646 20k. violet and pink . . 10 10

Each stamp is inscribed with a different line of verse from the Turkish National Anthem composed by Ersoy.

1956. Troy Commemoration. Inscr "TRUVA (TROIA)".
1647 – 15k. green . . . . . . 1·00 75
1648 **237** 20k. purple 50 60
1649 – 30k. brown . . . . . . 1·10 1·00
DESIGNS—HORIZ: 15k. Troy Amphitheatre; 30k. Trojan Horse.

238 Mobile X-ray Unit 239 Pres. Heuss

1957. T.B. Relief Campaign.
1650 **238** 25k. red and drab . . . 10 10

1957. Visit of President of West Germany.
1651 **239** 40k. brown and yellow (postage) 10 10
1652 40k. purple and pink (air) 10 10

240 View of Bergama

1957. Bergama Fair.
1653 **240** 30k. brown 10 10
1654 – 40k. green 10 10
DESIGN: 40k. Folk-dancing.

241

1957. Turkish-American Friendship.
1655 **241** 25k. violet 10 10
1656 40k. blue 10 10

242 Osman Hamdi Bey (founder) 243 Kemal Ataturk

1957. 75th Anniv of Fine Arts Academy, Istanbul.
1657 **242** 20k. drab, buff and black 10 10
1658 – 30k. grey, green & lt grn 10 10
DESIGN—HORIZ: 30k. Hittite relic of Alacahoyuk; Inscr "GUZEL SANATLAR AKADEMISI 75. YIL".

1957.
1659 **243** ½k. brown 10 10
1660 1k. blue 10 10
1661 2k. violet 10 10
1662 3k. orange 10 10
1663 5k. green 10 10
1664 6k. green 10 10
1665 10k. violet 10 10
1666 12k. green 10 10
1667 15k. green 10 10
1668 18k. mauve 10 10
1669 20k. sepia 10 10
1670 25k. brown 10 10
1671 30k. blue 10 10
1672 40k. slate 10 10
1673 50k. yellow 10 10
1674 60k. black 10 10
1675 70k. purple 10 10
1676 75k. olive 10 10
1677 – 100k. red 10 10
1678 – 250k. olive 20 10
Nos. 1677/8 are larger, 21 × 29 mm.

244 Mohammed Zahir Shah
245 Amasya Medical Centre

1957. Visit of Mohammed Zahir Shah of Afghanistan.
1679 **244** 45k. red and orange (postage) 10 10
1680 25k. deep green and green (air) 10 10

1957. 11th Congress of World Medical Association.
1681 **245** 25k. red and yellow . . 10 10
1682 – 65k. blue and yellow . . 10 10
DESIGN—HORIZ: 65k. Sultan Mohammed School, 1557.

246 Sultan Mohammed II Mosque

1957. 400th Anniv of the Suleiman Mosque, Istanbul.
1683 **246** 20k. green 10 10
1684 – 1l. brown 10 10
DESIGN—VERT: 1l. Mimar Koca Sinan (architect).

1957. 2nd Philatelic Exhibition, Istanbul. Surch **50 Kurus ISTANBUL Filatelik II. Sergisi 1957**.
1685 50k. on 2l. blue (No. 1487) 10 10

248 Forestry Map of Turkey

1957. Centenary of Forestry Teaching.
1686 **248** 20k. green and brown . . 10 10
1687 – 25k. green and blue . . 10 10
DESIGN—VERT: 25k. Planting fir-tree.

249 Fuzuli (poet)
250 Franklin

1957. Fuzuli Year.
1688 **249** 50k. multicoloured . . . 15 10

1957. 250th Birth Anniv of Benjamin Franklin.
1689 **250** 65k. purple 10 10
1690 65k. blue 10 10

251 Mevlana's Tomb, Konya
252 Adana

1957. 750th Birth Anniv of Mevlana (poet).
1691 **251** 50k. violet, blue and green 10 10
1692 – 100k. deep blue and blue 10 10
DESIGN—HORIZ: 100k. Konya Museum.

1958. Turkish Towns. As T **252**. (a) 26 × 21 mm.
1693 5k. brown (Adana) 10 10
1694 5k. mauve (Adapazari) . . . 10 10
1695 5k. red (Adiyaman) . . . 10 10
1696 5k. brown (Afyon) 10 10
1697 5k. green (Amasya) 10 10
1698 5k. blue (Ankara) 10 10
1699 5k. green (Antakya) 10 10
1700 5k. green (Antalya) 10 10
1701 5k. lilac (Artvin) 10 10
1702 5k. orange (Aydin) 10 10
1703 5k. violet (Balikesir) 10 10
1704 5k. green (Bilecik) 10 10
1705 5k. purple (Bingol) 10 10
1706 5k. blue (Bitlis) 10 10
1707 5k. purple (Bolu) 10 10
1708 5k. brown (Burdur) 10 10
1709 5k. green (Bursa) 10 10
1710 5k. blue (Canakkale) . . . 10 10
1711 5k. violet (Cankiri) . . . 10 10
1712 5k. blue (Corum) 10 10
1713 5k. blue (Denizli) 10 10
1714 5k. orange (Diyrbakir) . . . 10 10
1715 5k. violet (Edirne) 10 10
1716 5k. green (Elazig) 10 10
1717 5k. blue (Erzincan) 10 10
1718 5k. orange (Erzurum) . . . 10 10
1719 5k. green (Eskisehur) . . . 10 10
1720 5k. green (Gaziantep) . . . 10 10
1721 5k. blue (Giresun) 10 10
1722 5k. blue (Gumusane) . . . 10 10
1723 5k. purple (Hakkari) . . . 10 10
1724 5k. mauve (Isparta) . . . 10 10
1725 5k. blue (Istanbul) . . . 10 10
1726 5k. blue (Izmir) 10 10
1727 5k. blue (Izmit) 10 10
1728 5k. violet (Karakose) . . . 10 10
1729 5k. green (Kars) 10 10
1730 5k. mauve (Kastamonu) . . 10 10
1731 5k. green (Kayseri) . . . 10 10
1732 5k. brown (Kirklareli) . . . 10 10
1733 5k. orange (Kirsehir) . . . 10 10
1734 5k. blue (Konya) 10 10
1735 5k. violet (Kutahya) . . . 10 10
1736 5k. brown (Malatya) . . . 10 10
1737 5k. green (Manisa) 10 10
1738 5k. purple (Maras) 10 10
1739 5k. red (Mardin) 10 10
1740 5k. green (Mersin) 10 10
1741 5k. green (Mugla) 10 10
1742 5k. green (Mus) 10 10
1743 5k. green (Nevsehir) . . . 10 10
1744 5k. red (Nigde) 10 10
1745 5k. blue (Ordu) 10 10
1746 5k. violet (Rize) 10 10
1747 5k. purple (Samsun) . . . 10 10
1748 5k. brown (Siirt) 10 10
1749 5k. blue (Sinop) 10 10
1750 5k. green (Sivas) 10 10
1751 5k. blue (Tekirdag) . . . 10 10
1752 5k. red (Tokat) 10 10
1753 5k. blue (Trabzon) 10 10
1754 5k. orange (Tunceli) . . . 10 10
1755 5k. brown (Urfa) 10 10
1756 5k. green (Usak) 10 10
1757 5k. red (Van) 10 10
1758 5k. mauve (Yozgat) . . . 10 10
1759 5k. blue (Zonguldak) . . . 10 10

(b) 32½ × 22 mm.
1760 20k. brown (Adana) 10 10
1761 20k. mauve (Adapazari) . . 10 10
1762 20k. red (Adiyaman) 10 10
1763 20k. brown (Afyon) 10 10
1764 20k. green (Amasya) . . . 10 10
1765 20k. blue (Ankara) 10 10
1766 20k. blue (Antakya) . . . 10 10
1767 20k. green (Antalya) . . . 10 10
1768 20k. blue (Artvin) 10 10
1769 20k. orange (Aydin) . . . 10 10
1770 20k. purple (Balikesir) . . . 10 10
1771 20k. green (Bilecik) . . . 10 10
1772 20k. grey (Bingol) 10 10
1773 20k. violet (Bitlis) . . . 10 10
1774 20k. purple (Bolu) 10 10
1775 20k. brown (Burdur) . . . 10 10
1776 20k. green (Bursa) 10 10
1777 20k. blue (Canakkale) . . . 10 10
1778 20k. purple (Cankiri) . . . 10 10
1779 20k. grey (Corum) 10 10
1780 20k. blue (Denizli) 10 10
1781 20k. red (Diyrbakir) . . . 10 10
1782 20k. grey (Edirne) 10 10
1783 20k. green (Elazig) 10 10
1784 20k. blue (Erzincan) . . . 10 10
1785 20k. orange (Erzurum) . . . 10 10
1786 20k. green (Eskisehur) . . . 10 10
1787 20k. green (Gaziantep) . . . 10 10
1788 20k. blue (Giresun) 10 10
1789 20k. blue (Gumusane) . . . 10 10
1790 20k. purple (Hakkari) . . . 10 10
1791 20k. mauve (Isparta) . . . 10 10
1792 20k. blue (Istanbul) . . . 10 10
1793 20k. blue (Izmir) 10 10
1794 20k. green (Izmit) 10 10
1795 20k. violet (Karakose) . . . 10 10
1796 20k. green (Kars) 10 10
1797 20k. mauve (Kastamonu) . . 10 10
1798 20k. green (Kayseri) . . . 10 10
1799 20k. brown (Kirklareli) . . . 10 10
1800 20k. brown (Kirsehir) . . . 10 10
1801 20k. blue (Konya) 10 10
1802 20k. violet (Kutahya) . . . 10 10
1803 20k. brown (Malatya) . . . 10 10
1804 20k. green (Manisa) 10 10
1805 20k. purple (Maras) 10 10
1806 20k. red (Mardin) 10 10
1807 20k. green (Mersin) 10 10
1808 20k. green (Mugla) 10 10
1809 20k. green (Mus) 10 10
1810 20k. green (Nevsehir) . . . 10 10
1811 20k. red (Nigde) 10 10
1812 20k. blue (Ordu) 10 10
1813 20k. violet (Rize) 10 10
1814 20k. purple (Samsun) . . . 10 10
1815 20k. brown (Siirt) 10 10
1816 20k. blue (Sinop) 10 10
1817 20k. green (Sivas) 10 10
1818 20k. blue (Tekirdag) . . . 10 10
1819 20k. red (Tokat) 10 10
1820 20k. blue (Trabzon) 10 10
1821 20k. red (Tunceli) 10 10
1822 20k. brown (Urfa) 10 10
1823 20k. grey (Usak) 10 10
1824 20k. red (Van) 10 10
1825 20k. red (Yozgat) 10 10
1826 20k. blue (Zonguldak) . . . 10 10

253
254 Hierapolisat Pamukkale

1958. 75th Anniv of the Institute of Economics and Commerce, Ankara.
1827 **253** 20k. orange, blue & bistre 10 10
1828 25k. blue, orange & bistre 10 10

1958. Pamukkale Tourist Publicity. Inscr "PAMUKKALE".
1829 **254** 20k. brown 10 10
1830 – 25k. blue 10 10
DESIGN—HORIZ: 25k. Travertins (rocks) near Denizli.

255 Katib Celebi
256 Letters

1958. 300th Death Anniv of Katib Celebi (author).
1831 **255** 50k.+10k. black 10 10

1958. International Correspondence Week.
1832 **256** 20k. orange and black 10 10

257 Symbol of Industry
258 Symbol of "Europa"

1958. Industrial Fair, Istanbul.
1833 **257** 40k. black and blue . . 10 10

1958. Europa.
1834 **258** 25k. lilac and violet . . 10 10
1835 40k. blue and ultramarine 10 10

259 Bulldozer
260 Flame of Remembrance

1958. 35th Anniv of Republic.
1836 **259** 15k.+5k. orange 10 10
1837 – 20k.+5k. brown 10 10
1838 – 25k.+5k. green 10 10
DESIGNS—VERT: 20k. Portrait of Kemal Ataturk. HORIZ: 25k. Army tanks and Republic F-84G Thunderjets.

1958. 20th Death Anniv of Kemal Ataturk.
1839 **260** 25k. red 10 10
1840 – 75k. green 10 10
DESIGN: 75k. Sword, sprig and bust of Kemal Ataturk.

261
262 Blackboard

1959. 25th Anniv of Faculty of Agriculture, Ankara University.
1841 **261** 25k. yellow and violet 10 10

1959. 75th Anniv of Boys' High School, Istanbul.
1842 **262** 75k. black and yellow . . 10 10

263 Eagle
265 "Karadeniz" (liner)

264 Theatre, Ankara

1959. Air. Birds.
1843 – 40k. purple and mauve 25 10
1844 – 65k. myrtle and turquoise 30 10
1845 – 85k. blue and black . . 35 10
1846 **263** 105k. bistre and yellow 45 10
1847 – 125k. lilac and violet . . 65 10
1848 – 155k. green and yellow 75 15
1849 – 195k. blue and black . . 85 20
1850 – 245k. brown and orange 95 20
BIRDS (in flight)—HORIZ: 40k. Barnswallows; 65k. Cranes; 85k. Gulls. VERT: 125k. House martin; 155k. Demoisellecrane; 195k. Gulls; 245k. Turtledove.

1959. Centenary of Turkish Theatre.
1851 **264** 20k. brown and green . . 10 10
1852 – 25k. green and orange 10 10
DESIGN: 25k. Portrait of Sinasi and masks.

1959.
1853 – 1k. blue 10 10
1854 **265** 5k. blue 15 10
1855 – 10k. blue 10 10
1856 – 15k. brown 25 10
1857 – 20k. green 10 10
1858 – 25k. lilac 10 10
1859a – 30k. purple 20 10
1860 – 40k. blue 25 10
1861 – 45k. violet 30 10
1862 – 55k. brown 30 10
1863 – 60k. green 40 10
1864 – 75k. olive . . . . . . 1·60 10
1865 – 90k. blue . . . . . . 3·50 10
1866 – 100k. grey . . . . . . 5·25 10
1867 – 120k. purple . . . . . 1·60 10
1868 – 150k. orange . . . . . 1·60 10
1869 – 200k. green . . . . . 2·25 10
1870 – 250k. brown . . . . . 2·25 10
1871 – 500k. blue . . . . . . 3·50 10
DESIGNS—HORIZ: 1k. Vickers Viscount 700 airliner; 10k. Grain silo; 15k. Steel works; 20k. Euphrates Bridge; 25k. Zonguldak Harbour; 30k. Oil refinery; 40k. Rumeli Hisari Fortress; 45k. Sugarfactory; 55k. Coal mine; 150k. Combine-harvester. VERT: 60k. Telegraph pole; 75k. Railway; 90k. Crane loading "Kars" (container ship); 100k. Cement factory; 120k. Coast road; 200k. Electric transformer; 250, 500k. Portrait of Ataturk.

1959. Postage Due Stamps surch **20 = 20** for ordinary postage.
1872 **D 121** 20k. on 20pa. brown 10 10
1873 20k. on 2k. violet . . 10 10
1874 20k. on 3k. violet . . 10 10
1875 20k. on 5k. green . . 10 10
1876 20k. on 12k. red . . . 10 10

267 Northern Hemisphere and Stars

1959. 10th Anniv of N.A.T.O.
1877 **267** 105k. red 10 10
1878 195k. green 10 10

268 Amphitheatre, Aspendos
270 Basketball Players

1959. Aspendos Festival.
1879 **268** 20k. violet and bistre . . 10 10
1880 20k. brown and green . . 10 10

1959. 10th Anniv of Council of Europe. Surch **X. YIL** in circle of stars and **105 AVRUPAKONSEYI**.
1881 **259** 105k. on 15k.+5k. orange 10 10

1959. 11th European and Mediterranean Basketball Championships, Istanbul.
1882 **270** 25k. red and blue . . . 10 10

271 Marine Symbols

272 Goreme

1959. 50th Anniv of Turkish Merchant Marine College.
1883 **271** 30k. multicoloured . . . 10 10
1884 – 40k. multicoloured . . . 10 10
DESIGN: 40k. As 30k. but seahorse in place of anchor symbol.

1959. Tourist Publicity.
1885 **272** 105k.+10k. orange and violet 10 10

273 Mounted Warrior

1959. 888th Anniv of Battle of Malazgirt.
1886 **273** 2½l. purple and blue . . 15 10

274 Istanbul

1959. 15th International T.B. Conf, Istanbul.
1887 **274** 105k.+10k. blue and red 15 10

275 Ornamental Pattern

276 Kemal Ataturk

1959. 1st International Congress of Turkish Arts.
1888 **275** 30k. red and black . . . 10 10
1889 – 40k. blue, black and ochre 10 10
1890 – 75k. blue, yellow and red 10 10
DESIGNS—HORIZ: 40k. Sultan Mohammed II Mosque in silhouette. VERT: 75k. Circular ornament.

1959.
1891 **276** 500k. blue 65 20

277 Faculty Building 278 Crossed Sabres

1959. Centenary of Turkish Political Science Faculty.
1892 **277** 40k. brown and green . . 10 10
1893 40k. blue and brown . . 10 10
1894 – 1l. ochre and violet . . . 10 10
DESIGN—VERT: 1l. "S.B.F."emblem of Faculty.

1960. 125th Anniv of Territorial War College.
1895 **278** 30k. red and yellow . . 10 10
1896 – 40k. yellow, brown & red 10 10
DESIGN: 40k. Bayonet in bowl of fire.

279 "Uprooted Tree" and Globe

1960. World Refugee Year.
1897 **279** 90k. black and turquoise 10 10
1898 – 105k. black and yellow 10 10
DESIGN: 105k. "Uprooted Tree"" and houses representing refugee camp.

280 Mental Home, Manisa 281 Carnations

1960. ManisaFair. Inscr "MANISA MESIRBAYRAMI".
1899 **280** 40k.+5k. violet & mve 10 10
1900 40k.+5k. green & blue 10 10
1901 – 90k.+5k. purple & mve 10 10
1902 – 105k.+10k. mult 10 10
DESIGNS—VERT: 90k. Sultan Mosque, Manisa; 30½ × 42½ mm: 105k. Merkez Muslihittin Efendi (portrait).

1960. Spring Flowers Festival, Istanbul. Inscr "1960". Flowers in natural colours. Colours of inscriptions and backgrounds given.
1903 **281** 30k. red and yellow . . 10 10
1904 – 40k. green and grey . . 10 10
1905 – 75k. red and blue . . 20 10
1906 – 105k. green and pink . . 30 20
FLOWERS: 40k. Jasmine; 75k. Rose; 105k. Tulips.

282 Map of Cyprus

1960. Proclamation of Cyprus Republic. Inscr "KIBRISCUMHURIYETI".
1907 – 40k. mauve and blue . . 10 10
1908 **282** 105k. yellow, blue & grn 10 10
DESIGN: 40k. Town Centre, Nicosia.

283 Globe

1960. 16th Women's Int Council Meeting.
1909 **283** 30k. yellow and lilac . . 10 10
1910 – 75k. drab and blue . . . 10 10
DESIGN: 75k. Women, "W.I.C."emblem and nest.

283a Football

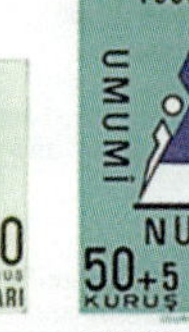

285 "Population"

1960. Olympic Games.
1911 30k. green (Type**283a**) . . . 10 10
1912 30k. black (Basketball) . . . 10 10
1913 30k. blue (Wrestling) . . . 10 10
1914 30k. purple (Hurdling) . . . 10 10
1915 30k. brown (Showjumping) 10 10

1960. Europa. As T **144a** of Switzerland but size 32½ × 22¼mm.
1916 75k. turquoise and green . . 25 10
1917 105k. light and deep blue . . 35 20

1960. National Census.
1918 – 30k.+5k. red and blue 10 10
1919 **285** 50k.+5k. blue & turq . . 10 10
DESIGN—HORIZ: 30k. Graph showing outlines of human faces.

286 "Justice"

287 Agah Efendi and Front Page of Newspaper "Turcamani Ahval"

1960. Trial of Ex-Government Officials.
1920 – 40k. bistre and violet . . 10 10
1921 – 105k. red and green . . 10 10
1922 **286** 195k. red and green . . 10 10
DESIGNS—HORIZ: 40k. Badge of Turkish Army; 105k. Trialscene.

1960. Turkish Press Centenary.
1923 **287** 40k. purple and blue . . 10 10
1924 60k. purple and ochre 10 10

288 U.N.Headquarters and Emblem

1960. 15th Anniv of U.N.O.
1925 – 90k. ultramarine and blue 10 10
1926 **288** 105k. brown and green 10 10
DESIGN—VERT: 90k. U.N. emblem,"XV" and hand holding torch.

289 Revolutionaries

1960. Revolution of 27 May1960.
1927 **289** 10k. grey and black . . 10 10
1928 – 30k. violet 10 10
1929 – 40k. red and black . . . 10 10
1930 – 105k. multicoloured . . 10 10
DESIGNS—HORIZ: 30k. Kemal Ataturk and hand with torch; 105k. Soldiers and wounded youth. VERT: 40k. Prancing horse breaking chain.

290 Faculty Building

1960. 25th Anniv of History and Geography Faculty.
1931 **290** 30k. black and green . . 10 10
1932 – 40k. black and buff . . 10 10
1933 – 60k. olive, buff and green 10 10
DESIGNS—HORIZ: 40k. Sun disc, cuneiform writing and map of Turkey. VERT: 60k. Ataturk's statue.

291 "Communications and Transport" 292

1961. 9th Central Treaty Organization Ministers' Meeting, Ankara.
1934 **291** 30k. black and violet . . 10 10
1935 – 40k. black and green . . 10 10
1936 – 75k. black and blue . . 10 10
DESIGNS: 40k. Road and rail construction,telephone and telegraph; 75k. Parliament building, Ankara.

1961. 1st Anniv of 27 May Revolution.
1937 **292** 30k. multicoloured . . . 10 10
1938 – 40k. green, cream & black 10 10
1939 – 60k. red, green and deep green 10 10
DESIGNS—HORIZ: 40k. Boz Kurt and warriors. VERT: 60k. "Progress".

293 North American F100 Jet and Rocket

1961. 50th Anniv of Turkish Air Force.
1940 – 38k. orange, lake & black 10 10
1941 **293** 40k. violet and red . . . 10 10
1942 – 75k. buff, grey and black 10 15
DESIGNS—HORIZ: 30k. Rockets. VERT: 75k. Ataturk, eagle and North American Super Sabrejets.

294 Old Observatory

1961. 50th Anniv of Kandilli Observatory, Istanbul.
1943 **294** 10k.+5k. turquoise and green 10 10
1944 – 30k.+5k. violet and black 10 10
1945 – 40k.+5k. brown and sepia 10 10
1946 – 75k.+5k. olive and green 10 10
DESIGNS—HORIZ: 30k. Observatory emblem; 75k. Observatory building. VERT: 40k. F.Gokmen.

295 Kemal Ataturk 295a

1961.
1947 **295a** 1k. brown 10 10
1948 5k. blue 10 10
1949 **295** 10k. mauve 85 10
1950 **295a** 10k. sepia 85 10
1951 30k. green . . . . . . 1·75 10
1952 10l. violet (22 × 32mm) 13·00 10

296 Doves

1961. Europa.
1960 **296** 30k. blue 10 10
1961 40k. grey 10 10
1962 75k. red 30 10

297 Tulip and Cogwheel 298 "The Constitution"

1961. Centenary of Professional and Technical Schools.
1963 **297** 30k. pink, silver and slate 10 10
1964 – 75k. red, black and blue 10 10
DESIGN—HORIZ: 75k. Inscr " 100 Yili 1861–1961" and tulip and cogwheel emblem.

1961. Opening of Turkish Parliament.
1965 **298** 30k. black, bistre and red 10 10
1966 75k. black, green and blue 10 10

299 Insecticide-sprayers ("Malaria Eradication") 300 N.A.T.O. and Anniversary Emblem

1961. 15th Anniv ofU.N.I.C.E.F.
1967 **299** 10k.+5k. turquoise . . . 10 10
1968 – 30k.+5k. violet 10 10
1969 – 75k.+5k. brown 10 10
DESIGNS—HORIZ: 30k. Mother and child ("Child Welfare"). VERT: 75k. Mother giving pasteurized milk to children ("Education on Nourishment").

1962. 10th Anniv of Turkish Admission to N.A.T.O.
1970 – 75k. black, silver and blue 10 10
1971 **300** 105k. black, silver and red 10 10
DESIGN—VERT: 75k. Peace dove overN.A.T.O. and Anniv emblems.

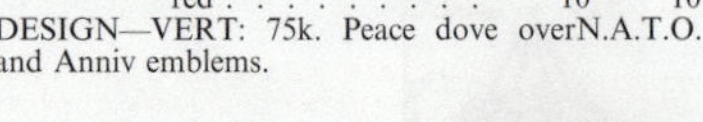

301 Mosquito on Map of Turkey 302 "Strelitziareginae"

1962. Malaria Eradication.
1972 **301** 30k.+5k. brown 10 10
1973 75k.+5k. mauve & blk 10 10

1962. Flowers. Multicoloured.
1974 30k.+10k. "Poinsettiapulcherrima" 15 10
1975 40k.+10k. Type**302** 20 10
1976 75k.+10k. "Nympheaalba" 20 10

303 Scouts in Camp

304 Soldier (Victory Monument, Ankara)

1962. 50th Anniv of Turkish Scout Movement.
1977 **303** 30k. red, black and green . . 10 10
1978 – 60k. red, black and lilac . . 15 10
1979 – 105k. red, black & brown 20 10
DESIGNS: 60k. Two scouts with flag; 105k. Wolf Cub and Brownie.

1962. 40th Anniv of Battle of Dumlupinar.
1980 **304** 30k. green 10 10
1981 – 40k. brown and black . . 10 10
1982 – 75k. grey 10 10
DESIGNS—HORIZ: 40k. Ox-cart carrying ammunition. (Victory Monument, Ankara). VERT: 75k. Kemal Ataturk.

305 Europa "Tree"

306 Shrine of the Virgin Mary

1962. Europa.
1983 **305** 75k. sepia and green . . 15 10
1984 105k. sepia and red . . . 15 10
1985 195k. sepia and blue . . 20 10

1962. Tourist Issue. Multicoloured.
1986 30k. Type **306** 10 10
1987 40k. Interior 10 10
1988 75k. Exterior 15 10
1989 105k. Statue of the Virgin 10 10
DESIGNS: The 40 and 75k. show horiz views of the Virgin Mary's house at Ephesus.

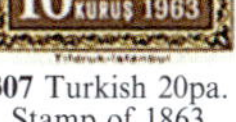
307 Turkish 20pa. Stamp of 1863

308 J-u-lian'sColumn,Ankara

1963. Stamp Centenary.
1990 **307** 10k. black, yellow & brn 10 10
1991 – 30k. black, pink and violet 10 10
1992 – 40k. black, blue & turq 10 10
1993 – 75k. black, pink & brown 10 10
DESIGNS—Turkish stamps of 1863: 30k.(1pi.); 40k. (2pi.); 75k. (5pi.).

1963.
1994 **308** 1k. green and olive . . . 10 10
1995 1k. violet 10 10
1996 – 5k. sepia and brown . . 15 10
1997 – 10k. mauve and green 20 10
1998 – 30k. black and violet . . 45 10
1999 – 50k. green, brown & yell 70 10
2000 – 60k. grey . . . . . . 1·75 10
2001 – 100k. brown 70 10
2002 – 150k. green . . . . . 6·75 10
DESIGNS—HORIZ: 5k. Ethnographic Museum; 10k. Citadel; 30k. Educational Establishment, Gazi; 50k. Ataturk's Mausoleum;60k. Presidential Palace, Ankara; 100k. Ataturk's house; 150k. National Museum, Ankara.

309 "Clinging to the World"

310 Wheat and Census Graph

1963. Freedom from Hunger.
2010 **309** 30k. deep blue and blue 10 10
2011 – 40k. deep brown & brown 10 10
2012 – 75k. deep green and green 10 10
DESIGNS: 40k. Sowers; 75k. Emblem and Globe within hands.

1963. Agricultural Census. Unissued stamps with "KASIM 1960" obliterated with bars. Inscr "UMUMI ZIRAATSAYIMI".
2013 **310** 40k.+5k. multicoloured 10 10
2014 – 60k.+5k. multicoloured 10 10
DESIGN—HORIZ: 60k. Wheat and chart.

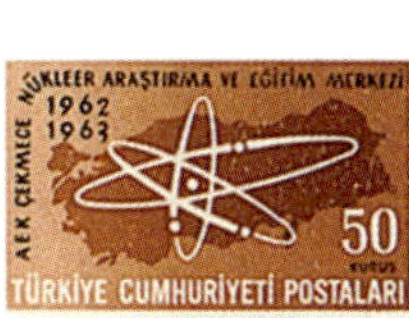
311 Atomic Symbol on Map

312 Ucserefili Mosque

1963. 1st Anniv of Opening of Turkish Nuclear Research Centre.
2015 **311** 50k. brown & deep brown 10 10
2016 – 60k. multicoloured . . . 10 10
2017 – 100k. blue & ultramarine 10 10
DESIGNS: 60k. Various symbols; 100k. Emblem of Turkish Atomic Energy Commission.

1963. 600th Anniv of Conquest of Edirne.
2018 **312** 10k. green, ultramarine and blue 10 10
2019 – 30k. blue and red . . . 10 10
2020 – 60k. multicoloured . . . 15 10
2021 – 100k. multicoloured . . 20 10
DESIGNS—HORIZ: 30k. Meric Bridge; 60k. Kum Kasri (building). VERT: 100k. Sultan Amurat I.

313 Soldier and Sun

1963. 600th Anniv of Turkish Army.
2022 **313** 50k. black, red and blue 10 10
2023 100k. black, red & bistre 10 10

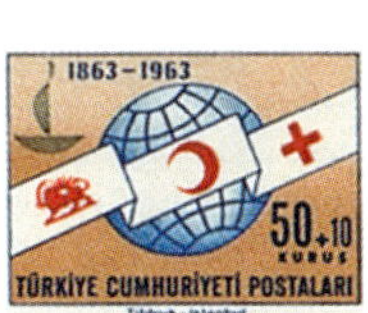
314 Globe and Emblems

315 Mithat Pasha (founder)

1963. Red Cross Centenary. Multicoloured.
2024 50k.+10k. Type **314** 10 10
2025 60k.+10k. "Flowers" emblem (vert) 10 10
2026 100k.+10k. Three emblems on flags 10 10

1963. Centenary of Turkish Agricultural Bank.
2027 – 30k. brown, green and yellow 10 10
2028 – 50k. blue and lilac . . . 10 10
2029 **315** 60k. green and black . . 10 10
DESIGNS—HORIZ: 30k. Ploughing and irrigation; 50k. Agricultural Bank, Ankara.

316 Exhibition Hall, Istanbul, and 5pi. stamp of 1863

1963. "Istanbul'63" International Stamp Exn.
2030 **316** 10k. salmon, black and yellow 10 10
2031 – 50k. green, red and black 10 10
2032 – 60k. sepia, black and blue 10 10
2033 – 100k. violet and purple 10 10
2034 – 130k. brown, orge & yell 10 10
DESIGNS: 50k. Sultan Ahmed's Mosque, Obelisk and 3pi. on 2pa. Nationalist Government (Angora) stamp of 1920; 60k. Istanbul skyline and 10pi. (Angora) stamp of 1922; 100k. Rumeli Fort and 6k. stamp of 1929/30; 130k. Ankara Fort and 12½k. air stamp of 1934.

317 "Co-operation"

1963. Europa.
2035 **317** 50k. orange, black and red 10 10
2036 130k. blue, black & green 15 10

318 Ataturk and Old Parliament House

319 Kemal Ataturk

1963. 40th Anniv of Turkish Republic. Multicoloured.
2037 30k. Type **318** 10 10
2038 50k. Ataturk and flag . . . 10 10
2039 60k. Ataturk and new Parliament House 15 10

1963. 25th Death Anniv of Kemal Ataturk.
2040 **319** 50k. multicoloured . . . 15 10
2041 60k. multicoloured . . . 15 10

320 R.S. Dag (painter)

321 N.A.T.O. Emblem and "XV"

1964. Cultural Celebrities.
2042 – 1k. black and red . . . 10 10
2043 – 5k. black and green . . 10 10
2044 **320** 10k. black and brown . . 15 10
2045 – 50k. black and blue . . 55 10
2046 – 60k. black and grey . . 65 10
2047 – 100k. ultramarine & blue 85 10
2048 – 130k. black and green 2·40 00
PORTRAITS: 1k. H. R. Gurpinar (romanticist, birth cent); 5k. J. H. Izmirli (savant, 20th death anniv); 10k. Type **320** (20th death anniv); 50k. R. Z. M. Ekrem (writer, 50th deathanniv); 60k. A. M. Pasa (comm and er, 125th birth anniv); 100k. A. Rasim (writer, birth cent); 130k. S. Zeki (mathematician, birthcent).

1964. 15th Anniv of N.A.T.O.
2049 **321** 50k. red, violet & turq 15 10
2050 – 130k. black and red . . 20 10
DESIGN: 130k. N.A.T.O. emblem and laurel sprig.

322 "Europa" holding Torch

1964. 15th Anniv of Council of Europe.
2051 **322** 50k. blue, brown & yell 10 10
2052 – 130k. orange, ultramarine and blue 15 10
DESIGN: 130k. Torch and circlet of stars.

323 Haga Mosque, Istanbul

324 Kars Castle

1964. Tourist Issue.
2053 **323** 50k. green and olive . . 10 10
2054 – 50k. red and purple . . 10 10
2055 – 50k. violet and blue . . 10 10
2056 – 60k. green, black & pur 10 10
2057 – 60k. brown and sepia . . 10 10
DESIGNS—HORIZ: No. 2054 Temple of Zeus, Silifke; 2055 Amasra. VERT: No. 2056 Mersin; 2057 Augustus' Temple, Ankara.

1964. 900th Anniv of Conquest of Kars.
2058 **324** 50k. black and lilac . . . 10 10
2059 – 130k. multicoloured . . 15 10
DESIGN: 130k. Alpaslan warrior.

325 Europa "Flower"

326 Grazing Cattle

1964. Europa.
2060 **325** 50k. blue, grey and orange 30 10
2061 130k. purple, green & bl 45 20

1964. Animal Protection Fund. Multicoloured.
2062 10k.+5k. Type **326** 10 10
2063 30k.+5k. Horned sheep . . 10 10
2064 50k.+5k. Horses 15 10
2065 60k.+5k. Three horned sheep 20 10
2066 100k.+5k. Dairy cows . . . 35 10
The 30k. and 60k. are vert.

327 Running

328 Mustafa Resit

1964. Olympic Games, Tokyo.
2067 **327** 10k.+5k. black, red and brown 15 10
2068 – 50k.+5k. black, red and olive 15 10
2069 – 60k.+5k. black, red and blue 15 10
2070 – 100k.+5k. black, red and violet 30 10
DESIGNS—VERT: 50k. Torch-bearer; 60k.Wrestling; 100k. Throwing the discus.

1964. 125th Anniv of Reformation Decrees. Multicoloured.
2071 50k. Mustafa Resit and the pashas (horiz 48 × 32mm) 20 10
2072 60k. Type **328** 20 10
2073 100k. As 50k. 25 10

329 Kemal Ataturk

330 Glider

1964.
2074 **329** 1k. green 10 10
2075 5k. blue 10 10
2076 10k. blue 45 10
2077 25k. green 85 10
2078 30k. purple . . . . . . 1·10 10
2079 50k. brown . . . . . . 1·75 10
2080 150k. orange . . . . . 5·00 10

1965. 40th Anniv of Turkish Civil Aviation League. Multicoloured.
2081 50k. Parachutist (vert) . . . 10 10
2082 90k. Type **330** 10 10
2083 130k. Ataturk and squadron of aircraft (vert) 10 10

331 CENTO Emblem

1965. Completion of CENTO Telecommunications Projects. Multicoloured.
2084 30k. Type **331** 10 10
2085 50k. Aerialmast (vert) . . . 10 10
2086 75k. H and pressing button (inaugural ceremony) . . 10 10

332 Monument and Soldiers

1965. 50th Anniv of Battle of the Dardanelles. Multicoloured.
2087 50k.+10k. Wreath and map 10 10
2088 90k.+10k. Type **332** 10 10
2089 130k.+10k. Dardanelles Monument and flag (vert) 10 10

333 Beach at Ordu

1965. Tourism. Multicoloured.
2090 30k. Type **333** 10 10
2091 50k. Manavgat Falls 10 10
2092 60k. Istanbul 10 10
2093 100k. Urfa 10 10
2094 130k. Alanya 10 10

334 I.T.U. Emblem and Symbols

1965. I.T.U. Centenary.
2095 **334** 50k. multicoloured . . . 10 10
2096 130k. multicoloured . . 10 10

335 I.C.Y. Emblem

1965. International Co-operation Year.
2097 **335** 100k. red, green and salmon 10 10
2098 130k. violet, green and grey 15 10

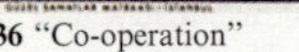

336 "Co-operation" **337** R.N. Guntekin

1965. 1st Anniv of Regional Development Co-operation Pact. Multicoloured.
2099 50k. Type **336** 10 10
2100 75k. Globe and flags of Turkey, Iran and Pakistan 10 10

1965. Cultural Celebrities.
2101 **337** 1k. black and red . . . 10 10
2102 – 5k. black and blue . . . 10 10
2103 – 10k. black and ochre . . 15 10
2104 – 25k. black and brown . . 20 10
2105 – 30k. black and grey . . 35 10
2106 – 50k. black and yellow . . 55 10
2107 – 60k. black and purple . . 50 10
2108 – 150k. black and green 80 10
2109 – 220k. black and brown 55 10
PORTRAITS: 5k. Dr. B. O Akalin; 10k. T. Fikret; 25k. T. Cemil; 30k. Ahmet Vefik Pasa; 50k. O. Seyfettin; 60k. K.Mimaroglu; 150k. H. Z. Usakligil; 220k. Y. K. Beyatli.

338 Kemal Ataturk and Signature **339** Tobacco Plant

1965.
2110 **338** 1k. black and mauve . . 10 10
2111 5k. black and green . . 15 10
2112 10k. black and blue . . 20 10
2113 50k. black and gold . . 20 10
2114 150k. black and silver . . 65 10
See also Nos. 2170/4.

1965. 2nd International Tobacco Congress. Mult.
2115 30k.+5k. Type **339** 10 10
2116 50k.+5k. Leander's Tower and tobacco leaves (horiz) 10 10
2117 100k.+5k. Tobacco leaf . . 10 10

340 Europa "Sprig"

1965. Europa.
2118 **340** 50k. green, blue and grey 40 15
2119 130k. green, blk & ochre 55 30

341 Civilians supporting Map

1965. National Census. Inscr "GENEL NUFUSSAYIMI".
2120 **341** 10k. multicoloured . . . 10 10
2121 – 50k. light green, green and black 10 10
2122 – 100k. black, blue & orge 15 10
DESIGNS—HORIZ: 50k. Year "1965". VERT: 100k. Human eye and figure.

342 Ankara Castle and Airliner

1965. "Ankara'65" National Stamp Exn. Inscr "I. MILLI PULSERGISI".
2123 **342** 10k. red, yellow and violet 10 10
2124 – 30k. multicoloured . . . 10 10
2125 – 50k. blue, red and olive 10 10
2126 – 100k. multicoloured 15 10
DESIGNS: 30k. Archer; 50k. Horseman; 100k.Three thematic "stamps" and medal.

343 Training-ship "Savarona" **344** Halide E. Adivar

1965. Turkish Naval Society Congress.
2128 **343** 50k. brown and blue . . 25 10
2129 – 60k. indigo and blue . . 30 10
2130 – 100k. brown and blue . . 45 10
2131 – 130k. purple and blue . . 55 15
2132 – 220k. black and blue . . 90 20
DESIGNS: 60k. Submarine "PiriReis"; 100k. Destroyer "Alpaslan"; 130k. Destroyer "Gelibolu"; 220k. Destroyer "Gemlik".

1966. Cultural Celebrities.
2133 – 25k. brown and grey . . 40 10
2134 – 30k. brown and mauve 15 10
2135 **344** 50k. black and blue 15 10
2136 – 60k. brown and green . . 40 10
2137 – 130k. black and blue . . 90 10
PORTRAITS: 25k. H. S. Arel; 30k. K. Akdik;60k. Abdurrahman Seref; 130k.Naima.

345 Roof Panel, Green Mausoleum, Burs **346** Volleyball

1966. Turkish Faience. Multicoloured.
2138 50k. Type **345** 25 10
2139 60k. "Spring Flowers", Sultan Mausoleum, Istanbul 90 50
2140 130k. 16th-cent tile, Iznik 60 25

1966. Int Military Volleyball Championships.
2141 **346** 50k. multicoloured . . . 10 10

347 Bodrum **348** Golden Pitcher

1966. Tourism. Multicoloured.
2142 10k. Type **347** 10 10
2143 30k. Kusadasi 15 10
2144 50k. Anadoluhisari (horiz) 10 10
2145 90k. Marmaris 10 10
2146 100k. Izmir (horiz) . . . 10 10

1966. Ancient Works of Art. Multicoloured.
2147 30k.+5k. Ivoryeagle and rabbit (horiz) 10 10
2148 50k.+5k. Deity in basalt . . 10 10
2149 60k.+5k. Bronze bull . . . 15 10
2150 90k.+5k. Type **348** 20 15

349 View of Dam

1966. Inaug of Keban Dam. Multicoloured.
2151 50k. Type **349** 10 10
2152 60k. Keban valley and bridge 10 10

350 King Faisal

1966. Visit of King of Saudi Arabia.
2153 **350** 100k. deep red and red 15 10

351 "Stamp" and "Postmark"

1966. "Balkanfila "Stamp Exhibition, Istanbul. Multicoloured.
2154 50k. Type **351** 10 10
2155 60k. Stamp "flower" 10 10
2156 75k. "Stamps" in form of display frames 10 10

353 Sultan Suleiman on Horseback **354** Europa"Ship"

1966. 400th Death Anniv of Sultan Suleiman. Multicoloured.
2158 60k. Type **353** 25 15
2159 90k. Mausoleum, Istanbul 50 20
2160 130k. Sultan Suleiman (profile) 75 45

1966. Europa.
2161 **354** 50k. ultramarine, bl & blk 25 15
2162 130k. purple, lilac & black 50 20

355 Grand Hotel Ephesus, Izmir

1966. 33rd International Fairs Union Congress, Izmir. Multicoloured.
2163 50k.+5k. Type**355** 10 10
2164 60k.+5k. Konak Square, Izmir (vert) 10 10
2165 130k.+5k. Izmir Fair . . . 10 10

356 "Education, Science and Culture"

1966. 20th Anniv of U.N.E.S.C.O.
2166 **356** 130k. chestnut, yellow and brown 10 10

357 University of Technology **358** Ataturk (equestrian statue)

1966. 10th Anniv of Middle East University of Technology. Multicoloured.
2167 50k. Type **357** 10 10
2168 100k. Atomic symbol . . . 10 10
2169 130k. Symbols of the sciences 15 10

1966. As Nos. 2110/14.
2170 **338** 25k. black and green . . 10 10
2171 30k. black and pink . . 15 10
2172 50k. black and violet . . 50 10
2173 90k. black and brown . . 70 10
2174 100k. black and drab . . 80 10

1966. Greetings Card Stamp.
2175 **358** 10k. black and yellow . . 10 10
See also Nos. 2218/9, 2257/8, 2303 and 2418.

359 DeHavill and Dragon Rapide **360** A. Mithat (author)

1967. Air. Aircraft.
2176 **359** 10k. black and pink . . 20 15
2177 – 60k. red, black and green 15 10
2178 – 130k. red, black and blue 35 10
2179 – 220k. red, sepia and ochre 45 10
2180 – 270k. red, blue and salmon 50 10
DESIGNS: 60k. Fokker F27 Friendship; 130k. Douglas DC-9-30; 220k. Douglas DC-3; 270k. Vickers Viscount 700.

1967. Cultural Celebrities.
2181 **360** 1k. black and green . . 10 10
2182 – 5k. black and ochre . . 15 10
2183 – 50k. black and violet . . 35 10
2184 – 100k. black and yellow 85 10
2185 – 150k. black and yellow 1·75 10
PORTRAITS: 5k. T. Reis (naval commander); 50k.S. Mehmet (statesman); 100k. Nedim (philosopher); 150k. O. Hamdi (painter).

361 Karogoz and Hacivat (puppets)

1967. International Tourist Year. Multicoloured.
2186 50k. Type **361** 30 10
2187 60k. Sword and shield game 35 15
2188 90k. Military Band 45 30
2189 100k. Karagoz (puppet) (vert) 70 35

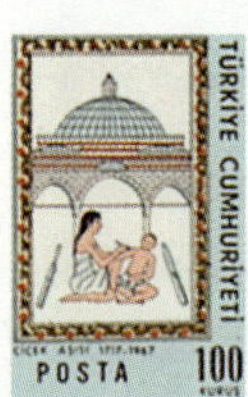

362 "Vaccination" **363** Fallow Deer

1967. 250th Anniv of 1st Smallpox Vaccination, Edirne.
2190 **362** 100k. multicoloured . . 15 10

1967. Game Animals. Multicoloured.
2191 50k. Type **363** 20 10
2192 60k. Wild goat 20 10
2193 100k. Brown bear 30 10
2194 130k. Wild boar 40 15

364 Emblem and Footballers **365** Cogwheels

1967. 20th Int Junior Football Tournament. Mult.
2195 50k. Type **364** 30 10
2196 130k. Footballers and emblem 45 15

1967. Europa.
2197 **365** 100k.+10k. mult 30 10
2198 130k.+10k. mult 50 35

366 Kemal Ataturk

367 Road Junction on Map

1967.

2199 **366** 10k. black and green . . 85 10
2200 50k. black and pink . . 1·25 10

1967. Opening of "E 5" Motorway. Mult.
2201 60k.+5k. Type **367** 15 10
2202 130k.+5k. Motorway map and emblem (vert) 30 15

368 Sivas Hospital

1967. 750th Anniv of Sivas Hospital.
2203 **368** 50k. multicoloured . . . 15 10

369 Selim Tarcan and Olympic Rings

1967. 1st Turkish Olympic Competitions, Istanbul. Multicoloured.
2204 50k. Type **369** 10 10
2205 60k. Pierrede Coubertin and Olympic Rings 10 10

370 St. John's Church, Ephesus

371 Common Kestrel

1967. Pope Paul VI's Visit to Virgin Mary's House, Ephesus. Multicoloured.
2206 130k. Interior of Virgin Mary's House, Ephesus 10 10
2207 220k. Type **370** 15 10

1967. Air. Birds.
2208 **371** 10k. brown and salmon 50 15
2209 – 60k. brown and yellow 40 10
2210 – 130k. purple and blue . . 90 10
2211 – 220k. sepia and green . . 95 10
2212 – 270k. brown and lilac . . 1·50 15
DESIGNS: 60k. Imperial eagle; 130k. Pallid harrier; 220k. Northern sparrow hawk; 270k. Common buzzard.

372 Exhibition Emblem

1967. International Ceramics Exn, Istanbul.
2213 **372** 50k. multicoloured . . . 10 10

373 Emblem and Istanbul Skyline

1967. Congress of International Large Dams Commission, Istanbul.
2214 **373** 130k. blue and drab . . 10 10

374 "Stamps" and Map

1967. "Izmir'67" Stamp Exhibition. Mult.
2215 50k. Type **374** 10 10
2216 60k. "Stamps" and grapes 15 10

1967. Greetings Card Stamps. As T **358**.
2218 10k. black and green . . . 10 10
2219 10k. black and red 10 10
DESIGNS: Equestrian statues of Ataturk at: No.2218 Samsun; No. 2219 Izmir.

375 Decade Emblem

376 Girl with Angora Cat

1967. International Hydrological Decade.
2220 **375** 90k. yellow, black & grn 15 10
2221 130k. yellow, black & lilac 20 10

1967. 125th Anniv of Turkish Veterinary Medical Service. Multicoloured.
2222 50k. Type **376** 15 10
2223 60k. Horse 20 10

377 Human Rights Emblem

378 Kemal Ataturk

1968. Human Rights Year.
2224 **377** 50k. multicoloured . . . 15 10
2225 130k. multicoloured . . 20 10

1968.

2226 **378** 1k. blue and light blue 10 10
2227 5k. green and light green 15 10
2228 50k. brown and yellow 1·10 10
2229 200k. brown and pink 2·75 10

379 "The Investiture"

1968. Turkish Book Miniatures. Multicoloured.
2230 50k. Type **379** 40 10
2231 60k. "Suleiman the Magnificent receiving an ambassador"" (vert) . . . 50 15
2232 90k. "The Sultan's Archery Practice" 70 35
2233 100k. "The Musicians" . . 80 40

380 Scales of Justice

1968. Turkish Courts Centenary. Multicoloured.
(a) Supreme Court.
2234 50k. Type **380** 15 10
2235 60k. Ahmet Cevdet Pasha (president) and scroll . . 20 10
(b) Court of Appeal.
2236 50k. Book 15 10
2237 60k. Mithat Pasha (first president) and scroll . . . 80 40

381 W.H.O. Emblem

1968. 20th Anniv of W.H.O.
2238 **381** 130k.+10k. yellow, black and blue 15 10

382 Europa "Key"

1968. Europa.
2239 **382** 100k. yellow, red and blue 55 25
2240 130k. yellow, red & green . . . . 1·10 35

383 Etem Pasha and Dr. Marko

1968. Turkish Red Crescent Fund. Multicoloured.
2241 50k.+10k. Type **383** 20 10
2242 60k.+10k. Omer Pasha and Dr. Abdullah 25 15
2243 100k.+10k. Kemal Ataturk and Dr. Refik Saydam in front of Red Crescent Headquarters (vert) . . . 30 20

384 "Kismet"

385 "Protection against Usury" (after Koseoglu)

1968. Sadun Boro's World Voyage in Ketch "Kismet".
2244 **384** 50k. multicoloured . . . 35 10

1968. Centenary of Pawnbroking Office, Istanbul.
2245 **385** 50k. multicoloured . . . 20 10

386 Battleof Sakarya and Obverse of Medal

1968. Independence Medal. Multicoloured.
2246 50k. Type **386** 10 10
2247 130k. National Anthem and reverse of medal 20 10

387 Old and New Emblems within "100"

1968. Centenary of Galatasaray High School. Multicoloured.
2248 50k. Type **387** 10 10
2249 60k. Gulbaba offering flowers to BayazetII . . . 20 10
2250 100k. Kemal Ataturk and School Building 30 10

388 President DeGaulle

389 Kemal Ataturk

1968. President De Gaulle's Visit to Turkey.
2251 **388** 130k. multicoloured . . 20 10

1968. 30th Death Anniv of Kemal Ataturk.
2252 **389** 30k. black and yellow . . 15 10
2253 – 50k. black and green . . 15 10
2254 – 60k. black and turquoise 45 10
2255 – 100k. black, green and bistre 35 10
2256 – 250k. multicoloured . . 50 15
DESIGNS: 50k. Ataturk's Cenotaph; 60k. Ataturkat railway carriage window. ($32\frac{1}{2}\times43$ mm): 100k. Ataturk's portrait and "address to youth"; 250k. Ataturk in military uniform.

1968. Greetings Card Stamps. As T **358** but dated "1968".
2257 10k. black and mauve . . . 10 10
2258 10k. black and blue 10 10
DESIGNS: Equestrian statues of Ataturk at: No.2257 Antakya; No. 2258 Zonguldak.

390 Ince Minara Mosque, Konya

391 Dove and N.A.T.O. Emblem

1968. Historic Buildings.
2259 **390** 1k. sepia and brown . . 10 10
2260 – 10k. maroon and purple 10 10
2261 – 50k. green and grey . . 20 10
2262 – 100k. green & light green 75 10
2263 – 200k. blue and light blue 40 10
DESIGNS: 10k. Doner Kumbet (tomb), Kayseri;50k. Karatay University, Konya; 100k. Ortakoy Mosque, Istanbul; 200k. Ulu Mosque, Divrigi.

1969. 20th Anniv of N.A.T.O.
2264 **391** 50k.+10k. black, blue and green 10 10
2265 – 130k.+10k. gold, blue and deep blue 25 15
DESIGN: 130k. Stars around globe and N.A.T.O. emblem.

392 "Education"

1969. Turkish Economy.
2266 **392** 1k. black and red . . . 10 10
2267 1k. black and green . . 10 10
2268 1k. black and violet . . 10 10
2269 1k. black and brown . . 10 10
2270 1k. black and grey . . . 10 10
2271 – 50k. brown and ochre 30 10
2272 – 90k. black and olive . . 50 10
2273 – 100k. red and black . . 25 10
2274 – 180k. violet and orange 1·40 10
DESIGNS: 50k. Farm workers and tractor ("Agriculture"); 90k. Ladle, factory and cogwheel ("Industry"); 100k. Road sign and graph ("Highways"); 180k. Derricks ("Oil Industry").

393 I.L.O. Emblem

1969. 50th Anniv of I.L.O.
2275 **393** 130k. red and black . . 10 10

394 "Hafsa Sultan" (unknown artist)

1969. Hafsa Sultan (medical pioneer) Commem.
2276 **394** 60k. multicoloured . . . 15 15

395 Colonnade

1969. Europa.
2277 **395** 100k. multicoloured . . 20 10
2278 130k. multicoloured . . 25 20

396 Kemal Ataturk in 1919 **397** Symbolic Map of Istanbul

1969. 50thAnniv of Kemal Ataturk's Landing at Samsun. Multicoloured.
2279 50k. Type **396** 15 10
2280 60k. Cargoliner "Bandirma" (horiz) 25 15

1969. 22nd Int Chambers of Commerce Congress, Istanbul.
2281 **397** 130k. multicoloured . . 10 10

398 "Suleiman the Great holding Audience" (16th-cent Turkish miniature) **399** Kemal Ataturk in Civilian Dress

1969. 5th Anniv of Regional Co-operation for Development Pact Miniatures. Multicoloured.
2282 50k. Type **398** 20 10
2283 80k. "Kneeling Servant" (17th-cent Persian) . . . 30 15
2284 130k. "Ladyon Balcony" (18th-cent Mogul–Pakistan) 40 20

1969. 50th Anniv of Erzurum Congress.
2285 **399** 50k. black and violet . . 10 10
2286 – 60k. black and green . . 15 10
DESIGN—HORIZ: 60k. Ataturk's statue, Erzurum.

401 Red Cross Societies' Emblems

1969. 21st International Red Cross Conf, Istanbul.
2291 **401** 100k.+10k. red, blue and ultramarine 10 10
2292 – 130k.+10k. mult 20 10
DESIGN: 130k. Conference emblem and silhouette of Istanbul.

402 Congress Hall

1969. 50th Anniv of Sivas Congress.
2293 **402** 50k. purple, black and red 10 10
2294 – 60k. olive, black & yellow 15 10
DESIGN: 60k. Congress delegates.

403 Halay Scarf Dance

1969. Turkish Folk-dances. Multicoloured.
2295 30k. Bardancers 10 10
2296 50k. Caydacira "candle" dance 20 10
2297 60k. Type **403** 25 10
2298 100k. Kilic-Kalkans word dance 35 10
2299 130k. Zeybekdance (vert) . . 40 15

404 Bleriot XI "Prince Celaladdin"

1969. 55th Anniv of First Turkish Airmail Service.
2300 **404** 60k. deep blue and blue 10 10
2301 – 75k. black and bistre . . 10 10
DESIGN: 75k. 1914 First Flight cover.

405 "Kutadgu Bilig"

1969. 900th Anniv of "Kutadgu Bilig" (political manual) Compilation.
2302 **405** 130k. brown, gold and bistre 10 10

1969. Greetings Card Stamp. As T **358**.
2303 10k. brown and green . . . 10 10
DESIGN: 10k. Equestrian statue of Ataturk at Bursa.

406 "Ataturk's Arrival" (S.Tuna)

1969. 50th Anniv of Kemal Ataturk's Arrival in Ankara. Multicoloured.
2304 50k. Type **406** 40 20
2305 60k. Ataturk's motorcade 40 25

407 "Erosion Control"

1970. Nature Conservation Year. Multicoloured.
2306 50k.+10k. Type **407** 15 10
2307 60k.+10k. "Protection of Flora" 10 10
2308 130k.+10k. "Protection of Wildlife" 30 15

408 Bosphorus Bridge (model) (½-size illustration)

1970. Commencement of Work on Bosphorus Bridge. Multicoloured.
2309 60k. Type **408** 25 10
2310 130k. Symbolic bridge linking Europe and Asia 45 20

409 Ataturk and Signature **410** Education Year Emblem

1970.
2311 **409** 1k. brown and red . . . 10 10
2312 50k. green and olive . . 20 10

1970. International Education Year.
2313 **410** 130k. blue, purple & mve 10 10

411 Turkish Pavilion Emblem **412** Kemal Ataturk

1970. World Fair "Expo '70", Osaka, Japan. Multicoloured.
2314 50k. Type **411** 10 10
2315 100k. Turkish pavilion and Expo emblem 15 10

1970.
2316 **412** 5k. black and silver . . . 10 10
2317 30k. black and bistre . . 25 10
2318 50k. black and pink . . 30 10
2319 75k. black and lilac . . . 45 10
2320 100k. black and blue . . 50 10

413 Opening Ceremony

1970. 50th Anniv of Turkish National Assembly. Multicoloured.
2321 50k. Type **413** 10 10
2322 60k. First Assembly in session 10 10

414 Emblem of Cartography Directorate

1970. "75 Years of Turkish Cartography". Multicoloured.
2323 50k. Type **414** 10 10
2324 60k. Dornier Do-28 airplane and contour map 15 10
2325 100k. Survey equipment . . 10 10
2326 130k. Lt.-Gen. Mehmet Sevki Pasha and relief map of Turkey 15 10
Nos. 2324 and 2326 are larger, size 48 × 33mm.

415 "Flaming Sun"

1970. Europa.
2327 **415** 100k. red, orange & black 25 10
2328 130k. green, orange & blk 45 25

416 NewU.P.U. Headquarters Building

1970. NewU.P.U. Headquarters Building, Berne.
2329 **416** 60k. black, blue & ltblue 10 10
2330 130k. black, green and light green 15 10

417 "Roe-deer" (Seker Ahmet Pasha) **418** "Turkish Folklore"

1970. Turkish Paintings. Multicoloured.
2331 250k. Type **417** 25 15
2332 250k. "Ladywith Mimosa" (Osman Hamdi) 25 15

Seealso Nos. 2349/50, 2364/5, 2396/7, 2416/17 and 2443/4.

1970. "Ankara70" National Stamp Exhibition. Multicoloured.
2333 10k. "Tree" of stamps and open album (vert) 10 10
2334 50k. Type **418** 10 10
2335 60k. Ataturk statue and "stamps" 15 10

419 Fethiye (Turkey)

1970. 6th Anniv of Regional Co-operation for Development. Multicoloured.
2337 60k. Type **419** 10 10
2338 80k. Seeyo-Se-Pol Bridge, Isfahan (Iran) 10 10
2339 130k. Saiful Malook Lake (Pakistan) 10 10
No.2338 is larger 41 × 26mm.

420 Tombof Haci Bektas Veli

1970. 700th Death Anniv of Haci Bektas Veli (mystic). Multicoloured.
2340 30k. Type **420** 10 10
2341 100k. Sultan Balim's tomb (vert) 25 10
2342 180k. Haci Bektas Veli(vert) 35 10
No.2342 is larger, size 32 × 49mm.

421 Symbolic "Fencer" and Globe

1970. World Fencing Championships.
2343 **421** 90k.+10k. black, blue and lightblue 10 10
2344 – 130k.+10k. orange, green, black and blue 15 10
DESIGN: 130k. Modern fencer, folk-dancer and globe.

422 I.S.O. Emblem

1970. 8th International St and ardization Organization General Assembly, Ankara.
2345 **422** 110k. red, gold and black 10 10
2346 150k. blue, gold and black 10 10

423 U.N. Emblem within Windmill

1970. 25th Anniv of United Nations. Mult.
2347 100k. Type **423** 10 10
2348 220k. World's people supporting U.N. (vert) . . 15 10

1970. Turkish Paintings. As T **417**. Mult.
2349 250k. "Fevzi Cakmak" (Avni Lifij) (vert) 35 10
2350 250k. "Fishing-boats" (Nazmi Ziya) (75 × 33mm) 30 10

424 Turkish Troops Advancing

1971. 50th Anniv of First Battle of Inonu.
2351 **424** 100k. multicoloured . . 20 10
See also No.2368.

425 Kemal Ataturk

429 Hands enclosing "Four Races"

428 "Turkish Village" (A. Sekur)

1971.

2352 **425** 5k. blue and grey . . . 10 10
2353 25k. red and grey . . . 30 10
2354 – 25k. brown and pink . . 10 10
2355 **425** 100k. violet and grey . . 50 10
2356 – 100k. green and flesh . . 50 10
2357 – 250k. blue and drab . . 95 10
2358 **425** 400k. green and bistre 2·10 10

DESIGNS: Nos. 2354, 2356 and 2357, Portraits similar to Type **425** but larger, 21 × 26 mm, and with face value at bottom right.

1971. Turkish Paintings. Multicoloured.
2364 250k. Type **428** 25 10
2365 250k. "Yildiz Palace Garden" (A. R. Bicakcilar) 25 10

See also Nos. 2396/7, 2416/17 and 2443/4.

1971. Racial Equality Year.
2366 **429** 100k. multicoloured . . 10 10
2367 250k. multicoloured . . 10 10

1971. 50th Anniv of Second Battle of Inonu. Design similar to T **424**. Multicoloured.
2368 100k. Turkish machine-gunners 20 10

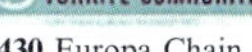

430 Europa Chain

431 Pres. C. Gursel

1971. Europa.
2369 **430** 100k. violet, yellow & bl 55 25
2370 150k. green, red & orange 70 40

1971. 11th Anniv of 27 May 1960 Revolution.
2371 **431** 100k. multicoloured . . 15 10

432 Lockhead Super Starfighter

433 "Careof Children"

1971. Air."60 Years of Turkish Aviation". Multicoloured.
2372 110k. Type **432** 35 10
2373 200k. Victory Monument, Afyon and aircraft . . . 50 10
2374 250k. Air Force emblem and jet fighters (horiz) 55 10
2375 325k. Lockheed Super Starfighters and pilot . . 95 15
2376 400k. Bleriot XI airplane of 1911 (horiz) 80 15
2377 475k. Hezarfen Celebi's "bird flight" from Galata Tower (horiz) . . . . . 1·10 20

1971. 50th Anniv of Children's Protection Society.
2378 **433** 50k.+10k. red, pur & blk 10 10
2379 – 100k.+15k. mult 10 10
2380 – 110k.+15k. mult 10 10

DESIGNS—VERT: 100k. Child standing on protective hand . HORIZ: 110k. Mother and child.

434 Selimiye Mosque, Edirne

1971. 7th Anniv of Regional Co-operation for Development Pact. Mosques. Multicoloured.
2381 100k. Type **434** 10 10
2382 150k. Chalharbagh Mosque School (Iran) 10 10
2383 200k. Badshahi Mosque (Pakistan) (horiz) 15 10

435 Alpaslan (Seljuk leader) and Cavalry

1971. 900th Anniv of Battle of Malazgirt.
2384 **435** 100k. multicoloured . . 20 10
2385 – 250k. red, yellow & black 35 15

DESIGN: 250k. Seljuk mounted archer.

436 Officer and Troop Column

1971. 50th Anniv of Battle of Sakarya.
2386 **436** 100k. multicoloured . . 20 10

437 Diesel Train and Map (Turkey–Iran Line)

1971. International RailLinks.
2387 – 100k. multicoloured . . 20 10
2388 – 110k. violet and blue . . 20 10
2389 **437** 250k. multicoloured . . 40 10

DESIGNS: 100k. Diesel train crossing bridge(Turkey–Bulgaria line); 110k. Train ferry "Orhan Atliman", Lake Van (Turkey–Iran line).

438 Football

1971. Mediterranean Games, Izmir.
2390 **438** 100k. black, violet & blue 15 10
2391 – 200k. multicoloured . . 15 10

DESIGN—VERT: 200k. "Athlete and stadium".

439 Tomb of Cyrus the Great

1971. 2500th Anniv of Persian Empire.
2393 **439** 25k. multicoloured . . . 10 10
2394 – 100k. multicoloured . . 15 10
2395 – 150k. brown and drab 25 10

DESIGNS—VERT: 100k. Persian mosaic of woman. HORIZ: 150k. Kemal Ataturk and Riza Shah Pahlavi.

1971. Turkish Paintings. As T **428**. Mult.
2396 250k. "Sultan Mohammed I and Entourage" 25 15
2397 250k. "Cinili Kosk Palace" 25 15

441 U.N.I.C.E.F. Emblem

442 Yunus Emre

1971. 25th Anniv of U.N.I.C.E.F.
2404 **441** 100k.+10k. mult 10 10
2405 250k.+15k. mult 10 10

1971. 650th Death Anniv of Yunus Emre (folk-poet).
2406 **442** 100k. multicoloured . . 10 10

443 First Turkish Map of the World (1072) and Book Year Emblem

1972. International Book Year.
2407 **443** 100k. multicoloured . . 30 10

444 Doves and N.A.T.O. Emblem

445 Human Heart

1972. 20th Anniv of Turkey's Membership of N.A.T.O.
2408 **444** 100k. black, grey & green 30 15
2409 250k. black, grey and blue 60 20

1972. World Health Day.
2410 **445** 250k.+25k. red, black and grey 10 10

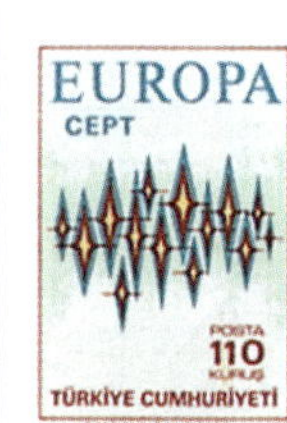

447 "Communications"

448 "Fisherman" (G. Dareli)

1972. Europa.
2414 **447** 110k. multicoloured . . 90 30
2415 250k. multicoloured . . 1·40 40

1972. Turkish Paintings. As T **428**. Multicoloured.
2416 250k. "Gebze" (Osman Hamdi) 25 15
2417 250k. "Forest"(S. A. Pasa) 25 15

1972. AsT **358**.
2418 25k. black and brown . . . 10 10

DESIGN: 25k. Equestrian statue of Ataturk at Ankara.

1972. Regional Co-operation for Development. Multicoloured.
2419 100k. Type **448** 40 15
2420 125k. "Will and Power" (Chughtai) 45 20
2421 150k. "Iranian Woman" (Behzad) 70 35

449 Olympic Rings

1972. Olympic Games, Munich.
2422 **449** 100k.+15k. mult 15 10
2423 – 110k.+25k. mult 10 10
2424 – 250k.+25k. mult 15 15

DESIGNS: 110k. "Athletes"; 250k. "Stadium".

450 Ataturkat Observation Post

1972. 50th Anniv of Turkish War of Liberation. Multicoloured. (a) The Great Offensive.
2425 100k. Type **450** 20 10
2426 110k. Artillery 25 10

(b)Comm and er-in-Chief's Offensive.
2427 100k. Hand-to-hand fighting 25 10

(c) Entry into Izmir.
2428 100k. Commanders in open car 25 10

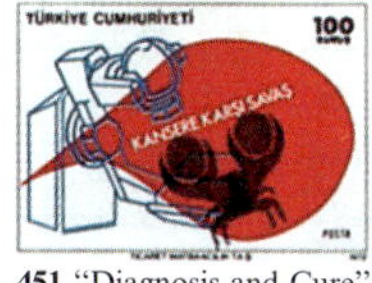

451 "Diagnosis and Cure"

452 Kemal Ataturk

1972. Fight against Cancer.
2429 **451** 100k. red, black and blue 10 10

1972. Various sizes.
2430 **452** 5k. light blue on blue 10 10
2430a 25k. orange on orange 10 10
2431 100k. lake on buff . . 55 10
2431a 100k. light grey on grey 15 10
2431b 100k. olive on green . . 20 10
2432 110k. blue on blue . . 50 10
2432a 125k. green and grey 60 10
2433 150k. brown on buff 50 10
2433a 150k. green on green 15 10
2434 175k. purple on yellow 75 10
2434a 200k. red on buff . . . 60 10
2434b 200k. brown on buff 20 10
2435 250k. lilac on pink . . 40 10
2435a 400k. turquoise on blue 25 10
2436 500k. violet on pink . . 1·00 10
2437 500k. blue on blue . . 45 10
2438 10l. mauve on pink . . 90 10

453 U.I.C. Emblem

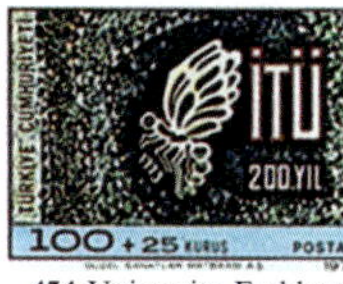

454 University Emblem

1972. 50th Anniv of International Railway Union.
2439 **453** 100k. brown, buff & grn 10 10

1973. Bicent of Technical University, Istanbul.
2440 **454** 100k.+25k. mult 10 10

455 Europa "Posthorn"

456 Helmet and Sword

1973. Europa.
2441 **455** 110k. multicoloured . . 50 30
2442 250k. multicoloured . . 1·10 50

1973. Turkish Painters. As T **428**. Multicoloured.
2443 250k. "Old Almshouses, Istanbul" (Ahmet Ziya Akbulut) (horiz) 25 15
2444 250k. "Flowersin Vase" (Suleyman Seyyit) (vert) 25 15

1973. Land Forces' Day.
2445 **456** 90k. green, brown & grey 10 10
2446 – 100k. green, brown and lightgreen 10 10

DESIGN: 100k. As Type **456**, butwreath enclosingdesign.

457 Carved Head, Tomb of Antiochus I (Turkey)
458 Peace Dove and "50"

1973. Regional Co-operation for Development. Multicoloured.
2447 100k. Type **457** 10 10
2448 150k. Statue, Lut excavations (Iran) 15 10
2449 200k. Street in Moenjodaro (Pakistan) 20 10

1973. 50th Anniv of Lausanne Peace Treaty.
2450 **458** 100k.+25k. mult 10 10

459 Minelayer "Nusret II"
460 "Al-Biruni" (from 16th-cent uryminiature)

1973. Bicentenary of Turkish Navy. Mult.
2451 5k. Type **459** 10 10
2452 25k. Destroyer "Istanbul" 15 10
2453 100k. Motortorpedo-boat "Simsek" 30 10
2454 250k. Cadetbrig "Nurud-i-Futuh" (48 × 32mm) . . . 90 20

1973. Millenary of Abu Reihanal-Biruni.
2455 **460** 250k. multicoloured . . 10 10

461 "Equal Opportunity"
463 "Balkanfila" Emblem

1973. Centenary of Darussafaka High School.
2456 **461** 100k. multicoloured . . 10 10

1973. "Balkanfila IV" Stamp Exhibition, Izmir (1st issue).
2458 **463** 100k. multicoloured . . 10 10
See also Nos.2462/3.

464 Sivas Sheepdog
465 Kemal Ataturk

1973. Animals.
2459 **464** 25k. blue, yellow & black 10 10
2460 – 100k. yellow, black & bl 20 10
DESIGN: 100k. Angoracat.

1973. 35th Death Anniv of Kemal Ataturk.
2461 **465** 100k. brown and drab 10 10

466 Bosphorus and "Stamps"
467 "Flower" Emblem

1973. "Balkanfila IV" Stamp Exhibition (2nd issue). Multicoloured.
2462 110k. Type **466** 10 10
2463 250k. "Balkanfila" in decorative script 15 10

1973. 50th Anniv of Republic.
2464 **467** 100k. red, violet and blue 10 10
2465 – 250k. multicoloured . . 15 10
2466 – 475k. yellow and blue . . 20 10
DESIGNS: 250k. "Hands" supporting "50"; 475k. Cogwheels and ears of corn.

468 Bosphorus Bridge
469 Bosphorus Bridge and U.N.I.C.E.F. Emblem

1973. Opening of Bosphorus Bridge, Istanbul. Multicoloured.
2468 100k. Type **468** 10 10
2469 150k. View of Bosphorus and bridge 20 10

1973. U.N.I.C.E.F. Ceremony. Children of Europe and Asia linked by Bosphorus Bridge.
2470 **469** 200k. multicoloured . . 25 10

470 Mevlana Celaleddin
471 Cotton

1973. 700th Death Anniv of Mevlana Celaleddin (poet and mystic).
2471 – 100k. green, blue & black 15 10
2472 **470** 250k. multicoloured . . 25 10
DESIGN: 100k. Tomb and dancing dervishes.

1973. Export Products.
2473 **471** 75k. grey, blue and black 15 10
2474 – 90k. bistre, blue and black 20 10
2475 – 100k. black, blue & green 25 10
2476 – 250k. multicoloured . . 1·75 10
2477 – 325k. yellow, blue & blk 50 10
2478 – 475k. black, blue & brn 45 10
DESIGNS: 90k. Grapes; 100k. Figs; 250k. Citrus fruits; 325k. Tobacco; 475k. Hazelnuts.

472 Fokker Fellowship
473 President Inonu

1973. Air. Multicoloured.
2479 110k. Type **472** 25 10
2480 250k. Douglas DC-10 . . . 55 10

1973. President Inonu's Death.
2481 **473** 100k. brown and buff . . 10 10

474 "Statue of a King" (Hittiteera)
475 Doctor and Patient

1974. Europa. Sculptures. Multicoloured.
2482 110k. Type **474** . . . . . . 1·25 50
2483 250k. "Statuette of a Child" (c. 2000 B.C.) . . . . . . 2·10 80

1974. 75th Anniv of Sisli Paediatrics Hospital.
2484 **475** 110k. black, grey and blue 10 10

476 Silver and Gold Idol
477 Population Year Emblem

1974. Archaeological Treasures. Multicoloured.
2485 125k. Type **476** 10 10
2486 175k. Paintedjar (horiz) . . 10 10
2487 200k. Bulls (statuettes) (horiz) 15 10
2488 250k. Jug 20 10

1974. World Population Year.
2489 **477** 250k.+25k. mult 15 10

479 Turkish Carpet

1974. Regional Co-operation for Development. Multicoloured.
2496 100k. Type **479** 45 25
2497 150k. Iranian carpet 80 40
2498 200k. Pakistani carpet . . . 1·25 50

480 Dove and Map of Cyprus

1974. Turkish Intervention in Cyprus.
2499 **480** 250k. multicoloured . . 15 10

481 "Getting to Grips"
482 Dove with Letter

1974. World Free-style Wrestling Championships, Ankara. Multicoloured.
2500 90k. Type **481** 10 10
2501 100k. "Throw" (vert) . . . 15 10
2502 250k. "Lock" 20 10

1974. Centenary of Universal Postal Union.
2503 **482** 110k. gold, dp blue & bl 10 10
2504 – 200k. brown and green 10 10
2505 – 250k. multicoloured . . 15 10
DESIGNS: 200k. Dove; 250k. Arrows encircling globe.

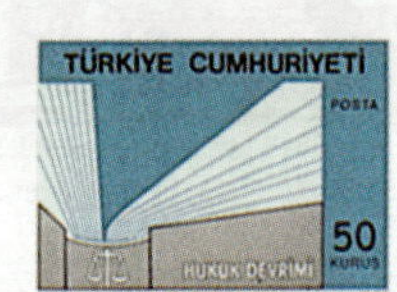

483 Open Book (Law Reform)

1974. Works and Reforms of Ataturk (1st series).
2506 **483** 50k. black and blue . . 10 10
2507 – 150k. multicoloured . . 15 10
2508 – 400k. multicoloured . . 15 10
DESIGNS—VERT: 150k. "Tree" ("National Economy"); 400k. Students facing sun ("Reform of Education").
See also Nos. 2543/5, 2566/8, 2597/9, 2639/41 and 2670/2.

484 Marconi
485 Arrows (3rd Five Year Development Programme)

1974. Birth Centenary of Marconi (radio pioneer).
2509 **484** 250k.+25k. black, brown and red 15 10

1974. "Turkish Development".
2510 **485** 25k. black and brown . . 10 10
2511 – 100k. grey and brown 15 10
DESIGNS—HORIZ: 100k. Map of Turkey within cogwheel (industrialization).

486 Volleyball
487 Dr. Albert Schweitzer

1974. BallGames.
2512 **486** 125k. black and blue . . 20 10
2513 – 175k. black and orange 20 10
2514 – 250k. black and green 30 10
DESIGNS: 175k. Basketball; 250k. Football.

1975. Birth Centenary of Dr. Albert Schweitzer.
2515 **487** 250k.+50k. mult 15 10

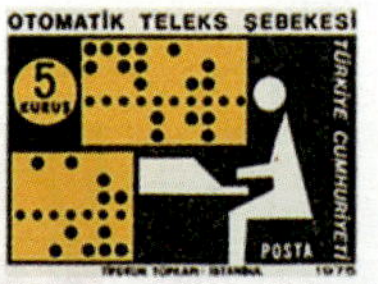

488 Automatic Telex Network

1975. Posts and Telecommunications.
2516 **488** 5k. black and yellow . . 10 10
2517 – 50k. green and orange 10 10
2518 – 100k. black and blue . 15 10
DESIGNS: 50k. Postal cheques; 100k. Radio link.

489 "Going to the Classroom" (I. Sivga)
490 Karacaoglan Monument (H. Gezer), Mut

1975. Children's Drawings. Multicoloured.
2519 25k. Type **489** 10 10
2520 50k. "View from a Village" (H. Dogru) 10 10
2521 100k. "Folklore" (B. Aktan) 10 10

1975. Karacaoglan (musician) Commem.
2522 **490** 110k. mauve, green & brn 10 10

491 "Orange-gatheringin Hatay" (C. Tollu)

1975. Europa. Paintings. Multicoloured.
2523 110k. Type **491** 65 55
2524 250k. "The Yoruks" (T. Zaim) . . . . 1·10 95

492 Turkish Porcelain Vase

493 Namibi allocated on Map of Africa

1975. Regional Co-operation for Development. Traditional Crafts. Multicoloured.
2525 110k. Type **492** 40 30
2526 200k. Ceramicplate (Iran) (horiz) 80 40
2527 250k. Camel-skinvase (Pakistan) . . . . 1·25 60

1975. Namibia Day.
2528 **493** 250k.+50k. mult 10 10

494 Horon Folk-dancers

1975. Turkish Folk Dances. Multicoloured.
2529 100k. Type **494** 20 15
2530 125k. Kasik 25 15
2531 175k. Bengi 30 15
2532 250k. Kasap 40 15
2533 325k. Kafkas (vert) 55 25

495 "Oguz Khan slaying Dragon"

498 Two Women and Symbol (Women's Participation in Public Life)

497 Turbot

1975. Tales of Dede Korkut. Multicoloured.
2534 90k. Type **495** 10 10
2535 175k. Tale of Duha Koca Oglu Deli Dumrul Hikayesi (horiz) 10 10
2536 200k. "Pillaging the Home of Salur Kazan" 10 10

1975. Fishes. Multicoloured.
2538 75k. Type **497** 60 55
2539 90k. Common carp 80 55
2540 175k. Brown trout . . . . 1·40 75
2541 250k. Red mullet . . . . 2·10 80
2542 475k. Gilthead seabream . . 2·75 95

1975. Works and Reforms of Ataturk (2nd series).
2543 **498** 100k. red, black and stone 10 10
2544 – 110k. multicoloured . . 10 10
2545 – 250k. multicoloured . . 15 10
DESIGNS—VERT: 110k. Symbol and inscription (Nationalization of Insurance Companies). HORIZ: 250k. Arrows (Orientation of the Fine Arts).

499 Z. Gokalp 500 Ceramic Plate

1976. Birth Cent of Ziya Gokalp (philosopher).
2546 **499** 200k.+25k. mult 10 10

1976. Europa. Multicoloured.
2547 200k. Type **500** . . . . . . 1·10 90
2548 400k. Dessert jug . . . . . 2·25 1·75

501 Silhouette of Istanbul

1976. 7th Islamic Conference, Istanbul.
2549 **501** 500k. multicoloured . . 15 10

502 "Lunchin Field" (S. Yucel)

1976. "Samsun'76" Youth Stamp Exn. Mult.
2550 50k. Type **502** 10 10
2551 200k. "Boats on the Bosphorus" (E. Kosemen) (vert) 10 10
2552 400k. "Winter View" (R. Cetinkaya) 15 10

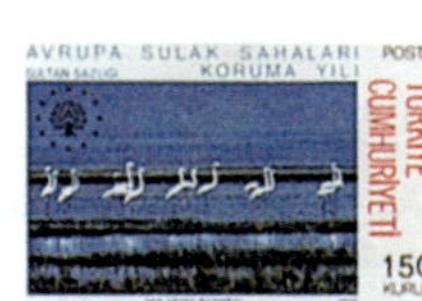

503 Sultan Marshes

1976. European Wetlands Conservation Year. Turkish Land scapes. Multicoloured.
2553 150k. Type **503** 20 10
2554 200k. Lake Manyas 20 10
2555 250k. Lake Borabey 30 10
2556 400k. Manavgat waterfalls 30 10

504 "Hodjawith Liver"

505 Games Emblem and Flame

1976. Nasreddin Hodja (humourist) Commem. "The Liver and the Kite". Multicoloured.
2557 150k. Type **504** 10 10
2558 250k. "Friend of fersrecipe" 10 10
2559 600k. "Kite takes liver, leaving recipe" 15 10

1976. Olympic Games, Montreal.
2560 **505** 100k. red and blue . . . 15 10
2561 – 400k. multicoloured . . 20 10
2562 – 600k. multicoloured . . 20 10
DESIGNS—HORIZ: 400k."Athlete" as "76". VERT: 600k. Games emblem.

506 Kemal Ataturk (Turkey)

1976. Regional Co-operation for Development. Heads of State. Multicoloured.
2563 100k. Type **506** 10 10
2564 200k. Riza Shah Pahlavi (Iran) 10 10
2565 250k. Mohammed Ali Jinnah (Pakistan) 15 10

507 Peace Dove and Sword (Army Reform)

508 White Spoonbill

1976. Works and Reforms of Ataturk (3rd series).
2566 **507** 100k. black and red . . 10 10
2567 – 200k. multicoloured . . 10 10
2568 – 400k. multicoloured . . 15 10
DESIGNS: 200k. Words, books and listeners (Ataturk's speeches); 400k. Peace doves and globe ("Peace throughout the World").

1976. Turkish Birds.Multicoloured.
2569 100k.+25k. Type **508** . . . 30 15
2570 150k.+25k. European roller 40 20
2571 200k.+25k. Greater flamingo 60 25
2572 400k.+25k. Waldrapp (horiz) . . . . 1·00 1·25

509 "Hora" (oil exploration ship)

510 Musical Symbols

1977.
2573 **509** 400k. multicoloured . . 20 10

1977. 150th Anniv of Presidential Symphony Orchestra.
2574 **510** 200k. multicoloured . . 10 10

511 Kemal Ataturk in"100"

1977. Centenary of Parliament.
2575 **511** 200k. black and red . . 10 10
2576 – 400k. black and brown 15 10
DESIGN: 400k. Hand placing ballot-paper in box.

512 Pamukkale

1977. Europa. Land scapes. Multicoloured.
2577 200k. Type **512** . . . . . . 1·00 90
2578 400k. Zelve . . . . 2·00 1·25

513 Edict of Karamanoglu Mehmet Bey and "Ongun" Bird

1977. 700th Anniv of Official Turkish Language.
2579 **513** 200k.+25k. black and green 10 10

514 Head-shaped Vase, Turkey

1977. Regional Co-operation for Development. Pottery. Multicoloured.
2580 100k. Type **514** 20 10
2581 255k. Earthenware pot (Iran) 35 10
2582 675k. Model bullock cart (Pakistan) 80 15

515 Stylized Sailing Yacht

523 Kemal Ataturk

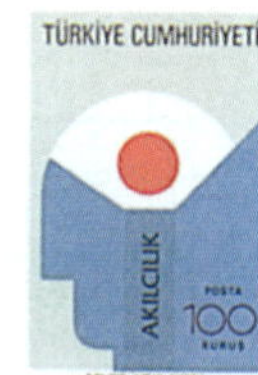

524 "Head and Book" (Rationalism)

522 "Globe" and Emblem

1977. European Finn Class Sailing Championships.
2584 **515** 150k. black, blue and light blue 10 10
2585 – 200k. blue and deep blue 20 10
2586 – 250k. black and blue . . 25 10
DESIGNS—HORIZ: 200k. VERT: 250k. Both showing stylized sailing yachts.

1977. Surch **10 KURUS**.
2592 **409** 10k. on 1k. brn & red 10 10

1977. 10th World Energy Conference.
2593 **522** 100k.+25k. black, brown and pink 10 10
2594 – 600k.+50k. red, black and blue 10 10
DESIGN: 600k. Similar design showing a "globe" and emblem.

1977. Size $20\frac{1}{4} \times 22\frac{1}{4}$mm.
2595 **523** 200k. blue on light blue 25 10
2596 250k. turquoise on blue 30 10
See also Nos.2619/25.

1977. Works and Reform of Ataturk (4th series). Multicoloured.
2597 100k. Type **524** 10 10
2598 200k. Words by Ataturk (National Sovereignty) . . 10 10
2599 400k. Symbol (Leadership for Liberation of Nations) 15 10

525 Allama Muhammad Iqbal

526 Overturned Car

1977. Birth Centenary of Allama Muhammad Iqbal (Pakistani poet).
2600 **525** 400k. multicoloured . . 15 10

1977. Road Safety.
2601 **526** 50k. black, blue and red 10 10
2602 – 150k. black, grey and red 10 10
2603 – 250k. black, brown & red 15 10
2604 – 500k. black, grey and red 25 10
2605 – 800k. deep green, green and red 35 10
2606 – 10l. green, red and black 45 10
DESIGNS—VERT: 150k. Arrow crossing white lines and pool of blood; 500k. "Children crossing" sign; 800k. "No overtaking" sign; 10l. Footprints in road and on pedestrian crossing. HORIZ: 250k. Tractor pulling trailer loaded with people.

527 Lighted Match and Trees

531 Riza Shah Pahlavi of Iran

530 Ishakpasa Palace, Dogubeyazit

1977. Forest Conservation.
2607 **527** 50k. black, red and green 10 10
2608 – 250k. black, green & grey 20 10
DESIGN: 250k. "Tree germination".
See also No.2699.

1978. Europa. Multicoloured.
2616 2½l. Type **530** 1·00 60
2617 5l. Anamur Castle 1·75 1·25

1978. Birth Centenary of Riza Shah Pahlavi of Iran.
2618 **531** 5l. multicoloured 10 10

1978. AsType **523** but larger, 19 × 25mm.
2619 10k. brown 10 10
2620 50k. grey 10 10
2621 1l. red 10 10
2622 2½l. lilac 10 10
2623 5l. blue 15 10
2624 25l. blue and light blue 50 10
2625 50l. orange and light orange 90 10

532 Athletics

1978. "Gymnasiade'78" World School Games.
2626 **532** 1l.+50k. deep green and green 10 10
2627 – 2½l.+50k. blue & orge 15 10
2628 – 5l.+50k. blue and pink 15 15
2629 – 8l.+50k. blue and green 25 15
DESIGNS: 2½l. Gymnastics; 5l. Table tennis; 8l. Swimming.

533 Salmon Rose

1978. Regional Co-operation for Development. Multicoloured.
2630 2½l. Type **533** 15 15
2631 3½l. Pink roses 25 15
2632 8l. Red roses 35 20

534 Anti-Apartheid Year Emblem
535 View of Ankara

1978. International Anti-Apartheid Year.
2633 **534** 10l. multicoloured 15 10

1978. Turkish–Libyan Friendship. Multicoloured.
2634 2½l. Type **535** 10 10
2635 5l. View of Tripoli 15 10

536 Ribbon and Chain

1978. 25th Anniv of European Convention on Human Rights.
2636 **536** 2½l.+50k. blue, green and black 20 10
2637 – 5l.+50k. red, blue and black 25 15
DESIGN: 5l. Ribbon and flower.

538 Independence Medal

1978. Works and Reforms of Ataturk (5th series).
2639 **538** 2½l. multicoloured 10 10
2640 – 3½l. red and black 10 10
2641 – 5l. multicoloured 15 10
DESIGNS—HORIZ: 3½l. Talking heads (Language reform). VERT: 5l. "ABC" in Arabic and Roman scripts (Adoption of Latin alphabet).

539 Bosphorus Waterside Residence of Koprulu Huseyin Pasa, Istanbul (1699)

1978. Traditional Turkish Houses. Multicoloured.
2642 1l. Type **539** 10 10
2643 2½l. Residence of Saatci Ali Efendi, Izmit, 1774 25 10
2644 3½l. House of Bey, Kula (vert) 35 15
2645 5l. House of Bahaeddin Aga, Milas (vert) 65 15
2646 8l. House of Safranbolu 90 20

541 Children with Globe as Balloon
542 MailTransport

1979. International Year of the Child.
2649 – 2½l.+50k. black, gold and red 10 10
2650 **541** 5l.+50k. multicoloured 10 10
2651 – 8l.+50k. multicoloured 15 10
DESIGNS: 2½l. Children embracing beneath hearts; 8l. Adult and child balancing globe.

1979. Europa.
2652 **542** 2½l. black, green and blue 30 10
2653 – 5l. orange and black 30 15
2654 – 7½l. black and blue 65 20
DESIGNS: 5l. Telex keyboard, morse key and telegraph poles; 7½l. Telephone dial and dishaerial.

543 Kemal Ataturk
544 "Turkish Harvest" (Namik Ismail)

1979.
2655 **543** 50k. green 10 10
2656 1l. green and light green 10 10
2657 2½l. lilac 15 10
2657a 2½l. blue 10 10
2748 2½l. orange 20 10
2658 5l. blue and light blue 15 10
2659 7½l. brown 25 10
2659a 7½l. red 25 10
2660 10l. mauve 35 10
2661a 10l. mauve (22 × 22mm) 15 10
2661 20l. grey 40 10

1979. Regional Co-operation for Development. Paintings. Multicoloured.
2662 5l. Type **544** 15 10
2663 7½l. "Iranian Goldsmith" (Kamal el Molk) 15 10
2664 10l. "Pakistan Village Scene" (Ustad Baksh) 25 10

545 Colemanite
546 Highway forming Figure 8

1979. 10th World Mining Congress. Mult.
2665 5l. Type **545** 10 10
2666 7½l. Chromite 15 10
2667 10l. Antimonite 20 10
2668 15l. Sulphur 55 10

1979. 8th European Communications Ministers' Symposium.
2669 **546** 5l. multicoloured 10 10

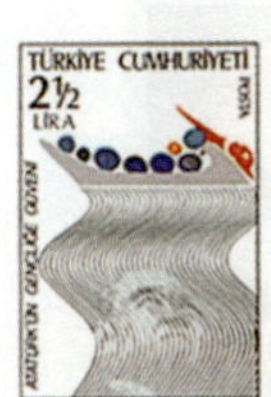

547 "Confidence in Youth"
548 Poppy ("P-apaversomniferum")

1979. Works and Reforms of Ataturk (6th series).
2670 **547** 2½l. multicoloured 10 10
2671 – 3½l. multicoloured 10 10
2672 – 5l. black and orange 15 10
DESIGNS—HORIZ: 3½l. "Secularism". VERT: 5l. "National Oath".

1979. Flowers (1st series). Multicoloured.
2673 5l. Type **548** 15 10
2674 7½l. Oleander ("Neriumoleander") 15 10
2675 10l. Latespider orchid ("Ophrysholosericea") 15 20
2676 15l. Mandrake ("M-andragoraautumnalis") 25 15
See also Nos.2705/8.

549 Ibrahim Muteferrika (first printer) and Presses

1979. 250th Anniv of Turkish Printing.
2678 **549** 10l. multicoloured 15 10

550 Black Partridge
551 Olives, Leaves and Globe in Oil-drop

1979. Wildlife Conservation. Multicoloured.
2679 5l.+1l. Type **550** 25 15
2680 5l.+1l. Great bustard 25 15
2681 5l.+1l. Demoiselle crane 25 15
2682 5l.+1l. Goitred gazelle 25 15
2683 5l.+1l. Mouflon 25 15
Nos. 2679/83 were issued together, se-tenant, forming a composite design.

1979. 2nd World Olive-oil Year.
2684 **551** 5l. multicoloured 10 10
2685 – 10l. yellow and green 15 10
DESIGN: 10l. Globe in oil drop.

553 Uskudarli Hoca Ali Riza (artist)

1980. Europa. Multicoloured.
2692 7½l. Type **553** 25 25
2693 10l. Ali Sami Boyar (artist) 45 35
2694 20l. Dr. Hulusi Behcet (skin specialist) 65 45

554 Flowers and Trees
555 Lighted Match and Trees

1980. Environmental Protection. Multicoloured.
2695 2½l.+1l. Type **554** 10 10
2696 7½l.+1l. Sun and water 10 10
2697 15l.+1l. Factory polluting atmosphere 15 10
2698 20l.+1l. Flower surrounded by oil 20 10

1980. Forest Conservation.
2699 **555** 50k. green, red and brown 10 10
See also No.2607.

556 Seismological Graph
557 Games Emblem and Pictograms

1980. 7th World Conference on Earthquake Engineering.
2700 – 7½l. brown, blue & orange 10 10
2701 **556** 20l. black, orange & blue 15 10
DESIGN: 7½l. Pictorial representation of earthquake within globe.

1980. 1st Islamic Games, Izmir. Multicoloured.
2702 7½l. Type **557** 10 10
2703 20l. AsNo. 2702 but with different sports around emblem 20 10

558 Ornamental Window
559 "Braconhebetor" and Larva of Dark Arches Moth

1980. 1400th Anniv of Hegira.
2704 **558** 20l. multicoloured 20 10

1980. Flowers(2nd series). As T **548**.Mult.
2705 2½l. Manisatulip ("Tulipahayatii") 10 10
2706 7½l. Ephesianbellflower ("Campanulaephesia") 15 10
2707 15l. C-rocus("Crocusancyrensis") 25 15
2708 20l. Anatolianorchid ("Orchisanatolica") 40 20

1980. Useful Insects (1st series). Multicoloured.
2709 2½l.+1l. "Rodoliacardinalis" (ladybird) and cottony cushion scale 20 10
2710 7½l.+1l. Type **559** 20 10
2711 15l.+1l. Caterpillar-hunter and larva of gypsy moth 30 15
2712 20l.+1l. "Deraeocorisrutilus" (leafbug) 35 20
See also Nos.2763/6.

560 Kemal Ataturk
561 Ibn Sina Teaching

1980.
2713 **560** 7½l. brown and pink 30 10
2714 10l. brown & lt brown 20 10
2719a 15l. blue 45 10
2715 20l. violet and mauve 30 10
2719b 20l. orange 25 10
2716 30l. grey and light grey 40 10
2717 50l. red and yellow 65 10
2719c 65l. green 90 10
2718 75l. green and lt green 1·25 10

2719d 90l. mauve 1·50 10
2719 100l. blue and light blue 1·40 10

1980. Birth Millenary of Ibn Sina (Avicenna) (philosopher and physician). Multicoloured.
2720 7½l. Type **561** 20 10
2721 20l. Ibn Sina (vert) 35 15

562 Ataturk and Figures "100"

563 Disabled Person in Wheelchair

1981. "Balkanfila VIII" Stamp Exhibition, Ankara.
2722 **562** 10l. red and black 20 10

1981. International Year of Disabled Persons.
2723 **563** 10l.+2½l. multicoloured 15 10
2724 20l.+2½l. multicoloured 25 15

564 Sultan Mohammed the Conqueror

565 Gaziantep

1981. 500th Death Anniv of Mohammed the Conqueror.
2725 **564** 10l. multicoloured 20 10
2726 20l. multicoloured 35 10

1981. Folk Dances and Europa (35, 70l.). Multicoloured.
2727 ½l. Type **565** 15 10
2728 10l. Balikesir 20 15
2729 15l. Kahramanmaras 30 15
2730 35l. Antalya 1·10 50
2731 70l. Burdur 1·75 70

566 Ataturkin 1919 (S.G. 2279)

568 Carpet

1981. Birth Centenary of Kemal Ataturk. Previous stamps showing Ataturk. Multicoloured.
2732 **566** 2½l. multicoloured 15 10
2733 – 7½l. black and brown 15 10
2734 – 10l. multicoloured 20 15
2735 – 20l. blue, red and black 30 20
2736 – 25l. black, red and orange 40 20
2737 – 35l. multicoloured 60 30
DESIGNS: 7½l. Ataturk in civilian dress (S.G. No. 2285); 10l. Ataturk and old Parliament House (S.G. No. 2037); 20l. Ataturk teaching Latin alphabet (S.G. No. 1222); 25l. Remilitarization of Dardanelles surcharged stamp (S.G. No. 1188); 35l. Ataturk in evening dress (from miniature sheet).

1981. Various stamps surch **10 LIRA**.
2739 – 10l.on 60k. red, black and green (No. 2177) 45 10
2740 **452** 10l. on 110k. blue on blue 45 10
2741 10l. on 400k. turquoise on blue 45 10
2742 – 10l. on 800k. green, turq & red (No. 2605) 45 10

1981. 2nd International Congress of Turkish Folklore. Multicoloured.
2743 7½l. Type **568** 10 10
2744 10l. Embroidery 15 10
2745 15l. Drum and "zurna" 20 10
2746 20l. Embroidered napkin 25 15
2747 30l. Rug 30 15

570 Ataturk Centenary and E.P.S. Emblem

1981. 5th European Physical Society General Congress.
2750 **570** 10l. multicoloured 25 15
2751 30l. multicoloured 45 15

571 F.A.O. Emblem

1981. World Food Day.
2752 **571** 10l. multicoloured 20 15
2753 30l. multicoloured 40 15

572 Olive Branch and Constitution on Map of Turkey

1981. Inauguration of Constituent Assembly.
2754 **572** 10l. multicoloured 30 15
2755 30l. multicoloured 55 15

574 Kemal Ataturk

575 Green Tiger Beetle

1981.
2762 **574** 2½l. red on grey 40 10

1981. Useful Insects (2nd series). Multicoloured.
2763 10l.+2½l. Type **575** 30 15
2764 20l.+2½l. "Syrphusvitripennis" (hoverfly) 45 25
2765 30l.+2½l. "Ascalaphusmacaronius" (owl-fly) 40 25
2766 40l.+2½l. "Empusafasciata" 70 35

576 Students and Silhouette of Ataturk

577 Sun

578 Kemal Ataturk

1981. Literacy Campaign.
2767 **576** 2½l. orange and blue 35 10

1982. Energy Conservation.
2768 **577** 10l. yellow, blue & green 20 10

1982.
2769 **578** 1l. green 10 10
2770 – 2½l. lilac 10 10
2771 – 5l. blue 15 10
2772 – 10l. red 30 10
2773 – 35l. brown 50 10
DESIGNS: 2½ to 35l. Different portraits of Ataturk.

579 "Magnolias"

580 Dr. Tevfik Saglam

1982. Birth Centenary of Ibrahim Calli (painter). Multicoloured.
2774 10l. Type **579** 20 10
2775 20l. "Fishermen" (horiz) 40 15
2776 30l. "Sewing Woman" 55 20

1982. Centenary of Discovery of Tubercle Bacillus. Multicoloured.
2777 10l.+2½l. Type **580** 15 10
2778 30l.+2½l. Dr. RobertKoch 30 25

582 Kul Tigin Monument

584 Demirkazik

583 Tanker and Emblem

1982. 1250th Anniv of Kul Tigin Monument. Multicoloured.
2780 10l. Type **582** 15 15
2781 30l. Head of Kul Tigin 30 15

1982. Inauguration of Pendik Shipyard.
2782 **583** 30l. multicoloured 35 15

1982. Anatolian Mountains. Multicoloured.
2783 7½l. Agri Dagi 20 10
2784 10l. Buzul Dagi (horiz) 25 10
2785 15l. Type **584** 30 15
2786 20l. Erciyes (horiz) 50 15
2787 30l. Kackar Dagi 65 25
2788 35l. Uludag (horiz) 80 25

585 Colorado Potato Beetle

1982. Insect Pests (1st series). Multicoloured.
2789 10l.+2½l. "Eurydemaspectabile" (shield-bug) 30 20
2790 15l.+2½l. Olive fruit-fly 45 20
2791 20l.+2½l. "K-lapperichicenviridissima" (cicada) 50 25
2792 20l.+2½l. Type **585** 70 35
2793 35l.+2½l. "Rhynchitesauratus" (weevil) 80 35
See also Nos.2830/4.

586 Open Book and Figures

1982. Centenary of Beyazit State Library.
2794 **586** 30l. multicoloured 35 15

587 Drum

1982. Musical Instruments. Multicoloured.
2796 7½l. Type **587** 25 15
2797 10l. Lute ("Baglama") 35 20
2798 15l. Horn ("Zurna") (horiz) 45 20
2799 20l. Stringed instrument ("Kemence") (horiz) 60 20
2800 30l. Flute ("Mey") 1·10 25

588 Temple of Artemis, Sart

1982. Ancient Cities.
2801 **588** 30l. multicoloured 35 20

589 Family on Map

1983. Family Planning and Mother and Child Health. Multicoloured.
2802 10l. Type **589** 20 10
2803 35l. Mother and child 25 15

590 Council Emblem

1983. 30th Anniv of Customs Co-operation Council.
2804 **590** 45l. multicoloured 45 15

591 People, Ballot Box and Constitution

1983. 1982 Constitution. Multicoloured.
2805 10l. Type **591** 15 10
2806 30l. Constitution, scales and olive branch 25 15

592 Richard Wagner

1983. Death Cent of Richard Wagner (composer).
2807 **592** 30l.+5l. multicoloured 30 20

593 Hamdi Bey

1983. 38th Death Anniv of Hamdi Bey (telegraphist).
2808 **593** 35l. multicoloured 30 20

594 Piri Reis (geographer) and Map

1983. Europa. Multicoloured.
2809 50l. Type **594** 4·00 5·00
2810 100l. Ulugh Bey (Central Asian ruler) and observatory 8·00 7·50

595 Olive Branch and Athletes

1983. Youth Week.
2811 **595** 15l. multicoloured 20 15

596 Junkers Ju 52/3m and Boeing 727

1983. 50th Anniv of Turkish State Airline. Multicoloured.
2812 50l. Type **596** 55 20
2813 70l. Airport at night 65 25
No. 2812 is wrongly inscribed "F-13".

597 Hellenic Statue of Eros

598 Oludeniz

1983. 18th Council of Europe Art Exhibition, Istanbul. Multicoloured.
2814 15l. Type **597** 35 15
2815 35l. Hittite carving of two-headed duck (horiz) . . . 60 20
2816 50l. Ottomanzinc flask and jug 85 15
2817 70l. Busts of Marcus Aurelius and his wife Faustina (horiz) . . . . . 1·10 25

1983. Coastal Protection. Multicoloured.
2818 10l. Type **598** 25 15
2819 25l. Olimpos 45 15
2820 35l. Kekova 65 20

1983. Nos.2655 and 2699 surch **5 LIRA**.
2821 **543** 5l. on 50k. green 20 10
2822 **555** 5l. on 50k. green, red and brown 20 10

600 Dove carrying Letter

601 Kemal Ataturk

1983. World Communications Year. Mult.
2823 15l. Type **600** 25 10
2824 50l. Telephone pole and telephone wires (horiz) . . 35 10
2825 70l. Telephone dial and letter within ornamental design 45 20

1983.
2826 **601** 15l. blue and light blue 20 10
2827 50l. blue and green . . . 65 10
2828 100l. blue and orange . . 1·50 10

602 Topkapi Serail, Istanbul

1983. Aga Khan Award for Architecture.
2829 **602** 50l. yellow, black & green 60 20

1983. Insect Pests (2nd series). As T **585**. Multicoloured.
2830 15l.+5l. Sun pest 20 20
2831 25l.+5l. "Phyllobiusnigrofasciatus" (weevil) 35 20
2832 35l.+5l. "Cercopsisintermedia" (froghopper) 40 25
2833 50l.+10l. Stripedbug 60 25
2834 75l.+10l. "Capnodismiliaris" 75 40

603 Map and Flag of Turkey

1983. 60th Anniv of Republic.
2836 **603** 15l. multicoloured . . . 25 15
2837 50l. multicoloured . . . 45 20

605 Temple of Aphrodite, Aphrodisias

1983. Ancient Cities.
2838 **605** 50l. multicoloured . . . 35 15

607 St. Sophia's from Sultan Ahmed Mosque, Istanbul

608 Police Badge and Ribbon protecting Citizens

1984. U.N.E.S.C.O. International Campaign for Istanbul and Goreme. Multicoloured.
2850 25l. Type **607** 20 15
2851 35l. Rock dwellings and chapels, Goreme 35 15
2852 50l. Suleymaniye district, Istanbul 45 25

1984. Turkish Police Organization.
2853 **608** 15l. multicoloured . . . 20 15

609 Bridge

610 Kaftan (16th-century)

1984. Europa. 25th Anniv of C.E.P.T.
2854 **609** 50l. multicoloured . . . 1·25 1·75
2855 100l. multicoloured . . . 3·75 2·40

1984. Topkapi Museum (1st series). Mult.
2856 20l.+5l. Type **610** 40 25
2857 70l.+15l. Ceremonialewer . . 90 50
2858 90l.+20l. Gold in laid and jewelled swords . . . . . 1·25 55
2859 100l.+25l. Kaabalock . . . 1·40 70
See also Nos. 2892/5, 2925/8 and 2967/70.

611 Mete Khan and Flag of Great Hun Empire

1984. Turkic States (1st series). Multicoloured.
2860 10l. Type **611** 30 20
2861 20l. Panu and flag of Western Hun Empire . . 55 25
2862 50l. Attila and flag of European Hun Empire . . 1·40 30
2863 70l. Aksunvar and flag of Ak Hun Empire . . . . 2·00 35
See also Nos. 2896/9, 2930/3 and 2971/4.

612 Peace Dove

1984. 10th Anniv of Turkish Forces in Cyprus.
2864 **612** 70l. multicoloured . . . 70 20

613 Olympic Colours

614 MarshMallow

1984. Olympic Games, Los Angeles. Mult.
2865 20l.+5l. Type **613** 30 25
2866 70l.+15l. Medallion of wrestler (vert) 90 30
2867 100l.+20l. Stylized athlete 1·50 45

1984. Wild Flowers. Multicoloured.
2868 5l. "Narcissustazetta" . . . 15 10
2868a 10l. Type **614** 15 10
2869 20l. Common poppy 15 10
2870 70l. "C-yclamenpseudoibericum" 75 10
2870a 100l. Falsechamomile . . . 1·25 10
2871 200l. Snowdrops . . . . . 1·50 10
2872 300l. "Tulipasintenesii" . . 2·25 10

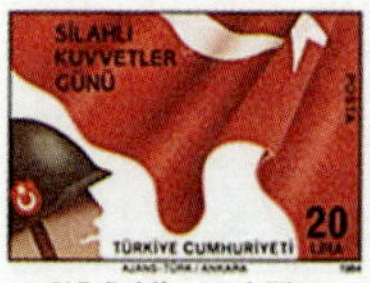

615 Soldier and Flag

616 Liquid amber

1984. Armed Forces Day.
2873 **615** 20l. multicoloured . . . 20 10
2874 – 50l. multicoloured . . . 40 10
2875 – 70l. red, blue and black 70 15
2876 – 90l. multicoloured . . . 95 20
DESIGNS: 50l. Olive branch as sword hilt; 70l. Emblem, soldier and flag; 90l. Soldier, olive branch and map.

1984. Forest Resources. Multicoloured.
2877 10l. Type **616** 25 20
2878 20l. Oriental spruce 40 25
2879 70l. Oriental beech . . . . 1·10 25
2880 90l. Cedar of Lebanon . . . 1·75 50

617 Pres. Inonu

618 Detail of 13th-century Seljukian Carpet

1984. Birth Cent of Ismet Inonu (Prime Minister 1923–37 and 1962–65; President1938–50).
2881 **617** 20l. multicoloured . . . 35 20

1984. 1st Int Congress on Turkish Carpets.
2882 **618** 70l. multicoloured . . . 65 20

619 Great Mosque and University, Harran

1984. Ancient Cities.
2883 **619** 70l. multicoloured . . . 1·10 20

620 Women and Ballot Box

1984. 50th Anniv of Turkish Women's Suffrage.
2884 **620** 20l. multicoloured . . . 25 10

621 "Icarus" (HansHerni)

1984. 40th Anniv of I.C.A.O.
2885 **621** 100l. multicoloured . . . 1·00 20

623 Glider and Parachutist

1985. 60th Anniv of Turkish Aviation League. Multicoloured.
2887 10l. Type **623** 20 10
2888 20l. Cameron Viva 77 hot-air balloon (vert) 30 15

624 Globe and Satellite

625 Score and Ulvi Cemal Erkin (composer)

1985. 20th Anniv of International Telecommunications Satellite Organization.
2889 **624** 100l. multicoloured . . . 90 20

1985. Europa. Music Year. Multicoloured.
2890 100l. Type **625** . . . . . . 2·75 1·50
2891 200l. Score and Mithat Fenmen (composer and pianist) . . . . 4·00 2·40

1985. Topkapi Museum (2nd series). As T **610**. Multicoloured.
2892 10l.+5l. Plate decorated with peacock 25 15
2893 20l.+10l. Jug and cup . . . 35 15
2894 100l.+15l. Porcelainewer and bowl . . . . 1·50 40
2895 120l.+20l. Chinese porcelain plate . . . . 1·75 50

1985. Turkic States (2nd series). As T **611**. Multicoloured.
2896 10l. Bilge Kagan and flag of Gokturk Empire 20 15
2897 20l. Bayan Kagan and flag of Avar Empire 30 15
2898 70l. Hazar Kagan and flag of Hazar Empire . . . . 1·60 20
2899 100l. Kutlug Kul Bilge Kagan and flag of Uygur Empire . . . . 1·90 35

626 Louis Pasteur working in Laboratory

627 I.Y.Y. Emblem within Globe and Profiles

1985. Centenary of Discovery of Anti-rabies Vaccine.
2900 **626** 100l.+15l. mult . . . . 1·40 25

1985. International Youth Year. Multicoloured.
2901 100l. Type **627** . . . . . . 1·00 15
2902 120l. Globe and I.Y.Y. Emblem . . . . 1·25 15

628 Postman and Couple Dancing

629 Aynalikavak Palace

1985. Introduction of Post Codes.
2903 **628** 10l. black, yellow & brn 15 10
2904 20l. black, yellow and red 25 10
2905 20l. black, yellow & green 25 10
2906 20l. black, yellow and blue 25 10
2907 70l. blue, yellow & purple 90 10
2908 100l. black, yellow and grey . . . . 1·25 10

1985. National Palaces Symposium. Multicoloured.
2909 20l. Type **629** 25 10
2910 100l. Beylerbeyi Palace . . . 1·25 15

630 U.N. Emblem, Headquarters and Flags in "40"

1985. 40thAnniv of U.N.O.
2911 **630** 100l. multicoloured . . . 1·25 15

631 Alanya

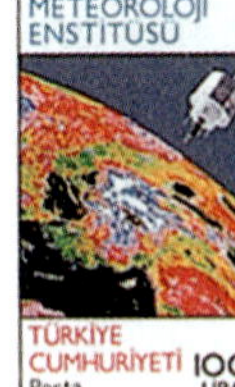

632 Satellite and Infra-red Picture of Earth's Surface

1985. Ancient Cities.
2912 **631** 100l. multicoloured . . . 1·25 15

1985. 60th Anniv of Meteorological Institute.
2913 **632** 100l. multicoloured . . . 1·25 15

633 Emblem

634 Kemal Ataturk

1985. Centenary of Isik Lyceum, Istanbul.
2914 **633** 20l. gold, blue and red 25 10

1985.
2915 **634** 10l. blue and cobalt . . 15 10
2916 20l. brown and lilac . . 20 10
2917 100l. purple and lilac . . 90 10

635 Girl and Flower

1986. International 23rd April Children's Festival, Ankara. Multicoloured.
2918 20l. Type **635** 20 15
2919 100l. Family 85 25
2920 120l. Balloon seller . . . . 2·25 35

636 Boy drawing in Smoke from Chimney

637 Trophy

1986. Europa. Multicoloured.
2921 100l. Type **636** . . . . . . 1·50 90
2922 200l. Plaster on dead half of leaf (vert) . . . . 2·25 1·50

1986. Ataturk International Peace Prize. Multicoloured.
2923 20l. Type **637** 20 15
2924 100l. Front view of trophy 1·10 25

1986. Topkapi Museum (3rd series). As T **610**. Multicoloured.
2925 20l.+5l. Censer 20 10
2926 100l.+10l. Jadeand jewelled tankard 70 20
2927 120l.+15l. Dagger and sheath . . . . 1·10 25
2928 200l.+30l. Willow buckler 1·50 35

638 "Abdulhamit"

639 Wrestler soiling Themselves

1986. Centenary of Turkish Submarine Fleet.
2929 **638** 20l. multicoloured . . . 40 15

1986. Turkic States (3rd series). As T **611**. Multicoloured.
2930 10l. Bilge Kul Kadir Khan and flag of Kara Khanids Empire 15 10
2931 20l. Alp Tekin and flag of Ghaznavids Empire 30 15
2932 100l. Seljukand flag of Great Seljuk Empire . . . . . 1·25 15
2933 120l. Muhammed Harezmsah and flag of Harezmsah State . . . . 1·60 20

1986. Kirkpinar Wrestling. Multicoloured.
2934 10l. Type **639** 15 15
2935 20l. Opening ceremony . . . 25 25
2936 100l. Wrestlers . . . . . . 1·40 35

640 Chateaude la Muette, Paris (headquarters)

1986. 25th Anniv of Organization for Economic Co-operation and Development.
2937 **640** 100l. multicoloured . . . 60 20

641 Benz "Einspur" Tricar, 1886

1986. Centenary of Motor Car. Multicoloured.
2938 10l. Type **641** 20 20
2939 20l. Rolls-Royce "Silver Ghost",1906 . . . . . . 40 20
2940 100l. Mercedes touring car, 1928 . . . . 1·50 60
2941 200l. Impression of speeding car . . . . 3·25 60

642 "Arrangement with Tulips" (Feyhaman Duran)

643 Celal Bayar

1986. Artists' Birth Centenaries. Multicoloured.
2942 100l. Type **642** 95 20
2943 120l. "Landscape with Fountain" (Huseyin Avni Lifij) (horiz) . . . . . . 1·10 25

1986. Celal Bayar (Prime Minister 1937–39; President 1950–60) Commemoration.
2944 **643** 20l. brown, gold and mauve 15 15
2945 – 100l. green, gold and mauve . . . . 1·10 15
DESIGN: 100l. Profile of Celal Bayar.

645 Kubad-Abad

1986. Ancient Cities.
2950 **645** 100l. multicoloured . . . 90 20

646 N.A.T.O. Emblem and Dove with Olive Branch

1986. 32nd N.A.T.O. Assembly, Istanbul.
2951 **646** 100l.+20l. mult . . . . 1·10 20

647 Ersoy and National Flag

648 Driverwearing SeatBelt

1986. 50th Death Anniv of Mehmet Akif Ersoy (composer of national anthem).
2952 **647** 20l. multicoloured . . . 25 20

1987. Road Safety.
2953 **648** 10l. violet, red and blue 10 10
2954 – 20l. red, blue and brown 15 10
2955 – 150l. brown, red & green 65 10
DESIGNS: 20l. Smashed drinking glass and road; 150l. Broken speed limit sign and road.

649 Spurge Hawk Moth

1987. Moths and Butterflies. Multicoloured.
2956 10l. Type **649** 40 25
2957 20l. Red admiral 80 35
2958 100l. Jersey tigermoth . . . 2·75 1·10
2959 120l. Clouded yellow . . . 3·50 1·90

650 Modern Housing and Emblem

651 Casting

1987. International Year of Shelter for the Homeless.
2960 **650** 200l. multicoloured . . . 90 20

1987. 50th Anniv of Turkish Iron and Steel Works. Multicoloured.
2961 50l. Type **651** 20 10
2962 200l. Karabuk Works . . . 75 15

652 Map of Turkey and Grand National Assembly Building, Ankara

1987. "Sovereignty belongs to the People".
2963 **652** 50l. multicoloured . . . 35 15

653 Turkish History Institution, Ankara (Turgut Cansever and Ertur Yener)

1987. Europa. Architecture. Multicoloured.
2964 50l. Type **653** 60 55
2965 200l. Social Insurance Institution, Zeyrek (Sedad Hakki Eldem) . . . . . 1·90 1·00

654 Olympic Rings as Flames

655 Men

1987. 92nd Session of International Olympic Committee, Istanbul.
2966 **654** 200l. multicoloured . . . 1·10 30

1987. Topkapi Museum (4th series). As T **610**. Multicoloured.
2967 20l.+5l. Crystals and jewelledewer 20 20
2968 50l.+10l. Emerald, gold and diamond ceiling pendant (horiz) 35 25
2969 200l.+15l. Sherbet jug . . . 1·00 50
2970 250l.+30l. Crystal, gold and jewelled writing drawer (horiz) . . . . 1·40 70

1987. Turkic States (4th series). As T **611**. Multicoloured.
2971 10l. Batu Khan and flag of Golden Horde State . . . 25 25
2972 20l. Timur (Tamerlane) and flag of Great Timur Empire 35 25
2973 50l. Babur Shah and flag of Mughal Empire 85 35
2974 200l. Osman Bey and flag of Ottoman Empire . . . . 3·75 1·00

1987. Paintings from Mehmet Siyah Kalem's "Album of the Conqueror". Multicoloured.
2975 10l. Type **655** 20 30
2976 20l. Donkey rider and attendants (horiz) 25 50
2977 50l. Man whipping fallen horse (horiz) 65 55
2978 200l. Demon . . . . 2·40 1·00

656 Cancer Cells and Pipette holding Drug

1987. 15th International Chemotherapy Congress, Istanbul.
2979 **656** 200l.+25l. mult 55 25

657 Ihlamur Pavilion

1987. Royal Pavilions (1st series). Multicoloured.
2980 50l. Type **657** 25 25
2981 200l. Kucuksu Pavilion . . 95 40
See also Nos.3019/20.

658 Suleiman receiving Barbarossa (miniature)

1987. Suleiman the Magnificent. Multicoloured.
2982 30l. Suleiman 20 30
2983 50l. Suleiman's tougra (horiz) 25 30
2984 200l. Type **658** . . . . 1·40 50
2985 270l. Sculpture of Suleiman from U.S. House of Representatives and inscribed scroll . . . . . 2·10 90

660 Sinanand Selimiye Mosque, Edrine

661 Means of Transport

1988. 400th Death Anniv of Mimar Sinan (architect). Multicoloured.

2987 50l. Type **660** 15 10
2988 200l. Suleiman Mosque . . 50 25

1988. Europa. Transport and Communications. Multicoloured.

2989 200l. Type **661** 65 60
2990 600l. Electric impulses forming globe between telephone and computer terminal (horiz) . . . . . 2·10 1·25

662 Syringes between Healthy and Sick Children

1988. Health. Multicoloured.

2991 50l. Type **662** 15 10
2992 200l. Capsules forming cross on bottle (vert) 25 10
2993 300l. Heart in cogwheel and heart-shaped worker . . . 40 10
2994 600l. Organs for transplant on open hands (vert) . . 1·00 10

663 American Standard Steam Locomotive, 1850s

1988. Locomotives. Each agate, light brown and brown.

2995 50l. Type **663** 80 25
2996 100l. Saronnoside-tank locomotive No. 3328, 1897 . . . . 1·40 35
2997 200l. Henschel Krupp steam locomotive No. 46020, 1933 . . . . 2·10 40
2998 300l. Type E 43001 electric locomotive, 1987 . . . . 2·75 70
2999 600l. MTE-Tulomsas diesel locomotive, 1984 . . . . 4·75 90

664 Articulated Lorry

1988. 21st International Road Transport Union World Congress, Istanbul.

3000 **664** 200l.+25l. mult 45 15

665 Scales and Map

1988. 120th Anniv of Court of Cassation (appeal court).

3001 **665** 50l. multicoloured . . . 25 20

666 Fatih Sultan Mohamed Bridge, Bosphorus

1988. Completion of Bridges. Multicoloured.

3002 200l. Type **666** . . . . . . 1·00 45
3003 300l. Seto Great road and rail Bridge, Japan . . . . 1·50 60

667 Telephone Dial and Wires over Villages

1988. Completion of Telephone Network to Every Village.

3004 **667** 100l. multicoloured . . . 30 10

669 Running **670** Weightlifting

1988. Olympic Games, Seoul. Multicoloured.

3005 100l. Type **669** 25 25
3006 200l. Archery 35 25
3007 400l. Weightlifting 75 35
3008 600l. Football (vert) . . . . 1·25 55

1988. Naim Suleymanoglu, Olympic and World Heavyweight Record Holder for Weightlifting.

3009 **670** 1000l. multicoloured . . 3·50 1·25

671 Lush Scene in Hands surrounded by Barren Earth **672** General Dynamics F-16 Fighters and Cogwheel

1988. European Campaign for Rural Areas. Multicoloured.

3010 100l.+25l. Type **671** 20 15
3011 400l.+50l. Rural scene in eye 70 25

1988. Turkish Aerospace Industries. Mult.

3012 50l. Type **672** 15 15
3013 200l. Birds forming jet fighter (horiz) 55 25

673 "Gonepteryxcleopatra"

1988. Butterflies. Multicoloured.

3014 100l. Type **673** (wrongly inscr "G. rhamni") . . . 1·10 1·75
3015 200l. Hermit . . . . 2·00 1·75
3016 400l. Eastern festoon . . . 3·50 2·10
3017 600l. Camberwell beauty . . 5·25 3·00

1988. Royal Pavilions (2nd series). As T **657**. Multicoloured.

3019 100l. Kasr-i Humayun Imperial Lodge, Maslak 25 15
3020 400l. Sale Pavilion, Yildiz 1·00 30

675 Large-leaved Lime

1988. Medicinal Plants. Multicoloured.

3022 150l. Type **675** 20 15
3023 300l. Common mallow . . . 40 15
3024 600l. Hen bane 70 20
3025 900l. Deadly nightshade . . 1·10 25

676 Seated Goddess with Child (clay statuette)

1989. Archaeology (1st series). Multicoloured.

3026 150l. Type **676** 40 20
3027 300l. Lead figurine of god and goddess 80 25
3028 600l. Clay human-shaped vase . . . . 1·25 35
3029 1000l. Hittite ivory figurine of mountain god . . . . 2·25 40

See also Nos. 3062/5, 3104/7 and 3134/7.

1989. Nos. 2826, 2915 and 2916 surch.

3030 **601** 50l. on 15l. blue and light blue 25 10
3031 **634** 75l. on 10l. blue and cobalt 30 10
3032 150l. on 20l. brown and lilac 50 10

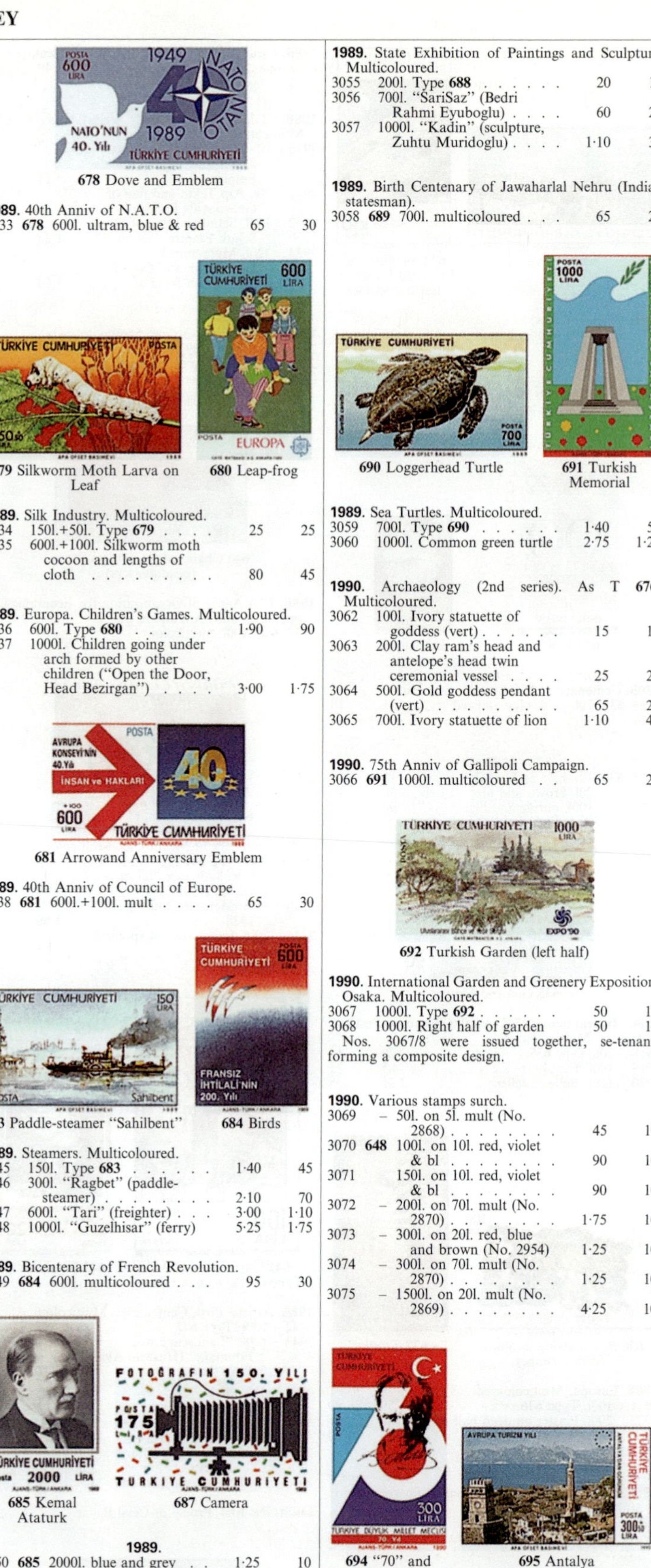

678 Dove and Emblem

1989. 40th Anniv of N.A.T.O.

3033 **678** 600l. ultram, blue & red 65 30

679 Silkworm Moth Larva on Leaf **680** Leap-frog

1989. Silk Industry. Multicoloured.

3034 150l.+50l. Type **679** 25 25
3035 600l.+100l. Silkworm moth cocoon and lengths of cloth 80 45

1989. Europa. Children's Games. Multicoloured.

3036 600l. Type **680** . . . . . . 1·90 90
3037 1000l. Children going under arch formed by other children ("Open the Door, Head Bezirgan") . . . . 3·00 1·75

681 Arrowand Anniversary Emblem

1989. 40th Anniv of Council of Europe.

3038 **681** 600l.+100l. mult 65 30

683 Paddle-steamer "Sahilbent" **684** Birds

1989. Steamers. Multicoloured.

3045 150l. Type **683** . . . . . . 1·40 45
3046 300l. "Ragbet" (paddle-steamer) . . . . 2·10 70
3047 600l. "Tari" (freighter) . . . 3·00 1·10
3048 1000l. "Guzelhisar" (ferry) 5·25 1·75

1989. Bicentenary of French Revolution.

3049 **684** 600l. multicoloured . . . 95 30

685 Kemal Ataturk **687** Camera

1989.

3050 **685** 2000l. blue and grey . . 1·25 10
3051 5000l. brown and grey 2·10 10

See also Nos. 3093/4, 3144 and 3199/3200.

1989. No. 2916 surch **LIRA 500**.

3052 **634** 500l.on 20l. brown and lilac 35 10

1989. 150th Anniv of Photography. Mult.

3053 175l. Type **687** 20 15
3054 700l. Coloured lens shutter 75 25

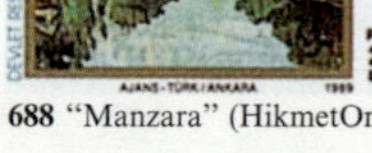

688 "Manzara" (HikmetOnat) **689** Nehru

1989. State Exhibition of Paintings and Sculpture. Multicoloured.

3055 200l. Type **688** 20 15
3056 700l. "SariSaz" (Bedri Rahmi Eyuboglu) 60 25
3057 1000l. "Kadin" (sculpture, Zuhtu Muridoglu) . . . . 1·10 30

1989. Birth Centenary of Jawaharlal Nehru (Indian statesman).

3058 **689** 700l. multicoloured . . . 65 25

690 Loggerhead Turtle **691** Turkish Memorial

1989. Sea Turtles. Multicoloured.

3059 700l. Type **690** . . . . . . 1·40 55
3060 1000l. Common green turtle 2·75 1·25

1990. Archaeology (2nd series). As T **676**. Multicoloured.

3062 100l. Ivory statuette of goddess (vert) 15 15
3063 200l. Clay ram's head and antelope's head twin ceremonial vessel 25 25
3064 500l. Gold goddess pendant (vert) 65 25
3065 700l. Ivory statuette of lion 1·10 40

1990. 75th Anniv of Gallipoli Campaign.

3066 **691** 1000l. multicoloured . . 65 25

692 Turkish Garden (left half)

1990. International Garden and Greenery Exposition, Osaka. Multicoloured.

3067 1000l. Type **692** 50 15
3068 1000l. Right half of garden 50 15

Nos. 3067/8 were issued together, se-tenant, forming a composite design.

1990. Various stamps surch.

3069 – 50l. on 5l. mult (No. 2868) 45 10
3070 **648** 100l. on 10l. red, violet & bl 90 10
3071 150l. on 10l. red, violet & bl 90 10
3072 – 200l. on 70l. mult (No. 2870) . . . . 1·75 10
3073 – 300l. on 20l. red, blue and brown (No. 2954) 1·25 10
3074 – 300l. on 70l. mult (No. 2870) . . . . 1·25 10
3075 – 1500l. on 20l. mult (No. 2869) . . . . 4·25 10

694 "70" and Ataturk **695** Antalya

1990. 70th Anniv of Establishment of Nationalist Provisional Government.

3076 **694** 300l. multicoloured 30 15

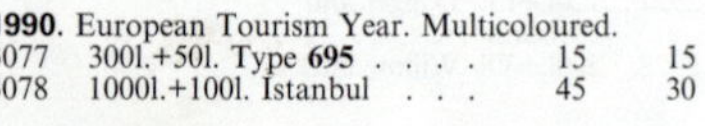

1990. European Tourism Year. Multicoloured.

3077 300l.+50l. Type **695** 15 15
3078 1000l.+100l. Istanbul . . . 45 30

696 Ankara Post Office **697** Map and Dove as Open Book

1990. Europa. Post Office Buildings. Mult.

3079 700l. Type **696** 90 90

3080 1000l. Istanbul Post Office (horiz) 1·75 1·75

1990. European Supreme Courts' Conference, Ankara.

3081 **697** 1000l. blue, dp blue & red 90 25

698 Fire Salamander

1990. World Environment Day. Multicoloured.

3082 300l. Type **698** 25 20

3083 500l. Banded newt 45 25

3084 1000l. Fire-bellied toads 70 35

3085 1500l. Common tree frog (vert) 1·25 40

699 "Ertugrul" (frigate) and Turkish and Japanese Women

701 Smoker's Bodyshattering

1990. Centenary of First Turkish Envoy to Japan.

3086 **699** 1000l. multicoloured 1·10 25

1990. Anti-addiction Campaign. Multicoloured.

3087 300l.on 50l. Type **701** 20 20

3088 1000l. on 100l. Addict injecting drug into skeletalarm (horiz) 65 35

702 "Self-portrait"

703 Emblem, Pen, Open Book and Globe

1990. Death Centenary of Vincent van Gogh (painter). Multicoloured.

3089 300l. Type **702** 70 35

3090 700l. "Boats in Saintes Maries" (horiz) 1·50 40

3091 1000l. "Sunflowers" 1·75 60

3092 1500l. "Road with Cypress" 2·25 75

1990. AsT **685** but inscription redrawn and dated "1990".

3093 **685** 500l. green and grey 50 10

3094 1000l. mauve and grey 70 10

1990. International Literacy Year.

3095 **703** 300l. multicoloured 50 15

704 "Portrait" (Nurullah Berk)

705 Tatar Courier and Modern Postal Transport

1990. State Exhibition of Painting and Sculpture. Multicoloured.

3096 300l. Type **704** 20 10

3097 700l. "Derya Kuzulari" (Cevat Dereli) 55 15

3098 1000l. "Artist's Mother" (bust) (Nijad Sirel) 80 25

1990. 150th Anniv of Ministry of Posts and Telecommunications. Multicoloured.

3099 200l. Type **705** 20 10

3100 250l. Computer terminal and Morse key 15 10

3101 400l. Manual and digital telephone exchanges 20 10

3102 1500l. Telegraph wires, dish aerial and satellite 1·00 10

1991. Archaeology (3rd series). As T **676**. Multicoloured.

3104 300l. Clay figurine of woman (vert) 20 15

3105 500l. Bronze sistrum (vert) 35 15

3106 1000l. Clay kettle on stand (vert) 65 20

3107 1500l. Clay ceremonial vessel (vert) 1·40 25

707 Lake Abant

708 Satellite and Map of Europe

1991. Lakes. Multicoloured.

3110 250l. Type **707** 20 10

3111 500l. Lake Egirdir 25 10

3112 1500l. Lake Van 95 20

1991. Europa. Europe in Space. Multicoloured.

3113 1000l. Type **708** 85 45

3114 1500l. Satellite and map of Europe (different) 1·40 55

709 Graph on Globe

1991. National Statistics Day.

3115 **709** 500l. multicoloured 25 10

710 Cable Ship, Map, Cable and Telephone Handset

711 Emblem

1991. Eastern Mediterranean Fibre Optic Cable System (EMOS-1).

3116 **710** 500l. multicoloured 25 10

1991. European Transport Ministers' Conference, Antalya.

3117 **711** 500l. multicoloured 30 15

712 Emre

713 Harpsichord, Score and Mozart

1991. "Yunus Emre (13th-century poet) Year of Love". Multicoloured.

3118 500l.+100l. Type **712** 25 10

3119 1500l.+100l. Globe, and Emre as tree 90 20

1991. Death Bicentenary of Wolfgang Amadeus Mozart (composer).

3120 **713** 1500l.+100l. mult 70 40

714 "Abdulcanbaz" (Turhan Selcuk)

715 13th-century Seljukian Wall Plaque

1991. Caricature. Multicoloured.

3121 500l. "Amcabey" (Cemal Nadir Guler) (horiz) 35 10

3122 1000l. Type **714** 70 25

1991. Turkish Ceramics. Multicoloured.

3123 500l. Type **715** 25 15

3124 1500l. Late 16th-century Ottoman wall plaque 80 30

716 Emblem

717 Dam, Water and Sun

1991. Turkish Grand National Assembly's Protection of Human Rights International Symposium, Ankara.

3125 **716** 500l. multicoloured 25 10

1991. South-eastern Anatolia Project (hydro-electric power and irrigation development).

3126 **717** 500l. multicoloured 25 10

718 Keloglan and Genie with Tray of Food

719 Sand Boa

1991. "Keloglan" (fairy tale). Multicoloured.

3127 500l. Type **718** 25 10

3128 1000l. Keloglan and dinner guests 45 15

3129 1500l. Keloglan ploughing 90 20

1991. World Environment Day. Snakes. Mult.

3130 250l. Type **719** 90 95

3131 500l. Four-lined snake 1·50 1·90

3132 1000l. Ottoman viper 3·00 2·00

3133 1500l. Caucasus viper 4·25 3·50

1992. Archaeology (4th series). As T **676**. Multicoloured.

3134 300l. Clay statuette of Mother Goddess (vert) 15 15

3135 500l. Bronze statuette (vert) 20 15

3136 1000l. Hittite clay vase (vert) 60 20

3137 1500l. Urartian lion (vert) 85 25

721 Emblem and People

722 Balloons

1992. 30th Anniv of Supreme Court.

3140 **721** 500l.+100l. mult 20 15

1992. Europa. 500th Anniv of Discovery of America by Columbus.

3141 – 1500l. blue and red 80 50

3142 **722** 2000l. multicoloured 1·25 75

DESIGN—HORIZ: 1500l. Stylized caravel.

723 Immigrant Ship

1992. 500th Anniv of Jewish Immigration.

3143 **723** 1500l. multicoloured 55 20

724 Kemal Ataturk

1992.

3144 – 250l. orange, ochre and gold 15 10

3145 **724** 10000l. blue, grey & gold 2·75 10

DESIGN: 250l. Portrait of Ataturk as in Type**685**.

725 Court Emblem

726 CongressEmblem

1992. 130th Anniv of Court of Accounts.

3146 **725** 500l. multicoloured 20 10

1992. 3rd Turkish Economy Congress, Izmir.

3147 **726** 1500l. multicoloured 55 20

727 Northern Lapwing

728 Ears of Grain, Cogwheel and Hands

1992. World Environment Day. Birds. Mult.

3148 500l. Type **727** 25 20

3149 1000l. Golden oriole 50 30

3150 1500l. Common shelduck 90 45

3151 2000l. White-throated kingfisher (vert) 1·00 60

1992. Black Sea Economic Co-operation Conference, Istanbul.

3152 **728** 1500l. multicoloured 45 20

729 Doves forming Olympic Flame

730 Soldiers and Old Woman

1992. Olympic Games, Barcelona. Multicoloured.

3153 500l. Type **729** 15 20

3154 1000l. Boxing 25 30

3155 1500l. Weightlifting 60 35

3156 2000l. Wrestling 1·00 60

1992. Legend of Anatolia. Multicoloured.

3157 500l. Type **730** 15 10

3158 1000l. Old woman filling trough with buttermilk 25 15

3159 1500l. Soldiers drinking from trough 30 25

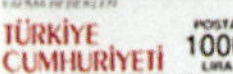

731 Bride and Mother-in-law Dolls from Merkez Kapikaya

732 Cherries

1992. Traditional Crafts. Multicoloured.
3160 500l. Knitted flowers from Ice l-Namrun (horiz) . . . 15 10
3161 1000l. Type **731** 25 15
3162 3000l. Woven saddlebag from Hakkari (horiz) . . 90 25

1992. Fruit (1st series). Multicoloured.
3163 500l. Type **732** 15 10
3164 1000l. Apricots 25 20
3165 3000l. Grapes 85 25
3166 5000l. Apples . . . . 1·50 35
See also Nos.3176/9.

734 Mountaineering

735 Sait Faik Abasiyanik

1992. 26th Anniv of Turkish Mountaineering Federation (3169) and 80th Anniv of Turkish Scout Movement (3170). Multicoloured.
3169 1000l.+200l. Type **734** . . . 25 20
3170 3000l.+200l. Scouts watering sapling (horiz) 80 35

1992. Anniversaries. No value expressed.
3171 **735** (T) blue, indigo and red 30 10
3172 – (T) blue, orange and violet 30 10
3173 – (M) blue, green & orange 85 10
3174 – (M) blue, red and indigo 85 10
3175 – (M) blue, red and green 85 10
DESIGNS: No. 3171, Type **935**(writer, 86th birth anniv); 3172, Fikret Mualla Saygi (painter, 25th deathanniv); 3173, Muhsin Ertugrul (actor and producer, birth centenary); 3174, Cevat Sakir Kabaagaeli (writer, 19th death anniv); 3175, Asik Veysel Satiroglu(poet, 98th birth anniv).
Nos. 3171/2were intended for greeting cards and Nos. 3173/5 for inland letters.

1993. Fruit (2nd series). As T **732**. Multicoloured.
3176 500l. Bananas 20 20
3177 1000l. Oranges 25 20
3178 3000l. Pears 90 20
3179 5000l. Pomegranates . . . . 1·50 30

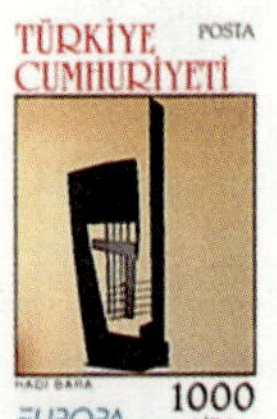

736 Sculpture (Hadi Bara)

737 Terraces

1993. Europa. Contemporary Art. Multicoloured.
3180 1000l. Type **736** 45 55
3181 3000l. Carved figure (Zuhtu Muridoglu) . . . . 1·40 75

1993. Campaign for the Preservation of Pamukkale. Multicoloured.
3182 1000l.+200l. Type **737** . . . 20 20
3183 3000l.+500l. Close-up of terrace 75 30

738 Buildings and Emblem

739 Rize

1993. Economic Co-operation Organization Conference, Istanbul.
3184 **738** 2500l. ultramarine, blue and gold 50 20

1993. Traditional Houses (1st series). Multicoloured.
3185 1000l. Type **739** 20 15
3186 2500l. Rize (different) (horiz) . 45 20
3187 3000l. Trabzon 55 25
3188 5000l. Black Sea houses (horiz) 95 45
See also Nos. 3222/5, 3256/9, 3283/6 and 3318/21.

740 Mausoleum

1993. 900th Birth Anniv of Hoca Ahmet Yesevi (philosopher).
3189 **740** 3000l. gold, blue & ltblue 45 15

741 Haci Arif Bey

1993. Death Anniversaries. No value expressed. Each brown and red.
3190 (T) Type **741** (composer, 109th) 45 10
3191 (T) Neyzen Tevfik Kolayli (singer, 40th) 45 10
3192 (M) Orhan Veli Kanik (poet, 43rd) 70 10
3193 (M) Cahit Sitki Taranci (poet, 27th) 70 10
3194 (M) Munir Nurettin Seluk (composer, 12th) 70 10
Nos. 3190/1 were intended for greetings cards and Nos. 3192/4 for inland letters.

742 Emblem

1993. Istanbul's Bid to host Summer Olympic Games in Year 2000.
3195 **742** 2500l. multicoloured . . 65 10

1993. As T **685** but inscription redrawn and dated "1993".
3199 **685** 5000l. violet and gold . . 1·25 10
3200 20000l. mauve and gold 5·00 10

744 Amphora on Sea-bed

1993. Mediterranean Treaty. Multicoloured.
3201 1000l. Type **744** 20 20
3202 3000l. Dolphin 80 30

745 Emblem

1993. U.N. Natural Disaster Relief Day.
3203 **745** 3000l.+500l. mult . . . 65 30

746 Prayer Mat

747 Laurel Wreath, Torch and Silhouette of Kemal Ataturk

1993. Handicrafts. Multicoloured.
3204 1000l. Type**746** 15 10
3205 2500l. Silver earrings . . . 20 15
3206 5000l. Crocheted purse . . . 70 20

1993. 70th Anniv of Republic.
3207 **747** 1000l. multicoloured . . 20 15

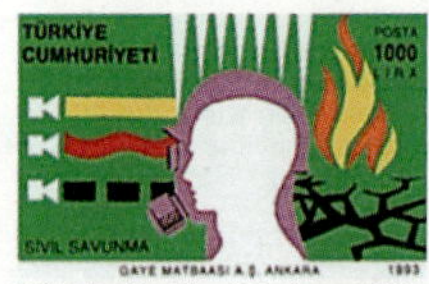

748 Manin Gas Mask and Fire

1993. Civil Defence.
3208 **748** 1000l. multicoloured . . 20 15

749 Satellite, Globe and Map

750 Ears of Corn

1994. "Turksat" Communications Satellite. Multicoloured.
3209 1500l. Type **749** 10 10
3210 5000l. Satellite and map showing satellite's "foot-print" 40 10

1994. 40th Anniv of Water Supply Company.
3211 **750** 1500l. multicoloured . . 25 15

751 Ezogel in Corbasi
752 Marie Curie

1994. Traditional Dishes. Multicoloured.
3212 1000l. Type **751** 15 15
3213 1500l. Karisikdolma 20 15
3214 3500l. Shishkebabs 25 25
3215 5000l. Baklava 60 25

1994. Europa. Discoveries. Multicoloured.
3216 1500l. Type **752** (discoverer ofradium) 30 35
3217 5000l. Albert Einstein and equation (formulator of Theory of Relativity) (horiz) 95 50

754 Faselis, Antalya

1994. Environment Day. Multicoloured.
3220 6000l. Type **754** 55 15
3221 8500l. Gocek, Mugla (vert) 80 20

755 Bursa

1994. Traditional Houses (2nd series). Multicoloured.
3222 2500l. Type **755** 20 15
3223 3500l. Uskudar 25 20
3224 6000l. Anadolu Hisari . . . 60 25
3225 8500l. Edirne 85 25

756 Trekking in Mountains

757 Centenary Emblem over City

1994. Tourism. Multicoloured.
3226 5000l. Type **756** 40 20
3227 10000l. White-water rafting (horiz) 90 30

1994. Centenary of International Olympic Committee.
3228 **757** 12500l.+500l. mult . . . 1·00 30

758 "2001"

1994. Seven Year Plan.
3229 **758** 2500l. multicoloured . . 20 15

759 Kusak Design

760 Kemal Ataturk

1994. Embroidery. Multicoloured.
3230 7500l. Type **759** 65 20
3231 12500l. Paalik design (horiz) 1·00 25

1994.
3232 **760** 50000l. violet, mve & red 2·00 10

761 Common Morel

762 "Platanusorientalis"

1994. Fungi. Multicoloured.
3233 2500l. Type **761** 20 25
3234 5000l. "Agaricusbernardii" 35 25
3235 7500l. Saffronmilk cap . . . 60 35
3236 12500l. Parasol mushroom 1·25 55

1994. Trees. Multicoloured.
3237 7500l.+500l. Type **762** . . . 75 30
3238 12500l.+1000l. "Cupressussempervirens" (vert) . . . . 1·10 50

763 Silver Jug

765 Starry Sky

1994. Traditional Crafts. Multicoloured.
3239 2500l. Type **763** 35 25
3240 5000l. Silver censer 40 25
3241 7500l. Necklace (horiz) . . . 60 40
3242 12500l. Goldbrooch (half horse and half fish) (horiz) . . . . 1·10 55

1995. Centenary of Motion Pictures.
3245 **765** 15000l. blue and red . . 95 10

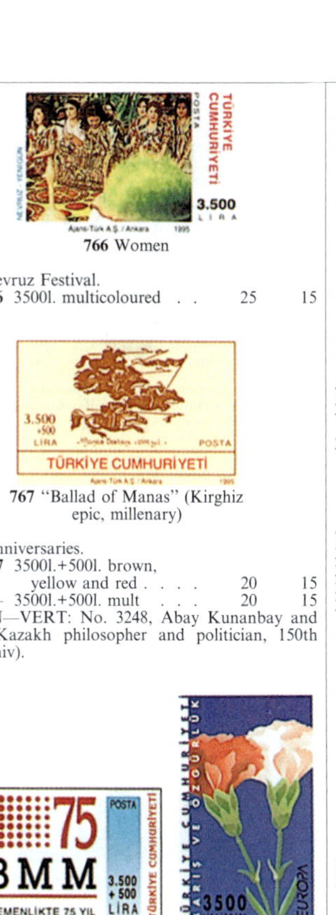

766 Women

1995. Nevruz Festival.
3246 **766** 3500l. multicoloured . . 25 15

767 "Ballad of Manas" (Kirghiz epic, millenary)

1995. Anniversaries.
3247 **767** 3500l.+500l. brown, yellow and red 20 15
3248 – 3500l.+500l. mult . . . 20 15
DESIGN—VERT: No. 3248, Abay Kunanbay and books (Kazakh philosopher and politician, 150th birth anniv).

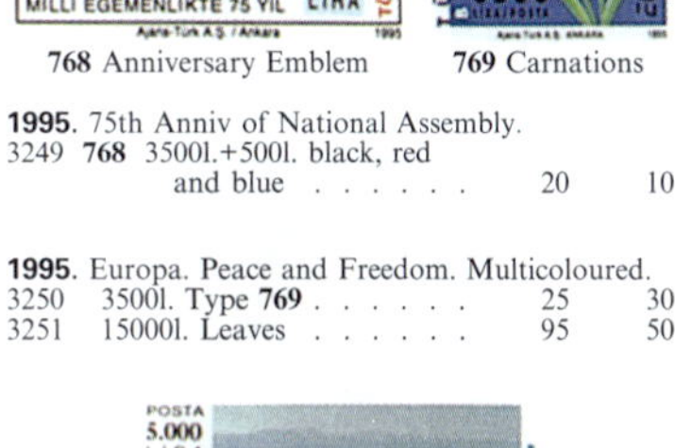

768 Anniversary Emblem   769 Carnations

1995. 75th Anniv of National Assembly.
3249 **768** 3500l.+500l. black, red and blue 20 10

1995. Europa. Peace and Freedom. Multicoloured.
3250 3500l. Type **769** 25 30
3251 15000l. Leaves 95 50

771 Beysehir Coast

1995. World Environment Day. National Parks. Multicoloured.
3253 5000l. Type **771** 15 15
3254 15000l. Yedi goller 60 15
3255 25000l. Ilgaz mountains . . 1·10 25

1995. Traditional Houses (3rd series). As T **755**. Multicoloured.
3256 5000l. Izmir (vert) 20 25
3257 10000l. Kula (vert) 35 35
3258 15000l. Mugla 70 50
3259 20000l. Birgi . . . . 1·10 55

772 Delegates, Flags and Globe

1995. 1st Muslim Parliamentary Members Congress, Islamabad.
3260 **772** 5000l. multicoloured . . 20 15

773 Painting of Townscape (left detail)

1995. "Istanbul96" International Stamp Exhibition. Multicoloured.
3261 7000l. Type **773** 30 15
3262 7000l. Aerial photo of bay (left detail) 30 15
3263 25000l. Painting of townscape (right detail) 1·40 20
3264 25000l. Aerial photo of bay (right detail) . . . . . . 1·40 20
Nos. 3261/4 were issued together, se-tenant, forming two composite designs.

774 Spirit embracing Earth   776 Death Cap

1995. 50th Anniversaries. Multicoloured.
3265 15000l. Type **774** (U.N.E.S.C.O.) 60 35
3266 30000l. Anniversary emblem (U.N.O.) . . . . 1·40 50

1995. Fungi. Multicoloured.
3268 5000l. Type **776** 15 15
3269 10000l. "Lepiotahelveola" 30 20
3270 20000l. Beef steak morel . . 80 30
3271 30000l. "Amanitagemmata" 1·60 35

777 Living in Harmony

1996. Aidfor Bosnia and Herzegovina.
3272 **777** 10000l.+2500l. mult . . 35 15

778 Rainbow, Flower, Sun and Hearts

1996. Children's Rights. Multicoloured.
3273 6000l. Type **778** 20 15
3274 10000l. Child drawing "A" 30 25

780 Nene Hatun (revolutionary)

1996. Europa. Famous Women. Multicoloured.
3276 10000l. Type **780** . . . . . 55 3·50
3277 40000l. Halide Edip Adivar (writer and politician) . . 2·00 5·00

781 Kemal Ataturk   782 Istanbul

1996.
3278 **781** 50000l. brown and pink 95 10
3279 – 100000l. blue and orange 2·40 10
DESIGN: 100000l. Ataturk (different).

1996. "HABITATII" Second United Nations Conference on Human Settlements, Istanbul.
3280 **782** 50000l. multicoloured . . 95 30

783 Player with Ball   788 Printing Works and Association Emblem

1996. European Football Championship, England. Multicoloured.
3281 15000l. Type **783** 45 35
3282 50000l. Football composed of participating countries' flags (horiz) . . . . . . 1·25 50

1996. Traditional Houses (4th series). As T **755**. Multicoloured.
3283 10000l. Kayseri 20 20
3284 15000l. Konya 30 25
3285 25000l. Ankara (vert) . . . 50 35
3286 50000l. Konya (vert) . . . . 1·40 45

1996. Various stamps surch. (a) Postcard Rate. Surch **T** and emblem.
3292 – T(10000l.) on 250l. orange, brown and gold (No.3144) 30 10
3293 **685** T(10000l.) on 2000l. blue andgrey 30 10

(b) Domestic Letter Rate. Nos. 3099 and 3101/2 surch **M**.
3294 **705** M(15000l.) on 200l. multicoloured 80 10
3295 – M(15000l.) on 400l. multicoloured 80 10
3296 – M(15000l.) on 1500l. multicoloured 80 10

1996. 50th Anniv of Journalists' Association.
3297 **788** 15000l. multicoloured . . 30 15

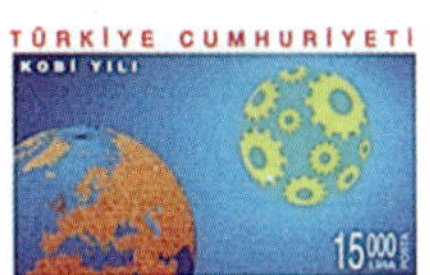

790 Cogwheels on Sphere and Globe

1996. Year of Small and Medium Businesses.
3299 **790** 15000l. multicoloured . . 35 20

791 Emblem

1996. 50th Anniv of Ankara University.
3300 **791** 15000l.+2500l. mult . . 35 20

792 Amasya Bayezit Public Library

1996. Historical Buildings. Multicoloured.
3301 10000l. Type **792** (500th anniv) 20 15
3302 15000l. Divrigi Mosque and Hospital 30 20

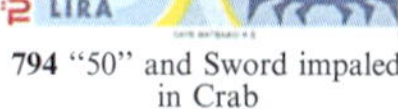

794 "50" and Sword impaled in Crab   795 Mohammed Ali Jinnah (first Governor-General)

1997. 50th Anniv of National Cancer Research and Prevention Association.
3304 **794** 25000l.+5000l. mult . . 40 20

1997. 50th Anniv of Independence of Pakistan.
3305 **795** 25000l.+5000l. mult . . 40 20

797 Cicgdem's Dreams (Cahit Ucuk)

1997. Europa. Tales and Legends. Multicoloured.
3307 25000l. Type **797** 40 25
3308 70000l. Bird of Zumrud-u Anka . . . . 1·10 45

798 Alphabet and Statue of Mehmet Bey   799 "Ophrystenthredinifera"

1997. Language Festival, Bayrami.
3309 **798** 25000l. multicoloured . . 30 20

1997. Orchids. Multicoloured.
3310 25000l. Type **799** 25 10
3311 70000l. Bee orchid 90 10

800 Erosion of Mountain Region

1997. Environment Day.
3312 **800** 35000l. multicoloured . . 45 20

801 Tulip and "XX5"   802 Urfa

1997. 25th Anniv of Istanbul Festival.
3313 **801** 15000l. blue, black & red 20 20
3314 25000l. mauve, blk & grn 30 20
3315 70000l. green, black & mve 85 20
3316 75000l. violet, black & bl 90 25
3317 100000l. turq, blk & pink 1·25 25

1997. Traditional Houses (5th series). Multicoloured.
3318 25000l. Type **802** 25 25
3319 40000l. Mardin (horiz) . . . 45 25
3320 80000l. Diyarbakir (horiz) 95 35
3321 100000l. Kemaliye . . . . . 1·25 45

804 Madonna Lily   805 Glider

1997. Plants. Multicoloured.
3324 40000l. Type **804** 35 10
3325 100000l. Poinsettia . . . . 1·25 10

1997. 1st International Aerial Sports Meeting. Multicoloured.
3326 40000l. Type **805** 50 25
3327 40000l. Hang-glider 50 25
3328 100000l. Hot-airballoon . . 1·40 35
3329 100000l. Kemal Ataturk at aerobatics display . . . . 1·40 35

806 Emblem

1997. International Forestry Congress, Ankara.
3330 **806** 50000l. multicoloured . . 60 10

807 Gymnast   808 Canakkale

1997. 15th European Gymnastics Congress.
3331 **807** 100000l. multicoloured . . . 1·10 50

1997. Traditional Women's Headdresses (1st series). Multicoloured.
3332 50000l. Type **808** 55 20
3333 50000l. Gaziantep 55 20
3334 100000l. Bursa . . . . . 1·10 25
3335 100000l. Isparta . . . . . 1·10 25
See also Nos. 3363/6, 3402/5, 3425/8 and 3455/8.

809 Alpine Skiing

1998. Winter Olympic Games, Nagano, Japan. Multicoloured.
3336 125000l. Type **809** 65 20
3337 125000l. Downhill skier . . . 65 20
Nos. 3336/7 were issued together, se-tenant, forming a composite design.

810 "With Great Respect to the Mehmetcik" Statue, Gallipoli

812 "Tulipaarmena"

1998. War Memorials. Multicoloured.
3338 125000l. Type **810** 55 20
3339 125000l. "Mother with Children", National War Memorial, Wellington, New Zealand 55 20

1998. International Tulip Festival, Bursa. Mult.
3341 50000l. "Tulipasylvestris" 40 10
3342 75000l. Type **812** 75 10
3343 100000l. "Tulipaarmena" (purple) . . . . 1·10 10
3344 125000l. "Tulipasaxatilis" 1·40 10

813 Ataturk and Parliament Building

1998. Europa. National Festivals. Multicoloured.
3345 100000l. Type **813** (Republic Day) 80 35
3346 150000l. Ataturk with children (Children's Festival) . . . . 1·25 60

816 Ballroom dancing

817 KemelAtaturk

1998. Contemporary Culture. Each red, black and yellow.
3353 75000l. Type **816** 45 10
3354 100000l. Cello player (vert) 55 10
3355 150000l. Ballet dancer (vert) 1·10 15

1998.
3356 **817** 150000l. brown & mve 95 10
3357 175000l. brown and blue 1·40 10
3358 250000l. mauve & brn 1·75 10
3359 500000l. blue and brown 3·50 15

818 State Flag

1998. 75th Anniv of Republic. Each red and black.
3360 175000l. Type **818** 85 25
3361 275000l. Silhouette of Ataturk and flag . . . . 1·40 25

1998. Traditional Women's Headdresses (2nd series). As T **808**. Multicoloured.
3363 75000l. Ankara 35 15
3364 75000l. Afyon 35 15
3365 175000l. Mugla 80 20
3366 175000l. Mus 80 20

819 Jigsaw Pieces

1998. 50th Anniv of Universal Declaration of Human Rights. Multicoloured.
3367 75000l.+25000l. Type **819** 40 25
3368 175000l.+25000l. Heart and human figures 85 45

820 Academy

1998. Centenary of Military Health Academy, Gata.
3369 **820** 75000l.+10000l. multicoloured 40 25

821 Feza Gursey (physicist, 6th anniv)

1998. Death Anniversaries. Value expressed by letter.
3370 **821** (T) orange, purple and brown 35 10
3371 – (T) violet and purple . . 35 10
3372 – (T) emerald, green and purple 35 10
3373 – (M) blue, violet and purple 80 10
3374 – (M) light purple, deep purple and purple . . 80 10
DESIGNS: No. 3371, Haldun Taner (writer, 12th anniv); 3372, Vasfi Riza Zobu (actor, 6th anniv); 3373, Ihap Hulusi Gorey (graphic designer, 12th anniv); 3374, Bedia Muvahhit (actress, 5th anniv).
Nos. 3370/2 were intended for greetings cards and Nos. 3373/4 for inland letters.

822 Ataturk and Monument (Tankut Oktem)

1999. Centenary of Kemal Ataturk's Entry into Military Academy.
3375 **822** 75000l.+5000l. mult . . 35 25

823 Anniversary Emblem

1999. 50th Anniv of North Atlantic Treaty Organization.
3376 **823** 200000l. blue, red and black 95 25

824 Council Ministers

1999. 700th Anniv of Foundation of Ottoman Empire. Multicoloured.
3377 175000l. Type **824** 75 25
3378 175000l. Horseman visiting Sultan 75 25
3379 175000l. Sultan on horseback and janissaries 75 25

825 Anniversary Emblem

826 Koprulu Canyon National Park

1999. 50th Anniv of Council of Europe.
3381 **825** 175000l.+10000l. mult 90 90

1999. Europa. Parks and Gardens. Multicoloured.
3382 175000l. Type **826** 80 45
3383 200000l. Kackarlar National Park (horiz) 95 60

830 "Degisim" (sculpture, Remzi Savas)

831 Templeof Zeus,Aizonoi

1999. Contemporary Art. Multicoloured.
3388 250000l. Type **830** 95 50
3389 250000l. "Anadolu' nun Gizemi" (painting, Zafer Gencaydin) 95 50

1999. World Tourism Day. Multicoloured.
3390 125000l. Type **831** 55 25
3391 125000l. Mosaic, Antakya Archaeological Museum (horiz) 55 25
3392 225000l. Yacht, Bodrum . . 1·10 50
3393 225000l. Golf course, Belek, Antalya . . . . 1·10 50

832 Cubuk-1Dam, Ankara

833 KemalAtaturk

1999. Dams. Multicoloured.
3394 225000l. Type **832** 95 55
3395 250000l. Ataturk Dam and hydro-electric power plant, River Euphrates . . 1·00 60

1999.
3396 **833** 225000l. mauve & green 90 10
3397 250000l. lilac and brown 1·00 10
3398 500000l. green & mauve 1·75 10
3399 1000000l. red and blue 3·50 10

834 Hands cradling Rubble and Daisies

1999. Thanks for Overseas Aid to Earthquake Victims. Multicoloured.
3400 225000l. Type **834** 70 35
3401 250000l. Rubble, rescue teams and handshake (horiz) 80 40

1999. Traditional Women's Headdresses (3rd series). As T **808**. Multicoloured.
3402 150000l. Manisa, Yunt Dagi 50 25
3403 150000l. Nigde 50 25
3404 250000l. Amasya, Merzifon 75 25
3405 250000l. Antalya 75 25

835 Sarapsa Fort, Alanya

1999. The Silk Road. Multicoloured.
3406 150000l. Type **835** 45 25
3407 250000l. Obruk Fort, Kanya 70 35

836 Globeas Brain and Satellite

2000. Millennium. Multicoloured.
3408 275000l. Type **836** 70 35
3409 300000l. Mediterranean monk seal 75 40

837 *Bug* (paddle-steamer)

2000. Ships. Multicoloured.
3410 125000l. Type **837** 70 35
3411 150000l. *Gulcemal* (liner) . . 75 40
3412 275000l. *Nusret* (paddle-steamer) 95 50
3413 300000l. *Bandirma* (cargoliner) . . . . 1·00 50

839 Flowers and Turkish Emblem

840 "Building Europe"

2000. 80th Anniv of Turkish National Assembly. Multicoloured.
3418 275000l. Type **839** 60 30
3419 300000l. Turkish emblem as flowers (horiz) 75 40

2000. Europa.
3420 **840** 300000l. multicoloured 60 40

841 Church, Mosque and Synagogue

2000. Tourism. Multicoloured.
3421 275000l.+10000l. Type **841** 60 55
3422 300000l.+10000l. Folk dancing 75 60

2000. Traditional Women's Headdresses (4th series). As T **808**. Multicoloured.
3425 275000l. Corum 60 35
3426 275000l. Trabzon 60 35
3427 275000l. Tunceli 60 35
3428 275000l. Izmir 60 35

844 Mausoleum, Ahlat

845 General Yakup Sevki Subasi

2000. Mausolea and Memorial. Multicoloured.
3429 150000l.+25000l. Type**844** 40 20
3430 200000l.+25000l. Memorial, Tunceli (horiz) 50 25
3431 275000l.+25000l. Domedmausoleum, Skopje, Macedonia 55 30
3432 300000l.+25000l. Mausoleum, Azerbaijan 65 35

2000. Military Leaders. Multicoloured.
3433 100000l. Type **845** 20 10
3434 200000l. General Musa Kazim Karabekir 45 20
3435 275000l. Marshal Mustafa Fevzi Cakmak 55 30
3436 300000l. General Cevat Cobanli 60 35

846 Gymnastics

2000. Olympic Games, Sydney. Multicoloured.
3437 125000l. Type **846** 30 10
3438 150000l. Swimming 35 15
3439 275000l. High jump 55 30
3440 300000l. Archery 60 30

847 *Crocuschrysanthus*

850 Globe, Satellite and Rocket

848 Arslan Baba

2000. Crocuses. Multicoloured.
3441 250000l. Type **847** 45 10
3442 275000l. *Crocusolivieri* 45 10
3443 300000l. *Crocusbiflorus* 50 10
3444 1250000l. *Crocussativus* 2·10 25

2000. Historic Buildings. Multicoloured.
3445 200000l. Type **848** 20 10
3446 275000l. Karasac Ana 30 10
3447 300000l. Hoca Ahmet Yesevi 30 10

2001. Launch of Turks at 2A Satellite.
3450 **850** 200000l. multicoloured 20 10

851 Afyon

852 Dudenbasi Waterfalls

2001. Women's Regional Costumes (1st series). Multicoloured.
3451 200000l. Type **851** 20 10
3452 200000l. Balikesir 20 10
3453 325000l. Kars 35 10
3454 325000l. Tokat 35 10
See also Nos.3494/7.

2001. Traditional Women's Headdresses (5th series). As T **808**. Multicoloured.
3455 200000l. Mersin-Silifke 20 10
3456 250000l. Sivas 25 10
3457 425000l. Aydin 45 10
3458 450000l. Hakkari 45 10

2001. Europa. Water Resources. Multicoloured.
3459 450000l. Type **852** 45 10
3460 500000l. Yerkopru Falls 50 10

853 Captain Mehmet Fethi Bey (pilot) and Muaret-I-Milliye

2001. 87th Anniv of First Istanbul–Cairo Flights by Turkish Crews. Multicoloured.
3461 250000l. Type **853** 25 10
3462 300000l. First Lieutenant Sadik Bey (navigator) and Muaret-I-Miliye 30 10
3463 450000l. First Lieutenant Nuri Bey (pilot) and Prince Celaleddin 45 10
3464 500000l. Captain Ismail Hakki Bey (navigator) and Prince Celaleddin 50 10

854 Ataturkand Turkish Flag

856 Myrtle (*Myrtuscommunis*)

2001. 120th Birth Anniv of Kemal Ataturk (President, 1923–38). Multicoloured.
3465 300000l. Type **854** 30 10
3466 450000l. Ataturk and building (horiz) 45 10

2001. Plants. Multicoloured.
3468 250000l. Type **856** 25 10
3469 300000l. Yarrow (*Achilleamillefolium*) 30 10
3470 450000l. St. John's Wort (*Hypericumperforatum*) 45 10
3471 500000l. Moyesrose (*Rosamoyesii*) 50 10
3472 1750000l. Whitethorn (*Crataegusoxyacantha*) 1·75 30

857 Mare and Foal

2001. Horses. Multicoloured.
3473 300000l. Type **857** 30 10
3474 450000l. Horses galloping 45 10
3475 450000l. Heads of three horses 45 10
3476 500000l. Horse (vert) 50 10

858 *Resitpasa*

2001. Merchant Ships. Multicoloured.
3477 250000l. Type **858** 25 10
3478 300000l. *Gulnihal* 30 10
3479 300000l. *Mithatpasa* 30 10
3480 500000l. *Aydin* 50 10

859 Obverse and Reverse of 1 Lira Coin, 1937

2001. Coins.Multicoloured.
3481 300000l.+25000l. Type **859** 35 15
3482 300000l.+25000l. Obverse and reverse of 100 Kurus coin, 1934 35 10
3483 450000l.+25000l. Obverse and reverse of Sultan Mehmet II gold coin, 1451 50 20
3484 500000l.+25000l. Obverse and reverse of Sultan Meliksah gold coin, 467 50 25

860 Sultan Tekes's Tomb, Turkmenistan

2001. Buildings.
3485 **860** 300000l. green and black 30 10
3486 – 300000l. red, yellow and black 30 10
3487 – 450000l. red, lilac and black 45 10
3488 – 500000l. blue and black 50 10
DESIGNS: No. 3486, Sirvansahlar Palace; 3487,Timur's Tomb, Samarkand; 3488, Yildirim Beyazit's Tomb.

861 Ashab-I Keff (13th-century)

2001. Caravanserais (inns) along the Silk Road. Multicoloured.
3489 300000l. + 25000l. Type **861** 55 20
3490 500000l. + 25000l. Horozlu (13th-century) 75 30

863N.A.T.O. Emblem on "50"

2002. 50th Anniv of Turkey's Membership of North Atlantic Treaty Organization.
3492 **863** 400000l. + 25000l. multicoloured 65 25

864 People Celebrating in Garden

865 Clown

2002. Sultan Nevruz Festival.
3493 **864** 400000l. multicoloured 40 10

2002. Women's Regional Costumes (2nd series). As T **851**. Multicoloured.
3494 350000l. Kastamonu 35 15
3495 400000l. Canakkale 40 10
3496 500000l. Amasya-Ilisu 50 10
3497 600000l. Elazig 60 10

2002. Europa. Circus.
3498 **865** 500000l. multicoloured 50 10

866 Referee and Footballers

2002. World Cup Football Championship, Japan and South Korea (1st issue). Multicoloured.
3499 400000l. Type **866** 40 10
3500 600000l. World cup, football and player 60 10
See also Nos. 3508/9.

867 Muzaffer Sarisozen (musician)

2002. Personalities.
3501 **867** 100000l. red, brown and black 10 10
3502 – 400000l. blue, indigo and black 40 10
3503 – 500000l. brown, deep brown and black 50 10
3504 – 600000l. lilac, purple and black 60 10
3505 – 2500000l. green, olive and black 2·25 35
DESIGNS: 400000l. Arif Nihat Asya (teacher, writer and politician); 500000l. Vedat Tek (architect); 600000l. Hilmi Ziya Ulken (philosopher); 2500000l. Ibrahim Calli (artist).

868 Anatolian Leopard (*Panthera pardus tulliana*)

2002. World Environment Day. Sheet 109 × 80 mm, containing T **868** and similar horiz designs. Multicoloured.
MS3506 400000l. Type **868**; 400000l. Eurasian lynx (*Lynx lynx*); 400000l. Tiger (*Panthera tigris*); 400000l. Caracal (*Felis caracal*) 1·60 1·60

869 Painted Top Shell and Edible Cockle

2002. Shells. Sheet 103 × 78 mm, containing T **869** and similar horiz designs. Multicoloured.
MS3507 400000l. Type **869**; 500000l. *Netted nassa*; 600000l. Common northern whelk; 750000l. Common periwinkle 2·25 2·25

870 Footballers

2002. World Cup Football Championship, Japan and South Korea (2nd issue). Multicoloured.
3508 400000l. Type **870** 40 10
3509 700000l. Turkish team (third place play-off winners) 70 10

871 Steam Locomotive

2002. Railways. Multicoloured.
3510 500000l.+250000l. Type **871** 75 10
3511 700000l.+250000l. Modern locomotive 95 15

872 Violin

2002. Musical Instruments. Multicoloured.
3512 450000l. Type **872** 45 10
3513 700000l. Double bass 70 10

873 *Ege*

2002. Merchant Ships. Multicoloured.
3514 450000l. Type **873** 45 10
3515 500000l. *Ayvalik* 50 10
3516 700000l. *Marakaz* 70 10
3517 700000l. *Karadeniz* 70 10

874 Pasha Gazi Kasim Mosque, Pecs

2002. Cultural Heritage. Sheet 105 × 65 mm, containing T **874** and similar square designs. Multicoloured.
MS3518 450l. Type **874**; 700l. Rakoczi Mansion, Tekirdag 15 15
Stamps of a similar design were issued by Hungary.

OBLIGATORY TAX STAMPS

T **101** Nurse bandaging Patient

T **102** Biplane

1926. Red Crescent.
T1035 – 1g. red, yellow & blk 25 15
T1036 T **101** 2½g. multicoloured 35 15
T1037 – 5g. multicoloured . . 50 20
T1038 – 10g. multicoloured 85 60
DESIGNS—VERT: 1g. Red crescent and decorative archway; 5g. Refugees. HORIZ: 10g. Stretcher bearers.

1926. Aviation Fund.
T1039 T **102** 20pa. brown & green 35 20
T1040 1g. green and stone 35 20
T1041 5g. violet and green 1·00 25
T1042 5g. red and green . . 19·00 2·50
The 5g. stamps are 40 × 29 mm.

T **103** Biplane over Ankara

٢٠ پاره
(T **104**)

1927. Aviation Fund.
T1043 T **102** 20pa. red and green 10 10
T1044 1g. green and ochre 20 10
T1045 T **103** 2g. brown and green 35 10
T1046 2½g. red and green 1·40 55
T1047 5g. blue and buff . . 30 10
T1048 10g. blue and pink 1·40 50
T1049 15g. green and yellow . . . . . 1·40 40
T1050 20g. brown and ochre . . . . . 2·10 90
T1051 50g. blue & light blue . . . . . 6·75 1·90
T1052 100g. red and blue 48·00 35·00
The 20pa. and 1g. are 25 × 15 mm.

1927. Red Crescent No. T1035 and charity labels surch with Type T **104** or similar types.
T1053 20pa. on 1g. red, yell & blk . . . . 2·50 30
T1054 20pa. on 1g. brown . . . 1·25 30
T1055 20pa. on 2½g. lilac . . . 1·25 30
DESIGNS: 26 × 21 mm. No. T1054 Hospital ship. No. T1055 Nurse tending patient.
No. T1053 has an extra line of Turkish characters in the surcharge.

T **105** Red Crescent on Map of Turkey

T **106** Cherubs holding Star

1928. Red Crescent. Various frames. Crescent in red.
T1067 T **105** ½pi. brown 15 10
T1068 1pi. purple 15 10
T1069 2½pi. orange 15 10
T1070 5pi. brown 55 15
T1071 10pi. green 55 20
T1072 20pi. blue 90 20
T1073 50pi. purple . . . . 3·00 15
See also Nos. T1171/4 and T1198/1212.

1928. Child Welfare.
T1074 T **106** 1g. olive and red . . 20 10
T1075 2½g. brown and red 20 10
T1076 5g. green and red . . 60 15
T1077 25g. black and red 1·90 45
See also Nos. T1160/1 and T1165/6.

1930. Aviation Fund. Nos. T1039, T1043, T1045 and T1049 surch.
T1099 T **102** Bir (1)k. on 20pa. brown and green 29·00 10·50
T1100 Bir (1)k. on 20pa. red and green . . 20 25
T1101 T **103** Yuz (100)pa. on 2g. brown and green 20 25
T1102 T **102** 5k. on 20pa. red and green 20 25
T1103 Bes (5)k. on 20pa. red and green . . 2·25 60
T1104 T **103** On (10)k. on 2g. brown and green 90 35
T1105 Elli (50)k. on 2g. brown and green 3·50 1·50
T1106 Bir (1)l. on 2g. brown and green 11·00 4·00
T1107 Bes (5)l. on 15g. green and yellow £600

T **114** Biplane over Ankara

T **118** Biplane

1931. Aviation Fund.
T1141 T **114** 20pa. black 30 10
See also Nos. T1154/6.

1932. Child Welfare. No. T1074 surch.
T1150 T **106** 20pa. on 1g. olive and red 45 20
T1153 3k. on 1g. olive and red . . . . 1·25 40

1932. Aviation Fund. As Type T **114** but larger, 22 × 30 mm, and with sky shaded.
T1154 1k. purple 20 10
T1155 5k. red 45 20
T1156 10k. green 80 20

1932. Red Crescent. Nos. T1067, T1069 and T1071 surch.
T1157 T **105** 1k. on 2½pi. orange 30 15
T1158 5k. on ½pi. brown . . 65 20
T1159 5k. on 10pi. green 1·00 40

1933. Child Welfare. As Type T **106** but inscr "IZMIR HIMAYEI ETFAL CEMIYETI"
T1160 1k. violet and red 40 35
T1161 5k. brown and red . . . . 1·90 60

1933. Aviation Fund.
T1162 T **118** On (10)pa. green . . 25 10
T1163 Bir (1)k. red 45 15
T1164 Bes (5)k. lilac . . . 60 15

1934. Child Welfare. As Type T **106** but inscr "Turkiye Himayeietfal Cemiyeti".
T1165 20pa. purple and red . . . 40 10
T1166 15k. green and red . . . 1·60 40

T **119** Red Crescent and Map of Turkey

1934. Inscr "TURKIYE HILALIAHMER CEMIYETI" (different frame on 5k.).
T1171 T **119** ½k. blue and red . . 20 10
T1172 1k. brown and red 40 10
T1173 2½k. brown and red 50 25
T1174 5k. green and red . . 90 35
See also Nos. T1198/1212.

1936. Child Welfare. Nos. T1074/5 and T1165 optd **P.Y.S.** or surch also.
T1186 T **106** 20pa. purple and red 2·10 65
T1187 1g. olive and red . . 50 35
T1188 3k. on 2½g. brn & red . . . . 2·10 65

1937. Red Crescent. As Types T **105** and T **119** but inscr "TURKIYE KIZILAY CEMIYETI". Various frames.
T1204 ¼k. blue and red 50 15
T1199 1k. mauve and red 35 15
T1200 2½k. orange and red . . . 55 25
T1201 5k. green and red . . . 1·10 25
T1209 5k. brown and red 60 15
T1202 10k. green and red . . . 1·10 50
T1203 20k. black and red . . . 2·10 60
T1211 50k. purple and red . . . 12·00 35
T1212 1l. blue and red . . . 48·00 2·10

1938. Child Welfare. No. T1075 surch. (a) Value in figures and words above **P. Y. S.**
T1213 T **106** 20pa. on 2½g. brown and red . . . . . 1·10 40
T1214 1k. on 2½g. brown and red . . . . . 1·10 40

(b) **P. Y. S.** above value in figures and words.
T1215 T **106** 20pa. on 2½g. brown and red . . . . . 1·90 75
T1216 1k. on 2½g. brown and red . . . . . 1·90 70

(c) **1 kurus**.
T1217 T **106** 1k. on 2½g. brown and red . . . . . 1·90 40

T **138** Laughing Child

T **139** Nurse and Baby

1940. Child Welfare. Star in red.
T1259 T **138** 20pa. green 15 10
T1260 1k. lilac 25 10
T1261 T **139** 1k. blue 20 15
T1262 2½k. mauve 70 25
T1263 T **138** 3k. black 25 10
T1264 T **139** 5k. lilac 20 10
T1265 10k. green 50 10
T1266 T **138** 15k. blue . . . . . 1·00 30
T1267 T **139** 25k. olive . . . . . 3·75 50
T1268 50k. olive . . . . . 4·50 60

T **145** Soldier and Map of Turkey

T **151** Child eating

1941. National Defence.
T1289 T **145** 1k. violet 20 10
T1290 2k. blue . . . . . 3·00 10
T1291 3k. brown . . . . . 4·25 40
T1292 4k. mauve . . . . . 1·60 15
T1293 5k. pink . . . . . 7·00 2·10
T1294 10k. blue . . . . . 20·00 12·00

1943. Child Welfare. Inscr "SEFKAT PULLARI 1943".
T1330 T **151** 0.50k. violet and red 15 10
T1331 0.50k. green and red 15 10
T1332 – 1k. blue and red . . 15 10
T1333 – 3k. red and orange 35 15
T1334 – 15k. black, buff and red 75 25
T1335 – 100k. blue and red 1·40 50
DESIGNS—VERT: 1k. Nurse with baby; 15k. Baby and emblem; 100k. President Inonu and child. HORIZ: 3k. Nurse and child.

T **152** Child Welfare Emblem

T **155** Pres. Inonu and Victim

1943. Child Welfare. Star in red.
T1337 T **152** 20pa. blue 15 10
T1338 – 1k. green 15 10
T1339 – 3k. brown 15 10
T1340 – 5k. orange . . . . . 1·60 15
T1341 – 5k. brown . . . . . 1·90 15
T1342 – 10k. red 85 10
T1343 – 15k. lilac . . . . . 1·75 10
T1344 – 25k. violet . . . . . 1·90 15
T1345 – 50k. blue . . . . . 2·75 20
T1346 – 100k. green . . . . 4·50 25
DESIGNS—VERT: 1k. Hospital; 3k. Nurse and children; 5k. Baby in cot; 10k. Nurse bathing baby; 15k. Nurse helping child to drink; 50k. Child. HORIZ: 25k. Baby with bottle; 100k. Hospital.

1944. Red Crescent. Inscr "TURKIYE KIZILAY CEMIYETI".
T1347 – 20pa. brown, flesh, red and blue . . . 25 10
T1348 T **155** 1k. olive, yellow, green and red . . 25 15
T1349 – 2½k. blue and red . . 45 15
T1350 – 5k. blue and red . . 1·90 25
T1351 – 10k. blue, green and red . . . . 1·90 25
T1352 – 50k. green, black and red . . . . 5·50 35
T1353 – 1l. yellow, black and red . . . . 10·50 70
DESIGNS—VERT: 20pa. Nurse tending dreaming patient; 5k. Soldier and nurse; 10k. Feeding victims; 50k. Wounded soldiers on raft; 1l. Nurse within red crescent. HORIZ: 2½k. Stretcher bearers and hospital ship.

T **156** Nurse helping Child to Drink

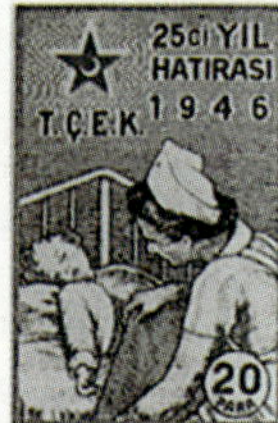

T **159** Nurse tucking Baby in Cot

1945. Child Welfare. Star in red.
T1354 – 1k. lilac 15 10
T1355 – 2½k. blue 35 15
T1356 T **156** 5k. green 40 35
T1357 – 10k. brown . . . . 2·25 60
T1358 – 250k. black . . . . 23·00 3·00
T1359 – 500k. violet . . . . 38·00 2·75
DESIGNS—VERT (21 × 20 mm): 1k. Nurse carrying baby; 2½k. Nurse holding child; 10k. Child sucking thumb. HORIZ (28 × 22 mm): 250, 500k. Emblem.

1946. 25th Anniv of Child Welfare Organization.
T1360 T **159** 20pa. brown and red 10 10
T1361 – 1k. blue and red . . 10 10
T1362 – 2½k. red 30 10
T1363 – 5k. brown and red 50 15
T1364 – 15k. purple and red 75 25
T1365 – 25k. green and red 1·25 40
T1366 – 50k. green and red 1·90 40
T1367 – 150k. brown and red 5·00 40
DESIGNS: 1k. Mother and baby; 2½k. Nurse holding child above head; 5k. Doctor examining baby; 15k. Nurse feeding baby; 25k. Nurse bathing baby; 50k. Nurse weighing baby; 150k. Nurse, and child in cot.

T **160** Pres. Inonu and Victim

T **169** Nurse and Children playing

1946. Red Crescent. As Nos. T1347/8, T1350 and T1353 and new design inscr "TURKIYE KIZILAY DERNEGI".
T1369 – 20pa. yellow, grey, blue and red . . 15 10
T1532 – 20pa. brown, yellow, violet and red . . 20 10
T1370 T **155** 1k. multicoloured . . 4·75 70
T1371 T **160** 1k. brown, blue and red 25 15
T1533 – 1k. green, blk & red 20 10
T1372 – 5k. blue and red . . 40 15
T1373 – 20k. red, blue & pur 1·25 75
T1374 – 1l. black, yell & red 5·50 2·75
T1375 – 250k. black, green and red . . . . 11·00 1·10
T1376 – 5l. black, pink and red . . . . 16·00 1·40
T1377 – 10l. blue and red 27·00 20·00
DESIGNS—VERT: 20pa. As No. T1347; 1k. (T1533), As No. T1352; 5k. As No. T1350; 1l. As No. T1353; 5l. Nurse tending patient; 10l. Soldier, red crescent and figure symbolizing Victory. HORIZ: 20k. Ankara Hospital; 250k. Nurse helping injured soldier.

1948. Child Welfare. Star in red.
T1399 T **169** 20pa. blue 15 10
T1400 – 20pa. mauve 15 10
T1401 – 1k. green 15 10
T1402 – 3k. purple 30 10
T1403 – 15k. grey 60 10
T1404 – 30k. orange . . . . 1·10 1·10
T1405 – 150k. green . . . . 5·75 45
T1406 – 300k. red . . . . . 11·50 3·50

DESIGNS—VERT: 20pa. (No. 1400) Nurse and children walking; 1k. Nurse feeding two children; 3k. Nurse with three children; 15k. Parents and two children; 150k. Nurse holding baby; 300k. Heads of nurse and child. HORIZ: 30k. Father handing baby to nurse.

T 177 Ruins and Tent

T 179 "Grief"

1949. Red Crescent.
T1422 T 177 5k. black, red & pur 55 25
T1423 10k. purple, red and flesh 55 25

1950. Red Crescent. Crescent in red.
T1425 T 179 ¼k. blue 1·40 10
T1426 1k. blue 15 10
T1427 2k. mauve 25 15
T1428 2½k. orange 25 65
T1429 3k. green 30 65
T1430 4k. drab 40 15
T1431 5k. blue 65 10
T1432 10k. pink 3·00 25
T1433 25k. brown 4·50 25
T1434 – 50k. blue 4·50 1·25
T1435 – 100k. green 8·00 1·25
DESIGN: 50, 100k. Plant with broken stem.

1952. (a) Red Crescent. Nos. T1427 and T1429/30 surch.
T1489 T 179 20pa. on 2k. mauve and red 80 25
T1490 20pa. on 3k. green and red 30 15
T1491 20pa. on 4k. drab and red 45 15

(b) Child Welfare. Nos. T1355, T1362 and T1339 surch.
T1492 – 1k. on 2½k. blue and red 75 20
T1493 – 1k. on 2½k. red 30 10
T1494 – 1k. on 3k. brown and red 40 15

T 208 Nurse and Baby

T 211 Globe and Flag

1954. Child Welfare. Inscr "SEFKAT PULLARI 1954".
T1534 – 20pa. yellow & orange 15 10
T1535 – 20pa. green and red 15 10
T1536 T 208 1k. blue and red 20 10
DESIGN: Nos. 1534/5, Nurse with two children.
See also Nos. T1569 and T1573/4.

1954. Red Crescent.
T1545 T 211 1k. multicoloured 20 10
T1546 – 5k. red, grey and green 20 10
T1547 – 10k. grey, green and red 35 10
DESIGNS: 5k. Nurse with wings on cloud; 10k. Arm and hand.
See also Nos. T1652, T1656/8, T1838 and T1840/3.

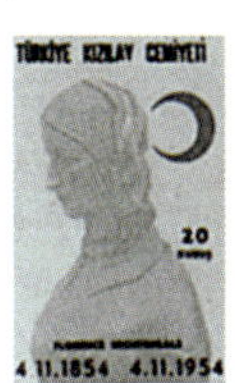
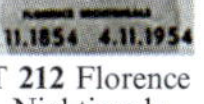
T 212 Florence Nightingale

T 215 Children Kissing

1954. Red Crescent. Centenary of Florence Nightingale's Arrival at Scutari.
T1551 T 212 20k. green, brown and red 25 10
T1552 – 30k. brown, black and red 30 10
T1553 – 50k. stone, black and red 30 10
DESIGNS: 30k. Florence Nightingale (three-quarter face); 50k. Selimiye Barracks.

1955. Child Welfare. Inscr "SEFKAT PULLARI 1955". Star in red.
T1564 T 215 20pa. blue 10 10
T1565 20pa. brown 10 10
T1566 1k. purple 10 10
T1567 3k. bistre 10 10
T1568 5k. orange 10 10
T1569 T 208 10k. green 50 10
T1570 – 15k. blue 30 25
T1571 – 25k. lake 40 25
T1572 – 50k. green 80 45
T1573 T 208 2½l. brown £170 70·00
T1574 10l. violet £550 £190
DESIGN: 15 to 50k. Nurse carrying baby.

1955. Red Crescent. Nos. T1373 and T1435 surch.
T1575 20pa. on 20k. red, blue and purple 15 10
T1576 20pa. on 100k. green and red 15 10

T 219 Nurse

T 227 Woman and Children

1955. Red Crescent. Congress of International Council of Nurses.
T1578 T 219 10k. brown, red and black 25 15
T1579 – 15k. green, red and black 30 15
T1580 – 100k. blue and red 1·25 60
DESIGNS—HORIZ: 15k. Nurses marching. VERT: 100k. Emblem, Red Cross and Red Crescent flags and nurses.

1956. Child Welfare. Star in red.
T1614 T 227 20pa. salmon 15 10
T1615 20pa. olive 15 10
T1616 1k. blue 20 10
T1617 1k. violet 20 10
T1618 3k. brown 75 25
T1619 – 10k. red 1·50 75
T1620 – 25k. green 2·10 75
T1621 – 50k. blue 3·50 80
T1622 – 2½l. lilac 7·00 2·10
T1623 – 5l. brown 14·00 5·00
T1624 – 10l. green 27·00 7·50
DESIGNS: 10k. to 50k. Flag and building; 2½l. to 10l. Mother and baby.

1956. Red Crescent. No. T1545 surch.
T1625 T 211 20pa. on 1k. mult 10 10
T1626 2.5k. on 1k. mult 10 10

1956. Child Welfare. Nos. 1399/1406 optd **IV. DUNYA Cocuk Gunu 1 Ekim 1956**. Nos. 1644/6 surch, also.
T1639 T 169 20pa. red and blue 4·50 4·50
T1640 – 20pa. mauve and red 4·50 4·50
T1641 – 1k. green and red 4·50 4·50
T1642 – 3k. purple and red 4·50 4·50
T1643 – 15k. grey and red 4·50 4·50
T1644 – 25k. on 30k. orange and red 4·50 4·50
T1645 – 100k. on 150k. green and red 4·50 4·50
T1646 – 250k. on 300k. deep red and red 4·50 4·50

1957. Red Crescent. As No. T1373 but inscr "TURKIYE KIZILAY CEMIYETI", new design and as Nos. T1545/6. Crescent in red.
T1651 – ½k. drab and brown 10 10
T1652 T 211 1k. black, bis & green 10 10
T1653 – 2½k. green & dp green 15 10
T1655 – 20k. red, brown and blue 1·75 15
T1656 T 211 25k. grey, black and green 1·50 25
T1657 50k. blue and green 2·40 25
T1658 100k. violet, black and green 4·50 25
DESIGNS—VERT: ½, 2½k. Flower being watered. HORIZ: 20k. Ankara hospital.

T 239 Two Babies

T 246 Nurse and Child

1957. Child Welfare.
T1659 T 239 20pa. green and red 10 10
T1660 20pa. pink and red 10 10
T1661 1k. blue and red 10 10
T1662 3k. orange and red 30 15
T1683 T 246 100k. brown and red 40 10
T1684 150k. green and red 40 10
T1685 250k. violet and red 75 10

T 254 Florence Nightingale

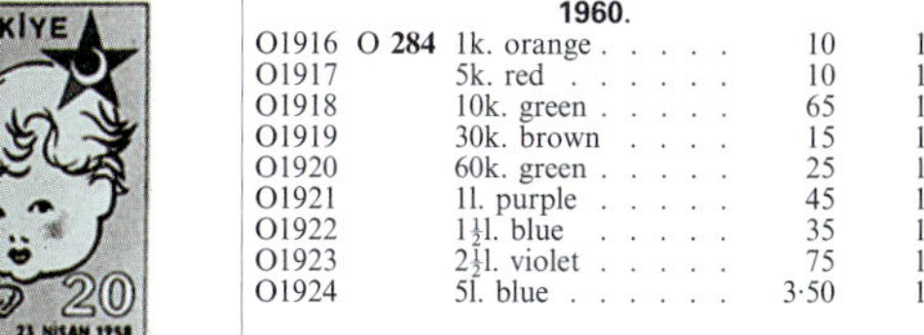
T 255 Child's Head and Butterfly

1958. Florence Nightingale Foundation. Crescent in red.
T1829 T 254 1l. green 20 10
T1830 1½l. grey 20 10
T1831 2½l. blue 20 10

1958. Child Welfare. Butterflies. Multicoloured.
T1832 20k. Typeno-wrap T /no-wrap255 30 25
T1833 25k. Brimstone 35 35
T1834 50k. Little tiger blue (horiz) 70 45
T1835 75k. Green-veined white (horiz) 95 70
T1836 150k. Peacock 1·40 90

1958. Red Crescent. As Nos. T1651/3, T1546 and T1656/8 but colours changed. Crescent in red.
T1837 – ½k. lilac 25 10
T1838 T 211 1k. black, brown and green 30 10
T1839 – 2½k. grey and red 50 10
T1840 – 5k. red, brown and green 90 10
T1841 T 211 25k. black, green and brown 3·75 25
T1842 50k. purple, black and green 4·50 25
T1843 100k. drab, black and green 7·00 45

OFFICIAL STAMPS

O 160

O 241

O 284

1947.
O1360 O 160 10pa. brown 10 10
O1361 1k. green 10 10
O1362 2k. purple 10 10
O1363 3k. orange 10 10
O1364 5k. turquoise 25·00 10
O1365 10k. brown 6·25 10
O1366 15k. violet 90 10
O1367 20k. blue 1·25 10
O1368 30k. olive 1·25 10
O1369 50k. blue 1·25 10
O1370 1l. green 1·90 10
O1371 2l. red 2·50 90

1951. Postage stamps optd **RESMI** between bars with star and crescent above.
O1458 165 0.25k. red 15 10
O1454 5k. blue 15 10
O1461 10k. brown 10 10
O1462 15k. violet 15 10
O1456 20k. blue 25 10
O1469 30k. brown 3·50 10
O1470 60k. black 3·75 15

1955. Postage stamps optd **RESMI** between wavy bars with star and crescent above or surch also.
O1568 165 0.25k. red 10 10
O1587 ½k. on 1k. black 10 10
O1569 1k. black 10 10
O1570 2k. purple 15 10
O1593 2k. on 4k. green 10 10
O1571 3k. orange 15 10
O1594 3k. on 4k. green 10 10
O1572 4k. green 15 10
O1573 5k. on 15k. violet 15 10
O1581 5k. blue 25 10
O1595 10k. on 12k. red 10 10
O1574 10k. on 15k. violet 15 10
O1575 15k. violet 15 10
O1576 20k. blue 25 10
O1585 30k. brown 15 10
O1577 40k. on 1l. olive 30 10
O1590 75k. on 1l. olive 20 10
O1578 75k. on 2l. brown 35 10
O1579 75k. on 5l. purple 8·50 10·00

1957.
O1655 O 241 5k. blue 10 10
O1843 5k. red 15 10
O1656 10k. brown 10 10
O1844 10k. olive 15 10
O1657 15k. violet 10 10
O1845 15k. red 10 10
O1658 20k. red 10 10
O1846 20k. violet 10 10
O1659 30k. olive 10 10
O1660 40k. purple 10 10
O1847 40k. blue 10 10
O1661 50k. grey 10 10
O1662 60k. green 10 10
O1848 60k. orange 25 10
O1663 75k. orange 10 10
O1849 75k. grey 25 10
O1664 100k. green 15 10
O1850 100k. violet 30 10
O1665 200k. lake 15 10
O1851 200k. brown 70 10

1960.
O1916 O 284 1k. orange 10 10
O1917 5k. red 10 10
O1918 10k. green 65 10
O1919 30k. brown 15 10
O1920 60k. green 25 10
O1921 1l. purple 45 10
O1922 1½l. blue 35 10
O1923 2½l. violet 75 10
O1924 5l. blue 3·50 10

O 303

O 320

1962.
O1977 O 303 1k. brown 10 10
O1978 5k. green 10 10
O1979 10k. brown 10 10
O1980 15k. blue 15 10
O1981 25k. red 35 10
O1982 30k. blue 20 10

1963. Surch.
O2003 O 303 50k. on 30k. blue 15 10
O2004 O 284 100k. on 60k. green 20 10

1963.
O2042 O 320 1k. green 10 10
O2043 5k. brown 10 10
O2044 10k. green 10 10
O2045 50k. red 15 10
O2046 100k. blue 25 10

O 329

O 344

1964.
O2074 O 329 1k. grey 10 10
O2075 5k. blue 10 10
O2076 10k. yellow 10 10
O2077 30k. red 25 10
O2078 50k. green 25 10
O2079 60k. brown 60 10
O2080 80k. turquoise 1·40 10
O2081 130k. blue 1·40 10
O2082 200k. purple 2·75 10

1965.
O2133 O 344 1k. green 10 10
O2134 10k. blue 10 10
O2135 50k. orange 20 10

O 358 Usak Carpet

O 372 Doves Emblem

O 383

1966. Turkish Carpets.
O2175 O 358 1k. orange 10 10
O2176 – 50k. green 10 10
O2177 – 100k. red 25 10
O2178 – 150k. blue 35 10
O2179 – 200k. bistre 40 10
O2180 – 500k. lilac 95 10
DESIGNS (Carpets of): 50k. Bergama; 100k. Ladik; 150k. Selcuk; 200k. Nomad; 500k. Anatolia.

1967.
O2213 O 372 1k. blue & light blue 10 10
O2214 50k. blue and orange 15 10
O2215 100k. blue & mauve 25 10

1968.
O2241 O 383 50k. brown and green 15 10
O2242 150k. black & orange 40 10
O2243 500k. brown and blue 60 10

O 400

O 427

O 440

1969.
O2287 O 400 1k. red and green 10 10
O2288 10k. blue and green 10 10

O2289 50k. brown and green 10 10
O2290 100k. mauve & green 20 10

1971.
O2359 O 427 5k. blue and brown 10 10
O2360 10k. red and blue 10 10
O2361 30k. violet & orange 10 10
O2362 50k. brown and blue 10 10
O2363 75k. green and buff 15 10

1971. Face-value and border colour given first.
O2398 O 440 5k. blue and grey 10 10
O2399 25k. green and brown 10 10
O2400 100k. brown & green 15 10
O2401 200k. brown & ochre 15 10
O2402 250k. purple & violet 15 10
O2403 500k. blue & light blue 40 10

O 446 O 462 O 478 Trellis Motif

1972.
O2411 O 446 5k. blue and brown 10 10
O2412 100k. green & brown 10 10
O2413 200k. red and brown 15 10

1973.
O2457 O 462 100k. blue and cream 10 10

1974.
O2490 O 478 10k. brown on pink 10 10
O2491 25k. purple on blue 10 10
O2492 50k. red on mauve 10 10
O2493 150k. brown on grn 15 10
O2494 250k. red on pink 25 10
O2495 500k. brown on yell 50 10

O 496 O 528 O 529

1975.
O2537 O 496 100k. red and blue 10 10

1977. Surch.
O2587 O 320 5k. on 1k. green 10 10
O2588 O 329 5k. on 1k. grey 10 10
O2589 O 344 5k. on 1k. green 10 10
O2590 O 358 5k. on 1k. orange 10 10
O2591 O 372 5k. on 1k. blue and light blue 10 10

1977.
O2609 O 528 250k. green and blue 10 10

1978.
O2610 O 529 50k. pink and red 10 10
O2611 2½l. buff and brown 10 10
O2612 4½l. lilac and green 15 10
O2613 5l. blue and violet 15 10
O2614 10l. light green and green 50 10
O2615 25l. yellow and red 95 10

O 540 O 552 O 573

1979.
O2647 O 540 50k. deep orange and orange 10 10
O2648 2½l. blue & light blue 10 10

1979.
O2686 O 552 50k. violet and pink 10 10
O2687 1l. red and green 10 10
O2688 2½l. mauve and light mauve 10 10
O2689 5l. purple and blue 10 10
O2690 7½l. blue and lilac 15 10
O2691 10l. blue and buff 20 10
O2692 35l. purple and silver 65 10
O2693 50l. blue and pink 1·00 10

1981.
O2756 O 573 5l. red and yellow 1·875 10
O2757 10l. red and pink 1·90 10
O2758 35l. mauve and grey 2·50 10
O2759 50l. blue and pink 3·75 10
O2760 75l. emerald & green 5·00 10
O2761 100l. blue & lt blue 5·75 10

O 606 O 644 O 720

1983.
O2839 O 606 5l. blue and yellow 35 10
O2840 15l. blue and yellow 40 10
O2841 20l. blue and grey 30 10
O2842 50l. blue & light blue 1·90 10
O2843 65l. blue and mauve 2·40 10
O2844 70l. blue and pink 60 10
O2845 90l. blue and brown 2·00 10
O2846 90l. blue & light blue 2·10 10
O2847 100l. blue and green 1·60 10
O2848 125l. blue and green 3·50 10
O2849 230l. blue and orange 2·50 10

1986.
O2946 O 644 5l. blue and yellow 10 10
O2947 10l. blue and pink 15 10
O2948 20l. blue and grey 20 10
O2949 50l. blue & light blue 30 10
O2950 100l. blue and green 1·25 10
O2951 300l. blue and lilac 1·90 10

1989. Various stamps surch.
O3039 O 644 500l. on 10l. blue and pink 1·00 10
O3040 O 606 500l. on 15l. blue and yellow 1·00 10
O3041 O 644 500l. on 20l. blue and grey 1·00 10
O3042 O 606 1000l. on 70l. blue and pink 2·00 10
O3043 1000l. on 90l. blue and brown 2·00 10
O3044 1250l. on 230l. blue and orange 3·00 10

1991. Nos. O2843 and O2846 surch.
O3108 O 606 100l. on 65l. blue and mauve 20 10
O3109 250l. on 90l. blue and light blue 60 10

1992.
O3138 O 720 3000l. deep brown and brown 1·10 10
O3139 5000l. green & lt grn 1·90 10

O 733 O 743 O 753

1992.
O3167 O 733 1000l. blue and green 20 10
O3168 10000l. green & blue 2·00 10

1993.
O3196 O 743 100l. green & brown 35 10
O3197 150l. green & brown 70 10
O3198 500l. brown & green 2·10 10

1994.
O3218 O 753 2500l. dp mve & mve 20 10
O3219 25000l. brn & stone 2·50 10

O 764 O 770 O 775

1995.
O3243 O 764 3500l. violet and light violet 50 10
O3244 17500l. green and light green 2·00 10

1995.
O3252 O 770 50000l. green and olive 1·90 10

1995.
O3267 O 775 5000l. red and orange 25 10

O 785 O 793 O 803

1996.
O3288 O 785 15000l. red and blue 30 10
O3289 – 20000l. violet and green 40 10
O3290 – 50000l. green and violet 1·10 10
O3291 – 100000l. blue and red 2·10 10

DESIGNS: 20000l. Hearts forming pattern; 50000l. Leaves forming pattern; 100000l. Ornate scroll pattern.

1997.
O3303 O 793 25000l. blue and mauve 35 10

1997.
O3322 O 803 40000l. violet and red 35 10
O3323 – 250000l. green and red 3·00 10

DESIGN: 250000l. Diamond-shaped pattern.

O 815 O 827 O 838

1998.
O3348 O 815 40000l. light blue and blue 25 10
O3349 – 75000l. lilac and orange 45 10
O3350 – 100000l. purple 50 10
O3351 – 200000l. green and brown 1·10 10
O3352 – 500000l. green and brown 2·25 10

DESIGNS: 75000l. Pattern forming St. Andrew's cross with fleur-de-lis finials; 100000l. Diamond-shaped pattern; 200000l. Pattern with central circle; 500000l. Pattern forming five crosses.

1999.
O3384 O 827 R (75000l.) lilac and blue 70 10
O3385 – RT (275000l.) grey and pink 1·90 10

DESIGN: No. O3385, Pattern of flowers.
No. O3384 was for use on Official letters and No. O3385 for use on Official registered letters.

2000.
O3414 O 838 50000l. pink and blue 15 10
O3415 – 75000l. grey and brown 20 10
O3416 – 500000l. blue and brown 1·10 10
O3417 – 1250000l. buff and blue 2·50 10

DESIGNS: 75000l. Squares and triangles; 500000l. Clover leaf pattern; 1250000l. Fleur de Lys pattern.

O 849 O 862 O 875

2000.
O3448 O 849 R yellow and blue 50 15
O3449 RT blue and ultramarine 50 15

No. O3448 was for use on Official letters and No. O3449 for use on Official registered letters.

2001.
O3491 O 862 R yellow and blue 50 15

No. O3491 was for use on Official letters.

2002.
O3519 O 875 50000l. blue and red 15 10
O3520 100000l. yellow and green 30 10
O3521 250000l. blue and red 55 15
O3522 500000l. orange and blue 1·00 30
O3523 1500000l. yellow, light green and green 2·75 1·60

POSTAGE DUE STAMPS

D 2 D 4

1863. Imperf.
D 7 D 2 20pa. black on brown 90·00 32·00
D 8 1pi. black on brown £110 38·00
D 9 2pi. black on brown £450 £110
D10 5pi. black on brown £325 £130

1865.
D18 D 4 20pa. brown 1·40 3·75
D19 1pi. brown 1·40 3·25
D74 2pi. brown 7·50 11·00
D70 5pi. brown 3·75 16·00
D76 25pi. brown 32·00 £100

1888. As T 9.
D117 9 20pa. black 3·25 10·00
D118 1pi. black 3·25 10·00
D119 2pi. black 3·25 10·00

1892. As T 15.
D146 15 20pa. black 4·50 4·00
D147 20pa. black on red 1·50 12·00
D148 1pi. black 15·00 4·75
D149 2pi. black 12·00 4·75

1901. As T 21.
D195 21 10pa. black on red 2·50 3·75
D196 20pa. black on red 2·10 6·00
D197 1pi. black on red 1·75 6·50
D198 2pi. black on red 1·25 7·75

1905. As T 23.
D228 23 1pi. black on red 1·40 3·75
D229 2pi. black on red 2·75 11·50

1908. As T 25.
D250 25 1pi. black on red 60·00 4·50
D251 2pi. black on red 4·25 35·00

1909. As T 28.
D288 28 1pi. black on red 12·50 65·00
D287 2pi. black on red 75·00 £130

1913. As T 30.
D347 30 2pa. black on red 45 65
D348 5pa. black on red 45 65
D349 10pa. black on red 45 65
D350 20pa. black on red 45 65
D351 1pi. black on red 1·50 5·00
D352 2pi. black on red 7·75 18·00

1913. Adrianople Issue surch.
D356 31 2pa. on 10pa. green 2·50 1·25
D357 5pa. on 20pa. red 2·50 1·25
D358 10pa. on 40pa. blue 7·50 2·50
D359 20pa. on 40pa. blue 17·00 12·00

D 49 D 50

D 51 D 52

1914.
D516 D 49 5pa. brown 40 11·00
D517 D 50 20pa. red 40 11·00
D518 D 51 1pi. blue 70 11·00
D519 D 52 2pi. blue 70 11·00

AD 26 D 101 Bridge over Kizil-Irmak

1921.
AD91 AD 26 20pa. green 30 1·00
AD92 1pi. green 35 1·40
AD93 2pi. brown 80 2·75
AD94 3pi. red 1·60 6·00
AD95 5pi. blue 2·75 7·00

1926.
D1035 D 101 20pa. orange 1·10 1·00
D1036 1gr. red 1·25 1·40
D1037 2gr. green 1·75 1·75
D1038 3gr. purple 2·50 3·00
D1039 5gr. violet 5·50 5·00

D 121

1936.
D1186 D 121 20pa. brown 10 10
D1187 2k. blue 10 10

D1188 3k. violet 10 10
D1189 5k. green 10 15
D1190 12k. red 10 30

PRINTED MATTER STAMPS

1879. Optd **IMPRIMES** in scroll.
N88 **9** 10pa. black and mauve . . £120 £100

(N **14**)

1891. Stamps of 1876 optd with Type N **14**.
N132 **9** 10pa. green . . . . 42·00 12·50
N134 20pa. pink . . . . 70·00 20·00
N136 1pi. blue . . . . £130 90·00
N138 2pi. yellow £350 £250
N139 5pi. brown £550 £375

1892. Stamps of 1892 optd with Type N **14**.
N150 **15** 10pa. green . . . . . . £250 65·00
N151 20pa. red £475 £130
N152 1pi. blue . . . . 75·00 90·00
N153 2pi. brown . . . . . . £120 90·00
N154 5pi. purple £1300 £1200

مطبوعه
(N **16**) (N **23**) (N **27**)

1894. Stamps of 1892 optd with Type N **16**.
N161 **15** 5pa. on 10pa. grn (160) 1·75 40
N155 10pa. green . . . . . . 70 1·50
N156a 20pa. red . . . . 1·90 1·25
N157 1pi. blue . . . . 1·90 1·25
N158 2pi. brown . . . . . . 21·00 7·75
N159 5pi. purple . . . . . . 65·00 48·00

1901. Stamps of 1901 optd with Type N **23**.
N183 **21** 5pa. violet . . . . 6·50 1·50
N184 10pa. green . . . . . . 22·00 1·40
N185 20pa. red . . . . 4·75 1·00
N186 1pi. blue . . . . 12·50 1·50
N187 2pi. orange . . . . . . 45·00 3·00
N188 5pi. mauve . . . . . . 90·00 22·00

1901. Stamps of 1901 optd with Type N **23**.
N189 **22** 5pa. brown 45 65
N190 10pa. green . . . . . . 2·25 4·50
N191 20pa. mauve . . . . . . 20·00 5·00
N192 1pi. blue . . . . 35·00 17·00
N193 2pi. blue . . . . 90·00 26·00
N194 5pi. brown . . . . . . £200 65·00

1905. Stamps of 1905 optd with Type N **23**.
N222 **23** 5pa. brown 90 55
N223 10pa. green . . . . . . 20·00 1·75
N224 20pa. pink 90 60
N225 1pi. blue 90 60
N226 2pi. blue . . . . 48·00 8·50
N227 5pi. brown . . . . . . £120 13·00

1908. Stamps of 1908 optd with Type N **27**.
N244 **25** 5pa. brown . . . . . . 10·00 35
N245 10pa. green . . . . . . 12·00 35
N246 20pa. red . . . . 12·00 35
N247 1pi. blue . . . . 65·00 1·50
N248 2pi. black . . . . . . £100 3·75
N249 5pi. purple . . . . . . £130 10·00

1909. Stamps of 1909 optd with Type N **27**.
N276 **28** 5pa. brown . . . . . . 2·50 90
N277 10pa. green . . . . . . 5·00 2·25
N278 20pa. red . . . . 42·00 2·50
N279 1pi. blue . . . . 75·00 8·50
N280 2pi. black . . . . . . £190 48·00
N281 5pi. purple . . . . . . £350 75·00

1911. New value of 1909 issue.
N332 **28** 2pa. olive 90 90

1920. No. 500 surch.
N961 5 on 4pa. brown 90 50

TURKMENISTAN Pt. 10

Formerly a constituent republic of the Soviet Union, Turkmenistan became independent on 27 October 1991.

1992. 100 kopeks = 1 rouble.
1994. 100 tenge = 1 manat.

1 19th-century Gold and Jewelled Bib

2 Asiatic Wild Ass

1992. Treasure in National Museum.
1 **1** 50k. multicoloured 10 10
See also No. 4.

1992. Animals of Central Asia. Multicoloured.
2 20k. Type **2** 10 10
3 40k. Cobra (vert) 10 10

3 President Saparmyrat Niyazov and Reverse of National Flag

1992. History and Culture.
4 10r. Type **1** 35 20
5 10r. Girl in traditional dress and Kopet-Daga Mountains 35 20
6 10r. Mollanepes Drama Theatre, Ashkhabad 35 20
7 10r. Akhaltekin horseman (vert) 35 20
8 15r. Arms (vert) 50 30
9 25r. Type **3** 75 50
For similar design to Type **3** but with flag reversed, see No. 12.

4 Traditional Musical Instruments

1992.
11 **4** 35k. multicoloured 15 10

5 National Flag and President Saparmyrat Niyazov

1992. 1st Anniv of Independence.
12 **5** 25r. multicoloured . . . . . 1·00 65
For similar design but with flag reversed, see No 9.

6 Carpet

1992.
13 **6** 1r. multicoloured 15 10

1992. Nos. 7/8 optd with horse's head.
14 10r. multicoloured 25 15
15 15r. multicoloured 60 40

8 Weightlifting

1993. Olympic Games, Barcelona. Multicoloured.
16 1r. Type **8** 10 10
17 3r. Show jumping 25 15
18 5r. Wrestling 40 30
19 10r. Canoeing . . . . 1·00 60
20 15r. National Olympic emblem 1·50 80

9 Presidents William Clinton and Niyazov

1993. Visit of President Saparmyrat Niyazov to United States of America. Type **9** with different dates. Multicoloured.
22 **9** 100r. Dated "21.03.93" . . . 45 30
23 100r. Dated "22.03.93" . . . 45 30
24 100r. Dated "23.03.93" . . . 45 30
25 100r. Dated "24.03.93" . . . 45 30
26 100r. Dated "25.03.93" . . . 45 30

1993. Nos. 16/20 surch.
27 10r. on 3r. Show jumping . . 10 10
28 15r. on 5r. Wrestling 25 15
29 15r. on 10r. Canoeing 40 30
30 25r. on 1r. Type **8** . . . . . . 1·00 60
31 50r. on 15r. National Olympic emblem . . . . 1·50 80

11 Seal on Ice

1993. The Caspian Seal. Multicoloured.
32 15r. Type **11** 10 10
33 25r. Seal on sandy beach . . . 15 10
34 50r. Seal on pebble beach . . 25 15
35 100r. Adult with young . . . 50 35
36 150r. Seal swimming . . . . . 1·00 75
37 500r. Seal on sandy beach (different) . . . . 2·75 1·75
Nos. 33 and 37 were issued together, se-tenant, forming a composite design.

12 Sulphur Spring, Cheleken

1994. 115th Anniv of Nobel Partnership to Exploit Black Sea Oil. Multicoloured.
38 1m. Type **12** 20 10
39 1m.50 "Turkmen" (oil tanker) 30 20
40 2m. Drilling in Cheleken . . . 40 30
41 3m. Nobel brothers and Petr Bilderling (partners) (vert) 65 40

13 Repetek Institute

1994. Repetek Nature Reserve. Multicoloured.
43 3m. Type **13** 15 10
44 5m. Dromedaries in Repetek Desert 20 15
45 5m. Saw-scaled viper 20 15
46 10m. Transcaspian desert monitor 45 30
47 20m. Tortoise 95 75

14 National Olympic Committee Emblem

1994. Centenary of International Olympic Committee.
49 **14** 11m.25 multicoloured . . . 70 50

16 Diesel Train

1996. 5th Anniv of Independence. Multicoloured.
52 100m. Type **16** (inauguration of Turkmenistan–Iran railway) 15 10
53 100m. Turkmenistan highlighted on globe (vert) 15 10
54 300m. Presidents Rafsanjani of Iran, Niyazov of Turkmenistan and Demirel of Turkey (opening of Turkmenistan–Iran–Turkey gas pipeline) 45 30
55 300m. Saparmyrat International Airport, Ashgabat (vert) 45 30
56 500m. Boutros Boutros-Ghali (United Nations Secretary General) and President Saparmyrat Niyazov (vert) 75 50
57 1000m. National flag and arms 1·40 1·00

17 Judo

1997. Olympic Games, Atlanta, U.S.A. Mult.
58 100m. Type **17** 25 15
59 300m. Athletics 80 60
60 300m. Greco-Roman wrestling 80 60
61 300m. Boxing 80 60
62 500m. Shooting . . . . 1·25 90

18 Woman in Red Dress and Blue Shawl

19 American Kestrel

1999. National Costumes. Multicoloured.
64 500m. Type **18** 20 10
65 1000m. Woman in red dress 35 25
66 1200m. Woman in pink dress 40 30
67 2500m. Woman in red dress and embroidered shawl . . 90 65
68 3000m. Woman in green dress 1·25 90

1999. Birds of Prey. Multicoloured.
69 1000m. Type **19** 40 30
70 1000m. Peregrine falcon "Falco peregrinus" facing left . . 40 30
71 1000m. Peregrine falcon facing right 40 30
72 2500m. Common kestrel on branch . . . . 1·00 75
73 3000m. Peregrine falcon on branch . . . . 1·40 1·10
Nos. 69/73 were issued together, se-tenant, with the backgrounds forming a composite design.

TURKS ISLANDS Pt. 1

A group of islands in the Br. W. Indies, S.E. of the Bahamas, now grouped with the Caicos Islands and using the stamps of Turks and Caicos Islands. A dependency of Jamaica until August 1962, when it became a Crown Colony.

12 pence = 1 shilling.

1

1867.
55 **1** 1d. brown . . . . 65·00 30·00
63 1d. red . . . . 2·50 2·25
2 6d. black . . . . 90·00 £120
59 6d. brown . . . . 2·50 2·75
3 1s. blue . . . . 90·00 60·00
6 1s. lilac £5000 £2000
60 1s. brown . . . . 4·00 2·75
52 1s. green £140 £120

1881. Surch with large figures.
17 **1** ½ on 1d. red . . . . 50·00 £110
7 ½ on 6d. black . . . . . . 75·00 £120
9 ½ on 1s. blue . . . . 95·00 £160
19 ½ on 1s. lilac . . . . 90·00 £170
34 2½ on 1d. red £600
28 2½ on 6d. black £150 £275
29 2½ on 1s. lilac £550 £850
38 2½ on 1s. blue £750
47 4 on 1d. red £700 £475
43 4 on 6d. black . . . . . . 75·00 £100
45 4 on 1s. lilac £400

31

34

1881.
70 31 ½d. green 2·25 1·75
56 2½d. brown 19·00 10·00
65 2½d. blue 2·50 2·00
50 4d. blue £110 60·00
57 4d. grey 16·00 2·25
71 4d. purple and blue 9·50 12·00
72 34 5d. olive and red 3·75 12·00

1889. Surch **One Penny**.
61 31 1d. on 2½d. brown 7·00 9·50

1893. Surch **½d.** and bar.
68 31 ½d. on 4d. grey £140 £150

TURKS AND CAICOS ISLANDS

Pt. 1

(See TURKS ISLANDS)

1900. 12 pence = 1 shilling;
20 shillings = 1 pound.
1969. 100 cents = 1 dollar.

35 Badge of the Islands

36

1900.
110 35 ½d. green 5·00 15
102 1d. red 3·50 75
103 2d. brown 1·00 1·25
104a 2½d. blue 1·75 1·00
112 3d. purple on yellow 2·25 6·00
105 4d. orange 3·75 7·00
106 6d. mauve 2·50 6·50
107 1s. brown 3·25 18·00
108 36 2s. purple 40·00 55·00
109 3s. red 55·00 75·00

37 Turk's-head Cactus

38

1909.
115 37 ¼d. mauve 1·75 1·00
116 ¼d. red 60 40
162 ¼d. black 80 1·00
117 38 ½d. green 75 40
118 1d. red 1·25 40
119 2d. grey 2·50 1·40
120 2½d. blue 2·50 3·75
121 3d. purple on yellow 2·50 2·00
122 4d. red on yellow 3·25 7·00
123 6d. purple 7·00 7·00
124 1s. black on green 7·00 8·50
125 2s. red and green 30·00 48·00
126 3s. black on red 30·00 40·00

39

1913.
129 39 ½d. green 50 1·75
130 1d. red 1·00 2·25
131 2d. grey 2·25 3·50
132 2½d. blue 2·25 3·00
133d 3d. purple on yellow 2·25 8·50
134a 4d. red on yellow 1·60 7·50
135 5d. green 6·50 22·00
136 6d. purple 2·50 3·50
137 1s. orange 1·50 5·00
138 2s. red on green 7·50 26·00
139 3s. black on red 15·00 26·00

1917. Optd **WAR TAX** in one line.
143 39 1d. red 10 1·25
144 3d. purple on yellow 60 1·75

1918. Optd **WAR TAX** in two lines.
150 39 1d. red 10 1·00
148 3d. purple on yellow 10 2·00

44

45

1922. Inscr "POSTAGE".
163a 44 ½d. green 2·00 3·00
164 1d. brown 50 3·25
165 1½d. red 6·00 15·00
166 3d. grey 50 5·00
167 2½d. purple on yellow 50 1·75
168 3d. blue 50 5·00
169 4d. red on yellow 1·25 15·00
170 5d. green 85 22·00
171 6d. purple 70 5·00
172 1s. orange 80 17·00
173 2s. red on green 2·00 9·00
175 3s. black on red 5·00 27·00

1928. Inscr "POSTAGE & REVENUE".
176 45 ½d. green 75 50
177 1d. brown 75 70
178 1½d. red 75 3·25
179 2d. grey 75 50
180 2½d. purple on yellow 75 5·00
181 3d. blue 75 6·50
182 6d. purple 75 7·50
183 1s. orange 3·75 7·50
184 2s. red on green 6·00 35·00
185 5s. green on yellow 11·00 35·00
186 10s. purple on blue 50·00 £100

1935. Silver Jubilee. As T **32a** of St. Helena.
187 ½d. black and green 30 75
188 3d. brown and blue 2·75 4·50
189 6d. blue and green 1·75 4·75
190 1s. grey and purple 1·75 3·25

1937. Coronation. As T **32b/c** of St. Helena.
191 ½d. green 10 10
192 2d. grey 50 40
193 3d. blue 60 40

46 Raking Salt

47 Salt Industry

1938.
194 46 ¼d. black 20 10
195a ½d. green 1·50 70
196 1d. brown 75 10
197 1½d. red 75 15
198 2d. grey 1·00 30
199a 2½d. orange 2·25 1·50
200 3d. blue 70 30
201 6d. mauve 12·00 1·50
201a 6d. brown 50 20
202 1s. brown 4·25 7·50
202a 1s. olive 50 20
203a 47 2s. red 17·00 17·00
204a 5s. green 35·00 21·00
205 10s. violet 12·00 7·50

1946. Victory. As T **33a** of St. Helena.
206 2d. grey 10 10
207 3d. blue 15 10

1948. Silver Wedding. As T **33b/c** of St. Helena.
208 1d. brown 15 10
209 10s. violet 7·50 11·00

50 Badge of the Islands

51 Blue Ensign bearing Dependency Badge

1948. Centenary of Dependency's Separation from the Bahamas.
210 50 ½d. green 1·00 15
211 2d. red 1·25 15
212 51 3d. blue 1·50 15
213 – 6d. violet 65 30
214 – 2s. black and blue 1·00 75
215 – 5s. black and green 1·10 3·75
216 – 10s. black and brown 1·10 3·75
DESIGNS—HORIZ: 6d. Map of Turks and Caicos Is; 2, 5, 10s. Queen Victoria and King George VI.

1949. 75th Anniv of U.P.U. As T **33d/g** of St. Helena.
217 2½d. orange 20 1·10
218 3d. blue 1·75 50
219 6d. brown 20 50
220 1s. olive 20 35

65 Bulk Salt Loading

66 Dependency's Badge

1950.
221 65 ½d. green 75 40
222 – 1d. brown 60 75
223 – 1½d. red 1·25 55
224 – 2d. orange 60 40
225 – 2½d. olive 1·00 50
226 – 3d. blue 50 40
227 – 4d. black and pink 2·50 70
228 – 6d. black and blue 2·00 50
229 – 1s. black and turquoise 80 40
230 – 1s.6d. black and red 8·00 3·25
231 – 2s. green and blue 2·75 4·50
232 – 5s. blue and black 17·00 8·50
233 66 10s. black and violet 17·00 18·00
DESIGNS—As Type **65**: 1d. Salt Cay; 1½d. Caicos mail; 2d. Grand Turk; 2½d. Diving for sponges; 3d. South Creek; 4d. Map; 6d. Grand Turk Light; 1s. Government House; 1s.6d. Cockburn Harbour; 2s. Govt Offices; 5s. Loading salt.

1953. Coronation. As T **33h** of St. Helena.
234 2d. black and orange 30 1·25

1955. As 1950 but with portrait of Queen Elizabeth II.
235 5d. black and green 60 70
236 8d. black and brown 2·50 70
DESIGNS—HORIZ—As Type **65**: 5d. M.V. "Kirksons"; 8d. Greater flamingos in flight.

69 Queen Elizabeth II (after Annigoni)

70 Bonefish

1957.
237 69 1d. blue and red 30 20
238 70 1½d. grey and orange 15 30
239 – 2d. brown and olive 15 15
240 – 2½d. red and green 20 15
241 – 3d. turquoise and purple 20 15
242 – 4d. lake and black 1·25 15
243 – 5d. green and brown 1·25 40
244 – 6d. red and blue 2·00 55
245 – 8d. red and black 3·25 20
246 – 1s. blue and black 1·25 10
247 – 1s.6d. sepia and blue 11·00 1·50
248 – 2s. blue and brown 11·00 2·50
249 – 5s. black and red 3·50 2·00
250 – 10s. black and purple 13·00 8·00
DESIGNS—As Type **70**: 2d. Red grouper; 2½d. Spiny lobster; 3d. Albacore; 4d. Mutton snapper; 5d. Permit; 6d. Queen or pink conch; 8d. Greater flamingoes; 1s. Spanish mackeral; 1s.6d. Salt Cay; 2s. "Uakon" (Caicos sloop); 5s. Cable Office. As Type **84**: 10s. Dependency's badge.

83 Map of the Turks and Caicos Is.

1959. New Constitution.
251 83 6d. olive and orange 45 70
252 8d. violet and orange 45 40

84 Brown Pelican

1960.
253 84 £1 brown and red 40·00 16·00

1963. Freedom from Hunger. As T **63a** of St. Helena.
254 8d. red 30 15

1963. Cent of Red Cross. As T **63b** of St. Helena.
255 2d. red and black 15 50
256 8d. red and blue 30 50

1964. 400th Birth Anniv of Shakespeare. As T **45a** of St. Lucia.
257 8d. green 30 10

1965. Cent of I.T.U. As T **64a** of St. Helena.
258 1d. red and brown 10 10
259 2s. green and blue 20 20

1965. I.C.Y. As T **64b** of St. Helena.
260 1d. purple and turquoise 10 15
261 8d. green and blue 20 15

1966. Churchill Commemoration. As T **64c** of St. Helena.
262 1d. blue 10 10
263 2d. green 20 10
264 8d. brown 35 10
265 1s.6d. violet 50 1·00

1966. Royal Visit. As T **48a** of St. Kitts-Nevis.
266 8d. black and blue 40 10
267 1s.6d. black and mauve 60 20

86 Andrew Symmer and Royal Warrant

1966. Bicent of "Ties with Britain".
268 – 1d. blue and orange 10 10
269 86 8d. red, blue and yellow 20 15
270 – 1s.6d. multicoloured 25 20
DESIGNS: 1d. Andrew Symmer going ashore; 1s.6d. Arms and Royal Cypher.

1966. 20th Anniv of U.N.E.S.C.O. As T **64f/h** of St. Helena.
271 1d. multicoloured 10 10
272 8d. yellow, violet and olive 20 10
273 1s.6d. black, purple and orange 30 40

88 Turk's-head Cactus

1967.
274 88 1d. yellow, red and violet 10 10
275 – 1½d. brown and yellow 40 10
276 – 2d. grey and yellow 20 10
277 – 3d. agate and green 20 10
278 – 4d. mauve, black & turq 1·75 10
279 – 6d. brown and blue 40 10
280 – 8d. yellow, turquoise & blue 40 10
281 – 1s. purple and turquoise 20 10
282 – 1s.6d. yellow, brown & blue 50 20
283 – 2s. multicoloured 60 1·75
284 – 3s. mauve and blue 55 40
285 – 5s. ochre, blue and light blue 1·25 2·75
286 – 10s. multicoloured 1·75 3·00
287 – £1 blue, silver and red 3·50 6·50
DESIGNS—HORIZ: 1½d. Boat-building; 4d. Conch industry; 1s. Fishing; 2s. Crawfish industry; 3s. Maps of Turks and Caicos Islands and West Indies; 5s. Fishing industry; 10s. Arms of Turks and Caicos Islands. VERT: 2d. Donkey; 3d. Sisal industry; 6d. Salt industry; 8d. Skin-diving; 1s.6d. Water-skiing; £1 Queen Elizabeth II.

102 Turks Islands 1d. Stamp of 1867

1967. Stamp Centenary.
288 102 1d. black and mauve 15 10
289 – 6d. black and grey 25 15
290 – 1s. black and blue 25 15
DESIGNS: 6d. Queen Elizabeth "stamp" and Turks Islands 6d. stamp of 1867; 1s. Turks Islands 1s. of 1867.

104 Human Rights Emblem and Charter

1968. Human Rights Year.
291 **104** 1d. multicoloured 10 10
292 8d. multicoloured 15 15
293 1s.6d. multicoloured . . . 15 15

105 Dr. Martin Luther King and "Freedom March"

1968. Martin Luther King. Commem.
294 **105** 2d. brown and blue . . . 10 10
295 8d. brown and lake . . . 15 15
296 1s.6d. brown and violet 15 15

1969. Decimal Currency. Nos. 274/87 surch, and new value in old design (¼c.).
297 ¼c. multicoloured (as No. 286) 10 10
298 1c. on 1d. yellow, red & violet 10 10
299 2c. on 2d. grey and yellow 10 10
300 3c. on 3d. agate and green 10 10
301 4c. on 4d. mauve, blk & turq . . . . 1·25 10
302 5c. on 6d. brown and blue 10 10
303 7c. on 8d. yellow, turq & bl 10 10
304 8c. on 1½d. brown and yellow 10 10
305 10c. on 1s. purple & turquoise 20 10
306 15c. on 1s.6d. yell, brn & bl 25 10
307 20c. on 2s. multicoloured . . 30 25
308 30c. on 3s. mauve and blue 55 35
309 50c. on 5s. ochre, blue & lt bl . . . . 1·25 45
310 $1 on 10s. multicoloured . . 2·50 1·00
311a $2 on £1 blue, silver and red 2·00 3·25

107 "The Nativity with John the Baptist"

109 Coat of Arms

1969. Christmas. Scenes from 16th-century "Book of Hours". Multicoloured.
312 1c. Type **107** 10 10
313 3c. "The Flight into Egypt" 10 10
314 15c. Type **107** 15 10
315 30c. As 3c. 25 20

1970. New Constitution.
316 **109** 7c. multicoloured 20 25
317 35c. multicoloured 35 25
For similar $10 design but without commemorative inscription, see No. 946.

110 "Christ bearing the Cross"

1970. Easter. Details from the "Small Engraved Passion" by Durer.
318 **110** 5c. grey and blue 10 10
319 – 7c. grey and red 10 10
320 – 50c. grey and brown . . . 50 90
DESIGNS: 7c. "Christ on the Cross"; 50c. "The Lamentation of Christ".

113 Dickens and Scene from "Oliver Twist"

1970. Death Cent of Charles Dickens.
321 **113** 1c. black & blue on yellow 10 50
322 – 3c. black and blue on flesh 10 40
323 – 15c. black & blue on flesh 20 20
324 – 30c. black & drab on blue 40 40
DESIGNS (showing Dickens and scene): 3c. "A Christmas Carol"; 15c. "Pickwick Papers"; 30c. "The Old Curiosity Shop".

114 Ambulance, 1870

1970. Cent of British Red Cross. Mult.
325 1c. Type **114** 10 20
326 5c. Ambulance, 1970 . . . . 20 10
327 15c. Type **114** 40 15
328 30c. As 5c. 50 20

115 Duke of Albemarle and Coat-of-Arms

1970. Tercentenary of Issue of Letters Patent. Multicoloured.
329 1c. Type **115** 10 30
330 8c. Arms of Charles II and Elizabeth II 20 40
331 10c. Type **115** 20 15
332 35c. As 8c. 40 75

116 Boat-building

1971. Designs as Nos. 274/87 but values in decimal currency as T **116**.
333 **88** 1c. yellow, red and violet 10 10
334 – 2c. grey and yellow (as No. 276) 10 10
335 – 3c. agate and green (as No. 277) 15 10
336 – 4c. mauve, black and turquoise (as No. 278) 1·25 10
337 – 5c. brown and blue (as No. 279) 40 10
338 – 7c. yellow, turquoise and blue (as No. 280) . . 30 10
339 **116** 8c. brown and yellow . . 1·25 10
340 – 10c. purple and turquoise (as No. 281) 75 10
341 – 15c. yellow, brown and blue (as No. 282) . . . 1·00 65
342 – 20c. mult (as No. 283) . . 1·50 3·00
343 – 30c. purple and blue (as No. 284) . . . . . . 2·00 1·25
344 – 50c. ochre, blue and light blue (as No. 285) . . . 3·00 2·00
345 – $1 mult (as No. 286) . . 3·00 3·00
346 – $2 blue, silver and red (as No. 287) . . . . . . 4·00 8·00

117 Lined Seahorse

119 The Wilton Diptych (Left Wing)

118 Pirate Sloop

1971. Tourist Development. Multicoloured.
347 1c. Type **117** 10 10
348 3c. Queen or pink conch shell 15 10
349 15c. Oystercatcher (horiz) . . 50 20
350 30c. Sailfish ("Blue marlin") (horiz) 35 25

1971. Pirates. Multicoloured.
351 2c. Type **118** 10 10
352 3c. Pirate treasure 10 10
353 15c. Marooned sailor 45 15
354 30c. Buccaneers 70 45

1971. Christmas. Multicoloured.
355 2c. Type **119** 10 10
356 2c. The Wilton Diptych (Right Wing) 10 10
357 8c. Type **119** 10 10
358 8c. As No. 356 . . . . 10 10
359 15c. Type **119** 20 10
360 15c. As No. 356 . . . . . . 20 10

120 Cape Kennedy Launching Area

1972. 10th Anniv of Colonel Glenn's Splashdown. Multicoloured.
361 5c. Type **120** 10 10
362 10c. "Friendship 7" space capsule 10 10
363 15c. Map of Islands and splashdown 15 10
364 20c. N.A.S.A. space medal (vert) 15 10

121 "Christ before Pilate" (Rembrandt)

122 Christopher Columbus

1972. Easter.
365 **121** 2c. black and lilac 10 10
366 – 15c. black and pink . . . 20 10
367 – 30c. black and yellow . . 30 15
DESIGNS—HORIZ: 15c. "The Three Crosses" (Rembrandt). VERT: 30c. "The Descent from the Cross" (Rembrandt).

1972. Discoverers and Explorers. Mult.
368 ¼c. Type **122** 15 30
369 8c. Sir Richard Grenville (horiz) 80 10
370 10c. Capt. John Smith . . . 90 10
371 30c. Juan Ponce de Leon (horiz) . . . . 1·75 90

1972. Royal Silver Wedding. As T **103** of St. Helena, but with Turk's-head cactus and spiny lobster in background.
372 10c. blue 15 10
373 20c. green 15 10

124 Treasure Hunting, c. 1700

126 Sooty Tern

125 Arms of Jamaica and Turks and Caicos Islands

1973. Treasure.
374 **124** 3c. multicoloured 10 10
375 – 5c. purple, silver and black 10 10
376 – 10c. purple, silver & black 20 10
377 – 30c. multicoloured 60 30
MS378 127 × 108 mm. Nos. 374/7 1·10 2·00
DESIGNS: 5c. Silver Bank medallion (obverse); 10c. Silver Bank medallion (reverse); 30c. Treasure hunting, 1973.

1973. Centenary of Annexation by Jamaica.
379 **125** 15c. multicoloured 25 10
380 35c. multicoloured 45 20

1973.
381 ¼c. Type **126** 10 40
382 1c. Magnificent frigate bird 30 60
383 2c. Common noddy 30 60
384 3c. Blue-grey gnatcatcher . . 85 50
385 4c. Little blue heron . . . . 35 1·25
386 5c. Catbird 30 30
387 7c. Black-whiskered vireo . . 4·50 30
388 8c. Osprey . . . . 5·00 2·75
389 10c. Greater flamingo 70 90
390 15c. Brown pelican . . . . . 1·25 50
459 20c. Parula warbler . . . . . 1·50 75
392 30c. Northern mockingbird 1·75 90
461 50c. Ruby-throated hummingbird . . . . . . 1·50 2·25
462 $1 Bananaquit . . . . 2·50 2·75
463 $2 Cedar waxwing . . . . . 6·00 4·50
464 $5 Painted bunting . . . . . 1·75 2·25

127 Bermuda Sloop

1973. Vessels. Multicoloured.
396 2c. Type **127** 15 80
397 5c. H.M.S. "Blanche" (screw sloop) 20 10
398 8c. "Grand Turk" (American privateer) and "Hinchinbrook II" (British packet), 1813 . . . . . . 25 80
399 10c. H.M.S. "Endymion" (frigate), 1790 . . . . . 25 15
400 15c. "Medina" (paddle-steamer) 25 80
401 20c. H.M.S. "Daring" (brig), 1804 . . . . 30 1·25
MS402 198 × 101 mm. Nos. 296/401 1·25 3·00

1973. Royal Wedding. As T **103a** of St. Helena.
403 12c. blue 10 10
404 18c. blue 10 10

128 Duho (stool)

1974. Lucayan Remains. Multicoloured.
405 6c. Type **128** 10 10
406 10c. Broken wood bowl . . . 15 10
407 12c. Greenstone axe 15 10
408 18c. Wood bowl 15 10
409 35c. Fragment of duho . . . 20 20
MS410 240 × 90 mm. Nos. 405/9 1·10 1·75

129 G.P.O., Grand Turk

1974. Centenary of U.P.U. Multicoloured.
426 4c. Type **129** 10 10
427 12c. Sloop and island map 20 10
428 18c. "U.P.U." and globe . . 20 10
429 55c. Posthorn and emblem 35 35

130 Churchill and Roosevelt

1974. Birth Cent of Sir Winston Churchill. Mult.
430 12c. Type **130** 15 15
431 18c. Churchill and vapour-trails 15 15
MS432 85×85 mm. Nos. 430/1 40 45

131 Spanish Captain circa 1492

132 Ancient Windmill Salt Cay

1975. Military Uniforms. Multicoloured.
433 5c. Type **131** 10 10
434 20c. Officer, Royal Artillery, 1783 20 15
435 25c. Officer, 67th Foot, 1798 25 15
436 35c. Private, 1st West India Regiment, 1833 35 25
MS437 145×88 mm. Nos. 433/6 1·00 2·00

1975. Salt-raking Industry. Multicoloured.
438 6c. Type **132** 15 10
439 10c. Salt pans drying in sun (horiz) 15 10
440 20c. Salt-raking (horiz) 25 25
441 25c. Unprocessed salt heaps 30 30

133 Star Coral

1975. Island Coral. Multicoloured.
442 6c. Type **133** 15 10
443 10c. Elkhorn coral 20 10
444 20c. Brain coral 35 15
445 25c. Staghorn coral 40 20

134 American Schooner

136 "The Virgin and Child with Flowers" (C. Dolci)

135 1s.6d. Royal Visit Stamp of 1966

1976. Bicent of American Revolution. Mult.
446 6c. Type **134** 25 15
447 20c. British ship of the line 30 20
448 25c. American privateer "Grand Turk" 30 25
449 55c. British ketch 40 65
MS450 95×151 mm. Nos. 446/9 1·00 4·00

1976. 10th Anniv of Royal Visit. Mult.
466 20c. Type **135** 30 30
467 25c. 8d. Royal Visit stamp 40 30

1976. Christmas. Multicoloured.
468 6c. Type **136** 10 10
469 10c. "Virgin and Child" with St. John and an Angel" (Studio of Botticelli) 10 10
470 20c. "Adoration of the Magi" (Master of Paraiso) 30 15
471 25c. "Adoration of the Magi" (French miniature) 30 20

137 Balcony Scene, Buckingham Palace

139 "Flight of the Holy Family" (Rubens)

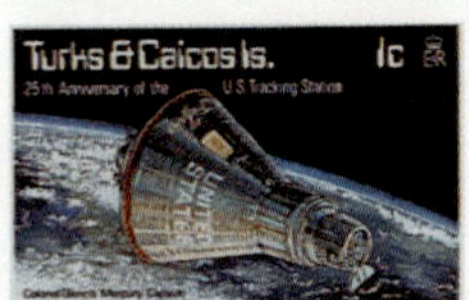

138 Col. Glenn's "Mercury" Capsule

1977. Silver Jubilee. Multicoloured.
472 6c. Queen presenting O.B.E. to E. T. Wood 10 10
473 25c. Queen with regalia 15 20
474 55c. Type **137** 30 45
MS475 120×97 mm. $5 Queen Elizabeth II 1·00 80

1977. 25th Anniv of U.S. Tracking Station. Multicoloured.
476 1c. Type **138** 10 10
477 3c. Moon buggy "Rover" (vert) 10 10
478 6c. Tracking Station, Grand Turk 10 10
479 20c. Moon landing craft (vert) 15 15
480 25c. Col. Glenn's rocket launch (vert) 20 20
481 50c. "Telstar 1" satellite 30 40

1977. Christmas. 400th Birth Anniv of Rubens. Multicoloured.
482 ¼c. Type **139** 10 10
483 ½c. "Adoration of the Magi" (1634) 10 10
484 1c. "Adoration of the Magi" (1624) 10 10
485 6c. "Virgin within Garland" 10 10
486 20c. "Madonna and Child Adored by Angels" 15 10
487 $2 "Adoration of the Magi" (1618) 1·25 1·25

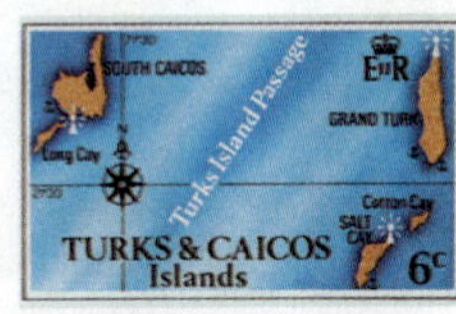

140 Map of Passage

1978. Turks Islands Passage. Multicoloured.
489A 6c. Type **140** 15 20
490A 20c. Caicos sloop passing Grand Turk Lighthouse 45 75
491A 25c. Motor cruiser 45 85
492A 55c. "Jamaica Planter" (freighter) 95 2·25
MS493A 136×88 mm. Nos. 489A/92A 1·10 2·50

141 "Queen Victoria" (Sir George Hayter)

142 Ampulla and Anointing Spoon

1978. 25th Anniv of Coronation. Multicoloured.

(a) Monarchs in Coronation robes.
494 6c. Type **141** 10 10
495 10c. "King Edward VII" (Sir Samuel Fildes) 10 10
496 25c. King George V 20 10
497 $2 King George VI 50 70
MS498 161×113 mm. $2.50 Queen Elizabeth II 75 75

(b) Coronation regalia. Self-adhesive.
499 15c. Type **142** 15 30
500 25c. St. Edward's Crown 15 30
501 $2 Queen Elizabeth II in Coronation robes 1·00 2·50

143 Wilbur Wright and Wright Type A

1978. 75th Anniv of Powered Flight. Mult.
502 1c. Type **143** 10 10
503 6c. Wright brothers and Cessna 337 Super Skymaster 10 10
504 10c. Orville Wright and Lockheed L.188 Electra 10 10
505 15c. Wilbur Wright and Douglas C-47 Skytrain 15 15
506 35c. Wilbur Wright and Britten Norman Islander 35 35
507 $2 Wilbur Wright and Wright Type A 1·00 2·00
MS508 111×84 mm. $1 Orville Wright and Wright glider No. III 60 1·60
No. 502 is inscr "FLYER III" in error.

144 Hurdling

1978. 11th Commonwealth Games, Edmonton. Multicoloured.
509 6c. Type **144** 10 10
510 20c. Weightlifting 15 15
511 55c. Boxing 20 30
512 $2 Cycling 50 1·25
MS513 105×79 mm. $1 Sprinting 55 1·50

145 Indigo Hamlet

1978. Fishes. Multicoloured.
514A 1c. Type **145** 15 50
515A 2c. Tobacco fish 75 50
516A 3c. Bar jack 50 30
517A 4c. Porkfish 75 50
518A 5c. Spanish grunt 50 40
519A 7c. Yellow-tailed snapper 1·00 1·25
520A 8c. Four-eyed butterflyfish 1·00 15
521A 10c. Yellow-finned grouper 50 15
522A 15c. Beau Gregory 1·50 30
523A 20c. Queen angelfish 50 30
524A 30c. Hogfish 1·75 40
525A 50c. Royal gramma ("Fairy basslet") 1·00 65
526A $1 Fin-spot wrasse 1·50 1·60
527A $2 Stoplight parrotfish 1·50 2·50
528A $5 Queen triggerfish 1·50 6·50
Some values exist both with or without imprint date at foot.

146 "Madonna of the Siskin"

1978. Christmas. Paintings by Durer. Mult.
529 6c. Type **146** 15 10
530 20c. "The Virgin and Child with St. Anne" 20 15
531 35c. "Paumgartner Nativity" (horiz) 35 15
532 $2 "Praying Hands" 85 1·40
MS533 137×124 mm. $1 "Adoration of The Magi" (horiz) 2·25 3·25

147 Osprey

1979. Endangered Wildlife. Multicoloured.
534 6c. Type **147** 75 20
535 20c. Green turtle 65 20
536 25c. Queen or pink conch 75 25
537 55c. Rough-toothed dolphin 90 50
538 $1 Humpback whale 2·00 2·50
MS539 117×85 mm. $2 Iguana 2·50 4·00

148 "The Beloved" (painting by D. G. Rossetti)

1979. International Year of the Child. Multicoloured.
540 6c. Type **148** 10 10
541 25c. "Tahitian Girl" (P. Gauguin) 15 10
542 55c. "Calmady Children" (Sir Thomas Lawrence) 25 20
543 $1 "Mother and Daughter" (detail, P. Gauguin) 45 45
MS544 112×85 mm. $2 "Marchesa Elena Grimalda" (A. van Dyck) 55 1·50

149 "Medina" (paddle-steamer) and Handstamped Cover

150 Cuneiform Script

1979. Death Centenary of Sir Rowland Hill.

(a) As T **149**. Multicoloured.
545 6c. Type **149** 10 10
546 20c. Sir Rowland Hill and map of Caribbean 15 15
547 45c. "Orinoco I" (mail paddle-steamer) and cover bearing Penny Black stamp 20 20
548 75c. "Shannon" (screw steamer) and letter to Grand Turk 30 30
549 $1 "Trent I" (paddle-steamer) and map of Caribbean 35 35
550 $2 Turks Islands 1867 and Turks and Caicos Islands 1900 1d. stamps 3·00 3·50
MS551 170×113 mm. As No. 550 70 1·50

(b) As T **150**. Self-adhesive.
552 **150** 5c. black and green 10 10
553 – 5c. black and green 10 10
554 – 5c. black and green 10 10
555 – 15c. black and blue 20 20
556 – 15c. black and blue 20 20
557 – 15c. black and blue 20 20
558 – 25c. black and blue 30 30
559 – 25c. black and blue 60 45
560 – 25c. black and blue 30 30
561 – 40c. black and red 45 45
562 – 40c. black and red 45 45
563 – 40c. black and red 45 45
564 – $1 black and yellow 70 1·25

DESIGNS—HORIZ: No. 533, Egyptian papyrus; No. 554, Chinese paper; No. 555, Greek runner; No. 556, Roman post horse; No. 557, Roman post ship; No. 558, Pigeon post; No. 559, Railway post; No. 560, Packet paddle-steamer; No. 561, Balloon post; No. 562, First airmail; No. 563, Supersonic airmail. VERT: No. 564, Original stamp press.

1979. "Brasiliana 79" International Stamp Exhibition, Rio de Janeiro. No. MS551 optd **BRASILIAN 79**.
MS565 170×113 mm. $2 Turks Islands 1867 and Turks and Caicos Islands 1900 1d. stamps 65 1·50

152 "St. Nicholas", Prikra, Ukraine

153 Pluto and Starfish

1979. Christmas. Religious Art. Multicoloured.
566 1c. Type **152** 10 10
567 3c. "Emperor Otto II with Symbols of Empire" (Master of the Registrum Gregorii) 10 10
568 6c. "Portrait of St. John" (Book of Lindisfarne) 10 10
569 15c. "Adoration of the Majestas Domini" (prayer book of Otto II) 10 10

570 20c. "Christ attended by Angels" (Book of Kells) 15 15
571 25c. "St. John the Evangelist" (Gospels of St. Medard of Soissons), Charlemagne 20 15
572 65c. "Christ Pantocrator", Trocany, Ukraine 30 35
573 $1 "Portrait of St. John" (Canterbury Codex Aureus) 45 60
MS574 106 × 133 mm. $2 "Portrait of St. Matthew" (Book of Lindisfarne) 70 1·50

1979. International Year of the Child. Walt Disney cartoon characters. At the Seaside. Multicoloured.
575 ½c. Type **153** 10 10
576 ½c. Minnie Mouse in summer outfit 10 10
577 1c. Mickey Mouse underwater 10 10
578 2c. Goofy and turtle 10 10
579 3c. Donald Duck and dolphin 10 10
580 4c. Mickey Mouse fishing 10 10
581 5c. Goofy surfing 10 10
582 25c. Pluto and crab 45 20
583 $1 Daisy water-skiing 75 2·25
MS584 126 × 96 mm. $1.50 Goofy after water-skiing accident 1·00 1·60

154 "Christina's World" (painting by Andrew Wyeth)

1979. Works of Art. Multicoloured.
585 6c. Type **154** 10 10
586 10c. Ivory leopards, Benin (19th-cent) 10 10
587 20c. "The Kiss" (painting by Gustav Klimt) (vert) 15 15
588 25c. "Portrait of a Lady" (painting by R. van der Weyden) (vert) 15 15
589 80c. Bull's head harp, Sumer, c. 2600 B.C. (vert) 20 30
590 $1 "The Wave" (painting by Hokusai) 25 50
MS591 110 × 140 mm. $2 "Holy Family" (painting by Rembrant) (vert) 70 1·25

155 Pied-billed Grebe

1980. Birds. Multicoloured.
592 20c. Type **155** 70 45
593 25c. Ovenbirds at nest 75 45
594 35c. Hen harrier 1·00 60
595 55c. Yellow-bellied sapsucker 1·25 65
596 $1 Blue-winged teal 1·50 2·25
MS597 107 × 81 mm. $2 Glossy ibis 2·75 2·25

156 Stamp, Magnifying Glass and Perforation Gauge

1980. "London 1980" Int Stamp Exhibition. Mult.
598 **156** 25c. black and yellow 15 15
599 – 40c. black and green 15 25
MS600 76 × 97 mm. $2 red, black and blue 70 1·10
DESIGN: 40c. Tweezers, stamp and perforation gauge; $2 Earls Court Exhibition Centre.

157 Atlantic Trumpet Triton

1980. Shells. Multicoloured.
601 14c. Type **157** 15 20
602 20c. Measled cowrie 20 25
603 30c. True tulip 25 35
604 45c. Lion's-paw scallop 30 45
605 55c. Sunrise tellin 40 55
606 70c. Crown cone 50 70

158 Queen Elizabeth the Queen Mother

1980. 80th Birthday of The Queen Mother.
607 **158** 80c. multicoloured 50 1·40
MS608 57 × 80 mm. **158** $1.50 multicoloured 80 2·00

159 Doctor examining Child and Lions International Emblem

1980. "Serving the Community". Mult.
609 10c. Type **159** 15 10
610 15c. Students receiving scholarships and Kiwanis International emblem 20 10
611 45c. Teacher with students and Soroptimist emblem 40 35
612 $1 Lobster trawler and Rotary International emblem 75 80
MS613 101 × 74 mm. $2 School receiving funds and Rotary International emblem 1·00 2·00
No. **MS**613 also commemorates the 75th anniv of Rotary International.

1980. Christmas. Scenes from Walt Disney's "Pinocchio". As T **153**. Multicoloured.
614 ½c. Scene from "Pinocchio" 10 10
615 ½c. As puppet 10 10
616 1c. Pinocchio changed into a boy 10 10
617 2c. Captured by fox 10 10
618 3c. Pinocchio and puppeteer 10 10
619 4c. Pinocchio and bird's nest nose 10 10
620 5c. Pinocchio eating 10 10
621 75c. Pinocchio with ass ears 1·00 90
622 $1 Pinocchio underwater 1·25 1·00
MS623 127 × 102 mm. $2 Pinocchio dancing (vert) 2·50 2·50

160 Martin Luther King Jr

1980. Human Rights. Personalities. Mult.
624 20c. Type **160** 15 10
625 30c. John F. Kennedy 30 25
626 45c. Roberto Clemente (baseball player) 45 35
627 70c. Sir Frank Worrel (cricketer) 1·50 1·10
628 $1 Harriet Tubman 1·10 1·25
MS629 103 × 80 mm. $2 Marcus Garvey 1·10 1·25

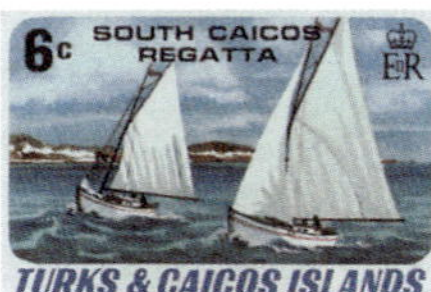
161 Yachts

1980. South Caicos Regatta. Multicoloured.
630 6c. Type **161** 10 10
631 15c. Trophy and yachts 15 15
632 35c. Spectators watching speedboat race 25 20
633 $1 Caicos sloops 60 65
MS634 113 × 85 mm. $2 Queen Elizabeth II and map of South Caicos (vert) 80 1·75

162 Night Queen Cactus

163 "Woman with Fan"

1981. Flowering Cacti. Multicoloured.
635 25c. Type **162** 20 25
636 35c. Ripsaw cactus 25 35
637 55c. Royal strawberry cactus 30 60
638 80c. Caicos cactus 40 1·00
MS639 72 × 68 mm. $2 Turks head cactus 1·00 2·00

1981. 50th Anniv of Walt Disney's Pluto (cartoon character). As T **153**. Multicoloured.
640 10c. Pluto listening to queen or pink conch shell 10 10
641 75c. Pluto on raft and porpoise 50 90
MS642 127 × 101 mm. $1.50 Pluto in scene from film "Simple Things" 1·25 2·25

1981. Easter. Walt Disney Cartoon Characters. As T **153**. Multicoloured.
643 10c. Donald Duck and Louie 20 20
644 25c. Goofy and Donald Duck 30 40
645 60c. Chip and Dale 40 1·00
646 80c. Scrooge McDuck and Huey 45 1·40
MS647 126 × 101 mm. $4 Chip (or Dale) 4·00 3·50

1981. Birth Centenary of Picasso. Mult.
648 20c. Type **163** 15 15
649 45c. "Woman with Pears" 20 15
650 80c. "The Accordionist" 30 40
651 $1 "The Aficionado" 45 60
MS652 102 × 127 mm. $2 "Girt with a Mandolin" 1·00 1·00

164 Kensington Palace **165** Lady Diana Spencer

1981. Royal Wedding. Multicoloured.
653 35c. Prince Charles and Lady Diana Spencer 15 10
654 65c. Type **164** 20 20
655 90c. Prince Charles as Colonel of the Welsh Guards 25 30
MS656 90 × 82 mm. $2 Glass Coach 50 55

1981. Royal Wedding. Multicoloured. Self-adhesive.
657 20c. Type **165** 25 30
658 $1 Prince Charles 35 70
659 $2 Prince Charles and Lady Diana Spencer 1·10 2·25

166 Marine Biology Observation

1981. Diving. Multicoloured.
660 15c. Type **166** 20 15
661 40c. Underwater photography 35 35
662 75c. Wreck diving 60 70
663 $1 Diving with dolphins 80 1·00
MS664 91 × 75 mm. $2 Diving flag 1·75 2·25

1981. Christmas. As T **153** showing scenes from Walt Disney's cartoon film "Uncle Remus".
665 ½c. multicoloured 10 10
666 ½c. multicoloured 10 10
667 1c. multicoloured 10 10
668 2c. multicoloured 10 10
669 3c. multicoloured 10 10
670 4c. multicoloured 10 10
671 5c. multicoloured 10 10
672 75c. multicoloured 1·00 80
673 $1 multicoloured 1·25 1·00

167 Map of Grand Turk, and Lighthouse

1981. Tourism. Multicoloured.
675 20c. Type **167** 50 50
676 20c. Map of Salt Cay, and "industrial archaeology" 50 50
677 20c. Map of South Caicos, and "island flying" 50 50
678 20c. Map of East Caicos, and "beach combing" 50 50
679 20c. Map of Central Grand Caicos, and cave exploring 50 50
680 20c. Map of North Caicos and camping and hiking 50 50
681 20c. Map of North Caicos, Parrot Cay, Dellis Cay, Fort George Cay, Pine Cay and Water Cay, and "environmental studies" 50 50
682 20c. Map of Providenciales, and scuba diving 50 50
683 20c. Map of West Caicos, and "cruising and bird sanctuary" 50 50
684 20c. Turks and Caicos Islands flag 50 50

168 "Junonia evarete" **169** Flag Salute on Queen's Birthday

1982. Butterflies. Multicoloured.
685 20c. Type **168** 30 30
686 35c. "Strymon maesites" 50 55
687 65c. "Agraulis vanillae" 90 1·25
688 $1 "Eurema dina" 1·40 2·00
MS689 72 × 56 mm. $2 "Anaea intermedia" 2·75 3·75

1982. 75th Anniv of Boy Scout Movement. Multicoloured.
690 40c. Type **169** 50 50
691 50c. Raft building 60 60
692 75c. Sea scout cricket match 1·10 1·60
693 $1 Nature study 1·50 1·75
MS694 100 × 70 mm. $2 Lord Baden-Powell and scout salute 1·50 3·00

170 Footballer **171** Washington crossing the Delaware and Phillis Wheatley (poetess)

1982. World Cup Football Championship, Spain.
695 **170** 10c. multicoloured 15 15
696 – 25c. multicoloured 20 20
697 – 45c. multicoloured 25 25
698 – $1 multicoloured 80 80
MS699 117 × 83 mm. $2 multicoloured 1·25 2·00
DESIGNS: 25c. to $2, Various footballers.

1982. 250th Birth Anniv of George Washington and Birth Centenary of Franklin D. Roosevelt.
700 20c. Type **171** 25 30
701 35c. George Washington and Benjamin Banneker (surveyor) 35 45
702 65c. Franklin D. Roosevelt meeting George Washington Carver (agricultural researcher) 50 80
703 80c. Roosevelt as stamp collector 60 1·00
MS704 100 × 70 mm. $2 Roosevelt with stamp showing profile of Washington 1·00 2·50

172 "Second Thoughts" 173 Princess of Wales

1982. Norman Rockwell (painter) Commemoration. Multicoloured.
705 8c. Type **172** 15 10
706 15c. "The Proper Gratuity" 20 20
707 20c. "Doctor's Office" (inscr "Before the Shot") 25 30
708 25c. "Bottom of the Sixth" (inscr "The Three Umpires") 25 30

1982. 21st Birthday of Princess of Wales. Multicoloured.
713 8c. Sandringham 15 35
714 35c. Prince and Princess of Wales . . . . 55 1·00
709 55c. As 8c. 35 45
710 70c. As 35c. 60 55
711 $1 Type **173** 90 80
715 $1.10 Type **173** . . . . . 80 2·00
MS712 102×76 mm. $2 Princess Diana (different) . . . . . 1·50 1·75

174 Cessna 337 Super Skymaster over Caicos Cays

1982. Aircraft. Multicoloured.
716 8c. Type **174** 15 15
717 15c. Lockheed JetStar II over Grand Turk 20 25
718 65c. Sikorsky S.58 helicopter over South Caicos 65 80
719 $1.10 Cessna 182 Skylan over Providenciales . . . . . 1·10 1·25
MS720 99×69 mm. $2 Boeing 727-200 over Turks and Caicos Islands . . . . 2·00 2·50

1982. Christmas. Scenes from Walt Disney's Cartoon film "Mickey's Christmas Carol". As T **153**. Multicoloured.
721 1c. Donald Duck, Mickey Mouse and Scrooge 10 10
722 1c. Goofy (Marley's ghost) and Scrooge 10 10
723 2c. Jiminy Cricket and Scrooge 10 10
724 2c. Huey, Dewey and Louie 10 10
725 3c. Daisy Duck and youthful Scrooge 10 10
726 3c. Giant and Scrooge . . . 10 10
727 4c. Two bad wolves, a wise pig and a reformed Scrooge 10 10
728 65c. Donald Duck and Scrooge . . . . 1·00 75
729 $1.10 Mortie and Scrooge . 1·60 1·25
MS730 126×101 mm. $2 Mickey and Minnie Mouse with Mortie 2·75 2·50

175 West Caicos Mule-drawn Wagon

1983. Trams and Locomotives. Multicoloured.
731 15c. Type **175** 20 25
732 55c. West Caicos steam locomotive 65 70
733 90c. East Caicos mule-drawn sisal train . . . . 90 1·00
734 $1.60 East Caicos steam locomotive . . . . 1·75 1·90
MS735 99×69 mm. $2.50 Steam sisal train . . . . 2·25 2·25

176 Policewoman on Traffic Duty

1983. Commonwealth Day. Multicoloured.
736 1c. Type **176** 40 50
737 8c. Stylized sun and weather vane 30 20
738 65c. Yacht . . . . 85 1·00
739 $1 Cricket . . . . 1·75 2·00

177 "St. John and the Virgin Mary" (detail) 179 First Hydrogen Balloon "The Globe", 1783

178 Minke Whale

1983. Easter. Designs showing details from the "Mond Crucifixion" by Raphael. Multicoloured.
740 35c. Type **177** 20 25
741 50c. "Two Women" 30 35
742 95c. "Angel with two jars" 40 60
743 $1.10 "Angel with one jar" 60 80
MS744 100×130 mm. $2.50 "Christ on the Cross" . . . . 2·00 2·00

1983. Whales. Multicoloured.
745 50c. Type **178** . . . . 2·00 2·00
746 65c. Black right whale . . . 2·25 2·25
747 70c. Killer whale . . . . . . 2·50 2·50
748 95c. Sperm whale . . . . . 2·75 2·75
749 $1.10 Cuvier's beaked whale 3·00 3·00
750 $2 Blue whale . . . . 5·00 5·00
751 $2.20 Humpback whale . . . 5·50 5·50
752 $3 Long-finned pilot whale 6·25 6·25
MS753 112×82 mm. $3 Fin whale 7·00 5·00

1983. Bicentenary of Manned Flight. Mult.
754 25c. Type **179** 20 25
755 35c. "Friendship 7" 30 35
756 70c. First hot air balloon "Le Martial", 1783 . . . . . . 50 70
757 95c. Space shuttle "Columbia" 70 90
MS758 112×76 mm. $2 Montgolfier balloon and space shuttle . . . 1·50 2·00

180 Fiddler Pig

1983. Christmas. Walt Disney Cartoon Characters. Multicoloured.
759 1c. Type **180** 10 10
760 1c. Fifer Pig 10 10
761 2c. Practical Pig 10 10
762 2c. Pluto 10 10
763 3c. Goofy 10 10
764 3c. Mickey Mouse 10 10
765 35c. Gyro Gearloose 55 35
766 50c. Ludwig von Drake . . . 85 60
767 $1.10 Huey, Dewey and Louie . . . . 1·25 1·25
MS768 127×102 mm. $2.50 Mickey and Minnie Mouse with Huey, Dewey and Louie . . . . . . 3·25 4·00

181 Bermudan Sloop

1983. Ships. Multicoloured.
769 4c. Arawak dug-out canoe 1·00 2·50
770 5c. "Santa Maria" . . . . . 1·00 2·50
771 8c. British and Spanish ships in battle . . . . 2·25 2·50
772 10c. Type **181** . . . . 2·25 1·50
773a 20c. U.S. privateer "Grand Turk" . . . . 50 2·00
774a 25c. H.M.S. "Boreas" (frigate) . . . . 60 2·00
775 30c. H.M.S. "Endymion" (frigate) attacking French ship, 1790s . . . . 3·00 1·50
776a 35c. "Caesar" (barque) . . . 60 2·50
777a 50c. "Grapeshot" (American schooner) . . . . 60 2·00
778a 65c. H.M.S. "Invincible" (battle cruiser) . . . . . . 2·50 3·25
779a 95c. H.M.S. "Magicienne" (cruiser) . . . . 2·50 3·25
780 $1.10 H.M.S. "Durban" (cruiser) . . . . 6·00 3·75
781a $2 "Sentinel" (cable ship) 2·50 6·00
782 $3 H.M.S. "Minerva" (frigate) . . . . 7·50 7·50
783 $5 Caicos sloop . . . . . . 7·50 13·00

182 Pres. Kennedy and Signing of Civil Rights Legislation

1983. 20th Death Anniv of J. F. Kennedy (U.S. President)
784 **182** 20c. multicoloured 20 15
785 $1 multicoloured . . . . 50 1·25

183 Clarabelle Cow Diving

1984. Olympic Games, Los Angeles. Mult. A. Inscr "1984 LOS ANGELES".
786A 1c. Type **183** 10 10
787A 1c. Donald Duck in 500 m kayak race 10 10
788A 2c. Huey, Dewey and Louie in 1000m kayak race . . 10 10
789A 2c. Mickey Mouse in single kayak 10 10
790A 3c. Donald Duck highboard diving 10 10
791A 3c. Minnie Mouse in kayak slalom 10 10
792A 25c. Mickey Mouse freestyle swimming 70 45
793A 75c. Donald Duck playing water-polo . . . . 2·00 2·00
794A $1 Uncle Scrooge and Donald Duck yachting 2·00 2·00
MS795A 117×90 mm. $2 Pluto platform diving . . . . 4·00 4·50

B. Inscr "1984 OLYMPICS LOS ANGELES" and Olympic emblem.
786B 1c. Type **183** 10 10
787B 1c. Donald Duck in 500 m kayak race 10 10
788B 2c. Huey, Dewey and Louie in 1000m kayak race . . 10 10
789B 2c. Mickey Mouse in single kayak 10 10
790B 3c. Donald Duck highboard diving 10 10
791B 3c. Minnie Mouse in kayak slalom 10 10
792B 25c. Mickey Mouse freestyle swimming 70 45
793B 75c. Donald Duck playing water-polo . . . . 2·00 2·00
794B $1 Uncle Scrooge and Donald Duck yachting 2·00 2·00
MS795B 117×90 mm. $2 Pluto platform diving . . . . 4·00 5·50

184 "Cadillac V-16", 1933

1984. Classic Cars and 125th Anniv of first Commercial Oil Well. Multicoloured.
796 4c. Type **184** 30 10
797 8c. Rolls-Royce "Phanton III", 1937 . . . . 40 15
798 10c. Saab "99", 1969 . . . . 40 15
799 25c. Maserati "Bora", 1973 90 40
800 40c. Datsun "260Z", 1970 . 1·25 65
801 55c. Porsche "917", 1971 . . 1·40 80
802 80c. Lincoln "Continental", 1939 . . . . 1·50 90
803 $1 Triumph "TR3A", 1957 1·60 1·25
MS804 70×100 mm. $2 Daimler, 1886 . . . . 2·00 2·50

185 "Rest during the Flight to Egypt, with St. Francis"

1984. Easter. 450th Death Anniv of Correggio (painter). Multicoloured.
805 15c. Type **185** 20 15
806 40c. "St. Luke and St. Ambrose" 45 40
807 60c. "Diana and her Chariot" 65 65
808 95c. "The Deposition of Christ" 80 80
MS809 100×79 mm. $2 "The Nativity with Saints Elizabeth and John the Younger" (horiz) . . 1·50 2·50

1984. Universal Postal Union Congress, Hamburg. Nos. 748/9 optd **19TH UPU CONGRESS, HAMBURG, WEST GERMANY. 1874–1984** and emblem. Multicoloured.
810 95c. Sperm whale . . . . . 2·50 2·75
811 $1.10 Goosebeak whale . . . 2·50 2·75
MS812 112×82 mm. $3 Fin whale 4·25 4·25

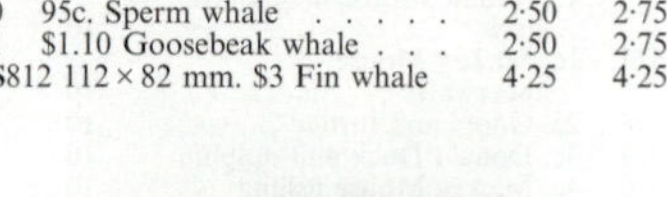

187 "The Adventure of the Second Stain"

1984. 125th Birth Anniv of Sir Arthur Conan Doyle (author). Multicoloured.
813 25c. Type **187** . . . . 2·50 1·50
814 45c. "The Adventure of the Final Problem" . . . . . 3·25 2·25
815 70c. "The Adventure of the Empty House" . . . . . 5·00 3·50
816 85c. "The Adventure of the Greek Interpreter" . . . . 6·00 4·00
MS817 100×70 mm. $2 Sir Arthur Conan Doyle . . . . 11·00 11·00

188 Orange Clownfish 190 Magnolia Warbler

189 Donald Duck cutting down Christmas Tree

1984. "Ausipex" International Stamp Exhibition, Melbourne. 175th Birth Anniv of Charles Darwin. Multicoloured.
818 5c. Type **188** 60 50
819 35c. Monitor lizard . . . . . 2·25 1·75
820 50c. Rainbow lory . . . . . 3·00 3·00
821 $1.10 Koalas . . . . 3·75 4·00
MS822 100×70 mm. $2 Eastern grey kangaroo . . . . 3·00 4·50

1984. Christmas. Walt Disney Cartoon Characters. Designs showing scenes form "Toy Tinkers". Multicoloured.
823 20c. Type **189** 85 45
824 35c. Donald Duck and Chip n' Dale playing with train set . . . . 1·10 75
825 50c. Donald Duck and Chip n' Dale playing with catapult . . . . 1·60 1·10
826 75c. Donald Duck, Chip n' Dale and Christmas tree 2·25 1·75
827 $1.10 Donald Duck, toy soldier and Chip 'n' Dale 2·50 2·50
MS828 126×102 mm. $2 Donald Duck as Father Christmas . . 3·25 4·00

1985. Birth Bicentenary of John J. Audubon (ornithologist). Multicoloured.
829 25c. Type **190** . . . . 2·00 75
830 45c. Short-eared owl . . . . 3·00 1·50
831 70c. Mourning dove and eggs 3·50 2·75
832 85c. Caribbean martin . . . 3·50 3·00
MS833 100×70 mm. $2 Oystercatcher and chicks . . . 4·50 4·50

191 Leonardo da Vinci and Illustration of Glider Wing (15th century)

1985. 40th Anniv of International Civil Aviation Organization. Pioneers. Multicoloured.

834 8c. Type **191** 65 40
835 25c. Sir Alliott Verdon Roe and Avro (Canada) CF-102 jetliner (1949) . . . . . . 1·75 55
836 65c. Robert H. Goddard and first liquid fuel rocket (1926) . . . . 2·50 1·75
837 $1 Igor Sikorsky and Vought-Sikorsky VS-300 helicopter prototype (1939) . . . . . 6·00 3·75
MS838 100 × 70 mm. $2 Amelia Earhart's Lockheed 10E Electra (1937) . . . . 2·75 3·25

192 Benjamin Franklin and Marquis de Lafayette

1985. Centenary of Statue of Liberty's Arrival in New York. Multicoloured.

839 20c. Type **192** 80 50
840 30c. Frederic Bartholdi (designer) and Gustave Eiffel (engineer) . . . . . 1·10 80
841 65c. "Isere" (French screw warship) arriving in New York with statue, 1885 . . 2·50 1·75
842 $1.10 United States fund raisers Louis Agassiz, Charles Sumner, H. W. Longfellow and Joseph Pulitzer . . . . 2·50 2·00
MS843 99 × 69 mm. $2 Dedication ceremony, 1886 . . . . 3·00 3·50

193 Sir Edward Hawke and H.M.S. "Royal George" (ship of the line), 1782

1985. Salute to Royal Navy. Multicoloured.

844 20c. Type **193** . . . . 2·25 1·75
845 30c. Lord Nelson and H.M.S. "Victory" (ship of the line), 1805 . . . . 2·75 2·25
846 65c. Admiral Sir George Cockburn and H.M.S. "Albion" (ship of the line), 1802 . . . . 3·75 3·00
847 95c. Admiral Sir David Beatty and H.M.S. "Indefatigable" (battle cruiser), 1916 . . . . . . 4·75 4·25
MS848 99 × 69 mm. $2 18th-century sailor and cannon (vert) . . . 3·25 4·00

194 Mark Twain riding on Halley's Comet

1985. International Youth Year. Birth Annivs of Mark Twain (150th) and Jakob Grimm (Bicentenary). Multicoloured.

849 25c. Type **194** . . . . 1·00 55
850 35c. "Grand Turk" (Mississippi river steamer) 1·75 70
851 50c. Hansel and Gretel and gingerbread house (vert) . . 2·00 1·25
852 95c. Rumpelstiltskin (vert) . . 2·75 2·50
MS853 99 × 68 mm. $2 Mark Twain and the Brothers Grimm . . . 3·50 5·00

195 The Queen Mother outside Clarence House

196 King George II and Score of "Zadok the Priest" (1727)

1985. Life and Times of Queen Elizabeth the Queen Mother. Multicoloured.

854 30c. Type **195** 70 45
855 50c. Visiting Biggin Hill airfield (horiz) . . . . . . 2·25 1·00
856 $1.10 80th birthday portrait 2·25 2·50
MS857 56 × 85 mm. $2 With Prince Charles at Garter ceremony, Windsor Castle, 1968 . . . . 2·00 3·00

1985. 300th Birth Anniv of George Frederick Handel (composer).

858 **196** 4c. multicoloured 65 50
859 – 10c. multicoloured . . . . 1·00 50
860 – 50c. multicoloured . . . . 2·50 2·50
861 – $1.10 multicoloured . . . 3·00 5·50
MS862 101 × 76 mm. $2 black, purple-blue . . . . 5·00 7·50

DESIGNS: 10c. Queen Caroline and score of "Funeral Anthem" (1737); 50c. King George I and score of "Water Music" (1714); $1.10, Queen Anne and score of "Or la Tromba" from "Rinaldo" (1711); $2 George Frederick Handel.

1985. 300th Birth Anniv of Johann Sebastian Bach (composer). As T **189a** of Sierra Leone. Mult.

863 15c. Bassoon . . . . 1·00 40
864 40c. Natural horn . . . . . 1·50 85
865 60c. Viola d'amore . . . . . 2·00 1·25
866 95c. Clavichord . . . . . . 2·25 2·25
MS867 102 × 76 mm. $2 Johann Sebastian Bach . . . . 4·00 4·00

197 Harley-Davidson Dual Cylinder (1915) on Middle Caicos

1985. Centenary of the Motor Cycle. Mult.

868 8c. Type **197** 85 30
869 25c. Triumph "Thunderbird" (1950) on Grand Turk . . 1·75 70
870 55c. BMW "K100RS" (1985) on North Caicos . . . . . 2·75 1·75
871 $1.20 Honda "1100 Shadow" (1985) on South Caicos . . 3·75 7·00
MS872 100 × 77 mm. $2 Daimler single track (1885) (vert) . . . 4·50 4·50

198 Pirates in Prison

1985. 30th Anniv of Disneyland, U.S.A. Designs showing scenes from "Pirates of the Caribbean" exhibition. Multicoloured.

873 1c. Type **198** 10 10
874 1c. The fate of Captain William Kidd 10 10
875 2c. Bartholomew Roberts . . 10 10
876 2c. Two buccaneers 10 10
877 3c. Privateers looting . . . 10 10
878 3c. Auction of captives . . . 10 10
879 35c. Singing pirates . . . . . 1·50 80
880 75c. Edward Teach—"Blackbeard" . . . . . . 3·00 3·25
881 $1.10 Sir Henry Morgan . . 3·50 4·00
MS882 123 × 86 mm. $2.50 Mary Read and Anne Bonney . . . 5·00 4·50

199 Brownies from China, Turks and Caicos and Papua New Guinea

1985. 75th Anniv of Girl Guide Movement and 35th Anniv of Grand Turk Company. Multicoloured.

883 10c. Type **199** 75 40
884 40c. Brownies from Surinam, Turks and Caicos and Korea . . . . 1·75 1·25
885 70c. Guides from Australia, Turks and Caicos and Canada . . . . 2·50 3·00
886 80c. Guides from West Germany, Turks and Caicos and Israel . . . . 2·75 3·00
MS887 107 × 76 mm. $2 75th anniv emblem . . . . 3·00 3·50

200 Iguana and Log

1986. Turks and Caicos Ground Iguana. Multicoloured.

888 8c. Type **200** . . . . 2·25 1·25
889 10c. Iguana on beach . . . . 2·25 1·25
890 20c. Iguana at nest . . . . . 3·50 2·50
891 35c. Iguana eating flowers . . 6·50 4·50
MS892 105 × 76 mm. $2 Map showing habitat . . . . 13·00 14·00

201 Duke and Duchess of York after Wedding

202 "Prophecy of Birth of Christ to King Achaz"

1986. Royal Wedding. Multicoloured.

893 35c. Type **201** . . . . 1·10 55
894 65c. Miss Sarah Ferguson in wedding carriage . . . . . 2·00 1·40
895 $1.10 Duke and Duchess of York on Palace balcony after wedding . . . . . . 2·50 2·75
MS896 85 × 85 mm. $2 Duke and Duchess leaving Westminster Abbey . . . . 4·00 4·50

1987. Christmas. Illuminated illustrations by Giorgio Clovio from "Farnese Book of Hours". Multicoloured.

897 35c. Type **202** . . . . 1·25 85
898 50c. "The Annunciation" . . 1·75 1·75
899 65c. "The Circumcision" . . 2·25 2·25
900 95c. "Adoration of the Kings" . . . . 3·25 4·00
MS901 76 × 106 mm. $2 "The Nativity" . . . . 4·75 6·00

203 H.M.S. "Victoria" (ship of the line), 1859, and Victoria Cross

1987. 150th Anniv of Accession of Queen Victoria. Multicoloured.

902 8c. Type **203** . . . . 1·75 1·00
903 35c. "Victoria" (paddle-steamer) and gold sovereign . . . . 3·00 2·25
904 55c. Royal Yacht "Victoria and Albert I" and 1840 Penny Black stamp . . . . 3·25 2·75
905 95c. Royal Yacht "Victoria and Albert II" and Victoria Public Library . . . . . . 4·50 5·00
MS906 129 × 76 mm. $2 "Victoria" (barque) . . . . 6·00 7·00

1987. Bicentenary of U.S. Constitution. As T **210a** of Sierra Leone. Multicoloured.

907 10c. State Seal, New Jersey 25 35
908 35c. 18th-century family going to church ("Freedom of Worship") (vert) 75 75
909 65c. U.S. Supreme Court, Judicial Branch, Washington (vert) . . . . 1·40 1·75
910 80c. John Adams (statesman) (vert) . . . . 1·60 2·25
MS911 105 × 75 mm. $2 George Mason (Virginia delegate) (vert) 1·75 3·75

204 "Santa Maria"

1988. 500th Anniv (1992) of Discovery of America by Columbus (1st issue). Multicoloured.

912 4c. Type **204** 45 30
913 25c. Columbus meeting Tainos Indians 95 60
914 70c. "Santa Maria" anchored off Indian village . . . . . 2·75 3·25
915 $1 Columbus in field of grain 2·75 3·25
MS916 105 × 76 mm. $2 "Santa Maria", "Pinta" and "Nina" 3·50 4·50

See also Nos. 947/51, 1028/36, 1072/80 and 1166/76.

205 Arawak Artifact and Scouts in Cave, Middle Caicos

207 Football

1988. World Scout Jamboree, Australia. Mult.

917 8c. Type **205** 20 15
918 35c. "Santa Maria" scouts and Hawks Nest Island (horiz) 55 55
919 65c. Scouts diving to wreck of galleon . . . . 95 1·25
920 95c. Visiting ruins of 19th-century sisal plantation (horiz) . . . . 1·40 1·75
MS921 118 × 82 mm. $2 Splashdown of John Glenn's "Mercury" capsule, 1962 . . . . 3·75 5·00

No. MS921 is inscribed "Sight" in error.

1988. Royal Ruby Wedding. Nos. 772, 774 and 781 optd **40TH WEDDING ANNIVERSARY H.M. QUEEN ELIZABETH II H.R.H. THE DUKE OF EDINBURGH**.

922 10c. Type **181** 75 50
923 25c. H.M.S. "Boreas" (frigate) . . . . 1·25 55
924 $2 "Sentinel" (cable ship) . . 3·50 4·50

1988. Olympic Games, Seoul. Multicoloured.

925 8c. Type **207** 45 15
926 30c. Yachting 80 50
927 70c. Cycling . . . . 3·50 2·00
928 $1 Athletics . . . . 1·75 2·25
MS929 102 × 71 mm. $2 Swimming 2·75 3·50

208 Game-fishing Launch and Swordfish

210 Coat of Arms

209 Princess Alexandra and Government House

1988. Billfish Tournament. Multicoloured.

930 8c. Type **208** 55 30
931 10c. Competitors with swordfish catch 55 30
932 70c. Game-fishing launch . . 2·25 3·00
933 $1 Atlantic blue marlin . . 2·75 3·50
MS934 119 × 85 mm. $2 Stylized sailfish . . . . 4·00 5·00

1988. Christmas. 500th Birth Anniv of Titian (artist). As T **183a** of St. Vincent, inscr "CHRISTMAS 1988" and with royal cypher at top right. Multicoloured.

935 15c. "Madonna and Child with Saint Catherine" . . . 40 30
936 25c. "Madonna with a Rabbit" 50 40
937 35c. "Virgin and Child with Saints" 60 50
938 40c. "The Gypsy Madonna" 70 60
939 50c. "The Holy Family and a Shepherd" 80 70

940 65c. "Madonna and Child" 95 85
941 $3 "Madonna and Child with Saints" 4·25 6·00
MS942 Two sheets, each 110×95 mm. (a) $2 "Adoration of the Magi" (detail). (b) $2 "The Annunciation" (detail) Set of 2 sheets 6·00 7·50

1988. Visit of Princess Alexandra. Mult.
943 70c. Type **209** 2·00 1·50
944 $1.40 Princess Alexandra and map of islands 5·50 4·25
MS945 92×72 mm. $2 Princess Alexandra (vert) 8·50 8·50

1988.
946 **210** $10 multicoloured 11·00 13·00

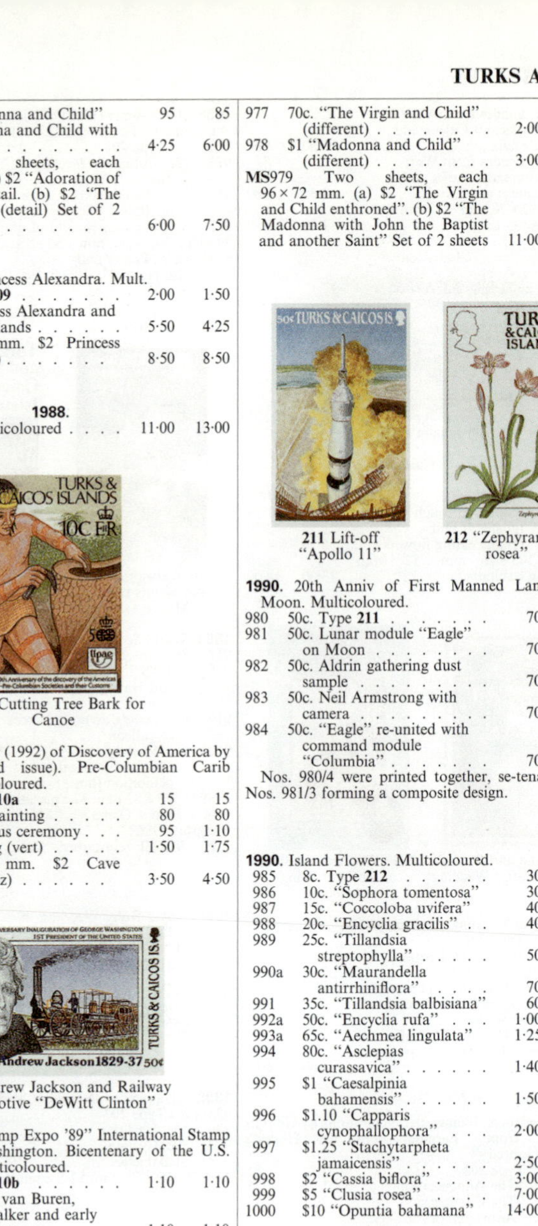

210a Cutting Tree Bark for Canoe

1989. 500th Anniv (1992) of Discovery of America by Columbus (2nd issue). Pre-Columbian Carib Society. Multicoloured.
947 10c. Type **210a** 15 15
948 50c. Body painting 80 80
949 65c. Religious ceremony 95 1·10
950 $1 Canoeing (vert) 1·50 1·75
MS951 87×70 mm. $2 Cave pictograph (horiz) 3·50 4·50

210b Andrew Jackson and Railway Locomotive "DeWitt Clinton"

1989. "World Stamp Expo '89" International Stamp Exhibition, Washington. Bicentenary of the U.S. Presidency. Multicoloured.
953 50c. Type **210b** 1·10 1·10
954 50c. Martin van Buren, Moses Walker and early baseball game 1·10 1·10
955 50c. William H. Harrison and campaign parade 1·10 1·10
956 50c. John Tyler, Davy Crockett and the Alamo, Texas 1·10 1·10
957 50c. James K. Polk, California gold miner and first U.S. postage stamp 1·10 1·10
958 50c. Zachary Taylor and Battle of Buena Vista, 1846 1·10 1·10
959 50c. Rutherford B. Hayes and end of Confederate Reconstruction 1·10 1·10
960 50c. James A. Garfield and Battle of Shiloh 1·10 1·10
961 50c. Chester A. Arthur and opening of Brooklyn Bridge, 1883 1·10 1·10
962 50c. Grover Cleveland, Columbian Exposition, Chicago, 1893, and commemorative stamp 1·10 1·10
963 50c. Benjamin Harrison, Pan-American Union Building and map of Americas 1·10 1·10
964 50c. William McKinley and Rough Rider Monument 1·10 1·10
965 50c. Hebert Hoover, Sonya Heine (skater) and Ralph Metcalf (athlete) 1·10 1·10
966 50c. Franklin D. Roosevelt with dog and in wheelchair 1·10 1·10
967 50c. Statue of Washington by Frazer and New York World's Fair, 1939 1·10 1·10
968 50c. Harry S. Truman, Veterans Memorial Building, San Francisco, and U.N. emblem 1·10 1·10
969 50c. Dwight D. Eisenhower and U.S. troops landing in Normandy, 1944 1·10 1·10
970 50c. John F. Kennedy and "Apollo 11" astronauts on Moon, 1969 1·10 1·10

1989. Christmas. Paintings by Bellini. As T **204a** of St. Vincent. Multicoloured.
971 15c. "Madonna and Child" 60 50
972 25c. "The Madonna of the Shrubs" 70 50
973 35c. "The Virgin and Child" 80 60
974 40c. "The Virgin and Child with a Greek Inscription" 90 70
975 50c. "The Madonna of the Meadow" 1·00 80
976 65c. "The Madonna of the Pear" 1·75 1·75
977 70c. "The Virgin and Child" (different) 2·00 2·00
978 $1 "Madonna and Child" (different) 3·00 3·00
MS979 Two sheets, each 96×72 mm. (a) $2 "The Virgin and Child enthroned". (b) $2 "The Madonna with John the Baptist and another Saint" Set of 2 sheets 11·00 13·00

211 Lift-off "Apollo 11"

212 "Zephyranthes rosea"

1990. 20th Anniv of First Manned Landing on Moon. Multicoloured.
980 50c. Type **211** 70 90
981 50c. Lunar module "Eagle" on Moon 70 90
982 50c. Aldrin gathering dust sample 70 90
983 50c. Neil Armstrong with camera 70 90
984 50c. "Eagle" re-united with command module "Columbia" 70 90
Nos. 980/4 were printed together, se-tenant, with Nos. 981/3 forming a composite design.

1990. Island Flowers. Multicoloured.
985 8c. Type **212** 30 20
986 10c. "Sophora tomentosa" 30 20
987 15c. "Coccoloba uvifera" 40 25
988 20c. "Encyclia gracilis" 40 30
989 25c. "Tillandsia streptophylla" 50 35
990a 30c. "Maurandella antirrhiniflora" 70 60
991 35c. "Tillandsia balbisiana" 60 50
992a 50c. "Encyclia rufa" 1·00 1·00
993a 65c. "Aechmea lingulata" 1·25 1·25
994 80c. "Asclepias curassavica" 1·40 1·50
995 $1 "Caesalpinia bahamensis" 1·50 1·60
996 $1.10 "Capparis cynophallophora" 2·00 2·75
997 $1.25 "Stachytarpheta jamaicensis" 2·50 3·00
998 $2 "Cassia biflora" 3·00 4·00
999 $5 "Clusia rosea" 7·00 9·00
1000 $10 "Opuntia bahamana" 14·00 17·00

213 Queen Parrotfish

1990. Fishes. Multicoloured.
1001 8c. Type **213** 25 20
1002 10c. Queen triggerfish 25 20
1003 25c. Sergeant major 60 45
1004 40c. Spotted goatfish 85 75
1005 50c. Neon goby 1·00 85
1006 75c. Nassau grouper 1·50 1·50
1007 80c. Yellow-headed jawfish 1·75 2·00
1008 $1 Blue tang 1·75 2·00
MS1009 Two sheets, each 115×80 mm. (a) $2 Butter hamlet. (b) $2 Queen angelfish Set of 2 sheets 13·00 14·00

214 Yellow-billed Cuckoo

1990. Birds (1st series). Multicoloured.
1010 10c. Type **214** 90 60
1011 15c. White-tailed tropic bird 1·25 60
1012 20c. Kirtland's warbler 1·75 85
1013 30c. Yellow-crowned night heron 1·75 85
1014 50c. Black-billed whistling duck ("West Indian tree duck") 2·25 1·10
1015 80c. Yellow-bellied sapsucker 3·00 2·50
1016 $1 American kestrel 3·00 2·50
1017 $1.40 Northern mockingbird 3·50 4·00
MS1018 Two sheets, each 104×78 mm. (a) $2 Yellow warbler. (b) $2 Osprey Set of 2 sheets 15·00 15·00
See also Nos. 1050/8.

215 "Anartia jatrophae"

216 Penny "Rainbow Trial" in Blue

215a Rock Beauty

1990. Butterflies (1st series). Multicoloured.
1019 15c. Type **215** 80 45
1020 25c. "Phoebis sennae" (horiz) 1·00 60
1021 35c. "Euptoieta hegesia" (horiz) 1·25 75
1022 40c. "Hylephila phylaeus" (horiz) 1·40 80
1023 50c. "Eurema chamberlaini" (horiz) 1·40 1·00
1024 60c. "Brephidium exilis" 1·60 1·40
1025 90c. "Papilio aristodemus" (horiz) 2·75 3·00
1026 $1 "Marpesia eleuchea" 2·75 3·00
MS1027 Two sheets, each 106×76 mm. (a) $2 "Hemiargus thomast" (horiz). (b) $2 "Danaus gilippus (horiz) Set of 2 sheets 11·00 12·00
See also Nos. 1081/9.

1990. 500th Anniv (1992) of Discovery of America by Columbus (3rd issue). New World Natural History–Fishes. Multicoloured.
1028 10c. Type **215a** 50 30
1029 15c. Coney 60 40
1030 25c. Red hind 85 60
1031 50c. Banded butterflyfish 1·40 1·25
1032 60c. French angelfish 1·75 1·50
1033 75c. Black-barred soldierfish 1·90 1·90
1034 90c. Stoplight parrotfish 2·00 2·25
1035 $1 French grunt 2·25 2·40
MS1036 Two sheets, each 109×75 mm. (a) $2 Blue chrornis. (b) $2 Grey angelfish Set of 2 sheets 9·00 10·00

1990. 150th Anniv of the Penny Black.
1037 **216** 25c. blue 1·25 60
1038 – 75c. brown 2·50 2·25
1039 – $1 blue 3·10 3·00
MS1040 144×111 mm. $2 black 5·00 5·50
DESIGNS: 75c. 1d. red-brown colour trial of December, 1840; $1 2d. blue of 1840; $2 Penny black.

217 Pillar Box No. 1, 1855

218 Queen Elizabeth the Queen Mother

1990. "Stamp World London 90" Int Stamp Exhibition. British Pillar Boxes.
1041 **217** 35c. brown and grey 80 65
1042 – 50c. blue and grey 1·25 1·10
1043 – $1.25 blue and grey 2·75 3·75
MS1044 143×111 mm. $2 red and black 5·50 6·00
DESIGNS: 50c. Penfold box, 1866; $1.25, Air mail box, 1935; $2 "k" type box, 1979.

1990. 90th Birthday of Queen Elizabeth the Queen Mother.
1045 **218** 10c. multicoloured 35 15
1046 – 25c. multicoloured 75 50
1047 – 75c. multicoloured 1·40 1·60
1048 – $1.25 multicoloured 2·00 2·50
MS1049 70×73 mm. $2 multicoloured 4·00 5·00
DESIGNS: 25, 75c., $2, Recent photographs of the Queen Mother.

219 Stripe-headed Tanager

1990. Birds (2nd series). Multicoloured.
1050 8c. Type **219** 90 55
1051 10c. Black-whiskered vireo (horiz) 90 55
1052 25c. Blue-grey gnatcatcher (horiz) 1·50 60
1053 40c. Lesser scaup (horiz) 2·00 1·00
1054 50c. Bahama pintail (horiz) 2·00 1·10
1055 75c. Black-necked stilt (horiz) 2·50 2·50
1056 80c. Oystercatcher 2·50 2·75
1057 $1 Louisiana heron (horiz) 3·00 3·25
MS1058 Two sheets, each 98×69 mm. (a) $2 American coot (horiz). (b) $2 Bahama woodstar (horiz) Set of 2 sheets 7·50 8·50

220 "Triumph of Christ over Sin and Death" (detail, Rubens)

221 Canoeing

1990. Christmas. 350th Death Anniv of Rubens. Multicoloured.
1059 10c. Type **220** 50 20
1060 35c. "St. Theresa Praying" (detail) 1·00 45
1061 45c. "St. Theresa Praying" (different detail) 1·10 60
1062 50c. "Triumph of Christ over Sin and Death" (different detail) 1·25 65
1063 65c. "St. Theresa Praying" (different detail) 1·75 1·10
1064 75c. "Triumph of Christ over Sin and Death" (different detail) 2·00 1·40
1065 $1.25 "St. Theresa Praying" (different detail) 2·50 3·75
MS1066 Two sheets, each 70×100 mm. (a) $2 "Triumph of Christ over Sin and Death" (different detail). (b) $2 "St. Theresa Praying" (different detail) Set of 2 sheets 9·50 11·00

1991. Olympic Games, Barcelona (1992). Mult.
1067 10c. Type **221** 35 25
1068 25c. 100 metre sprint 70 50
1069 75c. Pole vaulting 1·60 1·60
1070 $1.25 Javelin 2·25 3·00
MS1071 109×70 mm. $2 Basketball 5·00 5·00

1991. 500th Anniv (1992) of Discovery of America by Columbus (4th issue). History of Exploration. As T **220a** of St. Vincent. Multicoloured.
1072 5c. Henry Hudson in Hudson's Bay, 1611 65 40
1073 10c. Roald Amundsen's airship N.1 "Norge", 1926 65 40
1074 15c. Amundsen's "Gjoa" in the Northwest Passage, 1906 1·10 55
1075 50c. Submarine U.S.S. "Nautilus" under North Pole, 1958 1·40 65
1076 75c. Robert Scott's "Terra Nova", 1911 2·25 1·10
1077 $1 Byrd and Bennett's Fokker F.VIIa/3m "Josephine Ford" aircraft over North Pole, 1926 2·50 2·00
1078 $1.25 Lincoln Ellsworth's Northrop Gamma "Polar Star" on trans-Antarctic flight, 1935 3·00 3·50
1079 $1.50 Capt. James Cook in the Antarctic, 1772–75 3·75 4·25
MS1080 Two sheets, each 116×76 mm. (a) "Santa Maria" (vert). (b) $2 Bow of "Nina" (vert) Set of 2 sheets 8·50 9·00

222 "Anartia jatrophae"

1991. Butterflies (2nd series). Multicoloured.
1081 5c. Type **222** 35 40
1082 25c. "Historis osius" 80 50
1083 35c. "Agraulis vanillae" 90 65
1084 45c. "Junonia evarete" 1·10 90
1085 55c. "Dryas julia" 1·25 1·25
1086 65c. "Siproeta stelenes" 1·60 1·60
1087 70c. "Appias drusilla" 1·75 1·75
1088 $1 "Ascia monuste" 1·90 2·00
MS1089 Two sheets, each 114×72 mm. (a) $2 "Phoebis philea". (b) "Pseudolycaena marsyas" Set of 2 sheets 10·00 11·00

223 Protohydrochoerus

1991. Extinct Species of Fauna. Mult.
1090 5c. Type **223** 70 60
1091 10c. Phororhacos 70 60
1092 15c. Prothylacynus 85 60
1093 50c. Borhyaena 2·00 1·10
1094 75c. Smilodon 2·50 1·60
1095 $1 Thoatherium 2·75 2·00
1096 $1.25 Cuvieronius 3·00 3·25
1097 $1.50 Toxodon 3·00 3·50
MS1098 Two sheets, each 79 × 59 mm. (a) $2 Astrapotherium. (b) $2 Mesosaurus Set of 2 sheets 11·00 12·00

1991. 65th Birthday of Queen Elizabeth II. As T **220b** of St. Vincent. Multicoloured.
1099 25c. Queen and Prince Philip at St. Paul's Cathedral, 1988 65 45
1100 35c. Queen and Prince Philip 80 60
1101 65c. Queen and Prince Philip at Garter Ceremony, 1988 1·40 1·40
1102 80c. Queen at Windsor, May 1988 1·75 2·00
MS1103 68 × 90 mm. $2 Separate photographs of Queen and Prince Philip 4·00 5·00

224 "Pluteus chrysophlebius"

1991. Fungi. Multicoloured.
1104 10c. Type **224** 40 30
1105 15c. "Leucopaxillus gracillimus" 55 30
1106 20c. "Marasmius haematocephalus" 65 40
1107 35c. "Collybia subpruinosa" 85 45
1108 50c. "Marasmius atrorubens" (vert) 1·25 75
1109 65c. "Leucocoprinus birnbaumii" (vert) 1·50 1·25
1110 $1.10 "Trogia cantharelloides" (vert) 2·00 2·50
1111 $1.25 "Boletellus cubensis" (vert) 2·00 2·75
MS1112 Two sheets, each 85 × 59 mm. (a) $2 "Pynrhoglossum pyrrhum" (vert). (b) $2 "Gerronema citrinum" Set of 2 sheets 10·00 11·00

1991. 10th Wedding Anniv of the Prince and Princess of Wales. As T **220b** of St. Vincent. Multicoloured.
1113 10c. Prince and Princess of Wales, 1987 70 25
1114 45c. Separate photographs of Prince, Princess and sons 2·25 90
1115 50c. Prince Henry in fire engine and Prince William applauding 3·00 1·50
1116 $1 Princess Diana in Derbyshire, 1990, and Prince Charles 3·00 3·00
MS1117 68 × 90 mm. $2 Prince, Princess and Family, Majorca, 1990 5·00 5·50

1991. Death Centenary (1990) of Vincent van Gogh (artist). As T **215a** of St. Vincent. Multicoloured.
1118 15c. "Weaver with Spinning Wheel" 75 50
1119 25c. "Head of a Young Peasant with Pipe" (vert) 90 50
1120 35c. "Old Cemetery Tower at Nuenen" (vert) 1·00 60
1121 45c. "Cottage at Nightfall" 1·25 70
1122 50c. "Still Life with Open Bible" 1·25 75
1123 65c. "Lane, Jardin du Luxembourg" 1·75 1·40
1124 80c. "Pont du Carrousel and Louvre, Paris" 2·25 2·75
1125 $1 "Vase with Poppies, Cornflowers, Peonies and Chrysanthemums" (vert) 2·50 2·75
MS1126 Two sheets, each 117 × 80 mm. (a) $2 "Ploughed Field" (horiz). (b) $2 "Entrance to the Public Park" (horiz). Imperf Set of 2 sheets 8·50 9·00

225 Series "8550" Steam Locomotive, 1899

1991. "Phila Nippon '91" International Stamp Exhibition, Tokyo. Japanese Steam Locomotives. Multicoloured.
1127 8c. Type **225** 60 50
1128 10c. Class C57, 1937 60 40
1129 45c. Series 4110, 1913 1·40 70
1130 50c. Class C55, 1935 1·40 70
1131 65c. Series 6250, 1915 1·75 1·40
1132 80c. Class E10, 1948 1·90 2·00
1133 $1 Series 4500, 1902 1·90 2·25
1134 $1.25 Class C11, 1932 2·25 3·25
MS1135 Two sheets, each 112 × 80 mm. (a) $2 Class C58, 1938. (b) $2 Class C62, 1948 Set of 2 sheets 9·00 9·00

1991. Christmas. Religious Paintings by Gerard David. As T **241a** of St. Vincent. Multicoloured.
1136 8c. "Adoration of the Shepherds" (detail) 45 20
1137 15c. "Virgin and Child Enthroned with Two Angels" 65 25
1138 35c. "The Annunciation" (outer wings) 1·00 50
1139 45c. "The Rest on the Flight to Egypt" (different) 1·10 75
1140 50c. "The Rest on the Flight to Egypt" (different) 1·25 90
1141 65c. "Virgin and Child with Angels" 1·75 1·25
1142 80c. "Adoration of the Shepherds" 2·25 2·75
1143 $1.25 "Perussis Altarpiece" (detail) 2·75 3·75
MS1144 Two sheets, each 102 × 127 mm. (a) $2 "The Nativity". (b) $2 "Adoration of the Kings" Set of 2 sheets 8·00 9·00

1992. 40th Anniv of Queen Elizabeth II's Accession. As T **229a** of St. Vincent. Multicoloured.
1145 10c. Garden overlooking sea 55 40
1146 20c. Jetty 90 55
1147 25c. Small bay 1·00 60
1148 35c. Island road 1·10 75
1149 50c. Grand Turk 1·60 1·10
1150 65c. Beach 1·75 1·60
1151 80c. Marina 2·00 2·00
1152 $1.10 Grand Turk (different) 2·25 2·50
MS1153 Two sheets, each 75 × 97 mm. (a) $2 Beach (different). (b) $2 Foreshore, Grand Turk Set of 2 sheets 9·50 10·00

1992. "Granada '92" Int Stamp Exn, Spain. Religious Paintings. As T **250b** of Sierra Leone. Mult.
1154 8c. "St. Monica" (Luis Tristan) 50 20
1155 20c. "The Vision of Ezekiel: The Resurrection of the Flesh" (detail) (Francisco Collantes) 80 30
1156 45c. "The Vision of Ezekiel: The Resurrection of the Flesh" (different detail) (Collantes) 1·10 65
1157 50c. "The Martyrdom of St. Phillip" (Jose de Ribera) 1·25 65
1158 65c. "St. John the Evangelist" (Juan Ribalta) 1·50 1·25
1159 80c. "Archimedes" (De Ribera) 1·75 2·00
1160 $1 "St. John the Baptist in the Desert" (De Ribera) 2·00 2·25
1161 $1.25 "The Martyrdom of St. Phillip" (detail) (De Ribera) 2·25 2·75
MS1162 Two sheets, each 95 × 120 mm. (a) $2 "The Baptism of Christ" (Juan Fernández Navarrete). (b) $2 "Battle at EL Sotillo" (Francisco Zurbarán). Imperf Set of 2 sheets 9·00 10·00

226 Boy Scout on Duty at New York World's Fair, 1964

1992. 17th World Scout Jamboree, Korea. Multicoloured.
1163 $1 Type **226** 2·50 2·75
1164 $1 Lord Baden-Powell (vert) 2·50 2·75
MS1165 117 × 89 mm. $2 Silver Buffalo award 5·50 6·00

227 "Nina" and Commemorative Coin

1992. 500th Anniv of Discovery of America by Columbus (5th issue). Multicoloured.
1166 10c. Type **227** 65 40
1167 15c. Departure from Palos 80 40
1168 20c. Coat of arms of Columbus 80 50
1169 25c. Ships of Columbus 1·00 50
1170 30c. "Pinta" 1·00 50
1171 35c. Landfall in the New World 1·10 60
1172 50c. Christopher Columbus 1·25 1·00
1173 65c. "Santa Maria" 1·60 1·25
1174 80c. Erecting commemorative cross 1·60 1·75
1175 $1.10 Columbus meeting Amerindian 1·75 2·25
MS1176 Two sheets, each 70 × 100 mm. (a) $2 Coins showing ships of Columbus. (b) $2 Coins showing landing in the New World Set of 2 sheets 10·00 10·00

1992. Christmas. Religious Paintings. As T **241a** of St. Vincent. Multicoloured.
1177 8c. "Nativity" (detail) (Simon Bening) 50 15
1178 15c. "Circumcision" (detail) (Bening) 70 30
1179 35c. "Flight to Egypt" (detail) (Bening) 1·10 60
1180 50c. "Massacre of the Innocents" (detail) (Bening) 1·25 80
1181 65c. "The Annunciation" (Dieric Bouts) 1·60 1·25
1182 80c. "The Visitation" (Bouts) 2·00 2·25
1183 $1.10 "Adoration of the Angels" (Bouts) 2·25 2·50
1184 $1.25 "Adoration of the Wise Men" (Bouts) 2·25 2·50
MS1185 Two sheets, each 77 × 102 mm. (a) $2 "The Virgin seated with the Child" (detail) (Bouts). (b) $2 "The Virgin and Child" (detail) (Bouts) Set of 2 sheets 9·50 10·00

228 American Astronaut repairing Satellite

1993. Anniversaries and Events. Mult.
1186 25c. Type **228** 1·50 60
1187 50c. Dead and flourishing trees 1·75 90
1188 65c. Food and World map 2·25 1·60
1189 80c. Polluted and clean seas 2·75 2·75
1190 $1 Lions Club emblem 2·75 2·75
1191 $1.25 Projected orbiting quarantine modules 3·25 3·50
MS1192 Two sheets, each 107 × 80 mm. (a) $2 Projected orbital Martian vehicle. (b) $2 Industrialised town and clean beach Set of 2 sheets 11·00 12·00
ANNIVERSARIES AND EVENTS: Nos. 1186, 1191, **MS**1192a, International Space Year; 1187, 1189, **MS**1192b, Earth Summit '92, Rio; 1188, International Conference on Nutrition, Rome; 1190, 75th anniv of International Association of Lions Clubs.

1993. Visit of the Duke of Edinburgh. Nos. 1100/1 optd **Royal Visit HRH Duke of Edinburgh 20th March 1993.**
1193 35c. Queen and Prince Philip 1·50 75
1194 65c. Queen and Prince Philip at Garter Ceremony, 1988 2·25 1·75
MS1195 68 × 90 mm. $2 Separate photographs of Queen and Prince Philip 4·25 4·50

1993. 40th Anniv of Coronation. As T **256a** of St. Vincent.
1196 15c. multicoloured 50 65
1197 50c. multicoloured 1·00 1·25
1198 $1 green and black 1·50 1·60
1199 $1.25 multicoloured 1·50 1·60
MS1200 70 × 100 mm. $2 multicoloured 5·00 5·50
DESIGNS: 15c. Communion Chalice and Plate; 50c. Queen Elizabeth II at Coronation (photograph by Cecil Beaton); $1 Queen Elizabeth during Coronation ceremony; $1.25, Queen Elizabeth and Prince Philip. ($28\frac{1}{2} \times 42\frac{1}{2}$ mm.)—$2 "Queen Elizabeth II" (detail).

230 Omphalosaurus

1993. Prehistoric Animals. Multicoloured.
1201 8c. Type **230** 30 30
1202 15c. Coelophysis 40 30
1203 20c. Triceratops 45 30
1204 35c. Dilophosaurus 65 50
1205 50c. Pterodactylus 80 65
1206 65c. Elasmosaurus 1·10 1·00
1207 80c. Stegosaurus 1·25 1·40
1208 $1.25 Euoplocephalus 1·60 2·25
MS1209 Two sheets, each 100 × 70 mm. (a) $2 As 20c. (b) $2 As 35c. Set of 2 sheets 8·50 10·00

1993. Christmas. Religious Paintings. As T **256b** of St. Vincent. Black, yellow and red (Nos. 1210/12, 1217) or multicoloured (others).
1210 8c. "Mary, Queen of the Angels" (detail) (Durer) 50 20
1211 20c. "Mary, Queen of the Angels" (different detail) (Durer) 80 30
1212 35c. "Mary, Queen of the Angels" (different detail) (Durer) 1·10 50
1213 50c. "Virgin and Child with St. John the Baptist" (Raphael) 1·50 70
1214 65c. "The Canagiani Holy Family" (detail) (Raphael) 1·75 1·25
1215 80c. "The Holy Family with the Lamb" (detail) (Raphael) 2·00 2·00
1216 $1 "Virgin and Child with St. John the Baptist" (different detail) (Raphael) 2·50 2·50
1217 $1.25 "Mary, Queen of the Angels" (different detail) (Durer) 2·75 3·25
MS1218 Two sheets, each 102 × 127 mm. (a) $2 "Mary, Queen of the Angels" (different detail) (Durer). (b) $2 "The Canagiani Holy Family" (different detail) (Raphael) (horiz) Set of 2 sheets 8·00 9·00

231 Blue-headed Wrasse

1993. Fishes. Multicoloured.
1219 10c. Type **231** 30 20
1220 20c. Honeycomb cowfish 50 40
1221 25c. Glass-eyed snapper 50 40
1222 35c. Spotted drum 65 50
1223 50c. Jolt-headed porgy 90 70
1224 65c. Small-mouthed grunt 1·10 1·00
1225 80c. Candy basslet ("Peppermint bass") 1·25 1·50
1226 $1.10 Indigo hamlet 1·75 2·25
MS1227 Two sheets, each 106 × 75 mm. (a) $2 Bonnethead. (b) $2 Atlantic sharp-nosed shark Set of 2 sheets 7·50 8·00
The captions on No. **MS**1227 have been transposed in error.

232 Killdeer Plover ("Killdeer")

1993. Birds. Multicoloured.
1228 10c. Type **232** 85 60
1229 15c. Yellow-crowned night heron (vert) 1·25 60
1230 35c. Northern mockingbird 1·75 60
1231 50c. Eastern kingbird (vert) 2·00 1·00
1232 65c. Magnolia warbler 2·50 1·50
1233 80c. Cedar waxwing (vert) 2·75 2·75
1234 $1.10 Ruby-throated hummingbird 2·75 2·75
1235 $1.25 Painted bunting (vert) 3·00 3·25
MS1236 Two sheets, each 100 × 70 mm. (a) $2 Ruddy duck. (b) $2 American kestrel (vert) Set of 2 sheets 11·00 11·00

233 Sergio Goycoechea (Argentina)

1994. World Cup Football Championship, U.S.A. Multicoloured.
1237 8c. Type **233** 40 20
1238 10c. Bodo Illgner (Germany) 40 20
1239 50c. Nico Claesen (Belgium), Bossis and Amoros (France) 1·50 70
1240 65c. German players celebrating 1·75 1·10
1241 80c. Cameroun players celebrating 2·00 2·00
1242 $1 Cuciuffo (Argentina), Santin and Francescoli (Uruguay) 2·00 2·25
1243 $1.10 Hugo Sanchez (Mexico) 2·00 2·50
MS1244 Two sheets, each 100 × 70 mm. (a) $2 The Silverdome, Michigan. (b) $2 Michel Platini (France) (vert) Set of 2 sheets 6·50 7·50
No. 1237 is inscribed "Segio" and No. 1238 "Bado", both in error.

234 "Xerocomus guadelupae"

1994. Fungi. Multicoloured.
1245 5c. Type **234** 30 30
1246 10c. "Volvariella volvacea" 30 30
1247 35c. "Hygrocybe atrosquamosa" (horiz) . . 65 50
1248 50c. "Pleurotus ostreatus" (horiz) 90 65
1249 65c. "Marasmius pallescens" (horiz) . . . . 1·25 1·00
1250 80c. "Coprinus plicatilis" . . 1·40 1·50
1251 $1.10 "Bolbitius vitellinus" (horiz) . . . . 1·60 1·90
1252 $1.50 "Pyrrhoglossum lilaceipes" . . . . . . 2·00 2·50
MS1253 Two sheets, each 102 × 72 mm. (a) $2 "Russula cremeolilacina". (b) $2 "Lentinus edodes" (horiz) Set of 2 sheets 8·00 8·00

235 "The Annunciation"

1994. Christmas. Illustrations from 15th-century French Book of Hours. Multicoloured.
1254 25c. Type **235** 95 35
1255 50c. "The Visitation" . . . 1·75 75
1256 65c. "Annunciation to the Shepherds" . . . . 2·00 1·25
1257 80c. "The Nativity" . . . . 2·25 2·25
1258 $1 "Flight into Egypt" . . . 2·50 2·50
MS1259 63 × 86 mm. $2 "The Adoration of the Magi" . . . 5·00 5·50

236 "Dryas julia"

1994. Butterflies. Multicoloured.
1260 15c. Type **236** 40 35
1261 20c. "Urbanus proteus" . . 45 40
1262 25c. "Colobura dirce" . . . 50 40
1263 50c. "Papilio homerus" . . 90 65
1264 65c. "Chiodes catillus" . . 1·25 1·00
1265 80c. "Eurytides zonaria" . . 1·50 1·75
1266 $1 "Hypolymnas misippus" 1·60 1·75
1267 $1.25 "Phoebis avellaneda" 1·75 2·00
MS1268 Two sheets, each 100 × 70 mm. (a) $2 "Eurema adamst". (b) $2 "Morpho peleides" Set of 2 sheets . . . 6·50 7·00

237 General Montgomery and British Troops landing on Juno Beach

1994. 50th Anniv of D-Day. Multicoloured.
1269 10c. Type **237** 30 30
1270 15c. Admiral Ramsay and British commandos at Sword Beach 45 35
1271 35c. Gun crew on H.M.S. "Belfast" (cruiser) 65 45
1272 50c. Montgomery and Eisenhower with Air Chief Marshal Tedder 90 65
1273 65c. General Eisenhower and men of U.S. 101st Airborne Division . . . . 1·25 1·00
1274 80c. Lt-Gen. Bradley and U.S. troops landing on Omaha Beach . . . . . 1·40 1·50
1275 $1.10 Arrival of U.S. reinforcements . . . . . 1·60 1·75
1276 $1.25 Eisenhower at briefing 1·75 1·90
MS1277 Two sheets, each 100 × 70 mm. (a) $2 Landing craft and barrage balloon. (b) $2 Eisenhower and Montgomery Set of 2 sheets . . . . 6·50 7·00

238 "Cattleya deckeri"

1995. Orchids. Multicoloured.
1278 8c. Type **238** 50 20
1279 20c. "Epidendrum carpophorum" 70 30
1280 25c. "Epidendrum ciliare" 70 35
1281 50c. "Encyclia phoenicea" 95 70
1282 65c. "Bletia patula" . . . . 1·25 1·10
1283 80c. "Brassia caudata" . . . 1·40 1·50
1284 $1 "Brassavola nodosa" . . 1·60 1·60
1285 $1.25 "Bletia purpurea" . . 1·90 2·25
MS1286 Two sheets, each 100 × 70 mm. (a) $2 "Vanilla planifolia". (b) $2 "Ionopsis utricularioides" Set of 2 sheets 7·50 8·00

1995. 25th Anniv of First Manned Moon Landing. As T **284a** of St. Vincent. Multicoloured.
1287 10c. "Apollo 11" 30 30
1288 20c. Moon landing simulation 45 35
1289 25c. "Astronauts on the Moon" (detail) (Kovales) 50 35
1290 35c. First human foot on Moon 65 45
1291 50c. Astronaut Aldrin conducting solar wind experiment 90 65
1292 65c. Astronauts planting U.S.A. flag . . . . . . 1·25 1·00
1293 80c. Space module "Columbia" over lunar surface . . . . 1·40 1·50
1294 $1.10 "Apollo 11" after splashdown . . . . 1·60 1·90
MS1295 Two sheets, each 104 × 84 mm. (a) $2 Sample of Moon rock. (b) $2 "Apollo 11" lift-off, Cape Canaveral (vert) Set of 2 sheets . . . . 7·00 7·50

239 Elasmosaurus

1995. Jurassic Marine Reptiles. Multicoloured.
1296 35c. Type **239** 65 65
1297 35c. Plesiosaurus 65 65
1298 35c. Ichthyosaurus 65 65
1299 35c. Archelon 65 65
1300 35c. Askeptosaurus 65 65
1301 35c. Macroplata 65 65
1302 35c. Ceresiosaurus 65 65
1303 35c. Liopleurodon 65 65
1304 35c. Henodus 65 65
1305 35c. Muraenosaurus 65 65
1306 35c. Placodus 65 65
1307 35c. Kronosaurus 65 65
Nos. 1296/1307 were printed together, se-tenant, forming a composite design.
No. 1303 is inscribed "Lipoleurodon" in error.

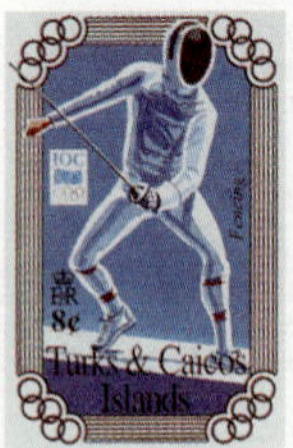

240 Fencing

1995. Centenary of Int Olympic Committee. Mult.
1308 8c. Type **240** 40 20
1309 10c. Speed skating 40 20
1310 15c. Diving 60 25
1311 20c. Cycling . . . . 1·75 70
1312 25c. Ice hockey . . . . . . 1·75 70
1313 35c. Figure skating . . . . 1·25 70
1314 50c. Football . . . . 1·50 90
1315 65c. Bobsleighing . . . . 1·50 1·25
1316 80c. Supergiant slalom . . . 1·50 1·60
1317 $1.25 Show jumping . . . 2·00 2·50
MS1318 Two sheets, each 89 × 110 mm. (a) $2 Downhill skiing. (b) $2 Gymnastics Set of 2 sheets . . . . 6·50 7·50
Both miniature sheets are incorrectly dated "1984–1994" on the margin.

241 Cat and Kitten **242** Belted Kingfisher

1995. Cats. Multicoloured.
1319 15c. Type **241** 80 40
1320 20c. Tabby on branch . . . 85 40
1321 35c. Cat and ladybird . . . 1·25 45
1322 50c. Black and white cat . . 1·50 75
1323 65c. Red cat with flower in paw . . . . 1·75 1·25
1324 80c. White cat on pink pillow . . . . 2·00 1·75
1325 $1 Siamese with flower in paws . . . . 2·00 2·00
1326 $1.25 Cats preening . . . . 2·25 2·75
MS1327 Two sheets, each 106 × 76 mm. (a) $2 Kitten and ladybirds. (b) $2 Kittens asleep Set of 2 sheets . . . . 8·50 8·50

1995. Birds. Multicoloured.
1328 10c. Type **242** 50 50
1329 15c. Clapper rail 60 50
1330 20c. American redstart . . . 70 50
1331 25c. Roseate tern 80 50
1332 35c. American purple gallinule ("Purple Gallinule") 90 55
1333 45c. Ruddy turnstone . . . 1·00 70
1334 50c. Barn owl . . . . 1·50 90
1335 60c. Brown booby . . . . . 1·25 90
1336 80c. Great blue heron . . . 1·50 1·25
1337 $1 Antillean nighthawk . . 2·00 2·00
1338 $1.25 Thick-billed vireo . . 2·25 2·25
1339 $1.40 Greater flamingo ("American Flamingo") 2·50 3·00
1340 $2 Wilson's plover . . . . 3·50 4·00
1341 $5 Blue-winged teal . . . . 8·00 9·00
1342 $10 Pair of reddish egrets (50 × 28 mm) . . . . . 15·00 16·00

1995. 95th Birthday of Queen Elizabeth the Queen Mother. As T **299a** of St. Vincent.
1344 50c. brown, light brown and black . . . . 1·50 1·50
1345 50c. multicoloured . . . . . 1·50 1·50
1346 50c. multicoloured . . . . . 1·50 1·50
1347 50c. multicoloured . . . . . 1·50 1·50
MS1348 102 × 127 mm. $2 multicoloured . . . . 4·50 4·50
DESIGNS: No. 1344, Queen Elizabeth the Queen Mother (pastel drawing); 1345, Wearing tiara; 1346, At desk (oil painting); 1347, Wearing blue dress; **MS**1348, wearing pale blue dress and hat.

1995. 50th Anniv of End of Second World War in Europe. As T **296a** of St. Vincent. Multicoloured.
1349 10c. Churchill, Roosevelt and Stalin at Yalta Conference 30 30
1350 15c. Liberated Allied prisoners of war 40 30
1351 20c. Meeting of American and Soviet soldiers at River Elbe 45 30
1352 25c. Pres. Roosevelt's funeral cortege 50 35
1353 60c. U.S. bugler sounding cease-fire . . . . 1·00 1·00
1354 80c. U.S. sailor kissing nurse, New York . . . . 1·40 1·50
1355 $1 Nuremburg Trials . . . 1·60 1·75
MS1356 104 × 74 mm. $2 Fireworks over Allied capital . . . . . . 3·00 3·75

243 William James Scuba, 1825

1995. "Singapore '95" International Stamp Exhibition. Deep Sea Diving. Multicoloured.
1357 60c. Type **243** . . . . . . 1·10 1·10
1358 60c. Rouquayrol apparatus, 1864 . . . . 1·10 1·10
1359 60c. Fluess oxygen-rebreathing apparatus, 1878 . . . . 1·10 1·10
1360 60c. Armoured diving suit, 1900 . . . . 1·10 1·10
1361 60c. Diving on the "Lusitania" in Peress armoured diving suit, 1935 . . . . 1·10 1·10
1362 60c. Cousteau Gagnan aqualung, 1943 . . . . 1·10 1·10
1363 60c. Underwater camera, 1955 . . . . 1·10 1·10
1364 60c. Sylvia Earle's record dive, 1979 . . . . 1·10 1·10
1365 60c. Spider propeller-driven rigid suit, 1984 . . . . . 1·10 1·10
MS1366 Two sheets, each 107 × 77 mm. (a) $2 Helmet diver, 1935. (b) $2 Jacques-Yves Cousteau (aqualung pioneer) Set of 2 sheets . . . . 6·00 6·50

1995. Christmas. Religious Paintings by Piero di Cosimo. As T **281a** of Sierra Leone. Mult.
1367 20c. "Madonna and Child with St. Giovannino" . . 80 50
1368 25c. "Adoration of the Child" 80 50
1369 60c. "Madonna and Child with St. Giovannino, St. Margherita and Angel" . . . . 1·75 1·00
1370 $1 "Madonna and Child with Angel" . . . . . . 2·00 2·50
MS1371 76 × 106 mm. $2 "Madonna and Child with Angels and Saints" (detail) . . . . 4·50 5·00

244 Daisies and Female Symbol ("Rights of Women and Children")

1996. 50th Anniv of the United Nations. Multicoloured.
1372 15c. Type **244** 30 25
1373 60c. Peace dove escaping from prison 80 80
1374 80c. Symbolic candles ("Human Rights") . . . 1·10 1·50
1375 $1 People on open book . . 1·40 1·75
MS1376 107 × 78 mm. $2 National flags forming "50" . . . . 3·25 4·00

245 Farmer on Tractor

1996. 50th Anniv of Food and Agriculture Organization. Sheet 111 × 80 mm.
MS1377 **245** $2 multicoloured . . 2·40 2·75

1996. 70th Birthday of Queen Elizabeth II. As T **323a** of St. Vincent. Multicoloured.
1378 80c. As Type **323a** of St. Vincent . . . . 1·10 1·25
1379 80c. In blue coat and hat . . 1·10 1·25
1380 80c. At Trooping the Colour 1·10 1·25
MS1381 125 × 104 mm. $2 In yellow dress and hat . . . . 3·75 4·00

246 Glaucus, God of Divers, 2500 B.C.

1996. "China '96" Asian International Philatelic Exhibition, Beijing. Underwater Exploration (1st series). Multicoloured.
1382 55c. Type **246** . . . . . . 1·10 1·10
1383 55c. Alexander the Great, 332 B.C. . . . . 1·10 1·10
1384 55c. Salvage diver, 1430 . . 1·10 1·10
1385 55c. Borelli's rebreathing device, 1680 . . . . . . 1·10 1·10
1386 55c. Edmund Halley's diving bell, 1690 . . . . . . 1·10 1·10
1387 55c. John Lethbridge's diving machine, 1715 . . 1·10 1·10
1388 55c. Klingert's diving apparatus, 1789 . . . . . 1·10 1·10
1389 55c. Drieberg's triton, 1808 1·10 1·10
1390 55c. Seibe's diving helmet, 1819 . . . . 1·10 1·10
MS1391 Two sheets, each 102 × 77 mm. (a) $2 12th-century Arab diver. (b) $2 Caribbean pearl diver, 1498 Set of 2 sheets . . 6·50 7·50
See also Nos. 1392/1401 and 1460/9.

1996. "Capex '96" World Stamp Exhibition, Toronto. Underwater Exploration (2nd series). As T **246**. Multicoloured.
1392 60c. Jim Jarrat exploring "Lusitania", 1935 . . . . 1·00 1·00
1393 60c. Cousteau's first use of scuba gear for exploration, 1952 . . . . 1·00 1·00

1394 60c. Discovery of oldest shipwreck, 1959 . . . . . 1·00 1·00
1395 60c. Raising of the "Vasa", 1961 . . . . 1·00 1·00
1396 60c. Mel Fisher discovering "Atocha", 1971 . . . . . 1·00 1·00
1397 60c. Barry Clifford discovering "Whydah", 1984 . . . . 1·00 1·00
1398 60c. Argo robot over the "Bismarck", 1989 . . . . 1·00 1·00
1399 60c. Discovery of "Land Tortoise" in Lake George, New York, 1991 . . . . 1·00 1·00
1400 60c. Nuclear submarine recovering artefacts from Roman shipwreck, 1994 1·00 1·00
MS1401 Two sheets, each 102 × 77 mm. (a) $2 Diver investigates the "Edmund Fitzgerald". (b) $2 Alvin exploring the "Titanic" Set of 2 sheets 5·50 7·00

247 Show Jumping

1996. Olympic Games, Atlanta. Sports on Medals. Multicoloured.
1402 55c. Type **247** . . . . . . 90 1·00
1403 55c. Cycling . . . . 90 1·00
1404 55c. Fencing . . . . 90 1·00
1405 55c. Gymnastics . . . . . 90 1·00
1406 55c. Pole vaulting . . . . . 90 1·00
1407 55c. Sprinting . . . . 90 1·00
1408 55c. Swimming . . . . . . 90 1·00
1409 55c. Diving . . . . 90 1·00
1410 55c. Hurdling . . . . 90 1·00
1411 55c. Long-distance running 90 1·00

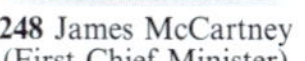

248 James McCartney (First Chief Minister)

249 Space Dog

1996. 20th Anniv of Ministerial Government.
1412 **248** 60c. multicoloured . . . 70 75

1996. Working Dogs. Multicoloured.
1413 25c. Type **249** 45 45
1414 25c. Greyhound 45 45
1415 25c. St. Bernard 45 45
1416 25c. Dog with medals . . . 45 45
1417 25c. Retriever 45 45
1418 25c. Dog with bone 45 45
1419 25c. "Hearing ear" dog . . 45 45
1420 25c. Husky 45 45
1421 25c. Police alsatian 45 45
1422 25c. Guard dog 45 45
1423 25c. Boxer 45 45
1424 25c. Sniffer dog 45 45
MS1425 Two sheets, each 106 × 76 mm. (a) $2 Labrador guide dog. (b) $2 Border sheep dog Set of 2 sheets . . . . 6·50 6·50

250 Winnie the Pooh asleep in Chair

1996. Christmas. "Winnie the Pooh". Mult.
1426 15c. Type **250** 60 40
1427 20c. Piglet holding star decoration 60 40
1428 35c. Tigger carrying presents 80 55
1429 50c. Pooh, Tigger and Piglet singing carols . . . . . . 1·00 80
1430 60c. Winnie and Rabbit . . 1·25 1·10
1431 80c. Tigger and Roo . . . . 1·75 1·50
1432 $1 Santa Pooh filling stockings . . . . 1·90 1·90
1433 $1.25 Christopher Robin and Winnie the Pooh . . 2·00 2·50
MS1434 Two sheets. (a) 124 × 98 mm. $2 Piglet decorating biscuits. (b) 98 × 124 mm. $2.60, Piglet placing star on tree Set of 2 sheets . . . . 8·50 8·50

251 Giant Milkweed

253 White Dove (face value at right)

252 Canterbury Cathedral Tower

1997. Flowers. Multicoloured.
1435 20c. Type **251** 55 65
1436 20c. Geiger tree 55 65
1437 20c. Passion flower 55 65
1438 20c. Hibiscus 55 65
1439 60c. Yellow elder 80 90
1440 60c. Prickly poppy 80 90
1441 60c. Frangipani 80 90
1442 60c. Seaside mahoe 80 90
MS1443 Two sheets, each 105 × 76 mm. (a) $2 Firecracker. (b) $2 Chain of love Set of 2 sheets 5·50 6·50

1997. 50th Anniv of U.N.E.S.C.O. Two sheets, each 127 × 102 mm, containing T **252** and similar horiz design. Multicoloured.
MS1444 (a) $2 Type **252**; (b) $2 High Altar, Canterbury Cathedral Set of 2 sheets . . . . 5·50 6·50
The miniature sheets of No. **MS**1444 are inscribed "CATHREDRAL" in error.

1997. 50th Anniv of U.N.I.C.E.F. Multicoloured.
1445 60c. Type **253** . . . . . . 1·25 1·50
1446 60c. White dove (with face value at left) . . . . . . 1·25 1·50
1447 60c. Three children . . . . 1·25 1·50
1448 60c. Two children with pets 1·25 1·50

1997. Golden Wedding of Queen Elizabeth and Prince Philip. As T **347a** of St. Vincent. Multicoloured.
1449 60c. Queen Elizabeth II . . 1·40 1·40
1450 60c. Royal coat of arms . . 1·40 1·40
1451 60c. Queen Elizabeth and Prince Philip in carriage 1·40 1·40
1452 60c. Queen Elizabeth and Prince Philip on royal visit . . . . 1·40 1·40
1453 60c. Windsor Castle . . . . 1·40 1·40
1454 60c. Prince Philip . . . . . 1·40 1·40
MS1455 100 × 70 mm. $2 Princess Elizabeth and Duke of Edinburgh on wedding day . . . . 4·25 4·50

1997. "Pacific '97" International Stamp Exhibition, San Francisco. Death Centenary of Heinrich von Stephan (founder of the U.P.U.). As T **347c** of St. Vincent.
1456 50c. mauve 75 85
1457 50c. brown 75 85
1458 50c. blue 75 85
MS1459 80 × 117 mm. $2 mauve and black . . . . 2·75 3·25
DESIGNS: No. 1456, British mail coach, 1700s; 1457, Von Stephan and Mercury; 1458, Space Shuttle; **MS**1459, Von Stephan and Ancient Greek messenger.

1997. "STAMPSHOW '97" 111th Annual A.P.S. Convention, Milwaukee. Underwater Exploration (3rd series). As T **246**. Multicoloured.
1460 20c. Edgerton underwater camera, 1954 . . . . . . 40 50
1461 20c. Conshelf habitat, 1963 40 50
1462 20c. "Sealab II", 1965 . . . 40 50
1463 20c. Research habitat Tektite, 1970 . . . . . . 40 50
1464 20c. Galapagos volcanic rift, 1974 . . . . 40 50
1465 20c. Epaulard robot survey craft, 1979 . . . . 40 50
1466 20c. Underwater sealife, 1995 . . . . 40 50
1467 20c. One-man research vessel, 1996 . . . . 40 50
1468 20c. Okhotsk Tower, Japan, 1996 . . . . 40 50
MS1469 Two sheets, each 72 × 103 mm. (a) $2 Coelacanth. (b) John Williamson making underwater movie Set of 2 sheets 6·00 7·00

254 "Adoration of an Angel" (detail) (Studio of Fra Angelico)

1997. Christmas. Religious Paintings. Mult.
1470 15c. Type **254** 35 25
1471 20c. "Scenes from the life of St. John the Baptist" (detail) (Master of Saint Severin) 40 30
1472 35c. "Archangel Gabriel" (Masolino de Panicale) . . 65 45
1473 50c. "Jeremiah with two Angels" (detail) (Gherardo Starnina) . . . 85 65
1474 60c. "Jeremiah with Two Angels" (different detail) (Starnina) 95 75
1475 80c. "The Annunciation" (detail) (Giovanni di Palo di Grazia) . . . . 1·25 1·40
1476 $1 "The Annunciation" (detail) (Carlo di Braccesco) . . . . 1·40 1·50
1477 $1.25 "The Nativity" (detail) (Benvenuto di Giovanni Guasta) . . . . 1·75 2·50
MS1478 Two sheets. (a) 130 × 105 mm. $2 "The Journey of the Magi" (detail) (Benozzo Gozzoli). (b) 105 × 130 mm. $2 "The Wilton Diptych" (right panel) (anon) Set of 2 sheets 6·00 7·00

255 Black-finned Snapper

1998. Endangered Species. International Year of the Reef. Fishes. Multicoloured.
1479 25c. Type **255** 45 50
1480 25c. Dog snapper 45 50
1481 25c. Cubera snapper 45 50
1482 25c. Mahogany snapper . . 45 50

256 Spotted Flamingo Tongue (John Petrak)

1998. 1st World Open Underwater Photographic Competition Prizewinners (1997). Multicoloured.
1483 20c. Type **256** 40 35
1484 50c. Feather duster (Dave Bothwell) 80 75
1485 60c. Squirrel fish (Waldermar Seifert) . . . 95 90
1486 80c. Queen angelfish (Ralph Oberlander) . . . . . . 1·25 1·40
1487 $1 Barracuda (Steve Rosenburg) . . . . 1·50 1·60
1488 $1.25 Royal gramma ("Fairy Basslet") (John Petrak) . . . . 1·90 2·25
MS1489 Two sheets, each 148 × 85 mm. (a) $2 Spotted Cleaning Shrimp (Micheal Boyer). (b) $2 Rough File Clam (Steve Rosenburg) Set of 2 sheets . . 6·00 7·00

257 Bird and Logo

258 University Arms on Banner (50th anniv of University of West Indies)

1998. International Year of the Ocean. Multicoloured.
1490 50c. Type **257** . . . . . . 80 1·00
1491 50c. Stylized crab . . . . . 80 1·00
1492 50c. Fish . . . . 80 1·00
1493 50c. Logo in cloverleaf . . . 80 1·00
MS1494 102 × 71 mm. $2 Queen and globe logo . . . . 3·00 3·50

1998. Anniversaries and Events. Multicoloured.
1495 20c. Type **258** 40 35
1496 60c. Global logo (U.N.E.S.C.O. World Solar Energy Programme Summit) . . . . 1·00 1·00
1497 80c. Flame (50th anniv of Universal Declaration of Human Rights) . . . . . 1·25 1·50
1498 $1 John Glenn (astronaut) (second space flight) . . . 1·75 2·00
MS1499 100 × 72 mm. $2 Space shuttle (John Glen's second space flight) . . . . 3·00 3·50

259 S.E. 5A Aircraft

1998. 80th Anniv of Royal Air Force. Multicoloured.
1500 20c. Type **259** 75 40
1501 50c. Sopwith Camel . . . . 1·10 85
1502 60c. Supermarine Spitfire . . 1·25 1·10
1503 80c. Avro Lancaster . . . . 1·50 1·50
1504 $1 Panavia Tornado . . . . 1·75 1·75
1505 $1.25 Hawker Hurricane . . 2·00 2·50
MS1506 Two sheets, each 100 × 80 mm. (a) $2 Hawker Siddley Harrier. (b) $2 Avro Vulcan Set of 2 sheets . . . . 7·50 7·50

260 Diana, Princess of Wales

261 "Magi's Visit"

1998. 1st Death Anniv of Diana, Princess of Wales.
1507 **260** 60c. multicoloured . . . 1·50 1·25

1998. Christmas. Paintings by Thomasita Fessler. Multicoloured.
1508 50c. Type **261** . . . . . . 90 1·00
1509 50c. "Flight into Egypt" . . 90 1·00
1510 50c. "Wedding Feast" . . . 90 1·00
1511 50c. "Maria" . . . . 90 1·00
1512 50c. "Annunciation and Visitation" (57 × 46 mm) 90 1·00
1513 50c. "Nativity" (57 × 46 mm) . . . . . . 90 1·00
MS1514 105 × 103 mm. $2 "Queen of Mothers" . . . . 3·00 3·50

262 Flamingos

1999. Marine Life. Multicoloured.
1515 20c. Type **262** 45 45
1516 20c. Sailing dinghies 45 45
1517 20c. Seagulls and lighthouse 45 45
1518 20c. House on beach . . . 45 45
1519 20c. Yellowtail snapper and pillar coral 45 45
1520 20c. Yellowtail snapper and elliptical star coral 45 45
1521 20c. Porkfish 45 45
1522 20c. Spotted eagle ray . . . 45 45
1523 20c. Large ivory coral . . . 45 45
1524 20c. Shy hamlet and mustard hill coral 45 45
1525 20c. Blue crust coral 45 45
1526 20c. Fused staghorn coral . 45 45
1527 20c. Queen angelfish and massive starlet coral . . . 45 45
1528 20c. Pinnate spiny sea fan . 45 45
1529 20c. Knobby star coral . . . 45 45
1530 20c. Lowridge cactus coral . 45 45
1531 20c. Orange telesto coral . . 45 45
1532 20c. Spanish hogfish and knobby ten-ray star coral 45 45
1533 20c. Clown wrasse and boulder brain coral . . . 45 45
1534 20c. Rainbow parrotfish and regal sea fan 45 45
1535 20c. Bluestriped grunt and great star coral 45 45
1536 20c. Blue tang and stinging coral 45 45

1537 20c. Lavender thin finger coral 45 45
1538 20c. Juvenile French grunt and brilliant sea fingers 45 45
MS1539 Two sheets, each 100 × 70 mm. (a) $2 Elkhorn coral. (b) Sea fan Set of 2 sheets . . 6·00 7·00

Nos. 1515/38 were printed together, se-tenant, with the backgrounds forming a composite design.

No. 1520 is inscribed "ELIPITICAL STAR CORAL" in error.

263 Prince Edward and Miss Sophie Rhys-Jones

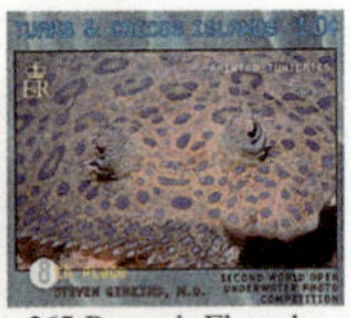

265 Peacock Flounder (M. Lynn)

264 Lady Elizabeth Bowes-Lyon, 1907

1999. Royal Wedding. Multicoloured.

1540 60c. Type **263** . . . . . . 1·10 1·10
1541 60c. Prince Edward . . . . 1·10 1·10
1542 60c. Miss Sophie Rhys-Jones 1·10 1·10
1543 60c. Prince Edward and Miss Sophie Rhys-Jones (different) . . . . 1·10 1·10
MS1544 Two sheets, each 75 × 60 mm. (a) $2 Prince Edward and Miss Sophie Rhys Jones in front of buliding. (b) $2 Prince Edward and Miss Sophie Rhys-Jones in front of tree Set of 2 sheets . . . . 6·50 7·00

1999. Queen Elizabeth the Queen Mother's 99th Birthday. Multicoloured.

1545 50c. Type **264** 65 70
1546 50c. Lady Elizabeth Bowes-Lyon, 1919 . . . . 65 70
1547 50c. On wedding day, 1923 65 70
1548 50c. With Princesses Elizabeth and Margaret, 1936 . . . . 65 70
1549 50c. King George VI and Queen Elizabeth during Second World War . . . 65 70
1550 50c. Queen Elizabeth the Queen Mother, 1958 . . . 65 70
1551 50c. Wearing blue outfit, 1960 . . . . 65 70
1552 50c. Wearing floral dress, 1970 . . . . 65 70
1553 50c. With Princes Charles and William, 1983 . . . . 65 70
1554 50c. Queen Mother, 1999 . . 65 70

No. 1549 is inscribed "GEORGE IV" in error.

1999. Winning Entries from 2nd World Open Underwater Photographic Competition. Mult.

1555 10c. Type **265** (inscr "Painted Tunicates (S. Genkins)" in error) . . 30 30
1555b 10c. Painted Tunicates (S. Genkins) 30 30
1556 20c. Peacock flounder (S. Genkins) (inscr "Peacock Flounder (M. Lynn)" in error) . . 50 50
1556b 20c. Type **265** 50 50
1557 50c. Squat anemone shrimps (M. Boyer) . . 1·00 80
1558 60c. Juvenile drum (N. Army) . . . . 1·10 1·00
1559 80c. Batwing coral crab (R. Jarnutowski) . . . . 1·40 1·50
1560 $1 Moon jellyfish (R. Kaufman) . . . . . 1·60 1·75
MS1561 Two sheets, each 85 × 68 mm. (a) $2 Christmas Tree Worms (B. Joubert) (48½ × 36 mm). (b) $2 Longhorn Nudibranch (Trina Lochlear) (48½ × 36 mm) Set of 2 sheets 6·50 7·00

266 Constellations over Earth and "2000"

1999. New Millennium. Multicoloured.

1562 20c. Type **266** 50 35
1563 50c. Big Ben, London (30 × 47 mm) . . . . . . 1·00 1·00
1564 50c. Flamingo, Turks and Caicos Islands (30 × 47 mm) . . . . . . 1·00 1·00
1565 50c. Empire State Building, New York (30 × 47 mm) 1·00 1·00
1566 50c. Roman Coliseum, Rome (30 × 47 mm) . . . 1·00 1·00
1567 50c. Dome of the Rock, Jerusalem (30 × 47 mm) 1·00 1·00
1568 50c. Eiffel Tower, Paris (30 × 47 mm) . . . . 1·00 1·00
1569 $1 As 20c. . . . . 1·75 2·00
MS1570 Two sheets, each 106 × 86 mm. (a) $2 Part of globe and Turks and Caicos Islands flag (30 × 47 mm). (b) $2 Part of globe and Turks and Caicos Islands coat of arms (30 × 47 mm). Set of 2 sheets . . . . 6·50 7·00

267 "The Mystic Marriage of Saint Catherine" (Anthony Van Dyck)

1999. Christmas. Multicoloured.

1571 20c. Type **267** 50 35
1572 50c. "Rest on the Flight into Egypt" . . . . 1·00 75
1573 $2 "Holy Family with Saints John and Elizabeth" . . . 3·50 4·00
MS1574 102 × 122 mm. $2 "The Madonna of the Rosary" . . . 3·00 3·50

No. 1571 is inscribed "Marrige" in error.

268 *Pholiota squarroides*

2000. Fungi. Multicoloured.

1575 50c. Type **268** . . . . . . 90 1·00
1576 50c. *Psilocybe squmosa* . . . 90 1·00
1577 50c. *Spathularia velutipes* . . 90 1·00
1578 50c. *Russula* . . . . 90 1·00
1579 50c. *Clitocybe clavipes* . . . 90 1·00
1580 50c. *Boletus frostii* . . . . . 90 1·00
MS1581 Two sheets, each 108 × 71 mm. (a) $2 *Strobilurus conigenoides* (horiz). (b) $2 *Stereum ostrea* (horiz) Set of 2 sheets . . . . 6·50 7·00

Nos. 1575/80 were printed together, se-tenant, with the background forming a composite design.

2000. Olympic Games, Sydney. As T **396b** of St. Vincent. Multicoloured.

1582 50c. Johan Oxenstierna (Swedish swimmer), 1932 90 1·00
1583 50c. Javelin . . . . 90 1·00
1584 50c. Aztec Stadium, Mexico City, 1968, and Mexican flag . . . . 90 1·00
1585 50c. Ancient Greek long-distance running . . . . 90 1·00

269 Bush Turkey ("Scrub Turkey")

2000. Caribbean Birds. Multicoloured.

1586 50c. Type **269** . . . . . . 90 1·00
1587 50c. Glaucous-winged gull ("Sickle Bill Gull") . . . 90 1·00
1588 50c. Black-capped chickadee ("Chickadee") . . . . . 90 1·00
1589 60c. Cattle egret ("Egret") 1·00 1·10
1590 60c. Royal tern ("Tern") . . 1·00 1·10
1591 60c. Osprey . . . . 1·00 1·10
1592 60c. Great blue heron . . . 1·00 1·10
1593 60c. Brown pelican ("Pelican") . . . . 1·00 1·10
1594 60c. Bahama pintail . . . . 1·00 1·10
MS1595 Two sheets, each 95 × 82 mm. (a) $2 Greater flamingo ("Flamingo"). (b) $2 Hyacinth macaw ("Macaw") Set of 2 sheets . . . . 7·00 7·50

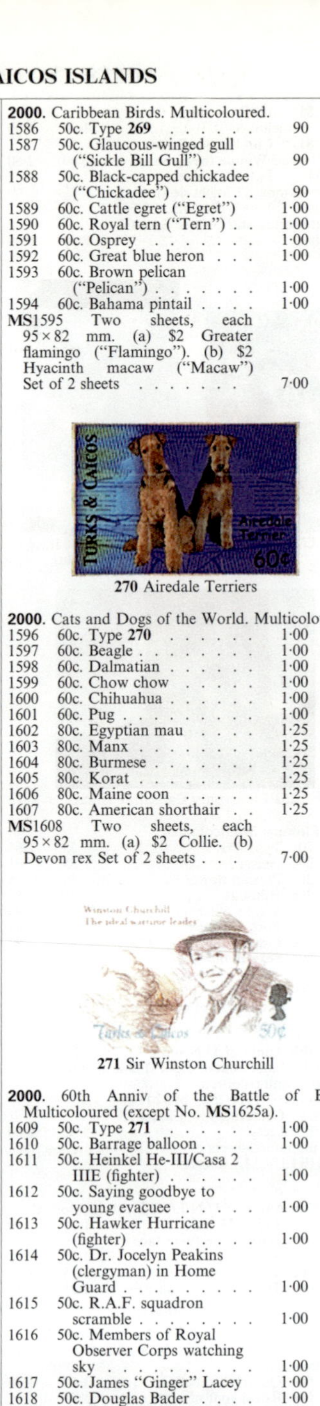

270 Airedale Terriers

2000. Cats and Dogs of the World. Multicoloured.

1596 60c. Type **270** . . . . . . 1·00 1·10
1597 60c. Beagle . . . . 1·00 1·10
1598 60c. Dalmatian . . . . . . 1·00 1·10
1599 60c. Chow chow . . . . . 1·00 1·10
1600 60c. Chihuahua . . . . . . 1·00 1·10
1601 60c. Pug . . . . 1·00 1·10
1602 80c. Egyptian mau . . . . 1·25 1·40
1603 80c. Manx . . . . 1·25 1·40
1604 80c. Burmese . . . . 1·25 1·40
1605 80c. Korat . . . . 1·25 1·40
1606 80c. Maine coon . . . . . 1·25 1·40
1607 80c. American shorthair . . 1·25 1·40
MS1608 Two sheets, each 95 × 82 mm. (a) $2 Collie. (b) Devon rex Set of 2 sheets . . . 7·00 7·50

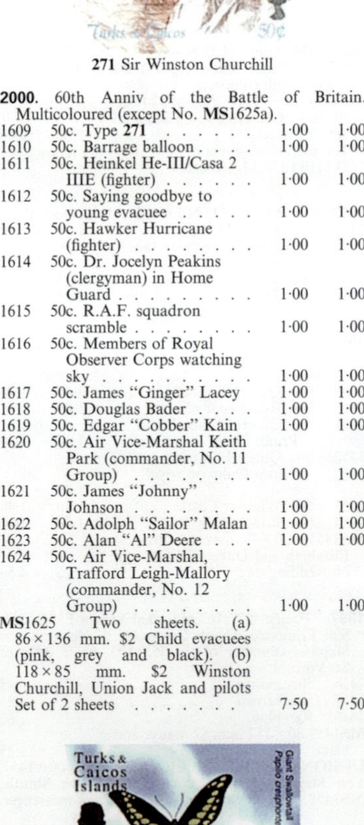

271 Sir Winston Churchill

2000. 60th Anniv of the Battle of Britain. Multicoloured (except No. **MS**1625a).

1609 50c. Type **271** . . . . . . 1·00 1·00
1610 50c. Barrage balloon . . . . 1·00 1·00
1611 50c. Heinkel He-III/Casa 2 IIIE (fighter) . . . . . . 1·00 1·00
1612 50c. Saying goodbye to young evacuee . . . . . 1·00 1·00
1613 50c. Hawker Hurricane (fighter) . . . . 1·00 1·00
1614 50c. Dr. Jocelyn Peakins (clergyman) in Home Guard . . . . 1·00 1·00
1615 50c. R.A.F. squadron scramble . . . . 1·00 1·00
1616 50c. Members of Royal Observer Corps watching sky . . . . 1·00 1·00
1617 50c. James "Ginger" Lacey 1·00 1·00
1618 50c. Douglas Bader . . . . 1·00 1·00
1619 50c. Edgar "Cobber" Kain 1·00 1·00
1620 50c. Air Vice-Marshal Keith Park (commander, No. 11 Group) . . . . 1·00 1·00
1621 50c. James "Johnny" Johnson . . . . 1·00 1·00
1622 50c. Adolph "Sailor" Malan 1·00 1·00
1623 50c. Alan "Al" Deere . . . 1·00 1·00
1624 50c. Air Vice-Marshal, Trafford Leigh-Mallory (commander, No. 12 Group) . . . . 1·00 1·00
MS1625 Two sheets. (a) 86 × 136 mm. $2 Child evacuees (pink, grey and black). (b) 118 × 85 mm. $2 Winston Churchill, Union Jack and pilots Set of 2 sheets . . . . . . 7·50 7·50

272 Giant Swallowtail

2000. Caribbean Butterflies. Multicoloured.

1626 50c. Type **272** . . . . . . 90 1·00
1627 50c. Common morpho . . . 90 1·00
1628 50c. Tiger pierid . . . . . 90 1·00
1629 50c. Banded king shoemaker 90 1·00
1630 50c. Figure-of-eight butterfly 90 1·00
1631 50c. Polydamas swallowtail 90 1·00
1632 50c. Clorinde . . . . 90 1·00
1633 50c. Blue night butterfly . . 90 1·00
1634 50c. Small lace-wing . . . . 90 1·00
1635 50c. Mosaic . . . . 90 1·00
1636 50c. Monarch . . . . 90 1·00
1637 50c. Grecian shoemaker . . 90 1·00
MS1638 Two sheets, each 68 × 98 mm. (a) $2 Orange-barred sulphur. (b) $2 White peacock Set of 2 sheets . . . . 7·50 7·50

Nos. 1626/31 and 1632/37 were each printed together, se-tenant, with the backgrounds forming composite designs.

273 *Neptune* (sailing packet)

2001. Sailing Ships of the World. Multicoloured.

1639 60c. Type **273** 75 80
1640 60c. American clipper (vert) 55 80
1641 60c. U.S.C.G. *Eagle* (cadet barque) 75 80
1642 60c. *Gloria* (Colombian cadet ship) 75 80
1643 60c. Viking longship 75 80
1644 60c. *Henri Grace a Dieu* (English galleon) 75 80
1645 60c. *Golden Hind* (Drake) 75 80
1646 60c. H.M.S. *Endeavour* (Cook) 75 80
1647 60c. *Anglo-Norman* (British barque) 75 80
1648 60c. *Libertad* (Argentine full-rigged cadet ship) . . 75 80
1649 60c. Northern European cog 75 80
1650 60c. 16th-century carrack . . 75 80
1651 60c. *Mayflower* (Pilgrim Fathers) 75 80
1652 60c. *Queen Anne's Revenge* (Blackbeard) 75 80
1653 60c. *Holkar* (British barque) 75 80
1654 60c. *Amerigo Vespucci* (Italian cadet ship) . . . 75 80
MS1655 Two sheets, each 48 × 67 mm. (a) $2 U.S.S. Constitution (frigate) (vert). (b) $2 Danmark (full-rigged Danish cadet ship) (vert) Set of 2 sheets 5·00 5·25

No 1642 is inscribed "Columbia" and 1648 "Liberated", both in error.

274 Beluga

2001. Whales and Dolphins. Multicoloured.

1656 50c. Type **274** 65 70
1657 50c. Dwarf sperm whale . . 65 70
1658 50c. Killer whale, swimming underwater 65 70
1659 50c. Shortfin pilot whale . . 65 70
1660 50c. Bowhead whale 65 70
1661 50c. Two killer whales . . . 65 70
1662 50c. Pygmy sperm whale . . 65 70
1663 50c. Right whale 65 70
1664 50c. Sperm whale with calf 65 70
1665 50c. California grey whale 65 70
1666 50c. Narwhal 65 70
1667 50c. Killer whale leaping . . 65 70
1668 50c. Bryde's whale 65 70
1669 50c. Two belugas 65 70
1670 50c. Sperm whale 65 70
1671 50c. Three pilot whales . . 65 70
MS1672 Two sheets, each 92 × 69 mm. (a) $2 Humpback whale and calf. (b) $2 Cuviers beacked whale Set of 2 sheets 5·00 5·25

274a Woman on beach

2001. United Nations Women's Human Rights Campaign. Multicoloured.

1673 90c. Type **274a** . . . . . . 1·10 1·25
1674 $1 "Caribbean Woman II" 1·25 1·40

2001. Death Centenary of Queen Victoria. As T **425** of St. Vincent. Multicoloured.

1675 60c. Queen Victoria in old age, wearing white cap . . 75 80
1676 60c. As a girl in evening dress 75 80
1677 60c. Bare-headed 75 80
1678 60c. Wearing diadem . . . 75 80
1679 60c. Holding fan 75 80
1680 60c. In Coronation robes (after Franz Winterhalter) 75 80

1681 60c. In carriage 75 80
1682 60c. As Empress of India . . 75 80
MS1683 Two sheets, each 82 × 113 mm. (a) $2 Queen Victoria carrying umbrella. (b) $2 Wearing white hat and veil Set of 2 sheets . . . . 5·25 5·50

2001. 75th Birthday of Queen Elizabeth II. As T **428** of St. Vincent. Multicoloured.
1684 60c. Queen Elizabeth wearing purple hat and coat 75 80
1685 60c. Wearing tiara and evening dress 75 80
1686 60c. In green hat and coat 75 80
1687 60c. Wearing diadem and ruby necklace 75 80
1688 60c. In red hat and coat . . 75 80
1689 60c. Wearing tiara and veil 75 80
MS1690 78 × 140 mm. $2 Queen Elizabeth robes of the Order of the Bath . . . . 2·50 2·75

275 "Rikaku II as a Fisherman" (Hirosada) **276** *Dismorphia cubana*

2001. "Philanippon '01" International Stamp Exhibition, Tokyo. Japanese Art. Multicoloured.
1691 60c. Type **275** 75 80
1692 60c. "Autumn Moon in Mirror" (Suzuki Harunobu) 75 80
1693 60c. "Musical Party" (Hishikawa Morunobu) 75 80
1694 60c. "Kannon and Four Farmers" (H. Gatto) . . 75 80
1695 60c. "Rain in Fifth Month" (I. Kunisada) 75 80
1696 60c. "The Lives of Women" (Utagawa Kuniyoshi) . . 75 80

2001. Butterflies. Multicoloured.
1697 10c. Type **276** 15 20
1698 15c. *Parides gundalachianus* (vert) 20 25
1699 20c. *Graphium androcles* . . 25 30
1700 25c. Eastern black swallowtail 30 35
1701 35c. *Papilio velvois* (vert) . . 45 50
1702 45c. Schaus swallowtail (vert) 60 65
1703 50c. Pipevine swallowtail (vert) 65 70
1704 60c. *Euploea Mniszechii* (vert) 75 80
1705 80c. *Papilio caiguanabus* (vert) . . . . 1·00 1·10
1706 $1 *Graphium encelades* (vert) 1·25 1·40
1707 $1.25 *Calisto zangis* . . . . 1·60 1·75
1708 $1.40 Eastern tiger swallowtail . . . . 1·75 1·90
1709 $2 *Graphium milon* (vert) . . 2·50 2·75
1710 $5 Palamedes swallowtail . . 6·50 6·75
1711 $10 Zebra swallowtail . . . 13·00 13·50
No. 1704 is inscribed "MNISZECKI", in error

277 Crossing Place Trail Monument, Middle Caicos **279** Duchess of York, 1923

278 Sooty Tern

2002. Golden Jubilee. Multicoloured (except Nos. 1718/19).
1712 25c. Type **277** 30 35
1713 25c. Wades Green Plantation, North Caicos 30 35
1714 25c. Underwater scenery, Grand Turk 30 35
1715 25c. St. Thomas Anglican Church, Grand Turk . . 30 35
1716 25c. Ripsaw Band, Grand Turk 30 35
1717 25c. Basket weaving 30 35
1718 60c. Princess Mary with cannon, Grand Turk, 1960 (black and gold) . . 75 80
1719 60c. Queen Elizabeth on South Caicos, 1966 (black, gold and blue) . . 75 80
1720 60c. Princess Alexandra on Providenciales, 1988 . . . 75 80
1721 60c. Duke of Edinburgh on Grand Turk, 1998 . . . . 75 80
1722 60c. Prince Andrew and aquarium, Grand Turk, 2000 . . . . 75 80
1723 80c. Salt gathering, Salt Cay 1·00 1·10
1724 80c. Space capsule, Grand Turk . . . . 1·00 1·10
1725 80c. Legislative Council Chamber, Grand Turk . . 1·00 1·10
1726 80c. Map of Turks and Caicos Islands . . . . . 1·00 1·10
1727 80c. National Museum, Grand Turk . . . . . . 1·00 1·10

2002. 20th World Scout Jamboree, Thailand. As T **116** of St. Kitts. Multicoloured.
1728 80c. Scout wood-working . . 1·00 1·10
1729 80c. Rifle shooting . . . . 1·00 1·10
1730 80c. Swinging over river . . 1·00 1·10
1731 80c. Scouts in tent at night 1·00 1·10
MS1732 107 × 127 mm. $2 Disabled scouts playing football . . . . 2·50 2·75

2002. International Year of Mountains. As T **115** of St. Kitts, but vert. Multicoloured.
1733 80c. Devil's Peak, South Africa . . . . 1·00 1·10
1734 80c. Drakensburg Mountains, South Africa 1·00 1·10
1735 80c. Mont Blanc, France . . 1·00 1·10
1736 80c. Roan Mountain, Tennessee, U.S.A. . . . . 1·00 1·10
1737 80c. Mount Sefton, New Zealand . . . . 1·00 1·10
1738 80c. Mount Cook, New Zealand . . . . 1·00 1·10
MS1739 107 × 127 mm. $2 North-west Highlands, Scotland . . . 2·50 2·75

2002. U.N. Year of Eco Tourism. As T **449** of St. Vincent. Multicoloured.
1740 60c. Humpback whale and lighthouse 75 80
1741 60c. Yacht 75 80
1742 60c. Two yachts racing . . . 75 80
1743 60c. Queen angelfish . . . 75 80
1744 60c. Manta and tropical fish 75 80
1745 60c. Turtle with boy wearing snorkle 75 80
MS1746 98 × 70 mm. $2 "Jojo" (Bottlenose Dolphin) (85 × 28 mm) 2·50 2·75
Nos. 1740/5 were printed together, se-tenant, forming a composite design.

2002. "United We Stand". Support for Victims of 11 September 2001 Terrorist Attacks. As T **114** of St. Kitts. Multicoloured.
1747 50c. U.S. and Turks and Caicos flags with Statue of Liberty's torch 65 70

2002. Birds and Insects. Multicoloured.
1748 60c. Type **278** 75 80
1749 60c. Magnificent frigatebird 75 80
1750 60c. American white pelican 75 80
1751 60c. Northern shoveler . . . 75 80
1752 60c. Northern oriole ("Baltimore Oriole") . . . 75 80
1753 60c. Roseate spoonbill . . . 75 80
1754 60c. Hawk moth 75 80
1755 60c. Burnet moth 75 80
1756 60c. Mammoth wasp . . . 75 80
1757 60c. Branch-boring beetle . . 75 80
1758 60c. Flower mantid on leaf 75 80
1759 60c. Flower mantid on tree trunk 75 80
MS1760 Two sheets, each 95 × 93 mm. (a) $2 Greater flamingo (vert). (b) $2 Tiphiid wasp Set of 2 sheets . . . . 5·25 5·50
Nos. 1748/53 (birds) and 1754/9 (insects) were each printed together, se-tenant, with the backgrounds forming composite designs.
No. 1753 is inscribed "ROSTATE" in error.

2002. Queen Elizabeth the Queen Mother Commemoration. Multicoloured.
1761 80c. Type **279** . . . . . . 1·00 1·10
1762 80c. Queen Elizabeth the Queen Mother on Remembrance Day . . . 1·00 1·10

280 Charles Lindbergh as a Young Man

2002. 75th Anniv of First Solo Transatlantic Flight. Multicoloured.
1763 60c. Type **280** 75 80
1764 60c. Lindbergh with *Spirit of St. Louis* 75 80
1765 60c. *Spirit of St. Louis* . . . 75 80
1766 60c. *Spirit of St. Louis* taking off from Roosevelt Field 75 80
1767 60c. *Spirit of St. Louis* above Atlantic 75 80
1768 60c. Lindbergh in Paris . . . 75 80

281 John Kennedy as a Young Man **282** "Madonna and Child" (Giovanni Bellini)

2002. Pres John Kennedy Commemoration. Multicoloured, centre colours given.
1769 **281** 60c. brown 75 80
1770 – 60c. mauve 75 80
1771 – 60c. grey 75 80
1772 – 60c. blue 75 80
1773 – 60c. violet 75 80
1774 – 60c. bistre 75 80
DESIGNS: Nos. 1770/4, Showing different portraits.

2002. Christmas. Religious Paintings. Mult.
1775 20c. Type **282** 25 30
1776 25c. "Adoration of the Magi" (Antonio Correggio) (horiz) 30 35
1777 60c. "Transfiguration of Christ" (Bellini) 75 80
1778 80c. "Polyptych of St. Vincent Ferrer," (Bellini) . . . . 1·00 1·10
1779 $1 "Miraculous Mass" (Simone Martini) . . . . 1·25 1·40
MS1780 90 × 125 $2 "Christ in Heaven with Four Saints" (Domenico Ghirlandaio) (horiz) 2·50 2·75
No. 1776 is inscribed "ADORATIO" in error.

TUSCANY Pt. 8

Formerly an independent duchy in C. Italy, now part of Italy.

1851. 60 quattrini = 20 soldi = 12 crazie = 1 Tuscan lira.
1859. 1 Tuscan lira = 1 Italian lira.

1 Arms of Tuscany **5** Arms of Savoy

1851. Imperf.
1 **1** 1q. black on blue £5000 £950
2 1q. black on grey £4750 £900
24 1q. black £600 £550
4 1s. orange on blue £8000 £1000
5 1s. orange on grey £6000 £950
25 1s. buff £18000 £2750
6 2s. red on blue £20000 £3000
7 1c. red on blue £3750 £110
9 1c. red on grey . . . . . . £3750 48·00
26 1c. red £4500 £250
10 2c. blue on blue £3750 £110
11 2c. blue on grey . . . . . . £1800 55·00
28 2c. blue . . . . £1000 50·00
13 4c. green on blue £4000 £140
14 4c. green on grey . . . . . £3000 60·00
30 4c. green . . . . £4250 85·00
16 6c. blue on blue £4000 £110
17 6c. blue on grey . . . . . . £5000 80·00
31 6c. blue . . . . £5000 95·00
20 9c. purple on blue £8000 £190
22 9c. purple on grey . . . . . £8000 90·00
33 9c. brown £16000 £2750
23 60c. red on blue £36000 £18000

1860. Imperf.
36 **5** 1c. purple £1100 £400
40 5c. green £5000 £150
43 10c. brown . . . . £1100 18·00
45 20c. blue . . . . £4250 80·00
48 40c. red £6000 £120
50 80c. red £14000 £600
51 3l. buff £100000 £40000

NEWSPAPER STAMP TAX

N 3

1854.
N1 **N 3** 2s. black . . . . 32·00

TUVA Pt. 10

A province lying between the Sajan and Tannu Ola range. Formerly known as North Mongolia and Tannu, Tuva was incorporated into the U.S.S.R. on 11 October 1944.

PRICES. The prices quoted in the used column are for stamps cancelled to order where these occur. Postally used copies are worth considerably more.

1926. 100 kopeks = 1 rouble.
1934. 100 kopeks = 1 tugrik.
1936. 100 kopeks = 1 aksha.

1 Wheel of Eternity

1926.
1 **1** 1k. red . . . . 1·25 1·10
2 2k. blue . . . . 1·25 1·10
3 5k. orange . . . . 1·25 1·10
4 8k. green . . . . 1·50 1·25
5 10k. violet . . . . 1·50 1·25
6 30k. brown . . . . 1·75 1·25
7 50k. black . . . . 1·75 1·25
8 1r. turquoise . . . . 2·50 2·25
9 3r. red . . . . 5·00 4·50
10 5r. blue . . . . 8·00 6·00
The rouble values are larger, $22\frac{1}{2} \times 30$ mm.

1927. Surch **TOUVA POSTAGE** and value.
11 **1** 8k. on 50k. black . . . . . 6·50 5·50
12 14k. on 1r. turquoise . . . . 7·50 5·50
13 18k. on 3r. red . . . . 10·00 9·00
14 28k. on 5r. blue . . . . . . 14·00 9·50

4 Tuvan Woman **5** Map of Tuva

6 Mongolian Sheep and Tents

7 Fording a River

8 Reindeer ($\frac{2}{3}$-size illustration)

1927.
15 **4** 1k. brown, red and black . . 60 35
16 – 2k. brown, green and violet 90 45
17 – 3k. green, yellow and black 1·40 50
18 – 4k. brown and blue 60 35
19 – 5k. blue, black and orange 60 35
20 **5** 8k. sepia, blue and red . . . 70 55
21 – 10k. red, black and green . . 4·50 75
22 – 14k. orange and blue . . . . 8·00 3·25
23 **6** 18k. brown and blue . . . . 8·00 3·50
24 – 28k. sepia and green . . . . 6·00 2·25
25 **7** 40k. green and red . . . . . 4·00 2·00
26 – 50k. brown, black and green 3·00 1·75
27 – 70k. bistre and red . . . . . 5·00 2·75
28 **8** 1r. violet and brown . . . . 8·00 5·50
DESIGNS—As Type **4**: 2k. Red deer; 3k. Common goral; 4k. Mongolian tent; 5k. Tuvan man. As Type **5**: 10k. Archers; 14k. Camel caravan. As Type **6**: 28k. Landscape. As Type **7**: 50k. Girl carpet-weaver; 70k. Horseman.

1932. Stamps of 1927 surch **TbBA POSTA** and value (10k. optd only).
29 **7** 1k. on 40k. green and red . . 5·50 6·50
30 – 2k. on 50k. brown, black and green . . . . 6·00 5·50
31 – 3k. on 70k. bistre and red . . 6·00 5·50
32 **5** 5k. on 8k. sepia, blue and red 7·50 5·50

No.	Type	Description	Unused	Used
33	–	10k. red, black and green	7·50	7·50
34	–	15k. on 14k. orange and blue	7·50	7·00

1932. Stamps of 1927 surch.

No.	Type	Description	Unused	Used
35	**5**	10k. on 8k. brown	£150	
36	–	15k. on 14k. orange and blue	£250	
37	**6**	35k. on 18k. brown and blue	60·00	60·00
38	–	35k. on 28k. sepia and green	70·00	70·00

1933. Fiscal stamps (20 × 39 mm) surch **Posta** and value. (a) Numerals 6 mm tall.

No.	Type	Description	Unused	Used
39		15k. on 6k. yellow	£120	£100
40		35k. on 15k. brown	£475	£400
		(b) Numerals 5¼ mm tall.		
41		15k. on 6k. yellow	£150	£140
42		35k. on 15k. brown	£500	£450

12 Mounted Hunter

13 Interior of Tent

14 Yak

1934. Perf or imperf.

No.	Type	Description	Unused	Used
43	**12**	1k. orange	1·00	40
44	–	2k. green	1·00	75
45	**13**	3k. red	1·00	75
46	–	4k. purple	2·50	1·50
47	**14**	5k. blue	2·50	1·50
48	–	10k. brown	2·50	1·50
49	–	15k. lake	2·50	1·50
50	–	20k. black	3·00	2·00

DESIGNS—As Type **12**: 2k. Hunter. As Type **13**: 4k. Tractor. As Type **14**: 10k. Camel caravan; 15k. Lassoing reindeer; 20k. Corsac fox-hunting.

15 Kalinin K-5 over Yaks

16 Western Capercaillie

1934. Air.

No.	Type	Description	Unused	Used
51	**15**	1k. red	1·00	75
52	–	5k. green	1·00	75
53	**16**	10k. brown	4·00	85
54	–	15k. red	2·00	75
55	–	25k. purple	2·00	75
56	**15**	50k. green	2·00	75
57	–	75k. red	2·00	75
58	**15**	1t. blue	2·00	1·25
59	–	2t. blue (55 × 28 mm)	3·00	2·25

DESIGNS—As Type **15**: 5, 15k. Tupolev ANT-25 over camels. As Type **16**: 25k. Junkers F-13 with skis over argali; 75k. Junkers F-13 over ox-cart; 2t. Tupolev ANT-9 over roe deer.

The 2t. also comes larger, 61 × 31 mm.

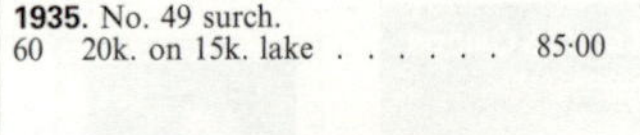

1935. No. 49 surch.

No.	Type	Description	Unused	Used
60		20k. on 15k. lake	85·00	

18 Map of Tuva

19 Rocky Outcrop

1935. Landscapes.

No.	Type	Description	Unused	Used
61	**18**	1k. orange	90	75
62	–	3k. green	90	75
63	–	5k. red	1·10	75
64	–	10k. violet	1·10	75
65	**19**	15k. green	1·25	95
66	–	25k. blue	1·25	95
67	–	50k. sepia	1·25	1·00

DESIGNS—As Type **18**: 3, 5, 10k. Views of River Yenisei. As Type **19**: 25k. Bei-kem rapids; 50k. Mounted hunter.

20 Eurasian Badger

21 Corsac Fox

22 Elk

1935. Animals.

No.	Type	Description	Unused	Used
68	**20**	1k. orange	1·10	85
69	–	3k. green	1·10	85
70	–	5k. mauve	1·10	90
71	**21**	10k. red	1·10	90
72	–	25k. red	1·50	1·00
73	–	50k. blue	1·50	1·00
74	**22**	1t. violet	1·50	1·00
75	–	2t. blue	1·50	1·00
76	–	3t. brown	1·50	1·10
77	–	5t. blue	1·50	1·25

DESIGNS—As Type **20**—VERT: 3k. Eurasian red squirrel. HORIZ: 5k. Sable. As Type **21**: 25k. European otter; 50k. Lynx. LARGER (61 × 31 mm): 2t. Yak; 3k. Bactrian camel. As Type **22**: 5t. Brown bear.

See also No. 115.

23 Arms of Republic

24 Wrestlers

25 Herdsman

26 Sports Meeting

27 Partisans

1936. 15th Anniv of Independence. (a) Postage.

No.	Type	Description	Unused	Used
78	**23**	1k. green	1·25	55
79	–	2k. sepia	1·25	55
80	–	3k. blue	1·75	60
81	**24**	4k. red	2·00	60
82	–	5k. purple	3·25	50
83	**24**	6k. green	3·00	50
84	–	8k. purple	3·00	55
85	–	10k. red	3·50	50
86	–	12k. agate	4·00	75
87	–	15k. green	5·00	55
88	–	20k. blue	5·00	75
89	**25**	25k. red	5·00	55
90	–	30k. purple	15·00	1·00
91	**25**	35k. red	5·00	55
92	–	40k. sepia	5·00	55
93	–	50k. blue	5·00	55
94	**26**	70k. plum	5·00	1·10
95	–	80k. green	5·00	1·10
96	**27**	1a. red	6·00	1·10
97		2a. red	5·75	1·10
98	–	3a. blue	5·75	1·10
99	–	5a. agate	5·75	1·10

DESIGNS—As Type **23**: 2k. President Gyrmittazi; 3k. Camel and driver. As Type **24**: 5, 8k. Archers; 10, 15k. Fishermen; 12, 20k. Brown bear hunt. As Type **25**: 30k. Bactrian camel and steam goods train; 40, 50k. Horse-racing. As Type **26**: 8k., 5a. 1921 war scene; 3a. Confiscation of cattle.

See also Nos. 116 and 118/19.

28 Yak Transport

29 Horseman and Airship

30 Seaplane over Waves

(b) Air.

No.	Type	Description	Unused	Used
100	**28**	5k. blue and flesh	2·00	75
101	–	10k. purple and brown	3·00	80
102	**28**	15k. agate and grey	3·00	80
103	**29**	25k. purple and cream	4·00	90
104	–	50k. red and cream	4·00	1·10
105	**29**	75k. green and yellow	4·00	1·10
106	**30**	1a. green and turquoise	4·00	1·25
107		2a. red and cream	5·00	1·25
108		3a. sepia and flesh	5·00	2·00

DESIGNS—As Type **28**: 10k. Horse-drawn reaper. As Type **29**: 50k. Feast of the women.

See also No. 117.

1938. Various stamps surch with large numerals and old values obliterated.

No.	Type	Description	Unused	Used
109		5k. on 2a. red (No. 97)		
110		5k. on 2a. red and cream (No. 107)		
111		10k. on 1t. blue (No. 58)		
112		20k. on 50k. sepia (No. 67)		
113		30k. on 2a. red and cream (No. 107)		
114		30k. on 3a. sepia and flesh (No. 108)		

See also Nos. 120/1.

1938. Previous types with designs modified and colours changed.

No.	Type	Description	Unused	Used
115		5k. green (No. 70)	£100	
116		10k. blue (No. 85)	£100	
117		15k. brown (No. 102)	£100	
118		20k. red (No. 88)	£225	
119		30k. purple (as No. 95)	£100	

In Nos. 116/19 the dates have been removed and in No. 117 "AIR MAIL" also.

1939. Nos. 58 and 67 surch with small thick numerals and old values obliterated.

No.	Type	Description	Unused	Used
120		1k. on 1t. blue		
121		20k. on 50k. sepia		

See also Nos. 122/3.

1940. Various stamps surch.

No.	Type	Description	Unused	Used
122		10k. on 1t. blue (No. 58)		
123		20k. on 50k. sepia (No. 67)		
124		20k. on 50k. blue (No. 73)		
125		20k. on 50k. blue (No. 93)		
126		20k. on 50k. red and cream (No. 104)		
127		20k. on 75k. green and yellow (No. 105)		
128		20k. on 80k. green (No. 95)		

1942. Nos. 98/9 surch.

No.	Type	Description	Unused	Used
129		25k. on 3a. blue		
130		25k. on 5a. agate		

34 Tuvan Woman

1942. 21st Anniv of Independence. Imperf.

No.	Type	Description	Unused	Used
131	**34**	25k. blue	£225	
132	–	25k. blue	£225	
133	–	25k. blue	£225	

DESIGNS: No. 132 Agricultural Exhibition building; No. 133 Government building.

35 Coat of Arms

36 Government Building

1943. 22nd Anniv of Independence. With or without gum.

134 **35** 25k. blue . . . . 30·00

135 25k. black . . . . 40·00

136 25k. green . . . . 80·00

137 **36** 50k. green . . . . 80·00

TUVALU Pt. 1

Formerly known as the Ellice Islands and sharing a joint administration with the Gilbert group. On 1 January 1976 the two island groups separated and the Ellice Is. were renamed Tuvalu.

100 cents = $1 Australian.

1 Tuvaluan and Gilbertese

1976. Separation. Multicoloured.

1 4c. Type **1** 35 80

2 10c. Map of the islands (vert) 50 1·00

3 35c. Gilbert and Ellice canoes 70 1·50

1976. Nos. 173/87 of Gilbert and Ellice Islands optd TUVALU.

14 1c. Cutting toddy 30 30

20 2c. Lagoon fishing 30 40

21 3c. Cleaning pandanus leaves 30 40

22 4c. Casting nets 30 45

5 5c. Gilbertese canoe 50 60

15 6c. De-husking coconuts . . . 30 30

6 8c. Weaving pandanus fronds 30 60

7 10c. Weaving a basket 30 65

16 15c. Tiger shark . . . . . . 1·00 40

23 20c. Beating a rolled pandanus leaf 30 60

24 25c. Loading copra 30 60

25 35c. Fishing at night 70 70

17 50c. Local handicrafts . . . 30 50

18 $1 Weaving coconut screen . . 35 60

19 $2 Coat of arms 50 60

3 50c. Coin and Octopus

4 Niulakita and Seven-ridged Leathery Turtle

1976. New Coinage. Multicoloured.

26 5c. Type **3** 30 15

27 10c. Red-eyed crab 40 20

28 15c. Flying fish 55 25

29 35c. Green turtle 70 50

1976. Multicoloured.

58 1c. Type **4** 50 15

59 2c. Nukulaelae and sleeping mat 20 25

60 4c. Nui and taro (vegetable) 20 15

61 5c. Nanumanga and grass skirt 25 15

62 6c. Nukufetau and coconut crab 20 35

63 8c. Funafuti and banana tree 20 25

64 10c. Map of Tuvalu 20 20

37 15c. Niutao and flying fish . . 75 20

38 20c. Vaitupu and maneapa (meeting hall) 35 40

66 25c. Nanumea and fish-hook 80 20

67 30c. Fatele (local dancing) . . 30 20

40 35c. Te Ano (game) 35 20

68 40c. Screw pine 30 15

41 50c. Canoe pole fishing . . . 35 20

42 $1 Reef fishing by flare . . . 35 20

43 $2 Living house 35 20

69 $5 M.V. "Nivanga" . . . . . 1·00 2·25

5 Title Page of New Testament

1976. Christmas. Multicoloured.

45 5c. Type **5** 20 25

46 20c. Lotolelei Church 20 25

47 25c. Kelupi Church 20 25

48 30c. Mataloa o Tuvala Church 25 25

49 35c. Palataise o Keliso Church 25 25

6 The Queen and Duke of Edinburgh after Coronation

1977. Silver Jubilee. Multicoloured.

50 15c. Type **6** 15 10

51 35c. Prince Philip carried ashore at Vaitupu 20 15

52 50c. The Queen and attendants 30 20

MS53 98 × 144 mm. Nos. 50/2 . . 1·00 1·00

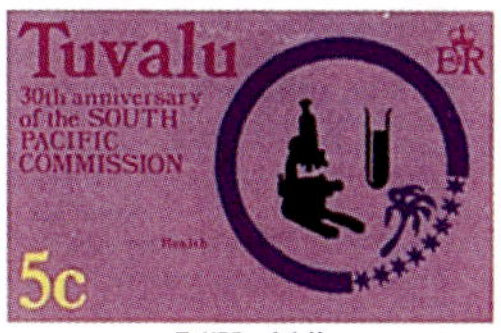

7 "Health"

1977. 30th Anniv of South Pacific Commission. Multicoloured.

54 5c. Type **7** 15 20

55 20c. "Education" 15 20

56 30c. "Fruit-growing" 15 20

57 35c. Map of S.P.C. area . . . 20 25

8 Scout Promise

1977. 50th Anniv of Scouting in the Central Pacific. Multicoloured.

73 5c. Type **8** 15 20

74 20c. Canoeing 15 20

75 30c. Scout shelter 20 25

76 35c. Lord Baden-Powell . . . 20 25

9 Hurricane Beach (Expedition photo)

1977. Royal Society Expeditions, 1896–97.

77 **9** 5c. multicoloured 15 15

78 – 20c. black and blue 15 20

79 – 30c. black and blue 20 20

80 – 35c. multicoloured 20 20

DESIGNS—VERT: 20c. Boring apparatus on H.M.S. "Porpoise"; 30c. Dredging chart. HORIZ: 35c. Charles Darwin and H.M.S. "Beagle".

10 Pacific Pigeon

13 White Frangipani

11 "Lawedua" (inter-island coaster)

1978. Wild Birds. Multicoloured.

81 8c. Type **10** 35 25

82 20c. Reef heron 40 40

83 30c. White tern ("Fairy Tern") 45 50

84 40c. Lesser frigate bird 45 55

1978. Ships. Multicoloured.

85 8c. Type **11** 15 15

86 20c. "Wallacia" (tug) 15 15

87 30c. "Cenpac Rounder" (freighter) 20 20

88 40c. "Pacific Explorer" (freighter) 20 20

1978. 25th Anniv of Coronation. As Nos. 422/5 of Montserrat. Multicoloured.

89 8c. Canterbury Cathedral . . . 10 10

90 30c. Salisbury Cathedral . . . 10 10

91 40c. Wells Cathedral 10 10

92 $1 Hereford Cathedral 30 30

MS93 137 × 108 mm. Nos. 89/92 45 70

1978. Independence. Nos. 63/4, 37/8, 67/40 and 68 optd **INDEPENDENCE 1ST OCTOBER 1978**.

94 8c. Funafuti and banana tree 10 10

95 10c. Map of Tuvalu 10 10

96 15c. Niutao and four-winged flyingfish 10 10

97 20c. Vaitupu and maneapa (house) 10 10

98 30c. Fatele (local dancing) . . 15 15

99 35c. Te Ano (game) 15 15

100 40c. Screw pine 15 15

1978. Wild Flowers. Multicoloured.

101 8c. Type **13** 10 10

102 20c. Susana 10 10

103 30c. Tiale 15 15

104 40c. Inato 20 25

14 Squirrelfish

1979. Fishes (1st series). Multicoloured.

105 1c. Type **14** 10 10

106 2c. Band-tailed goatfish . . 10 10

107 4c. Regal angelfish 10 10

108 5c. Melon butterflyfish . . . 10 10

109 6c. Semi-circle angelfish . . 10 10

110 8c. Blue-striped snapper . . 10 10

111 10c. Clown anemonefish . . 15 10

112 15c. Chevron butterflyfish 20 10

113 20c. Yellow-edged lyretail ("Fairy cod") 25 15

114 25c. Clown triggerfish . . . 25 20

115 30c. Long-nosed butterflyfish 25 10

116 35c. Yellow-finned tuna . . 30 15

117 40c. Spotted eagle ray . . . 30 10

117b 45c. Black-tipped grouper 1·50 2·00

118 50c. Hammerhead 30 20

119 70c. Lionfish (vert) 30 30

120 $1 Painted triggerfish (vert) 30 30

121 $2 Copper-banded butterflyfish ("Beaked coralfish") (vert) 50 30

122 $5 Tiger shark (vert) . . . 70 35

See also Nos. 770/81.

15 "Explorer of the Pacific"

1979. Death Bicent of Capt. James Cook. Mult.

123 8c. Type **15** 15 20

124 30c. "A new island is discovered" 15 20

125 40c. "Transit of Venus, Tahiti, 3 June, 1769" . . . 15 20

126 $1 Cook's death 15 30

16 Grumman Mackinnon Goose Flying Boat and Nukulaelae Island

1979. Internal Air Service. Multicoloured.

127 8c. Type **16** 15 15

128 20c. Goose and Vaitupu . . 15 15

129 30c. Goose and Nui 20 20

130 40c. Goose and Funafuti . . 25 30

17 Sir Rowland Hill, 1976 4c. Separation Commemorative and London's First Pillar Box, 1855

1979. Death Cent of Sir Rowland Hill. Mult.

131 30c. Type **17** 15 15

132 40c. Sir Rowland Hill, 1976 10c. Separation commemorative and Penny Black 15 15

133 $1 Sir Rowland Hill, 1976 35c. Separation commemorative and mail coach 25 30

MS134 148 × 140 mm. Nos. 131/3 70 1·25

18 Child's Face

1979. International Year of the Child.

135 **18** 8c. multicoloured 10 10

136 – 20c. multicoloured 10 10

137 – 30c. multicoloured 10 15

138 – 40c. multicoloured 15 25

DESIGN: 20c. to 40c. Children's faces.

19 Eyed Cowrie

1980. Cowrie Shells. Multicoloured.

139 8c. Type **19** 10 10

140 20c. Jester cowrie 10 10

141 30c. Closely-related carnelian cowrie 15 15

142 40c. Golden cowrie 25 20

20 Philatelic Bureau, Funafuti, and 1976 8c. Definitive

1980. "London 1980" Int Stamp Exhibition. Mult.

143 10c. Type **20** 10 10

144 20c. Nukulaelae postmark and 1976 2c. definitive . . 15 15

145 30c. Fleet Post Office, U.S. Navy, airmail cover, 1943 15 20

146 $1 Map and arms of Tuvalu 35 40

MS147 160 × 136 mm. Nos. 143/6 65 1·10

21 Queen Elizabeth the Queen Mother at Royal Variety Performance, 1978

1980. 80th Birthday of The Queen Mother.

148 **21** 15c. multicoloured 25 20

22 "Aethaloessa calidalis"

1980. Moths. Multicoloured.

149 8c. Type **22** 10 10

150 20c. "Parotis suralis" 15 10

151 30c. "Dudua aprobola" . . . 20 15

152 40c. "Decadarchis simulans" 20 15

23 Air Pacific De Havilland Heron 2

1980. Aviation Commemorations. Mult.
153 8c. Type **23** 10 10
154 20c. Hawker Siddeley H.S.748 15 10
155 30c. Short S.25 Sunderland flying boat 15 15
156 40c. Orville Wright and Wright Flyer III 20 15
COMMEMORATIONS: 8c. 1st regular air service to Tuvalu, 1964; 20c. Air service to Tuvalu; 30c. Wartime R.N.Z.A.F. flying boat service to Funafuti, 1945; 40c. Wright Brothers' 1st flight, 17 December, 1903.

1981. No. 118 surch **45 CENTS**.
157 45c. on 50c. Hammerhead 25 40

25 "Hypolimnas bolina" (male) **27** U.P.U. Emblem

26 "Elizabeth" (brig), 1809

1981. Butterflies. Multicoloured.
158 8c. Type **25** 15 10
159 20c. "Hypolimnas bolina" (female) 20 15
160 30c. "Hypolimnas bolina" (female) (different) 20 20
161 40c. "Precis villida" (male) 25 20

1981. Ships (1st series). Multicoloured.
162 10c. Type **26** 15 15
163 25c. "Rebecca" (brigantine), 1819 15 20
164 35c. "Independence II" (whaling ship), 1821 20 25
165 40c. H.M.S. "Basilisk" (paddle-sloop), 1872 25 30
166 45c. H.M.S. "Royalist" (screw-corvette), 1890 30 35
167 50c. "Olivebank" (barque), 1920 30 35
See also Nos. 235/40, 377/80, 442/5, 809/12 and 832/6.

1981. Royal Wedding. Royal Yachts. As T **14a/b** of St. Kitts. Multicoloured.
168 10c. "Carolina" 10 15
169 10c. Prince Charles and Lady Diana Spencer 35 50
170 45c. "Victoria and Albert III" 10 15
171 45c. As No. 169 40 65
172 $2 "Britannia" 25 50
173 $2 As No. 169 75 1·50
MS174 120 × 109 mm. $1.50, As No. 169 50 75

1981. U.P.U. Membership.
177 **27** 70c. blue 20 30
178 $1 brown 30 45
MS179 86 × 71 mm. Nos. 177/8 70 2·25

28 Map of Funafuti, and Anchor

1982. Amatuku Maritime School. Mult.
180 10c. Type **28** 10 10
181 25c. Motor launch 20 20
182 35c. School buildings and jetty 25 30
183 45c. School flag and freighter 30 35

29 Caroline of Brandenburg-Ansbach, Princess of Wales, 1714

1982. 21st Birthday of Princess of Wales. Multicoloured.
184 10c. Type **29** 10 10
185 45c. Coat of arms of Caroline of Brandenburg-Ansbach 10 10
186 $1.50 Diana, Princess of Wales 50 30

1982. Tonga Cyclone Relief. Nos. 170/1 optd **TONGA CYCLONE RELIEF 1982 +20c**.
187 45c.+20c. "Victoria and Albert III" 10 30
188 45c.+20c. Prince Charles and Lady Diana Spencer 30 1·10

1982. Birth of Prince William of Wales. Nos. 184/6 optd **ROYAL BABY**.
189 10c. Type **29** 10 10
190 45c. Coat of arms of Caroline of Brandenburg-Ansbach 10 10
191 $1.50 Diana, Princess of Wales 30 30

31 Tuvalu and World Scout Badge

1982. 75th Anniv of Boy Scout Movement. Multicoloured.
192 10c. Type **31** 15 15
193 25c. Campfire 25 40
194 35c. Parade 30 45
195 45c. Boy scout 40 55

32 Tuvalu Crest and Duke of Edinburgh's Standard

1982. Royal Visit. Multicoloured.
196 25c. Type **32** 15 20
197 45c. Tuvalu flag and Queen's Royal Standard 25 30
198 50c. Portrait of Queen Elizabeth II 25 30
MS199 104 × 85 mm. Nos. 196/8 60 1·75

33 Fisherman's Hat and Equipment

1983. Handicrafts. Multicoloured.
200 1c. Type **33** 15 10
201 2c. Cowrie shell handbags 15 10
202 5c. Wedding and baby food baskets 15 10
203 10c. Model canoe 15 10
203a 15c. Ladies' sun hats 2·25 2·00
204 20c. Palm climbing rope and platform with toddy pot 15 20
205 25c. Pandanus baskets 15 20
205a 30c. Basket tray and coconut stand 2·00 1·40
206 35c. Pandanus pillows and shell necklaces 25 30
207 40c. Round baskets and fans 20 35
208 45c. Reef sandals and fish trap 20 40
209 50c. Rat trap (vert) 20 45
209a 60c. Fisherman's waterproof boxes (vert) 2·25 1·40
210 $1 Pump drill and adze (vert) 20 45
211 $2 Fisherman's hat and canoe bailers (vert) 30 55
212 $5 Fishing rod, lures and scoop nets (vert) 60 75

34 "Te Tautai" (trawler)

1983. Commonwealth Day. Multicoloured.
213 20c. Type **34** 15 15
214 35c. Traditional dancing, Motufoua School 15 25
215 45c. Satellite view of Pacific 20 30
216 50c. "Morning Star" (container ship) 25 40

35 "Pantala flavescens"

1983. Dragonflies. Multicoloured.
217 10c. Type **35** 15 10
218 35c. "Anax guttatus" 20 35
219 40c. "Tholymis tillarga" 20 40
220 50c. "Diplacodes bipunctata" 25 50

36 Brigade Members Racing

1983. Centenary of Boys' Brigade. Mult.
221 10c. Type **36** 10 10
222 35c. B.B. members in outrigger canoe 20 30
223 $1 On parade 50 1·00

1983. No. 210 surch **60c**.
224 60c. on $1 Pump drill and adze 70 70

38 Montgolfier Balloon, 1783

1983. Bicentenary of Manned Flight. Mult.
225 25c. Type **38** 20 20
226 35c. Grumman Mackinnon Turbo Goose (horiz) 20 25
227 45c. Beech 200 Super King Air (horiz) 25 30
228 50c. "Double Eagle II" balloon 25 35
MS229 114 × 145 mm. Nos. 225/8 70 1·00

39 Early Communications

1983. World Communications Year. Mult.
230 25c. Type **39** 15 15
231 35c. Radio operator 20 20
232 45c. Modern teleprinter 20 20
233 50c. Funafuti transmitting station 25 25

1984. No. 208 surch **30c**.
234 30c. on 45c. Reef sandals and fish trap 35 40

1984. Ships (2nd series). As T **26**. Mult.
235 10c. "Titus" (freighter), 1897 25 15
236 20c. "Malaita" (freighter), 1905 25 15
237 25c. "Aymeric" (freighter), 1906 25 15
238 35c. "Anshun" (freighter), 1965 30 25
239 45c. "Beaverbank" (freighter), 1970 30 30
240 50c. "Benjamin Bowring" (freighter), 1981 30 30

41 Southern Pacific Railroad Class GS-4

1984. Leaders of the World. Railway Locomotives (1st series). As T **41**. The first in each pair shows technical drawings and the second the locomotive at work.
241 1c. multicoloured 10 10
242 1c. multicoloured 10 10
243 15c. multicoloured 20 25
244 15c. multicoloured 20 25
245 40c. multicoloured 25 30
246 40c. multicoloured 25 30
247 60c. multicoloured 35 40
248 60c. multicoloured 35 40
DESIGNS: Nos. 241/2, Southern Pacific Railroad Class GS-4, U.S.A. (1941); 243/4, New South Wales Govt Class AD 60, Australia (1952); 245/6, New South Wales Govt Class C38, Australia (1943); 247/8, Class "Achilles" "Lord of the Isles", Great Britain (1892).
See also Nos. 253/68, 273/80, 313/20 and 348/55.

42 "Ipomoea pes-caprae"

1984. Beach Flowers. Multicoloured.
249 25c. Type **42** 25 25
250 45c. "Ipomoea macrantha" 40 40
251 50c. "Triumfetta procumbens" 45 45
252 60c. "Portulaca quadrifida" 50 50

1984. Leaders of the World. Railway Locomotives (2nd series). As T **41**. The first design in each pair shows technical drawings and the second the locomotive at work.
253 10c. multicoloured 10 10
254 10c. multicoloured 10 10
255 15c. multicoloured 10 15
256 15c. multicoloured 10 15
257 20c. multicoloured 10 15
258 20c. multicoloured 10 15
259 25c. multicoloured 10 15
260 25c. multicoloured 10 15
261 40c. multicoloured 10 20
262 40c. multicoloured 10 20
263 50c. multicoloured 10 20
264 50c. multicoloured 10 20
265 60c. multicoloured 10 20
266 60c. multicoloured 10 20
267 $1 multicoloured 15 25
268 $1 multicoloured 15 25
DESIGNS: Nos. 253/4, Illinois Central Railroad "Casey Jones" type locomotive No. 382, U.S.A. (1896); 255/6, Erie Railroad Triplex type, U.S.A. (1914); 257/8, Class 370 Advanced Passenger Train, Great Britain (1981); 259/60, LMS Class 4F, Great Britain (1924); 261/2, GWR Class "Tornado Rover", Great Britain (1888); 263/4, Class 73 electric locomotive "Broadlands", Great Britain (1967); 265/6, "Locomotion", Great Britain (1825); 267/8, Class C57, Japan (1937).

43 Exhibition Emblem

1984. "Ausipex" International Stamp Exhibition, Melbourne. Multicoloured.
269 60c. Type **43** 20 30
270 60c. Arms of Tuvalu 20 30
271 60c. Tuvalu flag 20 30
272 60c. Royal Exhibition Building, Melbourne 20 30

1984. Leaders of the World. Railway Locomotives (3rd series). As T **41**. The first in each pair shows technical drawings and the second the locomotive at work.
273 1c. multicoloured 10 10
274 1c. multicoloured 10 10
275 15c. multicoloured 15 20
276 15c. multicoloured 15 20
277 30c. multicoloured 20 25
278 30c. multicoloured 20 25
279 $1 multicoloured 40 65
280 $1 multicoloured 40 65
DESIGNS: Nos. 273/4, Class 9700, Japan (1897); 275/6, Paris-Lyon-Mediterranee Class 231C/K, France (1909); 277/8, Class 640, Italy (1907); 279/80, Paris-Orleans Class 4500, France (1906).

44 A. Shrewsbury

1984. Leaders of the World. Cricketers. As T **44**. The first in each pair shows the cricketer in action and the second a head portrait.
281 5c. multicoloured 10 30
282 5c. multicoloured 10 30
283 30c. multicoloured 20 40
284 30c. multicoloured 20 40
285 50c. multicoloured 20 40
286 50c. multicoloured 20 40
287 60c. multicoloured 25 40
288 60c. multicoloured 25 40
DESIGNS: 281/2, A. Shrewsbury; 283/4, H. Verity; 285/6, E. H. Hendren; 287/8, J. Briggs.

45 Trees and Stars

1984. Christmas. Children's Drawings. Mult.
289 15c. Type **45** 10 10
290 40c. Fishing from outrigger canoes 20 20
291 50c. Three Wise Men bearing gifts 25 25
292 60c. The Holy Family 35 35

46 Morris Minor

1984. Leaders of the World. Automobiles (1st series). As T **46**. The first in each pair shows technical drawings and the second paintings.
293 1c. black, brown and yellow 10 10
294 1c. multicoloured 10 10
295 15c. black, pink and lilac 10 15
296 15c. multicoloured 10 15
297 50c. black, brown and mauve 20 20
298 50c. multicoloured 20 20
299 $1 black, green and blue 30 40
300 $1 multicoloured 30 40
DESIGNS: Nos. 293/4, "Morris Minor"; 295/6, Studebaker "Avanti"; 297/8, Chevrolet "International Six"; 299/300, Allard "J2".
See also Nos. 321/8, 356/71, 421/32 and 446/69.

47 Common Flicker

1985. Leaders of the World. Birth Bicentenary of John J. Audubon (ornithologist). Multicoloured.
301 1c. Type **47** 10 10
302 1c. Say's phoebe 10 10
303 25c. Townsend's warbler 20 30
304 25c. Bohemian waxwing 20 30
305 50c. Prothonotary warbler 20 50
306 50c. Worm-eating warbler 20 50
307 70c. Broad-winged hawk 30 65
308 70c. Hen harrier 30 65

48 Black-naped Tern

1985. Birds and their Eggs. Multicoloured.
309 15c. Type **48** 60 20
310 40c. White-capped noddy 1·10 50
311 50c. White-tailed tropicbird 1·10 60
312 60c. Sooty tern 1·25 70

1985. Leaders of the World. Railway Locomotives (4th series). As T **41**. The first in each pair shows technical drawings and the second the locomotive at work.
313 5c. multicoloured 10 10
314 5c. multicoloured 10 10
315 10c. multicoloured 10 10
316 10c. multicoloured 10 10
317 30c. multicoloured 30 35
318 30c. multicoloured 30 35
319 $1 multicoloured 50 80
320 $1 multicoloured 50 80
DESIGNS: Nos. 313/14, GWR "Churchward 28XX", Great Britain (1905); 315/16, Class KF No. 605, China (1935); 317/18, Class 99.77 No. 99773, Germany (1952); 319/20, Pearson type, Great Britain (1853).

1985. Leaders of the World. Automobiles (2nd series). As T **46**. The first in each pair shows technical drawings and the second paintings.
321 1c. black, green and deep green 10 10
322 1c. multicoloured 10 10
323 20c. black, pink and red 15 20
324 20c. multicoloured 15 20
325 50c. black, blue and violet 20 30
326 50c. multicoloured 20 30
327 70c. black, pink and brown 20 35
328 70c. multicoloured 20 35
DESIGNS: No. 321/2, Rickenbacker (1923); 323/4, Detroit-Electric two door brougham (1914); 325/6, Packard "Clipper" (1941); 327/8, Audi "Quattro" (1982).

49 Curtiss P-40N Warhawk

1985. World War II Aircraft. Multicoloured.
329 15c. Type **49** 2·00 1·00
330 40c. Consolidated B-24 Liberator 2·50 1·75
331 50c. Lockhead PV-1 Ventura 2·50 2·00
332 60c. Douglas C-54 2·50 2·25
MS333 110 × 108 mm. Nos. 329/32 5·00 4·00

50 Queen Elizabeth the Queen Mother

51 Guide playing Guitar

1985. Leaders of the World. Life and Times of Queen Elizabeth the Queen Mother. Various portraits.
334 **50** 5c. multicoloured 10 20
335 – 5c. multicoloured 10 20
336 – 30c. multicoloured 10 20
337 – 30c. multicoloured 10 20
338 – 60c. multicoloured 15 25
339 – 60c. multicoloured 15 25
340 – $1 multicoloured 15 40
341 – $1 multicoloured 15 40
MS342 85 × 114 mm. $1.20 mult; $1.20 mult 60 1·50
Each value issued in pairs showing a floral pattern across the bottom of the portraits which stops short of the left-hand edge on the first stamp and of the right-hand edge on the second.

1985. 75th Anniv of Girl Guide Movement. Multicoloured.
343 15c. Type **51** 15 20
344 40c. Building camp-fire 40 45
345 50c. Patrol leader with Guide flag 50 55
346 60c. Guide saluting 60 65
MS347 141 × 77 mm. Nos. 343/6 1·50 2·00

1985. Leaders of the World. Railway Locomotives (5th series). As T **41**. The first in each pair shows technical drawings and the second the locomotive at work.
348 10c. multicoloured 10 15
349 10c. multicoloured 10 15
350 40c. multicoloured 20 30
351 40c. multicoloured 20 30
352 65c. multicoloured 25 40
353 65c. multicoloured 25 40
354 $1 multicoloured 30 55
355 $1 multicoloured 30 55
DESIGNS: Nos. 348/49, LNER "Green Arrow", Great Britain (1936); 350/1, Conrail Class SD-50 diesel locomotive No. 6729, U.S.A. (1982); 352/3, "Flying Hamburger", Germany (1932); 354/5, Class 1070, Japan (1925. Dated "1908" in error).

1985. Leaders of the World. Automobiles (3rd series). As T **46**. The first in each pair shows technical drawings and the second paintings.
356 5c. black, grey and mauve 10 15
357 5c. multicoloured 10 15
358 10c. black, pink and red 10 20
359 10c. multicoloured 10 20
360 15c. black, brown and red 10 20
361 15c. multicoloured 10 20
362 35c. black, red and blue 15 30
363 35c. multicoloured 15 30
364 40c. black, light green & green 15 30
365 40c. multicoloured 15 30
366 55c. black, stone and green 15 30
367 55c. multicoloured 15 30
368 $1 black, deep brown & brown 25 40
369 $1 multicoloured 25 40
370 $1.50 black, pink and red 30 45
371 $1.50 multicoloured 30 45
DESIGNS: Nos. 356/7, Cord "L-29" (1929); 358/9, Horch "670 V-12" (1932); 360/1, Lanchester (1901); 362/3, Citroen "2 CV" (1950); 364/5, MGA (1957); 366/7, Ferrari "250 GTO" (1962); 368/9, Ford "V-8" (1932); 370/1, Aston Martin "Lagonda" (1977).

52 Stalk-eyed Ghost Crab

1986. Crabs. Multicoloured.
372 15c. Type **52** 80 90
373 40c. Red and white painted crab 1·00 1·25
374 50c. Red-spotted crab 1·00 1·75
375 60c. Red hermit crab 1·00 2·00

53 Chess Knight on Board and Flags of U.S. and U.S.S.R. (World Chess Championships)

1986. International Events. Sheet 148 × 127 mm, containing T **53** and similar vert design. Multicoloured.
MS376 $3 Type **53**; $3 Emblem (80th anniv of Rotary) 5·50 8·00

1986. Ships (3rd series). Missionary Vessels. As T **26**. Multicoloured.
377 15c. "Messenger of Peace" (schooner) 70 70
378 40c. "John Wesley" (brig) 85 1·00
379 50c. "Duff" (full-rigged ship) 85 1·25
380 60c. "Triton" (brigantine) 85 1·75

1986. 60th Birthday of Queen Elizabeth II. As T **167** of British Virgin Islands. Mult.
381 10c. Queen wearing ceremonial cloak, New Zealand, 1977 15 15
382 90c. Before visit to France, 1957 30 35
383 $1.50 Queen in 1982 45 80
384 $3 In Canberra, 1982 (vert) 60 1·50
MS385 85 × 115 mm. $4 Queen carring bouquet 3·00 6·00

54 Peace Dove carrying Wreath and Rainbow

1986. 25th Anniv of United States Peace Corps.
386 **54** 50c. multicoloured 80 1·00

55 Island and Flags of Tuvalu and U.S.A.

56 South Korean Player

1986. "Ameripex" Int Stamp Exhibition, Chicago.
387 **55** 60c. multicoloured 85 1·00

1986. World Cup Football Championship, Mexico. Multicoloured.
388 1c. Type **56** 10 10
389 5c. French player 10 10
390 10c. West German captain with World Cup trophy, 1974 10 10
391 40c. Italian player 50 50
392 60c. World Cup final, 1974 (59 × 39 mm) 65 65
393 $1 Canadian team (59 × 39 mm) 80 1·00
394 $2 Northern Irish team (59 × 39 mm) 1·25 2·00
395 $3 English team (59 × 39 mm) 1·75 3·00
MS396 Two sheets, each 85 × 114 mm. (a) $1.50 As No. 393; (b) $2.50 As No. 394 Set of 2 sheets 4·25 7·00

1986. Royal Wedding (1st issue). As T **164a** of St. Lucia. Multicoloured.
397 60c. Prince Andrew and Miss Sarah Ferguson 25 45
398 60c. Prince Andrew with prize-winning bull 25 45
399 $1 Prince Andrew at horse trials (horiz) 30 70
400 $1 Miss Sarah Ferguson and Princess Diana (horiz) 30 70
MS401 85 × 115 mm. $6 Duke and Duchess of York after wedding (horiz) 1·75 5·00
See also Nos. 433/6.

57 Mourning Gecko

1986. Lizards. Multicoloured.
402 15c. Type **57** 55 55
403 40c. Oceanic stump-toed gecko 1·00 1·00
404 50c. Azure-tailed skink 1·25 1·50
405 60c. Moth skink 1·50 2·00

1986. "Stampex '86" Stamp Exhibition, Adelaide. No. 386 optd **STAMPEX 86 ADELAIDE** and kangaroo.
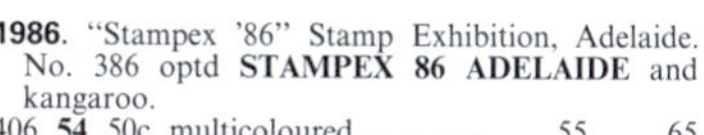
406 **54** 50c. multicoloured 55 65

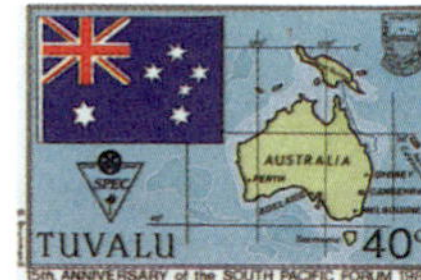

59 Map and Flag of Australia

1986. 15th Anniv of South Pacific Forum. Maps and national flags. Multicoloured.
407 40c. Type **59** 70 70
408 40c. Cook Islands 70 70
409 40c. Micronesia 70 70
410 40c. Fiji 70 70
411 40c. Kiribati 70 70
412 40c. Western Samoa 70 70
413 40c. Nauru 70 70
414 40c. Vanuatu 70 70
415 40c. New Zealand 70 70
416 40c. Tuvalu 70 70
417 40c. Tonga 70 70
418 40c. Solomon Islands 70 70
419 40c. Papua New Guinea 70 70
420 40c. Niue 70 70

1986. Automobiles (4th series). As T **46**. The first in each pair show technical drawings and the second paintings.
421 15c. multicoloured 15 15
422 15c. multicoloured 15 15
423 40c. multicoloured 20 25
424 40c. multicoloured 20 25
425 50c. multicoloured 20 30
426 50c. multicoloured 20 30
427 60c. multicoloured 20 35
428 60c. multicoloured 20 35
429 90c. multicoloured 25 35
430 90c. multicoloured 25 35
431 $1.50 multicoloured 30 45
432 $1.50 multicoloured 30 45
DESIGNS: Nos. 421/2, Copper "500" (1953); 423/4, Rover "2000" (1964); 425/6, Ruxton (1930); 427/8, Jowett "Jupiter" (1950); 429/30, Cobra "Daytona Coupe" (1964); 431/2, Packard Model F "Old Pacific" (1903).

1986. Royal Wedding (2nd issue). Nos. 397/400 optd **Congratulations to T.R.H. The Duke & Duchess of York.**
433 60c. Prince Andrew and Miss Sarah Ferguson 90 1·50
434 60c. Prince Andrew with prize-winning bull 90 1·50
435 $1 Prince Andrew at horse trials (horiz) 1·50 1·75
436 $1 Miss Sarah Ferguson and Princess Diana (horiz) 1·50 1·75

60 Sea Star

1986. Coral Reef Life (1st series). Mult.
437 15c. Type **60** 85 85
438 40c. Pencil urchin . . . . . 1·60 1·90
439 50c. Fragile coral . . . . . 1·75 2·00
440 60c. Pink coral . . . . 2·00 2·25
See also Nos. 498/501, 558/62 and 822/6.

1986. Centenary of Statue of Liberty. Vert views of Statue as T **121a** of Montserrat in separate miniature sheets. Multicoloured.
MS441 Nine sheets, each 85×115 mm. $1.25; $1.50; $1.80; $2; $2.25; $2.50; $3; $3.25; $3.50 Set of 9 sheets . . . . 6·00 9·00

1987. Ships (4th series). Missionary Steamers. As T **26**. Multicoloured.
442 15c. "Southern Cross IV" . . 1·10 1·10
443 40c. "John Williams VI" . . 2·25 2·50
444 50c. "John Williams IV" . . 2·50 2·75
445 60c. M.S. "Southern Cross" . 2·50 2·75

1987. Automobiles (5th series). As T **46**. The first in each pair shows technical drawings and the second paintings.
446 1c. multicoloured 10 10
447 1c. multicoloured 10 10
448 2c. multicoloured 10 10
449 2c. multicoloured 10 10
450 5c. multicoloured 10 10
451 5c. multicoloured 10 10
452 10c. multicoloured 15 20
453 10c. multicoloured 15 20
454 20c. multicoloured 20 25
455 20c. multicoloured 20 25
456 30c. multicoloured 25 30
457 30c. multicoloured 25 30
458 40c. multicoloured 30 35
459 40c. multicoloured 30 35
460 50c. multicoloured 30 40
461 50c. multicoloured 30 40
462 60c. multicoloured 30 40
463 60c. multicoloured 30 40
464 70c. multicoloured 30 45
465 70c. multicoloured 30 45
466 75c. multicoloured 30 45
467 75c. multicoloured 30 45
468 $1 multicoloured 40 70
469 $1 multicoloured 40 70
MS470 100×85 mm. Nos. 468/9 2·25 6·50
DESIGNS: Nos. 446/7, Talbot-Lago (1938); 448/9, Du Pont "Model G" (1930); 450/1, Riley "RM" (1950); 452/3, Chevrolet "Baby Grand" (1915); 454/5, Shelby "Mustang GT 500 KR" (1968); 456/7, Ferrari "212 Export Barchetta" (1952); 458/9, Peerless "Model 48-Six" (1912); 460/1, Sunbeam "Alpine" (1954); 462/3, Matra-Ford "MS 80" (1969); 464/5, Squire 1½ Litre (1934); 466/7, Talbot "105" (1931); 468/9, Plymouth "Model Q" (1928).

61 "Nephrolepis saligna" **62** Floral Arrangement

1987. Ferns. Multicoloured.
471 15c. Type **61** 50 65
472 40c. "Asplenium nidus" . . . 80 1·00
473 50c. "Microsorum scolopendria" . . . . 95 1·25
474 60c. "Pteris tripartita" . . . 1·10 1·50
MS475 62×62 mm. $1.50 "Psilotum nuclum" . . . . 2·25 2·50

1987. Flowers and "Fous". Designs showing either floral arrangements or "fous" (women's headdresses). Multicoloured.
476 15c. Type **62** 25 35
477 15c. "Fou" 25 35
478 40c. "Fou" 55 75
479 40c. Floral arrangement . . . 55 75
480 50c. Floral arrangement . . . 65 80
481 50c. "Fou" 65 80
482 60c. "Fou" 75 90
483 60c. Floral arrangement . . . 75 90

63 Queen Victoria, 1897 (photo by Downey)

1987. Royal Ruby Wedding and 150th Anniv of Queen Victoria's Accession.
484 **63** 40c. brown, black and green 70 55
485 – 60c. purple, black and green 85 75
486 – 80c. brown, black and blue 1·10 1·40
487 – $1 brown, black and purple 1·40 1·60
488 – $2 multicoloured . . . . . 2·00 2·75
MS489 86×101 mm. $3 black . . 2·50 4·00

DESIGNS: 60c. Wedding of Princess Elizabeth and Duke of Edinburgh, 1947; 80c. Queen, Duke of Edinburgh and Prince Charles, 1950; $1 Queen with Princess Anne, 1950; $2 Queen Elizabeth II, 1970; $3 Queen and Prince Charles at Princess Anne's christening, 1950.

64 Coconut Crab

1987. Crustaceans. Multicoloured.
490 40c. Type **64** . . . . 1·00 1·25
491 50c. Painted crayfish . . . . 1·25 1·50
492 60c. Ocean crayfish . . . . . 1·40 1·75

65 Aborigine and Ayers Rock

1987. World Scout Jamboree, Australia, and Bicent of Australian Settlement. Multicoloured.
493 40c. Type **65** 30 45
494 60c. Capt. Cook and H.M.S. "Endeavour" 70 90
495 $1 Scout saluting and Scout Park entrance 70 95
496 $1.50 Koala and kangaroo 80 1·25
MS497 115×85 mm. $2.50 Lord and Lady Baden Powell . . . . . 2·00 3·25

1988. Coral Reef Life (2nd series). As T **60**. Multicoloured.
498 15c. Spanish dancer 85 85
499 40c. Hard corals . . . . . . 1·00 1·40
500 50c. Feather stars . . . . . 1·00 1·60
501 60c. Staghorn corals . . . . 1·00 1·60

66 Red Junglefowl

1988. Birds. Multicoloured.
502 5c. Type **66** 10 15
503 10c. White tern 10 20
504 15c. Common noddy 15 20
505 20c. Phoenix petrel 20 40
506 25c. Pacific golden plover . . 20 45
507 30c. Crested tern 25 45
508 35c. Sooty tern 25 50
509 40c. Bristle-thighed curlew . . 25 40
510 45c. Bar-tailed godwit ("Eastern Bar-tailed Godwit") 25 45
511 50c. Eastern reef heron . . . 25 50
512 55c. Great frigate bird ("Greater Frigate-bird") . . . 30 70
513 60c. Red-footed booby . . . 30 75
514 70c. Rufous-necked sandpiper ("Red-necked Stint") . . . 30 1·00
515 $1 Long-tailed koel ("New Zealand Long-tailed Cuckoo") . . . . 30 1·50
516 $2 Red-tailed tropic bird . . 35 3·00
517 $5 Buff-banded rail ("Banded Rail") . . . . 65 6·00

67 Henri Dunant (founder)

69 "Ganoderma applanatum"

68 H.M.S. "Endeavour"

1988. 125th Anniv of International Red Cross.
518 **67** 15c. red and brown 10 20
519 – 40c. red and blue 20 40
520 – 50c. red and green 25 50
521 – 60c. red and purple 35 70
MS522 96×66 mm. $1.50 red and green . . . . 90 2·50
DESIGNS: 40c. Junior Red Cross members on parade; 50c. Red Cross worker with boy in wheelchair; 60c. First aid training; $1.50, Lecture.

1988. Voyages of Captain Cook. Multicoloured.
523 20c. Type **68** 70 80
524 40c. Stern of H.M.S. "Endeavour" . . . . 80 1·10
525 50c. Cook preparing to land at Tahiti (vert) . . . . . 90 1·25
526 60c. Maori chief (vert) . . . 90 1·40
527 80c. H.M.S. "Resolution" and Hawaiian canoe . . . 90 1·75
528 $1 "Captain Cook" (after Nathaniel Dance) (vert) . . 1·10 1·90
MS529 115×85 mm. $2.50 H.M.S. "Resolution" in Antarctic . . . 6·00 8·00

1988. Fungi (1st series). Multicoloured.
530 40c. Type **69** . . . . 80 1·40
531 50c. "Pseudoepicoccum cocos" (brown leaf spot) 90 1·50
532 60c. "Rigidoporus lineatus" ("Rigidoporus zonalis") . . 1·00 1·75
533 90c. "Rigidoporus microporus" . . . . 1·10 2·00
See also Nos. 554/7.

70 Rifle-shooting

1988. Olympic Games, Seoul. Multicoloured.
534 10c. Type **70** 35 65
535 20c. Judo 45 70
536 40c. Canoeing 70 90
537 60c. Swimming . . . . . . 90 1·25
538 80c. Sailing . . . . 1·10 1·75
539 $1 Gymnastics . . . . 1·40 1·75

71 Queen Elizabeth II in Ceremonial Canoe

1988. 10th Anniv of Independence.
540 **71** 60c. multicoloured 60 70
541 – 90c. multicoloured . . . . 90 1·10
542 – $1 multicoloured (horiz) . . 1·00 1·40
543 – $1.20 multicoloured . . . 1·25 1·75
MS544 Designs as Nos. 540/3 in separate miniature sheets, each 85×85 mm. Set of 4 sheets . . . 3·50 5·00
DESIGNS: 90c. to $1.20, Scenes from Royal Visit of 1982.

72 Virgin Mary

1988. Christmas. Multicoloured.
545 15c. Type **72** 55 55
546 40c. Christ Child 90 80
547 60c. Joseph . . . . 1·10 1·75
MS548 73×99 mm. $1.50 Angel 1·75 2·50

73 Dancing Skirt and Dancer

1989. Traditional Dancing Skirts. Designs showing skirts and dancer silhouettes.
549 **73** 40c. multicoloured 70 90
550 – 50c. multicoloured . . . . 80 1·00
551 – 60c. multicoloured . . . . 90 1·25
552 – 90c. multicoloured . . . . 1·40 1·75
MS553 110×75 mm. $1.50 multicoloured (dancer) (vert) 3·75 5·00

1989. Fungi (2nd series). As T **69**. Multicoloured.
554 40c. "Trametes marianna" ("Trametes muelleri") . . . 1·75 1·75
555 50c. "Pestalotiopsis palmarum" (grey leaf spot) 1·90 1·90
556 60c. "Trametes cingulata" . . 2·00 2·00
557 90c. "Schizophyllum commune" . . . . 2·75 2·75

1989. Coral Reef Life (3rd series). As T **60**. Multicoloured.
558 40c. Pennant coralfish . . . 1·75 1·75
559 50c. Orange-finned anemonefish . . . . . . 2·00 2·00
560 60c. Narrow-banned batfish 2·25 2·25
561 90c. Thread-finned butterflyfish . . . . 2·75 2·75
MS562 110×85 mm. Nos. 558/61 8·00 9·00

74 "Nivaga II"

1989. Delivery of "Nivaga II" (new inter-island ship). Sheet 116×85 mm.
MS563 **74** $1.50 multicoloured 4·00 5·50

75 Trumpet Triton Shell

76 "Cocus nucifera"

1989. Christmas. Multicoloured.
564 40c. Type **75** 85 85
565 50c. Posy of flowers . . . . 1·00 1·00
566 60c. Germinating coconut . . 1·25 1·25
567 90c. Jewellery . . . . 2·25 2·75

1990. Tropical Trees. Multicoloured.
568 15c. Type **76** 80 80
569 30c. "Rhizophora samoensis" 1·25 1·25
570 40c. "Messerschmidia argentea" . . . . 1·40 1·40
571 50c. "Pandanus tectorius" . . 1·60 1·75
572 60c. "Hernandia nymphaeifolia" . . . . . 1·75 1·90
573 90c. "Pisonia grandis" . . . 2·25 2·75

77 Penny Black with "Stamp World London 90" Emblem

1990. 150th Anniv of the Penny Black, and "Stamp World London 90" International Stamp Exhibition.
574 **77** 15c. multicoloured . . . . 1·50 1·50
575 40c. multicoloured . . . . 2·75 2·75
576 90c. multicoloured . . . . 4·50 5·00
MS577 115×85 mm. **77** $2 multicoloured . . . . 7·00 8·50

78 Japanese Camouflaged Freighter

1990. Second World War Ships (1st series). Multicoloured.

No.	Description	Mint	Used
578	15c. Type **78**	1·25	1·25
579	30c. U.S.S. "Unimack" (seaplane tender)	1·75	1·75
580	40c. "Amagiri" (Japanese destroyer)	1·90	1·90
581	50c. U.S.S. "Platte" (attack transport)	2·00	2·00
582	60c. Japanese "Shumushu" Class escort	2·25	2·25
583	90c. U.S.S. "Independence" (aircraft carrier)	3·00	3·00

See also Nos. 613/16.

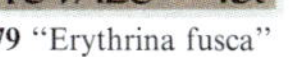

79 "Erythrina fusca"

81 Mary and Joseph travelling to Bethlehem

80 Land Resources Survey

1990. Flowers. Multicoloured.

No.	Description	Mint	Used
584	15c. Type **79**	30	50
585	30c. "Capparis cordifolia"	50	70
586	40c. "Portulaca pilosa"	60	80
587	50c. "Cordia subcordata"	75	90
588	60c. "Scaevola taccada"	80	1·00
589	90c. "Suriana maritima"	1·25	2·00

1990. 40th Anniv of United Nations Development Programme. Multicoloured.

No.	Description	Mint	Used
590	40c. Type **80**	80	80
591	60c. Satellite earth station	1·50	1·50
592	$1.20 "Te Tautai" (trawler)	3·25	4·25

1990. Christmas. Multicoloured.

No.	Description	Mint	Used
593	15c. Type **81**	55	55
594	40c. The Nativity	1·00	1·00
595	60c. Shepherds with flock	1·50	1·50
596	90c. Wise Men bearing gifts	2·00	2·50

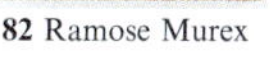
82 Ramose Murex

84 Green Turtle

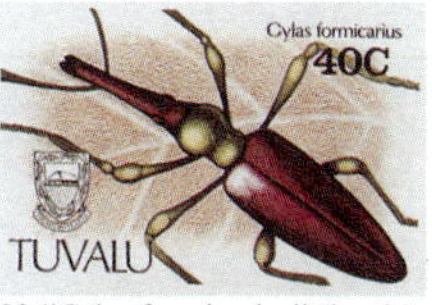

83 "Cylas formicarius" (beetle)

1991. Sea Shells. Multicoloured.

No.	Description	Mint	Used
597	40c. Type **82**	1·50	1·50
598	50c. Marble cone	1·60	1·60
599	60c. Commercial trochus	1·75	1·75
600	$1.50 Green map cowrie	3·50	4·00

1991. Insects. Multicoloured.

No.	Description	Mint	Used
601	40c. Type **83**	2·25	1·60
602	50c. "Heliothis armiger" (moth)	2·50	1·75
603	60c. "Spodoptera litura" (moth)	2·75	2·00
604	$1.50 "Agrius convolvuli" (moth)	7·00	8·50

1991. Endangered Marine Life. Multicoloured.

No.	Description	Mint	Used
605	40c. Type **84**	1·75	1·25
606	50c. Humpback whale	2·25	1·50
607	60c. Hawksbill turtle	2·25	1·60
608	$1.50 Sperm whale	5·00	6·50

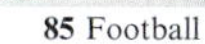

85 Football

87 Traditional Dancers

86 U.S.S. "Tennessee" (battleship)

1991. 9th South Pacific Games. Multicoloured.

No.	Description	Mint	Used
609	40c. Type **85**	1·75	1·25
610	50c. Volleyball	2·25	1·75
611	60c. Lawn tennis	3·50	2·50
612	$1.50 Cricket	7·50	8·00

1991. Second World War Ships (2nd series). Multicoloured.

No.	Description	Mint	Used
613	40c. Type **86**	2·50	2·00
614	50c. "Haguro" (Japanese cruiser)	2·75	2·00
615	60c. H.M.N.Z.S. "Achilles" (cruiser)	3·00	2·50
616	$1.50 U.S.S. "North Carolina" (battleship)	6·25	8·00

1991. Christmas. Multicoloured.

No.	Description	Mint	Used
617	40c. Type **87**	1·75	1·25
618	50c. Solo dancer	2·00	1·50
619	60c. Dancers in green costumes	2·50	1·75
620	$1.50 Dancers in multicoloured costumes	5·00	7·00

88 Southern Fish Constellation

1992. Pacific Star Constellations. Mult.

No.	Description	Mint	Used
621	40c. Type **88**	2·00	1·75
622	50c. Scorpion	2·25	1·75
623	60c. Archer	2·75	2·25
624	$1.50 Southern Cross	6·00	7·00

89 King George VI and Cargo Liner

1992. Cent of British Occupation of Tuvalu. Mult.

No.	Description	Mint	Used
625	40c. Type **89**	2·25	2·00
626	50c. King George V and freighter with barges at wharf	2·50	2·00
627	60c. King Edward VII and freighter	2·75	2·25
628	$1.50 Queen Victoria and warship	5·00	6·50

90 Columbus with King Ferdinand and Queen Isabella of Spain

1992. 500th Anniv of Discovery of America by Columbus.

No.	Description	Mint	Used
629 **90**	40c. blue and black	70	80
630 –	50c. purple and black	80	90
631 –	60c. green and black	90	1·10
632 –	$1.50 purple and black	2·25	3·50

DESIGNS: 50c. Columbus and Polynesians; 60c. Columbus and South American Indians; $1.50, Columbus and North American Indians.

91 Blue-spotted Butterflyfish

1992. Fishes. Multicoloured.

No.	Description	Mint	Used
633	15c. Type **91**	40	40
634	20c. Bridled parrotfish	45	40
635	25c. Clown surgeonfish	45	50
636	30c. Moon wrasse	55	50
637	35c. Harlequin filefish	60	50
638	40c. Bird wrasse	70	50
639	45c. Black-finned pigfish	75	50
640	50c. Blue damselfish	80	60
641	60c. Hump-headed wrasse	90	70
642	70c. Ornate butterflyfish (vert)	1·00	1·25
643	90c. Saddle butterflyfish (vert)	1·25	1·50
644	$1 Vagabond butterflyfish (vert)	1·40	1·60
645	$2 Pennant coralfish (vert)	2·25	3·00
646	$3 Moorish idol (vert)	3·00	4·00

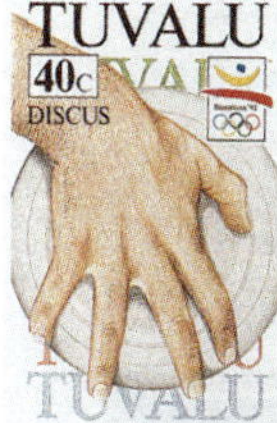
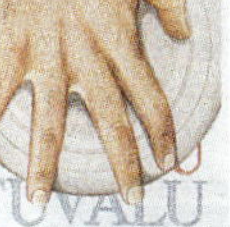

92 Discus Throwing

95 Fishermen and Angel

93 Blue Coral

1992. Olympic Games, Barcelona. Mult.

No.	Description	Mint	Used
647	40c. Type **92**	1·25	1·00
648	50c. Javelin throwing	1·50	1·25
649	60c. Shotput	1·75	1·50
650	$1.50 Competitor's foot	3·25	4·50
MS651	100 × 71 mm. $2 Olympic stadium, Barcelona	4·25	5·00

1992. Endangered Species. Blue Coral.

No.	Description	Mint	Used
652 **93**	10c. multicoloured	1·00	1·00
653 –	25c. multicoloured	2·00	2·00
654 –	30c. multicoloured	2·00	2·00
655 –	35c. multicoloured	2·25	2·25

DESIGNS: 25c. to 35c. Different coral formations.

1992. "Kuala Lumpur '92" International Philatelic Exhibition. Nos. 636, 638 and 640/1 optd **KL92 KUALA LUMPUR '92** and emblem.

No.	Description	Mint	Used
656	30c. Moon wrasse	1·60	1·60
657	40c. Bird wrasse	1·75	1·75
658	50c. Blue damselfish	2·00	2·00
659	60c. Hump-headed wrasse	2·00	2·00

1992. Christmas. Multicoloured.

No.	Description	Mint	Used
660	40c. Type **95**	90	70
661	50c. Fishing canoes following star	1·00	80
662	60c. Nativity scene	1·25	1·00
663	$1.50 Christmas gifts	2·25	3·25

96 "Calophyllum inophyllum"

1993. Flowers. Multicoloured.

No.	Description	Mint	Used
664	40c. Type **96**	30	35
665	50c. "Hibiscus tiliaceus"	35	40
666	60c. "Lantana camara"	40	45
667	$1.50 "Plumeria rubra"	1·10	1·25

97 Japanese Nakajima B5N "Kate" Bombers attacking Island

1993. 50th Anniv of War in the Pacific. Mult.

No.	Description	Mint	Used
668	40c. Type **97**	30	35
669	50c. Japanese anti-aircraft gun (vert)	35	40
670	60c. American troops storming beach	40	45
671	$1.50 Map of Funafuti Atoll (vert)	1·10	1·25

98 "Cepora perimale"

1993. "Indopex '93" International Stamp Exhibition", Surabaya, Indonesia. Sheet 81 × 111 mm.

No.	Description	Mint	Used
MS672 **98**	$1.50 multicoloured	1·10	1·25

99 Fluted Giant Clam

1993. Marine Life. Multicoloured.

No.	Description	Mint	Used
673	40c. Type **99**	30	35
674	50c. Anemone crab	35	40
675	60c. Octopus	40	45
676	$1.50 Green turtle	1·10	1·25

100 Queen Elizabeth II and Prince Philip in Land Rover

1993. 40th Anniv of Coronation.

No.	Description	Mint	Used
677 **100**	40c. multicoloured	30	35
678 –	50c. multicoloured	35	40
679 –	60c. multicoloured	40	45
680 –	$1.50 multicoloured	1·10	1·25
MS681	88 × 88 mm. $2 green, yellow and black	1·50	1·60

DESIGNS: 50c. Queen Elizabeth drinking kava; 60c. Queen Elizabeth with parasol; $1.50, Ceremonial welcome; $2 Crowning of Queen Elizabeth II, 1953.

1993. "Taipei '93" International Stamp Exhibition, Taiwan. Sheet, 85 × 85 mm, containing multicoloured design as T **98**.

No.	Description	Mint	Used
MS682	$1.50, "Geoffroyi godart" (vert)	1·10	1·25

1993. "Bangkok 1993" International Stamp Exhibition, Thailand. Sheet, 86 × 86 mm, containing horiz design as T **98**.

No.	Description	Mint	Used
MS683	$1.50 "Paradisea staudinger"	1·10	1·25

101 Hermit Crab and Shells on Beach

102 Virgin and Child with Christmas Tree

1993. Environmental Protection. Mult.

No.	Description	Mint	Used
684	40c. Type **101**	30	35
685	50c. Conch shell and starfish	35	40
686	60c. Crab, seaweed and shells	40	45
687	$1.50 Herring gull and human footprint on beach	1·10	1·25
MS688	126 × 80 mm. Nos. 684/7	2·10	2·50

1993. Christmas. Multicoloured.

No.	Description	Mint	Used
689	40c. Type **102**	30	35
690	50c. Candle	35	40
691	60c. Angel	40	45
692	$1.50 Decorated palm tree	1·10	1·25

1994. "Hong Kong '94" International Stamp Exhibition. Sheet 85 × 85 mm containing multicoloured design as T 98.

No.	Description	Mint	Used
MS693	$2 "Danaus plexippus" (vert)	1·50	1·60

103 Beach

1994. Island Scenery. Multicoloured.
694 40c. Type **103** 30 35
695 50c. Lagoon 35 40
696 60c. Distant island 40 45
697 $1.50 Launch and outrigger canoes on beach . . . . . 1·10 1·25

104 Irish Red Setter

105 World Cup, Australian Player and Sydney Opera House

1994. Chinese New Year ("Year of the Dog"). Multicoloured.
698 40c. Type **104** 30 35
699 50c. Golden retriever 35 40
700 60c. West Highland terrier . . 40 45
701 $1.50 German shepherd . . . 1·10 1·25

1994. World Cup Football Championship, U.S.A. Multicoloured.
702 40c. Type **105** 30 35
703 50c. English player and Big Ben, London 35 40
704 60c. Argentinian player and House of Assembly, Buenos Aires 40 45
705 $1.50 German player and Brandenburg Gate, Berlin 1·10 1·25
MS706 105 × 99 mm. $2 American player and Statue of Liberty, New York . . . . 1·50 1·60

106 Giant Button Top

107 Pekingese and Logo

1994. Sea Snails. Multicoloured.
707 40c. Type **106** 30 35
708 50c. Tapestry turban 35 40
709 60c. "Planaxis savignyi" . . . 40 45
710 $1.50 Green-lined paper bubble . . . . 1·10 1·25

1994. "Philakorea '94" International Stamp Exhibition, Seoul. Sheet 106 × 72 mm.
MS711 **107** $1.50 multicoloured 1·10 1·25

1994. "Singpex '94" Stamp Exhibition. Nos. 502/3 and 509/10 optd **SINGPEX '94 AUG 31-SEP 5 SINGAPORE** and emblem.
712 5c. Type **66** 10 10
713 10c. White tern 10 10
714 40c. Bristle-thighed curlew . . 30 35
715 45c. Bar-tailed godwit . . . 30 35

109 "Saturn V" Launch

1994. 25th Anniv of First Manned Moon Landing. Multicoloured.
716 40c. Type **109** 30 35
717 50c. "Apollo 11" capsule . . 35 40
718 60c. Neil Armstrong and American flag 40 45
719 $1.50 Capsule re-entry . . . 1·10 1·25

110 Boys swimming with Log

1994. Christmas. Local Customs. Multicoloured.
720 40c. Type **110** 30 35
721 50c. Fishermen landing catch 35 40
722 60c. Christmas dinner 40 45
723 $1.50 Traditional dancers . . 1·10 1·25

111 Pig asleep

1995. Chinese New Year ("Year of the Pig"). Multicoloured.
724 40c. Type **111** 30 35
725 50c. Two pigs and vegetation 35 40
726 60c. Three pigs 40 45
727 $1.50 Sow suckling piglets . . 1·10 1·25

112 Emblem and Man with Produce in Wheelbarrow

1995. 50th Anniv of F.A.O. Multicoloured.
728 40c. Type **112** 30 35
729 50c. Man holding basket of food 35 40
730 60c. Woman slicing produce 40 45
731 $1.50 Woman mixing food 1·10 1·25

113 Beach and Lagoon

1995. Visit South Pacific Year. Multicoloured.
732 40c. Type **113** 30 35
733 50c. Catamaran 35 40
734 60c. Traditional hut 40 45
735 $1.50 Village on beach . . . 1·10 1·25

114 "Dendrobium comptonii"

1995. Pacific Coastal Orchids. Multicoloured.
736 40c. Type **114** 30 35
737 50c. "Dendrobium involutum" 35 40
738 60c. "Dendrobium rarum" 40 45
739 $1.50 "Grammatophyllum scriptum" . . . . 1·10 1·25

115 Japanese Soldier and Maps of Tuvalu and Japan

1995. 50th Anniv of End of Second World War. Multicoloured.
740 40c. Type **115** 30 35
741 50c. American soldier and beach landing 35 40
742 60c. American marine and tree 40 45
743 $1.50 American soldier and atomic explosion . . . . . 1·10 1·25

116 Tuvalu Dancer

1995. "JAKARTA '95" Stamp Exhibition, Indonesia. Sheet 85 × 85 mm.
MS744 **116** $1 multicoloured . . 75 80

117 "Phalaenopsis amabilis"

118 Tuvaluans in Outrigger Canoes

1995. "Singapore '95" International Stamp Exhibition. Sheet 85 × 85 mm.
MS745 **117** $1 multicoloured . . 75 80

1995. 50th Anniv of United Nations. Sheet 83 × 70 mm, containing T **118** and similar vert design. Multicoloured.
MS746 $1 Type **118**; $1 U.N. headquarters, New York . . . 75 80

119 "Silent Night" and Aerial View of Airfield

1995. Christmas. Christmas Carols. Multicoloured.
747 40c. Type **119** 30 35
748 50c. "O Come all ye Faithful" and choir boys 35 40
749 60c. "The First Nowell" and choir girls 40 45
750 $1.50 "Hark the Herald Angels sing" and angel . . 1·10 1·25

120 1976 Separation 4c. Stamp

1996. 20th Anniv of Separation from Gilbert Islands and of First Tuvalu Postage Stamps. Sheet 108 × 82 mm, containing T **120** and similar horiz designs showing values from 1976 Separation issue.
MS751 40c. Type **120**; 60c. 1976 10c. stamp; $1 1976 35c. stamp . . 1·50 1·60

121 Rat with Jar

1996. Chinese New Year ("Year of the Rat"). Sheet 130 × 87 mm containing T **121** and similar vert design. Multicoloured.
MS752 50c. Type **121**; 50c. Rat drinking from jar 70 75

1996. "HONGPEX '96" International Stamp Exhibition. Sheet as No. **MS**752, but additionally inscr with "HONGPEX '96" emblem on sheet margin.
MS753 50c. Type **121**; 50c. Rat drinking from jar . . . . . . 1·10 1·40

1996. "indonesia 96" International Youth Stamp Exhibition, Bandung. No. **MS**744 optd **indonesia 96**.
MS754 85 × 85 mm. **116** $1 multicoloured . . . . 1·60 1·90

1996. "CHINA '96" 9th Asian International Stamp Exhibition, Peking. Sheet as No. **MS**752, but additionally inscr with "CHINA '96" emblem and puppet holding envelope on sheet margin.
MS755 50c. Type **121**; 50c. Rat drinking from jar . . . . . . 1·10 1·40

123 Volleyball

1996. Olympic Games, Atlanta. Multicoloured.
756 40c. Type **123** 30 35
757 50c. Swimming 35 40
758 60c. Weightlifting 40 45
759 $1.50 Boxing . . . . 1·10 1·25

1996. "TAIPEI '96" 10th Asian International Stamp Exhibition, Taiwan. No. 639 surch **$1.00 TAIPEI '96 21-27 OCTOBER** and emblem.
760 $1 on 45c. Black-finned pigfish 70 75

125 Children being immunized

1996. 50th Anniv of U.N.I.C.E.F. Multicoloured.
761 40c. Type **125** 30 35
762 50c. Teacher and children . . 35 40
763 60c. Domestic water tanks and child 40 45
764 $1.50 Children in hydroponic greenhouse . . . . 1·10 1·25

126 Wise Men following Star

1996. Christmas. Multicoloured.
765 40c. Type **126** 30 35
766 50c. Shepherds and star . . . 35 40
767 60c. Wise men presenting gifts 40 45
768 $1.50 The Nativity . . . . . 1·10 1·25

1997. Fishes (2nd series). As T **14**. Multicoloured.
770 25c. Sehel's grey mullet . . . 20 25
771 30c. Leatherback 20 25
772 40c. Hump-backed snapper ("Paddletail") 30 35
773 45c. Long-nosed emperor . . 30 35
774 50c. Blue-spined unicornfish 35 40
775 55c. Oblique-banded snapper 40 45
776 60c. Twin-spotted snapper ("Red bass") 40 45
777 70c. Rusty jobfish 50 55
778 90c. Leopard flounder . . . 65 70
779 $1 Ruby snapper 70 75
780 $2 Yellow-striped snapper . . 1·40 1·50
781 $3 Black jack . . . . 2·10 2·25

128 White Pekin Ducks

1997. "Pacific '97" International Stamp Exhibition, San Francisco. Ducks. Multicoloured.
782 40c. Type **128** 30 35
783 50c. Muscovy ducks 35 40
784 60c. Pacific black ducks . . . 40 45
785 $1.50 Mandarin ducks . . . 1·10 1·25

129 Korat King Cat

1997. Cats. Multicoloured.
786 40c. Type **129** 30 35
787 50c. Long-haired ginger kitten 35 40
788 60c. Shaded cameo 40 45
789 $1.50 Maine coon . . . . . 1·10 1·25

1997. Return of Hong Kong to China. Sheet, 130 × 90 mm, containing design as No. 780.
MS790 $2 Yellow-striped snapper 1·40 1·50

1997. Golden Wedding of Queen Elizabeth and Prince Philip. As T **87** of Kiribati. Multicoloured.
791 40c. Queen Elizabeth and Prince Philip in Land Rover 30 35
792 40c. Queen Elizabeth 30 35
793 50c. Queen Elizabeth accepting ceremonial gift 35 40
794 50c. Prince Philip 35 40

795 60c. Three portraits of Queen Elizabeth 40 45
796 60c. Queen Elizabeth and Prince Philip leaving Philatelic Bureau 40 45
MS797 110 × 70 mm. $2 Queen Elizabeth and Prince Philip in landau (horiz) . . . . 1·50 1·60

Nos. 791/2, 793/4 and 795/6 respectively were printed together, se-tenant, with the backgrounds forming composite designs.

130 Turtle Hunting

1997. Christmas. Multicoloured.
798 40c. Type **130** 30 35
799 50c. Pole fishing 35 40
800 60c. Canoe racing 40 45
801 $1.50 Traditional dancing . . 1·10 1·25

131 Tiger

1998. Chinese New Year ("Year of the Tiger"). Sheet 110 × 69 mm.
MS802 **131** $1.40 multicoloured 1·00 1·10

1998. Diana, Princess of Wales Commemoration. Sheet, 145 × 70 mm, containing vert designs as T **91** of Kiribati. Multicoloured.
MS803 80c. Wearing pearl drop earrings, 1990; 80c. Wearing black evening dress, 1995; 80c. Wearing tiara, 1992; 80c. Wearing beige coat (sold at $3.20 + 20c. charity premium) . . . . 2·40 2·50

1998. 80th Anniv of the Royal Air Force. As T **270** of Samoa. Multicoloured.
804 40c. Hawker Woodcock . . . 30 35
805 50c. Vickers Victoria 35 40
806 60c. Bristol Brigand 40 45
807 $1.50 De Havilland D.H.C.1 Chipmunk . . . . . . 1·10 1·25
MS808 110 × 77 mm. $1 Sopwith Pup; $1 Armstrong Whitworth F.K.8; $1 North American Harvard; $1 Vultee Vengeance 3·00 3·25

132 "Los Reyes" and "Santiago" (Alvare Mendana)

1998. Ships (5th series). Multicoloured.
809 40c. Type **132** 30 35
810 50c. "Morning Star II" (missionary schooner) . . . 35 40
811 60c. "The Light" (missionary brigantine) 40 45
812 $1.50 New Zealand missionary schooner . . . 1·10 1·25

133 Bottlenose Dolphin

1998. Dolphins and Porpoises. Multicoloured.
813 40c. Type **133** 30 35
814 50c. Dall's porpoise 35 40
815 60c. Harbour porpoise . . . 40 45
816 $1.50 Common dolphin . . . 1·10 1·25

134 Bikenibeu Paeniu, Teacher and Class

1998. 20th Anniv of Independence. Prime Ministers of Tuvalu. Multicoloured.
817 40c. Type **134** 30 35
818 60c. Kamuta Latasi and diagram of communications network 40 45
819 90c. Sir Tomasi Puapua and emblem of Trust Fund . . 65 70
820 $1.50 Sir Toaripi Lauti and emblem of Maritime School . . . . 1·10 1·25
MS821 115 × 81 mm. Nos. 817/20 2·50 2·75

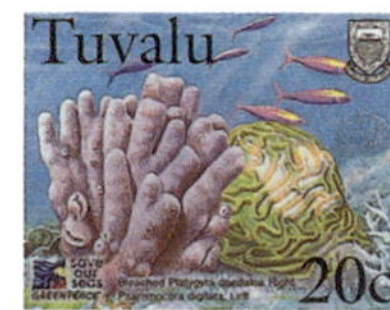

135 "Psammocra digitata" and Bleached "Platygyra daedalea"

1998. Coral Reef Life (4th series). Multicoloured.
822 20c. Type **135** 15 20
823 30c. Bleached "Acropora robusta" 20 25
824 50c. Bleached "Acropora hyacinthus" 35 40
825 $1 Bleached "Acropora danai" and "Montastrea curta" 70 75
MS826 74 × 54 mm. $1.50, Bleached "Seriatopora" and Bleached "Stylophora" . . . . 1·10 1·25

136 Mary and Joseph travelling to Bethlehem

1998. Christmas. Multicoloured.
827 40c. Type **136** 30 35
828 50c. Shepherds and angel . . 35 40
829 60c. The Nativity 40 45
830 $1.50 Visit of Wise Men . . 1·10 1·25

137 Rabbit playing Pipa and Chinese Lantern

1999. Chinese New Year ("Year of the Rabbit"). Sheet 115 × 75 mm.
MS831 **137** $2 multicoloured . . 1·50 1·60

138 "Heemskerk" (Tasman), 1642

1999. "Australia '99" World Stamp Exhibition, Melbourne. Ships (6th series). Multicoloured.
832 40c. Type **138** 30 35
833 50c. H.M.S. "Endeavour" (Cook), 1769 . . . . . . 35 40
834 90c. "Sophia Jane" (paddle-steamer), 1831 . . . . . . 65 70
835 $1.50 "Chusan I" (screw steamer), 1852 . . . . . 1·10 1·25
MS836 135 × 75 mm. $2 H.M.S. "Supply" (brig), 1788 . . . . 1·50 1·60

1999. Kosovo Relief Campaign. Nos. 505, 508, 512 and 515 optd **Kosovo Relief Fund**.
837 20c. Phoenix petrel 40 60
838 35c. Sooty tern 60 70
839 55c. Great frigate bird . . . 80 90
840 $1 Long-tailed koel . . . . . 1·25 1·50

1999. 30th Anniv of the First Manned Landing on Moon. As T **94a** of St. Kitts. Multicoloured.
841 40c. Lift-off 30 35
842 60c. Lander approaches Moon 40 45
843 90c. Lander leaving Moon . . 65 70
844 $1.50 Crew recovery . . . . 1·10 1·25
MS845 90 × 80 mm. $2 Earth as seen from Moon (circular, 40 mm diameter) . . . . 1·50 1·60

1999. "Queen Elizabeth the Queen Mother's Century". As T **199** of St. Helena. Multicoloured.
846 40c. King George VI and Queen Elizabeth inspecting bomb damage, 1940 . . . 30 35
847 60c. Queen Elizabeth with her daughters, 1951 . . . . . 40 45
848 90c. With Princes William and Harry, 1995 . . . . . 65 70
849 $1.50 Inspecting the Queen's Dragoon Guards . . . . . 1·10 1·25
MS850 145 × 70 mm. $2 Lady Elizabeth Bowes-Lyon aged 6, and Yuri Gagarin (first cosmonaut) 1·50 1·60

140 "Solandra maxima" (flower)

1999. Flowers. Multicoloured.
851 90c. Type **140** 65 70
852 90c. "Cistus" sp. 65 70
853 90c. "Pandorea jasminoides" 65 70
854 90c. "Grewia caffra" 65 70
855 90c. "Mandevilla x amabilis" 65 70
856 90c. "Punica granatum" (open flowers) 65 70
857 90c. "Cassytha filiformis" . . 65 70
858 90c. "Wollastonia biflora" . . 65 70
859 90c. "Portulacacae lueta" (without local inscr) . . . 65 70
860 90c. "Portulacacae lueta" (also inscr "TAMOLOC") 65 70
861 90c. "Vigna marina" 65 70
862 90c. "Punica granatum" (closed flowers) 65 70
MS863 97 × 104 mm. $3 "Cassia surattensis" (vert) . . . . . 2·25 2·40

No. MS863 is inscribed "SCRAMBLED EGGES" in error.

Nos. 851/6 and 857/62 were each printed together, se-tenant, with the backgrounds forming composite designs.

141 Lady of Peace

1999. New Millennium. Allegories of Peace. Mult.
864 90c. Type **141** 65 70
865 90c. Olive branch 65 70
866 90c. Dove 65 70
867 90c. Lion 65 70
868 90c. Lamb 65 70
869 90c. Cherub with bouquet ("War crowning Peace") 65 70
870 90c. As Type **142**, but with white frame 65 70
MS871 94 × 75 mm. $2 Sunrise and "2000" (46 × 28 mm). . . . . 1·50 1·60

Nos. 864/9 were printed together, se-tenant, forming a composite design.

142 Sand Tiger Shark showing Teeth

2000. Endangered Species. Sand Tiger Shark. Mult.
872 10c. Type **142** 10 10
873 30c. Sand tiger shark swimming 20 25
874 50c. Sand tiger shark over seaweed 35 40
875 60c. Group of sand tiger sharks 40 45
MS876 207 × 135 mm. As Nos. 872/5, but without WWF pander emblem . . . . 1·00 1·10

143 Chevron Butterflyfish

2000. Marine Life. Multicoloured.
877 90c. Type **143** 65 70
878 90c. Mandarin fish 65 70
879 90c. Bicoloured angelfish . . 65 70
880 90c. Copper-banded butterflyfish 65 70
881 90c. Clown anemonefish . . 65 70
882 90c. Lemon-peel angelfish . . 65 70
883 90c. Manta ray 65 70
884 90c. White shark 65 70
885 90c. Hammerhead shark . . 65 70
886 90c. Tiger shark 65 70
887 90c. Great barracuda 65 70
888 90c. Leatherback turtle . . . 65 70
889 90c. Common tern 65 70
890 90c. Red-billed tropic bird ("White-tailed Tropicbird") 65 70
891 90c. Emperor snapper . . . 65 70
892 90c. Clown triggerfish . . . 65 70
893 90c. Pennant coralfish ("Longfin Bannerfish") . . 65 70
894 90c. Harlequin tuskfish . . . 65 70
895 90c. Wilson's storm petrel . . 65 70
896 90c. Common dolphin . . . 65 70
897 90c. Yellow seahorse ("Spotted Seahorse") . . . 65 70
898 90c. Threeband demoiselle . . 65 70
899 90c. Coral hind 65 70
900 90c. Palette surgeonfish . . . 65 70
901 90c. Great frigatebird 65 70
902 90c. Brown booby 65 70
903 90c. Dugong 65 70
904 90c. Red knot 65 70
905 90c. Common starfish 65 70
906 90c. Hawksbill turtle 65 70
907 90c. Whale shark 65 70
908 90c. Six-blotched hind ("Sixspot Grouper") . . . 65 70
909 90c. Blue-streaked cleaner wrasse 65 70
910 90c. Lemon shark 65 70
911 90c. Spotted boxfish ("Spotted Trunkfish") . . 65 70
912 90c. Forceps butterflyfish ("Long-nosed Butterflyfish") 65 70
MS913 Three sheets, each 103 × 73 mm. (a) $3 Pygmy parrotfish. (b) $3 Picasso triggerfish. (c) $3 Sailfish Set of 3 sheets . . . . 6·50 6·75

Nos. 877/82, 883/8, 889/94, 895/900, 901/6 and 907/12 were each printed together, se-tenant, with the backgrounds forming composite designs.

144 Glasswing Butterfly

2000. South Pacific Butterflies. Multicoloured.
914 90c. Type **144** 65 70
915 90c. Leftwing butterfly . . . 65 70
916 90c. Moth butterfly 65 70
917 90c. Blue triangle 65 70
918 90c. Beak butterfly 65 70
919 90c. Plane butterfly 65 70
920 90c. Birdwing (vert) 65 70
921 90c. Tailed emperor (vert) . . 65 70
922 90c. Orchard shallowtail (vert) 65 70
923 90c. Union jack (vert) . . . 65 70
924 90c. Long-tailed blue (vert) 65 70
925 90c. Common jezebel (vert) 65 70
926 90c. Caper white (vert) . . . 65 70
927 90c. Common Indian crow (vert) 65 70
928 90c. Eastern flat (vert) . . . 65 70
929 90c. Cairns birdwing (vert) 65 70
930 90c. Monarch (vert) 65 70
931 90c. Meadow argus (vert) . . 65 70
MS932 Two sheets, each 70 × 100 mm. (a) $3 Great egg-fly (vert). (b) $3 Palmfly Set of 2 sheets . . . . 4·25 4·50

Nos. 914/19, 920/5 and 926/31 were each printed together, se-tenant, with the backgrounds forming composite designs.

145 Pekin Robin ("Red-Billed Leiothrix")

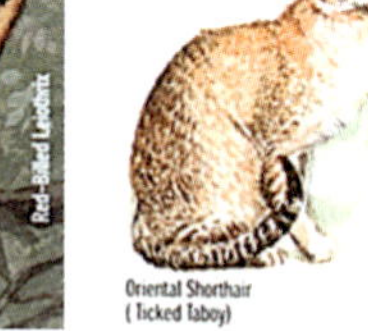

146 Oriental Shorthair

2000. South Pacific Birds. Multicoloured.
933 90c. Type **145** 65 70
934 90c. Grey shrike-thrush . . . 65 70
935 90c. Great frigatebird 65 70
936 90c. River kingfisher ("Common Kingfisher") . . 65 70
937 90c. Chestnut-breasted mannikin ("Chestnut-breasted Finch") 65 70
938 90c. White tern 65 70
939 90c. Rainbow lorikeet . . . 65 70
940 90c. White-throated tree creeper 65 70
941 90c. White-tailed kingfisher 65 70
942 90c. Golden whistler 65 70
943 90c. Grey plover ("Black-bellied Plover") 65 70
944 90c. Australian stone-curlew ("Beach Thick-knee") . . . 65 70
945 90c. White-collared kingfisher 65 70
946 90c. Peale's petrel ("Scaled Petrel") 65 70
947 90c. Blue wren ("Superb Blue Wren") 65 70
948 90c. Osprey 65 70
949 90c. Great cormorant 65 70
950 90c. Peregrine falcon 65 70
MS951 Two sheets. (a) 100 × 70 mm. $3 Broad-billed prion (horiz). (b) 70 × 100 mm $3 Morepork Set of 2 sheets . . . . 4·25 4·50

Nos. 933/8, 939/44 and 945/50 were each printed together, se-tenant, with the backgrounds forming composite designs.

No. 945 is inscribed "Kingisher" in error.

2000. Cats and Dogs. Multicoloured.
952 90c. Type **146** 65 70
953 90c. Balinese 65 70
954 90c. Somali 65 70
955 90c. Chinchilla Persian . . . 65 70
956 90c. Tonkinese 65 70
957 90c. Japanese bobtail 65 70
958 90c. Oriental shorthair (head) 65 70
959 90c. Balinese (head) 65 70
960 90c. Somali (head) 65 70
961 90c. Chinchilla Persian (head) 65 70
962 90c. Tonkinese (head) 65 70
963 90c. Japanese bobtail (head) 65 70
964 90c. Fox terrier (horiz) . . . 65 70
965 90c. Collie (horiz) 65 70
966 90c. Boston terrier (horiz) . . 65 70
967 90c. Welsh corgie (horiz) . . 65 70
968 90c. Pointer (horiz) 65 70
969 90c. Dalmatian (horiz) . . . 65 70
970 90c. Dalmatian (head) . . . 65 70
971 90c. Boston terrier (head) . . 65 70
972 90c. Fox terrier (head) . . . 65 70
973 90c. Pointer (head) 65 70
974 90c. Welsh corgi (head) . . . 65 70
975 90c. Collie (head) 65 70
MS976 Two sheets. (a) 96 × 70 mm. $3 Oriental shorthair. (b) 70 × 96 mm. $3 Scottish terrier (horiz) Set of 2 sheets . . . . 4·25 4·50

147 Common Noddy ("Brown Noddy")

2000. Fauna. Multicoloured.
977 90c. Type **147** 65 70
978 90c. Great frigatebird 65 70
979 90c. Emperor angelfish . . . 65 70
980 90c. Common dolphin . . . 65 70
981 90c. Hermit crab 65 70
982 90c. Threadfin butterflyfish 65 70
983 90c. Red-footed booby . . . 65 70
984 90c. Red-tailed tropicbird . . 65 70
985 90c. Grey plover ("Black-bellied Plover") 65 70
986 90c. Common tern 65 70
987 90c. Ruddy turnstone 65 70
988 90c. Sanderling 65 70
MS989 70 × 93 mm. $3 Great frigatebird (vert) . . . . 2·10 2·25
Nos. 977/82 and 983/8 were each printed together, se-tenant, with the backgrounds forming composite designs.

148 Green Dragon

2001. Chinese New Year ("Years of the Dragon and Snake"). Multicoloured.
990 40c. Type **148** 30 35
991 60c. Green snake with orange markings 45 50
992 90c. Orange snake with green markings 65 70
993 $1.05 Blue dragon 75 80

149 Anglo Specialist Rescue Unit

2000. Fire Service. Multicoloured.
994 60c. Type **149** 40 45
995 90c. Anglo 4800 water/foam tender 65 70
996 $1.50 Bronto 33-2T1 combined telescopic ladder/ hydraulic platform . . . . 1·10 1·25
997 $2 Anglo 450 LRX water tenders . . . . 1·40 1·50
MS998 105 × 55 mm. $3 Wormald "Arrestor" ARFFV in gateway to Motufoua Secondary School 2·10 2·25
Nos. 994/7 also commemorate the first anniv of the fire tragedy at Motufoua Secondary School.

150 Tuvaluan Boy with Japanese Family

2001. "Philanippon '01" International Stamp Exhibition, Tokyo. 13th Asian-Pacific Children's Convention, Fukuoka. Sheet 94 × 80 mm.
MS999 **150** $3 multicoloured . . 2·10 2·25

2001. 101st Birthday of Queen Elizabeth the Queen Mother. Nos. 846/9 optd or surch **101 birthday**.
1000 60c. Queen Elizabeth with her daughters, 1951 . . . 40 45
1001 90c. With Princes William and Harry, 1995 . . . . 65 70
1002 $1.50 Inspecting the Queen's Dragoon Guards . . . . 1·10 1·25
1003 $2 on 40c. King George VI and Queen Elizabeth inspecting bomb damage, 1940 . . . . 1·40 1·50
MS1004 145 × 70 mm. $5 on $2 Lady Elizabeth Bowes-Lyon aged 6, and Yuri Gagarin (first cosmonaut) 3·50 3·75

152 Tuvaluan Girl

2001. Inauguration of .tv Corporation (Internet Service Provider). Each featuring satellite dish and web address. Multicoloured.
1005 40c. Type **152** 30 35
1006 60c. Local dancers 40 45
1007 90c. Tuvaluan man blowing conch shell 65 70
1008 $1.50 Young child with flower garland around head . . . . 1·10 1·25
MS1009 85 × 50 mm. $2 Satellite dishes and web address . . . . 1·50 1·60

153 Mosquito

2001. Insects. Multicoloured.
1010 25c. Type **153** 20 25
1011 30c. Giant African snail . . 20 25
1012 40c. Cockroach 30 35
1013 45c. Stick insect 30 35
1014 50c. Green stink bug . . . 35 40
1015 55c. Dragonfly 40 45
1016 60c. Caterpillar of monarch butterfly 45 50
1017 70c. Coconut beetle 50 55
1018 90c. Honey bee 65 70
1019 $1 Monarch butterfly . . . 70 75
1020 $2 Common eggfly butterfly 1·40 1·50
1021 $3 Painted lady butterfly . . 2·10 2·25

2002. "United We Stand". Support for Victims of 11 September 2001 Terrorist Attacks. As T **445** of St. Vincent.
1022 $2 multicoloured (blue background) . . . . . . 1·40 1·50
1023 $2 multicoloured (yellow background) . . . . . . 1·40 1·50

154 The Paulownia Court

2002. Japanese Art. "The Tale of Genji" (Murasaki Shikibu). Multicoloured.
1024 40c. Type **154** 30 35
1025 40c. The Broom Tree . . . 30 35
1026 40c. The Shell of the Locust 30 35
1027 40c. Evening Faces 30 35
1028 40c. Lavender 30 35
1029 40c. The Safflower 30 35
1030 60c. The Festival of the Cherry Blossoms 45 50
1031 60c. Heartvine 45 50
1032 60c. The Sacred Tree . . . 45 50
1033 60c. The Orange Blossoms 45 50
1034 60c. Suma 45 50
1035 60c. Akashi 45 50
1036 90c. The Wormwood Patch 65 70
1037 90c. The Gate House . . . 65 70
1038 90c. A Picture Contest . . . 65 70
1039 90c. The Wind in the Pines 65 70
1040 90c. A Rack of Cloud . . . 65 70
1041 90c. The Morning Glory . . 65 70
MS1042 Three sheets, each 93 × 124 mm. (a) $4 An Autumn Excursion (chapter 7). (b) $4 Channel Buoys (chapter 14). (c) $4 The Maiden (chapter 21). Imperf Set of 3 sheets . . . . . . 8·50 9·00
Nos. 1024/9 (chapters 1/6), 1030/5 (chapters 8/13) and 1036/41 (chapters 15/20).

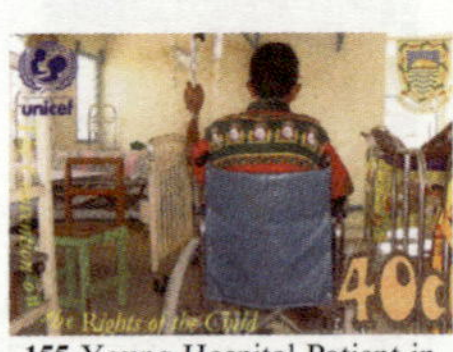

155 Young Hospital Patient in Wheelchair

2002. UNICEF. Rights of the Child. Multicoloured.
1043 40c. Type **155** 30 35
1044 60c. Children by roadside 45 50
1045 90c. Nauti Primary School, Funafuti 65 70
1046 $1.50 Mother and baby . . 1·10 1·25
MS1047 110 × 80 mm. $1 Taulosa Karl; $1 Simalua Jacinta Enele (Tuvalu representatives at UN special session on children) . . 1·40 1·50

2002. Golden Jubilee. As T **110** of St. Kitts. Multicoloured.
1048 $1.50 Princes William and Harry as young boys . . 1·10 1·50
1049 $1.50 Queen Elizabeth at garden party . . . . . . 1·10 1·50
1050 $1.50 Queen Elizabeth with Prince Philip wearing robes of Order of the Bath . . . . 1·10 1·50
1051 $1.50 Queen Elizabeth in red hat and coat . . . . 1·10 1·50
MS1052 76 × 108 mm. $4 Queen Elizabeth on horseback for Trooping the Colour . . . . . 3·00 3·25

2002. World Cup Football Championship, Japan and Korea. As T **113** of St. Kitts. Multicoloured.
1053 90c. Tom Finney (England) 65 70
1054 90c. Publicity poster, Germany, 1974 . . . . . 65 70
1055 90c. Portuguese player . . . 65 70
1056 90c. Uruguayan player . . . 65 70
1057 90c. Suwon Stadium, Korea (56 × 42 mm) 65 70
MS1058 64 × 86 mm. $4 Johann Cruyff (Holland) . . . . . . 3·00 3·25
No. **MS**1058 is inscribed "JOHAN CRUFF" in error.

156 Duchess of York, 1923

2002. Queen Elizabeth the Queen Mother Commemoration. Each multicoloured ($1.50) or black and lilac (others).
1059 60c. Type **156** 65 70
1060 60c. Duchess of York, 1923 (different) (face value at left) 65 70
1061 90c. Queen Mother at Sandringham, 1992 (29 × 25 mm) 65 70
1062 90c. Queen Mother accepting posy from child, 1989 (29 × 25 mm) 65 70
1063 90c. Queen Mother with teddy bear, Queen Charlotte's Hospital, 1989 (29 × 25 mm) 65 70
1064 90c. Queen Mother with family, Didcot, 1989 (29 × 25 mm) 65 70
1065 $1.50 Queen Mother at Tower Hamlets Memorial Garden, 2001 (40 × 30 mm) . . . . . . 1·10 1·25
MS1066 Two sheets, each 65 × 101 mm. (a) $2 Lady Elizabeth Bowes-Lyon with her brother David; $2 Queen Mother in old age. (b) $2 Queen Elizabeth smelling rose, 1950s; $2 Queen Mother, 1971(each 26 × 40 mm). Set of 2 sheets . . . . 4·25 4·50

157 Citizen of the World Badge

2002. 20th World Scout Jamboree, Thailand. Multicoloured.
1067 $1.50 Type **157** . . . . . . 1·10 1·25
1068 $1.50 First Aid badge . . . 1·10 1·25
1069 $1.50 Personal Fitness badge 1·10 1·25
1070 $1.50 Environmental Science badge . . . . 1·10 1·25
MS1071 66 × 85 mm. $5 Lord Baden-Powell (vert) . . . . . 3·50 3·75

158 Mt Fitzroy, Argentina

2002. International Year of Mountains. Muticoloured.
1072 $1.50 Type **158** . . . . . 1·10 1·25
1073 $1.50 Mt Foraker, U.S.A. . . 1·10 1·25
1074 $1.50 Mt Fujiyama, Japan 1·10 1·25
1075 $1.50 Mt Makalu, Nepal . . 1·10 1·25
MS1076 63 × 84 mm. $4 Mt Godwin-Austen (K2), Kashmir (vert) . . . . 3·00 3·25
No. 1072 is inscribed "CHILE" in error.

159 Palomino Horse

160 Ram in Bushes

2003. End of Chinese "Year of the Horse". Multicoloured.
1077 40c. Type **159** 30 35
1078 60c. White Arab horse . . . 45 50
1079 90c. Wild horse 65 70
1080 $2 Chestnut horse . . . . . 1·40 1·50
MS1081 75 × 75 mm. $1.50 Seahorse; $1.50 m Group of seahorses . . 2·10 2·25

2003. Chinese New Year ("Year of the Ram"). Multicoloured.
1082 75c. Type **160** 55 60
1083 75c. Side view of ram's head 55 60
1084 75c. Front view of ram's head 55 60

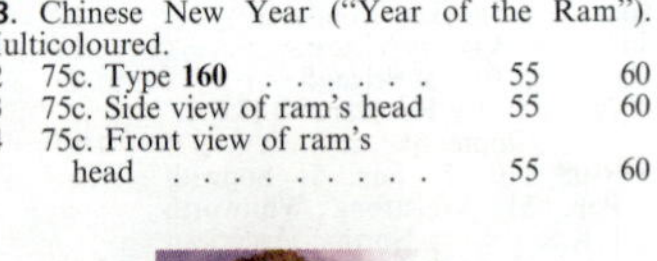

161 Diana, Princess of Wales

2003. 5th Death Anniv of Diana, Princess of Wales. Multicoloured.
1085 $1 Type **161** 70 75
1086 $1 Princess Diana wearing emerald necklace 70 75
1087 $1 Wearing blue evening dress 70 75
1088 $1 Wearing turquoise scarf 70 75
1089 $1 Wearing pink blouse . . 70 75
1090 $1 Wearing lace dress . . . 70 75
MS1091 90 × 105 mm. $4 Princess Diana and rose . . . . 3·00 3·25

OFFICIAL STAMPS

1981. Nos. 105/22 optd **OFFICIAL**.
O 1 **14** 1c. multicoloured 10 10
O 2 – 2c. multicoloured 10 10
O 3 – 4c. multicoloured 10 10
O 4 – 5c. multicoloured 10 10
O 5 – 6c. multicoloured 10 10
O 6 – 8c. multicoloured 10 10
O 7 – 10c. multicoloured . . . 15 15
O 8 – 15c. multicoloured . . . 15 15
O 9 – 20c. multicoloured . . . 20 20
O10a – 25c. multicoloured . . . 25 25
O11 – 30c. multicoloured . . . 25 20
O12 – 35c. multicoloured . . . 20 20
O13 – 40c. multicoloured . . . 20 20
O14 – 45c. multicoloured . . . 25 25
O15 – 50c. multicoloured . . . 30 30
O16 – 70c. multicoloured . . . 40 40
O17 – $1 multicoloured 40 40
O18a – $2 multicoloured 75 75
O19 – $5 multicoloured . . . . 1·00 75

1983. Nos. 202/3a, 205/12, 224 and 234 optd **OFFICIAL**.
O20 5c. Wedding and baby food baskets 10 40
O21 10c. Hand-carved model of canoe 10 40
O22 15c. Ladies' sun hats . . . 15 70
O23 25c. Pandanus baskets . . . 25 60

O24	30c. on 45c. Reef sandals and fish trap	50	70
O25	30c. Basket tray and coconut stand	30	70
O26	35c. Pandanus pillows and shell necklaces	40	75
O27	40c. Round baskets and fans	45	75
O28	45c. Reef sandals and fish trap	45	75
O29	50c. Rat trap	50	75
O30	60c. on $1 Pump drill and adze	75	75
O31	60c. Fisherman's waterproof boxes	60	1·00
O32	$1 Pump drill and adze	75	1·00
O33	$2 Fisherman's hat and canoe bailers	1·00	1·00
O34	$5 Fishing rod, lures and scoop nets	2·25	2·50

1989. Nos. 502/17 optd **OFFICIAL**.

O35	5c. Type **66**	30	55
O36	10c. White tern	30	55
O37	15c. Common noddy	45	55
O38	20c. Phoenix petrel	45	55
O39	25c. Pacific golden plover	50	75
O40	30c. Crested tern	50	75
O41	35c. Sooty tern	55	80
O42	40c. Bristle-thighed curlew	55	80
O43	45c. Bar-tailed godwit	65	85
O44	50c. Reef heron	70	90
O45	55c. Great frigate bird	70	90
O46	60c. Red-footed booby	70	90
O47	70c. Rufous-necked sandpiper	80	1·00
O48	$1 Long-tailed koel	1·10	1·10
O49	$2 Red-tailed tropic bird	2·00	1·90
O50	$5 Buff-banded rail	4·25	4·50

POSTAGE DUE STAMPS

D 1 Tuvalu Crest

1981.

D 1	D 1	1c. black and purple	10	10
D 2		2c. black and blue	10	10
D 3		5c. black and brown	10	10
D13		10c. black and green	10	10
D14		20c. black and brown	15	20
D 6		30c. black and orange	15	30
D 7		40c. black and blue	15	40
D 8		50c. black and green	20	45
D 9		$1 black and mauve	30	80

Some values exist with or without the imprint date at foot.

APPENDIX

The following stamps for individual islands of Tuvalu have either been issued in excess of postal needs, or have not been made available to the public in reasonable quantities at face value.

FUNAFUTI

1984.

Leaders of the World. Railway Locomotives (1st series). Two designs for each value, the first showing technical drawings and the second the locomotive at work. 15, 20, 30, 40, 50, 60c. each × 2.

Leaders of the World. Automobiles (1st series). Two designs for each value, the first showing technical drawings and the second the car in action. 1, 10, 40c., $1 each × 2.

Leaders of the World. Railway Locomotives (2nd series). Two designs for each value, the first showing technical drawings and the second the locomotive at work. 5, 15, 25, 35, 40, 55, 60c., $1 each × 2.

1985.

Leaders of the World. Automobiles (2nd series). Two designs for each value, the first showing technical drawings and the second the car in action. 1, 30, 55, 60c. each × 2.

Leaders of the World. Railway Locomotives (3rd series). Two designs for each value, the first showing technical drawings and the second the locomotive at work. 5, 15, 35, 40, 50c., $1 each × 2.

Leaders of the World. Life and Times of Queen Elizabeth the Queen Mother. Two designs for each value, showing different portraits. 5, 25, 80c., $1.05 each × 2.

1986.

60th Birthday of Queen Elizabeth II. 10, 50c., $1.50, $3.50.

Royal Wedding (1st issue). 60c., $1 each × 2.

Royal Wedding (2nd issue). Previous Royal Wedding stamps optd **Congratulations T.R.H. The Duke & Duchess of York**. 60c., $1 each × 2.

Railway Locomotives (4th series). Two designs for each value, the first showing technical drawings and the second the locomotive at work. 20, 40, 60c., $1.50 each × 2.

1987.

Automobiles (3rd series). Two designs for each value, the first showing technical drawings and the second the car in action. 10, 20, 40, 60, 75, 80c., $1.50 each × 2.

Royal Ruby Wedding. 20, 50, 75c., $1.20, $1.75.

1988.

Olympic Games, Seoul. 10, 20, 40, 50, 80, 90c.

NANUMAGA

1984.

Leaders of the World. Automobiles (1st series). Two designs for each value, the first showing technical drawings and the second the car in action. 5, 10, 25, 30, 40c., $1 each × 2.

Leaders of the World. British Monarchs. Two designs for each value, forming a composite picture. 10, 20, 30, 40, 50c., $1 each × 2.

Leaders of the World. Automobiles (2nd series). Two designs for each value, the first showing technical drawings and the second the car in action. 5, 10, 50c., $1 each × 2.

1985.

Leaders of the World. Railway Locomotives. Two designs for each value, the first showing technical drawings and the second the locomotive at work. 10, 25, 50, 60c. each × 2.

Leaders of the World. Flowers. 25, 30, 40, 50c. each × 2.

Leaders of the World. Automobiles (3rd series). Two designs for each value, the first showing technical drawings and the second the car in action. 10, 25, 75c., $1 each × 2.

Leaders of the World. Life and Times of Queen Elizabeth the Queen Mother. Two designs for each value, showing different portraits. 15, 55, 65, 90c. each × 2.

1986.

60th Birthday of Queen Elizabeth II. 5c., $1, $1.75, $2.50.

World Cup Football Championship, Mexico. 1, 2, 5, 5, 10, 20, 35, 50, 60, 75c., $1, $2, $4.

Royal Wedding (1st issue). 60c., $1 each × 2.

Royal Wedding (2nd issue). Previous Royal Wedding stamps optd as for Funafuti. 60c., $1 each × 2.

1987.

Automobiles (4th series). Two designs for each value, the first showing technical drawings and the second the car in action. 5, 10, 15, 20, 25, 40, 60c., $1 each × 2.

Royal Ruby Wedding. 15, 35, 60c., $1.50, $1.75.

NANUMEA

1984.

Leaders of the World. Railway Locomotives (1st series). Two designs for each value, the first showing technical drawings and the second the locomotive at work. 15, 20, 30, 40, 50, 60c. each × 2.

Leaders of the World. Famous Cricketers. Two designs for each value, the first showing a portrait and the second the cricketer in action. 1, 10, 40c., $1 each × 2.

1985.

Leaders of the World. Automobiles (1st series). Two designs for each value, the first showing technical drawings and the second the car in action. 5, 40, 50, 60c. each × 2.

Leaders of the World. Railway Locomotives (2nd series). Two designs for each value, the first showing technical drawings and the second the locomotive at work. 1, 35, 50, 60c. each × 2.

Leaders of the World. Automobiles (2nd series). Two designs for each value, the first showing technical drawings and the second the car in action. 15, 20, 50, 60c. each × 2.

Leaders of the World. Cats. 5, 30, 50c., $1 each × 2.

Leaders of the World. Life and Times of Queen Elizabeth the Queen Mother. Two designs for each value, showing different portraits. 5, 30, 75c., $1.05 each × 2.

1986.

60th Birthday of Queen Elizabeth II. 10, 80c., $1.75, $3.

World Cup Football Championship, Mexico. 1, 2, 5, 10, 25, 40, 50, 75, 90c., $1, $2.50, $4.

Royal Wedding (1st issue). 60c., $1 each × 2.

Royal Wedding (2nd issue). Previous Royal Wedding stamps optd as for Funafuti. 60c., $1 each × 2.

Automobiles (3rd series). Two designs for each value, the first showing technical drawings and the second the car in action. 10, 20, 35, 50, 75c., $2 each × 2.

1987.

Royal Ruby Wedding. 40, 60, 80c., $1, $2.

NIUTAO

1984.

Leaders of the World. Automobiles (1st series). Two designs for each value, the first showing technical drawings and the second the car in action. 15, 30, 40, 50c. each × 2.

Leaders of the World. Railway Locomotives (1st series). Two designs for each value, the first showing technical drawings and the second the locomotive at work. 5, 10, 20, 40, 50c., $1 each × 2.

1985.

Leaders of the World. Famous Cricketers. Two designs for each value, the first showing a portrait and the second the cricketer in action. 1, 15, 50c., $1 each × 2.

Leaders of the World. Birth Bicent of John J. Audubon (ornithologist). Birds. 5, 15, 25c., $1 each × 2.

Leaders of the World. Automobiles (2nd series). Two designs for each value, the first showing technical drawings and the second the car in action. 20, 25, 40, 60c. each × 2.

Leaders of the World. Railway Locomotives (2nd series). Two designs for each value, the first showing technical drawings and the second the locomotive at work. 10, 30, 45, 60, 75c., $1.20 each × 2.

Leaders of the World. Life and Times of Queen Elizabeth the Queen Mother. Two designs for each value, showing different portraits. 15, 35, 70, 95c. each × 2.

1986.

60th Birthday of Queen Elizabeth II. 5, 60c., $1.50, $3.50.

Royal Wedding (1st series). 60c., $1 each × 2.

Royal Wedding (2nd series). Previous Royal Wedding stamps optd as for Funafuti. 60c., $1 each × 2.

1987.

Royal Ruby Wedding. 60th Birthday of Queen Elizabeth II issue of 1986 optd **40th WEDDING ANNIVERSARY OF H.M. QUEEN ELIZABETH II**. 5, 60c., $1.50, $3.50.

NUI

1984.

Leaders of the World. Railway Locomotives (1st series). Two designs for each value, the first showing technical drawings and the second the locomotive at work. 15, 25, 30, 50c. each × 2.

Leaders of the World. British Monarchs. Two designs for each value, forming a composite picture. 1, 5, 15, 40, 50c., $1 each × 2.

1985.

Leaders of the World. Railway Locomotives (2nd series). Two designs for each value, the first showing technical drawings and the second the locomotive at work. 5, 15, 25c., $1 each × 2.

Leaders of the World. Automobiles (1st series). Two designs for each value, the first showing technical drawings and the second the car in action. 25, 30, 40, 50c. each × 2.

Leaders of the World. Famous Cricketers. Two designs for each value, the first showing a portrait and the second the cricketer in action. 1, 40, 60, 70c. each × 2.

Leaders of the World. Life and Times of Queen Elizabeth the Queen Mother. Two designs for each value, showing different portraits. 5, 50, 75, 85c. each × 2.

Leaders of the World. Automobiles (2nd series). Two designs for each value, the first showing technical drawings and the second the car in action. 5, 15, 40, 60, 90c., $1.10 each × 2.

1986.

60th Birthday of Queen Elizabeth II. 10, 80c., $1.75, $3.

Royal Wedding (1st issue). 60c., $1 each × 2.

Royal Wedding (2nd issue). Previous Royal Wedding stamps optd as for Funafuti. 60c., $1 each × 2.

1987.

Railway Locomotives (3rd series). Two designs for each value, the first showing technical drawings and the second the locomotive at work. 10, 25, 35, 40, 60, 75c., $1, $1.25 each × 2.

Royal Ruby Wedding. 20, 50, 75c., $1.20, $1.75.

1988.

Railway Locomotives (4th series). Two designs for each value, the first showing technical drawings and the second the locomotive at work. 5, 10, 20, 25, 40, 50, 60, 75c. each × 2.

NUKUFETAU

1984.

Leaders of the World. Automobiles (1st series). Two designs for each value, the first showing technical drawings and the second the car in action. 10, 25, 30, 50, 60c. each × 2.

Leaders of the World. British Monarchs. Two designs for each value, forming a composite picture. 1, 10, 30, 50, 60c., $1 each × 2.

1985.

Leaders of the World. Famous Cricketers. Two designs for each value, the first showing a portrait and the second the cricketer in action. 1, 10, 55c., $1 each × 2.

Leaders of the World. Railway Locomotives (1st series). Two designs for each value, the first showing technical drawings and the second the locomotive at work. 1, 10, 60, 70c. each × 2.

Leaders of the World. Automobiles (2nd series). Two designs for each value, the first showing technical drawings and the second the car in action. 5, 10, 15, 20, 50, 60, 75c., $1.50 each × 2.

Leaders of the World. Life and Times of Queen Elizabeth the Queen Mother. Two designs for each value, showing different portraits. 10, 45, 65c., $1 each × 2.

1986.

Leaders of the World. Railway Locomotives (2nd series). Two designs for each value, the first showing technical drawings and the second the locomotive at work. 20, 40, 60c., $1.50 each × 2.

60th Birthday of Queen Elizabeth II. 5, 40c., $2, $4.

Royal Wedding (1st issue). 60c., $1 each × 2.

Royal Wedding (2nd issue). Previous Royal Wedding stamps optd as for Funafuti. 60c., $1 each × 2.

1987.

Railway Locomotives (3rd series). Two designs for each value, the first showing technical drawings and the second the locomotive at work. 5, 10, 15, 25, 30, 50, 60c., $1 each × 2.

Royal Ruby Wedding. 60th Birthday of Queen Elizabeth II issue of 1986 optd as for Niutao. 5, 40c., $2, $4.

NUKULAELAE

1984.

Leaders of the World. Railway Locomotives (1st series). Two designs for each value, the first showing technical drawings and the second the locomotive at work. 5, 15, 40c., $1 each × 2.

Leaders of the World. Famous Cricketers. Two designs for each value, the first showing a portrait and the second the cricketer in action. 5, 15, 30c., $1 each × 2.

Leaders of the World. Railway Locomotives (2nd series). Two designs for each value, the first showing technical drawings and the second the locomotive at work. 5, 20, 40c., $1 each × 2.

1985.

Leaders of the World. Automobiles (1st series). Two designs for each value, the first showing technical drawings and the second the car in action. 5, 35, 50, 70c. each × 2.

Leaders of the World. Dogs. 5, 20, 50, 70c. each × 2.

Leaders of the World. Railway Locomotives (3rd series). Two designs for each value, the first showing technical drawings and the second the locomotive at work. 10, 25, 50c., $1 each × 2.

Leaders of the World. Automobiles (2nd series). Two designs for each value, the first showing technical drawings and the second the car in action. 10, 25, 35, 50, 75c., $1 each × 2.

Leaders of the World. Life and Times of Queen Elizabeth the Queen Mother. Two designs for each value, showing different portraits. 5, 25, 85c., $1 each × 2.

1986.

60th Birthday of Queen Elizabeth II. 10c., $1, $1.50, $3.

Railway Locomotives (4th series). Two designs for each value, the first showing technical drawings and the second the locomotive at work. 10, 15, 25, 40, 50, 80c., $1, $1.50 each × 2.

Royal Wedding (1st issue). 60c., $1 each × 2.

Royal Wedding (2nd issue). Previous Royal Wedding stamps optd as for Funafuti. 60c., $1 each × 2.

1987.

Royal Ruby Wedding. 15, 35, 60c., $1.50, $1.75.

VAITUPU

1984.

Leaders of the World. Automobiles (1st series). Two designs for each value, the first showing technical drawings and the second the car in action. 15, 25, 30, 50c. each × 2.

Leaders of the World. British Monarchs. Two designs for each value, forming a composite picture. 1, 5, 15, 40, 50c., $1 each × 2.

Leaders of the World. Automobiles (2nd series). Two designs for each value, the first showing technical drawings and the second the car in action. 5, 15, 25, 30, 40, 50, 60c. $1 each × 2.

1985.

Leaders of the World. Railway Locomotives (1st series). Two designs for each value, the first showing technical drawings and the second the locomotive at work. 10, 25, 50, 60c. each × 2.

Leaders of the World. Butterflies. 5, 15, 50, 75c. each × 2.

Leaders of the World. Automobiles (3rd series). Two designs for each value, the first showing technical drawings and the second the car in action. 15, 30, 40, 60c. each × 2.

Leaders of the World. Life and Times of Queen Elizabeth the Queen Mother. Two designs for each value, showing different portraits. 15, 40, 65, 90c. each × 2.

1986.

Leaders of the World. Railway Locomotives (2nd series). Two designs for each value, the first showing technical drawings and the second the locomotives at work. 5, 25, 80c., $1 each × 2.

60th Birthday of Queen Elizabeth II. 5, 60c., $2, $3.50.

Royal Wedding (1st issue). 60c., $1 each × 2.

Royal Wedding (2nd issue). Previous Royal Wedding stamps optd as for Funafuti. 60c., $1 each × 2.

1987.

Railway Locomotives (3rd series). Two designs for each value, the first showing technical drawings and the second the locomotive at work. 10, 15, 25, 35, 45, 65, 85c., $1 each × 2.

Royal Ruby Wedding. 60th Birthday of Queen Elizabeth II issue of 1986 optd as for Niutao. 5, 60c., $2, $3.50.

UBANGI-SHARI Pt. 6

Formerly part of the French Congo. Ubangi-Shari became a separate colony in 1904 (although stamps of the French Congo continued to be used until 1915). From 1915 to 1922 it shared a postal administration with Chad.

From 1936 to 1958 Ubangi-Shari was part of French Equatorial Africa. In December 1958 it became the autonomous state of the Central African Republic.

100 centimes = 1 franc.

A. UBANGI-SHARI-CHAD

1915. Stamps of Middle Congo optd **OUBANGUI-CHARI-TCHAD.**
1 **1** 1c. green and brown 20 3·00
2 2c. violet and brown 25 3·00
3 4c. blue and brown 35 3·25
4 5c. green and blue 1·10 2·75
19 5c. yellow and blue 3·00 3·25
5 10c. red and blue 1·40 80
20 10c. green and turquoise 2·75 3·25
5a 15c. purple and pink 3·75 4·00
6 20c. brown and blue 1·90 5·75
7 **2** 25c. blue and green 3·00 3·00
21 25c. green and black 2·50 3·00
8 30c. red and green 2·75 3·25
22 30c. red 2·50 3·25
9 35c. brown and blue 5·75 10·50
10 40c. green and brown 5·75 13·00
11 45c. violet and orange 6·00 13·00
12 50c. green and orange 5·00 14·50
23 50c. blue and green 2·50 3·50
13 75c. brown and blue 14·00 24·00
14 **3** 1f. green and violet 10·00 22·00
15 2f. violet and green 17·00 23·00
16 5f. blue and pink 55·00 60·00

1916. No. 5 surch **5c** and cross.
18 10c.+5c. red and blue 2·25 3·50

B. UBANGI-SHARI

1922. Stamps of Middle Congo, new colours, optd **OUBANGUI-CHARI.**
24 **1** 1c. violet and green 35 2·75
25 2c. green and pink 40 3·00
26 4c. brown and purple 1·75 3·50
27 5c. blue and pink 1·90 3·50
28 10c. green and turquoise 3·75 4·25
29 15c. pink and blue 4·00 4·75
30 20c. brown and pink 8·00 14·00
31 25c. violet and pink 4·50 10·50
32 30c. red 3·25 7·25
33 35c. violet and green 6·50 13·00
34 40c. blue and mauve 5·50 11·50
35 45c. brown and mauve 5·50 11·00
36 50c. blue and light blue 3·25 5·50
37 60 on 75c. violet on pink 4·25 7·75
38 75c. brown and pink 5·50 13·50
39 **3** 1f. green and blue 7·75 14·00
40 2f. green and pink 7·75 20·00
41 5f. green and brown 15·00 14·00

1924. Stamps of 1922 and similar stamps additionally optd **AFRIQUE EQUATORIALE FRANCAISE.**
42 **1** 1c. violet and green 10 2·50
43 2c. green and pink 10 3·00
44 4c. brown and chocolate 10 2·75
44c 4c. brown 1·40 4·00
45 5c. blue and pink 30 2·50
46 10c. green and turquoise 85 3·00
47 10c. red and blue 65 2·00
48 15c. pink and blue 55 3·50
49 20c. brown and pink 2·25 2·50
50 **2** 25c. violet and pink 1·75 95
51 30c. red 1·00 2·50
52 30c. brown and pink 50 1·10
53 30c. olive and green 2·50 2·25
54 35c. violet and green 30 2·50
55 40c. blue and mauve 1·40 2·00
56 45c. brown and mauve 1·90 3·00
57 50c. blue and light blue 1·75 2·00
58 50c. grey and blue 2·25 80
59 60 on 75c. violet on pink 1·10 2·25
60 65c. brown and blue 3·75 4·25
61 75c. brown and pink 2·50 3·50
62 75c. blue and light blue 2·00 2·50
63 75c. purple and brown 3·50 4·00
64 90c. pink and red 1·25 15·00
65a **3** 1f. green and blue 35 1·25
66 1f.10 brown and blue 3·50 6·00
67 1f.25 mauve and green 7·00 11·00
68 1f.50 ultramarine and blue 7·25 19·00
69 1f.75 brown and orange 9·50 12·00
70 2f. green and pink 3·00 3·00
71 3f. mauve on pink 6·50 12·00
72 5f. green and brown 5·25 5·00

1925. As last but new colours and surch.
73 **3** 65 on 1f. violet and brown 1·10 3·00
74 85 on 1f. violet and brown 80 4·00
75 90 on 75c. pink and red 2·75 2·75
76 1f.25 on 1f. blue & ultram 1·00 1·40
77 1f.50 on 1f. ultramarine & bl 3·00 2·75
78 3f. on 5f. brown and red 3·75 6·50
79 10f. on 5f. red and mauve 12·00 27·00
80 20f. on 5f. mauve and grey 30·00 42·00

1931. "International Colonial Exhibition" key-types inscr "OUBANGUI-CHARI".
103 E 40c. green 5·50 11·00
104 F 50c. mauve 4·50 3·50
105 G 90c. red 3·50 11·50
106 H 1f.50 blue 5·75 5·50

POSTAGE DUE STAMPS

1928. Postage Due type of France optd **OUBANGUI-CHARI A. E. F.**
D81 **D 11** 5c. blue 40 3·25
D82 10c. brown 55 3·25
D83 20c. olive 75 2·75
D84 25c. red 65 3·25
D85 30c. red 70 4·25
D86 45c. green 1·00 3·25
D87 50c. purple 80 5·00
D88 60c. brown on cream 90 4·75
D89 1f. red on cream 1·25 5·50
D90 2f. red 1·25 7·75
D91 3f. violet 1·25 7·75

D 12 Mobaye

D 13 E. Gentil

1930.
D 92 **D 12** 5c. olive and blue 25 2·25
D 93 10c. brown and red 25 3·25
D 94 20c. brown and green 60 3·50
D 95 25c. brown and blue 2·00 3·50
D 96 30c. green and brown 2·00 5·00
D 97 45c. olive and green 2·75 7·00
D 98 50c. brown and mauve 4·75 13·50
D 99 60c. black and violet 6·00 14·50
D100 **D 13** 1f. black and brown 2·50 6·25
D101 2f. brown and mauve 2·00 10·00
D102 3f. brown and red 2·25 14·50

UGANDA Pt. 1

A Br. Protectorate in Central Africa until it attained independence within the British Commonwealth in 1962. From 1903 to 1962 used the stamps listed under "Kenya, Uganda and Tanganyika".

1895. 200 cowries = 1 rupee.
1896. 16 annas = 1 rupee.
1962. 100 cents = 1 shilling.

'U G'
20
2

'V.96.R'
25
'Uganda'
3

1895. Typewritten in black.
17 **2** 5(c.) black £1500 £950
18 10(c.) black £1500 £1000
19 15(c.) black £1000 £1000
20 20(c.) black £1400 £650
21 25(c.) black £950 £950
6 30(c.) black £1400 £1400
7 40(c.) black £2500 £1200
8 50(c.) black £1200 £1000
9 60(c.) black £1600 £1600

1895. Typewritten in violet.
35 **2** 5(c.) violet £500 £500
36 10(c.) violet £475 £475
37 15(c.) violet £600 £425
38 20(c.) violet £375 £275
39 25(c.) violet £700 £700
40 30(c.) violet £950 £700
41 40(c.) violet £800 £800
42 50(c.) violet £800 £850
43 100(c.) violet £2500 £2500

1896. Typewritten in violet.
44 **3** 5(c.) violet £475 £500
45 10(c.) violet £425 £400
46 15(c.) violet £475 £500
47 20(c.) violet £275 £200
48 25(c.) violet £450
49 30(c.) violet £500 £650
50 40(c.) violet £550 £650
51 50(c.) violet £600 £650
52 60(c.) violet £1500
53 100(c.) violet £1300 £1500

4

8

1896.
55 **4** 1a. black 17·00 22·00
56 2a. black 23·00 27·00
57 3a. black 25·00 29·00
58 4a. black 24·00 28·00
59 8a. black 28·00 29·00
60 1r. black 75·00 95·00
61 5r. black £200 £325

1896. Optd with large **L.**
70 **4** 1a. black £180 £150
71 2a. black 85·00 £100
72 3a. black £200 £225
73 4a. black 95·00 £140
74 8a. black £170 £200
75 1r. black £350 £400
76 5r. black £11000 £11000

1898.
84a **8** 1a. red 2·00 1·00
86 2a. brown 2·00 7·00
87a 3a. grey 9·50 13·00
88 4a. green 4·00 6·50
89 8a. green 6·50 24·00
Larger type with lions at either side of portrait.
90 – 1r. blue 35·00 42·00
91 – 5r. brown 70·00 £100

1902. Stamps of British East Africa optd **UGANDA.**
92 **11** ½a. green 2·00 1·40
93 2½a. blue 2·75 3·00

11 Ripon Falls and Speke Memorial

1962. Centenary of Speke's Discovery of Source of Nile.
95 **11** 30c. black and red 15 20
96 50c. black and violet 15 10
97 1s.30 black and green 30 20
98 2s.50 black and blue 1·60 1·90

12 Murchison Falls

14 Mulago Hospital

1962. Independence.
99 **12** 5c. turquoise 10 10
100 – 10c. brown 10 10
101 – 15c. black, red and green 10 10
102 – 20c. plum and buff 10 10
103 – 30c. blue 10 10
104 – 50c. black and turquoise 10 10
105 **14** 1s. sepia, red and turquoise 15 10
106 – 1s.30 orange and violet 20 10
107 – 2s. black, red and blue 40 50
108 – 5s. red and deep green 4·00 1·00
109 – 10s. slate and brown 2·00 2·50
110 – 20s. brown and blue 3·50 13·00
DESIGNS—As Type **12**: 10c. Tobacco growing; 15c. Coffee growing; 20c. Ankole cattle; 30c. Cotton; 50c. Mountains of the Moon. As Type **14**: 1s.30, Cathedrals and mosque; 2s. Makerere College; 5s. Copper mining; 10s. Cement industry; 20s. Parliament Buildings.

15 South African Crowned Crane

16 Black BeeEater

18 Ruwenzori Turaco

1965. International Trade Fair, Kampala.
111 **15** 30c. multicoloured 10 10
112 1s.30 multicoloured 20 10

1965. Birds.
113 **16** 5c. multicoloured 10 10
114 – 10c. brown, black and blue 10 10
115 – 15c. yellow and brown 20 10
116 – 20c. multicoloured 20 10
117 – 30c. black and brown 1·50 10
118 – 40c. multicoloured 90 1·50
119 – 50c. blue and violet 25 10
120 – 65c. red, black and grey 2·50 2·50
121 **18** 1s. multicoloured 50 10
122 – 1s.30 brown, black & yell 5·50 30
123 – 2s.50 multicoloured 4·25 65
124 – 5s. multicoloured 7·00 4·00
125 – 10s. multicoloured 11·00 11·00
126 – 20s. multicoloured 21·00 38·00
DESIGNS—HORIZ (as Type **16**): 10c. African jacana; 30c. Sacred ibis; 65c. Red-crowned bishop. (As Type **18**): 2s.50, Great blue turaco; 10s. Black-collared lovebird. 20s. South African crowned crane ("Crowned Crane"). VERT (as Type **16**): 15c. Orange weaver; 20c. Narina's trogon ("Narina Trogon"); 40c. Blue-breasted kingfisher; 50c. Whale-headed stork. (As Type **18**): 1s.30, African fish eagle; 5s. Lilac-breasted roller.

19 Carved Screen

1967. 13th Commonwealth Parliamentary Association Conference. Multicoloured.
127 30c. Type **19** 10 10
128 50c. Arms of Uganda 10 10
129 1s.30 Parliamentary Building 10 10
130 2s.50 Conference Chamber 15 1·75

20 "Cordia abyssinica"

21 "Acacia drepanolobium"

1969. Flowers.
131a **20** 5c. brown, green & yellow 40 10
132 – 10c. multicoloured 10 10
133 – 15c. multicoloured 40 10
134 – 20c. violet, olive and green 15 10
135 – 30c. multicoloured 20 10
136 – 40c. violet, green and grey 20 10
137 – 50c. multicoloured 20 10
138 – 60c. multicoloured 45 1·50
139 – 70c. multicoloured 25 30
140 **21** 1s. multicoloured 20 10
141 – 1s.50 multicoloured 25 10
142a – 2s.50 multicoloured 1·25 10
143a – 5s. multicoloured 1·75 10
144a – 10s. multicoloured 3·75 10
145 – 20s. multicoloured 1·00 5·00
DESIGNS—As Type **20**: 10c. "Grewia similis"; 15c. "Cassia didymobotrya"; 20c. "Coleus barbatus"; 30c. "Ochna ovata"; 40c. "Ipomoea spathulata"; 50c. "Spathodea nilotica"; 60c. "Oncoba spinosa"; 70c. "Carissa edulis". As Type **21**: 1s.50, "Clerodendrum myricoides"; 2s.50, "Acanthus arboreus"; 5s. "Kigelia aethiopium"; 10s. "Erythrina abyssinica"; 20s. "Monodora myristica".

1975. Nos. 140, 142a and 145 surch.
146 2s. on 1s. multicoloured 2·00 1·50
147 3s. on 2s.50 multicoloured 20·00 40·00
148 40s. on 20s. multicoloured 5·50 3·50

23 Millet

24 Maize

1975. Ugandan Crops.
149 23 10c. black, green and brown 10 10
150 – 20c. multicoloured 10 10
151 – 30c. multicoloured 10 10
152 – 40c. multicoloured 10 10
153 – 50c. multicoloured 10 10
154 – 70c. black, green & turq 10 15
155 – 80c. multicoloured 10 15
156 24 1s. multicoloured 10 10
157 – 2s. multicoloured 30 30
158 – 3s. multicoloured 50 45
159 – 5s. multicoloured 50 75
160 – 10s. multicoloured 50 1·25
161 – 20s. green, black and purple 70 2·50
162 – 40s. green, blue and orange 1·10 4·50
DESIGNS—As Type **23**: 20c. Sugar; 30c. Tobacco; 40c. Onions; 50c. Tomatoes; 70c. Tea; 80c. Bananas. As Type **24**: 2s. Pineapples; 3s. Coffee; 5s. Oranges; 10s. Groundnuts; 20s. Cotton; 40s. Runner beans.
Face value colours: 5s. green; 10s. brown; 20s. mauve; 40s. orange.
For these values with colours changed, see Nos. 220/3.

1976. Telecommunications Development. As Nos. 56/60 of Kenya.
163 50c. Microwave tower 10 10
164 1s. Cordless switchboard 10 10
165 2s. Telephone 20 25
166 3s. Message Switching Centre 30 45
MS167 120 × 120 mm. Nos. 163/6 90 1·25

1976. Olympic Games, Montreal. As Nos. 61/5 of Kenya.
168 50c. Akii Bua, hurdler 10 10
169 1s. Filbert Bayi, runner 10 10
170 2s. Steve Muchoki, boxer 30 30
171 3s. East African flags 40 45
MS172 129 × 154 mm. Nos. 168/71 4·00 5·00

1976. Railway Transport. As Nos. 66/70 of Kenya.
173 50c. Diesel-hydraulic train, Tanzania–Zambia railway 15 10
174 1s. Nile Bridge, Uganda 15 10
175 2s. Nakuru Station, Kenya 50 45
176 3s. Uganda Railway Class A locomotive, 1896 55 55
MS177 154 × 103 mm. Nos. 173/6 2·25 2·50

1977. Game Fish of East Africa. As Nos. 71/5 of Kenya. Multicoloured.
178 50c. Nile perch 15 10
179 1s. Nile mouthbrooder 20 10
180 3s. Sailfish 60 40
181 5s. Black marlin 80 60
MS182 153 × 129 mm. Nos. 178/81 3·25 2·00

1977. Second World Black and African Festival of Arts and Culture. As Nos. 76/80 of Kenya. Multicoloured.
183 50c. Maasai manyatta (village), Kenya 10 10
184 1s. "Heartbeat of Africa" (Ugandan dancers) 10 10
185 2s. Makonde sculpture, Tanzania 25 55
186 3s. "Early man and technology" (skinning hippopotamus) 35 85
MS187 132 × 109 mm. Nos. 183/6 1·25 2·25

1977. 25th Anniv of Safari Rally. As Nos. 81/5 of Kenya. Multicoloured.
188 50c. Rally-car and villagers 10 10
189 1s. Starting-line 10 10
190 2s. Car fording river 25 35
191 5s. Car and elephants 80 1·00
MS192 126 × 93 mm. Nos. 188/91 1·50 2·50

1977. Centenary of Ugandan Church. As Nos. 86/90 of Kenya. Multicoloured.
193 50c. Canon Kivebulaya 10 10
194 1s. Modern Namirembe Cathedral 10 10
195 2s. Old Namirembe Cathedral 20 40
196 5s. Early congregation, Kigezi 45 1·10
MS197 126 × 89 mm. Nos. 193/6 1·00 1·75

1977. Design as No. 155 surch **80c.**
198 80c. on 60c. multicoloured 30 20

1977. Endangered Species. As Nos. 96/101 of Kenya. Multicoloured.
199 50c. Pancake tortoise 30 10
200 1s. Nile crocodile 45 10
201 2s. Hunter's hartebeest 1·25 40
202 3s. Red colobus monkey 1·50 75
203 5s. Dugong 1·50 1·00
MS204 127 × 101 mm. Nos. 200/3 4·50 4·00

1978. World Cup Football Championship, Argentina (1st issue). As Nos. 122/6 of Kenya. Multicoloured.
205 50c. Joe Kadenge and forwards 15 10
206 1s. Mohamed Chuma and cup presentation 15 10
207 2s. Omari Kidevu and goalmouth scene 30 45
208 5s. Polly Ouma and forwards 50 1·25
MS209 136 × 81 mm. Nos. 205/8 2·00 2·75

26 Shot Putting

1978. Commonwealth Games, Edmonton. Multicoloured.
210 50c. Type **26** 10 10
211 1s. Long jumping 15 10
212 2s. Running 20 40
213 5s. Boxing 40 1·10
MS214 114 × 85 mm. Nos. 210/13 1·25 3·00

1978. World Cup Football Championship, Argentina (2nd issue). As Nos. 205/8, but additionally inscr "WORLD CUP 1978".
215 50c. Polly Ouma and forwards 15 10
216 2s. Omari Kidevu and goalmouth scene 30 10
217 5s. Joe Kadenge and forwards 60 1·00
218 10s. Mohamed Chuma and cup presentation 90 1·75
MS219 140 × 87 mm. Nos. 215/18 2·00 2·75

1978. As Nos. 159/62, but colours changed.
220 5s. mult (face value in blue) 50 70
221 10s. mult (face value in mauve) 50 85
222 20s. mult (face value in brown) 55 85
223 40s. mult (face value in red) 65 1·10

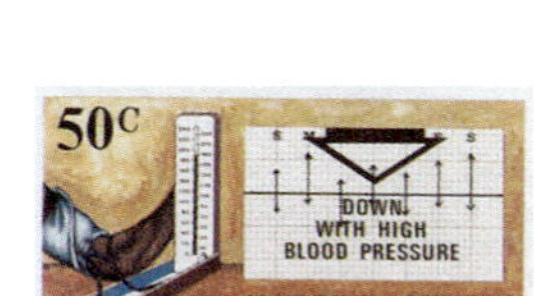

27 Measurements of High Blood Pressure

1978. "Down with High Blood Pressure". Multicoloured.
224 50c. Type **27** 15 10
225 1s. Hypertension and the heart 15 10
226 2s. Fundus of the eye in hypertension 40 45
227 5s. Kidney and high blood pressure 75 1·40
MS228 180 × 115 mm. Nos. 224/7 1·25 2·75

28 Off Loading Cattle

1978. 75th Anniv of Powered Flight. Multicoloured.
229 1s. Type **28** 15 10
230 1s.50 "Domestic services" (passengers boarding Britten Norman Islander) 25 15
231 2s.70 Export of Uganda coffee 25 35
232 10s. "Time machines in the air" (Wright Flyer III and Concorde) 75 1·25
MS233 166 × 110 mm. Nos. 299/32 1·75 2·75

29 Queen Elizabeth II leaving Owen Falls Dam

1979. 25th Anniv of Coronation (1978). Multicoloured.
234 1s. Type **29** 15 10
235 1s.50 Regalia 15 10
236 2s.70 Coronation ceremony 30 20
237 10s. Royal family on balcony of Buckingham Palace 50 1·25
MS238 150 × 102 mm. Nos. 234/7 1·40 1·25

30 Dr. Joseph Kiwanuka (first Ugandan bishop)

1979. Centenary of Catholic Church in Uganda. Multicoloured.
239 1s. Type **30** 10 10
240 1s.50 Lubaga Cathedral 10 10
241 2s.70 Ugandan pilgrimage to Rome, Holy Year, 1975 15 25
242 10s. Friar Lourdel-Mapeera (early missionary) 50 80
MS243 128 × 91 mm. Nos. 239/42 1·00 2·00

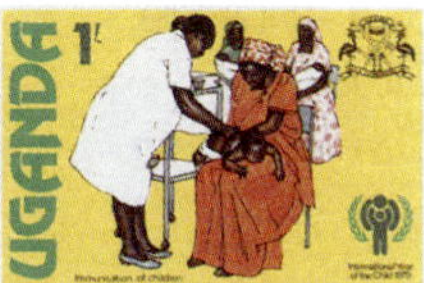

31 Immunization of Children

1979. International Year of the Child. Multicoloured.
244 1s. Type **31** 10 10
245 1s.50 Handicapped children at play 15 20
246 2s.70 Ugandan I.Y.C. emblem 15 35
247 10s. Children in class 40 1·10
MS248 136 × 113 mm. Nos. 244/7 1·10 2·00

1979. Liberation. Optd **UGANDA LIBERATED 1979**. (a) Nos. 149/62.
249 23 10c. black, green and brown 10 10
250 – 20c. multicoloured 10 10
251 – 30c. multicoloured 10 10
252 – 40c. multicoloured 10 10
253 – 50c. multicoloured 10 10
254 – 70c. black, green & turq 10 10
255 – 80c. multicoloured 10 10
256 24 1s. multicoloured 15 15
257 – 2s. multicoloured 20 25
258 – 3s. multicoloured 35 40
259 – 5s. multicoloured 55 60
260 – 10s. multicoloured 80 1·25
261 – 20s. green, black and purple 1·00 2·40
262 – 40s. green, black and orange 1·50 4·75

(b) Nos. 210/13.
263 50c. Type **26** 10 10
264 1s. Long jumping 15 20
265 2s. Running 25 30
266 5s. Boxing 60 65

(c) Nos. 207, 215, 217/18.
267 50c. Polly Ouma and forwards 10 10
268 2s. Omari Kidevu and goalmouth scene 20 30
269 5s. Joe Kadenge and forwards 55 65
270 10s. Mohamed Chuma and cup presentation 1·00 1·40

(d) Nos. 220/3.
271 5s. multicoloured 55 60
272 10s. multicoloured 60 1·25
273 20s. multicoloured 60 2·40
274 40s. multicoloured 75 4·75

(e) Nos. 229/32.
275 1s. Type **28** 35 20
276 1s.50 "Domestic services" 45 25
277 2s.70 Export of Uganda coffee 55 55
278 10s. "Time machines in the air" 2·00 2·00

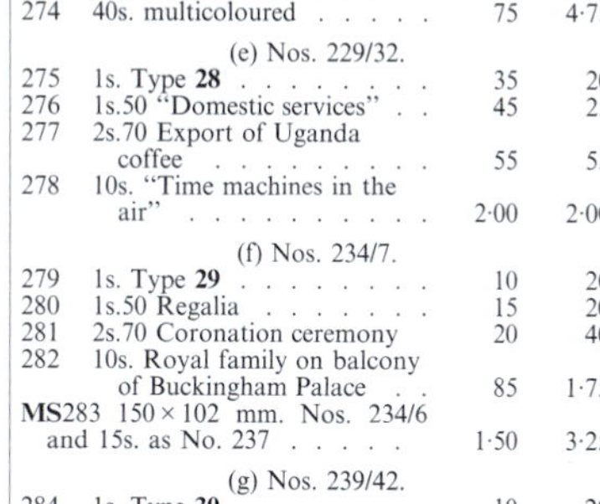

(f) Nos. 234/7.
279 1s. Type **29** 10 20
280 1s.50 Regalia 15 20
281 2s.70 Coronation ceremony 20 40
282 10s. Royal family on balcony of Buckingham Palace 85 1·75
MS283 150 × 102 mm. Nos. 234/6 and 15s. as No. 237 1·50 3·25

(g) Nos. 239/42.
284 1s. Type **30** 10 20
285 1s.50 Lubaga Cathedral 15 25
286 2s.70 Ugandan pilgrimage to Rome, Holy Year, 1975 30 50
287 10s. Friar Lourdel-Mapeera (early missionary) 90 1·75
MS288 128 × 91 mm. Nos. 239/42 1·75 2·75

(h) Nos. 244/8.
289 1s. Type **31** 20 20
290 1s.50 Handicapped children at play 25 25
291 2s.70 Ugandan I.Y.C. emblem 50 60
292 10s. Children in class 1·40 1·75
MS293 136 × 113 mm. Nos. 289/92 2·25 3·50

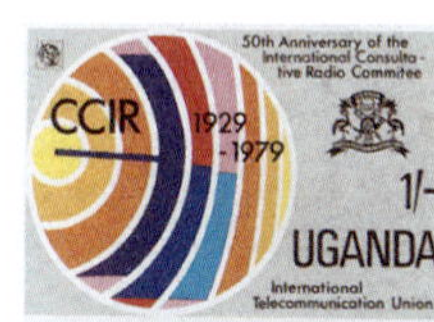

35 Radio Wave Symbol

1979. 50th Anniv of International Consultative Radio Committee and International Telecom-munications Union.
294 35 1s. multicoloured 10 10
295 1s.50 multicoloured 15 10
296 2s.70 multicoloured 15 35
297 10s. multicoloured 40 1·10

36 20s. Definitive Stamp of 1965 and Sir Rowland Hill

1979. Death Cent of Sir Rowland Hill. Mult.
298 1s. Type **36** 10 10
299 1s.50 1967 13th Commonwealth Parliamentary Association Conference 50c. commemorative 15 10
300 2s.70 1962 Independence 20s. commemorative 15 30
301 10s. Uganda Protectorate 1898 1a. 40 1·25
MS302 154 × 98 mm. Nos. 298/301 65 1·50

37 Impala

38 Lions with Cub

1979. Wildlife.
303A 10c. Type **37** 10 20
304A 20c. Large-spotted genet 10 20
305A 30c. Thomson's gazelle 10 20
306A 50c. Lesser bushbaby 10 10
307A 80c. Hunting dog 10 10
308A 1s. Type **38** 10 10
309A 1s.50 Gorilla 40 10
310B 2s. Common zebra 35 20
311A 2s.70 Leopard with cub 35 20
312A 3s.50 Black rhinoceros 50 55
313A 5s. Waterbuck 25 55
314A 10s. African buffalo 30 1·00
315A 20s. Hippopotamus 65 2·00
316A 40s. African elephant 1·00 3·50
SIZES—As Type **37**: 10c. to 80c. As Type **38**: 1s. to 40s.
See also Nos. 433/9.

1980. "London 1980" International Stamp Exhibition. Nos. 298/301 optd **LONDON 1980.**
317 36 1s. multicoloured 15 10
318 – 1s.50 multicoloured 20 10
319 – 2s.70 multicoloured 35 25
320 – 10s. multicoloured 80 80
MS321 154 × 99 mm. Nos. 317/20 1·40 1·75

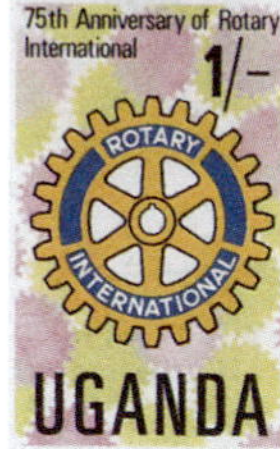

40 Rotary Emblem

1980. 75th Anniv of Rotary International. Multicoloured.
322 1s. Type **40** 10 10
323 20s. Paul P. Harris (founder) with wheel-barrow containing "Rotary projects" (horiz) 1·25 2·00
MS324 100 × 76 mm. Nos. 322/3. Imperf 1·75 2·50

41 Football

1980. Olympic Games, Moscow. Multicoloured.
325 1s. Type **41** 10 10
326 2s. Relay 10 10
327 10s. Hurdles 45 75
328 20s. Boxing 75 2·00
MS329 118 × 90 mm. 2s.70, 3s., 5s., 25s. As Nos. 325/8 1·25 2·25

1981. Olympic Medal Winners. Nos. 325/8 optd.
330 41 1s. multicoloured 10 10
331 – 2s. multicoloured 15 15
332 – 10s. multicoloured 55 80
333 – 20s. multicoloured 85 2·25
MS334 118 × 90 mm. 2s.70, 3s. 5s., 25s. As Nos. 330/3 1·00 2·50
OVERPRINTS: 1s. **FOOTBALL GOLD MEDALISTS, C.S.S.R.**; 2s. **RELAY GOLD MEDALIST U.S.S.R.**; 10s. **HURDLES 110m. GOLD MEDALIST THOMAS MUNKLET, D.D.R.**; 20s. **BOXING WELTERWEIGHT SILVER MEDALIST JOHN MUGABI, UGANDA.**

43 "Christ in the Storm on the Sea of Galilee" (painting, Rembrandt) (½-size illustration)

1980. Christmas. Sheet 79 × 101 mm. Imperf.
MS335 **43** 25s. multicoloured . . 4·25 4·75

44 Heinrich von Stephan and U.P.U. Emblem

1981. 150th Birth Anniv of Heinrich von Stephan (founder of U.P.U.). Multicoloured.
336 1s. Type **44** 10 10
337 2s. U.P.U. Headquarters . . 15 15
338 2s.70 Air mail, 1935 . . . . 40 20
339 10s. Mail transport by train, 1927 . . . . 1·10 80
MS340 112 × 95 mm. Nos. 336/9 2·25 1·90

45 Tower of London

1981. Royal Wedding. Multicoloured. (a) Previously unissued stamps surch.
341e 10s. on 1s. Prince Charles and Lady Diana Spencer 15 20
342e 50s. on 5s. Type **45** 20 30
343e 200s. on 20s. Prince Charles at Balmoral 45 80
MS344 95 × 80 mm. 250s. on 25s. Royal Mews . . . . 3·00 5·50

(b) Stamps reissued with new face values.
345 10s. As No. 341 . . . . . . 10 15
346 50s. Type **45** 15 20
347 200s. As No. 343 . . . . . 30 40
MS348 95 × 80 mm. 250s. As No. **MS**344 . . . . 50 65

48 "Sleeping Woman before Green Shutters"

1981. Birth Centenary of Picasso. Mult.
349 10s. Type **48** 10 10
350 20s. "Bullfight" 20 20
351 30s. "Detail of a Nude asleep in a Landscape" 25 30
352 200s. "Interior with a Girl Drawing" . . . . 1·10 3·25
MS353 120 × 146 mm. 250s. "Minotaure" (112 × 139 mm). Imperf . . . . 2·25 4·00

49 Deaf People using Sign Language

1981. Int Year of Disabled Persons. Mult.
354 1s. Type **49** 10 10
355 10s. Disabled teacher in classroom 15 10
356 50s. Teacher and disabled children 70 50
357 200s. Blind person with guide dog . . . . 1·40 2·00
MS358 122 × 93 mm. Nos. 354/7 3·00 4·00

50 Footballers

1981. World Cup Football Championship, Spain (1982).
359 **50** 1s. multicoloured 10 10
360 – 10s. multicoloured 15 10
361 – 50s. multicoloured 70 50
362 – 200s. multicoloured . . . 2·00 2·00
MS363 116 × 77 mm. 250s. multicoloured . . . . 3·00 3·00
DESIGNS: Nos. 360/63, various football scenes.

51 Mpoma Satellite Earth Station

1982. "Peaceful Use of Outer Space". Multicoloured.
364 5s. Type **51** 25 15
365 10s. "Pioneer II" (satellite) 35 35
366 50s. Space Shuttle . . . . . 1·00 2·00
367 100s. "Voyager 2" (satellite) 1·50 4·00
MS368 118 × 89 mm. 150s. Space Shuttle (different) . . . . . . 3·75 2·00

52 Dr. Robert Koch

54 Yellow-billed Hornbill ("Hornbill")

1982. Centenary of Robert Koch's Discovery of Tubercle Bacillus. Multicoloured.
369 1s. Type **52** 30 10
370 10s. Microscope 90 40
371 50s. Ugandans receiving vaccinations . . . . 2·25 2·50
372 100s. Tubercle virus . . . . 3·50 4·25
MS373 85 × 64 mm. 150s. Medical College classroom scence (horiz) 4·50 2·00

1982. 21st Birthday of Princess of Wales. Nos. 345/7 optd **21st BIRTHDAY HRH Princess of Wales JULY 1 1982**.
374 10s. Prince Charles and Lady Diana Spencer 20 10
375 50s. Type **45** 50 40
376 200s. Prince Charles at Balmoral . . . . 1·00 1·00
MS377 95 × 82 mm. 250s. Royal Mews . . . . 2·00 2·00

1982. Birds. Multicoloured.
378 1s. Type **54** 15 10
379 20s. Superb starling 60 35
380 50s. Bateleur ("Bateleur Eagle") . . . . 1·25 1·75
381 100s. Saddle-bill stork . . . 2·00 2·50
MS382 115 × 85 mm. 200s. Laughing dove . . . . 7·00 9·00

55 Scout Band

1982. 75th Anniv of Boy Scout Movement. Multicoloured.
383 5s. Type **55** 40 10
384 20s. Scout receiving Bata Shoe trophy . . . . 1·10 45
385 50s. Scouts with wheelchair patient . . . . 1·75 2·25
386 100s. First aid instruction . . 2·25 3·50
MS387 112 × 85 mm. 150s. Lord Baden-Powell . . . . 2·50 3·00

56 Swearing-in of Roosevelt

1982. 250th Birth Anniv of George Washington and Birth Centenary of Franklin D. Roosevelt. Multicoloured.
388 50s. Type **56** 30 30
389 200s. Swearing-in of Washington . . . . 75 1·25
MS390 100 × 69 mm. 150s. Washington at Mt Vernon . . 1·00 1·25
MS391 100 × 70 mm. 150s. Roosevelt at Hyde Park Mansion 1·00 1·25

57 Italy v. West Germany

1982. World Cup Football Championship Winners. Multicoloured.
392 10s. Type **57** 30 25
393 200s. Victorious Italian team 1·50 3·50
MS394 97 × 117 mm. 250s. Espana '82 emblem with Spanish and Italian flags . . . . 1·50 2·00

58 Dancers

1983. Commonwealth Day. Cultural Art. Multicoloured.
395 5s. Type **58** 10 10
396 20s. Traditional currency . . 15 20
397 50s. Homestead 35 55
398 100s. Drums . . . . 70 1·10

59 "St. George and the Dragon" (Raphael)

1983. 500th Birth Anniv of Raphael (painter). Multicoloured.
399 5s. Type **59** 10 10
400 20s. "St. George and the Dragon" (different) 25 20
401 50s. "Crossing the Red Sea" (detail) 50 60
402 200s. "The Expulsion of Heliodorus" (detail) . . . 90 3·00
MS403 126 × 101 mm. 250s. "The Meeting of Pope Leo the Great and Attila the Hun" (detail) . . 1·40 1·40

60 Map showing Namibia and U.N. Flag

1983. Commemorations. Multicoloured.
404 5s. Type **60** 10 10
405 200s. 7th Non-aligned Summit Conference logo 60 2·50

61 Elephants in Grassland

1983. Endangered Species (1st series). Mult.
406 5s. Elephants in "Elephants' Graveyard" . . . . 1·50 50
407 10s. Type **61** . . . . 1·75 50
408 30s. Elephants at waterhole 3·75 2·50
409 70s. Elephants having dust bath . . . . 6·00 7·00
MS410 87 × 64 mm. 300s. Grevy's zebra drinking (vert) . . . . 6·50 3·25
See also No. 642 for the 10s. redrawn and Nos. 988/91 for these designs with different face values.

1983. Centenary of Boys' Brigade. Nos. 383/6 optd **BOYS BRIGADE CENTENARY 1883-1983** or surch also.
411 5s. Type **55** 10 10
412 20s. Scout receiving Bata Shoe trophy 15 15
413 50s. Scouts with wheelchair patient 20 30
414 400s. on 100s. First aid instruction . . . . 1·50 3·00
MS415 112 × 85 mm. 150s. Lord Baden-Powell . . . . 70 1·25

63 Mpoma Satellite Earth Station

1983. World Communications Year. Mult.
416 20s. Type **63** 25 15
417 50s. Railroad computer and operator 55 85
418 70s. Cameraman filming lions 60 1·50
419 100s. Aircraft cockpit . . . . 70 2·00
MS420 128 × 103 mm. 300s. Communications satellite . . . 1·00 1·75

1983. Nos. 303, 305/9 and 313 surch.
421 100s. on 10c. Type **37** 85 60
422 135s. on 1s. Type **38** . . . . 1·00 80
423 175s. on 30c. Thomson's gazelle . . . . 1·25 1·25
424 200s. on 50c. Lesser bushbaby . . . . 1·25 1·40
425 400s. on 80c. Hunting dog . . 2·25 3·00
426 700s. on 5s. Waterbuck . . . 3·50 5·50
427 1000s. on 1s.50 Gorilla . . . 6·50 9·00

65 The Nativity

1983. Christmas. Multicoloured.
428 10s. Type **65** 10 10
429 50s. Shepherds and Angels 20 30
430 175s. Flight into Egypt . . . 60 1·25
431 400s. Angels blowing trumpets . . . . 1·00 2·75
MS432 85 × 57 mm. 300s. The Three Kings . . . . 1·40 1·75

1983. As Nos. 308/12 and 315/16, but with face values in revalued currency.
433 100s. Type **38** 90 35
434 135s. Gorilla . . . . 1·25 50
435 175s. Common zebra . . . . 1·40 80
436 200s. Leopard with cub . . . 1·75 90
437 400s. Black rhinoceros . . . 3·00 3·25
438 700s. African elephant . . . 5·00 6·50
439 1000s. Hippopotamus . . . . 7·50 8·50

66 Ploughing with Oxen

1984. World Food Day. Multicoloured.
440 10s. Type **66** 15 10
441 300s. Harvesting bananas . . 2·75 5·50

67 Ruth Kyalisiima, Sportsman of the Year 1983

1984. Olympic Games, Los Angeles. Mult.
442 5s. Type **67** 10 10
443 115s. Javelin-throwing . . . 65 1·00
444 155s. Wrestling . . . . . . 70 1·40
445 175s. Rowing . . . . 70 1·60

68 Entebbe Airport

1984. 40th Anniv of I.C.A.O. Mult.
447 5s. Type **68** 15 10
448 115s. Loading cargo plane 1·50 1·75
449 155s. Uganda police helicopter 2·50 2·75
450 175s. East African Civil Flying School, Soroti 2·75 3·25
MS451 100 × 70 mm. 250s. Balloon race 2·00 1·75

69 "Charaxes druceanus"

1984. Butterflies. Multicoloured.
452 5s. Type **69** 30 10
453 115s. "Papilio lormieri" 2·50 2·00
454 155s. "Druryia antimachus" 3·00 2·50
455 175s. "Salamis temora" 4·25 3·25
MS456 127 × 90 mm. 250s. "Colotis protomedia" 4·50 2·50

70 Blue-finned notho

1985. Lake Fishes. Multicoloured.
457 5s. Type **70** 30 40
458 10s. Semutundu 40 40
459 50s. Grey bichir 75 30
460 100s. Walking catfish 85 30
461 135s. Elephant-snout fish 1·25 1·00
462 175s. Lake Victoria squeaker 1·25 1·60
463 205s. Brown's haplochromis 1·25 2·00
464 400s. Nile perch 1·25 2·25
465 700s. African lungfish 1·25 2·75
466 1000s. Radcliffe's barb 1·25 3·00
467 2500s. Electric catfish 1·50 3·75

71 The Last Supper

1985. Easter. Multicoloured.
468 5s. Type **71** 10 10
469 115s. Christ showing the nail marks to Thomas 1·40 1·40
470 155s. The raising of the Cross 1·60 2·25
471 175s. Pentecost 1·90 2·75
MS472 99 × 70 mm. 250s. The last prayer in the Garden 80 1·25

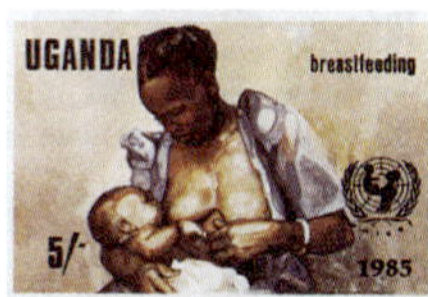

72 Breast Feeding

1985. U.N.I.C.E.F. Child Survival Campaign. Multicoloured.
473 5s. Type **72** 10 10
474 115s. Growth monitoring 1·75 1·75
475 155s. Immunization 2·25 2·25
476 175s. Oral re-hydration therapy 2·50 2·50
MS477 77 × 55 mm. 500s. Pregnant woman preparing nourishing food 4·25 5·00

73 Queen Elizabeth the Queen Mother
74 Sedge Warbler

1985. Life and Times of Queen Elizabeth the Queen Mother and Decade for Women. Multicoloured.
478 **73** 1000s. Type **73** 1·40 2·10
MS479 57 × 81 mm. 1500s. The Queen Mother inspecting Kings African Rifles, Kampala 2·25 3·50

1985. Birth Bicentenary of John J. Audubon (ornithologist) (1st issue). Multicoloured.
480 115s. Type **74** 2·00 1·50
481 155s. Cattle egret 2·25 1·75
482 175s. Crested lark 2·50 2·25
483 500s. Tufted duck 3·25 4·50
MS484 99 × 69 mm. 1000s. Twany owl 11·00 11·00
See also Nos. 494/8.

1985. Olympic Gold Medal Winners, Los Angeles. Nos. 442/5 optd or surch also.
485 5s. Type **67** (optd **GOLD MEDALIST BENITA BROWN-FITZGERALD USA**) 10 10
486 115s. Javelin-throwing (optd **GOLD MEDALIST ARTO HAERKOENEN FINLAND**) 60 30
487 155s. Wrestling (optd **GOLD MEDALIST ATSUJI MIYAHARA JAPAN**) 70 40
488 1000s. on 175s. Rowing (surch **GOLD MEDALIST WEST GERMANY**) 2·50 2·00
MS489 108 × 79 mm. 1200s. on 500s. Fund rasing walk (surch **MEN'S HURDLES EDWIN MOSES USA**) 2·25 2·50
On No. **MS**489 only the new value appears on the stamp the remainder of the surcharge is on the sheet margin.

76 Women carrying National Women's Day Banner
77 Man beneath Tree laden with Produce (F.A.O.)

76a Rock Ptarmigan

1985. Decade for Women. Multicoloured.
490 5s. Type **76** 10 10
491 115s. Girl Guides (horiz) 1·75 2·00
492 155s. Mother Teresa (Nobel Peace Prize winner, 1979) 3·00 3·25
MS493 85 × 59 mm. 1500s. As 115s. 4·00 4·00
No. 491 and **MS**493 also commemorates the 75th anniversary of Girl Guide movement.

1985. Birth Bicentenary of John J. Audubon (ornithologist) (2nd issue). Multicoloured.
494 5s. Type **76a** 55 10
495 155s. Sage grouse 2·00 1·75
496 175s. Lesser yellowlegs 2·00 2·25
497 500s. Brown-headed cowbird 3·25 4·50
MS498 72 × 102 mm. 1000s. Whooping crane 9·50 9·50

1986. 40th Anniv of U.N.O.
499 **77** 10s. multicoloured 10 10
500 – 180s. multicoloured 40 30
501 – 200s. blue, brown and green 40 35
502 – 250s. blue, black and red 40 40
503 – 2000s. multicoloured 1·25 5·00
MS504 69 × 69 mm. 2500s. multicoloured 1·75 2·75
DESIGNS—HORIZ: 180s. Soldier of U.N. Peace-keeping Force; 250s. Hands releasing peace dove. VERT: 200s. U.N. emblem; 2000s. Flags of U.N. and Uganda; 2500s. U.N. Building, New York, and Flags of member nations.

78 Goalkeeper catching Ball

1986. World Cup Football Championship, Mexico. Multicoloured.
505 10s. Type **78** 10 10
506 180s. Player with ball 85 55
507 250s. Two players competing for ball 1·00 65
508 2500s. Player running with ball 5·50 6·00
MS509 87 × 66 mm. 3000s. Player kicking ball (vert) 4·75 3·50

1986. Liberation by National Resistance Army. Nos. 462, 464/7 and **MS**493 optd **NRA LIBERATION 1986**.
510 175s. Lake Victoria squeaker 70 70
511 400s. Nile perch 1·25 1·25
512 700s. African lungfish 1·75 2·50
513 1000s. Radcliffe's barb 2·00 3·00
514 2500s. Electric catfish 3·00 6·00
MS514a 85 × 59 mm. 1500s. Girl Guides 5·00 2·50

1986. Appearance of Halley's Comet (1st issue). As T **191b** of Sierre Leone. Multicoloured.
515 50s. Tycho Brahe and Arecibo Radio Telescope, Puerto Rico 20 10
516 100s. Recovery of astronaut John Glenn from sea, 1962 35 15
517 140s. "The Star in the East" (painting by Giotto) 50 30
518 2500s. Death of Davy Crockett at the Alamo, 1835 3·75 6·00
MS519 102 × 70 mm. 3000s. Halley's Comet over Uganda 6·50 6·00
See also Nos. 544/8.

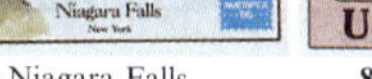
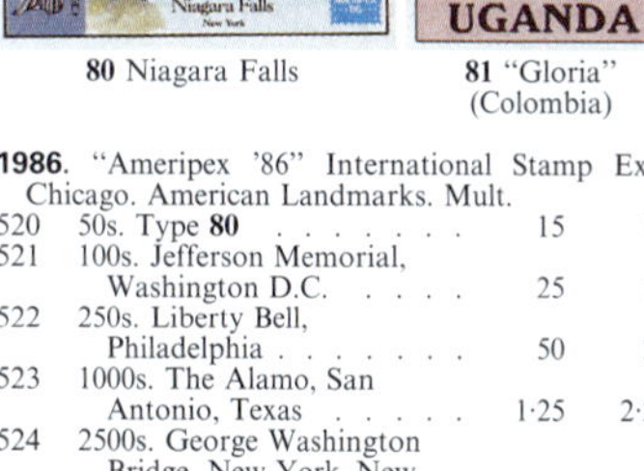

80 Niagara Falls
81 "Gloria" (Colombia)

1986. "Ameripex '86" International Stamp Exn, Chicago. American Landmarks. Mult.
520 50s. Type **80** 15 10
521 100s. Jefferson Memorial, Washington D.C. 25 15
522 250s. Liberty Bell, Philadelphia 50 35
523 1000s. The Alamo, San Antonio, Texas 1·25 2·25
524 2500s. George Washington Bridge, New York–New Jersey 1·75 5·00
MS525 87 × 64 mm. 3000s. Grand Canyon 2·00 3·25

1986. 60th Birthday of Queen Elizabeth II. As T **191c** of Sierre Leone.
526 100s. black and yellow 60 15
527 140s. multicoloured 60 20
528 2500s. multicoloured 3·25 4·25
MS529 120 × 85 mm. 3000s. black and brown 4·00 4·00
DESIGNS: 100s. Princess Elizabeth at London Zoo; 140s. Queen Elizabeth at race meeting, 1970; 2500s. With Prince Philip at Sandringham, 1982; 3000s. Engagement photograph, 1947.

1986. Centenary of Statue of Liberty. Cadet Sailing Ships. Multicoloured.
530 50s. Type **81** 60 20
531 100s. "Mircea" (Rumania) 95 30
532 140s. "Sagres II" (Portugal) (horiz) 1·60 1·00
533 2500s. "Gazela Primeiro" (U.S.A.) (horiz) 7·00 10·00
MS534 113 × 82 mm. 3000s. Statue of Liberty 3·25 3·50
No. 533 is inscribed "Primero" in error.

1986. Royal Wedding. As T **192c** of Sierre Leone. Multicoloured.
535 50s. Prince Andrew and Miss Sarah Ferguson (horiz) 10 10
536 140s. Prince Andrew with Princess Anne at shooting match (horiz) 20 20
537 2500s. Prince Andrew and Miss Sarah Ferguson at Ascot (horiz) 2·75 4·00
MS538 88 × 88 mm. 3000s. Prince Andrew and Miss Sarah Ferguson (different) 3·00 3·25

1986. World Cup Football Championship Winners, Mexico. Nos. 505/8 optd **WINNERS Argentina 3 W.Germany 2** or surch also.
539 50s. on 10s. Type **78** 10 10
540 180s. Player with ball 25 25
541 250s. Two players competing for ball 35 35
542 2500s. Player running with ball 2·75 4·50
MS543 87 × 66 mm. 3000s. Player kicking ball (vert) 4·75 3·25

1986. Appearance of Halley's Comet (2nd issue). Nos. 515/18 optd as T **198a** of Sierre Leone.
544 50s. Tycho Brahe and Arecibo Radio Telescope, Puerto Rico 20 15
545 100s. Recovery of astronaut John Glenn from sea, 1962 35 20
546 140s. "The Star in the East" (painting by Giotto) 55 40
547 2500s. Death of Davy Crockett at the Alamo, 1835 5·50 7·50
MS548 102 × 70 mm. 3000s. Halley's Comet over Uganda 5·50 5·00

83 St. Kizito

1986. Christian Martyrs of Uganda. Mult.
549 50s. Type **83** 15 10
550 150s. St. Kizito instructing converts 30 25
551 200s. Martyrdom of Bishop James Hannington, 1885 40 30
552 1000s. Burning of Bugandan Christians, 1886 1·60 3·00
MS553 89 × 59 mm. 1500s. King Mwanga of Buganda passing sentence on Christians 1·50 2·25

84 "Madonna of the Cherries" (Titian)

1986. Christmas. Religious Paintings. Mult.
554 50s. Type **84** 25 15
555 150s. "Madonna and Child" (Durer) (vert) 60 30
556 200s. "Assumption of the Virgin" (Titian) (vert) 70 40
557 2500s. "Praying Hands" (Durer) (vert) 5·50 8·00
MS558 Two sheets, each 102 × 76 mm. (a) 3000s. "Presentation of the Virgin in the Temple" (Titian). (b) 3000s. "Adoration of the Magi" (Durer) Set of 2 sheets 8·00 9·00

85 Red-billed Fire Finch and Glory Lily

1987. Flora and Fauna. Multicoloured.
559 2s. Type **85** 55 55
560 5s. African pygmy kingfisher and nandi flame 70 70
561 10s. Scarlet-chested sunbird and crown of thorns 85 70
562 25s. White rhinoceros and yellow-billed oxpecker 1·50 1·00
563 35s. Lion and elephant grass 1·00 1·10
564 45s. Cheetahs and doum palm 1·25 1·50
565 50s. Red-cheeked cordon-bleu and desert rose 2·00 2·00
566 100s. Giant eland and acacia 2·25 3·50
MS567 Two sheets, each 98 × 67 mm. (a) 150s. Carmine bee eaters and sausage tree. (b) 150s. Cattle egret and zebras Set of 2 sheets 7·00 8·00

86 Tremml's "Eagle" (longest man-powered flight), 1987

1987. Milestones of Transportation. Mult.
568 2s. Type **86** 20 50
569 3s. Junkers W.33 "Bremen" (first east-west transatlantic flight), 1928 20 50
570 5s. Lockheed Vega 5 "Winnie Mae" (Post's first solo round-the-world flight), 1933 30 60
571 10s. "Voyager" (first non-stop round-the-world flight), 1986 40 60
572 15s. Chanute biplane glider, 1896 70 80
573 25s. Airship N.1 "Norge" and polar bear (first transpolar flight), 1926 1·00 1·00
574 35s. Curtiss Golden Flyer biplane and U.S.S. "Pennsylvania" (battleship) (first take-off and landing from ship), 1911 1·40 1·25

575 45s. Shepard and "Freedom 7" spacecraft (first American in space), 1961 . . 1·60 1·50
576 100s. Concorde (first supersonic passenger flight), 1976 . . . . 5·50 5·50

87 Olympic Torch-bearer

1987. Olympic Games, Seoul (1988) (1st issue). Multicoloured.
577 5s. Type **87** 10 10
578 10s. Swimming 20 25
579 50s. Cycling . . . . 1·00 1·25
580 100s. Gymnastics . . . . . . 2·00 2·50
MS581 100 × 775 mm. 150s. Boxing 3·00 4·00
See also Nos. 628/32.

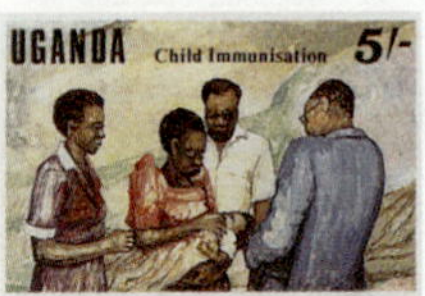

88 Child Immunization

1987. 25th Anniv of Independence.
582 **88** 5s. multicoloured 15 10
583 – 10s. multicoloured 30 25
584 – 25s. multicoloured 70 70
585 – 50s. multicoloured . . . . 1·25 1·50
MS586 90 × 70 mm. 100s. black, red and yellow . . . . 2·00 2·75
DESIGNS: 10s. Mulago Hospital, Kampala; 25s. Independence Mounument, Kampala City Park; 50s. High Court, Kampala; 100s. Stylized head of crested crane, "25" and Ugandan flag.

89 Eastern Golden-backed Weaver ("Golden-backed Weaver")

90 Hippocrates (physician) and Surgeons performing Operation

1987. Birds of Uganda. Multicoloured.
587 5s. Type **89** 85 80
588 10s. Hoopoe . . . . 1·75 1·25
589 15s. Red-throated bee eater . 1·90 1·25
590 25s. Lilac-breasted roller . . 2·50 1·60
591 35s. African pygmy goose ("Pygmy Goose") . . . . 2·50 1·75
592 45s. Scarlet-chested sunbird 2·75 2·50
593 50s. South African crowned crane ("Crowned Crane") 2·75 2·50
594 100s. Long-tailed fiscal ("Long-tailed Fiscal Shrike") . . . . . . 4·50 5·00
MS595 Two sheets, each 80 × 60 mm. (a) 150s. African fish eagle. (B) 150s. Barn owl Set of 2 sheets . . . . 6·50 8·00

1987. Great Scientific Discoveries. Mult.
596 5s. Type **90** 60 30
597 25s. Einstein and deep space (Theory of Relativity) . . . 2·50 1·75
598 35s. Isaac Newton and diagram from "Opticks" (Theory of Colour and Light) . . . . 2·75 2·50
599 45s. Karl Benz and early Benz and modern Mercedes car . . . . 3·25 3·00
MS600 97 × 70 mm. 150s. "Challenger" (space shuttle) (vert) 3·75 4·00

91 Scout with Stamp Album and Uganda Stamps

1987. World Scout Jamboree, Australia. Multicoloured.
601 5s. Type **91** 20 10
602 25s. Scouts planting tree . . 70 70
603 35s. Canoeing, Lake Victoria 1·25 85
604 45s. Hiking . . . . 1·75 1·10
MS605 95 × 65 mm. 150s. Jamboree and Uganda scout emblems . . 3·00 4·00

92 "The Annunciation"

1987. Christmas. Scenes from French diptych, c. 1250. Multicoloured.
606 5s. Type **92** 10 10
607 10s. "The Nativity" 20 25
608 50s. "Flight into Egypt" . . . 1·00 1·25
609 100s. "The Adoration of the Magi" . . . . 2·00 2·50

93 Class 12 Light Shunter Locomotive

94 Columbite-Tantalite

1988. Locomotives of East Africa Railways. Multicoloured.
611 5s. Type **93** 60 35
612 10s. Class 92 diesel-electric 70 45
613 15s. Steam locomotive No. 2506 . . . . 90 60
614 25s. Class 11 tank locomotive 1·25 85
615 35s. Class 24 steam locomotive . . . . 1·50 1·10
616 45s. Class 21 steam locomotive . . . . 1·75 1·40
617 50s. Class 59 Garratt steam locomotive, 1955 . . . . 2·00 1·60
618 100s. Class 87 diesel-electric locomotive . . . . 3·00 2·40
MS619 Two sheets, each 100 × 74 mm. (a) 150s. Class 31 steam locomotive. (b) 150s. Class 59 Garratt steam locomotive Set of 2 sheets . . . . 8·00 7·50

1988. Minerals. Multicoloured.
620 1s. Type **94** 15 15
621 2s. Galena 20 20
622 5s. Malachite 35 35
623 10s. Cassiterite 55 55
624 35s. Ferberite . . . . 1·50 1·50
625 50s. Emerald . . . . 2·00 2·00
626 100s. Monazite . . . . . . 3·00 3·00
627 150s. Microcline . . . . . . 4·00 4·00

95 Hurdling

1988. Olympic Games, Seoul (2nd issue). Mult.
628 5s. Type **95** 10 10
629 25s. High jumping 40 50
630 35s. Javelin throwing 45 55
631 45s. Long jumping 55 70
MS632 85 × 114 mm. 150s. Olympic medals . . . . 1·00 1·50

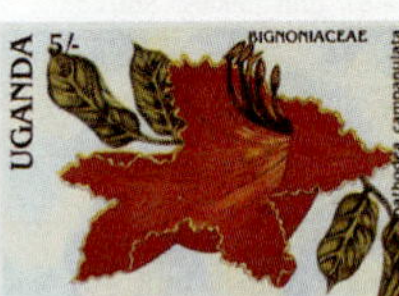

96 "Spathodea campanulata"

1988. Flowers. Multicoloured.
633 5s. Type **96** 15 15
634 10s. "Gloriosa simplex" . . . 15 15
635 20s. "Thevetica peruviana" (vert) 20 20
636 25s. "Hibiscus schizopetalus" 20 25
637 35s. "Aframomum sceptrum" 20 30
638 45s. "Adenium obesum" . . 20 35
639 50s. "Kigelia africana" (vert) 25 40
640 100s. "Clappertonia ficifolia" 35 75
MS641 Two sheets, each 109 × 79 mm. (a) 150s. "Costus spectabilis". (b) 150s. "Canarina abyssinica" (vert) Set of 2 sheets 2·00 2·75

97 Elephants in Grassland (Type **61** redrawn)

1988. Endangered Species (2nd series).
642 **97** 10s. multicoloured . . . . 65·00 4·00

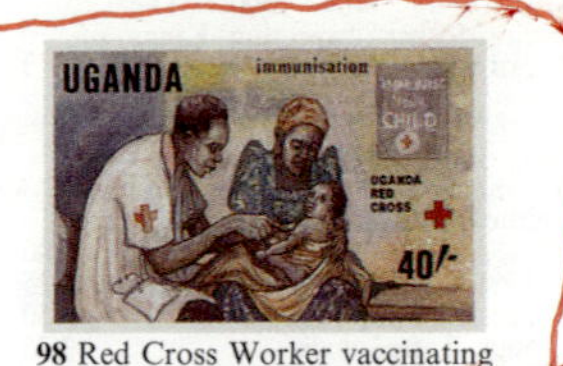

98 Red Cross Worker vaccinating Baby

1988. 125th Anniv of International Red Cross.
643 **98** 10s. red, yellow and black 25 15
644 – 40s. multicoloured 70 70
645 – 70s. multicoloured . . . . 1·50 2·00
646 – 90s. multicoloured . . . . 2·00 2·25
MS647 110 × 78 mm. 150s. multicoloured . . . . 1·00 1·60
DESIGNS—HORIZ: 10s. "AIDS" with test tube as "I"; 70s. Distributing food to refugees; 90s. Red Cross volunteers with accident victim. VERT: Henri Dunant (founder).

1988. 500th Birth Anniv of Titian (artist). As T **183a** of St. Vincent. Multicoloured.
648 10s. "Portrait of a Lady" . . 15 15
649 20s. "Portrait of a Man" . . 20 20
650 40s. "Isabella d'Este" 35 35
651 50s. "Vincenzo Mosti" . . . 45 45
652 70s. "Pope Paul III Farnese" 50 60
653 90s. "Violante" 60 75
654 100s. "Titian's Daughter Lavinia" 70 85
655 250s. "Dr. Parma" . . . . . 1·40 1·90
MS656 Two sheets, each 110 × 95 mm. (a) 350s. "The Speech of Alfonso D'Avalos" (detail). (b) 350s. "Cain and Abel" (detail) Set of 2 sheets . . . . 6·50 7·50

99 Giraffes, Kidepo Valley National Park

1988. National Parks of Uganda. Mult.
657 10s. Type **99** . . . . 1·25 30
658 25s. Zebras, Lake Mburo National Park . . . . . . 1·50 30
659 100s. African buffalo, Murchison Falls National Park . . . . 2·25 2·50
660 250s. Eastern white pelicans, Queen Elizabeth National Park . . . . 6·50 7·00
MS661 97 × 68 mm. 350s. Roan antelopes, Lake Mburo National Park . . . . 2·50 2·75

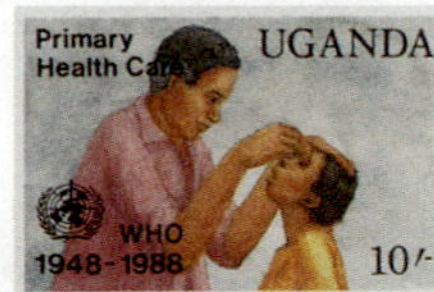

100 Doctor examining Child's Eyes

1988. 40th Anniv of W.H.O. Multicoloured.
662 10s. Type **100** 20 15
663 25s. Mental health therapist with patient 40 30
664 45s. Surgeon performing operation 60 60
665 100s. Dentist treating girl . . 1·25 1·50
666 200s. Doctor examining child 2·00 2·50
MS667 107 × 88 mm. 350s. Delegates approving Declaration of Alma-Ata, 1978 . . . . 2·50 3·50

1988. Christmas. "Santa's Helpers". As T **219a** of Sierre Leone showing Walt Disney cartoon characters. Multicoloured.
668 50s. Father Christmas with list . . . . 1·00 1·00
669 50s. Goofy carrying presents 1·00 1·00
670 50s. Mickey Mouse on toy train . . . . 1·00 1·00
671 50s. Reindeer at window . . 1·00 1·00
672 50s. Donald Duck's nephew with building blocks . . . 1·00 1·00
673 50s. Donald Duck holding sack . . . . 1·00 1·00
674 50s. Chip n' Dale on conveyor belt . . . . . . 1·00 1·00
675 50s. Donald Duck's nephew operating conveyor belt . . 1·00 1·00
MS676 Two sheets, each 127 × 102 mm. (a) 350s. Mickey Mouse loading sack of toys on sleigh (horiz). (b) 350s. Mickey Mouse and Chip n'Dale grooming reindeer. Set of 2 sheets . . . 7·50 8·50

Nos. 668/75 were printed together, se-tenant, as a composite design.

1989. Olympic Gold Medal Winners, Seoul. Nos. 628/31 optd or surch.
677 5s. Type **95** (optd **110 M HURDLES R. KINGDOM USA**) . . . 10 10
678 25s. High jumping (optd **HIGH JUMP G. AVDEENKO USSR**) 20 25
679 35s. Javelin throwing (optd **JAVELIN T. KORJUS FINLAND**) 25 30
680 300s. on 45s. Long jumping (optd **LONG JUMP C. LEWIS USA**) . . . . . 2·50 3·00
MS681 85 × 114 mm. 350s. on 150s. Olympic medals with medal table optd on sheet margin . . . . 3·00 4·00

102 Goalkeeper with Ball

103 1895 5 Cowries Stamp

1989. World Cup Football Championship, Italy (1990) (1st issue). Multicoloured.
682 10s. Type **102** 25 15
683 25s. Player kicking ball (horiz) 55 40
684 75s. Heading ball towards net (horiz) . . . . 1·25 1·10
685 200s. Tackling . . . . 2·25 2·75
MS686 118 × 87 mm. 300s. Football and World Cup trophy (horiz) 2·50 3·25
See also Nos. 849/53.

1989. Japanese Art. Paintings by Hokusai. As T **188a** of St. Vincent. Multicoloured.
687 10s. "Fuji and the Great Wave off Kanagawa" . . . 30 30
688 15s. "Fuji from Lake Suwa" 40 35
689 20s. "Fuji from Kajikazawa" 40 35
690 60s. "Fuji from Shichirigahama" . . . . 1·00 85
691 90s. "Fuji from Ejiri in Sunshu" . . . . 1·25 1·10
692 120s. "Fuji above Lightning" 1·50 1·25
693 200s. "Fuji from Lower Meguro in Edo" . . . . . . 2·25 2·00
694 250s. "Fuji from Edo" . . . 2·50 2·25
MS695 Two sheets, each 102 × 76 mm. (a) 500s. "The Red Fuji from the Foot". (b) 500s. "Fuji from Umezawa" Set of 2 sheets . . . . 9·00 9·00

1989. "Philexfrance 89" International Stamp Exhibition, Paris.
696 **103** 20s. black, red and brown 50 35
697 – 70s. black, green and blue 1·25 1·00
698 – 100s. black, violet & pink 1·50 1·50
699 – 250s. black, yell & lt yell 2·25 2·75
MS700 176 × 131 mm. Nos. 696/9 (sold at 500s.) . . . . 6·50 8·00
DESIGNS: 70s. 1895 10 on 50 cowries stamp; 100s. 1896 25 cowries stamp; 250s. 1896 1 rupee stamp.

104 Scout advising on Immunization

1989. 2nd All African Scout Jamboree, Uganda, and 75th Anniv of Uganda Scout Movement. Multicoloured.
701 10s. Type **104** 30 15
702 70s. Poultry keeping . . . . 1·10 90
703 90s. Scout on crutches leading family to immunization centre . . . 1·50 1·75
704 100s. Scouts making bricks . 1·50 1·75
MS705 99 × 67 mm. 500s. Ugandan Scout logo (vert) . . . . . . 3·25 4·50

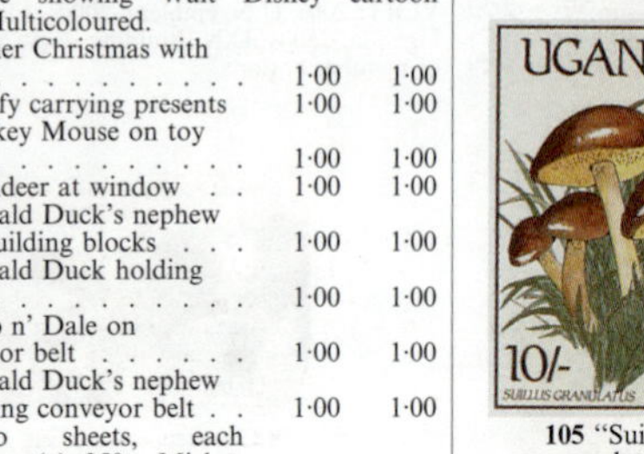

105 "Suillus granulatus"

106 Saddle-bill Stork

1989. Fungi. Multicoloured.
706 10s. Type **105** 40 30
707 15s. "Omphalotus olearius" . 55 40

708 45s. "Oudemansiella radicata" . . . . 1·25 1·00
709 50s. "Clitocybe nebularis" . . 1·25 1·10
710 60s. "Macrolepiota rhacodes" 1·40 1·25
711 75s. "Lepista nuda" . . . . 1·60 1·40
712 150s. "Suillus luteus" . . . . 2·75 3·00
713 200s. "Agaricus campestris" 3·00 3·25
MS714 Two sheets, each 100 × 68 mm. (a) 350s. "Bolbitius vitellinus" (b) 350s. "Schizophyllum commune" Set of 2 sheets . . . . 12·00 11·00

1989. Wildlife at Waterhole. Multicoloured.
715 30s. Type **106** 75 75
716 30s. Eastern white pelican . . 75 75
717 30s. Marabou stork 75 75
718 30s. Egyptian vulture 75 75
719 30s. Bateleur 75 75
720 30s. African elephant 75 75
721 30s. Giraffe 75 75
722 30s. Goliath heron 75 75
723 30s. Black rhinoceros 75 75
724 30s. Common zebra and oribi 75 75
725 30s. African fish eagle . . . 75 75
726 30s. Hippopotamus 75 75
727 30s. Black-backed jackal and eastern white pelican . . . 75 75
728 30s. African buffalo 75 75
729 30s. Olive baboon 75 75
730 30s. Bohar reedbuck 75 75
731 30s. Lesser flamingo and serval 75 75
732 30s. Whale-headed stork ("Shoebill Stork") 75 75
733 30s. South African crowned crane 75 75
734 30s. Impala 75 75
MS735 Two sheets, each 99 × 68 mm. (a) 500s. Lion. (b) 500s. Long-crested eagle Set of 2 sheets . . . . 6·50 8·00

Nos. 715/34 were printed together, se-tenant, forming a composite design showing wildlife at a waterhole.

107 Rocket on Launch Pad

1989. 20th Anniv of First Manned Landing on Moon. Multicoloured.
736 10s. Type **107** 30 20
737 20s. Lunar module "Eagle" on Moon 40 30
738 30s. "Apollo 11" command module 50 40
739 50s. "Eagle" landing on Moon 80 60
740 70s. Astronaut Aldrin on Moon . . . . 1·25 85
741 250s. Neil Armstrong alighting from "Eagle" (vert) . . . . 3·50 2·50
742 300s. "Eagle" over Moon . . 3·50 2·75
743 350s. Astronaut Aldrin on Moon (vert) . . . . 3·50 3·00
MS744 Two sheets, each 77 × 104 mm. (a) 500s. "Saturn" rocket (vert). (b) 500s. "Apollo 11" capsule on parachutes (vert) Set of 2 sheets 7·50 9·00

108 "Aphniolaus pallene"

1989. Butterflies. T **108** and similar vert designs showing "UGANDA" in black. Multicoloured.
745 5s. Type **108** 30 20
746 10s. "Hewitsonia boisduvali" 40 25
747 20s. "Euxanthe wakefieldi" 60 30
748 30s. "Papilio echerioides" . . 70 30
749 40s. "Acraea semivitrea" . . 75 40
750 50s. "Colotis antevippe" . . 75 50
751 70s. "Acraea perenna" . . 90 70
752 90s. "Charaxes cynthia" . . 90 70
753 100s. "Euphaedra neophron" 90 70
754 150s. "Cymothoe beckeri" . . 1·25 1·00
755 200s. "Vanessula milca" . . 1·25 1·25
756 400s. "Mimacraea marshalli" 1·50 2·50
757 500s. "Axiocerses amanga" 1·50 2·75
758 1000s. "Precis hierta" . . . . 2·00 4·50

For these, and similar designs showing "UGANDA" in blue, see Nos. 864/80.

109 John Hanning Speke and Map of Lake Victoria

1989. Exploration of Africa. Multicoloured.
760 10s. Type **109** 55 35
761 25s. Sir Richard Burton and map of Lake Tanganyika 75 50
762 40s. Richard Lander and Bakota bronze 80 65
763 90s. Rene Caillie and mosque, Timbuktu . . . . 1·25 1·00
764 125s. Sir Samuel Baker and dorcas gazelle . . . . . . 1·40 1·50
765 150s. Pharaoh Necho and ancient Phoenician merchant ship . . . . . . 1·60 1·75
766 250s. Vasco da Gama and 15th-century caravel . . . 2·50 2·75
767 300s. Sir Henry Morton Stanley and "Lady Alice" (sectional boat) . . . . . 2·75 3·00
MS768 Two sheets, each 73 × 103 mm. (a) 500s. Dr. David Livingstone and steam launch "Ma Robert" (b) 500s. Mary Kingsley and map of Ogooue River Set of 2 sheets . . . . . 8·50 9·50

110 Logo (25th anniv of African Development Bank)

1989. Anniversaries. Multicoloured.
769 10s. Type **110** 25 15
770 20s. Arrows and dish aerials (World Telecommunication Day) 25 20
771 75s. Two portraits of Nehru (birth centenary) . . . . 2·00 1·50
772 90s. Pan Am Boeing 314A flying boat "Dixie Clipper" (50th anniv of first scheduled trans-Atlantic airmail flight) . . . . . . 2·00 1·50
773 100s. George Stephenson and "Locomotion", 1825 (175th anniv of first practical steam locomotive) . . . . 2·25 1·60
774 150s. Concorde cockpit (20th anniv of first test flight) . . 3·50 3·00
775 250s. "Wapen von Hamburg" and "Leopoldus Primus" (galleons) (800th anniv of Port of Hamburg) . . . . 3·25 3·75
776 300s. Concorde and cockpit interior (20th anniv of first test flight) . . . . 4·00 4·00
MS777 Two sheets (a) 91 × 87 mm. 500s. Revolutionary with musket and Bastille, Paris (bicentenary of French Revolution). (b) 110 × 82 mm. 500s. Emperor Frederick I Barbarossa and Hamburg charter (800th anniv of Port of Hamburg) Set of 2 sheets 8·50 9·50

111 "Aerangis kotschyana"

112 "Thevetia peruviana"

1989. Orchids. Multicoloured.
778 10s. Type **111** 25 25
779 15s. "Angraecum infundibulare" 30 30
780 45s. "Cyrtorchis chailluana" 70 70
781 50s. "Aerangis rhodosticta" 75 75
782 100s. "Eulophia speciosa" . . 1·50 1·50
783 200s. "Calanthe sylvatica" . . 2·25 2·25
784 250s. "Vanilla imperialis" . . 2·40 2·40
785 350s. "Polystachya vulcanica" 2·75 2·75
MS786 Two sheets each 110 × 82 mm. (a) 500s. "Ansellia africana". (b) 500s. "Ancistrochilus rothschildianus" Set of 2 sheets . . . . 9·00 9·00

1989. Christmas. Paintings by Fra Angelico. As T **204a** of St. Vincent. Multicoloured.
787 10s. "Madonna and Child" 15 10
788 20s. "Adoration of the Magi" 20 15
789 40s. "Virgin and Child enthroned with Saints" . . 40 30
790 75s. "The Annunciation" . . 70 60
791 100s. "Virgin and Child" (detail, "St. Peter Martyr" triptych) 85 75
792 150s. "Virgin and Child enthroned with Saints" (different) . . . . 1·25 1·50
793 250s. "Virgin and Child enthroned" . . . . 1·75 2·25
794 350s. "Virgin and Child" (from Annalena altarpiece) 2·00 3·25
MS795 Two sheets, each 72 × 96 mm. (a) 500s. "Virgin and Child" (from Bosco ai Frati altarpiece). (b) 500s. "Madonna and Child with Twelve Angels" Set of 2 sheets . . . . 5·00 6·00

1990. "Expo '90" International Garden and Greenery Exhibition, Osaka (1st issue). Flowering Trees. Multicoloured.
796 10s. Type **112** 15 15
797 20s. "Acanthus eminens" . . 20 20
798 90s. "Gnidia glauca" 50 50
799 150s. "Oncoba spinosa" . . . 70 70
800 175s. "Hibiscus rosa-sinensis" 75 75
801 400s. "Jacaranda mimosifolia" . . . . . . 1·25 1·75
802 500s. "Erythrina abyssinica" 1·40 1·90
803 700s. "Bauhinia purpurea" 1·60 2·25
MS804 Two sheets, each 93 × 85 mm. (a) 1000s. "Delonix regia". (b) 1000s. "Cassia didymobotrya" Set of 2 sheets 10·00 11·00

See also Nos. 820/8.

1990. 50th Anniv of Second World War. As T **206a** of St. Vincent. Multicoloured.
805 5s. Allied penetration of German West Wall, 1944 25 25
806 10s. Flags of the Allies, VE Day, 1945 . . . . 35 35
807 20s. Capture of Okinawa, 1945 . . . . 45 45
808 75s. Appointment of Gen. De Gaulle to command all Free French forces, 1944 70 60
809 100s. Invasion of Saipan, 1944 . . . . 85 75
810 150s. Airborne landing, Operation Market Garden, 1944 . . . . 1·50 1·40
811 200s. MacArthur's return to Philippines, 1944 . . . . 1·60 1·50
812 300s. "Shoho" (Japanese aircraft carrier) under attack, Coral Sea, 1942 . . 1·75 1·75
813 350s. First Battle of El Alamein, 1942 . . . . . . 1·90 1·90
814 500s. Naval Battle of Guadalcanal, 1942 . . . . 2·25 2·50
MS815 112 × 83 mm. 1000s. Battle of Britain, 1940 (vert) . . . . . 3·75 4·50

1990. 90th Birthday of Queen Elizabeth the Queen Mother. As T **208a** of St. Vincent.
816 250s. black, mauve and blue 1·10 1·25
817 250s. black, mauve and blue 1·10 1·25
818 250s. black, mauve and blue 1·10 1·25
MS819 90 × 75 mm. 1000s. multicoloured . . . . 2·75 3·25

DESIGNS: No. 816, Queen Elizabeth with corgi; Nos. 817, **MS**819, Queen Elizabeth wearing feathered hat; No. 818, Queen Elizabeth at wartime inspection.

1990. "EXPO 90". International Garden and Greenery Exhibition, Osaka (2nd issue). Nos. 778/85 optd **EXPO '90** and emblem.
820 10s. Type **111** 60 40
821 15s. "Angraecum infundibulare" 60 40
822 45s. "Cyrtorchis chailluana" 95 45
823 50s. "Aerangis rhodosticta" 95 45
824 100s. "Eulophia speciosa" . . 1·50 80
825 200s. "Calanthe sylvatica" . . 2·25 2·25
826 250s. "Vanilla imperialis" . . 2·50 3·00
827 350s. "Polystachya vulcanica" 2·75 3·75
MS828 Two sheets, each 110 × 82 mm. (a) 500s. "Ansellia africana" (b) 500s. "Ancistrochilus rothschildianus" Set of 2 sheets 8·00 9·00

The overprint on No. **MS**828 occurs on the sheet margin and includes an additional inscription.

114 P.A.P.U. Emblem

1990. 10th Anniv of Pan-African Postal Union.
829 **114** 80s. multicoloured . . . . 1·00 70
MS830 97 × 67 mm. 750s. black and blue . . . . 3·50 4·50

DESIGN: 750s. Clasped hands.

115 Unissued G. B. "V R" Penny Black

1990. 150th Anniv of the Penny Black.
831 **115** 25s. multicoloured 40 15
832 – 50s. red, black and green 60 25
833 – 100s. multicoloured . . . 85 45
834 – 150s. multicoloured . . . 1·25 1·00
835 – 200s. multicoloured . . . 1·50 1·10
836 – 300s. multicoloured . . . 1·75 1·60
837 – 500s. multicoloured . . . 2·00 2·50
838 – 600s. multicoloured . . . 2·00 2·75
MS839 Two sheets (a) 107 × 77 mm. 1000s. multicoloured. (b) 119 × 85 mm. 1000s. black and red Set of 2 sheets . . . . 8·00 9·00

DESIGNS: 50s. Canada 1858–59 3d. Beaver; 100s. Baden 1851 9k. on green error; 150s. Basel 1845 2½r. Dove; 200s. U.S.A. 1918 24c. Inverted "Jenny" error; 300s. Western Australia 1854 1d. Black Swan; 500s. Uganda 1895 20c. "narrow" typewritten stamp; 600s. G.B. Twopenny blue; 1000s. (No. **MS**839a), Uganda 1895 20c. "wide" typewritten stamp; 1000s. (No. **MS**839b), Sir Rowland Hill.

No. **MS**839 also commemorates "Stamp World London 90" International Stamp Exhibition.

116 African Jacana

1990. Wild Birds of Uganda. Multicoloured.
840 10s. Type **116** 60 35
841 15s. Southern ground hornbill 60 35
842 45s. Kori bustard (vert) . . . 85 50
843 50s. Secretary bird 85 50
844 100s. Egyptian geese . . . . 1·25 85
845 300s. Goliath heron (vert) . . 2·25 2·75
846 500s. Ostrich with chicks (vert) . . . . 2·75 3·50
847 650s. Saddle-bill stork (vert) 3·00 4·00
MS848 Two sheets, each 98 × 69 mm. (a) 1000s. Lesser flamingo (vert). (b) 1000s. Vulturine guineafowl (vert) Set of 2 sheets . . . . 9·00 9·50

117 Roger Milla of Cameroon

1990. World Cup Football Championship, Italy (2nd issue). Multicoloured.
849 50s. Type **117** 35 25
850 100s. Ramzy of Egypt . . . 55 45
851 250s. David O'Leary of Ireland . . . . 1·50 1·25
852 600s. Littbarsky of West Germany . . . . 2·00 2·50
MS853 Two sheets, each 75 × 90 mm. (a) 1000s. Ali McCoist of Scotland. (b) 1000s. Ekstrom of Sweden Set of 2 sheets 8·00 9·00

118 Mickey and Minnie Mouse at Breakfast

1990. Health and Safety Campaign. Designs showing Walt Disney cartoon characters. Multicoloured.
854 10s. Type **118** 25 10
855 20s. Donald Duck's nephews doing kerb drill 30 15
856 50s. Donald and Mickey stopping Big Pete smoking 60 35
857 90s. Mickey stopping Donald choking . . . . 1·00 40
858 100s. Mickey and Goofy using seat belts . . . . . 1·10 45
859 250s. Mickey and Minnie dancing . . . . 2·00 2·00
860 500s. Donald Duck's fitness class . . . . 3·00 3·75
861 600s. Mickey's nephews showing lights at night . . 3·25 4·25
MS862 Two sheets, each 135 × 115 mm. (a) 1000s. Mickey weighing nephew (vert). (b) 1000s. Mickey and Pluto walking (vert) Set of 2 sheets . . . . 9·00 9·50

1990. As Nos. 746/55 and new values, showing butterflies, as T **108** with "UGANDA" in blue. Multicoloured.
864A 10s. "Hewitsonia boisduvali" 30 15
865A 20s. "Euxanthe wakefieldi" 40 20
866A 30s. "Papilio echerioides" 40 20
867A 40s. "Acraea semivitrea" . . 40 20
868B 50s. "Colotis antevippe" . . 50 30
869A 70s. "Acraea perenna" . . 50 30
870A 90s. "Charaxes cynthia" . . 60 30
871A 100s. "Euphaedra neophron" 60 40
872A 150s. "Cymothoe beckeri" 60 40
873B 200s. "Vanessula milca" . . 85 60

874B 400s. "Mimacraea marshalli" . . . . 1·25 1·25
875B 500s. "Axiocerses amanga" 1·25 1·25
876B 1000s. "Precis hierta" . . 2·50 2·75
877B 2000s. "Precis hierta" . . . 3·25 5·50
878A 3000s. "Euphaedra eusemoides" . . . . . . 6·00 8·50
879A 4000s. "Acraea natalica" 6·50 10·00
880A 5000s. "Euphaedra themis" 6·50 11·00

1990. Christmas. 350th Death Anniv of Rubens. As T **242a** of Sierra Leone, but inscr "CHRISTMAS 1990". Multicoloured.
881 10s. "Baptism of Christ" (detail) (vert) 10 10
882 20s. "St. Gregory the Great and other Saints" (detail) (vert) 15 10
883 100s. "Saints Nereus, Domitilla and Achilleus" (detail) (vert) 65 35
884 150s. "St. Gregory the Great and other Saints" (different detail) (vert) 90 60
885 300s. "Saint Augustine" (detail) (vert) . . . . . 1·50 1·75
886 400s. "St. Gregory the Great and other Saints" (different detail) (vert) . . . . . 1·60 1·90
887 500s. "Baptism of Christ" (different detail) (vert) . . 1·75 2·00
888 600s. "St. Gregory the Great and other Saints" (different detail) (vert) . . . . . . 1·90 2·75
MS889 Two sheets, each 110 × 71 mm. (a) 1000s. "The Triumph of Faith" (detail). (b) 1000s. "The Victory of Eucharistic Truth over Heresy" (detail). Set of 2 sheets . . . . 9·00 11·00

119 Census Emblem

1990. National Population and Housing Census. Multicoloured.
890 20s. Type **119** 30 30
MS891 105 × 73 mm. 1000s. Symbolic people and dwellings 4·50 5·00

120 Damselfly

1991. Fauna of Uganda's Wetlands. Mult.
892 70s. Type **120** 80 70
893 70s. Purple swamphen ("Gallinule") 80 70
894 70s. Sitatunga 80 70
895 70s. Western reef heron ("Purple heron") 80 70
896 70s. Bushpig 80 70
897 70s. Vervet monkey 80 70
898 70s. Long reed frog 80 70
899 70s. Malachite kingfisher . . 80 70
900 70s. Marsh mongoose 80 70
901 70s. Painted reed frog 80 70
902 70s. African jacana 80 70
903 70s. Charaxes butterfly . . . 80 70
904 70s. Nile crocodile 80 70
905 70s. Herald snake 80 70
906 70s. Dragonfly 80 70
907 70s. Lungfish 80 70
MS908 118 × 78 mm. 1000s. Nile monitor (horiz) . . . . 5·75 6·50
Nos. 892/907 were printed together, se-tenant, forming a composite design.

121 Slug Haplochromis

1991. Fishes of Uganda. Multicoloured.
909 10s. Type **121** 10 10
910 20s. Palmquist's notho . . . 15 15
911 40s. Silver distichodus . . . 20 20
912 90s. Sauvege's haplochromis 40 40
913 100s. Blue calliurum 45 45
914 350s. Johnston's haplochromis . . . . . . 1·10 1·25
915 600s. Colour-tailed haplochromis . . . . . . 2·25 2·50
916 800s. Jewel cichlid . . . . . 2·50 3·00
MS917 Two sheets, each 100 × 74 mm. (a) 1000s. Haplochromis. (b) 1000s. Striped panchax Set of 2 sheets . . . . 12·00 13·00

1991. Olympic Games, Barcelona (1992). As T **239a** of Sierra Leone. Multicoloured.
918 20s. Women's 100 metres hurdles 40 20
919 40s. Long jump 55 20
920 125s. Table tennis . . . . . 1·25 1·00
921 250s. Football . . . . 1·75 1·75
922 500s. Men's 800 metres . . . 2·25 3·25
MS923 Two sheets, each 110 × 71 mm. (a) 1200s. Opening Ceremony at Seoul Games (horiz). (b) 1200s. Women's 4 × 100 metres relay (horiz) Set of 2 sheets . . 10·00 12·00

122 South African Railways Class 15f Steam Locomotive, 1938–48

1991. African Railway Locomotives. Mult.
924 10s. Type **122** 70 30
925 20s. Rhodesian Railways 12th Class steam locomotive, 1900s 90 45
926 80s. Class "Tribal" steam locomotive, Tanzam Railway, 1951–56 . . . . . 1·75 80
927 200s. Steam locomotive, Egypt, 1905 . . . . 2·50 1·50
928 300s. Mikado steam locomotive, Sudan, 1930 2·50 2·00
929 400s. East African Railways Class 59 Garratt steam locomotive, 1955 . . . . . 2·75 2·50
930 500s. East African Railways Mallet steam locomotive, 1900 . . . . 2·75 2·50
931 1000s. Type 5 F 1 electric locomotive, South Africa, 1970 . . . . 3·00 3·50
MS932 Four sheets, each 100 × 70 mm. (a) 1200s. Atlantic steam locomotive, Egypt, 1900s. (b) 1200s. Rhodesian Railways 12th Class steam locomotive, 1930. (c) 1200s. Benguela Railway Class 11 steam locomotive, Angola, 1920. (d) 1200s. Natal Govt Mallet steam locomotive, 1905–19 Set of 4 sheets . . . . 16·00 17·00
No. 924 is incorrectly captioned as a Rhodesia Railways 10th Class locomotive.

123 Lord Baden-Powell and Scout Emblem

1991. World Scout Jamboree, Mount Sorak, Korea.
933 **123** 20s. multicoloured 50 30
934 – 80s. multicoloured 85 65
935 – 100s. multicoloured . . . 95 75
936 – 150s. black and green . . 1·40 1·00
937 – 300s. multicoloured . . . 2·00 1·75
938 – 400s. multicoloured . . . 2·00 1·90
939 – 500s. multicoloured . . . 2·25 2·00
940 – 1000s. multicoloured . . . 3·00 3·50
MS941 Two sheets. (a) 76 × 115 mm. 1200s. black and stone. (b) 115 × 76 mm. 1200s. black and blue Set of 2 sheets . . . . 12·00 12·00
DESIGNS: 80s. Scouts and Uganda 1982 100s. anniversary stamp; 100s. Scout encampment, New York World's Fair, 1939; 150s. Cover and illustration from "Scouting for Boys"; 300s. Cooking on campfire; 400s. Aldrin and Armstrong on Moon; 500s. Scout salutes; 1000s. Statue to the Unknown Scout, Gillwell Park; 1200s. (**MS**941a) Jamboree emblem; 1200s. (**MS**941b) Lord Baden-Powell, W. Boyce and Revd. L. Hadley.

1991. "Phila Nippon '91" International Stamp Exhibition, Tokyo. As T **221** of St. Vincent showing Walt Disney cartoon characters and Japanese traditions. Multicoloured.
942 10s. Uncle Scrooge celebrating Ga-No-Iwai . . 15 15
943 20s. Mickey Mouse removing shoes 25 20
944 70s. Goofy leading cart-horse 60 50
945 80s. Daisy Duck and Minnie Mouse exchanging gifts . . 70 60
946 300s. Minnie kneeling at doorway . . . . 1·75 1·75
947 400s. Donald Duck and Mickey taking a hot volcanic sand bath . . . . 1·90 1·90
948 500s. Clarabelle Cow burning incense . . . . 2·00 2·00
949 1000s. Mickey and Minnie writing New Year cards . . 2·75 3·00
MS950 Two sheets, each 127 × 112 mm. (a) 1200s. Mickey conducting (vert). (b) 1200s. Mickey in public bath (vert) Set of 2 sheets . . . . 11·00 11·00

1991. Death Cent (1990) of Vincent van Gogh (artist). As T **215a** of St. Vincent. Multicoloured.
951 10s. "Snowy Landscape with Arles" 35 30
952 20s. "Peasant Woman binding Sheaves" (vert) . . 45 30
953 60s. "The Drinkers" 70 50
954 80s. "View of Auvers" . . . 85 65
955 200s. "Mourning Man" (vert) 1·75 1·25
956 400s. "Still Life: Vase with Roses" . . . . 2·25 2·00
957 800s. "The Raising of Lazarus" . . . . 3·25 3·75
958 1000s. "The Good Samaritan" (vert) . . . . 3·25 3·75
MS959 Two sheets, each 102 × 76 mm. (a) 1200s. "First Steps" (95 × 71 mm). (b) 1200s. "Village Street and Steps in Auvers" (95 × 71 mm). Imperf Set of 2 sheets . . . . 12·00 13·00

1991. 65th Birthday of Queen Elizabeth II. As T **220b** of St. Vincent. Multicoloured.
960 70s. Queen and Prince Charles after polo match 1·25 45
961 90s. Queen at Balmoral, 1976 1·25 55
962 500s. Queen with Princess Margaret, August 1980 . . 2·75 2·25
963 600s. Queen and Queen Mother leaving St. George's Chapel, Windsor . . . . 3·00 2·75
MS964 68 × 90 mm. 1200s. Separate photographs of Queen and Prince Philip . . . . 4·50 4·50

1991. 10th Wedding Anniv of Prince and Princess of Wales. As T **220b** of St. Vincent. Multicoloured.
965 20s. Prince and Princess of Wales in July 1986 . . . . 70 15
966 100s. Separate photographs of Prince, Princess and sons . . . . 1·75 50
967 200s. Prince Henry and Prince William . . . . . . 1·90 1·00
968 1000s. Separate photographs of Prince and Princess in 1988 . . . . 6·00 6·00
MS969 68 × 90 mm. 1200s. Princess William and Henry on Majorca and Prince and Princess of Wales in Cameroun . . . . 6·00 5·50

124 General Charles de Gaulle

125 "Volvariella bingensis"

1991. Birth Centenary (1990) of Charles de Gaulle (French statesman). Multicoloured.
970 20s. Type **124** 25 20
971 70s. Liberation of Paris, 1944 55 45
972 90s. De Gaulle with King George VI, 1940 . . . . . 65 55
973 100s. Reviewing Free French troops, 1940 (horiz) . . . 70 60
974 200s. Broadcasting to France, 1940 (horiz) . . . . . . 1·25 1·00
975 500s. De Gaulle in Normandy, 1944 (horiz) . . 2·00 2·00
976 600s. De Gaulle at Albert Hall, 1940 (horiz) . . . . 2·00 2·25
977 1000s. Inauguration as President, 1959 . . . . . . 3·00 3·50
MS978 Two sheets. (a) 104 × 76 mm. 1200s. De Gaulle entering Paris, 1944. (b) 107 × 76 mm. 1200s. De Gaulle with Eisenhower, 1942 (horiz) Set of 2 sheets . . . . 9·50 10·00

1991. Fungi. Multicoloured.
979 20s. Type **125** 30 30
980 70s. "Agrocybe broadwayi" 55 55
981 90s. "Camarophyllus olidus" 65 65
982 140s. "Marasmius arborescens" 90 90
983 180s. "Marasmiellus subcinereus" . . . . 1·00 1·00
984 200s. "Agaricus campestris" 1·25 1·25
985 500s. "Chlorophyllum molybdites" . . . . 2·25 2·25
986 1000s. "Agaricus bingensis" 3·50 3·50
MS987 Two sheets, each 96 × 65 mm. (a) 1200s. "Leucocoprinus cepaestipes" (horiz). (b) 1200s. "Laccaria ohiensis" ("Laccaria lateritia") (horiz) Set of 2 sheets . . . . 8·50 9·00

1991. Endangered Species (3rd series). As Nos. 406/9, but with changed face values, and additional horiz designs as T **61**. Multicoloured.
988 100s. Elephants in "Elephants' Graveyard" . . 65 45
989 140s. Type **61** 85 75
990 200s. Elephants at waterhole 1·25 1·10
991 600s. Elephants having dust bath . . . . 2·50 3·75
MS992 Two sheets, each 102 × 74 mm. (a) 1200s. Giraffe. (b) 1200s. Rhinoceros and red-billed oxpecker Set of 2 sheets 16·00 16·00

126 "Anigozanthos manglesii"

1991. Botanical Gardens of the World. Mult.
993/1032 90s. × 20, 100s. × 20 Set of 40 . . . . 18·00 20·00
MS1033 Two sheets, each 110 × 75 mm. (a) 1400s. The Pagoda, Kew. (b) 1400s. Temple of the Winds, Melbourne Set of 2 sheets . . . . 13·00 14·00
Nos. 993/1032 were issued together, se-tenant, as two sheetlets of 20 containing designs as Type **126**. The 90 s values show "Anigozanthos manglesii", "Banksia grandis", "Clianthus formosus", "Gossypium sturtianum", "Callistemon lanceolatus", "Saintpaulia ionantha", "Calodendrum capense", "Aloe ferox x arborescens", "Bolusanthus speciousus", "Lithops schwantesii", "Protea repens", "Plumbago capensis", "Clerodendrum thomsoniae", "Thunbergia alata", "Schotia latifolia", "Epacris impressa", "Acacia pycnantha", "Telopea speciosissima", "Wahlenbergia gloriosa", "Eucalyptus globulus" from Melbourne, and the 100s. "Cypripedium calceolus", "Rhododendron thomsonii", "Ginkgo biloba", "Magnolia campbellii", "Wisteria sinensis", "Clerodendrum ugandense", "Eulophia horsfallii", "Aerangis rhodosticta", "Abelmoschus moschatus", "Gloriosa superba", "Carissa edulis", "Ochna kirkii", "Canarina abyssinica", "Nymphaea caerulea", "Ceropegia succulenta", "Strelitzia reginae", "Strongylodon macrobotrys", "Victoria amazonica", "Orchis militaris" and "Sophora microphylla" from Kew.

1991. Nos. 573, 597 and 614 surch **20/-**.
1034 20s. on 25s. Airship N.1 "Norge" and polar bear (first transpolar flight), 1926 . . . .
1035 20s. on 25s. Einstein and deep space (Theory of Relativity) . . . . . .
1035a 20s. on 25s. Tank locomotive No. 126 . .

1991. Christmas. Paintings by Piero della Francesca. As T **248a** of Sierra Leone. Multicoloured.
1036 20s. "Madonna with Child and Angels" 50 20
1037 50s. "The Baptism of Christ" 75 20
1038 80s. "Polyptych of Mercy" 1·00 40
1039 100s. "Polyptych of Mercy" (detail) . . . . 1·00 40
1040 200s. "The Annunciation" from "The Legend of the True Cross" . . . . . . 1·75 80
1041 500s. "Pregnant Madonna" 2·75 2·50
1042 1000s. "The Annunciation" from "Polyptych of St. Anthony" . . . . . . 4·00 4·50
1043 1500s. "The Nativity" . . . . 5·00 7·50
MS1044 Two sheets, each 102 × 127 mm. (a) 1800s. "The Brera Altarpiece". (b) 1800s. "Madonna and Child" from "Polyptych of St. Anthony" Set of 2 sheets . . . . 13·00 14·00

128 Boy Scout Monument, New York, and Ernest Thompson (first Chief Scout of U.S.A.)

1992. Anniversaries and Events. Multicoloured.
1045 20s. Type **128** 80 30
1046 50s. Treehouse design and Daniel Beard (vert) . . . 85 40
1047 400s. Lilienthal's signature and "Flugzeug Nr. 8" . . 1·50 1·75

1048 500s. Demonstator demolishing Berlin Wall 1·60 2·25
1049 700s. "The Magic Flute" . . 4·75 5·00
MS1050 Two sheets. (a) 114 × 85 mm. 1200s. Class VL8 electric locomotive leaving tunnel. (b) 117 × 89 mm. 1500s. Ugandan Boy Scout badge Set of 2 sheets 10·00 11·00

ANNIVERSARIES AND EVENTS: Nos. 1045/6, **MS**1050b, 50th death anniv of Lord Baden-Powell and World Scout Jamboree, Korea; No. 1047, Centenary of Otto Lilienthal's first gliding experiments; No. 1048, Bicentenary of Brandenburg Gate, Berlin; No. 1049, Death bicentenary of Mozart; **MS**1050a, Centenary of Trans-Siberian Railway.

129 U.S.S. "Vestal" (repair ship) under Attack

1992. 50th Anniv of Japanese Attack on Pearl Harbor. Multicoloured.
1051 200s. Type **129** . . . . . . 1·25 1·10
1052 200s. Japanese Mitsubishi A6M Zero-Sen . . . . . 1·25 1·10
1053 200s. U.S.S. "Arizona" (battleship) on fire . . . . 1·25 1·10
1054 200s. U.S.S. "Nevada" (battleship) passing burning ships . . . . . . 1·25 1·10
1055 200s. Japanese Aichi D3A "Val" bomber attacking 1·25 1·10
1056 200s. Douglas SBD Dauntless bombers attacking "Hiryu" (carrier) at Midway . . . 1·25 1·10
1057 200s. Japanese Mitsubishi A6M Zero-Sen aircraft attacking Midway Island 1·25 1·10
1058 200s. U.S. Marine Brewster F2A Buffalo (fighter) defending Midway . . . 1·25 1·10
1059 200s. American Grumman F6F Hellcat aircraft and carrier . . . . 1·25 1·10
1060 200s. U.S.S. "Yorktown" (carrier) torpedoed . . . 1·25 1·10

130 Three Modern Hot Air Balloons

1992. 120th Anniv (1990) of Paris Balloon Post. Multicoloured.
1061 200s. Type **130** . . . . . . 1·25 1·10
1062 200s. Sport balloons and top of "Double Eagle II" . . 1·25 1·10
1063 200s. Pro Juventute balloon and top of Branson's "Virgin Otsuka Pacific Flyer" . . . . 1·25 1·10
1064 200s. Blanchard and Jeffries' balloon . . . . 1·25 1·10
1065 200s. Nadar's "Le Geant" and centre of "Double Eagle II" . . . . 1·25 1·10
1066 200s. Branson's "Virgin Otsuka Pacific Flyer" . . 1·25 1·10
1067 200s. Montgolfier balloon 1·25 1·10
1068 200s. "Double Eagle II" basket and Paris balloon of 1870 . . . . 1·25 1·10
1069 200s. Henri Giffard's balloon "Le Grand Ballon Captif" . . . . 1·25 1·10

Nos. 1061/9 were printed together, se-tenant, forming a composite design.

1992. Mickey's World Tour. As T **250a** of Sierra Leone showing Walt Disney cartoon characters in different countries. Multicoloured.
1070 20s. Mickey Mouse and Goofy on African safari (horiz) 50 20
1071 50s. Mickey charming Pluto's tail, India (horiz) 70 20
1072 80s. Minnie Mouse, Donald and Daisy Duck as Caribbean calypso band (horiz) . . . . 1·00 25
1073 200s. Goofy pulling Donald and Daisy in rickshaw, China (horiz) . . . . 1·60 60
1074 500s. Mickey and Minnie on camel, Egypt (horiz) . . . 2·25 1·75
1075 800s. Donald and Pete sumo wrestling, Japan (horiz) 2·50 2·75
1076 1000s. Goofy bullfighting, Spain (horiz) . . . . . 2·50 2·75
1077 1500s. Mickey playing football, Italy (horiz) . . 3·00 4·00
MS1078 Two sheets, each 83 × 104 mm. (a) 2000s. Mickey as Cossack dancer, Russia. (b) 2000s. Daisy as Wagnerian diva, Germany Set of 2 sheets . . . 11·00 12·00

1992. 40th Anniv of Queen Elizabeth II's Accession. As T **220b** of St. Vincent. Multicoloured.
1079 100s. Lake Victoria 80 25
1080 200s. Lake and mountains 1·25 60
1081 500s. Lakeside fields . . . . 2·50 2·25
1082 1000s. River Nile . . . . . 3·75 4·25
MS1083 Two sheets, each 74 × 97 mm. (a) 1800s. Waterfalls. (b) 1800s. Owen Falls Dam Set of 2 sheets . . . . 12·00 11·00

1992. Prehistoric Animals. As T **250c** of Sierra Leone. Multicoloured.
1084 50s. Kentrosaurus 50 30
1085 200s. Iguanodon . . . . . 1·00 80
1086 250s. Hypsilophodon . . . 1·10 90
1087 300s. Brachiosaurus . . . . 1·25 1·10
1088 400s. Peloneustes . . . . . 1·40 1·40
1089 500s. Pteranodon . . . . . 1·50 1·50
1090 800s. Tetralophodon . . . . 2·00 2·50
1091 1000s. Megalosaurus . . . . 2·00 2·50
MS1092 Two sheets, each 100 × 70 mm. (a) 2000s. As 250s. (b) 2000s. As 1000s. Set of 2 sheets 14·00 13·00

131 "The Entry into Jerusalem" (detail) (Giotto)

132 Adungu

1992. Easter. Religious Paintings. Mult.
1093 50s. Type **131** 65 15
1094 100s. "Pilate and the Watch" (Psalter of Robert de Lisle) 85 20
1095 200s. "The Kiss of Judas" (detail) (Giotto) . . . . . 1·25 55
1096 250s. "Christ washing the Feet of the Disciples" (Vita Christi manuscript) 1·40 75
1097 300s. "Christ seized in the Garden" (Melissende Psalter) . . . . 1·50 85
1098 500s. "Doubting Thomas" (Vita Christi manuscript) 2·25 1·75
1099 1000s. "The Marys at the Tomb" (detail) (anon) . . 3·75 4·25
1100 2000s. "The Ascension" (Florentine manuscript) 5·50 7·50
MS1101 Two sheets, each 72 × 102 mm. (a) 2500s. "The Piercing of Christ's Side" (detail) (Limoges enamel). (b) 2500s. "Agony at Gethsemane" (detail) (Limoges enamel) Set of 2 sheets 13·00 14·00

1992. Traditional Musical Instruments. Mult.
1102 50s. Type **132** 40 20
1103 100s. Endingidi 55 35
1104 200s. Akogo 80 60
1105 250s. Nanga 85 70
1106 300s. Engoma 95 95
1107 400s. Amakondere . . . . . 1·10 1·25
1108 500s. Akakyenkye . . . . 1·40 1·50
1109 1000s. Ennanga . . . . . . 2·50 3·50

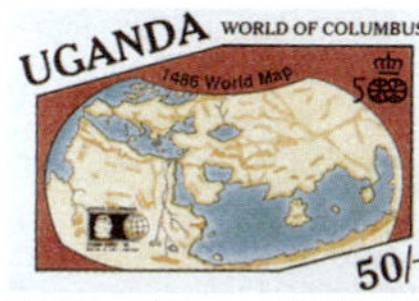

133 Map of Known World, 1486

1992. 500th Anniv of Discovery of America by Columbus and "World Columbian Stamp Expo '92" Exhibition, Chicago. Multicoloured.
1110 50s. Type **133** 20 20
1111 100s. Map of Africa, 1508 30 30
1112 150s. Map of West Indies, 1500 . . . . 50 50
1113 200s. "Nina" and astrolabe 60 60
1114 600s. "Pinta" and quadrant 1·50 1·50
1115 800s. Sand glass . . . . . 1·60 1·60
1116 900s. 15th-century compass 1·75 1·75
1117 2000s. Map of World, 1492 3·50 3·50
MS1118 Two sheets, each 95 × 75 mm. (a) 2500s. Sections of globe, 1492. (b) 2500s. Europe and Africa from map by Henricus Martellus, 1490 (vert) Set of 2 sheets . . . . 9·25 10·00

1992. Hummel Figurines. As T **215b** of St. Vincent. Multicoloured.
1119 50s. Girl with washing . . . 30 20
1120 200s. Girl scrubbing floor 70 50
1121 250s. Girl sweeping floor . . 80 60
1122 300s. Girl with baby 90 70
1123 600s. Boy mountaineer . . . 2·00 2·00
1124 900s. Girl knitting . . . . . 2·50 2·75
1125 1000s. Boy on stool . . . . 2·75 3·00
1126 1500s. Boy with telescope 3·00 3·50
MS1127 Two sheets, each 97 × 122 mm. (a) 500s. As No. 1119; 500s. As No. 1120; 500s. As No. 1121; 500s. As No. 1122. (b) 500s. As No. 1124; 500s. As No. 1123; 500s. As No. 1125; 500s. As No. 1126 Set of 2 sheets . . 9·50 11·00

134 Spotted Hyena

1992. Wildlife. Multicoloured.
1128 50s. Type **134** 35 15
1129 100s. Impala 45 25
1130 200s. Giant forest hog . . . 65 35
1131 250s. Pangolin 75 55
1132 300s. Golden monkey . . . 85 60
1133 800s. Serval . . . . 2·25 2·50
1134 1000s. Small-spotted genet ("Bush genet") . . . . . 2·25 2·75
1135 3000s. Waterbuck . . . . . 5·50 7·50
MS1136 Two sheets, each 100 × 70 mm. (a) 2500s. Gorilla. (b) 2500s. Hippopotamus Set of 2 sheets . . . . 9·00 10·00

1992. Olympic Games, Barcelona. As T **250d** of Sierra Leone. Multicoloured.
1137 50s. Men's javelin 30 20
1138 100s. Men's high jump (horiz) 40 30
1139 200s. Fencing (pentathlon) 60 45
1140 250s. Men's volleyball . . . 65 60
1141 300s. Women's platform diving 70 60
1142 500s. Men's team cycling . . 3·50 2·00
1143 1000s. Women's tennis . . . 4·00 4·25
1144 2000s. Boxing (horiz) . . . 4·75 7·00
MS1145 Two sheets, each 100 × 70 mm. (a) 2500s. Men's basketball. (b) 2500s. Baseball Set of 2 sheets . . . . 14·00 14·00

135 Red-headed Falcon
136 Goofy in "Hawaiian Holiday", 1937

1992. Birds. Multicoloured.
1146 20s. Type **135** 35 20
1147 30s. Yellow-billed hornbill 40 20
1148 50s. Purple heron 40 20
1149 100s. Regal sunbird 50 20
1150 150s. White-browed robin chat 60 25
1151 200s. Shining-blue kingfisher 70 30
1152 250s. Great blue turaco . . 80 40
1153 300s. African emerald cuckoo 90 60
1154 500s. Abyssinian roller . . . 1·25 1·00
1155 800s. South African crowned crane . . . . 1·75 1·75
1156 1000s. Doherty's bush shrike 2·00 2·25
1157 2000s. Splendid glossy starling . . . . 3·25 4·00
1158 3000s. Little bee eater . . . 4·50 6·50
1159 4000s. Red-faced lovebird ("Red-headed Lovebird") 6·00 8·00

1992. Postage Stamp Mega Event, New York. Sheet 100 × 70 mm. containing vert design as T **240a** of St. Vincent. Multicoloured.
MS1160 2500s. United Nations Headquarters . . . . 3·75 4·25

1992. 60th Anniv of Goofy. Multicoloured.
1162 50s. Type **136** 30 20
1163 100s. Riding pennyfarthing cycle, 1941 . . . . 40 20
1164 200s. Goofy and Mickey Mouse as firemen, 1935 60 35
1165 250s. Skiing, 1941 (horiz) . . 65 40
1166 300s. One man band, 1937 (horiz) 70 60
1167 1000s. Asleep against boat, 1938 (horiz) . . . . . 2·25 2·50
1168 1500s. Ancient Olympic champion, 1942 . . . . 3·25 3·75
1169 2000s. Pole vaulting, 1942 3·50 3·75
MS1170 Two sheets. (a) 105 × 115 mm. 3000s. Goofy and Wilbur the grasshopper, 1939 (horiz). (b) 92 × 116 mm. 3000s. Wyatt Goofy and Goofy today Set of 2 sheets . . . . 11·00 11·00

137 "The Annunciation" (Zurbaran)

1992. Christmas. Religious Paintings by Francisco Zurbaran. Multicoloured.
1171 50s. Type **137** 40 15
1172 200s. "The Annunciation" (different) 85 35
1173 250s. "The Virgin of the Immaculate Conception" 90 45
1174 300s. "The Virgin of the Immaculate Conception" (detail) . . . . 1·10 50
1175 800s. "Holy Family with Saints Anne, Joachim and John the Baptist" . . . . 2·75 3·00
1176 900s. "Holy Family with Saints Anne, Joachim and John the Baptist" (detail) 3·00 3·25
1177 1000s. "Adoration of the Magi" . . . . 3·00 3·25
1178 2000s. "Adoration of the Magi" (detail) . . . . . 4·25 6·00
MS1179 Two sheets, each 76 × 102 mm. (a) 2500s. "The Virgin of the Immaculate Conception" (different). (b) 2500s. "The Virgin of the Immaculate Conception" (different) Set of 2 sheets . . . . 13·00 14·00

138 Man cleaning Granary

1992. Anniversaries and Events. Multicoloured.
1180 50s. Type **138** 20 15
1181 200s. Mother breast feeding 55 40
1182 250s. Mother feeding baby 60 50
1183 300s. Boy collecting water from pump 60 75
1184 300s. "Voyager 2" passing Jupiter . . . . 2·00 1·25
1185 800s. Mother and baby . . 1·50 2·25
1186 800s. Impala . . . . 1·50 2·25
1187 1000s. Mountain zebra . . . 2·75 3·00
1188 1000s. Count Ferdinand von Zeppelin and airship . . . 3·00 3·00
1189 2000s. "Voyager 2" passing Neptune . . . . 7·00 7·00
1190 3000s. Count Ferdinand von Zeppelin and Clement-Bayard airship "Fleurus" 7·50 8·50
MS1191 Four sheets, each 115 × 85 mm. (a) 2500s. "Voyager 2" and Jupiter. (b) 2500s. Warthog. (c) 2500s. Count Ferdinand von Zeppelin with Robert Brothers and Colin Hullin balloon. (d) 2500s. Doctor inoculating boy Set of 4 sheets 21·00 22·00

ANNIVERSARIES AND EVENTS: Nos. 1180/3, 1185, United Nations World Health Organization Projects; Nos. 1184, 1189, **MS**1191a, International Space Year; Nos. 1186/7, **MS**1191b, Earth Summit '92, Rio; Nos. 1188, 1190, **MS**1191c, 75th death anniv of Count Ferdinand von Zeppelin (airship pioneer); **MS**1191d, 75th anniv of International Association of Lions Clubs.

139 Hands releasing Dove with Lubaga and Kampala Catholic Cathedrals

1993. Visit of Pope John Paul II. Mult.
1192 50s. Type **139** 50 10
1193 200s. Pope and Kampala Cathedral 90 30
1194 250s. Pope and Catholic worshipper . . . . 1·00 45
1195 300s. Ugandan bishops and Pope . . . . 1·10 60
1196 800s. Pope John Paul II waving . . . . 2·50 2·50
1197 900s. Pope and Kampala Cathedral (different) . . . 2·50 2·50

1198 1000s. Pope, national flag and Kampala Cathedral 2·50 2·50
1199 2000s. Pope and national flag 4·00 4·50
MS1200 Two sheets, each 100 × 70 mm. (a) 3000s. Pope on aircraft steps (vert). (b) 3000s. Pope delivering blessing (vert) Set of 2 sheets 13·00 13·00

1993. Bicentenary of the Louvre, Paris. Paintings by Rembrandt. As T **254a** of St. Vincent. Multicoloured.
1201 500s. "Self Portrait at Easel" 1·10 1·10
1202 500s. "Birds of Paradise" 1·10 1·10
1203 500s. "The Carcass of Beef" 1·10 1·10
1204 500s. "The Supper at Emmaus" 1·10 1·10
1205 500s. "Hendrickje Stoffels" 1·10 1·10
1206 500s. "The Artist's Son, Titus" 1·10 1·10
1207 500s. "The Holy Family" (left detail) 1·10 1·10
1208 500s. "The Holy Family" (right detail) 1·10 1·10
MS1209 100 × 70 mm. 2500s. "The philosopher in Meditation" (89 × 57 mm) 4·50 5·00

141 Gutierrez (Uruguay) and Voeller (Germany)

142 York Minster, England

1993. World Cup Football Championship, U.S.A. (1994) (1st issue). Multicoloured.
1245 50s. Type **141** 50 15
1246 200s. Tomas Brolin (Sweden) 1·00 40
1247 250s. Gary Lineker (England) 1·25 45
1248 300s. Munoz and Butragueno (Spain) 1·25 65
1249 800s. Carlos Valderrama (Colombia) 2·50 2·75
1250 900s. Diego Maradona (Argentina) 2·50 2·75
1251 1000s. Pedro Troglio (Argentina) 2·50 2·75
1252 2000s. Enzo Scifo (Belgium) 3·75 5·00
MS1253 Two sheets, each 103 × 72 mm. (a) 2500s. Brazilians celebrating. (b) 2500s. De Napoli (Italy) and Skuhravy (Czechoslovakia) (horiz) Set of 2 sheets 13·00 14·00
See also Nos. 1322/8.

140 Afghan Hound

1993. Dogs of the World. Multicoloured.
1210 50s. Type **140** 80 30
1211 100s. Newfoundland 1·10 30
1212 200s. Siberian huskies 1·60 50
1213 250s. Briard 1·60 65
1214 300s. Saluki 1·60 85
1215 800s. Labrador guide-dog (vert) 3·00 3·00
1216 1000s. Greyhound 3·25 3·25
1217 1500s. Pointer 3·75 4·50
MS1218 Two sheets, each 103 × 80 mm. (a) 2500s. Cape hunting dog. (b) 2500s. Norwegian elkhound pup Set of 2 sheets 16·00 16·00

1993. Cathedrals of the World. Multicoloured.
1254 50s. Type **142** 30 15
1255 100s. Notre Dame, Paris 45 20
1256 200s. Little Metropolis, Athens 75 40
1257 250s. St. Patrick's, New York 80 45
1258 300s. Ulm, Germany 85 50
1259 800s. St. Basil's, Moscow 2·25 2·50
1260 1000s. Roskilde, Denmark 2·25 2·50
1261 2000s. Seville, Spain 3·75 5·00
MS1262 Two sheets, each 70 × 100 mm. (a) 2500s. Namirembe, Uganda. (b) 2500s. St. Peter's, Vatican City Set of 2 sheets 9·00 10·00

1993. 40th Anniv of Coronation. As T **256a** of St. Vincent. Multicoloured.
1219 50s. Queen Elizabeth II at Coronation (photograph by Cecil Beaton) 30 35
1220 200s. Orb and Sceptre 50 60
1221 500s. Queen Elizabeth during Coronation 90 1·10
1222 1500s. Queen Elizabeth II and Princess Margaret 2·25 2·50
MS1223 69 × 100 mm. 2500s. "The Crown" (detail) (Grace Wheatley) (28½ × 42½ mm) 5·00 5·00

1993. Christmas. Religious Paintings. As T **265a** of St. Vincent. Black, yellow and red (Nos. 1263, 1265, 1267, 1270 and **MS**1271a) or multicoloured (others).
1263 50s. "Virgin with Carthusian Monks" (detail) (Durer) 40 10
1264 100s. "Sacred Family" (detail) (Raphael) 60 10
1265 200s. "Virgin with Carthusian Monks" (different detail) (Durer) 85 30
1266 250s. "The Virgin of the Rose" (Raphael) 90 35
1267 300s. "Virgin with Carthusian Monks" (different detail) (Durer) 1·00 40
1268 800s. "Sacred Family" (different detail) (Raphael) 2·50 2·75
1269 1000s. "Virgin with Beardless Joseph" (Raphael) 2·50 2·75
1270 2000s. "Virgin with Carthusian Monks" (different detail) (Durer) 4·00 5·50
MS1271 Two sheets, each 102 × 127 mm. (a) 2500s. "Virgin with Carthusian Monks" (different detail) (Dürer). (b) 2500s. "Sacred Family" (different detail) (Raphael) Set of 2 sheets 13·00 13·00
Nos. MS1271 is inscribed "Canthusian Monks" in error.

1993. Asian International Stamp Exhibitions. As T **263** of St. Vincent, but vert. Multicoloured. (a) "Indopex '93", Surabaya, Indonesia. Javanese Wayang Puppets
1224 600s. Bupati karma, Prince of Wangga 1·25 1·50
1225 600s. Rahwana 1·25 1·50
1226 600s. Sondjeng Sandjata 1·25 1·50
1227 600s. Raden Damar Wulan 1·25 1·50
1228 600s. Unidentified puppet 1·25 1·50
1229 600s. Hanaman 1·25 1·50
MS1230 135 × 105 mm. 2500s. Candi Mendut Temple, Java 6·00 7·00

(b) "Taipei '93", Taiwan. Funerary Pottery Figures
1231 600s. Tomb guardian god in green armour 1·25 1·50
1232 600s. Civil official and shrine 1·25 1·50
1233 600s. Tomb guardian god in green and gold armour 1·25 1·50
1234 600s. Civil official in red robe 1·25 1·50
1235 600s. Chimera (tomb guardian) 1·25 1·50
1236 600s. Civil official in red and green robe 1·25 1·50
MS1237 135 × 105 mm. 2500s. Statue of the Sacred Mother, Taiyuan 6·00 7·00

(c) "Bangkok '93", Thailand. Sculptured Figures
1238 600s. Standing Buddha in gilded red sandstone, 13th–15th century 1·25 1·50
1239 600s. Crowned Buddha in bronze, 13th century 1·25 1·50
1240 600s. Thepanom in stone, 15th century 1·25 1·50
1241 600s. Crowned Buddha in bronze, 12th century 1·25 1·50
1242 600s. Avalokitesvara in bronze, 9th century 1·25 1·50
1243 600s. Lop Buri standing Buddha in bronze, 13th century 1·25 1·50
MS1244 135 × 105 mm. 2500s. Buddha, Wat Mahathat 6·00 7·00

143 Mickey Mouse asleep on Stegosaurus

1993. Prehistoric Animals and Walt Disney Cartoon Characters. Multicoloured.
1272 50s. Type **143** 45 20
1273 100s. Minnie Mouse on pteranodon 55 20
1274 200s. Mickey being licked by mamenchisaurus 80 40
1275 250s. Mickey doing cave painting 90 45
1276 300s. Mickey wind-surfing on dinosaur 95 60
1277 500s. Mickey and Donald Duck sliding on diplodocus 1·50 1·25
1278 800s. Mamenchisaurus carrying Mickey 2·25 2·75
1279 1000s. Pluto on triceratops 2·25 2·75
MS1280 Two sheets, each 128 × 102 mm. (a) 2500s. Mickey and Minnie. (b) 2500s. Mickey feeding tyrannosaurus rex Set of 2 sheets 11·00 12·00
No. 1273 is inscribed "PTERANDOM" and No. 1278 "MAMENSHISAURUS", both in error.

144 "Woman in Yellow" (Picasso)

145 Passion Fruit

1993. Anniversaries and Events. Multicoloured.
1281 100s. Type **144** 40 15
1282 200s. Head of cow and syringe 50 30
1283 250s. "Gertrude Stein" (Picasso) 60 35
1284 500s. Early telescope 2·00 1·50
1285 800s. "Creation" (S. Witkiewicz after J. Glogowski) 2·00 2·50
1286 1000s. Modern telescope 3·00 3·25
1287 1000s. "For the Right to Work" (A. Strumillo) 2·25 3·25
MS1288 Three sheets. (a) 75 × 105 mm. 2500s. "Woman by a Window" (detail) (Picasso). (b) 105 × 75 mm. 2500s. Copernicus. (c) 105 × 75 mm. 2500s. "Temptation of Saint Antony I" (detail) (S. Witkiewicz) (horiz) Set of 3 sheets 13·00 14·00
ANNIVERSARIES AND EVENTS: Nos. 1281, 1283, **MS**1288a, 20th death anniv of Picasso (artist); No. 1282, Pan African Rinderpest Campaign; Nos. 1284, 1286, **MS**1288b, 450th death anniv of Copernicus (astronomer); Nos. 1285, 1287, 1288c, "Polska '93" International Stamp Exhibition, Poznan.

1994. Fruits and Crops. Multicoloured.
1289 50s. Type **145** 35 10
1290 100s. Sunflower 45 10
1291 150s. Bananas 60 25
1292 200s. Runner beans 70 30
1293 250s. Pineapple 75 55
1294 300s. Jackfruit 85 70
1295 500s. Sorghum 1·50 1·50
1296 800s. Maize 2·25 3·00
MS1297 Two sheets, each 101 × 71 mm. (a) 2000s. Sesame. (b) 2000s. Coffee (horiz) Set of 2 sheets 8·50 9·00

146 Ford Model "A", 1903

1994. Centenaries of Henry Ford's First Petrol Engine (Nos. 1298/1301, **MS**1306a) and Karl Benz's First Four-wheeled Car (others). Multicoloured.
1298 700s. Type **146** 1·25 1·50
1299 700s. Ford Model "T" snowmobile, 1932 1·25 1·50
1300 700s. Ford "Mustang" 1·25 1·50
1301 700s. Lotus-Ford racing car, 1965 1·25 1·50
1302 800s. Mercedes-Benz "S600" coupe, 1994 1·25 1·50
1303 800s. Mercedes-Benz "W196" racing car, 1955 1·25 1·50
1304 800s. Mercedes-Benz "W125" road speed record car, 1938 1·25 1·50
1305 800s. Benz "Viktoria", 1893 1·25 1·50
MS1306 Two sheets, each 85 × 85 mm. (a) 2500s. Henry Ford (vert). (b) 2500s. Karl Benz (vert) Set of 2 sheets 9·00 10·00

1994. "Hong Kong '94" International Stamp Exhibition (1st issue). As T **271a** of St. Vincent. Multicoloured.
1307 500s. Hong Kong 1988 60c. Catholic Cathedral stamp and religious shrines, Repulse Bay 80 1·00
1308 500s. Uganda 1993 2500s. Namirembe Cathedral stamp and religious shrines, Repulse Bay (different) 80 1·00
Nos. 1307/8 were printed together, se-tenant, forming a composite design.

1994. "Hong Kong '94" International Stamp Exhibition (2nd issue). Ching Dynasty Snuff Boxes. As T **271b** of St. Vincent, but vert. Multicoloured.
1309 200s. Glass box with pavilion design 40 50
1310 200s. Porcelain box with quail design 40 50
1311 200s. Porcelain box with floral design 40 50
1312 200s. Porcelain box with openwork design 40 50
1313 200s. Agate box with carved Lion-dogs 40 50
1314 200s. Agate box with man on donkey design 40 50
Captions for Nos. 1310/11 are transposed.

147 Meteorological Weather Station

1994. World Meteorological Day. Multicoloured.
1315 50s. Type **147** 50 15
1316 200s. Weather observatory at training school, Entebbe (vert) 1·10 40
1317 250s. Satellite link 1·25 60
1318 300s. Recording temperatures 1·40 75
1319 400s. Automatic weather station (vert) 1·60 1·75
1320 800s. Crops damaged by hailstones 2·50 3·75
MS1321 105 × 75 mm. 2500s. Barograph 5·50 6·50

1994. World Cup Football Championship, U.S.A. (2nd issue). As T **268** of Sierra Leone. Multicoloured.
1322 500s. Georges Grun (Belgium) 1·25 1·40
1323 500s. Oscar Ruggeri (Argentina) 1·25 1·40
1324 500s. Frank Rijkaard (Netherlands) 1·25 1·40
1325 500s. Magid "Tyson" Musisi (Uganda) 1·25 1·40
1326 500s. Ronald Koeman (Netherlands) 1·25 1·40
1327 500s. Igor Shalimov (Russia) 1·25 1·40
MS1328 Two sheets, each 70 × 100 mm. (a) 2500s. Ruud Gullit (Netherlands). (b) 2500s. Player and R.F.K. Stadium, Washington D.C. Set of 2 sheets 9·00 10·00
No. 1326 is inscribed "DONALD KOEMAN" in error.

148 Milking Cow

1994. 50th Anniv of Heifer Project International.
1329 **148** 100s. multicoloured 1·00 60

149 "Lobobunaea goodii"

150 Wooden Stool

1994. Moths. Multicoloured.
1330 100s. Type **149** 35 20
1331 200s. "Bunaeopsis hersilia" 65 40
1332 300s. "Rufoglanis rosea" 80 60
1333 350s. "Acherontia atropos" 85 75
1334 400s. "Rohaniella pygmaea" 95 95
1335 450s. "Euchloron megaera" 1·00 1·25
1336 500s. "Epiphora rectifascia" 1·10 1·25
1337 1000s. "Polyphychus coryndoni" 1·90 2·50
MS1338 Two sheets, each 117 × 88 mm. (a) 2500s. As Type **149**. (b) 2500s. "Lobobunaea goodii" (wings folded) Set of 2 sheets 9·50 10·00

1994. Crafts. Multicoloured.
1339 100s. Type **150** 25 10
1340 200s. Wood and banana fibre chair 45 30
1341 250s. Raffia and palm leaves basket 50 35
1342 300s. Wool tapestry showing tree planting 55 45
1343 450s. Wool tapestry showing hair grooming 85 90
1344 500s. Wood sculpture of a drummer 95 1·10
1345 800s. Gourds 1·75 2·25
1346 1000s. Bark cloth handbag 2·00 2·50
MS1347 Two sheets, each 100 × 70 mm. (a) 2500s. Raffia baskets. (b) 2500s. Papyrus hats Set of 2 sheets 9·50 10·00

151 Turkish Angora Cat and Blue Mosque

1994. Cats. Multicoloured.
1348 50s. Type **151** 50 25
1349 100s. Japanese bobtail and Mt. Fuji 65 25
1350 200s. Norwegian forest cat and windmill, Holland . . 85 40
1351 300s. Egyptian mau and pyramids (vert) 95 70
1352 450s. Rex and Stonehenge, England (vert) . . . . . 1·25 1·25
1353 500s. Chartreux and Eiffel Tower, France . . . . . 1·40 1·40
1354 1000s. Burmese and Shwe Dagon Pagoda (vert) . . 2·50 2·75
1355 1500s. Maine coon and Pemaquid Point Lighthouse (vert) . . . . 3·25 4·00
MS1356 Two sheets, each 100 × 76 mm. (a) 2500s. Russian blue. (b) 2500s. Manx Set of 2 sheets . . . . 11·00 11·00

152 Child carrying Building Block

1994. 75th Anniv of I.L.O.
1357 **152** 350s. multicoloured . . . 1·25 1·25

1994. 25th Anniv of First Manned Moon Landing. Astronauts. As Nos. 1977/89 of Antigua. Multicoloured.
1358 50s. Alan Shepard Jnr . . . 70 70
1359 100s. M. Scott Carpenter . . 80 80
1360 200s. Virgil Grissom . . . . 1·10 1·10
1361 300s. L. Gordon Cooper Jnr 1·25 1·25
1362 400s. Walter Schirra Jnr . . 1·40 1·40
1363 500s. Donald Slayton . . . 1·40 1·40
1364 600s. John Glenn Jnr . . . 1·40 1·40
MS1365 88 × 91 mm. 3000s. "Apollo 11" anniversary emblem 5·50 6·50

1994. Centenary of International Olympic Committee. Gold Medal Winners. As T **285a** of St. Vincent. Multicoloured.
1366 350s. John Akii-Bua (Uganda) (400 metres hurdles), 1972 (horiz) . . 60 45
1367 900s. Heike Herkel (Germany) (high jump), 1992 (horiz) . . . . . 1·25 1·75
MS1368 107 × 76 mm. 2500s. Aleski Urmanov (Russia) (figure skating), 1994 . . . . 5·00 5·50

1994. 50th Anniv of D-Day. As T **284b** of St. Vincent. Multicoloured.
1369 300s. Mulberry Harbour pier 50 40
1370 1000s. Mulberry Harbour floating bridge . . . . . 1·50 2·00
MS1371 105 × 76 mm. 2500s. Aerial view of Mulberry Harbour . . 4·00 4·50

1994. "Philakorea '94" International Stamp Exhibition, Seoul. As T **286a** of St. Vincent, but vert. Multicoloured.
1372 100s. Sari Pagoda, Paekyangsa 10 10
1373 350s. Ch'omsongdae 50 60
1374 1000s. Pulguksa Temple . . 1·40 2·00
MS1375 76 × 106 mm. 2500s. Bronze mural, Pagoda Park, Seoul . . 3·00 3·50

153 Ugandan family

1994. International Year of the Family.
1376 **153** 100s. multicoloured . . . 40 20

154 Baby Simba

1994. "The Lion King". Characters from Walt Disney's cartoon film. Multicoloured.
1377 100s. Type **154** 30 30
1378 100s. Mufasa, Simba and Sarabi 30 30
1379 100s. Young Simba and Nala 30 30
1380 100s. Timon 30 30
1381 100s. Rafiki 30 30
1382 100s. Pumbaa 30 30
1383 100s. The Hyenas 30 30
1384 100s. Scar 30 30
1385 100s. Zazu 30 30
1386 200s. Rafiki and Mufasa . . 35 35
1387 200s. Rafiki holding Simba with Mufasa and Sarabi 35 35
1388 200s. Rafiki holding Simba aloft 35 35
1389 200s. Scar and Zazu 35 35
1390 200s. Rafiki having vision 35 35
1391 200s. Simba and Scar . . . 35 35
1392 200s. Simba and Nala . . . 35 35
1393 200s. Simba with mane of leaves 35 35
1394 200s. Simba, Nala and Zazu 35 35
1395 250s. Scar and Simba . . . 40 40
1396 250s. Mufasa rescues Simba 40 40
1397 250s. Scar killing Mufasa . . 40 40
1398 250s. Simba falling off cliff 40 40
1399 250s. Timon, Pumbaa and Simba at pool 40 40
1400 250s. Simba, Timon and Pumbaa 40 40
1401 250s. Rafiki with staff . . . 40 40
1402 250s. Simba and Nala . . . 40 40
1403 250s. Simba looking into pool 40 40
MS1404 Three sheets. (a) 127 × 94 mm. 2500s. Jungle animals. (b) 127 × 102 mm. 2500s. Simba and Timon on branch. (c) 127 × 94 mm. 2500s. Simba with parents and Rafiki (vert) Set of 3 sheets . . . . 13·00 14·00

1994. Centenary (1992) of Sierra Club (environmental protection society). Endangered Species. As T **276a** of Sierra Leone. Multicoloured. (a) Vert designs.
1405 100s. Chimpanzee with arms folded 60 55
1406 200s. Head of chimpanzee 80 80
1407 250s. Head of African wild dog 80 80
1408 300s. Head of cheetah . . . 80 90
1409 500s. Geleda baboon . . . 90 1·00
1410 600s. Geleda baboon from back . . . . 1·00 1·10
1411 800s. Head of Grevy's zebra 1·10 1·25
1412 1000s. Geleda baboon sitting on rock . . . . 1·25 1·40

(b) Horiz designs.
1413 200s. Pair of cheetahs . . . 80 90
1414 250s. Cheetah cubs 80 90
1415 300s. African wild dog at rest . . . . 90 1·00
1416 500s. Head of African wild dog . . . . 1·00 1·10
1417 600s. Grevy's zebra . . . . 1·10 1·25
1418 800s. Chimpanzee lying down . . . . 1·25 1·40
1419 1000s. Grevy's zebra feeding 1·40 1·50

155 Terminal Building, Entebbe International Airport

1994. 50th Anniv of I.C.A.O. Mult.
1420 100s. Type **155** 75 20
1421 250s. Control tower, Entebbe International Airport . . . . 1·50 90

156 Game Poachers

157 "Adoration of the Christ Child" (Filippino Lippi)

1994. Ecology. Multicoloured.
1422 100s. Type **156** 40 10
1423 250s. Villagers at rubbish dump 80 45
1424 350s. Fishermen . . . . . . 1·10 1·10
1425 500s. Deforestation . . . . 1·75 1·90

1994. Christmas. Religious Paintings. Multicoloured.
1426 100s. Type **157** 30 10
1427 200s. "The Holy Family rests on the Flight into Egypt" (Annibale Carracci) 50 30
1428 300s. "Madonna with Christ Child and St. John" (Piero di Cosimo) 70 40
1429 350s. "The Conestabile Madonna" (Raphael) . . 80 65
1430 450s. "Madonna and Child with Angels" (after Antonio Rossellino) . . . 90 1·00
1431 500s. "Madonna and Child with St. John" (Raphael) 1·00 1·00
1432 900s. "Madonna and Child" (Luca Signorelli) . . . . 2·00 2·50
1433 1000s. "Madonna with the Child Jesus, St. John and an Angel" (pseudo Pier Francesco Fiorentino) . . 2·00 2·50
MS1434 Two sheets, each 115 × 95 mm. (a) 2500s. "The Madonna of the Magnificat" (detail) (Sandro Botticelli). (b) 2500s. "Adoration of the Magi" (detail) (Fra Angelico and Filippo Lippi) Set of 2 sheets . . . . . . 9·00 10·00
No. 1426 is inscribed "Fillipino" in error.

158 "Self-portrait" (Tintoretto)

1995. 400th Death Anniv (1994) of Jacopo Tintoretto (painter). Multicoloured.
1435 100s. Type **158** 25 10
1436 300s. "A Philosopher" . . . 65 45
1437 400s. "The Creation of the Animals" (detail) (horiz) 80 80
1438 450s. "The Feast of Belshazzar" (detail) (horiz) 85 85
1439 500s. "The Raising of the Brazen Serpent" 95 95
1440 1000s. "Elijah fed by the Angel" . . . . 1·90 2·50
MS1441 Two sheets. (a) 114 × 124 mm. 2000s. "Moses striking Water from a Rock" (detail). (b) 124 × 114 mm. 200s. "Finding of Moses" (detail) Set of 2 sheets . . . . 8·00 9·00

159 White-faced Whistling Duck ("White-faced Tree-duck")

1995. Waterfowl and Wetland Birds of Uganda. Multicoloured.
1442 200s. Type **159** 55 55
1443 200s. Common shoveler ("European Shoveler") . . 55 55
1444 200s. Hartlaub's duck . . . 55 55
1445 200s. Verreaux's eagle owl ("Milky Eagle-owl") . . . 55 55
1446 200s. Pied avocet ("Avocet") 55 55
1447 200s. African fish eagle . . 55 55
1448 200s. Spectacled weaver . . 55 55
1449 200s. Black-headed gonolek 55 55
1450 200s. Great crested grebe . . 55 55
1451 200s. Red-knobbed coot . . 55 55
1452 200s. Woodland kingfisher 55 55
1453 200s. Pintail 55 55
1454 200s. Squacco heron 55 55
1455 200s. Purple swamphen ("Purple Gallinule") . . . 55 55
1456 200s. African darter 55 55
1457 200s. African jacana 55 55
MS1458 Two sheets, each 106 × 76 mm. (a) 2500s. African pygmy goose. (b) 2500s. Fulvous whistling duck ("Fulvous Tree-duck") Set of 2 sheets . . . . 7·50 8·50
Nos. 1442/57 were printed together, se-tenant, forming a composite design.

1995. 18th World Scout Jamboree, Netherlands. Nos. 701/4 optd or surch **18th World Scout Jamboree Mondial, Holland, August 1995**.
1459 100s. Scouts making bricks 20 10
1460 450s. on 70s. Poultry keeping 85 55
1461 800s. on 90s. Scout on crutches leading family to immunization centre . . . 1·40 1·60
1462 1500s. on 10s. Type **104** . . 2·25 2·75
MS1463 115 × 76 mm. 2500s. on 1200s. Lord Baden-Powell, W. Boyce and Revd. L. Hadley 3·75 4·25

1995. 50th Anniv of End of Second World War in Europe. As T **296a** of St. Vincent. Multicoloured.
1464 500s. Soviet artillery in action 85 85
1465 500s. Soviet tanks on the Moltke Bridge 85 85
1466 500s. Kaiser Wilhelm Memorial Church, Berlin 85 85
1467 500s. Soviet tanks and Brandenburg Gate . . . 85 85
1468 500s. U.S. Boeing B-17 Flying Fortress 85 85
1469 500s. Soviet tanks enter Berlin 85 85
1470 500s. Ruins of the Chancellery 85 85
1471 500s. The Reichstag on fire 85 85
MS1472 104 × 74 mm. 2500s. Hoisting the Soviet flag on the Reichstag (57 × 42½ mm) . . . 3·50 4·25

161 Dove, Child, Dish Aerial, Food and Emblem
161a Woman peeling Maize

1995. 50th Anniv of United Nations. Multicoloured.
1473 450s. Type **161** 55 45
1474 1000s. Hands releasing bird and insects . . . . 1·50 2·25
MS1475 100 × 70 mm. 2000s. Child's hand holding adult's finger (horiz) 2·50 3·25

1995. 50th Anniv of F.A.O. Multicoloured.
1476 350s. Type **161a** 55 75
1477 500s. Woman and child with maize 65 85
1478 1000s. Woman and baby with maize . . . . 80 1·10
MS1479 100 × 70 mm. 2000s. Child and head of cow . . . . . . 2·50 3·25
Nos. 1476/8 were printed together, se-tenant, forming a composite design.

1995. 90th Anniv of Rotary International. As T **299** of St. Vincent, but vert. Multicoloured.
1480 2000s. Paul Harris (founder) and logo . . . . 2·00 2·75
MS1481 70 × 100 mm. 2000s. National flag and logo . . . . 2·25 3·00

1995. 95th Birthday of Queen Elizabeth the Queen Mother. As T **299a** of St. Vincent. Multicoloured.
1482 500s. brown, light brown and black . . . . 1·60 1·60
1483 500s. multicoloured . . . . 1·60 1·60
1484 500s. multicoloured . . . . 1·60 1·60
1485 500s. multicoloured . . . . 1·60 1·60
MS1486 102 × 127 mm. 2500s. multicoloured . . . . 4·25 4·50
DESIGNS: No. 1482, Queen Elizabeth the Queen Mother (pastel drawing); 1483, With bouquet of flowers; 1484, At desk (oil painting); 1485, Wearing turquoise-blue dress; **MS**1466, Wearing pale blue dress.

162 Australian Flag in Form of "VJ"

1995. 50th Anniv of End of Second World War in the Pacific. Designs showing national flags as "VJ".
1487 **162** 600s. red, violet and black . . . . 1·10 1·25
1488 – 600s. red, violet and black . . . . 1·10 1·25
1489 – 600s. red, violet and black . . . . 1·10 1·25
1490 – 600s. multicoloured . . . 1·10 1·25
1491 – 600s. red, orange and black . . . . 1·10 1·25
1492 – 600s. red and black . . . 1·10 1·25
MS1493 108 × 76 mm. 2500s. multicoloured . . . . 3·50 4·25
DESIGNS: No. 1488, Great Britain; 1489, New Zealand; 1490, United States of America; 1491, People's Republic of China; 1492, Canada; **MS**1493, American soldier and Flag.

163 Velociraptor

1995. Prehistoric Animals. Multicoloured.
1494 150s. Type **163** 75 65
1495 200s. Head of psittacosaurus 75 65
1496 300s. Archaeopteryx (vert) 90 90
1497 300s. Quetzalcoatlus and volcano (vert) 90 90
1498 300s. Pteranodon and volcano (vert) 90 90
1499 300s. Brachiosaurus (vert) 90 90
1500 300s. Tsintaosaur (vert) . . 90 90
1501 300s. Allosaur (vert) . . . 90 90
1502 300s. Tyrannosaurus (vert) 90 90
1503 300s. Apatosaur (vert) . . . 90 90
1504 300s. Giant dragonfly (vert) 90 90
1505 300s. Dimorphodon (vert) 90 90
1506 300s. Triceratops (vert) . . . 90 90
1507 300s. Compsognathus (vert) 90 90
1508 350s. Head of dilophosaurus 1·00 1·00
1509 400s. Kentrosaurus . . . . 1·10 1·10
1510 500s. Stegosaurus . . . . 1·25 1·25
1511 1500s. Pterodaustro . . . . 2·25 2·75
MS1512 Two sheets, each 106×75 mm. (a) 2000s. Head of parasaurolophus. (b) 2000s. Head of shunosaurus Set of 2 sheets 6·00 7·00

Nos. 1496/1507 were printed together, se-tenant, forming a composite design.

No. 1502 is inscribed "Tyranosaur" and No. 1506 "Tricreatops", both in error.

164 Rough-scaled Bush Viper

165 Bell's Hinged Tortoise

1995. Reptiles. Multicoloured.
1513 50s. Type **164** 10 10
1514 100s. Pygmy python . . . 10 10
1515 150s. Three-horned chameleon 10 15
1516 200s. African rock python 15 20
1516a 300s. Armadillo girdled lizard 25 30
1517 350s. Nile monitor 25 30
1518 400s. Savannah monitor . . 30 35
1519 450s. Bush viper 35 40
1520 500s. Nile crocodile 40 45
1520a 600s. Spotted sandveld lizard 45 50
1521 700s. Type **165** 55 60
1521a 700s. Bell's hinged tortoise 55 60
1522 900s. Rhinoceros viper . . 70 75
1523 1000s. Gabon viper 75 80
1524 2000s. Spitting cobra . . . 1·50 1·60
1525 3000s. Leopard tortoise . . 2·25 2·40
1526 4000s. Puff adder . . . . 3·00 3·25
1527 5000s. Common house gecko . . . . 3·75 4·00
1528 6000s. Dwarf chameleon . . 4·50 4·75
1529 10000s. Boomslang (snake) 7·75 8·00

SIZES—21×21 mm: 50, 100, 150, 200, 350, 400, 450, 500s.; 18×20 mm: 300, 600, 700s. (No. 1521a); 38½×24½ mm: 700s. (No. 1521), 900s. to 10000s.

166 Nsambya Church

1995. Local Anniversaries. Multicoloured.
1530 150s. Type **166** 35 20
1531 450s. Namilyango College 80 70
1532 500s. Figures with symbolic wheel 85 75
1533 1000s. Volunteers with food sacks . . . . 1·50 2·00

ANNIVERSARIES: Nos. 1530/1, Centenary of Mill Hill Missionaries in Uganda; 1532, Centenary of International Co-operative Alliance; 1533, 25th anniv of U.N. volunteers.

167 Bwindi Forest

1995. Landscapes. Multicoloured.
1534 50s. Type **167** 25 20
1535 100s. Karamoja 30 20
1536 450s. Sunset, Lake Mburo National Park 80 70
1537 500s. Sunset, Gulu District 85 75
1538 900s. Mist, Kabale District 1·50 2·00
1539 1000s. Ruwenzori Mountains . . . . 1·60 2·00

1995. Waterfalls. As T **167**. Multicoloured.
1540 50s. Sipi Falls (vert) 25 20
1541 100s. Murchison Falls . . . 30 20
1542 450s. Bujagali Falls 80 70
1543 500s. The Two Falls at Murchison 85 75
1544 900s. Falls, Ruwenzori Mountains (vert) . . . . 1·50 2·00
1545 1000s. Falls, Ruwenzori Mountains (different) (vert) . . . . 1·60 2·00

168 Peter Rono (1500 m), 1988

1995. Olympic Games, Atlanta (1996). Multicoloured.
1546 50s. Type **168** 20 10
1547 350s. Reiner Klimke (dressage), 1984 . . . . . 70 40
1548 450s. German team (cycling time trials), 1988 . . . . 1·50 70
1549 500s. Grace Birungi (athlete) 90 70
1550 900s. Francis Ogola (athlete) 1·40 1·75
1551 1000s. Nyakana Godfrey (boxer) . . . . 1·50 1·75
MS1552 Two sheets, each 106×76 mm. (a) 2500s. Sebastian Coe (1500 metres), 1980 and 1984. (b) 2500s. Rolf Dannenberg (discus), 1984 (vert) Set of 2 sheets 6·00 7·00

169 Common Peafowl ("Peafowl")

1995. Domestic Animals. Multicoloured.
1553 200s. Type **169** 50 50
1554 200s. Pouter pigeon 50 50
1555 200s. Feral rock dove ("Rock Doves") 50 50
1556 200s. Mallard ("Rouen Duck") 50 50
1557 200s. Guineafowl 50 50
1558 200s. Donkey 50 50
1559 200s. Shetland ponies . . . 50 50
1560 200s. Palomino horse . . . 50 50
1561 200s. Pigs 50 50
1562 200s. Border collie 50 50
1563 200s. Merino sheep 50 50
1564 200s. Milch goat 50 50
1565 200s. Black dutch rabbit . . 50 50
1566 200s. Lop rabbit 50 50
1567 200s. Somali cat 50 50
1568 200s. Asian cat 50 50
MS1569 Two sheets, each 106×76 mm. (a) 2500s. Saddle-bred horses. (b) 2500s. Oxen Set of 2 sheets . . . . . . 7·50 7·50

Nos. 1553/68 were printed together, se-tenant, forming a composite design.

170 Scouts putting Child on Scales

171 Hermann Staudinger (1953 Chemistry)

1995. Uganda Boy Scouts in the Community. Multicoloured.
1570 150s. Type **170** 40 20
1571 350s. Scouts carrying children 75 45
1572 450s. Checking health cards (horiz) 80 70
1573 800s. Holding child for immunization (horiz) . . 1·50 1·75
1574 1000s. Weighing child before immunization . . . . . 1·60 1·75

1995. Centenary of Nobel Prize Trust Fund. Multicoloured.
1575 300s. Type **171** 65 65
1576 300s. Fritz Haber (1918 Chemistry) 65 65
1577 300s. Bert Sakmann (1991 Medicine) 65 65
1578 300s. Adolf Windaus (1926 Chemistry) 65 65
1579 300s. Wilhelm Wien (1911 Physics) 65 65
1580 300s. Ernest Hemingway (1954 Literature) 65 65

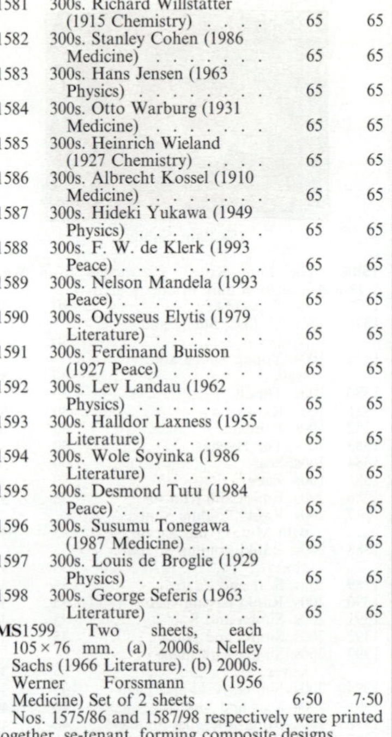

1581 300s. Richard Willstatter (1915 Chemistry) 65 65
1582 300s. Stanley Cohen (1986 Medicine) 65 65
1583 300s. Hans Jensen (1963 Physics) 65 65
1584 300s. Otto Warburg (1931 Medicine) 65 65
1585 300s. Heinrich Wieland (1927 Chemistry) 65 65
1586 300s. Albrecht Kossel (1910 Medicine) 65 65
1587 300s. Hideki Yukawa (1949 Physics) 65 65
1588 300s. F. W. de Klerk (1993 Peace) 65 65
1589 300s. Nelson Mandela (1993 Peace) 65 65
1590 300s. Odysseus Elytis (1979 Literature) 65 65
1591 300s. Ferdinand Buisson (1927 Peace) 65 65
1592 300s. Lev Landau (1962 Physics) 65 65
1593 300s. Halldor Laxness (1955 Literature) 65 65
1594 300s. Wole Soyinka (1986 Literature) 65 65
1595 300s. Desmond Tutu (1984 Peace) 65 65
1596 300s. Susumu Tonegawa (1987 Medicine) 65 65
1597 300s. Louis de Broglie (1929 Physics) 65 65
1598 300s. George Seferis (1963 Literature) 65 65
MS1599 Two sheets, each 105×76 mm. (a) 2000s. Nelley Sachs (1966 Literature). (b) 2000s. Werner Forssmann (1956 Medicine) Set of 2 sheets . . . 6·50 7·50

Nos. 1575/86 and 1587/98 respectively were printed together, se-tenant, forming composite designs.

1995. Christmas. Religious Paintings. As T **281a** of Sierra Leone. Multicoloured.
1600 150s. "The Virgin and Child" (Holbein the Younger) 30 20
1601 350s. "Madonna" (Procaccini) 55 35
1602 500s. "The Virgin and Child" (Pisanello) 80 50
1603 1000s. "Madonna and Child" (Crivelli) . . . . . 1·50 1·75
1604 1500s. "The Nativity of the Virgin" (Le Nain) . . . 2·00 2·75
MS1605 Two sheets, each 102×127 mm. (a) 2500s. "Madonna and Child" (detail) (Bellini). (b) 2500s. "The Holy Family" (detail) (Andrea del Sarto) Set of 2 sheets . . . . . 7·50 7·50

172 "Ansellia africana"

1995. Orchids. Multicoloured.
1606 150s. Type **172** 50 40
1607 350s. "Aerangis iuteoalba" 60 60
1608 350s. "Satyrium sacculatum" 60 60
1609 350s. "Bolusiella maudiae" 60 60
1610 350s. "Habenaria attenuata" 60 60
1611 350s. "Cyrtorchis arcuata" 60 60
1612 350s. "Eulophia angolensis" 60 60
1613 350s. "Tridactyle bicaudata" 60 60
1614 350s. "Eulophia horsfallii" 60 60
1615 350s. "Diaphananthe fragrantissima" 60 60
1616 450s. "Satyricum crassicaule" 75 75
1617 500s. "Polystachya cultriformis" 80 80
1618 800s. "Disa erubescens" . . 1·25 1·40
MS1619 Two sheets, each 66×76 mm. (a) 2500s. "Rangaeris amaniensis". (b) 2500s. "Diaphananthe pulchella" Set of 2 sheets . . . . 7·50 8·00

173 Rat and Purple Grapes

1996. Chinese New Year ("Year of the Rat"). Multicoloured.
1620 350s. Type **173** 40 50
1621 350s. Rat and radishes . . . 40 50
1622 350s. Rat eating corn . . . 40 50
1623 350s. Rat eating cucumber 40 50
MS1624 100×74 mm. Nos. 1620/3 1·10 1·40
MS1625 106×76 mm. 2000s. Rat and green grapes . . . . 2·25 2·50

174 Wild Dog and Pup

1996. Wildlife of Uganda. Multicoloured. (a) Horiz designs.
1626 150s. Type **174** 40 35
1627 200s. African fish eagle . . 45 40
1628 250s. Hippopotamus 45 40
1629 350s. Leopard 50 50
1630 400s. Lion 50 60
1631 450s. Lioness 55 65
1632 500s. Meerkats 55 65
1633 550s. Pair of black rhinoceroses 75 75

(b) Vert designs.
1634 150s. Gorilla 40 35
1635 200s. Cheetah 45 40
1636 250s. African elephant . . . 50 45
1637 350s. Thomson's gazelle . . 50 50
1638 400s. Crowned crane . . . 60 60
1639 450s. Saddlebill 65 70
1640 500s. Vulture 65 70
1641 550s. Zebra 65 70
MS1642 Two sheets. (a) 72×102 mm. 200s. Grey heron (horiz). (b) 102×72 mm. 2000s. Giraffe Set of 2 sheets . . . . 5·50 6·00

175 Mickey Mouse and Goofy on Platform at Calais

1996. Mickey's Orient Express. Walt Disney Cartoon Characters. Multicoloured.
1643 50s. Type **175** 30 30
1644 100s. Mickey and Goofy at Athens 35 30
1645 150s. Mickey showing Donald Duck his Pullman ticket 50 30
1646 200s. Daisy and Donald Duck in Pullman car . . 65 30
1647 250s. Mickey and Minnie Mouse in dining car . . . 75 40
1648 300s. Goofy as guard assisting Mickey and Minnie 85 50
1649 600s. Mickey and Donald preparing for bed . . . . 1·50 1·75
1650 700s. Mickey and Minnie at Orient Express accident, Frankfurt, 1901 . . . . . 1·60 1·90
1651 800s. Mickey and Goofy building snowman and Orient Express in snowdrift, 1929 . . . . . 1·75 2·00
1652 900s. Disney characters filming "Murder on the Orient Express" . . . . . 1·90 2·25
MS1653 Two sheets, each 132×106 mm. (a) 2500s. Donald driving Orient Express. (b) 2500s. Mickey, Minnie and Goofy on Observation platform Set of 2 sheets . . . . 8·50 9·50

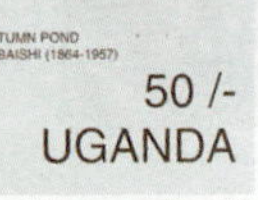

176 "Autumn Pond"

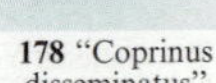
178 "Coprinus disseminatus"

177 Tomb Mural, Xi'an (½-size illustration)

1996. "CHINA '96" 9th Asian International Stamp Exhibition, Peking. Paintings by Qi Baishi. Multicoloured.

1654 50s. Type **176** 20 20
1655 100s. "Partridge and Smartweed" 25 20
1656 150s. "Begonias and Mynah" 30 20
1657 200s. "Chrysanthemums, Cocks and Hens" 30 20
1658 250s. "Crabs" 30 25
1659 300s. "Wisterias and Bee" 35 30
1660 350s. "Smartweed and Ink-drawn Butterflies" 40 40
1661 400s. "Lotus and Mandarin Ducks" 45 50
1662 450s. "Lichees and Locust" 50 55
1663 500s. "Millet and Praying Mantis" 55 60
MS1664 135 × 114 mm. 800s. "Morning Glories and Locust" (50 × 38 mm); 800s. "Shrimps" (50 × 38 mm) . . . . 3·00 3·00

The painting titles on 150s. and 200s. are transposed in error, with "CHRYSANTHEMUMS" shown as "RYSANTHEMUMS".

1996. "CHINA '96" 9th Asian International Stamp Exhibition, Peking (2nd issue). Sheet 140 × 90 mm.
MS1664a **177** 500s. multicoloured 1·00 1·10

1996. African Fungi. Multicoloured.

1665 150s. Type **178** 50 50
1666 300s. "Coprinus radians" . . 60 60
1667 350s. "Hygrophorus coccineus" 60 60
1668 400s. "Marasmius siccus" 70 70
1669 450s. "Cortinarius collinitus" 80 80
1670 500s. "Cortinarius cinnabarinus" 80 80
1671 550s. "Coltricia cinnamomea" 85 90
1672 1000s. "Mutinus elegans" 1·50 1·75
MS1673 Two sheets, each 110 × 80 mm. (a) 2500s. "Inocybe sororia". (b) 2500s. "Flammulina velutipes" Set of 2 sheets . . . 6·00 6·50

179 "Catopsilia philea"

1996. Butterflies. Multicoloured.

1674 50s. Type **179** 40 45
1675 100s. "Dione vanillae" . . . 40 45
1676 150s. "Metamorpha dido" 45 50
1677 200s. "Papilio sesostris" . . 50 55
1678 250s. "Papilio neophilus" . . 50 55
1679 300s. "Papilio thoas" . . . 50 55
1680 350s. "Diorina periander" 55 60
1681 400s. "Morpho cipris" . . . 55 60
1682 450s. "Catonephele numilia" 60 65
1683 500s. "Heliconius doris" . . 60 65
1684 550s. "Prepona antimache" 60 65
1685 600s. "Eunica alcmena" . . 65 70
MS1686 Two sheets, each 100 × 70 mm. (a) 2500s. "Caligo martia" (b) 2500s. "Heliconius doris" (different) Set of 2 sheets 5·00 5·50

1996. 70th Birthday of Queen Elizabeth II. As T **323a** of St. Vincent. Different photographs. Multicoloured.

1687 500s. Queen Elizabeth II . . 1·00 1·00
1688 500s. In evening dress . . . 1·00 1·00
1689 500s. Wearing red coat and hat . . . . 1·00 1·00
MS1690 125 × 103 mm. 2000s. Queen Elizabeth II . . . . . . 2·75 2·75

179a Asian Children

1996. 50th Anniv of U.N.I.C.E.F. Multicoloured.

1691 450s. Type **179a** 75 85
1692 500s. South American children 80 90
1693 550s. Boy holding pencil . . 90 1·00
MS1694 74 × 104 mm. 2000s. African mother and child . . . 2·50 3·00

179b Darien National Park, Panama

1996. 50th Anniv of U.N.E.S.C.O. Multicoloured.

1695 450s. Type **179b** 75 85
1696 500s. Los Glaciares National Park, Argentina 80 90
1697 550s. Tubbatha Reef Marine Park, Philippines . . . . 90 1·00
MS1698 104 × 74 mm. 2500s. Ruwenzori Mountains National Park, Uganda . . . . 2·25 2·75

No. **MS**1698 is inscribed "RWENZORI" in error.

180 Statue of Menorah, Knesset

1996. 3000th Anniv of Jerusalem. T **180** and similar vert designs. Multicoloured.

MS1699 114 × 95 mm. 300s. Type **180**, 500s. Jerusalem Theatre. 1000s. Israel Museum 3·25 3·25
MS1700 104 × 74 mm. 2000s. Grotto of the Nativity . . . . 3·25 3·25

1996. Centenary of Radio. Entertainers. As T **326** of St. Vincent. Multicoloured.

1701 200s. Ella Fitzgerald 35 20
1702 300s. Bob Hope 70 40
1703 500s. Nat "King" Cole . . . 80 70
1704 800s. George Burns and Gracie Allen . . . . . . 1·25 1·50
MS1705 74 × 104 mm. 2000s. Jimmy Durante . . . . 3·00 3·25

181 Electric Locomotive, 1968 (Japan)

1996. Railway Locomotives. Multicoloured.

1706 450s. Type **181** 80 80
1707 450s. Stephenson's "Rocket", 1829 . . . . . 80 80
1708 450s. William Norris's "Austria", 1843 . . . . . 80 80
1709 450s. Early American steam locomotive 80 80
1710 450s. Steam locomotive, 1947 (India) 80 80
1711 450s. Class 103 electric locomotive (Germany) . . 80 80
1712 550s. GWR steam locomotive "Lady of Lynn" (England) 80 80
1713 550s. Steam locomotive, 1930 (China) 80 80
1714 550s. Meyer-Kitson steam locomotive (Chile) 80 80
1715 550s. Union Pacific "Centennial" diesel locomotive No. 6900 (U.S.A.) 80 80
1716 550s. Type 581 diesel locomotive (Japan) . . . 80 80
1717 550s. Class 120 electric locomotive (Germany) . . 80 80
MS1718 Two sheets, each 106 × 76 mm. (a) 2500s. Type 99 steam locomotive (Germany); (b) 2500s. LNER Class A4 steam locomotive "Mallard", Great Britain Set of 2 sheets . . . . 6·50 7·00

182 Postal and Telecommunications Corporation Emblem

1996. Centenary of Postal Services. Multicoloured.

1719 150s. Type **182** 25 20
1720 450s. Loading postbus . . . 1·00 1·00
1721 500s. Modern postal transportation . . . . . 1·25 1·25
1722 550s. 1896 25c. violet and 1r. black stamps . . . . 1·25 1·40

183 Two American River Steamers and 1904 Games, St. Louis

1996. Olympic Games, Atlanta (1st issue). Multicoloured.

1723 350s. Type **183** 60 45
1724 450s. George Finnegan (U.S.A.) (boxing), 1904 65 65
1725 500s. Chariot racing 75 75
1726 800s. John Flanagan (U.S.A.) (hammer), 1904 (vert) . . . . 1·10 1·40

See also Nos. 1764/81.

184 Mango

185 Traditional Costumes from Western Uganda

1996. Fruit. Multicoloured.

1727 150s. Type **184** 35 20
1728 350s. Orange 75 50
1729 450s. Pawpaw 85 75
1730 500s. Avocado 90 85
1731 550s. Watermelon (horiz) . . 1·00 1·10

1996. Christmas. Religious Paintings. As T **337** of St. Vincent. Multicoloured.

1732 150s. "Annunciation" (Lorenzo di Credi) . . . 35 20
1733 350s. "Madonna of the Loggia" (detail) (Botticelli) 70 40
1734 400s. "Virgin in Glory with Child and Angels" (Lorenzetti) 75 60
1735 450s. "Adoration of the Child" (Lippi) 80 80
1736 500s. "Madonna of the Loggia" (Botticelli) . . . 90 90
1737 550s. "The Strength" (Botticelli) . . . . . . 1·00 1·25
MS1738 Two sheets, each 106 × 76 mm. (a) 2500s. "Holy Allegory" (Bellini) (horiz); (b) 2500s. "The Virgin on the Throne with Child and the Saints" (ghirlandaio) (horiz) Set of 2 sheets . . . . 7·50 8·00

1996. 20th Anniv of "Rocky" (film). Sheet 143 × 182 mm, containing vert design as T **338** of St. Vincent. Multicoloured.
MS1739 800s. × 3 Sylvester Stallone in "Rocky III" . . . . 3·50 4·00

1997. Traditional Costumes. Multicoloured.

1740 150s. Type **185** 30 20
1741 300s. Acholi headdress . . . 65 75
1742 300s. Alur headdress 65 75
1743 300s. Bwola dance headdress 65 75
1744 300s. Madi headdress . . . 65 75
1745 300s. Karimojong headdress with plume 65 75
1746 300s. Karimojong headdress with two feathers 65 75
1747 350s. Karimojong women 70 60
1748 450s. Ganda traditional dress (horiz) 80 80
1749 500s. Acholi traditional dress (horiz) 85 85

186 Ox

1997. Chinese New Year ("Year of the Ox"). Multicoloured.

1750 350s. Type **186** 50 60
1751 350s. Cow suckling calf . . 50 60
1752 350s. Cow and calf lying down 50 60
1753 350s. Ox lying down 50 60
MS1754 111 × 83 mm. Nos. 1750/3 1·40 1·60
MS1755 76 × 106 mm. 1500s. Young calf (vert) . . . . 1·40 1·60

187 Giraffe running

1997. Endangered Species. Rothschild's Giraffe. Multicoloured.

1756 300s. Type **187** 70 70
1757 300s. Two adult giraffes . . 70 70
1758 300s. Head of giraffe . . . 70 70
1759 300s. Giraffe with calf . . . 70 70
MS1760 75 × 109 mm. 2500s. Head of giraffe (different) (horiz) . . 4·75 4·75

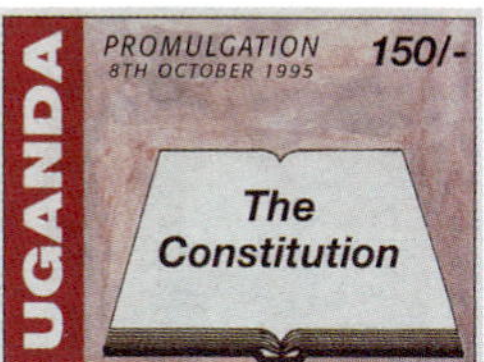

188 "The Constitution" on Open Book

1997. Promulgation of New Constitution (8 Oct 1995). Multicoloured.

1761 150s. Type **188** 30 20
1762 350s. "The Constitution" on scroll 60 50
1763 550s. "THE CONSTITUTION" on closed book (vert) . . . . 90 1·10

189 Kitel Son (Japan) (marathon), 1936

190 "Red Plum Blossom and Daffodil"

1997. Olympic Games, Atlanta (2nd issue). Previous Gold Medal Winners. Multicoloured.

1764 150s. Type **189** 40 50
1765 150s. Bob Hayes (U.S.A.) (100 m), 1964 . . . . . 40 50
1766 200s. Walter Davis (U.S.A.) (high jump), 1952 . . . . 45 55
1767 200s. Rod Milburn (110 m hurdles), 1972 . . 45 55
1768 250s. Matthes (swimming), 1968 . . . . 50 60
1769 250s. Filbert Bayi (Tanzania) (athletics), 1976 . . . . 50 60
1770 300s. Akii Bua (Uganda) (400 m hurdles), 1972 . . 55 65
1771 300s. H. Kipchoge Keino (Kenya) (steeplechase), 1972 . . . . 55 65
1772 350s. Nordwig (Germany) (pole vault), 1972 . . . . 60 70
1773 350s. Ron Ray (U.S.A.) (athletics), 1976 . . . . 60 70
1774 400s. Wilma Rudolph (U.S.A.) (100 m relay), 1960 . . . . 65 75
1775 400s. Joe Frazer (U.S.A.) (boxing), 1976 . . . . . 65 75
1776 450s. Abebe Bikila (Ethiopia) (marathon), 1964 . . . . 70 80
1777 450s. Carl Lewis (U.S.A.) (100 m), 1984 . . . . . 70 80
1778 500s. Edwin Moses (U.S.A.) (400 m hurdles), 1984 . . 75 85
1779 500s. Gisela Mauermayer (Germany) (discus), 1936 75 85
1780 550s. Rady Williams (U.S.A.) (long jump), 1972 . . . . 80 90
1781 550s. Dietmar Mogenburg (Germany) (high jump), 1984 . . . . 80 90

Nos. 1764, 1766, 1768, 1770, 1772, 1774, 1776, 1778 and 1780 and 1765, 1767, 1769, 1771, 1773, 1775, 1777, 1779 and 1781 respectively were printed together, se-tenant, with the backgrounds forming composite designs.

No. 1769 is incorrectly inscribed "Eiilbert" and is dated "1976"; Filbert Bayi did not participate in the 1976 Games. No. 1779 is incorrectly inscribed "Mauemayer" and wrongly identifies the event as the shotput.

1997. "HONG KONG '97" International Stamp Exhibition. Paintings by Wu Changshuo. Mult.

1782 50s. Type **190** 25 35
1783 100s. "Peony" 35 45
1784 150s. "Rosaceae" 45 50
1785 200s. "Pomegranate" . . . 50 55
1786 250s. "Peach, Peony and Plum Blossom" 50 55
1787 300s. "Calyx Canthus" . . 55 60
1788 350s. "Chrysanthemum" . . 55 60
1789 400s. "Calabash" 60 65
1790 450s. "Chrysanthemum" (different) 65 70
1791 500s. "Cypress Tree" . . . 65 70
MS1792 137 × 105 mm. 550s. "Litchi" (50 × 37 mm); 1000s. "Water Lily" (50 × 37 mm). . . . 2·00 2·50

191 Woody

1997. Disney's "Toy Story" (cartoon film). Multicoloured.

1793 100s. Type **191** 50 50
1794 100s. Buzz Lightyear . . . 50 50
1795 100s. Bo Peep 50 50
1796 100s. Hamm 50 50
1797 100s. Slinky 50 50
1798 100s. Rex 50 50
1799 150s. Woody on bed (horiz) 55 55
1800 150s. Woody at microphone (horiz) 55 55
1801 150s. Bo Peep (horiz) . . . 55 55
1802 150s. Buzz Lightyear (horiz) 55 55
1803 150s. Slinky and Rex (horiz) 55 55
1804 150s. Woody hiding (horiz) 55 55
1805 150s. "Halt! Who goes there" (horiz) 55 55
1806 150s. Rex, Slinky and Buzz Lightyear (horiz) 55 55
1807 150s. "You're just an action figure!" (horiz) 55 55
1808 200s. "I'm the only sheriff in these parts" (horiz) . . . 55 55
1809 200s. Green toy soldiers (horiz) 55 55
1810 200s. Woody and Buzz (horiz) 55 55
1811 200s. Woody pointing (horiz) 55 55
1812 200s. Buzz Lightyear (horiz) 55 55
1813 200s. Green aliens (horiz) 55 55
1814 200s. "This is an intergalactic emergency" (horiz) 55 55
1815 200s. Buzz and Woody argue (horiz) 55 55
1816 200s. Buzz and Woody in buggy (horiz) 55 55
MS1817 Three sheets, each 133 × 108 mm. (a) 133 × 108 mm. 2000s. Woody; (b) 108 × 133 mm. 2000s. Buzz Lightyear, Rex and other toys; (c) 2000s. Buzz Lightyear Set of 3 sheets . . . 13·00 13·00

192 "Pioneer 10"

1997. Space Exploration. Multicoloured.

1818 250s. Type **192** 60 65
1819 250s. "Voyager 1" 60 65
1820 250s. "Viking Orbiter" . . . 60 65
1821 250s. "Pioneer – Venus 1" 60 65
1822 250s. "Mariner 9" 60 65
1823 250s. "Galileo" Entry Probe 60 65
1824 250s. "Mariner 10" 60 65
1825 250s. "Voyager 2" 60 65
1826 300s. "Sputnik 1" 60 65
1827 300s. "Apollo" spacecraft 60 65
1828 300s. "Soyuz" spacecraft . . 60 65
1829 300s. "Intelsat 1" 60 65
1830 300s. Manned manoeuvring Unit 60 65
1831 300s. "Skylab" 60 65
1832 300s. "Telstar 1" 60 65
1833 300s. Hubble Telescope . . 60 65
MS1834 Two sheets, each 103 × 73 mm. (a) 2000s. Space Shuttle *Challenger* (35 × 61 mm). (b) 2000s. "Viking Lander" on Mars (61 × 35 mm) Set of 2 sheets 6·00 6·50

Nos. 1818/25 and 1826/33 respectively were printed together, se-tenant, with the backgrounds forming composite designs.

193 Deng Xiaoping and Port

1997. Deng Xiaoping (Chinese statesman) Commemoration.

1835 **193** 500s. multicoloured . . . 75 75
1836 550s. multicoloured . . . 85 85
1837 1000s. multicoloured . . 1·50 2·00
MS1838 100 × 70 mm. 200s. multicoloured (Deng Xiaoping and Shenzhen) . . . . . . 2·75 3·25

194 Water Hyacinth and Pebbles
195 Men's Slalom

1997. Environmental Protection. Multicoloured.

1839 500s. Water hyacinth and Lake Victoria (inscr at top left) 75 75
1840 500s. Water hyacinth and Lake Victoria (inscr at top right) 75 75
1841 500s. Type **194** 75 75
1842 500s. Larger clump of water hyacinth and pebbles . . 75 75
1843 550s. Buffalo 75 75
1844 550s. Uganda kob 75 75
1845 550s. Vulturine guineafowl ("Guinea Fowl") 75 75
1846 550s. Marabou stork . . . 75 75
MS1847 106 × 76 mm. 2500s. Gorilla 4·50 4·50

Nos. 1839/42 and 1843/6 respectively were printed together, se-tenant, with the backgrounds forming composite designs.

No. 1845 is inscribed "GUINEA FOWEL" and No. 1846 "MALIBU STORK", both in error.

1997. 10th Anniv of Chernobyl Nuclear Disaster. As T **347** of St. Vincent.

1848 500s. As Type **347** of St. Vincent . . . . . . 1·00 1·00
1849 700s. As No. 1848 but inscribed "CHABAD'S CHILDREN OF CHERNOBYL" at foot 1·25 1·25

1997. 50th Death Anniv of Paul Harris (founder of Rotary International). As T **347a** of St. Vincent. Multicoloured.

1850 1000s. Paul Harris and child drinking . . . . . . 1·75 2·25
MS1851 78 × 107 mm. 2500s. The first Rotarians . . . . 2·50 3·25

1997. Golden Wedding of Queen Elizabeth and Prince Philip. As T **347b** of St. Vincent. Multicoloured.

1852 200s. Queen Elizabeth II . . 1·00 1·10
1853 200s. Royal coat of arms . . 1·00 1·10
1854 200s. Queen Elizabeth and Prince Philip at reception 1·00 1·10
1855 200s. Queen Elizabeth and Prince Philip on royal visit . . . . . . 1·00 1·10
1856 200s. Buckingham Palace . . 1·00 1·10
1857 200s. Prince Philip in military uniform . . . . 1·00 1·10
MS1858 100 × 70 mm. 2000s. Princess Elizabeth in wedding dress . . . . 2·75 3·00

1997. "Pacific '97" International Stamp Exhibition, San Francisco. Death Centenary of Heinrich von Stephan (founder of the U.P.U.). As T **347c** of St. Vincent.

1859 800s. blue . . . . 1·10 1·25
1860 800s. brown . . . . . . 1·10 1·25
1861 800s. green . . . . . . 1·10 1·25
MS1862 82 × 119 mm. 2500s. deep blue and blue . . . . 3·00 3·25

DESIGNS: No. 1859, Chinese post boat; 1860, Von Stephan and Mercury; 1861, Russian post cart; **MS**1862, Von Stephan and French postman on stilts.

1997. Winter Olympic Games, Nagano, Japan (1998). Multicoloured.

1863 350s. Type **195** 50 35
1864 450s. Two-man bobsled . . 60 45
1865 500s. Ski jumping (horiz) . . 70 75
1866 500s. Giant slalom (horiz) 70 75
1867 500s. Cross-country skiing (horiz) 70 75
1868 500s. Ice hockey (horiz) . . 70 75
1869 500s. Pairs figure skating (man) (horiz) 70 75
1870 500s. Pairs figure skating (woman) (horiz) 70 75
1871 800s. Women's slalom (horiz) . . . . 1·10 1·25
1872 2000s. Men's speed skating (horiz) . . . . 2·25 2·75
MS1873 Two sheets, each 103 × 72 mm. (a) 2500s. Downhill skiing (horiz). (b) 2500s. Women's figure skating (horiz) Set of 2 sheets . . . . 6·50 7·50

Nos. 1865/70 were printed together, se-tenant, with the backgrounds forming a composite design.

196 Main Building, Makerere University

1997. 75th Anniv of Makerere University. Multicoloured.

1874 150s. Type **196** 30 20
1875 450s. East African School of Librarianship building (vert) 65 65
1876 500s. Buyana Stock Farm, Makerere University . . . 75 75
1877 550s. Ceramic dish from School of Architecture and Fine Arts 80 90

1997. World Cup Football Championship, France (1998). As T **351a** of St. Vincent. Multicoloured (except Nos. 1878, 1880, 1883 and 1886).

1878 200s. Fritz Walter, Germany (brown) 40 25
1879 250s. Paulo Rossi (horiz) . . 40 40
1880 250s. Mario Kempes (black) (horiz) 40 40
1881 250s. Gerd Muller (horiz) 40 40
1882 250s. Grzegorz Lato (horiz) 40 40
1883 250s. Joseph Gaetjens (black) (horiz) 40 40
1884 250s. Eusebio Ferreica da Silva (horiz) 40 40
1885 250s. Salvatore Schillaci (horiz) 40 40
1886 250s. Leonidas da Silva (black) (horiz) 40 40
1887 250s. Gary Lineker (horiz) 40 40
1888 250s. Argentine and West German player chasing ball (horiz) 40 40
1889 250s. Azteca Stadium (horiz) 40 40
1890 250s. Maradona holding World Cup (horiz) . . . 40 40
1891 250s. Argentine and West German players with goalkeeper (horiz) 40 40
1892 250s. West German player tackling Argentine player (horiz) 40 40
1893 250s. Ball in back of net (horiz) 40 40
1894 250s. Argentine team (horiz) 40 40
1895 250s. Players competing to head ball (horiz) 40 40
1896 300s. Daniel Pasarella, Argentina 45 45
1897 450s. Dino Zoff, Italy . . . 60 65
1898 500s. Bobby Moore, England 70 75
1899 550s. Franz Beckenbaur, West Germany 75 85
1900 600s. Diego Maradona, Argentina . . . . 80 1·00
MS1901 Two sheets. (a) 102 × 127 mm. 2000s. Celebrating West German players, 1990 (horiz). (b) 127 × 102 mm. 2000s. Bobby Moore, 1966 (horiz) Set of 2 sheets . . . . 7·00 7·50

No. 1883 is inscribed "ADEMIR" in error.

197 Mahatma Gandhi

1997. 50th Death Anniv of Mahatma Gandhi (1998) (1st issue).

1902 **197** 600s. brown and black 1·10 1·25
1903 – 700s. brown and black 1·25 1·40
MS1904 73 × 103 mm. 1000s. multicoloured . . . . 2·25 2·25

DESIGNS: 700s., 1000s. Different portait.

See also Nos. 2021/2.

198 "Cupid and Dolphin" (Andrea del Verrocchio)

1997. Christmas. Paintings and Sculptures. Multicoloured.

1905 200s. Type **198** 40 20
1906 300s. "The Fall of the Rebel Angels" (Pieter Brueghel the Elder) 55 30
1907 400s. "The Immaculate Conception" (Bartolome Murillo) 70 50
1908 500s. "Music-making Angel" (Rosso Fiorentino) . . . 75 75
1909 600s. "Cupid and Psyche" (Adolphe-William Bouguereau) . . . . . . 85 1·00
1910 700s. "Cupid and Psyche" (Antonio Canova) . . . . 95 1·25
MS1911 Two sheets, each 105 × 96 mm. (a) 2500s. Mary and Angels (detail, "The Assumption of the Virgin") (El Greco) (horiz). (b) 2500s. Angel holding baby (detail, "The Assumption of the Virgin") (El Greco) (horiz) Set of 2 sheets . . . . 7·00 7·50

199 Diana, Princess of Wales

1997. Diana, Princess of Wales Commemoration.

1912 **199** 600s. multicoloured . . . 1·25 1·40

200 Tiger

1998. Chinese New Year ("Year of the Tiger"). Multicoloured.

1913 350s. Type **200** 55 60
1914 350s. Tiger leaping 55 60
1915 350s. Tiger resting 55 60
1916 350s. Tiger yawning 55 60
MS1917 106 × 76 mm. 1500s. Tiger 2·00 2·25

201 Mountain Gorilla
202 Namugongo Martyrs Shrine, Kampala

1998. 18th Anniv of Pan African Postal Union.

1918 **201** 300s.+150s. mult . . . . 1·10 1·50

1998. Tourist Attractions. Multicoloured.

1919 300s. Type **202** 40 30
1920 400s. Kasubi Tombs, Kampala (horiz) 50 40
1921 500s. Tourist launch in Kazinga Channel, Queen Elizabeth Park (horiz) . . 70 65
1922 600s. Elephant, Queen Elizabeth Park (horiz) . . 95 95
1923 700s. Bujagali Falls, River Nile at Jinja (horiz) . . . 1·10 1·25

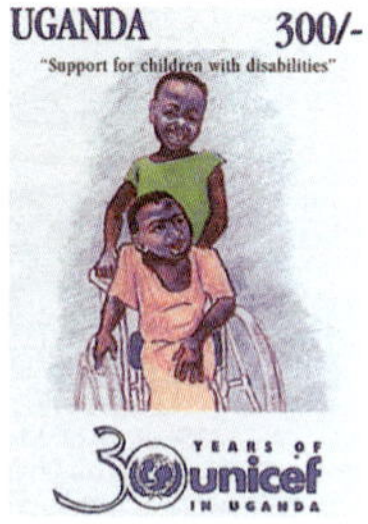

203 Mother Teresa, 1928 **204** Child in Wheelchair

1998. Mother Teresa Commemoration. Mult.
1924 300s. Type **203** 60 60
1925 300s. Holding child (56 × 42 mm) 60 60
1926 300s. Mother Teresa at United Nations, 1975 (56 × 42 mm) 60 60
1927 300s. Facing left 60 60
1928 300s. Full face portrait . . . 60 60
1929 300s. With children (56 × 42 mm) 60 60
1930 300s. Mother Teresa rescuing child (56 × 42 mm) 60 60
1931 300s. Smiling 60 60
MS1932 95 × 81 mm. 2000s. Mother Teresa with Diana, Princess of Wales (50 × 37 mm) . . . . . 4·25 4·25

1998. 30th Anniv of U.N.I.C.E.F. Multicoloured.
1933 300s. Type **204** 45 30
1934 400s. Child receiving oral vaccination against polio 60 45
1935 600s. Children outside toilet 85 1·00
1936 700s. Children in class . . . 90 1·10

205 Pteranodon

1998. Prehistoric Animals. Multicoloured.
1937 300s. Type **205** 45 30
1938 400s. Diplodocus 55 45
1939 500s. Lambeosaurus 70 60
1940 600s. Centrosaurus 75 85
1941 600s. Cetiosaurus (vert) . . 75 85
1942 600s. Brontosaurus (vert) . . 75 85
1943 600s. Brachiosaurus (vert) 75 85
1944 600s. Deinonychus (vert) . . 75 85
1945 600s. Dimetrodon (vert) . . 75 85
1946 600s. Megalosaurus (vert) 75 85
1947 700s. Parasaurolophus . . . 85 95
MS1948 Two sheets, each 73 × 103 mm. (a) 2500s. Tyrannosaurus rex (42 × 56 mm). (b) 2500s. Iguanodon (42 × 56 mm) Set of 2 sheets . . 7·50 8·00
Nos. 1941/6 were printed together, se-tenant, with the backgrounds forming a composite design.

206 Rita Dove

1998. U.N.E.S.C.O. World Literacy Campaign. 20th-century Afro-American Writers. Multicoloured.
1949 300s. Type **206** 80 80
1950 300s. Mari Evans 80 80
1951 300s. Sterling A. Brown . . 80 80
1952 300s. June Jordan 80 80
1953 300s. Stephen Henderson . . 80 80
1954 300s. Zora Neale Hurston 80 80

207 Mickey Mouse and Monster

1998. 70th Birthday of Mickey Mouse. Scenes from cartoon film "Runaway Brain". Multicoloured.
1955 400s. Type **207** 85 85
1956 400s. Mickey and Pluto with newspaper 85 85
1957 400s. Mickey and Pluto in front of television 85 85
1958 400s. Mickey and Minnie fleeing 85 85
1959 400s. Mickey on television screen 85 85
1960 400s. Monster and hostage Minnie Mouse clinging to skyscraper 85 85
1961 400s. Mickey Mouse throwing lasso 85 85
1962 400s. Mickey circling Monster on lasso 85 85
1963 400s. Mickey and Minnie on rope 85 85
MS1964 Two sheets, each 127 × 102 mm. (a) 3000s. Mickey and Minnie hugging on roof. (b) 3000s. Mickey and Minnie on liferaft (vert). Set of 2 sheets 11·00 11·00

1998. "Israel 98" International Stamp Exhibition, Tel-Aviv. Nos. **MS**1699/1700 optd with **98** and logo and each further optd "**ISRAEL 98 - WORLD STAMP EXHIBITION TEL-AVIV 13-21 MAY 1998**" on margin.
MS1965 114 × 95 mm. 300s. Type **180**; 500s. Jerusalem Theatre; 1000s. Israel Museum 3·00 3·00
MS1966 104 × 74 mm. 2000s. Grotto of the Nativity . . . . 3·00 3·00

209 "Santa Maria" (Columbus)

1998. Ships of the World. Multicoloured.
1967 1000s. Type **209** . . . . . 1·40 1·60
1968 1000s. "Mayflower" (Pilgrim Fathers) . . . . 1·40 1·60
1969 1000s. Barque . . . . . . 1·40 1·60
1970 1000s. Fishing schooner . . 1·40 1·60
1971 1000s. Chesapeake oyster boat . . . . 1·40 1·60
1972 1000s. Java Sea schooner . . 1·40 1·60
MS1973 Two sheets, each 100 × 70 mm. (a) 3000s. Thames barge (27 × 41 mm); (b) 3000s. Felucca (41 × 27 mm) Set of 2 sheets . . . . 8·00 8·50

210 Grumman F4F Wildcat (U.S.A.)

1998. Aircraft. Multicoloured.
1974 500s. Type **210** 75 75
1975 500s. Mitsubishi A6M Zero-Sen (Japan) 75 75
1976 500s. Supermarine Seafire ("Spitfire") (Great Britain) 75 75
1977 500s. Hawker Siddeley Harrier (Great Britain) . . 75 75
1978 500s. S3A Viking (U.S.A.) 75 75
1979 500s. Corsair (U.S.A.) . . . 75 75
1980 600s. Dornier Do-X (flying boat) (1929) 75 75
1981 600s. German Zucker mail rocket (1930) 75 75
1982 600s. North American X-15 rocket plane (1959) . . . 75 75
1983 600s. Goddard's rocket (1930s) 75 75
1984 600s. Wright Brothers' "Flyer I" (1903) 75 75
1985 600s. 16 0R Sikorsky (first helicopter) (1939) 75 75
MS1986 Two sheets. (a) 85 × 110 mm. 2500s. P-40 Tomahawk (U.S.A.) (1940). (b) 110 × 85 mm. 2500s. SH-346 Seabat recovery helicopter (U.S.A.) Set of 2 sheets . . . . 7·50 7·50
Nos. 1974/9 and 1980/5 respectively were printed together, se-tenant, forming composite designs.

211 "Onosma" sp. **213** Diana, Princess of Wales

212 Bohemian Waxwing

1998. Flowers of the Mediterranean. Multicoloured.
1987 300s. Type **211** 55 55
1988 300s. "Rhododendron luteum" 55 55
1989 300s. "Paeonia mascula" . . 55 55
1990 300s. "Geranium macrorrhizum" 55 55
1991 300s. "Cyclamen graecum" 55 55
1992 300s. "Lilium rhodopaedum" 55 55
1993 300s. "Narcissus pseudonarcissus" . . . 55 55
1994 300s. "Paeonia rhodia" . . 55 55
1995 300s. "Aquilegia amaliae" 55 55
1996 600s. "Paeonia peregrina" (horiz) 75 75
1997 600s. "Muscari comutatum" (horiz) 75 75
1998 600s. "Sternbergia" sp. (horiz) 75 75
1999 600s. "Dianthus" sp. (horiz) 75 75
2000 600s. "Verbascum" sp. (horiz) 75 75
2001 600s. "Aubrieta gracilis" (horiz) 75 75
2002 600s. "Galanthus nivalis" (horiz) 75 75
2003 600s. "Campanula incurva" (horiz) 75 75
2004 600s. "Crocus sieberi" (horiz) 75 75
MS2005 Two sheets. (a) 70 × 100 mm. 2000s. "Paeonia parnassica" (b) 100 × 70 mm. 2000s. "Pancratium maritimum" Set of 2 sheets . . . . 6·50 7·00

1998. Christmas. Birds. Multicoloured.
2006 300s. Type **212** 45 30
2007 400s. House sparrow . . . 55 40
2008 500s. Black-capped chickadee 65 50
2009 600s. Northern bullfinch ("Eurasian Bullfinch") . . 75 65
2010 700s. Painted bunting . . . 85 80
2011 1000s. Common cardinal ("Northern Cardinal") . . 1·25 1·50
MS2012 Two sheets, each 70 × 97 mm. (a) 2500s. Winter wren (vert). (b) 2500s. Red-winged blackbird (vert) Set of 2 sheets 7·50 7·50
No. **MS**2012a is inscribed "Winter Wreu" in error.

1998. 25th Death Anniv of Pablo Picasso (painter). As T **373** of St. Vincent. Multicoloured.
2013 500s. "Woman Reading" (vert) 65 65
2014 600s. "Portrait of Dora Maar" (vert) 75 80
2015 700s. "Les Demoiselles d'Avignon" . . . . . . 85 1·00
MS2016 127 × 101 mm. 2500s. "Night Fishing at Antibes" (vert) 3·25 3·50
No. 2015 is inscribed "Des Moiselles D'Avignon" in error.

1998. 19th World Scout Jamboree, Chile. As T **373b** of St. Vincent. Multicoloured (except **MS**2020).
2017 700s. Cub Scouts greeting President Eisenhower, 1956 . . . . 85 95
2018 700s. Scout with "Uncle Dan" Beard, 1940 . . . . 85 95
2019 700s. Vice-President Hubert Humphrey as Scout leader, 1934 . . . . . . 85 95
MS2020 70 × 100 mm. 2000s. Scout with pet beaver (purple, grey & brown) . . . . 3·00 3·25

1998. 50th Death Anniv of Mahatma Gandhi (2nd issue). As T **373c** of St. Vincent.
2021 600s. multicoloured . . . . 2·00 2·00
MS2022 98 × 58 mm. 2500s. brown, mauve and black . . . . . . 3·75 4·00
DESIGN—HORIZ: 600s. Gandhi as a young man. VERT: 2500s. Gandhi in Bombay law office.

1998. 1st Death Anniv of Diana, Princess of Wales.
2023 **213** 700s. multicoloured . . . 1·40 1·60

214 Rabbit

1999. Chinese New Year ("Year of the Rabbit"). Multicoloured.
2024 350s. White rabbit 50 60
2025 350s. Rabbit with carrot . . 50 60
2026 350s. Brown and white rabbit 50 60
2027 350s. Type **214** 50 60
MS2028 106 × 76 mm. 1500s. Rabbit 1·75 2·00

215 Post Office Emblem and Slogan

1999. Uganda Post Limited Commemoration.
2029 **215** 300s. multicoloured . . . 60 35

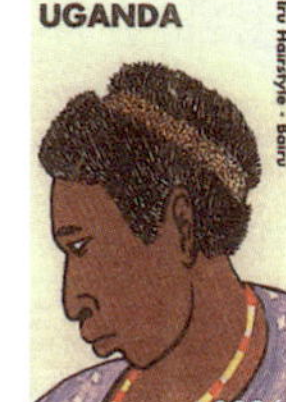

216 Iru Hairstyle

1999. Hairstyles. Multicoloured.
2030 300s. Type **216** 40 30
2031 500s. Enshunju hairstyle . . 60 50
2032 550s. Elemungole hairstyle 65 65
2033 600s. Lango hairstyle . . . 70 70
2034 700s. Ekikuura hairstyle . . 75 80

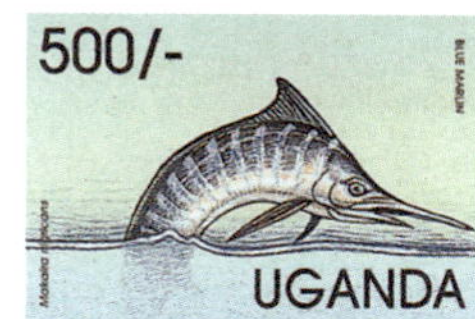

217 Blue Marlin

1999. International Year of the Ocean. Multicoloured.
2035 500s. Type **217** 60 65
2036 500s. Arctic tern 60 65
2037 500s. Common dolphin . . 60 65
2038 500s. Blacktip shark 60 65
2039 500s. Manta ray 60 65
2040 500s. Blackedge moray . . . 60 65
2041 500s. Loggerhead turtle . . 60 65
2042 500s. Sail-finned tang . . . 60 65
2043 500s. Two-spotted octopus 60 65
2044 500s. Atlantic wolffish . . . 60 65
2045 500s. Equal sea star 60 65
2046 500s. Purple sea urchin . . 60 65
2047 500s. Mountain crab 60 65
MS2048 Two sheets, each 110 × 85 mm. (a) 2500s. Sea nettle jellyfish. (b) 2500s. "Decatopecten striatus" (scallop) Set of 2 sheets 6·50 7·00
Nos. 2035/43 and Nos. 2044/7 respectively were printed together, se-tenant, with the backgrounds forming a composite design.
No. 2036 is inscribed "ARTIC TERN" in error.

218 Cows feeding (income generation)

1999. International Year of the Elderly. Mult.
2049 300s. Type **218** 40 30
2050 500s. Elderly man reading with child 60 55
2051 600s. Playing board game 70 70
2052 700s. Food distribution . . 80 90

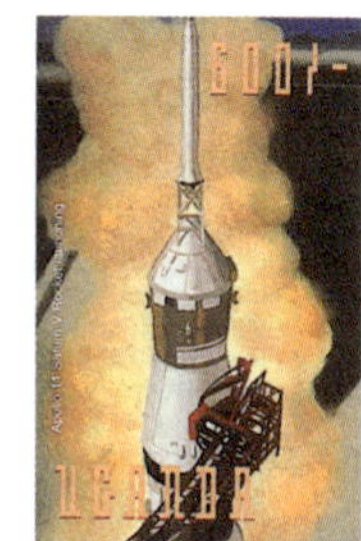

219 L'Hoest's Monkey **220** Saturn V Rocket Launch

1999. Primates. Multicoloured.
2053 300s. Type **219** 40 30
2054 400s. Diademed monkey ("Sykes/Blue Monkey") 50 40
2055 500s. Patas monkey 60 50
2056 600s. Red-tailed monkey . . 70 70
2057 700s. Eastern black and white colobus 80 85
2058 1000s. Mountain gorilla . . 1·10 1·40
MS2059 73 × 54 mm. 2500s. Olive baboon (35 × 26 mm) . . . . 3·50 4·00

1999. 150th Death Anniv of Katsushika Hokusai (Japanese artist). As T **384b** of St. Lucia. Multicoloured.
2060 700s. "Dragon flying over Mount Fuji" (detail) . . . 85 85
2061 700s. "Famous Poses from the Kabuki Theatre" (one woman) 85 85
2062 700s. "Kitsune No Yomeiri" 85 85
2063 700s. "Dragon flying over Mount Fuji" (complete picture) 85 85

2064 700s. "Famous Poses from the Kabuki Theatre" (man and woman) 85 85
2065 700s. "Girl holding Cloth" 85 85
MS2066 100 × 70 mm. 3000s. "Japanese Spaniel" . . . . 4·25 4·50

No. 2065 is inscribed "GIRL HOLDING CLOTHE" in error.

1999. "Queen Elizabeth the Queen Mother's Century". As T **386a** of St. Vincent.

2067 1200s. multicoloured . . . . 1·40 1·50
2068 1200s. black and gold . . . 1·40 1·50
2069 1200s. black and gold . . . 1·40 1·50
2070 1200s. multicoloured . . . 1·40 1·50
MS2071 152 × 155 mm. 3000s. multicoloured . . . . 4·25 4·50

DESIGNS: No. 2067, Duchess of York wearing evening cape; 2068, Wedding of Duke and Duchess of York, 1923; 2069, Formal portrait of Queen Mother; 2070, Queen Mother at evening reception; **MS**2071, Queen Mother visiting Cambridge, 1961.

No. **MS**2071 also shows the Royal Arms embossed in gold.

1999. 30th Anniv of First Manned Landing on Moon. Multicoloured.

2072 600s. Type **220** 70 75
2073 600s. Command and service module "Columbia" . . . 70 75
2074 600s. Edwin E. Aldrin descending ladder 70 75
2075 600s. Saturn V rocket on launch pad 70 75
2076 600s. Lunar module "Eagle" 70 75
2077 600s. Edwin E. Aldrin on Moon surface 70 75
2078 700s. Mercury mission "Freedom 7", 1961 . . . 75 80
2079 700s. "Gemini 4", 1965 . . 75 80
2080 700s. "Apollo 11" command and service module "Columbia" 75 80
2081 700s. "Vostok 1", 1961 . . 75 80
2082 700s. Saturn V rocket . . 75 80
2083 700s. "Apollo 11" lunar module "Eagle" 75 80
MS2084 Two sheets, each 76 × 106 mm. (a) 3000s. Edwin E. Aldrin with scientific experiment. (b) 3000s. "Apollo 11" command module re-entering Earth's atmosphere . . 7·50 8·00

Nos. 2078/83 were each printed together, se-tenant, with the backgrounds forming a composite design.

221 African Penduline Tit ("Penduline Tit")

222 "Epiphora bauhiniae" (moth)

1999. Birds of Uganda. Multicoloured.

2085 300s. Type **221** 60 45
2086 500s. Grey-headed kingfisher 70 75
2087 500s. Green-headed sunbird 70 75
2088 500s. Speckled pigeon . . . 70 75
2089 500s. Grey parrot 70 75
2090 500s. Barn owl 70 75
2091 500s. South African crowned crane ("Grey Crowned Crane") 70 75
2092 500s. Whale-headed stork ("Shoebill") 70 75
2093 500s. Black heron 70 75
2094 600s. Scarlet-chested sunbird 45 50
2095 600s. Lesser honeyguide . . 45 50
2096 600s. African palm swift . . 45 50
2097 600s. Swamp flycatcher . . 45 50
2098 600s. Lizard buzzard . . . 45 50
2099 600s. Osprey 45 50
2100 600s. Cardinal woodpecker 45 50
2101 600s. Pearl-spotted owlet . . 45 50
2102 700s. Speke's weaver ("Fox's Weaver") 80 90
2103 700s. Chin spot puff-backed flycatcher ("Chin-spot Flycatcher") 80 90
2104 700s. Blue swallow 80 90
2105 700s. Purple-breasted sunbird 80 90
2106 700s. Comb duck ("Knob-billed Duck") 80 90
2107 700s. Red-collared whydah ("Red-collared Widowbird") 80 90
2108 700s. Ruwenzori turaco . . 80 90
2109 700s. African cuckoo hawk 80 90
2110 1000s. Yellow-fronted tinkerbird . . . . 1·10 1·25
2111 1200s. Zebra waxbill . . . . 1·25 1·50
2112 1800s. Sooty chat ("Sooty Anteater Chat") . . . . . 1·75 2·00
MS2113 Two sheets, each 76 × 106 mm. (a) 3000s. Four-banded sandgrouse. (b) 3000s. Paradise whydah Set of 2 sheets 7·50 8·00

Nos. 2086/93, 2094/2101 and 2102/9 were each printed together, se-tenant, with the backgrounds forming composite designs.

Nos. 2100/1 are inscribed "Cardinal Woopecker" or "Glaucidium periatum", both in error.

2000. Moths. Multicoloured.

2114 300s. Type **222** 25 30
2115 400s. "Phylloxiphia formosa" (horiz) 30 35
2116 500s. "Bunaea alcinoe" . . 40 45
2117 600s. "Euchloron megaera" (horiz) 45 50
2118 700s. "Argema mimosae" . . 55 60
2119 1800s. "Denephila nerii" (horiz) . . . . 1·40 1·50
MS2120 75 × 52 mm. 3000s. "Lobobunaea angasana" (horiz) 2·25 2·40

223 Postman with Women and Child

224 *Eulophia paivenna*

2000. 125th Anniv of the Universal Postal Union. Multicoloured.

2121 600s. Type **223** 45 50
2122 700s. American mother and child reading letter by post box 55 60
2123 1200s. Mail coach 90 95

2000. Orchids. Multicoloured.

2124 600s. Type **224** 45 50
2125 600s. *Ansellia gigantea* . . . 45 50
2126 600s. *Anglaecopsis gracillima* 45 50
2127 600s. *Bonatea steudneri* . . . 45 50
2128 600s. *Bulbophyllum falcatum* 45 50
2129 600s. *Aerangis citrata* . . . 45 50
2130 600s. *Eulophiella Elisabethae* 45 50
2131 600s. *Aerangis rhodosticta* 45 50
2132 600s. *Angraecum scottianum* 45 50
2133 600s. *Angraecum eichcerianum* 45 50
2134 600s. *Angraecum leonis* . . . 45 50
2135 600s. *Arpophyllum giganteum* 45 50
2136 600s. *Bulbophyllum barbigerum* 45 50
2137 600s. *Angeraelum giryamae* 45 50
2138 600s. *Aeraungis ellisii* . . . 45 50
2139 600s. *Disa uniflora* 45 50
2140 600s. *Eulophia alta* 45 50
2141 600s. *Ancistrochilius stylosa* 45 50
2142 700s. *Eulophia orthoplectra* 55 60
2143 700s. *Cirrhopetalum umbellatum* 55 60
2144 700s. *Eulophiella rolfei* . . . 55 60
2145 700s. *Eulophia porphyroglossa* 55 60
2146 700s. *Eulophia petersii* . . . 55 60
2147 700s. *Cyrtorchis arcuata* . . 55 60
2148 700s. *Eurychone rothschildiana* 55 60
2149 700s. *Eulophia quartiniana* 55 60
2150 700s. *Eulophia stenophylia* (single flower) 55 60
2151 700s. *Grammangis ellisii* . . 55 60
2152 700s. *Eulophia stenophylia* (several flowers) 55 60
2153 700s. *Oeoniella polystachys* 55 60
2154 700s. *Cymbidiella humblotii* 55 60
2155 700s. *Polystachya bella* . . . 55 60
2156 700s. *Vanilla polycepis* . . . 55 60
2157 700s. *Eulophiella roemplerana* 55 60
2158 700s. *Habenaria englerana* 55 60
2159 700s. *Ansella frallana* . . . 55 60
MS2160 Four sheets, each 95 × 65 mm. (a) 3000s. *Cymbidiella rhodochila* (horiz). (b) 3000s. *Calanthe corymbosa* (horiz). (c) 3000s. *Ancistrochilus rothschildianus* (horiz). (d) 3000s. *Polystachya tayloriana* (horiz) Set of 4 sheets . . . . . . 9·00 9·50

Nos. 2124/32, 2133/41, 2142/50 and 2151/9 were each printed together, se-tenant, with the backgrounds forming composite designs.

225 Short-tailed Admiral

2000. "The Stamp Show 2000" International Stamp Exhibition, London. Butterflies. Multicoloured.

2161 300s. Type **225** 25 30
2162 400s. Guineafowl 30 35
2163 500s. *Charaxes anticlea* . . 40 45
2164 500s. *Epitola posthumus* . . 40 45
2165 500s. Beautiful monarch . . 40 45
2166 500s. Blue-banded nymph 40 45
2167 500s. *Euxanthe crossleyi* . . 40 45
2168 500s. African map butterfly 40 45
2169 500s. Western blue charaxes 40 45
2170 500s. Noble butterfly . . . 40 45
2171 600s. Green-veined charaxes 45 50
2172 600s. Ansorge's leaf butterfly 45 50
2173 600s. Crawshay's sapphire blue 45 50
2174 600s. *Palla ussheri* 45 50
2175 600s. Friar 45 50
2176 600s. Blood-red cymothoe 45 50
2177 600s. Mocker swallowtail . . 45 50
2178 600s. Green charaxes ("Charaxes eupale") . . . 45 50
2179 700s. *Acraea pseudolycia* . . 55 60
2180 700s. *Colotis protomedia* ("Veined Yellow") . . . 55 60
2181 700s. Buxton's hairstreak . . 55 60
2182 700s. *Iolaus iosmenias* . . . 55 60
2183 700s. Veined swallowtail . . 55 60
2184 700s. Fig-tree blue 55 60
2185 700s. Scarlet tip 55 60
2186 700s. Gaudy commodore ("Precis octavia") 55 60
2187 1200s. Club-tailed charaxes 90 95
2188 1800s. *Cymothoe egesta* . . 1·40 1·50
MS2189 Two sheets, each 63 × 69 mm. (a) 3000s. African monarch. (b) 3000s. Kigezi swordtail Set of 2 sheets . . . 4·50 4·75

Nos. 2163/70, 2171/8 and 2179/86 were each printed together, se-tenant, with the backgrounds forming composite designs.

No. 2165 is inscribed "Danasus formosa", No. 2169 "Western Blue Caraxes" and No. 2183 "Graphium lionidas", all in error.

225a King Philip II of France, 1180–1223

2000. Monarchs of the Millennium.

2190 **225a** 900s. grey, brown and bistre 70 75
2191 – 900s. grey, brown and bistre 70 75
2192 – 900s. grey, brown and bistre 70 75
2193 – 900s. purple, brown and bistre 70 75
2194 – 900s. multicoloured . . 70 75
2195 – 900s. multicoloured . . 70 75
2196 – 900s. grey, brown and bistre 70 75
2197 – 900s. grey, brown and bistre 70 75
2198 – 900s. grey, brown and bistre 70 75
MS2199 Two sheets. (a) 117 × 137 mm. 3000s. multicoloured. (b) 116 × 136 mm. 3000s. multicoloured Set of 2 sheets . . . . 4·50 4·75

DESIGNS: No. 2191, King Richard I of England, 1189–99; 2192, King William I of England, 1066–87; 2193, Tsar Boris III of Bulgaria, 1918–43; 2194, Emperor Charles V of Holy Roman Empire, 1519–58; 2195, Emperor Pedro II of Brazil, 1831–89; 2196, Empress Elizabeth of Austria, 1854–98; 2197, Emperor Francis Joseph of Austria, 1848–1916; 2198, King Frederik of Bohemia, 1619–20; **MS**2199a, King Mutesa I of Buganda; No. **MS**2199b, King Cwa II of Kabaleega.

No. 2198 is inscribed "FREDRICH" in error.

225b Pope Agapitus II, 946–55

2000. Popes of the Millennium. Multicoloured (except **MS**2206).

2200 900s. Type **225b** 70 75
2201 900s. Alexander II, 1061–73 70 75
2202 900s. Anastasius IV, 1153–54 . . . . 70 75
2203 900s. Benedict VIII, 1012–24 70 75
2204 900s. Benedict VII, 974–83 70 75
2205 900s. Callistus, 1119–24 . . 70 75
MS2206 116 × 137 mm. 3000s. Celestine III, (grey, brown and buff) . . . . 2·25 2·50

225c Bow of Merchant Ship (opening of Japan to foreign trade, 1853)

2000. New Millennium. People and Events of Nineteenth Century (1850–1900). Multicoloured.

2207 300s. Type **225c** 25 30
2208 300s. First elevator, 1854 . . 25 30
2209 300s. Ladle of molten steel (Bessemer Process, 1854) 25 30
2210 300s. Florence Nightingale (founder of nursing, 1854) 25 30
2211 300s. Louis Pasteur (French chemist, discovered bacteriology, 1856) . . . 25 30
2212 300s. Oil gusher (first oil well, 1859) 25 30
2213 300s. Charles Darwin (*The Origin of Species*, 1859) 25 30
2214 300s. Gregor Mendel (law of heredity, 1866) 25 30
2215 300s. Alfred Nobel (invention of dynamite, 1867) 25 30
2216 300s. Modern freighter in Canal (opening of Suez Canal, 1869) 25 30
2217 300s. Early telephone (invented 1876) 25 30
2218 300s. Light bulb (invention of electric light, 1879) . . 25 30
2219 300s. Clocks (World's time zones established, 1884) 25 30
2220 300s. Electric motor (invented 1888) 25 30
2221 300s. Cinema projector (first motion pictures, 1895) . . 25 30
2222 300s. *Monitor* and *Merrimack* (ironclad warships) (American Civil War, 1861–65) (59 × 39 mm) 25 30
2223 300s. Olympic Torch and Rings (revival of Games, 1896) 25 30

226 Education in the Millennium

2000. Anniversaries and Events. Multicoloured.

2224 300s. Type **226** 40 30
2225 500s. Controlled and open borders (6th anniv of Comesa Treaty) 65 50
2226 600s. Flags of member countries (50th anniv of Commonwealth) 75 75
2227 600s. Aspects of the River Nile in the Millennium . . 75 75
2228 700s. Non-traditional exports in the Millennium 75 80
2229 1200s. World map (50th anniv of Commonwealth) 1·40 1·50
2230 1400s. People and exports crossing border (6th anniv of Comesa Treaty) . . . 1·50 1·75
2231 1800s. Tourism in the Millennium . . . . 1·75 2·00

227 Kenya Railways Class A 60 Steam Locomotive

2000. African Railway Locomotives. Multicoloured.

2232 300s. Type **227** 25 30
2233 400s. Mozambique Railways Baldwin type 30 35
2234 600s. Uganda Railways Class 73 diesel locomotive 45 50
2235 700s. South Africa Railways Baby Garratt type 55 60
2236 700s. Uganda Railways Class 36 diesel locomotive (from back) 55 60
2237 700s. Rhodesian Railways 12th Class 55 60
2238 700s. Rhodesian Railways Garratt type 55 60
2239 700s. Uganda Railways Class 62 diesel locomotive 55 60
2240 700s. South African Railways Beyer-Garratt type 55 60
2241 700s. Sudan Railways oil-burning locomotive . . . 55 60
2242 700s. Nigerian Railways coal train 55 60
2243 700s. South Africa Railways steam locomotive 55 60

2244 700s. Uganda Railways Class 36 diesel locomotive (from front) 55 60
2245 700s. South African Railways Class 19D 55 60
2246 700s. Algeria Railways Garratt type 55 60
2247 700s. Cameroon Railways locomotive No. 194 55 60
2248 700s. South Africa Railways electric freight locomotive 55 60
2249 700s. Rhodesian Railways Class 14A 55 60
2250 700s. Egyptian Railways British-built locomotive 55 60
2251 700s. Uganda Railways Class 73 diesel locomotive 55 60
2252 1200s. Uganda Railways Class 82 diesel locomotive 90 95
2253 1400s. East Africa Railways Beyer-Garratt type 1·10 1·25
2254 1800s. Rhodesian Railways Beyer-Garratt type 1·40 1·50
2255 2000s. East African Railways Garratt type 1·50 1·60
MS2256 Three sheets, each 106 × 76 mm. (a) 3500s. East Africa Railways steam locomotive (56 × 42 mm). (b) 3500s. Egyptian State Railways locomotive No. 402 (56 × 42 mm). (c) 3500s. Rhodesian Railways Alco type (56 × 42 mm) Set of 2 sheets 8·25 8·50

No. 2237 also shows part of the inscription for No. 2236 in error.

228 "The Nativity" (Drateru Oliver)

2000. Christmas. Young People's Paintings. Mult.
2257 300s. Type **228** 40 30
2258 400s. "Baby Jesus and Donkey" (Brenda Tumwebaze) (horiz) 50 35
2259 500s. "Angels" (Joseph Mukiibi) 65 45
2260 600s. "Holy Family in Stable" (Paul Serunjogi) (horiz) 75 50
2261 700s. "Holy Family with Oxon" (Edward Maswere) (horiz) 85 60
2262 1200s. "Children worshipping baby Jesus" (Ndeba Harriet) (horiz) 1·50 1·75
2263 1800s. "Madonna and Child with Shepherd" (Jude Kasagga) 2·00 2·50
MS2264 Two sheets, each 85 × 110 mm. (a) 3000s. "King with Gift and Christmas Tree" (Nicole Kwiringira). (b) 3000s. "Adoration of the Shepherds" (Michael Tinkamanyire) Set of 2 sheets 7·50 8·00

229 Snake

2001. Chinese New Year ("Year of the Snake") and "Hong Kong 2001" Stamp Exhibition. Showing different snakes. Multicoloured.
2265 600s. Type **229** 70 80
2266 600s. Snake coiled around man 70 80
2267 600s. Snakes showing fangs 70 80
2268 600s. Snake on branch 70 80
MS2269 115 × 75 mm. 2500s. Cobra 3·00 3·25

230 Bongo

2001. Endangered Wildlife. Multicoloured.
2270 600s. Type **230** 80 85
2271 600s. Black rhinoceros 80 85
2272 600s. Leopard (vert) 80 85
MS2273 Two sheets. (a) 110 × 85 mm. 3000s. Mountain gorillas. (b) 85 × 110 mm. 3000s. Parrot (vert) Set of 2 sheets 7·50 8·00

231 Holy Family
233 Anemometer
232 East African School of Library and Information Science, Makerere

2001. 2000th Birth Anniv of Jesus Christ. Multicoloured.
2274 300s. Type **231** 40 30
2275 700s. Madonna and child 80 85
2276 1200s. The Nativity (horiz) 1·25 1·50

2001. East African Universities. Multicoloured.
2277 300s. Type **232** 40 30
2278 400s. Nairobi University 50 35
2279 1200s. Nkrumah Hall, University of Dar-es-Salaam 1·40 1·60
2280 1800s. Makerere, Kenyata and Open Universities (vert) 1·90 2·25

2001. 50th Anniv (2000) of World Meteorological Organization. Multicoloured.
2281 300s. Type **233** 50 30
2282 2000s. Tropical sun recorder (horiz) 2·25 2·50

234 Working in the Fields

2001. 50th Anniv of United Nations High Commissioner for Refugees. Economic Development. Multicoloured.
2283 300s. Type **234** 40 30
2284 600s. Community building project 70 50
2285 1200s. Carpentry class 1·25 1·50
2286 1800s. New water supply 1·75 2·25

235 "Segawa Kikunojo and Ichikawa Danjuro as Samurai" (Kiyonobu II)

2001. "Philanippon '01" International Stamp Exhibition, Tokyo. Japanese Woodcuts. Multicoloured.
2287 600s. Type **235** 45 50
2288 700s. "Tchimura Kamezo as Warrior" (Kiyohiro) 55 60
2289 1000s. "Ichikawa Danjuro as Shirobei Tadanobu" (Kiyomitsu) 75 80
2290 1200s. "Actor Arashi Sangoro" (Shunsho) 90 95
2291 1400s. "Matsumoto Koshiro IV as Juro Sukenari" (Kiyonaga) 1·10 1·25
2292 2000s. "Pheasant on Pine Branch" (Kiyomasu II) 1·50 1·60
MS2293 68 × 105 mm 3500s. Depicts "Tale of Ise" (Eishi) 2·75 3·00

236 Blue and Cream Shorthair

2001. Cats and Dogs. Multicoloured.
2294 400s. Tabby British shorthair (vert) 30 35
2295 600s. Type **236** 45 50
2296 600s. Manx 45 50
2297 600s. Angora 45 50
2298 600s. Red and white British shorthair 45 50
2299 600s. Turkish cat 45 50
2300 600s. Egyptian mau 45 50
2301 700s. Rottweiler 55 60
2302 700s. Flat-coated retriever 55 60
2303 700s. Samoyed 55 60
2304 700s. Poodle 55 60
2305 700s. Maltese 55 60
2306 700s. Irish terrier 55 60
2307 900s. Turkish cat (vert) 70 75
2308 1100s. German shepherd (vert) 85 90
2309 1200s. Irish setter (vert) 90 95
2310 1300s. English sheepdog 1·00 1·10
2311 1300s. German shepherd 1·00 1·10
2312 1300s. Great Dane 1·00 1·10
2313 1300s. Boston terrier 1·00 1·10
2314 1300s. Bull terrier 1·00 1·10
2315 1300s. Australian terrier 1·00 1·10
2316 1400s. Red tabby shorthair 1·10 1·25
2317 1400s. Japanese bobtail 1·10 1·25
2318 1400s. Siamese 1·10 1·25
2319 1400s. Tabby Persian 1·10 1·25
2320 1400s. Black and white Persian 1·10 1·25
2321 1400s. Russian blue 1·10 1·25
MS2322 Four sheets. (a) 106 × 76 mm. 3500s. American calico shorthair (vert). (b) 76 × 106 mm. 3500s. Blue-eyed british shorthair (vert). (c) 106 × 76 mm. 3500s. Bloodhound (vert). (d) 106 × 76 mm. 3500s. Pointer Set of 4 sheets 11·00 12·00

2001. Death Centenary of Queen Victoria. As T **101** of St. Kitts. Multicoloured.
2323 1000s. Queen Victoria wearing brown 75 80
2324 1000s. Queen Victoria in white bonnet 75 80
2325 1000s. Wearing feathered hat 75 80
2326 1000s. In evening dress 75 80
2327 1000s. Queen Victoria wearing choker with pendant 75 80
2328 1000s. In black dress, looking down 75 80
MS2329 107 × 83 mm. 3500s. Queen Victoria in furred hat 2·75 3·00

2001. 75th Death Anniv of Claude-Oscar Monet (French painter). As T **103** of St. Kitts. Multicoloured.
2330 1200s. "Storm, Belle-Ile Coast" 90 95
2331 1200s. "Manneporte, Etretat" 90 95
2332 1200s. "Rocks at Low Tide, Pourville" 90 95
2333 1200s. "Wild Sea" 90 95
MS2334 137 × 109 mm. 3500s. "Sunflowers" (vert) 2·75 3·00

2001. 75th Birthday of Queen Elizabeth II. As T **104** of St. Kitts. Multicoloured.
2335 1000s. Princess Elizabeth as a baby, 1926 75 80
2336 1000s. Princess Elizabeth aged 5, 1931 75 80
2337 1000s. Princess Elizabeth in 1939 75 80
2338 1000s. Queen Elizabeth in 1955 75 80
2339 1000s. Queen Elizabeth wearing tiara, 1963 75 80
2340 1000s. Queen Elizabeth in 1999 75 80
MS2341 82 × 106 mm. 3500s. Queen Elizabeth in uniform for Trooping the Colour 2·75 3·00

237 "Woman combing her Hair" (Toulouse-Lautrec)

2001. Death Centenary of Henri de Toulouse-Lautrec (French painter). Multicoloured.
2342 1500s. Type **237** 1·10 1·25
2343 1500s. "The Toilette" 1·10 1·25
2344 1500s. "English Girl at the Star Inn, Le Havre" 1·10 1·25
MS2345 74 × 109 mm. 3500s. "Aristide Bruant" 2·75 3·00

2001. Centenary of Royal Navy Submarine Service. As T **107** of St. Kitts. Multicoloured.
2346 1000s. H.M.S. *Tribune* (submarine) (vert) 75 80
2347 1000s. H.M.S. *Royal Oak* (battleship, launched 1914) (vert) 75 80
2348 1000s. H.M.S. *Invincible* (aircraft carrier) (vert) 75 80
2349 1000s. H.M.S. *Dreadnought* (nuclear submarine) (vert) 75 80
2350 1000s. H.M.S. *Ark Royal* (aircraft carrier, launched 1950) (vert) 75 80
2351 1000s. H.M.S. *Cardiff* (destroyer) (vert) 75 80
MS2352 70 × 57 mm. 3500s. H.M.S. Triad (submarine) 2·75 3·00

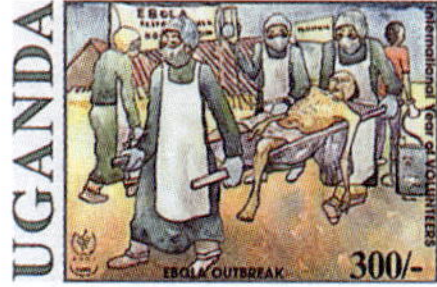
238 Carrying Ebola Victim on Stretcher

2001. U.N. Year of Dialogue among Civilizations (3000s.) and International Year of Volunteers (others). Multicoloured.
2353 300s. Type **238** 40 30
2354 700s. Blood donor session 90 65
2355 2000s. Provision of clean water 2·00 2·50
2356 3000s. Children encircling Globe (vert) 2·75 3·50

239 *Amanita excelsa*

2001. Fungi. Multicoloured.
2357 300s. Type **239** 25 30
2358 500s. *Coprinus cinereus* 40 45
2359 600s. *Scleroderma aurantium* 45 50
2360 700s. *Armillaria mellea* 55 60
2361 1200s. *Leopiota procera* 90 95
2362 2000s. *Flammulina velutipes* 1·50 1·75
MS2363 Two sheets, each 100 × 70 mm. (a) 3000s. *Amanita phalloides*. (b) 3000s. *Amanita fulva* Set of 2 sheets 5·00 5·25

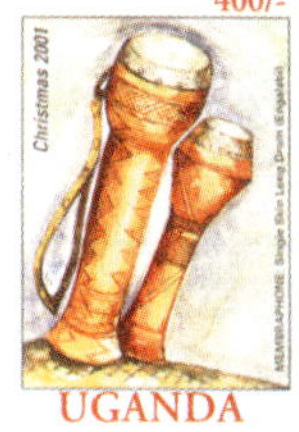
240 Long Drums

242 White Horse

241 Namugongo Shrine, Uganda

2001. Christmas. Musical Instruments. Mult.
2364 400s. Type **240** 30 35
2365 800s. Animal horn trumpets (horiz) 60 65
2366 1000s. Bugisu clay drum 75 80
2367 1200s. Musical bows 90 95
2368 1400s. Pan pipes 1·10 1·25
2369 2000s. Two-man xylophone (horiz) 1·50 1·60
MS2370 Two sheets. (a) 85 × 110 mm. 3500s. Eight-stringed giant bow harp. (b) 110 × 85 mm. 3500s. Nativity (horiz) Set of 2 sheets 5·50 5·75

2002. Historical Sites of East Africa. Multicoloured.
2371 400s. Type **241** 30 35
2372 800s. Maruhubi Palace ruins, Zanzibar 60 65
2373 1200s. Kings' Burial Grounds, Mparo, Hoima 85 90
2374 1400s. Old Law Courts, Mombasa (vert) 1·10 1·25

2002. Chinese New Year ("Year of the Horse"). Multicoloured.
2375 1200s. Type **242** 85 90
2376 1200s. Piebald horse 85 90
2377 1200s. Dun horse 85 90
MS2378 75 × 105 mm. 3000s. Rearing horse 2·25 2·40

2002. Golden Jubilee. As T **110** of St. Kitts. Multicoloured.
2379 1500s. Young Queen Elizabeth looking to her left 1·10 1·25
2380 1500s. Queen Elizabeth in striped hat 1·10 1·25

2381 1500s. Queen Elizabeth in evening dress . . . . . . 1·10 1·25
2382 1500s. As No. 2379, but Queen Elizabeth looking to her right . . . . 1·10 1·25
MS2383 76 × 108 mm. 3500s. Queen Elizabeth wearing straw hat . . 2·75 3·00

2002. "United We Stand". Support for Victims of 11 September 2001 Terrorist Attacks. As T **179** of St. Kitts, but showing Ugandan flag.
2384 1500s. multicoloured . . . . 1·10 1·25

2002. International Year of Mountains. As T **115** of St. Kitts. Multicoloured.
2385 2000s. Mount Tateyama, Japan . . . . 1·50 1·60
2386 2000s. Mount Nikko Semdjoda-Hara, Japan . . 1·50 1·60
2387 2000s. Mount Hodaka, Japan . . . . 1·50 1·60
MS2388 70 × 55 mm. 3500s. Mount Fuji, Japan . . . . 2·75 3·00

2002. 20th World Scout Jamboree, Thailand. As T **116** of St. Kitts. Multicoloured.
2389 1400s. Scout from 1930s in forest . . . . 1·10 1·25
2390 1400s. Scout from 1930s saluting . . . . 1·10 1·25
2391 1400s. Two scouts with packs . . . . 1·10 1·25
2392 1400s. International Scouts symbol . . . . 1·10 1·25
MS2393 60 × 78 mm. 3500s. Lord Baden-Powell (vert) . . . . . 2·75 3·00

243 Two Women with Symbol and Makerere University

2002. 8th International Interdisciplinary Congress on Women, Kampala. Multicoloured.
2394 400s. Type **243** 30 35
2395 1200s. Arms of Makerere University (vert) 90 95

2002. Winter Olympic Games, Salt Lake City. As T **111** of St. Kitts. Multicoloured.
2396 1200s. Cross-country skiing (vert) 90 95
2397 1200s. Ski-jumping (vert) . . 90 95
MS2398 82 × 113 mm. Nos. 2396/7 1·75 1·90

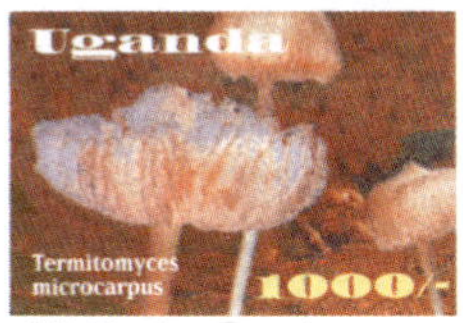

244 *Termitomyces microcarpus* (fungus)

2002. Flora and Fauna. Multicoloured.
2399 400s. White rhinoceros (vert) 30 35
2400 800s. *Macrotermes subhyalinus* (insect) (vert) 60 65
2401 1000s. Type **244** 75 80
2402 1000s. *Agaricus trisulphuratus* 75 80
2403 1000s. *Macrolepiota zeyheri* 75 80
2404 1000s. *Lentinus stupeus* . . . 75 80
2405 1000s. *Lentinus sajor-caju* . 75 80
2406 1000s. *Lentinus velutinus* . . 75 80
2407 1000s. *Nudaurelia cytherea* (caterpillar) 75 80
2408 1000s. *Locusta migratoria* (locust) 75 80
2409 1000s. *Anacridium aegyptium* (grasshopper) 75 80
2410 1000s. *Sternotomis bohemanni* (longhorn beetle) 75 80
2411 1000s. *Papilio dardanus* (butterfly) 75 80
2412 1000s. *Mantis polyspilota* (mantid) 75 80
2413 1200s. Uganda kob 90 95
2414 1200s. Hartebeest 90 95
2415 1200s. Topi 90 95
2416 1200s. Olive baboon 90 95
2417 1200s. Lion 90 95
2418 1200s. Common warthog . . 90 95
2419 1200s. *Canarina eminii* . . . 90 95
2420 1200s. *Vigna unguiculata* . . 90 95
2421 1200s. *Gardenia ternifolia* . . 90 95
2422 1200s. *Canavalia rosea* . . . 90 95
2423 1200s. *Hibiscus calyphyllus* 90 95
2424 1200s. *Nymphaea lotus* . . . 90 95
2425 1200s. *Gloriosa superba* (flower) (vert) 90 95
2426 1400s. *Cyptotrama asprata* (fungus) (vert) . . . . . 1·10 1·25
MS2427 Four sheets, each 95 × 70 mm. (a) 4000s. *Podoscypha parvula* (fungus). (b) 4000s. *Glossina austeni* (tsetse fly). (c) 4000s. Waterbuck (vert). (d) 4000s. *Abutilon grandiflorum* (flower) Set of 4 sheets . . . . . . 12·00 12·50
Nos. 2401/6 (fungi), 240712 (insects), 2423/28 (mammals) and 2419/24 (flowers) were each printed together, se-tenant, with the backgrounds forming composite designs.

245 Cetiosaurus

2002. Prehistoric Animals. Multicoloured.
2428 600s. Type **245** 45 50
2429 600s. Brontosaurus 45 50
2430 600s. Brachiosaurus 45 50
2431 600s. Deinonychus 45 50
2432 600s. Dimetrodon 45 50
2433 600s. Megalosaurus 45 50

POSTAGE DUE STAMPS

The Postage Due stamps of Kenya, Uganda and Tanganyika were used in Uganda until 2 January 1967.

D 1

D 3 Lion

1967.
D 7 D **1** 5c. red . . . . 15 2·50
D 8 10c. green . . . . 15 2·50
D 9 20c. blue . . . . 25 3·00
D10 30c. brown . . . . . . 35 4·00
D11 40c. purple . . . . . . 55 4·50
D17 1s. orange . . . . 1·75 11·00
These stamps exist in limited quantities overprinted **UGANDA LIBERATED 1979**.

1979. Liberation. As Nos. D7/11 and D17 optd **LIBERATED 1979**.
D18 D **1** 5c. red 15 40
D19 10c. green 15 40
D20 20c. blue 20 40
D21 30c. brown 20 60
D22 40c. purple 20 60
D23 1s. orange 20 60

1985. Animals.
D24 D **3** 5s. black and turquoise 15 50
D25 – 10s. black and lilac . . . 15 50
D26 – 20s. black and orange . . 30 60
D27 – 40s. black and lilac . . . 60 90
D28 – 50s. black and blue . . . 60 90
D29 – 100s. black and mauve 1·00 1·60
DESIGNS: 10s. African buffalo; 20s. Kob; 40s. African elephant; 50s. Common zebra; 100s. Black rhinoceros.

UKRAINE Pt. 10

A district of S.W. Russia, which issued stamps during its temporary independence after the Russian Revolution. In 1923 it became a constituent republic of the U.S.S.R.

In 1991 it became an independent republic.

1918. 100 shahiv = 1 hryvna (grivna); 2 hriven = 1 rouble.
1992. 100 kopeks = 1 rouble.
1992. Karbovanets (coupon currency).
1996. 100 kopiykas = 1 hryvna.

(L 6)

(L 8)

1918. Arms types of Russia optd with Trident device in various types according to the district. Imperf or perf.
L 51 **22** 1k. orange 10 10
L 52 2k. green 10 10
L 53 3k. red 10 10
L 54 **23** 4k. red 10 10
L 55 **22** 5k. red 10 10
L138 7k. blue 10 10
L 57 **23** 10k. blue 10 10
L 58 **22** 10k. on 7k. blue 15 10
L159 **9** 14k. red and blue 15 20
L 60 15k. blue and purple . . 10 10
L 61 **14** 20k. red and blue 10 10
L 62 **9** 20k. on 14k. red and blue 10 10
L145 25k. mauve and green . . 10 25
L 64 35k. green and purple . . 10 10
L 65 **14** 50k. green and purple . . 10 10
L 66 **9** 70k. orange and brown 10 10
L 47 **15** 1r. orange and brown . . 15 15
L 72 **11** 3r.50 grey and black . . 10·00 16·00
L212 3r.50 green and brown 20 20
L 49 **20** 5r. blue and green . . . 40 60
L 73 **11** 7r. yellow and black . . . 7·00 10·00
L 14 7r. pink and green . . . 90 2·00
L 36 **20** 10r. grey, red and yellow 5·50 6·50

1 Trident (from Arms of Grand Duke Vladimir the Great)

2 Peasant

3 Ceres

4 Trident

5

1918. Without inscription on back. Imperf.
1 **1** 10s. brown 20 50
2 **2** 20s. brown 20 50
3 **3** 30s. blue 20 50
4 **4** 40s. green 20 50
5 **5** 50s. red 20 50

1918. With trident and four lines of inscription on back.
6 **1** 10s. brown . . . . 2·50 5·00
7 **2** 20s. brown . . . . 2·50 5·00
8 **3** 30s. blue . . . . 2·50 5·00
9 **4** 40d. green . . . . 2·50 5·00
10 **5** 50s. red . . . . 2·50 5·00

6a Trident

6b Parliament Building

Stamps of the above and similar designs were prepared for use but never used.

7 Spectre of Famine

8 T. G. Shevchenko (Ukrainian poet)

1923. Charity.
12 **7** 10+10k. blue and black . . . 1·00 2·25
13 **8** 20+20k. brown and orange 1·00 2·25
14 – 90+30k. black and bistre . . 2·00 4·50
15 – 150+50k. red and black . . 4·00 6·00
DESIGNS—VERT: 90k. "Death" and peasant; 150k. "Ukraine" (woman) distributing bread.

11 Cossack Chief with Musician and Standard Bearer

12 Galician Emigrant Couple

1992. 500th Anniv (1990) of Ukraine Cossacks.
20 **11** 15k. multicoloured 15 10

1992. Centenary (1991) of Ukrainian Emigration to Canada.
21 **12** 15k. multicoloured 15 10

13 Mykola Lysenko and Score from "Taras Bulba"

1992. 150th Birth Anniv of Mykola Lysenko (composer).
22 **13** 1r. brown, red and bistre . . 10 10

14 Mykola Kostomarov, Quill Pen and Scroll

15 Ceres

1992. 175th Birth Anniv of Mykola Kostomarov (historian).
23 **14** 20k. brown and light brown 10 10

1992.
46 **15** 50k. blue 10 10
47 70k. brown 10 10
48 1r. green 10 10
49 2r. violet 10 10
50 5r. blue 10 10
51 10r. red 15 10
52 20r. green 30 20
53 50r. brown 75 50

16 Rhythmic Gymnastics

17 State Flag and Trident Symbol

1992. Olympic Games, Barcelona. Multicoloured.
54 3r. Type **16** 10 10
55 4r. Pole vaulting 10 10
56 5r. Type **16** 10 10

1992. 1st Anniv of Regained Independence.
57 **17** 2r. multicoloured 10 10

18 Three Cranes on Globe

1992. World Congress of Ukrainians, Kyiv.
58 **18** 2r. multicoloured 10 10

20 U.P.U. Emblem and Hand writing

1992. Correspondence Week.
60 **20** 5r. multicoloured 10 10

21 Congress Emblem

1992. World Congress of Ukrainian Jurists, Kyiv.
61 **21** 15r. multicoloured 15 10

22 Embroidery

1992. Ukraine Folk Art.
62 **22** 0.50k. black and orange . . 10 10

23 Arms of Austria and Ukraine with Traditional Costumes of Galicia and Bukovina

1992. Ukrainians in Austria.
63 **23** 5k. multicoloured 15 10

24 Students and Academy, 1632 (after I. Shyrsky)

1992. 360th Anniv of Mogilyanska's Academy, Kyiv.
64 **24** 1k.50 black, blue and brown 10 10

26 Lviv Arms 27 Cardinal Slipyj

1993. Regional Arms.
66 **26** 3k. blue, deep blue and gold 10 10
67 – 5k. lake, gold and red . . . 20 15
DESIGN: 5k. Kyiv.

1993. Birth Centenary (1992) of Cardinal Josyf Slipyj.
68 **27** 15k. multicoloured 45 30

28 Hansa Brandenburg C-I

1993. 75th Anniv of First Vienna–Cracow–Lviv–Kyiv Flight.
69 **28** 35k. black, blue and mauve 30 20
70 – 50k. multicoloured 40 30
DESIGN: 50k. Airbus Industrie A300.

29 Candles and Traditional Foods

1993. Easter.
71 **29** 15k. multicoloured 40 30

30 "Country Wedding in Lower Austria" (Ferdinand Georg Waldmuller) 31 National Famine Monument, Kyiv

1993. 45th Anniv of Declaration of Human Rights.
72 **30** 5k. multicoloured 30 20

1993. 60th Anniv of Famine Deaths.
73 **31** 75k. brown 10 10

32 1918 10sh. Stamp

1993. Stamp Day. 75th Anniv of First Ukrainian Postage Stamps.
74 **32** 100k. blue and brown . . . 15 10

33 Kyiv 34 Mowing

1993. 50th Anniv of Liberation of Kyiv.
75 **33** 75k. multicoloured 15 10

1993. Agricultural Scenes.
76 **34** 50k. green 10 10
77 – 100k. blue 10 10
78 – 150k. red 10 10
79 – 200k. orange 10 10
80 – 300k. purple 10 10
81 – 500k. brown 20 15
DESIGNS: 100k. Laden bullock carts; 150, 300k. Shepherd and flock; 200, 500k. Women cutting corn.

35 Madonna and Child (Albrecht Durer) 36 St. Ahapit

1994. Ukrainian Health Fund.
82 **35** 150k.+20k. black, gold and red 10 10

1994. St. Ahapit (medieval doctor).
83 **36** 200k. black and red 10 10

37 Dog's-tooth Violet ("Erythronium denscanis") 38 Laden Bullock Carts

1994. Red Book of Ukraine. Multicoloured.
84 200k. Type **37** 15 10
85 200k. Lady's slipper ("Cypripedium calceolus") 15 10

1994. Agricultural Scenes. Value expressed by Cyrillic letter.
86 – A (5000k.) red 25 15
87 **38** V (10000k.) blue 75 50
DESIGN: A, Shepherd and flock.
The Cyrillic "V" on No. 87 resembles a "B".

39 Women cutting Corn 40 Cutting Hay

1994. Agricultural Scenes. Value expressed by Cyrillic letter.
88 **39** B (100k.) brown 10 10
89 **40** G (250k.) green 10 10

42 Kyiv University

1994. 160th Anniv of Kyiv University.
91 **42** 10000k. multicoloured . . . 40 30

43 Map and Airplanes (Liberation of Ukraine)

1994. 50th Anniv of Liberation. Multicoloured.
93 500k. Map and rocket launchers (Russia) 10 10
94 500k. Type **43** 10 10
95 500k. Map, tank and soldiers (Byelorussia) 10 10

44 Ploughing 45 Fishing

1994. Agricultural Scenes. Value expressed by Cyrillic letter.
96 **44** D (100k.) mauve 10 10
97 **45** Zh (5300k.) blue 30 10

46 Bee-Keeping 47 Potter at Wheel

1994. Agricultural Scenes. Value expressed by Cyrillic letter.
98 **46** Ye (1800k.) brown 15 10
99 **47** E (17000k.) red 95 40

48 Ceramics and Map 49 Reader and Arms

1994. 100th Anniv of Excavation of Tripillya.
100 **48** 4000k. multicoloured . . . 10 10

1994. 500th Anniv of First Book printed in Ukrainian Language, "Book of Hours" by Sh. Fiol.
101 **49** 4000k. multicoloured . . . 10 10

50 Repin and Study of Soldier

1994. 150th Birth Anniv of Ilya Repin (painter).
102 **50** 4000k. multicoloured . . . 10 10

51 Sofiyivka Park and Statue

1994. Bicent of Sofiyivka Nature Park, Uman.
103 **51** 5000k. multicoloured . . . 10 10

52 Uzhhorod Castle

1995. 1100th Anniv of Uzhhorod.
104 **52** 5000k. multicoloured . . . 10 10

53 Ivan Franko (writer) 54 Peregrine Falcon

1995. Personalities. Multicoloured.
105 3000k. Type **53** 10 10
106 3000k. Ivan Pulyui (physicist) (vert) 10 10
107 3000k. Lesya Ukrainka (writer) 10 10

1995. Red Book of Ukraine. Birds. Multicoloured.
108 5000k. Type **54** 35 25
109 10000k. Common crane . . . 75 50

55 Rylskyi 56 Doves, Bell Tower and River

1995. Birth Centenary of Maksym Rylskyi (writer).
110 **55** 50000k. multicoloured . . 45 30

1995. 50th Anniv of End of Second World War.
111 **56** 100000k. multicoloured . . 75 60

57 Figures around Globe on Map of Ukraine

1995. 70th Anniv of Artek International Children's Holiday Camps, Crimea
112 **57** 5000k. multicoloured . . . 10 10

58 Ivan Kotlyarevski and Scene from "Eneida" (poem)

1995. Writers. Multicoloured.
113 1000k. Type **58** 10 10
114 3000k. Taras Shevchenko and cover of "Kobzar" 10 10

59 Siege of Theodosia

1995. 17th-century Hetmans. Petro Konashevich-Sahaidachnyi.
115 **59** 30000k. multicoloured . . 25 15

60 Lugansk

1995. Regional Arms.
116 **60** 10000k. multicoloured . . 10 10

61 Bell Tower of Domition Church, National Museum and Dominican Cathedral

1995. National Stamp Exhibition, Lviv.
117 **61** 50000k.+5000k. mult . . . 35 20

62 St. Elias's Church, Subotov, and Battle Scene

1995. 17th-century Hetmans. Bohdan Khimelnytskyi.
118 **62** 40000k. multicoloured . . 25 15

63 St. Michael's Cathedral, Kyiv

1995. 17th-century Hetmans. Ivan Mazepa.
119 **63** 30000k. multicoloured . . 25 15

64 Part of Rainbow and White Stork

65 Girl carrying Water Pails

1995. European Nature Conservation Year.
120 **64** 50000k. multicoloured . . 35 20

1995. Regional Arms. As T **60**.
121 10000k. multicoloured . . . 10 10
DESIGN: 10000k. Chernihiv.

1995. International Children's Day.
122 **65** 50000k. multicoloured . . 35 20

66 Anniversary Emblem

67 Hrushevskyi

1995. 50th Anniv of U.N.O.
123 **66** 50000k. blue, violet and black 35 20

1995. 60th Death Anniv (1994) of Mykhailo Hrushevskyi (first President).
124 **67** 50000k. multicoloured . . 35 20

68 Karpenko-Karyi

69 Shafaryk

1995. 150th Birth Anniv of Ivan Karpenko-Karyi (dramatist).
125 **68** 50000k. multicoloured . . 35 20

1995. Birth Bicentenary of Pavel Shafaryk (historian and philologist).
126 **69** 30000k. green 25 15

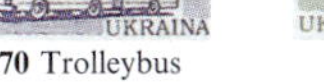

70 Trolleybus

71 Tramcar

72 Bus

1995. Transport. Value expressed by Cyrillic letter.
127 **70** I (1000k.) blue 35 20
128 **71** K (2000k.) green 50 30
129 **72** Z (3000k.) pink 75 50

74 Research Aids

75 Krymskyi

1996. 150th Anniv of Observatory, Taras Shevchenko University, Kyiv. Multicoloured.
131 20000k. Type **74** 15 10
132 30000k. Telescope 25 15
133 50000k. Sun over observatory buildings 40 30

1996. 125th Birth Anniv of Ahatanhel Krymskyi (writer).
134 **75** 20000k. brown and ochre 15 10

76 Kozlovskyi

77 Animals

1996. 3rd Death Anniv of Ivan Kozlovskyi (tenor).
135 **76** 20000k. multicoloured . . 15 10

1996. Centenary of Kharkiv Zoo.
136 **77** 20000k. olive, green and blue 15 10

78 Dovshenko and Birthplace

1996. Birth Centenary of Oleksandr Dovshenko (film producer and set designer).
137 **78** 4000k. multicoloured . . . 10 10

79 Lighted Candle within Tower

80 Vasyl Fedorovych, Volodymyr Levkovich and Levko Platonovych Symyrenko

1996. 10th Anniv of Chernobyl Nuclear Disaster.
138 **79** 20000k. multicoloured . . 15 10

1996. Symyrenko Family.
139 **80** 20000k. multicoloured . . 15 10
Vasil was a sugar refiner; Volodimir and Levko fruit growers and researchers.

81 Stefanik

1996. 60th Death Anniv of Vasyl Stefanyk (writer and politician).
140 **81** 20000k. multicoloured . . 15 10

82 Miklukho-Maklai

1996. 150th Birth Anniv of Mikola Mikolaiovich Miklukho-Maklai (explorer and philologist).
141 **82** 40000k. multicoloured . . 30 20

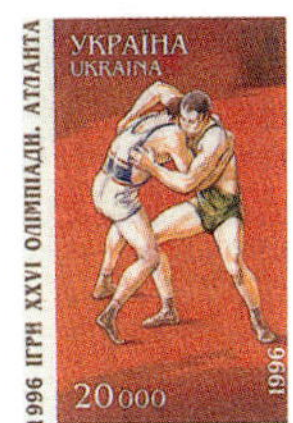

83 Wrestling

1996. Olympic Games, Atlanta, U.S.A. Mult.
142 20000k. Type **83** 15 10
143 40000k. Handball 30 20

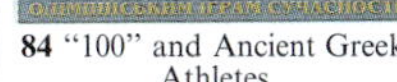

84 "100" and Ancient Greek Athletes

85 Trident Emblem and "V" in National Colours

1996. Centenary of Modern Olympic Games.
145 **84** 40000k. bistre, turquoise and blue 30 20

1996. 5th Anniv of Independence.
146 **85** 20000k. multicoloured . . 15 10

86 "Sich-1"

87 Series OD Steam Locomotive

1996. 1st Ukrainian Satellite.
147 **86** 20000k. multicoloured . . 15 10

1996. Railway Locomotives. Multicoloured.
148 20000k. Type **87** 30 20
149 40000k. Class 2TE-116 diesel locomotive 65 45

88 Antonov

89 Piddubnyi

1996. 90th Birth Anniv of Oieh Antonov (aircraft designer). Multicoloured.
150 20000k. Type **88** 20 15
151 20000k. Antonov An-2 biplane 20 15
152 40000k. Antonov An-124 airliner 40 25
153 40000k. Antonov An-225 piggybacking airplane . . . 40 25

1996. 125th Birth Anniv of Ivan Piddubnyi (weightlifting world champion).
154 **89** 40k. multicoloured 30 20

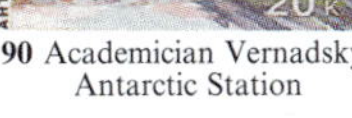

90 Academician Vernadskyi Antarctic Station

91 Eidelwiess

1996. 1st Ukrainian Antarctic Expedition.
155 **90** 20k. multicoloured 20 15

1996. Protected Flowers. Multicoloured.
156 20k. Type **91** 20 10
157 40k. "Narcissus anqustifolius" 30 20

92 Emblem

93 Kosenko

1996. 50th Anniv of U.N.E.S.C.O.
158 **92** 20k. multicoloured 15 10

1996. Birth Centenary of W. S. Kosenko (composer).
159 **93** 20k. multicoloured 15 10

94 St. Sophia Cathedral, Kyiv

1996. Churches. Multicoloured.
160 20k. Type **94** 15 10
161 20k. St. Elias's Church, Subotov 15 10
162 20k. St. George's Church, Drogobych 15 10
163 20k. Trinity Cathedral, Novomoskovsk 15 10

95 Mohyla

1996. 400th Birth Anniv of Petro Mohyla (Metropolitan of Kyiv).
164 **95** 20k. black and brown . . . 15 10

96 Mother and Child within Emblem

1996. 50th Anniv of U.N.I.C.E.F.
165 **96** 20k. multicoloured 15 10

97 Lynx

1997. Protected Animals. Multicoloured.
166 20k. Type **97** 15 10
167 20k. Brown bear 15 10

98 Cathedral of the Holy Cross, Poltava

1997. Religious Buildings. Multicoloured.
168 20k. Type **98** 15 10
169 20k. St. George's Cathedral, Lviv 15 10
170 20k. St. Mary's Church, Sythtsi 15 10

100 Taras Shevchenko Monument, Stamps and Exhibition Hall

1997. 4th National Stamp Exhibition, Cherkasy.
172 **100** 10k. multicoloured . . . 10 10

101 Kondratyuk and Diagram of Space Orbit

1997. Birth Centenary of Yury Kondratyuk (space pioneer).
173 **101** 20k. multicoloured . . . 15 10

102 Arms, Map on Open Book and Assembly Building

1997. 1st Anniv of Constitution.
174 **102** 20k. multicoloured . . . 15 10

103 Fire, Fern and Couple 104 Princess Olga (regent of Kyiv, 945–55)

1997. Midsummer Festival of Ivana Kupala.
175 **103** 20k. multicoloured . . . 15 10

1997. Famous Women. Multicoloured.
176 40k. Type **104** 30 20
177 40k. Roxolana (wife of Sultan Suleiman II of Turkey) 30 20

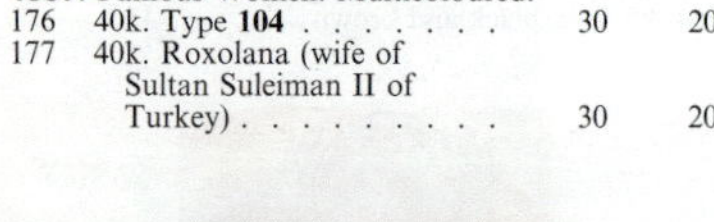

105 Taras Shevchenko Monument, Buenos Aires

1997. Centenary of First Ukranian Emigration to Argentina.
178 **105** 20k. multicoloured . . . 15 10

106 For Military Service for Ukraine 108 Kruschenlnytska

107 Dmytro Vyshnevetskyi Baida

1997. Orders and Medals.
179 **106** 20k. multicoloured . . . 10 10
180 – 20k. multicoloured . . . 10 10
181 – 30k. grey, red and blue 20 15
182 – 40k. multicoloured . . . 25 20
183 – 60k. multicoloured . . . 35 25
DESIGNS: No. 180, For Meritorious Service; 181, For Valour; 182, Order of Bohdan Khmelnytskyi; 183, For Special Contributions.

1997. Hetmans. Multicoloured.
185 20k. Type **107** 15 10
186 20k. Stockholm, Pylyp Orlik and Thessalonika 15 10

1997. 125th Birth Anniv of Solomiya Kruschenlnytska (opera singer).
187 **108** 20k. multicoloured . . . 15 10

109 Antonov An-74 TK-200

1997. Aircraft. Multicoloured.
188 20k. Type **109** 15 10
189 40k. Antonov An-38-100 . . 30 20

110 "Zavetnyi" (torpedo boat), 1903 111 "Columbia" (space shuttle) and Flags

1997. Ships. Multicoloured.
190 20k. Type **110** 15 10
191 40k. "Akademik Sergei Korolov" (research ship), 1970 . . . . 30 20

1997. Ukraine–U.S.A. Space Flight.
192 **111** 40k. multicoloured . . . 40 30

112 Krichevskyi 113 "Nativity" (icon)

1997. 125th Birth Anniv of Vasyl Krichevskyi (painter and architect).
193 **112** 10k. stone, brown & black 10 10

1997. Christmas.
194 **113** 20k. multicoloured . . . 15 10

114 Painted Rooster, Dnipropetrovsk

1997. Folk Art. Multicoloured. Buff margins.
195 20k. Type **114** 15 10
196 20k. Fur-trimmed waistcoat, Chernivtsi 15 10
197 40k. Ceramic ram, Poltava 25 20
198 40k. Wooden plate, Ivano-Frankivsk 25 20

115 Skovoroda 116 Arms of Zakarpattskaya Oblast

1997. 275th Birth Anniv of Grigorii Skovoroda (philosopher).
200 **115** 60k. multicoloured . . . 40 30

1997. Regional Arms.
201 **116** 20k. multicoloured . . . 10 10

118 Sosyura 119 Figure Skating

1998. Birth Centenary of Volodimyr Sosyura (poet).
203 **118** 20k. blue, black and brown 10 10

1998. Winter Olympic Games, Nagano, Japan. Multicoloured.
204 20k. Type **119** 10 10
205 20k. Biathlon 10 10

120 City Walls

1998. 2500th Anniv of Bilhorod-Dnistrovskyi.
206 **120** 20k. multicoloured . . . 10 10

121 "Hetman Sagaidachnyi" (frigate)

1998.
207 **121** 30k. multicoloured . . . 25 20

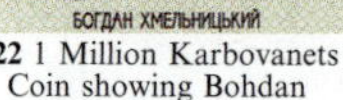

122 1 Million Karbovanets Coin showing Bohdan Khmelnytskyi 123 Festival of Ivana Kupala

1998. Coins.
208 **122** 30k. black, green & purple 20 15
209 – 30k. black, green & purple 20 15
210 – 60k. brown, green and purple 30 25
211 – 60k. brown, green and purple 35 25
212 – 1h. brown, green & purple 60 40
213 – 1h. black, green and purple 60 40
DESIGNS: No. 209, 10 hryven coin showing Petro Mohila; 210, 500 hryven coin showing Virgin Mary; 211, 200 hryven coin showing Taras Shevchenko; 212, Gold coin of Vladymyr Svyatoslavich; 213, Silver coin of Vladymyr Svyatoslavich.

1998. Europa. National Festivals.
214 **123** 40k. multicoloured . . . 30 20

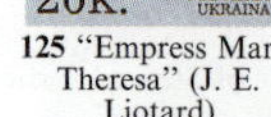

125 "Empress Maria Theresa" (J. E. Liotard) 128 Armoured Rider and Swordsman

127 Askold and Dir

1998. Paintings. Multicoloured.
216 20k. Type **125** 15 10
217 20k. "Man playing Cello" (G. Honthorst) 15 10
218 40k. "Madonna and Child" (icon) 25 20

1998. 1st Rulers of Kyiv.
221 **127** 3h. purple and bistre . . 95 85

1998. 350th Anniv of Start of Campaign for Independence. Each brown, green and purple.
222 30k. Type **128** 15 10
223 30k. Warriors with staves and swordsman 15 10
224 40k. Stavesman, swordsman and archer 20 15
225 40k. Group of archers . . . 20 15
226 60k. Rider 30 20
227 2h. Hetman Bohdan Khmelnytskyi 65 65
Nos. 222/7 were issued together, se-tenant, forming a composite design.

129 Crown of Prince Danylo Galitsky

1998. 1100th Anniv of the Town of Halich.
228 **129** 20k. multicoloured . . . 10 10

130 Anna Yaroslavna

1998. Anna Yaroslavna (daughter of King Yaroslav of Kyiv and wife of King Henri I of France).
229 **130** 40k. multicoloured . . . 20 15

131 Lisyansky

1998. 225th Birth Anniv of Yurii Fyodorovich Lisyansky (first Ukrainian to circumnavigate world).
230 **131** 40k. multicoloured . . . 20 15

132 Natalia Uzhvii

1998. Birth Centenary of Natalia Uzhvii (actress).
231 **132** 40k. brown and gold . . 20 15

133 V. L. Kyrpychov (first Director)

1998. Centenary of Kyiv Technical University. Multicoloured.
232 10k. Type **133** 10 10
233 20k. E. Paton (metallurgist) and bridge in Kyiv 20 15
234 20k. Stefan Timoshenko (materials scientist) and formula 20 15
235 30k. Igor Sikorsky (aircraft designer) and test flight in Kyiv 30 20
236 40k. Sergei Korolev (space scientist) and spacecraft . . 40 25

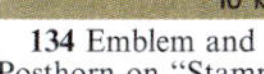

134 Emblem and Posthorn on "Stamp"

135 Monk Nestor (early chronicler)

1998. World Post Day.
237 **134** 10k. multicoloured . . . 10 10

1998. Millenary of Book Production in Ukraine.
238 **135** 20k. multicoloured . . . 10 10

136 Cathedral of the Transfiguration, Chernigov

1998. Cathedrals. Multicoloured.
239 20k. Type **136** 10 10
240 20k. Pokrovsky Cathedral, Kharkov 10 10

137 Red-breasted Geese

1998. Endangered Species. The Red-breasted Goose. Multicoloured.
241 20k. Type **137** 10 10
242 30k. Goose 15 10
243 40k. Goose with chicks . . . 20 15
244 60k. Geese with chicks . . . 30 20

138 Battle of Chyhyryn, Doroshenko and Volokolamsk

1998. Hetmans. Petro Doroshenko.
246 **138** 20k. multicoloured . . . 10 10

139 Antonov An-140

1998. Aircraft. Multicoloured.
247 20k. Type **139** 10 10
248 40k. Antonov An-70 . . . . 20 15

140 Hrinchenko and his Dictionary

1998. 135th Birth Anniv of B. Hrinchenko (philologist).
249 **140** 20k. multicoloured . . . 10 10

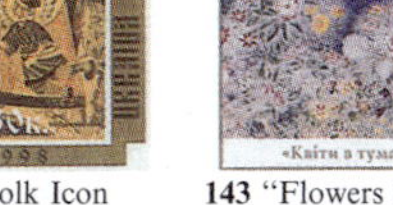

141 Folk Icon

143 "Flowers in Fog"

142 Map of Australia and Waratah

1998. Christmas.
250 **141** 30k. multicoloured . . . 10 10

1998. 50th Anniv of Ukrainians in Australia.
251 **142** 40k. multicoloured . . . 15 10

1998. 50th Anniv of Universal Declaration of Human Rights. Paintings by Kateryna Bilokur. Multicoloured.
252 30k. Type **143** 10 10
253 50k. "Bouquet of Flowers" 20 15

144 Meteorites striking Earth

1998. Illinetsk Meteorite Impact Site.
254 **144** 40k. multicoloured . . . 20 10

145 Paradzhanov

1999. 75th Birth Anniv of Sergei Paradzhanov (film director).
255 **145** 40k. multicoloured . . . 20 15

146 Ivasyuk

1999. 50th Birth Anniv of Volodymyr Ivasyuk (composer).
256 **146** 30k. multicoloured . . . 10 10

147 Quiver

1999. Scythian Gold. Multicoloured.
257 20k. Type **147** 10 10
258 40k. Statuette of boar 15 10
259 50k. Statuette of young elk 15 10
260 1h. Pectoral 30 20

148 Girls in Central Ukrainian National Costume

149 Lake and Carpathian Mountains

1999. Spring.
261 **148** 30k. multicoloured . . . 10 10

1999. Europa. Parks and Gardens. Synievyr Lake National Park. Multicoloured.
262 50k. Type **149** 10 10
263 1h. Lake and European grayling 25 15
Nos. 262/3 were issued together, se-tenant, forming a composite design.

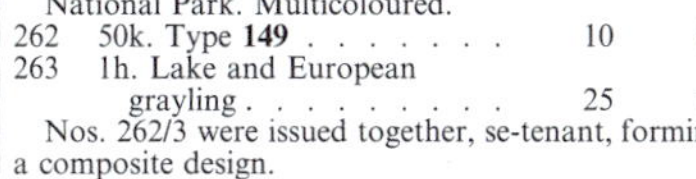

150 Mirny

1999. 150th Birth Anniv of Panas Mirny (writer).
264 **150** 40k. multicoloured . . . 10 10

151 Balzac

1999. Birth Bicentenary of Honore de Balzac (writer).
265 **151** 40k. black, gold and red 10 10

152 Anniversary Emblem and Headquarters, Strasbourg

1999. 50th Anniv of Council of Europe.
266 **152** 40k. multicoloured . . . 10 10

153 Pushkin

156 St. George on Horseback (15th-century icon)

154 Baidak

1999. Birth Bicentenary of Aleksandr Sergyevich Pushkin (poet).
267 **153** 40k. multicoloured . . . 10 10

1999. Traditional Warships. Multicoloured.
268 30k. Type **154** 10 10
269 30k. Chaika 10 10

1999. Centenary of National Art Museum, Kyiv. Multicoloured.
271 30k. Type **156** 10 10
272 60k. "The Girl in the Red Hat" (O. O. Murashko) . . 15 10

157 Heraldic Lion (emblem of Lviv) and Armoured Knight

1999. 800th Anniv of Galitsian-Volynian State.
273 **157** 50k. multicoloured . . . 10 10

158 Honey Bee on Flower

159 Monument, Berne

1999. Bee-keeping.
274 **158** 30k. multicoloured . . . 10 10

1999. 125th Anniv of Universal Postal Union.
275 **159** 30k. multicoloured . . . 10 10

160 Crest and Scroll

161 Order of Princess Olga

1999. 1100th Anniv of Poltava.
276 **160** 30k. multicoloured . . . 10 10

1999. Orders and Medals.
277 **161** 30k. multicoloured . . . 10 10

163 Red Deer (Stuzhitsya Regional Landscape Park)

1999. Animals of the East Carpathian Mountains. Multicoloured.
280 1h.40 Type **163** 35 25
281 1h.40 Wild cat (Bieszczadzki National Park) 35 25

164 Bank Emblem

1999. 160th Anniv of National Bank.
282 **164** 3h. multicoloured 75 50

165 Vyhovskyi and Battle of Konotop

1999. Hetmans. Ivan Vyhovskyi.
284 **165** 30k. multicoloured . . . 10 10

166 Three Wise Men

1999. Christmas. Multicoloured.
285 30k. Type **166** 10 10
286 60k. Nativity 15 10

168 Space Rocket and Car on Moon (Ivan Kovalevskyi)

1999. Winning Entries in Children's Stamp Design Competition. Multicoloured.
287 10k. Type **168** 10 10
288 10k. Elephant wearing space helmet (Ivan Chuev) . . . 10 10
289 10k. Aliens and space ship (Dmitro Verzhbyikyi) . . . 10 10

169 Russian Desman

1999. Endangered Species. Multicoloured.
290 40k. Type **169** 10 10
291 40k. Stag beetle (*Lucanus cervus*) 10 10
292 60k. Griffon vulture 15 10

170 Angel and Church, Kyiv **171** Boot-lace Fungus

1999. St. Andriya Pervozvannoho Commemoration.
293 **170** 60k. multicoloured . . . 15 10

1999. Fungi. Multicoloured.
294 30k. Type **171** 10 10
295 30k. Velvet-footed pax (*Paxillus atrotomentosus*) 10 10
296 30k. Oyster mushroom (*Pleurotus ostreatus*) . . . 10 10
297 30k. Chanterelle (*Cantharellus cibarius*) 10 10
298 30k. Field mushroom (*Agaricus campestris*) . . . 10 10

172 KRAZ-65032 Lorry

1999. Motor Vehicles. Multicoloured.
299 30k. Type **172** 10 10
300 30k. Tavriya car 10 10

173 Girl wearing New Year's Costume

1999. New Year.
301 **173** 50k. multicoloured . . . 10 10

174 Ships, Polubotok and St. Petersburg

1999. Hetmans. Pavel Polubotok.
302 **174** 30k. multicoloured . . . 10 10

175 "Pea Wild"

1999. Paintings by Mariya Primachenko. Mult.
303 30k. Type **175** 10 10
304 30k. "Wild Boar" 10 10

176 Gulebichibna

1999. 425th Birth Anniv (2000) of Galshka Gulebichibna.
305 **176** 30k. multicoloured . . . 10 10

179 Moscow Bridge, 1976

2000. Bridges in Kyiv. Multicoloured.
308 10k. Type **179** 10 10
309 30k. Ye. O. Paton Bridge, 1953 . . . . 10 10
310 40k. Pedestrian bridge, 1957 10 10
311 60k. Metro bridge, 1965 . . . 15 10

182 Petrusenko **183** Churai

2000. Birth Centenary of Oksana Petrusenko (singer). Multicoloured.
314 **182** 30k. multicoloured . . . 10 10

2000. Marusia Churai (songwriter) Commemoration.
315 **183** 40k. multicoloured . . . 10 10

184 Cossack Forces attacking Derbent Fortress, Danylo Apostol and Church

2000. Hetmans. Multicoloured.
316 30k. Type **184** 10 10
317 30k. Kozacha Dibrova (Cossack council), Ivan Samoilovych and Tobol'sk 10 10

185 Globe and Emblem **186** "Building Europe"

2000. 50th Anniv of World Meteorological Organization.
318 **185** 30k. multicoloured . . . 10 10

2000. Europa.
319 **186** 3h. multicoloured . . . . 1·40 1·40

189 Sunflower, Map and Emblem (Donetsk)

2000. Regions. Multicoloured.
322 30k. Type **189** 10 10
323 30k. Statue, map and churches (Kyiv) 10 10

190 Buildings and Emblem

2000. National Stamp Exhibition, Donetsk.
324 **190** 30k. multicoloured . . . 10 10

191 Buildings **192** High Jump

2000. 900th Anniv of Ostroh.
325 **191** 30k. multicoloured . . . 10 10

2000. Olympic Games, Sydney. Multicoloured.
326 30k. Type **192** 10 10
327 30k. Boxing 10 10
328 70k. Sailing 20 10
329 1h. Rhythmic gymnastics . . 25 10

193 Prokopovych

2000. 150th Death Anniv of Petro Prokopovych (beekeeper).
330 **193** 30k. multicoloured . . . 10 10

194 *St. Paul* (ship of the line) **195** "Leafy Plants with Flowers–1950s Series"

2000. Ships. Multicoloured.
331 40k. Type **194** 10 10
332 70k. *St. Nicholas* (frigate) . . 20 10

2000. Paintings by Tetiana Pata. Multicoloured.
333 40k. Type **195** 10 10
334 40k. "Viburnum Berries and Bird" 10 10

196 Tower and Arms **197** Women harvesting

2000. 900th Anniv of Dubno.
335 **196** 30k. multicoloured . . . 10 10

2000. Harvest Festival.
336 **197** 30k. multicoloured . . . 10 10

198 Presidential Flag

2000. Official Presidential Symbols. Multicoloured.
337 60k. Type **198** 15 10
338 60k. Mace 15 10
339 60k. Seal 15 10
340 60k. Chain of office 15 10

199 Elk, Map and Arms

2000. Regions. Volynska.
341 **199** 30k. multicoloured . . . 10 10

200 Kyiv General Post Office, Anniversary Emblem and Figures

2000. 225th Anniv of Kyiv General Post Office.
342 **200** 30k. blue, green and silver 10 10

201 Common Newts (*Triturus vulgaris*)

2000. Endangered Amphibians. Multicoloured.
343 30k. Type **201** 10 10
344 70k. European fire salamander (*Salamandra salamandra*) 20 10

202 Drogobych

2000. 250th Birth Anniv of Yuri Drogobych (Kotermack) (first Ukrainian Doctor and author of the first book printed in Slav).
345 **202** 30k. multicoloured . . . 10 10

204 Marigolds

2000. Flora. Sheet 130 × 150 mm containing T **204** and similar vert designs. Multicoloured.
MS347 30k. Type **204**; 30k. Camomile; 30k. Hollyhocks; 30k. Poppies; 30k. Periwinkle; 30k. Cornflower; 30k. Morning glory; 30k. Martagon lily; 30k. Peony; 30k. Bluebells 70 70

205 Grapes, Map and Lastivske Hnizdo Castle

2000. Regions. Crimea.
348 **205** 30k. multicoloured . . . 10 10

206 Young Boy and Witch

2000. Animated Children's Folk Tales. Multicoloured.
349 30k. Type **206** 10 10
350 30k. Elderly couple and duck ("Crooked Duck") 10 10
351 30k. Cat and rooster 10 10

207 Bridge joining Globes and Father Frost carrying Tree

2000. New Year.
352 **207** 30k. multicoloured . . . 10 10

208 St. Onufius Church, Lviv **209** Prince Volodymyr the Great

2000. Churches. Multicoloured.

353	30k. Type **208**	10	10
354	30k. Church of Christ's Birth, Velyke	10	10
355	70k. Church of the Resurrection, Sumy	10	10

2000. 2000 Years of Christianity. Sheet 78 × 96 mm.

MS356	209 2h. multicoloured	45	45

UMM AL QIWAIN — Pt. 19

One of the Trucial States in the Persian Gulf. In July 1971 formed the United Arab Emirates with five other Gulf Shaikdoms.

1964. 100 naye paise = 1 rupee.
1967. 100 dirhams = 1 riyal.

1 Shaikh Ahmed bin Rashid al Moalla and Mountain Gazelles

1964. Multicoloured. (a) Size as T **1**.

1	1n.p. Type **1**	15	15
2	2n.p. Snake	15	15
3	3n.p. Striped hyena	15	15
4	4n.p. Clown triggerfish	15	15
5	5n.p. Lionfish	15	15
6	10n.p. Diamond fingerfish	15	15
7	15n.p. Palace	15	15
8	20n.p. Town buildings	15	15
9	30n.p. Tower	25	20

(b) Size 42½ × 27 mm.

10	40n.p. Type **1**	25	20
11	50n.p. Snake	40	25
12	50n.p. Striped hyena	55	30
13	1r. Clown triggerfish	1·00	40
14	1r.50 Lionfish	1·25	50
15	2r. Diamond fingerfish	1·75	95

(c) Size 53½ × 33½ mm.

16	3r. Palace	2·75	1·60
17	5r. Town buildings	4·25	2·50
18	10r. Tower	6·75	4·50

2 Discus Thrower and Stadium

1964. Olympic Games, Tokyo. Multicoloured.

19	50n.p. Type **2**	20	15
20	1r. Main stadium	35	30
21	1r.50 Swimming pool	55	40
22	2r. Main stadium	70	55
23	3r. Komazawa gymnasium	1·10	95
24	4r. Stadium entrance	1·90	1·40
25	5r. Type **2**	2·40	1·90

3 Cortege leaving White House

1965. Pres. Kennedy Commemoration. Each black and gold on coloured paper as given below.

26	**3** 10n.p. blue	15	15
27	– 15n.p. stone	15	15
28	– 50n.p. stone	20	15
29	– 1r. pink	40	30
30	– 2r. stone	75	60
31	– 3r. lilac	1·25	95
32	– 5r. blue	2·25	1·90
33	– 7r.50 buff	3·25	2·25

DESIGNS—As T **3** (Funeral scenes): 15n.p. Coffin-bearers; 50n.p. Hearse; 1r. Presidents Eisenhower and Truman; 2r. Foreign dignitaries. 33 × 51 mm: 3r. Mrs. Kennedy and family at grave; 5r. Last salute; 7r.50, Pres. Kennedy.

1965. Air. Designs similar to Nos. 1/9 but inscr "AIR MAIL". Multicoloured. (a) Size 43 × 26½ mm.

34	15n.p. Type **1**	15	15
35	25n.p. Snake	15	15
36	35n.p. Striped hyena	25	15
37	50n.p. Clown triggerfish	45	20
38	75n.p. Lionfish	75	30
39	1r. Diamond fingerfish	85	40

(b) Size 53 × 34 mm.

40	2r. Palace	1·60	35
41	3r. Town buildings	2·25	65
42	5r. Tower	3·00	1·10

4 Tribute to Ruler (reverse of 10n.p. piece)

1965. Arabian Gulf Area Monetary Conf. Circular designs on silver foil, backed with paper inscr overall "Walsall Security Paper" in English and Arabic. Imperf. (a) Diameter 43 mm.

43	**4** 10n.p. purple and black	15	15
44	– 25n.p. blue and green	15	15

(b) Diameter 55½ mm.

45	**4** 1r. red and violet	40	40
46	– 2r. green and orange	45	45

(c) Diameter 64 mm.

47	**4** 3r. blue and mauve	1·00	1·00
48	– 5r. purple and blue	1·75	1·75

SILVER PIECES: Nos. 44, 46, 48 each show the obverse side (Shaikh Ahmed).

5 "Penny Black" and Egyptian 5p. Stamp of 1866

1966. Centenary Stamp Exhibition, Cairo.

49	**5** 3n.p. multicoloured	10	10
50	– 5n.p. multicoloured	10	10
51	– 7n.p. multicoloured	15	15
52	– 10n.p. multicoloured	15	15
53	– 15n.p. multicoloured	15	15
54	– 25n.p. multicoloured	15	15
55	– 50n.p. multicoloured	35	20
56	– 75n.p. multicoloured	45	20
57	– 1r. multicoloured	65	25
58	– 2r. multicoloured	1·10	55

DESIGNS: As Type **5** with Egyptian 5p. stamp: 7n.p. Brazil 30r. "Bull's-eye" of 1843; 15n.p. Mauritius "Post Office" One Penny of 1847; 50n.p. Belgium 10c. "Epaulettes" of 1849; 1r. New South Wales One Penny and Victoria One Penny of 1850. As Type **5**, but with Egyptian "Pyramid and Star" watermark of 1866: 5n.p. Basel 2½r. "Dove" of 1845, Geneva 5c.+5c. "Double Eagle" and Zurich 4r. "Numeral" of 1843; 10n.p. U.S. St. Louis "Bears" 5c., Baltimore 5c. and New York 5c. "Postmasters" stamps of 1845; 25n.p. France 20c. "Ceres" of 1849; 75n.p. Bavaria 1k. of 1850; 2r. Spain 6c. of 1850.

6 Sir Winston Churchill with Lord Alanbrooke and Field Marshal Montgomery

1966. Churchill Commemoration. Multicoloured designs each including Churchill.

59	3n.p. Type **6**	10	10
60	4n.p. With Roosevelt and Stalin at Yalta	10	10
61	5n.p. In garden at No. 10 Downing Street, London	10	10
62	10n.p. With Eisenhower	15	15
63	15n.p. With Lady Churchill in car	15	15
64	50n.p. Painting in Morocco	25	15
65	75n.p. Walking – on holiday	40	15
66	1r. Funeral cortege	65	20
67	3r. Lying-in-state, Westminster Hall	1·60	60
68	5r. Churchill giving "Victory" sign	2·40	1·10

7 Communications Satellite

1966. Centenary (1965) of I.T.U. Communications Satellites. Multicoloured.

70	5n.p. Type **7**	15	15
71	10n.p. "Tiros"	20	15
72	25n.p. "Telstar"	20	15
73	50n.p. "Ariel"	50	15
74	75n.p. "Ranger"	65	15
75	1r. "Alouette"	95	25
76	2r. "Vanguard 1"	1·75	40
77	3r. "Explorer 10"	2·50	50
78	5r. "Early Bird"	4·75	90

NEW CURRENCY SURCHARGES. In 1967 various issues appeared surcharged in dirhams and riyals. The 1964 definitives, 1965 air stamps and officials with this surcharge are listed as there is evidence of their postal use. Nos. 19/33 and 49/68 also exist with these surcharges.

1967. Various issues with currency names changed by overprinting. (i) Nos. 1/18 (1964 Definitives).

80	1d. on 1n.p.	10	10
81	2d. on 2n.p.	10	10
82	3d. on 3n.p.	10	10
83	4d. on 4n.p.	10	10
84	5d. on 5n.p.	15	10
85	10d. on 10n.p.	15	10
86	15d. on 15n.p.	1·75	70
87	20d. on 20n.p.	1·75	70
88	30d. on 30n.p.	1·75	70
89	40d. on 40n.p.	45	15
90	50d. on 50n.p.	55	25
91	70d. on 70n.p.	70	30
92	1r. on 1r.	1·25	35
93	1r.50 on 1r.50	1·75	60
94	2r. on 2r.	2·00	70
95	3r. on 3r.	4·50	1·60
96	5r. on 5r.	6·25	2·50
97	10r. on 10r.	9·00	4·25

(ii) Nos. 34/42 (Airmails).

98	15d. on 15n.p.	15	10
99	25d. on 25n.p.	20	10
100	35d. on 35n.p.	25	20
101	50d. on 50n.p.	75	25
102	75d. on 75n.p.	85	35
103	1r. on 1r.	95	45
104	2r. on 2r.	1·60	1·25
105	3r. on 3r.	2·10	2·10
106	5r. on 5r.	3·25	3·25

9 Blue-spotted Boxfish

1967. Fish of the Arabian Gulf. Multicoloured. (a) Postage. (i) Size 46 × 21 mm.

116	1d. Type **9**	10	10
117	2d. Parrotfish	10	10
118	3d. Striped sweetlips	10	10
119	4d. Black-wedged butterflyfish	10	10
120	5d. Japanese bonyhead	10	10
121	10d. Reticulate damselfish	20	10
122	15d. Picasso triggerfish	20	10
123	20d. Undulate triggerfish	30	10
124	30d. Black-saddled pufferfish	45	10

(ii) Size 56 × 26 mm.

125	40d. Type **9**	50	10
126	50d. As 2d.	60	15
127	70d. As 3d.	85	15
128	1r. As 4d.	1·00	15
129	1r.50 As 5d.	1·60	25
130	2r. As 10d.	1·75	35
131	3r. As 15d. (No. 122)	2·50	45
132	5r. As 20d.	4·25	75
133	10r. As 30d.	6·50	1·50

(b) Air. Size 70 × 35 mm.

134	15d. Type **9**	20	10
135	25d. As 2d.	30	10
136	35d. As 3d.	45	10
137	50d. As 4d.	60	15
138	75d. As 5d.	85	15
139	1r. As 10d.	1·00	15
140	2r. As 15d. (No. 122)	1·75	35
141	3r. As 20d.	2·50	45
142	5r. As 30d.	4·25	75

OFFICIAL STAMPS

1965. Designs similar to Nos. 1/9, additionally inscr "ON STATE'S SERVICE". Multicoloured. (a) Postage. Size 42½ × 27 mm.

O49	25n.p. Type **1**	15	15
O50	40n.p. Snake	20	15
O51	50n.p. Striped hyena	25	15
O52	75n.p. Clown triggerfish	80	20
O53	1r. Lionfish	1·75	40

(b) Air. (i) Size 42½ × 27 mm.

O54	75n.p. Diamond fingerfish	75	20

(ii) Size 53 × 34 mm.

O55	2r. Palace	1·40	60
O56	3r. Town buildings	2·10	85
O57	5r. Tower	3·50	1·25

1967. Nos. O49/57 with currency names changed by overprinting.

O107	25d. on 25n.p. (postage)	30	15
O108	40d. on 40n.p.	35	15
O109	50d. on 50n.p.	45	25
O110	75d. on 75n.p.	85	35
O111	1r. on 1r.	95	45
O112	75d. on 75d. (air)	85	35
O113	2r. on 2r.	1·90	1·25
O114	3r. on 3r.	2·10	1·75
O115	5r. on 5r.	3·50	2·75

For later issues see **UNITED ARAB EMIRATES**.

APPENDIX

The following stamps have either been issued in excess of postal needs or have not been available to the public in reasonable quantities at face value. Such stamps may later be given full listing if there is evidence of regular postal use.

1967.

Self-portraits of Famous Painters. Postage 10, 15, 25, 50, 75d., 1, 1r.50; Air 1r.25, 2, 2r.50, 3, 5r.

Dogs. Postage 15, 25, 50, 75d., 1r.; Air 1r.25, 2r.50, 4r.

"Expo 67" World Fair, Montreal. Famous Paintings. 25, 50, 75d., 1, 1r.50, 2, 3r.

1968.

Falcons. Postage 15, 25, 50, 75d., 1r.; Air 1r.50, 3, 5r.

Winter Olympic Games, Grenoble. Postage 10, 25, 75d., 1r.; Air 1r.50, 2, 3, 5r.

Famous Paintings. Postage 25, 50, 75d., 1, 1r.50, 2r.50; Air 1, 2, 3, 4, 5r.

Olympic Games, Mexico (1st issue). Optd on (a) 1964 Tokyo Olympic Games Issue. Postage 1r.50, 2, 4, 5r. (b) 1968 Winter Olympic Games issue. Air 1r.50, 2, 5r.

Robert Kennedy Memorial. Optd on 1965 Pres. Kennedy issue. Postage 3, 5, 7r.50.

Olympic Games, Mexico (2nd issue). Postage 10, 25, 50d., 1, 2r.; Air 2r.50, 3, 4, 5r.

Still Life Paintings. Postage 25, 50d., 1, 1r.50, 2r.; Air 1r.25, 2r.50, 3, 3r.50, 5r.

Mexico Olympic Medal Winners. Optd on Olympic Games, Mexico issue. Postage 10, 25, 50d., 1, 2r.; Air 2r.50, 3, 4, 5r.

Aviation History. Aircraft. Postage 25, 50d., 1, 1r.50, 2r.; Air 1r.25, 2r.50, 3, 5r.

1969.

"Apollo 8" Moon Orbit. Optd on 1968 Aviation History issue. Postage 25, 50d., 1, 1r.50, 2r.; Air 1r.25, 2r.50, 3, 5r.

Horses (1st series). Postage 25, 50, 75d., 1, 2r.; Air 1r.50, 2r.50, 4, 5r.

Olympic Games, Munich, 1972 (1st issue). Optd on 1968 Olympic Games, Mexico issue. Postage 10, 25, 50d., 1, 2r.; Air 2r.50, 3, 4, 5r.

Winter Olympic Games, Sapporo 1972 (1st issue). Optd on 1968 Winter Olympics Grenoble issue. Postage 10, 25, 75d., 1r.; Air 1r.50, 2, 3, 5r.

Veteran and Vintage Cars. Postage 15d. × 8, 25d. × 8, 50d. × 8, 75d. × 8; Air 1r. × 8, 2r. × 8.

Famous Films. Postage 10, 15, 25, 50, 75d., 1r.; Air 1r.50, 2r.50, 3, 4, 5r.

"Apollo 12" Moon Landing. 10, 20, 30, 50, 75d., 1r.

1970.

"Apollo 13" Astronauts. 10, 30, 50d.

"Expo 70" World Fair, Osaka, Japan. 5, 10, 20, 40d., 1, 1r.25.

150th Anniv of British Landing on Trucial Coast. Uniforms. 10, 20, 30, 50, 75d., 1r.

1971.

Animals. Postage 10, 15, 20, 25d.; Air 5r.

Winter Olympic Games, Saporro, 1972 (2nd issue). Postage 5, 10, 15, 20, 25d.; Air 50, 75d., 1, 3, 5r.

Olympic Games, Munich, 1972 (2nd issue). Postage 5, 10, 15, 20, 25d.; Air 50, 75d., 1, 3, 5r.

1972.

Durer's Religious Paintings. Postage 5, 10, 15, 20, 25d.; Air 3r.

Horses (2nd series). Postage 10, 15, 20, 25d.; Air 50d., 3r.

Locomotives (plastic surfaced). Postage 5, 10, 20, 40, 50d.; Air 6r.

Winter Olympic Games, Sapporo, 1972 (3rd issue) (plastic surfaced). Postage 5, 10, 20, 40, 50d.; Air 6r.

Easter, Religious Paintings. Postage 5, 10, 20, 50d.; Air 1, 3r.

Kennedy Brothers Memorial. Postage 5, 10, 15, 20d.; Air 1, 3r.

Winston Churchill Memorial. Postage 5, 10, 15, 20d.; Air 3r.

Arab Rulers. Postage 5d. × 6, 10d. × 6, 15d. × 6, 20d. × 6; Air 3r. × 6.

13th World Jamboree, 1971 (plastic surfaced). Postage 5, 10, 20, 40, 50d.; Air 6r.

Fish. Postage 5, 10, 20, 40, 50d.; Air 6r.

International Airlines. Postage 5, 10, 15, 20, 25d.; Air 50d.

"Apollo 15" Moon Mission. Postage 5, 10, 15, 20, 25d.; Air 50, 75d., 1, 3, 5r.

Olympic Games, Munich, 1972 (3rd issue) (plastic surfaced). Postage 5, 10, 20, 40, 50d.; Air 6r.

2500th Anniv of Founding of Persian Empire. Postage 10, 20, 30, 40, 50, 60d.; Air 1r.

Portraits of Charles de Gaulle. 5, 10, 15, 20, 25d.

Paintings of Napoleon. Postage 5, 10, 15, 20, 25d.; Air 5r.

Butterflies. Postage 5, 10, 15, 20, 25d.; Air 3r.

Penguins. Postage 5, 10, 15, 20d.; Air 50d., 4r.

Cars. Postage 5, 10, 15, 20, 25d.; Air 3r.

Masks (1st series). Postage 5, 10, 15, 20, 25d.; Air 50d., 1, 3r.

Dogs and Cats. Postage 5, 5, 10, 10, 15, 15, 20, 20, 25, 25d.; Air 5, 5r.

Roses. Postage 10, 15, 20, 25d.; Air 50d., 5r.

Marine Fauna. Postage 5, 10, 15, 20, 25, 50d.; Air 1, 3r.

Masks (2nd series). Postage 5, 10, 15, 20, 25d.; Air 50d., 1, 3r.

Navigators. Postage 5, 10, 15, 20, 25, 50d.; Air 1, 3r.

Exotic Birds (1st series). Horiz and vert designs. Air 1r. × 16.

Exotic Birds (2nd series). Horiz designs. Air 1r. × 16.

In common with the other states of the United Arab Emirates the Umm al Qiwain stamp contract was terminated on 1 August 1972 and any further new issues released after that date were unauthorized.

UNITED ARAB EMIRATES Pt. 19

Following the withdrawal of British forces from the Gulf and the ending of the Anglo-Trucial States treaties six of the states, Abu Dhabi, Ajman, Dubai, Fujeira, Sharjah and Umm al Qiwain, formed an independent union on 2 December 1971. The seventh state, Ras al Khaima, joined during February 1972. Each emirate continued to use its own stamps, pending the introduction of a unified currency. A Union Postal administration came into being on 1 August 1972 and the first stamps appeared on 1 January 1973.

For Abu Dhabi stamps optd U.A.E., etc, see under that heading.

100 fils = 1 dirham.

1 U.A.E. Flag and Map of Gulf

1973. Multicoloured. (a) Size 42 × 25 mm.

No.	Type	Description	Unused	Used
1		5f. Type **1**	10	10
2		10f. Type **1**	10	10
3		15f. Eagle emblem	20	15
4		35f. As 15f.	35	35
		(b) Size 46 × 30 mm.		
5		65f. Almaqta Bridge, Abu Dhabi	70	70
6		75f. Khor Fakkan, Sharjah	85	85
7		1d. Clock Tower, Dubai	1·10	1·10
8		1¼d. Buthnah Fort, Fujeira	1·75	2·50
9		2d. Alfalaj Fort, Umm al Qiwain	21·00	5·25
10		3d. Khor Khwair, Ras al Khaima	5·00	5·00
11		5d. Ruler's Palace, Ajman	5·50	5·50
12		10d. President Shaikh Zaid	11·00	11·00

2 Youth and Girl within Shield

1973. National Youth Festival. Multicoloured.

No.	Type	Description	Unused	Used
13		10f. Type **2**	2·40	15
14		1d.25 Allegory of Youth	5·75	4·25

3 Traffic Lights and Road Sign

1973. Traffic Week. Multicoloured.

No.	Type	Description	Unused	Used
15		35f. Type **3**	1·75	95
16		75f. Pedestrian-crossing (horiz)	3·25	1·75
17		1d.25 Traffic policeman	5·75	2·75

4 "Three Races of the World"

1973. 25th Anniv of Declaration of Human Rights.

No.	Type	Description	Unused	Used
18	4	35f. black, yellow and blue	95	40
19		65f. black, yellow and red	2·50	85
20		1¼d. black, yellow and green	4·00	1·60

5 U.P.U. Emblem

1974. Centenary of Universal Postal Union.

No.	Type	Description	Unused	Used
21	5	25f. multicoloured	1·00	35
22		60f. multicoloured	1·75	85
23		1¼d. multicoloured	3·25	1·40

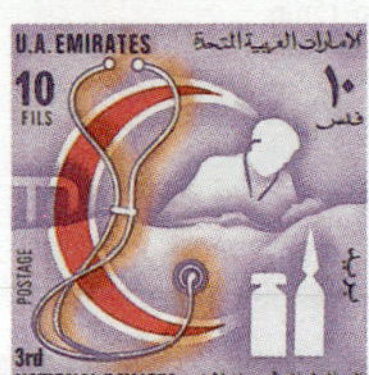

6 Medical Equipment (Health Service)

1974. Third National Day.

No.	Type	Description	Unused	Used
24	6	10f. red, brown and lilac	65	10
25	–	35f. gold, green and blue	1·25	50
26	–	65f. brown, sepia and blue	1·75	95
27	–	1¼d. multicoloured	3·75	2·40

DESIGNS—49 × 30 mm: 35f. Children reading (Education); 65f. Tools and buildings (Construction); 1¼d. U.A.E. flag with emblems of U.N. and Arab League.

7 Arab Couple with Candle and Book

1974. International Literacy Day.

No.	Type	Description	Unused	Used
28	7	35f. multicoloured	1·25	20
29	–	65f. black, blue and brown	1·50	60
30	–	1d.25 black, blue and brown	3·25	1·40

DESIGN—VERT: 65f., 1f.25, Arab couple with book.

8 Oil De-gassing Installation

1975. 9th Arab Oil Conference. Multicoloured.

No.	Type	Description	Unused	Used
31		25f. Type **8**	60	25
32		50f. "Al Ittiad" (offshore oil drilling platform)	1·75	45
33		100f. Underwater storage tank	2·50	1·10
34		125f. Marine oil production platform	3·00	1·75

9 Station and Dish Aerial

1975. Inauguration of Jabal Ali Satellite Earth Station. Multicoloured.

No.	Type	Description	Unused	Used
36		15f. Type **9**	70	25
37		35f. Satellite beaming information to Earth	1·75	40
38		65f. As 35f.	2·75	55
39		2d. Type **9**	5·75	3·00

10 "Snapshots" within Eagle Emblem

11 Symbols of Learning

1975. Fourth National Day. Multicoloured.

No.	Type	Description	Unused	Used
40		10f. Type **10**	35	15
41		35f. Shaikh Mohamed bin Hamad al Sharqi of Fujeira	1·00	45
42		60f. Shaikh Rashid bin Humaid al Naimi of Ajman	1·50	60
43		80f. Shaikh Ahmed bin Rashid al Moalla of Umm al Qiwain	2·25	1·00
44		90f. Shaikh Sultan bin Mohammed al Qasimi of Sharjah	2·50	1·50
45		1d. Shaikh Saqr bin Mohammed al Qasimi of Ras al Khaima	2·50	1·50
46		1d.40 Shaikh Rashid bin Said of Dubai	3·75	2·75
47		5d. Shaikh Zaid bin Sultan al Nahayyan of Abu Dhabi, President of U.A.E	14·00	10·00

1976. Arab Literacy Day. Multicoloured.

No.	Type	Description	Unused	Used
48		15f. Type **11**	40	10
49		50f. Arabs seeking enlightenment	75	55
50		3d. As 50f.	4·50	3·25

1976. No. 6 surch **50** in English and Arabic.

No.	Type	Description	Unused	Used
50a		50f. on 75f. multicoloured	13·00	8·00

12 Man and Road Signs

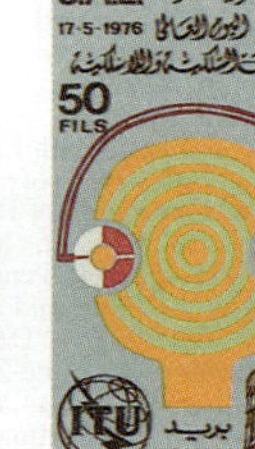

13 Headphones

1976. Traffic Week. Multicoloured.

No.	Type	Description	Unused	Used
51		15f. Type **12**	40	40
52		80f. Example of dangerous driving and road signals (horiz)	2·00	2·00
53		140f. Children on road crossing (horiz)	3·50	3·50

1976. International Telecommunications Day.

No.	Type	Description	Unused	Used
54	13	50f. multicoloured	65	25
55		80f. multicoloured	1·40	50
56		2d. multicoloured	4·00	1·75

14 U.A.E. Crest

15 President Shaikh Zaid

1976.

No.	Type	Description	Unused	Used
57	14	5f. red	10	30
58		10f. brown	15	20
59		15f. pink	20	20
60		35f. brown	35	10
61		50f. violet	55	15
62		60f. bistre	70	15
63		80f. green	80	25
64		90f. blue	85	65
65		1d. blue	1·25	75
66		140f. green	1·50	95
67		250f. violet	1·75	1·10
68		2d. grey	2·25	1·50
69		5d. blue	5·75	3·75
70		10d. mauve	11·50	7·75

1976. Fifth National Day.

No.	Type	Description	Unused	Used
71	15	15f. multicoloured	1·00	20
72		140f. multicoloured	4·00	2·00

16 Falcon's Head and Gulf

17 Mohammed Ali Jinnah (Quaid-i-Azam)

1976. International Falconry Congress, Abu Dhabi.

No.	Type	Description	Unused	Used
73	16	80f. multicoloured	1·75	70
74		2d. multicoloured	4·25	2·00

1976. Birth Centenary of Mohammed Ali Jinnah (founder of Pakistan).

No.	Type	Description	Unused	Used
75	17	50f. multicoloured	2·50	80
76		80f. multicoloured	3·50	1·60

19 A.P.U. Emblem

20 U.A.E. Crest

1977. 25th Anniv of Arab Postal Union.

No.	Type	Description	Unused	Used
78	19	50f. multicoloured	2·00	80
79		80f. multicoloured	3·00	1·50

1977.

No.	Type	Description	Unused	Used
80	20	5f. red and black	15	35
81		10f. brown and black	20	25
82		15f. pink and black	30	25
83		35f. brown and black	60	15
84		50f. mauve and black	85	20
85		60f. bistre and black	1·50	40
86		80f. green and black	1·50	30
87		90f. blue and black	1·60	15
88		1d. blue and black	2·25	35
89		1d.40 green and black	3·00	75
90		1d.50 violet and black	3·50	95
91		2d. grey and black	4·25	1·25
92		5d. blue and black	10·00	4·00
93		10d. purple and black	18·00	8·00

21 Arab Scholar and Emblems

1977. International Literacy Day.

No.	Type	Description	Unused	Used
94	21	50f. multicoloured	1·50	50
95		3d. multicoloured	6·00	4·00

22 Armoured Cars

1977. Sixth National Day. Multicoloured.

No.	Type	Description	Unused	Used
96		15f. Type **22**		
97		50f. Anti-aircraft missiles		
98		150f. Soldiers marching		
		Set of 3	£400	

Nos. 96/8 were withdrawn from sale on day of issue as the date in Arabic was wrongly inscribed backwards.

23 Posthorn Dhow

24 Koran on Map of World

1979. 2nd Gulf Postal Organization Conf, Dubai.

No.	Type	Description	Unused	Used
99	23	50f. multicoloured	50	30
100		5d. multicoloured	4·00	3·25

1980. The Arabs.

No.	Type	Description	Unused	Used
101	24	50f. multicoloured	50	30
102		1d.40 multicoloured	1·25	90
103		3d. multicoloured	2·75	2·00

25 Dassault Mirage III Jet Fighters and Sud Aviation Alouette III Helicopter

1980. Ninth National Day.
104 **25** 15f. multicoloured 30 15
105 50f. multicoloured 90 30
106 80f. multicoloured . . . . 1·25 90
107 150f. multicoloured . . . . 2·50 1·90

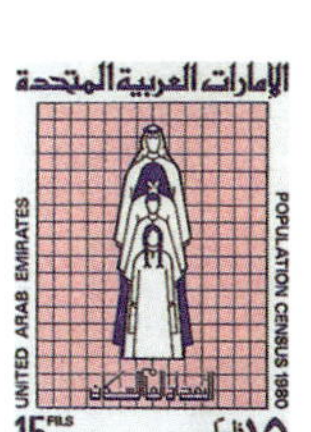

26 Family on Graph **27** Mosque and Kaaba, Mecca

1980. Population Census.
109 **26** 15f. blue and pink 30 15
110 – 80f. brown and grey . . . 1·25 50
111 – 90f. brown and buff . . . 1·40 75
112 **26** 2d. blue and cobalt . . . 4·25 3·50
DESIGN: 80, 90f. Figure standing in doorway.

1980. 1400th Anniv of Hejira.
113 **27** 15f. multicoloured 30 15
114 80f. multicoloured 90 50
115 90f. multicoloured . . . . 1·10 65
116 140f. multicoloured . . . . 2·75 1·75

28 Figures supporting O.P.E.C. Emblem **29** Policeman helping Child across Road

1980. 20th Anniv of Organization of Petroleum Exporting Countries. Multicoloured.
118 50f. Type **28** 60 35
119 80f. Type **28** . . . . 1·00 55
120 90f. O.P.E.C. emblem and globe . . . . 1·25 70
121 140f. As No. 120 . . . . . . 2·25 1·75

1981. Traffic Week. Multicoloured.
123 15f. Type **29** 30 15
124 50f. Policeman and traffic signs (21 × 31 mm) 60 35
125 80f. Type **29** 90 50
126 5d. As No. 124 . . . . . . 3·75 3·25

30 Symbols of Industry

1981. Tenth National Day.
127 **30** 25f. blue and black 30 15
128 – 150f. multicoloured . . . . 1·60 1·10
129 – 2d. red, green and black . . 2·75 1·90
DESIGNS: 150f. Soldiers; 2d. Flag and U.N. and U.A.E emblems.

31 Helping the Disabled (pictogram) and I.Y.D.P. Emblem **32** U.A.E. Crest

1981. Int Year of Disabled Persons. Mult.
130 25f. Type **31** 45 15
131 45f. Disabled person in wheelchair (pictogram) (vert) 80 35
132 150f. As No. 131 . . . . . . 1·75 1·50
133 2d. Type **31** . . . . 2·75 2·25

1982. Multicoloured. Background colour given.
(a) Size 17 × 21 mm.
134 **32** 5f. pink 10 10
135 10f. green 10 10
136 15f. violet 10 10
137 25f. brown 15 10
138 35f. brown 20 15
139 50f. blue 30 25
140 75f. yellow 50 40
141 100f. grey 65 50
142 110f. green 65 50
143 125f. mauve 80 60
144 150f. blue . . . . 1·00 80
145 175f. blue . . . . 1·25 75

(b) Size 23 × 27 mm.
146 **32** 2d. green . . . . 1·40 1·25
147 250f. pink . . . . 1·50 1·40
148 3d. blue . . . . 1·90 1·75
149 5d. yellow . . . . 2·50 2·25
150 10d. brown . . . . 5·00 5·00
151 20d. silver . . . . 8·00 8·00
151c 50d. purple . . . . 20·00 18·00

33 Flags of Competing Countries and Emblem

1982. 6th Arab Gulf Football Championships. Multicoloured.
152 25f. Type **33** 50 20
153 75f. American bald eagle holding ball over stadium (vert) . . . . 1·60 85
154 125f. Footballers (vert) . . . 1·60 1·10
155 3d. As No. 153 . . . . . . 4·50 4·00

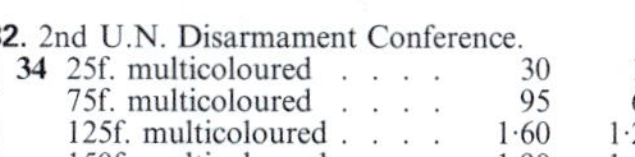

34 Figure breaking Gun

1982. 2nd U.N. Disarmament Conference.
156 **34** 25f. multicoloured 30 15
157 75f. multicoloured 95 65
158 125f. multicoloured . . . . 1·60 1·25
159 150f. multicoloured . . . . 1·90 1·40

35 National Emblems

1982. 11th National Day. Multicoloured.
160 25f. Type **35** 35 15
161 75f. Dove and flag (vert) . . 1·00 60
162 125f. As 75f. . . . . 1·75 95
163 150f. Type **35** . . . . 1·90 1·40

36 Arab writing **37** W.C.Y. Emblem

1983. Arab Literacy Day.
164 – 25f. multicoloured . . . . 10·00
165 **36** 35f. brown, violet and black 30 30
166 – 75f. yellow, black & mauve 13·00
167 **36** 3d. brown, yellow and black . . . . 2·00 2·00
DESIGN: 25, 75f. Koran and lamp.

1983. World Communications Year.
168 **37** 25f. multicoloured 50 15
169 150f. multicoloured . . . . 1·25 1·10
170 2d. multicoloured . . . . 1·90 1·50
171 3d. multicoloured . . . . 3·00 2·75

38 Satellite Orbit within "20"

1984. 20th Anniv of International Telecommunications Satellite Consortium.
172 **38** 2d. blue, purple & deep blue . . . . 2·50 2·00
173 2½d. blue, purple and green 3·50 3·00

39 Shaikh Hamad bin Mohamed al Sharqi and Buthnah Fort, Fujeira

1984. 13th National Day. Multicoloured.
174 1d. Type **39** . . . . 1·25 95
175 1d. Shaikh Rashid bin Ahmed al Moalla and Alfalaj Fort, Umm al Qiwain . . . . 1·25 95
176 1d. Shaikh Humaid bin Rashid al Naimi and Palace, Ajman . . . . . . 1·25 95
177 1d. Shaikh Saqr bin Mohammed al-Qasimi and harbour, Ras al Khaima 1·25 95
178 1d. Shaikh Zaid bin Sultan al Nahayyan and refinery, Abu Dhabi . . . . 1·25 95
179 1d. Shaikh Sultan bin Mohammed al Qasimi, oil well and mosque, Sharjah 1·25 95
180 1d. Shaikh Rashid bin Said and building, Dubai . . . 1·25 95

40 Pictograms of Refuse Collection **41** Globe and Knights

1985. Tidy Week.
181 **40** 5d. orange and black . . . 4·75 4·75

1985. World Junior Chess Championship, Sharjah.
182 **41** 2d. multicoloured . . . . 2·75 1·75
183 250f. multicoloured . . . . 3·75 2·50

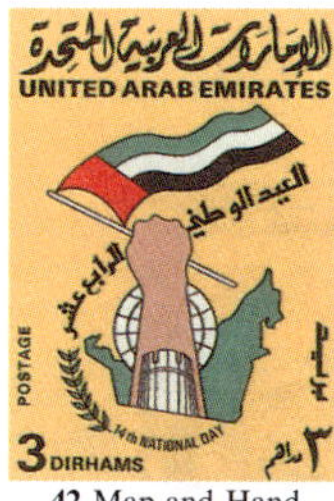

42 Map and Hand holding Flag **43** Stylized People and Map

1985. 14th National Day.
184 **42** 50f. multicoloured 40 20
185 3d. multicoloured . . . . 3·00 1·75

1985. Population Census.
186 **43** 50f. multicoloured 40 20
187 1d. multicoloured 90 45
188 3d. multicoloured . . . . 2·75 1·60

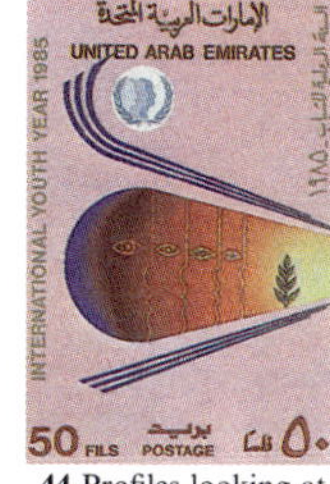

44 Profiles looking at Sapling **45** Emblem

1985. International Youth Year. Multicoloured.
189 50f. Type **44** 30 20
190 175f. Open book, flame and people between hemispheres (horiz) . . . . 1·25 90
191 2d. Youth carrying globe on back . . . . 1·50 1·00

1986. Arabic Woman and Family Day.
192 **45** 1d. multicoloured 75 45
193 3d. multicoloured . . . . 2·00 1·50

46 Globe, Map and Posthorn **47** Sakar Falcon

1986. 1st Anniv of General Postal Authority. Multicoloured.
194 50f. Type **46** 40 20
195 1d. Banner around globe (vert) 85 50
196 2d. As No. 195 . . . . . . 1·60 1·40
197 250f. Type **46** . . . . 1·90 1·75

1986.
198 **47** 50f. gold, blue and green 90 75
199 75f. gold, blue and mauve 1·40 1·10
200 125f. gold, blue and grey 2·40 1·75

48 Container Ship in Dock **49** Dawn, Satellite, Emblem and Dish Aerials

1986. 10th Anniv of United Arab Shipping Company. Multicoloured.
201 2d. Type **48** . . . . 2·25 1·60
202 3d. Container ship at sea (vert) . . . . 3·25 2·25

1986. 10th Anniv of Emirates Telecommunications Corporation.
203 250f. Type **49** . . . . 2·10 1·50
204 3d. As Type **49** but with sun behind emblem . . . . . 2·50 1·90

50 Emblem, Boeing 737 Airliner and Camel Rider **51** Emblem and Member States' Crests

1986. 1st Anniv of Emirates Airlines. Multicoloured.
205 50f. Type **50** 50 40
206 175f. Boeing 737, emblem and national colours . . . 2·75 2·10

1986. 7th Supreme Council Session of Gulf Co-operation Council, Abu Dhabi.
207 50f. Type **51** 50 30
208 1d.75 Emblem beneath tree 1·75 1·50
209 3d. As No. 208 . . . . . . 2·75 2·75
The face value of No. 208 is wrongly shown as "1.75 FILS".

52 Dubai Trade Centre

1986. 27th Chess Olympiad, Dubai. Mult.
210 50f. Type **52** 70 50
211 2d. Chess players (miniature from King Alfonso X's "Book of Chess, Dice and Tablings") (horiz) . . . . 3·00 2·50
212 250f. Chess players (miniature) (different) (horiz) . . . . 3·50 3·00

53 Dhow, Oil Rig, Tower Block and Sun's Rays

1986. 15th National Day. Multicoloured.
214 50f. Type **53** 45 20
215 1d. Type **53** 90 50
216 175f. Flag and hands holding Arabic "15" (vert) . . . . 1·75 1·40
217 2d. As No. 216 . . . . . . 2·25 2·00

54 Emblem

1986. Arab Police Day.
218 **54** 50f. multicoloured 70 50
219 1d. multicoloured . . . . 1·40 1·10

55 Emblem on Landscape

56 Boeing 737 Airliner and Map

1987. Municipalities and Environment Week.
220 **55** 50f. multicoloured 45 35
221 1d. multicoloured 90 75

1987. 1st Anniv of United Arab Emirates Flight Information Region.
222 **56** 200f. multicoloured . . . . 2·00 2·00
223 250f. multicoloured . . . . 2·50 2·50

57 Flower in Droplet

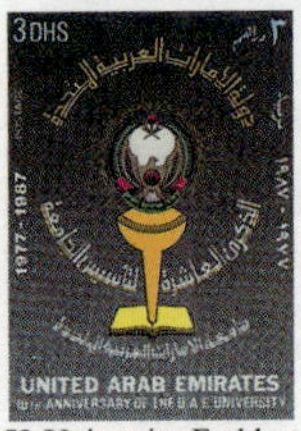

58 University Emblem

1987. "Save Energy". Multicoloured.
224 50f. Type **57** 50 50
225 2d. Globe as sun over oil derrick . . . . 5·00 5·00

1987. 10th Anniv of U.A.E. University.
226 **58** 1d. multicoloured 80 80
227 3d. multicoloured . . . . 2·25 2·25

59 Oil Rig

1987. 25th Anniv of First Crude Oil Shipment from Abu Dhabi.
228 **59** 50f. multicoloured 50 45
229 – 1d. light blue, black and blue 90 85
230 – 175f. grey, black and blue 1·60 1·50
231 – 2d. multicoloured . . . . 2·00 2·00
DESIGNS—VERT: 1d. Aerial view of drilling platform; 175f. Rig workers with drill head. HORIZ: 2d. Oil tanker at sea.

60 Trees and Dates in Arched Window

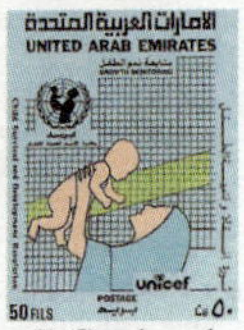

61 Graph and Woman holding Baby

1987. Arab Palm Tree and Dates Day. Multicoloured.
232 50f. Type **60** 45 45
233 1d. Trees and fruit 85 85

1987. U.N.I.C.E.F Child Survival Campaign.
234 **61** 50f. multicoloured 35 35
235 – 1d. blue, black and pink 65 65
236 – 175f. black, green & emer 1·10 1·10
237 – 2d. multicoloured . . . . 1·50 1·50
DESIGNS—VERT: 1d. Vaccinating baby; 175f. Oral rehydration therapy. HORIZ: 2d. Mother breastfeeding.

62 Emblem on Man's Head and Globe

63 Salim bin Ali al-Owais

1987. International Year of Shelter for the Homeless.
238 **62** 2d. multicoloured . . . . 1·60 1·60
239 250f. multicoloured . . . . 1·90 1·90

1987. Birth Centenary of Salim bin Ali al-Owais (poet).
240 **63** 1d. multicoloured . . . . 1·10 1·10
241 2d. multicoloured . . . . 2·40 2·40

64 Lockheed TriStar 500 and Terminal Building

1987. 6th Anniv of Abu Dhabi Int Airport. Mult.
242 50f. Type **64** 50 50
243 50f. Reception area 50 50
244 100f. Lockheed TriStar 500 over air traffic control centre . . . . 1·25 1·25
245 100f. Lockheed TriStar 500 and Boeing 737 at gangways . . . . 1·25 1·25

65 Writing in Sand, Black-lip Pearl Oyster and Pearls

1988. National Arts Festival.
246 **65** 50f. multicoloured 50 50
247 250f. multicoloured . . . . 1·75 1·75

66 Fisherman on Shore (Layla Mohammed Khalfan)

1988. Children's Paintings. Multicoloured.
248 50f. Type **66** 45 30
249 1d. Woman and flowers (Zeinab Nasir Mohammed) (vert) 80 65
250 1d.75 Flowers with girls' faces (Fatma Ali Abdullah) (vert) . . . . 1·40 1·10
251 2d. Teddy bear, cat and girls playing (Saaly Mohammed Jowda) . . . . 1·50 1·25

67 Masked Youth

68 Emblem and Urban and Desert Scenes

1988. Palestinian "Intifida" Movement.
252 **67** 2d. multicoloured . . . . 1·40 1·40
253 250f. multicoloured . . . . 1·75 1·75

1988. National Banking Anniversaries. Mult.
254 50f. Type **68** (20th anniv of National Bank of Abu Dhabi) . . . . 1·00 1·00
255 50f. Emblem (25th anniv of National Bank of Dubai Ltd) . . . . 1·00 1·00

69 Map, Fork-lift Truck and Container Lorry

70 Swimming

1988. 16th Anniv of Port Rashid. Multicoloured.
256 50f. Type **69** 35 35
257 1d. Container ship and view of port 70 70
258 175f. Ro-ro ferry and small boats at anchorages . . . 1·25 1·25
259 2d. Container ship at dockside . . . . 1·60 1·60

1988. Olympic Games, Seoul. Multicoloured.
260 2d. Type **70** . . . . 1·50 1·50
261 250f. Cycling . . . . 1·75 1·75

71 Vase

1988. 1st Anniv of Ras al Khaimah National Museum. Multicoloured.
262 50f. Type **71** 30 30
263 3d. Gold ornament (horiz) . . 1·60 1·60

72 Emblem

1988. 18th Arab Scouts Conference, Abu Dhabi.
264 **72** 1d. multicoloured 55 55

73 Dahlia

1989. 10th Tree Day. Multicoloured.
265 50f. Ghaf tree 30 30
266 100f. Palm tree 60 60
267 250f. Type **73** . . . . 1·40 1·40

74 Airport

1989. 10th Anniv of Sharjah International Airport.
268 **74** 50f. multicoloured 40 40
269 100f. multicoloured 90 90

75 Short S.23 Flying Boat

1989. 80th Anniv of Gulf Postal Services. Multicoloured.
270 50f. Type **75** 35 35
271 3d. "Bombala" (freighter) . . 2·25 2·00

76 Newspaper

1989. 20th Anniv of "Al-Ittihad" (newspaper). Multicoloured.
272 50f. Type **76** 30 30
273 1d. Newspaper offices 60 60

77 Emblem and Map

1989. 5th Anniv of Gulf Investment Corporation.
274 **77** 50f. multicoloured 25 25
275 2d. multicoloured . . . . 1·00 1·00

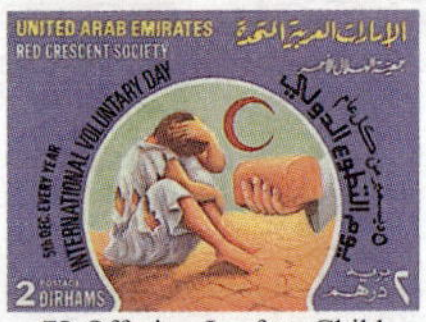

78 Offering Leaf to Child

1989. International Volunteer Day. U.A.E. Red Crescent Society. Multicoloured.
276 2d. Type **78** . . . . 1·00 1·00
277 250f. Crippled child in open hands (vert) . . . . 1·40 1·40

79 Bank Emblem and Buildings

80 Compass and Dhow

1989. 20th Anniv of Commercial Bank of Dubai. Multicoloured.
278 50f. Type **79** 30 30
279 1d. Bank building 60 60

1989. Bin Majid (15th-century navigator) Heritage Revival. Multicoloured.
280 1d. Type **80** 70 70
281 3d. Dhow (vert) . . . . . . 1·75 1·75

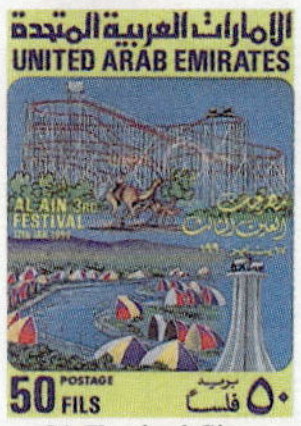

81 Festival Sites

82 Saker Falcon

1990. 3rd National Arts Festival, Al-Ain.
282 **81** 50f. multicoloured 30 30
283 1d. multicoloured 60 60

1990. Multicoloured, background colour given.
(a) Size 18 × 23 mm.
284 **82** 5f. blue 15 10
285 20f. mauve 15 10
286 25f. pink 25 15
287 50f. brown 45 25
288 100f. bistre 85 45
289 150f. green . . . . 1·40 70
290 175f. green . . . . 1·50 80
(b) Size 21 × 26 mm.
291 **82** 2d. lilac . . . . 1·75 90
292 250f. blue . . . . 2·00 1·10
293 3d. pink . . . . 2·50 1·40
294 5d. orange . . . . 4·00 2·25
295 10d. yellow . . . . 8·00 4·50
296 20d. green . . . . 16·00 9·00
297 50d. green . . . . 39·00 22·00

83 Children and Leaves
84 Leaning Tower of Pisa, Flag and U.A.E. Mascot

1990. Children's Culture Festival.
301 **83** 50f. multicoloured 30 30
302 250f. multicoloured . . . . 1·40 1·40

1990. World Cup Football Championship, Italy. Multicoloured.
303 50f. Type **84** 30 30
304 1d. Desert, flag and mascot (vert) 55 55
305 2d. Mascot on ball (vert) . . 1·10 1·10
306 250f. Flags around mascot . . 1·40 1·40

85 Projects and Buildings

1990. 25th Anniv of Dubai Chamber of Commerce and Industry. Multicoloured.
308 **85** 50f. multicoloured 50 50
309 1d. multicoloured . . . . 1·00 1·00

86 Weeping Eyes and Child on Globe
87 Periwinkle ("Catharanthus roseus")

1990. Child Survival Programme. Multicoloured.
310 175f. Type **86** 90 90
311 2d. Emaciated child and newspapers . . . . 1·00 1·00

1990. Flowers. Multicoloured.
312 50f. "Centavrea pseudo sinaica" 30 30
313 50f. Ushar bush ("Calotropis procera") 30 30
314 50f. "Argyrolobeum roseum" 30 30
315 50f. "Lamranthus roseus" . . 30 30
316 50f. "Hibiscus rosa sinensis" 30 30
317 50f. "Nerium oleander" . . . 30 30
318 50f. Type **87** 30 30
319 50f. "Bougainvillaea glabra" (wrongly inscr "Bogainvillea") 30 30

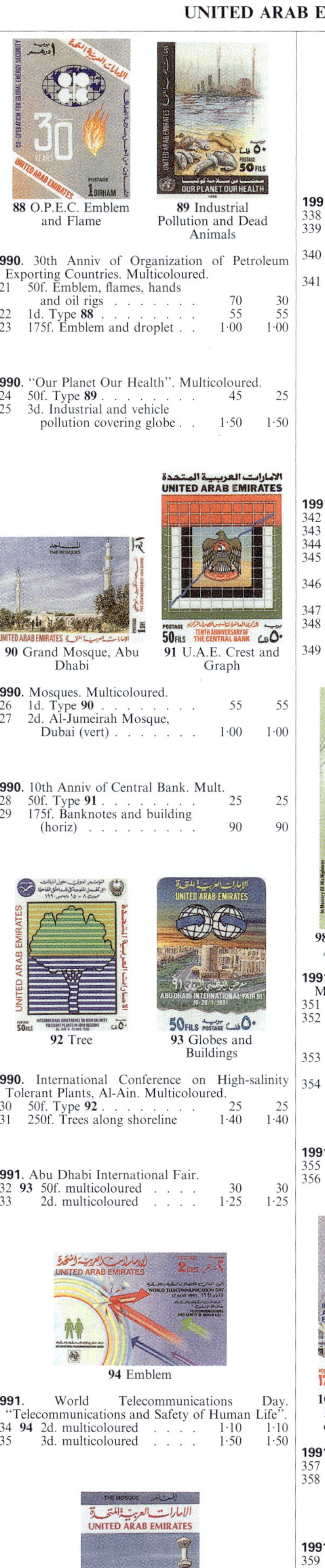

88 O.P.E.C. Emblem and Flame
89 Industrial Pollution and Dead Animals

1990. 30th Anniv of Organization of Petroleum Exporting Countries. Multicoloured.
321 50f. Emblem, flames, hands and oil rigs 70 30
322 1d. Type **88** 55 55
323 175f. Emblem and droplet . . 1·00 1·00

1990. "Our Planet Our Health". Multicoloured.
324 50f. Type **89** 45 25
325 3d. Industrial and vehicle pollution covering globe . . 1·50 1·50

90 Grand Mosque, Abu Dhabi
91 U.A.E. Crest and Graph

1990. Mosques. Multicoloured.
326 1d. Type **90** 55 55
327 2d. Al-Jumeirah Mosque, Dubai (vert) . . . . 1·00 1·00

1990. 10th Anniv of Central Bank. Mult.
328 50f. Type **91** 25 25
329 175f. Banknotes and building (horiz) 90 90

92 Tree
93 Globes and Buildings

1990. International Conference on High-salinity Tolerant Plants, Al-Ain. Multicoloured.
330 50f. Type **92** 25 25
331 250f. Trees along shoreline 1·40 1·40

1991. Abu Dhabi International Fair.
332 **93** 50f. multicoloured 30 30
333 2d. multicoloured . . . . 1·25 1·25

94 Emblem

1991. World Telecommunications Day. "Telecommunications and Safety of Human Life".
334 **94** 2d. multicoloured . . . . 1·10 1·10
335 3d. multicoloured . . . . 1·50 1·50

95 Shaikh Saqr Mosque, Ras al Khaimah

1991. Mosques. Multicoloured.
336 1d. Type **95** 55 55
337 2d. King Faisal Mosque, Sharjah . . . . 1·10 1·10
See also Nos. 371/2 and 411/12.

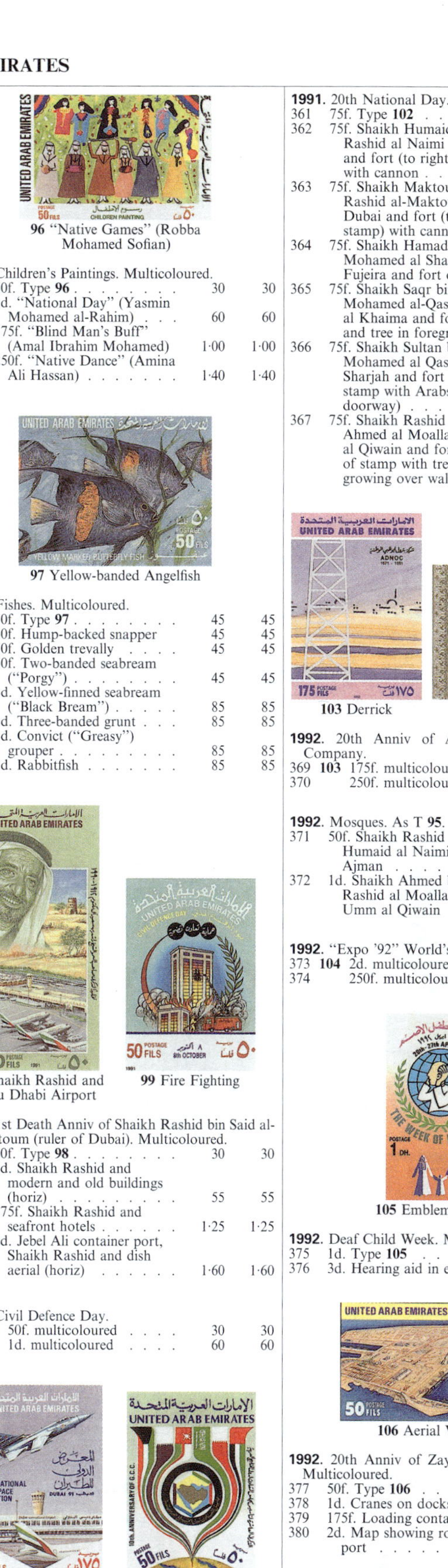

96 "Native Games" (Robba Mohamed Sofian)

1991. Children's Paintings. Multicoloured.
338 50f. Type **96** 30 30
339 1d. "National Day" (Yasmin Mohamed al-Rahim) . . . 60 60
340 175f. "Blind Man's Buff" (Amal Ibrahim Mohamed) 1·00 1·00
341 250f. "Native Dance" (Amina Ali Hassan) . . . . 1·40 1·40

97 Yellow-banded Angelfish

1991. Fishes. Multicoloured.
342 50f. Type **97** 45 45
343 50f. Hump-backed snapper 45 45
344 50f. Golden trevally 45 45
345 50f. Two-banded seabream ("Porgy") 45 45
346 1d. Yellow-finned seabream ("Black Bream") 85 85
347 1d. Three-banded grunt . . . 85 85
348 1d. Convict ("Greasy") grouper 85 85
349 1d. Rabbitfish 85 85

98 Shaikh Rashid and Abu Dhabi Airport
99 Fire Fighting

1991. 1st Death Anniv of Shaikh Rashid bin Said al-Maktoum (ruler of Dubai). Multicoloured.
351 50f. Type **98** 30 30
352 1d. Shaikh Rashid and modern and old buildings (horiz) 55 55
353 175f. Shaikh Rashid and seafront hotels . . . . . . 1·25 1·25
354 2d. Jebel Ali container port, Shaikh Rashid and dish aerial (horiz) . . . . . . 1·60 1·60

1991. Civil Defence Day.
355 **99** 50f. multicoloured 30 30
356 1d. multicoloured 60 60

100 Panavia Tornado F Mk 3 Jet Fighter over Dubai Airport
101 Flags and Emblem

1991. Int Aerospace Exhibition, Dubai. Mult.
357 175f. Type **100** 90 90
358 2d. View of under-side of Panavia Tornado over Dubai airport . . . . . . 1·00 1·00

1991. 10th Anniv of Gulf Co-operation Council.
359 **101** 50f. multicoloured 25 25
360 3d. multicoloured . . . . 1·50 1·50

102 Shaikh Zaid bin Sultan al Nahayyan of Abu Dhabi (President of U.A.E.)

1991. 20th National Day. Multicoloured.
361 75f. Type **102** 45 45
362 75f. Shaikh Humaid bin Rashid al Naimi of Ajman and fort (to right of stamp) with cannon 45 45
363 75f. Shaikh Maktoum bin Rashid al-Maktoum of Dubai and fort (to left of stamp) with cannon . . . 45 45
364 75f. Shaikh Hamad bin Mohamed al Sharqi of Fujeira and fort on hillock 45 45
365 75f. Shaikh Saqr bin Mohamed al-Qasimi of Ras al Khaima and fort (tower and tree in foreground) . . 45 45
366 75f. Shaikh Sultan bin Mohamed al Qasimi of Sharjah and fort (to left of stamp with Arabs in doorway) 45 45
367 75f. Shaikh Rashid bin Ahmed al Moalla of Umm al Qiwain and fort (to right of stamp with trees growing over walls) 45 45

103 Derrick
104 Fort Jahili, Al Ain

1992. 20th Anniv of Abu Dhabi National Oil Company.
369 **103** 175f. multicoloured . . . 90 90
370 250f. multicoloured . . . 1·25 1·25

1992. Mosques. As T **95**. Multicoloured.
371 50f. Shaikh Rashid bin Humaid al Naimi Mosque, Ajman 30 30
372 1d. Shaikh Ahmed bin Rashid al Moalla Mosque, Umm al Qiwain 60 60

1992. "Expo '92" World's Fair, Seville.
373 **104** 2d. multicoloured . . . . 1·10 1·10
374 250f. multicoloured . . . 15·00 15·00

105 Emblem and Family

1992. Deaf Child Week. Multicoloured.
375 1d. Type **105** 60 60
376 3d. Hearing aid in ear . . . 1·50 1·50

106 Aerial View of Port

1992. 20th Anniv of Zayed Sea Port, Abu Dhabi. Multicoloured.
377 50f. Type **106** 40 40
378 1d. Cranes on dockside . . . 80 80
379 175f. Loading container ship 1·25 1·25
380 2d. Map showing routes from port . . . . 1·50 1·50

107 Yachting
108 Football Match (Najla Saif Mohamed Harib)

1992. Olympic Games, Barcelona. Multicoloured.
381 50f. Type **107** 40 30
382 1d. Running 60 60
383 175f. Swimming 90 90
384 250f. Cycling . . . . 1·25 1·25

1992. Children's Paintings. Multicoloured.
386 50f. Type **108** 30 30
387 1d. Children in park (Anoud Adnan Ali Mohamed) . . 60 60

388 2d. Family at playground (Ahlam Ibrahim Ahmed) . . . 1·10 1·10
389 250f. Children playing amongst trees (Dallal Ali Salih) . . . . 1·25 1·25

109 Bank Building 110 Tambourah

1992. 15th Anniv of Emirates Bank International.
390 **109** 50f. multicoloured 30 30
391 – 175f. gold, brown and red 90 90
DESIGN—33 × 40 mm: 175f. Bank emblem.

1992. Musical Instruments. Multicoloured.
392 50f. Type **110** 30 30
393 50f. Oud (stringed instrument) 30 30
394 50f. Rababah (stringed instrument with bow) . . . 30 30
395 1d. Mizmar (wind instrument) and shindo (drum) (horiz) 60 60
396 1d. Marwas and duff (hand-held drums) (horiz) 60 60
397 1d. Tabel (drum) and hibban (bagpipe) (horiz) 60 60

111 Emblem

1992. 13th Supreme Council Session of Gulf Co-operation Council, Abu Dhabi.
399 **111** 50f. multicoloured 30 30
400 2d. multicoloured . . . . 1·10 1·10

112 Camel Race

1992. The Dromedary. Multicoloured.
401 50f. Type **112** 30 30
402 1d. Camel riders and mother with young (vert) 55 55
403 175f. Camels at well and mother with young 90 90
404 2d. Camels (vert) . . . . . . 1·10 1·10

113 Golf 114 Club Building

1993. Tourism. Multicoloured.
405 50f. Type **113** 30 30
406 1d. Fishing (vert) 70 70
407 2d. Sailing . . . . 1·40 1·40
408 250f. Sight-seeing by car . . 1·40 1·40

1993. Dubai Creek Golf and Yacht Club. Mult.
409 2d. Type **114** . . . . 1·10 1·10
410 250f. Club building and sea shore . . . . 1·75 1·75

1993. Mosques. As T **95**. Multicoloured.
411 50f. Thabit bin Khalid Mosque, Fujeira 30 30
412 1d. Sharq al Morabbah Mosque, Al-Ain 55 55

115 National Crest and Sports

1993. National Youth Festival. Multicoloured.
413 50f. Type **115** 30 30
414 3d. National crest and sciences . . . . 1·60 1·60

116 Textile Cone

1993. Sea Shells. Multicoloured.
415 25f. Type **116** 15 10
416 50f. Atlantic pearl oyster . . 25 25
417 100f. Woodcock murex . . . 50 50
418 150f. "Natica pulicaris" . . . 75 75
419 175f. Giant spider conch . . 90 90
420 200f. "Cardita bicolor" . . . 1·00 1·00
421 250f. Gray's cowrie . . . . . 1·25 1·25
422 300f. "Cymatium trilineatum" 1·50 1·50

117 Addict within Capsule

1993. Anti-drugs Campaign. Multicoloured.
423 50f. Type **117** 30 30
424 1d. Family on skull, globe and drugs (vert) 60 60

118 Commercial Buildings 119 Aerial View of Port

1993. 25th Anniv of Abu Dhabi National Bank. Multicoloured.
425 50f. Type **118** 30 30
426 1d. Bank emblem 60 60
427 175f. Bank building and emblem . . . . 1·10 1·10
428 2d. Commercial buildings within shield . . . . 1·25 1·25

1993. Dubai Ports Authority. Multicoloured.
429 50f. Type **119** 30 30
430 1d. Cranes loading containers 60 60
431 2d. Aerial view of port (different) . . . . 1·10 1·10
432 250f. Arrowed routes on globe . . . . 1·50 1·50

120 Soldiers on Parade (Mouza Musabah al-Mazroui)

1993. National Day. Children's Paintings. Multicoloured.
433 50f. Type **120** 30 30
434 1d. Woman and children (Shreen Naeem Hassan Radwan) (vert) 60 60
435 175f. Flag and dhow (Samiha Mohamad Sultan) . . . . 1·25 1·25
436 2d. Decorations and fireworks (Omer Abdulla Rabia Thani) . . . . . . 1·25 1·25

121 Hili Tomb

1993. Archaeological Finds from Al-Ain. Multicoloured.
437 50f. Type **121** 30 30
438 1d. Hili decorative tile . . . 60 60
439 175f. Qattarah figure . . . . 1·00 1·00
440 250f. Hili bowl . . . . 1·50 1·50

122 Horse rearing

1994. Arab Horses. Multicoloured.
441 50f. Type **122** 30 30
442 1d. Grey (horiz) 60 60
443 175f. Bay with white blaze . . 1·00 1·00
444 250f. Piebald (horiz) . . . . 1·50 1·50

123 Children with Flags and Balloons

1994. 10th Children's Festival, Sharjah. Children's Paintings. Multicoloured.
445 50f. Type **123** 30 30
446 1d. Children in forest 60 60
447 175f. Children with balloons and child painting . . . . 1·00 1·00
448 2d. Children in garden . . . 1·10 1·10

124 Dubai, Map and Emblems 125 Holy Kaaba and Globe

1994. 10th Arab Towns Organization Congress, Dubai. Multicoloured.
449 50f. Type **124** 25 25
450 1d. Different view of Dubai, map and emblems (horiz) 55 55

1994. Pilgrimage to Mecca. Multicoloured.
451 50f. Type **125** 25 25
452 2d. Crowds around Holy Kaaba . . . . 1·10 1·10

126 Homes (Arab Housing Day) 127 Covered Vessel

1994. Anniversaries and Events. Multicoloured.
453 1d. Type **126** 55 55
454 1d. Children playing and couple (International Year of the Family) (horiz) . . . 55 55
455 1d. National Olympic Committee emblem, rings and sports (cent of Int Olympic Committee) (horiz) 55 55
456 1d. Paper, pen-nib and dove (10th anniv of Emirates Writers' Association) . . . 55 55

1994. Archaeological Finds from Al-Qusais, Dubai. Multicoloured.
457 50f. Type **127** 25 25
458 1d. Jug (horiz) 55 55
459 175f. Jug (different) (horiz) . . 95 95
460 250f. Bowl (horiz) . . . . . 1·25 1·25

128 Arabian Leopard

1994. Environmental Protection. The Cat Family. Multicoloured.
461 50f. Type **128** 30 30
462 1d. Gordon's wildcat 60 60
463 2d. Caracal . . . . 1·25 1·25
464 250f. Sandcat . . . . 1·75 1·75

129 Little Green Bee Eaters

1994. Birds. Multicoloured.
465 50f. Type **129** 50 50
466 175f. White-collared kingfishers . . . . 1·60 1·60
467 2d. Crab plovers . . . . . . 1·75 1·25
468 250f. Indian rollers . . . . . 2·75 1·75

130 Championship Emblem 131 Horse's Head

1994. 12th Arab Gulf Football Championship, Abu Dhabi. Multicoloured.
470 50f. Type **130** 25 25
471 3d. Match scene (horiz) . . . 1·60 1·60

1995. Archaeological Finds from Mulaiha, Sharjah. Multicoloured.
472 50f. Type **131** 25 25
473 175f. Coin 95 95
474 2d. Ancient writing on leather 1·10 1·10
475 250f. Stone tablet (horiz) . . 1·25 1·25

132 Al-Naashat

1995. National Dances. Multicoloured.
476 50f. Type **132** 25 25
477 175f. Al-Ayaalah 95 95
478 2d. Al-Shahhoh . . . . . . 1·10 1·10

133 Helicopters 134 Arab League

1995. International Defence Exhibition and Conference, Abu Dhabi. Multicoloured.
479 50f. Type **133** 25 25
480 1d. Exhibition emblem . . . 50 50
481 175f. Missile corvettes (horiz) 90 90
482 2d. Artillery (horiz) . . . . . 1·00 1·00

1995. 50th Anniversaries. Anniversary Emblems. Multicoloured.
483 1d. Type **134** 50 50
484 2d. F.A.O. . . . . 1·00 1·00
485 250f. U.N.O. . . . . 1·25 1·25

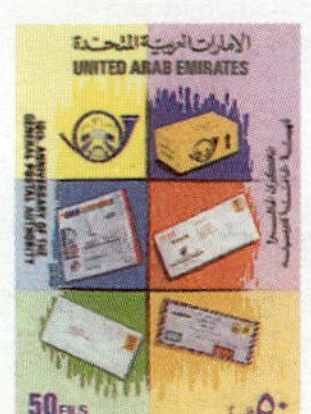

135 Symbols of Postal Services

1995. 10th Anniv of General Postal Authority.
486 **135** 50f. multicoloured 20 20

136 Exhibition Emblem

1995. 1st Gulf Co-operation Council Stamp Exhibition, Abu Dhabi.
487 **136** 50f. multicoloured 20 20

137 Bowling Hoop

138 Lesser Kestrel

1995. National Games. Multicoloured.
488 50f. Type **137** 20 20
489 175f. Swinging 65 65
490 2d. Sticks in stone square game 75 75
491 250f. Stone game 95 95

1995. Birds. Multicoloured.
492 50f. Type **138** 20 20
493 175f. Socotra cormorant . . 75 75
494 2d. Cream-coloured courser 90 90
495 250f. Hoopoe . . . . 1·10 1·10

139 Figures and Tower Block

1995. Population and Housing Census. Mult.
496 50f. Type **139** 15 15
497 250f. City and stylized family 85 85

140 "Folklore Show" (Ibtisam Mussa)

1995. National Day. Children's Paintings. Multicoloured.
498 50f. Type **140** 15 15
499 175f. "Children dancing" (Shimaa Mohamed Abdullah Khoury) 60 60
500 2d. "Children holding balloons" (Khoula Ibrahim) 70 70
501 250f. "Car festival" (Fatima Jumaa) 85 85

141 Dugongs

1996. Environmental Protection. Sea Mammals. Multicoloured.
502 50f. Type **141** 20 15
503 2d. Common dolphins . . . 70 70
504 3d. Humpback whales . . . 1·00 1·00

142 Competitor

143 Earthenware Urn (Bathna-Fujaira)

1996. Hobie Cat 16 World Championships. Mult.
506 50f. Type **142** 15 15
507 3d. Hobie 1b catamaran and building . . . . 1·00 1·00

1996. Archaeological Finds. Multicoloured.
508 50f. Type **143** 15 15
509 175f. Earthenware pot with handles (Bidya-Fujaira) . . 60 60
510 250f. Bronze bangle (Qidfa-Fujaira) 85 85
511 3d. Bronze ring (Dibba-Fujaira) (horiz) . . . . . 1·00 1·00

144 Shooting

1996. Olympic Games, Atlanta. Multicoloured.
512 50f. Type **144** 15 15
513 1d. Cycling (vert) 35 35
514 250f. Running (vert) 85 85
515 350f. Swimming . . . . . . 1·25 1·25

145 Emblem

146 Emblem, Landmarks and Players

1996. 21st Anniv of Women's Union. Multicoloured.
516 50f. Type **145** 15 15
517 3d. Woman's hands and emblem (horiz) . . . . . . 1·00 1·00

1996. 11th Asian Football Cup Championship. Multicoloured.
518 1d. Type **146** 35 35
519 250f. Player with ball 85 85

147 "Drug" Snake crushing weeping Globe

1996. Anti-drugs Campaign. Multicoloured.
520 50f. Type **147** 15 15
521 3d. Healthy man and drug-wrecked skull . . . . . . 1·00 1·00

148 Shaikh Said and House

1996. Centenary of Shaikh Said al Maktoum House (museum). Multicoloured.
522 50f. Type **148** 15 15
523 250f. Shaikh Said and close-up view of House 85 85
524 350f. House at sunset . . . . 1·25 1·25

149 Chestnut-bellied Sandgrouse

150 Head forming Waterfall (Abdullah Muhammed Abdullah al-Sharhan)

1996. Birds. Multicoloured.
525 50f. Type **149** 15 15
526 150f. Striated scops owl . . . 50 50
527 250f. Grey hypocolius . . . 85 85
528 3d. White-throated robin . . 1·00 1·00
529 350f. Sooty falcon . . . . . 1·25 1·25

1996. Children's Paintings. Multicoloured.
530 50f. Type **150** 15 15
531 1d. Dhows (Hamda Muhammed Abdullah) (horiz) 35 35
532 250f. Flowers (Hind Muhammed bin Dhahi) . . 85 85
533 350f. Girl and tent (Lin Atta Yaghi) . . . . 1·25 1·25

151 Emirates Rulers

152 U.A.E. Crest

153 Shaikh and Trees

1996. 25th National Day. Multicoloured.
534 50f. Type **151** 15 15
535 1d. Emirates crest and flag 35 35
536 150f. Type **151** 50 50
537 3d. As No. 535 . . . . . . 1·00 1·00

1996. 30th Anniv of Accession of Shaikh Zaid ibn Sultan al Nahayyan of Abu Dhabi and 25th Anniv of United Arab Emirates. (a) Type **152**.
539 **152** 50f. multicoloured 15 15
540 1d. multicoloured 35 35

(b) As T **153**. Multicoloured.
541 50f. Type **153** 15 15
542 1d. Shaikh and dates 35 35
543 250f. Type **153** 85 85
544 350f. As No. 542 . . . . . . 1·10 1·10

154 Loew's Blue

1997. Butterflies. Multicoloured.
546 50f. Type **154** 15 15
547 1d. Swallowtail 35 35
548 150f. Blue argus 50 50
549 250f. African monarch . . . 85 85

155 Festival Poster

1997. Shopping Festival, Dubai. Multicoloured.
550 50f. Type **155** 15 15
551 250f. Emblem (vert) 85 85

156 Helicopter lifting Vehicle

157 Sky and Anniversary Emblem

1997. International Defence Exhibition and Conference, Abu Dhabi. Multicoloured.
552 50f. Type **156** 15 15
553 1d. Exhibition emblem . . . 35 35
554 250f. Weapons demonstration 85 85
555 350f. Frigates and submarine 1·10 1·10

1997. 20th Anniv of Emirates Bank Group. Multicoloured.
556 50f. Type **157** 15 15
557 1d. Anniversary emblem . . 35 35

158 "TEND" and Emblem

160 Stamps and Magnifying Glass

159 Silver Coins spilling from Pot

1997. Technological, Education and National Development. Multicoloured.
559 50f. Type **158** 15 15
560 250f. Emblem 85 85

1997. Sharjah Heritage. Multicoloured.
561 50f. Type **159** 15 15
562 3d. Courtyard and minarets 1·00 1·00

1997. Emirates Philatelic Association. Multicoloured.
563 50f. Type **160** 15 15
564 250f. Magnifying glass, tweezers and "river" of stamps (horiz) 75 75

161 Cats and Kittens

1997. Children's Paintings. Multicoloured.
565 50f. Type **161** 15 15
566 1d. Fashion parade 35 35
567 250f. Group of children (vert) 85 85
568 3d. Abstract . . . . 1·00 1·00

162 Cliffs

1997. Fine Arts. Multicoloured.
569 50f. Type **162** 15 15
570 50f. Still-life (vert) 15 15
571 50f. Modern painting in blues and yellows 15 15
572 50f. Couple (vert) 15 15
573 50f. Waterfall and rocks . . 15 15
574 50f. Coral hind (fish) (vert) 15 15

163 Jet Fighter over Airport

1997. International Aerospace Exhibition, Dubai. Multicoloured.
576 250f. Type **163** 85 85
577 3d. Buildings, airplane and oil rig . . . . 1·00 1·00

164 Park

1997. 26th National Day. Environmental Protection. Multicoloured.
578 50f. Type **164** 15 15
579 1d. Mountains and forest . . 35 35
580 150f. Mountains and river . . 50 50
581 250f. Landscaped road verge 85 85

165 Emblems and Venue

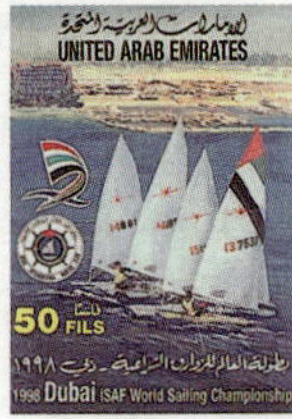

167 Laser Dinghies

166 "Blepharopsis mendica" (praying mantis)

1997. 3rd Afro–Arab Trade Fair, Sharjah. Mult.
582 150f. Type **165** 50 50
583 350f. Organization of African Unity and Arab League emblems' handclasp over Fair emblem (horiz) . . . 1·10 1·10

1998. Insects. Multicoloured.
584 50f. Type **166** 15 15
585 150f. "Galeodes" sp. (spider) 50 50
586 250f. "Crocothemis arythraea" (darter) 85 85
587 350f. "Xylocopa aestuans" (carpenter bee) . . . . . . 1·10 1·10

1998. World Sailing Championships, Dubai. Multicoloured.
588 50f. Type **167** 15 15
589 1d. Racing yachts (horiz) . . 35 35
590 250f. High-performance 2-man dinghies (horiz) . . . 85 85
591 3d. Catamarans . . . . . . 1·00 1·00

168 Military Personnel

1998. Triple International Defence Exhibition and Conference, Abu Dhabi. Multicoloured.
592 50f. Type **168** 15 15
593 1d. Exhibition emblem and city (vert) 35 35
594 150f. Radar equipment (vert) 50 50
595 350f. Rocket launcher and communications equipment (vert) . . . . 1·10 1·10

169 Emblem and City Landmarks

170 Oryx on Hillside

1998. Sharjah, Arab Cultural Capital. Multicoloured.
596 50f. Type **169** 15 15
597 3d. Emblem and tower . . . 1·00 1·00

1998. Protection of the Environment. Multicoloured.
598 1d. Type **170** 35 35
599 350f. Palm tree and sun . . . 1·10 1·10

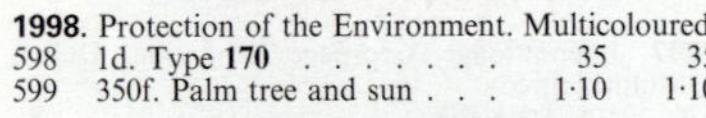

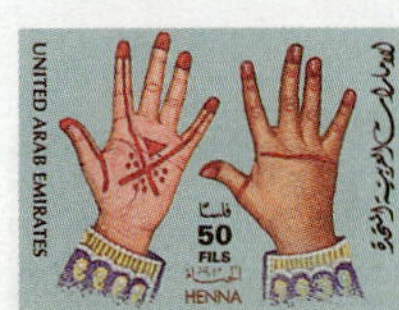

171 Decorated Hands

1998. Henna.
600 **171** 50f. multicoloured 15 15
601 – 1d. multicoloured 35 35
602 – 150f. multicoloured . . . 50 50
603 – 2d. multicoloured 65 65
604 – 250f. multicoloured . . . 85 85
605 – 3d. multicoloured . . . . 1·00 1·00
DESIGNS: 1d. to 3d. Different hand decorations.

172 Underwater Scene (Rashid al Shayaa)

1998. Paintings. Multicoloured.
606 50f. Type **172** 15 15
607 1d. Woman and cradle (Nadia Othman al Baroot) 35 35
608 250f. Village scene (Mahmoud Hassan) (vert) 85 85
609 350f. Rural still life (Shaikha Saeed) . . . . 1·10 1·10

173 Mountain Road

1998. 27th National Day. Tourism. Multicoloured.
610 50f. Type **173** 15 15
611 350f. Dubai Harbour . . . . 1·10 1·10

174 "Indigofera arabica"

1998. Wild Flowers. Multicoloured.
612 25f. Type **174** 10 10
613 50f. "Centaureum pulchellum" 15 15
614 75f. "Lavandula citriodora" 25 25
615 1d. "Taverniera glabra" . . . 35 35
616 150f. "Convolvulus deserti" 50 50
617 2d. "Capparis spinosa" . . . 65 65
618 250f. "Rumex vesicrius" . . 85 85
619 3d. "Anagallis arvensis" . . . 1·00 1·00
620 350f. "Tribulus arabicus" . . 1·10 1·10
621 5d. "Reichardia tinitana" . . 1·60 1·60

175 "Anthia duodecimguttata" (ground beetle)

177 U.P.U. Emblem

176 Emblem

1999. Insects and Arachnids. Multicoloured.
622 50f. Type **175** 15 15
623 150f. Oleander hawk moth 50 50
624 250f. "Acorypha glaucopsis" 85 85
625 350f. "Androctonus crassicauda" . . . . 1·10 1·10

1999. International Monuments Day. Multicoloured.
626 150f. Type **176** 50 50
627 250f. Al Faheidi fort, Dubai 85 85

1999. 125th Anniv of Universal Postal Union. Mult.
628 50f. Type **177** 15 15
629 350f. U.P.U. emblem and "125" . . . . 1·25 1·25

178 Jellyfish

1999. Protection of the Environment. Multicoloured.
631 50f. Feather star 15 15
632 150f. Type **178** 50 50
633 250f. Spanish dancer 85 85
634 3d. Sponge . . . . 1·00 1·00

179 Woman braiding

180 Championship Emblem

1999. Crafts. Multicoloured.
635 50f. Type **179** 15 15
636 1d. Braided trousers 35 35
637 250f. Weaving palm leaves 85 85
638 350f. Woven palm leaf products . . . . 1·25 1·25

1999. 14th World Tenpin Bowling Championship, Abu Dhabi. Multicoloured.
639 50f. Type **180** 15 15
640 250f. Competitor 85 85

181 Couple outside House

1999. Children's Paintings. Multicoloured.
641 50f. Type **181** 15 15
642 1d. Pattern 35 35
643 150f. Underwater scene . . . 50 50
644 250f. Family having picnic 85 85

182 "2000" and Dove

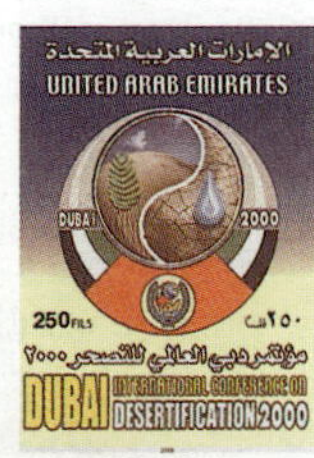

184 Conference Emblem

183 Dubai Port

1999. Year 2000.
645 **182** 50f. black and silver . . . 15 15
646 – 250f. blue and gold . . . 85 85
DESIGN: 250f. "2000" and dove (different).

2000. Centenary of Dubai Ports and Customs. Multicoloured.
647 50f. Type **183** 15 15
648 3d. Dubai Customs House . . 1·00 1·00

2000. Int Conference on Desertification, Dubai.
649 **184** 250f. multicoloured . . . 85 85

185 River

2000. Environmental Protection. Multicoloured.
650 50f. Type **185** 20 20
651 250f. Beach 85 85

186 Swimming

2000. Olympic Games, Sydney. Multicoloured.
652 50f. Type **186** 10 10
653 2d. Athletics 65 65
654 350f. Shooting . . . . 1·25 1·25

187 Ribbon and Award

188 Map of United Arab Emirates and Barometer

2000. International Holy Koran Award. Mult.
655 50f. Type **187** 20 20
656 250f. Pres. Shaikh Zaid ibn Sultan al Nahayyan (recipient of award) 85 85

2000. 50th Anniv of World Meteorological Organization. Multicoloured.
657 50f. Type **188** 20 20
658 250f. Old map of Gulf region and sun dial 85 85

189 Airplanes

2000. Expansion of Dubai International Airport.
659 **189** 50f. multicoloured 20 20
660 350f. multicoloured . . . 1·25 1·25

190 White Crescent forming Smile

2001. Development and Environment.
661 **190** 50f. green 20 20
662 – 2d.50 green and deep green 95 95
663 – 3d. green, light green and deep green . . . . . . 1·10 1·10
664 – 3d.50 light green, green and deep green . . . . 1·25 1·25
DESIGNS: 250f. White flower casting shadow; 3d. Heart-shaped leaf; 350f. Heart-shaped world map.

UNITED NATIONS Pt. 22; Pt. 8; Pt. 2

A. NEW YORK HEADQUARTERS

For use on mail posted at the Post Office at U.N. Headquarters, New York.

NOTE: Similar designs, but in different colours and values in Swiss Francs (F.S.) are issues of the Geneva office. Those with face values in Austrian Schillings are issues of the Vienna office. These are listed after the New York issues.

100 cents = 1 dollar.

1 "Peoples of the World"

3 U.N. Emblem

1951.
1 **1** 1c. mauve 10 15
2 – 1½c. green 10 15
3 **3** 2c. violet 10 15
4 – 3c. blue and purple 10 15
5 – 5c. blue 10 15
6 **1** 10c. brown 10 15
7 – 15c. blue and violet 10 20
8 – 20c. brown 30 30
9 – 25c. blue and black 30 30
10 – 50c. blue . . . . 2·30 2·00
11 **3** $1 red . . . . 1·20 85
DESIGNS—VERT: 1½, 50c. U.N. Headquarters, New York; 5c. Clasped hands. HORIZ: 3, 15, 25c. U.N. flag; 20c. Hemispheres and U.N. emblem.

A 7 Seagull and Airplane

1951. Air.
A12 A 7 6c. red 10 10
A13 10c. green 10 10
A14 – 15c. blue 10 10
A15 – 25c. black 10 10
DESIGN: 15, 25c. Swallows and U.N. emblem.

7 Veterans' War Memorial Building, San Francisco

1952. 7th Anniv of Signing of U.N. Charter.
12 7 5c. blue 15 15

8 "Flame of Freedom"

1952. Human Rights Day.
13 8 3c. green 10 10
14 5c. blue 15 15

9 Homeless Family

1953. Protection for Refugees.
15 9 3c. brown 10 10
16 5c. blue 20 20

10 "Universal Postal Union"

1953. Universal Postal Union.
17 10 3c. sepia 15 20
18 5c. blue 40 40

11 Gearwheels and U.N. Emblem

12 "Flame of Freedom"

1953. Technical Assistance for Underdeveloped Areas.
19 11 3c. grey 10 15
20 5c. green 20 20

1953. Human Rights Day.
21 12 3c. blue 15 10
22 5c. red 70 30

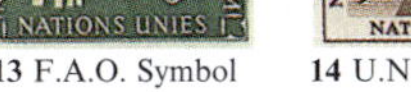

13 F.A.O. Symbol

14 U.N. Emblem and Anvil

1954. Food and Agriculture Organization.
23 13 3c. yellow and green 25 15
24 8c. yellow and blue 60 35

NOTE. In the following issues the majority of the values unillustrated have the commemorative inscription or initials in another language.

1954. International Labour Organization.
25 14 3c. brown 15 15
26 8c. mauve 90 45

15 U.N. European Office, Geneva

16 Mother and Child

1954. United Nations Day.
27 15 3c. violet . . . . 1·60 85
28 8c. red 20 15

1954. Human Rights Day.
29 16 3c. orange . . . . 5·50 1·60
30 8c. green 15 20

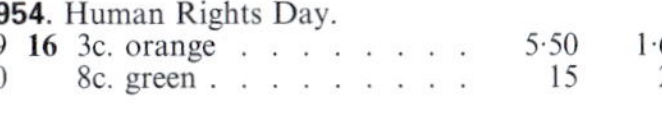

17 "Flight"

1955. International Civil Aviation Organization.
31 17 3c. blue . . . . 1·30 50
32 8c. red 50 80

18 U.N.E.S.C.O. Symbol

1955. U.N. Educational, Scientific and Cultural Organization.
33 18 3c. mauve 10 15
34 8c. blue 15 15

19 U.N. Charter

20 "Flame of Freedom"

1955. 10th Anniv of U.N.
35 19 3c. red 70 40
36 4c. green 25 10
37 8c. black 15 20

1955. Human Rights Day.
39 20 3c. blue 10 15
40 8c. green 20 20

21 "Telecommunication"

22 Staff of Aesculapius

1956. International Telecommunication Union.
41 21 3c. blue 10 15
42 8c. red 20 25

1956. World Health Organization.
43 22 3c. blue 10 15
44 8c. brown 20 25

23 General Assembly

1956. United Nations Day.
45 23 3c. slate 10 10
46 8c. olive 10 10

24 "Flame of Freedom"

25 Weather Balloon

1956. Human Rights Day.
47 24 3c. purple 10 10
48 8c. blue 10 10

1957. World Meteorological Organization.
49 25 3c. blue 10 10
50 8c. red 10 10

26 U.N.E.F. Badge

A 26 "Flight"

1957. United Nations Emergency Force.
51 26 3c. blue 05 10
52 8c. red 10 05

1957. Air.
A51 A 26 4c. brown 15 15
A52 5c. red 15 15
A53 – 7c. blue 15 15
DESIGNS—HORIZ: 7c. U.N. flag and Douglas DC-8-60 airplane.
On the 5c. value inscriptions are redrawn larger than those on Type A **26**.

27 U.N. Emblem over Globe

28 "Flames of Freedom"

1957. U.N. Security Council.
55 27 3c. brown 10 10
56 8c. green 10 10

1957. Human Rights Day.
57 28 3c. brown 10 10
58 8c. black 10 10

29 Atomic Symbol

30 Central Hall, Westminster (site of first General Assembly)

1958. International Atomic Energy Agency.
59 29 3c. olive 10 10
60 8c. blue 15 10

1958. U.N. General Assembly Buildings.
61 30 3c. blue 10 10
62 8c. purple 10 10
See also Nos. 69/70, 77/8 and 123/4.

31 U.N. Seal

32 Cogwheels

1958.
63 31 4c. orange 10 10
64 8c. blue 10 10

1958. Economic and Social Council.
65 32 4c. turquoise 10 10
66 8c. red 15 10

33 Hands holding Globe

1958. Human Rights Day.
67 33 4c. green 10 10
68 8c. brown 15 10

34 New York City Building, Flushing Meadows (1946–50)

35 Emblems of U.N. Industry and Agriculture

1959. U.N. General Assembly Buildings.
69 34 4c. mauve 10 10
70 8c. turquoise 10 10

1959. U.N. Economic Commission for Europe.
71 35 4c. blue 10 10
72 8c. red 25 15

36 "The Age of Bronze" (Rodin)

37 "Protection for Refugees"

1959. U.N. Trusteeship Council.
73 36 4c. red 10 10
74 8c. green 25 15

1959. World Refugee Year.
75 37 4c. red and bistre 10 10
76 8c. blue and bistre 15 10

38 Palais de Chaillot, Paris (1948, 1951)

1960. U.N. General Assembly Buildings.
77 38 4c. blue and purple 10 10
78 8c. brown and green 25 10

39 Steel Girder and Map

1960. U.N. Economic Commission for Asia and the Far East ("ECAFE").
79 39 4c. purple, buff and turquoise 10 10
80 8c. green, pink and blue . . 20 15

40 Tree and Emblems

41 U.N. Headquarters and Emblem

1960. 5th World Forestry Congress, Seattle.
81 **40** 4c. multicoloured 10 05
82 8c. multicoloured 05 10

1960. 15th Anniv of U.N.
83 **41** 4c. blue 10 05
84 8c. black 20 05

42 Double Block and Hook

43 Scales of Justice

1960. International Bank for Reconstruction and Development ("World Bank").
86 **42** 4c. multicoloured 10 05
87 8c. multicoloured 15 05

1961. International Court of Justice.
88 **43** 4c. black, brown and yellow 15 05
89 8c. black, green and yellow 15 05

44 I.M.F. Emblem

1961. International Monetary Fund.
90 **44** 4c. blue 20 15
91 7c. brown and yellow . . . 20 10

45 "Peace"

53 Globe and Weather Vane

52 Flags

1961.
92 **45** 1c. multicoloured 10 05
93 – 2c. multicoloured 15 15
94 – 3c. multicoloured 10 05
95 – 5c. red 10 05
96 – 7c. brown, black and blue 20 15
97 – 10c. black, green and blue 25 15
98 – 11c. gold, light blue and blue 20 05
99 **52** 30c. multicoloured 35 30
100 **53** 50c. multicoloured 95 40
DESIGNS—HORIZ: 32×23 mm: 2c. Map of the World; 10c. Three figures on globe ("Races United"). 30½×23½ mm: 3c. U.N. Flag. 36½×23½ mm: 5c. Hands supporting "UN" and globe. 37½×22½ mm: 11c. U.N. emblem across globe. VERT—21×26 mm: 7c. U.N. emblem as flowering plant.
For 1c. in same design, but smaller, see No. 146 and for 5c. multicoloured see No. 165.

54 Cogwheel and Map of S. America

55 Africa Hall, Addis Ababa

1961. Economic Commission for Latin America.
101 **54** 4c. red, olive and blue . . 10 10
102 11c. purple, red and green 20 15

1961. Economic Commission for Africa.
103 **55** 4c. multicoloured 10 10
104 11c. multicoloured 15 10

56 Bird feeding Young

57 "Housing and Community Facilities"

1961. 15th Anniv of U.N.I.C.E.F.
105 **56** 3c. multicoloured 10 05
106 4c. multicoloured 10 05
107 13c. multicoloured 15 10

1962. U.N. Housing and Related Community Facilities Programme.
108 **57** 4c. multicoloured 15 10
109 7c. multicoloured 15 10

58 Mosquito and W.H.O. Emblem

59 U.N. Flag at Half-mast

1962. Malaria Eradication.
110 **58** 4c. multicoloured 10 10
111 11c. multicoloured 25 10

1962. Dag Hammarskjold (U.N. Secretary-General, 1953–61) Memorial Issue.
112 **59** 5c. indigo, blue and black 10 10
113 15c. blue, grey and black 20 20

60 Congo on World Map

61 "Peace in Space"

1962. U.N. Congo Operation.
114 **60** 4c. multicoloured 15 10
115 11c. multicoloured 15 10

1962. U.N. Committee on Peaceful Uses of Outer Space.
116 **61** 4c. blue 10 05
117 11c. mauve 25 10

62 Conference Emblem

63 Wheat

1963. Science and Technology Conf, Geneva.
118 **62** 5c. multicoloured 10 10
119 11c. multicoloured 25 10

1963. Freedom from Hunger.
120 **63** 5c. yellow, green and orange 10 05
121 11c. yellow, red and orange 25 10

A 65 "Flight"

64 "Bridge" over Map of West New Guinea

1963. Air. Multicoloured.
A122 6c. "Space" 35 30
A123 8c. Type A **65** 10 05
A124 13c. "Bird" 20 15
A125 15c. "Birds in Flight" . . . 10 10
A126 25c. Douglas DC-8 and airmail envelope 20 10

SIZES—HORIZ: 6c. As Type A **65**; 13, 25c. 30½×23 mm. VERT: 15c. 23×30½ mm.

1963. United Nations Temporary Executive Authority (UNTEA) in West New Guinea.
122 **64** 25c. green, blue and drab 40 25

65 General Assembly Building and Flags

66 "Flame of Freedom"

1963. U.N. General Assembly Buildings.
123 **65** 5c. multicoloured 10 10
124 11c. multicoloured 20 15

1963. 15th Anniv of Declaration of Human Rights.
125 **66** 5c. multicoloured 10 10
126 11c. multicoloured 20 15

67 Ships at Sea

1964. Inter-Governmental Maritime Consultative Organization (I.M.C.O.).
127 **67** 5c. multicoloured 15 15
128 11c. multicoloured 30 25

68 "Trade and Development"

1964. U.N. Trade and Development Conf, Geneva.
129 **68** 5c. yellow, black and red 15 15
130 11c. yellow, black and bistre 15 15

69 Opium Poppy and Reaching Hands

70 Atomic Explosion and Padlock

1964. Narcotics Control.
131 **69** 5c. red and black 15 15
132 11c. green and black . . . 50 35

1964. Cessation of Nuclear Testing.
133 **70** 5c. sepia and brown . . . 15 15

71 "Teaching"

72 Key, Globe and "Graph"

1964. "Education for Progress".
134 **71** 4c. multicoloured 15 15
135 5c. multicoloured 15 20
136 11c. multicoloured 15 15

1965. U.N. Special Fund.
137 **72** 5c. multicoloured 15 15
138 11c. multicoloured 15 20

73 Cyprus "Leaves" and U.N. Emblem

74 "From Semaphore to Satellite"

1965. Peace-keeping Force in Cyprus.
139 **73** 5c. olive, black and orange 10 15
140 11c. green, black & lt green 15 15

1965. I.T.U. Centenary.
141 **74** 5c. multicoloured 15 10
142 11c. multicoloured 25 20

75 I.C.Y. Emblem

76 "Peace"

1965. 20th Anniv of United Nations and International Co-operation Year.
143 **75** 5c. blue 25 15
144 15c. mauve 25 30

1965.
146 **76** 1c. multicoloured 10 10
147 – 15c. multicoloured 25 10
148 – 20c. multicoloured 30 15
149 – 25c. ultramarine and blue 45 15
150 – $1 blue and turquoise . . . 2·00 1·30
DESIGNS—24½×30 mm: 15c. Opening words, U.N. Charter. 22×32 mm: 20c. U.N. emblem and Headquarters. 24×24 mm: 25c. U.N. emblem. 33×23 mm: $1 U.N. emblem encircled.

81 "Expanding Population"

82 Globe and Flags

1965. Population Trends and Development.
151 **81** 4c. multicoloured 10 10
152 5c. multicoloured 10 10
153 11c. multicoloured 20 20

1966. World Federation of United Nations Assns. (W.F.U.N.A.).
154 **82** 5c. multicoloured 10 10
155 15c. multicoloured 20 20

83 W.H.O. Building

1966. Inaug of W.H.O. Headquarters, Geneva.
156 **83** 5c. multicoloured 10 10
157 11c. multicoloured 20 20

84 Coffee

1966. International Coffee Agreement of 1962.
158 **84** 5c. multicoloured 10 10
159 11c. multicoloured 20 20

85 Military Observer

86 Children in Closed Railway Wagon

1966. U.N. Military Observers.
160 **85** 15c. multicoloured 25 25

1966. 20th Anniv of U.N.I.C.E.F. Multicoloured.
161 4c. Type **86** 10 10
162 5c. Children in locomotive and tender 20 10
163 11c. Children in open railway wagon 40 20

89 U.N. Headquarters and World Map

91 "UN" and Emblem

1967.

164 **89** 1½c. multicoloured 10 10
165 – 5c. multicoloured 15 10
166 – 6c. multicoloured 15 10
167 **91** 13c. blue, gold and black 25 15

DESIGNS—HORIZ: 5c. As No. 95. 23 × 34 mm: 6c. Aerial view of U.N. Headquarters.

92 "Progress through Development"

93 U.N. Emblem and Fireworks

1967. U.N. Development Programme.

168 **92** 5c. multicoloured 10 10
169 11c. multicoloured 20 10

1967. New Independent Nations Commem.

170 **93** 5c. multicoloured 10 10
171 11c. multicoloured 20 15

94 "Peace"

99 Baggage Labels

1967. "Expo 67", World Fair, Montreal.

172 **94** 4c. brown and red 10 10
173 – 5c. brown and blue 10 10
174 – 8c. multicoloured 15 10
175 – 10c. brown and green . . . 15 10
176 – 15c. chestnut and brown 20 25

DESIGNS—VERT: 5c. "Justice"; 10c. "Fraternity"; 15c. "Truth". HORIZ (32 × 23½ mm): 8c. Facade of U.N. Pavilion.

The above stamps are expressed in Canadian currency and were valid for postage only from the U.N. Pavilion at the World Fair.

1967. International Tourist Year.

177 **99** 5c. multicoloured 20 10
178 15c. multicoloured 65 20

100 "Towards Disarmament"

101 "The Kiss of Peace" (part of Chagall's stained glass window)

1967. Disarmament Campaign.

179 **100** 6c. multicoloured 10 10
180 13c. multicoloured 20 15

1967. United Nations Art (1st issue). Chagall's Memorial Window in U.N. Secretariat Building.

181 **101** 6c. multicoloured 15 15

See also Nos. 185/6, 201/2, 203/4, 236/7 and 251/2.

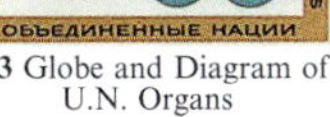

103 Globe and Diagram of U.N. Organs

104 Starcke's Statue

1968. U.N. Secretariat.

183 **103** 6c. multicoloured 15 15
184 13c. multicoloured 20 15

1968. United Nations Art (2nd issue). Henrik Starcke's Statue in U.N. Trusteeship Council Chamber.

185 **104** 6c. multicoloured 15 15
186 75c. multicoloured . . . . 1·20 75

105 Industrial Skyline

1968. U.N. Industrial Development Organization (U.N.I.D.O.).

187 **105** 6c. multicoloured 15 15
188 13c. multicoloured 15 15

A **106** "Winged Envelopes"

A **107** Aircraft and U.N. Emblem

1968. Air.

A189 A **106** 10c. multicoloured . . 15 15
A190 A **107** 20c. multicoloured . . 25 15

106 Radar Scanner

1968. World Weather Watch.

189 **106** 6c. multicoloured 15 10
190 20c. multicoloured 30 20

107 Human Rights Emblem

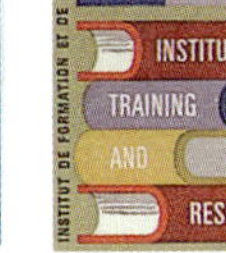

108 Textbooks

1968. Human Rights Year.

191 **107** 6c. gold, ultramarine & bl 15 15
192 13c. gold, red and pink 20 15

1969. United Nations Institute for Training and Research (U.N.I.T.A.R.).

193 **108** 6c. multicoloured 15 10
194 13c. multicoloured 20 15

In the 13c. the name and value panel is at foot of stamp.

109 U.N. Building, Santiago

1969. U.N. Building, Santiago, Chile.

195 **109** 6c. blue, light blue & green 15 15
196 15c. purple, red and buff 20 15

110 "Peace Through International Law"

1969. 20th Anniv of Session of U.N. Int Law Commission.

197 **110** 6c. multicoloured 15 15
198 13c. multicoloured 20 15

111 "Labour and Development"

1969. 50th Anniv of I.L.O.

199 **111** 6c. multicoloured 15 15
200 20c. multicoloured 15 15

112 "Ostrich"

114 Peace Bell

1969. United Nations Art (3rd issue). 3rd-century A.D. Tunisian Mosaic, Delegates' North Lounge. Multicoloured.

201 6c. Type **112** 15 15
202 13c. "Ring-necked Pheasant" 15 15

1970. United Nations Art (4th issue). Japanese Peace Bell.

203 **114** 6c. multicoloured 15 15
204 25c. multicoloured 30 20

115 River, Power Lines and Map

1970. Lower Mekong Basin Development Project.

205 **115** 6c. multicoloured 15 15
206 13c. multicoloured 15 15

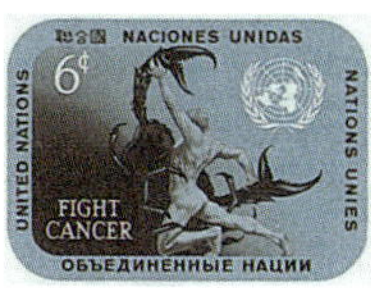

116 "Fight Cancer"

1970. 10th Int Cancer Congress, Houston, Texas.

207 **116** 6c. black and blue 15 15
208 13c. black and olive . . . 15 15

117 Laurel Branch

120 Scales and Olive-branch

1970. 25th Anniv of United Nations.

209 **117** 6c. multicoloured 15 15
210 13c. multicoloured 15 15
211 – 25c. gold, light blue & blue 30 25

DESIGN—VERT: 25c. U.N. emblem.

On No. 210 the inscription is in French.

1970. "Peace, Justice and Progress" (Aims of the United Nations).

213 **120** 6c. multicoloured 15 15
214 13c. multicoloured 15 15

121 U.N. Emblem on Sea-bed

122 "Refugees" (sculpture, Kaare Nygaard)

1971. Peaceful Uses of the Sea-bed.

215 **121** 6c. multicoloured 10 10

1971. U.N. Work with Refugees.

216 **122** 6c. black, yellow & brown 15 15
217 13c. black, turq & blue 15 15

123 Wheatsheaf on Globe

124 New U.P.U. H.Q. Building

1971. World Food Programme.

218 **123** 13c. multicoloured 15 15

1971. Opening of New U.P.U. Headquarters Building, Berne.

219 **124** 20c. multicoloured 20 20

125 Four-leafed Clover

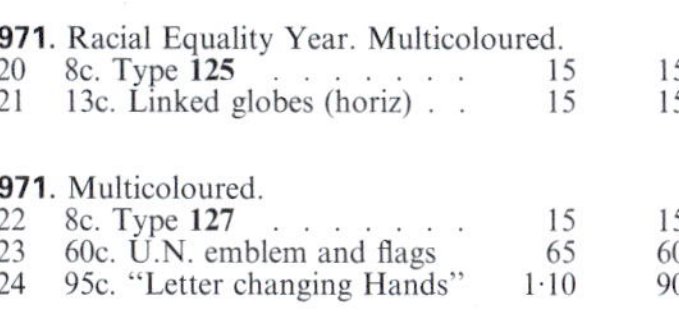

127 U.N. H.Q., New York

1971. Racial Equality Year. Multicoloured.

220 8c. Type **125** 15 15
221 13c. Linked globes (horiz) . . 15 15

1971. Multicoloured.

222 8c. Type **127** 15 15
223 60c. U.N. emblem and flags 65 60
224 95c. "Letter changing Hands" 1·10 90

130 "Maia" (Picasso)

131 "X" over Atomic Explosion

1971. U.N. International Schools.

225 **130** 8c. multicoloured 15 15
226 21c. multicoloured 25 15

1972. Non-proliferation of Nuclear Weapons.

227 **131** 8c. blue, black and pink 10 10

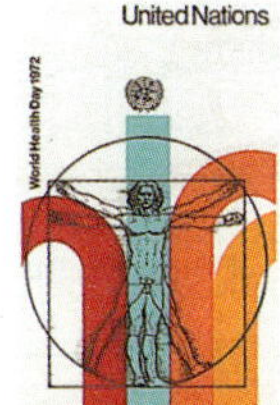

132 "Proportions of Man" (Leonardo da Vinci)

A 134 Birds in Flight

1972. World Health Day.

228 **132** 15c. multicoloured 20 15

1972. Air.

A229 – 9c. multicoloured . . 15 15
A230 A **134** 11c. multicoloured . . 15 15
A231 – 17c. orange, yellow and red 25 15
A232 – 21c. multicoloured . . 35 20

DESIGNS—23 × 31 mm: 9c. "Contemporary Flight". 38 × 23 mm: 17c. Clouds. 33 × 23 mm: 21c. "U.N." jetstream.

137 Environmental Emblem

138 Europe "Flower"

1972. U.N. Environmental Conservation Conf, Stockholm.

233 **137** 8c. multicoloured 15 15
234 15c. multicoloured 20 15

1972. Economic Commission for Europe (E.C.E.).

235 **138** 21c. multicoloured 35 25

139 "World United" (detail, Sert mural, Geneva)

140 Laurel and Broken Sword

1972. United Nations Art (5th issue).
236 **139** 8c. brown, gold & lt brown 15 15
237 15c. brown, gold and green 25 15

1973. Disarmament Decade.
238 **140** 8c. multicoloured 15 15
239 15c. multicoloured 30 25

141 Skull on Poppy

142 Emblems within Honeycomb

1973. "Stop Drug Abuse" Campaign.
240 **141** 8c. multicoloured 15 15
241 15c. multicoloured 30 25

1973. U.N. Volunteers Programme.
242 **142** 8c. multicoloured 15 15
243 21c. multicoloured 30 25

143 Namibia on Map of Africa

1973. U.N. Resolution on Namibia (South West Africa).
244 **143** 8c. multicoloured 15 15
245 15c. multicoloured 30 25

144 Human Rights Flame

1973. 25th Anniv of Declaration of Human Rights.
246 **144** 8c. multicoloured 15 15
247 21c. multicoloured 30 20

145 H.Q. Building

1973. Inauguration of New I.L.O. Headquarters Building, Geneva.
248 **145** 10c. multicoloured 15 15
249 21c. multicoloured 30 20

146 Globe within Posthorn

1974. Centenary of U.P.U.
250 **146** 10c. multicoloured 20 15

147 "Children's Choir" (mural detail, C. Portinari)

148 Peace Dove

1974. United Nations Art (6th issue). Brazilian Peace Mural, Delegates' Lobby.
251 **147** 10c. multicoloured 15 15
252 18c. multicoloured 35 25

1974.
253 **148** 2c. blue and ultramarine 15 15
254 – 10c. multicoloured 15 15
255 – 18c. multicoloured 25 15
DESIGNS—VERT: 10c. U.N. Headquarters, New York; 18c. Globe over U.N. emblem and flags.

A **151** Globe and Jet Aircraft

154 Young Children with Globe

1974. Air. Multicoloured.
A256 13c. Type A **151** 20 15
A257 18c. "Channels of Communication" (38 × 23 mm) 25 15
A258 26c. Dove in flight and U.N. Headquarters . . . 40 30

1974. World Population Year.
259 **154** 10c. multicoloured 15 15
260 18c. multicoloured 35 20

155 Ship and Fish

156 Satellite, Globe and Symbols

1974. U.N. Conference on "Law of the Sea".
261 **155** 10c. multicoloured 15 15
262 26c. multicoloured 50 20

1975. Peaceful Uses of Outer Space.
263 **156** 10c. multicoloured 15 15
264 26c. multicoloured 35 25

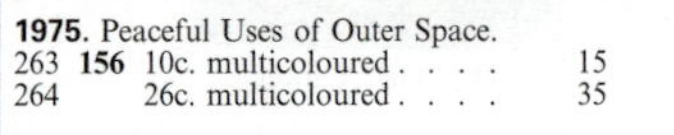

157 "Sex Equality"

158 "The Hope of Mankind"

1975. International Women's Year.
265 **157** 10c. multicoloured 15 15
266 18c. multicoloured 35 20

1975. 30th Anniv of U.N.O.
267 **158** 10c. multicoloured 15 15
268 26c. multicoloured 40 25

160 Cupped Hand

161 Wild Rose and Barbed Wire

1975. "Namibia—United Nations Direct Responsibility".
270 **160** 10c. multicoloured 15 15
271 18c. multicoloured 30 15

1975. U.N. Peace-keeping Operations.
272 **161** 13c. blue 20 15
273 26c. mauve 40 35

162 "Bird of Peace"

166 Linked Ribbons

1976. Multicoloured.
274 3c. Type **162** 15 15
275 4c. "Gathering of Peoples" (39 × 23 mm) 15 15
276 30c. U.N. flag (23 × 39 mm) 40 25
277 50c. "Universal Peace" (Dove and rainbow) (23 × 39 mm) 75 50

1976. World Federation of U.N. Associations.
278 **166** 13c. multicoloured 15 15
279 26c. multicoloured 30 25

167 Globe and Crate

168 Houses bordering Globe

1976. U.N. Conf on Trade and Development.
280 **167** 13c. multicoloured 15 15
281 31c. multicoloured 35 25

1976. U.N. Conf on Human Settlements.
282 **168** 13c. multicoloured 15 15
283 25c. multicoloured 35 25

169 Magnifying Glass and Emblem

170 Stylized Ear of Wheat

1976. 25th Anniv of U.N. Postal Administration.
284 **169** 13c. multicoloured 15 15
285 31c. multicoloured . . . . 1·20 1·00

1976. World Food Council.
286 **170** 13c. multicoloured 20 15

171 U.N. Emblem

173 Rain Drops and Funnel

172 W.I.P.O. Headquarters Building

1976.
287 **171** 9c. multicoloured 15 15

1977. World Intellectual Property Organization Headquarters.
288 **172** 13c. multicoloured 15 15
289 31c. multicoloured 40 25

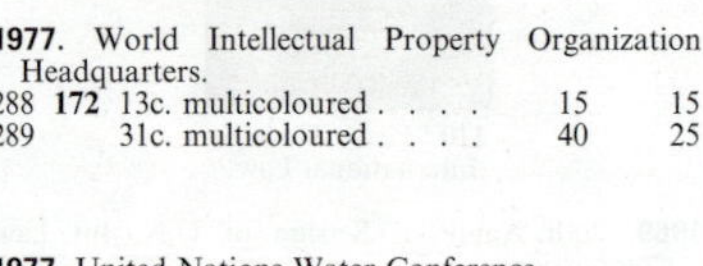

1977. United Nations Water Conference.
290 **173** 13c. multicoloured 15 15
291 25c. multicoloured 40 25

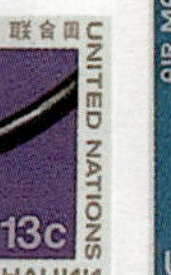

174 Severed Fuse

175 Winged Airmail Letter

1977. Security Council.
292 **174** 13c. multicoloured 15 15
293 31c. multicoloured 40 25

1977. Air. Multicoloured.
A294 25c. Type **175** 40 25
A295 31c. Globe and airplane (horiz) 45 35

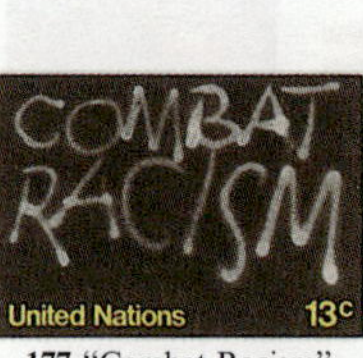

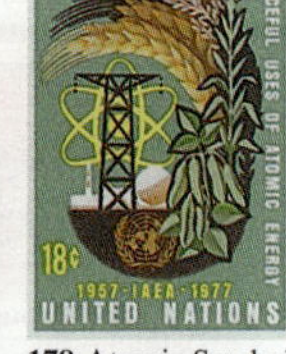

177 "Combat Racism"

178 Atomic Symbol and Produce

1977. Campaign Against Racial Discrimination.
296 **177** 13c. black and yellow . . 15 15
297 25c. black and red 35 25

1977. Peaceful Uses of Atomic Energy.
298 **178** 13c. multicoloured 15 15
299 18c. multicoloured 30 20

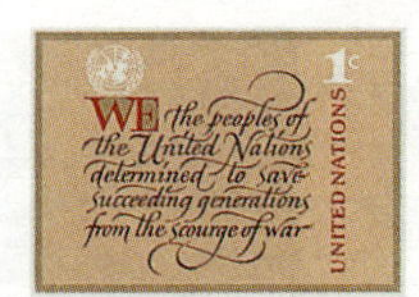

179 U.N. Charter

1978. Multicoloured.
300 1c. Type **179** 15 15
301 25c. Knotted flags 30 25
302 $1 Multi-racial group 95 85

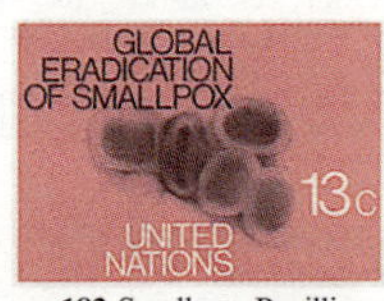

182 Smallpox Bacilli

1978. Global Eradication of Smallpox.
303 **182** 13c. black and red 15 15
304 31c. black and blue . . . 40 30

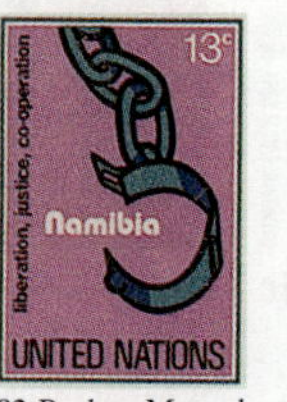

183 Broken Manacle

184 Clouds within Ribbon

1978. "Namibia: Liberation, Justice, Co-operation".
305 **183** 13c. multicoloured 15 15
306 18c. multicoloured 25 15

1978. International Civil Aviation Organization—Safety in the Air.
307 **184** 13c. multicoloured 15 15
308 25c. multicoloured 35 25

185 General Assembly

1978. General Assembly.
309 **185** 13c. multicoloured 25 15
310 18c. multicoloured 30 20

186 Hemispheres within Cogwheels

187 Hand holding Olive Branch

1978. Technical Co-operation among Developing Countries.
311 **186** 13c. multicoloured 15 15
312 31c. multicoloured 40 30

1979. Multicoloured.
313 5c. Type **187** 15 15
314 14c. Multiple "tree" 15 15
315 15c. Globe and peace dove 25 20
316 20c. Doves crossing globe 25 20

191 Fire and Flood

1979. U.N. Disaster Relief Co-ordinator.
317 **191** 15c. multicoloured 20 15
318 20c. multicoloured 30 25

192 Child's Drawing

193 Olive Branch and Map of Namibia

1979. International Year of the Child.
319 **192** 15c. multicoloured 15 15
320 31c. multicoloured 40 25

1979. "For a Free and Independent Namibia".
321 **193** 15c. multicoloured 15 15
322 31c. multicoloured 35 25

194 Sword and Scales of Justice

195 Graph

1979. International Court of Justice.
323 **194** 15c. olive, green and black 15 15
324 20c. blue, lt blue & black 35 25

1980. New International Economic Order. Multicoloured.
325 15c. Type **195** 15 15
326 31c. Key 40 35

197 Doves

1980. U.N. Decade for Women.
327 **197** 15c. multicoloured 15 15
328 20c. multicoloured 25 20

198 Helmet

1980. Peace-keeping Operations.
329 **198** 15c. blue and black 20 15
330 – 31c. multicoloured 40 30
DESIGN: 31c. "Peace-keeping".

200 "35" composed of Flags

203 Flag of Bangladesh

1980. 35th Anniv of United Nations. Mult.
331 15c. Type **200** 15 15
332 31c. Stylized flower 35 25

1980. Flags of Member Nations (1st series). Multicoloured.
334 15c. Type **203** 15 15
335 15c. Guinea 15 15
336 15c. Mali 15 15
337 15c. Surinam 15 15
338 15c. Cameroun 15 15
339 15c. Hungary 15 15
340 15c. Madagascar 15 15
341 15c. Rwanda 15 15
342 15c. El Salvador 15 15
343 15c. France 15 15
344 15c. Venezuela 15 15
345 15c. Yugoslavia 15 15
346 15c. Fiji 15 15
347 15c. Luxembourg 15 15
348 15c. Turkey 15 15
349 15c. Vietnam 15 15
See also Nos. 359/74, 383/98, 408/23, 434/9, 458/74, 486/501, 508/23, 537/52, 563/78, 710/17, 744/51, 785/92 and 849/56.

204 Various Emblems forming Bunch of Flowers

1980. Economic and Social Council. Mult.
350 15c. Type **204** 25 20
351 20c. Economic and social emblems 35 25

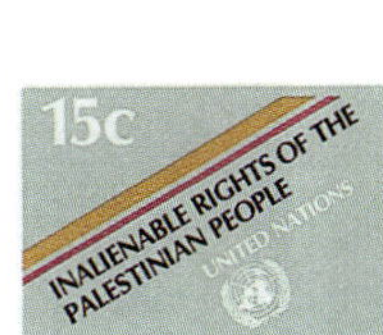

206 Text and U.N. Emblem

207 Jigsaw

1981. Inalienable Rights of the Palestinian People.
352 **206** 15c. multicoloured 20 20

1981. International Year of Disabled Persons.
353 **207** 20c. multicoloured 25 15
354 – 35c. black and orange 45 30
DESIGN: 35c. Disabled person.

209 "Sebastocrator Kaloyan and his Wife Desislava" (13th-cent Bulgarian fresco)

210 Sun and Sea

1981. Art.
355 **209** 20c. multicoloured 25 20
356 31c. multicoloured 40 40

1981. New and Renewable Sources of Energy.
357 **210** 20c. multicoloured 25 20
358 – 40c. gold and blue 45 40
DESIGN: 40c. U.N. energy conference emblem.

1981. Flags of Member Nations (2nd series). As T **203**. Multicoloured.
359 20c. Djibouti 20 15
360 20c. Sri Lanka 20 15
361 20c. Bolivia 20 15
362 20c. Equatorial Guinea 20 15
363 20c. Malta 20 15
364 20c. Czechoslovakia 20 15
365 20c. Thailand 20 15
366 20c. Trinidad and Tobago 20 15
367 20c. Ukrainian S.S.R. 20 15
368 20c. Kuwait 20 15
369 20c. Sudan 20 15
370 20c. Egypt 20 15
371 20c. United States 20 15
372 20c. Singapore 20 15
373 20c. Panama 20 15
374 20c. Costa Rica 20 15

212 Grafted Plant

214 "Respect for Human Rights"

1981. 10th Anniv of U.N. Volunteers Programme. Multicoloured.
375 18c. Type **212** 30 20
376 28c. "10" enclosing symbols of services 55 40

1982. Multicoloured.
377 17c. Type **214** 25 15
378 28c. "Granting of Independence to Colonial Countries and Peoples" 40 25
379 40c. "Second Disarmament Decade" 65 45

217 Hand holding Seedling

219 Olive Branch and U.N. Emblem

1982. Human Environment. Multicoloured.
380 20c. Type **217** 20 20
381 40c. Symbols of the environment 65 50

1982. Second United Nations Conference on Exploration and Peaceful Uses of Outer Space.
382 **219** 20c. ultramarine, blue and green 40 25

1982. Flags of Member Nations (3rd series). As T **203**. Multicoloured.
383 20c. Austria 20 15
384 20c. Malaysia 20 15
385 20c. Seychelles 20 15
386 20c. Ireland 20 15
387 20c. Mozambique 20 15
388 20c. Albania 20 15
389 20c. Dominica 20 15
390 20c. Solomon Islands 20 15
391 20c. Philippines 20 15
392 20c. Swaziland 20 15
393 20c. Nicaragua 20 15
394 20c. Burma 20 15
395 20c. Cape Verde 20 15
396 20c. Guyana 20 15
397 20c. Belgium 20 15
398 20c. Nigeria 20 15

220 Tree (flora)

222 Interlocking Arrows

1982. Conservation and Protection of Nature. Multicoloured.
399 20c. Type **220** 30 25
400 28c. Butterfly (insects) 50 40

1983. World Communications Year. Mult.
401 20c. Type **222** 40 20
402 40c. Cable network 60 50

224 Ship and Buoy

226 Giving Food

1983. Safety at Sea: International Maritime Organization. Multicoloured.
403 20c. Type **224** 35 20
404 37c. Stylized liner 50 40

1983. World Food Programme.
405 **226** 20c. red 30 25

227 Coins and Cogwheels

229 "Window Right"

1983. Trade and Development. Multicoloured.
406 20c. Type **227** 25 20
407 28c. Emblems of trade 55 45

1983. Flags of Member Nations (4th series). As T **203**. Multicoloured.
408 20c. United Kingdom 25 15
409 20c. Barbados 25 15
410 20c. Nepal 25 15
411 20c. Israel 25 15
412 20c. Malawi 25 15
413 20c. Byelorussian S.S.R. 25 15
414 20c. Jamaica 25 15
415 20c. Kenya 25 15
416 20c. China 25 15
417 20c. Peru 25 15
418 20c. Bulgaria 25 15
419 20c. Canada 25 15
420 20c. Somalia 25 15
421 20c. Senegal 25 15
422 20c. Brazil 25 15
423 20c. Sweden 25 15

1983. 35th Anniv of Declaration of Human Rights. Multicoloured.
424 20c. Type **229** 25 20
425 40c. "Treaty with Nature" 60 50

231 World Population

1984. International Conference on Population, Mexico.
426 **231** 20c. multicoloured 25 20
427 40c. multicoloured 60 45

232 Fertilizing Crops

1984. World Food Day. Multicoloured.
428 20c. Type **232** 25 20
429 40c. Planting rice 50 45

234 Grand Canyon, U.S.A

236 Mother with Baby

1984. World Heritage—U.N. Educational, Scientific and Cultural Organization. Multicoloured.
430 20c. Type **234** 20 15
431 50c. Polonnaruwa, Sri Lanka 60 55

1984. Future for Refugees.
432 **236** 20c. brown and black 35 25
433 – 50c. black and blue 85 65
DESIGN: 50c. Mother with child.

1984. Flags of Member Nations (5th series). As T **203**. Multicoloured.
434 20c. Burundi 45 30
435 20c. Pakistan 45 30
436 20c. Benin 45 30
437 20c. Italy 45 30
438 20c. Poland 45 30
439 20c. Papua New Guinea 45 30
440 20c. Uruguay 45 30
441 20c. Chile 45 30
442 20c. Paraguay 45 30
443 20c. Bhutan 45 30
444 20c. Central African Republic 45 30
445 20c. Australia 45 30
446 20c. Tanzania 45 30
447 20c. United Arab Emirates 45 30
448 20c. Ecuador 45 30
449 20c. Bahamas 45 30

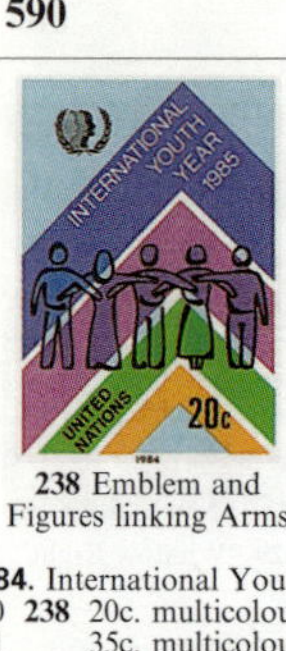

238 Emblem and Figures linking Arms

239 Turin Centre Emblem

1984. International Youth Year.

450 **238** 20c. multicoloured 40 25

451 35c. multicoloured . . . . 1·10 85

1985. 20th Anniv of Turin Centre of International Labour Organization.

452 **239** 23c. blue 50 35

240 Farming and Mediums of Communication

1985. 10th Anniv of United Nations University, Tokyo.

453 **240** 50c. multicoloured . . . . 1·10 80

241 People of Various Nations

1985. Multicoloured.

454 22c. Type **241** 30 25

455 $3 Paintbrush and emblem 3·25 2·00

243 "Snow Scene" (Andrew Wyeth)

1985. 40th Anniv of U.N.O. Multicoloured.

456 22c. Type **243** 40 25

457 45c. "Harvest Scene" (Andrew Wyeth) . . . . . 1·10 65

1985. Flags of Member Nations (6th series). As T **203**. Multicoloured.

459 22c. Grenada 45 40

460 22c. Federal Republic of Germany 45 40

461 22c. Saudi Arabia 45 40

462 22c. Mexico 45 40

463 22c. Liberia 45 40

464 22c. Mauritius 45 40

465 22c. Chad 45 40

466 22c. Dominican Republic . . 45 40

467 22c. Oman 45 40

468 22c. Ghana 45 40

469 22c. Sierra Leone 45 40

470 22c. Finland 45 40

471 22c. Uganda 45 40

472 22c. St. Thomas and Prince Islands 45 40

473 22c. U.S.S.R. 45 40

474 22c. India 45 40

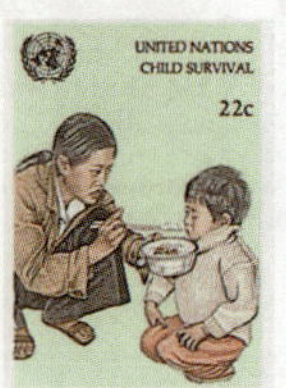

246 Woman feeding Child

248 "Africa in Crisis"

1985. U.N.I.C.E.F. Child Survival Campaign. Multicoloured.

475 32c. Type **246** 30 25

476 33c. Mother breast-feeding child 55 45

1986. Africa in Crisis.

477 **248** 22c. multicoloured 40 35

249 Dam

1986. Development Programme. Water Resources. Multicoloured.

478 22c. Type **249** . . . . 1·30 80

479 22c. Working in the fields . . 1·30 80

480 22c. Girls at waterhole . . . 1·30 80

481 22c. Women at well . . . . 1·30 80

Nos. 478/81 were printed together, se-tenant, forming a composite design.

253 Magnifying Glass and Stamp

1986. Philately: The International Hobby.

482 **253** 22c. lilac and blue 35 20

483 – 44c. brown and green . . 75 55

DESIGN: 44c. Engraver.

255 Peace Doves

1986. International Peace Year.

484 **255** 22c. multicoloured 45 30

485 – 33c. multicoloured . . . . 1·30 1·00

DESIGN: 33c. Words for "Peace" around U.N. emblem.

1986. Flags of Member Nations (7th series). As T **203**. Multicoloured.

486 22c. New Zealand 50 35

487 22c. Laos 50 35

488 22c. Burkina Faso 50 35

489 22c. Gambia 50 35

490 22c. Maldives 50 35

491 22c. Ethiopia 50 35

492 22c. Jordan 50 35

493 22c. Zambia 50 35

494 22c. Iceland 50 35

495 22c. Antigua and Barbuda . . 50 35

496 22c. Angola 50 35

497 22c. Botswana 50 35

498 22c. Rumania 50 35

499 22c. Togo 50 35

500 22c. Mauritania 50 35

501 22c. Colombia 50 35

258 Trygve Lie (after Harald Dal)

259 Men with Surveying Equipment and Blueprints

1987. 9th Death Anniv of Trygve Lie (first U.N. Secretary-General).

503 **258** 22c. multicoloured 75 60

1987. International Year of Shelter for the Homeless.

504 **259** 22c. deep brown, brown and black 35 20

505 – 44c. multicoloured . . . . 1·10 80

DESIGN: 44c. Cutting bamboo.

261 Construction Workers

1987. Anti-drugs Campaign. Multicoloured.

506 22c. Type **261** 55 40

507 33c. University graduates . . 1·10 80

1987. Flags of Member Nations (8th series). As T **203**. Multicoloured.

508 22c. Comoros 50 40

509 22c. People's Democratic Republic of Yemen . . . 50 40

510 22c. Mongolia 50 40

511 22c. Vanuatu 50 40

512 22c. Japan 50 40

513 22c. Gabon 50 40

514 22c. Zimbabwe 50 40

515 22c. Iraq 50 40

516 22c. Argentina 50 40

517 22c. Congo 50 40

518 22c. Niger 50 40

519 22c. St. Lucia 50 40

520 22c. Bahrain 50 40

521 22c. Haiti 50 40

522 22c. Afghanistan 50 40

523 22c. Greece 50 40

263 Family and U.N. Building, New York

265 Measles

1987. United Nations Day. Multicoloured.

524 22c. Type **263** 35 25

525 39c. Dancers 60 50

1987. "Immunize Every Child". Multicoloured.

526 22c. Type **265** . . . . 1·00 45

527 44c. Tetanus . . . . 1·50 1·00

267 Wheat as U.N. Emblem

1988. "For a Better World".

528 **267** 3c. yellow, brown and black 30 15

268 Fisherman

1988. International Fund for Agricultural Development "For a World Without Hunger" Campaign. Multicoloured.

529 22c. Type **268** 40 30

530 33c. Farmers ploughing with oxen 85 65

270 Tropical Rain Forest Canopy

272 Teacher at Blackboard

1988. "Survival of the Forests". Multicoloured.

531 25c. Type **270** . . . . 1·80 80

532 44c. Tropical rain forest floor 2·30 1·30

Nos. 531/2 were printed together, se-tenant, forming a composite design.

1988. International Volunteer Day. Mult.

533 25c. Type **272** 40 30

534 50c. Teaching basketry (horiz) 95 80

274 Cycling

276 Flame

1988. "Health in Sports". Multicoloured.

535 25c. Type **274** 60 35

536 38c. Marathon (horiz) . . . 1·10 85

1988. Flags of Member Nations (9th series). As T **203**. Multicoloured.

537 25c. Spain 50 35

538 25c. St. Vincent and Grenadines 50 35

539 25c. Ivory Coast 50 35

540 25c. Lebanon 50 35

541 25c. Yemen 50 35

542 25c. Cuba 50 35

543 25c. Denmark 50 35

544 25c. Libya 50 35

545 25c. Qatar 50 35

546 25c. Zaire 50 35

547 25c. Norway 50 35

548 25c. German Democratic Republic 50 35

549 25c. Iran 50 35

550 25c. Tunisia 50 35

551 25c. Samoa 50 35

552 25c. Belize 50 35

1989. 40th Anniv of Declaration of Human Rights.

553 **276** 25c. multicoloured 45 30

278 Electricity Production

280 "Blue Helmet" Soldier

1989. World Bank. Multicoloured.

555 25c. Type **278** 65 35

556 45c. Planting rice . . . . . . 1·30 80

1989. Award of Nobel Peace Prize to United Nations Peace-keeping Forces.

557 **280** 25c. multicoloured 40 30

281 U.N. Headquarters, New York

1989.

558 **281** 45c. multicoloured 60 45

282 Satellite Image of Storm over Chesapeake Bay Area

284 Band

1989. 25th Anniv of World Weather Watch. Multicoloured.

559 25c. Type **282** 65 40

560 36c. Typhoon Abby approaching China . . . . 1·50 1·30

1989. 10th Anniv of United Nations Vienna International Centre. Multicoloured.

561 25c. Type **284** . . . . 2·10 40

562 90c. Mountain and butterfly as tree . . . . 2·50 1·40

1989. Flags of Member Nations (10th series). As T **203**. Multicoloured.

563 25c. Indonesia 55 45

564 25c. Lesotho 55 45

565 25c. Guatemala 55 45

566 25c. Netherlands 55 45

567 25c. Algeria 55 45

568 25c. Brunei 55 45

569 25c. St. Kitts and Nevis . . . 55 45

570 25c. United Nations 55 45

571 25c. Honduras 55 45

572 25c. Kampuchea 55 45

573 25c. Guinea-Bissau 55 45

574 25c. Cyprus 55 45

575 25c. South Africa 55 45

576 25c. Portugal 55 45

577 25c. Morocco 55 45

578 25c. Syria 55 45

286 "Table of Universal Brotherhood" (Jose Clemente Orozco) (Article 1)

1989. Declaration of Human Rights (1st series). Multicoloured.

579 25c. Type **286** 35 25

580 45c. "Composition II" (V. Kandinsky) (Article 2) 75 65

See also Nos. 592/3, 609/10, 626/7 and 637/8.

288 Port Activities

1990. International Trade Centre.

581 **288** 25c. multicoloured . . . . 1·30 1·00

289 "AIDS" **291** Madagascar Periwinkle

1990. Anti-AIDS Campaign. Multicoloured.
582 25c. Type **289** 40 30
583 40c. Group at risk . . . . . 1·30 80

1990. Medicinal Plants. Multicoloured.
584 25c. Type **291** 65 50
585 90c. American ginseng . . . 1·70 1·20

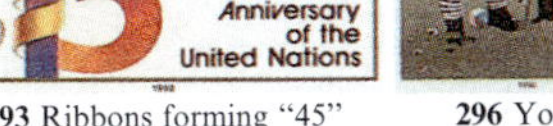

293 Ribbons forming "45" **296** Youth waylaying Elderly Man

1990. 45th Anniv of U.N.O. Multicoloured.
586 25c. Type **293** 65 55
587 45c. "45" and U.N. Emblem 2·30 1·20

1990. Crime Prevention. Multicoloured.
590 25c. Type **296** 95 55
591 36c. Burglars leaving burning building . . . . 2·10 1·00

1990. Universal Declaration of Human Rights (2nd series). As T **286**. Multicoloured.
592 25c. Sarcophagus of Plotinus (detail) (Article 7) . . . 40 25
593 45c. "Combined Chambers of High Court of Appeal" (Charles Paul Renouard, from "The Dreyfus Case") (Article 8) 75 60

300/303 Alpine Lake and Wildlife (½-size illustration)

1991. Economic Commission for Europe. "For a Better Environment".
594 **300** 30c. multicoloured 95 70
595 **301** 30c. multicoloured 95 70
596 **302** 30c. multicoloured 95 70
597 **303** 30c. multicoloured 95 70
Nos. 594/7 were printed together, se-tenant, forming the composite design illustrated.

304 Desert **306** U.N. Building

1991. 1st Anniv of Namibian Independence. Multicoloured.
598 30c. Type **304** 85 50
599 50c. Open grassland . . . . 1·50 1·20

1991.
600 **306** $2 blue . . . . 2·50 1·60

307 Children around Globe (Nicole Delia Legnani)

1991. 30th Anniv (1989) of U.N. Declaration on the Rights of the Child and 1990 World Summit on Children, New York. Children's Drawings. Multicoloured.
601 30c. Type **307** . . . . 1·10 80
602 70c. Dove, rainbow and houses (Alissa Duffy) . . . 2·75 1·80

309 Bubbles of Toxin approaching City

1991. Banning of Chemical Weapons. Mult.
603 30c. Type **309** . . . . 1·50 1·10
604 90c. Hand pushing back barrels of toxins . . . . . 2·75 1·70

311 U.N. Flag

1991. Multicoloured.
605 30c. Type **311** 75 45
606 50c. "The Golden Rule" (mosaic, Norman Rockwell) (vert) . . . . . 1·30 80

313 1951 1c. Stamp

1991. 40th Anniv of United Nations Postal Administration.
607 **313** 30c. red on cream 95 70
608 – 40c. purple on cream . . 1·60 1·00
DESIGN: 40c. 1951 2c. stamp.

1991. Declaration of Human Rights (3rd series). As T **286**. Multicoloured.
609 30c. "The Last of England" (Ford Maddox Brown) (Article 13) 50 35
610 50c. "The Emigration to the East" (Tito Salas) (Article 14) . . . . 1·10 80

317 Uluru National Park, Australia **319/20** Sea Life (½-size illustration)

1992. 20th Anniv of U.N.E.S.C.O. World Heritage Convention. Multicoloured.
611 30c. Type **317** 60 45
612 50c. Great Wall of China . . 1·10 80

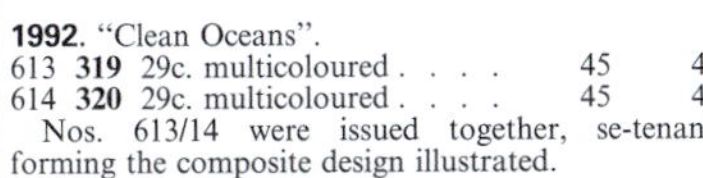

1992. "Clean Oceans".
613 **319** 29c. multicoloured 45 45
614 **320** 29c. multicoloured 45 45
Nos. 613/14 were issued together, se-tenant, forming the composite design illustrated.

321/324 Planet Earth (½-size illustration)

1992. 2nd U.N. Conference on Environment and Development, Rio de Janeiro.
615 **321** 29c. multicoloured 75 45
616 **322** 29c. multicoloured 75 45
617 **323** 29c. multicoloured 75 45
618 **324** 29c. multicoloured 75 45
Nos. 615/18 were issued together, se-tenant, forming the composite design illustrated.

325/326 "Mission Planet Earth" (⅔-size illustration)

1992. International Space Year. Roul.
619 **325** 29c. multicoloured . . . . 2·75 2·30
620 **326** 29c. multicoloured . . . . 2·75 2·30
Nos. 619/20 were issued together, se-tenant, forming the composite design illustrated.

327 Winged Man with V.D.U.

1992. Commission on Science and Technology for Development. Multicoloured.
621 29c. Type **327** 40 35
622 50c. Man sitting in crocodile's mouth 70 55

329 Aerial View of Building

1992. United Nations University, Tokyo. Mult.
623 4c. Type **329** 15 15
624 40c. Front elevation of building 60 45

331 U.N. Headquarters, New York **334** Family Life

1992.
625 **331** 29c. multicoloured 75 60

1992. Universal Declaration of Human Rights (4th series). As T **286**. Multicoloured.
626 29c. "Lady writing a letter with her Maid" (Johannes Vermeer) (Article 19) . . . 75 60
627 50c. "The Meeting"(Ester Almqvist) (Article 20) . . . 95 95

1993. "Ageing: Dignity and Participation". 10th Anniv (1992) of International Plan of Action on Ageing. Multicoloured.
628 29c. Type **334** 85 60
629 52c. Health and nutrition . . 1·50 1·10

336 Queensland Hairy-nosed Wombat

1993. Endangered Species (1st series). Multicoloured.
630 29c. Type **336** 45 40
631 29c. Whooping crane ("Grus americana") 45 40
632 29c. Giant clams ("Tridacnidae") 45 40
633 29c. Sable antelope ("Hippotragus niger") . . 45 40
See also Nos. 649/52, 667/70, 694/7, 720/3, 755/8, 803/6, 819/22, 841/4 and 875/8.

340 "United Nations"

1993.
634 **340** 5c. multicoloured 60 40

341 Personal Environment

1993. 45th Anniv of W.H.O. Multicoloured.
635 29c. Type **341** 95 65
636 50c. Family environment . . 1·10 80

1993. Declaration of Human Rights (5th series). As T **286**. Multicoloured.
637 29c. "Shocking Corn" (Thomas Hart Benton) (Article 25) 75 50
638 35c. "The Library" (Jacob Lawrence) (Article 26) . . 1·10 80

345/348 Peace (½-size illustration)

1993. International Peace Day. Roul.
639 **345** 29c. multicoloured . . . . 1·70 1·20
640 **346** 29c. multicoloured . . . . 1·70 1·20
641 **347** 29c. multicoloured . . . . 1·70 1·20
642 **348** 29c. multicoloured . . . . 1·70 1·20
Nos. 639/42 were issued together, se-tenant, forming the composite design illustrated.

349 Chameleon

1993. The Environment—Climate. Mult.
643 29c. Type **349** 70 60
644 29c. Storm 40 60
645 29c. Antelopes fleeing from flood 70 60
646 29c. Lesser bird of paradise 40 60
Nos. 643/6 were issued together, se-tenant, forming a composite design.

353 Equality across Generations

1994. Int Year of the Family. Mult.
647 29c. Type **353** . . . . 1·10 80
648 45c. Poor family . . . . . . 1·70 1·20

1994. Endangered Species (2nd series). As T **336**. Multicoloured.
649 29c. Chimpanzees ("Pan troglodytes") 50 40
650 29c. St. Lucia amazon ("Amazona versicolor") . . 50 40
651 29c. American crocodile ("Crocodylus acutus") . . 50 40
652 29c. Addra gazelles ("Gazelle dama") 50 40

359 "Dove of Peace" (mosaic) **362** Refugee crossing Bridge of Hands

1994.
653 **359** 10c. multicoloured 15 15
654 – 19c. multicoloured 55 30
655 – $1 brown . . . . 2·10 1·60
DESIGNS: 19c. "Sleeping Child" (stained-glass window after drawing by Stanislaw Wyspianski); $1 "Mourning Owl" (Vanessa Isitt).

1994. United Nations High Commissioner for Refugees.
656 **362** 50c. multicoloured . . . . 1·10 80

363/366 Shattered Globe and "Warning" (⅔-size illustration)

1994. International Decade for Natural Disaster Reduction.
657 **363** 29c. multicoloured . . . . 1·50 1·00
658 **364** 29c. multicoloured . . . . 1·50 1·00
659 **365** 29c. multicoloured . . . . 1·50 1·00
660 **366** 29c. multicoloured . . . . 1·50 1·00
Nos. 657/60 were issued together, se-tenant, forming the composite design illustrated.

367 Children Playing (health and family planning)

1994. International Population and Development Conference, Cairo. Multicoloured.
661 29c. Type **367** 65 45
662 52c. Family unit (demographic changes) . . 1·10 80

369 Map and Looped Ribbon

371 Anniversary Emblem

1994. 30th Anniv of United Nations Conference on Trade and Development. Multicoloured.
663 29c. Type **369** 45 40
664 50c. Map and coiled ribbon . . . 80 55

1995. 50th Anniv of U.N.O. (1st issue).
665 **371** 32c. multicoloured . . . . 1·10 70
See also Nos. 673/4 and 679/90.

372 "Social Summit 1995"

1995. World Summit for Social Development, Copenhagen.
666 **372** 50c. multicoloured 95 80

1995. Endangered Species (3rd series). As T **336**. Multicoloured.
667 32c. Giant armadillo ("Priodontes maximus") . . 55 45
668 32c. American bald eagle ("Haliaeetus leucocephalus") 55 45
669 32c. Fijian banded iguana ("Brachylophus fasciatus") 55 45
670 32c. Giant panda ("Ailuropoda melanoleuca") 55 45

377 Man looking out to Sea

1995. "Youth: Our Future". 10th Anniv of International Youth Year. Multicoloured.
671 32c. Type **377** 85 35
672 55c. Family cycling . . . . . 1·20 65

379 Signing U.N. Charter

1995. 50th Anniv of U.N.O. (2nd issue).
673 **379** 32c. black 55 35
674 – 50c. purple 85 55
DESIGN: 50c. Veterans' Memorial Hall and Opera House, San Francisco (venue for signing of Charter).

382 Mother and Child

1995. 4th World Conference on Women, Peking.
676 32c. Type **382** 65 30
677 40c. Harpist and cranes . . . 95 40

384 U.N. Headquarters, New York

1995.
678 **384** 20c. multicoloured 30 15

385/387 (½-size illustration)

388/390 (½-size illustration)

391/393 (½-size illustration)

394/396 (½-size illustration)

1995. 50th Anniv of U.N.O. (3rd issue).
679 **385** 32c. multicoloured . . . . 1·10 65
680 **386** 32c. multicoloured . . . . 1·10 65
681 **387** 32c. multicoloured . . . . 1·10 65
682 **388** 32c. multicoloured . . . . 1·10 65
683 **389** 32c. multicoloured . . . . 1·10 65
684 **390** 32c. multicoloured . . . . 1·10 65
685 **391** 32c. multicoloured . . . . 1·10 65
686 **392** 32c. multicoloured . . . . 1·10 65
687 **393** 32c. multicoloured . . . . 1·10 65
688 **394** 32c. multicoloured . . . . 1·10 65
689 **395** 32c. multicoloured . . . . 1·10 65
690 **396** 32c. multicoloured . . . . 1·10 65
Nos. 679/81 and 682/4 form the left and right halves respectively of a composite design, and Nos. 685/7 and 688/90 another composite design.

397 Rainbow and Faces within "Sun"

398 Mural

1996. 50th Anniv of World Federation of United Nations Associations.
691 **397** 32c. multicoloured 40 25

1996. Murals by Fernand Leger in General Assembly, U.N. Headquarters. Multicoloured.
692 32c. Type **398** 40 25
693 60c. Mural (different) 85 60

1996. Endangered Species (4th series). As T **336**. Multicoloured.
694 32c. "Masdevallia veitchiana" 65 50
695 32c. Saguaro ("Carnegiea gigantea") 65 50
696 32c. West Australian pitcher plant ("Cephalotus follicularis") 65 50
697 32c. "Encephalartos horridus" 65 50

404 Deer under Tree

1996. "Habitat II" Second United Nations Conference on Human Settlements, Istanbul, Turkey. Multicoloured.
698 32c. Type **404** 70 45
699 32c. City and countryside . . 70 45
700 32c. Walking in city park . . 70 45
701 32c. City and village 70 45
702 32c. Village and parrot . . . 70 45
Nos. 698/702 were issued together, se-tenant, forming a composite design.

409 Basketball

1996. Sport and the Environment. Multicoloured.
703 32c. Type **409** 85 60
704 50c. Volleyball . . . . 1·20 1·20

412 Two Birds

1996. "A Plea for Peace". Winners of China Youth Design Competition. Multicoloured.
706 32c. Type **412** 55 35
707 60c. Peace dove . . . . 1·10 40

414 "Yeh-Shen" (Chinese tale)

416 Cherry Tree

1996. 50th Anniv of U.N.I.C.E.F. Children's Stories.
708 32c. Type **414** 55 40
709 60c. "The Ugly Duckling" (Hans Christian Andersen) 1·30 1·00

1997. Flags of Member Nations (11th series). As T **203**. Multicoloured.
710 32c. Liechtenstein 55 40
711 32c. Republic of Korea . . . 55 40
712 32c. Kazakhstan 55 40
713 32c. Latvia 55 40
714 32c. Tajikistan 55 40
715 32c. Georgia 55 40
716 32c. Armenia 55 40
717 32c. Namibia 55 40

1997. Multicoloured.
718 8c. Type **416** 35 25
719 55c. Rose "Peace" (horiz) . . 1·10 55

1997. Endangered Species (5th series). As T **336**. Multicoloured.
720 32c. African elephant ("Loxodonta africana") . . 55 40
721 32c. Major Mitchell's cockatoo ("Cacatua leadbeateri") 55 40
722 32c. Black-footed ferret ("Mustela nigripes") . . . 55 40
723 32c. Puma ("Felis concolor") 55 40

422/425 Ocean Scene (⅔-size illustration)

1997. "Earth Summit + 5". 5th Anniv of United Nations Conference on Environment and Development.
724 **422** 32c. multicoloured 95 65
725 **423** 32c. multicoloured 95 65
726 **424** 32c. multicoloured 95 65
727 **425** 32c. multicoloured 95 65
Nos. 724/7 were issued together, se-tenant, forming the composite design illustrated.

427 Clipper

432 1986 22c. Philately Stamp

1997. 50th Anniversaries of Economic Commission for Europe and Economic and Social Commission for Asia and the Pacific. Multicoloured.
729 32c. Type **427** 55 25
730 32c. Sail/steam ship 55 25
731 32c. Liner 55 25
732 32c. Hovercraft 55 25
733 32c. Hydrofoil 55 25
Nos. 729/33 were issued together, se-tenant, forming a composite design.

1997. "Tribute to Philately". Multicoloured.
734 32c. Type **432** 70 55
735 50c. 1986 44c. Philately stamp . . . . 1·20 70

434 Kneeling Warrior

1997. 25th Anniv of World Heritage Convention. Terracotta Warriors from Emperor Qin Shi Huang's Tomb, Xian, China. Multicoloured.

736 8c. Type **434** 25 25
737 8c. Ranks of armoured warriors 25 25
738 8c. Head 25 25
739 8c. Group in wrap-over tunics 25 25
740 8c. Head and shoulders . . . 25 25
741 8c. Group in armour 25 25
742 32c. Type **434** 60 25
743 60c. As No. 737 . . . . . . 1·10 65

1998. Flags of Member Nations (12th series). As T **203**.

744 32c. blue, grey and black . . 65 40
745 32c. multicoloured 65 40
746 32c. multicoloured 65 40
747 32c. multicoloured 65 40
748 32c. multicoloured 65 40
749 32c. red, grey and black . . . 65 40
750 32c. multicoloured 65 40
751 32c. black, blue and grey . . 65 40

FLAGS: No. 744, Micronesia; 745, Slovakia; 746, Democratic People's Republic of Korea; 747, Azerbaijan; 748, Uzbekistan; 749, Monaco; 750, Czech Republic; 751, Estonia.

440 Boy holding Dove

1998. Multicoloured.

752 1c. Type **440** 15 15
753 2c. Birds 15 15
754 21c. Dancing around U.N. emblem 40 15

1998. Endangered Species (6th series). As T **366**. Multicoloured.

755 32c. Lesser bushbaby ("Galago senegalensis") . . 55 25
756 32c. Hawaiian goose ("Branta sandvicensis") 55 25
757 32c. Golden birdwing ("Troides aeacus") 55 25
758 32c. Sun bear ("Helarctos malayanus") 55 25

447 Turtles

1998. International Year of the Ocean. Multicoloured.

759 32c. Type **447** 55 25
760 32c. Rays 55 40
761 32c. Sunfishes 55 40
762 32c. Head of whale 55 40
763 32c. Dugongs 55 40
764 32c. Striped fishes 55 40
765 32c. Dolphin (fish) and orca 55 40
766 32c. Jellyfish and seahorse . . 55 40
767 32c. Sealions, seahorse and fishes 55 40
768 32c. Dolphins, octopus and diver's head 55 40
769 32c. Submersible 55 40
770 32c. Sharks 55 40

448 Jaguar

1998. Rainforest Preservation.

771 **448** 32c. multicoloured 55 40

450 Soldier holding Binoculars

1998. 50 Years of United Nations Peacekeeping. Multicoloured.

773 33c. Type **450** 70 45
774 40c. Soldiers sitting on tank 75 30

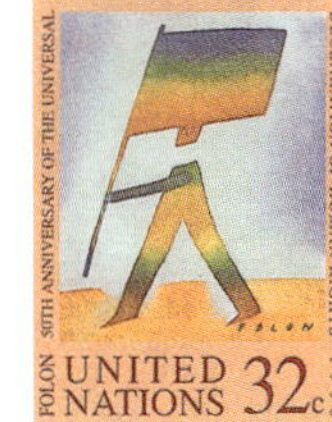

452 Man carrying Flag

1998. 50th Anniv of Universal Declaration of Human Rights. Multicoloured.

775 32c. Type **452** 65 35
776 55c. Walking pens . . . . . 1·10 60

454 Blue and White Vase (Mirror Room)

1998. World Heritage Site. Schonbrunn Palace, Vienna. Multicoloured.

777 11c. Type **454** 35 30
778 11c. Detail of wall hanging (Johann Wenzl Bergl) . . . 35 30
779 11c. Porcelain stove 35 30
780 15c. Palace facade (horiz) . . 40 40
781 15c. Great Palm House (horiz) 40 40
782 15c. Gloriette (horiz) 40 40
783 33c. As No. 782 . . . . . . 65 40
784 60c. As No. 778 . . . . . . 1·00 45

1999. Flags of Member Nations (13th series). As T **203**. Multicoloured.

785 33c. Lithuania 60 35
786 33c. San Marino 60 35
787 33c. Turkmenistan 60 35
788 33c. Marshall Islands 60 35
789 33c. Moldova 60 35
790 33c. Kyrgyzstan 60 35
791 33c. Bosnia and Herzegovina 60 35
792 33c. Eritrea 60 35

460 Man putting Banner of Flags around Globe

1999. Multicoloured.

793 33c. Type **460** 55 25
794 $5 Roses . . . . 7·25 2·50

462 Tasmanian Wilderness

1999. World Heritage Sites in Australia. Mult.

795 5c. Type **462** 15 15
796 5c. Wet Tropics, Queensland 15 15
797 5c. Great Barrier Reef . . . 15 15
798 15c. Uluru-Kata Tjuta National Park 25 25
799 15c. Kakadu National Park 25 25
800 15c. Willandra Lakes Region 25 25
801 33c. As No. 800 . . . . . . 70 60
802 60c. As No. 796 . . . . . . 1·00 1·20

1999. Endangered Species (7th series). As T **336**. Multicoloured.

803 33c. Tiger ("Panthera tigris") 55 15
804 33c. Secretary bird ("Sagittarius serpentarius") 55 15
805 33c. Green tree python ("Chondropython viridis") 55 15
806 33c. Long-tailed chinchilla ("Chinchilla lanigera") . . 55 15

472/473 International Planetary Exploration (½-size illustration)

1999. 3rd Conference on Exploration and Peaceful Uses of Outer Space, Vienna.

807 **472** 33c. multicoloured 80 45
808 **473** 33c. multicoloured 80 45

Nos. 807/8 were issued together, se-tenant, forming the composite design illustrated.

475/478 19th-century Mail Transport (½-size illustration)

1999. 125th Anniv of Universal Postal Union

810 **475** 33c. multicoloured 55 25
811 **476** 33c. multicoloured 55 25
812 **477** 33c. multicoloured 55 25
813 **478** 33c. multicoloured 55 25

Nos. 810/13 were issued together, se-tenant, forming the composite design illustrated.

479 U.N. Headquarters, New York

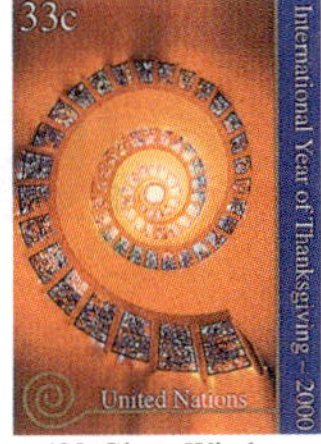

483 Glory Window (Gabrielle Loire), Chapel of Thanksgiving, Dallas

481 Couple with Books

1999. "In Memoriam: Fallen in the Cause of Peace".

814 **479** 37c. multicoloured . . . . 1·70 1·40

1999. Education: Keystone to the 21st Century. Multicoloured.

816 33c. Type **481** 55 25
817 60c. Heart and open book . . 1·10 45

2000. International Year of Thanksgiving.

818 **483** 33c. multicoloured 75 60

2000. Endangered Species (8th series). As T **336**. Mult.

819 33c. Brown bear (*Ursus arctos*) 55 25
820 33c. Black-bellied bustard (*Lissotis melanogaster*) . . 55 25
821 33c. Chinese crocodile lizard (*Shinisaurus crocodilurus*) 55 25
822 33c. Pygmy chimpanzee (*Pan paniscis*) 55 25

488 "Crawling Toward the Millennium" (Sam Yeates)

2000. "Our World 2000" International Art Exhibition, New York. Entries in Millennium Painting Competition. Multicoloured.

823 33c. Type **488** 55 25
824 60c. "Crossing" (Masakazu Takahata) (vert) . . . . . 1·10 45

491 Auditorium, General Assembly Building, 1956

2000. 55th Anniv of the United Nations and 50th Anniv of Opening of U.N. Headquarters, New York.

826 **491** 33c. blue, green and ochre 55 25
827 – 55c. blue, green and ochre 95 45

DESIGN: 55c. Headquarters, 1951.

493 Globe, Sun and Olympic Rings (Mateja Prunk)

2000. Winning Entry in "International Flag of Peace" Children's Design Competition.

829 **493** 33c. multicoloured 55 25

496 Granada

2000. World Heritage Sites in Spain. Multicoloured.

831 5c. Type **496** 15 15
832 5c. Cliff-top Houses, Cuence 15 15
833 5c. Roman Aqueduct, Segovia 15 15
834 15c. Archaeological Site, Merida 25 25
835 15c. Toledo 25 25
836 15c. Guell Park, Barcelona 25 25
837 33c. As No. 831 . . . . . . 55 25
838 60c. As No. 834 . . . . . . 1·10 45

502 Family of Refugees

2000. 50th Anniv of United Nations High Commissioner for Refugees.

839 **502** 33c. multicoloured 55 25

2001. Endangered Species (9th series). As T **336**. Multicoloured.

841 34c. Spotted phalanger (*Phalanger maculatus*) . . . 55 25
842 34c. Resplendent quetzal (*Pharomachrus mocinno*) . . 55 25
843 34c. Gila monster (*Heloderma suspectum*) 55 25
844 34c. Eastern black and white colobus (*Colobus guereza*) 55 25

508 Landscape and Silhouette (Jose Zaragoza)

2001. United Nations International Year of Volunteers. Multicoloured.
845 34c. Type **508** 55 25
846 80c. Piano keys, hands and music score (John Terry) 1·30 65

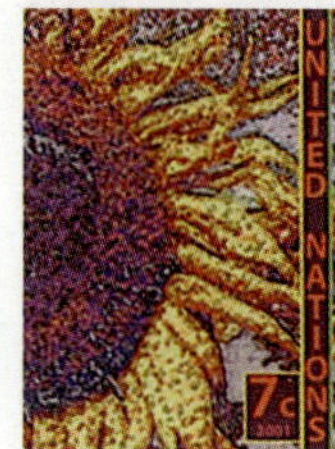

510 Sunflower

2001. Multicoloured.
847 7c. Type **510** 15 15
848 34c. Rose 55 25

2001. Flags of Member Nations (14th series). As T **203**. Multicoloured.
849 34c. Slovenia 55 25
850 34c. Palau 55 25
851 34c. Tonga 55 25
852 34c. Croatia 55 25
853 34c. Macedonia 55 25
854 34c. Kiribati 55 25
855 34c. Andorra 55 25
856 34c. Nauru 55 25

512 Pagoda, Kyoto

2001. World Heritage Sites in Japan. Multicoloured.
857 5c. Type **512** 15 15
858 5c. Imperial Palace, Nara . . 15 15
859 5c. Himeji Castle 15 15
860 20c. Shirakawa-go and Gokayama Villages 35 30
861 20c. Itsukushima Shinto Shrine 35 30
862 20c. Temple, Nikko 35 30
863 34c. As No. 857 . . . . . . 55 25
864 70c. As No. 860 . . . . . . 1·20 55

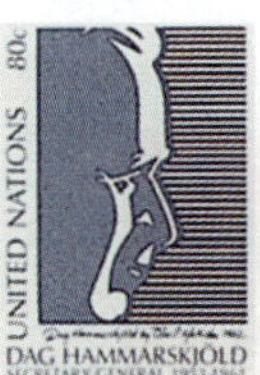

518 Hammarskjold

519 "Stamps" and Ribbons

2001. 40th Death Anniv of Dag Hammarskjold (United Nations Secretary General, 1953–61).
865 **518** 80c. blue . . . . 1·30 65

2001. 50th Anniv of United Nations Postal Administration. Multicoloured.
866 34c. Type **519** 55 25
867 80c. Presents . . . . 1·30 65

522 Landscape, Butterfly and Goose

2001. Climate Change. Multicoloured.
869 34c. Type **522** 55 25
870 34c. Penguin and tomato plant 55 25
871 34c. Palm tree and solar panel 55 25
872 34c. Hand planting sapling 55 25
Nos. 869/72 were issued together, se-tenant, forming a composite design.

526 United Nations Flag

2001. Kofi Annan, Winner of Nobel Peace Prize, 2001.
873 **526** 34c. multicoloured 55 25

527 Children carrying Stamps

2002.
874 **527** 80c. multicoloured . . . . 1·10 40

2002. Endangered Species (10th series). As T **336**. Multicoloured.
875 34c. Hoffmann's two-toed sloth (*Choloepus hoffmanni*) 50 25
876 34c. American bighorn (*Ovis canadensis*) 50 25
877 34c. Cheetah (*Acinonyx jubatus*) 50 25
878 34c. San Esteban Island chuckwalla (*Sauromalus varius*) 50 25

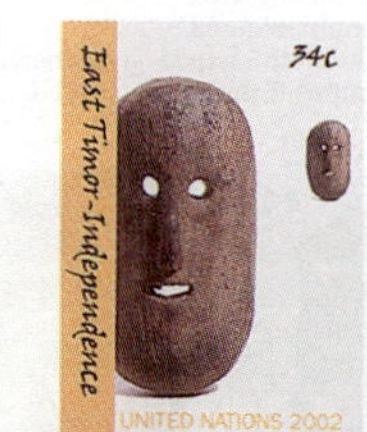

532 Wooden Mask, Dili

2002. East Timor Independence. Multicoloured.
879 34c. Type **532** 45 20
880 57c. Traditional wooden door panels 70 30

534 Khan-Tengri, Kyrgyzstan

2002. International Year of Mountains. Multicoloured.
881 34c. Type **534** 45 20
882 34c. Kilimanjaro, Tanzania 45 20
883 80c. Mt. Foraker, U.S.A . . 1·00 40
884 80c. Paine Grande, Chile . . 1·00 40

538 Sun, Earth and Planets

2002. World Summit on Sustainable Development, Johannesburg. Multicoloured.
885 37c. Type **538** 45 20
886 37c. Women's profile 45 20
887 60c. Yacht 75 30
888 60c. Figures wearing fashionable dress 75 30

542 Duomo di Sant'Andrea, Amalfi Coast

2002. World Heritage Sites in Italy. Multicoloured.
889 5c. Type **542** 10 10
890 5c. View across Islands, Aeolian Islands 10 10
891 5c. Del Moro Fountain, Rome 10 10
892 15c. Santa Maria del Fiore, Florence 20 20
893 15c. Leaning Tower, Pisa . . 20 20
894 15c. The Forum, Pompeii . . 20 20
895 37c. As No. 892 . . . . . . 45 20
896 70c. As No. 889 . . . . . . 85 35

548 AIDS Symbol on U. N. Secretariat Building, New York

2002. AIDS. Awareness Campaign. Multicoloured.
897 70c. Type **548** 85 35
MS898 80 × 80 mm. 37c.+6c. 549 on UN Secretariat Building, New York at night AIDS symbol 60 25
The premium was for AIDS charities.

B. GENEVA HEADQUARTERS

For use on mail posted at the United Nations Geneva Headquarters. Before 1969 the Swiss PTT issued stamps for use at the Palais des Nations; these are listed at the end of Switzerland.

100 centimes = 1 Swiss franc.

NOTE: References to numbers and types in this section. other than to those with a "G" prefix are to the United Nations (New York Office) listing. Designs adapted for the Geneva issue are inscribed in French and have face values in francs.

G **4** Palais des Nations, Geneva

G **5** Palais des Nations, Geneva

1969. Existing United Nations (New York) designs adapted with new colours and values in Swiss francs (F.S.). 30 and 40c. new designs. Multicoloured unless otherwise stated.
G 1 – 5c. (As No. 164) 10 10
G 2 – 10c. (As No. 94) 10 10
G 3 – 20c. (As No. 97) 20 10
G 4 G **4** 30c. multicoloured . . . 25 15
G 5 G **5** 40c. multicoloured . . . 30 25
G 6 – 50c. (As No. 147, but scroll inscr in French) 40 25
G 7 – 60c. gold, red and brown (As No. 98) . . . 40 25
G 8 – 70c. red, gold and black (As No. 167) . . . 50 35
G 9 – 75c. (As No. A125) . . 50 45
G10 – 80c. (As No. 148) . . 55 45
G11 **52** 90c. (Inscr in French) . . 65 50
G12 – 1f. deep green and green (As No. 149) . . . 75 40
G13 **53** 2f. multicoloured . . . . 1·50 1·20
G14 **104** 3f. multicoloured . . . . 2·40 2·10
G15 **3** 10f. blue . . . . 7·75 7·25

1971. Peaceful Uses of the Sea-bed.
G16 **121** 30c. multicoloured . . . 35 35

1971. United Nations Work with Refugees.
G17 **122** 50c. black, orange and red 55 55

1971. World Food Programme.
G18 **123** 50c. multicoloured . . . 55 55

1971. Opening of New Universal Postal Union Headquarters Building, Berne.
G19 **124** 75c. multicoloured . . . 85 85

1971. Racial Equality Year. Designs as Nos. 220/1, with background colours changed.
G20 30c. Type **125** 40 35
G21 50c. Linked globes (horiz) 40 35

1971. U.N. International Schools.
G22 **130** 1f.10 multicoloured . . . 85 75

1972. Non-proliferation of Nuclear Weapons.
G23 **131** 40c. multicoloured . . . 65 65

1972. World Health Day.
G24 **132** 80c. multicoloured . . . 75 75

1972. United Nations Environmental Conservation Conference, Stockholm.
G25 **137** 40c. multicoloured . . . 45 45
G26 80c. multicoloured . . . 70 70

1972. Economic Commission for Europe (ECE).
G27 **138** 1f.10 multicoloured . . . 1·30 1·30

1972. United Nations Art.
G28 **139** 40c. multicoloured . . . 45 45
G29 80c. multicoloured . . . 80 80

1973. Disarmament Decade.
G30 **140** 60c. multicoloured . . . 50 50
G31 1f.10 multicoloured . . . 85 85

1973. "No Drugs" Campaign.
G32 **141** 60c. multicoloured . . . 60 60

1973. U.N. Volunteers Programme.
G33 **142** 80c. multicoloured . . . 70 70

1973. "Namibia" (South West Africa).
G34 **143** 60c. multicoloured . . . 60 60

1973. 25th Anniv of Declaration of Human Rights.
G35 **144** 40c. multicoloured . . . 30 30
G36 80c. multicoloured . . . 70 70

1973. Inauguration of New I.L.O. Headquarters, Geneva.
G37 **145** 60c. multicoloured . . . 40 40
G38 80c. multicoloured . . . 90 90

1973. Centenary of Universal Postal Union.
G39 **146** 30c. multicoloured . . . 25 25
G40 60c. multicoloured . . . 50 50

1974. Brazilian Peace Mural.
G41 **147** 60c. multicoloured . . . 55 55
G42 1f. multicoloured 80 80

1974. World Population Year.
G43 **154** 60c. multicoloured . . . 70 70
G44 80c. multicoloured . . . 75 75

1974. U.N. Conference on "Law of the Sea".
G45 **155** 1f.30 multicoloured . . . 1·20 1·20

1975. Peaceful Uses of Outer Space.
G46 **156** 60c. multicoloured . . . 50 50
G47 90c. multicoloured . . . 90 90

1975. International Women's Year.
G48 **157** 60c. multicoloured . . . 55 55
G49 90c. multicoloured . . . 80 80

1975. 30th Anniv of U.N.O.
G50 **158** 60c. multicoloured . . . 45 45
G51 90c. multicoloured . . . 70 70

1975. "Namibia—U.N. Direct Responsibility".
G53 **160** 50c. multicoloured . . . 45 45
G54 1f.30 multicoloured . . . 85 85

1975. U.N. Peace Keeping Operations.
G55 **161** 60c. blue 80 80
G56 70c. violet 65 65

1976. World Federation of U.N. Associations.
G57 **166** 90c. multicoloured . . . 75 75

1976. U.N. Conf on Trade and Development.
G58 **167** 1f.10 multicoloured . . . 95 95

1976. U.N. Conf on Human Settlements.
G59 **168** 40c. multicoloured . . . 35 35
G60 1f.50 multicoloured . . . 1·20 1·20

G **46** U.N. Emblem within Posthorn

G **49** Rain Drop and Globe

1976. 25th Anniv of U.N. Postal Administration.
G61 G **46** 80c. multicoloured . . . 2·25 2·00
G62 1f.10 multicoloured . . 2·25 2·10

1976. World Food Council Publicity.
G63 **170** 70c. multicoloured . . . 55 55

1977. World Intellectual Property Organization Publicity.
G64 **172** 80c. multicoloured . . . 70 70

1977. U.N. Water Conference.
G65 G **49** 80c. multicoloured . . . 70 70
G66 1f.10 multicoloured . . 90 90

G **50** Protective Hands

1977. Security Council Commemoration.
G67 G **50** 80c. multicoloured . . . 70 70
G68 1f.10 multicoloured . . 90 90

G **51** "Intertwining of Races"

1977. "Combat Racism".
G69 G **51** 40c. multicoloured . . . 30 30
G70 1f.10 multicoloured . . 90 90

G **52** Atoms and Laurel Leaf

G **53** Tree and Birds

1977. "Peaceful Uses for Atomic Energy".
G71 G **52** 80c. multicoloured . . . 70 70
G72 1f.10 multicoloured . . 90 90

1978.
G73 G **53** 35c. multicoloured . . . 30 30

G **54** Smallpox Bacilli and Globe

G **56** Aircraft Flightpaths

1978. Global Eradication of Smallpox.
G74 G **54** 80c. multicoloured . . . 70 70
G75 1f.10 multicoloured . . 90 90

1978. "Namibia: Liberation, Justice, Co-operation".
G76 **183** 80c. multicoloured . . . 70 70

1978. International Civil Aviation Organization—Safety in the Air.
G77 G **56** 70c. multicoloured . . . 55 55
G78 80c. multicoloured . . . 65 65

G **57** Globe, Flags and General Assembly Interior

1978. General Assembly.
G79 G **57** 70c. multicoloured . . . 55 55
G80 1f.10 multicoloured . . 90 90

1978. Technical Co-operation among Developing Countries.
G81 **186** 80c. multicoloured . . . 80 80

G **59** "Disaster"

1979. United Nations Disaster Relief Co-ordinator.
G82 G **59** 80c. multicoloured . . . 65 65
G83 1f.50 multicoloured . . 1·40 1·40

G **60** Children and Rainbow

G **62** Int Court of Justice and Scales

1979. International Year of the Child.
G84 G **60** 80c. multicoloured . . . 75 75
G85 1f.10 multicoloured . . 1·10 1·10

1979. "For a Free and Independent Namibia".
G86 **193** 1f.10 multicoloured . . . 1·00 1·00

1979. International Court of Justice.
G87 G **62** 80c. multicoloured . . . 70 70
G88 1f.10 multicoloured . . 95 95

G **63** Key symbolizing Unity of Action

G **64** Emblem

1980. New International Economic Order.
G89 G **63** 80c. multicoloured . . . 70 70

1980. U.N. Decade for Women.
G90 G **64** 40c. multicoloured . . . 30 30
G91 70c. multicoloured . . . 50 50

1980. Peace Keeping Operations.
G92 **198** 1f.10 blue and green . . 95 95

1980. 35th Anniv of United Nations.
G93 – 40c. black and blue . . . 35 35
G94 **200** 70c. multicoloured . . . 60 60
DESIGN: 40c. Dove and "35".

1980. Economic and Social Council.
G96 **204** 40c. multicoloured . . . 35 35
G97 – 70c. blue, red and black 60 60
DESIGN: 70c. Human figures ascending graph.

1981. Inalienable Rights of the Palestinian People.
G98 **206** 80c. multicoloured . . . 70 70

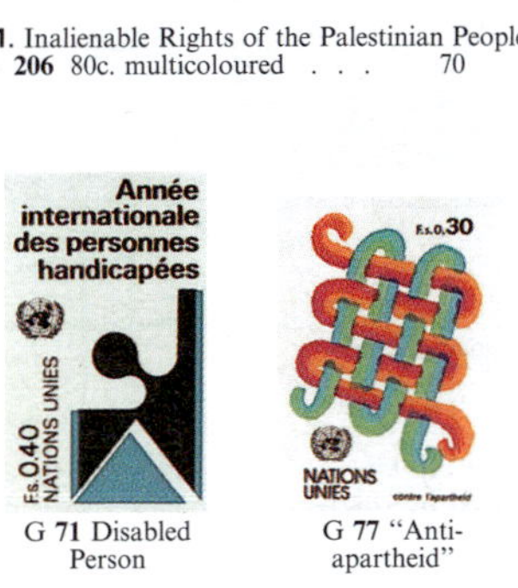

G **71** Disabled Person

G **77** "Anti-apartheid"

1981. International Year of Disabled Persons.
G 99 G **71** 40c. black and blue . . 40 40
G100 – 1f.50 black and red . . 1·30 1·30
DESIGN: 1f.50, Knot pattern.

1981. Art.
G101 **209** 80c. multicoloured . . . 70 70

1981. New and Renewable Sources of Energy.
G102 **210** 1f.10 multicoloured . . 95 95

1981. 10th Anniv of U.N. Volunteers Programme. Multicoloured.
G103 40c. Type **212** 35 35
G104 70c. Emblems of science, agriculture and industry 60 60

1982. Multicoloured.
G105 30c. Type G **77** 30 30
G106 1f. Flags 85 85

1982. Human Environment. Multicoloured.
G107 40c. Leaves 35 35
G108 1f.20 Type **217** . . . . . 1·10 1·10

1982. Second United Nations Conference on Exploration and Peaceful Uses of Outer Space.
G109 **219** 80c. violet, pink & green 70 70
G110 – 1f. multicoloured . . . 80 80
DESIGN: 1f. Satellite and emblems.

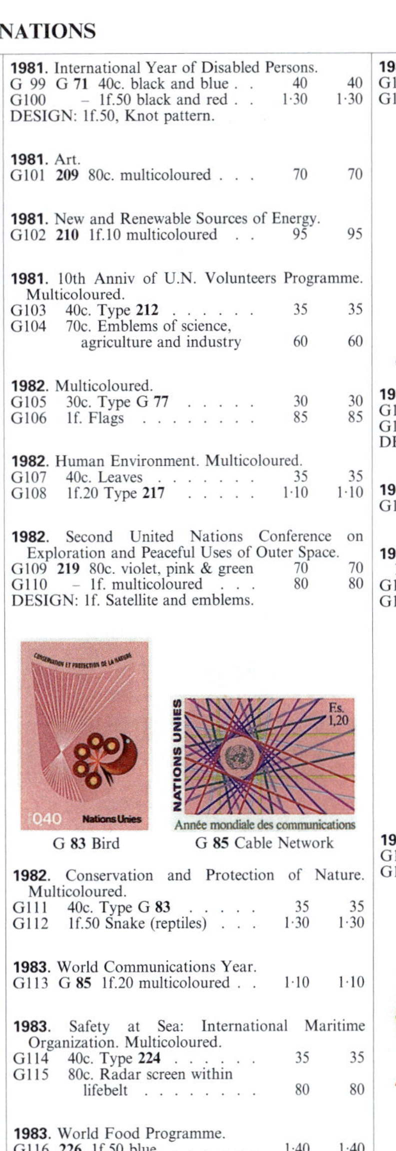

G **83** Bird

G **85** Cable Network

1982. Conservation and Protection of Nature. Multicoloured.
G111 40c. Type G **83** 35 35
G112 1f.50 Snake (reptiles) . . . 1·30 1·30

1983. World Communications Year.
G113 G **85** 1f.20 multicoloured . . 1·10 1·10

1983. Safety at Sea: International Maritime Organization. Multicoloured.
G114 40c. Type **224** 35 35
G115 80c. Radar screen within lifebelt 80 80

1983. World Food Programme.
G116 **226** 1f.50 blue . . . . . . 1·40 1·40

1983. Trade and Development. Multicoloured.
G117 80c. Type **227** 75 75
G118 1f.10 Exports . . . . . . 1·00 1·00

G **91** "Homo Humus Humanitas"

G **93** World Housing

1983. 35th Anniv of Universal Declaration of Human Rights. Multicoloured.
G119 40c. Type G **91** 50 50
G120 1f.20 "Droit de Creer" . . 1·20 1·20

1984. International Conference on Population, Mexico City.
G121 G **93** 1f.20 multicoloured . . 1·10 1·10

G **94** Fishing

1984. World Food Day. Multicoloured.
G122 50c. Type G **94** 65 65
G123 80c. Planting saplings . . . 75 75

G **96** Fort St. Angelo, Malta (wrongly inscr "Valetta")

1984. World Heritage—U.N.E.S.C.O. Mult.
G124 50c. Type G **96** 55 55
G125 70c. Los Glaciares, Argentina 65 65

G **98** Man and Woman

G **100** Heads

1984. Future for Refugees.
G126 G **98** 35c. black and green 35 35
G127 – 1f.50 black and brown 1·40 1·40
DESIGN: 1f.50, Head of woman.

1984. International Youth Year.
G128 G **100** 1f.20 multicoloured 1·20 1·20

1985. 20th Anniv of Turin Centre of International Labour Organization.
G129 **239** 80c. red 75 75
G130 V **43** 1f.20 green . . . . . 1·10 1·10

G **103** Ploughing and Group of People

1985. 10th Anniv of U.N. University, Tokyo.
G131 G **103** 50c. multicoloured . . 65 65
G132 80c. multicoloured . . 80 80

G **104** Postman

G **108** Children

1985.
G133 G **104** 20c. multicoloured . . 20 20
G134 – 1f.20 blue and black 95 95
DESIGN: 1f.20, Doves.

1985. 40th Anniv of United Nations Organization. Multicoloured.
G135 50c. Type **243** 50 50
G136 70c. "Harvest Scene" (Andrew Wyeth) 65 65

1985. U.N.I.C.E.F. Child Survival Campaign. Multicoloured.
G138 50c. Type G **108** 40 40
G139 1f.20 Child drinking . . . 1·30 1·30

G **110** Children raising Empty Bowls to weeping Mother

G **111** Herring Gulls

1986. Africa in Crisis.
G140 G **110** 1f.40 multicoloured 1·50 1·50

1986.
G141 G **111** 5c. multicoloured . . 15 15

G **112** Tents in Clearing

1986. Development Programme. Timber Production. Multicoloured.
G142 35c. Type G **112** . . . . . 2·50 2·30
G143 35c. Felling tree . . . . . 2·50 2·30
G144 35c. Logs on lorries . . . . 2·50 2·30
G145 35c. Girls with sapling . . 2·50 2·30
Nos. G142/5 were printed together, se-tenant, forming a composite design.

1986. Philately: The International Hobby.
G146 **253** 50c. green and red . . . 55 55
G147 – 80c. black and orange 95 95
DESIGN: 80c. United Nations stamps (as Type V **56**).

G **118** Ribbon forming Dove

1986. International Peace Year. Multicoloured.
G148 45c. Type G **118** 55 55
G149 1f.40 "Paix" and olive branch . . . . 1·50 1·60

1987. 9th Death Anniv of Trygve Lie (first U.N. Secretary-General).
G151 **258** 1f.40 multicoloured . . 1·50 1·50

G **122** Abstract
G **124** Mixing Cement and Carrying Bricks

1987. Multicoloured.
G152 90c. Type G **122** 90 90
G153 1f.40 Armillary Sphere, Geneva Centre (30 × 30 mm) . . . . . . 1·40 1·40

1987. International Year of Shelter for the Homeless.
G154 G **124** 50c. green and black 60 60
G155 – 90c. blue, turquoise and black . . . . 1·10 1·10
DESIGN: 90c. Fitting windows and painting.

G **126** Mother and Baby

1987. Anti-drugs Campaign. Multicoloured.
G156 80c. Type G **126** . . . . . 1·10 1·10
G157 1f.20 Workers in paddy field . . . . 1·60 1·60

G **128** People in Boat and Palais des Nations, Geneva
G **130** Whooping Cough

1987. United Nations Day. Multicoloured.
G158 35c. Type G **128** 45 45
G159 50c. Dancers 75 75

1987. "Immunize Every Child". Multicoloured.
G160 90c. Type G **130** . . . . . 1·00 1·00
G161 1f.70 Tuberculosis . . . . 1·90 1·90

G **132** Goatherd
G **134** People

1988. International Fund for Agricultural Development "For a World Without Hunger" Campaign. Multicoloured.
G162 35c. Type G **132** 55 55
G163 1f.40 Women and baskets of fruit . . . . 1·50 1·50

1988.
G164 G **134** 50c. multicoloured . . 50 50

G **135** Mountains and Pine Forest
G **137** Instruction in Fruit Growing

1988. "Survival of the Forests". Multicoloured.
G165 50c. Type G **135** . . . . . 4·75 4·50
G166 1f.10 Pine forest and lake shore . . . . 4·75 4·50
Nos. G165/6 were printed together, se-tenant, forming a composite design.

1988. International Volunteer Day. Mult.
G167 80c. Type G **137** 80 80
G168 90c. Teaching animal husbandary (horiz) . . . 95 95

G **139** Football
G **142** Communications

1988. "Health in Sports". Multicoloured.
G169 50f. Type G **139** 55 55
G170 1f.40 Swimming . . . . . 1·60 1·60

1988. 40th Anniv of Declaration of Human Rights.
G171 **276** 90c. multicoloured . . . 1·00 1·00

1989. World Bank. Multicoloured.
G173 80c. Type G **142** 85 85
G174 1f.40 Industry . . . . . . 1·50 1·50

1989. Award of Nobel Peace Prize to United Nations Peace-keeping Forces.
G175 **280** 90c. multicoloured . . . 1·10 1·10

G **145** Cold Arctic Air over Europe
G **147** Tree and Birds

1989. 25th Anniv of World Weather Watch.
G176 90c. Type G **145** . . . . . 1·00 1·00
G177 1f.10 Surface temperatures of Kattegat . . . . . . 1·30 1·30

1989. 10th Anniv of United Nations Vienna International Centre.
G178 50c. Type G **147** 75 75
G179 2f. Woman and flower . . 2·10 2·10

G **149** "Young Mother sewing" (Mary Cassatt) (Article 3)

1989. Universal Declaration of Human Rights (1st series). Multicoloured.
G180 35f. Type G **149** 80 80
G181 80f. "Runaway Slave" (Albert Mangones) (Article 4) . . . . 1·80 1·80
See also Nos. G193/4, G209/10, G224/5 and G234/5.

1990. International Trade Centre.
G182 **288** 1f.50 multicoloured . . 1·80 1·80

G **152** Palais des Nations
G **155** Frangipani

1990.
G183 G **152** 5f. multicoloured . . 5·00 5·00

1990. Anti-AIDS Campaign. Multicoloured.
G184 50c. Type **289** 65 65
G185 80c. "Man" (Leonardo da Vinci) . . . . 1·10 1·10

1990. Medicinal Plants. Multicoloured.
G186 90c. Type G **155** . . . . . 1·00 1·00
G187 1f.40 "Cinchona officinalis" 1·60 1·60

G **157** Projects forming "45"

1990. 45th Anniv of U.N.O. Multicoloured.
G188 90c. Type G **157** . . . . . 1·10 1·10
G189 1f.10 Dove and "45" . . . 1·50 1·50

G **159** Men making Deal over Painting

1990. Crime Prevention. Multicoloured.
G191 50c. Type G **159** 65 65
G192 2f. Man spilling waste from cart . . . . 2·50 2·50

1990. Universal Declaration of Human Rights (2nd series). As Type G **149**.
G193 35c. multicoloured . . . . 1·20 1·20
G194 90c. black and flesh . . . . 3·00 3·00
DESIGNS: 35c. "Prison Courtyard" (Vincent van Gogh) (Article 9); 90c. "Katho's Son Redeems the Evil Doer from Execution" (Albrecht Durer) (Article 10).

G **163/166** Lake (½-size illustration)

1991. Economic Commission for Europe. "For a Better Environment".
G195 G **163** 90c. multicoloured . . 2·00 2·00
G196 G **164** 90c. multicoloured . . 2·00 2·00
G197 G **165** 90c. multicoloured . . 2·00 2·00
G198 G **166** 90c. multicoloured . . 2·00 2·00
Nos. G195/8 were issued together, se-tenant, forming the composite design illustrated.

G **167** Mountains
G **169** Papers and Ballot Box

1991. 1st Anniv of Namibian Independence. Multicoloured.
G199 70c. Type G **167** 85 75
G200 90c. Baobab . . . . 1·00 95

1991. Multicoloured.
G201 80c. Type G **169** 90 90
G202 1f.50 U.N. emblem . . . . 1·70 1·70

G **171** Baby in Open Hands (Ryuta Nakajima)

1991. 30th Anniv (1989) of U.N. Declaration of the Rights of the Child and 1990 World Summit on Children, New York. Children's Drawings. Multicoloured.
G203 80c. Type G **171** . . . . . 1·00 1·00
G204 1f.10 Children playing amongst flowers (David Popper) . . . . 1·20 1·20

G **173** Bubble of Toxin, City and Drums

1991. Banning of Chemical Weapons. Mult.
G205 80c. Type G **173** 95 95
G206 1f.40 Hand pushing back gas mask . . . . 1·50 1·50

G **175** U.N. (New York) 1951 15c. Stamp

1991. 40th Anniv of United Nations Postal Administration.
G207 G **175** 50c. blue and lilac on cream 60 60
G208 – 1f.60 blue on cream 1·90 1·90
DESIGN: 1f.60, U.N. (New York) 1951 50c. stamp.

1991. Declaration of Human Rights (3rd series). As Type G **149**. Multicoloured.
G209 50c. "Early Morning in Ro, 1925" (Paul Klee) (Article 15) . . . . . . 1·70 1·70
G210 90c. "The Marriage of Arnolfini" (Jan van Eyck) (Article 16) . . . 3·25 3·25

G **179** Sagarmatha National Park, Nepal
G **181** U.N. Headquarters, New York

1992. 20th Anniv of U.N.E.S.C.O. World Heritage Convention. Multicoloured.
G211 50c. Type G **179** 60 60
G212 1f.10 Stonehenge, United Kingdom . . . . 1·70 1·70

1992.
G213 G **181** 3f. multicoloured . . 3·00 3·00

G **182/183** Sea Life (½-size illustration)

1992. "Clean Oceans".
G214 G **182** 80c. multicoloured . . 1·40 1·40
G215 G **183** 80c. multicoloured . . 1·40 1·40
Nos. G214/15 were issued together, se-tenant, forming the composite design illustrated.

G 184/187 Planet Earth (½-size illustration)

1992. 2nd U.N. Conference on Environment and Development, Rio de Janeiro.

G216	G **184**	75c. multicoloured	1·10	1·10
G217	G **185**	75c. multicoloured	1·10	1·10
G218	G **186**	75c. multicoloured	1·10	1·10
G219	G **187**	75c. multicoloured	1·10	1·10

Nos. G216/19 were issued together, se-tenant, forming the composite design illustrated.

G 188/189 "Mission Planet Earth" (½-size illustration)

1992. International Space Year. Roul.

G220	G **188**	1f.10 multicoloured	1·60	1·60
G221	G **189**	1f.10 multicoloured	1·60	1·60

Nos. G220/1 were issued together, se-tenant, forming the composite design illustrated.

G 190 Women in Science and Technology

G 194 Voluntary Work

1992. Commission on Science and Technology for Development. Multicoloured.

G222	90c. Type G **190**	1·10	1·10
G223	1f.60 Graduate using V.D.U.	1·90	1·90

1992. Universal Declaration of Human Rights (4th series). As Type G **149**. Multicoloured.

G224	50c. "The Oath of the Tennis Court" (Jacques Louis David) (Article 21)	1·70	1·70
G225	90c. "Rocking Chair I" (Henry Moore) (Article 22)	3·25	3·25

1993. "Ageing: Dignity and Participation". 10th Anniv (1992) of International Plan of Action on Ageing. Multicoloured.

G226	50c. Type G **194**	60	60
G227	1f.60 Security of employment	1·80	1·80

G 196 Gorilla

1993. Endangered Species (1st series). Multicoloured.

G228	80c. Type G **196**	90	90
G229	80c. Peregrine falcon ("Falco peregrinus")	90	90
G230	80c. Amazon manatee ("Tricheous inunguis")	90	90
G231	80c. Snow leopard ("Panthera uncia")	90	90

See also Nos. G246/9, G264/7, G290/3, G308/11, G333/6, G372/5, G389/92, G409/12 and G433/6.

G 200 Neighbourhood and Community Environment

1993. 45th Anniv of W.H.O. Multicoloured.

G232	60c. Type G **200**	75	75
G233	1f. Urban environment	1·20	1·20

1993. Declaration of Human Rights (5th series). As Type G **149**. Multicoloured.

G234	50c. "Three Musicians" (Pablo Picasso) (Article 27)	1·40	1·40
G235	90c. "Voice of Space" (Rene Magritte) (Article 28)	2·75	2·75

G 204/207 Peace (½-size illustration)

1993. International Peace Day. Roul.

G236	G **204**	60c. multicoloured	95	95
G237	G **205**	60c. multicoloured	95	95
G238	G **206**	60c. multicoloured	95	95
G239	G **207**	60c. multicoloured	95	95

Nos. G236/9 were issued together, se-tenant, forming the composite design illustrated.

G 208 Polar Bears

1993. The Environment—Climate. Multicoloured.

G240	1f.10 Type G **208**	1·60	1·60
G241	1f.10 Whale in melting ice	1·60	1·60
G242	1f.10 Elephant seal	1·60	1·60
G243	1f.10 Adelie penguins	1·60	1·60

Nos. G240/3 were issued together, se-tenant, forming a composite design.

G 212 Father calling Child

G 218 Hand delivering Refugee to New Country

1994. International Year of the Family. Mult.

G244	80c. Type G **212**	85	85
G245	1f. Three generations	1·20	1·60

1994. Endangered Species (2nd series). As Type G **196**. Multicoloured.

G246	80c. Mexican prairie dogs ("Cynomys mexicanus")	90	90
G247	80c. Jabiru ("Jabiru mycteria")	90	90
G248	80c. Blue whale ("Balaenoptera musculus")	90	90
G249	80c. Golden lion tamarin ("Leontopithecus rosalia")	90	90

1994. U.N. High Commissioner for Refugees.

G250	G **218**	1f.20 multicoloured	1·50	1·50

G 219/222 Shattered Globe and "Evaluation" (½-size illustration)

1994. International Decade for Natural Disaster Reduction.

G251	G **219**	60c. multicoloured	1·00	1·00
G252	G **220**	60c. multicoloured	1·00	1·00
G253	G **221**	60c. multicoloured	1·00	1·00
G254	G **222**	60c. multicoloured	1·00	1·00

Nos. G251/4 were issued together, se-tenant, forming the composite design illustrated.

G 223 Mobilization of Resources in Developing Countries

1994. International Population and Development Conference, Cairo. Multicoloured.

G255	60c. Type G **223**	65	65
G256	80c. Internal migration of population	85	85

G 225 Palais des Nations, Geneva

1994. Multicoloured.

G257	60c. Type G **225**	70	70
G258	80c. "Creation of the World" (detail of tapestry, Oili Maki)	95	95
G259	1f.80 Palais des Nations	1·90	1·90

G 228 Map and Linked Ribbons

1994. 30th Anniv of United Nations Conference on Trade and Development.

G260	80c. Type G **228**	1·00	1·00
G261	1f. Map and ribbons	1·20	1·20

1995. 50th Anniv of U.N.O. (1st issue).

G262	**371**	80c. multicoloured	95	95

See also Nos. G270/1 and G275/86.

G 231 "Social Summit 1995"

1995. World Summit for Social Development, Copenhagen.

G263	G **231**	1f. multicoloured	1·40	1·40

1995. Endangered Species (3rd series). As Type G **196**. Multicoloured.

G264	80c. Crowned lemur ("Lemur coronatus")	90	95
G265	80c. Giant scops owl ("Otus gurneyi")	90	95
G266	80c. Painted frog ("Atelopus varius zeteki")	90	95
G267	80c. American wood bison ("Bison bison athabascae")	90	95

G 236 Field in Summer

1995. "Youth: Our Future". 10th Anniv of International Youth Year. Multicoloured.

G268	80c. Type G **236**	95	95
G269	1f. Field in winter	1·20	1·20

1995. 50th Anniv of U.N.O. (2nd issue).

G270	**379**	60c. purple	75	75
G271	–	1f.80 green	1·90	1·90

DESIGN: 1f.80, Veteran's Memorial Hall and Opera House, San Francisco (venue for signing of Charter).

G 240 Woman and Cranes

G 254 Catching Fish

1995. 4th World Conference on Women, Peking. Multicoloured.

G273	60c. Type G **240**	80	80
G274	1f. Women worshipping (30×49 mm)	1·20	1·20

1995. 50th Anniv of U.N.O. (3rd issue).

G275	**385**	30c. multicoloured	40	40
G276	**386**	30c. multicoloured	40	40
G277	**387**	30c. multicoloured	40	40
G278	**388**	30c. multicoloured	40	40
G279	**389**	30c. multicoloured	40	40
G280	**390**	30c. multicoloured	40	40
G281	**391**	30c. multicoloured	40	40
G282	**392**	30c. multicoloured	40	40
G283	**393**	30c. multicoloured	40	40
G284	**394**	30c. multicoloured	40	40
G285	**395**	30c. multicoloured	40	40
G286	**396**	30c. multicoloured	40	40

Nos. G275/80 and G281/6 respectively were issued together, se-tenant, forming two composite designs.

1996. 50th Anniv of World Federation of United Nations Associations.

G287	G **254**	80c. multicoloured	1·10	1·10

G 255 "Galloping Horse treading on a Flying Swallow" (Chinese bronze sculpture, Han Dynasty)

1996. Multicoloured.

G288	40c. Type G **255**	40	45
G289	70c. Palais des Nations, Geneva	75	85

1996. Endangered Species (4th series). As Type G **196**. Multicoloured.

G290	80c. "Paphiopedilum delenatii"	85	85
G291	80c. "Pachypodium baronii"	85	85
G292	80c. Yellow amaryllis ("Sternbergia lutea")	85	85
G293	80c. Cobra plant ("Darlingtonia californica")	85	85

G 261 Family on Verandah of House

1996. "Habitat II" Second United Nations Conference on Human Settlements, Istanbul, Turkey. Multicoloured.

G294	70c. Type G **261**	85	85
G295	70c. Women in traditional dress in gardens	1·10	1·10
G296	70c. Produce seller and city	1·10	1·10
G297	70c. Boys playing on riverside	1·10	1·10
G298	70c. Elderly couple reading newspaper	1·10	1·10

Nos. G294/8 were issued together, se-tenant, forming a composite design.

G 266 Cycling

G 268 Birds in Treetop

1996. Sport and the Environment. Multicoloured.
G299 70c. Type G **266** 75 75
G300 1f.10 Running (horiz) . . . 1·30 1·30

1996. "A Plea for Peace". Winning Entries in China Youth Design Competition. Multicoloured.
G302 90c. Type G **268** 95 95
G303 1f.10 Flowers growing from bomb . . . . 1·30 1·30

G **270** "The Sun and the Moon" (South American legend)

1996. 50th Anniv of U.N.I.C.E.F. Multicoloured.
G304 70c. Type G **270** 80 80
G305 1f.80 "Ananse" (African spider tale) . . . . . . 1·70 1·70

G **272** U.N. Flag

1997.
G306 10c. Type G **272** 15 15
G307 1f.10 "Building Palais des Nations" (detail of fresco, Massimo Campigli) . . . . 1·10 1·10

1997. Endangered Species (5th series). As Type G **196**. Multicoloured.
G308 80f. Polar bear ("Ursus maritimus") 85 85
G309 80f. Blue crowned pigeon ("Goura cristata") . . . 85 85
G310 80f. Marine iguana ("Amblyrhynchus cristatus") 85 85
G311 80f. Guanaco ("Lama guanicoe") 85 85

G **278/281** Sunrise over Mountains ($\frac{2}{3}$-size illustration)

1997. "Earth Summit + 5". 5th Anniv of United Nations Conference on Environment and Development.
G312 G **278** 45f. multicoloured . . 60 60
G313 G **279** 45f. multicoloured . . 60 60
G314 G **280** 45f. multicoloured . . 60 60
G315 G **281** 45f. multicoloured . . 60 60
Nos. G312/15 were issued together, se-tenant, forming the composite design illustrated.

G **282** Fokker F.7 Trimotor and Airship

1997. 50th Anniversaries of Economic Commission for Europe and Economic and Social Commission for Asia and the Pacific. Multicoloured.
G317 70f. Type G **282** . . . . . 1·00 1·00
G318 70f. Lockheed Constellation and Boeing 314 flying boat . . . . 1·00 1·00
G319 70f. De Havilland D.H.106 Comet and Boeing 747 jetliners . . . . 1·00 1·00
G320 70f. Ilyushin and Boeing 747 jetliners . . . . . . 1·00 1·00
G321 70f. Concorde Supersonic jetliner . . . . 1·00 1·00

Nos. 317/21 were issued together, se-tenant, forming a composite design.

1997. "Tribute to Philately". Multicoloured.
G322 70c. Type G **432** 85 85
G323 1f.10 1986 80c. philately stamp (as Type V **227**) 1·20 1·20

1997. 25th Anniv of World Heritage Convention. Terracotta Warriors from Emperor Qin Shi Huang's Tomb, Xian, China. Multicoloured.
G324 10c. As Type **434** 35 35
G325 10c. As No. 737 . . . . 55 55
G326 10c. As No. 738 . . . . 25 25
G327 10c. As No. 739 . . . . 25 25
G328 10c. As No. 740 . . . . 25 25
G329 10c. As No. 741 . . . . 25 25
G330 45c. As No. 738 . . . . 50 50
G331 70c. As No. 739 . . . . 70 70

G **295** Palais des Nations, Geneva

1998.
G332 G **295** 2f. multicoloured . . 2·10 2·10

1998. Endangered Species (6th series). As Type G **196**. Multicoloured.
G333 80c. Tibetan stump-tailed macaques ("Macaca thibetana") 85 85
G334 80c. Greater flamingoes ("Phoenicopterus ruber") 85 85
G335 80c. Queen Alexandra's birdwings ("Ornithoptera alexandrae") 85 85
G336 80c. Fallow deer ("Cervus dama") 85 85

G **300** Bull Seal

1998. International Year of the Ocean. Multicoloured.
G337 45c. Type G **300** 50 50
G338 45c. Polar bears 50 50
G339 45c. Polar bear, musk oxen, king penguins and seal on ice 50 50
G340 45c. Diver 50 50
G341 45c. Seals 50 50
G342 45c. Narwhal 50 50
G343 45c. Fishes and shark . . . 50 50
G344 45c. Shark's tail, seal and horned puffin 50 50
G345 45c. Fishes and gentoo penguin's back 50 50
G346 45c. Fish and jellyfishes . . . 50 50
G347 45c. Seal, gentoo penguin and squid 50 50
G348 45c. gentoo penguin hunting fishes 50 50

G **301** Orang-utan with Young

1998. Rainforest Preservation.
G349 G **301** 70c. multicoloured . . 85 85

G **302** Soldier with Children

1998. 50 Years of United Nations Peacekeeping. Multicoloured.
G351 70c. Type G **302** 75 75
G352 90c. Soldier holding baby 1·00 1·00

G **304** Birds

1998. 50th Anniv of Universal Declaration of Human Rights. Multicoloured.
G353 90c. Type G **304** . . . . . 1·00 1·00
G354 1f.80 Hand releasing birds 2·00 2·00

1998. World Heritage Site. Schonbrunn Palace, Vienna. Multicoloured.
G355 10c. As No. 780 . . . . . 50 55
G356 10c. As No. 781 . . . . . 60 60
G357 10c. As No. 782 . . . . . 30 30
G358 30c. As Type **454** 40 45
G359 30c. As No. 778 . . . . . 40 45
G360 30c. As No. 779 . . . . . 40 45
G361 70c. As No. 781 . . . . . 60 60
G362 1f.10 As Type **454** . . . . 1·20 1·30

G **312** Palais Wilson, Geneva

1999. Headquarters of United Nations High Commissioner for Human Rights.
G363 G **312** 1f.70 red . . . . 1·90 1·90

1999. World Heritage Sites in Australia. Mult.
G364 10c. As Type **462** 25 25
G365 10c. As No. 796 . . . . . 20 20
G366 10c. As No. 797 . . . . . 20 20
G367 20c. As No. 798 . . . . . 30 30
G368 20c. As No. 799 . . . . . 30 30
G369 20c. As No. 800 . . . . . 30 30
G370 90c. As No. 801 . . . . . 1·10 1·10
G371 1f.10 As No. 802 . . . . . 1·30 1·30

1999. Endangered Species (7th series). As Type G **196**. Multicoloured.
G372 90c. Asiatic wild ass ("Equus hemionus") . . 95 95
G373 90c. Hyacinth macaw ("Anodorhynchus hyacinthinus") 95 95
G374 90c. Jamaican boa ("Epicrates subflavus") 95 95
G375 90c. Bennett's tree kangaroo ("Dendrolagus bennettianus") 95 95

G **323/324** Satellite-aided Agriculture ($\frac{1}{2}$-size illustration)

1999. 3rd Conference on Exploration and Peaceful Uses of Outer Space, Vienna.
G376 G **323** 45c. multicoloured . . 60 60
G377 G **324** 45c. multicoloured . . 60 60
Nos. G376/7 were issued together, se-tenant, forming the composite design illustrated.

G **325/328** Early 20th-century Mail Transport ($\frac{1}{2}$-size illustration)

1999. 125th Anniv of Universal Postal Union.
G380 G **325** 70c. multicoloured . . 85 85
G381 G **326** 70c. multicoloured . . 85 85
G382 G **327** 70c. multicoloured . . 85 85
G383 G **328** 70c. multicoloured . . 85 85
Nos. G380/3 were issued together, se-tenant, forming the composite design illustrated.

G **329** Palais des Nations, Geneva

1999. "In Memoriam: Fallen in the Cause of Peace".
G384 G **329** 1f.10 multicoloured 1·30 1·30

G **331** Couple on Globe

1999. Education: Keystone to the 21st Century.
G386 90c. Type G **331** . . . . . 1·00 1·00
G387 1f.80 "Environment" . . . 2·10 2·10

2000. International Year of Thanksgiving. Mult.
G388 90c. As Type **483** . . . . 1·30 1·30

2000. Endangered Species (8th series). As Type G **196**. Multicoloured.
G389 90c. Hippopotamus (*Hippopotamus amphibius*) 1·40 1·40
G390 90c. Coscoroba swan (*Coscoroba coscoroba*) . . 1·40 1·40
G391 90c. Emerald monitor (*Varanus prasinus*) . . . 1·40 1·40
G392 90c. Sea otter (*Enhydra lutris*) . . . . 1·40 1·40

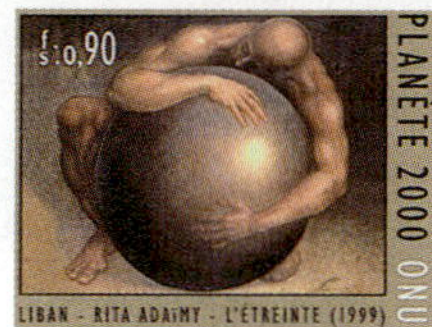

G **338** "The Embrace" (Rita Adaimy)

2000. "Our World 2000" International Art Exhibition, New York. Entries in Millennium Painting Competition. Multicoloured.
G393 90c. Type G **338** . . . . . 1·30 1·30
G394 1f.10 "Living Single" (Richard Kimanthi) (vert) 1·30 1·30

G **340** Corner Stone Dedication, 1949

2000. 55th Anniv of the United Nations and 50th Anniv of Opening of U.N. Headquarters, New York.
G395 G **340** 90c. red, blue and ochre . . . . . . 1·20 1·20
G396 – 1f.40 red, blue and ochre . . . . . . 1·50 1·50
DESIGN: 1f.40, Window cleaner, Secretariat Building, 1951.

2000. World Heritage Sites in Spain. Multicoloured.
G399 10c. As Type **496** 25 25
G400 10c. As No. 832 . . . . . 25 25
G401 10c. As No. 833 . . . . . 25 25
G402 20c. As No. 834 . . . . . 25 25
G403 20c. As No. 835 . . . . . 25 25
G404 20c. As No. 836 . . . . . 25 25
G405 1f. As No. 837 . . . . . 1·10 1·10
G406 1f.20 As No. 838 . . . . . 1·20 1·20

G 350 Family of Refugees

2000. 50th Anniv of United Nations High Commissioner for Refugees.
G407 G **350** 80c. multicoloured . . 1·10 1·10

2001. Endangered Species (9th series). As Type G **196**. Multicoloured.
G409 90c. Lynx (*Felis lynx canadensis*) . . . . . . 1·10 1·10
G410 90c. Green peafowl (*Pavo muticus*) . . . . 1·10 1·10
G411 90c. Galapagos tortoise (*Geochelone elephantopus*) 1·10 1·10
G412 90c. Lemur (*Lepilemur* sp.) 1·10 1·10

G **356** Hands forming Heart (Ernest Pignon-Ernest)

2001. United Nations International Year of Volunteers. Multicoloured.
G413 90c. Type G **356** . . . . . 1·10 1·10
G414 1f.30 Women's head and white dove (Paul Siche) 1·20 1·20

2001. World Heritage Sites in Japan. Multicoloured.
G415 10c. As Type **512** 20 20
G416 10c. As No. 858 . . . . . 20 20
G417 10c. As No. 859 . . . . . 20 20
G418 30c. As No. 860 . . . . . 40 40
G419 30c. As No. 861 . . . . . 40 40
G420 30c. As No. 862 . . . . . 40 40
G421 1f.10 As No. 858 . . . . . 1·20 1·20
G422 1f.30 As No. 861 . . . . . 1·00 1·60

2001. 40th Death Anniv of Dag Hammarskjold (United Nations Secretary General, 1953–61).
G423 **518** 2f. red . . . . 1·30 1·30

G **365** Postman and "Stamps" G **368** Flowers and Coastline

2001. 50th Anniv of United Nations Postal Administration. Multicoloured.
G424 90c. Type G **365** 95 95
G425 1f.30 Trumpets and "Stamps" . . . . 1·40 1·40

2001. Climate Change. Multicoloured.
G427 90c. Type G **368** 95 95
G428 90c. Wind-powered generators and brick making 95 95
G429 90c. Power station inside glass dome 95 95
G430 90c. Couple sitting beside lake 95 95
Nos. G427/30 were issued together, se-tenant, forming a composite design.

2001. Kofi Annan, Winner of Nobel Peace Prize, 2001.
G431 **526** 90c. multicoloured . . . 95 95

G **373** Armillary Sphere, Ariana Park

2002.
G432 G **373** 1f.30 multicoloured 1·00 1·00

2002. Endangered Species (10th series). As Type G **196**. Multicoloured.
G433 90c. Bald uakari (*Cacajao calvus*) 95 95
G434 90c. Ratel (*Mellivora capensis*) 95 95
G435 90c. Pallas's cat (*Otocolobus manul*) 95 95
G436 90c. Savannah monitor (*Varanus exanthematicus*) 95 95

2002. East Timor Independence. As T **532**. Multicoloured.
G437 90c. Wooden statue 75 75
G438 1f.30 Carved wooden container . . . . 1·10 1·10

2002. International Year of Mountains. As T **534**. Multicoloured.
G439 70c. Type Weisshorn, Switzerland 55 55
G440 70c. Mount Fuji, Japan . . 55 55
G441 1f.20 Vinson Massif, Antarctica 95 95
G442 1f.20 Kamet, India 95 95

G **384** Sun, Water, Birds and Flowers

2002. World Summit on Sustainable Development, Johannesburg. Multicoloured.
G443 90c. Type G **384** 75 75
G444 90c. Figure's wearing fashionable dress 75 75
G445 1f.80 Women's profile . . . 1·50 1·50
G446 1f.80 Yacht . . . . 1·50 1·50

2002. World Heritage Sites in Italy. As T **542**. Multicoloured.
G447 10c. Duomo di Sant'Andrea, Amalfi Coast 10 10
G448 10c. View across Islands, Aeolian Islands 10 10
G449 10c. Del Moro Fountain, Rome 10 10
G450 20c. Santa Maria del Fiore, Florence 20 20
G451 20c. Leaning Tower, Pisa 20 20
G452 20c. The Forum, Pompeii 20 20
G453 90c. As No. G451 . . . . 80 80
G454 1f.30 As No. G448 . . . . 1·20 1·20

2002. AIDS Awareness Campaign. As T **548**.
G455 1f.30 AIDS Symbol on UN Secretariat Building, New York 1·20 1·20
MSG456 80 × 80 mm. 90c.+30c. AIDS symbol on UN Secretariat Building, New York at night 1·20 1·20
The premium was for AIDS charities.

G **396** Doves

2002.
G457 G **396** 3f. multicoloured . . 2·75 2·75

C. VIENNA HEADQUARTERS.

For use on mail posted at the United Nations Vienna International Centre and by the International Atomic Energy Agency.

1979. 100 groschen = 1 schilling.
2002. 100 cents = 1 euro.

NOTE. Reference to numbers and types in this section, other than those with a "V" prefix, are to the United Nations (New York or Geneva) Headquarters listing. Designs adapted for the Vienna issues are inscribed in Austrian and have face values in schillings.

V **4** Donaupark Complex

1979. Some designs adapted from issues of New York or Geneva Headquarters. Multicoloured.
V1 50g. Type G **53** 10 10
V2 1s. As No. 94 . . . . 10 10
V3 2s.50 Type **162** 30 30
V3a 3s. "... for a better world" 35 35
V4 4s. Type V **4** 35 35
V5 5s. Type A **134** 45 40
V6 6s. Aerial view of Donaupark (vert) 55 50
V7 10s. As Type **52**, but without frame 90 85

1980. New International Economic Order.
V8 **195** 4s. multicoloured . . . . 1·10 1·10

V **9** Dove and World Map

1980. U.N. Decade for Women.
V 9 V **9** 4s. multicoloured 40 40
V10 6s. multicoloured 60 60

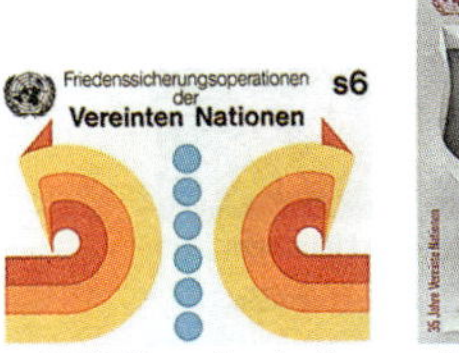

V **10** "Peace-keeping" V **11** Dove and "35"

1980. Peace-keeping Operations.
V11 V **10** 6s. multicoloured . . . 70 70

1980. 35th Anniv of U.N.O.
V12 V **11** 4s. black and red . . . 40 40
V13 – 6s. multicoloured . . . 60 60
DESIGN: 6s. Stylized flower.

V **13** Economic and Social Emblems

1980. Economic and Social Council. Multicoloured.
V15 V **13** 4s. multicoloured . . . 40 40
V16 – 6s. green, red and black 60 60
DESIGN: 6s. Figures ascending graph.

1981. "Inalienable Rights of the Palestinian People".
V17 **206** 4s. multicoloured 40 40

1981. International Year of Disabled Persons.
V18 **207** 4s. multicoloured 40 40
V19 – 6s. orange and black . . 60 60
DESIGN: 6s. Knot pattern.

1981. Art.
V20 **209** 6s. multicoloured 65 65

V **19** U.N. Energy Conference Emblem

1981. New and Renewable Sources of Energy.
V21 V **19** 7s.50 gold and mauve 85 85

V **20** Symbols of Services

1981. 10th Anniv of U.N. Volunteers Programme. Multicoloured.
V22 5s. Type V **20** 50 50
V23 7s. Emblems of science, agriculture and industry 75 75

V **22** Symbols of the Environment V **24** Satellite and Emblems

1982. Human Environment. Multicoloured.
V24 5s. Type V **22** 50 50
V25 7s. Leaves 75 75

1982. Second United Nations Conference on Exploration and Peaceful Uses of Outer Space.
V26 V **24** 5s. multicoloured . . . 55 55

V **25** Fish V **28** Radar Screen within Lifebelt

1982. Conservation and Protection of Nature. Multicoloured.
V27 5s. Type V **25** 45 45
V28 7s. Elephant (mammals) . . 80 80

1983. World Communications Year.
V29 **222** 4s. multicoloured 40 40

1983. Safety at Sea: International Maritime Organization. Multicoloured.
V30 4s. Type V **28** 40 40
V31 6s. Stylized liner 60 60

1983. World Food Programme.
V32 **226** 5s. green 50 45
V33 7s. brown 70 70

V **31** Exports V **33** "Die Zweite Haut"

1983. Trade and Development. Multicoloured.
V34 5s. Type V **31** 45 45
V35 8s.50 Emblems of trade . . . 90 90

1983. 35th Anniv of Declaration of Human Rights. Multicoloured.
V36 5s. Type V **33** 80 80
V37 7s. "Recht auf Traume" . . 1·10 1·10

V **35** World Agriculture

1984. International Conference on Population, Mexico City.
V38 V **35** 7s. multicoloured . . . 80 80

V **36** Irrigation

1984. World Food Day. Multicoloured.
V39 4s.50 Type V **36** 45 45
V40 6s. Combine harvesters . . . 65 65

V **38** Serengeti National Park, Tanzania V **40** Woman with Child

1984. World Heritage—U.N.E.S.C.O. Mult.
V41 3s.50 Type V **38** 35 35
V42 15s. Schibam, Yemen . . . . 1·50 1·50

1984. Future for Refugees.
V43 V **40** 4s.50 black and brown 50 50
V44 – 8s.50 black and yellow 90 90
DESIGN: 8s.50, Woman.

V 42 Stylized Figures V 43 U Thant Pavilion

1984. International Youth Year.
V45 V 42 3s.50 multicoloured . . 35 35
V46 6s.50 multicoloured . . 75 75

1985. 20th Anniv of Turin Centre of International Labour Organization.
V47 V 43 7s.50 violet 85 85

V 44 Rural Scene and Researcher with Microscope

1985. 10th Anniv of United Nations University, Tokyo.
V48 V 44 8s.50 multicoloured . . 1·00 1·00

V 45 "Boat" V 49 Oral Immunization

1985. Multicoloured.
V49 4s.50 Type V 45 . . . . . 50 45
V50 15s. Sheltering under U.N. umbrella . . . . 1·60 1·40

1985. 40th Anniv of United Nations Organization. Multicoloured.
V51 6s.50 Type 243 . . . . . 70 70
V52 8s.50 "Harvest Scene" (Andrew Wyeth) 90 90

1985. U.N.I.C.E.F. Child Survival Campaign. Multicoloured.
V54 4s. Type V 49 . . . . . . 60 60
V55 6s. Mother and baby 85 85

V 51 "Africa in Crisis" V 52 Growing Crops

1986. "Africa in Crisis".
V56 V 51 8s. multicoloured . . . 1·00 1·00

1986. Development Programme. Village Scene. Multicoloured.
V57 4s.50 Type V 52 . . . . . . 75 75
V58 4s.50 Villagers with livestock 75 75
V59 4s.50 Woodwork instructor 75 75
V60 4s.50 Nutrition instructor . . 75 75
Nos. V57/60 were issued together, se-tenant, forming a composite design.

V 56 United Nations Stamps

1986. Philately: The International Hobby.
V61 V 56 3s.50 blue and brown 55 55
V62 – 6s.50 blue and red . . . 90 90
DESIGN: 6s.50, Engraver.

V 58 Olive Branch and Rainbow

1986. International Peace Year. Multicoloured.
V63 5s. Type V 58 . . . . . . 70 70
V64 6s. Doves on U.N. emblem 85 85

1986. 9th Death Anniv of Trygve Lie (first U.N. Secretary-General).
V66 259 8s. multicoloured . . . . 1·20 1·20

V 62 Family looking at New Houses

1987. International Year of Shelter for the Homeless.
V67 V 62 4s. orange, blk & yell 60 60
V68 – 9s.50 orange and black 1·30 1·30
DESIGN: 9s.50, Family entering door of new house.

V 64 Footballers

1987. Anti-drugs Campaign. Multicoloured.
V69 5s. Type V 64 . . . . . . 70 70
V70 8s. Family . . . . 1·20 1·20

V 66 U.N. Centre, Vienna

1987. Multicoloured.
V71 2s. Type V 66 . . . . . . 25 25
V72 17s. Wreath of olive leaves and doves around globe 2·10 1·80

V 68 Dancers and Vienna Headquarters V 70 Poliomyelitis

1987. United Nations Day. Multicoloured.
V73 5s. Type V 68 . . . . . . 65 65
V74 6s. Dancers 75 75

1987. "Immunize Every Child". Multicoloured.
V75 4s. Type V 70 . . . . . . 60 60
V76 9s.50 Diphtheria . . . . . . 1·40 1·40

V 72 Woman planting

1987. International Fund for Agricultural Development "For a World without Hunger" Campaign. Multicoloured.
V77 4s. Type V 72 . . . . . . 60 60
V78 6s. Women and foodstuffs 85 85

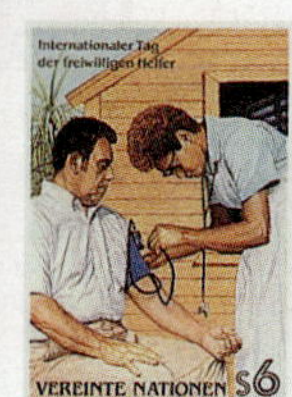

V 74 Hills and Forest in Autumn V 76 Testing Blood Pressure

1988. "Survival of the Forests". Multicoloured.
V79 4s. Type V 74 . . . . . . 2·75 2·75
V80 5s. Forest in autumn . . . . 3·00 3·00
Nos. V79/80 were issued together, se-tenant, forming a composite design.

1988. International Volunteer Day. Multicoloured.
V81 6s. Type V 76 . . . . . . 85 85
V82 7s.50 Building houses (horiz) 1·00 1·00

V 78 Skiing V 81 Transport

1988. "Health in Sports". Multicoloured.
V83 6s. Type V 78 . . . . . . 85 85
V84 8s. Tennis (horiz) . . . . . 1·00 1·00

1988. 40th Anniv of Declaration of Human Rights.
V85 276 5s. multicoloured 70 70

1989. World Bank. Multicoloured.
V87 5s.50 Type V 81 . . . . . 85 85
V88 8s. Health and education . . 1·10 1·10

1989. Award of Nobel Peace Prize to United Nations Peace-keeping Forces.
V89 280 6s. multicoloured 85 85

V 84 Depression over Italy V 86 Man in Winter Clothes

1989. 25th Anniv of World Weather Watch.
V90 4s. Type V 84 . . . . . . 60 60
V91 9s.50 Short-range rainfall forecast for Tokyo . . . . 1·30 1·30

1989. 10th Anniv of United Nations Vienna International Centre. Multicoloured.
V92 5s. Type V 86 . . . . . . 70 70
V93 7s.50 Abstract . . . . 1·10 1·10

V 88 "Prisoners" (Kathe Kollwitz) (Article 5)

1989. Universal Declaration of Human Rights (1st series).
V94 V 88 4s. black 45 45
V95 – 6s. multicoloured 70 70
DESIGN: 6s. "Jurisprudence" (Raphael) (Article 6).
See also Nos. V107/8, V122/3, V138/9 and V149/150.

1990. International Trade Centre.
V96 287 12s. multicoloured . . . 1·60 1·60

V 91 "Earth" (painting by Kurt Regschek in I.A.E.A. Building)

1990.
V97 V 91 1s.50 multicoloured . . 20 20

1990. Anti-AIDS Campaign. Multicoloured.
V98 5s. Type 289 . . . . 70 70
V99 11s. Attacking infected blood 1·50 1·50

V 94 Annatto V 96 "45"

1990. Medicinal Plants. Multicoloured.
V100 4s.50 Type V 94 . . . . . 60 60
V101 9s.50 Cundeamor . . . . . 1·30 1·30

1990. 45th Anniv of U.N.O. Multicoloured.
V102 7s. Type V 96 . . . . . . 95 95
V103 9s. "45" (different) . . . . 1·20 1·20

V 98 Men fighting

1990. Crime Prevention. Multicoloured.
V105 6s. Type V 98 . . . . . . 85 85
V106 8s. Masked man damaging painting . . . . 1·10 1·10

1990. Universal Declaration of Human Rights (2nd series). As Type V 88. Multicoloured.
V107 4s.50 "Before the Judge" (Sandor Bihari) (Article 11) 95 55
V108 7s. "Young Man greeted by Woman writing Poem" (Suzuki Harunobu) (Article 12) . . . . . . 1·00 80

V 102/105 Mediterranean Coastline and Wildlife (½-size illustration)

1991. Economic Commission for Europe. "For a Better Environment".
V109 V 102 5s. multicoloured . . 65 65
V110 V 103 5s. multicoloured . . 65 65
V111 V 104 5s. multicoloured . . 65 80
V112 V 105 5s. multicoloured . . 65 65
Nos. V109/12 were issued together, se-tenant, forming the composite design illustrated.

V 106 Scrubland V 108 Different Races

1991. 1st Anniv of Namibian Independence. Multicoloured.
V113 6s. Type V 106 . . . . . 85 85
V114 9s.50 Sand dune . . . . . 1·30 1·30

1991.
V115 V 108 20s. multicoloured . . 2·50 2·50

V 109 Boy and Girl (Anna Harmer)

1991. 30th Anniv (1989) of U.N. Declaration of the Rights of the Child and 1990 World Summit on Children, New York. Children's Drawings. Multicoloured.
V116 7s. Type V 109 . . . . . . 95 95
V117 9s. Child's world (Emiko Takegawa) . . . . 1·30 1·30

V 111 City, Bubbles of Toxin and Gas Mask

1991. Banning of Chemical Weapons. Mult.
V118 5s. Type V 111 . . . . . 75 75
V119 10s. Hand pushing back cloud of toxin sprayed from airplane . . . . . 1·25 1·10

V **113** U.N. (New York) 1951 20c. Stamp

1991. 40th Anniv of United Nations Postal Administration.
V120 V **113** 5s. brown on cream 75 75
V121 – 8s. blue on cream . . 1·20 1·20
DESIGN: 8s. U.N. (New York) 1951 5c. stamp.

1991. Declaration of Human Rights (3rd series). As Type V **88**. Multicoloured.
V122 4s.50 Ancient Mexican pottery (Article 17) . . . 60 60
V123 7s. "Windows, 1912" (Robert Delaunay) (Article 18) 90 90

V **117** Iguacu National Park, Brazil

V **119/120** Sea Life (½-size illustration)

1992. 20th Anniv of U.N.E.S.C.O. World Heritage Convention. Multicoloured.
V124 5s. Type V **117** 80 80
V125 9s. Abu Simbel, Egypt . . . 1·40 1·40

1992. "Clean Oceans".
V126 V **119** 7s. multicoloured . . 95 90
V127 V **120** 7s. multicoloured . . 1·10 90
Nos. V126/7 were issued together, se-tenant, forming the composite design illustrated.

V **121/124** Planet Earth (½-size illustration)

1992. 2nd U.N. Conference on Environment and Development, Rio de Janeiro.
V128 V **121** 5s.50 multicoloured 70 70
V129 V **122** 5s.50 multicoloured 70 70
V130 V **123** 5s.50 multicoloured 70 70
V131 V **124** 5s.50 multicoloured 70 70
Nos. V128/131 were issued together, se-tenant, forming the composite design illustrated.

V **125/126** "Mission Planet Earth" (⅔-size illustration)

1992. International Space Year. Roul.
V132 V **125** 10s. multicoloured . . 1·40 1·40
V133 V **126** 10s. multicoloured . . 1·40 1·40
Nos. V132/3 were printed together, se-tenant, forming the composite design illustrated.

V **127** Woman with Book emerging from V.D.U.

V **129** Woman's Profile, Birds, Butterfly and Rose

1992. Commission on Science and Technology for Development. Multicoloured.
V134 5s.50 Type V **127** 80 75
V135 7s. Flowers growing from thumb . . . . 1·00 1·00

1992. Multicoloured.
V136 5s.50 Type V **129** 75 70
V137 7s. Vienna International Centre (horiz) 95 90

1992. Universal Declaration of Human Rights (4th series). As Type V **88**. Multicoloured.
V138 6s. "The Builders" (Fernand Leger) (Article 23) 85 85
V139 10s. "Sunday Afternoon on the Island of La Grande Jatte" (Georges Seurat) (Article 24) . . . . . . 1·40 1·40

V **133** Housing and Environment

V **135** Grevy's Zebra

1993. "Ageing: Dignity and Participation". 10th Anniv (1992) of International Plan of Action on Ageing. Multicoloured.
V140 5s.50 Type V **133** 90 80
V141 7s. Education . . . . . . 1·00 95

1993. Endangered Species (1st series). Multicoloured.
V142 7s. Type V **135** 85 85
V143 7s. Humboldt penguin ("Spheniscus humboldti") 85 85
V144 7s. Desert monitor ("Varanus griseus") . . . 85 85
V145 7s. Wolf ("Canis lupus") . . 85 85
See also Nos. V161/4, V179/82, V205/8, V223/6, V249/52, V288/91, V304/7, V324/7 and V353/6.

V **139** Globe, Doves and U.N. Emblem

V **140** Regional and National Environment

1993.
V146 V **139** 13s. multicoloured . . 1·90 1·80

1993. 45th Anniv of W.H.O. Multicoloured.
V147 6s. Type V **140** 90 85
V148 10s. Continental and global environment . . . . . . 1·40 1·40

1993. Declaration of Human Rights (5th series). As Type V **88**. Multicoloured.
V149 5s. "Lower Austrian Peasants' Wedding" (Ferdinand Waldmuller) (Article 29) 70 70
V150 6s. "Outback" (Sally Morgan) (Article 30) . . 85 85

V **144/147** Peace (½-size illustration)

1993. International Peace Day. Roul.
V151 V **144** 5s.50 multicoloured 70 70
V152 V **145** 5s.50 multicoloured 70 70
V153 V **146** 5s.50 multicoloured 70 70
V154 V **147** 5s.50 multicoloured 70 70

Nos. V151/4 were issued together, se-tenant, forming the composite design illustrated.

V **148** Monkeys

1993. The Environment—Climate. Multicoloured.
V155 7s. Type V **148** 90 90
V156 7s. Eastern bluebird and factory chimneys 90 90
V157 7s. Volcano, smokestacks and tree stumps 90 90
V158 7s. Great horned owl in desert 90 90
Nos. V155/8 were issued together, se-tenant, forming a composite design.

V **152** Family holding Hands

1994. International Year of the Family. Mult.
V159 5s.50 Type V **152** 90 90
V160 8s. Family at work . . . . 1·30 1·30

1994. Endangered Species (2nd series). As Type V **135**. Multicoloured.
V161 7s. Ocelot ("Felis pardalis") 85 85
V162 7s. White-crested white eye ("Zosterups albogularis") 85 85
V163 7s. Mediterranean monk seals ("Monachus monachus") 85 85
V164 7s. Indian elephant ("Elephas maximus") . . 85 85

V **158** Tree and Doves

V **161** Hands ready to help Refugees

1994. Multicoloured.
V165 50g. Type V **158** 15 15
V166 4s. Herring gulls 60 60
V167 30s. Globe and dove . . . 4·00 4·00

1994. United Nations High Commissioner for Refugees.
V168 V **161** 12s. multicoloured . . 1·80 1·80

V **162/165** Shattered Globe and "Preparation" (⅔-size illustration)

1994. International Decade for Natural Disaster Reduction.
V169 V **162** 6s. multicoloured . . 85 75
V170 V **163** 6s. multicoloured . . 85 75
V171 V **164** 6s. multicoloured . . 85 75
V172 V **165** 6s. multicoloured . . 75 75
Nos. V169/72 were issued together, se-tenant, forming the composite design illustrated.

V **166** Enhancing Role of Women

1994. International Population and Development Conference, Cairo. Multicoloured.
V173 5s.50 Type V **166** 85 90
V174 7s. Relationship of population and environment . . . . . . 1·00 1·10

V **168** Map and Crossed Ribbons

1994. 30th Anniv of United Nations Conference on Trade and Development. Multicoloured.
V175 6s. Type V **168** 85 90
V176 7s. Map and ribbons forming star . . . . . . 1·00 1·10

1995. 50th Anniv of U.N.O. (1st issue).
V177 **371** 7s. multicoloured . . . 1·00 1·10
See also Nos. V185/6 and V190/201.

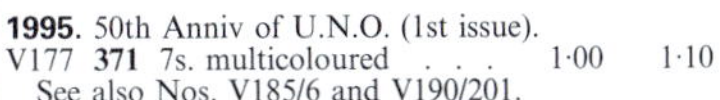

V **171** "Social Summit 1995"

1995. World Summit for Social Development, Copenhagen.
V178 V **171** 14s. multicoloured . . 2·40 2·75

1995. Endangered Species (3rd series). As Type V **135**. Multicoloured.
V179 7s. Black rhinoceros ("Diceros bicornis") . . . 80 85
V180 7s. Golden conure ("Aratinga guarouba") 80 85
V181 7s. Variegated langur ("Pygathrix nemaeus") 80 85
V182 7s. Arabian oryx ("Oryx leucoryx") 80 85

V **176** Village in Winter

1995. "Youth: Our Future". 10th Anniv of International Youth Year. Multicoloured.
V183 6s. Type V **176** 85 90
V184 7s. Wheat stacks in field . . 1·00 1·10

1995. 50th Anniv of U.N.O. (2nd issue).
V185 **379** 7s. green . . . . 1·00 1·10
V186 – 10s. black . . . . . . 1·50 1·70
DESIGN: 10s. Veterans' Memorial Hall and Opera House, San Francisco (venue for signing of U.N. Charter).

V **180** Women in Jungle

V **194** Jester holding Dove

1995. 4th World Conference on Women, Peking. Multicoloured.
V188 5s.50 Type V **180** 85 90
V189 6s. Woman reading book (28 × 48 mm) 85 95

1995. 50th Anniv of U.N.O. (3rd issue).
V190 **385** 3s. multicoloured . . . 40 45
V191 **386** 3s. multicoloured . . . 40 45
V192 **387** 3s. multicoloured . . . 40 45
V193 **388** 3s. multicoloured . . . 40 45
V194 **389** 3s. multicoloured . . . 40 45
V195 **390** 3s. multicoloured . . . 40 45
V196 **391** 3s. multicoloured . . . 40 45
V197 **392** 3s. multicoloured . . . 40 45
V198 **393** 3s. multicoloured . . . 40 45
V199 **394** 3s. multicoloured . . . 40 45
V200 **395** 3s. multicoloured . . . 40 45
V201 **396** 3s. multicoloured . . . 40 40
Nos. V190/5 and V196/201 respectively were issued together, se-tenant, forming two composite designs.

1996. 50th Anniv of World Federation of United Nations Associations. Multicoloured.
V202 V **194** 7s. multicoloured . . 1·00 1·10

V **195** U.N. Flag

V **201** Family with Agricultural Products

1996. Multicoloured.
V203 1s. Type V **195** 20 20
V204 10s. Abstract painting (Karl Korab) . . . . 1·40 1·50

1996. Endangered Species (4th series). As Type V **135**. Multicoloured.
V205 7s. Venus slipper orchid ("Cypripedium calceolus") 80 85
V206 7s. "Aztekium ritteri" . . . 80 85
V207 7s. "Euphorbia cremersii" 80 85
V208 7s. "Dracula bella" 80 85

1996. "Habitat II" Second U.N. Conf on Human Settlements, Istanbul, Turkey. Mult.
V209 6s. Type V **201** 75 80
V210 6s. Women with sacks of grain 75 80
V211 6s. Woman and city 75 80
V212 6s. Ploughing with oxen . . 75 80
V213 6s. Villlage and elephant . . 75 80
Nos. V209/13 were issued together, se-tenant, forming a composite design.

V **206** Gymnastics

1996. Sport and the Environment. Multicoloured.
V214 6s. Type V **206** . . . . . 90 1·00
V215 7s. Hurdling . . . . 1·10 1·20

V **208** Dove and Butterflies

1996. "A Plea for Peace". Winners of China Youth Design Competition. Multicoloured.
V217 7s. Type V **208** . . . . . 1·10 1·20
V218 10s. Children and flowers in dove . . . . 1·40 1·50

V **210** "Hansel and Gretel" (Brothers Grimm)
V **212** Red Phoenix

1996. 50th Anniv of U.N.I.C.E.F. Children's Stories.
V219 5s.50 Type V **210** 75 85
V220 8s. "How Maui Stole Fire from the Gods" (Pacific Islands myth) . . . . . 1·00 1·10

1997. Details of "Phoenixes flying Down" by Sagenji Yoshida. Multicoloured.
V221 5s. Type V **212** 70 75
V222 6s. Green phoenix 85 90

1997. Endangered Species (5th series). As Type V **135**. Multicoloured.
V223 7s. Barbary ape ("Macaca sylvanus") 80 85
V224 7s. Stanley crane ("Anthropoides paradisea") 80 85
V225 7s. Przewalski's horse ("Equus przewalskii") . . 80 85
V226 7s. Giant anteater ("Myrmecophaga tridactyla") 80 85

V **218/221** River Scene (⅔-size illustration)

1997. "Earth Summit + 5". 5th Anniv of United Nations Conference on Environment and Development.
V227 V **218** 3s.50 multicoloured 45 35
V228 V **219** 3s.50 multicoloured 45 35
V229 V **220** 3s.50 multicoloured 45 35
V230 V **221** 3s.50 multicoloured 45 65
Nos. V227/30 were issued together, se-tenant, forming the composite design illustrated.

V **222** Stephenson's Locomotive "Rocket" and Darraque Motor Car (1901)
V **227** 1986 3s.50 Philately Stamp

1997. 50th Anniversaries of Economic Commission for Europe and Economic and Social Commission for Asia and the Pacific. Multicoloured.
V232 7s. Type V **222** 85 85
V233 7s. Russian steam locomotive and American streetcar 85 85
V234 7s. Diesel train and British double-decker bus . . . 85 85
V235 7s. Diesel locomotive and articulated trailer lorry 85 85
V236 7s. High speed electric train and electric-powered car 85 85
Nos. V232/6 were issued together, se-tenant, forming a composite design.

1997. "Tribute to Philately". Multicoloured.
V237 6s.50 Type V **227** 55 65
V238 7s. 1986 6s.50 Philately stamp 55 65

1997. 25th Anniv of World Heritage Convention. Terracotta Warriors from Emperor Qin Shi Huang's Tomb, Xian, China. Multicoloured.
V239 1s. As Type **434** 40 45
V240 1s. As No. 737 . . . . . . 55 60
V241 1s. As No. 738 . . . . . . 25 30
V242 1s. As No. 739 . . . . . . 25 30
V243 1s. As No. 740 . . . . . . 25 30
V244 1s. As No. 741 . . . . . . 25 30
V245 3s. As No. 740 . . . . . . 35 35
V246 6s. As No. 741 . . . . . . 55 60

V **235** Japanese Peace Bell, Vienna

1998. Multicoloured.
V247 6s.50 Type V **235** 85 95
V248 9s. Underground train passing Vienna Centre . . 1·30 1·40

1998. Endangered Species (6th series). As Type V **135**. Multicoloured.
V249 7s. Green turtle ("Chelonia mydas") 80 85
V250 7s. Burrowing owl ("Speotyto cunicularia") 80 85
V251 7s. Raja Brooke's birdwing ("Trogonoptera brookiana") 80 85
V252 7s. Lesser panda ("Ailurus fulgens") 80 85

V **241** Shark

1998. International Year of the Ocean. Multicoloured.
V253 3s.50 Type V **241** 55 60
V254 3s.50 Diver and submersible 55 60
V255 3s.50 Diver and dolphins 55 60
V256 3s.50 School of fishes above diver and submersible . . 55 60
V257 3s.50 Sealions 55 60
V258 3s.50 Diver and underwater camera 55 60
V259 3s.50 Angelfishes 55 60
V260 3s.50 Fishes and diver . . . 55 60
V261 3s.50 Turtle 55 60
V262 3s.50 Butterflyfishes 55 60
V263 3s.50 Anemonefish, other fishes and starfish 55 60
V264 3s.50 Starfish and butterflyfishes 55 60

V **242** Ocelot

1998. Rainforest Preservation.
V265 V **242** 6s.50 multicoloured 1·00 1·10

V **243** Soldier distributing Supplies

1998. 50 Years of United Nations Peacekeeping. Multicoloured.
V267 4s. Type V **243** 55 65
V268 7s.50 Voters . . . . 1·10 1·30

V **245** Open Head
V **253** "Volcanic Landscape" (detail, Peter Pongratz)

1998. 50th Anniv of Universal Declaration of Human Rights. Multicoloured.
V269 4s.50 Type V **245** 75 85
V270 7s. Cogwheels . . . . . . 1·10 1·00

1998. World Heritage Site. Schonbrunn Palace, Vienna. Multicoloured.
V271 1s. As Type **454** 60 55
V272 1s. As No. 778 . . . . . . 70 80
V273 1s. As No. 779 . . . . . . 30 35
V274 2s. As No. 780 . . . . . . 30 35
V275 2s. As No. 781 . . . . . . 30 35
V276 2s. As No. 782 . . . . . . 35 35
V277 3s.50 As No. 780 . . . . . 80 80
V278 7s. As No. 779 . . . . . . 2·10 2·10

1999.
V279 V **253** 8s. multicoloured . . 1·20 1·40

1999. World Heritage Sites in Australia. Mult.
V280 1s. As Type **462** 40 45
V281 1s. As No. 796 . . . . . . 55 60
V282 1s. As No. 797 . . . . . . 20 20
V283 2s. As No. 798 . . . . . . 25 30
V284 2s. As No. 799 . . . . . . 25 30
V285 2s. As No. 800 . . . . . . 30 35
V286 4s.50 As No. 801 . . . . . 45 55
V287 6s.50 As No. 802 . . . . . 75 70

1999. Endangered Species (7th series). As Type V **135**. Multicoloured.
V288 7s. Orang-utan ("Pongo pygmaeus") 80 85
V289 7s. Dalmatian pelican ("Pelecanus crispus") . . 80 85
V290 7s. Yellow anaconda ("Eunectes notaeus") . . 80 85
V291 7s. Caracal ("Caracal caracal") 80 85

V **264/265** Global Weather Forecasting (½-size illustration)

1999. Third Conference on Exploration and Peaceful Uses of Outer Space, Vienna.
V292 V **264** 3s.50 multicoloured 55 60
V293 V **265** 3s.50 multicoloured 55 60

Nos. V292/3 were issued together, se-tenant, forming the composite design illustrated.

V **266/269** Modern Communications (½-size illustration)

1999. 125th Anniv of Universal Postal Union
V295 V **266** 33c. multicoloured . . 95 1·00
V296 V **267** 33c. multicoloured . . 95 1·00
V297 V **268** 33c. multicoloured . . 95 1·00
V298 V **269** 33c. multicoloured . . 95 1·00
Nos. V295/8 were issued together, se-tenant, forming the composite design illustrated.

V **270** U.N. Centre, Vienna

1999. "In Memoriam: Fallen in the Cause of Peace".
V299 V **270** 6s.50 multicoloured 1·10 1·20

V **272** Couple leaping over Open Book

1999. Education: Keystone to the 21st Century.
V301 7s. Type V **272** . . . . . 1·00 1·10
V302 13s. Group of readers . . . 2·00 2·20

DENOMINATION. From Nos. V303 to V346, United Nations Vienna Centre stamps are denominated both in Austrian schillings and in euros. As no cash for the latter was in circulation the catalogue uses the schilling value.

2000. International Year of Thanksgiving.
V303 **483** 7s. multicoloured . . . 95 1·00

2000. Endangered Species (8th series). As Type V **135**. Multicoloured.
V304 7s. Leopard (*Panthera pardus*) 80 85
V305 7s. White spoonbill (*Platalea leucorodia*) . . . 80 85
V306 7s. Chilean guemal (*Hippocamelus bisulcus*) 80 85
V307 7s. Killer whale (*Orcinus orca*) 80 85

V **279** "Tomorrow's Dream" (Voltaire Perez)

2000. "Our World 2000" International Art Exhibition, New York. Entries in Millennium Painting Competition. Multicoloured.
V308 7s. Type V **279** . . . . . 95 1·00
V309 8s. "Remembrance" (Dimitris Nalbandis) . . 1·10 1·20

V **281** Dome of General Assembly Hall, 1951

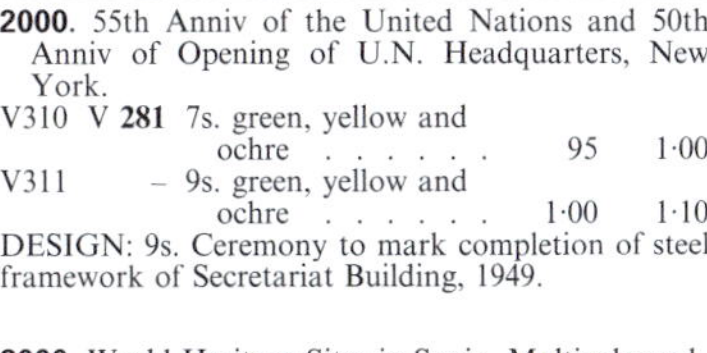

2000. 55th Anniv of the United Nations and 50th Anniv of Opening of U.N. Headquarters, New York.

V310 V **281** 7s. green, yellow and ochre . . . . 95 1·00
V311 – 9s. green, yellow and ochre . . . . . . 1·00 1·10

DESIGN: 9s. Ceremony to mark completion of steel framework of Secretariat Building, 1949.

2000. World Heritage Sites in Spain. Multicoloured.

V314 1s. As Type **496** 40 40
V315 1s. As No. 832 . . . . . . 45 50
V316 1s. As No. 833 . . . . . . 20 20
V317 2s. As No. 834 . . . . . . 25 30
V318 2s. As No. 835 . . . . . . 25 30
V319 2s. As No. 836 . . . . . . 30 35
V320 4s.50 As No. 837 . . . . . 65 65
V321 6s.50 As No. 838 . . . . . 80 80

V **291** Family of Refugees

2000. 50th Anniv of United Nations Commissioner for Refugees.

V322 V **291** 7s. multicoloured . . 1·00 1·10

2001. Endangered Species (9th series). As Type V **135**. Multicoloured.

V324 7s. Spectacled bear (*Tremarctos ornatus*) . . 80 85
V325 7s. Laysan duck (*Anas laysanensis*) 80 85
V326 7s. Aardwolf (*Proteles cristatus*) 80 85
V327 7s. Silver langur (*Trachypithecus cristatus*) 80 85

V **297** Couple (Nguyen Thanh Chuong)

2001. United Nations International Year of Volunteers. Multicoloured.

V328 10s. Type V **297** . . . . . 1·30 1·40
V329 12s. Hands and heart (Ikko Tanaka) . . . . 1·25 1·40

2001. World Heritage Sites in Japan.

V330 1s. As Type **512** 45 50
V331 1s. As No. 858 . . . . . . 15 15
V332 1s. As No. 859 . . . . . . 15 15
V333 2s. As No. 860 . . . . . . 25 25
V334 2s. As No. 861 . . . . . . 25 25
V335 2s. As No. 862 . . . . . . 25 30
V336 7s. As No. 859 . . . . . . 65 70
V337 15s. As No. 862 . . . . . 1·30 1·40

2001. 40th Death Anniv of Dag Hammarskjold (United Nations Secretary General, 1953–61).

V338 **518** 7s. green 85 90

V **306** Balloons

V **309** Futuristic Electric Car and Solar Panels

2001. 50th Anniv of United Nations Postal Administration.

V339 7s. Type V **306** 85 90
V340 8s. Cake 95 80

2001. Climate Change. Multicoloured.

V342 7s. Type V **309** . . . . . . 90 1·00
V343 7s. Airship, cyclists and horse rider . . . . 90 1·00
V344 7s. Couple walking, balloon and coastline . . . . . . 90 1·00
V345 7s. Train and traffic signs in glass dome . . . . 90 1·00

Nos. V342/5 were issued together, se-tenant, forming a composite design.

2001. Kofi Annan, Winner of Nobel Peace Prize, 2001.

V346 **526** 7s. multicoloured . . . 1·00 1·10

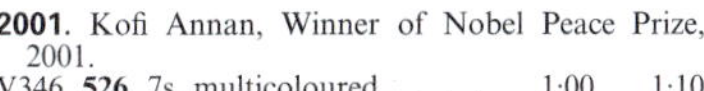

V **314** Semmering Railway

2002. Multicoloured.

V347 7c. Type V **314** 15 15
V348 51c. Pferdeschwemme, Salzburg 80 85
V349 58c. Aggstein Ruin . . . . 90 1·00
V350 73c. Hallstatt . . . . 1·10 90
V351 87c. Melk Abbey . . . . . 1·60 95
V352 €2.03 Kapitelschwemme, Salzburg . . . . 1·90 1·90

2002. Endangered Species (10th series). As Type V **135**. Multicoloured.

V353 51c. Siamang gibbon (*Hylobates syndactylus*) 80 85
V354 51c. Jackass penguin (*Spheniscus demersus*) . . 80 85
V355 51c. Banded linsang (*Prionodon linsang*) . . . 80 85
V356 51c. Sonoran green toad (*Bufo retiformis*) 80 85

2002. East Timor Independence. As T **532**. Multicoloured.

V357 51c. Carved deer horn container 75 75
V358 €1.09 Weaving loom . . . 1·50 1·50

2002. International Year of Mountains. As T **534**. Multicoloured.

V359 22c. Mt. Cook, New Zealand 30 30
V360 22c. Mt. Robson, Canada 30 30
V361 51c. Rakaposhi, Pakistan 75 75
V362 51c. Sagarmatha, Nepal . . 75 75

V **330** Rainbow

2002. World Summit on Sustainable Development, Johannesburg. Multicoloured.

V363 51c. Type V **330** 75 75
V364 51c. Women's profiles . . . 75 75
V365 58c. Figures wearing fashionable dress 80 80
V366 58c. Wave and doves . . . 80 80

2002. World Heritage Sites in Italy. As T **542**. Multicoloured.

V367 7c. Duomo di Sant'Andrea, Amalfi Coast 10 10
V368 7c. View across Islands, Aeolian Islands 10 10
V369 7c. Del Moro Fountain, Rome 10 10
V370 15c. Santa Maria del Fiore, Florence 25 25
V371 15c. Leaning Tower, Pisa 25 25
V372 15c. The Forum, Pompeii 25 25
V373 51c. As No. 372 . . . . . 75 75
V374 58c. As No. 369 . . . . . 80 80

2002. AIDS Awareness Campaign. A T **549**. Multicoloured.

V375 €1.53 AIDS Symbol on UN Secretariat Building, New York 2·10 2·10
MSV376 80 × 80 mm. 51c.+25c. AIDS Symbol on UN Secretariat Building, New York at night 1·10 1·10

The premium was for AIDS charities.

E. EAST TIMOR

UNITED NATIONS TRANSITIONAL ADMINISTRATION IN EAST TIMOR

100 cents = 1 dollar.

Following negotiations between Portugal and Indonesia a referendum was conducted on 30 August 1999 with the majority voting for independence for East Timor. On the 20 September 1999 the first United Nations peace keeping troops arrived in East Timor and the Indonesian troops began to withdraw. By October the United Nations had established the International Force for East Timor (I.N.T.E.R.F.E.T.). On the 19 October 1999 the Indonesian Consultative Assembly confirmed the establishment and on the 25 October 1999 the United Nations voted to replace I.N.T.E.R.F.E.T. with a force to help with the establishment of a United Nations Transitional Administration of East Timor (U.N.T.A.E.T.). The East Timor National Council (E.T.N.C.), which was formed to help with policy recommendations, held it's first meeting on 11 December 1999.

1 Man with Arms Raised

2000. (a) Inscr "Dom.".

1 **1** (21c.) multicoloured 25 25

(b) Inscr "Int.".

2 **1** ($1.05) multicoloured . . . . 1·30 1·30

No. 1 was for use on Domestic mail and No. 2 was for use on International mail.

F. Kosovo

United Nations Interim Administration Mission

The following stamps were issued by the United Nations Interim Administration Mission (U.N.M.I.K.) and the Post & Telecommunications of Kosovo for postal purposes in Kosovo. They were for local use only for the first two months with international use commencing in May 2000.

K **1** Orpheus (mosaic, 5–6th century, Podujeve))

K **2** Bird

2000. Artefacts. Multicoloured.

K1 20pf. Type K **1** 10 10
K2 30pf. "Dardanian idol", 3500 B.C. 20 20
K3 50pf. Obverse and reverse of 4th-century B.C. silver coin, Damastion 30 30
K4 1m. Mother Teresa (statue, Prizren) 65 65
K5 2m. Map of Kosovo showing various sites . . . . 1·25 1·25

2001. Art. Multicoloured designs.

K 6 20pf. Type K **2** 10 10
K 7 30pf. Musician 20 20
K 8 50pf. Butterfly and pear (horiz) 30 30
K 9 1m. Children and stars . . . 65 65
K10 2m. Handprints surrounding globe . . . . 1·25 1·25

Nos. K6/10 have the face values shown in deutsche Marks and euros.

UNITED STATES OF AMERICA

Pt. 22

A Federal Republic in N. America, consisting of 50 states and one federal district.

100 cents = 1 dollar.

PRICES. On the issues before 1890 the gum is rarely complete and the unused prices quoted are for stamps with part original gum.

1 Franklin (after drawings by James B. Longacre)

2 Washington (after painting by Stuart)

1847. Imperf.

1 **1** 5c. brown £4000 £400
2 **2** 10c. black £16000 £1100

The 5c. blue and 10c. orange, both imperf, come from miniature sheets isssued in 1947 to commemorate the Centenary Philatelic Exhibition, New York.

3 Franklin (after bust by Caffieri)

4 Washington (after bust by Houdon)

5 Jefferson

6 Washington

7 Washington

8 Washington

9 Franklin (after bust by Caffieri)

10 Washington (after Trumbull painting)

1851. Imperf.

11 **3** 1c. blue . . . . £250 75·00
13a **4** 3c. red . . . . £225 7·50
14 **5** 5c. brown £10000 £500
16 **6** 10c. green £1200 £140
19 **7** 12c. black £3000 £190

1857. Perf.

26 **3** 1c. blue . . . . £110 28·00
28 **4** 3c. red . . . . 45·00 4·00
33 **5** 5c. brown £375 £160
39 **6** 10c. green . . . . £150 45·00
40c **7** 12c. black £250 £100
41 **8** 24c. lilac £800 £225
42 **9** 30c. orange £650 £300
43 **10** 90c. blue £1200 £1000

DESIGNS: Types **5**, **6**, **7** and **8** are after paintings by Stuart.

11 Franklin

12 Washington

13 Jefferson

14 Washington

15 Washington

16 Washington

17 Franklin

18 Washington

19 Andrew Jackson (after miniature by J. W. Dodge)

20 Lincoln (from a photograph)

1861.

60b **11** 1c. blue . . . . 80·00 26·00
69 **19** 2c. black . . . . £300 30·00
62 **12** 3c. red . . . . 45·00 2·30
63 **13** 5c. yellow £10000 £325
72 5c. brown . . . . £325 90·00
64 **14** 10c. green . . . . £400 25·00
65 **15** 12c. black . . . . £325 49·00
73 **20** 15c. black . . . . £1100 95·00
66c **16** 24c. blue £4500 £375
74 24c. lilac . . . . £600 80·00
74b 24c. grey . . . . £600 80·00
67 **17** 30c. orange . . . . £900 90·00
68a **18** 90c. blue £1500 £275

21 Franklin (after Houdon bust)

22 Post Rider

23 Baldwin Steam Locomotive

24 Washington (after Stuart)

25 Shield and Eagle

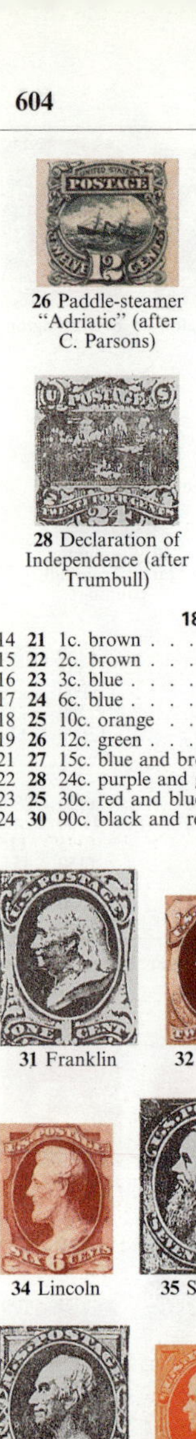

26 Paddle-steamer "Adriatic" (after C. Parsons)

27 Landing of Columbus (after Vanderlyn)

28 Declaration of Independence (after Trumbull)

30 Lincoln (from a photograph)

1869.

114	21	1c. brown	£400	85·00
115	22	2c. brown	£300	40·00
116	23	3c. blue	£130	8·75
117	24	6c. blue	£950	95·00
118	25	10c. orange	£650	80·00
119	26	12c. green	£650	75·00
121	27	15c. blue and brown	£1100	£150
122	28	24c. purple and green	£3500	£550
123	25	30c. red and blue	£2750	£325
124	30	90c. black and red	£6500	£1500

31 Franklin

32 Jackson

33 Washington

34 Lincoln

35 Stanton

36 Jefferson

37 Henry Clay

38 Daniel Webster

39 General Winfield Scott

40 Alexander Hamilton

41 Commodore Perry

42 General Zachary Taylor (from a daguerreotype)

1870.

207	31	1c. blue	40·00	50
148	32	2c. brown	90·00	4·25
185		2c. red	70·00	2·30
208	33	3c. green	43·00	55
219		3c. red	40·00	37·00
161	34	6c. red	£200	6·25
151	35	7c. red	£475	49·00
210	36	10c. brown	70·00	3·25
153	37	12c. purple	£800	70·00
191	38	15c. orange	£190	16·00
155	39	24c. violet	£800	65·00
192	40	30c. black	£325	35·00
222		30c. brown	£275	60·00
193	41	90c. red	£1400	£140
223		90c. violet	£600	£130

1875.

181	42	5c. blue	£160	11·00

43 Garfield (from a photograph)

44 Washington (after bust by Houdon)

45 Jackson (after bust by Powers)

46 Franklin

47 Franklin

1882.

217	46	1c. blue	55·00	1·00
213	44	2c. brown	25·00	40
218		2c. green	19·00	40
214	45	4c. green	£150	10·00
220		4c. red	£100	12·00
211	43	5c. brown	£150	6·00
221		5c. blue	£120	7·75

1890. No triangles in upper corners.

224	47	1c. blue (Franklin)	20·00	40
225a	–	2c. red (Washington)	16·00	35
226	–	3c. violet (Jackson)	50·00	4·00
227	–	4c. sepia (Lincoln)	50·00	2·00
228	–	5c. brown (Grant)	50·00	1·60
229	–	6c. red (Garfield)	50·00	13·50
230	–	8c. purple (Sherman)	49·00	6·25
231	–	10c. green (Webster)	£100	2·00
232	–	15c. blue (Clay)	£140	14·50
233	–	30c. black (Jefferson)	£225	20·00
234	–	90c. orange (Perry)	£375	70·00

58 Columbus in Sight of Land

83 Jefferson

1893. Columbian Exposition, Chicago.

235	58	1c. blue	16·00	25
236	–	2c. purple	14·50	30
237	–	3c. green	46·00	10·00
238	–	4c. blue	70·00	5·75
239	–	5c. brown	70·00	5·75
240	–	6c. violet	65·00	15·00
241	–	8c. red	60·00	7·75
242	–	10c. sepia	£100	5·50
243	–	15c. green	£190	48·00
244	–	30c. orange	£250	55·00
245	–	50c. slate	£450	£110
246	–	$1 red	£1200	£375
247	–	$2 lake	£1300	£450
248	–	$3 green	£1900	£850
249	–	$4 red	£2500	£950
250	–	$5 black	£2750	£1200

DESIGNS: 2c. Landing of Columbus; 3c. "Santa Maria", flagship of Columbus; 4c. Fleet of Columbus; 5c. Columbus soliciting aid of Isabella; 6c. Columbus welcomed at Barcelona, Ferdinand (left) and Balboa (right); 8c. Columbus restored to favour; 10c. Columbus presenting natives; 15c. Columbus announcing his discovery; 30c. Columbus at La Rabida; 50c. Recall of Columbus; $1 Isabella pledging her jewels; $2 Columbus in chains; $3 Columbus describing his third voyage; $4 Isabella and Columbus; $5 Columbus, America and Liberty.

1894. Triangles in upper corners as T 83. Same portraits as issue of 1890, except dollar values.

267	–	1c. blue	4·25	30
283	–	1c. green	7·75	35
270	–	2c. red	4·50	30
271	–	3c. violet	27·00	1·20
285	–	4c. brown	24·00	95
273	–	5c. brown	27·00	1·50
286	–	5c. blue	22·00	85
274	–	6c. brown	65·00	3·75
287a	–	6c. purple	21·00	3·25
275	–	8c. brown	47·00	95
276	–	10c. green	65·00	1·20
289	–	10c. brown	80·00	1·90
277	–	15c. blue	£200	7·25
290	–	15c. green	£110	7·00
278	83	50c. orange	£250	11·50
279	–	$1 black (Perry)	£425	48·00
281a	–	$2 blue (Madison)	£500	£140
282	–	$5 green (Marshall)	£1800	£350

88 Father Marquette on the Mississippi

97 "City of Alpena" (Great Lakes steamer)

1898. Trans-Mississippi Exposition, Omaha.

291	88	1c. green	24·00	4·00
292	–	2c. red	20·00	1·00
293	–	4c. orange	£120	16·00
294	–	5c. blue	£120	12·50
295	–	8c. purple	£140	27·00
296	–	10c. violet	£170	16·00
297	–	50c. green	£450	£120
298	–	$1 black	£1200	£350
299	–	$2 brown	£1900	£650

DESIGNS: 2c. Farming in the West; 4c. Indian hunting American bison; 5c. Fremont on Rocky Mountains; 8c. Troops guarding emigrant train; 10c. Hardships of emigration; 50c. Western mining prospector; $1 Western cattle in storm; $2 Eads Bridge over Mississippi at St. Louis and paddle-steamer "Grey Eagle".

1901. Pan-American Exhibition, Buffalo. Inscr "COMMEMORATIVE SERIES, 1901."

300	97	1c. black and green	17·00	2·00
301	–	2c. black and red	14·50	60
302	–	4c. black and brown	60·00	9·25
303	–	5c. black and blue	48·00	9·75
304	–	8c. black and brown	75·00	33·00
305	–	10c. black and brown	£120	16·00

DESIGNS: 2c. "Empire State Express"; 4c. Automobile; 5c. Railway bridge below Niagara Falls; 8c. Canal locks at Sault Sainte Marie; 10c. "Saint Paul" (liner).

103 Franklin

104 Washington

105 Jackson

106 Grant

107 Lincoln

108 Garfield

109 Martha Washington

110 Webster

111 Harrison

112 Clay

113 Jefferson

114 Farragut

115 Madison

116 Marshall

1902. Inscr "SERIES 1902". 1, 4 and 5c. perf or imperf.

306	103	1c. green	6·50	20
307	104	2c. red	9·75	20
308a	105	3c. violet	33·00	1·40
309a	106	4c. brown	38·00	75
310	107	5c. blue	43·00	95
311	108	6c. lake	49·00	1·70
312	109	8c. violet	32·00	1·40
313	110	10c. brown	48·00	1·20
314	111	13c. purple	32·00	5·00
315	112	15c. olive	£110	3·50
316	113	50c. orange	£325	16·00
317	114	$1 black	£550	40·00
485	115	$2 blue	£275	28·00
486	116	$5 green	£250	28·00

117 Washington (after Stuart)

118 Robert R. Livingston (after Stuart)

1903. Perf or imperf.

326	117	2c. red	4·00	25

1904. International Exposition, St. Louis, and Louisiana Purchase. Inscr "COMMEMORATIVE SERIES OF 1904".

330	118	1c. green	26·00	3·00
331	–	2c. red	20·00	1·10
332	–	3c. violet	65·00	21·00
333	–	5c. blue	80·00	12·50
334	–	10c. brown	£150	22·00

DESIGNS: 2c. Thomas Jefferson; 3c. James Monroe (after Vanderlyn); 5c. William McKinley; 10c. Map of Louisiana Purchase.

123 Capt. John Smith, Pocahontas and Powhatan (after painting)

1907. Jamestown Exposition.

335	123	1c. green	21·00	2·50
336	–	2c. red	27·00	2·40
337	–	5c. blue	£120	16·00

DESIGN: 2c. Founding of Jamestown, 1607; 5c. Princess Pocahontas.

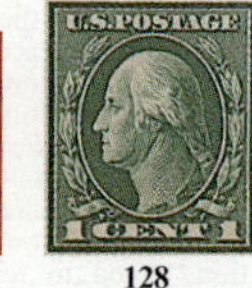

126 Franklin

127

128

1908. 1 to 5c. perf or imperf.

338	126	1c. green	5·50	20
505	128	1c. green	25	25
339	127	2c. red	5·75	20
506	128	2c. red	25	20
537		3c. violet	1·70	30
510		4c. brown	10·00	25
503		5c. blue	3·75	75
513		6c. orange	10·50	1·40
514		7c. black	24·00	85
344		8c. green	33·00	1·70
345		10c. yellow	55·00	1·10
346		13c. green	35·00	14·50
347		15c. blue	50·00	4·25
348		50c. violet	£250	14·00
349		$1 black	£400	55·00

DESIGNS: Types 127 and 128, Washington (after Houdon bust).

129 Lincoln (detail of statue by Saint Gaudens in Grant Park, Chicago)

1909. Birth Centenary of Abraham Lincoln. Perf or imperf.

374	129	2c. red	4·75	1·10

130 Wm. H. Seward

131 "Clermont" and "Half Moon" on Hudson River

1909. Alaska–Yukon–Pacific Exposition. Perf or imperf.

377	130	2c. red	6·00	1·30

1909. Hudson–Fulton Celebration. Perf or imperf.

379	131	2c. red	8·75	2·75

133 Franklin (after Caffieri bust)

138 Franklin (after Caffieri bust)

1912.

515	133	8c. olive	10·50	90
516		9c. pink	11·50	1·50
517		10c. yellow	14·00	20
518		11c. green	7·75	2·50
519		12c. brown	7·75	55
520		13c. green	9·25	4·50
521		15c. grey	30·00	75
522		20c. blue	41·00	25
523		30c. orange	34·00	90
524		50c. lilac	60·00	70
525		$1 black	55·00	1·30
526	138	$2 black and orange	£650	£130
527		$2 black and red	£170	23·00
528		$5 black and green	£225	25·00

134 Balboa

135 Panama Canal (after model of Pedro Miguel Locks)

1913. Panama–Pacific Exposition. Inscr "SAN FRANCISCO 1915".

423	134	1c. green	13·50	1·20
424	135	2c. red	15·00	45
425	–	5c. blue	60·00	4·25
426	–	10c. yellow	£110	17·00

DESIGNS: 5c. Golden Gate, San Francisco; 10c. Discovery of San Francisco Bay (after painting by Mathew).

A 139 Curtiss JN-4 "Jenny"

139 Liberty and Allies' Flags

1918. Air.

A546	A 139	6c. orange	7·75	2·50
A547		16c. green	90·00	28·00
A548		24c. blue and red	95·00	36·00

1919. Victory

546	139	3c. violet	6·00	2·50

140 The "Mayflower"

1920. Tercentenary of Landing of Pilgrim Fathers. Inscr as in T **140**.

556 **140** 1c. green 3·25 2·30
557 – 2c. red 5·00 1·40
558 – 5c. blue 33·00 11·00

DESIGNS: 2c. Landing of the Pilgrims (after drawing by White); 5c. Signing the Compact.

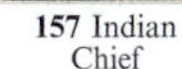

144 Franklin **157** Indian Chief **158** Statue of Liberty

159 Golden Gate **165** America

176 Wilson

1922. Perf or imperf (1, 1½, 2c.).

559 – ½c. brown (Hale) 20 20
632 **144** 1c. green 15 15
612 – 1½c. brown (Harding) 20 15
634 – 2c. red (Washington) 10 15
636a – 3c. violet (Lincoln) 20 15
637 – 4c. brown (Martha Washington) 1·50 15
608 – 5c. blue (T. Roosevelt) 1·40 30
639 – 6c. orange (Garfield) 1·40 15
640 – 7c. black (McKinley) 1·40 15
641 – 8c. green (Grant) 1·40 15
642 – 9c. pink (Jefferson) 1·40 15
610 – 10c. orange (Monroe) 2·20 25
571a – 11c. blue (Hayes) 1·00 30
571b – 11c. green (Hayes) 1·00 40
693 – 12c. violet (Cleveland) 3·75 20
694 – 13c. green (B. Harrison) 1·30 20
695 **157** 14c. blue 2·50 40
696 **158** 15c. grey 6·00 20
697 **176** 17c. black 3·25 20
698 **159** 20c. red 7·00 20
699 – 25c. green (Niagara) 7·25 20
700 – 30c. brown (American bison) 11·00 20
701 – 50c. lilac (Arlington Amphitheatre and Unknown Soldier's Tomb) 30·00 20
579 – $1 brown (Lincoln Memorial) 38·00 35
580 – $2 blue (Capitol, Washington) 90·00 8·50
581 **165** $5 blue and red £140 12·00

The 25c. to $2 are horiz designs as T **159**, the remainder vert as T **144**.

A **166** Airplane Radiator and Propeller A **168** De Havilland D.H.4M "Liberty"

1923. Air.

A614 A **166** 8c. green 45 20
A615 – 16c. blue 65·00 23·00
A616 A **168** 24c. red 70·00 24·00

DESIGN: 16c. Air mail service insignia.

166 Harding **167** "Nieu Nederland" (emigrant ship)

1923. President Harding Memorial.

614 **166** 2c. black 50 10

1924. Huguenot–Walloon Tercentenary.

618 **167** 1c. green 2·10 2·75
619 – 2c. red 5·00 1·90
620 – 5c. blue 19·00 11·00

DESIGNS: 2c. Landing at Fort Orange; 5c. Ribault Memorial, Mayport, Florida.

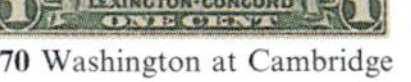

170 Washington at Cambridge **173** Sloop "Restaurationen"

1925. 150th Anniv of Battle of Lexington and Concord.

621 **170** 1c. green 2·00 2·30
622 – 2c. red 3·75 3·50
623 – 5c. blue 17·00 10·00

DESIGNS: 2c. Battle of Lexington-Concord; 5c. Statue of "Minute Man".

1925. Norse-American Centennial. Dated "1825 1925".

624 **173** 2c. black and red 2·75 2·40
625 – 5c. black and blue 10·00 9·25

DESIGN: 5c. "Raven" (replica Viking longship).

A **177** De Havilland D.H.4M Biplanes and Relief Map of U.S.A.

1926. Air.

A628 A **177** 10c. blue 2·20 35
A629 15c. brown 4·75 2·75
A630 20c. green 6·00 1·60

177 Liberty Bell

1926. 150th Anniv of Independence and Sesquicentennial Exhibition.

628 **177** 2c. red 2·75 45

178 Ericsson Memorial (J. E. Fraser) in Washington, D.C. **179** Alexander Hamilton's Battery (after painting by E. F. Ward)

1926. John Ericsson Commemoration.

629 **178** 5c. violet 5·50 3·50

1926. 150th Anniv of Battle of White Plains.

644 **179** 2c. red 1·30 1·50

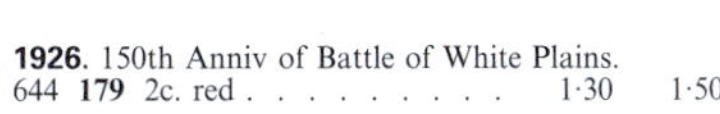

A **180** "Spirit of St. Louis"

1927. Air. Lindbergh's Transatlantic Flight.

A646 A **180** 10c. blue 75 85

181 Green Mountain Boy **182** Surrender of Gen. Burgoyne (after painting by Trumbull)

1927. 150th Anniv of Independence of Vermont and Battle of Bennington.

646 **181** 2c. red 1·00 80

1927. 150th Anniv of Burgoyne Campaign.

647 **182** 2c. red 2·40 1·90

183 Washington at Valley Forge (after engraving by J. C. McRae) A **184** Air Beacon, Sherman Hill, Rocky Mountains

1928. 150th Anniv of Valley Forge.

648 **183** 2c. red 60 40

1928. Air.

A649 A **184** 5c. blue and red 2·75 3·00

1928. 150th Anniv of Discovery of Hawaii. Optd **HAWAII 1778 - 1928**.

649 2c. red (No. 634) 4·00 4·00
650 5c. blue (No. 608) 8·25 10·50

1928. 150th Anniv of Battle of Monmouth. Optd **MOLLY PITCHER**.

651 2c. red (No. 634) 70 70

186 Wright Flyer I

1928. Civil Aeronautics Conference and 25th Anniv of Wright Brothers' First Flight.

652 **186** 2c. red 75 75
653 – 5c. blue 4·00 3·00

DESIGN: 5c. Globe and Ryan B-5 Brougham biplane.

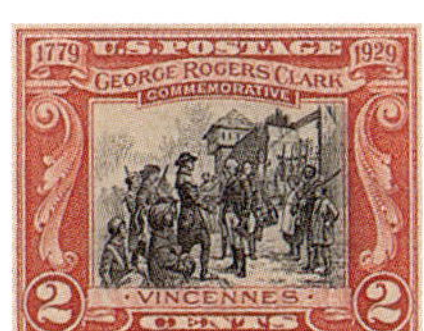

188 George Rogers Clark at Vincennes (from painting by F. C. Yohn)

1929. 150th Anniv of Surrender of Fort Sackville.

654 **188** 2c. black and red 40 50

1929. Stamps of 1922 optd. (a) **Kans.**

655 **144** 1c. green 2·00 1·70
656 **166** 1½c. brown 3·00 2·00
657 – 2c. red 3·50 90
658 – 3c. violet 16·00 10·00
659 – 4c. brown 14·50 6·50
660 – 5c. blue 10·00 6·75
661 – 6c. orange 21·00 12·50
662 – 7c. black 22·00 17·00
663 – 8c. olive 70·00 50·00
664 – 9c. red 11·00 8·50
665 – 10c. yellow 17·00 9·00

(b) **Nebr.**

666 **144** 1c. green 2·75 1·50
667 **166** 1½c. brown 2·75 1·80
668 – 2c. red 2·75 1·30
669 – 3c. violet 10·50 7·50
670 – 4c. brown 16·00 10·50
671 – 5c. blue 15·00 10·50
672 – 6c. orange 34·00 16·00
673 – 7c. black 19·00 12·50
674 – 8c. olive 28·00 17·00
675 – 9c. red 33·00 18·00
676 – 10c. yellow 95·00 15·00

191 Edison's Original Lamp **192** Maj.-Gen. Sullivan

1929. 50th Anniv of Edison's First Electric Lamp.

678 **191** 2c. red 45 20

1929. 150th Anniv of Maj.-Gen. Sullivan's Western Campaign.

680 **192** 2c. red 50 40

193 Gen. Wayne Memorial in Fallen Timbers Park, by E. W. Laville **194** Ohio River Lock No. 5, Monongahela R.

1929. 135th Anniv of Battle of Fallen Timbers.

681 **193** 2c. red 65 65

1929. Completion of Ohio River Canalization.

682 **194** 2c. red 40 45

A **195** Air Mail Pilot's Badge

1930. Air.

A684 A **195** 5c. violet 65 85
A685 6c. orange 15 15
A686 8c. green 55 15

195 Seal of the Colony **196** Governor and Indian

1930. Massachusetts Bay Colony Tercentenary.

683 **195** 2c. red 40 40

1930. 250th Anniv of Original Settlement near Charleston.

684 **196** 2c. red 1·00 1·10

A **197** Over the Atlantic

1930. Air. Airship "Graf Zeppelin" Europe–Pan-American Flight.

A687 A **197** 65c. green £200 £180
A688 – $1.30 brown £425 £325
A689 – $2.60 blue 60 45

DESIGNS: $1.30, Between continents; $2.60, Over the globe.

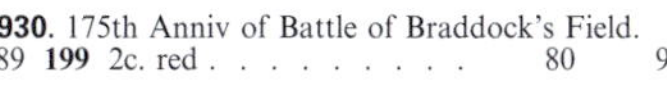

197 Harding **199** George Washington (after statue by F. Vittor in Braddock, Pa.)

1930.

685 **197** 1½c. brown 30 10
686 – 4c. brown 80 10

DESIGN: 4c. Taft.

1930. 175th Anniv of Battle of Braddock's Field.

689 **199** 2c. red 80 90

200 Gen. Wilhelm von Steuben (from medallion by Karl Dautert) **201** Gen. Casimir Pulaski (from etching by H. B. Hall)

1930. Birth Bicentenary of Gen. von Steuben.

690 **200** 2c. red 30 45

1931. 150th Death Anniv of Gen. Pulaski.

691 **201** 2c. red 15 15

202 Red Cross Nurse (from poster "The World's Greatest Mother") **203** Rochambeau, Washington, De Grasse (Washington, after painting by Trumbull, others from old engravings)

1931. 50th Anniv of American Red Cross Society.

702 **202** 2c. black and red 15 15

1931. 150th Anniv of Surrender of Cornwallis at Yorktown.

703 **203** 2c. black and red 20 25

204 George Washington **205** George Washington

1932. Birth Bicentenary of George Washington. Portraits dated "1732 1932".

704 **204** ½c. sepia 10 15
705 **205** 1c. green 15 15
706 – 1½c. brown 20 15
707 – 2c. red 10 15
708 – 3c. violet 40 20
709 – 4c. brown 15 15

710 – 5c. blue 95 20
711 – 6c. orange 2·10 20
712 – 7c. black 15 20
713 – 8c. olive 1·90 70
714 – 9c. red 1·50 25
715 – 10c. yellow 7·00 20
For 3c. as No. 707, see No. 720.

216 Skiing 217 Tree-planting

1932. Winter Olympic Games, Lake Placid.
716 **216** 2c. red 25 20

1932. 60th Anniv of Establishment of Arbor Day.
717 **217** 2c. red 10 15

218 Sprinter 219 Discus Thrower 221 Wm. Penn

1932. Summer Olympic Games, Los Angeles.
718 **218** 3c. violet 1·00 15
719 **219** 5c. blue 1·60 25

1932. As No. 707, but without date.
720 3c. violet 15 15

1932. 250th Anniv of Penn's Arrival in America.
723 **221** 3c. violet 15 20

222 Webster 223 Gen. Oglethorpe 224 Washington's H.Q.

1932. 150th Birth Anniv of Daniel Webster.
724 **222** 3c. violet 20 20

1933. Bicentenary of Founding of Georgia.
725 **223** 3c. violet 15 20

1933. 150th Anniv of Proclamation of Peace after War of Independence.
726 **224** 3c. violet 15 15

225 Fort Dearborn (after painting by Dwight Benton) 226 Federal Building

1933. "Centenary of Progress" International Exhibition, Chicago.
727 **225** 1c. green 15 15
728 **226** 3c. violet 15 15

227 Agriculture, Commerce and Industry

1933. National Recovery Act.
729 **227** 3c. violet 10 15

A 230 Chicago Federal Building, "Graf Zeppelin" and Friedrichshafen Hangar

1933. Air. "Graf Zeppelin" Chicago Flight.
A732 A **230** 50c. green 60·00 50·00

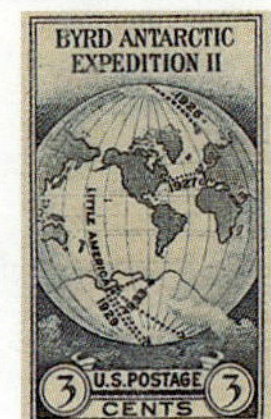

230 Routes of various Admiral Byrd Flights

1933. Byrd Antarctic Expedition.
752 **230** 3c. blue 35 50

231 Gen. Kosciuszko (from statue in Lafayette Park, Washington)

233 The "Ark" and the "Dove" (from drawing by E. Tunis)

1933. 150th Anniv of Naturalization of Kosciuszko.
733 **231** 5c. blue 30 25

1934. Maryland Tercentenary.
735 **233** 3c. red 10 15

234 "Portrait of my Mother" by Whistler

1934. Mothers' Day. Perf or imperf.
736 **234** 3c. violet 10 15

235 Nicolet's Landing at Green Bay (after painting by E. W. Deming)

1934. Tercentenary of Wisconsin.
738 **235** 3c. violet 10 15

236 "El Capitan", Yosemite

237 Grand Canyon

1934. National Parks.
739 **236** 1c. green 10 15
740 **237** 2c. red 10 15
741 – 3c. violet 10 15
742 – 4c. brown 20 30
743 – 5c. blue 40 45
744 – 6c. blue 70 80
745 – 7c. black 40 70
746 – 8c. green 1·10 1·10
747 – 9c. red 1·00 50
748 – 10c. grey 2·00 70
DESIGNS—VERT: 5c. "Old Faithful" geyser, Yellowstone; 8c. Great White Throne, Zion; 10c. Mount le Conte, Smoky Mountain. HORIZ: 3c. Mirror Lake, Mt. Rainier; 4c. Cliff dwellings, Mesa Verde; 6c. Crater Lake and Wizard Is; 7c. Great Head, Acadia; 9c. Mt. Rockwell and Two Medicine Lake Glacier.

248 The Charter Oak

1935. Connecticut Tercentenary.
771 **248** 3c. purple 10 10

249 Exhibition Grounds, Point Loma and San Diego Bay

1935. California Pacific Int Exn, San Diego.
772 **249** 3c. violet 10 10

250 Boulder Dam, Nevada

251 Seal of Michigan

1935. Dedication of Boulder Dam.
773 **250** 3c. violet 10 10

1935. Michigan Centenary.
774 **251** 3c. violet 10 10

A 253 Martin M-130 Flying Boat

1935. Air. Trans-Pacific Air Mail.
A775 – 20c. green 10 10
A776 A **253** 25c. blue 10 10
A777 – 50c. red 9·00 4·50
Nos. A775 and A777 are as Type A **253** but without the date.

252 S. Houston, S. F. Austin, and the Alamo

253 Roger Williams (from statue in Roger Williams Park, Providence, R. I.)

1936. Centenary of Declaration of Texan Independence.
775 **252** 3c. violet 10 10

1936. Rhode Island Tercentenary.
776 **253** 3c. violet 10 10

255 First Settlement, Old State House and Capitol

1936. Centenary of Arkansas.
778 **255** 3c. violet 10 10

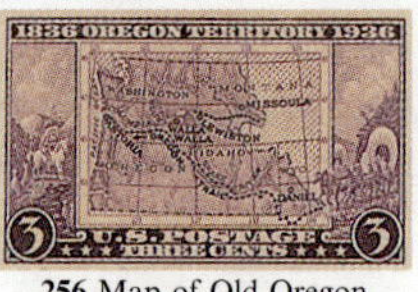

256 Map of Old Oregon Territory

257 Susan B. Anthony (detail from statue by Adelaide Johnson in Capitol)

1936. Centenary of Oregon.
779 **256** 3c. violet 10 10

1936. 16th Anniv of Women's Suffrage.
780 **257** 3c. purple 10 10

258 Washington and Greene, Mt. Vernon in background

263 Jones, Barry and Battle of Flamborough Head

1936. Army and Navy Heroes. (a) Army.
781 **258** 1c. green 10 10
782 – 2c. red 10 10
783 – 3c. purple 10 10
784 – 4c. blue 15 20
785 – 5c. blue 30 20
DESIGNS: 2c. Jackson, Scott and the Hermitage; 3c. Sherman, Grant and Sheridan; 4c. Lee, Jackson and Stratford Hall; 5c. West Point Military Academy.

(b) Navy.
786 **263** 1c. green 10 10
787 – 2c. red 10 10
788 – 3c. purple 10 10
789 – 4c. blue 15 20
790 – 5c. blue 30 20
DESIGNS: 2c. Decatur, MacDonough and U.S.S. "United States" (frigate); 3c. Farragut, Porter and U.S.S. "Hartford" (steam frigate); 4c. Sampson, Dewey and Schley; 5c. Seal of Naval Academy and cadets.

268 Cutler, Putnam and Map of N. W. Territory

1937. 150th Anniv of Enactment of North West Territory Ordinance.
791 **268** 3c. violet 10 10

269 Virginia Dare

1937. 350th Birth Anniv of Virginia Dare.
792 **269** 5c. blue 15 20

271 Signing the Constitution (after painting by J. B. Stearns)

1937. 150th Anniv of U.S. Constitution.
794 **271** 3c. mauve 10 10

272 Statue to Kamehameha I, Honolulu

273 Mt. McKinley, Alaska

274 Fortaleza Castle, Puerto Rico

275 Charlotte Amalie (St. Thomas), Virgin Islands

1937. Territorial Issue.
795 **272** 3c. violet 10 15
796 **273** 3c. violet 10 10
797 **274** 3c. violet 10 10
798 **275** 3c. mauve 10 10

276 Benjamin Franklin

A **308** American Bald Eagle and Shield

1938. Presidential Series.
799 **276** ½c. orange 10 10
800 – 1c. green 10 10
801 – 1½c. brown 10 10
802 – 2c. red 10 10
803 – 3c. violet 10 10
804 – 4c. purple 50 10
805 – 4½c. grey 10 15
806 – 5c. blue 10 10
807 – 6c. red 20 10
808 – 7c. brown 20 10
809 – 8c. green 25 10
810 – 9c. pink 40 10
811 – 10c. red 25 10
812 – 11c. blue 50 10
813 – 12c. mauve 70 10
814 – 13c. green . . . . 1·00 15
815 – 14c. blue 65 10
816 – 15c. slate 35 10
817 – 16c. black 65 40
818 – 17c. red 65 10
819 – 18c. purple . . . . 1·20 10
820 – 19c. mauve . . . . 1·00 55
821 – 20c. green 50 10
822 – 21c. blue 90 20
823 – 22c. red 70 55
824 – 24c. black . . . . 2·75 25
825 – 25c. mauve 50 10
826 – 30c. blue . . . . 3·00 10
827 – 50c. lilac . . . . 4·00 10
828 – $1 black and purple . . . 5·00 15
830 – $2 black and green . . . 15·00 4·00
831 – $5 black and red . . . . 70·00 4·25

DESIGNS: 1c. Washington; 1½c. Martha Washington; 2c. John Adams; 3c. Jefferson; 4c. Madison; 4½c. White House; 5c. James Monroe; 6c. John Quincy Adams; 7c. Jackson; 8c. Martin van Buren; 9c. Wm. Henry Harrison; 10c. John Tyler; 11c. James K. Polk; 12c. Zachary Taylor; 13c. Millard Fillmore; 14c. Franklin Pierce; 15c. James Buchanan; 16c. Lincoln; 17c. Johnson; 18c. Grant; 19c. Rutherford B. Hayes; 20c. James A. Garfield; 21c. Chester A. Arthur; 22c. Grover Cleveland; 24c. Benjamin Harrison; 25c. William McKinley; 30c. Theodore Roosevelt; 50c. Taft; $1 Woodrow Wilson; $2 Harding; $5 Coolidge.

1938. Air.
A845 A **308** 6c. red and blue . . . 15 10

308 Colonial Court House

1938. 150th Anniv of Ratification of U.S. Constitution.
845 **308** 3c. violet 15 10

309 Landing of the Swedes and Finns from "Calmare Nyckel" (after S. Arthurs)

310 Colonization of the West (from statue by G. Borglum at Marietta, Ohio)

1938. Tercentenary of Scandinavian Settlement in America.
846 **309** 3c. mauve 10 10

1938. North West Territory Sesquicentennial.
847 **310** 3c. violet 10 10

311 Old Capitol Building, Iowa

312 Tower of the Sun

1938. Iowa Territory Centennial.
848 **311** 3c. violet 10 10

1939. Golden Gate Int Exn, San Francisco.
849 **312** 3c. purple 10 10

313 Trylon and Perisphere

314 Inauguration of Washington

1939. New York World's Fair.
850 **313** 3c. violet 10 10

1939. 150th Anniv of Election of Washington as First President.
851 **314** 3c. purple 20 10

A **315** Winged Globe

1939. Air.
A852 A **315** 30c. blue . . . . . . 1·00 15

315 Baseball

1939. Baseball Centenary.
852 **315** 3c. violet 45 10

316 T. Roosevelt, Goethals and "Andrea F. Luckenbach" (freighter) in Gaillard Cut

317 Stephen Daye Press (from sketch by G. F. Trenholm)

1939. 25th Anniv of Opening of Panama Canal.
853 **316** 3c. purple 15 10

1939. Tercent of Printing in Colonial America.
854 **317** 3c. violet 10 15

318 Washington, Montana, N. and S. Dakota

319 Washington Irving

324 Henry W. Longfellow

329 Horace Mann

334 John James Audubon

339 Stephen Collins Foster

344 Gilbert Charles Stuart

349 Eli Whitney

1939. 50th Anniv of Statehood of Washington, Montana and N. and S. Dakota.
855 **318** 3c. mauve 10 10

1940. Famous Americans. (a) Authors.
856 **319** 1c. green 10 10
857 – 2c. red 10 10
858 – 3c. purple 10 10
859 – 5c. blue 15 20
860 – 10c. brown . . . . . . 90 1·20

PORTRAITS: 2c. J. Fenimore Cooper; 3c. Ralph Waldo Emerson; 5c. Louisa May Alcott; 10c. Samuel L. Clemens ("Mark Twain").

(b) Poets.
861 **324** 1c. green 10 10
862 – 2c. red 10 10
863 – 3c. purple 10 10
864 – 5c. blue 20 25
865 – 10c. brown . . . . . . 95 1·70

PORTRAITS: 2c. John Greenleaf Whittier; 3c. James Russell Lowell; 5c. Walt Whitman; 10c. James Whitcomb Riley.

(c) Educationalists.
866 **329** 1c. green 10 10
867 – 2c. red 10 15
868 – 3c. purple 10 10
869 – 5c. blue 20 25
870 – 10c. brown . . . . . . 85 1·30

PORTRAITS: 2c. Mark Hopkins; 3c. Charles W. Eliot; 5c. Frances E. Willard; 10c. Booker T. Washington.

(d) Scientists.
871 **334** 1c. green 10 10
872 – 2c. red 10 10
873 – 3c. purple 10 10
874 – 5c. blue 15 20
875 – 10c. brown . . . . . . 70 1·10

PORTRAITS: 2c. Dr. Crawford W. Long; 3c. Luther Burbank; 5c. Dr. Walter Reed; 10c. Jane Addams.

(e) Composers.
876 **339** 1c. green 10 10
877 – 2c. red 10 10
878 – 3c. purple 10 10
879 – 5c. blue 20 25
880 – 10c. brown . . . . . . 2·50 1·30

PORTRAITS: 2c. John Philip Sousa; 3c. Victor Herbert; 5c. Edward A. MacDowell; 10c. Ethelbert Nevin.

(f) Artists.
881 **344** 1c. green 10 10
882 – 2c. red 10 10
883 – 3c. purple 10 10
884 – 5c. blue 25 20
885 – 10c. brown . . . . . . 1·20 1·50

PORTRAITS: 2c. James A. McNeill Whistler; 3c. Augustus Saint-Gaudens; 5c. Daniel Chester French; 10c. Frederic Remington.

(g) Inventors.
886 **349** 1c. green 10 10
887 – 2c. red 10 10
888 – 3c. purple 15 10
889 – 5c. blue 75 40
890 – 10c. brown . . . . . . 8·00 2·40

PORTRAITS: 2c. Samuel F. B. Morse; 3c. Cyrus Hall McCormick; 5c. Elias Howe; 10c. Alexander Graham Bell.

354 "Pony Express"

355 "The Three Graces" (after Botticelli's "Spring")

1940. 80th Anniv of Inauguration of Pony Express.
891 **354** 3c. red 15 20

1940. 50th Anniv of Pan-American Union.
892 **355** 3c. mauve 15 15

356 State Capitol, Boise

357 Wyoming State Seal

1940. 50th Anniv of Idaho.
893 **356** 3c. violet 10 10

1940. 50th Anniv of Wyoming.
894 **357** 3c. purple 10 10

358 Coronado and His Captains (after painting by Gerald Cassidy)

360 Anti-aircraft Gun

1940. 400th Anniv of Coronado Expedition.
895 **358** 3c. violet 10 10

1940. National Defence.
896 – 1c. green 10 10
897 **360** 2c. red 10 10
898 – 3c. violet 10 15

DESIGNS: 1c. Statue of Liberty; 3c. Hand holding torch.

362 Emancipation Monument (from statue by Thomas Ball, Lincoln Park, Washington)

363 State Capitol Building, Montpelier

1940. 75th Anniv of Abolition of Slavery.
899 **362** 3c. violet 10 15

1941. 150th Anniv of Vermont.
900 **363** 3c. violet 10 10

A **364** Mail Plane

1941. Air.
A901 A **364** 6c. red 10 15
A902 8c. green 10 10
A903 10c. violet 45 25
A904 15c. red 10 10
A905 20c. green 10 10
A906 30c. blue 15 20
A907 50c. orange 15 20

364 Daniel Boone and Companions viewing Kentucky (from mural by Gilbert White in State Capitol, Frankfort)

365 Symbolical of Victory

1942. 150th Anniv of Kentucky.
901 **364** 3c. violet 15 10

1942. Independence Day.
902 **365** 3c. violet 10 10

366 Lincoln and Sun Yat-sen

367 Allegory of Victory

1942. Chinese War Effort.
903 **366** 5c. blue 30 20

1943. Allied Nations.
904 **367** 2c. red 10 10

368 Liberty holding Torch of Freedom and Enlightenment

369 Flag of Poland

1943. Four Freedoms.
905 **368** 1c. green 10 10

1943. Flags of Oppressed Nations. Frames in violet, flags in national colours.

906	5c. Type **369**	25	20
907	5c. Czechoslovakia	25	20
908	5c. Norway	15	20
909	5c. Luxembourg	15	20
910	5c. Netherlands	15	20
911	5c. Belgium	15	20
912	5c. France	15	20
913	5c. Greece	30	40
914	5c. Yugoslavia	15	25
915	5c. Albania	15	25
916	5c. Austria	15	20
917	5c. Denmark	15	20
918	5c. Korea	15	30

382 "Golden Spike Ceremony" (mural, John McQuarrie)

1944. 75th Anniv of First Transcontinental Railway.
919 **382** 3c. violet 10 10

383 Paddle-steamer "Savannah"

1944. 125th Anniv of Transatlantic Crossing of "Savannah."
920 **383** 3c. violet 10 10

384 "What Hath God Wrought"

1944. Centenary of First Telegraph Message.
921 **384** 3c. mauve 10 10

385 View of Corregidor

1944. Defence of Corregidor.
922 **385** 3c. violet 10 10

386 Open-air Cinema

1944. 50th Anniv of Motion Pictures.
923 **386** 3c. violet 20 15

387 Gates of St. Augustine, State Seal and Capitol

1945. Centenary of Statehood of Florida.
924 **387** 3c. purple 10 10

388 "Toward United Nations"

1945. San Francisco Conference.
925 **388** 5c. blue 10 10

389 Franklin D. Roosevelt and Hyde Park

393 Raising U.S.A. Flag at Iwo Jima

1945. Pres. Roosevelt Commemoration. Inscr "1882 1945".

926	**389**	1c. green	10	10
927	–	2c. red	15	10
928	–	3c. violet	15	10
929	–	5c. blue	15	10

DESIGNS: 2c. "Little White House", Warm Springs, Georgia; 3c. "White House", Washington; 5c. Western Hemisphere and Four Freedoms.

1945. U.S. Marines.
930 **393** 3c. green 15 15

394 U.S. Troops marching through Paris

1945. U.S. Army.
931 **394** 3c. olive 15 10

395 U.S. Sailors

1945. U.S. Navy.
932 **395** 3c. blue 15 10

396 "Arthur Middleton" (supply ship) and Coastguard Landing Craft)

397 Alfred E. Smith

1945. U.S. Coastguard.
933 **396** 3c. green 15 10

1945. Alfred E. Smith (Governor of New York) Commemoration.
934 **397** 3c. violet 15 10

398 Flags of U.S.A. and Texas

1945. Centenary of Texas Statehood.
935 **398** 3c. blue 15 10

399 "Liberty" type Freighter unloading Cargo

400 Honourable Discharge Emblem

1946. U.S. Mercantile Marine.
936 **399** 3c. green 15 10

1946. Honourable Discharged Veterans of Second World War.
937 **400** 3c. violet 15 10

401 Andrew Jackson, John Sevier and Tennessee State Capitol

1946. 150th Anniv of Tennessee Statehood.
938 **401** 3c. violet 15 10

402 Iowa State Flag and Map

1946. Centenary of Iowa Statehood.
939 **402** 3c. blue 15 10

403 Smithsonian Institution

1946. Centenary of Smithsonian Institution.
940 **403** 3c. purple 15 10

A **404** Douglas DC-4

1946. Air.
A941 A **404** 5c. red 15 10

404 Entry into Santa Fe (after painting by Kenneth M. Chapman)

405 Thomas A. Edison

1946. Centenary of Entry of Stephen Watts Kearny Expedition into Santa Fe.
941 **404** 3c. purple 15 10

1947. Birth Cent of Thomas Edison (scientist).
942 **405** 3c. violet 15 10

A **406** Douglas DC-4

406 Joseph Pulitzer (from portrait by J. S. Sargent)

1947. Air.

A943	A **406**	5c. red	15	10
A944		6c. red	15	10

1947. Birth Centenary of Joseph Pulitzer (journalist and newspaper publisher).
943 **406** 3c. violet 15 10

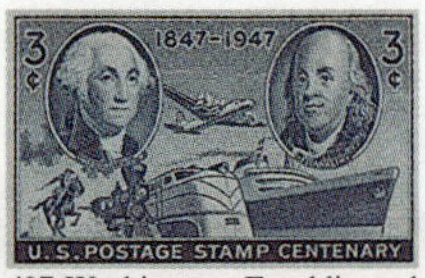

407 Washington, Franklin and Evolution of Postal Transport

1947. U.S. Postage Stamp Centenary.
944 **407** 3c. blue 25 10

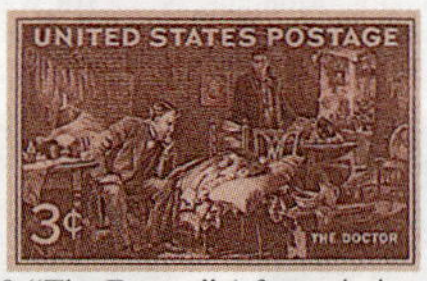

409 "The Doctor" (after painting by Sir Luke Fildes)

1947. Medical Profession.
946 **409** 3c. purple 15 10

410 Pioneer Caravan

1947. Centenary of Utah.
947 **410** 3c. violet 15 10

A **411** Pan-American Union Building, Washington

1947. Air.

A948	A **411**	10c. black	15	10
A949	–	15c. green	15	10
A950	–	25c. blue	15	10

DESIGNS: 15c. Statue of Liberty and New York City; 25c. San Francisco–Oakland Bay Suspension Bridge.

411 U.S.S. "Constitution"

412 Great Blue Heron and Map of Florida

1947. 150th Anniv of Launching of Frigate U.S.S. "Constitution" ("Old Ironsides").
948 **411** 3c. green 25 15

1947. Dedication of Everglades National Park, Florida.
949 **412** 3c. green 30 15

413 George Washington Carver

414 Sutter's Mill, Coloma

1948. 5th Death Anniv of George Washington Carver (scientist).
950 **413** 3c. violet 15 10

1948. Cent of Discovery of Gold in California.
951 **414** 3c. violet 15 10

415 Gov. Winthrop Sargent, Map and Seal of Mississippi Territory (from portrait by Gilbert Stuart)

1948. 150th Anniv of Mississippi Territory.
952 **415** 3c. purple 15 10

416 Four Chaplains and Liner "Dorchester"

1948. 5th Death Anniv of George Fox, Clark Poling, John Washington and Alexander Goode (who gave up life-jackets).
953 **416** 3c. black 15 10

417 Scroll and State Capitol, Madison

1948. Centenary of Statehood of Wisconsin.
954 **417** 3c. violet 15 10

418 Pioneer and Covered Wagon

1948. Centenary of Swedish Pioneers in Middle West.
955 **418** 5c. blue 15 10

419 Elizabeth Stanton, Carrie C. Catt, and Lucretia Mott

A 420 Map of New York, Ring and Planes (from Poster by G. A. Lorimer)

1948. Progress of American Women.
956 **419** 3c. violet 15 10

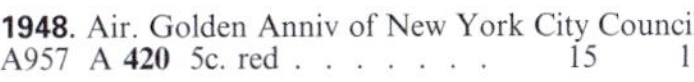

1948. Air. Golden Anniv of New York City Council.
A957 A **420** 5c. red 15 15

420 William Allen White

421 Niagara Railway Suspension Bridge (from print by H. Peters)

1948. Honouring W. A. White (editor and author).
957 **420** 3c. purple 15 10

1948. Centenary of Friendship between United States and Canada.
958 **421** 3c. blue 15 15

422 Francis Scott Key

1948. Honouring F. S. Key (author of "Star Spangled Banner").
959 **422** 3c. red 15 15

423 Boy and Girl Students

1948. Salute to Youth.
960 **423** 3c. blue 15 15

424 John McLoughlin, Jason Lee and Covered Wagon

425 Harlan Fiske Stone

1948. Oregon Territory Centennial.
961 **424** 3c. red 15 15

1948. Honouring Chief Justice H. F. Stone.
962 **425** 3c. purple 15 15

426 Palomar Mountain Observatory

427 Clara Barton and Cross

1948. Dedication of Palomar Observatory.
963 **426** 3c. blue 15 15

1948. Honouring Clara Barton (founder of American Red Cross).
964 **427** 3c. red 15 15

428 Light Brahma Rooster

1948. Centenary of American Poultry Industry.
965 **428** 3c. brown 15 15

429 Star and Palm Branch

430 Fort Kearny and Pioneers (Pioneer group from sculpture on Nebraska State Capitol)

1948. Honouring Bereaved Mothers.
966 **429** 3c. yellow 15 10

1948. Centenary of Fort Kearny, Nebraska.
967 **430** 3c. violet 15 10

431 Peter Stuyvesant and Fire Engines (from painting in Library of Congress)

1948. Tercentenary of Volunteer Firemen.
968 **431** 3c. red 15 10

432 Indian Seals and Map of Oklahoma

1948. Centenary of Five Civilized Indian Tribes of Oklahoma.
969 **432** 3c. brown 15 10

433 Statue of Capt. William Owen "Bucky" O'Neill, Prescott, Arizona (S. H. Borglum)

1948. 50th Anniv of Organization of Rough Riders.
970 **433** 3c. purple 15 10

434 Juliette Gordon Low

435 Will Rogers

1948. Honouring Juliette Gordon Low (founder of U.S.A. Girl Scouts).
971 **434** 3c. green 15 10

1948. Honouring Will Rogers (political commentator).
972 **435** 3c. purple 15 10

436 Rocket Testing

437 Moina Michael and Poppies

1948. Centenary of Fort Bliss.
973 **436** 3c. red 15 15

1948. Honouring Moina Michael (founder of Memorial Poppy).
974 **437** 3c. red 15 10

438 Abraham Lincoln (from statue by D. C. French at Lincoln, Neb.)

439 Torch and Emblem

1948. 85th Anniv of Gettysburg Address.
975 **438** 3c. blue 20 10

1948. Centenary of American Turners' Society.
976 **439** 3c. red 20 10

440 Joel Chandler Harris

441 Pioneer and Red River Ox Cart

1948. Birth Centenary of J. C. Harris (author).
977 **440** 3c. purple 15 10

1949. Cent of Territorial Status of Minnesota.
978 **441** 3c. green 15 10

442 Washington, Lee and University Building

1949. Bicentenary of Washington and Lee University, Lexington, Virginia.
979 **442** 3c. blue 15 10

443 Puerto Rican, Cogwheel and Ballot Box

1949. 1st Gubernatorial Election in Puerto Rico.
980 **443** 3c. green 15 10

A 444 Wings, Seal, Carlyle House and Gadsby's Tavern

1949. Air. Bicentenary of Alexandria, Virginia.
A981 A **444** 6c. red 15 10

444 Map, "Het Vergulde Vsanker" (sailing barge) and Shield

1949. Tercentenary of Annapolis, Maryland.
981 **444** 3c. green 20 10

445 Young and Old Soldiers

446 Edgar Allan Poe

1949. Final National Encampment of the Grand Army of the Republic.
982 **445** 3c. red 15 10
For similar stamp see No. 995.

1949. Death Centenary of Edgar Allan Poe (poet and author).
983 **446** 3c. purple 25 10

A 447 U.P.U Monument, Berne and P.O. Department, Washington

1949. Air. 75th Anniv of U.P.U.
A984 A **447** 10c. violet 15 10
A985 – 15c. blue 15 10
A986 – 25c. red 15 10
DESIGNS: 15c. Globe and birds; 25c. Globe and Boeing 377 Stratocruiser.

A 450 Wright Brothers and Wright Flyer I

1949. Air. 46th Anniv of Wright Brothers' First Flight.
A987 A **450** 6c. purple 15 10

447 Symbolic of Investments

448 Samuel Gompers

1950. 75th Anniv of American Bankers' Assn.
984 **447** 3c. green 15 10

1950. Birth Centenary of Samuel Gompers (labour leader).
985 **448** 3c. purple 15 10

449 Statue of Freedom (by Crawford) on Capitol Dome

450 The White House

1950. National Capital Sesquicentennial.
986 **449** 3c. blue 25 15
987 **450** 3c. green 25 15
988 – 3c. violet 20 10
989 – 3c. purple 15 10
DESIGNS—HORIZ: No. 988, U.S. Supreme Court building; 989, Capitol, Washington.

453 Casey Jones, Locomotive No. 382 and "Rocket" Diesel Train

1950. Honouring Railway Engineers.
990 **453** 3c. purple 20 10

454 Kansas City in 1850 and 1950

1950. Centenary of Kansas City.
991 **454** 3c. violet 15 10

455 Scouts and Badge

1950. American Boy Scouts.
992 **455** 3c. brown 20 10

456 First Capitol and W. H. Harrison

1950. Sesquicentennial of Indiana.
993 **456** 3c. blue 20 10

457 Pioneers

1950. Centenary of California.
994 **457** 3c. yellow 15 10

1951. Final Reunion of United Confederate Veterans. As T **445**, but initials at left and in hat badge changed to "UCV".
995 **445** 3c. grey 15 10

458 Log Cabin

1951. Centenary of Nevada.
996 **458** 3c. olive 15 10

459 Cadillac Disembarking

1951. 250th Anniv of Landing of Cadillac at Detroit.
997 **459** 3c. blue 15 10

460 Mount of the Holy Cross, State Seal and Capitol

1951. 75th Anniv of Colorado.
998 **460** 3c. violet 15 10

461 Emblem and Chemical Plant

1951. 75th Anniv of American Chemical Society.
999 **461** 3c. purple 20 10

462 Washington at Brooklyn

1951. 175th Anniv of Battle of Brooklyn.
1000 **462** 3c. violet 15 10

463 Betsy Ross and Flag

1952. Birth Bicentenary of Betsy Ross (maker of First American flag).
1001 **463** 3c. red 15 10

464 Emblem and Young Club Members

1952. 50th Anniv of 4-H Clubs.
1002 **464** 3c. green 15 10

465 Horse-drawn "Pioneer" Coach, "Tom Thumb" (1829) and Diesel Locomotive

1952. 125th Anniv of Baltimore and Ohio Railway.
1003 **465** 3c. blue 20 10

466 Cars of 1902 and 1952 **467** "Torch of Freedom"

1952. 50th Anniv of American Automobile Assn.
1004 **466** 3c. blue 20 10

1952. 3rd Anniv of N.A.T.O.
1005 **467** 3c. violet 15 10

A **467** Diamond Head, Oahu, Honolulu

1952. Air.
A1005 A **467** 80c. purple . . . . 5·00 1·10

468 Grand Coulee Dam

1952. 50th Anniv of Columbia Basin Reclamation.
1006 **468** 3c. green 15 10

469 Lafayette and Flags

1952. 175th Anniv of Lafayette's Arrival in America.
1007 **469** 3c. blue 20 10

470 Mt. Rushmore National Memorial **471** Bridges in 1852 and 1952

1952. 25th Anniv of Mt. Rushmore National Memorial.
1008 **470** 3c. green 15 10

1952. Centenary of American Society of Civil Engineers.
1009 **471** 3c. blue 15 10

472 Women in Uniform

1952. Women's Services Commemoration.
1010 **472** 3c. blue 15 10

473 Gutenberg and Elector of Mainz (after Edward Laning)

1952. 500th Anniv of Printing of First Book from Movable Type.
1011 **473** 3c. violet 15 10

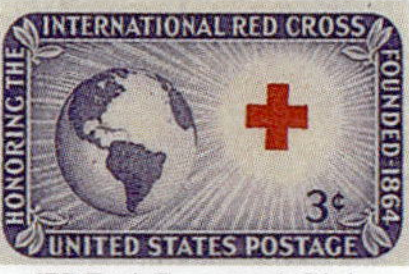

474 Newspaperboy and Torch of Free Enterprise

1952. Newspaperboys Commemoration.
1012 **474** 3c. violet 15 10

475 Red Cross and Globe

1952. International Red Cross.
1013 **475** 3c. blue and red 20 10

476 Guardsman and Amphibious Landing

1953. National Guard.
1014 **476** 3c. blue 15 10

477 Map and Seal of Ohio

1953. 150th Anniv of Ohio.
1015 **477** 3c. sepia 20 10

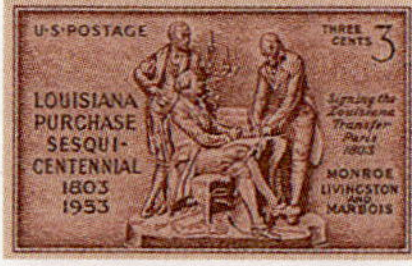

478 Seal of Washington Territory and Settlers

1953. Centenary of Washington Territory.
1016 **478** 3c. green 15 10

479 Monroe, Livingston and Marbois signing Transfer (from sculpture plaque by Karl Bitter)

1953. 150th Anniv of Louisiana Purchase.
1017 **479** 3c. purple 20 10

A **480** Wright Flyer I and Boeing 377 Stratocruiser

1953. Air. 50th Anniv of Aviation.
A1018 A **480** 6c. red 15 10

480 Commodore Perry and U.S.S. "Susquehanna" and "Mississippi" (paddle-gunboats) in Tokyo Bay

1953. Centenary of Opening of Japan to Foreign Trade.
1018 **480** 5c. turquoise 30 15

481 "Wisdom", "Justice and Divine Inspiration" and "Truth"

1953. 75th Anniv of American Bar Association.
1019 **481** 3c. violet 15 10

482 "Sagamore Hill"

1953. Opening of Theodore Roosevelt's Home.
1020 **482** 3c. green 15 10

483 Young Farmer and Landscape

1953. 25th Anniv of "Future Farmers of America".
1021 **483** 3c. blue 15 10

484 Truck and Distant City

1953. 50th Anniv of Trucking Industry.
1022 **484** 3c. violet 15 10

485 Gen. Patton and Tanks in Action

1953. Gen. George Patton and U.S. Armoured Forces.
1023 **485** 3c. violet 15 10

486 New York in 1653 and 1953

1953. Tercent of Foundation of New York City.
1024 **486** 3c. purple 20 10

487 Pioneer Family

1953. Centenary of Gadsden Purchase.
1025 **487** 3c. chestnut 15 10

488 Low Memorial Library

1954. Bicentenary of Columbia University.
1026 **488** 3c. blue 15 10

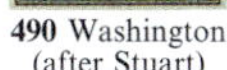
490 Washington (after Stuart)

492 Mount Vernon

501 Statue of Liberty

516 "The Sower" and Mitchell Pass (from statue on Capitol, Lincoln, Neb)

1954. Liberty Issue.

1027	–	½c. red	15	10
1028	**490**	1c. green	15	10
1029	–	1¼c. turquoise	15	10
1030	**492**	1½c. lake	15	10
1031	–	2c. red	15	10
1032	–	2½c. blue	15	10
1033	**501**	3c. violet	15	10
1034	–	4c. mauve	15	10
1035	–	4½c. green	15	10
1036	–	5c. blue	15	10
1037	–	6c. red	20	10
1038	–	7c. red	20	10
1039	**501**	8c. red and blue	25	10
1040	–	8c. red and blue	20	10
1041	–	8c. brown	20	10
1042	–	9c. purple	30	10
1043	–	10c. red	25	10
1044	–	11c. blue and red	20	10
1045	–	12c. red	35	10
1046	–	15c. red	65	10
1047	–	20c. blue	45	10
1059	–	25c. turquoise	50	20
1049	–	30c. black	1·10	10
1050	–	40c. lake	1·70	10
1051	–	50c. violet	1·50	10
1052	–	$1 violet	4·50	10
1053	–	$5 black	70·00	6·25

DESIGNS—As Type **490**: ½c. Benjamin Franklin; 2c. Jefferson; 4c. Lincoln; 5c. Monroe; 6c. Theodore Roosevelt; 7c. Woodrow Wilson; 8c. (No. 1040), As Type **501** but torch flame below "P"; 8c. (No. 1041), Gen. John J. Pershing; 11c. As No. 1040; 12c. Benjamin Harrison; 15c. John Jay; 25c. Paul Revere; 30c. Robert E. Lee; 40c. John Marshall; 50c. Susan B. Anthony; $1 Patrick Henry; $5 Alexander Hamilton. As Type **492**—VERT: 2½c. Bunker Hill Monument and Massachusetts flag. HORIZ: 1¼c. Palace of the Governors, Santa Fe; 4½c. The Hermitage; 9c. The Alamo; 10c. Independence Hall; 20c. Monticello, Thomas Jefferson's home.

1954. Centenary of Nebraska Territory.
1062 **516** 3c. violet 15 10

517 Pioneers and Cornfield

518 George Eastman

1954. Centenary of Kansas Territory.
1063 **517** 3c. salmon 15 10

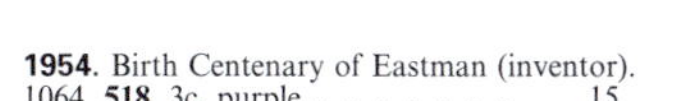

1954. Birth Centenary of Eastman (inventor).
1064 **518** 3c. purple 15 10

519 Landing on Riverbank, Missouri

A 520 American Bald Eagle in Flight

1954. 150th Anniv of Lewis and Clark Expedition.
1065 **519** 3c. purple 15 10

1954. Air.
A1066 A **520** 4c. blue 15 10
A1067 5c. red 25 10

520 "Peale in his Museum" (self-portrait)

521 Open Book and Symbols of Subjects taught

1955. 150th Anniv of Pennsylvania Academy of Fine Arts.
1066 **520** 3c. purple 15 10

1955. Centenary of First Land-Grant Colleges.
1067 **521** 3c. green 15 10

522 Torch, Globe and Rotary Emblem

1955. 50th Anniv of Rotary International.
1068 **522** 8c. blue 15 10

523 Marine, Coastguard, Soldier, Sailor and Airman

1955. Armed Forces Reserve.
1069 **523** 3c. purple 15 10

524 "The Old Man of the Mountains"

525 The Great Lakes and "Altadoc" (freighter)

1955. 150th Anniv of Discovery of "The Old Man of the Mountains" (New Hampshire landmark).
1070 **524** 3c. turquoise 20 10

1955. Soo Locks Centenary.
1071 **525** 3c. blue 15 10

526

1955. "Atoms for Peace".
1072 **526** 3c. blue 20 10

527 Plan of Fort, Ethan Allen and Artillery

528 Mellon (after Edward Birley)

1955. Bicentenary of Fort Ticonderoga.
1073 **527** 3c. brown 20 10

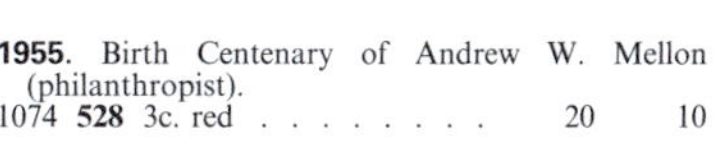

1955. Birth Centenary of Andrew W. Mellon (philanthropist).
1074 **528** 3c. red 20 10

529 Benjamin Franklin (after painting by Benjamin West)

530 Log Cabin

1956. 250th Birth Anniv of Franklin.
1075 **529** 3c. red 15 10

1956. Birth Centenary of Booker T. Washington.
1076 **530** 3c. blue 15 10

532 New York Coliseum and Columbus Monument

1956. 5th International Philatelic Exn, New York.
1078 **532** 3c. violet 15 10

533 Common Turkey

536 H. W. Wiley

1956. Wild Life Conservation.
1079 **533** 3c. purple 15 10
1080 – 3c. sepia 15 10
1081 – 3c. green 20 10
DESIGNS: No. 1080, Pronghorns; 1081, Chinook "king" salmon.

1956. 50th Anniv of Pure Food and Drug Laws.
1082 **536** 3c. green 20 10

537 Wheatland

538 Mosaic by L. M. Winter, A.F.L.-C.I.O. Headquarters

1956. Home of James Buchanan.
1083 **537** 3c. sepia 20 10

1956. Labour Day.
1084 **538** 3c. blue 20 10

539 Nassau Hall (contemporary engraving by Dawkins)

540 Devils Tower

1956. Bicentenary of Nassau Hall.
1085 **539** 3c. black on orange 20 10

1956. 50th Anniv of Devils Tower National Monument.
1086 **540** 3c. violet 15 10

541 "The Key to World Peace"

1956. Children's Friendship.
1087 **541** 3c. blue 15 10

542 Alexander Hamilton and Federal Hall, New York

543 Women, Children and Shield

1957. Birth Bicentenary of Alexander Hamilton.
1088 **542** 3c. red 15 10

1957. Infantile Paralysis Relief Campaign.
1089 **543** 3c. mauve 15 10

544 Survey Flag and Coastguard Vessels "Pathfinder", "Explorer" and "Surveyor"

1957. 150th Anniv of Coast and Geodetic Survey.
1090 **544** 3c. blue 15 10

545 Ancient and Modern Capitals

546 Eagle and Ladle

1957. Cent of American Institute of Architects.
1091 **545** 3c. mauve 15 10

1957. Centenary of American Steel Industry.
1092 **546** 3c. blue 15 10

547 Festival Emblem and Aircraft Carrier U.S.S. "Forrestal"

1957. Jamestown Festival and Int Naval Review.
1093 **547** 3c. green 15 10

548 Arrow piercing Atomic Symbol

1957. 50th Anniv of Oklahoma Statehood.
1094 **548** 3c. blue 15 10

549 Teacher with Pupils

1957. Teachers of America Commemoration.
1095 **549** 3c. red 15 10

550 U.S. Flag

1957. Flag Issue.
1096 **550** 4c. red and blue 20 15

A **551** Boeing B-52 Stratofortress and Lockheed F-104 Starfighters

551 "Virginia of Sagadahock" (shallop) and Arms of Maine

1957. Air. 50th Anniv of U.S. Air Force.
A1097 A **551** 6c. blue 15 10

1957. 350th Anniv of American Shipbuilding.
1097 **551** 3c. violet 15 10

552 Pres. Magsaysay of the Philippines (medallion)

553 Marquis de Lafayette (portrait by Court in Versailles Museum)

1953. Pres. Magsaysay Commemoration.
1098 **552** 8c. ochre, blue and red 25 10

1957. Birth Bicentenary of Marquis de Lafayette.
1099 **553** 3c. red 15 10

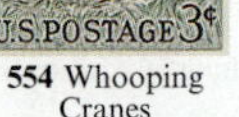

554 Whooping Cranes

555 "Religious Freedom"

1957. Wild Life Conservation.
1100 **554** 3c. blue, orange and green 15 10

1957. Tercentenary of Flushing Remonstrance.
1101 **555** 3c. black 15 10

556 "Abundance"

557 U.S. Pavilion

1958. Gardening and Horticulture Commem.
1102 **556** 3c. green 15 10

1958. Brussels International Exhibition.
1103 **557** 3c. purple 15 10

558 James Monroe (portrait by Stuart)

1958. Birth Bicentenary of Pres. James Monroe.
1104 **558** 3c. violet 15 10

559 Lake in Minnesota

1958. Centenary of Minnesota Statehood.
1105 **559** 3c. green 15 10

560 Sun's Surface and Hands (after Michelangelo's "The Creation of Adam")

1958. I.G.Y.
1106 **560** 3c. red and black 15 10

561 Gunston Hall (after drawing by Rene Clarke)

562 Mackinac Bridge

1958. Bicentenary of Gunston Hall, Virginia (home of George Mason, patriot).
1107 **561** 3c. green 15 10

1958. Mackinac Bridge Commemoration.
1108 **562** 3c. turquoise 15 10

563 Simon Bolivar (after painting by Ricardo Arcevedo-Bernal)

A **564** Silhouette of Jet Airliner

1958. Bolivar Commemoration.
1109 **563** 4c. ochre 15 10
1110 8c. brown, blue and red 15 15
See also Nos. 1116/17, 1124/5, 1135/6, 1146/7, 1158/9, 1164/5, 1167/8 and 1173/4.

1958. Air.
A1111 A **564** 7c. blue 20 15
A1112 7c. red 25 10

564 Globe, Neptune and Mermaid

1958. Centenary of Inaug of Atlantic Cable.
1111 **564** 4c. purple 15 10

565 Abraham Lincoln (from painting by G. Healy)

570 Hand with Quill Pen and Printing Press

1958. 150th Birth Anniv of Lincoln.
1112 **565** 1c. green 15 10
1113 – 3c. red 20 10
1114 – 4c. brown 25 10
1115 – 4c. blue 25 10
DESIGNS: No. 1113, Bust of Lincoln; 1114, Addressing Electorate; 1115, Lincoln Statue, Washington.

1958. Lajos Kossuth Commemoration. Medallion portrait as T **563**.
1116 4c. green 15 10
1117 8c. brown, blue and red . . 25 15

1958. Freedom of the Press.
1118 **570** 4c. black 15 10

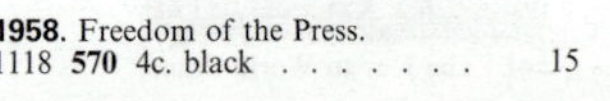

571 Mail Coach under Attack

572 Noah Webster (engraving by G. Parker after painting by James Herring)

1958. Overland Mail Centenary.
1119 **571** 4c. red 15 10

1958. Birth Bicentenary of Noah Webster (lexicographer).
1120 **572** 4c. red 15 10

573 Forest Pines

574 British Forces occupying Fort Duquesne (from etching by T. B. Smith)

1958. Forest Conservation.
1121 **573** 4c. yellow, green & brown 15 10

1958. Bicentenary of Fort Duquesne.
1122 **574** 4c. blue 15 10

A **575** Stars on Alaskan Map

1959. Air. Alaska Statehood.
A1123 A **575** 7c. blue 15 10

575 Covered Wagon and Mt. Hood

577 N.A.T.O. Emblem

1959. Centenary of Oregon Statehood.
1123 **575** 4c. green 20 10

1959. San Martin Commemoration. Medallion portrait as T **563**.
1124 4c. blue 15 10
1125 8c. ochre, red and blue . . . 25 20

1959. 10th Anniv of N.A.T.O.
1126 **577** 4c. blue 20 10

578 Peary with Dog-team and Submarine U.S.S. "Nautilus"

1959. Arctic Explorations by Robert Peary (50th anniv of reaching North Pole) and U.S.S. "Nautilus".
1127 **578** 4c. blue 15 10

579

1959. World Peace through World Trade.
1128 **579** 8c. red 25 15

580 Discovery of Silver at Mt. Davidson, Nevada (from a print)

1959. Cent of Discovery of Silver in Nevada.
1129 **580** 4c. black 15 10

581 Maple Leaf linked with American Eagle

1959. Opening of St. Lawrence Seaway.
1130 **581** 4c. blue and red 15 10

582 New U.S. Flag (with 49 stars)

1959. Inauguration of New United States Flag.
1131 **582** 4c. red, blue and orange 15 10

A **583** John Wise's Balloon "Jupiter"

A **584** Hawaiian Warrior, Map and Star

1959. Air. Centenary of Balloon "Jupiter's" Mail-carrying Flight.
A1132 A **583** 7c. red and blue . . 15 10

1959. Air. Hawaii Statehood.
A1133 A **584** 7c. red 20 10

583 "The Good Earth"

584 Oil Derrick

1959. Soil Conservation.
1132 **583** 4c. green, brown and blue 15 10

1959. Centenary of First Oil-well at Titusville, Pennsylvania.
1133 **584** 4c. brown 25 10

A **585** Runner with Olympic Torch

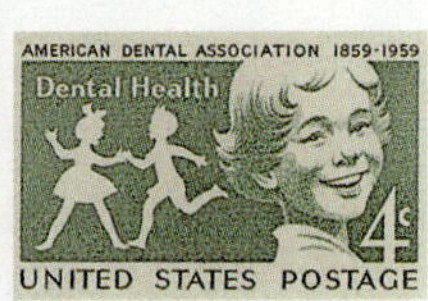

585 "Happy Children with Healthy Teeth"

1959. Air. 3rd Pan-American Games, Chicago.
A1134 A **585** 10c. red and blue . . 20 10

1959. Dental Health. Centenary of American Dental Association.
1134 **585** 4c. green 20 10

1959. Ernst Reuter Commemoration. Medallion portrait as T **563**.
1135 4c. grey 20 10
1136 8c. ochre, red and blue . . . 15 15

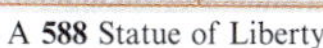
A **588** Statue of Liberty

587 Dr. E. McDowell (from painting)

1959. Air.
A1137 – 10c. black and green 15 10
A1138 – 13c. black and red 20 10
A1139 A **588** 15c. black & orge (A) 20 10
A1140 15c. black & orge (B) 20 10
A1141 – 25c. black and brown 20 10
DESIGNS: 10, 13c. Liberty Bell; 15c. Statue has double frame-line (A) or single frame-line (B); 25c. Abraham Lincoln.

1959. 150th Anniv of First Recorded Successful Abdominal Operation.
1137 **587** 4c. purple 15 10

588

1960. "American Credo" series.
1138 **588** 4c. red and blue 20 10
1139 – 4c. green and bistre 20 10
1140 – 4c. red and grey 25 10
1141 – 4c. blue and red 25 10
1142 – 4c. green and purple 20 10
1143 – 4c. brown and green 20 10
INSCRIPTIONS: No. 1139, "Fear to do ill, and you need fear Nought else" (Franklin); 1140, "I have sworn ... Hostility against every form of TYRANNY over the mind of man" (Jefferson); 1141, "And this be our Motto in GOD is our TRUST" (Francis Scott Key); 1142, "Those who Deny freedom to others Deserve it not for Themselves" (Lincoln); 1143, "Give me LIBERTY or give me DEATH" (P. Henry).

594 Scout Saluting

595 Olympic Rings and Snow Crystal

1960. 50th Anniv of American Boy Scout Movement.
1144 **594** 4c. ochre, red and blue 15 10

1960. Winter Olympic Games.
1145 **595** 4c. blue 15 10

1960. Thomas Masaryk Commemoration. Medallion portrait as T **563**.
1146 4c. blue 15 10
1147 8c. ochre, red and blue 25 15

597 "Towards the Light"

1960. World Refuge Year.
1148 **597** 4c. black 20 15

598 "Irrigation"

599 S.E.A.T.O. Emblem

1960. Water Conservation Campaign.
1149 **598** 4c. green, brown and blue 15 10

1960. S.E.A.T.O. Conference.
1150 **599** 4c. blue 15 10

600 Mother and Child

601 New U.S. Flag (with 50 stars)

1960. American Womanhood Commemoration.
1151 **600** 4c. violet 15 10

1960. New United States Flag (50 stars).
1152 **601** 4c. red and blue 15 10

602 Pony Express

1960. Centenary of Pony Express.
1153 **602** 4c. brown 15 10

603 Cripple operating Press

604 Congress Seal

1960. Employment of the Handicapped Campaign.
1154 **603** 4c. blue 15 10

1960. 5th World Forestry Congress, Seattle.
1155 **604** 4c. green 15 10

605 Dolores Bell (Mexico)

606 Washington Monument and Cherry Blossom

1960. 150th Anniv of Mexican Independence.
1156 **605** 4c. red and green 15 10

1960. Centenary of U.S.–Japan Treaty.
1157 **606** 4c. red and turquoise 15 10

1960. Jan Paderewski Commemoration. Medallion portrait as T **563**.
1158 4c. blue 15 10
1159 8c. ochre, red and blue 25 15

608 Robert A. Taft

609 Steering Wheel, Motor Transport and Globes

1960. Robert A. Taft Memorial Issue.
1160 **608** 4c. violet 15 10

1960. "Wheels of Freedom" (Motor Industry).
1161 **609** 4c. blue 15 10

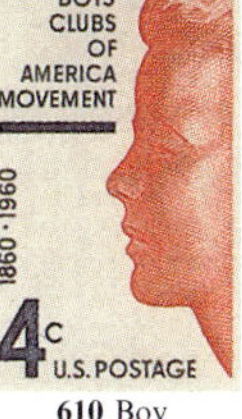

610 Boy

611 New P.O. Building

1960. Cent of Boys' Clubs of America Movement.
1162 **610** 4c. red, black and indigo 15 10

1960. Inauguration of 1st U.S. Automated P.O., Providence, Rhode Island.
1163 **611** 4c. blue and red 15 10

1960. Marshal Mannerheim Commem. Medallion portrait as T **563**.
1164 4c. blue 15 10
1165 8c. ochre, red and blue 25 20

613 Camp Fire Girls Emblem

615 George

1960. 50th Anniv of Camp Fire Girls Movement.
1166 **613** 4c. red and blue 15 10

1960. Garibaldi Commem. Medallion portrait as T **563**.
1167 4c. green 15 10
1168 8c. ochre, red and blue 20 20

1960. Senator Walter F. George Memorial Issue.
1169 **615** 4c. violet 15 10

616 Andrew Carnegie

617 Dulles

1960. Andrew Carnegie.
1170 **616** 4c. red 15 10

1960. John Foster Dulles Memorial Issue.
1171 **617** 4c. violet 15 10

618 "Echo I" Communications Satellite

1960. "Communications for Peace".
1172 **618** 4c. violet 20 10

1961. Mahatma Gandhi Commemoration. Medallion portrait as T **563**.
1173 4c. red on orange 15 10
1174 8c. ochre, red and blue 25 20

620 Trail Boss and Prairie

621 Horace Greeley (from steel engraving by A. H. Ritchie)

1961. Range Conservation.
1175 **620** 4c. black, orange and blue 15 10

1961. Horace Greeley (editor).
1176 **621** 4c. violet 15 10

622 Sea Coast Gun

1961. Civil War Centennial. Battles.
1177 **622** 4c. green 30 10
1178 – 4c. black on pink 25 10
1179 – 5c. indigo and blue 25 10
1180 – 5c. black and red 25 15
1181 – 5c. black and blue 40 10
DESIGNS—HORIZ: No. 1178, Rifleman (Shiloh); 1179, Armed combat (Gettysburg); 1180, Artillery crew (Wilderness). VERT: No. 1181, Soldier and rifles (Appomattox).

627 Sunflower and Pioneers

1961. Centenary of Kansas Statehood.
1182 **627** 4c. red, green and brown on yellow 15 10

628 Senator G. W. Norris

1961. Birth Centenary of George W. Norris.
1183 **628** 4c. green 15 10

629 Curtiss A-1 Seaplane, 1911 (Navy's first plane)

1961. 50th Anniv of U.S. Naval Aviation.
1184 **629** 4c. blue 15 10

630 "Balanced Judgement"

631 "The Smoke Signal" (after Remington)

1961. 150th Anniv of Workmen's Compensation Law.
1185 **630** 4c. blue 15 10

1961. Birth Centenary of Frederic Remington (painter).
1186 **631** 4c. multicoloured 15 10

632 Dr. Sun Yat-sen

633 Basketball

1961. 50th Anniv of Republic of China.
1187 **632** 4c. blue 20 10

1961. Birth Centenary of Dr. James A. Naismith (inventor of basketball).
1188 **633** 4c. brown 20 10

634 Nurse lighting Candle of Dedication

635 Ship Rock, New Mexico

1961. Nursing.
1189 **634** 4c. multicoloured 20 10

1962. 50th Anniv of Statehood of New Mexico.
1190 **635** 4c. lake, ochre & turq 15 10

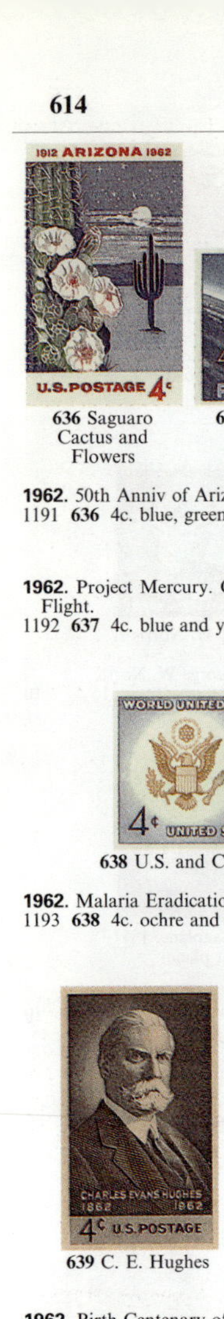

636 Saguaro Cactus and Flowers

637 "U.S. Man in Space"

1962. 50th Anniv of Arizona Statehood.
1191 **636** 4c. blue, green and red . . . 15 10

1962. Project Mercury. Colonel John Glenn's Space Flight.
1192 **637** 4c. blue and yellow . . . 15 10

638 U.S. and Campaign Emblems

1962. Malaria Eradication.
1193 **638** 4c. ochre and blue . . . 15 10

639 C. E. Hughes

640 Space Needle and Monorail

1962. Birth Centenary of Chief Justice Hughes.
1194 **639** 4c. black on buff 15 10

1962. "Century 21" Exn ("World's Fair"), Seattle.
1195 **640** 4c. blue and red 15 10

641 Mississippi Sternwheel Steamer

1962. 150th Anniv of Lousiana Statehood.
1196 **641** 4c. myrtle, red and blue 15 10

642 Settlers' Homestead

1962. Centenary of Homestead Act.
1197 **642** 4c. grey 15 10

643 Girl Scout and Flag

1962. 50th Anniv of U.S. Girl Scouts.
1198 **643** 4c. red 15 10

644 Senator McMahon and Atomic Symbol

1962. Brien McMahon.
1199 **644** 4c. violet 15 10

645 "Transfer of Skill"

646 Sam Rayburn

1962. 25th Anniv of National Apprenticeship Act.
1200 **645** 4c. black on olive . . . 15 10

1962. Sam Rayburn (Speaker of House of Representatives) Commemoration.
1201 **646** 4c. brown and blue . . . 15 10

647 Dag Hammarskjold and U.N. Headquarters

648 Christmas Laurel Wreath

1962. Hammarskjold.
1202 **647** 4c. brown, yellow & black 15 10
1203 4c. brown, yellow & black 15 15
No. 1203 has the yellow colour inverted and comes from a special printing made after a few examples had been discovered.

1962. Christmas.
1204 **648** 4c. green and red 15 10

649 "Lamp of Learning" and Map

1962. Higher Education.
1205 **649** 4c. black and green . . . 15 10

651 Washington (after Houdon)

A **652** Capitol, Washington, and Douglas DC-8

1962.
1206 – 1c. green 15 10
1207 **651** 5c. blue 15 10
DESIGN: 1c. Andrew Jackson.

1962. Air.
A1210 A **652** 8c. red 15 10

652 "Breezing Up" (after Winslow Homer)

653 U.S. Flag and White House

1962. Winslow Homer.
1210 **652** 4c. multicoloured 15 10

1963.
1211 **653** 5c. red and blue 15 10

654 Charter and Quill

1963. 300th Anniv of Carolina Charter.
1212 **654** 5c. sepia and red 25 10

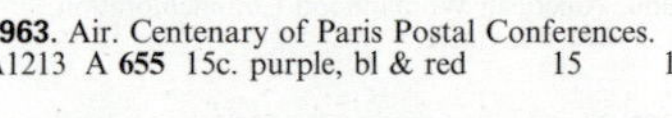

A **655** P. M. G. Montgomery Blair, Letters and Globe (after portrait by Thomas Sully)

655 "Food for Peace"

1963. Air. Centenary of Paris Postal Conferences.
A1213 A **655** 15c. purple, bl & red 15 10

1963. Freedom from Hunger.
1213 **655** 5c. brown, green and red 15 10

656 Map and State Capitol, Charleston

A **657** American Bald Eagle

1963. Centenary of West Virginia Statehood.
1214 **656** 5c. red, black and green 15 10

1963. Air.
A1215 A **657** 6c. red 15 10

657 Broken Link

A **658** Amelia Earhart and Lockheed "Electra"

1963. Centenary of Emancipation Proclamation.
1215 **657** 5c. black, blue and red 15 10

1963. Air. Amelia Earhart Commemoration.
A1216 A **658** 8c. purple and red 15 10

658 Torch of Progress

659 Cordell Hull

1963. "Alliance for Progress".
1216 **658** 5c. green and blue . . . 15 10

1963. Cordell Hull Commemoration.
1217 **659** 5c. turquoise 20 10

660 Eleanor Roosevelt

1963. Eleanor Roosevelt Commemoration.
1218 **660** 5c. violet 20 10

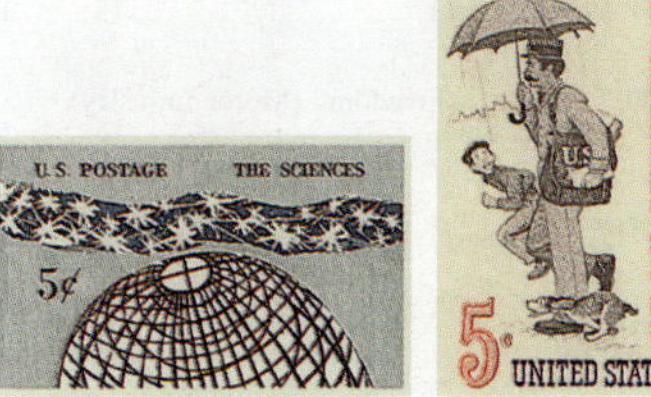

661 "The Sciences"

662 City Mail Postman

1963. Centenary of National Academy of Science.
1219 **661** 5c. black, red and blue 15 10

1963. Centenary of City Mail Delivery.
1220 **662** 5c. black and turquoise 15 10

663 Red Cross Flag and S.S. "Morning Light"

664 Christmas Tree

1963. Red Cross Centenary.
1221 **663** 5c. black and red 15 10

1963. Christmas.
1222 **664** 5c. black, blue and red 15 10

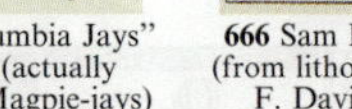

665 "Columbia Jays" (print) (actually Collie's Magpie-jays)

666 Sam Houston (from lithograph by F. Davignon)

1963. John James Audubon Commemoration.
1223 **665** 5c. multicoloured 20 10
See also No. A1304.

1964. Sam Houston Commemoration.
1224 **666** 5c. black 15 10

667 "Jerked Down"

1964. Birth Centenary of C. M. Russell (artist).
1225 **667** 5c. multicoloured 15 10

668 Mall with Unisphere and "The Rocket Thrower" (after De Lue)

669 John Muir (naturalist) and Forest

1964. New York World's Fair.
1226 **668** 5c. turquoise 15 15

1964. John Muir Commemoration.
1227 **669** 5c. brown, emerald & green 15 10

670 Pres. Kennedy and "Eternal Flame"

671 Philip Carteret at Elizabethtown (1664) (after painting in Union County Courthouse)

1964. President Kennedy Memorial Issue.
1228 **670** 5c. blue on grey 25 10

1964. Tercentenary of New Jersey.
1229 **671** 5c. blue 20 10

672 Virginia City in 19th Century

673 U.S. Flag

1964. Centenary of Nevada Statehood.
1230 **672** 5c. multicoloured 15 10

1964. "Register and Vote" Campaign.
1231 **673** 5c. red and blue 15 10

674 Shakespeare

675 Drs. William and Charles Mayo (after J. E. Fraser)

1964. 400th Birth Anniv of William Shakespeare.
1232 **674** 5c. sepia on buff 20 10

1964. Mayo Brothers (founders of Mayo Clinic) Commemoration.
1233 **675** 5c. green 20 10

A **676** R. H. Goddard, "Atlas" Rocket and Launching Tower

1964. Air. Robert H. Goddard Commem.
A1234 A **676** 8c. blue, red & yellow 15 10

676 Lute, Horn and Music Score

1964. American Music.
1234 **676** 5c. black, red and blue on light blue 15 10

677 Sampler

1964. "Homemakers" Commemoration.
1235 **677** 5c. multicoloured 15 10

678 Holly

682 Verrazano-Narrows Bridge

1964. Christmas. Each red, green and black.
1236 5c. Type **678** 20 15
1237 5c. Mistletoe 20 15
1238 5c. Poinsettia 20 15
1239 5c. Pine cone 20 15

1964. Opening of Verrazano-Narrows Bridge, New York.
1240 **682** 5c. green 15 10

683 "Abstract Art" (from lithograph by S. Davis)

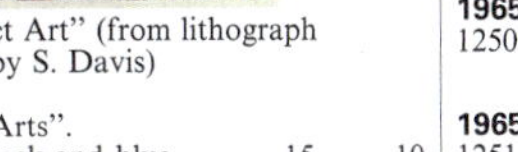

1964. "To the Fine Arts".
1241 **683** 5c. red, black and blue 15 10

684 Radio Waves

685 General Jackson leading Troops into Battle

1964. Amateur Radio.
1242 **684** 5c. purple 20 10

1965. 150th Anniv of Battle of New Orleans.
1243 **685** 5c. red, blue and black 20 10

686 Discus-thrower (Washington statue)

687 Microscope and Stethoscope

1965. Centenary of Sokol Physical Fitness Organization in the U.S.A.
1244 **686** 5c. blue and lake 15 10

1965. Crusade Against Cancer.
1245 **687** 5c. black, violet and red 15 10

688 Sir Winston Churchill (from photo by Karsh)

1965. Churchill Commemoration.
1246 **688** 5c. black 15 10

689 Procession of Barons, and King John's Crown

1965. 750th Anniv of Magna Carta.
1247 **689** 5c. black, yellow & violet 15 10

690 I.C.Y. Emblem

691 "One hundred years of service"

1965. International Co-operation Year.
1248 **690** 5c. black and blue . . . 15 10

1965. Centenary of Salvation Army.
1249 **691** 5c. black, red and blue 15 10

692 Dante

693 Herbert Hoover

1965. 700th Anniv of Dante's Birth.
1250 **692** 5c. red on flesh 15 10

1965. Hoover Commemoration.
1251 **693** 5c. red 15 10

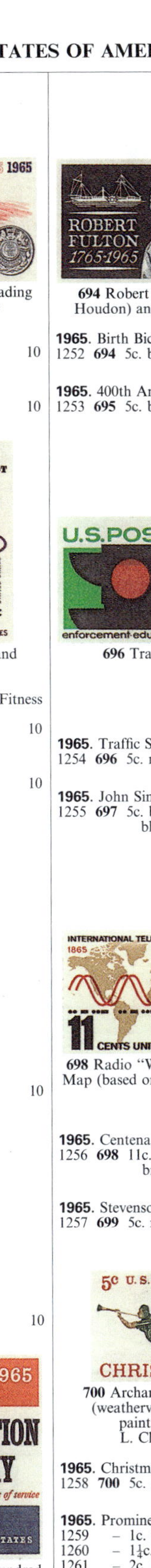

694 Robert Fulton (after Houdon) and "Clermont"

695 Spanish Knight and Banners

1965. Birth Bicent of Robert Fulton (inventor).
1252 **694** 5c. black and blue . . . 15 10

1965. 400th Anniv of Florida Settlement.
1253 **695** 5c. black, red and yellow 15 10

696 Traffic Signal

697 Elizabeth Clarke Copley (from "The Copley Family" by John S. Copley)

1965. Traffic Safety.
1254 **696** 5c. red, black and green 15 10

1965. John Singleton Copley.
1255 **697** 5c. brown, drab and black 15 10

698 Radio "Waves" on World Map (based on Galt projection)

699 Adlai Stevenson (from photo by P. Halsman)

1965. Centenary of I.T.U.
1256 **698** 11c. red, black and brown 30 20

1965. Stevenson Commemoration.
1257 **699** 5c. multicoloured 15 10

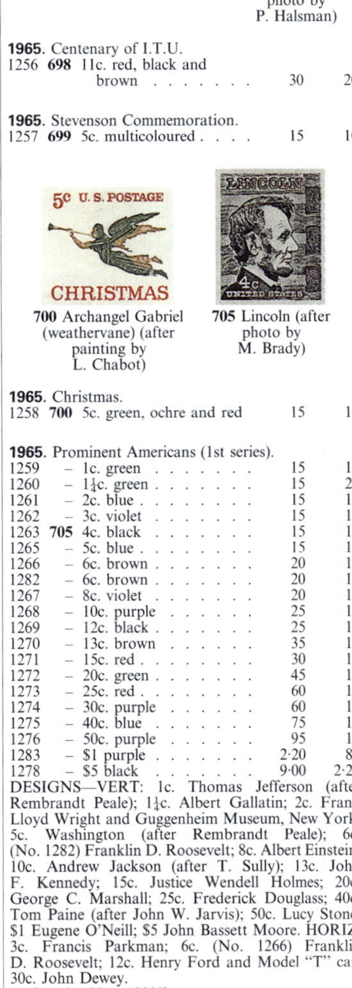

700 Archangel Gabriel (weathervane) (after painting by L. Chabot)

705 Lincoln (after photo by M. Brady)

1965. Christmas.
1258 **700** 5c. green, ochre and red 15 10

1965. Prominent Americans (1st series).

1259	–	1c. green	15	10
1260	–	1¼c. green	15	20
1261	–	2c. blue	15	10
1262	–	3c. violet	15	10
1263	**705**	4c. black	15	10
1265	–	5c. blue	15	10
1266	–	6c. brown	20	10
1282	–	6c. brown	20	10
1267	–	8c. violet	20	10
1268	–	10c. purple	25	10
1269	–	12c. black	25	10
1270	–	13c. brown	35	10
1271	–	15c. red	30	10
1272	–	20c. green	45	10
1273	–	25c. red	60	10
1274	–	30c. purple	60	10
1275	–	40c. blue	75	10
1276	–	50c. purple	95	10
1283	–	$1 purple	2·20	80
1278	–	$5 black	9·00	2·20

DESIGNS—VERT: 1c. Thomas Jefferson (after Rembrandt Peale); 1¼c. Albert Gallatin; 2c. Frank Lloyd Wright and Guggenheim Museum, New York; 5c. Washington (after Rembrandt Peale); 6c. (No. 1282) Franklin D. Roosevelt; 8c. Albert Einstein; 10c. Andrew Jackson (after T. Sully); 13c. John F. Kennedy; 15c. Justice Wendell Holmes; 20c. George C. Marshall; 25c. Frederick Douglass; 40c. Tom Paine (after John W. Jarvis); 50c. Lucy Stone; $1 Eugene O'Neill; $5 John Bassett Moore. HORIZ: 3c. Francis Parkman; 6c. (No. 1266) Franklin D. Roosevelt; 12c. Henry Ford and Model "T" car; 30c. John Dewey.

See also Nos. 1383/9.

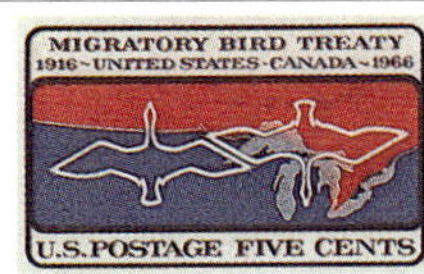

719 "Migratory Birds"

1966. 50th Anniv of Migratory Bird Treaty.
1286 **719** 5c. red, blue and black 15 10

720 Dog

721 Seal, Emblem and Map

1966. Humane Treatment of Animals.
1287 **720** 5c. black and brown . . 15 10

1966. 150th Anniv of Indiana Statehood.
1288 **721** 5c. blue, brown & yellow 15 10

722 Lou Jacobs (clown)

723 SIPEX "Letter"

1966. The American Circus.
1289 **722** 5c. multicoloured 20 10

1966. 6th Int Philatelic Exn, Washington (SIPEX).
1290 **723** 5c. multicoloured 15 10

725 "Freedom" opposing "Tyranny"

726 Polish Eagle

1966. 175th Anniv of Bill of Rights.
1292 **725** 5c. red, indigo and blue 15 10

1966. Polish Millennium.
1293 **726** 5c. red 15 10

727 N.P.S. Emblem

728 Marines Past and Present

1966. 50th Anniv of National Park Service.
1294 **727** 5c. black, green & yellow 15 10

1966. 50th Anniv of Marine Corps Reserve.
1295 **728** 5c. multicoloured 15 10

729 Women of 1891 and 1966

730 Johnny Appleseed and Apple

1966. 75th Anniv of General Federation of Women's Clubs.
1296 **729** 5c. black, pink and blue 15 10

1966. Johnny Appleseed.
1297 **730** 5c. black, red and green 15 10

731 Jefferson Memorial, Washington

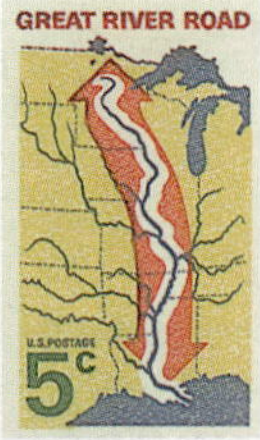

732 Map of Great River Road

1966. "Beautification of America" Campaign.
1298 **731** 5c. black, green and pink 15 10

1966. Opening of Great River Road.
1299 **732** 5c. red, yellow and blue 15 10

733 Statue of Liberty and U.S. Flag (after photo by B. Noble)

734 "Madonna and Child" (after Memling)

1966. 25th Anniv of U.S. Savings Bond Programme and Tribute to U.S. Servicemen.
1300 **733** 5c. multicoloured 15 10

1966. Christmas.
1301 **734** 5c. multicoloured 15 10

735 "The Boating Party' (after Mary Cassatt)

A **736** Tlingit Totem, Southern Alaska

1966. Mary Cassatt.
1302 **735** 5c. multicoloured 15 10

1967. Air. Centenary of Alaska Purchase.
A1303 A **736** 8c. brown 15 10

736 Recruiting Poster

A **737** "Columbia Jays" by Audubon

1967. Centenary of National Grange (farmers' organization).
1303 **736** 5c. multicoloured 15 10

1967. Air.
A1304 A **737** 20c. multicoloured 15 10
See also No. 1223.

737 Canadian Landscape

1967. Canadian Centennial.
1304 **737** 5c. multicoloured 15 10

738 Canal Barge

1967. 150th Anniv of Erie Canal.
1305 **738** 5c. multicoloured 15 10

739 Peace Dove Emblem

1967. "Search for Peace" (Lions Int essay theme).
1306 **739** 5c. black, red and blue 15 10

740 H. D. Thoreau

742 Radio Tower and "Waves"

741 Hereford Bull

1967. 150th Birth Anniv of Henry Thoreau (writer).
1307 **740** 5c. black, red and green 15 10

1967. Centenary of Nebraska Statehood.
1308 **741** 5c. multicoloured 15 10

1967. "Voice of America". 25th Anniv of Radio Branch of United States Information Agency.
1309 **742** 5c. black, red and blue 15 10

743 Davy Crockett and Pine

1967. Davy Crockett Commemoration.
1310 **743** 5c. black, green & yellow 15 10

744 Astronaut in Space

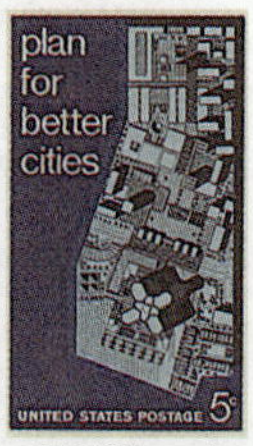

746 "Planned City"

1967. U.S. Space Achievements. Multicoloured.
1311 5c. Type **744** 30 15
1312 5c. "Gemini 4" over Earth 30 20
Nos. 1311/12 were issued together se-tenant, forming a composite design.

1967. Urban Planning.
1313 **746** 5c. ultramarine, black & blue 15 10

747 Arms of Finland

748 "The Biglin Brothers racing" (Eakins)

1967. 50th Anniv of Finnish Independence.
1314 **747** 5c. blue 15 10

1967. Thomas Eakins.
1315 **748** 5c. multicoloured 15 10

749 "Madonna and Child with Angels" (Memling)

750 Magnolia

1967. Christmas.
1316 **749** 5c. multicoloured 15 10

1967. 150th Anniv of Mississippi Statehood.
1317 **750** 5c. brown, green and turquoise 15 10

A **751** "Fifty Stars"

751 U.S. Flag and The White House

1968. Air.
A1318 A **751** 10c. red 15 10

1968. Flag Issue.
1318 **751** 6c. multicoloured 20 10
1320 8c. multicoloured 20 10

752 Homestead and Cornfield

753 Map of the Americas

1968. 150th Anniv of Illinois Statehood.
1323 **752** 6c. multicoloured 20 10

1968. "HemisFair '68" Exn, San Antonio.
1324 **753** 6c. blue, pink and white 20 10

754 Eagle with Pennant (after late 19th-century wood carving)

1968. "Airlift".
1325 **754** $1 brown, blue and buff 2·20 1·90
No. 1325 was issued primarily for a special reduced-rate parcels service to forces personnel overseas and in Alaska, Hawaii and Puerto Rico.

755 Boys and Girls

756 Policeman with Small Boy

A **756** Curtiss JN-4 "Jenny"

1968. Youth Programme of Elks Benevolent Society.
1326 **755** 6c. blue and red 20 10

1968. Air. 50th Anniv of Scheduled Airmail Services.
A1327 A **756** 10c. black, red & blue 25 20

1968. "Law and Order".
1328 **756** 6c. blue, red and black 20 10

757 Eagle Weathervane

758 Fort Moultrie, 1776

1968. "Register and Vote".
1329 **757** 6c. yellow, orange & black 20 10

1968. Historic Flags.
1330 **758** 6c. blue 30 25
1331 – 6c. red and blue 20 25
1332 – 6c. green and blue . . . 20 25
1333 – 6c. red and blue 20 25
1334 – 6c. blue, yellow and red 20 25
1335 – 6c. red and blue 20 25
1336 – 6c. blue, red and green 20 25
1337 – 6c. red and blue 20 25
1338 – 6c. blue, red and yellow 20 25
1339 – 6c. red, yellow and blue 20 25
FLAGS: No. 1331, U.S. (Fort McHenry), 1795–1818; 1332, Washington's Cruisers, 1775; 1333, Bennington, 1777; 1334, Rhode Island, 1775; 1335, First Stars and Stripes, 1777; 1336, Bunker Hill, 1775; 1337, Grand Union, 1776; 1338, Philadelphia Light Horse, 1775; 1339, First Navy Jack, 1775.

768 Walt Disney (after portrait by P. E. Wenzel)

769 Father Jacques Marquette (explorer) with Jolliet and Indians Canoeing

1968. Walt Disney Commemoration.
1340 **768** 6c. multicoloured 35 10

1968. Marquette Commemoration.
1341 **769** 6c. multicoloured 20 10

770 Rifle, Tomahawk, Powder-horn and Knife

1968. Daniel Boone Commemoration.
1342 **770** 6c. multicoloured 20 10

771 Ship's Wheel and River Tanker

1968. Arkansas River Navigation Project.
1343 **771** 6c. black, blue & lt blue 20 10

772 "Leif Erikson" (statue by Stirling Calder, Reykjavik, Iceland)

773 Pioneers racing to Cherokee Strip

1968. Leif Erikson Commemoration.
1344 **772** 6c. sepia and brown . . 20 10

1968. 75th Anniv of Opening of Cherokee Strip to Settlers.
1345 **773** 6c. brown 20 10

774 "Battle of Bunker's Hill" (detail) (after John Trumbull)

775 Wood Ducks

1968. John Trumbull.
1346 **774** 6c. multicoloured 20 10

1968. Waterfowl Conservation.
1347 **775** 6c. multicoloured 20 10

776 "The Annunciation" (Jan van Eyck)

777 "Chief Joseph" (after C. Hall)

1968. Christmas.
1348 **776** 6c. multicoloured 20 10

1968. "The American Indian".
1349 **777** 6c. multicoloured 20 10

A **778** "U.S.A." and Jet Aircraft

1968. Air.
A1350 A **778** 20c. red, blue & blk 45 15
A1351 21c. blue, red & blk 40 15

778 Capitol and Flowers ("Cities")

1969. "Beautification of America" Campaign.
1352 **778** 6c. multicoloured 40 15
1353 – 6c. multicoloured 40 15
1354 – 6c. multicoloured 40 15
1355 – 6c. multicoloured 40 15
DESIGNS: No. 1353, Potomac River and flowers ("Parks"); 1354, Motorway and flowers ("Highways"); 1355, Road and trees ("Streets").

782 "Eagle" (U.S. Seal)

783 "July Fourth"

1969. 50th Anniv of American Legion.
1356 **782** 6c. black, blue and red 20 10

1969. Grandma Moses (Mrs. A. M. R. Moses).
1357 **783** 6c. multicoloured 20 10

784 Earth and Moon's Surface (from an astronaut's photograph)

785 W. C. Handy (statue, Memphis)

1969. Moon Flight of "Apollo 8".
1358 **784** 6c. ochre, blue and black 20 10

1969. Handy (composer) Commemoration.
1359 **785** 6c. mauve, blue and violet 20 10

786 Belfry, Carmel Mission

787 Powell exploring Colorado River

1969. Bicentenary of California.
1360 **786** 6c. multicoloured 20 10

1969. John Wesley Powell (geologist). Centenary of Colorado River Exploration.
1361 **787** 6c. multicoloured 20 10

788 Camellia and Common Flicker

1969. 150th Anniv of Alabama Statehood.
1362 **788** 6c. multicoloured 20 10

791 Ocotillo

1969. 11th International Botanical Congress, Seattle. Multicoloured.
1363 6c. Douglas fir 40 15
1364 6c. Lady's slipper 40 15
1365 6c. Type **791** 40 15
1366 6c. Franklinia 40 15

A **793** Astronaut setting foot on Moon

1969. Air. 1st Man on the Moon.
A1367 A **793** 10c. multicoloured 25 15

793 Daniel Webster and Dartmouth Hall

794 Striker

1969. 150th Anniv of Dartmouth College Legal Case.
1368 **793** 6c. green 20 10

1969. Centenary of Professional Baseball.
1369 **794** 6c. multicoloured 85 10

795 Footballer and Coach

1969. Centenary of Intercollegiate Football.
1370 **795** 6c. green and red 40 10

796 Dwight D. Eisenhower (from photograph by B. Noble)

1969. Eisenhower Commemoration.
1371 **796** 6c. black, blue and lake 20 10

797 "Winter Sunday in Norway, Maine" (unknown artist)

1969. Christmas.
1372 **797** 6c. multicoloured 20 10

798 Rehabilitated Child

800 "Old Models" (William Harnett)

1969. Rehabilitation of the Handicapped.
1373 **798** 6c. multicoloured 20 10
No. 1373 also commemorates the 50th anniv of the National Society for Crippled Children and Adults.

1969. William M. Harnett.
1376 **800** 6c. multicoloured 20 10

804 Prehistoric Creatures (from mural by R. Zallinger in Yale's Peabody Museum)

1970. Natural History. Centenary of American Natural History Museum. Multicoloured.
1377 6c. American bald eagle . . 20 15
1378 6c. African elephant herd . . 20 15
1379 6c. Haida ceremonial canoe 20 15
1380 6c. Type **804** 20 15

805 "The Lighthouse at Two Lights" (painting by Edward Hopper in Metropolitan Museum of Art, New York

1970. Maine Statehood Sesquicentennial.
1381 **805** 6c. multicoloured 20 10

806 American Bison

1970. Wildlife Conservation.
1382 **806** 6c. black on brown . . . 20 10

807 Dwight D. Eisenhower

809 Benjamin Franklin

1970. Prominent Americans (2nd series).
1383 **807** 6c. blue 20 10
1384 **809** 7c. blue 20 10
1392 **807** 8c. maroon 20 10
1390 8c. black, blue and red 20 10
1386 – 14c. black 25 15
1387 – 16c. brown 30 15
1388 – 18c. violet 40 15
1389 – 21c. green 40 10
DESIGNS: VERT: 14c. F. H. La Guardia; 16c. Ernest T. Pyle; 18c. Dr. Elizabeth Blackwell; 21c. Amadeo P. Giannini (after painting by J. Kozlowski).

822 Edgar Lee Masters

823 Suffragettes, 1920, and Woman operating Voting Machine

1970. Edgar Lee Masters (poet) Commem.
1401 **822** 6c. black and bistre . . . 20 10

1970. 50th Anniv of Women's Suffrage.
1402 **823** 6c. blue 20 10

824 Symbols of South Carolina

1970. 300th Anniv of South Carolina.
1403 **824** 6c. multicoloured 20 10

825 Stone Mountain Memorial

1970. Dedication of Stone Mountain Confederate Memorial.
1404 **825** 6c. black 20 10

826 Fort Snelling and Keel Boat

1970. 150th Anniv of Fort Snelling, Minnesota.
1405 **826** 6c. multicoloured 20 10

828 City Park

1970. Prevention of Pollution.
1406 6c. Wheat 20 15
1407 6c. Type **828** 20 15
1408 6c. Blue-gilled sunfish . . . 20 15
1409 6c. Western gull 20 15

832 Toy Steam Locomotive (after drawing by C. Hemming)

1970. Christmas. Multicoloured.
1410 6c. "The Nativity" (L. Lotto) (vert) 20 10
1411 6c. Type **832** 30 15
1412 6c. Toy horse on wheels . . 30 15
1413 6c. Mechanized tricycle . . 30 15
1414 6c. Doll's pram 30 15
Nos. 1412/14 are taken from "Golden Age of Toys" by Fondin and Remise.

836 "U.N." and Emblem

1970. 25th Anniv of U.N.O.
1415 **836** 6c. red, blue and black 20 10

837 "Mayflower" and Pilgrims

838 Disabled American Veterans Emblem

1970. 350th Anniv of Landing of the Pilgrim Fathers in America.
1416 **837** 6c. multicoloured 20 10

1970. 50th Anniv of Disabled American Veterans Organization, and Armed Forces Commemoration.
1417 **838** 6c. multicoloured 20 15
1418 – 6c. black, blue and red 20 15
DESIGN: No. 1418, Inscriptions—"Prisoners of War", "Missing and Killed in Action".

840 Ewe and Lamb

841 General Douglas MacArthur

1970. 450th Anniv of Introduction of Sheep into North America.
1419 **840** 6c. multicoloured 20 10

1971. 91st Birth Anniv of General Douglas MacArthur.
1420 **841** 6c. black, blue and red 20 10

842 "Giving Blood Saves Lives"

1971. Salute to Blood Donors.
1421 **842** 6c. deep blue, red & blue 20 10

A **844** Jet Aircraft

A **845** Winged Letter

1971. Air.
A1422 – 9c. red 20 20
A1423 A **844** 11c. red 20 10
A1424 A **845** 13c. red 20 10
DESIGN—HORIZ: 9c. Delta-wing plane.

846 "Settlers and Indians" (after mural "Independence and the Opening of the West" by Thomas H. Benton)

1971. 150th Anniv of Missouri Statehood.
1427 **846** 8c. multicoloured 20 10

847 Rainbow Trout

1971. Wildlife Conservation. Multicoloured.
1428 8c. Type **847** 20 15
1429 8c. Alligator 20 15
1430 8c. Polar bear and cubs . . 20 15
1431 8c. California condor . . . 20 15

851 Antarctic Map Emblem

852 Postal Service Emblem

1971. 10th Anniv of Antarctic Treaty.
1432 **851** 8c. blue and red 20 10

1971. Reorganization of U.S. Post Office as U.S. Postal Service.
1433 **852** 8c. multicoloured 20 10

853 Bicentennial Emblem

A **854** Head of Statue of Liberty

1971. American Revolution Bicent. Bicentennial Commisssion Emblem.
1434 **853** 8c. multicoloured 20 10

1971. Air.
A1435 A **854** 17c. blue, red & grn 40 20

855 "The Wake of the Ferry" (John Sloan)

1971. Birth Centenary of John Sloan (artist).
1436 **855** 8c. multicoloured 20 10

856 Landing Module on Moon

858 Emily Dickinson

1971. Decade of U.S. Space Achievements. Mult.
1437 8c. Type **856** 20 15
1438 8c. Astronauts in lunar rover 20 15
Nos. 1437/8 were issued together, se-tenant, forming a composite design.

1971. 85th Death Anniv of Emily Dickinson (poet).
1439 **858** 8c. multicoloured on green 20 10

859 Watch-tower, El Morro, San Juan

860 Drug Victim

1971. 450th Anniv of San Juan, Puerto Rico.
1440 **859** 8c. multicoloured 20 10

1971. Drug Abuse Prevention Week.
1441 **860** 8c. black, lt blue & blue 20 10

861 Hands reaching to "CARE"

866 "Adoration of the Shepherds" (Giorgione)

862 Decatur House, Washington D.C.

1971. 25th Anniv of "CARE" (Co-operative for American Relief Everywhere).
1442 **861** 8c. multicoloured 20 10

1971. Historic Preservation.
1443 **862** 8c. black & flesh on cream 20 15
1444 – 8c. black & flesh on cream 20 15
1445 – 8c. black & flesh on cream 20 15
1446 – 8c. black & flesh on cream 20 10
DESIGNS: No. 1444, Whaling ship "Charles W. Morgan", Mystic, Conn; 1445, San Francisco cable car; 1446, San Xavier del Bac Mission, Tucson, Arizona.

1971. Christmas. Multicoloured.
1447 8c. Type **866** 20 10
1448 8c. "Partridge in a Pear Tree" 20 10

868 Sidney Lanier

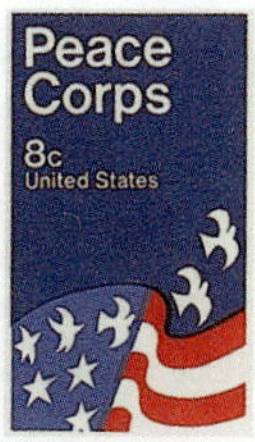

869 Peace Corps Poster (D. Battle)

1972. 90th Death Anniv (1971) of Sidney Lanier (poet).
1449 **868** 8c. black, brown and blue 20 10

1972. Peace Corps.
1450 **869** 8c. red, light blue & blue 20 10

870/873 Cape Hatteras National Seashore

875 "Old Faithful", Yellowstone Park

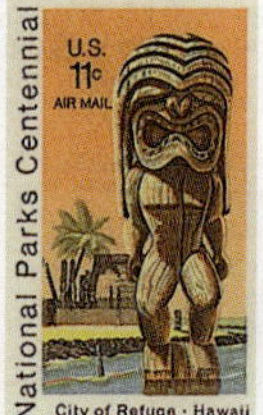

A **877** Statue and Temple, City of Refuge, Hawaii

1972. Centenary of National Parks.
1451 **870** 2c. multicoloured (postage) 10 10
1452 **871** 2c. multicoloured . . 10 10
1453 **872** 2c. multicoloured . . 10 10
1454 **873** 2c. multicoloured . . 10 10
1455 – 6c. multicoloured . . 20 10
1456 **875** 8c. multicoloured . . 20 10
1457 – 15c. multicoloured 25 25
A1458 A **877** 11c. mult (air) . . . 20 15

DESIGNS—HORIZ (As Type A **877**): 6c. Theatre at night, Wolf Trap Farm, Virginia; 15c. Mt. McKinley, Alaska.

878 American Family

879 Glassblower

1972. Family Planning.
1459 **878** 8c. multicoloured 20 10

1972. Bicentenary of American Revolution. American Colonial Craftsmen.
1460 **879** 8c. brown on yellow . . 20 20
1461 – 8c. brown on yellow . . 20 20
1462 – 8c. brown on yellow . . 20 20
1463 – 8c. brown on yellow . . 20 20
DESIGNS: No. 1461, Silversmith; 1462, Wigmaker; 1463, Hatter.

883 Cycling

1972. Olympic Games, Munich and Sapporo, Japan. Multicoloured.
1464 6c. Type **883** (postage) . . 20 10
1465 8c. Bobsleighing 20 10
1466 15c. Running 35 25
A1467 11c. Skiing (air) 25 20

887 Classroom Blackboard

1972. 75th Anniv of Parent Teacher Association.
1468 **887** 8c. black and yellow . . 20 10

888 Northern Fur Seals

1972. Wildlife Conservation. Multicoloured.
1469 8c. Type **888** 20 15
1470 8c. Common cardinal (bird) 20 15
1471 8c. Brown pelicans 20 15
1472 8c. American bighorn . . . 20 15

892 19th-century Country Post Office and Store

1972. Centenary of Mail Order Business.
1473 **892** 8c. multicoloured 20 10

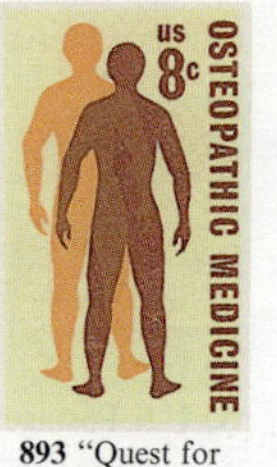

893 "Quest for Health"

894 "Tom Sawyer" (N. Rockwell)

1972. 75th Anniv of American Osteopaths.
1474 **893** 8c. multicoloured 20 10

1972. "The Adventures of Tom Sawyer" by Mark Twain.
1475 **894** 8c. multicoloured 20 10

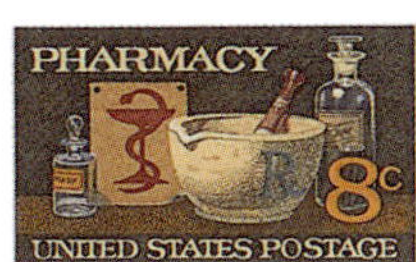

895 "Angels" (detail, "Mary, Queen of Heaven" by Master of the St. Lucy Legend)

897 Pharmaceutical Equipment

1972. Christmas. Multicoloured.
1476 8c. Type **895** 20 10
1477 8c. Santa Claus 20 10

1972. 120th Anniv of American Pharmaceutical Association.
1478 **897** 8c. multicoloured 25 10

898 Five Cent Stamp of 1847 under Magnifier

1972. 125th Anniv of 1st U.S. Stamp, and Stamp Collecting Promotion.
1479 **898** 8c. brown, black & green 20 10

899 "LOVE"

1973. Greetings Stamp.
1480 **899** 8c. red, green and blue 20 10

900 Pamphleteers with Press

1973. American Revolution Bicentennial. Colonial Communications.
1481 **900** 8c. green, blue and red 20 10
1482 – 8c. black, red and blue 20 10
1483 – 8c. multicoloured 20 10
1484 – 8c. multicoloured 20 10
DESIGNS: No. 1482, Posting a broadside; 1483, Post-rider; 1484, Drummer.

904 George Gershwin (composer) and Scene from "Porgy and Bess"

908 Nicolas Copernicus (after 18th-cent engraving)

1973. American Arts Commemoration. Mult.
1485 8c. Type **904** 20 10
1486 8c. Robinson Jeffers (poet) and people of Carmel . . 20 10
1487 8c. Henry Tanner (painter) and palette 20 10
1488 8c. Willa Cather (novelist) and pioneer family . . . 20 10

1973. 500th Birth Anniv of Copernicus (astronomer).
1489 **908** 8c. black and yellow . . 20 10

909 Counter Clerk

919 Harry S. Truman

1973. Postal Service Employees. Multicoloured.
1490 8c. Type **909** 20 15
1491 8c. Collecting mail 20 15
1492 8c. Sorting on conveyor belt 20 15
1493 8c. Sorting parcels 20 15
1494 8c. Cancelling letters 20 15
1495 8c. Sorting letters by hand 20 15
1496 8c. Coding desks 20 15
1497 8c. Loading mail-van . . . 20 15
1498 8c. City postman 20 15
1499 8c. Rural postman 20 15

1973. Pres. Harry Truman Commemoration.
1500 **919** 8c. black, red and blue 20 10

920/923 Boston Tea Party (½-size illustration)

1973. American Revolution Bicentennial. The Boston Tea Party.
1501 **920** 8c. multicoloured 20 15
1502 **921** 8c. multicoloured 20 15
1503 **922** 8c. multicoloured 20 15
1504 **923** 8c. multicoloured 20 15

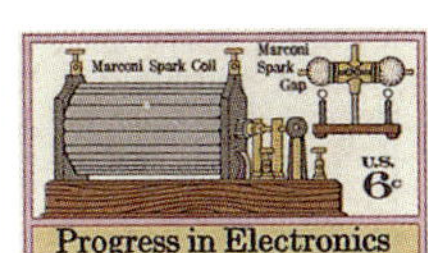

924 Marconi's Spark Coil and Gap (1901)

1973. Progress in Electronics. Multicoloured.
1505 6c. Type **924** (postage) . . 20 10
1506 8c. Modern transistor circuit 25 15
1507 15c. Early microphone and radio speaker, radio and T.V. camera tubes . . . 25 25
A1508 11c. DeForest audions (1915) (air) 20 15

928 Lyndon B. Johnson (from painting by Elizabeth Shoumatoff)

929 Angus and Longhorn Cattle (painting by F. C. Murphy)

1973. Pres. Lyndon B. Johnson Commem.
1509 **928** 8c. multicoloured 20 10

1973. "Rural America" Centenaries.
1510 8c. Type **929** 20 10
1511 10c. Institute marquee . . . 20 10
1512 10c. Steam train crossing wheatfield 20 10
CENTENARIES: No. 1510, Introduction of Aberdeen Angus cattle into United States; 1511, Foundation of Chautauqua Institution (adult education organization); 1512, Introduction of hard winter wheat into Kansas.

932 "Small Cowper Madonna" (Raphael)

933 Christmas Tree in Needlepoint

1973. Christmas.
1513 **932** 8c. multicoloured 20 10
1514 **933** 8c. multicoloured 20 10

934 U.S. Flags of 1777 and 1973

935 Jefferson Memorial

936 "Mail Transport" (from poster by R. McDougall)

937 Liberty Bell

1973.
1519 **937** 6.3c. red 20 10
1515 **934** 10c. red and blue 20 10
1516 **935** 10c. blue 20 10
1517 **936** 10c. multicoloured . . . 25 10

A **938** Statue of Liberty

1974. Air.
A1521 A **938** 18c. black, red & bl 35 35
A1522 – 26c. black, bl & red 45 15
DESIGN: 26c. Mt. Rushmore National Memorial.

940 "VFW" and Emblem

941 Robert Frost

1974. 75th Anniv of Veterans of Foreign Wars Organization.
1523 **940** 10c. red and blue 20 10

1974. Birth Centenary of Robert Frost (poet).
1524 **941** 10c. black 20 10

942 "Cosmic Jumper" and "Smiling Sage" ("Preserve the Environment" theme)

1974. "Expo 74" World Fair, Spokane.
1525 **942** 10c. multicoloured . . . 20 10

943 Horse-racing

1974. Centenary of Kentucky Derby.
1526 **943** 10c. multicoloured . . . 20 10

944 "Skylab" in Orbit

1974. "Skylab" Space Project.
1527 **944** 10c. multicoloured . . . 20 10

945 "Michelangelo" (detail from "School of Athens" by Raphael)

1974. Centenary of U.P.U. Multicoloured.
1528 10c. Type **945** 20 20
1529 10c. "Five Feminine Virtues" (Hokusai) . . . 20 20
1530 10c. "Old Scraps" (J. F. Peto) 20 20
1531 10c. "The Lovely Reader" (J. Liotard) 20 20
1532 10c. "The Lady Writing Letter" (G. Terborch) . . 20 20
1533 10c. "Inkwell and Quill" (detail from "Young Boy with Top" by J. Chardin) 20 20
1534 10c. "Mrs. John Douglas" (T. Gainsborough) . . . 20 20
1535 10c. "Don Antonio Noriega" (F. Goya) . . . 20 20

955 Amethyst

957 Covered Wagon at Fort Harrod

1974. Mineral Heritage. Multicoloured.
1536 10c. Petrified wood 20 15
1537 10c. Tourmaline 20 15
1538 10c. Type **955** 20 15
1539 10c. Rhodochrosite 20 15

1974. Bicentenary of Fort Harrod, First Settlement in Kentucky.
1540 **957** 10c. multicoloured . . . 20 10

959 "We ask but for peace ..." (First Continental Congress)

962 Slogan, Molecules and Petrol Drops

1974. American Revolution Bicentennial. First Continental Congress.
1541 – 10c. blue and red 20 15
1542 **959** 10c. grey, blue and red 20 15
1543 – 10c. grey, red and blue 20 15
1544 – 10c. red and blue 20 15
DESIGNS: No. 1541, Carpenters' Hall, Philadelphia; 1543, "Deriving their just powers ..." (Declaration of Independence); 1544, Independence Hall, Philadelphia.

1974. Energy Conservation.
1545 **962** 10c. multicoloured . . . 20 10

963 "The Headless Horseman"

964 Child clasping Hand

1974. Washington Irving's "Legend of Sleepy Hollow".

1546	963	10c. multicoloured . . .	20	10

1974. Help for Retarded Children.

1547	964	10c. lake and brown . .	20	10

966 "The Road — Winter" (from a Currier and Ives print, drawn by O. Knirsch)

1974. Christmas. Multicoloured.

1548		10c. "Angel" (detail, Perussis altarpiece) (vert)	20	10
1549		10c. Type **966**	20	15
1550		10c. Dove weathervane, Mount Vernon	20	20

No. 1550 has self-adhesive gum.

968 "Benjamin West" (self-portrait)

969 "Pioneer" Spacecraft passing Jupiter

1975. Benjamin West (painter) Commem.

1551	968	10c. multicoloured . . .	20	10

1975. U.S. Unmanned Space Missions. Mult.

1552		10c. Type **969**	20	10
1553		10c. "Mariner 10", Venus and Mercury	20	10

971 Overlapping Circles

1975. Collective Bargaining in Labour Relations.

1554	971	10c. multicoloured . . .	20	10

972 Sybil Ludington on Horseback

1975. American Revolution Bicent. Contributors to the Cause.

1555	972	8c. multicoloured	20	10
1556	–	10c. multicoloured . . .	20	10
1557	–	10c. multicoloured . . .	20	10
1558	–	18c. multicoloured . . .	30	20

DESIGNS: No. 1556, Salem Poor loading musket; 1557, Haym Salomon writing in ledger; 1558, Peter Francisco carrying cannon.

976 "Lexington" (from painting "Birth of Liberty" by H. Sandham)

977 Paul Laurence Dunbar (poet)

1975. American Revolution Bicentennial. Battles of Lexington and Concord.

1559	976	10c. multicoloured . . .	20	10

1975. Dunbar Commemoration.

1560	977	10c. multicoloured . . .	20	15

978 D. W. Griffith (film producer)

1975. Griffith Commemoration.

1561	978	10c. multicoloured . . .	20	10

979 "Bunker Hill, 1775", (John Trumbull)

980 Marine with Musket

1975. Bicentenary of American Revolution. Battle of Bunker Hill.

1562	979	10c. multicoloured . . .	20	10

1975. American Revolution Bicentennial. U.S. Military Services. Multicoloured.

1563		10c. Type **980**	20	15
1564		10c. Militiaman with musket	20	15
1565		10c. Soldier with flintlock	20	15
1566		10c. Sailor with grappling-iron	20	15

984 Docking Manoeuvre

1975. "Apollo–Soyuz" Space Test Project. Mult.

1567		10c. Type **984**	20	15
1568		10c. Spacecraft docked . . .	20	15

986 "Worldwide Equality"

1975. International Women's Year.

1569	986	10c. multicoloured . . .	20	15

987 Stagecoach and Modern Lorry

1975. Bicentenary of Postal Services. Mult.

1571		10c. Type **987**	20	10
1572		10c. Early steam and modern diesel locomotives	20	15
1573		10c. Curtiss JN-4 "Jenny" and Boeing 747-100 jetliner	20	15
1574		10c. Telecommunications satellite	20	15

991 Law Book, Gavel and Globe

1975. "World Peace through Law".

1575	991	10c. brown, blue & green	20	15

992 Coins and Engine-turned Motif

1975. "Banking and Commerce".

1576	992	10c. multicoloured . . .	20	10
1577	–	10c. multicoloured . . .	20	15

DESIGN: No. 1577, As Type **992**, but design reversed with different coins.

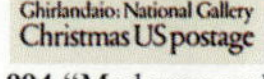

994 "Madonna and Child" (Ghirlandaio)

995 "Christmas Card" (from early design by Louis Prang)

1975. Christmas.

1578	994	(10c.) multicoloured . .	20	15
1579	995	(10c.) multicoloured . .	20	10

Nos. 1578/9 were each sold at 10c. Because of an imminent increase in the postage rates the two designs were issued without face values.

1002 Early Printing Press

1020 Flag over Independence Hall

1975.

1580	–	1c. deep blue on grey	15	10
1581	–	2c. red on cream . . .	15	10
1582	–	3c. olive on green . .	15	10
1597b	–	3.1c. lake on yellow	15	15
1598	–	3.5c. lilac on yellow	15	20
1582a	–	4c. red on cream . . .	15	10
1599	–	7.7c. brown on yellow	20	20
1600	–	7.9c. red on yellow . .	20	20
1601	–	8.4c. blue on yellow	20	20
1583	–	9c. green on grey . .	30	10
1584	–	9c. green	60	45
1585	–	10c. purple on grey	20	10
1585a	1002	11c. orange on grey	20	10
1585b	–	12c. brown on cream	25	10
1586	–	13c. brown on cream	30	10
1595	–	13c. multicoloured . .	25	10
1596	–	15c. blue, red and black	35	10
1605	–	16c. blue	30	10
1589	–	24c. red on blue . . .	45	10
1589a	–	28c. brown on blue . .	55	10
1590	–	29c. blue on light blue	55	30
1591	–	30c. green on turquoise	55	15
1592	–	50c. black, red & brn	90	15
1593	–	$1 multicoloured . . .	2·00	25
1594	–	$2 multicoloured . . .	3·75	60
1594a	–	$5 multicoloured . . .	9·00	1·90

DESIGNS: 1c. Inkwell and quill; 2c. Speaker's stand; 3c. Ballot box; 3.1c. Guitar; 3.5c. Weaver violins; 4c. Books, spectacles and bookmark; 7.7c. Saxhorns; 7.9c. Drum; 8.4c. Grand piano; 9c. (both) Dome of Capitol; 10c. "Contemplation of Justice" (statue, J. E. Fraser); 12c. Statue of Liberty torch; 13c. (No. 1586) Liberty Bell; 13c. (No. 1595) Eagle and shield; 15c. Fort McHenry flag; 16c. Statue of Liberty; 24c. Old North Church, Boston; 28c. Fort Nisqually, Washington; 29c. Sandy Hook Lighthouse, N.J.; 30c. Morris Township School; 50c. Iron "Betty" lamp; $1 Rush lamp and candle holder; $2 Kerosene lamp; $5 Railway conductor's lantern.

1975.

1606	1020	13c. red and blue . . .	25	15
1606c	–	13c. red and blue . . .	30	20

DESIGN: No. 1606c, Flag over Capitol, Washington.

1021 Drummer Boy (after A. M. Willard)

1024 Boeing 737 Jetliner

1976. American Revolution Bicentennial. "The Spirit of '76". Multicoloured.

1607		13c. Type **1021**	20	15
1608		13c. Old drummer	20	15
1609		13c. Fifer	20	15

Nos. 1607/9 were issued together, se-tenant, forming a composite design.

1976. Air.

A1610	1024	25c. black, blue & red	55	15
A1611	–	31c. black, blue & red	60	15

DESIGN: 31c. As 25c. but with background of U.S. flag.

1026 "Interphil 76"

1976. "Interphil 76" International Stamp Exhibition, Philadelphia.

1612	1026	13c. red and blue . . .	25	10

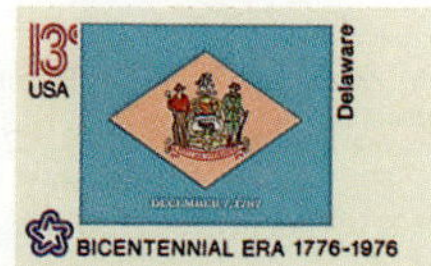

1027 Delaware Flag

1976. Bicentenary of American Revolution. State Flags. Multicoloured.

1613	13c. Type **1027**	25	30
1614	13c. Pennsylvania	25	30
1615	13c. New Jersey	25	30
1616	13c. Georgia	25	30
1617	13c. Connecticut	25	30
1618	13c. Massachusetts	25	30
1619	13c. Maryland	25	30
1620	13c. South Carolina	25	30
1621	13c. New Hampshire . . .	25	30
1622	13c. Virginia	25	30
1623	13c. New York	25	30
1624	13c. North Carolina	25	30
1625	13c. Rhode Island	25	30
1626	13c. Vermont	25	30
1627	13c. Kentucky	25	30
1628	13c. Tennessee	25	30
1629	13c. Ohio	25	30
1630	13c. Louisiana	25	30
1631	13c. Indiana	25	30
1632	13c. Mississippi	25	30
1633	13c. Illinois	25	30
1634	13c. Alabama	25	30
1635	13c. Maine	25	30
1636	13c. Missouri	25	30
1637	13c. Arkansas	25	30
1638	13c. Michigan	25	30
1639	13c. Florida	25	30
1640	13c. Texas	25	30
1641	13c. Iowa	25	30
1642	13c. Wisconsin	25	30
1643	13c. California	25	30
1644	13c. Minnesota	25	30
1645	13c. Oregon	25	30
1646	13c. Kansas	25	30
1647	13c. West Virginia	25	30
1648	13c. Nevada	25	30
1649	13c. Nebraska	25	30
1650	13c. Colorado	25	30
1651	13c. North Dakota	25	30
1652	13c. South Dakota	25	30
1653	13c. Montana	25	30
1654	13c. Washington	25	30
1655	13c. Idaho	25	30
1656	13c. Wyoming	25	30
1657	13c. Utah	25	30
1658	13c. Oklahoma	25	30
1659	13c. New Mexico	25	30
1660	13c. Arizona	25	30
1661	13c. Alaska	25	30
1662	13c. Hawaii	25	30

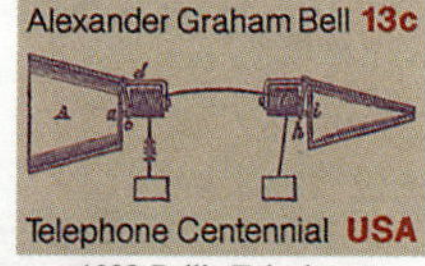

1028 Bell's Telephone

1976. Telephone Centenary.

1663	1028	13c. violet, black and red on brown	25	10

1029 Stout Air Pullman and Laird Swallow Biplane

1976. Commercial Aviation.

1664	1029	13c. multicoloured . . .	25	10

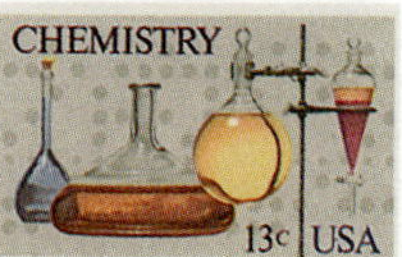

1030 Laboratory Equipment

1976. Centenary of American Chemical Society.
1665 **1030** 13c. multicoloured . . . 25 10

1035 Benjamin Franklin and 1776 Map of North America

1040 Diving

1036/1039 "Signing the Declaration of Independence" (John Turnbull) ($\frac{1}{2}$-size illustration)

1976. American Revolution Bicentennial.
1667 **1035** 13c. multicoloured . . . 25 10

1976. American Revolution Bicentennial.
1668 **1036** 13c. multicoloured . . . 40 15
1669 **1037** 13c. multicoloured . . . 40 15
1670 **1038** 13c. multicoloured . . . 40 15
1671 **1039** 13c. multicoloured . . . 40 15
Nos. 1668/71 were issued together, se-tenant, forming the composite design illustrated.

1976. Olympic Games, Innsbruck and Montreal. Multicoloured.
1672 13c. Type **1040** 30 15
1673 13c. Skiing 30 15
1674 13c. Running 30 15
1675 13c. Skating 30 15

1044 Clara Maass

1045 A. S. Ochs

1976. Birth Centenary of Clara Maass (martyr to yellow fever).
1676 **1044** 13c. multicoloured . . . 30 15

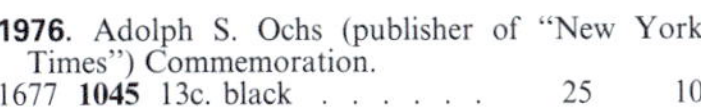

1976. Adolph S. Ochs (publisher of "New York Times") Commemoration.
1677 **1045** 13c. black 25 10

1046 "Winter Pastime" (N. Currier)

1976. Christmas.
1678 13c. Type **1046** 25 10
1679 13c. "Nativity" (John S. Copley) 25 10

1048 "Washington at Princeton" (Peale)

1050 Zia Pot

1049 Early Gramophone

1977. American Revolution Bicentennial.
1680 **1048** 13c. multicoloured . . . 25 10

1977. Centenary of Sound Recording.
1681 **1049** 13c. multicoloured . . . 25 10

1977. American Folk Art. Pueblo Art.
1682 13c. Type **1050** 25 15
1683 13c. San Ildefonso pot . . . 25 15
1684 13c. Hopi pot 25 15
1685 13c. Acoma pot 25 15

1054 "Spirit of St. Louis"

1977. 50th Anniv of Lindbergh's Transatlantic Flight.
1686 **1054** 13c. multicoloured . . . 25 10

1055 Columbine and Rocky Mountains

1056 American Swallowtail

1977. Centenary (1976) of Colorado Statehood.
1687 **1055** 13c. multicoloured . . . 25 10

1977. Butterflies. Multicoloured.
1688 13c. Type **1056** 25 15
1689 13c. Checkerspot 25 15
1690 13c. Dogface 25 15
1691 13c. Falcate orange-tip . . . 25 15

1060 Marquis de Lafayette

1977. American Revolution Bicent. Bicentenary of Lafayette's Landing on Coast of South Carolina.
1692 **1060** 13c. black, blue and red 25 10

1061 Seamstress

1977. American Revolution Bicentenary. "Skilled Hands for Independence". Multicoloured.
1693 13c. Type **1061** 25 15
1694 13c. Blacksmith 25 15
1695 13c. Wheelwright 25 15
1696 13c. Leatherworker 25 15

1065 Peace Bridge and Dove

1977. 50th Anniv of Opening of Peace Bridge.
1697 **1065** 13c. blue 25 10

1066 "Herkimer at Oriskany" (F. Yohn)

1977. American Revolution Bicent. Bicentenary of Battle of Oriskany.
1698 **1066** 13c. multicoloured . . . 25 10

1067 Farmhouses, El Pueblo

1977. Bicentenary of First Civil Settlement in Alta California.
1699 **1067** 13c. multicoloured . . . 25 10

1068 Members of the Continental Congress

1977. Bicentenary of Drafting of the Articles of Constitution.
1700 **1068** 13c. brown and red . . 25 10

1069 "Vitaphone" Projector and Sound Equipment

1977. 50th Anniv of Talking Pictures.
1701 **1069** 13c. multicoloured . . . 25 10

1070 "Surrender of Burgoyne at Saratoga" (J. Trumbull)

1977. American Revolution Bicent. Surrender of General Burgoyne.
1702 **1070** 13c. multicoloured . . . 25 10

1071 "Conservation"

1073 Washington at Valley Forge (after Leyendecker)

1977. Energy Conservation and Development.
1703 **1071** 13c. multicoloured . . . 25 15
1704 – 13c. multicoloured . . . 25 15
DESIGN: No. 1704, "Development".

1977. Christmas.
1705 **1073** 13c. multicoloured . . . 25 10
1706 – 13c. multicoloured . . . 25 10
DESIGN: No. 1706, Rural mailbox.

1075 Carl Sandburg

1076 Indian Head Penny

1978. Birth Centenary of Carl Sandburg (poet and biographer).
1707 **1075** 13c. black and brown 25 10

1978.
1708 **1076** 13c. brown & blue on buff 25 10

1077 Captain James Cook (after Nathaniel Dance)

1079 Harriet Tubman and Slaves

1978. Bicentenary of Capt. Cook's Visits to Hawaii and Alaska.
1709 **1077** 13c. blue 25 15
1710 – 13c. green 25 15
DESIGN—HORIZ: No. 1710, H.M.S. "Resolution" and H.M.S. "Discovery" at Hawaii (after John Webber).

1978. Black Heritage. Harriet Tubman (organizer of slave "underground railway").
1711 **1079** 13c. multicoloured . . . 30 10

1082 Quilt Design

1978. American Folk Art. Quilts.
1712 – 13c. brown and grey . . 25 15
1713 – 13c. red and grey . . . 25 15
1714 **1082** 13c. multicoloured . . . 25 15
1715 – 13c. multicoloured . . . 25 15
DESIGNS: No. 1712, Chequered; 1713, Dotted; 1715, Striped.

1084 Ballet

1978. American Dance.
1716 **1084** 13c. blue, mauve & black 25 15
1717 – 13c. orange, red & black 25 15
1718 – 13c. green, yellow & black 25 15
1719 – 13c. blue, ultram & black 25 15
DESIGNS: No. 1717, Theatre; 1718, Folk dance; 1719, Modern.

1088 "Louis XVI and Benjamin Franklin" (statuette, C. G. Sauvage)

1089 Dr. Papanicolaou

1978. Bicentenary of French Alliance.
1720 **1088** 13c. black, blue and red 25 10

1978. Dr. George Papanicolaou (developer of Pap (cancer detection) test) Commemoration.
1721 **1089** 13c. brown 25 10

1090 American Eagle

1091 Jimmie Rodgers

1978. No value expressed.
1722 **1090** (15c.) orange 30 10
For "B" stamp see No. 1843, for "C" stamp Nos. 1909/10 and for "D" stamp Nos. 2137/8.

1978. Performing Arts and Artists. Jimmie Rodgers, "Father of Country Music".

1725 **1091** 13c. multicoloured . . . 25 10

1093 Camera and Accessories

1094 George M. Cohan

1978. Photography.

1727 **1093** 15c. multicoloured . . . 35 10

1978. Performing Arts. Birth Centenary of George M. Cohan (actor and playwright).

1728 **1094** 15c. multicoloured . . . 45 10

1095 "Red Masterpiece" and "Medallion" Roses

1096 "Viking 1" Lander scooping Soil from Mars

1978. Roses.

1729 **1095** 15c. red, orange & grn 30 10

1978. 2nd Anniv of "Viking 1" Landing on Mars.

1730 **1096** 15c. multicoloured . . . 35 10

1097 Great Grey Owl

1101 Wright Brothers and Wright Flyer I

1978. Wildlife Conservation. American Owls. Mult.

1731 15c. Type **1097** 30 15

1732 15c. Saw-whet owl 30 15

1733 15c. Barred owl 30 15

1734 15c. Great horned owl . . . 30 15

1978. Air. 75th Anniv of First Powered Flight. Multicoloured.

A1735 31c. Type **1101** 60 15

A1736 31c. Wright Flyer I and Wright Brothers (in bowler hats) 60 15

1103 White Pine

1107 "Madonna and Child with Cherubim" (Andrea della Robbia)

1978. American Trees. Multicoloured.

1737 15c. Type **1103** 25 15

1738 15c. Giant sequoia 25 15

1739 15c. Grey birch 25 15

1740 15c. White oak 25 15

1978. Christmas. Multicoloured.

1741 15c. Type **1107** 30 10

1742 15c. Child on rocking horse 30 10

1109 Robert F. Kennedy

1110 Martin Luther King

1979. Robert F. Kennedy Commemoration.

1743 **1109** 15c. blue 30 10

1979. Black Heritage. Martin Luther King (Civil Rights leader).

1744 **1110** 15c. multicoloured . . . 35 10

1111 Children of Different Races

1112 John Steinbeck

1979. International Year of the Child.

1745 **1111** 15c. red 30 10

1979. Literary Arts. John Steinbeck (novelist).

1746 **1112** 15c. blue 30 10

1113 Einstein

1114 Chanute and Glider

1979. Birth Cent of Albert Einstein (physicist).

1747 **1113** 15c. brown 30 10

1979. Air. Aviation Pioneers. Octave Chanute. Multicoloured.

A1748 21c. Type **1114** 55 30

A1749 21c. Chanute and glider (different) 55 30

1116 Coffee Pot

1120 Virginia Rotunda (Thomas Jefferson)

1979. American Folk Art. Pennsylvania Toleware. Multicoloured.

1750 15c. Type **1116** 25 15

1751 15c. Tea caddy 25 15

1752 15c. Sugar bowl with lid . . 25 15

1753 15c. Coffee pot with gooseneck spout 25 15

1979. American Architecture. Each black and red.

1754 15c. Type **1120** 35 15

1755 15c. Baltimore Cathedral (Benjamin Latrobe) . . . 35 15

1756 15c. Boston State House (Charles Bulfinch) 35 15

1757 15c. Philadelphia Exchange (William Strickland) . . . 35 15

1124 Persistent Trillium

1128 Guide Dog

1979. Endangered Flora. Multicoloured.

1758 15c. Type **1124** 35 15

1759 15c. Hawaiian wild broadbean 35 15

1760 15c. Contra costa wallflower 35 15

1761 15c. Antioch dunes evening primrose 35 15

1979. 50th Anniv of First U.S. Guide Dog Programme.

1762 **1128** 15c. multicoloured . . . 30 10

1129 Child with Medal

1130 Throwing the Javelin (Decathlon)

1979. Special Olympic Games for the Handicapped.

1763 **1129** 15c. multicoloured . . . 30 10

1979. Olympic Games, Moscow (1980). Mult.

1764 10c. Type **1130** (postage) 25 20

1765 15c. Running (horiz) . . . 20 15

1766 15c. Swimming (horiz) . . 25 20

1767 15c. Rowing (horiz) . . . 25 20

1768 15c. Show jumping (horiz) 25 20

A1769 31c. High jumping (horiz) (air) 55 35

1136 John Paul Jones (after Peale)

1137 "Rest on the Flight to Egypt" (G. David)

1979. American Revolution Bicentennial. John Paul Jones (naval commander).

1770 **1136** 15c. multicoloured . . . 30 10

1979. Christmas. Multicoloured.

1771 15c. Type **1137** 30 10

1772 15c. Santa Claus tree ornament 30 10

1139 Will Rogers

1140 Vietnam Service Medal Ribbon

1979. Performing Arts and Artists. Will Rogers (cowboy philosopher).

1773 **1139** 15c. multicoloured . . . 30 10

1979. Vietnam Veterans.

1774 **1140** 15c. multicoloured . . . 35 10

1141 Wiley Post

1143 W. C. Fields

1979. Air. Aviation Pioneers. Wiley Post. Mult.

A1775 25c. Type **1141** . . . . . 1·00 40

A1776 25c. Wiley Post and Lockheed Vega "Winnie Mae" . . . . 1·00 40

1980. Performing Arts and Artists. W. C. Fields (comedian).

1777 **1143** 15c. multicoloured . . . 35 10

1144 Speed Skating

1148 Robertson Windmill, Williamsburg, Va.

1980. Winter Olympic Games, Lake Placid. Mult.

1778 15c. Type **1144** 35 20

1779 15c. Downhill skiing 35 20

1780 15c. Ski jumping 35 20

1781 15c. Ice hockey 35 20

1980. Windmills.

1782 **1148** 15c. brown on yellow 35 10

1783 – 15c. brown on yellow 35 10

1784 – 15c. brown on yellow 35 10

1785 – 15c. brown on yellow 35 10

1786 – 15c. brown on yellow 35 10

DESIGNS: No. 1783, Replica of old windmill, Portsmouth, R.I.; 1784, Cape Cod windmill, Eastham, Mass.; 1785, Dutch mill, Fabyan Park Forest Preserve, Ill.; 1786, Southwestern windmill, Texas.

1153 Benjamin Banneker

1980. Black Heritage. Benjamin Banneker (astronomer and mathematician).

1787 **1153** 15c. multicoloured . . . 35 10

1154 Photograph and Envelope

1157 "P.S. Write Soon"

1980. National Letter Writing Week.

1788 **1154** 15c. multicoloured . . . 35 15

1789 **1157** 15c. multicoloured (purple background) 35 15

1790 – 15c. multicoloured . . . 35 15

1791 **1157** 15c. multicoloured (green background) 35 15

1792 – 15c. multicoloured . . . 35 15

1793 **1157** 15c. blue, black and red 35 15

DESIGNS—As T **1154**: No. 1790, Flowers and envelope; 1792, Capitol and envelope.

1158 Frances Perkins

1159 Dolley Madison (after Stuart)

1980. Frances Perkins (first woman Cabinet member) Commemoration.

1794 **1158** 15c. blue 30 10

1980.

1795 **1159** 15c. dp brown & brown 30 10

1160 Emily Bissell

1161 Helen Keller and Anne Sullivan

1980. Emily Bissell (crusader against tuberculosis) Commemoration.

1796 **1160** 15c. black and red . . . 30 10

1980. Birth Centenary of Helen Keller.

1797 **1161** 15c. multicoloured . . . 30 10

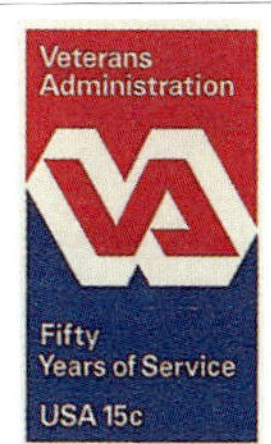

1162 Veterans Administration Emblem

1163 Statue of Gen. Galvez, Mobile

1980. 50th Anniv of Veterans Administration.

1798	**1162**	15c. red and blue . . .	30	10

1980. General Bernardo de Galvez (leader of Spanish forces in Louisiana during American Revolution) Commemoration.

1799	**1163**	15c. multicoloured . . .	30	10

1164 Brain Corals

1168 American Bald Eagle

1980. Coral Reefs. Multicoloured.

1800	15c. Type **1164**	30	15
1801	15c. Elkhorn coral	30	15
1802	15c. Chalice coral	30	15
1803	15c. Finger coral	30	15

1980. Organized Labour.

1804	**1168**	15c. multicoloured . . .	30	10

1169 Edith Wharton

1170 "Homage to the Square: Glow" (J. Albers)

1980. Literary Arts. Edith Wharton (novelist).

1805	**1169**	15c. violet	35	10

1980. American Education.

1806	**1170**	15c. multicoloured . . .	40	10

1171 Heiltsuk, Bella Bella

1980. American Folk Art, Indian Masks. Mult.

1807	15c. Type **1171**	35	15
1808	15c. Chilkat Tlingit	35	15
1809	15c. Tlingit	35	15
1810	15c. Bella Coola	35	15

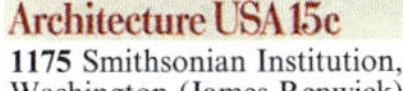

1175 Smithsonian Institution, Washington (James Renwick)

1179 Philip Mazzei

1980. American Architecture.

1811	**1175**	15c. black and red . . .	25	15
1812	–	15c. black and red . . .	25	15
1813	–	15c. black and red . . .	25	15
1814	–	15c. black and red . . .	25	15

DESIGNS: No. 1812, Trinity Church, Boston (Henry Hobson Richardson); 1813, Penn Academy, Philadelphia (Frank Furness); 1814, Lyndhurst, Tarrytown, New York (Alexander Jackson Davis).

1980. Air. 250th Birth Anniv of Philip Mazzei (patriot).

A1815	**1179**	40c. multicoloured . .	80	15

1180 "Madonna and Child" (Epiphany Window, Washington Cathedral)

1181 Antique Toys

1980. Christmas.

1816	**1180**	15c. multicoloured . . .	30	10
1817	**1181**	15c. multicoloured . . .	35	10

1191 Sequoyah (Cherokee scholar) (after C. B. Wilson)

1203 Blanche Stuart Scott and Curtiss Golden Flyer

1980. Great Americans. With "c" after face value.

1818	–	1c. black	15	10
1819	–	2c. black	15	10
1820	–	3c. green	15	10
1821	–	4c. violet	15	10
1822	–	5c. red	15	10
1823	–	10c. blue	20	10
1824	–	13c. red	30	10
1825	–	17c. green	30	15
1826	–	18c. blue	30	15
1827	**1191**	19c. brown	30	15
1828	–	20c. purple	40	15
1829	–	20c. green	45	15
1830	–	20c. black	45	10
1831	–	30c. green	55	10
1832	–	35c. black	70	15
1833	–	37c. blue	70	15
1834	–	40c. green	80	15

DESIGNS: 1c. Dorothea Dix (social pioneer); 2c. Igor Stravinsky (composer); 3c. Henry Clay (politician); 4c. Carl Schurz (reformer); 5c. Pearl Buck (author) (after F. Elliot); 10c. Richard Russell (politician); 13c. Crazy Horse (Sioux chief) (after K. Ziolkowski); 17c. Rachel Carson (scientist); 18c. George Mason (patriot); 20c. (No. 1828), Ralph Bunche (U.N. Secretariat member); 20c. (No. 1829), Thomas H. Gallaudet (educator of the deaf); 20c. (No. 1830), Pres. Harry S. Truman; 30c. Frank C. Laubach (literacy educator); 35c. Charles R. Drew (surgeon); 37c. Robert Millikan (physicist); 40c. Lillian M. Gilbreth (engineer).

For similar designs without "c", see Nos. 2108/36.

1980. Air. Aviation Pioneers. Multicoloured.

A1839	28c. Type **1203**	65	15
A1840	35c. Glenn Curtiss and Curtiss "June Bug" . .	85	20

1205 Everett Dirksen

1206 Whitney Moore Young

1981. Senator Everett Dirksen Commemoration.

1841	**1205**	15c. grey	30	10

1981. Black Heritage. Whitney Moore Young (civil rights leader).

1842	**1206**	15c. multicoloured . . .	30	10

1981. Non-denominational "B" stamp. As T **1090**.

1843	(18c.) lilac	35	10

1207 Rose

1981. Flowers. Multicoloured.

1846	18c. Type **1207**	40	15
1847	18c. Camellia	40	15
1848	18c. Dahlia	40	15
1849	18c. Lily	40	15

1211 ". . . for amber waves of grain"

1212 Stars

1981.

1851	**1212**	6c. blue and red	70	30
1850	**1211**	18c. brown, red and blue	40	20
1852	–	18c. lilac, red and blue	65	25
1853	–	18c. brown, blue and red	40	10

DESIGNS—As T **1211**: No. 1852, "... for purple mountain majesties"; 1853, "... from sea to shining sea".

1215 Nurse and Child

1216 Money Box

1981. Centenary of American Red Cross.

1854	**1215**	18c. multicoloured . . .	40	10

1981. 150th Anniv of First Savings and Loans Association.

1855	**1216**	18c. multicoloured . . .	40	15

1217 American Bighorn

1238 Detroit Electric Auto, 1917

1981. Wildlife.

1856	**1217**	18c. brown	80	20
1857	–	18c. brown	80	20
1858	–	18c. brown	80	20
1859	–	18c. brown	80	20
1860	–	18c. brown	80	20
1861	–	18c. brown	80	20
1862	–	18c. brown	80	20
1863	–	18c. brown	80	20
1864	–	18c. brown	80	20
1865	–	18c. brown	80	20

DESIGNS: No. 1857, Puma; 1858, Common seal; 1859, American bison; 1860, Brown bear; 1861, Polar bear; 1862, Red deer; 1863, Elk; 1864, White-tailed deer; 1865, Pronghorn.

1981. Transport. With "c" after face value.

1866	–	1c. violet	15	10
1867	–	2c. black	15	10
1868	–	3c. green	15	10
1869	–	4c. brown	15	10
1870	–	5c. green	15	10
1871	–	5.2c. red	20	15
1872	–	5.9c. blue	20	20
1873	–	7.4c. brown	20	20
1874	–	9.3c. red	25	20
1875	–	10.9c. mauve	30	20
1876	–	11c. red	25	20
1877	**1238**	17c. blue	40	20
1878	–	18c. brown	40	15
1879	–	20c. red	40	10

DESIGNS: 1c. Omnibus, 1880s; 2c. Steam locomotive, 1870s; 3c. Railway handcar, 1880s; 4c. Concord stagecoach, 1890s; 5c. Pope motor-cycle, 1913; 5.2c. Sleigh, 1880s; 5.9c. Bicycle, 1870s; 7.4c. Baby buggy, 1880s; 9.3c. Mail wagon, 1880s; 10.9c. Hansom cab, 1890s; 11c. Railway caboose, 1890s; 18c. Surrey, 1890s; 20c. Amoskeag fire pumper, 1860s.

For similar designs without "c", see Nos. 2150/74 and 2477/82.

1247 Exploring the Moon ("Apollo" mission)

1255 Joseph Wharton (founder of Wharton School)

1981. Space Achievements.

1886	**1247**	18c. multicoloured . . .	35	20
1887	–	18c. multicoloured . . .	35	20
1888	–	18c. multicoloured . . .	35	20
1889	–	18c. multicoloured . . .	35	20
1890	–	18c. multicoloured . . .	35	20
1891	–	18c. multicoloured . . .	35	20
1892	–	18c. multicoloured . . .	35	20
1893	–	18c. multicoloured . . .	35	20

DESIGNS: No. 1887, Space Shuttle loosing boosters; 1888, Space Shuttle performing experiment; 1889, Understanding the Sun ("Skylab"); 1890, Probing the Planets ("Pioneer II"); 1891, Space Shuttle launch; 1892, Space Shuttle landing; 1893, Comprehending the Universe (space telescope).

Nos. 1886/93 were issued together in se-tenant blocks of eight, each block forming a composite design.

1981. Cent of Professional Management Education.

1894	**1255**	18c. blue and black . .	40	10

1256 Great Blue Heron

1260 Disabled Man using Microscope

1981. Wildlife Habitats.

1895	**1256**	18c. multicoloured . . .	40	15
1896	–	18c. multicoloured . . .	40	15
1897	–	18c. multicoloured . . .	40	15
1898	–	18c. multicoloured . . .	40	15

DESIGNS: No. 1896, American badger; 1897, Brown bear; 1898, Ruffed grouse.

1981. International Year of Disabled Persons.

1899	**1260**	18c. multicoloured . . .	40	10

1261 Edna St. Vincent Millay

1262 "Alcoholism. You can beat it!"

1981. Edna St. Vincent Millay (poet) Commem.

1900	**1261**	18c. multicoloured . . .	40	10

1981. Anti-alcoholism Campaign.

1901	**1262**	18c. blue and black . .	50	10

1263 New York University Library (Stanford White)

1267 Bobby Jones (golfer)

1981. American Architecture (3rd series).

1902	**1263**	18c. black and brown	45	15
1903	–	18c. black and brown	45	15
1904	–	18c. black and brown	45	15
1905	–	18c. black and brown	45	15

DESIGNS: No. 1903, Biltmore House, Asheville, North Carolina (Richard Morris Hunt); 1904, Palace of Arts, San Francisco (Bernard Maybeck); 1905, Bank, Owatonna, Minnesota (Louis Sullivan).

1981. American Sports Personalities.

1906	**1267**	18c. green	1·10	10
1907	–	18c. red	55	10

DESIGN: No. 1907, Babe Zaharias (golfer and athlete).

1269 "Coming through the Rye"

1981. Frederic Remington (sculptor) Commem.

1908	**1269**	18c. brown, green and light brown	40	10

1981. Non-denominational "C" stamp. As T **1090** but inscribed "Domestic Mail".

1909	(20c.) brown (19 × 22 mm)	45	15
1910	(20c.) brown (15 × 18½ mm)	50	15

1271 James Hoban and White House

1981. 150th Death Anniv of James Hoban (architect).
1912 **1271** 18c. multicoloured . . . 40 15
1913 20c. multicoloured . . . 40 10

1272 Map of Yorktown Peninsula
1274 "Madonna and Child" (Botticelli)

1981. Bicentenary of Battles of Yorktown and Virginia Capes. Multicoloured.
1914 18c. Type **1272** 35 15
1915 18c. French ships blocking Chesapeake Bay 35 15

1981. Christmas. No value expressed. Mult.
1916 (20c.) Type **1274** 40 10
1917 (20c.) Teddy bear on sleigh 40 10

1276 John Hanson
1277 Barrel Cactus

1981. John Hanson (American revolutionary leader) Commemoration.
1918 **1276** 20c. multicoloured . . . 40 10

1981. Desert Plants. Multicoloured.
1919 20c. Type **1277** 40 15
1920 20c. Agave (horiz) 40 15
1921 20c. Saguaro 40 15
1922 20c. Beavertail cactus (horiz) 40 15

1281 Flag over Supreme Court
1282 American Bighorn

1981.
1923c **1281** 20c. black, red and blue 40 10

1982.
1926 **1282** 20c. blue 40 10

1283 Franklin D. Roosevelt

1982. Birth Centenary of President Franklin D. Roosevelt.
1927 **1283** 20c. blue 40 10

1284 Flowers spelling "Love"
1285 George Washington

1982. Greetings Stamp.
1928 **1284** 20c. multicoloured . . . 80 15

1982. 250th Birth Anniv of George Washington.
1929 **1285** 20c. multicoloured . . . 40 10

1286 Common Flicker (inscr "Yellow-hammer") and Camellia (Alabama)
1287 Stripes in National Colours

1982. State Birds and Flowers. Multicoloured.
1930 20c. Type **1286** 45 40
1931 20c. Willow grouse (inscr "Ptarmigan") and forget-me-not (Alaska) 45 40
1932 20c. Cactus wren and saguaro cactus blossom (Arizona) 45 40
1933 20c. Northern mockingbird and apple blossom (Arkansas) 45 40
1934 20c. California quail and California poppy (California) 45 40
1935 20c. Lark bunting and Rocky Mountain columbine (Colorado) . . 45 40
1936 20c. American robin and mountain laurel (Connecticut) 45 40
1937 20c. Blue hen chicken and peach blossom (Delaware) 45 40
1938 20c. Northern mockingbird and orange blossom (Florida) 45 40
1939 20c. Brown thrasher and Cherokee rose (Georgia) 45 40
1940 20c. Hawaiian goose and hibiscus (Hawaii) 45 40
1941 20c. Mountain bluebird and syringa (Idaho) 45 40
1942 20c. Common cardinal and violet (Illinois) 45 40
1943 20c. Common cardinal and peony (Indiana) 45 40
1944 20c. American (inscr "Eastern") goldfinch and wild rose (Iowa) 45 40
1945 20c. Western meadowlark and sunflower (Kansas) 45 40
1946 20c. Common cardinal and goldenrod (Kentucky) . . 45 40
1947 20c. Brown pelican and magnolia (Louisiana) . . 45 40
1948 20c. Black-capped chickadee, white pine cone and tassel (Maine) . . . 45 40
1949 20c. Northern (inscr "Baltimore") oriole and black-eyed susan (Maryland) 45 40
1950 20c. Black-capped chickadee and mayflower (Massachusetts) 45 40
1951 20c. American robin and apple blossom (Michigan) 45 40
1952 20c. Great northern diver (inscr "Common Loon") and showy lady slipper (Minnesota) 45 40
1953 20c. Northern mockingbird and magnolia (Mississippi) 45 40
1954 20c. Eastern bluebird and red hawthorn (Missouri) 45 40
1955 20c. Western meadowlark and bitterroot (Montana) 45 40
1956 20c. Western meadowlark and goldenrod (Nebraska) 45 40
1957 20c. Mountain bluebird and sagebrush (Nevada) . . 45 40
1958 20c. Purple finch and lilac (New Hampshire) 45 40
1959 20c. American goldfinch and violet (New Jersey) . . . 45 40
1960 20c. Road-runner and yucca flower (New Mexico) . . 45 40
1961 20c. Eastern bluebird and rose (New York) 45 40
1962 20c. Common cardinal and flowering dogwood (North Carolina) 45 40
1963 20c. Western meadowlark, and wild prairie rose (North Dakota) 45 40
1964 20c. Common cardinal and red carnation (Ohio) . . . 45 40
1965 20c. Scissor-tailed flycatcher and mistletoe (Oklahoma) 45 40
1966 20c. Western meadowlark and Oregon grape (Oregon) 45 40
1967 20c. Ruffed grouse and mountain laurel (Pennsylvania) 45 40
1968 20c. Rhode Island red and violet (Rhode Island) . . 45 40
1969 20c. Carolina wren and Carolina jessamine (South Carolina) 45 40
1970 20c. Common pheasant ("Ring-necked Pheasant") and pasque flower (South Dakota) 45 40
1971 20c. Northern mockingbird and iris (Tennessee) . . . 45 40
1972 20c. Northern mockingbird and bluebonnet (Texas) 45 40
1973 20c. California gull and sego lily (Utah) 45 40
1974 20c. Hermit thrush and red clover (Vermont) 45 40
1975 20c. Common cardinal and flowering dogwood (Virginia) 45 40
1976 20c. American goldfinch and rhododendron (Washington) 45 40
1977 20c. Common cardinal ("Cardinal") and "Rhododendron maximum" (West Virginia) 45 40
1978 20c. American robin and wood violet (Wisconsin) 45 40
1979 20c. Western meadowlark and Indian paint bush (Wyoming) 45 40

1982. Bicent of U.S.A.–Netherlands Diplomatic Relations.
1980 **1287** 20c. red, blue and black 40 10

1288 Library of Congress
1289 Garment Tag

1982. Library of Congress.
1981 **1288** 20c. black and red . . . 40 10

1982. Consumer Education.
1982 **1289** 20c. blue 75 25

1290 Solar Energy
1294 Frontispiece from "Ragged Dick"

1982. Knoxville World's Fair.
1983 **1290** 20c. multicoloured . . . 45 15
1984 – 20c. multicoloured . . . 45 15
1985 – 20c. blue, light blue and black 45 15
1986 – 20c. blue, black and brown 45 15
DESIGNS: No. 1984, Synthetic fuels; 1985, Breeder reactor; 1986, Fossil fuels.

1982. 150th Birth Anniv of Horatio Alger (novelist).
1987 **1294** 20c. black and red on buff 40 10

1295 Family Group
1296 John, Ethel and Lionel Barrymore

1982. Ageing Together.
1988 **1295** 20c. red 40 10

1982. Performing Arts and Artists. The Barrymores (theatrical family).
1989 **1296** 20c. multicoloured . . . 45 10

1297 Dr. Mary Walker
1298 Maple Leaf and Rose

1982. Dr. Mary Walker (army surgeon) Commem.
1990 **1297** 20c. multicoloured . . . 40 10

1982. 50th Anniv of International Peace Garden (on U.S.A.–Canada border).
1991 **1298** 20c. multicoloured . . . 40 10

1299 Typographic Design
1300 Jackie Robinson

1982. America's Libraries.
1992 **1299** 20c. red and black . . . 40 10

1982. Black Heritage. Jackie Robinson (baseball player).
1993 **1300** 20c. multicoloured . . . 1·60 20

1301 Touro Synagogue

1982. Touro Synagogue, Newport, Rhode Island.
1994 **1301** 20c. multicoloured . . . 45 10

1302 Open Air Theatre

1982. Wolf Trap Farm Park, Vienna, Virginia.
1995 **1302** 20c. multicoloured . . . 40 10

1303 Fallingwater, Mill Run, Pennsylvania (Frank Lloyd Wright)

1982. American Architecture.
1996 **1303** 20c. black and brown 60 20
1997 – 20c. black and brown 60 20
1998 – 20c. black and brown 60 20
1999 – 20c. black and brown 60 20
DESIGNS: No. 1997, Illinois Institute of Technology, Chicago (Mies van der Rohe); 1998, Gropius House, Lincoln, Massachusetts (Walter Gropius); 1999, Dulles Airport, Washington D.C. (Eero Saarinen).

1307 St. Francis and Doves

1982. 800th Birth Anniv of St. Francis of Assisi.
2000 **1307** 20c. multicoloured . . . 40 10

1308 Ponce de Leon and Map of Florida
1309 "Madonna and Child" (Tiepolo)

1982. Ponce de Leon (explorer) Commemoration.
2001 **1308** 20c. multicoloured . . . 45 10

1982. Christmas. Multicoloured.
2002 20c. Type **1309** 40 10
2003 20c. Building a snowman (horiz) 60 20
2004 20c. Sledging (horiz) 60 20
2005 20c. Decorating a Christmas tree (horiz) 60 20
2006 20c. Skating (horiz) 60 20

1314 Puppy and Kitten **1316** Industrial Complex

1982.
2007 **1314** 13c. multicoloured . . . 30 10

1983. Science and Industry.
2015 **1316** 20c. multicoloured . . . 40 10

1317 Benjamin Franklin and Great Seal of Sweden

1983. Bicentenary of Sweden–U.S.A. Treaty of Amity and Commerce.
2016 **1317** 20c. indigo, brown and black 25 10

1319/1320 Hot Air Ballooning

1983. Bicentenary of Manned Flight. Mult.
2017 20c. "Intrepid", 1861 (vert) 40 20
2018 20c. Type **1319** 40 20
2019 20c. Type **1320** 40 20
2020 20c. Stratosphere balloon "Explorer II", 1935 (vert) 40 20

1322 C.C.C. Workers repairing Trail

1983. 50th Anniv of Civilian Conservation Corps.
2021 **1322** 20c. multicoloured . . . 40 10

1323 Shot Putting **1327** Joseph Priestley (after G. Stuart)

1983. Air. Olympic Games, Los Angeles (1984) (1st issue). Multicoloured.
A2022 40c. Type **1323** 90 30
A2023 40c. Gymnastics 90 30
A2024 40c. Swimming 90 30
A2025 40c. Weightlifting 90 30
See also Nos. A2034/7, 2040/3, A2058/61 and 2079/82.

1983. 250th Birth Anniv of Joseph Priestley (discoverer of oxygen).
2026 **1327** 20c. multicoloured . . . 40 10

1328 Reaching Hands

1983. Voluntary Work.
2027 **1328** 20c. black and red . . . 50 15

1329 "Concord"

1983. 300th Anniv of First German Settlers in America.
2028 **1329** 20c. brown 45 15

1330 Joggers and Electrocardiograph Trace

1983. Physical Fitness.
2029 **1330** 20c. multicoloured . . . 50 15

1331 Brooklyn Bridge, New York

1983. Centenary of Brooklyn Bridge.
2030 **1331** 20c. blue 45 15

1332 Norris Hydro-electric Dam

1983. 50th Anniv of Tennessee Valley Authority.
2031 **1332** 20c. multicoloured . . . 40 10

1333 Army, Air Force and Navy Medals of Honour **1334** Scott Joplin

1983. Medal of Honour.
2032 **1333** 20c. multicoloured . . . 40 15

1983. Black Heritage. Scott Joplin (ragtime composer).
2033 **1334** 20c. multicoloured . . . 70 15

1335 Gymnastics **1339** Babe Ruth

1983. Air. Olympic Games, Los Angeles (1984) (2nd issue). Multicoloured.
A2034 28c. Type **1335** 80 30
A2035 28c. Hurdling 80 30
A2036 28c. Basketball 80 30
A2037 28c. Football 80 30

1983. American Sports Personalities. Babe Ruth (baseball player).
2038 **1339** 20c. blue . . . . 1·90 15

1340 Hawthorne (after C. G. Thompson) **1341** Discus

1983. Literary Arts. Nathaniel Hawthorne (writer).
2039 **1340** 20c. multicoloured . . . 40 10

1983. Olympic Games, Los Angeles (1984) (3rd issue). Multicoloured.
2040 13c. Type **1341** 40 20
2041 13c. High jump 40 20
2042 13c. Archery 40 20
2043 13c. Boxing 40 20

1345 American Bald Eagle and Moon

1983.
2044 **1345** $9.35 multicoloured . . 20·00 11·50

1346 Signing the Treaty of Paris (after Benjamin West) **1347** Text in Early and Modern Type

1983. Bicentenary of Treaty of Paris.
2045 **1346** 20c. multicoloured . . . 40 10

1983. Centenary of Civil Service.
2046 **1347** 20c. stone, red and black 45 10

1348 Part of Proscenium and Modern Facade

1983. Centenary of Metropolitan Opera, New York.
2047 **1348** 20c. yellow and purple 40 10

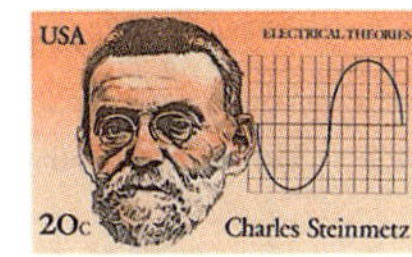

1349 Charles Steinmetz and Graph

1983. American Inventors.
2048 **1349** 20c. pink and black . . 50 20
2049 – 20c. pink and black . . 50 20
2050 – 20c. pink and black . . 50 20
2051 – 20c. pink and black . . 50 20
DESIGNS: No. 2049, Edwin Armstrong and frequency modulator; 2050, Nikola Tesla and induction motor; 2051, Philo T. Farnsworth and television camera.

1353 "John Mason" Streetcar, New York City, 1832

1983. Streetcars. Multicoloured.
2052 20c. Type **1353** 40 20
2053 20c. Electric streetcar, Montgomery, Alabama, 1886 . . . . 40 20
2054 20c. "Bobtail" horsecar, Sulphur Rock, Arkansas, 1926 . . . . 40 20
2055 20c. St. Charles streetcar, New Orleans, 1923 . . . 40 20

1357 "Madonna and Child" (Raphael) **1358** Santa Claus

1983. Christmas.
2056 **1357** 20c. multicoloured . . . 40 10
2057 **1358** 20c. multicoloured . . . 40 15

1359 Fencing

1983. Air. Olympic Games, Los Angeles (1984) (4th issue). Multicoloured.
A2058 35c. Type **1359** 90 35
A2059 35c. Cycling 90 45
A2060 35c. Volleyball 90 35
A2061 35c. Pole vault 90 35

1363 Martin Luther **1364** Reindeer and Pipeline

1983. 500th Birth Anniv of Martin Luther.
2062 **1363** 20c. multicoloured . . . 40 10

1984. 25th Anniv of Alaska Statehood.
2063 **1364** 20c. multicoloured . . . 40 10

1365 Ice Dancing **1369** Column and "$" Sign

1984. Winter Olympic Games, Sarajevo. Mult.
2064 20c. Type **1365** 60 20
2065 20c. Downhill skiing 60 20
2066 20c. Cross-country skiing . . 60 20
2067 20c. Ice hockey 60 20

1984. 50th Anniv of Federal Deposit Insurance Corporation.
2068 **1369** 20c. multicoloured . . . 40 10

1370 "Love" **1371** Carter G. Woodson

1984. Greetings Stamp.
2069 **1370** 20c. multicoloured . . . 40 15

1984. Black Heritage. Carter G. Woodson (historian).
2070 **1371** 20c. multicoloured . . . 40 10

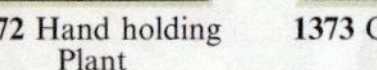

1372 Hand holding Plant **1373** Coin and "$" Sign

1984. 50th Anniv of Soil and Water Conservation Movement.
2071 **1372** 20c. multicoloured . . . 40 10

1984. 50th Anniv of Credit Union Act.
2072 **1373** 20c. multicoloured . . . 40 10

1374 Wild Pink

1984. Orchids. Multicoloured.
2073 20c. Type **1374** 50 20
2074 20c. Yellow lady's slipper 50 20
2075 20c. Spreading pogonia 50 20
2076 20c. Pacific calypso . . . 50 20

1378 Eastern Polynesian Canoe and Pacific Golden Plover

1984. 25th Anniv of Hawaii Statehood.
2077 **1378** 20c. multicoloured . . . 55 10

1379 Silhouettes of Lincoln and Washington **1380** Diving

1984. 50th Anniv of National Archives.
2078 **1379** 20c. black, olive and red 45 10

1984. Olympic Games, Los Angeles (5th issue). Multicoloured.
2079 20c. Type **1380** 75 20
2080 20c. Long jump 75 20
2081 20c. Wrestling 75 20
2082 20c. Canoeing 75 20

1384 Bayou Wildlife

1984. Louisiana World Exposition, New Orleans.
2083 **1384** 20c. multicoloured . . . 40 10

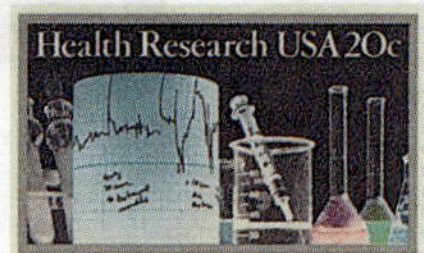

1385 Laboratory Equipment

1984. Health Research.
2084 **1385** 20c. multicoloured . . . 45 10

1386 Fairbanks in Film Roles **1387** Jim Thorpe

1984. Performing Arts and Artists. Douglas Fairbanks (film actor).
2085 **1386** 20c. multicoloured . . . 50 10

1984. American Sports Personalities. Jim Thorpe (athlete, footballer and baseball player).
2086 **1387** 20c. brown 45 10

1388 John McCormack **1389** St. Lawrence Seaway

1984. Performing Arts and Artists. John McCormack (singer).
2087 **1388** 20c. multicoloured . . . 45 10

1984. 25th Anniv of St. Lawrence Seaway.
2088 **1389** 20c. multicoloured . . . 40 10

1390 "Mallards dropping In" (Jay Norwood Darling)

1984. 50th Anniv of Migratory Bird Hunting and Conservation Stamp Act.
2089 **1390** 20c. blue 60 10

1391 Galleon "Elizabeth" **1392** Melville (after J. O. Eaton)

1984. Explorers. 400th Anniv of First Raleigh Expedition to Roanoke Island, North Carolina.
2090 **1391** 20c. multicoloured . . . 40 10

1984. Literary Arts. Herman Melville (novelist).
2091 **1392** 20c. green 40 10

1393 Horace Moses **1394** Smokey Bear and American Black Bear Cub clinging to burnt Tree

1984. Horace Moses (founder of Junior Achievement (training organization) Commem.
2092 **1393** 20c. orange and black 50 10

1984. Smokey Bear (symbol of forest fire prevention campaign).
2093 **1394** 20c. multicoloured . . . 45 10

1395 Clemente and Flag of Puerto Rico **1396** Beagle and Boston Terrier

1984. American Sports Personalities. Roberto Clemente (baseball player).
2094 **1395** 20c. multicoloured . . . 2·00 25

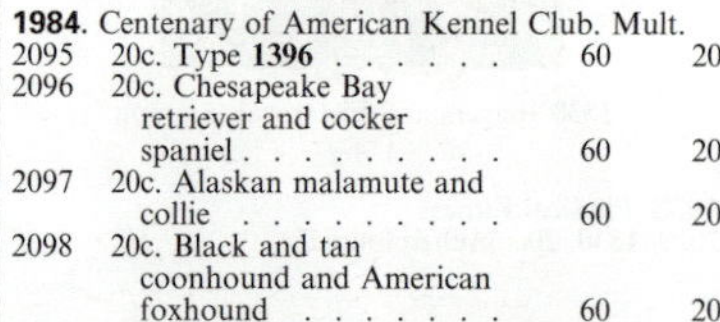

1984. Centenary of American Kennel Club. Mult.
2095 20c. Type **1396** 60 20
2096 20c. Chesapeake Bay retriever and cocker spaniel 60 20
2097 20c. Alaskan malamute and collie 60 20
2098 20c. Black and tan coonhound and American foxhound 60 20

1400 McGruff (campaign character) **1401** "Family Unity"

1984. National Crime Prevention Month.
2099 **1400** 20c. multicoloured . . . 40 10

1984. National Stamp Collecting Month.
2100 **1401** 20c. black, red and blue 60 10

1402 Eleanor Roosevelt **1403** Abraham Lincoln reading to his Son, Tad

1984. Eleanor Roosevelt Commemoration.
2101 **1402** 20c. blue 40 10

1984. "Nation of Readers".
2102 **1403** 20c. brown and red . . 45 10

1404 "Madonna and Child (Fra Filippo Lippi) **1406** Uniformed Group and Flag

1984. Christmas.
2103 20c. Type **1404** 40 10
2104 20c. Santa Claus 40 10

1984. Hispanic Americans.
2105 **1406** 20c. multicoloured . . . 40 10

1407 Memorial (Maya Ying Lin)

1984. Vietnam Veterans Memorial, Washington, D.C.
2106 **1407** 20c. black, green and deep green 55 10

1408 Kern **1409** Margaret Mitchell (writer)

1985. Performing Arts and Artists. Birth Centenary of Jerome Kern (composer).
2107 **1408** 22c. multicoloured . . . 45 10

1985. Great Americans. Without "c" after face value.
2108 **1409** 1c. brown 15 10
2109 – 2c. blue 15 10
2110 – 3c. blue 15 10
2111 – 4c. blue 15 10
2112 – 5c. green 15 10
2113 – 6c. red 20 15
2114 – 7c. red 20 10
2115 – 8c. brown 20 15
2116 – 9c. green 20 15
2117 – 10c. red 30 10
2118 – 11c. blue 20 10
2119 – 14c. green 30 10
2120 – 14c. red 25 10
2121 – 15c. purple 35 10
2122 – 17c. green 40 10
2123 – 21c. purple 45 15
2124 – 22c. blue 45 10
2125 – 23c. violet 45 15
2126 – 25c. blue 50 15
2127 – 28c. green 50 25
2128 – 39c. mauve 75 15
2129 – 45c. blue 85 20
2130a – 50c. brown 70 30
2131 – 56c. red . . . . 1·00 30
2132 – 65c. blue . . . . . . 1·10 25
2133 – $1 green . . . . . . 3·00 25
2134a – $1 blue . . . . 1·80 25
2135 – $2 violet . . . . . . 3·75 50
2136 – $5 brown . . . . . . 9·25 1·50

DESIGNS: 2c. Mary Lyon (educator); 3c. Paul Dudley White (cardiologist); 4c. Father Flanagan (founder of Boys Town); 5c. Hugo L. Black (Supreme Court Justice); 6c. Walter Lippmann (journalist); 7c. Abraham Baldwin (politician); 8c. General Henry Knox; 9c. Sylvanus Thayer (military educator) (after R. Weir); 10c. Red Cloud (Oglala Sioux chief); 11c. Alden Partridge (educationist); 14c. (No. 2119) Sinclair Lewis (writer) (after S. Melik); 14c. (No. 2120) Julia Ward Howe (author of "Battle Hymn of the Republic") (after J. Elliott); 15c. Buffalo Bill Cody (showman); 17c. Belva Ann Lockwood (women's rights campaigner); 21c. Chester Carlson (inventor of photocopying); 22c. J. J. Audubon (ornithologist); 23c. Mary Cassatt (artist); 25c. Jack London (writer); 28c. Sitting Bull (Hunkpapa Sioux chief); 39c. Grenville Clark (peace activist); 45c. Dr. Harvey Cushing (neurosurgeon); 50c. Admiral Chester W. Nimitz; 56c. John Harvard (philanthropist) (after D. C. French); 65c. Gen. Henry Harley "Hap" Arnold; $1 (No. 2133) Bernard Revel (scholar); $1 (No. 2134) Johns Hopkins (philanthropist); $2 William Jennings Bryan (politician); $5 Bret Harte (writer).

1985. Non-denominational "D" stamp. As T **1090** but inscribed "Domestic Mail".
2137 (22c.) green (18 × 21 mm) . . 55 10
2138 (22c.) green (15 × 18 mm) . . 70 15

1438 Alfred V. Verville and Verville-Sperry R-3

1985. Air. Aviation Pioneers.
A2142 33c. Type **1438** 70 15
A2143 39c. Lawrence and Elmer Sperry and Curtiss F flying boat 70 15

1440 Loading Mail into "China Clipper" **1441** Mary McLeod Bethune

1985. Air. 50th Anniv of Martin M-130 Flying Boat, First Transpacific Airmail Flight.
A2144 **1440** 44c. multicoloured . . 80 25

1985. Black Heritage. Mary McLeod Bethune (social activist).
2145 **1441** 22c. multicoloured . . . 45 10

1442 Lesser Scaup ("Broadbill") Decoy, 1890 (Ben Holmes)
1446 Omnibus, 1880s

1985. American Folk Art. Duck Decoys. Mult.

No.	Type	Description	Unused	Used
2146		22c. Type **1442**	1·40	20
2147		22c. Mallard decoy, 1900 (Percy Grant)	1·40	20
2148		22c. Canvasback decoy, 1929 (Bob McGraw)	1·40	20
2149		22c. Redhead decoy, 1925 (Keyes Chadwick)	1·40	20

1985. Transport. Without "c" after face value.

No.	Type	Description	Unused	Used
2150	**1446**	1c. violet	15	10
2151	–	2c. black	20	10
2152	–	3c. purple	15	10
2153	–	3.4c. green	15	10
2154	–	4.9c. black	15	15
2155	–	5c. black	15	15
2156	–	5.3 black	15	15
2157	–	5.5c. red	15	15
2158	–	6c. brown	20	15
2159	–	7.1c. red	20	20
2160	–	7.6c. brown	20	15
2161	–	8.3c. green	20	20
2162	–	8.4c. purple	20	10
2163	–	8.5c. green	20	20
2163a	–	10c. blue	20	15
2164	–	10.1c. grey	20	20
2165	–	11c. black	25	20
2166	–	12c. blue	35	20
2167	–	12.5c. green	25	20
2167b	–	13c. black	25	30
2168	–	13.2c. green	25	20
2169	–	14c. blue	25	20
2170	–	15c. violet	30	20
2170b	–	16.7c. red	30	20
2171	–	17c. blue	45	20
2172	–	17.5c. violet	40	20
2172b	–	20c. purple	40	20
2172c	–	20.5c. red	55	25
2172d	–	21c. green	45	20
2173	–	24.1c. blue	55	30
2174	–	25c. brown	50	15

DESIGNS: 2c. Steam locomotive, 1870s; 3c. Conestoga wagon, 1800s; 3.4c. School bus, 1920s; 4.9c. Buckboard, 1880s; 5c. Milk wagon, 1900s; 5.3c. Lift, 1900s; 5.5c. Star Route truck, 1910s; 6c. Tricycle, 1880s; 7.1c. Tractor, 1920s; 7.6c. Carreta, 1770s; 8.3c. "McKean" ambulance, 1860s; 8.4c. Wheelchair, 1920s; 8.5c. Tow truck, 1920s; 10c. Canal barge, 1880s; 10.1c. Oil wagon, 1890s; 11c. Stutz "Bearcat", 1933; 12c. Stanley "Steamer", 1909; 12.5c. Pushcart, 1880s; 13c. Police patrol wagon, 1880s; 13.2c. Coal wagon, 1870s; 14c. Iceboat, 1880s; 15c. Tug, 1900s; 16.7c. Popcorn wagon, 1902; 17c. Dog sledge, 1920s; 17.5c. Marmon "Wasp", 1911; 20c. Cable car, 1880s; 20.5c. Ahrens-Fox fire engine, 1900s; 21c. Railway mail van, 1920s; 24.1c. Pope tandem, 1890s; 25c. Bread wagon, 1880s.

The 5.3, 7.6, 8.4, 13, 13.2, 16.7, 21 and 24.1c. were only issued with precancelled inscription of the type of service in red and the 20.5c. in black. Prices in the unused column are for stamps with full gum.

1471 Ice Skating, Skiing and Emblem
1472 Flag over Capitol, Washington

1985. Winter Special Olympic Games, Park City, Utah.

No.	Type	Description	Unused	Used
2175	**1471**	22c. multicoloured	45	10

1985.

No.	Type	Description	Unused	Used
2176	**1472**	22c. black, red and blue	50	10
2178	–	22c. black, red and blue	50	10

DESIGN—40 × 22 mm: No. 2178, Flag over Capitol, Washington, and inscription "Of the People By the People For the People".

1474 Frilled Dogwinkle
1479 Coloured Lines and "Love"

1985. Sea Shells.

No.	Type	Description	Unused	Used
2179	**1474**	22c. red and black	35	10
2180	–	22c. red, purple and black	35	10
2181	–	22c. red and black	35	10
2182	–	22c. purple and black	35	10
2183	–	22c. red, purple and black	35	10

DESIGNS: No. 2180, Reticulated cowrie helmet; 2181, New England neptune; 2182, Calico scallop; 2183, Lightning whelk.

1985. Greetings Stamp.

No.	Type	Description	Unused	Used
2184	**1479**	22c. multicoloured	45	10

1480 American Bald Eagle and Moon

1985.

No.	Type	Description	Unused	Used
2185	**1480**	$10.75 multicoloured	20·00	9·25

1481 Electricity Pole and Rural Landscape

1985. 50th Anniv of Rural Electrification Administration.

No.	Type	Description	Unused	Used
2186	**1481**	22c. multicoloured	45	10

1482 1c. Franklin Stamp, 1870
1483 Abigail Adams

1985. "Ameripex 86" International Stamp Exhibition, Chicago.

No.	Type	Description	Unused	Used
2187	**1482**	22c. multicoloured	45	10

1985. Abigail Adams (wife of Pres. John Adams and writer) Commemoration.

No.	Type	Description	Unused	Used
2188	**1483**	22c. multicoloured	45	15

1484 Bartholdi (after J. Frappa) and Statue of Liberty

1985. Frederic Auguste Bartholdi (sculptor of Statue of Liberty) Commemoration.

No.	Type	Description	Unused	Used
2189	**1484**	22c. multicoloured	45	10

1485 Troops in Mountain Pass

1985. Korean War Veterans.

No.	Type	Description	Unused	Used
2190	**1485**	22c. green and red	55	10

1486 Disabled and Needy People

1985. 50th Anniv of Social Security Act.

No.	Type	Description	Unused	Used
2191	**1486**	22c. blue and deep blue	45	10

1487 Junipero Serra and Mission San Gabriel

1985. Air. Death Bicentenary (1984) of Father Junipero Serra (missionary).

No.	Type	Description	Unused	Used
A2192	**1487**	44c. multicoloured	95	20

1488 "Battle of the Marne" (Harvey Dunn)

1985. World War I Veterans.

No.	Type	Description	Unused	Used
2193	**1488**	22c. green and red	45	10

1489 Quarter Horse
1493 Alphabet, Spectacles, Quill and Apple

1985. Horses. Multicoloured.

No.	Type	Description	Unused	Used
2194		22c. Type **1489**	90	55
2195		22c. Morgan horse	90	55
2196		22c. Saddlebred horse	90	55
2197		22c. Appaloosa	90	55

1985. Public Education.

No.	Type	Description	Unused	Used
2198	**1493**	22c. multicoloured	90	10

1494 Y.M.C.A. Youth Camping (centenary)

1985. International Youth Year. Multicoloured.

No.	Type	Description	Unused	Used
2199		22c. Type **1494**	70	20
2200		22c. Boy Scouts of America (75th anniv)	70	20
2201		22c. Big Brothers and Big Sisters	70	20
2202		22c. Camp Fire Inc. (75th anniv)	70	20

1498 Hungry Faces
1499 Envelopes

1985. "Help End Hunger".

No.	Type	Description	Unused	Used
2203	**1498**	22c. multicoloured	45	10

1985.

No.	Type	Description	Unused	Used
2204	**1499**	21.1c. multicoloured	45	30

No. 2204 exists both with and without precancel "ZIP + 4".

1500 "Genoa Madonna" (Luca della Robbia)
1502 George Washington (after Stuart) and Washington Monument

1985. Christmas.

No.	Type	Description	Unused	Used
2205	**1500**	22c. multicoloured	45	10
2206	–	22c. red, green and black	45	10

DESIGN—HORIZ: No. 2206, Poinsettias.

1985.

No.	Type	Description	Unused	Used
2207	**1502**	18c. multicoloured	50	25

No. 2207 exists both with and without precancel "PRESORTED FIRST-CLASS".

1503 Old State House, Little Rock

1986. 150th Anniv of Arkansas State.

No.	Type	Description	Unused	Used
2208	**1503**	22c. multicoloured	45	10

1504 Sheet of Stamps, Handstamp and Magnifying Glass
1508 Puppy

1986. "Ameripex 86" International Stamp Exhibition, Chicago. Stamp Collecting. Mult.

No.	Type	Description	Unused	Used
2209		22c. Type **1504**	45	20
2210		22c. Boy holding stamp in tweezers	45	20
2211		22c. Mounted stamps and 3c. U.S. stamp under glass	45	20
2212		22c. "Ameripex" miniature sheet on cover and handstamp	45	20

1986. Greetings Stamp.

No.	Type	Description	Unused	Used
2213	**1508**	22c. multicoloured	45	10

1509 Sojourner Truth
1510 Texan Flag and Santa Anna's Spur

1986. Black Heritage. Sojourner Truth (human rights activist).

No.	Type	Description	Unused	Used
2214	**1509**	22c. multicoloured	50	10

1986. 150th Anniv of Battle of San Jacinto.

No.	Type	Description	Unused	Used
2215	**1510**	22c. red, blue and black	45	10

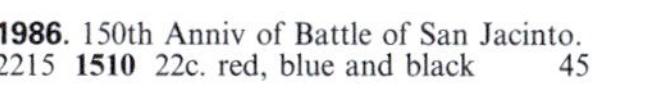

1511 Muskellunge

1986. Fishes. Multicoloured.

No.	Type	Description	Unused	Used
2216		22c. Type **1511**	1·10	20
2217		22c. Atlantic cod	1·10	20
2218		22c. Large-mouthed black bass	1·10	20
2219		22c. Blue-finned tuna	1·10	20
2220		22c. Bullhead catfish	1·10	20

1516 Modern Hospital
1517 Ellington

1986. Public Hospitals. 250th Anniv of Bellevue Hospital Centre, New York.

No.	Type	Description	Unused	Used
2221	**1516**	22c. multicoloured	45	10

1986. Performing Arts and Artists. Duke Ellington (jazz musician).

No.	Type	Description	Unused	Used
2222	**1517**	22c. multicoloured	45	10

1519 Elisha Kent Kane and Polar Brig "Advance"
1523 Head of Statue

1986. Polar Explorers. Multicoloured.

No.	Type	Description	Unused	Used
2224		22c. Type **1519**	85	20
2225		22c. Adolphus W. Greely	85	20
2226		22c. Vilhjalmur Stefansson	85	20
2227		22c. Robert E. Peary and Matthew Henson	85	20

1986. Centenary of Statue of Liberty.

No.	Type	Description	Unused	Used
2228	**1523**	22c. blue and red	45	10

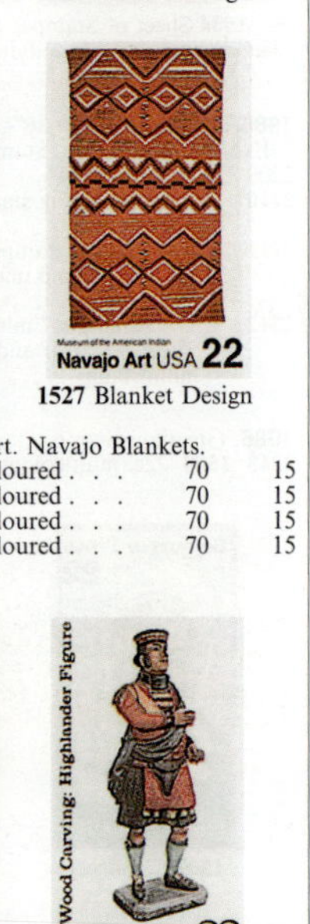

1524 Blanket Design **1525** Blanket Design

1526 Blanket Design **1527** Blanket Design

1986. American Folk Art. Navajo Blankets.
2229 **1524** 22c. multicoloured . . . 70 15
2230 **1525** 22c. multicoloured . . . 70 15
2231 **1526** 22c. multicoloured . . . 70 15
2232 **1527** 22c. multicoloured . . . 70 15

1528 T. S. Eliot **1529** Highlander Figure (tobacconist)

1986. Literary Arts. Thomas Stearns Eliot (poet).
2233 **1528** 22c. red 45 10

1986. American Folk Art. Carved Wooden Figures. Multicoloured.
2234 22c. Type **1529** 60 15
2235 22c. Ship's figurehead . . . 60 15
2236 22c. Nautical figure (nautical instrument maker) 60 15
2237 22c. Indian (cigar store) . . 60 15

1533 "Madonna" (Il Perugino) **1535** White Pine and Lake Huron

1986. Christmas. Multicoloured.
2238 22c. Type **1533** 45 10
2239 22c. Winter village 45 10

1987. 150th Anniv of Michigan Statehood.
2240 **1535** 22c. multicoloured . . . 45 10

1536 Stylized Runner **1537** Heart

1986. 10th Pan-American Games, Indianapolis.
2241 **1536** 22c. multicoloured . . . 45 10

1987. Greetings Stamp.
2242 **1537** 22c. multicoloured . . . 45 10

1538 Du Sable **1539** Caruso as Duke of Mantua in "Rigoletto"

1987. Black Heritage. Jean Baptiste Pointe du Sable (founder of Chicago).
2243 **1538** 22c. multicoloured . . . 45 10

1987. Performing Arts and Artists. Enrico Caruso (operatic tenor).
2244 **1539** 22c. multicoloured . . . 45 10

1540 Badges

1987. 75th Anniv of Girl Scouts of America.
2245 **1540** 22c. multicoloured . . . 45 10

1541 "Congratulations!"

1987. Greetings Stamps. Multicoloured.
2246 22c. Type **1541** 70 30
2247 22c. "Get Well!" (18 × 33 mm) 70 30
2248 22c. "Thank You!" (18 × 33 mm) 70 30
2249 22c. "Love You, Dad!" . . 70 30
2250 22c. "Best Wishes!" (18 × 21 mm) 70 30
2251 22c. "Happy Birthday!" (18 × 21 mm) 70 30
2252 22c. "Love You, Mother!" 70 30
2253 22c. "Keep in Touch!" (18 × 21 mm) 70 30

1549 Ethnic Faces **1550** Flag and Fireworks

1987. Centenary of United Way Volunteer Organization.
2254 **1549** 22c. multicoloured . . . 45 10

1987.
2255 **1550** 22c. multicoloured . . . 45 10

1551 Barn Swallows **1552** State Seal

1987. "Capex '87" International Stamp Exhibition, Toronto. North American Wildlife. Multicoloured.
2256 22c. Type **1551** 85 30
2257 22c. Monarch butterflies on field thistle 85 30
2258 22c. Bighorn sheep 85 30
2259 22c. Broad-tailed hummingbird on Colorado columbine . . . 85 30
2260 22c. Rabbit and red clover 85 30
2261 22c. Osprey 85 30
2262 22c. Mountain lion 85 30
2263 22c. Luna moth on trumpet honeysuckle 85 30
2264 22c. Mule deer 85 30
2265 22c. Grey squirrel on red oak 85 30
2266 22c. Armadillo and Texas prickly pear 85 30
2267 22c. Eastern chipmunk and European white birch . . 85 30
2268 22c. Moose 85 30
2269 22c. Black bear 85 30
2270 22c. Tiger swallowtail butterflies on orange milkweed 85 30
2271 22c. Northern bobwhite ("Bobwhite") and purple coneflower 85 30
2272 22c. Ringtail and Cape marigold 85 30
2273 22c. Red-winged blackbird on common cattail . . . 85 30
2274 22c. American lobster . . . 85 30
2275 22c. Black-tailed hare and beavertail 85 30
2276 22c. Scarlet tanager and American basswood . . . 85 30
2277 22c. Woodchuck and dandelion 85 30
2278 22c. Roseate spoonbill and red mangrove 85 30
2279 22c. American bald eagle . . 85 30
2280 22c. Alaskan brown bear . . 85 30
2281 22c. Iiwi on "Ohia lehua" 85 30
2282 22c. Badger 85 30
2283 22c. Pronghorns 85 30
2284 22c. River otter 85 30
2285 22c. Ladybird on rose . . . 85 30
2286 22c. Beaver, maple and quaking aspen 85 30
2287 22c. White-tailed deer . . . 85 30
2288 22c. Blue jays on Table Mountain pine 85 30
2289 22c. Pikas 85 30
2290 22c. Bison 85 30
2291 22c. Snowy egret 85 30
2292 22c. Grey wolf 85 30
2293 22c. Mountain goat 85 30
2294 22c. Deer mouse 85 30
2295 22c. Black-tailed prairie dog 85 30
2296 22c. Box turtle and Virginia creeper 85 30
2297 22c. Wolverine 85 30
2298 22c. American elk 85 30
2299 22c. California sea-lion . . . 85 30
2300 22c. Northern mockingbird on royal poinciana . . . 85 30
2301 22c. Racoon 85 30
2302 22c. Bobcat 85 30
2303 22c. Black-footed ferret . . 85 30
2304 22c. Canada goose 85 30
2305 22c. Red fox and red maple 85 30

1987. Bicentenary of Delaware Statehood.
2306 **1552** 22c. multicoloured . . . 60 10

1553 Arabesque from Door, Dar Batha Palace, Fez **1554** Faulkner (after M. L. Goldsborough)

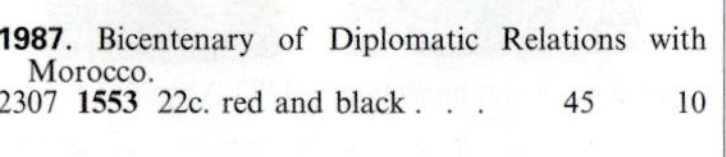

1987. Bicentenary of Diplomatic Relations with Morocco.
2307 **1553** 22c. red and black . . . 45 10

1987. Literary Arts. 25th Death Anniv of William Faulkner (novelist).
2308 **1554** 22c. green 40 10

1555 Squash Blossoms (Ruth Maxwell)

1556 Floral Design (Mary McPeek)

1557 Floral Design (Leslie Saari)

1558 Dogwood Blossoms (Trenna Ruffner)

1987. American Folk Art. Lacemaking.
2309 **1555** 22c. white, blue and ultramarine 65 15
2310 **1556** 22c. white, blue and ultramarine 65 15
2311 **1557** 22c. white, blue and ultramarine 65 15
2312 **1558** 22c. white, blue and ultramarine 65 15

1559 Independence Hall

1987. Bicentenary of Pennsylvania Statehood.
2313 **1559** 22c. multicoloured . . . 65 10

1560 "The Bicentennial ..."

1987. Bicentenary of United States Constitution (1st issue). Multicoloured.
2314 22c. Type **1560** 65 15
2315 22c. "We the people ..." . . 65 15
2316 22c. "Establish justice ..." 65 15
2317 22c. "And secure ..." . . . 65 15
2318 22c. "Do ordain ..." 65 15
See also No. 2320.

1565 Farmer with Basket of Produce **1566** First Page of Constitution and Hand holding Quill Pen

1987. Bicentenary of New Jersey Statehood.
2319 **1565** 22c. mullticoloured . . . 60 10

1987. Bicentenary of United States Constitution (2nd issue).
2320 **1566** 22c. multicoloured . . . 55 15

1567 Ledger Page and Pen Nib **1568** "Stourbridge Lion", 1829

1987. Centenary of American Institute of Certified Public Accountants.
2321 **1567** 22c. multicoloured . . . 2·40 25

1987. Steam Railway Locomotives. Multicoloured.
2322 22c. Type **1568** 70 20
2323 22c. "Best Friend of Charleston", 1830 . . . . 70 20
2324 22c. "John Bull", 1831 . . . 70 20
2325 22c. "Brother Jonathan", 1832 . . . . 70 20
2326 22c. "Gowan and Marx", 1839 . . . . 70 20

1573 "A Gentleman in Adoration before the Madonna" (detail, Giovanni Battista Moroni) **1575** Oak Tree

1987. Christmas. Multicoloured.
2327 22c. Type **1573** 45 10
2328 22c. Baubles on tree (horiz) 45 10

1988. Bicentenary of Georgia Statehood.
2329 **1575** 22c. multicoloured . . . 60 10

1576 "Charles W. Morgan" (whaling ship) and Mystic Town

1577 Slalom

1988. Bicentenary of Connecticut Statehood.
2330 **1576** 22c. multicoloured . . . 60 10

1988. Winter Olympic Games, Calgary.
2331 **1577** 22c. multicoloured . . . 45 10

1578 Koala and American Bald Eagle

1579 Johnson and Music Score

1988. Bicentenary of Australian Settlement.
2332 **1578** 22c. multicoloured . . . 45 10

1988. Black Heritage. James Weldon Johnson (writer, lyricist and diplomat).
2333 **1579** 22c. multicoloured . . . 45 10

1580 Siamese and Exotic Shorthair Cats

1584 "A Southwest View of the Statehouse, Boston" (S. Hill)

1988. Cats. Multicoloured.
2334 22c. Type **1580** 60 20
2335 22c. Abyssinian and Himalayan cats 60 20
2336 22c. Maine coon and Burmese cats 60 20
2337 22c. American shorthair and Persian cats 60 20

1988. Bicentenary of Massachusetts Statehood.
2338 **1584** 22c. blue, black and red 60 10

1585 St. Anne's Church, "Clarence Crockett" (yacht) and Statehouse, Annapolis

1586 Rockne

1988. Bicentenary of Maryland Statehood.
2339 **1585** 22c. multicoloured . . . 60 10

1988. American Sports Personalities. Birth Centenary of Knute Rockne (football player and coach).
2340 **1586** 22c. multicoloured . . . 50 10

1587 Earth

1588 Map, Settlers, Indians, "Calmare Nyckel" and "Fagel Grip"

1988. No value expressed.
2341 **1587** (25c.) multicoloured . . 55 10

1988. Air. 350th Anniv of Founding of New Sweden (settlement in America).
A2345 **1588** 44c. multicoloured . . 1·10 45

1589 Common Pheasant

1590 Flag and Clouds

1988.
2346 **1589** 25c. multicoloured . . . 65 10

1988.
2347 **1590** 25c. multicoloured . . . 50 10

1591 "Aerodrome No. 5" and Langley

1593 Flag over Half Dome, Yosemite National Park

1988. Air. Aviation Pioneers. Samuel Pierpont Langley.
A2348 **1591** 45c. multicoloured . . 95 20

1988.
2352 **1593** 25c. blue, red and green 55 10

1594 Palmetto Trees and Sea Grass

1595 Rose-breasted Grosbeak on Dogwood

1988. Bicentenary of South Carolina Statehood.
2353 **1594** 25c. multicoloured . . . 60 10

1988. Multicoloured.
2354 25c. Type **1595** 50 10
2355 25c. Saw-whet owl on Eastern hemlock 50 10

1597 Ouimet

1598 Old Man of the Mountain

1988. American Sports Personalities. 75th Anniv of Francis Ouimet's Open Golf Championship Victory.
2356 **1597** 25c. multicoloured . . . 75 10

1988. Bicentenary of New Hampshire Statehood.
2357 **1598** 25c. multicoloured . . . 35 10

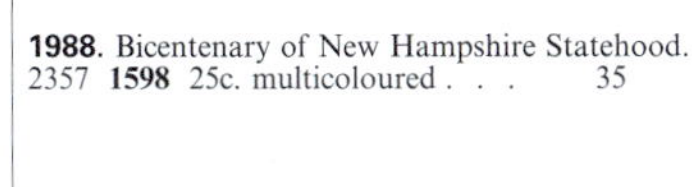

1599 Sikorsky and Vought Sikorsky VS-300 Helicopter Prototype

1600 Carriage and Capitol Building, Williamsburg

1988. Air. Aviation Pioneers. Igor Sikorsky.
A2358 **1599** 36c. multicoloured . . 70 25

1988. Bicentenary of Virginia Statehood.
2359 **1600** 25c. multicoloured . . . 60 10

1601 Rose

1602 Trinity Church, Wall Street and Federal Hall, New York City

1988. Greetings Stamp.
2360 **1601** 25c. multicoloured . . . 50 10

1988. Bicentenary of New York Statehood.
2361 **1602** 25c. multicoloured . . . 60 10

1603 Roses

1604 Gymnast

1988. Greetings Stamp.
2362 **1603** 45c. multicoloured . . . 85 20

1988. Olympic Games, Seoul.
2363 **1604** 25c. multicoloured . . . 50 10

1605 Locomobile, 1928

1610 Honey Bee on Clover

1988. Classic Cars. Multicoloured.
2364 25c. Type **1605** . . . . . . 1·10 35
2365 25c. Pierce-Arrow, 1929 . . 1·10 35
2366 25c. Cord, 1931 . . . . . . 1·10 35
2367 25c. Packard, 1932 . . . . 1·10 35
2368 25c. Duesenberg, 1935 . . . 1·10 35

1988.
2369 **1610** 25c. multicoloured . . . 55 10

1611 Nathaniel Palmer (after Samuel Waldo) and "Hero"

1615 Buck (Gustav Dentzel)

1988. Antarctic Explorers. Multicoloured.
2370 25c. Type **1611** 80 20
2371 25c. Charles Wilkes (after Samuel Bell Waugh) and "Polar Star" 80 20
2372 25c. Richard E. Byrd and Ford Trimotor "Floyd Bennett" 80 20
2373 25c. Lincoln Ellsworth and Northrop Gamma "Polar Star" 80 20

1988. American Folk Art. Carousel Animals. Mult.
2374 25c. Type **1615** 85 20
2375 25c. Armoured horse (Daniel C. Muller) . . . 85 20
2376 25c. Camel (Charles Looff) 85 20
2377 25c. Goat (Charles Looff) 85 20

1619 American Bald Eagle and Moon

1988.
2378 **1619** $8.75 multicoloured . . 16·00 7·50

1620 "Madonna and Child" (detail, Sandro Botticelli)

1622 "Happy Birthday"

1988. Christmas.
2379 25c. Type **1620** 50 10
2380 25c. "White Christmas" (horiz) 55 10

1988. Greetings Stamps. Multicoloured.
2381 25c. Type **1622** 85 25
2382 25c. "Thinking of you" . . 85 25
2383 25c. "Love you" 85 25
2384 25c. "Best Wishes" 85 25

1626 "C.M. Russell and Friends" (Charles M. Russell)

1627 A. Philip Randolph

1989. Centenary of Montana Statehood.
2385 **1626** 25c. multicoloured . . . 60 15

1989. Black Heritage. A. Philip Randolph (trade union activist).
2386 **1627** 25c. multicoloured . . . 50 10

1628 Grain Elevator and Buckboard

1629 Mt. Rainer and Canoe on Reflection Lake

1989. Centenary of North Dakota Statehood.
2387 **1628** 25c. multicoloured . . . 55 15

1989. Centenary of Washington Statehood.
2388 **1629** 25c. multicoloured . . . 55 10

1630 "Experiment", 1788–90

1989. Paddle-steamers. Multicoloured.
2389 25c. Type **1630** 70 15
2390 25c. "Phoenix", 1809 . . . 70 15
2391 25c. "New Orleans", 1812 70 15
2392 25c. "Washington", 1816 . . 70 15
2393 25c. "Walk in the Water", 1818 . . . . 70 15

1635 Cancelled 1869 90c. Lincoln Stamp

1636 Toscanini

1989. "World Stamp Expo'89" International Stamp Exhibition, Washington D.C.
2394 **1635** 25c. red, black & brown 50 10

1989. Performing Arts and Artists. Arturo Toscanini (conductor).
2395 **1636** 25c. multicoloured . . . 55 10

1637 "Car of History" Clock (Carlo Franzoni)

1638 Eagle and Shield over Vice-President's Chair

1989. Bicentenary of House of Representatives.
2396 **1637** 25c. multicoloured . . . 55 10

1989. Bicentenary of Senate.
2397 **1638** 25c. multicoloured . . . 55 10

1639 George Washington (statue, J. Q. A. Ward)

1640 Pasque Flowers, Pioneer Woman and House

1989. Bicentenary of Executive Branch.
2398 **1639** 25c. multicoloured . . . 60 15

1989. Centenary of South Dakota Statehood.
2399 **1640** 25c. multicoloured . . . 50 10

1641 Gehrig

1643 Hemingway

1642 Liberty, Equality and Fraternity

1989. American Sports Personalities. Lou Gehrig (baseball player).
2400 **1641** 25c. multicoloured . . . 85 10

1989. Air. Bicentenary of French Revolution.
A2401 **1642** 45c. multicoloured . . 90 25

1989. Literary Arts. Ernest Hemingway (novelist).
2402 **1643** 25c. multicoloured . . . 55 10

1644 Astronauts planting Flag on Moon

1645 Dogwood Blossoms

1989. 20th Anniv of First Manned Moon Landing
2403 **1644** $2.40 multicoloured . . 5·00 2·40

1989. Bicentenary of North Carolina Statehood.
2404 **1645** 25c. multicoloured . . . 60 10

1646 Letter Carriers

1647 Eagle and Flag as Shield

1989. Centenary of National Association of Letter Carriers.
2405 **1646** 25c. multicoloured . . . 50 10

1989. Bicentenary of Bill of Rights.
2406 **1647** 25c. black, red and blue 70 15

1648 Tyrannosaurus Rex

1652 Mimbres Ritual Figure

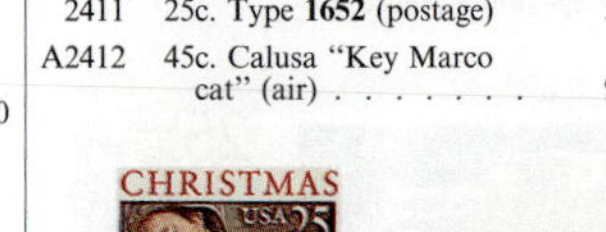

1989. Prehistoric Animals. Multicoloured.
2407 25c. Type **1648** 85 35
2408 25c. Pteranodon 85 35
2409 25c. Stegosaurus 85 35
2410 25c. Brontosaurus 85 35

1989. America. Pre-Columbian Carvings. Mult.
2411 25c. Type **1652** (postage) 50 15
A2412 45c. Calusa "Key Marco cat" (air) 90 25

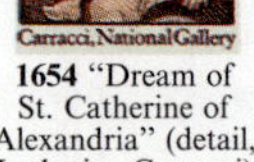

1654 "Dream of St. Catherine of Alexandria" (detail, Ludovico Carracci)

1656 Eagle and Shield

1989. Christmas. Multicoloured.
2413 25c. Type **1654** 50 10
2415 25c. Gifts on sleigh (horiz) 55 10

1989. Self-adhesive. Imperf.
2416 **1656** 25c. multicoloured . . . 60 15

1658 Western Stagecoach

1663 Hypersonic Airliner

1989. 20th U.P.U. Congress, Washington D.C. (1st issue). Classic Mail Transport. Multicoloured.
2418 25c. Type **1658** 75 25
2419 25c. "Chesapeake" (Mississippi river steamer) 75 25
2420 25c. Curtiss JN-4 "Jenny" biplane 75 25
2421 25c. Motor car 75 25
See also Nos. A2423/6.

1989. Air. 20th Universal Postal Union Congress, Washington D.C. (2nd issue). Mail Transport of the Future. Multicoloured.
A2423 45c. Type **1663** 95 35
A2424 45c. Hovercar 95 35
A2425 45c. Rover vehicle delivering mail to space colony 95 35
A2426 45c. Space shuttle delivering mail to space station 95 35

1668 Mountain Bluebird

1669 Lovebirds

1990. Centenary of Idaho Statehood.
2428 **1668** 25c. multicoloured . . . 45 10

1990. Greetings Stamp.
2429 **1669** 25c. multicoloured . . . 45 10

1670 Ida Wells

1671 John Marshall

1990. Black Heritage. Ida B. Wells (civil rights activist).
2431 **1670** 25c. multicoloured . . . 65 15

1990. Bicentenary of Supreme Court.
2432 **1671** 25c. multicoloured . . . 60 10

1672 Beach Umbrella

1674 Luis Munoz Marin

1990.
2433 **1672** 15c. multicoloured . . . 35 20

1990. Great Americans. (a) Ordinary Gum.
2435 **1674** 5c. red 25 15
2437 – 20c. red 30 15
2439 – 29c. blue 50 20
2440 – 29c. black 50 15
2442 – 32c. brown 60 25
2443 – 32c. green 60 50
2444 – 32c. red 60 50
2445 – 32c. blue 60 50
2448 – 35c. black 55 20
2450 – 40c. blue 65 25
2452 – 46c. red 80 60
2454 – 52c. lilac . . . . . . 1·00 20
2456 – 55c. green 85 45
2458 – 75c. red . . . . 1·10 30
2460a – 78c. violet . . . . . 1·20 80

(b) Self-adhesive Gum.
2464 – 55c. black . . . . 00 1·00
2466 – 77c. blue . . . . 1·30 90

DESIGNS: 20c. Virginia Agpar; 29c. (No. 2439) Earl Warren; 29c. (No. 2440) Thomas Jefferson (President, 1801–09); 32c. (No. 2442) Milton S. Hershey; 32c. (No. 2443) Cal Farley; 32c. (No. 2444) Henry Luce; 32c. (No. 2445) Lila and DeWitt Wallace (after Paul Calle); 35c. Dennis Chavez; 40c. Lt-Gen. Claire Chennault; 46c. Ruth Benedict; 52c. Hubert Humphrey (Vice-president, 1965–69); 55c. (No. 2456) Dr. Alice Hamilton; 55c. (No. 2464) Justin Morrill; 75c. Wendell Wilkie; 77c. Mary Breckinridge; 78c. Alice Paul.

1710 "High Mountain Meadows" (Conrad Schwiering)

1990. Centenary of Wyoming Statehood.
2471 **1710** 25c. multicoloured . . . 55 10

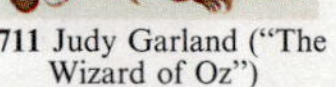

1711 Judy Garland ("The Wizard of Oz")

1715 Marianne Moore

1990. Classic Films. Multicoloured.
2472 25c. Type **1711** . . . . . 1·20 35
2473 25c. Clark Gable and Vivien Leigh ("Gone with the Wind") . . . . 1·20 35
2474 25c. Gary Cooper ("Beau Geste") . . . . 1·20 35
2475 25c. John Wayne ("Stagecoach") . . . . . 1·20 35

1990. Literary Arts. Marianne Moore (poet).
2476 **1715** 25c. multicoloured . . . 45 10

1717 Circus Wagon, 1900s ("05")

1755 Admiralty Head, Nugent Sound

1990. Transport.
2477 – 4c. purple 15 15
2478 **1717** 5c. red 15 15
2484 – 5c. red 15 15
2485 – 5c. brown 15 15
2487 – 5c. red 15 15
2486 – 10c. green 20 20
2479 – 20c. green 30 20
2480 – 23c. blue 35 20
2481 – 32c. blue 50 20
2482 – $1 blue and red . . . . 1·40 35

DESIGNS: 4c. Richard Dudgeon steam carriage, 1866; 5c. (Nos. 2485, 2487) Birch bark canoe, 1800s; 5c. (No. 2484) Circus wagon 1900s ("5c."); 10c. Tractor trailer, 1930s; 20c. Mt. Washington Cog Railway, 1870s; 23c. Lunch wagon, 1890s; 32c. Ferryboat, 1900s; $1 Benoist Type XIV flying boat.

1990. Lighthouses. Multicoloured.
2516 25c. Type **1755** 80 20
2517 25c. Cape Hatteras 80 20
2518 25c. West Quoddy Head . . 65 20
2519 25c. American Shoals . . . 80 20
2520 25c. Sandy Hook, New York Harbour 80 20

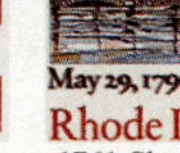

1760 Stars and Stripes

1761 Slater Mill

1990. Self-adhesive. Imperf.
2521 **1760** 25c. red and blue . . . 60 55

1990. Bicentenary of Rhode Island Statehood.
2522 **1761** 25c. multicoloured . . . 60 10

1763 Bobcat

1990. Wildlife.
2523 **1763** $2 multicoloured . . . 2·50 50

1769 Jesse Owens

1990. American Olympic Medal Winners. Mult.
2530 25c. Type **1769** 70 20
2531 25c. Ray Ewry 70 20
2532 25c. Hazel Wightman . . . 70 20
2533 25c. Eddie Eagan 70 20
2534 25c. Helene Madison . . . 70 20

1774 Assiniboine

1990. American Folk Art. Indian Headdresses. Multicoloured.
2535 25c. Type **1774** 60 30
2536 25c. Cheyenne 60 30
2537 25c. Comanche 60 30
2538 25c. Flathead 60 30
2539 25c. Shoshone 60 30

1779 Micronesian Outrigger Canoe and Flag

1990. 4th Anniv of Ratification of Marshall Islands and Micronesia Compacts of Free Association. Multicoloured.

2540	25c. Type **1779**	55	20
2541	25c. Marshallese stick chart, outrigger canoe and flag	55	20

1781 Killer Whales

1990. Marine Mammals. Multicoloured.

2542	25c. Type **1781**	70	20
2543	25c. Northern sea lions	70	20
2544	25c. Sea otter	70	20
2545	25c. Common dolphin	70	20

1785 Grand Canyon

1990. America. Natural World. Multicoloured.

2546	25c. Type **1785** (postage)	55	15
A2547	45c. Tropical island coastline (air)	1·00	20

1787 Eisenhower and Soldiers

1788 "Madonna and Child" (Antonello da Messina)

1990. Birth Cent of Dwight David Eisenhower (President, 1953–61).

2548	**1787** 25c. multicoloured	60	15

1990. Christmas. Multicoloured.

2549	25c. Type **1788**	50	15
2551	25c. Christmas tree	50	15

1790 Tulip

1791

This U.S. stamp, along with 25¢ of additional U.S. postage, is equivalent to the 'F' stamp rate

1991. No value expressed.

2552	**1790** (29c.) multicoloured	65	15

1991. No value expressed. Make-up rate stamp.

2556	**1791** (4c.) red and brown	15	10

1792 Stars and Stripes

1991. No value expressed. Self-adhesive. Imperf.

2557	**1792** (29c.) red, blue and black	70	35

1794 Federal Palace, Berne, and Capitol, Washington

1795 Farm

1991. 700th Anniv of Swiss Confederation.

2559	**1794** 50c. multicoloured	1·10	30

1991. Bicentenary of Vermont Statehood.

2560	**1795** 29c. multicoloured	65	15

1796 Fawn

1797 Flag over Mt. Rushmore

1991.

2561	**1796** 19c. multicoloured	40	10

1991.

2562	**1797** 29c. red, brown & black	55	15

1798 Tulip

1799 Wood Duck

1991.

2564	**1798** 29c. multicoloured	55	20

1991. (a) Inscriptions in black.

2565	**1799** 29c. multicoloured	60	15

(b) Inscriptions in red.

2567	**1799** 29c. multicoloured	65	15

1800 Flag and Olympic Rings

1801 Quimby and Bleriot XI Airplane

1991.

2569	**1800** 29c. multicoloured	55	15

1991. Air. Aviation Pioneers. Harriet Quimby (first American woman pilot).

A2570	**1801** 50c. multicoloured	95	30

1802 American Bald Eagle

1803 Heart-shaped Globe

1991. 50th Anniv of "E Series" Defence Bonds.

2571	**1802** 29c. multicoloured	55	15

1991. Greetings Stamps. Multicoloured.

2572	29c. Type **1803**	55	15
2574	52c. Fischer's lovebirds (21 × 35 mm)	1·10	15

1805 Hot-air Balloon

1806 Piper and Piper J-3 Cub

1991.

2575	**1805** 19c. multicoloured	40	20

1991. Air. Aviation Pioneers. William Piper.

A2576	**1806** 40c. multicoloured	85	25

1807 Saroyan

1808 Flags on Parade

1991. Literary Arts. 10th Death Anniv of William Saroyan (dramatist and novelist).

2578	**1807** 29c. multicoloured	55	15

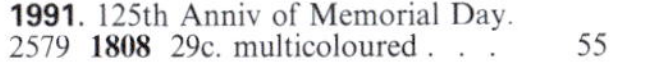

1991. 125th Anniv of Memorial Day.

2579	**1808** 29c. multicoloured	55	15

1809 Royal Wulff

1814 Porter and Score

1991. Fishing Flies. Multicoloured.

2580	29c. Type **1809**	1·10	20
2581	29c. Jock Scott	1·10	20
2582	29c. Apte tarpon fly	1·10	20
2583	29c. Lefty's deceiver	1·10	20
2584	29c. Muddler minnow	1·10	20

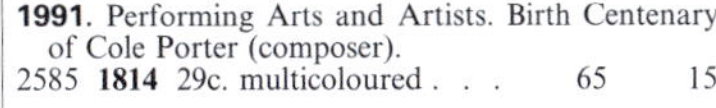

1991. Performing Arts and Artists. Birth Centenary of Cole Porter (composer).

2585	**1814** 29c. multicoloured	65	15

1815 American Bald Eagle

1991. U.S. Olympic Festival.

2586	**1815** $9.95 multicoloured	17·00	7·25

1816 U.S.S. "Glacier" (ice-breaker) near Palmer Station

1817 American Kestrel

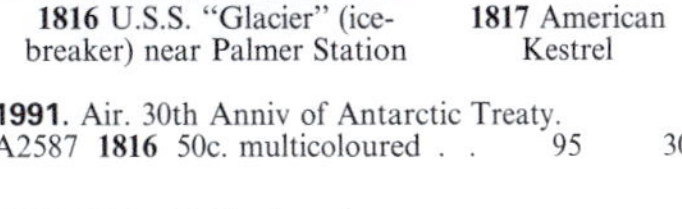

1991. Air. 30th Anniv of Antarctic Treaty.

A2587	**1816** 50c. multicoloured	95	30

1991. Birds. Multicoloured.

2588	1c. Type **1817**	15	10
2589	3c. Eastern bluebird	15	15
2590	30c. Common cardinal ("Cardinal")	50	20

For Nos. 2588/9 and 2c. but with face value expressed as "1c" etc see No. 3023 etc.

1823 Liberty Torch

1824 South-West Asia Service Medal

1991. Self-adhesive. Imperf.

2591	**1823** 29c. green, gold & black	65	30

1991. Operations Desert Shield and Desert Storm (liberation of Kuwait).

2592	**1824** 29c. multicoloured	55	15

1825 American Bald Eagle

1991.

2594	**1825** $2.90 multicoloured	5·50	2·50

1826 Pole Vaulting

1831 Rowing Boat

1991. Olympic Games, Barcelona (1992). Mult.

2595	29c. Type **1826**	60	20
2596	29c. Throwing the discus	60	20
2597	29c. Running	60	20
2598	29c. Throwing the javelin	60	20
2599	29c. Hurdling	35	15

1991.

2600	**1831** 19c. multicoloured	25	10

1832 Coins and Banknotes

1833 Shot at Goal

1991. Cent Convention of American Numismatic Association.

2603	**1832** 29c. multicoloured	65	15

1991. Centenary of Basketball.

2604	**1833** 29c. multicoloured	65	15

1834 Stan Laurel and Oliver Hardy

1991.

2605	**1834** 29c. black, violet and red	1·00	20
2606	– 29c. black, red and violet	50	20
2607	– 29c. black, violet and red	50	20
2608	– 29c. black, violet and red	50	20
2609	– 29c. black, red and violet	70	20

DESIGNS: No. 2606, Edgar Bergen and Charlie McCarthy; 2607, Jack Benny; 2608, Fanny Brice; 2609, Bud Abbott and Lou Costello.

1839 American Bald Eagle

1991.

2610	**1839** $14 multicoloured	23·00	13·00

1840 Burma Road Convoy

1991. 50th Anniv of America's Entry into Second World War. Multicoloured.

2611	29c. Type **1840**	65	60
2612	29c. America's first peacetime draft	65	60
2613	29c. Lend-Lease Act	65	60
2614	29c. Roosevelt and Churchill (Atlantic Charter)	65	60
2615	29c. Munitions factory	65	60
2616	29c. Sinking of "Reuben James" (destroyer)	65	60
2617	29c. Gas mask (Civil Defence)	65	60
2618	29c. Delivery of "Patrick Henry" (first "Liberty" freighter)	65	60
2619	29c. U.S.S. "West Virginia" and U.S.S. "Tennessee" ablaze, Pearl Harbor	65	60
2620	29c. US Declaration of War on Japan	65	60

1850 Pennsylvania Avenue, 1903

1851 Matzeliger

1991. Bicentenary of District of Columbia.
2621 **1850** 29c. multicoloured . . . 55 15

1991. Black Heritage. Jan Ernst Matzeliger (inventor of shoe lasting machine).
2622 **1851** 29c. multicoloured . . . 55 15

1852 Flag

1853 Postal Service Emblem and Olympic Rings

1991.
2623 **1852** 23c. blue, red and black 30 15

1991.
2624 **1853** $1 multicoloured . . . 1·60 60

1854 "Mariner 10" and Mercury

1991. Space Exploration. Multicoloured.
2625 29c. Type **1854** 60 25
2626 29c. Venus and "Mariner 2" 60 25
2627 29c. Earth and "Landsat" 60 25
2628 29c. Moon and Lunar Orbiter 60 25
2629 29c. "Viking" Orbiter and Mars 60 25
2630 29c. Jupiter and "Pioneer 11" 60 25
2631 29c. "Voyager 2" and Saturn 60 25
2632 29c. Uranus and "Voyager 2" 60 25
2633 29c. Neptune and "Voyager 2" 60 25
2634 29c. Pluto 60 25

1864 Early Explorers from Asia

1865 "Madonna and Child with Donor" (detail, Antoniazzo Romano)

1991. Air. America. Voyages of Discovery.
A2635 **1864** 50c. multicoloured . . 95 35

1991. Christmas. No value expressed. Mult.
2636 (29c.) Type **1865** 55 15
2637 (29c.) Santa Claus in chimney (horiz) 65 15
2639 (29c.) Santa Claus checking list (horiz) 60 20
2640 (29c.) Santa Clause leaving by chimney (horiz) . . . 60 20
2642 (29c.) Santa Claus on sleigh (horiz) 60 20

1871 Eagle and Shield

1872 Ice Hockey

1991. Inscr "Bulk Rate USA".
2644 **1871** (10c.) multicoloured . . 20 15
For design T **1871** but inscribed "USA Bulk Rate" see Nos. 2800/1.

1992. Winter Olympic Games, Albertville. Mult.
2645 29c. Type **1872** 50 20
2646 29c. Figure skating 50 20
2647 29c. Speed skating 50 20
2648 29c. Skiing 50 20
2649 29c. Two-man bobsleigh . . 50 20

1877 1869 15c. Columbus Stamp

1878 Du Bois

1992. "World Columbian Stamp Expo'92", Chicago.
2650 **1877** 29c. multicoloured . . . 55 15

1992. Black Heritage. William Edward Burghardt Du Bois (founder of Niagara Movement (precursor of National Association for Advancement of Colored People)).
2651 **1878** 29c. multicoloured . . . 65 15

1879 Heart in Envelope

1880 Catcher and Baserunner

1992. Greetings Stamp.
2652 **1879** 29c. multicoloured . . . 55 15

1992. Addition of Baseball to Olympic Games.
2653 **1880** 29c. multicoloured . . . 85 15

1881 Flag over White House

1882 Seeking Queen Isabella's Support

1992. Bicentenary of White House.
2654 **1881** 29c. red and blue . . . 50 15

1992. 500th Anniv of Discovery of America by Columbus. Multicoloured.
2655 29c. Type **1882** 60 20
2656 29c. Crossing the Atlantic 60 20
2657 29c. Approaching land . . . 60 20
2658 29c. Coming ashore 60 20

1886 Exchange Facade and Trading Floor

1893 Russian Cosmonaut and Space Shuttle

1992. Bicentenary of New York Stock Exchange.
2659 **1886** 29c. green, black and red 55 15

1992. International Space Year. Multicoloured.
2661 29c. Type **1893** 65 20
2662 29c. American astronaut and "Mir" space station . . . 65 20
2663 29c. "Apollo" and "Vostok" spacecraft and Sputnik . . 65 20
2664 29c. "Soyuz", "Mercury" and "Gemini" spacecraft 65 20

1897 Army Lorry using New Highway

1898 My Old Kentucky Home State Park, Bardstown

1992. 50th Anniv of Alaska Highway.
2665 **1897** 29c. multicoloured . . . 55 15

1992. Bicentenary of Kentucky Statehood.
2666 **1898** 29c. multicoloured . . . 55 15

1899 Football

1904 Ruby-throated Hummingbird

1992. Olympic Games, Barcelona. Multicoloured.
2667 29c. Type **1899** 60 30
2668 29c. Gymnastics 60 30
2669 29c. Volleyball 60 30
2670 29c. Boxing 60 30
2671 29c. Swimming 60 30

1992. Hummingbirds. Multicoloured.
2672 29c. Type **1904** 65 20
2673 29c. Broad-billed hummingbird 65 20
2674 29c. Costa's hummingbird 65 20
2675 29c. Rufous hummingbird 65 20
2676 29c. Calliope hummingbird 65 20

1909 Flag in "USA"

1910 Indian Paintbrush

1992. Presorted First Class stamp.
2678 **1909** 23c. multicoloured . . . 45 20

1992. Wild Flowers. Multicoloured.
2680 29c. Type **1910** 55 30
2681 29c. Fragrant water lily . . 55 30
2682 29c. Meadow beauty 55 30
2683 29c. Jack-in-the-pulpit . . . 55 30
2684 29c. California poppy . . . 55 30
2685 29c. Large-flowered trillium 55 30
2686 29c. Tickseed 55 30
2687 29c. Shooting star 55 30
2688 29c. Stream violet 55 30
2689 29c. Bluets 55 30
2690 29c. Herb Robert 55 30
2691 29c. Marsh marigold . . . 55 30
2692 29c. Sweet white violet . . . 55 30
2693 29c. Claret cup cactus . . . 55 30
2694 29c. White mountain avens 55 30
2695 29c. Sessile bellwort 55 30
2696 29c. Blue flag 55 30
2697 29c. Harlequin lupine . . . 55 30
2698 29c. Twinflower 55 30
2699 29c. Common sunflower . . 55 30
2700 29c. Sego lily 55 30
2701 29c. Virginia bluebells . . . 55 30
2702 29c. Ohi'a lehua 55 30
2703 29c. Rosebud orchid 55 30
2704 29c. Showy evening primrose 55 30
2705 29c. Fringed gentian 55 30
2706 29c. Yellow lady's slipper . . 55 30
2707 29c. Passionflower 55 30
2708 29c. Bunchberry 55 30
2709 29c. Pasqueflower 55 30
2710 29c. Round-lobed hepatica 55 30
2711 29c. Wild columbine 55 30
2712 29c. Fireweed 55 30
2713 29c. Indian pond lily . . . 55 30
2714 29c. Turk's cap lily 55 30
2715 29c. Dutchman's breeches 55 30
2716 29c. Trumpet honeysuckle 55 30
2717 29c. Jacob's ladder 55 30
2718 29c. Plains prickly pear . . 55 30
2719 29c. Moss campion 55 30
2720 29c. Bearberry 55 30
2721 29c. Mexican hat 55 30
2722 29c. Harebell 55 30
2723 29c. Desert five spot 55 30
2724 29c. Smooth Solomon's seal 55 30
2725 29c. Red maids 55 30
2726 29c. Yellow skunk cabbage 55 30
2727 29c. Rue anemone 55 30
2728 29c. Standing cypress . . . 55 30
2729 29c. Wild flax 55 30

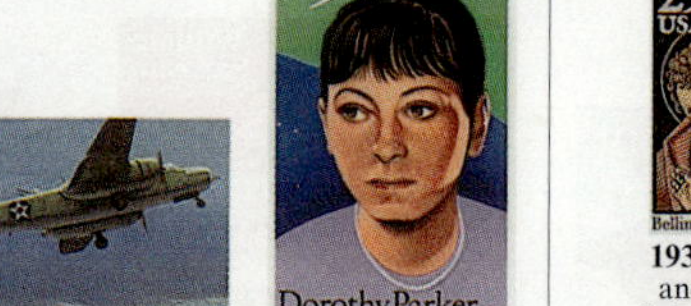

1911 Doolittle Raid on Tokyo

1921 Dorothy Parker

1992. United States Participation in Second World War. Multicoloured.
2730 29c. Type **1911** 65 50
2731 29c. Ration stamps 65 50
2732 29c. Douglas SBD-3 Dauntless on aircraft carrier (Battle of Coral Sea) 65 50
2733 29c. Japanese occupation of Corregidor 65 50
2734 29c. Japanese invasion of Aleutian Islands 65 50
2735 29c. Allies decipher enemy codes 65 50
2736 29c. U.S.S. "Yorktown" ablaze (Battle of Midway) 65 50
2737 29c. Woman engaged in war effort 65 50
2738 29c. Marines landing at Guadalcanal 65 50
2739 29c. Allied tanks in North Africa 65 50

1992. Literary Arts. Dorothy Parker (short story writer, poet and critic).
2740 **1921** 29c. multicoloured . . . 55 15

1922 Von Karman and Rocket

1923 Flag and "I pledge allegiance ..."

1992. Theodore von Karman (space pioneer).
2741 **1922** 29c. multicoloured . . . 55 15

1992. Centenary of Pledge of Allegiance.
2742 **1923** 29c. mult (value in blk) 55 15
2743 29c. mult (value in red) 65 25

1924 Azurite

1928 Eagle and Shield

1992. Minerals. Multicoloured.
2744 29c. Type **1924** 65 15
2745 29c. Copper 65 20
2746 29c. Variscite 65 20
2747 29c. Wulfenite 65 20

1992. Self-adhesive. Imperf.
2748 **1928** 29c. mult (inscr in red) 65 20
2749 29c. mult (inscr in grn) 65 20
2750 29c. mult (inscr in brn) 65 20

1929 Spanish Galleon, Map and Cabrillo

1930 Giraffe

1992. 450th Anniv of Discovery of California by Juan Rodriguez Cabrillo.
2751 **1929** 29c. multicoloured . . . 55 15

1992. Wild Animals. Multicoloured.
2752 29c. Type **1930** 50 20
2753 29c. Giant panda 50 20
2754 29c. Greater flamingo ("Flamingo") 50 20
2755 29c. King penguins 50 20
2756 29c. White Bengal tiger . . 50 20

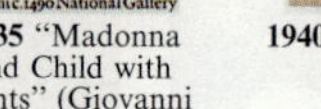

1935 "Madonna and Child with Saints" (Giovanni Bellini)

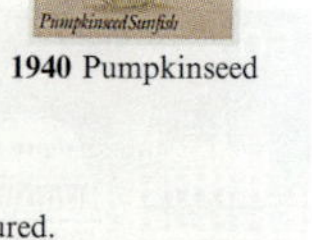

1940 Pumpkinseed

1992. Christmas. Multicoloured.
2757 29c. Type **1935** 55 15
2758 29c. Wheeled racing horse (horiz) 65 15
2759 29c. Toy steam locomotive (horiz) 65 20

2760 29c. Toy steam engine (horiz) 65 20
2761 29c. Toy steamer (horiz) . . 65 20
No. 2759 also comes imperf and self-adhesive.

1992.
2767 **1940** 45c. multicoloured . . . 70 20

1941 Rooster

1992. New Year.
2768 **1941** 29c. multicoloured . . . 65 15

1942 Elvis Presley

1943 Spacecraft and Ringed-planet

1993. Elvis Presley (rock singer and actor).
2769 **1942** 29c. multicoloured . . . 70 20
For similar design but inscr "ELVIS PRESLEY" see Type **1987**.

1993. Space Fantasy. Multicoloured.
2770 29c. Type **1943** 55 20
2771 29c. Space capsules 55 20
2772 29c. Astronauts 55 20
2773 29c. Spaceship 55 20
2774 29c. Spacecraft and planet 55 20

1948 Julian

1949 Route Map

1993. Black Heritage. Percy Lavon Julian (research chemist).
2775 **1948** 29c. multicoloured . . . 55 15

1993. 150th Anniv of Oregon Trail.
2776 **1949** 29c. multicoloured . . . 55 15

1950 Athletes

1951 Princess Grace

1993. World University Games, Buffalo.
2777 **1950** 29c. multicoloured . . . 55 15

1993. 10th Death Anniv of Princess Grace of Monaco (former Grace Kelly).
2778 **1951** 29c. blue 75 15

1952 "Oklahoma"

1993. Broadway Musicals. Multicoloured. (a) No frame. Size 36 × 28 mm.
2779 29c. Type **1952** 55 15

(b) With frame. Size 35 × 27 mm.
2780 29c. "Show Boat" 65 20
2781 29c. "Porgy and Bess" . . . 65 20
2782 29c. Type **1952** 65 20
2783 29c. "My Fair Lady" . . . 65 20

1956 Clown

1993. Bicentenary of First Circus Performance in America. Multicoloured.
2784 29c. Type **1956** 65 20
2785 29c. Ringmaster 65 20
2786 29c. Trapeze artiste 65 20
2787 29c. Elephant 65 20

1960 Pioneers racing to Cherokee Strip

1961 Acheson

1993. Centenary of Cherokee Strip Land Run.
2789 **1960** 29c. multicoloured . . . 55 15

1993. Birth Centenary of Dean Acheson (Secretary of State, 1949–53).
2790 **1961** 29c. green 55 15

1962 Steeplechase

1966 Hyacinths

1993. Equestrian Sports. Multicoloured.
2791 29c. Type **1962** 65 20
2792 29c. Thoroughbred racing 65 20
2793 29c. Harness racing 65 20
2794 29c. Polo 65 20

1993. Garden Flowers. Multicoloured.
2795 29c. Type **1966** 55 20
2796 29c. Daffodils 55 20
2797 29c. Tulips 55 20
2798 29c. Irises 55 20
2799 29c. Lilac 55 20

1971 Eagle and Shield

1972 Atlantic Convoy

1993. Coil stamps. Inscr "USA Bulk Rate". Multicoloured, colours of eagle given.
2800 **1971** (10c.) yellow and brown 20 15
2801 (10c.) gold and brown 20 15
No. 2802 exists with both ordinary gum and self-adhesive gum.
For design as Type **1971** but inscr "Bulk Rate USA" see No. 2644.

1993. United States Participation in Second World War. Multicoloured.
2803 29c. Type **1972** 65 50
2804 29c. Treating the wounded 65 50
2805 29c. Allied attack on Sicily 65 50
2806 29c. Consolidated B-24 Liberators bombing Ploesti refineries 65 50
2807 29c. G.I.s with mail from home 65 50
2808 29c. Allied invasion of Italy 65 50
2809 29c. War Savings stamps and bonds 65 50
2810 29c. Willie and Joe (cartoon characters) 65 50
2811 29c. Gold Star emblem . . . 65 50
2812 29c. Marine assault on Tarawa, Gilbert Islands 65 50

1982 Futuristic Space Shuttle

1993.
2813 **1982** $2.90 multicoloured . . 5·00 2·10

1983 Hank Williams

1993. Country Music. Multicoloured. (a) No frame.
2815 29c. Type **1983** 70 35
2816 29c. Patsy Cline 70 45
2817 29c. Carter Family 70 45
2818 29c. Bob Wills 70 45

(b) With frame.
2819 29c. Type **1983** 70 20
2820 29c. Carter Family 70 20
2821 29c. Patsy Cline 70 20
2822 29c. Bob Wills 70 20

1987 Elvis Presley

1994 Louis

1993. Rock and Rhythm and Blues Music. Mult. (a) No frame.
2823 29c. Type **1987** 70 30
2824 29c. Buddy Holly 70 30
2825 29c. Ritchie Valens 70 30
2826 29c. Bill Haley 70 30
2827 29c. Dinah Washington . . 70 30
2828 29c. Otis Redding 70 30
2829 29c. Clyde McPhatter . . . 70 30

(b) With frame.
2830 29c. Type **1987** 70 20
2831 29c. Bill Haley 70 20
2832 29c. Clyde McPhatter . . . 70 20
2833 29c. Ritchie Valens 70 20
2834 29c. Otis Redding 70 20
2835 29c. Buddy Holly 70 20
2836 29c. Dinah Washington . . 70 20

1993. Joe Louis (boxer).
2837 **1994** 29c. multicoloured . . . 1·75 15

1995 Red Squirrel

1996 Benjamin Franklin, Liberty Hall, Philadelphia, Post Rider and Printing Press

1993. Self-adhesive. Imperf.
2838 **1995** 29c. multicoloured . . . 65 20

1993. Inauguration of National Postal Museum, Washington. Multicoloured.
2839 29c. Type **1996** 65 20
2840 29c. Pony Express rider, Civil War soldier and stagecoach 65 20
2841 29c. Curtiss JN-4 "Jenny" biplane, pilot, railway mail/baggage car and mail truck 65 20
2842 29c. Gold rush miner's letter and stamps 65 20

2000 Red Rose

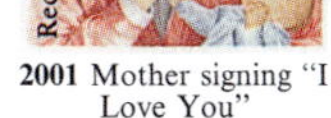

2001 Mother signing "I Love You"

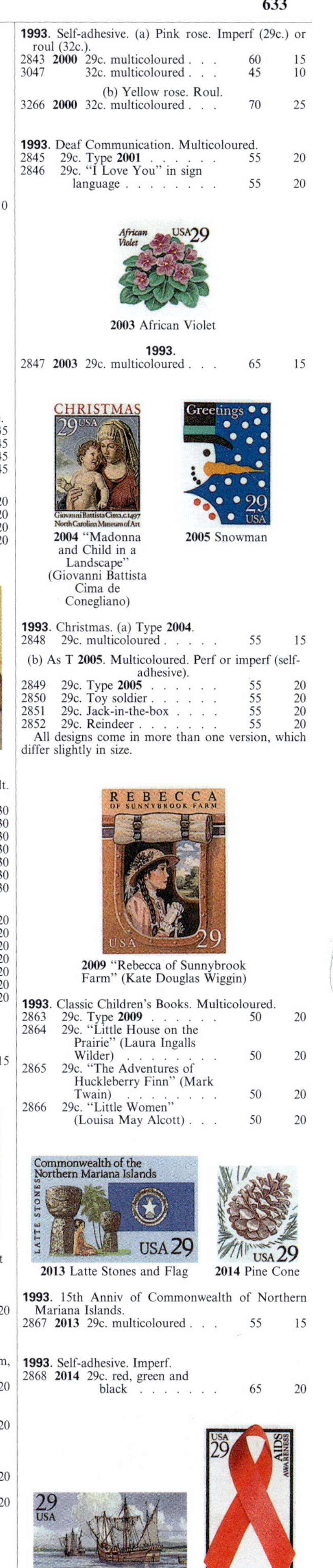

1993. Self-adhesive. (a) Pink rose. Imperf (29c.) or roul (32c.).
2843 **2000** 29c. multicoloured . . . 60 15
3047 32c. multicoloured . . . 45 10

(b) Yellow rose. Roul.
3266 **2000** 32c. multicoloured . . . 70 25

1993. Deaf Communication. Multicoloured.
2845 29c. Type **2001** 55 20
2846 29c. "I Love You" in sign language 55 20

2003 African Violet

1993.
2847 **2003** 29c. multicoloured . . . 65 15

2004 "Madonna and Child in a Landscape" (Giovanni Battista Cima de Conegliano)

2005 Snowman

1993. Christmas. (a) Type **2004**.
2848 29c. multicoloured 55 15

(b) As T **2005**. Multicoloured. Perf or imperf (self-adhesive).
2849 29c. Type **2005** 55 20
2850 29c. Toy soldier 55 20
2851 29c. Jack-in-the-box 55 20
2852 29c. Reindeer 55 20
All designs come in more than one version, which differ slightly in size.

2009 "Rebecca of Sunnybrook Farm" (Kate Douglas Wiggin)

1993. Classic Children's Books. Multicoloured.
2863 29c. Type **2009** 50 20
2864 29c. "Little House on the Prairie" (Laura Ingalls Wilder) 50 20
2865 29c. "The Adventures of Huckleberry Finn" (Mark Twain) 50 20
2866 29c. "Little Women" (Louisa May Alcott) . . . 50 20

2013 Latte Stones and Flag

2014 Pine Cone

1993. 15th Anniv of Commonwealth of Northern Mariana Islands.
2867 **2013** 29c. multicoloured . . . 55 15

1993. Self-adhesive. Imperf.
2868 **2014** 29c. red, green and black 65 20

2015 Caravels off Puerto Rico

2016 Red Ribbon

1993. 500th Anniv of Columbus's Landing at Puerto Rico.
2869 **2015** 29c. multicoloured . . . 55 15

1993. World AIDS Day.
2870 **2016** 29c. red and black . . . 55 15

2017 Skiing **2022** Murrow

1994. Winter Olympic Games. Lillehammer. Mult.
2872 29c. Type **2017** 55 40
2873 29c. Luge 55 40
2874 29c. Ice dancing 55 40
2875 29c. Cross-country skiing . . 55 40
2876 29c. Ice hockey 55 40

1994. 29th Death Anniv of Edward Murrow (radio and television journalist).
2877 **2022** 29c. brown 55 15

2023 Heart-shaped Sun **2024** Davis

1994. Greetings Stamp. Self-adhesive. Imperf.
2878 **2023** 29c. multicoloured . . . 65 25

1994. Black Heritage. Dr. Allison Davis (educationist).
2879 **2024** 29c. sepia and brown 55 25

2025 American Bald Eagle **2026** Pekingese

1994. Self-adhesive. Imperf.
2880 **2025** 29c. multicoloured . . . 65 25

1994. New Year.
2881 **2026** 29c. multicoloured . . . 95 25

2027 Dove on Heart-shaped Bouquet of Roses **2029** Troopers on Western Frontier

1994. Greetings Stamps. Multicoloured.
2882 29c. Type **2027** (16 × 24½ mm) . . . 35 15
2883 29c. Type **2027** (18 × 27 mm) 60 15
2884 52c. Doves on flower arrangement . . . . . . 1·00 50

1994. "Buffalo Soldiers" (U.S. Army black regiments).
2885 **2029** 29c. multicoloured . . . 55 15

2030 Rudolph Valentino **2040** Lilies

1994. Silent Screen Stars.
2886 **2030** 29c. black, violet and red 50 00
2887 – 29c. black, violet and red 50 40
2888 – 29c. black, red and violet . . . . 1·10 40
2889 – 29c. black, red and violet 50 40
2890 – 29c. black, violet and red 50 40
2891 – 29c. black, red and violet 50 40
2892 – 29c. black, violet and red 50 40
2893 – 29c. black, violet and red 50 40
2894 – 29c. black, red and violet 50 40
2895 – 29c. black, red and violet 50 40

DESIGNS: No. 2887, Clara Bow; 2888, Charlie Chaplin; 2889, Lon Chaney; 2890, John Gilbert; 2891, Zasu Pitts; 2892, Harold Lloyd; 2893, Keystone Cops; 2894, Theda Bara; 2895, Buster Keaton.

1994. Garden Flowers. Multicoloured.
2896 29c. Type **2040** 50 25
2897 29c. Zinnias 50 25
2898 29c. Gladioli 50 25
2899 29c. Marigolds 50 25
2900 29c. Roses . . . . 1·20 40

2045 Surrender at Saratoga (after John Trumbull) **2046** U.S.A. Player kicking Ball

1994.
2901 **2045** $1 blue . . . . 2·25 1·25

1994. World Cup Football Championship, U.S.A. Multicoloured.
2902 29c. Type **2046** 65 25
2903 40c. Controlling the ball . . 75 40
2904 50c. Heading the ball . . . 95 55

2050 Liberating New Guinea **2060** Statue of Liberty

1994. United States Participation in Second World War. Multicoloured.
2906 29c. Type **2050** 65 85
2907 29c. P-51 escorting B-17 bombers 65 85
2908 29c. Normandy Landings 65 85
2909 29c. Glider and paratroops 65 85
2910 29c. Submarine crew 65 85
2911 29c. Liberating Rome . . . 65 85
2912 29c. Troops clearing Saipan bunkers 65 85
2913 29c. Red Ball Express truck 65 85
2914 29c. U.S.S. "Pennsylvania" (battleship) (Battle of Leyte Gulf) 65 85
2915 29c. Battle of the Bulge . . 65 85

1994. Self-adhesive. Imperf.
2918 **2060** 29c. multicoloured . . . 65 20
3273 32c. multicoloured . . . 75 30

2061 "Triple Self-portrait"

1994. Birth Centenary of Norman Rockwell (illustrator).
2919 **2061** 29c. multicoloured . . . 60 15

2063 Astronauts planting Flag on Moon

1994. 25th Anniv of First Manned Moon Landing.
2921 **2063** $9.95 multicoloured . . 17·00 18·00

2065 William Hudson's "General", 1855

1994. Locomotives. Multicoloured.
2923 29c. Type **2065** 60 25
2924 29c. Walter McQueen's "Jupiter", 1868 . . . . . 60 25
2925 29c. Wilson Eddy's No. 242, 1874 . . . . 60 25
2926 29c. Theodore Ely's No. 10, 1881 . . . . 60 25
2927 29c. William Buchanan's No. 999, 1893 . . . . . 60 25

2070 Meany **2072** Al Jolson

2071 Presidents Washington and Jackson

1994. Birth Centenary of George Meany (trades unionist).
2928 **2070** 29c. blue 55 15

1994.
2929 **2071** $5 green . . . . 7·50 3·00

1994. Popular Music. Multicoloured.
2930 29c. Type **2072** 75 65
2931 29c. Bing Crosby 75 65
2932 29c. Ethel Waters 75 65
2933 29c. Nat "King" Cole . . . 75 65
2934 29c. Ethel Merman 75 65

2077 "Male Type (eastern seaboard)" **2078** Bessie Smith

1994. Literary Arts. Birth Centenary of James Thurber (writer and cartoonist).
2935 **2077** 29c. multicoloured . . . 55 15

1994. Jazz and Blues Music. Multicoloured.
2936 29c. Type **2078** 85 50
2937 29c. Muddy Waters 85 50
2938 29c. Billie Holiday 85 50
2939 29c. Robert Johnson 85 50
2940 29c. Jimmy Rushing 85 50
2941 29c. "Ma" Rainey 85 50
2942 29c. Mildred Bailey 85 50
2943 29c. Howlin' Wolf 85 50

2086/9 Sea Life (½-size illustration)

1994. Wonders of the Seas.
2944 **2086** 29c. multicoloured . . . 50 25
2945 **2087** 29c. multicoloured . . . 50 25
2946 **2088** 29c. multicoloured . . . 50 25
2947 **2089** 29c. multicoloured . . . 50 25
Nos. 2944/7 were issued together, se-tenant, forming the composite design illustrated.

2090 Black-necked Crane **2092** Home on the Range

1994. Cranes. Multicoloured.
2948 29c. Type **2090** 65 25
2949 29c. Whooping crane . . . 65 25

1994. Legends of the West. Multicoloured.
2950 29c. Type **2092** 65 70
2951 29c. Buffalo Bill (William Cody) 65 70
2952 29c. Jim Bridger 65 70
2953 29c. Annie Oakley 65 70
2954 29c. Native American culture 65 70
2955 29c. Chief Joseph 65 70
2956 29c. Bill Pickett 65 70
2957 29c. Bat Masterson 65 70
2958 29c. John Fremont 65 70
2959 29c. Wyatt Earp 65 70
2960 29c. Nellie Cashman 65 70
2961 29c. Charles Goodnight . . 65 70
2962 29c. Geronimo 65 70
2963 29c. Kit Carson 65 70
2964 29c. Wild Bill Hickok . . . 65 70
2965 29c. Western wildlife 65 70
2966 29c. Jim Beckwourth . . . 65 70
2967 29c. Bill Tilghman 65 70
2968 29c. Sacagawea 65 70
2969 29c. Overland mail 65 70
Each stamp is inscribed on the back, under the gum, with a brief history of the subject depicted.

2097 "Virgin and Child" (Elisabetta Sirani) **2100** Common Cardinal

1994. Christmas. Multicoloured. (a) Perf.
2970 29c. Type **2097** 55 15
2972 29c. Stocking 55 15

(b) Self-adhesive. Imperf.
2973 29c. Santa Claus 65 30
2974 29c. Type **2100** 65 40
Nos. 2972/3 are as Type **2097** in size.

2102 Dove with Olive Branch **2103** Old Glory

1994. Make-up Rate stamp. No value expressed.
2976 **2102** (3c.) blue, brn & red . . 20 20

1994. With service indicator. (a) Nonprofit Presort. Green background.
2978 **2103** (5c.) multicoloured . . 25 40

(b) Postcard rate. Yellow background.
2979 **2103** (20c.) mult (black "G") 30 25
2980 (20c.) mult (red "G") 45 30

(c) First-Class Presort. Blue background.
2981 **2103** (25c.) multicoloured . . 55 50

2104 Old Glory **2106** Boar

1994. No value expressed. Perf (Nos. 2982, 2984); perf or imperf (self-adhesive) (No. 2986).
2982 **2104** (32c.) mult (red "G") 65 25
2984 (32c.) mult (blue "G") 75 40
2986 (32c.) mult (black "G") 80 25

1994. New Year.
2991 **2106** 29c. multicoloured . . . 65 50

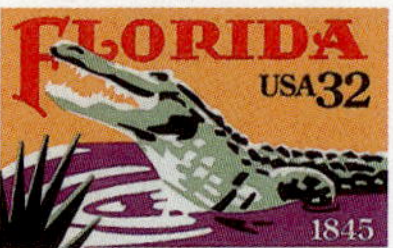

2107 Cherub (detail from "Sistine Madonna" by Raphael) **2108** Alligator

1995. Greetings Stamp. No value expressed. (a) Size 20 × 26 mm.
2992 **2107** (32c.) multicoloured . . 60 20

(b) Size 18 × 22 mm. Self-adhesive. Imperf.
2993 **2107** (32c.) multicoloured . . 70 15
For Type **2107** but with face value "32", see No. 3035.

1995. 150th Anniv of Florida Statehood.
2994 **2108** 32c. multicoloured . . . 65 25

2109 Butte

2110 Front of Motor Car

1995. Non-profit Organizations Stamp. Ordinary or self-adhesive gum.
2995 **2109** (5c.) orange, blue and yellow 15 25

1995. Bulk Rate Stamp. Ordinary or self-adhesive gum.
2997 **2110** (10c.) vermilion, black and red 20 25

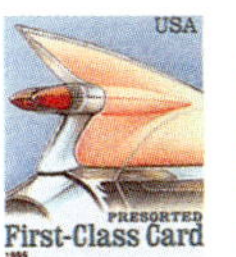

2111 Motor Car Tail Fin

2112 Juke Box

2113 Flag over Field

1995. Presorted First Class Postcard Stamp. Ordinary or self-adhesive gum.
2999 **2111** (15c.) multicoloured . . 30 30

1995. Presorted First Class Stamp. Ordinary or self-adhesive gum.
3003 **2112** (25c.) multicoloured . . 50 50

1995. Self-adhesive. Imperf.
3007 **2113** 32c. multicoloured . . . 70 40

2115 Flag over Porch

2116 Globe in Bath (Christy Millard)

1995. Perf or imperf (self-adhesive).
3008 **2115** 32c. multicoloured . . . 60 40

1995. 25th Anniv of Earth Day. Multicoloured.
3017 32c. Type **2116** 65 30
3018 32c. Solar energy (Jennifer Michalove) 65 30
3019 32c. Youth planting tree (Brian Hailes) 65 30
3020 32c. Family cleaning up beach (Melody Kiper) . . 65 25

2119 Nixon

2120 Bessie Coleman

1995. 1st Death Anniv of Richard Nixon (President, 1968–74).
3021 **2119** 32c. multicoloured . . . 60 25

1995. Black Heritage. Bessie Coleman (aviator).
3022 **2120** 32c. black and red . . . 60 25

1995. Birds. Value expressed as "1c" etc. Mult.
3023 1c. As T **1817** 15 10
3024 2c. Red-headed woodpecker 15 20
3025 3c. As No. 2589 . . . . . 15 15
No. 3023 also comes self-adhesive.

2125 Cherub

1995. Greetings Stamps. Details from "Sistine Madonna" by Raphael. Ordinary gum (Nos. 3035/6) or self-adhesive (Nos. 3038/9). Perf (Nos. 3035/6, 3038) or imperf (No. 3039).
3035 **2107** 32c. multicoloured (19½ × 27 mm) . . . 60 25
3038 32c. multicoloured (18½ × 22 mm) . . . 60 30
3036 **2125** 55c. multicoloured (27 × 20½ mm) . . . 1·00 50
3039 55c. multicoloured (21½ × 19 mm) . . . 1·00 55

2126 Golf

1995. Sports. Multicoloured.
3040 32c. Type **2126** 70 45
3041 32c. Volleyball 70 45
3042 32c. Baseball 70 45
3043 32c. Bowls 70 45
3044 32c. Tennis 70 45

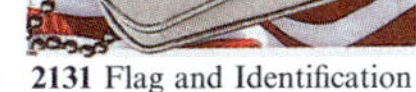

2131 Flag and Identification Tags

2132 Marilyn Monroe

1995. Memorial Day.
3045 **2131** 32c. multicoloured . . . 60 30

1995. Legends of Hollywood.
3046 **2132** 32c. multicoloured . . . 85 40

2133 Blue Jay

2134 Horseman carrying Flag

1995. Ordinary or self-adhesive gum.
3048 **2133** 20c. multicoloured . . . 45 15

1995. 150th Anniv of Texas Statehood.
3051 **2134** 32c. multicoloured . . . 70 25

2135 Split Rock, Lake Superior

2140 "Challenger" (space shuttle)

1995. Great Lakes Lighthouses. Multicoloured.
3052 32c. Type **2135** 65 30
3053 32c. St. Joseph, Lake Michigan 65 30
3054 32c. Spectacle Reef, Lake Huron 65 30
3055 32c. Marblehead, Lake Erie 65 30
3056 32c. Thirty Mile Point, Lake Ontario 65 30

1995.
3057 **2140** $3 multicoloured . . . 5·00 2·00

2141 Emblem

2142 U.S.S. "Monitor" and C.S.S. "Virginia" (ironclads) in Battle

1995. 50th Anniv of U.N.O.
3058 **2141** 32c. blue 60 30

1995. 130th Anniv of End of American Civil War. Multicoloured.
3059 32c. Type **2142** 75 75
3060 32c. Gen. Robert E. Lee (Confederate) 75 75
3061 32c. Clara Barton (Union nurse) 75 75
3062 32c. Gen. Ulysses Grant (Union) 75 75
3063 32c. Battle of Shiloh 75 75
3064 32c. Jefferson Davis (Confederate President) 75 75
3065 32c. Vice-Admiral David Farragut (Union) 75 75
3066 32c. Frederick Douglass (journalist and diplomat) 75 75
3067 32c. Rear-Admiral Raphael Semmes (Confederate) . . 75 75
3068 32c. Abraham Lincoln (U.S. President, 1861–65) . . 75 75
3069 32c. Harriet Tubman (black rights campaigner) 75 75
3070 32c. Brig.-Gen. Stand Watie (Confederate) 75 75
3071 32c. Gen. Joseph Johnston (Confederate) 75 75
3072 32c. Major-Gen. Winfield Hancock (Union) 75 75
3073 32c. Mary Chesnut (Confederate diarist) . . . 75 75
3074 32c. Battle of Chancellorsville 75 75
3075 32c. Major-Gen. William Sherman (Union) 75 75
3076 32c. Phoebe Pember (Confederate nurse) . . . 75 75
3077 32c. Lt.-Gen. Thomas "Stonewall" Jackson (Confederate) 75 75
3078 32c. Battle of Gettysburg . . 75 75
Each stamp is inscribed on the back, under the gum, with a brief history of the subject depicted.

2147 Peaches

1995. Multicoloured. Ordinary or self-adhesive gum.
3079 32c. Type **2147** 65 20
3080 32c. Pear 65 20

2149 King Horse, 1910 (Stein and Goldstein)

2150 Indian Pony, 1905 (Daniel Muller)

2151 Armoured Horse, 1912 (Stein and Goldstein)

2152 Lillie Belle, 1917 (C. W. Parker Co)

1995. Carousel Horses.
3085 **2149** 32c. multicoloured . . . 75 25
3086 **2150** 32c. multicoloured . . . 75 25
3087 **2151** 32c. multicoloured . . . 75 25
3088 **2152** 32c. multicoloured . . . 75 25

2153 Launch of Space Shuttle "Endeavour"

1995.
3089 **2153** $10.75 multicoloured 17·00 8·25

2154 1913 and 1976 Women's Rights Marches

1995. 75th Anniv of Ratification of 19th Amendment (giving women the right to vote).
3090 **2154** 32c. multicoloured . . . 60 25

2155 Coleman Hawkins

1995. Jazz Musicians. Multicoloured. (a) With value in white.
3091 32c. Louis Armstrong . . . 85 50

(b) With value in black.
3092 32c. Type **2155** 85 80
3093 32c. Louis Armstrong . . . 85 80
3094 32c. James Johnson 85 80
3095 32c. Jelly Roll Morton . . . 85 80
3096 32c. Charlie Parker 85 80
3097 32c. Eubie Blake 85 80
3098 32c. Charles Mingus 85 80
3099 32c. Thelonious Monk . . . 85 80
3100 32c. John Coltrane 85 80
3101 32c. Erroll Garner 85 80

2165 Marines raising Flag on Iwo Jima

2175 Asters

1995. United States Participation in Second World War. Multicoloured.
3102 32c. Type **2165** 70 70
3103 32c. Liberation of Manila 70 70
3104 32c. Troops advancing on Okinawa 70 70
3105 32c. Bridge across River Elbe 70 70
3106 32c. Liberation of concentration camp survivors 70 70
3107 32c. German Surrender at Reims 70 70
3108 32c. Refugees 70 70
3109 32c. President Truman announcing Japanese surrender 70 70
3110 32c. News of victory reaches America 70 70
3111 32c. Honouring returned service personnel 70 70

1995. Garden Flowers. Multicoloured.
3112 32c. Type **2175** 65 30
3113 32c. Chrysanthemums . . . 65 30
3114 32c. Dahlias 65 30
3115 32c. Hydrangea 65 30
3116 32c. Rudbeckias 65 30

2180 Rickenbacker

2181 Racoon Butterflyfish, Soldierfish, Shell and Palau Flag

1995. Aviation Pioneers. Eddie Rickenbacker (fighter pilot).
3117 **2180** 60c. multicoloured . . . 1·10 40

1995. 1st Anniv of Independence of Palau.
3118 **2181** 32c. multicoloured . . . 60 25

2182 Santa Claus on Rooftop

2186 The Yellow Kid

1995. Christmas (1st issue). Victorian Designs from writing tablet (T **2182**) or postcards (others). Ordinary or self-adhesive gum.
3119 32c. Type **2182** 60 25
3120 32c. Boy holding jumping jack 60 25
3121 32c. Boy holding tree . . . 60 25
3122 32c. Santa Claus making toy sleigh 60 25
See also Nos. 3153/7.

1995. Centenary of Comic Strips. Multicoloured.
3131 32c. Type **2186** 65 70
3132 32c. Katzenjammer Kids . . 65 70
3133 32c. Little Nemo in Slumberland 65 70
3134 32c. Bringing Up Father . . 65 70
3135 32c. Krazy Kat 65 70
3136 32c. Rube Goldberg's Inventions 65 70
3137 32c. Toonerville Folks . . . 65 70
3138 32c. Gasoline Alley 65 70
3139 32c. Barney Google 65 70
3140 32c. Little Orphan Annie . . 65 70
3141 32c. Popeye 65 70
3142 32c. Blondie 65 70
3143 32c. Dick Tracy 65 70
3144 32c. Alley Oop 65 70
3145 32c. Nancy 65 70

3146 32c. Flash Gordon 65 70
3147 32c. Li'l Abner 65 70
3148 32c. Terry and the Pirates 65 70
3149 32c. Prince Valiant 65 70
3150 32c. Brenda Starr, Reporter 65 70

Each stamp is inscribed on the back, under the gum, with a brief history of the subject depicted.

2187 "Swift" (racing sloop) and Academy Chapel

1995. 150th Anniv of Naval Academy, Annapolis.
3151 **2187** 32c. multicoloured . . . 60 25

2188 Williams and Streetcars

1995. Literary Arts. Tennessee Williams (dramatist).
3152 **2188** 32c. multicoloured . . . 60 25

2189 "Enthroned Madonna and Child" (Giotto)

2190 Midnight Angel (after Ellen Clapsaddle)

2191 Children Sledding

2192 Polk

1995. Christmas (2nd issue). (a) Ordinary gum. Perf.
3153 **2189** 32c. multicoloured . . . 60 25

(b) Self-adhesive. Roul (No. 3137) or imperf (No. 3187).
3155 **2190** 32c. multicoloured . . . 75 25
3157 **2191** 32c. multicoloured . . . 75 40

1995. Birth Bicentenary of James K. Polk (President, 1844–49).
3158 **2192** 32c. brown 60 20

2193 Columbia Battery-powered Car, 1898

2198 Delicate Arch, Arches National Park

1996. Veteran Cars. Multicoloured.
3159 32c. Type **2193** 60 65
3160 32c. Winton Car, 1899 . . . 60 65
3161 32c. White Steam-powered Car, 1901 . . . . 60 65
3162 32c. Duryea Car, 1893 . . . 60 65
3163 32c. Haynes Car, 1894 . . . 60 65

1996. Centenary of Utah Statehood.
3164 **2198** 32c. multicoloured . . . 65 25

2199 Crocus

2204 Just

1996. Garden Flowers. Multicoloured.
3165 32c. Type **2199** 65 30
3166 32c. Winter aconites 65 30
3167 32c. Pansies 65 30
3168 32c. Snowdrops 65 30
3169 32c. Anemones 65 30

1996. Black Heritage. Ernest Just (marine biologist).
3170 **2204** 32c. multicoloured . . . 65 25

2205 The Castle (first Smithsonian building)

1996. 150th Anniv of Smithsonian Institution.
3171 **2205** 32c. multicoloured . . . 55 25

2206 Rat

1996. New Year.
3172 **2206** 32c. multicoloured . . . 65 25

2207 Frederic Ives (halftone process)

2211 Face, Map and Compass

1996. Pioneers of Communication. Multicoloured.
3173 32c. Type **2207** 60 40
3174 32c. William Dickson (motion pictures) 60 40
3175 32c. Eadweard Muybridge (photography) 60 40
3176 32c. Ottmar Mergenthaler (linotype) 60 40

1996. 50th Anniv of Fulbright Scholarships (international educational exchange programme).
3177 **2211** 32c. multicoloured . . . 55 25

2212 Jacqueline Cochran

2213 Mountains

1996. Aviation Pioneers. Jacqueline Cochran (first woman to fly faster than speed of sound).
3178 **2212** 50c. multicoloured . . . 90 50

1996. Non-profit Organizations. No value expressed. Ordinary or self-adhesive gum.
3179 **2213** (5c.) multicoloured . . 15 25

2214 Runners

2215 Decathlon

1996. 100th Boston Marathon.
3183 **2214** 32c. multicoloured . . . 55 25

1996. Olympic Games, Atlanta. Multicoloured.
3184 32c. Type **2215** 65 65
3185 32c. Men's canoeing 65 65
3186 32c. Women's running . . . 65 65
3187 32c. Women's diving 65 65
3188 32c. Men's cycling 65 65
3189 32c. Freestyle wrestling . . 65 65
3190 32c. Women's gymnastics . . 65 65
3191 32c. Women's sailboarding . 65 65
3192 32c. Men's putting the shot 65 65
3193 32c. Women's football . . . 65 65
3194 32c. Beach volleyball . . . 65 65
3195 32c. Men's rowing 65 65
3196 32c. Men's sprinting 65 65
3197 32c. Women's swimming . . 65 65
3198 32c. Women's softball . . . 65 65
3199 32c. Men's hurdling 65 65
3200 32c. Men's swimming . . . 65 65
3201 32c. Men's gymnastics . . . 65 65
3202 32c. Show jumping 65 65
3203 32c. Men's basketball . . . 65 65

2216 "Red Poppy"

2217 State Capitol, Nashville

1996. 10th Death Anniv of Georgia O'Keeffe (painter).
3204 **2216** 32c. multicoloured . . . 60 25

1996. Bicentenary of Tennessee. Ordinary or self-adhesive gum.
3205 **2217** 32c. multicoloured . . . 60 30

2218 Fancy Dance

2223 Mastodon

1996. Traditional Amerindian Dances.
3207 32c. Type **2218** 65 40
3208 32c. Butterfly dance 65 40
3209 32c. Traditional dance . . . 65 40
3210 32c. Raven dance 65 40
3211 32c. Hoop dance 65 40

1996. Prehistoric Animals.
3212 32c. Type **2223** 65 40
3213 32c. Sabre-tooth tiger . . . 65 40
3214 32c. Eohippus 65 40
3215 32c. Woolly mammoth . . . 65 40

2227 Woman and Ribbon

2228 James Dean

1996. Breast Cancer Awareness Campaign.
3216 **2227** 32c. multicoloured . . . 75 25

1996. Legends of Hollywood.
3217 **2228** 32c. multicoloured . . . 75 30

2229 Mighty Casey

2233 "The Discus Thrower" (Miron)

1996. Folk Heroes. Multicoloured.
3218 32c. Type **2229** 65 50
3219 32c. Paul Bunyan 65 50
3220 32c. John Henry 65 50
3221 32c. Pecos Bill 65 50

1996. Centenary of Modern Olympic Games.
3222 **2233** 32c. brown 65 25

2234 "Young Corn" (Grant Wood)

2235 Early Postal Carrier and Horse-drawn Mail Wagon

1996. 150th Anniv of Iowa Statehood. Ordinary or self-adhesive gum.
3223 **2234** 32c. multicoloured . . . 60 30

1996. Centenary of Free Rural Postal Deliveries.
3225 **2235** 32c. multicoloured . . . 60 25

2236 "Robert E. Lee"

1996. 19th-century Paddle-steamers. Self-adhesive.
3226 32c. Type **2236** 65 40
3227 32c. "Sylvan Dell" 65 40
3228 32c. "Far West" 65 40
3229 32c. "Rebecca Everingham" 65 40
3230 32c. "Bailey Gatzert" . . . 65 40

2241 Count Basie

1996. Big Band Leaders (Nos. 3231/4) and Songwriters (Nos. 3235/8). Multicoloured.
3231 32c. Type **2241** 75 40
3232 32c. Tommy and Jimmy Dorsey 75 40
3233 32c. Glenn Miller 75 40
3234 32c. Benny Goodman . . . 75 40
3235 32c. Harold Arlen 75 40
3236 32c. Johnny Mercer 75 40
3237 32c. Dorothy Fields 75 40
3238 32c. Hoagy Carmichael . . 75 40

2249 Fitzgerald

1996. Birth Centenary of Francis Scott Fitzgerald (writer).
3239 **2249** 23c. multicoloured . . . 45 25

2250 Black-footed Ferret

1996. Endangered Species. Multicoloured.
3240 32c. Type **2250** 65 65
3241 32c. Thick-billed parrot . . 65 65
3242 32c. Hawaiian monk seal . . 65 65
3243 32c. American crocodile . . 65 65
3244 32c. Ocelot 65 65
3245 32c. Schaus swallowtail . . 65 65
3246 32c. Wyoming toad 65 65
3247 32c. Brown pelican 65 65
3248 32c. California condor . . . 65 65
3249 32c. Gila trout 65 65
3250 32c. San Francisco garter snake 65 65
3251 32c. Woodland caribou . . 65 65
3252 32c. Florida panther 65 65
3253 32c. Piping plover 65 65
3254 32c. Florida manatee . . . 65 65

2251 Circuit Boards covering Brain

1996. Computer Technology. 50th Anniv of ENIAC (Army computer system).
3255 **2251** 32c. multicoloured . . . 55 30

2252 Family at Fireside

2256 Ice Skaters

1996. Christmas (1st issue). Multicoloured. Ordinary or self-adhesive gum (Nos. 3256/9), self-adhesive (No. 3264).
3256 32c. Type **2252** 65 25
3257 32c. Decorating Christmas tree 65 25
3258 32c. Santa Claus in chimney and child sleeping 65 25

3259 32c. Mother and child carrying gifts 65 25
3264 32c. Type **2256** 70 40
See also No. 3268.

2257 Lighted Candles

2258 Madonna and Child (detail from "Adoration of the Shepherds", Paolo de Matteis)

1996. Festival of Hanukkah. Self-adhesive.
3265 **2257** 32c. multicoloured . . . 60 25
3693 33c. multicoloured . . . 55 25

1996. Christmas (2nd issue). Ordinary or self-adhesive gum.
3268 **2258** 32c. multicoloured . . . 55 25

2260 Ox

2261 Davis on Inspection Tour in France, 1944

1997. New Year.
3271 **2260** 32c. multicoloured . . . 65 40

1997. Black Heritage. Brigadier-General Benjamin Davis. Self-adhesive.
3272 **2261** 32c. blk, lt grey & grey 65 30

2262 Mute Swans

1997. Greetings Stamps. Mult. Self-adhesive.
3274 32c. Type **2262** 70 30
3275 55c. Mute swans (horiz) . . 95 60

2264 Adult and Child with Book

2265 Beetle, Moth and Lava on Citron

1997. Helping Children Learn. Self-adhesive.
3276 **2264** 32c. multicoloured . . . 70 30

1997. 350th Birth Anniv of Maria Sibylla Merian (painter). Self-adhesive. (a) Size 18½ × 24½ mm. Multicoloured.
3277 32c. Type **2265** 70 65
3278 32c. Cockroaches on flowering pineapple . . . 70 30

(b) Size 19½ × 27½ mm.
3279 32c. Type **2265** 65 30
3280 32c. As No. 3278 . . . . . 65 30

2267 U.S. Mail Coach

1997. "Pacific 97" International Stamp Exhibition, San Francisco.
3281 **2267** 32c. red 65 55
3282 – 32c. blue 65 55
DESIGN: No. 3282, "Richard S. Ely" (clipper).

2269 Wilder (after Michael Deas)

1997. Literary Arts. Birth Centenary of Thornton Wilder (novelist, playwright and essayist).
3283 **2269** 32c. multicoloured . . . 60 25

2270 Holocaust Survivors and Wallenberg

1997. Raoul Wallenberg (Swedish diplomat) Commemoration.
3284 **2270** 32c. multicoloured . . . 60 30

2271 Ceratosaurus

1997. Prehistoric Animals. Multicoloured.
3285 32c. Type **2271** 65 70
3286 32c. Camptosaurus (38½ × 30mm) 65 70
3287 32c. Camarasaurus (38½ × 30 mm) 65 70
3288 32c. Brachiosaurus (30 × 38 mm) 65 70
3289 32c. Stegosaurus (38½ × 30 mm) 65 70
3290 32c. Allosaurus (38½ × 30 mm) 65 70
3291 32c. Goniopholis 65 70
3292 32c. Opisthias 65 70
3293 32c. Parasaurolophus . . . 65 70
3294 32c. Edmontonia (38½ × 30 mm) 65 70
3295 32c. Einiosaurus (38½ × 30 mm) 65 70
3296 32c. Daspletosaurus (30 × 38½ mm) 65 70
3297 32c. Corythosaurus (38½ × 30 mm) 65 70
3298 32c. Ornithomimus (38½ × 30 mm) 65 70
3299 32c. Palaeosaniwa 65 70
Nos. 3285/99 were issued together, se-tenant, forming two composite designs.

2272 Bugs Bunny

2274 Map of Europe and General George Marshall

1997. Bugs Bunny (cartoon character). Self-adhesive.
3300 **2272** 32c. multicoloured . . . 60 30

1997. 50th Anniv of European Recovery Program ("Marshall Plan").
3303 **2274** 32c. multicoloured . . . 60 25

2275 North American P-51 Mustang Fighter

1997. American Aircraft. Multicoloured.
3304 32c. Type **2275** 60 65
3305 32c. Wright Model B biplane 60 65
3306 32c. Piper J-3 Cub light airplane 60 65
3307 32c. Lockheed Vega 60 65
3308 32c. Northrop Alpha . . . 60 65
3309 32c. Martin B-10 bomber 60 65
3310 32c. Vought Corsair fighter 60 65
3311 32c. Boeing B-47 Stratojet 60 65
3312 32c. Gee Bee 60 65
3313 32c. Beech Staggerwing . . 60 65
3314 32c. Boeing B-17 Flying Fortress bomber 60 65
3315 32c. Stearman PT-13 biplane 60 65
3316 32c. Lockheed Constellation 60 65
3317 32c. Lockheed P-38 Lightning fighter 60 65
3318 32c. Boeing P-26 "Peashooter" fighter . . . 60 65
3319 32c. Ford Trimotor "Tin Goose" 60 65
3320 32c. Douglas DC-3 . . . . 60 65
3321 32c. Boeing 314 Clipper flying boat 60 65
3322 32c. Curtiss JN-4 "Jenny" trainer 60 65
3323 32c. Grumman F4F Wildcat fighter 60 65
Each stamp is inscribed on the back, under the gum, with a description of the airplane depicted.

2276 Bear Bryant

1997. Football Coaches. Multicoloured. (a) With red line above coach's name.
3324 32c. Type **2276** 65 50
3325 32c. Pop Warner 65 50
3326 32c. Vince Lombardi . . . 65 50
3327 32c. George Halas 65 50

(b) Without red line.
3328 32c. Type **2276** 65 80
3329 32c. As No. 3325 . . . . . 65 80
3330 32c. As No. 3326 . . . . . 65 80
3331 32c. As No. 3327 . . . . . 65 80

2280 "Alabama Baby" (Ella Smith) and Cloth Doll by Martha Chase

2281 Humphrey Bogart

1997. American Dolls. Multicoloured.
3332 32c. Type **2280** 75 65
3333 32c. "The Columbian Doll" (Emma Adams and Marietta Adams Ratta) 75 65
3334 32c. "Raggedy Ann" (John Gruelle) 75 65
3335 32c. Cloth doll by Martha Chase 75 65
3336 32c. "American Child" (Dwees Cochran) 75 65
3337 32c. "Baby Coos" 75 65
3338 32c. Plains Indian doll . . . 75 65
3339 32c. Moulded doll by Izannah Walker 75 65
3340 32c. "Babyland Rag" . . . 75 65
3341 32c. "Scootles" (Rose O'Neill) 75 65
3342 32c. Doll with papier-mache head, cloth body and leather arms by Ludwig Greiner 75 65
3343 32c. "Betsy McCall" 75 65
3344 32c. "Skippy" 75 65
3345 32c. "Maggie Mix-up" . . . 75 65
3346 32c. Wooden moveable dolls by Albert Schoenut . . . 75 65

1997. Legends of Hollywood.
3347 **2281** 32c. multicoloured . . . 65 30

2282 Flag and Bandsmen

2283 Lily Pons as Rosina in "The Barber of Seville" and as Lucia in "Lucia di Lammermoor"

1997. Centenary of "The Stars and Stripes Forever" by John Philip Sousa.
3348 **2282** 32c. multicoloured . . . 60 15

1997. Opera Singers. Multicoloured.
3349 32c. Type **2283** 75 50
3350 32c. Richard Tucker as the Duke in "Rigoletto" and in "Carmen" 75 50
3351 32c. Lawrence Tibbet as the Toreador in "Carmen" . . 75 50
3352 32c. Rosa Ponselle in "Norma" 75 50

2287 Leopold Stokowski (Philadelphia Symphony Orchestra)

2295 Varela

1997. Classical Conductors (Nos. 3353/6) and Composers (Nos. 3357/60). Multicoloured.
3353 32c. Type **2287** 75 50
3354 32c. Arthur Fiedler (Boston Pops Orchestra) 75 50
3355 32c. George Szell (Cleveland Orchestra) 75 50
3356 32c. Eugene Ormandy (Philadelphia Symphony Orchestra) 75 50
3357 32c. Samuel Barber 75 50
3358 32c. Ferde Grofe 75 50
3359 32c. Charles Ives 75 50
3360 32c. Louis Moreau Gottschalk 75 50

1997. Father Felix Varela (social reformer).
3361 **2295** 32c. violet 55 50

2296 U.S.A.F. Thunderbirds flying in Formation

1997. 50th Anniv of United States Air Force.
3362 **2296** 32c. multicoloured . . . 55 30

2297 Lon Chaney as The Phantom of the Opera

1997. Movie Monsters. Multicoloured.
3363 32c. Type **2297** 65 50
3364 32c. Bela Lugosi as Dracula 65 50
3365 32c. Boris Karloff in "Frankenstein" 65 50
3366 32c. Boris Karloff as The Mummy 65 50
3367 32c. Lon Chaney Jr. as The Wolf Man 65 50

2302 Bell XS-1 Rocket Airplane

1997. 50th Anniv of First Supersonic Flight (by Charles Yeager). Self-adhesive.
3368 **2302** 32c. multicoloured . . . 60 30

2303 Uniformed Women

1997. Women in Military Service.
3369 **2303** 32c. multicoloured . . . 60 30

2304 Family

1997. Kwanzaa Festival. Self-adhesive.
3370 **2304** 32c. multicoloured . . . 60 25
3694 33c. multicoloured . . . 55 25

2305 "Madonna and Child with Saints and Angels" (Sano di Pietro)

2306 Holly

1997. Christmas (1st issue). Self-adhesive.
3371 **2305** 32c. multicoloured . . . 60 25

1997. Christmas (2nd issue). Self-adhesive.
3372 **2306** 32c. multicoloured . . . 60 25

2308 Tiger

2309 Skier

1998. New Year.
3374 **2308** 32c. multicoloured . . . 65 30

1998. Alpine Skiing.
3375 **2309** 32c. multicoloured . . . 65 30

2310 Madam Walker

1998. Black Heritage. Madam C. J. Walker (designer of cosmetics for black women). Self-adhesive.
3376 **2310** 32c. brown, grey and black 65 30

2311 Model T Ford

2312 Charlie Chaplin as the Little Tramp

1998. The Twentieth Century (1st series). (a) The 1900s. Red (No. 3389) or multicoloured (others).
3377 32c. Type **2311** 55 65
3378 32c. President Theodore Roosevelt 55 65
3379 32c. Film frame from "The Great Train Robbery", 1903 . . . . 55 65
3380 32c. Box of Crayola crayons, 1903 . . . . . . 55 65
3381 32c. Children with ice cream cones, St. Louis World's Fair, 1904 . . . . . . 55 65
3382 32c. Advertisement for "unfailing" elixir (Pure Food and Drugs Act, 1904) 55 65
3383 32c. Wright Brothers' Flyer I (first powered flight, Kitty Hawk, 1903) . . . 55 65
3384 32c. "Stag at Sharkey's" (detail, George Bellows) (Ash Can Painters) . . . 55 65
3385 32c. Immigrants arriving at Ellis Island 55 65
3386 32c. John Muir (preservationist) and mountains 55 65
3387 32c. Teddy bear (created 1902) 55 65
3388 32c. W. E. B. Du Bois (civil rights activist) 55 65
3389 32c. Gibson Girl (fashionable "look" created by Charles Gibson) 55 65
3390 32c. Baseball player (first World Series championship, 1903) . . . 55 65
3391 32c. Robie House (Frank Lloyd Wright), Chicago 55 65

(b) The 1910s. Blue (No. 3397) or multicoloured (others).
3392 32c. Type **2312** 55 65
3393 32c. Eagle (Federal Reserve System (regulation of financial institutions), 1913) 55 65
3394 32c. George Washington Carver (botanist) and microscope (increased commercial use of peanuts and sweet potatoes) . . . 55 65
3395 32c. Couple viewing "Nude Descending a Staircase, No. 2" (Marcel Duchamp) (Armory Show of avant-garde art, 1913) 55 65
3396 32c. Linesmen and flag (first transcontinental telephone line, 1914) 55 65
3397 32c. Freighter in lock (opening of Panama Canal, 1914) 55 65
3398 32c. Jim Thorpe (gold medal winner in pentathlon and decathlon at Olympic Games, Stockholm, 1912) 55 65
3399 32c. Grand Canyon (designation as National Park, 1919) 55 65
3400 32c. First World War recruitment poster . . . 55 65
3401 32c. Scouts and camp (formation of Boy Scouts of America (1910) and Girl Scouts (1912)) . . . 55 65
3402 32c. President Woodrow Wilson (Nobel Peace Prize, 1919) 55 65
3403 32c. Grids and hand holding pencil (first crossword puzzle created by Arthur Wynne, 1913) 55 65
3404 32c. Jack Dempsey (World heavyweight boxing champion, 1919–25) . . . 55 65
3405 32c. Boy with construction toys 55 65
3406 32c. Girl beside loom (child labour reform) 55 65

See also Nos. 3421/35, 3496/3510, 3550/64, 3606/20, 3652/66, 3705/19, 3726/40 and 3763/77.

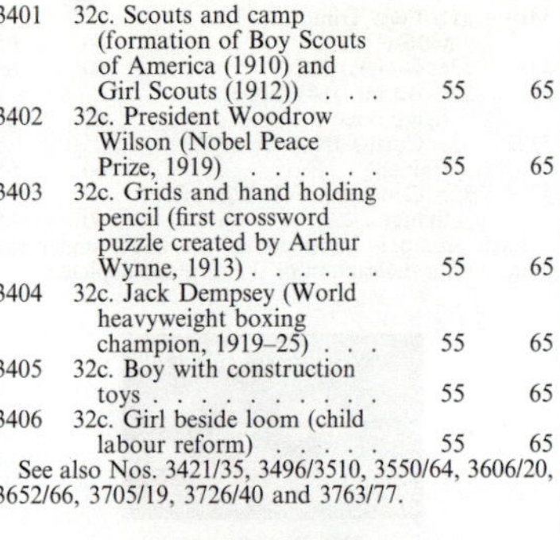

2313 U.S.S. "Maine"

1998. Centenary of Sinking of the "Maine" (battleship) (cause of Spanish–American War).
3407 **2313** 32c. black and red . . . 65 30

2314 Southern Magnolia

2319 "Black Cascade, 13 Verticals"

1998. Flowers and Fruits. Self-adhesive.
3408 32c. Type **2314** 60 40
3409 32c. Blue paloverde 60 40
3410 32c. Yellow poplar 60 40
3411 32c. Prairie crab apple . . . 60 40
3412 32c. Pacific dogwood . . . 60 40

1998. Birth Centenary of Alexander Calder (sculptor).
3413 **2319** 32c. black, grey and red 65 40
3414 – 32c. multicoloured . . . 65 40
3415 – 32c. black, grey and red 65 40
3416 – 32c. multicoloured . . . 65 40
3417 – 32c. black, red and grey 65 40
DESIGNS: No. 3414, "Untitled"; 3415, "Rearing Stallion"; 3416, "Portrait of a Young Man"; 3417, "Un Effet du Japonais".

2324 Dancers in Traditional Costumes

2325 Sylvester and Tweety

1998. Cinco de Mayo Festival. Self-adhesive.
3418 **2324** 32c. multicoloured . . . 65 25
3594 33c. multicoloured . . . 55 25

1998. Sylvester and Tweety (cartoon characters). Self-adhesive.
3419 **2325** 32c. multicoloured . . . 55 15

2326 Babe Ruth (baseball player)

2327 Wisconsin

1998. The Twentieth Century (2nd series). The 1920s. Brown (Nos. 3432/3) or mult (others).
3421 32c. Type **2326** 55 65
3422 32c. The Gatsby style ("The Great Gatsby" by F. Scott Fitzgerald, 1925) 55 65
3423 32c. Federal agents pouring away wine (after Ben Shahn) (prohibition) . . . 55 65
3424 32c. Electric model steam train 55 65
3425 32c. Woman voter (19th Amendment, 1920) . . . 55 65
3426 32c. Dinner plate and cutlery (Emily Post's writings on etiquette) . . 55 65
3427 32c. Margaret Mead (anthropologist) 55 65
3428 32c. Flapper doing the Charleston (after John Held jr.) 55 65
3429 32c. Radio 55 65
3430 32c. Chrysler Building, New York (Art Deco style) . . 55 65
3431 32c. Jazz trombonists . . . 55 65
3432 32c. Notre Dame's Four Horsemen (college football players) 55 65
3433 32c. Charles Lindbergh and "Spirit of St. Louis" (first non-stop solo trans-Atlantic flight) 55 65
3434 32c. "Automat" (detail, Edward Hopper) (American Realism) . . . 55 65
3435 32c. Torn banknote (Stock Market crash, 1929) . . . 55 65

1998. 150th Anniv of Wisconsin Statehood.
3436 **2327** 32c. multicoloured . . . 55 45

2328 Diner

2329 Wetlands

1998. Presorted First-Class Mail coil stamp. Ordinary or self-adhesive gum.
3437 **2328** (25c.) multicoloured . . 40 50

1998. With service indication. Ordinary or self-adhesive gum.
3439 **2329** (5c.) multicoloured . . 20 40

2331 Family watching Douglas C-54 Transport

1998. 50th Anniv of Berlin Airlift (relief during Soviet blockade).
3443 **2331** 32c. multicoloured . . . 60 25

2332 Leadbelly

1998. Folk Music. Multicoloured.
3444 32c. Type **2332** 65 25
3445 32c. Woody Guthrie 65 50
3446 32c. Sonny Terry 65 50
3447 32c. Josh White 65 50

2336 Mission of San Miguel

1998. 400th Anniv of Spanish Settlement at San Gabriel.
3448 **2336** 32c. multicoloured . . . 55 30

2337 Mahalia Jackson

1998. Gospel Music. Multicoloured.
3449 32c. Type **2337** 65 50
3450 32c. Roberta Martin 65 50
3451 32c. Clara Ward 65 50
3452 32c. Sister Rosetta 65 50

2341 Benet

2342 Woman

1998. Literary Arts. Birth Centenary of Stephen Vincent Benet (poet).
3453 **2341** 32c. multicoloured . . . 55 15

1998. Breast Cancer Awareness Campaign. Inscr "First Class". Self-adhesive.
3454 **2342** (32c.+8c.) mult 65 60

2343 Antillean Euphonia

2347 Common Pheasant ("Ringed-necked Pheasant")

1998. Tropical Birds. Multicoloured.
3455 32c. Type **2343** 65 50
3456 32c. Green-throated carib 65 50
3457 32c. Crested honeycreeper 65 50
3458 32c. Cardinal honeyeater . . 65 40

1998. Self-adhesive.
3459 **2347** 20c. multicoloured . . . 35 40

2348 Alfred Hitchcock (director)

2349 Couple swapping Hearts

1998. Legends of Hollywood.
3465 **2348** 32c. black and silver . . 65 25
No. 3465 includes a cut-out of Hitchcock's trademark caricature above his right shoulder.

1998. Organ and Tissue Donation Campaign. Self-adhesive.
3466 **2349** 32c. multicoloured . . . 60 25

2350 Red Fox

2351 Bicycle Handlebars

1998. Self-adhesive.
3467 **2350** $1 multicoloured . . . 1·40 50

1998. Ordinary or self-adhesive gum.
3468 **2351** (10c.) black, grn & vio 25 25

2352 Dog

1998. "Bright Eyes". Multicoloured. Self-adhesive.
3470 32c. Type **2352** 60 25
3471 32c. Cat 60 50
3472 32c. Hamster 60 50
3473 32c. Goldfish 60 50
3474 32c. Parakeet 60 50

2357 Gold Prospectors

1998. Centenary of Klondike Gold Rush.
3475 **2357** 32c. multicoloured . . . 60 45

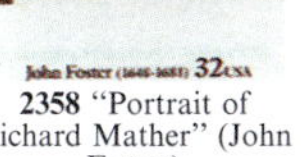

2358 "Portrait of Richard Mather" (John Foster)

2359 Pres. Franklin D. Roosevelt making Radio Broadcast

1998. American Art. Multicoloured.
3476 32c. Type **2358** 60 65
3477 32c. "Mrs. Elizabeth Freake and Baby Mary" (The Freake Limner) 60 65
3478 32c. "Girl in Red Dress with Cat and Dog" (Ammi Phillips) 60 65
3479 32c. "Rubens Peale with Geranium" (Rembrandt Peale) 60 65
3480 32c. "Long-billed Curlew, Numenius longrostris" (John James Audubon) 60 65
3481 32c. "Boatmen on the Missouri" (George Caleb Bingham) 60 65
3482 32c. "Kindred Spirits" (Asher B. Durand) . . . 60 65
3483 32c. "Westwood Children" (Joshua Johnson) 60 65
3484 32c. "Music and Literature" (William Harnett) 60 65
3485 32c. "Fog Warning" (Winslow Homer) 60 65
3486 32c. "White Cloud, Head Chief of the Iowas" (George Catlin) 60 65
3487 32c. "Cliffs of Green River" (Thomas Moran) 60 65
3488 32c. "Last of the Buffalo" (Albert Bierstadt) 60 65
3489 32c. "Niagara" (Frederic Edwin Church) 60 65
3490 32c. "Breakfast in Bed" (Mary Cassatt) 60 65
3491 32c. "Nighthawks" (Edward Hopper) 60 65
3492 32c. "American Gothic" (Grant Wood) 60 65
3493 32c. "Two against the White" (Charles Sheeler) 60 65
3494 32c. "Mahoning" (Franz Kline) 60 65
3495 32c. "No. 12" (Mark Rothko) 60 65

1998. The Twentieth Century (3rd series). The 1930s. Blue (No. 3497) or multicoloured (others).
3496 32c. Type **2359** 55 65
3497 32c. Empire State Building (completed 1931) 55 65
3498 32c. Front cover of "Life" magazine's first issue, 1936 . . . . 55 65
3499 32c. Eleanor Roosevelt (First Lady) and child . . 55 65
3500 32c. New Deal economic recovery plan 55 65
3501 32c. Superman (first comic book super hero, 1938) 55 65
3502 32c. Electric food mixer (household conveniences) 55 65
3503 32c. "Snow White and the Seven Dwarfs" (first feature-length animated film, 1937) 55 65
3504 32c. "Gone with the Wind" (novel by Margaret Mitchell) (published 1936) 55 65
3505 32c. Jesse Owens (athlete) 55 65
3506 32c. "New 20th Century Limited" (streamlined steam train) 55 65
3507 32c. Inauguration of Golden Gate Bridge, San Francisco, 1937 . . . . . 55 65
3508 32c. Florence Owens Thompson (photograph by Dorothea Lange, 1936) (Great Depression) . . . 55 65
3509 32c. Bobby Jones (golfer) (only person to win Grand Slam, 1930) . . . 55 65
3510 32c. Monopoly board (first produced commercially, 1933) 55 65

2360 Ballerina

2361 City Domes and Vehicle

1998. 50th Anniv of New York City Ballet.
3511 **2360** 32c. multicoloured . . . 60 25

1998. Future of Space Travel. Multicoloured.
3512 32c. Type **2361** 60 40
3513 32c. Capsule preparing to land 60 40
3514 32c. Space pioneer on rock 60 40
3515 32c. Capsule taking off and pioneer with vehicle . . . 60 40
3516 32c. Dome and bridge over canyon 60 40

Nos. 3512/16 were issued together, se-tenant, forming a composite design.

2366 Flower and Bee

1998. "Giving and Sharing". Self-adhesive.
3517 **2366** 32c. multicoloured . . . 60 30

2367 "Florentine Madonna and Child" (sculpture, anon)

2368 Evergreen Wreath

1998. Christmas. Multicoloured. Self-adhesive.

(a) Size $19\frac{1}{2} \times 26\frac{1}{2}$ mm.
3518 32c. Type **2367** 60 25
3519 32c. Type **2368** 60 50
3520 32c. Victorian wreath . . . 60 50
3521 32c. Chilli wreath 60 50
3522 32c. Tropical wreath 60 50

(b) Size 17 × 22 mm.
3523 32c. Type **2368** 65 50
3524 32c. As No. 3520 . . . . . 65 50
3525 32c. As No. 3521 . . . . . 65 50
3526 32c. As No. 3522 . . . . . 65 50

2372 Uncle Sam's Hat

2373 Rooster Weathervane

1998. First-Class Rate stamps. No value expressed. Ordinary or self-adhesive gum.
3527 **2372** (33c.) multicoloured . . 60 25

1998. No value expressed. Make-up Rate stamps.
3533 **2373** (1c.) multicoloured (blue imprint date) (21 × 17 mm) 20 15
3534 (1c.) multicoloured (black imprint date) (21 × 18 mm) 20 20

2374 Uncle Sam

2375 Space Shuttle landing

1998. Self-adhesive.
3535 **2374** 22c. multicoloured . . . 40 30

1998. Multicoloured. Self-adhesive.
3538 $3.20 Type **2375** . . . . . 5·25 1·20
3539 $11.75 Space shuttle on transport plane . . . . . 20·00 10·00

2377 Eagle and Shield

2378 Rabbit

1998. Presorted coil stamp. Ordinary or self-adhesive gum.
3540 **2377** (10c.) multicoloured . . 20 25

1999. Chinese New Year.
3545 **2378** 33c. multicoloured . . . 60 50

2379 Malcolm X

2380 Heart of Pink Roses

1999. Black Heritage. Malcolm X (el-Hajj Malik el-Shabazz) (black nationalist leader). Self-adhesive.
3546 **2379** 33c. green, grey and black 65 25

1999. Greetings Stamps. Multicoloured. Self-adhesive.
3547 33c. Type **2380** 60 25
3548 55c. Heart of red roses . . . 95 65

Nos. 3547/8 are die-cut to shape around the design.

2382 Butterfly and Hospice

2383 Uncle Sam and Soldiers (World War II)

1999. Hospice Care. Self-adhesive.
3549 **2382** 33c. multicoloured . . . 60 25

1999. The Twentieth Century (4th series). The 1940s. Brown (No. 3560) or mult (others).
3550 33c. Type **2383** 55 65
3551 33c. Penicillin (development of antibiotics) 55 65
3552 33c. Jackie Robinson (baseball player) 55 65
3553 33c. President Harry Truman 55 65
3554 33c. Women's War Effort poster ("We Can Do It") 55 65
3555 33c. Filming of television programme 55 65
3556 33c. Couple jitterbugging . . 55 65
3557 33c. Jackson Pollock at work (Abstract Expressionism) 55 65
3558 33c. Soldier studying (Servicemen's Readjustment Act (GI Bill), 1944) 55 65
3559 33c. Big Band music 55 65
3560 33c. United Nations building, New York (International Style of architecture) 55 65
3561 33c. Postwar baby boom (front cover of "The Saturday Evening Post", 2 November 1946) 55 65
3562 33c. Slinky (coiled wire toy) 55 65
3563 33c. Poster for Broadway production of "A Streetcar Named Desire" (Tennessee Williams), 1947 . . . . 55 65
3564 33c. Scene from Orson Welles's "Citizen Kane" (film), 1941 . . . . 55 65

A brief description of the subject is printed under the gum on the back of each stamp.

2384 Flag and Skyscrapers

2385 Irish Immigration Ship

1999. Ordinary or self-adhesive gum.
3565 **2384** 33c. multicoloured . . . 55 25

1999. Irish Immigration.
3570 **2385** 33c. multicoloured . . . 55 40

2386 Alfred Lunt and Lynn Fontanne (actors)

1999. Preforming Arts and Artists.
3571 **2386** 33c. multicoloured . . . 55 40

2387 Arctic Hare

2392 Flag and Alphabet on Board

1999. Arctic Animals. Multicoloured.
3572 33c. Type **2387** 60 40
3573 33c. Arctic fox 60 40
3574 33c. Snowy owl 60 40
3575 33c. Polar bear 60 40
3576 33c. Grey wolf 60 40

1999. Automatic Teller Machine stamp.
3577 **2392** 33c. multicoloured . . . 60 40

2395 Blueberries

2399 Daffy Duck

1999. Berries. Self-adhesive. Multicoloured.
3579 33c. Type **2395** 55 50
3580 33c. Raspberries 55 50
3581 33c. Strawberries 55 50
3582 33c. Blackberries 55 50

1999. Daffy Duck (cartoon character). Self-adhesive.
3591 **2399** 33c. multicoloured . . . 55 40

2400 Ayn Rand

2401 Bird-of-Paradise Flower

1999. Literary Arts. Ayn Rand (novelist).
3593 **2400** 33c. multicoloured . . . 55 25

1999. Tropical Flowers. Self-adhesive. Mult.
3595 33c. Type **2401** 55 65
3596 33c. Royal poinciana . . . 55 65
3597 33c. Gloriosa lily 55 65
3598 33c. Chinese hibiscus . . . 55 65

A 2405 Rio Grande

2410 "Franklinia alatamaha" (after William Bartram)

1999. Air. Self-adhesive. Multicoloured.
A3599 40c. Type A **2405** . . . 65 60
A3600 48c. Niagara Falls . . . 90 70
A3601 60c. Grand Canyon . . . 1·00 85
A3602 60c. Acadia National Park, Maine 80 20
A3603 70c. Nine-mile Piaine, Nebrasska 90 20
A3600a 80c. Mt. Mckinley, Alaska . . . . 1·10 25

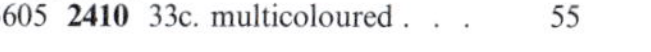

1999. 300th Birth Anniv of John and 260th Birth Anniv of William Bartram (botanists). Self-adhesive.
3605 **2410** 33c. multicoloured . . . 55 30

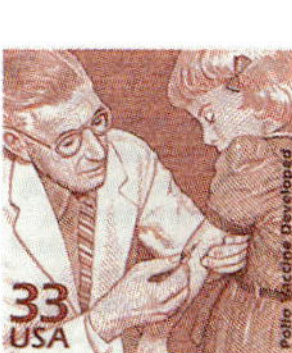
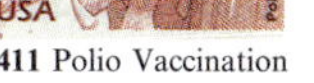

2411 Polio Vaccination

2412 Male Gender Sign

1999. The Twentieth Century (5th series). The 1950s. Red (No. 3606) or multicoloured (others).

3606 33c. Type **2411** 55 65
3607 33c. Teen fashions 55 65
3608 33c. Baseball (The "Shot Heard 'Round the World") 55 65
3609 33c. Rocket launch, 1958 . . 55 65
3610 33c. U.S. soldiers in snow (Korean War, 1950–53) 55 65
3611 33c. Desegregation of state ("public") schools 55 65
3612 33c. Tailfin of car ("Tail Fins and Chrome") . . . 55 65
3613 33c. "The Cat in the Hat" (reading primer by Theodor Seuss, 1957) . . 55 65
3614 33c. Drive-in movies 55 65
3615 33c. Stadium and badges for New York Yankees and Brooklyn Dodgers baseball teams (World Series Rivals) 55 65
3616 33c. Rocky Marciano (world heavyweight boxing champion, 1952–56) . . . 55 65
3617 33c. Lucille Ball and Desi Arnaz in "I Love Lucy" (television series) 55 65
3618 33c. Singer/guitarist and jivers (Rock 'n' Roll) . . 55 65
3619 33c. Stock car race 55 65
3620 33c. Audience at 3-D movie 55 65

A brief description of the subject is printed under the gum on the back of each stamp.

1999. Prostate Cancer Awareness Campaign. Self-adhesive.

3621 **2412** 33c. multicoloured . . . 55 30

2413 Prospectors

1999. 150th Anniv of California Gold Rush.

3622 **2413** 33c. multicoloured . . . 55 30

2414 Long-horned Cowfish, Black-tailed Damselfish, Cleaner Shrimp and Flame Hawkfish

2415 Copper-band Butterflyfish, Mushroom Polyps and Blue Starfish

2416 Powder-blue Surgeonfish and Long-spined Sea Urchin

2417 Clown Anemonefish and Red Hermit Crab

2418 Skateboarding

1999. Aquarium Fishes. Self-adhesive.

3623 **2414** 33c. multicoloured . . . 55 65
3624 **2415** 33c. multicoloured . . . 55 65
3625 **2416** 33c. multicoloured . . . 55 65
3626 **2417** 33c. multicoloured . . . 55 40

Nos. 3623/6 were issued together, se-tenant, forming a composite design.

1999. "Xtreme" Sports. Self-adhesive. Mult.

3627 33c. Type **2418** 60 40
3628 33c. BMX biking 60 40
3629 33c. Snowboarding 60 40
3630 33c. Inline skating 60 40

2422 Free-blown Glass

2426 James Cagney

1999. American Glass. Multicoloured.

3631 33c. Type **2422** 55 40
3632 33c. Mould-blown glass . . 55 65
3633 33c. Pressed glass 55 40
3634 33c. Art glass 55 40

1999. Legends of Hollywood.

3635 **2426** 33c. multicoloured . . . 60 65

2427 Mitchell and SPAD XVI Biplane

2428 Rose

1999. 120th Birth Anniv of Billy Mitchell (aviation pioneer). Self-adhesive.

3636 **2427** 55c. multicoloured . . . 95 80

1999. Self-adhesive.

3637 **2428** 33c. multicoloured . . . 55 25

2429 Flag

1999. "Honoring Those Who Served". Self-adhesive.

3638 **2429** 33c. red, blue and black 55 25

2430 Stars

1999. 125th Anniv of Universal Postal Union.

3639 **2430** 45c. blue and red . . . 75 60

2431 "Daylight"

1999. Trains. Multicoloured.

3640 33c. Type **2431** 55 40
3641 33c. "20th Century Limited" 55 40
3642 33c. "Super Chief" 55 40
3643 33c. "Congressional" . . . 55 40
3644 33c. "Hiawatha" 55 40

Details of the trains are printed under the gum on the back of each stamp.

2436 Olmsted (after John Singer Sargent) and Central Park, New York

1999. 77th Birth Anniv of Frederick Law Olmsted (landscaper).

3645 **2436** 33c. multicoloured . . . 55 25

2437 Max Steiner

1999. Hollywood Composers. Multicoloured.

3646 33c. Type **2437** 75 65
3647 33c. Dimitri Tiomkin . . . 75 65
3648 33c. Bernard Herrmann . . 75 65
3649 33c. Franz Waxman 75 65
3650 33c. Alfred Newman 75 65
3651 33c. Erich Wolfgang Korngold 75 65

2443 Martin Luther King (Civil Rights leader)

1999. The Twentieth Century (6th series). The 1960s. Black (No. 3654) or mult (others).

3652 33c. Type **2443** 55 65
3653 33c. Bird on guitar neck (Woodstock Music Festival, 1969) 55 65
3654 33c. Footprint (first manned moon landing, 1969) . . . 55 65
3655 33c. Members of Green Bay Packers football team . . 55 65
3656 33c. Starship "Enterprise" (television series "Star Trek") 55 65
3657 33c. Peace Corps volunteers 55 65
3658 33c. Troops disembarking from helicopter (Vietnam War) 55 65
3659 33c. Ford Mustang sportscar 55 65
3660 33c. Barbie doll 55 65
3661 33c. Integrated circuit . . . 55 65
3662 33c. Lasers 55 65
3663 33c. Ticket to football match (Super Bowl I) . . 55 65
3664 33c. Peace symbol 55 65
3665 33c. Roger Maris (baseball player) 55 65
3666 33c. Yellow submarine (The Beatles pop group) . . . 55 65

A brief description of the subject is printed under the gum on the back of each stamp.

2444 Ira and George Gershwin

1999. Broadway Songwriters. Multicoloured.

3667 33c. Type **2444** 75 65
3668 33c. Alan Jay Lerner and Frederick Loewe 75 65
3669 33c. Lorenz Hart 75 65
3670 33c. Richard Rodgers and Oscar Hammerstein II . . 75 65
3671 33c. Meredith Willson . . . 75 65
3672 33c. Frank Loesser 75 65

2450 Black Widow

1999. Insects and Spiders. Multicoloured.

3673 33c. Type **2450** 55 65
3674 33c. Elderberry longhorn . . 55 65
3675 33c. Ladybird ("Lady beetle") 55 65
3676 33c. Yellow garden spider 55 65
3677 33c. Dogbane beetle 55 65
3678 33c. Flower fly 55 65
3679 33c. Assassin bug 55 65
3680 33c. Ebony jewelwing . . . 55 65
3681 33c. Velvet ant 55 65
3682 33c. Monarch (caterpillar) 55 65
3683 33c. Monarch (butterfly) . . 55 65
3684 33c. Eastern Hercules beetle 55 65
3685 33c. Bombadier beetle . . . 55 65
3686 33c. Dung beetle 55 65
3687 33c. Spotted water beetle . . 55 65
3688 33c. True katydid 55 65
3689 33c. Spiny-backed spider . . 55 65
3690 33c. Periodical cicada . . . 55 65
3691 33c. Scorpionfly 55 65
3692 33c. Jumping spider 55 65

Descriptions of the subject are printed under the gum on the back of each stamp.

2451 Dove with Laurel

1999. 50th Anniv of North Atlantic Treaty Organization.

3695 **2451** 33c. multicoloured . . . 55 25

2452 "Madonna and Child" (Bartolomeo Vivarini)

2453 Stag

1999. Christmas. Self-adhesive. (a) Size 20 × 27 mm.

3696 **2452** 33c. multicoloured . . . 55 40

(b) Size 27 × 20½ mm.

3697 **2452** 33c. gold and red . . . 55 25
3698 33c. gold and blue . . . 55 25
3699 33c. gold and violet . . 55 25
3700 33c. gold and green . . 55 50

(c) Size 21½ × 19½ mm.

3701 **2453** 33c. gold and red . . . 65 15
3702 33c. gold and blue . . . 65 15
3703 33c. gold and violet . . 65 40
3704 33c. gold and green . . 65 40

2454 Hands holding Globe (first Earth Day, 1970)

2455 New Year Baby

1999. The Twentieth Century (7th series). The 1970s. Blue (Nos. 3712, 3714) or multicoloured (others).

3705 33c. Type **2454** 55 65
3706 33c. Scene from "All in the Family" (television series) 55 65
3707 33c. Big Bird (character from children's television series "Sesame Street") . . 55 65
3708 33c. Disco dancers 55 65
3709 33c. American football helmet (winning of four Super Bowls by Pittsburgh Steelers) . . . 55 65
3710 33c. Statue of Liberty and fireworks (bicentenary of United States, 1976) . . . 55 65
3711 33c. Secretariat (racehorse) (winner of Triple Crown, 1973) 55 65
3712 33c. Video cassette recorder 55 65
3713 33c. "Pioneer 10" (launch of Jupiter space probe, 1972) 55 65
3714 33c. Emblem of Women's Rights Movement 55 65
3715 33c. 1970s fashion 55 65
3716 33c. Cameraman filming American football match (television series "Monday Night Football") 55 65
3717 33c. "Smiley face" badges 55 65
3718 33c. Girl gazing at Boeing jumbo jet 55 65
3719 33c. Scan of skull ("Medical imaging") 55 65

A brief description of the subject is printed under the gum on the back of each stamp.

1999. Year 2000. Self-adhesive.

3720 **2455** 33c. multicoloured . . . 65 40

2456 Dragon

2000. New Year.

3725 **2456** 33c. multicoloured . . . 55 25

2457 Space Shuttle "Columbia"

2458 Patricia Harris

2000. The Twentieth Century (8th series). The 1980s. Multicoloured.

3726 33c. Type **2457** 55 65
3727 33c. Poster for "Cats" (stage musical) 55 65
3728 33c. San Francisco 49ers (American football team) 55 65
3729 33c. Welcome in Washington for homecoming of hostages held in siege of U.S. Embassy, Teheran 55 65
3730 33c. Figure skater 55 65
3731 33c. Dish aerials (cable TV) 55 65

3732 33c. Vietnam Veterans Memorial 55 65
3733 33c. Compact disc 55 65
3734 33c. Cabbage Patch doll . . 55 65
3735 33c. Opening shot of "The Cosby Show" (television comedy series) 55 65
3736 33c. Fall of the Berlin Wall 55 65
3737 33c. Children playing video game 55 65
3738 33c. "E.T." the Extra-Terrestrial (film) 55 65
3739 33c. Personal computer . . 55 65
3740 33c. Hip-hop culture 55 65

A brief description of the subject is printed under the gum on the back of each stamp.

2000. Black Heritage. Patricia Roberts Harris (diplomat). Self-adhesive.
3741 **2458** 33c. multicoloured . . . 55 25

2459 S-Class Submarine

2000. Centenary of United States Navy Submarine Fleet. Multicoloured.
3743 22c. Type **2459** 35 15
3744 33c. Los Angeles Class . . . 55 65
3745 55c. Ohio Class 85 40
3746 60c. U.S.S. *Holland I*, 1900 95 45
3747 $3.20 Gato Class (77 × 22 mm) . . . . . . 4·75 6·50

2466 "Silent Music I"

2467 "Royal Tide I"

2468 "Black Chord"

2469 "Nightsphere-Light"

2470 "Dawn's Wedding Chapel I" **2471** Eagle Nebula

2000. Birth Centenary of Louise Nevelson (sculptress).
3749 **2466** 33c. multicoloured . . . 55 65
3750 **2467** 33c. multicoloured . . . 55 65
3751 **2468** 33c. multicoloured . . . 55 65
3752 **2469** 33c. multicoloured . . . 55 65
3753 **2470** 33c. multicoloured . . . 55 65

2000. 10th Anniv of Hubble Space Telescope. Mult.
3754 33c. Type **2471** 55 40
3755 33c. Ring Nebula 55 40
3756 33c. Lagoon Nebula 55 40
3757 33c. Egg Nebula 55 40
3758 33c. Galaxy NGC 1316 . . 55 40

A brief description of the subject is printed under the gum on the back of each stamp.

2476 Sunuitao Peak, Ofu Island and Alia (fishing catamaran)

2000. Centenary of Samoa's Status as an Unorganized United States Territory.
3759 **2476** 33c. multicoloured . . . 55 15

2477 Main Reading Room, Thomas Jefferson Building, Library of Congress

2478 Road Runner and Wile E. Coyote

2000. Bicentenary of Library of Congress, Washington, D.C.
3760 **2477** 33c. multicoloured . . . 55 40

2000. Wile E. Coyote and Road Runner (cartoon characters). Self-adhesive.
3761 **2478** 33c. multicoloured . . . 55 25

2479 Baseball and Newspaper Headline

2000. The Twentieth Century (9th series). The 1990s. Multicoloured.
3763 33c. Type **2479** 55 65
3764 33c. Soldier and Chinook helicopters (Iraqi invasion of Kuwait, 1990) 55 65
3765 33c. Set from *Seinfeld* (television comedy show) 55 65
3766 33c. Snowboarder (increased popularity in extreme sports) 55 65
3767 33c. Child writing (improvement in quality of education) 55 65
3768 33c. Hand and butterfly (computer generated art) 55 65
3769 33c. Peregrine falcon (recovery of endangered species) 55 65
3770 33c. Space shuttle *Discovery* (John Glenn's (first American to orbit Earth) return to space, 1998) . . 55 65
3771 33c. Olympic gold medal (30th anniv of special Olympics, 1998) 55 65
3772 33c. Man using virtual reality game 55 65
3773 33c. Tyrannosaurus rex (*Jurassic Park* (film), 1993) 55 65
3774 33c. Poster for *Titanic* (film), 1997 . . . . 55 65
3775 33c. Increase in popularity of off-road vehicles . . . 55 65
3776 33c. Computer keyboard (introduction of the Internet and the World Wide Web) 55 65
3777 33c. Man using mobile phone (increase in use of cellular phones) 55 65

A brief description of the subject is printed under the gum on the back of each stamp.

2480 John L. Hines and 4th Division Insignia (Distinguished Service Cross and Medal)

2000. Distinguished Soldiers. Multicoloured.
3778 33c. Type **2480** 60 40
3779 33c. Omar N. Bradley and First Army Insignia (Army Chief of Staffs) . . 60 40
3780 33c. Alvin C. York and 82nd Division Insignia (Medal of Honor) 60 40
3781 33c. Audie L. Murphy and 3rd Infantry Division Insignia (Medal of Honor) 60 40

2484 Athletes

2000. Summer Sports. Lilac Bloomsday Run, Washington.
3782 **2484** 33c. multicoloured . . . 55 30

2485 Stylized Man and Woman **2486** Basketball

2000. Adoption Awareness. Self-adhesive.
3783 **2485** 33c. multicoloured . . . 55 25

2000. Youth Team Sports.
3784 33c. Type **2486** 60 40
3785 33c. American football . . . 60 40
3786 33c. Soccer 60 40
3787 33c. Baseball 60 40

2490 Sons of Liberty Flag, 1775 **2491** Blackberries

2000. History of the American Flag.
3788 **2490** 33c. red and black . . . 55 65
3789 – 33c. multicoloured . . . 55 65
3790 – 33c. red and black . . . 55 65
3791 – 33c. red, blue and black 55 65
3792 – 33c. red, blue and black 55 65
3793 – 33c. red and black . . . 55 65
3794 – 33c. red, blue and black 55 65
3795 – 33c. red, blue and black 55 65
3796 – 33c. red, blue and black 55 65
3797 – 33c. blue, red and black 55 65
3798 – 33c. red, blue and black 55 65
3799 – 33c. red, blue and black 55 65
3800 – 33c. red, blue and black 55 65
3801 – 33c. red, blue and black 55 65
3802 – 33c. red, blue and black 55 65
3803 – 33c. red, blue and black 55 65
3804 – 33c. red, blue and black 55 65
3805 – 33c. red, blue and black 55 65
3806 – 33c. red, blue and black 55 65
3807 – 33c. red, blue and black 55 65

DESIGNS: No. 3789, New England flag, 1775; 3790, Forster flag, 1775; 3791, Continental Colors, 1776; 3792, Francis Hopkinson flag, 1777; 3793, Brandywine flag, 1777; 3794, John Paul Jones flag, 1779; 3795, Pierre L'Enfant flag, 1783; 3796, Indian Peace flag, 1803; 3797, Easton flag, 1814; 3798, Star-Spangled Banner, 1814; 3799, Bennington flag, 1820; 3800, Great Star flag, 1837; 3801, 29-Star flag, 1847; 3802, Fort Sumter flag, 1861; 3803, Centennial flag, 1876; 3804, 38-Star flag, 1877; 3805, Peace flag, 1891; 3806, 48-Star flag, 1912; 3807, 50-Star flag, 1960.

A brief history of the subject is printed under the gum on the back of each stamp.

2000. Berries. Self-adhesive. Multicoloured.
3808 33c. Type **2491** 55 15
3809 33c. Raspberries 55 15
3810 33c. Blueberries 55 15
3811 33c. Strawberries 55 25

2495 Jackie Robinson

2000. Legends of Baseball. Self-adhesive. Mult.
3812 33c. Type **2495** 55 65
3813 33c. Eddie Collins 55 65
3814 33c. Christy Mathewson . . 55 65
3815 33c. Ty Cobb 55 65
3816 33c. George Sisler 55 65
3817 33c. Rogers Hornsby . . . 55 65
3818 33c. Mickey Cochrane . . . 55 65
3819 33c. Babe Ruth 55 65
3820 33c. Walter Johnson 55 65
3821 33c. Roberto Clemente . . . 55 65
3822 33c. Lefty Grove 55 65
3823 33c. Tris Speaker 55 65
3824 33c. Cy Young 55 65
3825 33c. Jimmie Foxx 55 65
3826 33c. Pie Traynor 55 65
3827 33c. Satchel Paige 55 65
3828 33c. Honus Wagner 55 65
3829 33c. Josh Gibson 55 65
3830 33c. Dizzy Dean 55 65
3831 33c. Lou Gehrig 55 65

2501 "Astronauts" (Zachary Canter) **2507** Joseph W. Stillwell

2000. "Stampin' the Future". Winning Entries in Children's International Painting Competition. Self-adhesive. Multicoloured.
3833 33c. Type **2501** 55 40
3834 33c. "Children" (Sarah Lipsey) 55 40
3835 33c. "Rocket" (Morgan Hill) 55 40
3836 33c. "Dog" (Ashley Young) 55 40

2000. Great Americans. (a) Ordinary gum.
3839 **2507** 10c. black and red . . . 20 25
3846 – 33c. black and red . . . 55 15

(b) Self-adhesive.
3857 – 76c. black and red . . . . 1·10 65

DESIGNS: 33c. Claude Pepper; 76c. Hattie W. Caraway.

2538 Coastline **2539** Edward G. Robinson

2000. 150th Anniv of Californian Statehood.
3870 **2538** 33c. multicoloured . . . 55 40

2000. Legends of Hollywood.
3871 **2539** 33c. multicoloured . . . 55 40

2540 Fanfin Anglerfish

2000. Deep Sea Creatures. Multicoloured.
3872 33c. Type **2540** 55 15
3873 33c. Sea cucumber 55 15
3874 33c. Fangtooth 55 15
3875 33c. Amphipod 55 40
3876 33c. Medusa 55 40

2545 Wolfe

2000. Birth Centenary of Thomas Wolfe (writer).
3877 **2545** 33c. multicoloured . . . 55 25

2546 North Facade **2547** Lion Statue, New York Public Library

2000. Bicentenary of The White House as President's Residence. Self-adhesive.
3878 **2546** 33c. multicoloured . . . 55 25

2000. Presorted coil stamp. Self-adhesive.
3879 **2547** (10c.) multicoloured . . 20 25

2548 Farm and Flag

2000. Ordinary or self-adhesive gum.
3880 **2548** (34c.) multicoloured . . 55 50

2549 Statue of Liberty **2550** Statue of Liberty

2000. First-Class Rate stamps. (a) Ordinary or self-adhesive gum.
3883 **2549** (34c.) multicoloured . . 55 80

(b) Self-adhesive gum.
3885 **2550** (34c.) multicoloured . . 55 65

2551 Lily **2552** Freesia **2553** Lily

2554 Orchid **2555** Statue of Liberty

2556 Statue of Liberty

2000. Flowers. Self-adhesive.
3886 **2551** (34c.) multicoloured . . 55 50
3887 **2552** (34c.) multicoloured . . 55 50
3888 **2553** (34c.) multicoloured . . 55 50
3889 **2554** (34c.) multicoloured . . 55 50

2001. (a) Ordinary or Self-adhesive gum.
3894 **2555** 34c. multicoloured . . . 55 80

(b) Self-adhesive.
3895 **2556** 34c. multicoloured . . . 55 50

2557 Red Rose and "LOVE" **2558** Snake

2001. Greeting Stamps. First-Class Rate stamp. Self-adhesive.
3897 **2557** (34c.) multicoloured . . 55 65

2001. New Year.
3898 **2558** 34c. multicoloured . . . 55 25

2559 Roy Wilkins **2560** Capitol, Washington

2001. Black Heritage. Roy Wilkins (civil rights pioneer). Self-adhesive.
3899 **2559** 34c. blue and black . . 55 25

2001. Self-adhesive.
3900 $3.50 Type **2560** . . . . . 5·50 5·00
3901 $12.25 Washington Monument . . . . 18·00 16·00

Nos. 3900/1 each incorporate an additional hidden inscription "PRIORITY MAIL" (No. 3900) or "EXPRESS MAIL" (No. 3901) visible only under a special decoder.

No. 3900 was intended mainly for Priority mail and No. 3901 for Express Mail Service but they could be used on other mail as well.

2562 "First in the Fight, Always Faithful" (recruitment poster, James Montgomery Flagg) **2563** Farm and Flag

2001. American Illustrators. Black (No. 3918) or multicoloured (others). Self-adhesive.
3902 34c. Type **2562** 55 65
3903 34c. "Interlude (The Lute Players)" (mural, Maxfield Parrish) 55 65
3904 34c. Couple dancing (advertisement, Joseph Christian Leyendecker) . . 55 65
3905 34c. Man sawing ice (advertisement, Robert Fawcett) 55 65
3906 34c. Couple in car (advertisement, Coles Philips) 55 65
3907 34c. Woman combing hair ("How I Make a Picture") (Al Parker) 55 65
3908 34c. Br'er Rabbit (Arthur Burdett Frost) 55 65
3909 34c. "An Attack on a Galleon" (illustration, Howard Pyle) 55 65
3910 34c. Kewpies (Rose O'Neill)
3911 34c. Steam boat (magazine cover illustration, Dean Cornwell) 55 65
3912 34c. "Galahad's Departure" (detail of mural, Edwin Austin Abbey) 55 65
3913 34c. "The First Lesson" (magazine cover illustration, Jessie Willcox Smith) 55 65
3914 34c. Woman holding artist's palette (magazine cover illustration, Neysa McMein) 55 65
3915 34c. "Back Home for Keeps" (advertisement, Jon Whitcomb) 55 65
3916 34c. "Something for Supper" (Harvey Dunn) 55 65
3917 34c. "A Dash for the Timber" (Frederic Remington) 55 65
3918 34c. Scene from *Moby Dick* (book illustration, Rockwell Kent) 55 65
3919 34c. "Captain Bill Bones" (book illustration, Newell Convers Wyeth) 55 65
3920 34c. Doctor and child (magazine cover illustration, Norman Rockwell) 55 65
3921 34c. "The Girl He Left Behind" (John Held Jr.) 55 65

A brief biography of the artist is printed on the backing paper on the back of each stamp.

2001. Ordinary or Self-adhesive gum.
3922 **2563** 34c. multicoloured . . . 55 50

2564 Lily **2565** Freesia **2566** Lily

2567 Orchid

2001. Flowers. Self-adhesive.
3930 **2564** 34c. multicoloured . . . 55 50
3931 **2565** 34c. multicoloured . . . 55 65
3932 **2566** 34c. multicoloured . . . 85 65
3933 **2567** 34c. multicoloured . . . 35 65

2568 Rose and "LOVE" **2569** Rose and "LOVE"

2001. Greetings Stamps. Self-adhesive.
3938 **2568** 34c. multicoloured . . . 55 15
3939 **2569** 55c. multicoloured . . . 55 15
3940 57c. multicoloured . . . 85 65

2570 George Washington **2571** Bison

2001. Self-adhesive.
3941 **2570** 20c. red 35 65
3942 23c. green . . . . . . 1·10 35

2001. Self-adhesive.
3951 **2571** 21c. multicoloured . . . 35 65
3961 57c. multicoloured . . . 85 65

2572 Art Deco Eagle **2573** Apple

2001. Self-adhesive.
3960 **2572** 55c. multicoloured . . . 85 15

2001. Fruit. Self-adhesive.
3965 34c. Type **2573** 55 15
3966 34c. Orange 55 15

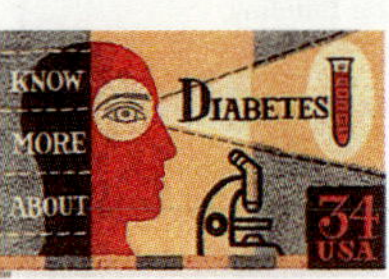

2576 Head, Test-tube and Microscope

2001. Diabetes Awareness Campaign. Self-adhesive.
3969 **2576** 34c. multicoloured . . . 55 30

2577 Obverse of Medals and Alfred Nobel (founder)

2001. Centenary of Nobel Prizes.
3970 **2577** 34c. yell, lt brn & brn 55 80

2578 1c. Stamp with Inverted Centre

2581 Exposition Emblem

2001. Centenary of Pan-American Exposition.
3971 **2578** 1c. black and green . . 30 15
3972 – 2c. black and red . . . 30 15
3973 – 4c. black and brown . . 30 15
3974 **2581** 80c. red and blue . . . 85 30

DESIGNS: No. 3972, 2c. stamp with inverted centre; 3973, 4c. stamp with inverted centre.

2583 Great Plains Prairie (1/2-size illustration)

2001. Nature of America. Sheet 233 × 172 mm. Forming the overall design T **2583**. Multicoloured. Self-adhesive.
MS3975 34c. Canada geese and Pronghorn deer; 34c. Bison, burrowing owls and buffalo grass; 34c. Bison, wild alfalfa and prairie dogs (horiz); 34c. Black-tailed prairie dog; 34c. Painted lady butterfly, coneflower and wild rose (horiz); 34c., Camel cricket and western meadow lark; 34c. Badger and buffalo grass; 34c. Eastern short-horned lizard and plains pocket gopher; 34c. Plains spadefoot and dung beetle (horiz); 34c. Two-striped grasshopper and Ord's kangaroo rat . . . . . 4·50 1·40

The back of the sheet has a description of the plains prairie and a key to the flora and fauna in the design.

2584 Snoopy as World War I Flying Ace (Charles M. Schultz)

2001. "Peanuts" (comic strip). Self-adhesive.
3976 **2584** 34c. multicoloured . . . 45 15

2585 Flag **2586** Kahlo

2001. "Honoring Veterans". Self-adhesive.
3977 **2585** 34c. multicoloured . . . 45 15

2001. Frida Kahlo (artist) Commemoration.
3978 **2586** 34c. multicoloured . . . 45 15

2587 Ebbets Field, Brooklyn **2588** Atlas (statue), Rockefeller Centre, New York City

2001. Baseball Fields. Multicoloured. Self-adhesive.
3979 34c. Type **2587** 45 15
3980 34c. Tiger Stadium, Detroit 45 15
3981 34c. Crosley Field, Cincinnati 45 15
3982 34c. Yankee Stadium, New York City 45 15
3983 34c. Polo Grounds, New York City 45 15
3984 34c. Forbes Field, Pittsburgh 45 15
3985 34c. Fenway Park, Boston 45 15
3986 34c. Comiskey Park, Chicago 45 15
3987 34c. Shibe Park, Philadelphia 45 15
3988 34c. Wrigley Field, Chicago 45 15

A brief description of the stadium is included on the backing paper of each stamp.

2001. Presorted coil stamp. Multicoloured. Self-adhesive.
3989 **2588** (10c.) multicoloured . . 15 10

2589 Leonard Bernstein (composer) **2590** Car

2001.
3990 **2589** 34c. black 45 15

2001. Presorted First-Class Card coil stamp. Self-adhesive.
3991 **2590** (15c.) multicoloured . . 20 10

2591 Lucille Ball

2592 Diamond in Square

2593 Lone Star

2594 Sunshine and Shadow

2595 Double Ninepatch

2001. Legends of Hollywood. Self-adhesive.

3992	**2591**	34c. multicoloured . . .	45	15

2001. Amish Quilts. Self-adhesive.

3993	**2592**	34c. multicoloured . . .	45	15
3994	**2593**	34c. multicoloured . . .	45	15
3995	**2594**	34c. multicoloured . . .	45	15
3996	**2595**	34c. multicoloured . . .	45	15

2596 Venus Flytrap

2600 Calligraphy

2001. Carnivorous Plants. Multicoloured. Self-adhesive.

3997	34c. Type **2596**	45	15
3998	34c. Yellow trumpet	45	15
3999	34c. Cobra lily	45	15
4000	34c.25 99 English sundew	45	15

2001. Eid al-Fitr and Eid al-Adha (Islamic festivals). Self-adhesive.

4001	**2600**	34c. gold, blue and brown	45	15

2601 Fermi

2602 Porky Pig delivering Letter

2001. Birth Centenary of Enrico Fermi (nuclear physicist).

4002	**2601**	34c. multicoloured . . .	45	15

2001. Porky Pig (cartoon character). Self-adhesive.

4003	**2603**	34c. multicoloured . . .	45	15
MS4004		87 × 130 mm. No. 4003	60	25

2603 "Virgin and Child" (Lorenzo Costa)

2604 Santa Claus with Armful of Presents

2001. Christmas. (1st issue). Self-adhesive gum.

4005	**2603**	34c. multicoloured . . .	45	15

2001. Christmas (2nd issue). Mulicoloured. Self-adhesive. (a) Size18 × 25 mm.

4006	34c. Type **2604**	45	15
4007	34c. Wearing blue outfit . .	45	15
4008	34c. Wearing red outfit with fur collar	45	15
4009	34c. Wearing holly wreath	45	15

(b) Size18 × 21 mm.

4010	34c. As T **2640**	45	15
4011	34c. As No. 4007	45	15
4012	34c. As No. 4008	45	15
4013	34c. As No. 4009	45	15

2608 Madison

2001. 250th Birth Anniv of James Madison (fourth president of United States).

4018	**2608**	34c. green and black . .	45	15

2609 Cornucopia

2610 Flag

2001. Thanksgiving Festival. Self-adhesive.

4019	**2609**	34c. multicoloured . . .	45	15

2001. Hanukkah and Kawanzaa Festivals. As Nos. 3265 and 3370 but with face values changed. Self-adhesive.

4020	**2257**	34c. multicoloured . . .	45	15
4021	**2304**	34c. multicoloured . . .	45	15

See also Nos. 3693/4.

2001. "United We Stand". Self-adhesive.

4022	**2610**	34c. multicoloured . . .	45	15

CERTIFIED MAIL

C 524 Postman

1955.

C1070	**C 524**	15c. red	45	30

NEWSPAPER STAMPS

N 21 Washington (½-size illustration)

1865. 5c. with coloured or white border.

N78	**N 21**	5c. blue	£175
N80	–	10c. green	£130
N81	–	25c. red	£140

DESIGNS: 10c. Franklin; 20c. Lincoln.

N 42 "Freedom"

N 87 "Freedom"

1875. Different Frames.

N252	**N 42**	1c. black	15·00	5·00
N291	**N 87**	1c. black	4·00	4·00
N228	**N 42**	2c. black	14·00	3·75
N292	**N 87**	2c. black	4·25	3·25
N229	**N 42**	3c. black	17·00	4·75
N230		4c. black	17·00	4·75
N293	**N 87**	5c. black	6·75	5·00
N231	**N 42**	6c. black	28·00	10·00
N232		8c. black	28·00	10·00
N185		9c. black	£160	55·00
N233		10c. black	26·00	10·00
N294	**N 87**	10c. black	4·25	3·25
N253	A	12c. red	38·00	13·50
N254		24c. red	40·00	13·50
N295		25c. red	8·25	10·00
N255		36c. red	65·00	20·00
N256		48c. red	£110	30·00
N296		50c. red	10·00	12·50
N191		60c. red	£100	43·00
N258		72c. red	£140	47·00
N240		84c. red	£225	£110
N241		96c. red	£160	80·00
N242	–	$1.92 brown	£120	70·00
N297	–	$2 red	13·50	20·00
N243	–	$3 red	£110	70·00
N298	–	$5 blue	23·00	27·00
N244	–	$6 blue	£170	£110
N245	–	$9 orange	£140	75·00
N299	–	$10 green	23·00	27·00
N246	–	$12 green	£200	95·00
N300	–	$20 black	25·00	28·00
N247	–	$24 purple	£220	£120
N248	–	$36 red	£275	£130
N249	–	$48 brown	£350	£180
N301	–	$50 red	33·00	28·00
N250	–	$60 violet	£325	£180
N302	–	$100 violet	37·00	33·00

DESIGNS: A, Astraea or "Justice"; $1.92, Ceres; $2, $3 "Victory"; $5, $6 Clio; $9 Minerva; $10, $12 Vesta; $20, $24 "Peace"; $36, $50 "Commerce"; $48 Hebe; $60, $100 Minnehaha.

OFFICIAL STAMPS

For list of stamps used on correspondence from individual Government Departments, between 1873 and 1879, see the Stanley Gibbons Part 22 (U.S.A.) Catalogue.

O 1315 Eagle O 1438 O 1588

1983.

O2008	**O 1315**	1c. blue, red & blk	10	20
O2009		4c. blue, red & blk	15	20
O2010		13c. blue, red & blk	25	65
O2011		14c. blue, red & blk	25	35
O2012		17c. blue, red & blk	30	75
O2015		20c. blue, red & blk	85	1·10
O2016		22c. blue, red & blk	45	1·20
O2013		$1 blue, red & blk	1·30	2·30
O2014		$5 blue, red & blk	10·50	13·00

1985. No value expressed. (a) Inscr "Postal Card Rate D".

O2140	**O 1438**	(14c.) bl, red & blk	3·25	3·25

(b) Inscr "Domestic Letter Rate D"

O2141	–	(22c.) blue, red and black	3·00	2·00

1988. No value expressed.

O2344	**O 1588**	(25c.) bl, blk & red	75	1·00

O 1592 O 1793 O 2001

1988.

O2348	**O 1592**	1c. blue, black & red	10	10
O2349		4c. blue, black & red	10	15
O2350		15c. blue, blk & red	35	25
O2352		19c. blue, blk & red	30	40
O2353		20c. blue, blk & red	45	35
O2351		23c. blue, blk & red	40	35
O2354		25c. blue, blk & red	45	55
O2355		29c. blue, blk & red	55	85

1991. Value expressed as "F".

O2558	**O 1793**	(29c.) blue, blk & red	1·10	55

1993.

O2844	**O 2001**	1c. blue, blk & red	10	10
O2845		10c. blue, blk & red	10	20
O2846		20c. blue, blk & red	25	35
O2847		23c. blue, blk & red	25	35
O2849		32c. blue, blk & red	35	25
O2850		33c. blue, blk & red	35	40
O2851		34c. blue, blk & red	35	35
O2848		$1 blue, blk & red	1·60	1·50

No. O2844 has the face value expressed as "1c."

The line above the face value consists of "USA" and the year date repeated several times.

1994. Value expressed as "G".

O2990	**O 1793**	(32c.) blue, blk & red	35	40

PARCEL POST STAMPS

P 134 Post Office Clerk

1912.

P423	**P 134**	1c. red	3·00	80
P424	–	2c. red	3·50	60
P425	–	3c. red	12·00	4·00
P426	–	4c. red	20·00	1·60
P427	–	5c. red	29·00	1·20
P428	–	10c. red	38·00	1·40
P429	–	15c. red	48·00	6·50
P430	–	20c. red	80·00	13·50
P431	–	25c. red	70·00	3·50
P432	–	50c. red	£150	24·00
P433	–	75c. red	50·00	19·00
P434	–	$1 red	£190	19·00

DESIGNS: 2c. City carrier; 3c. Railway postal clerk; 4c. Rural carrier; 5c. Steam mail train; 10c. "Kronprinz Wilhelm" (liner) and mail tender; 15c. Automobile service; 20c. Wright Type A biplane carrying mail; 25c. Manufacturing (Pullman works); 50c. Dairying; 75c. Harvesting; $1 Fruit growing.

PARCEL POST POSTAGE DUE STAMPS

PD 134

1912.

PD423	**PD 134**	1c. green	7·25	3·00
PD424		2c. green	55·00	12·50
PD425		5c. green	10·00	3·50
PD426		10c. green	£120	32·00
PD427		25c. green	70·00	3·25

POSTAGE DUE STAMPS

D 43

D 87

1879.

D207	**D 43**	1c. brown	36·00	4·75
D222		2c. brown	40·00	3·25
D209		3c. brown	32·00	2·50
D224		5c. brown	£225	14·50
D225		10c. brown	£200	10·50
D226		30c. brown	£120	26·00
D213		50c. brown	£275	50·00

1891.

D235	**D 43**	1c. red	20·00	80
D236		2c. red	23·00	60
D237		3c. red	41·00	6·25
D238		5c. red	50·00	6·25
D239		10c. red	75·00	13·50
D240		30c. red	£275	£110
D241		50c. red	£300	£110

1894.

D529	**D 87**	½c. red	70	15
D530		1c. red	7·50	60
D531		2c. red	8·50	70
D532		3c. red	7·25	15
D533		5c. red	7·25	15
D534		10c. red	11·50	15
D535a		30c. red	60·00	20
D536		50c. red	85·00	20

D 201 D 202

D 581

1931.

D702	**D 201**	½c. red	60	10
D703		1c. red	15	10
D704		2c. red	15	10
D705		3c. red	15	10
D706		5c. red	25	10
D707		10c. red	90	10
D708		30c. red	6·50	20
D709		50c. red	7·50	15
D699a	**D 202**	$1 red	20·00	15
D700a		$5 red	29·00	15

1959. Centres in black.

D1130	D **581**	½c. red	1·10	90
D1131		1c. red	15	10
D1132		2c. red	15	10
D1133		3c. red	15	10
D1134		4c. red	15	10
D1135		5c. red	15	10
D1136		6c. red	15	10
D1137		7c. red	15	10
D1138		8c. red	15	10
D1139		10c. red	15	10
D1140		11c. red	25	15
D1141		13c. red	25	15
D1142		17c. red	25	25
D1143		30c. red	50	10
D1144		50c. red	85	10
D1145		$1 red	1·90	10
D1146		$5 red	7·75	15

In the dollar values the numerals are double-lined and vertical.

REGISTERED LETTER STAMP

R **133** American Bald Eagle

1911.

R404	R **133**	10c. blue	80·00	3·75

SPECIAL DELIVERY AIR STAMPS

AE **247** Great Seal of U.S.A.

1934.

AE750	AE **247**	16c. blue	55	60
AE751		16c. blue and red	30	15

SPECIAL DELIVERY STAMPS

E **46** Messenger Running

1885. Inscr "AT A SPECIAL DELIVERY OFFICE".

E217	E **46**	10c. blue	£190	28·00

1888. Inscr "AT ANY POST OFFICE".

E283	E **46**	10c. blue	£200	6·25
E251		10c. orange	£120	12·50

E **117** Messenger on Bicycle

1917.

E529	E **117**	10c. blue	14·00	90

E **129** Hat of Mercury and Olive-branch

E **143** Delivery by Motor Cycle

1908.

E374	E **129**	10c. green	44·00	26·00

1922.

E648	E **143**	10c. blue	50	10
E648a		10c. violet	50	15
E649		13c. blue	35	10
E650		15c. orange	60	45
E651		17c. yellow	2·75	2·20

E **144** Delivery by Van

1925.

E652	E **144**	20c. black	1·50	20

E **520** Delivery by Hand

1954.

E1066	E **520**	20c. blue	55	10
E1067		30c. lake	60	10

E **799** Arrows

1969.

E1374	E **799**	45c. red and blue	1·20	20
E1375		60c. blue and red	1·20	15

SPECIAL HANDLING STAMPS

SH **173**

1925.

SH624	SH **173**	10c. green	1·10	65
SH625		15c. green	1·10	60
SH626		20c. green	1·75	1·20
SH628		25c. green	17·00	6·50

UNITED STATES POSTAL AGENCY IN SHANGHAI Pt. 17

These stamps were valid for use on mail despatched from the U.S. Postal Agency in Shanghai to addresses in the United States. This agency was closed on 31 December 1922.

100 cents = 1 dollar (Chinese).

1919. United States stamps of 1908–12 surch **SHANGHAI CHINA** and new value.

1	**128**	2c. on 1c. green	19·00	21·00
17		2Cts. on 1c. green	90·00	85·00
2		4c. on 2c. pink	19·00	21·00
18		4Cts. on 2c. red	80·00	75·00
3		6c. on 3c. violet	38·00	50·00
4		8c. on 4c. brown	40·00	50·00
5		10c. on 5c. blue	48·00	50·00
6		12c. on 6c. orange	60·00	70·00
7		14c. on 7c. black	65·00	85·00
8	**133**	16c. on 8c. olive	42·00	45·00
9		18c. on 9c. orange	45·00	55·00
10		20c. on 10c. yellow	42·00	45·00
11a		24c. on 12c. red	50·00	55·00
12		30c. on 15c. grey	60·00	90·00
13		40c. on 20c. blue	90·00	£140
14		60c. on 30c. red	85·00	£120
15		$1 on 50c. lilac	£350	£425
16		$2 on $1 black	£300	£350

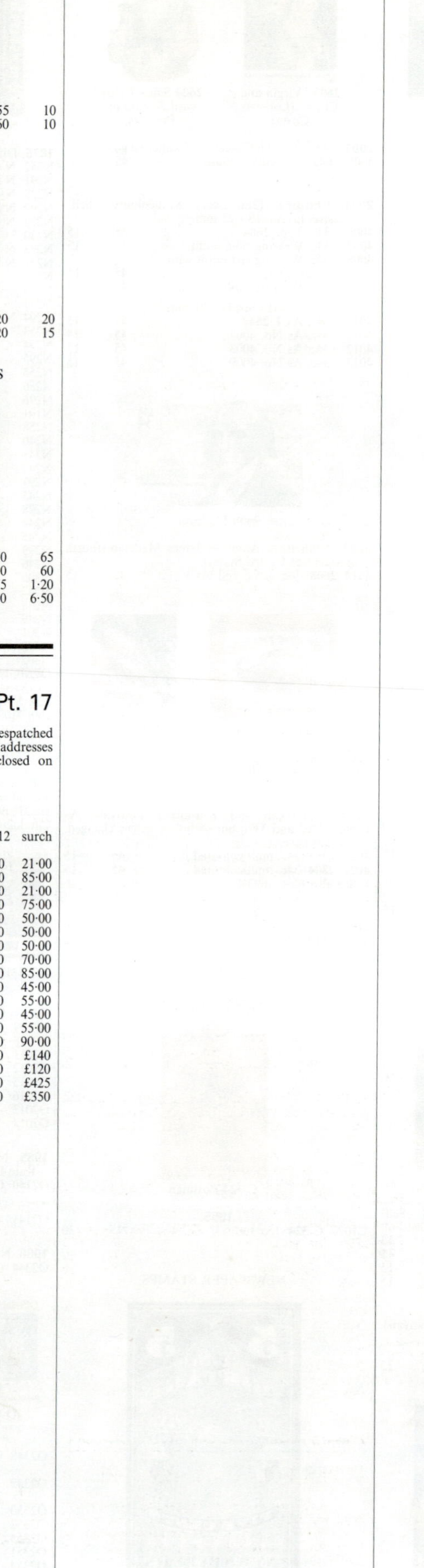

UPPER SENEGAL AND NIGER

Pt. 6

A French Colony in W. Africa, E. of Senegal, formerly called Senegambia and Niger, and became part of French Sudan in 1920.

100 centimes = 1 franc.

1906. "Faidherbe", "Palms" and "Balay" key-types inscr "HT-SENEGAL-NIGER" in blue (10, 40c., 5f.) or red (others).
35 I 1c. grey 55 75
36 2c. brown 60 1·25
37 4c. brown on blue 2·25 2·25
38 5c. green 4·00 2·00
39 10c. red 5·25 80
40 15c. violet 4·25 5·50
41 J 20c. black on blue 1·75 3·50
42 25c. blue 9·00 2·50
43 30c. brown on pink 3·50 10·00
44 35c. black on yellow 1·40 1·75
45 40c. red on blue 5·25 10·00
46 45c. brown on green 7·00 10·50
47 50c. violet 5·75 7·50
48 75c. green on orange 6·25 12·00
49 K 1f. black on blue 15·00 25·00
50 2f. blue on red 35·00 48·00
51 5f. red on yellow 70·00 80·00

7 Touareg

1914.
59 7 1c. violet and purple 10 2·50
60 2c. purple and grey 10 1·60
61 4c. blue and black 1·50 1·75
62 5c. green and light green 10 1·25
63 10c. carmine and red 55 3·00
64 15c. yellow and brown 75 3·00
65 20c. black and purple 2·25 3·50
66 25c. blue and ultramarine 85 2·75
67 30c. chocolate and brown 2·00 3·25
68 35c. violet and red 2·00 3·75
69 40c. red and grey 1·75 3·25
70 45c. brown and blue 1·50 3·25
71 50c. green and black 2·50 3·25
72 75c. brown and yellow 2·00 3·50
73 1f. purple and brown 3·75 5·50
74 2f. blue and green 2·00 5·00
75 5f. black and violet 15·00 12·00

1915. Red Cross. Surch **5c** and red cross.
76 7 10c.+5c. carmine and red 2·25 2·75

POSTAGE DUE STAMPS

1906. "Natives" key-type inscr "HT-SENEGAL-NIGER".
D52 L 5c. green and red 1·60 1·40
D53 10c. purple and blue 3·50 3·25
D54 15c. blue and red on blue 4·75 6·25
D55 20c. black & red on yellow 5·50 6·00
D56 50c. violet and red 21·00 17·00
D57 60c. black and red on buff 14·00 21·00
D58 1f. black and red on flesh 32·00 35·00

1915. "Figures" key-type inscr "HT. SENEGAL-NIGER".
D77 M 5c. green 1·10 2·75
D78 10c. red 1·25 2·75
D79 15c. grey 1·25 3·00
D80 20c. brown 1·10 3·00
D81 30c. blue 2·00 4·50
D82 50c. black 2·00 4·00
D83 60c. orange 5·50 8·50
D84 1f. violet 3·25 7·00

For later issues see **FRENCH SUDAN**.

UPPER SILESIA

Pt. 7

Stamps issued during a plebiscite held in 1921 to decide the future of the district. After the plebiscite it was divided between Germany and Poland.

100 pfenning = 1 mark.

Coal-mine in Silesia

1920.
1 1 2½pf. grey 35 50
2 3pf. brown 30 65
3 5pf. green 15 25
4 10pf. brown 15 30
5 15pf. violet 15 25
6 20pf. blue 15 25
7 50pf. purple 3·50 6·00
8 1m. pink 3·50 7·00
9 5m. orange 3·50 8·00

1920. Surch.
10 1 5pf. on 15pf. violet 42·00 18·00
12 5pf. on 20pf. blue 10 15
14 10pf. on 20pf. blue 10 10
17 50pf. on 5m. orange 10·00 22·00

1920.
19 9 2½pf. grey 15 10
20 3pf. purple 20 10
21 5pf. green 10 10
22 10pf. red 10 10
23 15pf. violet 10 10
24 20pf. blue 10 10
25 25pf. brown 15 10
26 30pf. yellow 10 10
27 40pf. green 10 10

Same design, but larger.
28 9 50pf. grey 10 10
29 60pf. blue 20 15
30 75pf. green 60 40
31 80pf. purple 50 40
32 1m. mauve 30 15
33 2m. brown 30 30
34 3m. violet 50 30
35 5m. orange 1·10 85

1921. Optd **Plebiscite 20 mars 1921.**
36 9 10pf. red 2·00 6·00
37 15pf. violet 2·00 6·00
38 20pf. blue 2·00 9·00
39 25pf. brown 5·00 15·00
40 30pf. yellow 5·00 15·00
41 40pf. green 5·00 15·00
42 50pf. grey 5·00 18·00
43 60pf. blue 6·00 15·00
44 75pf. green 6·00 18·00
45 80pf. purple 7·00 26·00
46 1m. mauve 12·00 45·00

1922. Type **9** in new colours and surch.
47 9 4m. on 60pf. green 60 1·00
48 10m. on 75pf. red 90 2·50
49 20m. on 80pf. orange 5·00 10·00

OFFICIAL STAMPS

1920. Stamps of Germany optd **C.I.H.S.** within a circle. (a) Stamps of 1902 and 1916.
O 1 24 2pf. grey — £900
O 2 2½pf. grey £1500 £500
O 3 10 3pf. brown — £600
O 4 5pf. green £800 £400
O 5 24 7½pf. orange £1400 £700
O 6 10 10pf. red £500 £225
O 7 24 15pf. violet £550 £190
O 8 10 20pf. blue £550 £225
O 9 25pf. black & red on yell — £900
O10 30pf. blk & orge on pink £900 £225
O11 24 35pf. brown £900 £200
O12 10 40pf. black and red £600 £200
O13 50pf. black & pur on pink £600 £200
O14 60pf. purple £800 £200
O15 75pf. black and green £500 £200
O16 80pf. black and red on red — £750
O17 12 1m. red £1500 £500
O18 13 2m. blue — £750

(b) War Charity. Nos. 105/6.
O19 10 10+5pf. red
O20 24 15+5pf. violet

(c) National Assembly at Weimar. Nos. 107/10.
O21 26 10pf. red £650 £650
O22 27 15pf. blue and brown — £650
O23 28 25pf. red and green — £650
O24 30pf. red and purple £650 £650

1920. Official stamps of Germany optd **C.G.H.S.** (a) As Types O **31** and O **32** (with figures "21").
O25 5pf. green 15 25
O26 10pf. red 15 25
O27 15pf. brown 15 25
O28 20pf. blue 15 25
O29 30pf. orange on buff 15 25
O30 50pf. violet on buff 30 50
O31 1m. red on buff 4·25 7·00

(b) As Types O **31** and O **32** but without figures.
O32 5pf. green 55 1·75
O33 10pf. red 10 10
O34 15pf. purple 10 10
O35 20pf. blue 10 10
O36 30pf. orange on buff 10 10
O37 40pf. red 10 10
O38 50pf. violet on buff 10 10
O39 60pf. brown 10 10
O40 1m. red on buff 10 10
O41 1m.25 blue on yellow 10 10
O43 2m. blue 10 20
O44 5m. brown on yellow 10 20

UPPER VOLTA

Pt. 6; Pt. 14

Formerly part of Upper Senegal and Niger, Upper Volta was created a separate colony in 1919. In 1932 it was divided among French Sudan, Ivory Coast and Niger but was reconstituted as a separate territory in 1947 from when it used the stamps of French West Africa.

In 1958 it became an autonomous republic within the French Community and attained full independence in 1960.

In 1984 the name of the state was changed to Burkina Faso.

100 centimes = 1 franc.

1920. Stamps of Upper Senegal and Niger optd **HAUTE-VOLTA.**
1 7 1c. violet and purple 20 2·25
2 2c. purple and grey 10 2·50
3 4c. blue and black 10 2·50
4 5c. green and light green 90 3·25
18 5c. chocolate and brown 40 2·25
5 10c. carmine and red 60 3·25
19 10c. green and light green 15 2·50
20 10c. blue and mauve 30 3·00
6 15c. yellow and brown 50 3·25
7 20c. black and purple 75 3·75
8 25c. blue and ultramarine 2·75 3·75
21 25c. green and black 50 2·75
9 30c. chocolate and brown 3·00 4·50
22 30c. carmine and red 45 3·50
23 30c. red and violet 50 3·50
23a 30c. turquoise and green 2·00 3·75
10 35c. violet and red 1·25 3·75
11 40c. red and grey 55 3·25
12 45c. brown and blue 55 3·25
13 50c. green and black 50 7·75
24 50c. blue and ultramarine 80 3·00
25 50c. blue and orange 25 2·75
26 60c. red 20 2·50
26a 65c. blue and brown 2·50 4·00
14 75c. brown and yellow 1·75 4·50
15 1f. purple and brown 80 4·00
16 2f. blue and green 1·90 4·00
17 5f. black and violet 2·00 7·50

1922. Surch in figures and bars.
27 7 0,01 on 15c. yellow & brown 1·75 4·00
28 0,02 on 15c. yellow & brown 70 4·00
29 0,05 on 15c. yellow & brown 30 4·00
30 25c. on 2f. blue and green 1·50 4·00
31 25c. on 5f. black and violet 1·50 3·75
32 60 on 75c. violet on pink 55 2·75
33 65 on 45c. brown and blue 1·50 3·75
34 85 on 45c. brown and yellow 2·00 4·25
35 90c. on 75c. pink and red 1·25 4·75
36 1f.25 on 1f. lt blue & blue 65 4·00
37 1f.50 on 1f. ultram & bl 1·25 4·25
37a 3f. on 5f. brown and pink 2·00 6·50
38 10f. on 5f. pink and green 14·50 24·00
39 20f. on 5f. violet and brown 15·00 38·00

3 Hausa Man

5 Hausa Warrior

1928.
40 3 1c. blue and green 35 2·25
41 2c. brown and mauve 15 3·00
42 4c. black and yellow 15 2·75
43 5c. indigo and blue 65 2·75
44 10c. blue and pink 1·25 3·75
45 15c. brown and blue 1·75 4·50
46 20c. brown and green 1·10 4·25
47 – 25c. brown and yellow 1·40 2·75
48 – 30c. deep green and green 1·60 3·75
49 – 40c. black and pink 2·25 3·25
50 – 45c. brown and blue 2·00 4·50
51 – 50c. black and green 2·00 2·00
52 – 65c. indigo and blue 2·50 5·25
53 – 75c. black and mauve 2·75 4·25
54 – 90c. red and mauve 2·50 4·25
55 5 1f. brown and green 2·75 4·75
56 1f.10 blue and mauve 3·25 4·75
57 1f.50 blue 3·00 6·50
58 2f. black and blue 4·00 7·75
59 3f. brown and yellow 4·00 9·00
60 5f. brown and mauve 4·50 9·00
61 10f. black and green 12·00 29·00
62 20f. black and pink 22·00 42·00
DESIGN—VERT: 25c. to 90c. Hausa woman.

1931. "Colonial Exhibition" key-types inscr "HAUTE-VOLTA".
63 E 40c. green and black 4·00 7·50
64 F 50c. mauve and black 3·75 7·25
65 G 90c. red and black 1·50 7·25
66 B 1f.50 blue and black 1·50 10·00

6 President Coulibaly

8 President Yameogo

8a C.C.T.A. Emblem

7 Antelope Mask

1959. 1st Anniv of Republic.
67 6 25f. purple and black 40 20

1960. Animal Masks.
68 7 30c. violet and red 10 10
69 40c. purple and ochre 10 10
70 50c. olive and turquoise 10 10
71 – 1f. black, brown and red 15 10
72 – 2f. multicoloured 10 10
73 – 4f. black, violet and blue 20 10
74 – 5f. red, brown and bistre 20 10
75 – 6f. purple and turquoise 20 20
76 – 8f. brown and red 20 20
77 – 10f. purple and green 20 20
78 – 15f. blue, brown and red 40 20
79 – 20f. green and blue 40 30
80 – 25f. purple, green and blue 50 30
81 – 30f. black, brown & turquoise 70 30
82 – 40f. black, red and blue 80 40
83 – 50f. brown, green and mauve 1·00 40
84 – 60f. blue and brown 1·25 65
85 – 85f. blue and turquoise 2·00 1·00
MASKS: 1f. to 4f. Wart-hog; 5f. to 8f. Monkey; 10f. to 20f. Buffalo; 25f. Antelope; 30f. to 50f. Elephant; 60f., 85f. Secretary bird.

1960.
86 8 25f. purple and grey 40 20

1960. 10th Anniv of African Technical Co-operation Commission.
87 8a 25f. indigo and blue 50 40

8b Conseil de l'Entente Emblem

1960. 1st Anniv of Conseil de l'Entente.
88 8b 25f. multicoloured 50 30

9

1960. Proclamation of Independence.
89 9 25f. brown, red and black 55 40

10 Holste Broussard Airplane and Map

1961. Air.
90 10 100f. blue, green and red 1·90 80
91 – 200f. brown, red and green 4·75 1·40
92 – 500f. multicoloured 11·00 5·00
DESIGNS: 200f. Scene at Ouagadougou Airport; 500f. Aerial view of Champs Elysees, Ouagadougou.

11 W.M.O. Emblem, Sun and Meteorological Instruments

1961. 1st World Meteorological Day.
93 11 25f. red, blue and black 55 35

12 Arms of Republic

1961. Independence Festival.
94 12 25f. multicoloured 45 30

1962. Air. "Air Afrique" Airline. As T **47a** of Senegal.
95 25f. mauve, green and purple 55 30

13 W.M.O. Emblem, Weather Station and Crops

1962. World Meteorological Day.
96 **13** 25f. blue, green and black . . . 55 40

1962. Malaria Eradication. As T **47b** of Senegal.
97 25f.+5f. red 70 70

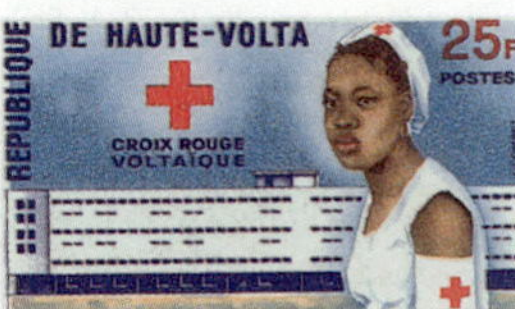

14 Nurse and Hospital

1962. Establishment of Red Cross in Upper Volta.
98 **14** 25f. brown, blue and red . . 60 40

15 African Buffalo at Water-hole

1962. Hunting and Tourism.
99 **15** 5f. green, blue and sepia 35 20
100 – 10f. green, yellow & brown 45 35
101 – 15f. green, yellow & brown 1·10 60
102 – 25f. green, blue and mauve 1·10 60
103 – 50f. green, blue and mauve 1·60 1·40
104 – 85f. green, blue and brown 3·75 2·40
DESIGNS—VERT: 15f. Waterbuck; 85f. Kob. HORIZ: 10f. Lion and lioness; 25f. Arly Camp; 50f. Diapaga Camp.

15a Football

1962. Abidjan Games, 1961. Multicoloured.
105 20f. Type **15a** 45 30
106 25f. Cycling 65 35
107 85f. Boating . . . . 1·40 70

1962. 1st Anniv of Union of African and Malagasy States. As T **47c** of Senegal.
108 30f. multicoloured . . . . . 1·10 75

16 Flag and U.N. Emblem

1962. Air. 2nd Anniv of Admission to U.N.
109 **16** 50f. multicoloured 65 35
110 100f. multicoloured . . . . 1·40 65

17 G.P.O., Ouagadougou

1962. Air. Opening of Ouagadougou P.O.
111 **17** 100f. multicoloured . . . . 1·40 60

1963. Freedom from Hunger. As T **47d** of Senegal.
112 25f.+5f. blue, brn & myrtle 70 70

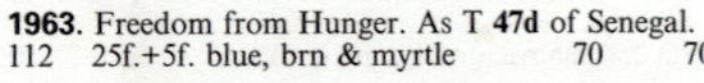

18 Rainfall Map **19** Basketball

1963. World Meteorological Day.
113 **18** 70c. multicoloured 85 55

1963. Dakar Games. Centres in black and red.
114 **19** 20f. violet 35 20
115 – 25f. ochre (Discus) 45 20
116 – 50f. blue (Judo) 90 40

20 "Argyreia nervosa"

1963. Flowers. Multicoloured.
117 50c. "Hibiscus rosa-sinensis" 10 10
118 1f. "Oldenlandia grandiflora" 10 10
119 1f.50 "Portulaca grandiflora" 10 10
120 2f. "Nicotiana tabacum" . . 10 10
121 4f. "Ipomaea stolonifera" . . 15 10
122 5f. "Striga senegalensis" . . . 15 10
123 6f. "Vigna" 20 10
124 8f. "Lepidagathis heudelotiana" 30 20
125 10f. "Euphorbia splendens" 30 15
126 15f. "Hippeastrum equestre" 40 30
127 25f. Type **20** 55 30
128 30f. "Quisqualis indica" . . 70 35
129 40f. "Nymphea lotus" . . . 1·25 50
130 50f. "Plumeria alba" . . . 1·40 55
131 60f. "Crotalaria retusa" . . . 1·75 80
132 85f. "Hibiscus esculentus" . . 2·40 1·10
The 50c. to 10f. are vert.

21 Douglas DC-8 in Flight

1963. Air. 1st Jet-flight, Ouagadougou–Paris.
133 **21** 200f. multicoloured . . . . 4·25 1·25

1963. Air. African and Malagasy Posts and Telecommunications Union. As T **5a** of Rwanda.
134 85f. multicoloured . . . . . 1·25 60

22 Centenary Emblem and Globe **24** "Declaration universelle. . ."

1963. Red Cross Centenary.
135 **22** 25f. multicoloured 90 65

1963. Air. 1st Anniv of "Air Afrique". Surch **AIR AFRIQUE 19-11-63 50F.**
136 **21** 50f. on 200f. multicoloured 1·10 65

1963. 15th Anniv of Declaration of Human Rights.
137 **24** 25f. multicoloured 60 40

25 "Europafrique" **26** "Telecommunications"

1964. Air. "Europafrique".
138 **25** 50f. multicoloured . . . . 1·25 70

1964. Admission of Upper Volta to I.T.U.
139 **26** 25f. multicoloured 45 30

27 Rameses II, Abu Simbel

1964. Air. Nubian Monuments Preservation.
140 **27** 25f. purple and green . . . 65 45
141 100f. brown and blue . . . 2·25 1·75

28 Barograph, Landscape and W.M.O. Emblem

1964. World Meteorological Day.
142 **28** 50f. mauve, blue and green 85 55

29 Dove and Letters

1964. 1st Anniv of Admission to U.P.U.
143 **29** 25f. sepia and blue 45 30
144 – 60f. sepia and orange . . . 90 65
DESIGN: 60f. Jet airliner and letters.

30 Head of Athlete (bronze) **31** Symbols of Solar Research

1964. Air. Olympic Games, Tokyo.
145 **30** 15f. green, red and sepia 35 15
146 – 25f. green, red and sepia 50 20
147 – 85f. green, red and brown 1·10 70
148 – 100f. chocolate, red & brn 1·60 85
DESIGNS: 25f. Seated athlete (bronze); 85f. "Victorious athlete" (bronze); 100f. Venus de Milo.

1964. International Quiet Sun Years.
149 **31** 30f. red, ochre and green 60 40

32 Grey Woodpecker **33** President Kennedy

1964. Air.
150 **32** 250f. multicoloured . . . . 13·00 4·50

1964. French, African and Malagasy Co-operation. As T **60a** of Senegal.
151 70f. brown, red and blue . . 1·00 55

1964. Air. Pres. Kennedy Commemoration.
152 **33** 100f. multicoloured . . . . 1·60 1·10

34 Independence Hotel **35** Pygmy Sunbird

1964. Opening of Independence Hotel, Ouagadougou.
153 **34** 25f. multicoloured . . . . 1·75 65

1965. Birds. Multicoloured.
154 10f. Type **35** (postage) 1·25 40
155 15f. Olive-bellied sunbird . . 1·40 60
156 20f. Splendid sunbird . . . . 2·50 80
157 500f. Abyssinian roller (27 × 48 mm) (air) . . . . 28·00 8·75

36 Sun and Emblems

1965. Air. World Meterological Day.
158 **36** 50f. multicoloured 85 35

37 Grand Cascade, Banfora

1965. Banfora Waterfalls.
159 – 5f. brown, blue and green 15 10
160 **37** 25f. blue, green and red . . 55 20
DESIGN—VERT: 5f. Comoe Cascade.

38 Hughes Telegraph and Modern Telephone

1965. Air. I.T.U. Centenary.
161 **38** 100f. red, green & turquoise . . . . 1·90 85

39 I.C.Y. Emblem

1965. Air. International Co-operation Year.
162 **39** 25f. multicoloured 45 20
163 100f. multicoloured . . . . 1·25 50

40 Football, Boots and Net **42** "Early Bird" Satellite in Orbit

41 Sacred Alligator of Sabou

1965. 1st African Games, Brazzaville.
164 **40** 15f. green, red and purple 30 20
165 – 25f. purple, orange and blue 40 25
166 – 70f. red and green . . . . 1·00 55
DESIGNS: 25f. Boxing gloves and ring; 70f. Tennis racquets, ball and net.

1965. Air. Fauna.
167 **41** 60f. green, turquoise & brn 2·25 65
168 – 85f. brown, bistre and green . . . . 2·75 85
DESIGN—VERT: 85f. Lion.

1965. Air. Space Telecommuncations.
169 **42** 30f. red, brown and blue 55 30

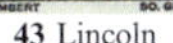

43 Lincoln **45** Dromedary

44 President Yameogo

1965. Death Centenary of Abraham Lincoln.
170 **43** 50f. multicoloured 65 40

1965. Pres. Yameogo.
171 **44** 25f. multicoloured 45 20

1966. Insects and Fauna. Multicoloured.
172 1f. "Nemopistha imperatrix" (vert) 10 10
173 2f. Python (vert) 10 10
174 3f. "Sphodromantis lineola" 10 10
175 4f. "Staurocleis magnifica occidentalis" 15 10
176 5f. Warthog (vert) 20 10
177 6f. "Pandinus imperator" . . 20 10
178 8f. Savanna monkey (vert) . . 35 15
179 10f. Type **45** 35 20
180 15f. Leopard (vert) 65 25
181 20f. African buffalo 90 30
182 25f. Pygmy hippopotamus (vert) . . . . 1·00 35
183 30f. Agama (lizard) 70 35
184 45f. Viper (vert) . . . . . . 1·40 40
185 50f. Chameleon (vert) . . . . 1·75 55
186 60f. "Ugada limbata" (vert) 2·25 80
187 85f. African elephant . . . . 2·40 1·00
The 1, 3, 4, 6 and 60f. are insects, the remainder are fauna.

46 Communications Satellite **47** Ritual Mask

1966. Air. World Meteorological Day.
188 **46** 50f. black, lake and blue 55 30

1966. World Festival of Negro Arts, Dakar. Multicoloured.
189 20f. Type **47** 40 15
190 25f. Plumed head-dress . . . 45 20
191 60f. Dancer . . . . 1·10 40

48 Bobo-Dioulasso Mosque

1966. Religious Buildings. Multicoloured.
192 25f. Type **48** 45 30
193 25f. Po Church 45 30

49 Satellite "FR 1" and Ouagadougou Tracking Station

1966. Air. Inauguration of Ouagadougou Tracking Station.
194 **49** 250f. lake, brown and blue 4·00 1·90

50 W.H.O. Building

1966. Air. Inauguration of W.H.O. Headquarters, Geneva.
195 **50** 100f. black, blue and yellow . . . . 1·60 70

51 Nurse and Red Cross on Globe **52** Scouts by Campfire

1966. Red Cross.
196 **51** 25f. multicoloured 55 30

1966. Scouting.
197 **52** 10f. multicoloured 35 15
198 – 15f. black, brown and buff 35 15
DESIGN: 15f. Scouts on cliff.

53 Inoculating Cattle

1966. Prevention of Cattle Plague Campaign.
199 **53** 25f. black, yellow and blue 85 45

1966. Air. Inauguration of DC-8F Air Services. As T **76a** of Senegal.
200 25f. olive, black and brown 55 35

54 Ploughing with Donkey

1966. Rural Education (25f.) and 3rd Anniv of Kamboince Centre (30f.). Multicoloured.
201 25f. Type **54** 40 20
202 30f. "Rotation of crops", Kamboince Centre 45 20

55 Sir Winston Churchill

1966. Air. Churchill Commemoration.
203 **55** 100f. green and red . . . . 1·60 65

56 Pope Paul and Dove over U.N. General Assembly Building

1966. Air. Pope Paul's Peace Appeal before U.N.
204 **56** 100f. violet and blue . . . 1·60 65

57 U.N.E.S.C.O. Emblem

1966. 20th Anniv of U.N.E.S.C.O. and U.N.I.C.E.F.
205 **57** 50f. red, blue and black . . 65 40
206 – 50f. violet, purple and red 65 40
DESIGN: No. 206, U.N.I.C.E.F. emblem and child-care theme.

58 Arms of Upper Volta **59** Man and Woman holding Emblems

1967.
207 **58** 30f. multicoloured 55 15

1967. Europafrique.
208 **59** 60f. multicoloured 90 40

60 Acclaiming Lions Emblem

1967. Air. 50th Anniv of Lions International.
209 **60** 100f. ultramarine, bl & brn 1·60 65

61 W.M.O. Emblem and Landscape **62** "Diamant" Rocket

1967. Air. World Meteorological Day.
210 **61** 50f. green, turquoise & blue 85 40

1967. Air. French Space Achievements.
211 **62** 5f. green, orange and blue 15 10
212 – 20f. lilac, purple and blue 40 15
213 – 30f. green, blue and red . . 55 20
214 – 100f. green, violet & purple 1·40 60
DESIGNS—HORIZ: 20f. "FR-1" satellite; 100f. "D1-D" satellite. VERT: 30f. "D1-C" satellite.

63 Dr. Schweitzer and Organ Pipes

1967. Air. 2nd Death Anniv of Dr Albert Schweitzer.
215 **63** 250f. black and purple . . 4·00 1·90

64 Scout waving Hat

1967. World Scout Jamboree, Idaho. Mult.
216 5f. Type **64** (postage) 35 10
217 20f. Scouts' handclasp . . . 80 45
218 100f. Jamboree emblem and world map (48 × 27 mm) (air) . . . . 1·40 65

65 "Virgin and Child" (by 15th-century master) **67** Postman on Cycle

66 Bank Book and Coins

1967. Air. Religious Paintings. Multicoloured.
219 30f. Type **65** 50 30
220 50f. "The Deposition of Christ" (Dirk Bouts) . . . 85 40
221 100f. "Christ giving Blessing" (Bellini) . . . . 1·40 80
222 250f. "The Evangelists" (Jordaens) . . . . 4·00 1·90
See also Nos. 237/40.

1967. National Savings Bank.
223 **66** 30f. green, brown & orange 45 20

1967. Air. 5th Anniv of U.A.M.P.T. As T **86a** of Senegal.
224 100f. green, lake and blue . . 1·40 55

1967. Stamp Day.
225 **67** 30f. brown, green and blue 65 45

1967. 5th Anniv of West African Monetary Union. As T **89a** of Togo.
226 30f. violet and blue 30 15

68 Les Deux Alpes **69** Human Rights Emblem

1967. Winter Olympic Games, Grenoble (1968).
227 – 15f. green, blue and brown 40 30
228 **68** 50f. blue and green 70 40
229 – 100f. green, blue and red 1·60 1·00
DESIGNS—HORIZ: 15f. St. Nizier-du-Moucherotte; 100f. Cable-car, Villard-de-Lans.

1968. Human Rights Year.
230 **69** 20f. red, gold and blue . . 40 15
231 30f. red, gold and green . . 45 20

70 Student and School

1968. National School of Administration.
232 **70** 30f. blue, turquoise & brn 45 20

71 Sud Aviation Caravelle "Ouagadougou"

1968. Air.
233 **71** 500f. black, blue and purple . . . . 9·00 4·50

72 W.M.O. Emblem, Sun and Cloud-burst

1968. Air. World Meteorological Day.
234 **72** 50f. blue, red and green . . 85 35

73 Human Figures and W.H.O. Emblem

1968. 20th Anniv of W.H.O.
235 **73** 30f. indigo, red and blue 45 20
236 50f. blue, brown and green 65 35

1968. Air. Paintings. Old Masters in the Louvre. As T **65**. Multicoloured.
237 20f. "Still Life" (Gauguin) (36 × 50 mm) 35 30
238 60f. "Anne of Cleves" (Holbein the Younger) (36 × 50 mm) 65 50
239 90f. "The Pawnbroker and His Wife" (Quentin Metsys) (38 × 40 mm) . . . 1·00 70
240 200f. "The Cart" (Le Nain) (50 × 37 mm) . . . . . . 2·40 1·60

74 "Europafrique"

1968. Air. "Europafrique".
241 **74** 50f. red, black and ochre 70 35

75 Telephone Exchange

1968. Inauguration of Automatic Telephone Exchange, Bobo-Dioulasso.
242 **75** 30f. multicoloured 55 30

76 Colima Acrobat with Bells

1968. Air. Olympic Games, Mexico.
243 **76** 10f. brown, yellow and red 35 20
244 – 30f. blue, red and green . . 50 30
245 – 60f. lake, brown and blue 1·10 45
246 – 100f. lake, blue and green 1·40 70
DESIGNS—VERT: 30f. Pelota-player (Veracruz); 60f. Javelin-thrower (Colima). HORIZ: 100f. Athlete with cape (Jalisco).
The designs represent early Mexican statuary.

77 Weaving

1968. Handicrafts.
247 – 5f. black, purple and brown (postage) 20 10
248 **77** 30f. brown, orange and mauve 50 20
249 – 100f. purple, red and yellow (air) . . . . . . 1·40 65
250 – 150f. black, blue & brown 2·25 1·00
DESIGNS—As Type **77**: 5f. Metal-work; 48 × 27 mm: 100f. Pottery; 150f. Basket-making.

1968. Air. "Philexafrique" Stamp Exhibition, Abidjan (Ivory Coast, 1969) (1st issue). As T **98a** of Senegal. Multicoloured.
251 100f. "Too Late" or "The Letter" (A. Cambon) . . . 2·50 2·25
See also No. 256.

78 Mahatma Gandhi

79 "Grain for the World"

1968. Air. "Workers for Peace".
252 **78** 100f. black, yellow & green 1·40 80
253 – 100f. black, light green and red . . . . 1·40 80
DESIGNS: No. 253, Albert Luthuli.

1969. World Food Programme.
255 **79** 30f. purple, slate and blue 45 20

1969. Air. "Philexafrique" Stamp Exn, Abidjan (Ivory Coast) (2nd issue). As T **101a** of Senegal. Multicoloured.
256 50f. Dancers of Tengrela and stamp of 1928 . . . . . . 2·50 2·25

80 Loom and I.L.O. Emblem

1969. 50th Anniv of I.L.O.
257 **80** 30f. blue, lake and green 50 30

81 Cattle and Labourer

1969. Air. World Meteorological Day.
258 **81** 100f. brown, blue and green . . . . 2·50 1·40

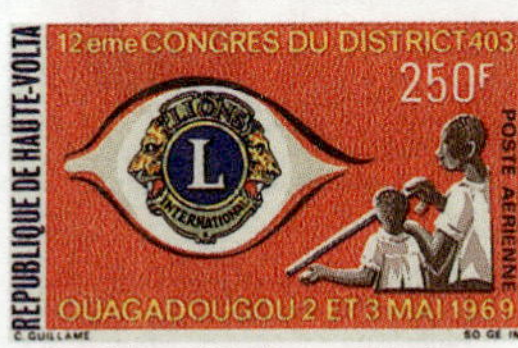

82 "Lions" Emblem within Eye

1969. Air. 12th Congress of 403 District, Lions International, Ouagadougou.
259 **82** 250f. multicoloured . . . . 2·75 1·40

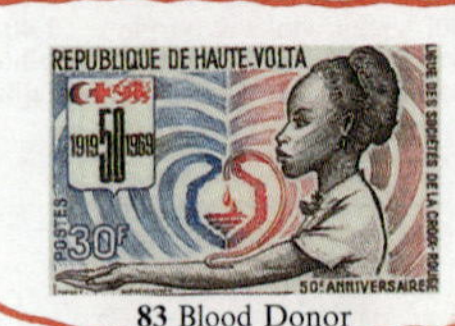

83 Blood Donor

1969. 50th Anniv of League of Red Cross Societies.
260 **83** 30f. black, red and blue . . 60 40

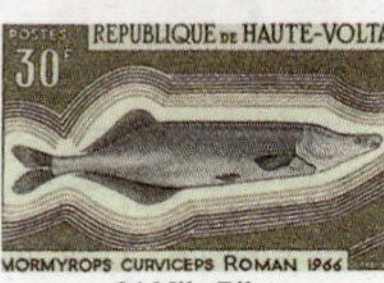

84 Nile Pike

1969. Fishes.
261 – 20f. buff, brown and blue (postage) . . . . 1·10 55
262 – 25f. purple, brown and blue . . . . 1·10 55
263 **84** 30f. black and olive . . 1·60 85
264 – 55f. olive, yellow and green 2·00 1·10
265 – 85f. blue, mauve and brown . . . . 3·75 2·40
266 – 100f. blue, yell & pur (air) 2·25 1·50
267 – 150f. blue, black and red 3·75 1·90
DESIGNS: 20f. Gudgeon tetra; 25f. Poll's tetra; 55f. Half-striped characin; 85f. Sharp-toothed tetra. 48 × 27 mm: 100f. Roman's tetra; 150f. Arnoult's squeaker.

85 Astronaut and Moon

1969. Air. Moon Flight of "Apollo 8". Embossed on gold foil.
268 **85** 1,000f. gold . . . . 18·00

1969. Air. 1st Man on the Moon. No. 214 optd **L'HOMME SUR LA LUNE JUILLET 1969** and "Apollo 11" emblem.
269 100f. green, violet and purple 3·25 3·25

87 "Bonaparte crossing the Great St. Bernard" (J. L. David)

1969. Air. Birth Bicent of Napoleon Bonaparte. Multicoloured.
270 50f. Type **87** . . . . 1·60 80
271 150f. "First Presentation of the Legion of Honour" (Debret) . . . . . 5·00 2·00
272 250f. "Napoleon before Madrid" (C. Vernet) . . . 6·75 3·25

1969. 5th Anniv of African Development Bank.
273 30f. brown, emerald and green 35 15

88 Millet 89 Stylized Tree

1969. Agricultural Produce.
274 **88** 15f. brown, green and yellow (postage) 45 20
275 – 30f. blue and mauve . . . 55 35
276 – 100f. brown and violet (air) 1·40 40
277 – 200f. green and red . . . 2·50 80
DESIGNS: 30f. Cotton. LARGER—48 × 27mm: 100f. Ground-nuts; 200f. Rice.

1969. Air. Europafrique.
278 **89** 100f. multicoloured 90 55

1969. 10th Anniv of Aerial Navigation Security Agency for Africa and Madagascar (A.S.E.C.N.A.). As T **112** of Senegal.
279 100f. brown . . . . 1·25 75

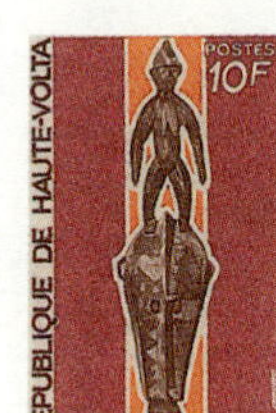

90 "Niadale" 91 Lenin

1970. Figurines and Masks in National Museum.
280 **90** 10f. brown, orange and red 20 10
281 – 30f. brown, blue and violet 40 20
282 – 45f. brown, blue and green 70 30
283 – 80f. brown, purple, & violet . . . . 1·25 60
DESIGNS: 30f. "Niaga"; 45f. "Iliu bara"; 80f. "Karan Weeba".

1970. Air. Birth Centenary of Lenin.
284 **91** 20f. brown and ochre . . . 35 20
285 – 100f. red, blue and green 1·25 80
DESIGN—HORIZ: 100f. "Lenin addressing workers" (A. Serov).

92 African Huts and City Buildings 93 Cauris Dancers

1970. Linked Cities' Day.
286 **92** 30f. brown, blue and red 50 30

1970. Upper Volta Dances. Multicoloured.
287 5f. Mask of Nebwa Gnomo dance (horiz) 20 15
288 8f. Type **93** 30 15
289 20f. Gourmantches dancers 40 15
290 30f. Larlle dancers (horiz) . . 50 20

94 "Pupils", Sun and Emblem of Education Year

1970. Int Education Year. Multicoloured.
291 40f. Type **94** 40 20
292 90f. Visual aids and emblem 95 45

95 New U.P.U. Headquarters Building, U.P.U. Monument and Abraham Lincoln

1970. New U.P.U. Headquarters Building.
293 **95** 30f. grey, red and brown 50 20
294 60f. purple, green & brown 85 35

96 Footballers and Cup

1970. Air. World Cup Football Championship, Mexico.
295 **96** 40f. lake, green and brown 45 30
296 – 100f. brown, purple & green . . . . 1·10 55
DESIGN: 100f. Goalkeeper saving ball, Globe and footballers.

97 Franklin D. Roosevelt

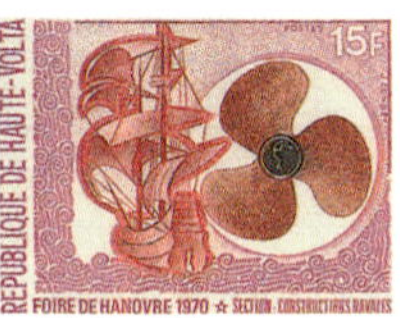

98 Naval Construction

1970. Air. 25th Anniv of Roosevelt's Death.
297 **97** 10f. brown, black and green 20 20
298 – 200f. red, violet and grey 1·60 80
DESIGN—HORIZ: 200f. Roosevelt with his stamp collection.

1970. Hanover Fair.
299 **98** 15f. multicoloured 70 35
300 – 45f. green, blue and black 60 35
301 – 80f. purple, brown & black 1·40 50
DESIGNS: 45f. Test-tubes and retorts ("Chemistry"); 80f. Power transmission lines and pylons ("Electro-techniques").

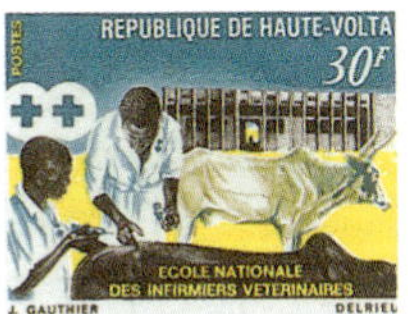

99 Inoculating Cattle

1970. National Veterinary School.
302 **99** 30f. multicoloured 55 35

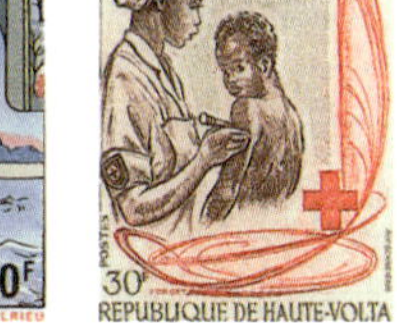

100 "Manchurian Cranes and Seashore" and Expo Monorail Coach

101 Nurse attending Patient

1970. Air. World Fair "EXPO 70" Osaka, Japan.
303 50f. Type **100** . . . . . . 1·40 60
304 150f. "Geisha", rocket and satellite . . . . 1·40 80

1970. Upper Volta Red Cross.
305 **101** 30f. brown, red and green 60 35

102 "Nurse and Child" (F. Hals)

103 U.N. Emblem and Dove

1970. "Europafrique". Multicoloured.
306 25f. Type **102** 50 20
307 30f. "Courtyard in Delft" (Hoogh) 60 35
308 150f. "Christina of Denmark" (Holbein) . . . 2·25 90
309 250f. "Hofburg Courtyard, Innsbruck" (Durer) . . . . 4·00 1·40

1970. Air. 25th Anniv of U.N.O.
310 **103** 60f. ultramarine, bl & grn 65 30
311 – 250f. violet, brown & grn 2·75 1·10
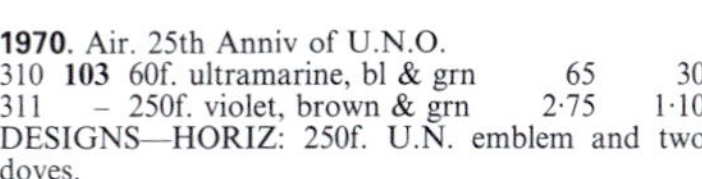
DESIGNS—HORIZ: 250f. U.N. emblem and two doves.

104 Front of Car

1970. Paris Motor Show.
312 **104** 25f. green, lake and brown 90 35
313 – 40f. blue, purple and green . . . . 1·10 55
DESIGN: 40f. Old and new cars.

105 "Holy Family"

1970. Christmas.
314 **105** 300f. silver . . . . 6·75
315 1000f. gold . . . . 18·00

106 Centre Buildings

1970. Inauguration of Austro-Voltaic Centre.
316 **106** 50f. orange, green and red 55 30

107 Arms and Stork

1970. 10th Anniv of Independence.
317 **107** 30f. multicoloured (postage) 45 20
318 – 500f. blk, red & gold (air) 5·50
DESIGN—27 × 37 mm: 500f. Family and flag. No. 318 is embossed on gold foil.

108 U.N. "Key" and Split Globe

1970. 10th Anniv of U.N. Declaration on Colonies.
319 **108** 40f. red, blue and brown 60 35
320 – 50f. multicoloured 55 30
DESIGN: 50f. Two maps of Africa showing former colonies.

109 Pres. Nasser

111 Heads of Different Races

110 Beingolo Hunting Horn

1971. Air. Pres. Nasser Commemoration.
321 **109** 100f. multicoloured . . . 90 40

1971. Musical Instruments.
322 **110** 5f. brown, red and blue 20 15
323 – 15f. brown, red and green 35 20
324 – 20f. red, grey and blue . . 65 20
325 – 25f. drab, green and red 80 40
INSTRUMENTS—VERT: 15f. Mossi "guitar"; 20f. Gurunssi "flutes". HORIZ: 25f. Lunga "drum".

1971. Racial Equality Year.
326 **111** 50f. brown, red & turq . . 55 30

112 "The Purple Herons" (Egypt, 1354)

1971. Air. Muslim Miniatures. Multicoloured.
327 100f. Type **112** . . . . 1·40 60
328 250f. Page from the Koran (Egypt, c. 1368–88) (vert) 2·75 1·25

113 Telephone and Hemispheres

1971. World Telecommunications Day.
329 **113** 50f. violet, grey and brown 60 30

114 Olympic Rings and Events

1971. Air. "Pre-Olympic Year".
330 **114** 150f. red, violet and blue 2·25 1·10

115 Cutting Cane and Sugar Factory, Banfora

117 Scout and Pagodas

116 "Gonimbrasia hecate"

1971. Local Industries. Multicoloured.
331 10f. Type **115** 20 10
332 35f. Cotton-plant and textiles ("Voltex" project) 35 20

1971. Butterflies. Multicoloured.
333 1f. Type **116** 10 10
334 2f. "Hamanumida daedalus" 10 10
335 3f. "Ophideres materna" . . 20 10
336 5f. "Danaus chrysippus" . . 45 20
337 40f. "Hypolimnas misippus" 2·25 1·10
338 45f. "Danaus petiverana" . . 3·25 1·40

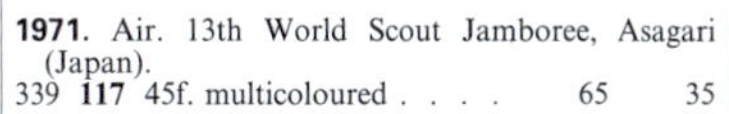
1971. Air. 13th World Scout Jamboree, Asagari (Japan).
339 **117** 45f. multicoloured 65 35

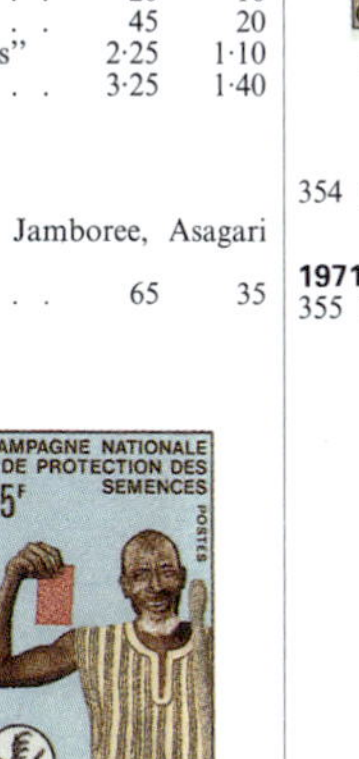

118 Actor with Fan

119 African with Seed-packet

1971. "Philatokyo" Stamp Exn, Tokyo. Mult.
340 25f. Type **118** 35 20
341 40f. Actor within mask . . . 50 25

1971. National Seed-protection Campaign. Multicoloured.
342 35f. Grading seeds (horiz) . . 40 20
343 75f. Type **119** 60 30
344 100f. Harvesting crops (horiz) 60 35

1971. 10th Anniv of Volta Red Cross. Surch **Xe ANNIVERSAIRE** and new value.
345 **101** 100f. on 30f. brown, red and purple . . . . . . 1·25 65

121 Teacher and Class

122 Soldier and Tractors

1971. "Women's Access to Education". Multicoloured.
346 35f. Type **121** 45 20
347 50f. Family learning alphabet 60 35

1971. Dakiri Project. Military Aid for Agriculture. Multicoloured.
348 15f. Type **122** 45 15
349 40f. Soldiers harvesting (horiz) 65 40

123 General De Gaulle and Map

1971. Air. De Gaulle Commemoration.
350 **123** 40f. multicoloured 55 55
351 – 500f. gold and green . . . 10·50 9·50
DESIGN—VERT (30 × 40 mm): 500f. De Gaulle. No. 351 is embossed on gold foil.

1971. Air. 10th Anniv of African and Malagasy Posts and Telecommunications Union. As No. 432 of Rwanda. Multicoloured.
352 100f. U.A.M.P.T. H.Q. and Mossi dancer . . . . . . 1·10 50

124 "Simulium damnosum" and Preventive Measures

1971. Regional Anti-onchocerciasis Campaign.
353 **124** 40f. multicoloured 55 35

125 Pres. Lamizana

126 Children acclaiming Emblem

1971.
354 **125** 35f. multicoloured 30 20

1971. 25th Anniv of U.N.I.C.E.F.
355 **126** 45f. multicoloured 50 35

127 Peulh Straw Hut

1971. Traditional Housing (1st series). Mult.
356 10f. Type **127** 15 10
357 20f. Gourounsi house 30 15
358 35f. Mossi huts 45 30
See also Nos. 370/2.

128 Town Halls of Bobo-Dioulasso and Chalons-sur-Marne, France

1971. "Twin Cities" Co-operation.
359 **128** 40f. multicoloured 65 40

129 Ice-hockey **130** Running

1972. Air. Winter Olympic Games, Sapporo, Japan.
360 **129** 150f. purple, blue and red 1·90 1·00

1972. Air. U.N.E.S.C.O. "Save Venice" Campaign. As T **145** of Senegal. Multicoloured.
361 100f. "La Musica" (P. Longhi) (vert) . . . . 1·90 1·00
362 150f. "Panorama da Ponte della Marina" (detail, Caffi) (horiz) . . . . . . 2·75 1·25

1972. Air. Olympic Games, Munich.
363 **130** 65f. brown, blue and green 60 45
364 – 200f. brown and blue . . 1·90 1·25
DESIGN: 200f. Throwing the discus.

131 Louis Armstrong

1972. Famous Negro Musicians. Multicoloured.
366 45f. Type **131** (postage) . . . 1·25 65
367 500f. Jimmy Smith (air) . . . 6·75 4·50

132 Globe and Emblems

1972. World Red Cross Day.
368 **132** 40f. multicoloured (postage) 55 40
369 100f. multicoloured (air) 1·10 45

133 Bobo House **134** Hair Style

1972. Traditional Housing (2nd series). Mult.
370 45f. Type **133** 55 30
371 50f. Dagari house 65 35
372 90f. Interior of Bango house (horiz) . . . . 1·25 50

1972. Upper Volta Hair Styles.
373 **134** 25f. multicoloured 35 15
374 – 35f. multicoloured 50 20
375 – 75f. multicoloured . . . . 1·10 45
DESIGNS: 35, 75f. Similar hair styles.

135 "Teaching"

1972. 2nd National Development Plan.
376 **135** 10f. mauve, green and turquoise (postage) . . 10 10
377 – 15f. brown, orange & green 20 15
378 – 20f. brown, green and blue 30 15
379 – 35f. brown, blue and green 50 20
380 – 40f. brown, green & purple 55 30
381 – 85f. black, red & blue (air) 70 50
DESIGNS: 15f. Doctor and patient ("Health"); 20f. Factory and silos ("Industry"); 35f. Cattle ("Cattle-raising"); 40f. Rice-planting ("Agriculture"); 85f. Road-making machine ("Infrastructure").

1972. 10th Anniv of West African Monetary Union. As T **156** of Senegal.
382 40f. grey, blue and mauve . . 45 20

136 Lottery Building

1972. 5th Anniv of National Lottery.
383 **136** 35f. multicoloured 50 20

137 Presidents Pompidou and Lamizana

1972. Air. Visit of Pres. Pompidou to Upper Volta.
384 **137** 40f. multicoloured . . . . 1·60 1·60
385 – 250f. multicoloured . . . 6·00 6·00
DESIGN: 250f. As T **137** but frame differs and portraits are embossed on gold.

138 Mary Peters (pentathlon)

1972. Air. Gold Medal-winners, Olympic Games, Munich. Multicoloured.
386 40f. Type **138** 35 15
387 65f. Ragno-Lonzi (fencing) 55 20
388 85f. Touritcheva (gymnastics) 80 30
389 200f. Maury (sailing) . . . . 1·60 65
390 300f. Meyfarth (high-jumping) . . . . 2·75 1·10

139 Donkeys

1972. Animals. Multicoloured.
392 5f. Type **139** 10 10
393 10f. Spur-winged geese . . . 55 20
394 30f. Goat 55 20
395 50f. Bull 80 30
396 65f. Dromedaries . . . . . . 1·10 40

140 "The Nativity" (Della Notte)

1972. Air. Christmas. Religious Paintings. Multicoloured.
397 100f. Type **140** . . . . 1·10 65
398 200f. "The Adoration of the Magi" (Durer) . . . . . . 2·25 1·60

141 Mossi Hair-style and Village

1973. Air.
399 **141** 5f. multicoloured 10 10
400 40f. multicoloured 55 20

1973. 25th Anniv of W.H.O. No. 353 surch **O. M. S. 25 Anniversaire 45F.**
401 **124** 45f. on 40f. multicoloured 50 30

1973. 12th Anniv of African and Malagasy Posts and Telecommunications Union. As T **170** of Senegal.
402 100f. purple, red and yellow 1·00 55

1974. 15th Anniv of Council of Accord. As T **176** of Togo.
403 40f. multicoloured 30 20

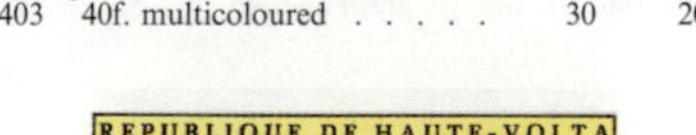

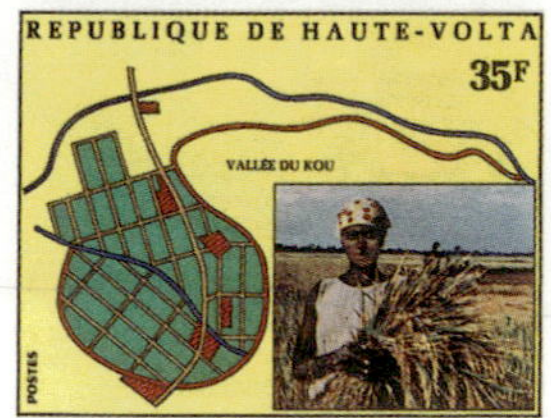

143 Map and Harvester

1974. Kou Valley Project.
404 **143** 35f. multicoloured 55 35

144 Woman, Globe and I.W.Y. Emblem

1975. International Women's Year.
405 **144** 65f. multicoloured 65 45

145 Mgr. Joanny Thevenoud and Cathedral

1975. 75th Anniv of Evangelization of Upper Volta.
406 **145** 55f. black, brown & green 65 35
407 – 65f. black, brown & green 80 45
DESIGN: 65f. Father Guillaume Templier and Cathedral.

146 Farmer's Hat, Hoe and Emblem **147** Diseased People

1975. Development of the Volta Valleys.
408 **146** 15f. multicoloured 15 10
409 50f. multicoloured 50 25

1976. Campaign against Onchocerciasis (roundworm).
410 **147** 75f. mauve, orange & grn 85 35
411 250f. sepia, orange & brn 2·50 1·10

148 Globe and Emblem

1976. Non-aligned Countries' Summit Conference, Colombo, Sri Lanka. Multicoloured.
412 55f. Type **148** 45 20
413 100f. Globe, dove and emblem 90 50

149 Washington at Trenton

1976. "Interphil '76" International Stamp Exhibition, Philadelphia. Multicoloured.
414 60f. Type **149** (postage) . . . 55 15
415 90f. Seat of Government, Pennsylvania 80 20
416 100f. Siege of Yorktown (air) 80 30
417 200f. Battle of Cape St. Vincent . . . . 1·60 60
418 300f. Peter Francisco's act of bravery . . . . 2·40 80

150 U.P.U. and U.N. Emblems

1976. 25th Anniv of U.N. Postal Administration.
420 **150** 200f. blue, bronze and red 1·60 90

151 Tenkodogo Commune **152** Bronze Statuette

1977. Arms. Multicoloured.
421 10f. Type **151** 15 10
422 20f. Ouagadougou 20 10
423 55f. Type **151** 55 20
424 100f. As 20f. 70 35

1977.
425 **152** 55f. multicoloured 45 20
426 – 65f. multicoloured 45 20
DESIGN: 65f. Bronze statuette of woman with bowl.

153 Samo Granary **154** Gouin Basket

1977. Millet Granaries. Multicoloured.
427 5f. Type **153** 10 10
428 35f. Boromo 30 20
429 45f. Banfora 45 20
430 55f. Mossi 55 30

1977. Local Handicrafts. Baskets and Bags. Multicoloured.
431 30f. Type **154** 20 15
432 40f. Bissa 40 20
433 60f. Lobi 60 25
434 70f. Mossi 65 30

155 "Crinum ornatum" **156** General De Gaulle

1977. Fruits and Flowers. Multicoloured.
435 2f. "Cordia myxa" 10 10
436 3f. "Opilia celtidifolia" . . . 15 10
437 15f. Type **155** 20 10
438 25f. "Haemanthus multiflorus" 20 10
439 50f. "Hannoa undulata" . . 10 10
440 90f. "Cochlospermum planchonii" . . . . 1·00 40
441 125f. "Clitoria ternatea" . . 1·10 50
442 150f. "Cassia alata" . . . . 1·40 90
443 175f. "Nauclea latifolia" (horiz) . . . . 1·60 1·00
444 300f. "Bombax costatum" (horiz) . . . . 2·50 1·40
445 400f. "Eulophia cucullata" 4·25 1·40

1977. Personalities. Multicoloured.
446 100f. Type **156** . . . . 1·60 50
447 200f. King Baudouin . . . . 1·60 50

157 Queen Elizabeth II

1977. Silver Jubilee of Queen Elizabeth II. Multicoloured.
448 200f. Type **157** . . . . 1·60 50
449 300f. Queen Elizabeth II taking salute at Trooping the Colour . . . . 2·25 60

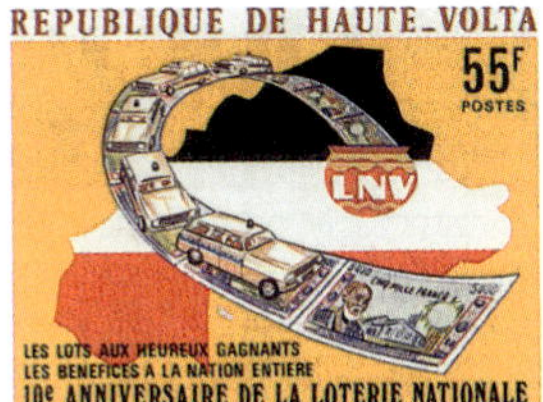

158 Cars on "Road" of Banknotes

1977. 10th Anniv of National Lottery.
451 **158** 55f. multicoloured 55 40

159 Selma Lagerlof and Bean Geese

1977. Nobel Prize Winners. Multicoloured.
452 55f. Type **159** (Literature, 1909) 80 25
453 65f. Guglielmo Marconi and early transmitter (Physics, 1909) 45 20
454 125f. Bertrand Russell, laurel, book and dove (Literature, 1950) 95 30
455 200f. L. C. Pauling, formula and atomic explosion (Chemistry, 1954) . . . . 1·40 50
456 300f. Robert Koch, slide and X-ray plate (Medicine, 1905) . . . . 2·40 70

160 "The Three Graces"

1977. 400th Birth Anniv of Rubens.
458 55f. "Heads of Four Negroes" (horiz) 40 10
459 65f. Type **160** 50 15
460 85f. "Bathsheba at the Fountain" 50 20
461 150f. "The Drunken Silenus" 1·25 45
462 200f. "The Story of Maria de Medici" (detail) . . . . 1·60 55
463 300f. "The Story of Maria de Medici" (different detail) 2·50 70

161 Lenin

1977. 60th Anniv of Russian Revolution. Multicoloured.
465 10f. Type **161** 15 10
466 85f. Lenin Monument and Kremlin 65 40
467 200f. Lenin with children (horiz) . . . . 1·90 1·10
468 500f. Lenin and Pres. Brezhnev (horiz) . . . . . 4·50 2·25

162 Stadium and Brazil 5cr.80 Stamp of 1950

1978. World Cup Football Championship, Argentina. Multicoloured.
469 55f. Type **162** 35 10
470 65f. Brazil 1969 Pele stamp 45 15
471 125f. G.B. 1966 England winners stamp 90 30
472 200f. Chile 1962 World Cup stamp . . . . 1·40 45
473 300f. Switzerland 1954 World Cup stamp . . . . 2·00 65

163 Jean Mermoz

1978. Aviation History. Multicoloured.
475 65f. Type **163** 60 20
476 75f. Anthony Fokker 65 30
477 85f. Wiley Post 75 35
478 90f. Otto Lilienthal (vert) . . 85 35
479 100f. Concorde . . . . . . 1·10 40

164 "Crateva religiosa" **165** Microwave Antennae

1978. Trees of Upper Volta. Multicoloured.
481 55f. Type **164** 55 35
482 75f. "Ficus sp." 65 45

1978. World Telecommunications Day.
483 **165** 65f. multicoloured 55 40

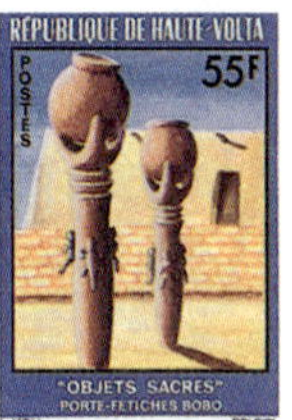

166 Bobo Fetish Portals

1978. Sacred Objects. Multicoloured.
484 55f. Type **166** 55 30
485 65f. Mossi fetish 65 40

167 U.P.U. Emblem over Globe

1978. Air. Centenary of Paris Postal Congress.
486 **167** 350f. multicoloured . . . 2·75 1·60

168 Capt. Cook and H.M.S. "Endeavour"

1978. 250th Birth Anniv of Captain James Cook. Multicoloured.
487 65f. Type **168** . . . . 1·00 40
488 85f. Death of Captain Cook 55 15
489 250f. Cook and navigation instruments . . . . 1·60 55
490 350f. Cook and H.M.S. "Resolution" . . . . . . 3·50 2·25

169 Yuri Gagarin and Spacecraft

1978. "Conquest of Space". Multicoloured.
491 50f. Type **169** 40 20
492 60f. Jules Verne, "Apollo 11" badge and Neil Armstrong in space-suit . . . . 2·75 90
493 100f. Montgolfier medallion and balloon, Bleriot XI and Concorde 85 40

170 I.A.Y. Emblem

1978. Air. Anti-Apartheid Year.
494 **170** 100f. multicoloured . . . 80 45

1978. 25th Anniv of Coronation of Queen Elizabeth II. Nos. 448/9 optd **ANNIVERSAIRE DU COURONNEMENT 1953-1978**.
495 **157** 200f. multicoloured . . . 1·40 90
496 – 300f. multicoloured . . . 2·25 1·40

1978. Air. "Philexafrique" Stamp Exhibition, Libreville (Gabon), and Int Stamp Fair, Essen, West Germany (1st series). As T **237a** of Senegal. Multicoloured.
498 100f. River kingfisher and Hanover 1850 1ggr. stamp 2·00 1·40
499 100f. Hippopotamus and 1964 250f. Grey woodpecker stamp . . . . 2·00 1·40
See also Nos. 518/19.

172 "Trent Castle"

1978. 450th Death Anniv of Albrecht Durer. Multicoloured.
500 65f. Type **172** 55 15
501 150f. "Virgin and Child" (vert) . . . . 1·10 35
502 250f. "Saints George and Eustace" (vert) . . . . . . 1·90 60
503 350f. "H. Holzschuher" (vert) 2·75 90

173 Horus **174** Jules Verne

1978. Air. U.N.E.S.C.O. Campaign: "Save the Philae Temples". Multicoloured.
504 200f. Type **173** . . . . 1·40 65
505 300f. Stylized falcon . . . . 2·00 1·00

1978. 150th Birth Anniv of Jules Verne (author).
506 **174** 20f. purple, blue and green . . . . 1·60 90

175 Human Rights Flame

1978. 30th Anniv of Declaration of Human Rights.
507 **175** 55f. multicoloured 50 30

1979. World Cup Football Championship Winners. Nos. 469/73 optd.
508 **162** 55f. multicoloured 45 25
509 – 65f. multicoloured 50 30
510 – 125f. multicoloured . . . 95 55
511 – 200f. multicoloured . . . 1·40 85
512 – 300f. multicoloured . . . 2·10 1·10
OPTS.: 55f. **VAINQUEURS 1950 URUGUAY 1978 ARGENTINE**; 65f. **VAINQUEURS 1970 BRESIL 1978 ARGENTINE**; 125f. **VAINQUEURS 1966 GRANDE BRETAGNE 1978 ARGENTINE**; 200f. **VAINQUEURS 1962 BRESIL 1978 ARGENTINE**; 300f. **VAINQUEURS 1954 ALLEMAGNE (RFA) 1978 ARGENTINE**.

177 Radio Station

1979. 10th Anniv of Posts and Telecommunications Organization. Multicoloured.
514 55f. Type **177** 40 20
515 65f. Loading mail aboard Beech A100 King Air monoplane 50 30

178 Children listening to Story

1979. International Year of the Child.
516 **178** 75f. multicoloured 85 45

179 Wave Pattern and Human Figures

1979. World Telecommunications Day.
517 **179** 70f. multicoloured 55 35

180 Basket Weaving and Upper Volta 50c. Stamp of 1963

1979. "Philexafrique" Exhibition, Libreville, Gabon (2nd series). Multicoloured.
518 100f. Type **180** . . . . 1·60 1·40
519 100f. Concorde, van, shouting man and U.P.U. emblem 1·60 1·40

181 Volta Squeaker

1979. Freshwater Fish. Multicoloured.
520 20f. Type **181** 50 25
521 50f. Como tetra . . . . . . 1·40 75
522 85f. Airbreathing catfish . . . 2·00 1·00

182 Class 241-P Steam Locomotive, France

1979. Death Centenary of Sir Rowland Hill. Multicoloured.
523 65f. Type **182** 55 20
524 165f. Class 215 diesel locomotive, Germany . . . 1·25 50
525 200f. Class "Warship" diesel locomotive, Great Britain 1·40 60
526 300f. French TGV express train . . . . 2·40 90

183 Kob

1979. Endangered Animals. Multicoloured.
528 30f. Type **183** 20 10
529 40f. Roan antelope 35 10
530 60f. Caracal 65 10
531 100f. African elephant . . . 1·00 35
532 175f. Hartebeest . . . . . . 1·60 45
533 250f. Leopard . . . . 2·50 55

184 Teacher and Class

1979. World Literacy Day. Multicoloured.
534 55f. Farmer reading book (vert) 45 35
535 250f. Type **184** . . . . 2·00 1·25

185 Telecommunications

1979. 3rd World Telecommunications Exhibition, Geneva.
536 **185** 200f. multicoloured . . . 1·40 70

186 King Vulture

1979. Protected Birds. Multicoloured.
537 5f. Type **186** 45 10
538 10f. Hoopoe 45 15
539 15f. Ruppell's griffon 55 20
540 25f. Intermediate egret . . . 75 25
541 35f. Ostrich . . . . 1·25 30
542 45f. Crowned crane . . . . 1·50 35
543 125f. Cassin's hawk eagle . . 3·25 1·40

187 Airport

1979. 20th Anniv of A.S.E.C.N.A. (Air Navigation Security Agency).
544 **187** 65f. multicoloured 60 40

188 Headquarters Building

1979. Opening of West African Savings Bank Building, Dakar, Senegal.
545 **188** 55f. multicoloured 50 30

189 Jamot, Map and Tsetse Fly

1979. Birth Centenary of Eugene Jamot (discoverer of cure for sleeping sickness).
546 **189** 55f. multicoloured 85 45

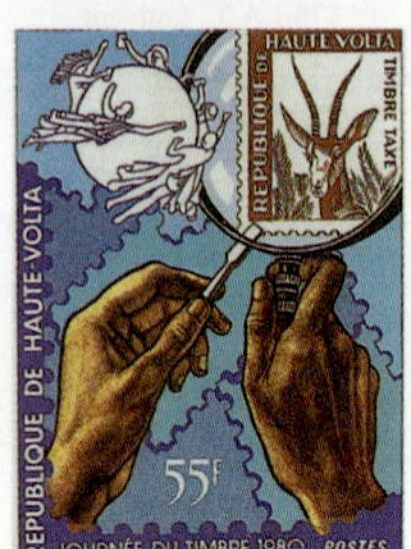

190 Stamp under Magnifying Glass

1980. Stamp Day.
547 **190** 55f. multicoloured 50 25

191 Electric Locomotives

1980. 25th Anniv of World Locomotive Speed Record.
548 **191** 75f. multicoloured . . . . 1·40 45
549 100f. multicoloured . . . 2·10 65

192 Pope John Paul II

1980. Papal Visit. Multicoloured.
550 55f. Pres. Lamizana, Pope and Cardinal Pau Zoungrana (horiz) 85 35
551 100f. Type **192** . . . . 1·40 85

193 Telephone

194 Mountains and Statue

1980. World Telecommunications Day.
552 **193** 50f. multicoloured 40 20

1980. Solar Energy. Multicoloured.
553 65f. Sun and Earth 50 20
554 100f. Type **194** 80 40

195 Downhill Skiing (L. Stock)

1980. Winter Olympic Games Winners. Mult.
555 65f. Type **195** 45 15
556 100f. Women's downhill skiing (A. Moser-Proell) . . 65 20
557 200f. Figure skating (A. Poetzsch) . . . . . . 1·40 35
558 350f. Slalom (I. Stenmark) (vert) . . . . 2·25 60

196 Map of Europe and Africa

197 Hand pushing back Sand Dune

1980. Europafrique.
560 **196** 100f. red, black and green 90 45

1980. Operation "Green Sahara". Multicoloured.
561 50f. Type **197** 50 20
562 55f. Hands planting saplings 60 35

198 Cyclists

1980. Air. Olympic Games, Moscow. Cycling.
563 **198** 65f. multicoloured 55 15
564 – 150f. multicoloured (vert) 1·10 40
565 – 250f. multicoloured . . . 1·90 55
566 – 350f. multicoloured . . . 2·75 90
DESIGNS: 150f. to 350f. Different cyclists.

199 Installation of Chief

1980. National History. Multicoloured.
568 30f. Type **199** 35 15
569 55f. Moro Naba, Emperor of Mossis 55 30
570 65f. Princess Guimbe Ouattara (vert) 60 30

200 Gourounsi Mask

201 Tractor, Cattle and Grain (Agriculture)

1980. World Tourism Conference, Manila.
571 **200** 65f. multicoloured 55 30

1980. 5th Anniv of West African Economic Council. Multicoloured.
572 55f. Type **201** 35 15
573 65f. "Communications" . . . 90 35
574 75f. Dam and highway . . . 45 30
575 100f. "Industry" . . . . . . 1·40 50

1980. Air. Olympic Winners. Nos. 563/6 optd.
576 **198** 65f. multicoloured 30 25
577 – 150f. multicoloured . . . 75 50
578 – 250f. multicoloured . . . 1·25 90
579 – 350f. multicoloured . . . 1·60 1·00
OVERPRINTS: 65f. **SOUKHOROUCHENKOV (URSS)**; 150f. **HESSLICH (RDA)**; 250f. **LANG (POL)**; 350f. **DILL-BUNDI (SUISSE)**.

203 Coat of Arms and Map

1980. 20th Anniv of Independence.
581 **203** 500f. multicoloured . . . 4·25 2·50

204 "Sistine Madonna" (detail)

205 "Scarabaeus sacer"

1980. Christmas. Multicoloured.
582 60f. Type **204** 45 15
583 150f. "Virgin de l'Impannata" . . . . . 1·10 40
584 250f. "Alba Madonna" . . . 1·75 55

1980. 5th Anniv of African Post and Telecommunications. As T **272a** of Togo.
585 55f. multicoloured 50 30

1981. Insects. Multicoloured.
586 5f. Type **205** 10 10
587 10f. "Gryllus campestris" . . 10 10
588 15f. Termites 15 10
589 20f. "Mantis religiosa" (vert) 25 10
590 55f. "Nyctaon pyri" 75 25
591 65f. "Locusta migratorius" (vert) 85 35

206 Bobo Mask, Hounde

207 College Emblem

1981. Masks. Multicoloured.

592	45f. Type **206**	40	15
593	55f. Bwa mask	45	20
594	85f. Kouroumba mask	60	35
595	105f. Gourounsi mask	80	40

1981. 25th Anniv of Notre-Dame College, Kologh'naba.

596	**207** 55f. multicoloured	45	20

208 Von Stephan and U.P.U. Emblem

1981. 150th Birth Anniv of Heinrich von Stephan (founder of U.P.U.).

597	**208** 65f. multicoloured	60	35

209 Ribbons forming Caduceus, I.T.U. and W.H.O. Emblems

210 Series ZE Diesel-electric Train

1981. World Telecommunications Day.

598	**209** 90f. multicoloured	60	35

1981. Abidjan–Niger Railway. Multicoloured.

599	25f. Type **210**	50	15
600	30f. "La Gazelle" express train	90	25
601	40f. "Le Belier" express train	1·10	60

211 Group of Trees

1981. Tree Month.

602	**211** 70f. multicoloured	70	40

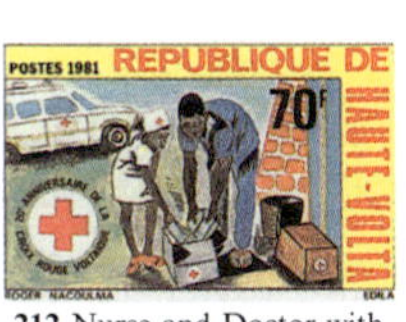

212 Nurse and Doctor with Medical Equipment

213 Handicapped Sculptor

1981. 25th Anniv of Upper Volta Red Cross.

603	**212** 70f. multicoloured	60	40

1981. International Year of Disabled People.

604	**213** 70f. multicoloured	60	35

214 Koudougou

1981. Landscapes. Multicoloured.

605	35f. Type **214**	30	15
606	45f. Toma	40	20
607	85f. Volta Noire	65	30

215 Agricultural Scenes within Map

1981. World Food Day.

608	**215** 90f. multicoloured	70	45

216 Topi

1981. Wildlife Protection. Multicoloured.

609	5f. Type **216**	10	10
610	15f. Waterbuck	15	15
611	40f. Roan antelopes	35	20
612	60f. Dorcas gazelle	60	35
613	70f. African elephant	1·00	55

217 Campaign Emblem

219 Donkey

218 Papaya

1981. Anti-Apartheid Campaign.

614	**217** 90f. red	60	35

1981. Fruit and Vegetables. Multicoloured.

615	20f. Type **218**	15	10
616	35f. Fruit and vegetables	30	15
617	75f. Mangoes (vert)	50	30
618	90f. Melons	60	35

1981. Stock Breeding. Multicoloured.

619	10f. Type **219**	10	10
620	25f. Pig	20	10
621	70f. Cow	55	20
622	90f. Helmeted guineafowl (vert)	80	40
623	250f. Rabbit	1·75	90

220 Women carrying Rice

221 Father and Son

1981. 10th Anniv of West African Rice Development Association.

625	**220** 90f. multicoloured	90	45

1982. 20th Anniv of World Food Programme.

626	**221** 50f. multicoloured	40	15

222 Morhonaba Palace, Ouagadougou

1982. Traditional Houses. Multicoloured.

627	30f. Type **222**	20	10
628	70f. Bobo (horiz)	50	20
629	100f. Gourounsi (horiz)	70	30
630	200f. Peulh (horiz)	1·40	60
631	250f. Dagari (horiz)	1·60	65

223 Hexagonal Pattern

1982. World Telecommunications Day.

632	**223** 90f. multicoloured	85	40

224 Symbols of National Life

225 Passing Ball

1982. National Life.

633	**224** 90f. multicoloured	60	30

1982. Air. World Cup Football Championship, Spain. Multicoloured.

634	70f. Type **225**	50	15
635	90f. Tackle	60	30
636	150f. Running with ball	1·10	40
637	300f. Receiving ball	2·00	85

226 Water Lily

227 Symbols of Communication on Map of Africa

1982. Flowers. Multicoloured.

639	25f. Type **226**	15	10
640	40f. Kapoka	35	10
641	70f. Frangipani	60	35
642	90f. "Cochlospermum planchonii"	80	45
643	100f. Cotton	90	45

1982. African Post and Telecommunications Union.

644	**227** 70f. multicoloured	45	15
645	90f. multicoloured	65	35

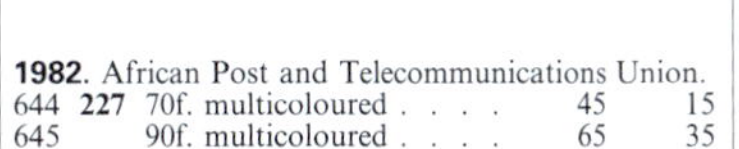

228 Children holding Torch

1982. 25th Anniv of Cultural Aid Fund.

646	**228** 70f. multicoloured	50	30

229 Hairstyle

1983.

647	**229** 90f. multicoloured	65	30
648	120f. multicoloured	90	35
649	170f. multicoloured	1·25	50

230 Audience watching Film

1983. 8th Film Festival, Ouagadougou. Mult.

650	90f. Type **230**	85	55
651	500f. Dumarou Ganda	4·25	2·50

231 Joseph Montgolfier and First Demonstration of Hot-air Balloon, 1783

1983. Bicentenary of Manned Flight. Mult.

652	15f. Type **231** (postage)	10	10
653	25f. Jean-Francois Pilatre de Rozier and first manned flight, 1783	15	10
654	70f. Jacques Charles and hydrogen balloon "The Globe", 1783	50	10
655	90f. John Jeffries and first Channel crossing, 1785	65	20
656	100f. Wilhelmine Reichardt and ascent on a horse, 1798 (air)	85	30
657	250f. Salomon Andree and Spitzbergen–Expedition, 1897	1·60	55

232 Campaign Emblem and River

233 Man reading Letter

1983. International Drinking Water Decade. Mult.

659	60f. Type **232**	45	20
660	70f. Woman carrying water	55	35

1983. World Communications Year. Multicoloured.

661	30f. Type **233**	20	15
662	35f. Type **233**	30	15
663	45f. Canoe and Boeing 727 airliner	40	20
664	90f. Woman on telephone	65	35

234 Space Shuttle "Challenger"

1983. Air. World Events. Multicoloured.

665	90f. Type **234**	60	20
666	120f. World Cup football final	85	30
667	300f. World Cup football final (different)	1·90	60
668	450f. Royal wedding	2·50	85

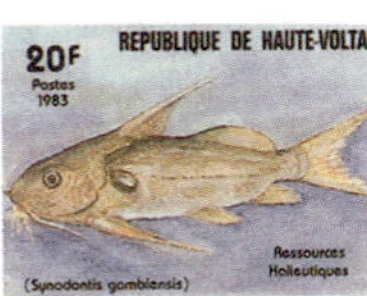

235 Gambian Squeaker

1983. Fishery Resources. Multicoloured.

670	20f. Type **235**	30	20
671	30f. Gunther's krib	75	45
672	40f. Line fishing (vert)	75	45
673	50f. Net fishing	85	55
674	75f. Trap fishing	1·25	85

236 Soling Class Yacht

1983. Air. Pre-Olympic Year. Multicoloured.

675	90f. Type **236**	65	20
676	120f. Type 470 yacht	1·00	30
677	300f. Windsurfing	2·25	60
678	400f. Windsurfing (different)	2·75	85

237 Planting a Sapling

1983. Campaign for Control of the Desert. Multicoloured.

680	10f. Type **237**	15	10
681	50f. Plantation	40	10
682	100f. Control of forest fires	90	35
683	150f. Woman cooking	1·40	60
684	200f. Control of timber trade (vert)	1·60	90

238 Arms of Upper Volta

1983. 25th Anniv of Republic. Multicoloured.

685	90f. Type **238**	55	30
686	500f. Family with flag	3·25	1·40

239 "Self-portrait" (Picasso)

1983. Celebrities' Anniversaries. Multicoloured.

687	120f. Type **239**	1·40	35
688	185f. "Self-portrait with a Palette" (Manet (1832–1883))	1·40	45
689	300f. Fresco detail (Raphael (1483–1520)) (horiz)	2·25	60
690	350f. Fresco detail (Raphael) (different) (horiz)	2·50	85
691	500f. J. W. Goethe (1749–1832) (portrait by Georg Oswald)	3·50	1·10

240 "Adoration of the Shepherds"

1983. Air. Christmas. Multicoloured.

692	120f. Type **240**	85	30
693	350f. "Virgin of the Garland"	2·40	65
694	500f. "Adoration of the Magi"	3·00	1·00

242 Handball

1984. Air. Olympic Games, Los Angeles. Multicoloured.

695	90f. Type **242**	55	20
696	120f. Volleyball	80	30
697	150f. Handball (horiz)	1·10	35
698	250f. Basketball (horiz)	1·60	50
699	300f. Football (horiz)	2·00	65

243 Greater Flamingo

1984. Air. Birds. Multicoloured.

701	90f. Type **243**	1·25	45
702	185f. Kori bustard (vert)	2·00	1·10
703	200f. Red-billed oxpecker (vert)	2·40	1·10
704	300f. Southern ground hornbill	3·25	1·75

244 Pres. Houari Boumedienne of Algeria

1984. Air. Celebrities. Multicoloured.

705	5f. Type **244**	10	10
706	125f. Gottlieb Daimler (automobile designer) and car	90	30
707	250f. Louis Bleriot (aviator) and Bleriot XI airplane	1·60	50
708	300f. Pres. Abraham Lincoln of U.S.A. and White House	2·25	55
709	400f. Henry Dunant (founder of Red Cross), red cross and battle of Solferino	2·75	70
710	450f. Auguste Piccard and bathyscaphe "Trieste"	3·00	1·40
711	500f. Robert Baden-Powell (founder of Boy Scout movement) and scouts	3·25	95
712	600f. Anatole Karpov, 1978 world chess champion	3·75	1·10

245 Seedling and Clasped Hands within Circle of Flags

246 "Polystictus leoninus"

1984. 25th Anniv of Council of Unity.

714 **245**	90f. multicoloured	65	30
715	100f. multicoloured	80	35

1984. Fungi and Flowers. Multicoloured.

716	25f. Type **246** (postage)	40	20
717	185f. "Pterocarpus lucens"	1·60	60
718	200f. "Phlebopus colossus sudanicus"	3·25	1·25
719	250f. "Cosmos suplhureus"	2·25	85
720	300f. "Trametes versicolour" (air)	4·50	1·40
721	400f. "Ganoderma lucidum"	5·50	1·75

247 Cheetah with Cubs

1984. Protected Animals. Multicoloured.

723	15f. Type **247** (postage)	10	10
724	35f. Two cheetahs	30	10
725	90f. Cheetah	65	20
726	120f. Cheetah with cubs (different)	90	35
727	300f. Baboons (air)	2·25	55
728	400f. Marabou stork and African white-backed vulture	3·50	80

248 CC 2400 Diesel Locomotive and Lumber Train

1984. Transport. Multicoloured. (a) Locomotives.

730	40f. Type **248**	40	10
731	100f. Steam locomotive No. 1806	1·00	20
732	145f. Steam locomotive "Livingstone"	1·90	40
733	450f. Class C51 steam locomotive, Japan	5·00	1·00
	(b) Ships.		
734	20f. "Maiden Queen"	15	10
735	60f. "Scawfell"	50	15
736	120f. "Harbinger"	1·00	35
737	400f. "True Briton"	3·25	1·25

For later issues see **BURKINA FASO**.

OFFICIAL STAMPS

O 18 African Elephant

1963.

O112 **O 18**	1f. sepia and brown	10	10
O113	5f. sepia and green	15	15
O114	10f. sepia and violet	20	20
O115	15f. sepia and orange	25	25
O116	25f. sepia and purple	35	35
O117	50f. sepia and green	65	65
O118	60f. sepia and red	75	75
O119	85f. sepia and myrtle	1·25	1·25
O120	100f. sepia and blue	1·50	1·50
O121	200f. sepia and mauve	2·75	2·75

POSTAGE DUE STAMPS

1920. Postage Due stamps of Upper Senegal and Niger, "Figures" Key-type, optd **HAUTE-VOLTA**.

D18 M	5c. green	15	3·25
D19	10c. red	15	3·25
D20	15c. grey	15	3·25
D21	20c. brown	25	3·75
D22	30c. blue	40	4·25
D23	50c. black	35	4·25
D24	60c. orange	40	4·25
D25	1f. violet	50	4·75

1927. Surch.

D40 M	2f. on 1f. mauve	1·25	8·75
D41	3f. on 1f. brown	1·75	9·75

1928. "Figures" key-type inscr "HAUTE-VOLTA".

D63 M	5c. green	35	75
D64	10c. red	35	75
D65	15c. grey	50	95
D66	20c. brown	50	95
D67	30c. blue	65	1·25
D68	50c. black	1·75	3·00
D69	60c. orange	2·25	4·00
D70	1f. violet	3·50	6·50
D71	2f. purple	6·75	10·00
D72	3f. brown	7·50	11·00

D 13 Red-fronted Gazelle

1962. Figures of value in black.

D 95 **D 13**	1f. blue	10	10
D 96	2f. orange	10	10
D 97	5f. blue	15	15
D 98	10f. purple	30	30
D 99	20f. green	55	55
D100	50f. red	1·40	1·40

APPENDIX

The following stamps have either been issued in excess of postal needs or have not been available to the public in reasonable quantities at face value. Such stamps may later be given full listing if there is evidence of regular postal use.

1973.

Gold Medal Winners, Munich Olympic Games (2nd series). Air 50, 60, 90, 150, 350f.

Christmas 1972. Paintings of the Madonna and Child. Air 50, 75, 100, 125, 150f.

Moon Mission of "Apollo 17". Air 50, 65, 100, 150, 200f.

Gold Medal Winners, Munich Olympic Games (3rd series). Air 35, 45, 75, 250, 400f.

Exploration of the Moon. Air 50, 65, 100, 150, 200f.

Wild Animals. Air 100, 150, 200, 250, 500f.

10th Anniv of Organization of African Unity. Air 45f.

Europafrique. European Paintings. Air 50, 65, 100, 150, 200f.

Historic Railway Locomotives, French Railway Museum, Mulhouse. Air 10, 40, 50, 150, 250f.

Upper Volta Boy Scouts. Postage 20f.; Air 40, 75, 150, 200f.

Pan-African Drought Relief. Surch on values of 1973 Europafrique issue. Air 100f. on 65f., 200f. on 150f.

10th Death Anniv of President John Kennedy. Rockets. Postage 5, 10, 30f.; Air 200, 300f.

50th Anniv of International Police Organization (Interpol). 50, 65, 70, 150f.

Tourism. Postage 35, 40f.; Air 100f.

Religious Buildings. Postage 35, 40f.; Air 200f.

Folk-dancers. Postage 35, 40f.; Air 100, 225f.

Famous Men. 5, 10, 20, 25, 30, 50, 60, 75, 100, 175, 200, 250f.

1974.

World Cup Football Championship, Munich (1st issue). Postage 5, 40f.; Air 75, 100, 250f.

Pres. De Gaulle Commemoration. Postage 35, 40, 60f.; Air 300f.

World Cup Football Championship (2nd issue). Postage 10, 20, 50f.; Air 150, 300f.

Centenary of Universal Postal Union. Postage 35, 40, 85f.; Air 100, 200, 300f.

World Cup Football Championship (3rd issue). Previous Finals. Postage 10, 25, 50f.; Air 150, 200, 250f.

Centenary of Berne Convention. 1974 U.P.U. issue optd. Postage 35, 40, 85f., Air 100, 200, 300f.

Bouquets of Flowers. Postage 5, 10, 30, 50f.; Air 300f.

1975.

Birth Centenary of Sir Winston Churchill. 50, 75, 100, 125, 300f.

Bicentenary of American Revolution (1st issue). 35, 40, 75, 100, 200, 300f.

Railway Locomotives. Postage 15, 25, 50f.; Air 100, 200f.

Vintage and Veteran Cars. Postage 10, 30, 35f.; Air 150, 200f.

Bicent of American Revolution (2nd issue). Postage 30, 40, 50f.; Air 200, 300f.

Birth Cent of Dr Albert Schweitzer. Postage 5, 15f.; Air 150, 175, 200f.

"Apollo–Soyuz" Joint Space Test Project. Postage 40, 50f.; Air 100, 200, 300f.

Paintings by Picasso. Postage 50, 60, 90f.; Air 150, 350f.

"Expo '75" Exhibition, Okinawa, Japan. Postage 15, 25, 45, 50, 60f.; Air 150f.

Winter Olympic Games, Innsbruck. Postage 35, 45, 85f.; Air 100, 200f.

1976.

Olympic Games, Montreal (1st issue). "Pre-Olympic Year" (1975). Postage 40, 50, 100f.; Air 125, 150f.

Olympic Games, Montreal (2nd issue). Postage 30, 55, 75f.; Air 150, 200f.

Zeppelin Airships. Postage 10, 40, 50f.; Air 100, 200, 300f.

"Viking" Space Flight. Postage 30, 55, 75f.; Air 200, 300f.

1977.

Olympic Games Medal Winners, 1976 Olympic Games issue optd. Postage 30, 55, 75f.; Air 150, 200f.

1983.

Bicentenary of Manned Flight. Air 1500f.

UPPER YAFA Pt. 19

A Sultanate of South Arabia, formerly part of the Western Aden Protectorate. Independent from September to December 1967 and then part of the People's Democratic Republic of Yemen.

1000 fils = 1 dinar.

1 Flag and Map

1967.

UY 1	1	5f. mult (postage)	15	15
UY 2		10f. multicoloured	15	15
UY 3		20f. multicoloured	20	20
UY 4		25f. multicoloured	25	20
UY 5		40f. multicoloured	40	25
UY 6		50f. multicoloured	50	30
UY 7	–	75f. multicoloured (air)	65	50
UY 8	–	100f. multicoloured	85	60
UY 9	–	250f. multicoloured	2·00	2·00
UY10	–	500f. multicoloured	3·50	3·50

DESIGNS: UY7/10, Arms of Sultanate.

APPENDIX

The following stamps have either been issued in excess of postal needs or have not been available to the public in reasonable quantities at face value. Such stamps may later be given full listing if there is evidence of regular postal use.

1967.

Olympic Games, Mexico (1968). Postage 15, 25, 50, 75f.; Air 150f.

Sculptures. Postage 10, 30, 60, 75f.; Air 150f.

Paintings from the Louvre. Postage 50f.; Air 100, 150, 200, 250f.

World Cup Football Championship, England (1966). Postage 5, 10, 50f.; Air 100f.

Paintings by Old Masters. Postage 10, 15, 20, 25, 30, 40, 50, 60, 75f.; Air 150f.

Human Rights Year and 5th Death Anniv of J. F. Kennedy. Postage 5, 10, 50, 75f.; Air 125f.

Persian Miniatures. 10, 20, 30, 40, 50f.

Ballet Paintings. 20, 30, 40, 50, 60f.

Portraits by Old Masters. Postage 25, 50, 75f.; Air 100, 125, 150, 175, 200, 225, 250f.

Winter Olympic Games, Grenoble (1968). 1967 World Cup issue optd. Postage 5f. × 2, 10f. × 2, 50f. × 2; Air 100f. × 2.

20th Anniv of UNICEF. Paintings. Postage 50, 75f.; Air 100, 125, 250f.

Flower Paintings. Postage 5, 10, 50f.; Air 100, 150f.

URUGUAY Pt. 20

A republic in S. America, bordering on the Atlantic Ocean, independent since 1828.

1856. 120 centavos = 1 real.
1859. 1000 milesimos = 100 centesimos = 1 peso.

1

1856. Imperf.

1	1	60c. blue	£190
2		80c. green	£170
3		1r. red	£150

3

4

1858. Imperf.

5	3	120c. blue	£130	£120
6		180c. green	38·00	55·00
7		240c. red	38·00	£225

1859. Imperf.

15	4	60c. purple	15·00	13·50
16		80c. yellow	£130	25·00
17		100c. red	38·00	29·00
18		120c. blue	25·00	9·50
12		180c. green	9·50	11·50
13		240c. red	35·00	35·00

6 8 9

1864. Imperf.

20a	6	6c. red	5·75	3·75
21		8c. green	9·75	9·75
22		10c. yellow	13·50	9·25
23		12c. blue	5·75	4·50

1866. Surch in figures. Imperf.

24	6	5c. on 12c. blue	9·50	19·00
25		10c. on 8c. green	9·50	25·00
26		15c. on 10c. yellow	11·50	29·00
27a		20c. on 6c. red	13·50	29·00

1866. Imperf.

28	8	1c. black	95	1·50
29	9	5c. blue	1·50	85
30		10c. green	5·50	2·25
31		15c. yellow	9·25	3·75
32		20c. red	11·00	3·75

1866. Perf.

37	8	1c. black	2·25	2·25
33	9	5c. blue	2·00	35
34		10c. green	3·75	35
35		15c. yellow	2·00	1·40
36		20c. red	4·50	1·10

10

11

1877. Roul. Various frames.

42	10	1c. brown	25	20
43	11	5c. green	30	15
44	10	10c. red	40	15
45		20c. bistre	60	25
46		50c. black	3·00	1·10
47		1p. blue	17·00	5·50

15 J. Suarez

16

1881. Perf.

60a	15	7c. blue	75	90

1882.

62	16	1c. green	40	40
63	–	2c. red	35	35

The central device on the 2c. shows a mountain.

18 Arms

20 Gen. Maximo Santos

21 General Artigas

26

1883.

66	18	1c. green	50	30
67		2c. red	60	40
68	20	5c. blue	75	60
69	21	10c. brown	1·10	75

1883. Optd **1883 Provisorio**. Roul.

75	11	5c. green	50	40

1884. Optd **PROVISORIO 1884** or surch **1 CENTESIMO** also.

76	10	1c. on 10c. red	15	15
77	–	2c. red (No. 63)	50	50

1884.

79	26	5c. blue	1·00	50

28 29 31 Gen. Artigas

32 M. Santos 33 34

1884. Roul.

100	28	1c. green	20	20
83a		1c. grey	40	30
101	29	2c. red	20	25
85a	28	5c. blue	1·00	15
86		5c. lilac	25	10
87	31	7c. brown	95	60
103		7c. orange	60	40
88	32	10c. brown	20	20
89	33	20c. mauve	75	30
105		20c. brown	75	40
90	34	25c. lilac	1·40	50
106		25c. red	1·10	60

35

36

1887. Roul.

99	35	10c. mauve	70	40

1888. Roul.

104	36	10c. violet	25	25

1889. Optd **Provisorio**. Roul.

114	28	5c. lilac	15	15

38

39 40

41 42 43

44 Figure of Justice

45 Mercury

46

1889. Perf.

115	38	1c. green	40	20
116	39	2c. red	20	25
117	40	5c. blue	20	15
118	41	7c. brown	60	25
119	42	10c. green	1·50	25
120	43	20c. orange	1·10	30
121	44	20c. brown	2·00	40
122	45	50c. blue	3·50	1·10
123	46	1p. violet	8·50	2·00

See also Nos. 142/52, 220, 222 224 and 236/7.

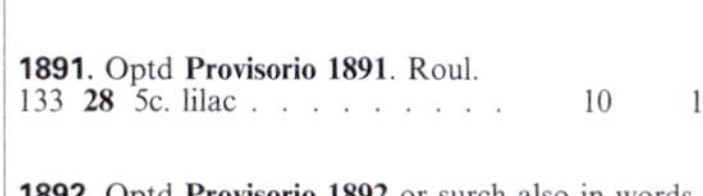

1891. Optd **Provisorio 1891**. Roul.

133	28	5c. lilac	10	10

1892. Optd **Provisorio 1892** or surch also in words.

135	28	1c. green	40	40
137	43	1c. on 20c. orange	15	10
136	41	5c. on 7c. brown	15	30

50

51

52

53 54

55

1892. Perf.

138	50	1c. green	20	15
139	51	2c. red	25	20
140	52	5c. blue	20	15
141	53	10c. orange	90	40

1894.

142	38	1c. blue	20	25
143	39	2c. brown	25	25
144	40	5c. red	50	20
145	41	7c. green	2·75	1·10
146	42	10c. orange	1·50	30
147	43	20c. brown	2·75	75
148	44	25c. red	3·50	1·50
149	45	50c. purple	6·25	2·25
150	46	1p. blue	11·00	3·00
151	54	2p. red	11·50	7·00
152	55	3p. purple	11·50	7·00

56 Gaucho

57 Solis Theatre

58 Steam Locomotive

59 Bull's Head

60 Ceres 61 Steamer "Elbe"

62 Amazon

63 Mercury

64

65 Montevideo Fortress

66 Montevideo Cathedral

1895.

153	56	1c. bistre	20	20
154	57	2c. blue	20	20
155	58	5c. red	4·00	20
156	59	7c. green	3·75	1·00
157	60	10c. brown	85	30
158	61	20c. black and green	7·00	55
159	62	25c. black and brown	2·75	60
160	63	50c. black and blue	3·50	1·50
161	64	1p. black and brown	5·50	2·00
162	65	2p. green and violet	11·50	7·75
163	66	3p. blue and red	11·50	6·25

For further stamps in these types, see Nos. 183/93 and 221.

67 J. Suarez

68 J. Suarez Monument

72

1896. Unveiling of President Joaquin Suarez Monument.
177 **67** 1c. black and red 20 15
178 **68** 5c. black and blue 25 20
179 – 10c. black and lake 45 25
DESIGN: 10c. Larger stamp showing whole Suarez Monument.

1897. Optd **PROVISORIO 1897**.
180 **67** 1c. black and red 30 30
181 **68** 5c. black and blue 40 30
182 – 10c. black and lake 50 50

1897.
183 **56** 1c. blue 20 15
184 **57** 2c. purple 30 20
185 **58** 5c. green . . . . 3·50 15
186 **59** 7c. orange . . . . 1·75 60
187 **72** 10c. red 85 35
188 **61** 20c. black and mauve . . . 6·50 40
189 **62** 25c. blue and red . . . . 1·50 35
190 **63** 50c. brown and green . . . 2·75 70
191 **64** 1p. blue and brown . . . . 4·50 1·40
192 **65** 2p. red and yellow . . . . 4·50 65
193 **66** 3p. red and lilac . . . . 4·25 1·10
See also No. 223.

1897. End of Civil War. Optd with palm leaf and **PAZ 1897**.
197 **56** 1c. blue 40 30
198 **57** 2c. purple 55 55
199 **58** 5c. green . . . . 3·25 2·50
200 **72** 10c. red . . . . 1·40 1·40

1898. Surch **PROVISIONAL ½ CENTESIMO**.
209 **38** ½c. on 1c. blue 15 15
210 **56** ½c. on 1c. bistre 15 15
211 **67** ½c. on 1c. black and red . . 15 15
212 **57** ½c. on 2c. blue 15 15
213 **68** ½c. on 5c. black and blue . . 20 15
214 **59** ½c. on 7c. green 20 15

75 Liberty

76 Monument to Gen. Artigas

1898.
215 **75** 5m. red 20 20
216 5m. violet 25 25

1899.
217 **76** 5m. blue 25 15
218 5m. orange 25 15
220 **39** 2c. orange 20 20
221a **58** 5c. blue . . . . 2·75 15
222 **41** 7c. red . . . . 2·25 1·10
223 **72** 10c. purple 30 25
224 **43** 20c. blue . . . . 1·10 20

1900. No. 182 surch **1900 5 CENTESIMOS** and bar.
229 5c. on 10c. black and lake . . 25 15

78 **79** **80**

81 **82**

1900.
230 **78** 1c. green 30 15
231a **79** 2c. red 10 15
232b **80** 5c. blue 60 15
233 **81** 7c. brown 85 30
234 **82** 10c. lilac 45 20
236 **45** 50c. red . . . . 3·50 35
237 **46** 1p. green . . . . 11·00 75

85 General Artigas **86**

87 **88**

89 **90**

91

1904.
251 **85** 5m. yellow 30 15
252 **86** 1c. green 50 15
253a **87** 2c. orange 20 15
254b **88** 5c. blue 40 10
255 **89** 10c. lilac 40 20
256 **90** 20c. green . . . . 1·40 40
257 **91** 25c. bistre . . . . 1·50 40

1904. End of the Civil War. Optd **Paz-1904**.
258 **86** 1c. green 35 30
259 **87** 2c. orange 40 35
260 **88** 5c. blue . . . . 1·00 50

95 **96**

1906.
268 **95** 5c. blue 50 15

1906.
269 **96** 5c. blue 20 10
270 7c. brown 40 25
271 50c. red . . . . 2·25 40

98 Cruiser "Montevideo" and Cadet Ship "Diez-y-Ocho de Julio"

1908. 83rd Anniv of Revolt of the "Immortal 33" under Levalleja. Roul.
279 **98** 1c. green and red . . . . 1·25 85
280 2c. green . . . . 1·25 85
281 5c. green and orange . . . 1·25 85

99 Montevideo Port

1909. Opening of the Port of Montevideo.
282 **99** 2c. black and brown . . . 1·75 80
283 5c. black and red . . . . 1·75 80

1909. Surch **Provisorio** and value.
284 **82** 8c. on 10c. violet 40 30
285 **44** 23c. on 25c. brown 75 30

103 Centaur

1910. Centenary of 1810 Argentine Revolution.
286 **103** 2c. red 30 20
287 5c. blue 30 20

1910. Surch **PROVISORIO 5 MILESIMOS** (or **CENTESIMOS**) **1910**.
294 **78** 5m. on 1c. green 10 20
295 **45** 5c. on 50c. red 15 30
296 **96** 5c. on 50c. red 40 30

107 Artigas **108**

1910.
297 **107** 5m. purple 15 10
298 1c. green 15 10
299 2c. red 20 10
324 2c. pink 25 10
319 4c. yellow 30 10
300 5c. blue 20 10
301 8c. black 40 15
327 8c. blue 25 10
302 20c. brown 70 20
303 **108** 23c. blue . . . . 4·00 50
330 50c. orange . . . . 9·00 90
331 1p. red . . . . 9·00 1·25

109

114 Liberty offering Peace to Uruguay

1911. 1st Pan-American Postal Congress.
306 **109** 5c. black and red 35 25

1911. Centenary of Battle of Las Piedras. Surch **ARTIGAS**, value and **1811-1911**.
314 **81** 2c. on 7c. brown 35 25
315 5c. on 7c. brown 35 20

1913. Centenary of 1813 Conference. Optd **CENTENARIO DE LAS INSTRUCCIONES DEL AÑO XIII.**
332 **107** 2c. brown 30 40
333 4c. yellow 30 40
334 5c. blue 30 40

1918. Promulgation of New Constitution.
347 **114** 2c. brown and green . . . 35 25
348 5c. blue and brown . . . 35 25

115 Montevideo Harbour

116 Statue of Liberty, New York

118 J. E. Rodo

1919.
349 **115** 5m. grey and violet . . . 20 10
350 1c. grey and green . . . 25 10
351 2c. grey and red 25 10
352 4c. grey and orange . . . 60 10
353 5c. grey and blue 70 10
354 8c. brown and blue . . . 85 20
355 20c. grey and brown . . . 3·00 35
356 23c. brown and green . . . 4·25 70
357 50c. blue and brown . . . 4·75 3·25
358 1p. blue and red . . . . 11·50 2·75

1919. Peace Commemoration.
359 **116** 2c. brown and red 20 10
360 4c. brown and orange . . 30 10
361 5c. brown and blue . . . 35 10
362 8c. blue and brown . . . 50 20
363 20c. black and bistre . . . 1·40 40
364 23c. black and green . . . 2·00 70

1920. Honouring J. E. Rodo (writer).
372 **118** 2c. black and lake 35 45
373 4c. blue and orange . . . 40 30
374 5c. brown and blue . . . 50 35

1921. Air. Optd with airplane and **CORREO AEREO**.
377 **44** 25c. brown . . . . 2·10 1·50

120 Mercury

122 Damaso A. Larranaga

1921.
378 **120** 5m. mauve 30 10
410 5m. black 20 10
380 1c. green 30 10
411 1c. mauve 25 10
411a 1c. violet 25 10
412 2c. orange 35 10
412a 2c. red 40 10
384 3c. green 40 20
385 4c. yellow 25 10
386 5c. blue 25 10
413 5c. brown 40 10
414 8c. red 55 50
388 12c. blue . . . . 1·10 50
389 36c. olive . . . . 4·50 1·50

1921. 150th Birth Anniv of D. A. Larranaga.
390 **122** 5c. slate 75 55

127 Artigas Monument

128 Southern Lapwing

1923. Unveiling of Monument to Artigas.
418 **127** 2c. brown and red 30 10
419 5c. brown and violet . . . 30 10
420 12c. brown and blue . . . 40 20

1923. Various sizes.
450 **128** 5m. grey 35 20
422 1c. yellow 25 30
451 1c. pink 60 30
477 1c. purple . . . . 1·10 40
528 1c. violet 25 40
423 2c. mauve 25 30
529 2c. red 25 40
453 3c. green 80 30
454 5c. blue 60 20
455 8c. red 80 30
456 10c. green 60 20
457 12c. blue 90 30
458 15c. mauve 80 30
459 20c. brown . . . . 1·50 30
429 36c. green . . . . 4·00 1·50
460 36c. red . . . . 6·50 1·25
430 50c. orange . . . . 7·50 2·10
461 50c. olive . . . . 7·50 1·75
431 1p. red . . . . 30·00 17·00
462 1p. buff . . . . 11·00 4·00
432 2p. green . . . . 30·00 17·00
463 2p. lilac . . . . 27·00 12·00

130

131 Biplane

1923. Centenary of Battle of Sarandi.
433 **130** 2c. green 35 25
434 5c. red 35 25
435 12c. blue 35 25

1924. Air.
436 **131** 6c. blue 75 85
437 10c. red . . . . 1·10 1·25
438 20c. green . . . . 2·00 2·00

134 "Victory" of Samothrace

1924. Uruguayan Football Victory in Olympic Games.
464 **134** 2c. red . . . . 8·50 6·25
465 5c. purple . . . . 8·50 6·25
466 12c. blue . . . . 8·50 6·25

135 Landing of Lavalleja

1925. Centenary of Rising against Brazilian Rule.
467 **135** 2c. grey and red 60 70
468 5c. grey and mauve . . . 60 70
469 12c. grey and blue 60 70

136 Parliament House

1925. Inauguration of Parliament House.
470 **136** 5c. black and violet . . . 60 40
471 12c. black and blue . . . 60 40

137 White-necked Heron
138 Gen. F. Rivera

139 Gaucho Cavalryman at Rincon

1925. Air. Centenary of Assembly of Florida.
(a) Inscr "MONTEVIDEO".
472 **137** 14c. black and blue . . . 15·00 7·75
(b) Inscr "FLORIDA".
473 **137** 14c. black and blue . . . 15·00 7·75

1925. Centenary of Battle of Rincon.
474 **138** 5c. pink (postage) 40 30
475 **139** 45c. green (air) . . . . . — 4·50

140 Battle of Sarandi

1925. Centenary of Battle of Sarandi.
482 **140** 2c. green 60 55
483 5c. mauve 60 55
484 12c. blue 75 60

141 Albatross
145 New G.P.O., Montevideo

1926. Air. Imperf.
495 **141** 6c. blue 70 70
496 10c. red 95 95
497 20c. green . . . . 1·40 1·40
498 25c. violet . . . . 1·40 1·40
See also Nos. 569/80.

1927. Philatelic Exhibition, Montevideo. Imperf.
534 **145** 2c. green . . . . 2·00 2·00
535 5c. red . . . . 2·00 2·00
536 8c. blue . . . . 2·00 2·00

1928. Opening of San Carlos–Rocha Railway. Surch **Inauguracion Ferrocarril SAN CARLOS a ROCHA 14/1/928** and value.
537 **128** 2c. on 12c. blue . . . . 2·25 2·25
538 5c. on 12c. blue . . . . 2·25 2·25
539 10c. on 12c. blue . . . 2·25 2·25
540 15c. on 12c. blue . . . 2·25 2·25

147 Gen. F. Rivera (after M. Bucasso)

1928. Centenary of Conquest of Las Misiones.
541 **147** 5c. red 30 15

148 Artigas
149 Artigas Statue, Paysandu

1928.
542 **148** 5m. black 10 10
762 5m. brown 10 10
868 5m. orange 10 10
543 1c. violet 10 10
544 1c. purple 10 10
869 1c. blue 10 10
687 15m. black 25 15
545 2c. green 10 10
764 2c. brown 10 10
870 2c. red 10 10
546 3c. bistre 20 10
871 3c. green 10 10
548 5c. red 15 10
549 5c. olive 15 10
766 5c. blue 15 10
767 5c. turquoise 30 10
872 5c. violet 10 10
550 7c. red 15 10
551 8c. blue 20 10
552 8c. brown 20 10
553 10c. orange 30 15
768 12c. blue 30 10
556 15c. blue 45 10
557 17c. violet 40 15
558 20c. brown 55 15
757 20c. buff 70 35
770 20c. red 40 30
771 20c. violet 35 10
560 24c. red 70 40
561 24c. yellow 40 35
562 36c. olive 70 40
563 50c. grey . . . . 1·75 95
564 50c. black . . . . 2·25 85
772 50c. sepia . . . . 1·10 45
566 1p. green . . . . 4·00 1·50
567 **149** 2p. brown and blue . . . 5·00 2·75
568 3p. black and red . . . . 6·25 6·25

1928. Air. Re-issue of T **141**. Perf.
634 **141** 4c. brown . . . . 1·50 1·50
569 10c. green 75 70
570 20c. orange . . . . . . 1·10 85
571 30c. blue . . . . 1·10 85
572 38c. green . . . . 1·75 1·50
573 40c. yellow . . . . . . 2·10 2·00
574 50c. violet . . . . 2·25 2·25
575 76c. orange . . . . . . 4·25 4·25
576 1p. red . . . . 3·50 3·50
577 1p.14 blue . . . . . . 10·00 8·75
578 1p.52 yellow . . . . . 15·00 15·00
579 1p.90 violet . . . . . 18·00 17·00
580 3p.80 red . . . . 50·00 45·00

150 Goal Posts
151 General Garzon

1928. Uruguayan Football Victories in 1924 and 1928 Olympic Games.
581 **150** 2c. purple . . . . 4·50 3·75
582 5c. red . . . . 4·50 3·75
583 8c. blue . . . . 4·50 3·75

1928. Unveiling of Monument to Gen. Garzon. Imperf.
584 **151** 2c. red 75 75
585 5c. green 75 75
586 8c. blue 75 75

154 Artigas
156 Pegasus

1929.
759 **154** 1p. brown . . . . 3·00 1·40
596 2p. green . . . . 5·00 2·75
597 2p. red . . . . 11·00 7·75
760 2p. blue . . . . 5·75 5·50
598 3p. blue . . . . 7·00 5·00
761 3p. black . . . . 8·75 7·00
600 4p. violet . . . . 11·00 8·50
601 4p. green . . . . 11·00 7·75
602 5p. red . . . . 13·50 11·00
603 5p. orange . . . . . . 11·00 7·75
604 10p. blue . . . . 38·00 35·00
605 10p. red . . . . 38·00 35·00

1929. Air. Size 34½ × 23½ mm.
617 **156** 1c. mauve 25 25
659 1c. blue 25 25
618 2c. yellow 25 25
660 2c. olive 25 25
619 4c. blue 45 40
661 4c. lake 45 40
620 6c. violet 25 40
662 6c. brown 25 40
621 8c. orange . . . . . . 1·10 1·10
663 8c. grey . . . . 1·25 1·10
664 8c. green 35 30
622 16c. blue . . . . 1·10 75
665 16c. red . . . . 1·10 1·10
623 24c. purple 95 95
666 24c. violet . . . . 1·25 1·10
624 30c. brown . . . . . . 1·10 1·10
667 30c. green 60 30
625 40c. brown . . . . . . 2·00 2·00
668 40c. orange . . . . . . 2·00 1·75
626 60c. blue . . . . 1·75 1·25
669 60c. green . . . . 3·00 2·25
670 60c. red 95 60
627 80c. blue . . . . 3·00 3·00
671 80c. green . . . . 5·00 4·00
628 90c. blue . . . . 3·00 2·10
672 90c. olive . . . . 5·00 4·00
629 1p. red . . . . 2·25 2·00
630 1p.20 olive . . . . . . 7·00 7·00
673 1p.20 red . . . . 11·00 9·25
631 1p.50 purple . . . . . 7·00 5·50
674 1p.50 sepia . . . . . . 3·75 3·50
632 3p. red . . . . 11·50 11·00
675 3p. blue . . . . 7·75 7·75
633 4p.50 black . . . . . . 20·00 18·00
676 4p.50 lilac . . . . . . 14·00 12·50
677 10p. blue . . . . 7·00 5·50
For stamps as Type **156**, but smaller, see Nos. 725/44.

157 Rio Negro Railway Bridge
159 "Peace"

1930. Independence Centenary.
639 **157** 5m. black 55 15
640 – 1c. sepia 20 15
641 **159** 2c. lake 20 15
642 – 3c. green 25 20
643 – 5c. blue 25 20
644 – 8c. red 35 20
645 – 10c. violet 25 35
646 – 15c. green 30 25
647 – 20c. blue . . . . 2·00 70
648 – 24c. lake 60 30
649 – 50c. red . . . . 4·00 1·75
650 – 1p. black . . . . 3·00 1·50
651 – 2p. blue . . . . 7·00 4·50
652 – 3p. red . . . . 10·00 7·00
653 – 4p. orange . . . . 11·50 8·50
654 – 5p. lilac . . . . 17·00 10·00
DESIGNS—HORIZ: 1c. Gaucho horse-breaker; 5c. Head of Liberty and Uruguayan flag; 10c. "Artigas", from picture by Blanes; 15c. Seascape; 20c. Montevideo harbour, 1830; 24c. Head of Liberty and Arms of Uruguay; 50c. Montevideo Harbour, 1930. VERT: 3c. Montevideo; 8c. Allegorical figure with torch; 1p. to 5p. Artigas Monument.

161
163 J. Zorrilla de San Martin

1930. Fund for Old People.
655 **161** 1c.+1c. violet 20 15
656 2c.+2c. green 25 25
657 5c.+5c. red 30 30
658 8c.+8c. blue 30 30

1932.
679 **163** 1½c. purple 20 10
680 3c. green 30 10
681 7c. blue 35 10
682 12c. blue 30 35
683 1p. brown . . . . 9·25 6·25

1932. Surch.
684 **161** 1½c. on 2c.+2c. green . . 25 15

167 J. Zorrilla de San Martin
168 Flag of the Race

1933. Various portraits.
689 – 15m. red (Lavalleja) . . . 15 10
690 – 3c. green (Rivera) 10 10
691 **167** 7c. grey 15 10

1933. 441st Anniv of Columbus' Departure from Palos.
692 **168** 3c. green 15 20
693 5c. pink 20 25
694 7c. blue 20 20
695 8c. red 60 30
696 12c. blue 25 25
697 17c. violet 75 40
698 20c. brown . . . . 1·50 95
699 24c. bistre . . . . 2·00 95
700 36c. red . . . . 2·25 1·10
701 50c. brown . . . . 2·75 1·40
702 1p. brown . . . . 7·75 3·50

169 Sower

1933. Opening of the 3rd National Assembly.
703 **169** 3c. green 20 15
704 5c. violet 35 25
705 7c. blue 30 20
706 8c. red 40 40
707 12c. blue 75 45

170 Map and Albatross

1933. 7th Pan-American Conference, Montevideo.
708 **170** 3c. green, brown and black . . . . 1·10 1·10
709 7c. blue, black and brown 60 45
710 12c. blue, red and grey . . 95 75
711 17c. red, blue and grey . . 2·10 2·10
712 20c. yellow, green and blue . . . . 2·25 2·25
713 36c. red, yellow and black 3·00 3·00

1934. Air. Closure of the 7th Pan-American Conference. Optd **SERVICIO POSTAL AEREO 1-1-34** in circle.
714 **170** 17c. red, blue and grey . . 7·75 6·25
715 36c. red, yellow and black 7·25 6·25

172

1934. 1st Anniv of Third Republic.
716 **172** 3c. green 25 35
717 7c. red 25 35
718 12c. blue 60 30
719 17c. brown and pink . . . 75 70
720 20c. yellow and grey . . . 95 75
721 36c. violet and green . . . 95 95
722 50c. grey and blue . . . . 2·50 2·00
723 1p. red and mauve . . . 6·25 4·00

1935. Air. As T **156**, but size 31½ × 21½ mm.
725 15c. yellow 95 75
726 22c. red 60 50
727 30c. purple 95 75
728 37c. purple 50 40
729 40c. red 75 50
730 47c. red . . . . 1·50 1·40
731 50c. blue 50 50
732 52c. blue . . . . 1·50 1·40
733 57c. blue 75 70
734 62c. green 70 50
735 87c. green . . . . 2·10 1·75
736 1p. olive . . . . 1·40 85
737 1p.12 brown . . . . . . 1·40 85
738 1p.20 brown . . . . . . 4·50 3·75
739 1p.27 brown . . . . . . 4·50 3·75
740 1p.62 red . . . . 3·00 3·00
741 2p. lake . . . . 5·00 4·50
742 2p.12 grey . . . . 5·00 4·50
743 3p. blue . . . . 4·50 4·50
744 5p. orange . . . . 16·00 16·00

173 Friendship of Uruguay and Brazil
174 Florencio Sanchez

1935. Visit of President Vargas of Brazil.
747 **173** 5m. brown 50 30
748 15m. black 25 25
749 3c. green 30 25
750 7c. orange 35 20
751 12c. blue 50 50
752 50c. brown . . . . 2·00 1·50

1935. 25th Death Anniv of F. Sanchez (dramatist).
753 **174** 3c. green 15 10
754 7c. brown 20 10
755 12c. blue 55 35

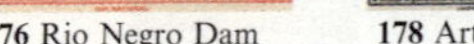

176 Rio Negro Dam **178** Artigas

1937.
780 **176** 1c. violet (postage) 30 10
781 10c. blue 20 10
782 15c. red 75 50
783 1p. brown 3·00 1·10
793 8c. green (air) 35 35
794 20c. green 75 50
785 35c. brown 2·10 2·00
786 62c. green 25 20
787 68c. orange 60 40
788 68c. brown 50 20
789 75c. violet 2·10 60
790 1p. red 75 55
791 1p.38 red 7·00 6·25
792 3p. blue 3·75 75

1939. (a) Plain background.
806 **178** 5m. orange 10 10
807 1c. blue 10 10
808 2c. violet 10 10
809 5c. brown 15 10
810 8c. red 20 10
811 10c. green 35 10
812 15c. blue 40 30
813 1p. brown 1·25 30
1008 1p. purple 1·25 30
814 2p. lilac 3·00 1·25
815 4p. orange 3·75 1·50
816 5p. red 5·25 2·50
Nos. 806/12 are size 16 × 19 mm. No. 1008 is 18 × 22 mm. and Nos. 813/6 are 24 × 29½ mm.

(b) Lined background. (i) Size 17 × 22 mm.
835 **178** 5m. orange 10 10
848 5m. black 10 10
849 5m. blue 10 10
836 1c. blue 10 10
837 1c. purple 10 10
838 2c. violet 10 10
839 2c. orange 15 10
840a 2c. brown 10 10
1152 2c. grey 10 10
841 3c. green 15 10
842 5c. brown 15 10
843b 7c. blue 10 10
844 8c. red 25 10
845 10c. green 15 10
851 10c. brown 25 10
852 12c. blue 25 10
853 20c. mauve 70 15
846 50c. bistre 3·00 60
847 50c. green 2·10 75
1153 50c. brown 10 10

(ii) Size 23½ × 29½ mm.
1024 **178** 2p. brown 3·50 1·50

180 Airplane over "La Carreta" (sculpture, Jose Bellini)

1939. Air.
817 **180** 20c. blue 30 25
818 20c. violet 20 25
820 35c. red 25 20
821 50c. orange 25 20
822 75c. pink 30 15
823 1p. blue 85 10
824 1p.38 violet 1·50 60
825 1p.38 orange 1·40 1·25
826a 2p. blue 2·25 45
827 5p. lilac 3·00 60
828 5p. green 3·75 1·50
829 10p. red 23·00 15·00

181 Congress of Montevideo

1939. 50th Anniv of 1st International Juridical Congress, Montevideo.
830 **181** 1c. red 20 10
831 2c. green 25 20
832 5c. red 25 20
833 12c. blue 30 35
834 50c. violet 1·10 75

183 Juan Manuel Blanes (artist) **185** Francisco Acuna de Figueroa

1941. 40th Death Anniv of Blanes.
855 **183** 5m. brown 20 10
856 1c. brown 20 10
857 2c. green 20 10
858 5c. red 50 10
859 12c. blue 60 45
860 50c. violet 2·75 2·10

1942. 80th Death Anniv of Figueroa (author of words of National Anthem).
863 **185** 1c. brown 15 15
864 2c. green 15 15
865 5c. red 30 15
866 12c. blue 60 40
867 50c. violet 1·75 1·50

1943. Surch **Valor $ 0.005.**
873 **178** 5m. on 1c. blue

187 **189** Clio

1943.
874 **187** 1c. on 2c. brown 10 10
875 2c. on 2c. brown 15 10

1943. Centenary of Historical and Geographical Institute, Montevideo.
878 **189** 5m. violet 20 10
879 1c. blue 20 10
880 2c. red 35 15
881 5c. brown 35 20

191 **192** Emblems of Y.M.C.A.

1944. 75th Anniv of Founding of Swiss Colony.
889 **191** 1c. on 3c. green 10 10
890 5c. on 7c. brown 20 10
891 10c. on 12c. blue 40 25

1944. Centenary of Young Men's Christian Assn.
892 **192** 5c. blue 10 10

1944. Air. Air stamps of 1935, Nos. 730, etc, surch.
893 40c. on 47c. red 25 40
894 40c. on 57c. blue 30 25
895 74c. on 1p.12 brown 30 25
896 79c. on 87c. green 1·10 75
897 79c. on 1p.27 brown 1·50 1·25
898 1p.20 on 1p.62 red 85 60
899 1p.43 on 2p.12 grey 1·10 75

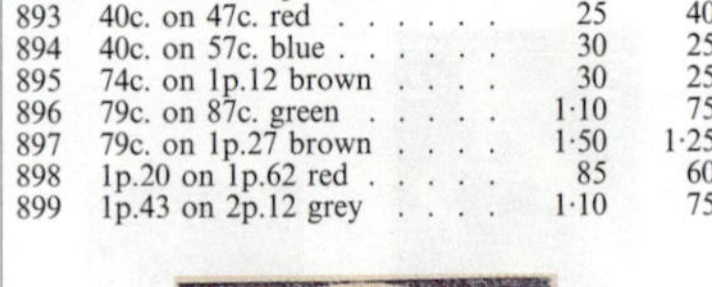

194 Legislative Palace

1945. Air.
900 **194** 2p. blue 1·75 70

195 Book **198** Statue

1945. Birth Centenary of Jose Pedro Varela (writer).
901 **195** 5m. green 15 10
902 – 1c. brown (Varela) 15 10
903 – 2c. red (Statue) 15 10
904a **198** 5c. blue 15 10
Nos. 902/3 are vert.

205 Eduardo Acevedo (statesman) **200** Jose Pedro Varela (writer)

1945.
905 – 5m. violet 10 10
911 – 1c. brown 10 10
912 **205** 2c. purple 10 10
945 – 3c. green 10 10
906 **200** 5c. red 15 10
907 – 10c. blue 25 15
946 – 20c. brown and green 55 30
PORTRAITS: 5m. Santiago Vazquez (statesman); 1c. Sylvestre Blanco (statesman); 3c. Bruno Mauricio de Zabala (founder of Montevideo); 10c. Jose Ellauri (President, 1873–75); 20c. Col. Luis de Larrobla (first Postmaster).

206 Full-rigged Ship "La Eolo"

1945. Air.
913 **206** 8c. green 2·50 45

1945. Air. Victory. Surch with figure as "Victory of Samothrace", **1945** and new value. No. 908 optd **VICTORIA** also.
914 **180** 14c. on 50c. orange 35 30
915 23c. on 50c. orange 40 35
916 23c. on 1p.38 orange 50 40
908 **156** 44c. on 75c. brown 70 40
917 **180** 1p. on 1p. 38 orange 2·00 1·10

1946. Inaug of Rio Negro Hydro-electric Power Plant. Optd **INAUGURACION DICIEMBRE, 1945**, No. 918 also surch **CORREO 20 CENTS.**
918 **176** 20c. on 68c. brown (postage) 80 35
919 62c. green (air) 50 45

1946. As T **187**. (a) Postage. Optd **CORREOS** and Caduceus.
920 **187** 5m. orange 10 10
921 2c. brown 10 10
922 3c. green 10 10
923 5c. blue 10 10
924 10c. brown 15 10
925 20c. green 50 15
926 50c. brown 1·10 60
927 3p. red 4·25 2·25

(b) Air. Optd **SERVICIO AEREO** and an airplane.
928 **187** 8c. red 10 10
929 50c. brown 40 25
930 1p. blue 50 30
931 2p. olive 2·25 1·10
932 3p. red 2·25 1·10
933 5p. red 4·50 3·00

217 Douglas DC-4 **215** National Airport

1947. Air.
947 **217** 3c. brown 10 10
948 8c. red 15 10
949 10c. black 10 10
950 10c. red 10 10
951 14c. blue 25 15
952 15c. brown 15 10
953 20c. purple 15 15
954 21c. lilac 20 15
955 23c. green 25 20
956 27c. green 20 10
957 31c. brown 30 15
958 36c. blue 20 10
959 36c. black 20 15
960 50c. turquoise 35 25
961 50c. blue 25 10
962 62c. blue 40 25
963 65c. red 40 25
964 84c. orange 55 40
941 **215** 1p. brown and red 95 20
965 **217** 1p.08 plum 65 45
966 2p. blue 1·10 40
942 **215** 3p. brown and blue 1·75 95
967 **217** 3p. orange 1·25 50
943 **215** 5p. brown and green 3·75 2·00
968 **217** 5p. green 2·50 1·10
969 5p. grey 1·50 75
944 **215** 10p. brown and purple 4·00 3·00
970 **217** 10p. green 6·25 3·50

1947. As T **187** but surch in figures above shield and wavy lines.
976 2c. on 5c. blue 10 10
977 3c. on 5c. blue 10 10

219 "Ariel" **221** Bas-reliefs

1948. Unveiling of Monument to J. E. Rodo (writer).
978 **219** 1c. brown and olive 10 10
979 – 2c. brown and violet 10 10
980 **221** 3c. brown and green 15 10
981 5c. brown and mauve 20 10
982 10c. brown and red 20 10
983 12c. brown and blue 25 15
984 **219** 20c. brown and purple 55 35
985 – 50c. brown and red 1·50 70
DESIGN: 2, 50c. Bust of J. E. Rodo.

The 5c. and 12c. are as Type **221** but inscr "UN GRAN AMOR ES EL ALMA MISMA DE QUIEN AMA".

1948. Air. As T **187**, optd **AVIACION** and airplane.
986 12c. blue 20 10
987 24c. green 35 15
988 36c. grey 50 25

223 Paysandu **225** River Santa Lucia Railway Bridge

1948. Industrial and Agricultural Exhibitions, Paysandu.
989 **223** 3c. green 15 10
990 – 7c. blue 20 10
DESIGN—HORIZ: 7c. Livestock, sower and arms of Paysandu.

1948. Uruguayan–Brazilian Friendship.
991 **225** 10c. blue 75 20
992 50c. green 2·75 70

226 Ploughing

1949. 4th American Labour Conference.
993 **226** 3c. green 15 10
994 – 7c. blue 20 10
DESIGN—HORIZ: 7c. Horseman herding cattle.

227 Medical Faculty

1949. Air. Centenary of Montevideo University.
995 – 15c. red 10 10
996 **227** 27c. brown 15 10
997 – 31c. blue 25 10
998 – 36c. green 30 10
DESIGNS: 15c. Architectural faculty; 31c. Engineering faculty; 36c. View of University.

228 Cannon and Buildings **229** Kicking Football

1950. Bicentenary of Cordon (district of Montevideo).
1003 **228** 1c. mauve 10 10
1004 3c. green 10 10
1005 7c. blue 15 10

1951. 4th World Football Championship.
1006 **229** 3c. green 50 15
1007 7c. blue 75 35

230 Gen. Artigas

231 Emigration from Eastern Provinces

1952. Death Cent of Artigas. Dated "1950".
1009 **230** 5m. blue 10 10
1010 – 1c. black and blue 10 10
1011 – 2c. brown and violet 10 10

1012 **231** 3c. sepia and green . . . 10 10
1013 – 5c. black and orange . . 15 10
1014 **231** 7c. black and olive . . . 15 10
1015 – 8c. black and red 25 10
1016 – 10c. red, blue and brown 25 10
1017 – 14c. blue 30 10
1018 – 20c. red, blue and yellow 45 20
1019 – 50c. olive and brown . . 80 35
1020 – 1p. olive and blue . . . 1·75 70

DESIGNS (all show Artigas except 10c. and 20c.)—As Type **230**: 1c. at Las Huerfanas; 2c. at Battle of Las Piedras; 5c. in Cerrito; 14c. at Ciudadela; 20c. Arms; 50c. in Paraguay; 1p. Bust. As Type **231**: 7c. Dictating instructions; 8c. in Congress; 10c. Flag.

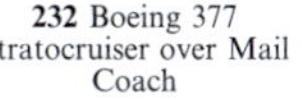

232 Boeing 377 Stratocruiser over Mail Coach

234 Franklin D. Roosevelt

1952. 75th Anniv of U.P.U. (1949).
1021 **232** 3c. green 10 10
1022 7c. black 15 10
1023 12c. blue 20 10

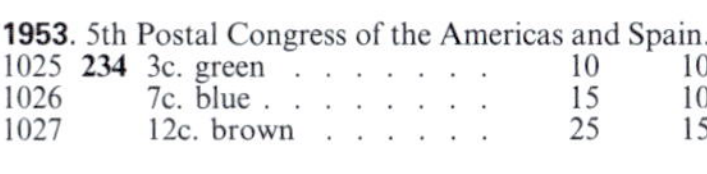

1953. 5th Postal Congress of the Americas and Spain.
1025 **234** 3c. green 10 10
1026 7c. blue 15 10
1027 12c. brown 25 15

235 Ceibo (National Flower)

236 Ombu Tree

237 Parliament House

239 Exhibition Entrance

1954.
1028 **235** 5m. multicoloured . . . 10 10
1029 – 1c. black and red 10 10
1030 **236** 2c. green and brown . . 10 10
1031 – 3c. multicoloured 10 10
1032 **237** 5c. brown and lilac . . . 10 10
1033 – 7c. green and brown . . 10 10
1034 – 8c. blue and red 20 10
1035 **236** 10c. green and orange 20 10
1036 – 12c. sepia and blue . . . 15 10
1037 – 14c. black and purple . . 20 10
1038 **235** 20c. multicoloured . . . 25 10
1039 – 50c. multicoloured . . . 55 20
1040 **237** 1p. brown and red . . . 95 30
1041 – 2p. sepia and red . . . . 2·00 80
1042 – 3p. green and lilac . . . 2·10 60
1043 – 4p. blue and brown . . . 5·50 2·50
1044 **236** 5p. green and blue . . . 5·00 3·00

DESIGNS—As T **235**: 3c., 50c. Passion flower. As T **236**—HORIZ: 1c., 14c. Gaucho breaking-in horse. VERT: 7c., 3p. Montevideo Citadel. As T **237**—VERT: 8c., 4p. Isla de Lobos lighthouse and southern sealions. HORIZ: 12c., 2p. Outer Gateway of Montevideo, 1836.

1956. 1st National Production Exhibition.
1050 **239** 3c. green (postage) . . . 10 10
1051 7c. blue 10 10
1052 – 20c. blue (air) 30 20
1053 – 31c. green 35 30
1054 – 36c. red 60 35

DESIGN—HORIZ: Nos. 1052/4, Exhibition symbol and two airliners.

241 Uruguay's First Stamp and "Diligencia"

1956. Air. Centenary of First Uruguay Stamps. Stamp in blue.
1055 **241** 20c. green and yellow . . 35 20
1056 31c. brown and blue . . 40 25
1057 36c. red and pink . . . 50 35

242 Pres. Jose Battle y Ordonez

248 High Diver

1956. Birth Centenary of Jose Batlle y Ordonez (President, 1903–07 and 1911–15).
1058 **242** 3c. red (postage) 10 10
1059 – 7c. sepia 10 10
1060 – 10c. mauve (air) 10 10
1061 **242** 20c. slate 15 10
1062 – 31c. brown 20 15
1063 – 36c. green 30 20

PORTRAIT OF PRESIDENT—VERT: 7c. Wearing overcoat; 10c. Similar to Type **242**; 36c. Profile, facing right. HORIZ: 31c. Seated at desk.

1957. Surch **5** or **10 Cts.**
1071 **242** 5c. on 3c. red 10 10
1072 – 10c. on 7c. sepia (No. 1059) 10 10

1958. 14th S. American Swimming Championships, Montevideo. Inscr as in T **248**.
1073 **248** 5c. green 15 10
1074 – 10c. blue 35 15

DESIGN—HORIZ: 10c. Diving.

249 Dr. E. Acevedo

250 Flags

1958. Birth Centenary of Dr. Eduardo Acevedo (lawyer).
1075 **249** 5c. black and green . . . 10 10
1076 10c. black and blue . . . 15 10

1958. Air. Day of the Americas.
1077 **250** 23c. black and blue . . . 15 15
1078 34c. black and green . . 20 15
1079 44c. black and mauve . . 35 20

251 Baygorria Dam

252 "Flame of Freedom"

1958. Inauguration of Baygorria Hydro-electric Power Station.
1080 **251** 5c. black and green . . . 10 10
1081 10c. black and brown . . 10 10
1082 – 1p. black and blue . . . 40 15
1083 – 2p. black and mauve . . 60 35

DESIGN: 1, 2p. Aerial view of dam.

1958. Air. 10th Anniv of Declaration of Human Rights.
1084 **252** 23c. black and blue . . . 15 10
1085 34c. black and green . . 20 15
1086 44c. black and red . . . 35 25

1958. Nos. 1028, 1031 and 1033 surch with Caduceus and value.
1087 5c. on 3c. multicoloured . . 10 10
1088 10c. on 7c. green and brown 10 10
1089 20c. on 5m. multicoloured 15 10

254 Statue on Capt. Boiso Lanza Monument

1959. Air. Centres in black.
1090 **254** 3c. brown 10 10
1091 8c. mauve 10 10
1092 38c. black 10 10
1093 50c. yellow 15 10
1094 60c. violet 15 10
1095 90c. olive 20 15
1096 1p. blue 30 15
1097 2p. orange 70 50
1098 3p. green 85 50
1099 5p. purple . . . . 1·10 85
1100 10p. red . . . . 3·75 2·50

See also Type **266**.

255 Santos-Dumont and his Biplane "14 bis"

1959. Air. Santos-Dumont Commemoration.
1101 **255** 31c. multicoloured . . . 15 15
1102 36c. multicoloured . . . 15 15

257 "Tourism in Uruguay"

258 Gabriela Mistral (poet)

1959. Air. Tourist Publicity and 50th Anniv of Punta del Este.
1103 **257** 10c. blue and ochre . . . 10 10
1104 – 38c. buff and green . . . 15 10
1105 – 60c. buff and violet . . . 25 15
1106 **257** 90c. green and red . . . 30 20
1107 – 1p.05 buff and blue . . . 35 25

DESIGN: 38, 60c., 1p.05, Beach and compass.

1959. 2nd Death Anniv of Gabriela Mistral.
1108 **258** 5c. green 10 10
1109 10c. blue 10 10
1110 20c. red 15 10

259 Dr. Vaz Ferreira

260 Emblem of Y.M.C.A.

1959. Honouring Dr. Carlos Vaz Ferreira (philosopher).
1111 **259** 5c. black and blue . . . 10 10
1112 10c. black and ochre . . 10 10
1113 20c. black and red . . . 10 10
1114 50c. black and violet . . 25 10
1115 1p. black and green . . 40 20

1959. Air. 50th Anniv of Y.M.C.A. in Uruguay.
1116 **260** 38c. black, grey and green 25 25
1117 50c. black, grey and blue 30 20
1118 60c. black, grey and red 35 35

261 Boy and Dam

262 Artigas and Washington

1959. National Recovery.
1119 **261** 5c.+10c. green and orange (postage) . . . 10 10
1120 10c.+10c. blue & orange 10 10
1121 1p.+10c. violet & orange 40 30
1122 38c.+10c. brown and orange (air) 20 20
1123 60c.+10c. green & orge 30 30

1960. Air. Visit of President Eisenhower.
1124 **262** 38c. black and red . . . 15 15
1125 50c. black and blue . . . 20 15
1126 60c. black and green . . 25 15

1960. Air. Surch with caduceus and **20 c.**
1128 **217** 20c. on 27c. green . . . 10 10

265 Martinez

266 Statue on Lanza Monument

1960. Birth Centenary of Dr. Martin C. Martinez.
1129 **265** 3c. black and purple . . 10 10
1130 5c. black and violet . . . 10 10
1131 10c. black and blue . . . 10 10
1132 20c. black and brown . . 10 10
1133 1p. black and grey . . . 25 10
1134 2p. black and orange . . 55 15
1135 3p. black and olive . . . 85 30
1136 4p. black and brown . . 1·10 65
1137 5p. black and red . . . 1·25 70

1960. Air.
1138 **266** 3c. black and lilac . . . 10 10
1139 20c. black and red . . . 10 10
1140 38c. black and blue . . . 10 10
1141 50c. black and buff . . . 10 10
1142 60c. black and green . . 15 10
1143 90c. black and red . . . 25 15
1144 1p. black and grey . . . 30 15
1145 2p. black and green . . . 45 25
1146 3p. black and purple . . 40 20
1147 5p. black and salmon . . 60 40
1148 10p. black and yellow . . 1·10 65
1149 20p. black and blue . . 2·50 1·25

267 Refugees

268 Scene of Revolution

1960. World Refugee Year.
1150 – 10c. black & bl (postage) 10 10
1151 **267** 60c. black and mauve (air) 20 20

DESIGN: 10c. "Uprooted tree".

1960. 150th Anniv of Argentine May Revolution.
1154 **268** 5c. black & blue (postage) 10 10
1155 10c. brown and blue . . 10 10
1156 38c. olive and blue (air) 15 10
1157 59c. red and blue 15 15
1158 60c. violet and blue . . . 25 15

269 Pres. M. Oribe

270 Pres. Gronchi

1961. 104th Death Anniv of Manuel Oribe (President, 1835–38).
1159 **269** 10c. black and blue . . . 10 10
1160 20c. black and brown . . 10 10
1161 40c. black and green . . 15 10

1961. Air. Visit of President of Italy.
1162 **270** 90c. multicoloured . . . 25 20
1163 1p.20 multicoloured . . 30 25
1164 1p.40 multicoloured . . 35 30

271 Carrasco Airport Building

1961. Air. Carrasco National Airport.
1165 **271** 1p. grey and violet . . . 20 20
1166 2p. grey and olive . . . 45 10
1167 3p. grey and yellow . . . 35 35
1168 4p. grey and purple . . . 55 20
1169 5p. grey and turquoise 60 30
1170 10p. grey and blue . . . 1·10 45
1171 20p. grey and red . . . 2·00 1·25

272 "Charging Horsmen" (by C. M. Herrera)

1961. 150th Anniv of 28 February Revolution.
1172 **272** 20c. black and blue . . . 15 10
1173 40c. black and green . . 25 10

273 Welfare, Justice and Education

1961. Latin-American Economic Commission Conference, Punta del Este. (a) Postage. Centres in bistre.
1174 **273** 2c. violet 10 10
1175 5c. orange 10 10
1176 10c. red 10 10
1177 20c. green 10 10
1178 50c. lilac 10 10
1179 1p. blue 25 15
1180 2p. yellow 55 35
1181 3p. grey 55 35
1182 4p. blue 85 45
1183 5p. brown 95 60

(b) Air. Centres in black.
1184 **273** 20c. orange 10 10
1185 45c. green 15 10
1186 50c. purple 15 10
1187 90c. violet 20 15
1188 1p. red 25 20
1189 1p.40 lilac 35 25
1190 2p. ochre 20 25
1191 3p. blue 30 35
1192 4p. yellow 40 50
1193 5p. blue 55 40
1194 10p. green . . . . 1·10 70
1195 20p. mauve . . . . 2·00 1·50

274 Gen. Rivera

275 Symbols of Swiss Settlers

1962. Honouring Gen. Fructuoso Rivera (1st President, 1830–35).
1196 **274** 10c. black and red . . . 10 10
1197 20c. black and ochre . . 10 10
1198 40c. black and green . . 15 10

1962. Centenary of First Swiss Settlers.
1199 **275** 10c. red, black and blue (postage) 10 10
1200 20c. red, black and green 10 10
1201 – 90c. black, red and orange (air) 20 20
1202 – 1p.40 black, red and blue 30 30
DESIGN—HORIZ: 90c., 1p.40, Wheatsheaf, harvester and Swiss flag.

276 B. P. Berro

277 Red-crested Cardinal

1962. Bernardo Prudencio Berro (President, 1860–64).
1203 **276** 10c. black and blue . . . 10 10
1204 20c. black and brown . . 10 10

1962. Birds.
1205 – 2c. brown, pink and black (postage) . . . 25 10
1206 – 50c. brown and black . . 75 15
1207 – 1p. brown and black . . 1·00 40
1208 – 2p. black, brown and grey . . . . 1·50 75
1209 **277** 20c. red, black and grey (air) 25 15
1210 – 45c. red, blue and black 45 15
1211 – 90c. brown, black and red . . . . 1·10 15
1212 – 1p. blue, black and brown 75 25
1213 – 1p.20 multicoloured . . 1·50 25
1214 – 1p.40 brown, black and blue . . . . 2·25 45
1215 – 2p. yellow, black & brown . . . . 1·50 45
1216 – 3p. black, yellow & brown . . . . 2·25 70
1217 – 5p. black, blue and green 4·00 1·00
1218 – 10p. multicoloured . . 7·00 2·10
1219 – 20p. orange, black and grey . . . . 15·00 7·25

BIRDS—HORIZ: 2c. Rufous-bellied thrush; 45c. Diademed tanager; 50c. Rufous hornero; 1p. (1207), Chalk-browed mockingbird; 1p. (1212), Shiny-headed cowbird; 1p.20, Great kiskadee; 2p. (1208), Rufous-collared sparrow; 2p. (1215), Yellow cardinal; 3p. Hooded siskin; 5p. Sayaca tanager; 10p. Blue and yellow tanager; 20p. Scarlet-headed blackbird. VERT: 90c. Vermilion flycatcher; 1p.40, Fork-tailed flycatcher.

Nos. 1208, 1210, 1212 and 1215 have no frame; Nos. 1206 and 1214 have a thin frame line; the others are as Type **277**.

278 D. A. Larranaga

1963. 85th Death Anniv of Damaso Antonio Larranaga (founder of National Library).
1220 **278** 20c. sepia and turquoise 20 20
1221 40c. sepia and drab . . . 20 20

279 U.P.A.E. Emblem

1963. 50th Anniv of Postal Union of the Americas and Spain.
1222 **279** 20c. blue & black (postage) 10 10
1223 45c. green and black (air) 10 10
1224 90c. red and black . . . 20 15

280 Campaign Emblem

281 Anchors

1963. Freedom from Hunger.
1225 **280** 10c. yell & grn (postage) 10 10
1226 20c. yellow and brown 10 10
1227 90c. yellow and red (air) 20 15
1228 1p.40 yellow and violet 25 20

1963. World Voyage of "Alferez Campora".
1229 **281** 10c. vio & orge (postage) 10 10
1230 20c. grey and red . . . 10 10
1231 – 90c. green & orange (air) 30 10
1232 – 1p.40 blue and yellow . . 40 25
DESIGN: 90c., 1p.40, Sailing ship "Alferez Campora".

282 Large Intestine Congress Emblem

1963. 1st Uruguayan Proctological Congress, Punta del Este.
1233 **282** 10c. red, black and green 10 10
1234 20c. red, black and ochre 10 10

283 Centenary Emblem

1964. Red Cross Centenary.
1235 **283** 20c. red and blue 10 10
1236 40c. red and grey . . . 15 10

284 L. A. de Herrera

1964. 5th Death Anniv of Luis A. de Herrera (statesman).
1237 **284** 20c. black, green and blue 10 10
1238 40c. black, lt blue & blue 10 10
1239 80c. black, yellow & blue 15 10
1240 1p. black, lilac and blue 15 10
1241 2p. black, slate and blue 25 20

285 Pres. De Gaulle

1964. Air. Visit of President of France. Multicoloured.
1242 1p.50 Type **285** 40 15
1243 2p.40 Flags of France and Uruguay 50 40

286 Reliefs from Abu Simbel

1964. Nubian Monuments Preservation. Multicoloured.
1244 20c. Type **286** (postage) . . 10 10
1245 1p.30 Sphinx, Sebua (air) . . 30 15
1246 2p. Rameses II, Abu Simbel 65 30
Nos. 1245/6 are vert.

292 Arms

288 Pres. Kennedy

1965. Air.
1261 **292** 20p. multicoloured . . . 1·25 70
1248 – 50p. blue, yellow and grey . . . . 3·75 3·00
DESIGN—HORIZ (38 × 27 mm) 50p. National flag.

1965. Pres. Kennedy Commemoration. Frame and laurel in gold.
1249 **288** 20c. blk & grn (postage) 10 10
1250 40c. black and brown . . 10 10
1251 1p.50 black and lilac (air) 20 10
1252 2p.40 black and blue . . 30 15

289 "Tete-beche" Pair of Uruguayan 8c. Stamps of 1864

290 6c. "Arms-type" of 1964

1965. 1st River Plate Stamp Exn, Montevideo. (a) Postage. T **289**.
1253 40c. green and black 10 10

(b) Air. As T **290** showing Arms-type stamps of 1864 (values in brackets).
1254 1p. black and blue (12c.) . . 10 10
1255 1p. black and orange (T **290**) 10 10
1256 1p. black and green (8c.) . . 10 10
1257 1p. black and bistre (10c.) 10 10
1258 1p. black and red (6c.) . . . 10 10

Nos. 1254/8 were issued together in sheets of 10 (5 × 2), each design arranged in a vertical pair with "URUGUAY" either at top or bottom.

291 B. Nardone

1965. 1st Death Anniv of Benito Nardone (statesman).
1259 **291** 20c. black and green . . 10 10
1260 – 40c. black and green . . 10 10
DESIGN—VERT: 40c. Portrait as Type **291**, but Nardone with microphone.

293 Part of Artigas' Speech before the 1813 Congress

1965. Birth Bicent (1964) of Gen. Jose Artigas.
1262 **293** 20c. red, blue and yellow (postage) 10 10
1263 – 40c. olive, black and blue 10 10
1264 – 80c. multicoloured . . . 10 10
1265 – 1p. multicoloured (air) 10 10
1266 – 1p.50 multicoloured . . 15 15
1267 **293** 2p.40 multicoloured . . 25 20
DESIGNS—HORIZ: 40c. Bust of Artigas; 80c. Artigas and his army flag; 1p.50, Bust, flag and exodus of his followers to Argentina. VERT: 1p. Artigas' statue.

295 Football

1965. Olympic Games, Tokyo (1964).
1269 **295** 20c. orange, black and green (postage) . . . 10 10
1270 – 40c. olive, black & brown 10 10
1271 – 80c. red, black and drab 10 10
1272 – 1p. green, black and blue 10 10
1273 – 1p. grey, black & red (air) 10 10
1274 – 1p.50 blue, black & grn 15 15
1275 – 2p. blue, black and red 15 15
1276 – 2p.40 orange, black & bl 20 15
1277 – 3p. yellow, black and lilac 25 20
1278 – 20p. pink, blue & indigo 70 50
DESIGNS: 40c. Basketball; 80c. Cycling; 1p. (No. 1272) Swimming; 1p. (No. 1273) Boxing; 1p.50, Running; 2p. Fencing; 2p.40, Sculling; 3p. Pistol-shooting; 20p. Olympic "Rings".

1965. Surch with caduceus and value.
1280 **178** 10c. on 7c. blue 10 10

1966. 50th Anniv of Uruguay Architects' Assn. Surch **CINCUENTENARIO Sociedad Arquitectos del Uruguay** and value.
1281 **261** 4c. on 5c.+10c. green and orange 10 10

298 I.T.U. Emblem and Satellite

1966. Air. Centenary of I.T.U.
1282 **298** 1p. deep blue, red & blue 15 10

299 Sir Winston Churchill

1966. Churchill Commemoration.
1283 **299** 40c. brown, red and blue (postage) 10 10
1284 – 2p. brn, red & gold (air) 20 10
DESIGN—VERT: 2p. Churchill-full-face portrait and signed quotation.

300 Arms and View of Rio de Janeiro

1966. 400th Anniv of Rio de Janeiro.
1285 **300** 40c. grn & brn (postage) 10 10
1286 80c. red and brown (air) 10 10

301 I.C.Y. Emblem

1966. Air. I.C.Y.
1287 **301** 1p. black and green . . 15 10

302 Army Engineer **304** Pres. Shazar

1966. 50th Anniv of Army Engineers.
1288 **302** 20c. multicoloured . . . 15 10

1966. Air. Visit of President of Israel.
1291 **304** 7p. multicoloured . . . 40 30

305 Crested Screamer **306** Jules Rimet Cup, Ball and Globe

1966. Air.
1292 **305** 100p. multicoloured . . 8·00 2·40

1966. Air. World Cup Football Championship.
1293 **306** 10p. yellow and violet 50 30

307 Hereford Bull **308** L. Batlle Berres (1947–51 and 1955–56)

1966. Air. Cattle-breeding.
1294 **307** 4p. brown, chest & sepia 15 10
1295 – 6p. black, green & turq 25 10
1296 – 10p. mauve, green & turq 35 20
1297 – 15p. black, red and orange 30 30
1298 – 20p. brown, yell & grey 50 40
1299 – 30p. brown and yellow 75 55
1300 – 50p. brown, grey & green . . . . 1·25 85
DESIGNS (Cattle breeds): 6p. Dutch; 10p. Shorthorn; 15p. Aberdeen Angus; 20p. Norman; 30p. Jersey; 50p. Charolais.

1966. Former Uruguayan Presidents.
1301 **308** 20c. black and red . . . 10 10
1302 – 20c. black and blue . . 10 10
1303 – 20c. brown and blue . . 10 10
PRESIDENTS: No. 1302, Daniel Fernandez Crespo (1963–64); 1303, Dr. Washington Beltran (1965–66).

309 Gutenberg Press **310** Capt. Boiso Lanza

1966. 50th Anniv of State Printing Works.
1304 **309** 20c. sepia, green & brown 10 10

1966. Air. Honouring Boiso Lanza (pioneer military aviator).
1305 **310** 25c. black, blue & ultram 75 55

311 Fireman **313** General J. A. Lavalleja

1966. 50th Anniv of Firemen's Corps.
1306 **311** 20c. black and red . . . 25 15

1966. 2nd River Plate Stamp Exn, Montevideo. (a) Postage. No. 1253 optd **Segunda Muestra y Jornadas Rioplatenses**, etc.
1307 **187** 40c. green and black . . 10 10

(b) Air. Nos. 1254/8 optd **CENTENARIO DEL SELLO ESCUDITO RESELLADO**, etc.
1308 1p. blue 10 10
1309 1p. orange 10 10
1310 1p. green 10 10
1311 1p. bistre 10 10
1312 1p. red 10 10
Nos. 1308/12 commemorate the centenary of Uruguay's first surcharged stamps.

1966. Heroes of War of Independence.
1313 **313** 20c. brown, red and blue 10 10
1314 – 20c. blue, black and grey 10 10
1315 – 20c. black and blue . . . 10 10
DESIGNS—VERT: No. 1314, Gen. L. Gomez. HORIZ: 1315, Gen. A. Saravia on horseback.

1966. Air. 40th Anniv of Uruguayan Philatelic Club. No. 1036 surch **40 ANIVERSARIO Club Filatelico del Uruguay $ 1.00 aereo.**
1316 1p. on 12p. sepia and blue 10 10

315 Dante **316** Sunflower

1966. Air. 700th Birth Anniv (1965) of Dante (writer).
1317 **315** 50c. brown and sepia . . 10 10

1967. 20th Anniv of Young Farmers' Movement.
1318 **316** 40c. sepia, yellow & brn 10 10

317 Planetarium

1967. 10th Anniv of Montevideo Planetarium.
1319 **317** 40c. blk & mve (postage) 15 10
1320 – 5p. black and blue (air) 35 15
DESIGN: 5p. Planetarium projector.

318 Pres. Makarios **319** Dr. Schweitzer

1967. Air. Visit of President of Cyprus.
1321 **318** 6p.60 black and mauve 20 15

1967. Air. Schweitzer Commemoration.
1322 **319** 6p. multicoloured . . . 20 15

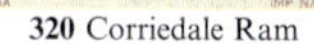

320 Corriedale Ram **322** Church, San Carlos

321 Uruguayan Flag and Globe

1967. Air. Uruguayan Sheep-breeding.
1323 **320** 3p. black, bistre and red 10 10
1324 – 4p. black, bistre and green 15 10
1325 – 5p. black, bistre and blue 20 10
1326 – 10p. black, bistre & yellow 35 30
DESIGNS (sheep breeds): 4p. "Ideal"; 5p. Romney Marsh; 10p. Australian merino.

1967. Air. Heads of State Meeting, Punta del Este.
1327 **321** 10p. gold, blue and black 25 20

1967. Bicentenary of San Carlos.
1328 **322** 40c. black, red and blue 10 10

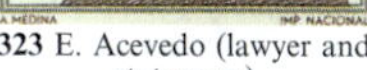

323 E. Acevedo (lawyer and statesman) **325** Ansina

324 "Numeral" Stamps of 1866

1967. Eduardo Acevedo Commemoration.
1329 **323** 20c. brown and green . . 10 10
1330 40c. green and orange 10 10

1967. Air. Centenary of "Numeral" Stamps of 1866.
1331 **324** 3p. blue, green and black 20 10
1332 – 6p. ochre, red and black 35 15
DESIGN: 6p. As T **324**, but depicting 15c. and 20c. stamps of 1866.

1967. Air. Honouring Ansina (servant of Gen. Artigas).
1334 **325** 2p. red, blue and black 10 10

326 Douglas DC-4 over Runway **327** Making Basket

1967. Air. 30th Anniv of PLUNA Airline.
1335 **326** 10p. multicoloured . . . 35 25

1967. Air. World Basketball Championships, Montevideo. Multicoloured.
1336 5p. Type **327** 20 10
1337 5p. Running 20 10
1338 5p. Holding 20 10
1339 5p. Pivot 20 10
1340 5p. Dribbling 20 10

1967. Air. Nos. 1210 and 1223 surch with new value in figures only.
1343 – 5p.90 on 45c. red, bl & blk 55 20
1344 **279** 5p.90 on 45c. green & blk 20 15

330 "Don Quixote and Sancho Panza" (after Denry Torres)

1967. Air. 420th Birth Anniv of Cervantes (writer).
1345 **330** 8p. brown and bistre . . 25 15

331 Arms of Carmelo **332** J. E. Rodo

1967. 150th Anniv of Founding of Carmelo.
1346 **331** 40c. deep blue, ochre and blue 10 10

1967. 50th Death Anniv of Jose E. Rodo (writer). Multicoloured.
1347 1p. Type **332** 10 10
1348 2p. Portrait and sculpture 10 10
The 2p. is horiz.

333 S. Rodriguez (founder), Steam Locomotive and Diesel Railcar **334** Child and Map of Americas

1967. Centenary of 1st National Railway in Uruguay.
1349 **333** 2p. brown and ochre . . 30 10

1967. 40th Anniv of Inter-American Children's Institute.
1350 **334** 1p. red and violet . . . 15 10

1967. No. 1033 surch **1.00 PESO** and caduceus.
1351 1p. on 7c. green and brown 10 10

336 Primitive Club **337** Level Crossing and Traffic Sign

1967. Air. Archaeological Discoveries. Each black and grey.
1352 15p. Type **336** 10 10
1353 20p. Lance-head 20 10
1354 30p. Axe-head 45 15
1355 50p. Sculptured "bird of El Polonio" 60 25
1356 75p. Cooking pot 60 40
1357 100p. Sculptured "bird" of Balizas (horiz) 85 35
1358 150p. Bolas . . . . 1·10 40
1359 200p. Arrow-heads . . . . 1·50 85

1967. Air. Pan American Highways Congress.
1360 **337** 4p. black, yellow and red 30 10

338 Lions Emblem and Map **339** Boy Scout

1967. Air. 50th Anniv of Lions International.
1361 **338** 5p. violet, yellow & green 15 10

1968. Air. Lord Baden-Powell Commemoration.
1362 **339** 9p. brown and orange 15 10

340 Cocoi Heron **341** Sun, Transport and U.N. Emblem

1968. Birds.
1363 – 1p. brown and buff . . . 1·10 25
1364 **340** 2p. black and green . . 1·40 25
1365 – 3p. purple, black & orge 1·50 25
1366 – 4p. black and brown . . 3·50 55
1367 – 4p. black and orange . . 3·50 55
1368 – 5p. black, yellow & brown . . . . 4·00 75
1369 – 10p. violet and black . . 7·00 1·25
BIRDS—VERT: 1p. Great horned owl; 4p. (No. 1367), Black-tailed stilt. HORIZ: 3p. Brown-hooded gull; 4p. (No. 1366), White-faced whistling duck; 5p. Wattled jacana; 10p. Snowy egret.

1968. Air. International Tourist Year (1967).
1370 **341** 10p. multicoloured . . . 65 15

342 Presidents of Uruguay and Brazil, and Concord Bridge **343** Footballer

1968. Opening of Concord Bridge between Uruguay and Brazil.
1371 **342** 6p. brown 15 10

1968. Penarol Club's Victory in Intercontinental Soccer Championships.
1372 **343** 1p. black and lemon . . 15 10

344 St. John Bosco

1968. 75th Anniv of "Don Bosco Workshops".
1373 **344** 2p. black and brown . . 10 10

345 Octopus

1968. Air. Uruguayan Marine Fauna.
1374 **345** 15p. black, blue and turquoise 45 15
1375 – 20p. brown, blue & green 40 15
1376 – 25p. multicoloured . . . 45 20
1377 – 30p. black, green and blue 50 25
1378 – 50p. salmon, blue and green 95 40
DESIGNS—HORIZ: 20p. River Plate pejerrey; 25p. Dorado. VERT: 30p. Spotted sorubim; 50p. Short-finned squid.

346 Sailors' Monument, Montevideo

1968. 150th Anniv of Uruguayan Navy.
1379 **346** 2p. black and green (postage) 10 10
1380 – 6p. black and green . . 10 10
1381 – 12p. black and blue . . 50 15
1382 – 4p. black, red & blue (air) 10 10
1383 – 6p. multicoloured . . . 10 10
1384 – 10p. red, yellow and blue 15 10
1385 – 20p. black and blue . . 90 15
DESIGNS—HORIZ: 4p. Tailplane (Naval Air Force); 6p. (No. 1383), Naval Arms; 12p. Screw gunboat "Suarez"; 20p. Artigas's privateer "Isabel". VERT: 6p. (No. 1380), Buoy and lighthouse; 10p. Mast-head and signal flags.

347 President Gestido

1968. 1st Death Anniv of President Oscar D. Gestido.
1386 **347** 6p. brown, red and blue 10 10

348 Sculling

1969. Air. Olympic Games, Mexico.
1387 **348** 30p. black, brown & blue 30 20
1388 – 50p. black, brown & yell 45 30
1389 – 100p. black, brown & grn 75 50
DESIGNS: 50p. Running; 100p. Football.

349 Cogwheel, Ear of Wheat and Two Heads

1969. 25th Anniv of Uruguay Trades University.
1390 **349** 2p. black and red . . . 10 10

350 Cycling

1969. World Cycling Championships, Montevideo (1968).
1391 **350** 6p. blue, orange and green (postage) . . . 20 10
1392 – 20p. multicoloured (air) 30 15
DESIGN—VERT: 20p. Cyclist and globe.

351 EFIMEX "Stamp" on Easel

1969. Air. "EFIMEX" Stamp Exhibition, Mexico City (1968).
1393 **351** 20p. red, green and blue 20 15

353 Gymnasts and Emblem **354** Pres. Baltasar Brum

1969. 75th Anniv of "L'Avenir" Gymnastics Club.
1395 **353** 6p. black and red . . . 15 10

1969. 36th Death Anniv of Baltasar Brum (President, 1919–23).
1396 **354** 6p. black and red . . . 15 10

356 Sun and Fair Emblem (½-size illustration)

1969. 2nd World Industrial Fair, Montevideo.
1399 **356** 2p. multicoloured . . . 15 10

357 Emblem, Quill and Book **358** Modern Diesel Locomotive

1969. Air. 10th Latin-American Notaries' Congress, Montevideo.
1400 **357** 30p. black, orange & grn 35 25

1969. Centenary of Uruguayan Railways.
1401 **358** 6p. black, red and blue 40 25
1402 – 6p. black, red and blue 40 25
DESIGN: No. 1402 Steam locomotive and diesel train.

360 Automobile Club Badge **362** I.L.O. Emblem

361 Belloni and "Combat" (monument). (½-size illustration)

1969. Air. 50th Anniv of Uruguay Automobile Club.
1404 **360** 10p. blue and red . . . 15 10

1969. 4th Death Anniv of Jose Belloni (sculptor).
1405 **361** 6p. green, black and gold 10 10

1969. Air. 50th Anniv of I.L.O.
1406 **362** 30p. turquoise and black 30 20

363 Training Centre Emblem **364** Exhibition Emblem

1969. 25th Anniv (1967) of Reserve Officers' Training Centre.
1407 **363** 1p. lemon and blue . . . 10 10
1408 – 2p. brown and blue . . . 15 10
DESIGN: 2p. Reservist in uniform and civilian dress.

1969. Air. "ABUEXPO 69" Philatelic Exhibition, Sao Paulo, Brazil.
1409 **364** 20p. yellow, blue & green 25 10

365 Rotary Emblem and Hemispheres **366** Dr. Morquio and Child

1969. Air. South American Regional Rotary Conference, and 50th Anniv of Rotary Club, Montevideo.
1410 **365** 20p. gold, ultram & blue 40 10

1969. Air. Birth Cent (1967) of Dr. Luis Morquio (pediatrician).
1411 **366** 20p. brown and red . . 20 10

1969. Air. New Year. No. 1345 surch **FELIZ ANO 1970 6.00 PESOS**.
1412 **330** 6p. on 8p. brown & bis 10 10

368 Pres. Tomas Berreta **369** Mahatma Gandhi

1969. 22nd Death Anniv of Dr. Tomas Berreta (President, 1947).
1413 **368** 6p. red and black . . . 15 10

1970. Air. Birth Cent (1969) of Mahatma Gandhi.
1414 **369** 100p. brown, ochre & blue 85 85

370 Teju Lizard **371** Dr. E. C. Ciganda

1970. Air. Fauna.
1415 – 20p. black, green & pur 95 25
1416 **370** 30p. black, green & yell 40 20
1417 – 50p. black, brown & yell 40 35
1418 – 100p. brown, bistre and orange 60 55
1419 – 150p. brown and green 95 80
1420 – 200p. black, brown & red . . . . 1·25 1·25
1421 – 250p. black, blue and grey . . . . 1·50 1·50
DESIGNS—VERT: 20p. Greater rhea. HORIZ: 50p. Capybara; 100p. Mulita armadillo; 150p. Puma; 200p. Coypu; 250p. South American fur seal.

1970. Air. Birth Centenary of Evaristo C. Ciganda (pioneer of teachers' pensions law).
1422 **371** 6p. brown and green . . 10 10

372 Garibaldi **373** Bank Emblem

1970. Air. Centenary of Garibaldi's Participation in Defence of Uruguay against Brazil and Argentina.
1423 **372** 20p. mauve and pink . . 15 10

1970. 11th Inter-American Development Bank Governors' Meeting, Punta del Este.
1424 **373** 10p. blue and gold . . . 15 10

374 Stylized Tree **375** Footballer and Emblem

1970. 2nd National Forestry Exhibition.
1425 **374** 2p. black, green and red 10 10

1970. Air. World Cup Football Championship, Mexico.
1426 **375** 50p. multicoloured . . . 55 30

376 Artigas' House, Sauce

1970. 120th Death Anniv of Artigas.
1427 **376** 15p. black, blue and red 15 10

377 "U.N."

1970. Air. 25th Anniv of United Nations.
1428 **377** 32p. blue, gold and light blue 25 15

378 Sun, Sea and Map

1970. Tourist Publicity.
1429 **378** 5p. blue 10 10

379 Eisenhower and U.S. Flag

1970. Air. 1st Death Anniv of Dwight D. Eisenhower (American soldier and statesman).
1430 **379** 30p. blue, red and grey 30 15

380 First Man on the Moon

1970. Air. 1st Anniv of Moon Landing from "Apollo 11".
1431 **380** 200p. multicoloured . . 1·50 1·50

381 Mt. Fuji

1970. "EXPO 70" World Fair, Osaka, Japan. Each with EXPO emblem and arms of Uruguay.
1432 **381** 25p. blue, green & yellow 25 15
1433 – 25p. blue, orange & green 25 15
1434 – 25p. blue, yellow & violet 25 15
1435 – 25p. blue, violet & orange 25 15
DESIGNS: No. 1433, Geishas; 1434, Tower of the Sun; 1435, Youth totem.

382 Flag of 1825

1970. Air. 145th Anniv of Revolt of the "Immortal 33" under Levalleja.
1436 **382** 500p. black, red and blue 3·50 3·50

383 Rheumatology Congress Emblem

1970. Air. 5th Pan-American Rheumatology Congress, Punta del Este.
1437 **383** 30p. deep blue, blue and yellow 30 15

384 Street Scene

1970. 290th Anniv of Colonia del Sacramento (1st European settlement in Uruguay).
1439 **384** 5p. multicoloured . . . 10 10

385 "Mother and Son" (statue, E. Prati)

386 Flags of Member Countries

1970. "Homage to Mothers".
1440 **385** 10p. black and green . . 15 10

1970. Air. 10th Anniv of Founding of Latin-American Association for Free Trade by the Montevideo Treaty.
1441 **386** 22p. multicoloured . . . 30 15

387 "Stamp" Emblem

389 Dr. Alfonso Espinola

388 "Playing Ring-o-Roses" (Ana Gaye)

1970. "URUEXPO 70" Stamp Exn, Montevideo.
1442 **387** 15p. violet, blue & brown 15 10

1970. International Education Year. Children's Drawings. Multicoloured.
1443 10p. Type **388** 20 15
1444 10p. "Two Girls" (Andrea Burcatovsky) (vert) . . . 20 15
1445 10p. "Boy at Desk" (Humberto Abel Garcia) (vert) 20 15
1446 10p. "Spaceman" (Aquiles Vaxelaire) 20 15

1971. 125th Birth Anniv (1970) of Dr. Alfonso Espinola (physician and philanthropist).
1447 **389** 5p. black and orange . . 15 10

391 "Stamps" and Poster (½-size illustration)

1971. "EFU 71" Stamp Exn, Montevideo.
1449 **391** 15p. multicoloured . . . 20 10

392 5c. Coin of 1840 (obverse)

1971. Numismatics Day.
1450 **392** 25p. black, brown & blue 40 30
1451 – 25p. black, brown & blue 40 30
DESIGN: No. 1451, Reverse of coin showing "Sun" emblem.

393 Dr. Domingo Arena (from caricature by A. Sifredi)

395 Dr. Jose Arias

394 Opening Bars of Anthem

1971. Birth Centenary (1970) of Arena (lawyer and statesman).
1452 **393** 5p. lake 10 10

1971. National Anthem Commemoration.
1453 **394** 15p. black, blue and gold 40 25

1971. 1st Death Anniv of Dr Jose Arias (statesman).
1454 **395** 5p. brown 15 10

396 "Yellow Fever" (J. M. Blanes)

1971. Air. 70th Death Anniv of Juan Blanes (artist).
1455 **396** 50p. multicoloured . . . 30 30

397 Eduardo Fabini

1971. 21st Death Anniv of Eduardo Fabini (composer).
1456 **397** 5p. black and red . . . 40 10

398 "Two Races"

1971. Air. Racial Equality Year.
1457 **398** 27p. black, pink and gold 30 15

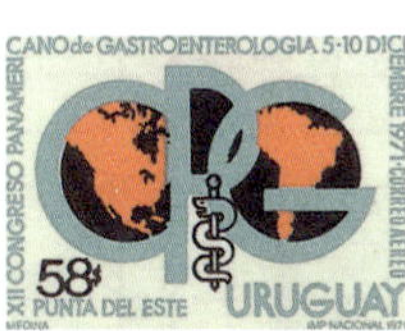

399 Congress Emblem

1971. Air. 12th Pan-American Gastro-enterological Congress, Punta del Este.
1458 **399** 58p. orange, black & grn 55 35

400 J. E. Rodo and U.P.A.E. Emblem

1971. Birth Centenary of Jose E. Rodo (writer and first delegate to U.P.A.E.).
1459 **400** 15p. black and blue . . 20 15

401 Old Water-cart and Tap

1971. Centenary of Montevideo's Water Supply.
1460 **401** 5p. multicoloured . . . 15 10

402 Sheep and Roll of Cloth

1971. Wool Production.
1461 **402** 5p. green, grey & lt green 10 10
1462 – 15p. grey, violet and blue 20 10
DESIGN: 15p. Sheep, and loading bales of cloth.

403 Dr. Jose Elorza and Sheep

1971. 12th Death Anniv of Dr. Jose Elorza (sheep-breeder).
1463 **403** 5p. black, green and blue 15 10

404 Creole Horse

1971. Uruguayan Horse-breeding.
1464 **404** 5p. black, blue and orange 20 10

405 Bull, Sheep and Ears of Corn

1971. Cent of Uruguayan Rural Association.
1465 **405** 20p. multicoloured . . . 30 15

406 Police Emblem

1971. Honouring Police Heroes.
1466 **406** 10p. blue, black and grey 25 10
1467 – 20p. multicoloured . . . 45 15
DESIGN: 20p. Policeman and flag.

407 1896 10 Peso Banknote (obverse)

1971. 75th Anniv of Uruguayan State Bank.
1468 **407** 25p. green, black and gold 30 25
1469 – 25p. green, black and gold 30 25
DESIGN: No. 1469 Reverse of banknote showing rural scene.

408 Labourer and Arms

1971. 150th Anniv of Town of Durazno.
1470 **408** 20p. multicoloured . . . 25 10

409 Shield and Laurel (½-size illustration)

1971. Uruguay's Victory in Liberators' Cup Football Championships.
1471 **409** 10p. gold, red and blue 20 10

411 Voter and Ballot-box

1971. General Election.
1473 **411** 10p. black and blue . . 10 10
1474 – 20p. black and blue . . 25 15
DESIGN—HORIZ: 20p. Voters in line.

412 C.I.M.E. Emblem and Globe

1971. Air. 20th Anniv of Inter-Governmental Committee for European Migration (C.I.M.E.).
1475 **412** 30p. multicoloured . . . 35 25

413 Exhibition Emblem and Map of Uruguay

414 Juan Lindolfo Cuestas (1897–1903)

1971. "EXPO LITORAL" Industrial Exhibition, Paysandu.
1476 **413** 20p. purple and blue . . 35 15

1971. Uruguayan Presidents. Each brown and blue.
1477 10p. Type **414** 10 10
1478 10p. J. Herrara y Obes (1890–94) 10 10
1479 10p. Claudio Williman (1907–11) 10 10
1480 10p. Jose Serrato (1923–27) 10 10
1481 10p. Andres Martinez Trueba (1951–55) 10 10

415 Llama Emblem

417 Olympic Symbols

1971. Air. "EXFILIMA" Stamp Exn, Lima, Peru.
1482 **415** 37p. multicoloured . . . 35 30

1972. Air. Olympic Games, Munich (1st issue).
1484 **417** 50p. black, red and yellow 20 10
1485 – 100p. multicoloured . . 40 30
1486 – 500p. grey, red and blue 1·10 1·10
DESIGNS: 100p. Athlete and torch; 500p. Discus-thrower.
See also Nos. 1493/4.

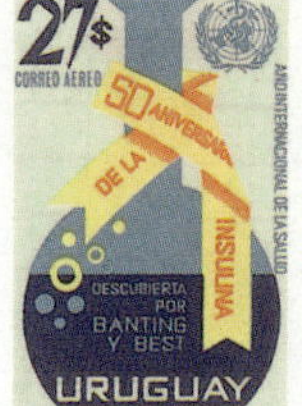

418 Chemical Jar

419 Bartolome Hidalgo

1972. Air. 50th Anniv of Discovery of Insulin.
1487 **418** 27p. multicoloured . . . 20 10

1972. 150th Death Anniv (1973) of Bartolome Hidalgo (Gaucho poet).
1488 **419** 5p. black, red and brown 20 10

420 "Flagship"

421 "Face" on Beethoven Score

1972. Air. American Stamp Day.
1489 **420** 37p. multicoloured . . . 25 15

1972. 12th Eastern Uruguay Choral Festival.
1491 **421** 20p. black, green & purple 25 10

422 Dove supporting Wounded Bird (after Maria Mullin)

424 Columbus Monument, Colon

423 Footballer and 1928 Gold Medal

1972. Dionisio Diaz (9 year-old hero) Commemoration.
1492 **422** 10p. multicoloured . . . 15 10

1972. Air. Olympic Games, Munich. Mult.
1493 100p. Type **423** 40 30
1494 300p. Olympic flag (vert) . . 70 75

1972. Centenary of Colon (suburb of Montevideo).
1495 **424** 20p. black, blue and red 10 10

1972. Uruguay's Victory in Intercontinental Football Cup Championships. No. 1471 surch **COPA INTER CONTINENTAL 1971**, football cup and **50**.
1496 **409** 50p. on 10p. gold, red and blue 35 30

426 Sapling and Spade

428 U.N.C.T.A.D. Emblem

427 Cross of Remembrance

1972. Tree Planting Campaign.
1497 **426** 20p. black, myrtle & grn 15 10

1972. Air. 2nd Death Anniv of Dan Mitrione (U.S. police instructor assassinated by terrorists in Uruguay).
1498 **427** 37p. violet and gold . . 15 10

1972. Air. 3rd United Nations Conference on Trade and Development (U.N.C.T.A.D.), Santiago, Chile.
1499 **428** 30p. multicoloured . . . 15 10

429 Brazilian "Bull's-Eye" Stamp of 1843

1972. Air. "EXFILBRA 72" Stamp Exhibition, Rio de Janeiro.
1500 **429** 50p. multicoloured . . . 20 10

430 Compass Rose and Map of South America

431 "Birds' Nests in Tree"

1972. Air. Campaign for Extension of Territorial Waters to 200 Mile Limit.
1501 **430** 37p. multicoloured . . . 15 10

1972. National Building Project for Communal Dwellings.
1502 **431** 10p. multicoloured . . . 10 10

432 Amethyst

1972. Uruguayan Mineralogy. Rocks and Gems.
1503 **432** 5p. multicoloured . . . 15 10
1504 – 9p. multicoloured . . . 20 10
1505 – 15p. green, brown & blk 35 15
DESIGNS: 9p. Agate; 15p. Chalcedony.

433 "The Three Holy Kings" (R. Barradas)

1972. Air. Christmas.
1506 **433** 20p. multicoloured . . . 20 15

435 Infantry Uniform of 1830

436 Red Cross over Map

1972. Military Uniforms. Multicoloured.
1509 10p. Type **435** 15 10
1510 20p. Artigas cavalry regiment uniform 30 15

1972. 75th Anniv of Uruguayan Red Cross.
1511 **436** 30p. multicoloured . . . 30 10

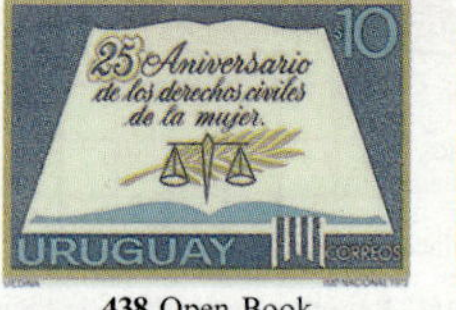

438 Open Book

439 General Jose Artigas

1972. 25th Anniv of Full Civil Rights for Uruguayan Women.
1513 **438** 10p. gold, blue & lt blue 10 10

1972.
1514 **439** 5p. yellow 10 10
1515 10p. brown 10 10
1516 15p. green 10 10
1517 20p. lilac 10 10
1518 30p. blue 20 10
1519 40p. orange 20 10
1520 50p. red 15 10
1521 75p. green 25 15
1522 100p. green 30 15
1523 150p. brown 15 25
1524 200p. blue 25 30
1525 250p. violet 30 35
1526 500p. grey 60 75
1527 1000p. blue . . . . . . 1·10 1·10

440 Cup and Ear of Wheat on Map

441 E. Fernandez and J. P. Varela (founders)

1973. 30th Anniv of Inter-American Institute for Agricultural Sciences.
1531 **440** 30p. black, yellow and red 15 10

1973. Centenary (1968) of Friends of Popular Education Society.
1532 **441** 10p. black, green & brn 10 10

442 Columbus and Map

1973. American Tourist Year.
1533 **442** 50p. purple 20 15

443 Carlos Ramirez

1973. Eminent Uruguayan Jurists. Each black, brown and bistre.
1534 10p. Type **443** 10 10
1535 10p. Justino Jimenez de Arechaga 10 10
1536 10p. Juan Ramirez 10 10
1537 10p. Justino E. Jimenez de Arechaga 10 10

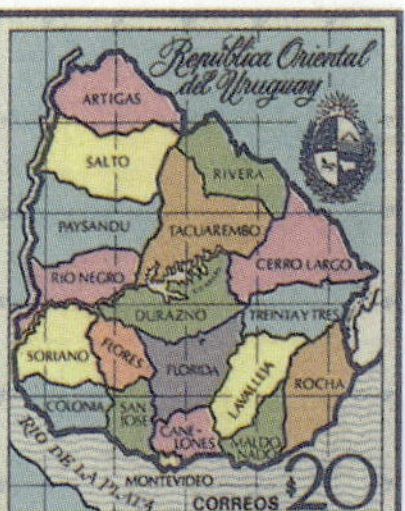

444 Departmental Map

447 Priest, Indians and Soriano Church

446 Francisco de los Santos and Artigas

1973. Uruguayan Departments.
1538 **444** 20p. multicoloured . . . 30 15
See also No. 1844.

1973. Francisco de los Santos (courier) Commem.
1540 **446** 20p. emerald, black and green 20 10

1973. Villa Santo Domingo Soriano (first Spanish Settlement in Uruguay) Commemoration.
1541 **447** 20p. black, violet and blue 15 10

448 "SOYP" and Fish

1973. Inauguration of 1st Fishery Station of Oceanographic and Fishery Service (S.O.Y.P.).
1542 **448** 100p. multicoloured . . 35 15

449 Flower and Sun 451 Luis A. de Herrera

1973. Italian Chamber of Commerce in Uruguay.
1543 **449** 100p. multicoloured . . 25 15

1973. Birth Centenary of Luis A. de Herrera (conservative leader).
1545 **451** 50p. brown, sepia & grey 20 10

452 Festival Emblem

1973. "Festival of Nations", Montevideo.
1546 **452** 50p. multicoloured . . . 20 10

453 Artery and Heart within "Arm" 454 "Madonna" (R. Barradas)

1973. 3rd Pan-American Voluntary Blood Donors' Congress.
1547 **453** 50p. black, red and pink 20 10

1973. Christmas.
1548 **454** 50p. black, yellow & grn 15 10

455 Copernicus (½-size illustration)

1973. 500th Birth Anniv of Nicholas Copernicus (astronomer).
1549 **455** 50p. multicoloured . . . 15 10

456 Hands in Prayer, and Andes 457 O.E.A. Emblem and Map

1973. Rescue of Survivors from Andes Air-crash.
1550 **456** 50p. green, blue and black 15 10
1551 – 75p. multicoloured . . . 20 15
DESIGN: 75p. Flower with broken stem, and Christ of the Andes statue.

1974. 25th Anniv of Organization of American States (O.E.A.).
1552 **457** 250p. multicoloured . . 40 50

458 Games' Emblem

1974. 1st International Scout Games, Montevideo.
1553 **458** 250p. multicoloured . . 40 50

459 Hector Sedes and Motor-car 462 "The Three Gauchos"

1974. Hector Sedes (motor-racing driver) Commemoration.
1554 **459** 50p. brown, black & grn 15 10

1974. Centenary of Antonio Lussich's Poem "Los Tres Gauchos".
1560 **462** 50p. multicoloured . . . 15 10

463 Rifle, Target and Swiss Flag

1974. Centenary of Swiss Rifle Club, Nueva Helvecia.
1561 **463** 100p. multicoloured . . 30 15

464 Compass Rose on Map 465 Emblem and Stadium

1974. Military Geographical Service.
1562 **464** 50p. black, emerald & grn . . . 15 10

1974. World Cup Football Championship, Munich. Multicoloured.
1563 50p. Type **465** 15 10
1564 75p. Emblem and footballer (horiz) . . . 20 15
1565 1000p. Emblem and footballer (different) (horiz) . . . . 11·00 7·50

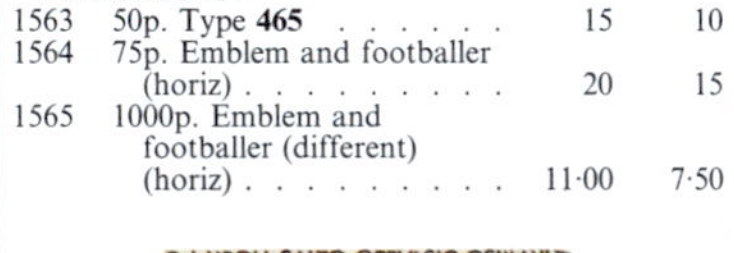

466 Old and New School Buildings, and Founders

1974. Centenary of Osimani-Llerena Technical School, Salto.
1566 **466** 75p. black and brown . . 20 15

467 Carlos Gardel 468 "Ball and Net"

1974. 39th Death Anniv of Carlos Gardel (singer).
1567 **467** 100p. multicoloured . . 35 15

1974. 1st Women's World Cup Volleyball Championships.
1568 **468** 200p. purple, yellow & blk 45 25

469 "Protect Your Heart" 470 Vidal and Statue

1974. Uruguayan "Pro Cardias" Heart Foundation.
1569 **469** 75p. red, yellow and green 20 15

1974. Bicentenary (1973) of Founding of San Jose by Eusebio Vidal.
1570 **470** 75p. blue and light blue 15 10
No. 1570 is incorrectly inscr "1873–1973".

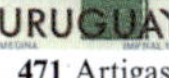

471 Artigas Monument 472 W.P.Y. Emblem

1974. Dedication of Artigas Monument, Buenos Aires, Argentine Republic.
1571 **471** 75p. multicoloured . . . 15 10

1974. Air. World Population Year.
1572 **472** 500p. red, black and grey 55 70

473 Montevideo Citadel Gateway and Emblem 474 Mast and Radio Waves

1974. Air. Events of 1974.
1573 **473** 200p. multicoloured . . 55 40
1574 300p. multicoloured . . 70 60

1974. 50th Anniv of Broadcasting in Uruguay.
1575 **474** 100p. multicoloured . . 20 10

475 "Sheet of Stamps" and "URUEXPO 74" Emblem

1974. 10th Anniv of "Circulo Filatelico" Journal of Montevideo Stamp Club.
1576 **475** 100p. blue, red and black 20 10

476 Envelopes and Emblem

1974. Centenary of Universal Postal Union.
1577 **476** 100p. multicoloured . . 10 10
1578 – 200p. black, gold and lilac 20 10
DESIGN—VERT: 200p. U.P.U. emblem on envelope, laurel and globe.

477 Mexican Official Stamp of 1884 and Arms

1974. Air. "EXFILMEX" Interamerican Philatelic Exhibition, Mexico City.
1579 **477** 200p. multicoloured . . 20 10

478 Artigas Monument

1974. Dedication of Artigas Monument. Ventura Hill, Minas.
1580 **478** 100p. multicoloured . . 10 10

479 Early Map of Montevideo

1974. 250th Anniv of Montevideo's Fortifications.
1581 **479** 300p. brown, red & green 50 20

480 Naval Vessel in Dry-dock and Badge

1974. Centenary of Montevideo Naval Arsenal.
1582 **480** 200p. multicoloured . . 40 30

481 Balloon

1974. History of Aviation. Multicoloured.
1583 100p. Type **481** 25 15
1584 100p. Farman H.F.III biplanes 25 15
1585 100p. Castaibert's Morane Saulnier Type I 25 15
1586 100p. Bleriot XI 25 15
1587 150p. Military and civil pilots' "wings" 35 20
1588 150p. Nieuport 17 biplane 35 20
1589 150p. Breguet Bidon biplane 35 20
1590 150p. Caproni Ca 5 biplane 35 20

482 Pan de Azucar Mountain and Cross

1974. Centenary of Pan de Azucar (town).
1591 **482** 150p. multicoloured . . 25 20

483 Adoration of the Kings

1974. Christmas. Multicoloured.
1592 100p. Type **483** (postage) . . 10 10
1593 150p. Kings with Gifts . . . 15 10
1594 240p. Kings following the Star (air) 20 15

484 Rowers, Fireworks and Nike of Samothrace Statue

1975. Centenary of Montevideo Rowing Club.
1596 **484** 150p. multicoloured . . 15 10

485 "Treaty of Purificacion, 1817" (J. Zorrilla de San Martin)

1975. Recognition of Artigas Government by Great Britain in Treaty of Purificacion, 1817.
1597 **485** 100p. multicoloured . . 10 10

486 Spanish 6c. Stamp of 1850, and National Colours

1975. Air. "ESPANA 75" Stamp Exhibition, Madrid.
1598 **486** 400p. multicoloured . . 35 20

487 Rose

1975. Bicentenary of Rosario.
1600 **487** 150p. multicoloured . . 20 10

488 "The Oath of the Thirty-three" (J. M. Blanes)

1975. 150th Anniv of 1825 Liberation Movement.
1601 **488** 150p. multicoloured . . 20 10

489 Michelangelo's Motif for Floor of Capitol, Rome

1975. Air. 500th Birth Anniv of Michelangelo.
1602 **489** 1p. multicoloured . . . 60 50

490 Columbus and Caravel

492 Emblem of Montreal Olympics (1976) and World Cup Football Championship (Argentina, 1978)

491 Sun and 4p.50 Air Stamp of 1929

1975. Spanish–American Stamp Day.
1603 **490** 1p. multicoloured . . . 1·00 60

1975. Air. Uruguayan Stamp Day.
1604 **491** 1p. black, yellow and grey . . . . 2·50 1·40

1975. Air. "Exfilmo-Espamer 75" Stamp Exhibition, Montevideo. Multicoloured.
1605 1p. Type **492** 40 60
1606 1p. "Independence" (U.S. and Uruguayan flags) . . 40 60
1607 1p. Emblems of U.P.U. and Spanish-American Postal Union 40 60

493 Jose Artigas and J. Francisco de Larrobla

1975. 150th Anniv of Independence.
1608 **493** 50c. multicoloured . . . 40 35

494 Col. L. Oliveira and Fortress

1975. 150th Anniv of Capture of Santa Teresa Fortress.
1609 **494** 10c. multicoloured . . . 20 10

495 Battle Scene from Painting by D. Hequet

1975. 150th Anniv of Battle of Rincon.
1610 **495** 15c. black and gold . . . 20 10
See also Nos. 1620/1.

496 Florencio Sanchez

1975. Birth Cent of Florencio Sanchez (dramatist). Multicoloured.
1611 20c. Type **496** 30 10
1612 20c. "En Familia" 30 10
1613 20c. "Barranca Abajo" . . 30 10
1614 20c. "Mi Hijo el Doctor" . . 30 10
1615 20c. "Camilita" 30 10
Nos. 1612/15 show scenes from plays and are horiz 38 × 26 mm.

1975. Surch in revalued currency.
1616 **439** 10c. on 20p. lilac 10 10
1617 15c. on 40p. orange . . 10 10
1618 50c. on 50p. red 35 20
1619 1p. on 1000p. blue . . . 40 40

1975. 150th Anniv of Artigas' Exile and Battle of Sarandi. As T **495**. Multicoloured.
1620 15c. Artigas' house, Ibiray (Paraguay) 20 10
1621 25c. Battle scene 40 20

498 Maria E. Vaz Ferreira (poetess)

1975. Birth Centenaries.
1622 **498** 15c. black, yellow & pur 20 10
1623 – 15c. black, orange & pur 20 10
DESIGN: No. 1623, Julio Herrera y Reissig (poet).

499 "Virgin and Child" (stained-glass window)

500 Colonel L. Latorre

1975. Christmas. Multicoloured.
1624 20c. Type **499** 35 15
1625 30c. "Virgin and Child" (different) 50 30
1626 60c. "Fireworks" (horiz) . . 40 40

1975. 59th Death Anniv of Col. Lorenzo Latorre (President, 1876–80).
1627 **500** 15c. multicoloured . . . 15 10

501 "Ariel", Stars and Book

1976. 75th Anniv of Publication of "Ariel" by Jose Rodo.
1628 **501** 15c. multicoloured . . . 15 10

502 "Oncidium bifolium" (orchid)

1976. Air. Multicoloured.
1629 50c. Type **502** 45 20
1630 50c. Geoffroy's cat 45 20

503 "Water Sports"

504 Telephone Receiver

1976. 23rd South American Swimming, Diving and Water-polo Championships, Maldonado.
1631 **503** 30c. multicoloured . . . 20 15

1976. Telephone Centenary.
1632 **504** 83c. multicoloured . . . 30 25

505 Dornier Wal Flying Boat "Plus Ultra"

506 Dornier Wal Flying Boat and Airliner rising around Hour-glass

1976. 50th Anniv of "Plus Ultra" Spain–South America Flight.
1633 **505** 63c. multicoloured . . . 60 25

1976. 50th Anniv of Lufthansa Airline.
1634 **506** 83c. multicoloured . . . 55 35

507 Louis Braille and word "Braille"

1976. 150th Anniv of Braille System for the Blind.
1635 **507** 60c. black and brown . . 40 25

508 Signing of Declaration of Independence

1976. Bicentenary of American Revolution.
1636 **508** 1p.50 multicoloured . . 1·25 95

509 "Candombe" (Pedro Figari)

1976. 150th Anniv of Abolition of Slavery.
1637 **509** 30c. multicoloured . . . 15 10

510 Rivera Monument

511 Southern Lapwing

1976. Dedication of General Rivera Monument.
1638 **510** 5p. on 10p. multicoloured . . . . 2·00 95

1976.

1639	**511**	1c. violet	20	10
1640	–	5c. green	10	10
1641	–	15c. red	15	10
1642	–	20c. black	10	10
1643	–	30c. grey	15	10
1644	–	45c. blue	10	10
1645	–	50c. green	25	10
1646	–	1p. brown	45	10
1646b	–	1p. yellow	25	10
1647	–	1p.75 green	35	10
1648	–	1p.95 grey	40	10
1649	–	2p. green	90	70
1649a	–	2p. mauve	35	10
1650	–	2p.65 violet	45	15
1651	–	5p. blue	2·00	2·00
1651a	–	10p. brown	3·25	2·00

DESIGNS—VERT: 5c. Passion flower; 15c. National flower; 20c. Indian lance-head; 30c. Indian statue; 45c., 1p. (No. 1646b), 1p.75, 1p.95, 2p. (both), 2p.65, 5, 10p., Artigas; 1p. (No. 1646), "At Dawn" (J. M. Blanes). HORIZ: 50c. "Branding Cattle" (J. M. Blanes).

513 Office Building and Reverse of First Uruguayan Coin of 1840

1976. 150th Anniv of State Accounting Office.
1652 **513** 30c. black, brown & blue 25 15

514 Hand-pump within Flames

516 Championship Emblem

515 Uruguay 60c. Stamp of 1856 and "Commemorative Postmark"

1976. Centenary of Fire Service.
1653 **514** 20c. black and red . . . 15 10

1976. 50th Anniv of Uruguay Philatelic Club.
1654 **515** 30c. red, blue and bistre 15 10

1976. 5th World Universities' Football Championships, Montevideo.
1655 **516** 83c. multicoloured . . . 40 20

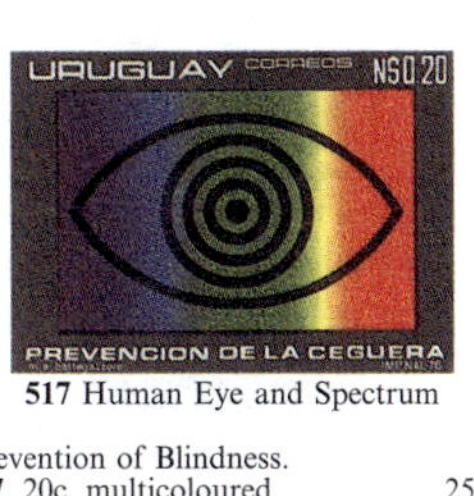

517 Human Eye and Spectrum

1976. Prevention of Blindness.
1656 **517** 20c. multicoloured . . . 25 10

518 Map of Montevideo

1976. 250th Anniv of Montevideo. Multicoloured.
1657 30c. Type **518** 15 10
1658 45c. Montevideo panorama. 1842 . . . . 20 10
1659 70c. First settlers, 1726 . . . 35 15
1660 80c. Montevideo coin (vert) 40 20
1661 1p.15 Montevideo's first arms (vert) 55 30

519 "VARIG" Emblem

1977. 50th Anniv of VARIG Airline.
1662 **519** 80c. multicoloured . . . 50 40

520 Artigas Mausoleum

1977. Mausoleum of General Jose Artigas.
1663 **520** 45c. multicoloured . . . 30 10

521 Arch on Map

1977. Cent of Salesian Education in Uruguay.
1664 **521** 45c. multicoloured . . . 30 10

522 Globe and Emblems

1977. Air. 150th Anniv of Uruguayan Postal Services.
1665 **522** 8p. multicoloured . . . 2·75 2·50

523 Children

524 "Windmills"

1977. 50th Anniv of Inter-American Children's Institute.
1667 **523** 45c. multicoloured . . . 30 10

1977. Hispanidad Day.
1668 **524** 70c. red, yellow and black 35 15

525 Sun on "Stamp" and Stripes of Uruguayan Flag

1977. Stamp Day.
1669 **525** 45c. multicoloured . . . 20 10

527 Globe and Aircraft

1977. 30th Anniv of International Civil Aviation Organization.
1670 **527** 45c. multicoloured . . . 15 10

528 "The Holy Family"

1977. Christmas.
1671 **528** 45c. multicoloured . . . 15 10
1672 – 70c. red, yellow and black 20 10
DESIGN—HORIZ: (45 × 26 mm): 70c. "Santa Claus".

529 Arms, Map and Products

530 Postman clearing Mail-box

1977. Rio Negro Department.
1673 **529** 45c. multicoloured . . . 15 10

1977. 150th Anniv of National Mail Service. Multicoloured.
1674 50c. Type **530** 15 10
1675 50c. Loading mail-van . . . 15 10
1676 50c. Post Office counter, Montevideo G.P.O . . . 15 10
1677 50c. Post-boxes area 15 10
1678 50c. Sorting mail 15 10
1679 50c. Postal sorters 15 10
1680 50c. Postmen sorting "walks" 15 10
1681 50c. Postman on rounds . . 15 10
1682 50c. Postmen on motor-scooters 15 10
1683 50c. Postal counter, Carrasco Airport 15 10

531 Edison's First "Phonograph"

1977. Centenary of Sound Recording.
1684 **531** 50c. purple and yellow 15 10

532 "R" and Spectrum

1977. World Rheumatism Year.
1685 **532** 50c. multicoloured . . . 15 10

533 Emblem, Diploma, Sword and Flag

1978. 50th Anniv of Military College.
1686 **533** 50c. multicoloured . . . 15 10

534 Arms and Map

537 "Wandering Angels" (detail)

1978. Department of Artigas.
1687 **534** 45c. multicoloured . . . 40 20

1978. Air. "Riccione" and "Europhil 78" Stamp Exhibitions, Italy and Urphila Stamp Exhibition, Uruguay. Optd **EUROPA 1978 ITALIA Riccione 78 urphila '78**.
1689 **522** 8p. multicoloured . . . 3·00 2·50

1978. National Artists. Luis A. Solari. Multicoloured.
1690 1p.50 Type **537** 30 20
1691 1p.50 "Wandering Angels" (horiz 38 × 30 mm) . . . 30 20
1692 1p.50 "Wandering Angels" (detail) 30 20

538 Bernardo O'Higgins

1978. Birth Bicentenary of Bernardo O'Higgins (national hero of Chile).
1693 **538** 1p. multicoloured . . . 25 10

539 Telephone Dials and "Antel" Emblem

1978. Telephone Automation.
1694 **539** 50c. multicoloured . . . 10 10

540 San Martin and Army of the Andes Monument (J. M. Ferrari)

541 Spanish Tiles

1978. Birth Bicentenary of General Jose de San Martin.
1695 **540** 1p. multicoloured . . . 25 10

1978. Hispanidad.
1696 **541** 1p. blue, yellow and black 25 10

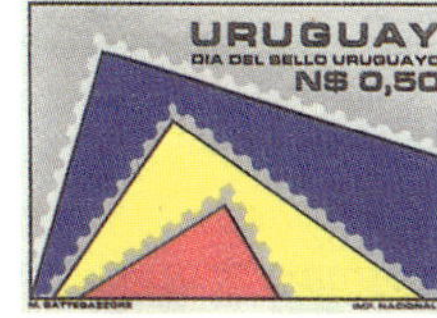

542 Corners of "Stamps"

1978. Stamp Day.
1697 **542** 50c. multicoloured . . . 10 10

543 Boeing 727 in Flight

545 Flag Monument, Montevideo

544 Angel blowing Trumpet

1978. PLUNA Airline Inaugural Boeing 727 Flight.
1698 **543** 50c. multicoloured . . . 15 10

1978. Christmas.
1699 **544** 50c. green, orange & black 10 10
1700 1p. blue, red and black 20 10

1978. Homage to the National Flag.
1701 **545** 1p. multicoloured . . . 25 10

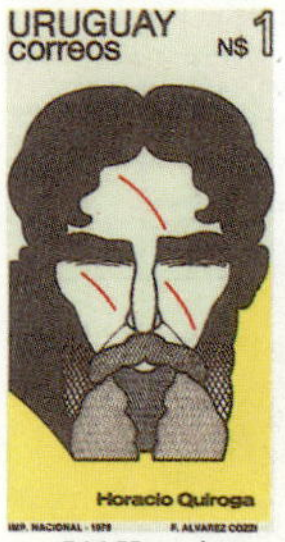

546 Horacio Quiroga

547 Arms and Map of Paysandu

1978. Birth Centenary of Horacio Quiroga (playwright).
1702 **546** 1p. black, yellow and red 25 10

1979. Department of Paysandu.
1703 **547** 45c. multicoloured . . . 10 10

548 Olympic Rings and Ciudadela

1979. Olympic Games, Moscow (1980) and Winter Olympics, Lake Placid (1980). Multicoloured.
1704 5p. Type **548** 90 85
1705 7p. Lake Placid emblem . . 1·10 1·25
See also Nos. 1728/9.

549 Arms and Map of Salto

1979. Department of Salto.
1706 **549** 45c. multicoloured . . . 10 10

550 Artilleryman, 1830

551 Arms and Map of Maldonado

1979. Uruguayan Military Uniforms. Mult.
1707 5p. Type **550** 85 85
1708 5p. Sapper, 1837 . . . . . 85 85

1979. Department of Maldonado.
1709 **551** 45c. multicoloured . . . 10 10

552 Salto Grande Dam

1979. Salto Grande Dam.
1710 **552** 2p. multicoloured . . . 50 15

553 Centenary Symbol and Branch

1979. Centenary of Crandon Uruguayan–American High School.
1711 **553** 1p. blue and violet . . . 20 10

554 Kites

1979. International Year of the Child (1st issue).
1712 **554** 2p. multicoloured . . . 35 15
See also Nos. 1715, 1718 amd 1720.

555 Arms and Map of Cerro Largo

1979. Department of Cerro Largo.
1713 **555** 45c. multicoloured . . . 10 10

556 Arms and Map of Trienta y Tres

1979. Department of Trienta y Tres.
1714 **556** 50c. multicoloured . . . 10 10

557 Cinderella

1979. International Year of the Child (2nd issue).
1715 **557** 2p. multicoloured . . . 35 20

558 National Coat of Arms

1979. 150th Anniv of First National Coat of Arms.
1716 **558** 8p. multicoloured . . . 1·10 1·10

559 U.P.U. Emblem and Arrow

1979. 18th U.P.U. Congress, Rio de Janeiro.
1717 **559** 5p. multicoloured . . . 85 50

560 "Chico Carlo" (Juana de Ibarbourou)

561 Drawing by J. M. Torres-Garcia

1979. International Year of the Child (3rd issue).
1718 **560** 1p. multicoloured . . . 20 10

1979. 31st Death Anniv of Joaquin Torres-Garcia (artist).
1719 **561** 10p. yellow and black . . 1·40 1·25

562 Madonna and Child

1979. Christmas and International Year of the Child (4th issue).
1720 **562** 10p. multicoloured . . . 1·40 1·25

563 Arms and Map of Durazno

1979. Department of Durazno.
1721 **563** 50c. multicoloured . . . 15 10

564 Dish Aerial and Sun

1979. 3rd World Telecommunications Exposition, Geneva.
1722 **564** 10p. black, yellow & lav 95 80

565 Caravel

1979. Hispanidad Day.
1723 **565** 10p. multicoloured . . . 1·75 85

566 10c. Coin of 1877

1979. Centenary of 1st Silver Coinage. Multicoloured.
1724 **566** 10c. silver, black & green 10 10
1725 – 20c. silver, black & green 10 10
1726 – 50c. silver, black and blue 10 10
1727 – 1p. silver, black and blue 20 10
DESIGNS: 20c. 1877 20c. coin; 50c. 1877 50c. coin; 1p. 1877 1p. coin.

1980. Events. Multicoloured.
1728 3p. Type **548** 60 25
1729 3p. As No. 1705 . . . . . 60 25
1730 5p. Olympic rings 90 40
1731 5p. "Uruguay 79" stamp exhibition emblem 90 40
1732 7p. Chessboard and rook (23rd Chess Olympiad, Buenos Aires, 1978) . . . 1·25 55
1733 7p. Detail from Greek vase (Olympic Games) . . . . 1·25 55
1734 10p. Detail from Greek vase (different) . . . . 1·75 80

568 Thomas Edison and Lamp

1980. Centenary of Electric Light.
1736 **568** 2p. multicoloured . . . 40 20

569 Arms of Colonia

571 Association Emblem

1980. Colonia.
1737 **569** 50c. multicoloured . . . 15 10

1980. 50th Anniv of Uruguayan Printers' Association.
1739 **571** 1p. yellow, mauve & blue 20 15

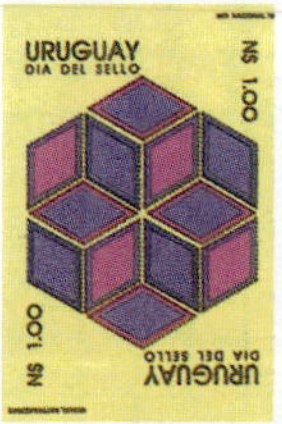

572 Geometric Design

573 Zorilla de San Martin and Page of "La Leyenda Patria"

1980. Stamp Day.
1740 **572** 1p. multicoloured . . . 20 10

1980. "La Leyenda Patria".
1741 **573** 1p. multicoloured . . . 20 10

574 Boeing 747-200C Cargo Airplane

1980. Inauguration of Lufthansa Cargo Container Service.
1742 **574** 2p. multicoloured . . . 40 20

575 Conference Emblem and Flags

1980. 8th World Hereford Conference, Punta del Este, and Livestock Exhibition, Prado, Montevideo.
1743 **575** 2p. multicoloured . . . 40 20

576 Lions Emblem and Map of South America

1980. 9th Latin-American Lions Forum.
1744 **576** 1p. multicoloured . . . 20 10

579 Rotary Emblem and Globe

580 Hand stubbing out Cigarette

1980. 75th Anniv of Rotary International.
1747 **579** 5p. multicoloured . . . 85 70

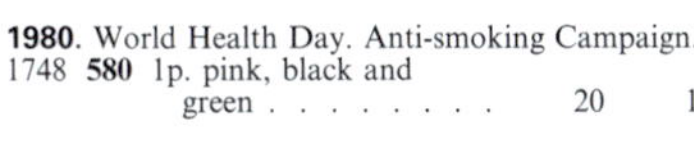

1980. World Health Day. Anti-smoking Campaign.
1748 **580** 1p. pink, black and green 20 10

581 Jose Artigas

582 Angel blowing Trumpet

1980.
1749 **581** 10c. blue 10 10
1750 20c. orange 10 10
1751 50c. red 10 10
1752 60c. yellow 10 10
1753 1p. grey 15 15
1754 2p. brown 35 15
1755 3p. green 55 30
1756 4p. blue 65 40
1757 5p. green 30 10
1757a 6p. orange 10 10
1758 7p. purple 95 70
1759 10p. blue 50 25
1760 12p. black 20 10
1761 15p.50 green 25 15
1762 20p. purple . . . . . . 1·00 85
1763 30p. brown . . . . . . 1·25 1·25
1764 50p. blue . . . . 2·00 2·00

1980. Christmas.
1765 **582** 2p. multicoloured . . . 30 15

583 Title Page of Constitution

1980. 150th Anniv of Constitution.
1766 **583** 4p. blue and gold . . . 70 35

584 Montevideo Football Stadium

585 Conquistador

1980. Gold Cup Football Championship, Montevideo.
1767 **584** 5p. multicoloured . . . 50 35
1768 – 5p. yellow, black and red 50 35
1769 – 10p. multicoloured . . . 1·10 1·10
DESIGNS—As T **584**. No. 1768, Gold cup. 25×79 mm: No. 1769, Mascot and flags of participating countries.

1981. Hispanidad Day.
1771 **585** 2p. multicoloured . . . 35 15

586 U.P.U. Emblem

587 Alexander von Humboldt

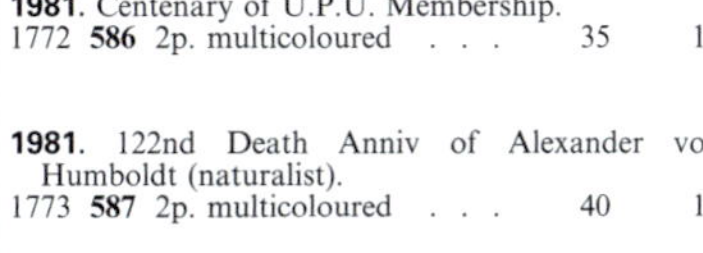

1981. Centenary of U.P.U. Membership.
1772 **586** 2p. multicoloured . . . 35 15

1981. 122nd Death Anniv of Alexander von Humboldt (naturalist).
1773 **587** 2p. multicoloured . . . 40 15

588 Trophy and Open Book

1981. International Education Exhibition and Congress, Montevideo.
1774 **588** 2p. green, black and lilac 35 15

589 Flags and Trophy

590 Musical Notes over Map of the Americas

1981. Uruguayan Victory in Gold Cup Football Championship.
1775 **589** 2p. multicoloured . . . 40 15
1776 5p. multicoloured . . . 60 35

1981. 40th Anniv of Inter-american Institute of Musicology.
1777 **590** 2p. multicoloured . . . 40 15

591 Boeing 707

1981. Inaugural Flight to Madrid of Pluna Airline.
1778 **591** 2p. multicoloured . . . 40 15
1779 5p. multicoloured . . . 60 40
1780 10p. multicoloured . . . 1·25 70
Nos 1778/80 are inscribed "BOEING 737".

592 Cavalryman of Gen. Manuel Oribe, 1843

1981. Army Day. Multicoloured.
1781 2p. Type **592** 40 15
1782 2p. Infantry of Montevideo, 1843 . . . . 40 15

593 Conference Emblem on Suitcase

1981. World Tourism Conference, Manila (1980).
1783 **593** 2p. multicoloured . . . 35 15

594 Peace Dove and Atomic Emblem

596 Arms and Map of Rocha

595 Footballer

1981. 25th Anniv of National Atomic Energy Commission.
1784 **594** 2p. multicoloured . . . 35 15

1981. Europe–South America Football Cup.
1785 **595** 2p. multicoloured . . . 40 15

1981. Department of Rocha.
1786 **596** 2p. multicoloured . . . 40 15

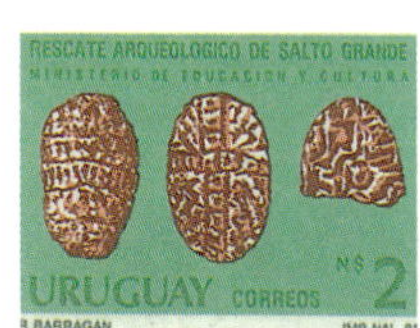

597 Carved Stone Tablets

1981. Salto Grande Archaeological Rescue Excavations.
1787 **597** 2p. multicoloured . . . 40 15

598 Artigas Monument, Minas

599 A.N.C.A.P. Anniversary Emblem

1981. 10th Lavalleja Week.
1788 **598** 4p. multicoloured . . . 70 35

1981. 50th Anniv of National Administration for Combustible Fuels, Alcohol and Portland Cement.
1789 **599** 2p. multicoloured . . . 35 15

600 I.Y.D.P. Emblem

1981. International Year of Disabled Persons.
1790 **600** 2p. deep blue, red and blue 35 15

601 Sun Disc

1981. Senior Level Meeting on Environmental Law, Montevideo.
1791 **601** 5p. multicoloured . . . 60 35

602 Hands holding Knife and Fork

1981. World Food Day.
1792 **602** 2p. multicoloured . . . 40 15

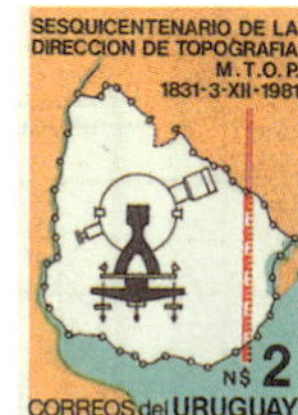

603 Theodolite and Measuring Rod on Map of Uruguay

1981. 150th Anniv of Topographic Survey.
1793 **603** 2p. multicoloured . . . 40 15

604 Bank of Uruguay

1981. 85th Anniv of Bank of Uruguay.
1794 **604** 2p. multicoloured . . . 40 15

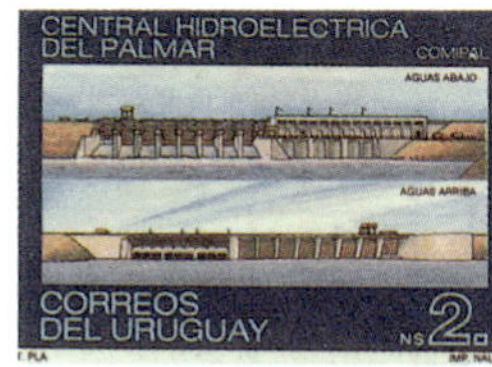

605 Palmar Dam

1981. Palmar Central Hydro-electric Project.
1795 **605** 2p. multicoloured . . . 40 15

606 Father Christmas

607 Joaquin Suarez

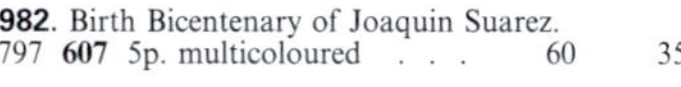

1981. Christmas.
1796 **606** 2p. multicoloured . . . 40 15

1982. Birth Bicentenary of Joaquin Suarez.
1797 **607** 5p. multicoloured . . . 60 35

608 Lockheed Super Constellation and Route Map

1982. 25th Anniv of 1st Germany–Uruguay Lufthansa Flight. Multicoloured.
1798 3p. Type **608** 50 30
1799 7p. Boeing 747-200 and route map 90 70

609 American Air Forces Co-operation Emblem

610 Private, Florida Battalion, 1865

1982. 22nd American Air Forces' Commanders Conference.
1800 **609** 10p. multicoloured . . . 1·25 80

1982. Army Day. Multicoloured.
1801 3p. Type **610** 55 20
1802 3p. Captain of Artillery, 1872 . . . . 55 20

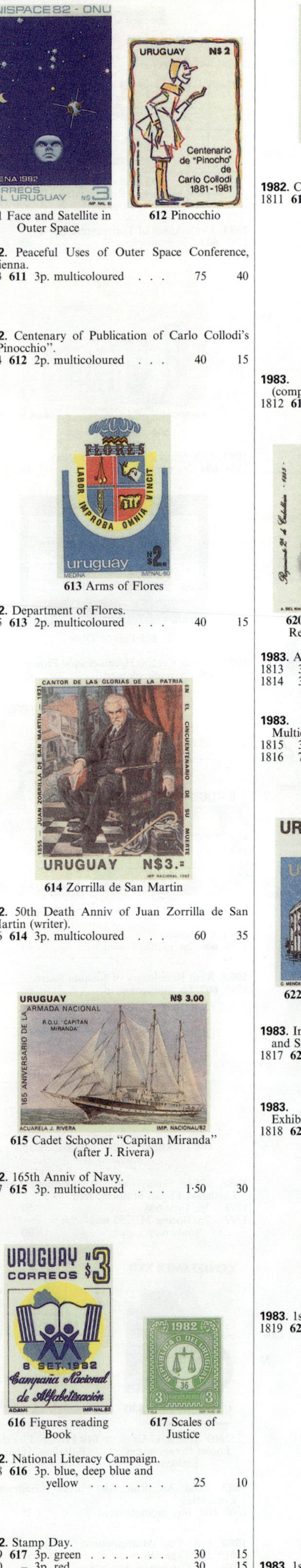

611 Face and Satellite in Outer Space

612 Pinocchio

1982. Peaceful Uses of Outer Space Conference, Vienna.
1803 **611** 3p. multicoloured . . . 75 40

1982. Centenary of Publication of Carlo Collodi's "Pinocchio".
1804 **612** 2p. multicoloured . . . 40 15

613 Arms of Flores

1982. Department of Flores.
1805 **613** 2p. multicoloured . . . 40 15

614 Zorrilla de San Martin

1982. 50th Death Anniv of Juan Zorrilla de San Martin (writer).
1806 **614** 3p. multicoloured . . . 60 35

615 Cadet Schooner "Capitan Miranda" (after J. Rivera)

1982. 165th Anniv of Navy.
1807 **615** 3p. multicoloured . . . 1·50 30

616 Figures reading Book

617 Scales of Justice

1982. National Literacy Campaign.
1808 **616** 3p. blue, deep blue and yellow 25 10

1982. Stamp Day.
1809 **617** 3p. green 30 15
1810 – 3p. red 30 15
DESIGN: No. 1810, Volcano.

618 Star, Family and Symbols of Economic Progress

1982. Christmas.
1811 **618** 3p. multicoloured . . . 30 15

619 Fabini

1983. Birth Centenary of Edouardo Fabini (composer).
1812 **619** 3p. deep brown & brown 30 15

620 2nd Cavalry Regiment, 1885

621 "Santa Maria" on Globe

1983. Army Day. Multicoloured.
1813 3p. Type **620** 40 15
1814 3p. Military College, 1885 40 15

1983. Visit of King and Queen of Spain. Multicoloured.
1815 3p. Type **621** . . . . 2·00 30
1816 7p. Royal couple and Uruguayan and Spanish flags (44 × 31 mm) 80 40

622 Headquarters Building

623 Exhibition Emblem

1983. Inauguration of Postal Union of the Americas and Spain H.Q., Montevideo.
1817 **622** 3p. black, blue and brown 30 15

1983. "Brasiliana 83" International Stamp Exhibition, Rio de Janeiro.
1818 **623** 3p. multicoloured . . . 30 15

624 Space Shuttle "Columbia"

1983. 1st Flight of Space Shuttle "Columbia".
1819 **624** 7p. multicoloured . . . 65 30

625 "Delin 1900" Car

1983. 1st Imported Car.
1820 **625** 3p. blue and black . . . 30 15

626 Goethe and Scene from "Faust"

1983. 150th Death Anniv (1982) of Johann Wolfgang von Goethe (writer).
1821 **626** 7p. blue and black . . . 65 30

627 "Moonlit Landscape"

628 Statue of Lavelleja

1983. 6th Death Anniv of Jose Cuneo (artist).
1822 **627** 3p. multicoloured . . . 30 15

1983. Bicentenary of Minas City.
1823 **628** 3p. multicoloured . . . 30 15

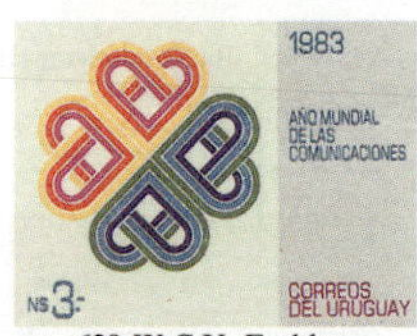

629 W.C.Y. Emblem

1983. World Communications Year.
1824 **629** 3p. multicoloured . . . 20 10

630 Garibaldi

1983. Death Centenary (1982) of Guiseppe Garibaldi (Italian revolutionary).
1825 **630** 7p. multicoloured . . . 50 30

631 "Graf Zeppelin"

1983. Zeppelin Flight over Montevideo (1934).
1826 **631** 7p. black, blue and mauve 90 35

632 Footballers, World Cup and Italian Team Badge

1983. Italy's Victory in World Cup Football Championship (1982).
1827 **632** 7p. multicoloured . . . 65 30

633 Virgin, Child and Star

1983. Christmas.
1828 **633** 4p.50 multicoloured . . 25 10

634 "50" on Telephone Dial

1984. 50th Anniv of Automatic Telephone Dialling.
1829 **634** 4p.50 multicoloured . . 25 10

635 Leandro Gomez

636 Emblem, Map, Flag and Tanker

1984. General Leandro Gomez Commemoration.
1830 **635** 4p.50 blue, light blue and black 25 10

1984. 25th Anniv (1983) of International Maritime Organization.
1831 **636** 4p.50 multicoloured . . 50 15

637 Flags and Emblem

638 Map of Uruguay and Bank Emblem

1984. American Women's Day.
1832 **637** 4p.50 multicoloured . . 25 10

1984. 25th Annual Meeting of Governors of International Development Bank, Punta del Este.
1833 **638** 10p. blue, gold and black 55 20

639 Simon Bolivar

1984. Birth Bicentenary (1983) of Simon Bolivar.
1834 **639** 4p.50 lt brown & brown 25 10

640 Club Emblem and Radio Waves

1984. 50th Anniv (1983) of Uruguay Radio Club.
1835 **640** 7p. multicoloured . . . 40 20

641 Monument

1984. 1930 World Cup Football Championship Monument.
1836 **641** 4p.50 multicoloured . . 25 10

642 National Emblem within "200"

1984. Bicentenary (1983) of San Jose de Mayo.
1837 **642** 4p.50 multicoloured . . 25 10

643 Emblem

1984. 50th Anniv of Tourist Organization.
1838 **643** 4p.50 gold, violet and blue 25 10

644 Artillery Uniform, 1895

645 Artigas on Horseback

1984. Army Day. Multicoloured.
1839 4p.50 Type **644** 25 15
1840 4p.50 2nd Battalion Cazadores uniform, 1894 25 15

1984.
1841 **645** 4p.50 black and blue . . 25 15
1842 8p.50 brown and blue . . 45 25

646 Trophy

1984. Penarol Athletic Club. Winners of European-South American Football Cup, 1982.
1843 **646** 4p.50 black, yellow and deep yellow 25 10

1984. Uruguayan Departments.
1844 **444** 4p.50 multicoloured . . 25 10

647 Child holding Flower and "50 ANOS"

1984. 50th Anniv of Children's Council.
1845 **647** 4p.50 multicoloured . . 25 10

648 Christmas Tree with Candles

649 Pelota Player and Flags

1984. Christmas.
1846 **648** 6p. multicoloured . . . 30 10

1985. 1st Junior Pelota World Championship.
1847 **649** 4p.50 multicoloured . . 25 10

650 Bruno Mauricio de Zabala

652 Carlos Gardel

651 Emblems of Los Angeles and Sarajevo Games and Olympic Rings

1985. 300th Birth Anniv (1983) of Don Bruno Mauricio de Zabala (Governor of Buenos Aires and founder of Montevideo).
1848 **650** 4p.50 multicoloured . . 25 10

1985. 90th Anniv of International Olympic Committee.
1849 **651** 12p. multicoloured . . . 45 25

1985. 50th Death Anniv of Carlos Gardel (entertainer).
1850 **652** 6p. grey, blue and brown 25 10

653 Emblem and Flags of Member States

1985. 25th Anniv of American Air Forces' Co-operation System.
1851 **653** 12p. multicoloured . . . 20 10

654 Icarus

1985. 40th Anniv of I.C.A.O.
1852 **654** 4p.50 deep blue, green and blue 10 10

655 Stylized Factory and "50"

1985. 50th Anniv of FUNSA Tyre Factory.
1853 **655** 6p. multicoloured . . . 10 10

656 Cross and Clasped Hands

1985. Centenary of Catholic Workers Circle.
1854 **656** 6p. multicoloured . . . 10 10

657 I.Y.Y. Emblem

1985. International Youth Year.
1855 **657** 12p. red and black . . . 20 10

658 Peace Dove and Sun

1985. "Return to Democracy".
1856 **658** 20p. blue, yellow and violet 30 15

659 Books forming "8"

661 Map and Arms

660 Emblem

1985. 8th International Book Exhibition.
1857 **659** 20p. multicoloured . . . 30 15

1985. Centenary of Military School.
1858 **660** 10p. multicoloured . . . 20 10

1985. Centenary of Flores Department.
1859 **661** 6p. multicoloured . . . 10 10

662 Father Christmas

1985. Christmas.
1860 **662** 10p. multicoloured . . . 20 10
1861 22p. multicoloured . . . 35 20

663 Monument to Isabel the Catholic

1985. Hispanidad Day.
1862 **663** 12p. black, red and brown 15 10

664 Emblem and Meeting Logo

1986. 3rd Inter-American Agriculture Co-operation Institute Meeting.
1863 **664** 12p. yellow, red and black 20 10

665 Emblem and Flag

1986. World Post Day.
1864 **665** 15p.50 multicoloured . . 25 10

666 Map and Symbolic House

1986. 6th Population and 4th Housing Census (1985).
1865 **666** 10p. black, blue and yellow 20 10

667 Emblem

1986. 50th Anniv (1985) of Conaprole Milk and Cattle Co-operative.
1866 **667** 10p. gold, blue and light blue 20 10

668 U.N. Emblem and Population Diagram

1986. 40th Anniv (1985) of U.N.O.
1867 **668** 20p. multicoloured . . . 30 15

669 Emblem

670 Manuel Oribe

1986. 50th Anniv (1985) of National Brokers and Auctioneers Association.
1868 **669** 10p. black, deep blue and blue 15 10

1986. Liberation Heroes.
1869 **670** 1p. green (postage) . . 10 10
1870 2p. red 10 10
1871 A 3p. blue 10 10
1872 5p. blue 10 10
1872a **670** 5p. blue 10 10
1873 7p. brown 10 10
1874 B 10p. mauve 10 10
1875 C 10p. green 10 10
1875a **670** 10p. green 10 10
1876 15p. blue 10 10
1877 B 17p. blue 15 10
1877a **670** 20p. brown 15 10
1877b A 25p. orange 10 10
1878 B 26p. brown 10 10
1879 C 30p. orange 20 15
1879a A 30p. blue 10 10
1879b B 45p. red 25 20
1880 C 50p. ochre 30 20
1880a A 50p. mauve 30 20
1881 C 60p. grey 40 40
1881a A 60p. orange 10 20
1881b B 60p. mauve 10 10
1881c 75p. red 10 10
1881d 90p. red 10 10

1882 C 100p. red 60 75
1882a 100p. brown 30 30
1882b 150p. green 35 35
1883 200p. green . . . . . 1·25 1·10
1883a 300p. blue 60 60
1883b 500p. red . . . . . 1·25 1·25
1883c 1000p. red . . . . . 2·00 2·00

1884 B 22p. violet (air) 15 10
DESIGNS: A, Lavalleja; B, Jose Fructuoso Rivera; C, Jose Gervasio Artigas.

671 Mosaic in National Colours

1986. Italian Chamber of Commerce in Uruguay.
1885 **671** 20p. multicoloured . . . 20 10

672 Armenian Flag and Monument

673 Emblem and Footballer

1986. 71st Anniv of Armenian Genocide.
1886 **672** 10p. black, red and blue 10 10

1986. World Cup Football Championship, Mexico.
1887 **673** 20p. multicoloured . . . 20 15

674 Newspaper Page

675 Alan Garcia

1986. Centenary of "El Dia".
1888 **674** 10p. gold, black and red 10 10

1986. Visit of President of Peru.
1889 **675** 20p. brown, red and blue 15 15

676 Map, Gen. Sucre and Simon Bolivar

677 Jose Sarney

1986. Visit of Pres. Jaime Lusinchi of Venezuela.
1890 **676** 20p. multicoloured . . . 15 15

1986. Visit of President of Brazil.
1891 **677** 20p. multicoloured . . . 15 15

678 Michelini

1986. 10th Death Anniv of Zelmar Michelini (senator).
1892 **678** 10p. blue and red . . . 10 10

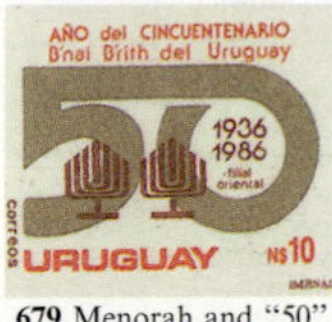

679 Menorah and "50"

1986. 50th Anniv of B'nai B'rith in Uruguay.
1893 **679** 10p. brown, gold and red 10 10

680 Handshake across "GATT"

1986. General Agreement on Tariffs and Trade Assembly, Punta del Este.
1894 **680** 10p. multicoloured . . . 10 10

681 Dr. Raul Alfonsin

1986. Visit of President of Argentina.
1895 **681** 20p. orange, black & blue 15 15

682 Fishes in Sea

1986. Quality Exports. Multicoloured.
1896 20p. Type **682** 30 15
1897 20p. Lambs 15 15

683 Flags and Dr. Blanco

1986. Visit of Dr. Salvador Jorge Blanco, President of Dominican Republic.
1898 **683** 20p. multicoloured . . . 15 15

684 Dr. Pertini

1986. Visit of Dr. Sandro Pertini, President of Italy.
1899 **684** 20p. yellow and green . . 15 15

685 Douglas DC-10 and DC-3 Aircraft and Flags

1986. 40th Anniv of First Scheduled Spain-Uruguay Flight.
1900 **685** 20p. multicoloured . . . 45 15

686 Statue of Sts. Philip and John and Montevideo Cathedral

1987. Hispanidad Day.
1901 **686** 10p. red and black . . . 10 10

687 Emblem

1987. 50th Anniv (1986) of Juventus Catholic Cultural Organization.
1902 **687** 10p. yellow, black and blue 10 10

688 Ruiz

1987. 10th Death Anniv (1986) of Hector Gutierrez Ruiz (Chamber of Deputies member).
1903 **688** 10p. brown and red . . 10 10

689 Emblem

690 "Arrowhead" of Flying Doves

1987. International Science and Technology Symposium, Montevideo and Punta del Este (1986).
1904 **689** 20p. multicoloured . . . 15 15

1987. Visit of Pope John Paul II.
1905 **690** 50p. orange and grey . . 35 45

691 Dr. Arias and Emblem

692 "70" and Menorah

1987. Birth Centenary of Dr. Jose F. Arias (founder of Uruguay Trades University).
1906 **691** 10p. multicoloured . . . 10 10

1987. 70th Anniv of Uruguayan Jewish Community.
1907 **692** 10p. blue, orange & black 10 10

693 De Havilland Dragon Fly

1987. 50th Anniv (1986) of Pluna National Airline. Multicoloured.
1908 10p. Type **693** 10 10
1909 20p. Douglas DC-3 . . . . 15 10
1910 25p. Vickers Viscount 810 15 15
1911 30p. Boeing 707 . . . . . . 20 15

694 Artigas Antarctic Base

1987.
1912 **694** 20p. multicoloured . . . 15 15

695 Sun, Symbolic House and "75"

1987. 75th Anniv of Uruguayan Mortgage Bank.
1913 **695** 26p. multicoloured . . . 20 15

696 Dairy Products

697 "Holy Family"

1987. Uruguayan Quality Exports. Multicoloured.
1914 51p. Type **696** 35 20
1915 51p. Map and cattle 35 20

1987. Christmas. Stained Glass Windows. Multicoloured.
1916 17p. Type **697** 15 10
1917 66p. "Angels" 45 55

698 Pres. Duarte

699 Airplane and Globe forming "60"

1988. Visit of Pres. Jose Napoleon Duarte of El Salvador.
1918 **698** 20p. blue and yellow . . 15 15

1988. 60th Anniv (1987) of VARIG (airline).
1919 **699** 66p. blue, yellow & black 45 50

700 Emblem and Globe

1988. International Peace Year (1986).
1920 **700** 10p. multicoloured . . . 10 10

701 Flags and Beret

702 Farman "Shorthorn" within Airplane Wing

1988. 75th Anniv (1987) of Basque Immigration.
1921 **701** 66p. multicoloured . . . 45 45

1988. 75th Anniv of Air Force.
1922 **702** 17p. multicoloured . . . 20 10

703 Lantern and "75"

1988. 75th Anniv (1987) of UTE (hydro-electric dam programme).
1923 **703** 17p. multicoloured . . . 15 10
1924 – 17p. black, blue and green 15 10
1925 – 51p. black and blue . . 35 20
1926 – 51p. black, blue and red 35 20
1927 – 66p. blue, black & yellow 45 25

DESIGNS: No. 1924, Baygorria Dam; 1925, Dr. Gabriel Terra Dam; 1926, Constitucion Dam; 1927, Map showing dam sites on River Negro.

704 Flag and Globe

1988. 75th Anniv (1986) of Postal Union of the Americas and Spain.
1928 **704** 66p. multicoloured . . . 45 45

705 Menorah in "40"

1988. 40th Anniv of Israel.
1929 **705** 66p. blue and black . . 45 45

706 Airmail Envelope and Postman

1988. "Post, Messenger of Peace".
1930 **706** 66p. multicoloured . . . 45 45

707 Emblem on Map

709 Col. Pablo Banales (founder)

708 Matos Rodriguez

1988. 60th Anniv of Inter-American Institute for the Child.
1931 **707** 30p. lt green, green & blk 20 15

1988. Gerardo H. Matos Rodriguez (composer) Commemoration.
1932 **708** 17p. black and violet . . 15 10
1933 – 51p. brown on lt brown 35 20
DESIGN: 51p. Matos Rodriguez and score of "La Cumparsita".

1988. Centenary (1987) of Fire Service. Mult.
1934 17p. Type **709** 15 10
1935 26p. Fireman, 1900 . . . . 20 15
1936 34p. Emblem (horiz) 20 15
1937 51p. Merryweather fire engine, 1907 (horiz) . . . 35 20
1938 66p. 8-man hand pump, 1888 (horiz) 45 25
1939 100p. Magirus mechanical ladder, 1921 (44 × 25 mm) 70 40

710 Route Map and "Capitan Miranda"

1988. 1st World Voyage of "Capitan Miranda".
1940 **710** 30p. multicoloured . . . 90 30

711 Citrus Fruits

1988. Exports. Multicoloured.
1941 30p. Type **711** 20 15
1942 45p. Rice 35 20
1943 55p. Shoes 40 20
1944 55p. Clothes 40 20

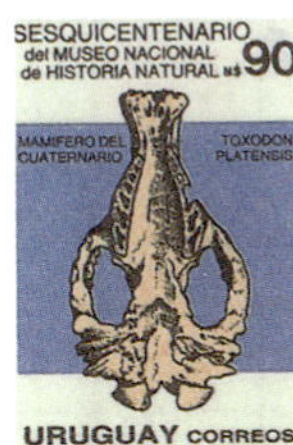

712 "Toxodon platensis" (mammal bone)

713 Bird posting Letter

1988. 150th Anniv of National Natural History Museum, Montevideo.
1945 – 30p. brown, yellow & blk 50 20
1946 **712** 90p. brown, blue & black 65 60
DESIGN: 30p. "Usnea densirostra" (moss).

1988. Postal Officers' Day. Unissued stamp surch.
1947 **713** 30p. on 10p.+5p. yellow, black and blue 10 10

714 Abstract

1988. 150th Anniv (1986) of Battle of Carpinteria.
1948 **714** 30p. multicoloured . . . 10 10

715 Virgin and Child

716 "Self-portrait" (Joaquin Torres Garcia)

1988. Christmas.
1949 **715** 115p. multicoloured . . 55 55

1988. Uruguayan Painters. Multicoloured.
1950 115p. Type **716** 50 50
1951 115p. Poster for Pedro Figari exhibition, Montevideo 50 50
1952 115p. "Squares and Rectangles LXXVIII" (Jose P. Costigliolo) . . . 50 50
1953 115p. "Manolita Pina, 1920" (Joaquin Torres Garcia) 50 50

717 "Santa Maria"

1989. Hispanidad Day.
1954 **717** 90p. multicoloured . . . 75 45
1955 115p. multicoloured . . 90 55

718 Emblem

1989. Cent of Armenian Organization Hnchakian.
1956 **718** 210p. blue, yellow and red 40 35

719 Plumb Line suspended on Frame

1989. Bicentenary of French Revolution. Each black, red and blue.
1957 50p. Type **719** 10 10
1958 50p. Tree of Liberty 10 10
1959 210p. Eye in centre of sunburst 40 35
1960 210p. "Liberty", "Equality", "Fraternity" around phrygian cap 40 35

720 Map

1989. "Use the Post Code". Each black and red.
1961 50p. Type **720** 10 10
1962 210p. Map showing numbered zones (vert) . . 40 35

721 Map, Cow, Factory and Baby

722 "Tiradentes"

1989. 3rd Pan-American Milk Congress.
1963 **721** 170p. deep blue and blue 30 25

1989. Birth Bicentenary of Joaquin Jose da Silver Xavier.
1964 **722** 170p. multicoloured . . 30 25

723 Emblem and Flag

1989. Interparliamentary Union Centenary Conference, London.
1965 **723** 210p. red, blue and black 40 35

724 F.A.O. Emblem, Map and Fruit Slices

1989. 8th Intergovernmental Group on Citrus Fruits Meeting.
1966 **724** 180p. multicoloured . . 30 25

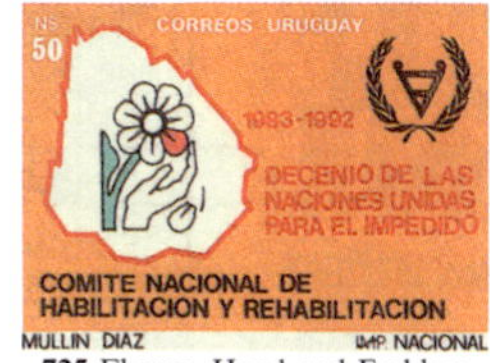

725 Flower, Hand and Emblem

1989. U.N. Decade for Disabled People. Mult.
1967 50p. Type **725** 10 10
1968 210p. Disabled people and emblem 40 35

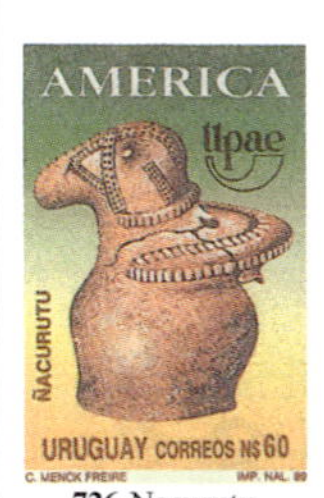

726 Nacurutu Artefact

727 Virgin of the Thirty Three

1989. America. Pre-Columbian Culture.
1969 **726** 60p. multicoloured . . . 10 10
1970 180p. multicoloured . . 30 25

1989. Christmas. Multicoloured.
1971 70p. Type **727** 10 10
1972 210p. "Adoration of the Animals" (Barradas) (horiz) 15 15

728 Old and Modern Buildings

1989. Bicentenary of Pando.
1973 **728** 60p. multicoloured . . . 10 10

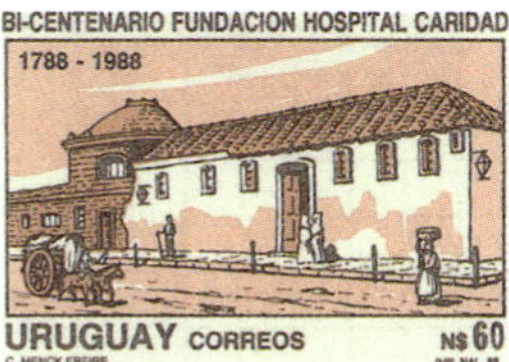

729 Hospital Building

1990. Bicentenary of Charity Hospital.
1974 **729** 60p. flesh, black & brown 10 10

730 Map and Arms of Soriano

731 Luisa Luisi

1990. Departments. Multicoloured.
1975 70p. Type **730** 10 10
1976 70p. Florida (vert) 10 10
1977 90p. San Jose (vert) 10 10
1978 90p. Canelones 10 10
1979 90p. Lavalleja (vert) 10 10
1980 90p. Rivera 10 10

1990. Writers. Multicoloured.
1981 60p. Type **731** 10 10
1982 60p. Javier de Viana 10 10
1983 75p. J. Zorilla de San Martin 10 10
1984 75p. Dekmira Agustini . . . 10 10
1985 170p. Julio Casal 45 45
1986 170p. Alfonsina Storni . . . 45 45
1987 210p. Juana de Ibarbourou 55 55
1988 210p. Carlos Roxlo 55 55

732 Mercedes Church

733 Ear of Wheat and Tractor

1990. Bicentenary of Mercedes.

1989	**732**	70p. multicoloured	10	10

1990. 10th Anniv of International Agricultural Fund.

1990	**733**	210p. multicoloured	55	55

734 Glass and Smashed Car

1990. Road Safety. Multicoloured.

1991		70p. Type **734**	70	70
1992		70p. Traffic waiting at red light	70	70
1993		70p. Road signs	70	70
1994		70p. Children crossing road at green light	70	70

735 Sculpture of Artigas

736 Woman

1990. Artigas Day.

1995	**735**	60p. blue and red	10	10

1990. International Women's Day.

1996	**736**	70p. multicoloured	10	10

737 Gonzalo Ramirez

1990. Centenary of 1st International Juridical Congress, Montevideo.

1997	**737**	60p. black, yellow & mve	55	55
1998	–	60p. black, blue & mauve	55	55
1999	–	60p. multicoloured	55	55
2000	–	60p. multicoloured	55	55

DESIGNS: No. 1998, Ildefonso Garcia; 1999, Flags and left half of 50th anniversary memorial; 2000, Flags and right half of memorial.

738 Microphone and Radio Mast

1990. The Media. Multicoloured.

2001		70p. Type **738**	70	70
2002		70p. Newspaper vendor	70	70
2003		70p. Television screen, camera and aerial	70	70
2004		70p. Books and type	70	70

739 Burning Trees

741 "Nativity" (Juan B. Maino)

740 American Deer

1990. Fire Prevention.

2005	**739**	70p. black, yellow and red	70	70

1990. America. The Natural World. Mult.

2006		120p. Type **740**	10	10
2007		360p. "Peltophorum dubium" (vert)	85	85

1990. Christmas.

2008	**741**	170p. multicoloured	40	40
2009		830p. multicoloured	2·00	2·00

742 Carlos Federico Saez

1990. Artists. Multicoloured.

2010		90p. Type **742**	10	10
2011		90p. Pedro Blanes Viale	10	10
2012		210p. Edmundo Prati	55	55
2013		210p. Jose L. Zorrilla de San Martin	55	55

743 Mechanical Digger

1991. 75th Anniv of Army Engineers Division.

2014	**743**	170p. multicoloured	40	40

744 Drum and Masks

1991. Carnival.

2015	**744**	170p. multicoloured	40	40

745 Campaign Emblem

1991. Campaign against AIDS.

2016	**745**	170p. multicoloured	40	40
2017		830p. multicoloured	2·00	2·00

746 Anniversary Emblem

1991. Centenary of Organization of American States.

2018	**746**	830p. yellow, blue & blk	2·00	2·00

747 Textiles

1991. Uruguayan Quality Exports. Multicoloured.

2019		120p. Type **747**	10	10
2020		120p. Clothes (vert)	10	10
2021		400p. Semi-precious stones and granite	55	60

748 Flint Axe and Stone Monument

1991. Education. Multicoloured.

2022		120p. Type **748**	10	10
2023		120p. Wheel and pyramids	10	10
2024		330p. Printing press and diagram of planetary orbits	45	45
2025		330p. Space probe and computer diagram	45	45

749 Sword piercing Crab

1991. Anti-cancer Day.

2026	**749**	360p. red and black	45	45

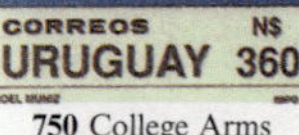

750 College Arms

751 College Building

1991. Centenary of Holy Family College.

2027	**750**	360p. multicoloured	45	45

1991. Centenary of Immaculate Heart of Mary College.

2028	**751**	1370p. multicoloured	1·60	1·60

752 Emblem

1991. 7th Pan-American Maccabiah Games.

2029	**752**	1490p. multicoloured	1·75	1·75

753 World Map and Dornier Wal Flying Boat "Plus Ultra"

1991. "Espamer '91" Spain–Latin America Stamp Exhibition, Buenos Aires.

2030	**753**	1510p. multicoloured	2·00	2·00

754 "Oath of the Constitution" (P. Blanes Viale)

1991. 1830 Constitution.

2031	**754**	360p. multicoloured	45	45

755 Gateway, Sacramento

756 "William Tell" (statue) and Flags

1991.

2032	**755**	360p. brown and yellow	45	45
2033	–	540p. grey and blue	65	65
2034	**755**	600p. brown, yellow & blk	55	55
2035	–	825p. grey, blue and black	1·10	1·10
2036	–	1510p. brown and green	2·00	2·00
2037	–	2500p. brown, grn & blk	2·50	2·50

DESIGNS: 540, 825p. First locomotive in Uruguay, 1869; 1510, 2500p. Horse tram.

For 800p. as Type **755** see No. 2103.

1991. 700th Anniv of Swiss Confederation.

2038	**756**	1510p. multicoloured	2·50	2·50

757 Yacht

758 Emblem

1991. Whitbread Regatta.

2040	**757**	1510p. multicoloured	1·75	1·75

1991. 50th Anniv of Uruguayan Society of Actors.

2041	**758**	450p. black and red	50	50

759 Camera and Photograph

1991. 150th Anniv of First Photograph in Rio de la Plata.

2042	**759**	1370p. multicoloured	1·50	1·50

760 Anniversary Emblem

1991. 25th Anniv of CREA (livestock organization).

2043	**760**	450p. multicoloured	50	50

761 Margarita Xirgu

1991. 22nd Death Anniv of Margarita Xirgu (actress).

2044	**761**	360p. brown, light brown and yellow	40	40

762 "General Rivera" (gunboat)

1991. Centre for Study of Naval and Maritime History. Multicoloured.
2045 450p. Type **762** 45 45
2046 450p. "Salto" (coastguard patrol boat) 45 45
2047 1570p. "Uruguay" (cruiser) 1·60 1·60
2048 1570p. "Pte. Oribe" (tanker) 1·60 1·60

763 "Rio de la Plata, 1602" (woodcut)

1991. America. Voyages of Discovery.
2049 **763** 450p. brown and yellow 50 50
2050 – 1740p. green and brown 1·90 1·90
DESIGN—HORIZ: 1740p. Amerigo Vespucci.

764 "The Tree is the Fountain of Life"

1991. World Food Day.
2051 **764** 1740p. multicoloured . . 1·75 1·75

765 "The Table" (Zoma Baitler)

1991.
2052 **765** 360p. multicoloured . . 40 40

766 Gladiator, 1902

1991. Old Cars. Multicoloured.
2053 360p. Type **766** 40 40
2054 1370p. E.M.F., 1909 . . . . 1·50 1·50
2055 1490p. Renault, 1912 . . . 1·50 1·50
2056 1510p. Clement-Bayard, 1903 (vert) . . . . 1·75 1·75

767 Emblem **768** Club Badge and Trophy

1991. 60th General Assembly of Interpol, Punta del Este.
2057 **767** 1740p. multicoloured . . 1·75 1·75

1991. National Football Club, Winners of World Cup Football Cup, 1988, and the Toyota Cup. Multicoloured.
2058 450p. Type **768** 50 50
2059 450p. Trophies on football pitch (horiz) 50 50

769 School and Pupils

1991. Centenary of Maria Auxiliadora Institute.
2060 **769** 450p. blue, black and red 50 50

770 "LATU"

1991. 25th Anniv of Uruguay Technological Laboratory.
2061 **770** 1570p. blue and deep blue . . . . 1·50 1·50

771 Emblem and Couple **772** Theodolite and Measuring Rod on Map of Uruguay

1991. World AIDS Day.
2062 **771** 550p. black, yellow & bl 55 55
2063 2040p. black, lilac & grn 2·00 2·00

1991. 160th Anniv of Topographic Survey.
2064 **772** 550p. multicoloured . . 55 55

773 Angel

1991. Christmas. Multicoloured.
2065 550p. Type **773** 55 55
2066 2040p. "Adoration of the Angels" . . . . 1·90 1·90

774 Anibal Troilo

1992. Musicians.
2067 **774** 450p. black, mauve & bl 40 40
2068 – 450p. black, orange & red 40 40
2069 – 450p. black, light green and green 40 40
2070 – 450p. black, blue & mve 40 40
DESIGNS: No. 2068, Francisco Canaro; 2069, Pintin Castellanos; 2070, Juan de Dios Filiberto.

775 Worker and Factory Building

1992. Quality Exports.
2071 **775** 120p. multicoloured . . 15 15

776 Pres. Aylwin **777** Trophy

1992. Visit of President Patricio Aylwin of Chile.
2072 **776** 550p. multicoloured . . 50 50

1992. Penarol F.C., Three-times World Club Football Champions.
2073 **777** 600p. black and yellow 55 55

778 Hands holding Hammer and Chisel **779** No Smoking Emblem

1992. 120th Anniv of La Paz.
2075 **778** 550p. multicoloured . . 50 50

1992. World No Smoking Day.
2076 **779** 2500p. red, black & brn 2·00 2·00

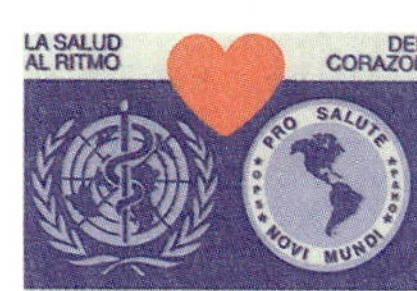

780 Heart and Emblems

1992. World Health Day. "Health in Rhythm with the Heart".
2077 **780** 2500p. ultramarine, blue and red . . . . 2·10 2·10

781 Map of South America and Food Products

1992. Mercosur (South American economic organization).
2078 **781** 2500p. multicoloured . . 2·10 2·10

782 Stamp

1992. "Olymphilex 92" International Olympic Stamps Exhibition, Barcelona.
2079 **782** 2900p. multicoloured . . 2·25 2·25

783 Emblems

1992. 22nd Latin American–Caribbean Regional Conference of Food and Agricultural Organization.
2080 **783** 2500p. multicoloured . . 1·75 1·75

784 Children with Basket of Food

1992. International Nutrition Conference, Rome.
2081 **784** 2900p. multicoloured . . 2·10 2·10

785 Vallejo

1992. Birth Centenary of Cesar Vallejo (painter and poet).
2082 **785** 2500p. brown & lt brown . . . . 1·75 1·75

786 Monument and Route Map **787** Ruins of Sacramento and Lighthouse

1992. Centenary of Christopher Columbus Monument, Durazno.
2083 **786** 700p. black, blue & green 50 50

1992. 500th Anniv of Discovery of America by Columbus.
2084 **787** 700p. multicoloured . . 50 50

788 Caravel **789** Emblem

1992. America. 500th Anniv of Discovery of America by Columbus. Multicoloured.
2085 700p. Type **788** 50 50
2086 2900p. Globe showing Americas and old map (horiz) . . . . 2·10 2·10

1992. Centenary of Christopher Columbus Philanthropic Society.
2087 **789** 700p. black, mauve and magenta 50 50

790 Emblem

1992. 500th Anniv of Presence of Jews in America.
2088 **790** 2900p. multicoloured . . 2·10 2·10

791 Arms

1992. 50th Anniv of Jose Pedro Varela Teachers' College.
2089 **791** 700p. multicoloured . . 50 50

792 Cambadu Building **793** Emblem

1992. Centenary of Chamber of Wholesale and Retail Traders.
2090 **792** 700p. grey, black and red . . . 50 50

1992. 50th Anniv of Lebanon Club of Uruguay.
2091 **793** 2900p. multicoloured . . 2·10 2·10

794 Nativity **796** Immigrant

795 Map and Emblem

1992. Christmas. Multicoloured.
2092 800p. Type **794** 55 55
2093 3200p. Star . . . . 2·10 2·10

1992. 22nd Latin American and Carribean Lions Clubs Forum.
2094 **795** 2700p. multicoloured . . 1·75 1·75

1992. Immigrants Day.
2095 **796** 800p. green and black . . 55 55

797 Oribe **799** Anniversary Emblem

798 Anniversary Emblem

1992. Birth Bicentenary of Manuel Oribe (Liberation hero). Multicoloured.
2096 800p. Type **797** 55 55
2097 800p. Oribe (founder) and Eastern University (horiz) . . 55 55

1992. 90th Anniv of Pan-American Health Organization.
2098 **798** 3200p. multicoloured . . 2·10 2·10

1992. 50th Anniv of Jose H. Molaguero S.A.
2099 **799** 800p. brown and stone . . 55 55

800 Satellite and Map

1992. 70th Anniv of ANDEBU (association of broadcasting stations).
2100 **800** 2700p. multicoloured . . 1·75 1·75

801 Emblem and Shanty Town

1992. 30th Anniv of Caritas Uruguaya.
2101 **801** 3200p. multicoloured . . 2·00 2·00

802 Gonzalez Pecotche (founder) and Emblem

1992. 60th Anniv of Logosofia.
2102 **802** 800p. yellow and blue . . 55 55

1993. Size 35 × 24 mm.
2103 **755** 800p. olive and green . . 30 15

Currency Reform
1 (new) peso = 1000 (old) pesos.

803 Wilson Ferreira Aldunate **804** Post Car

1993.
2104 **803** 80c. red, black and grey . . 30 15

1993.
2105 **804** 1p. blue and yellow . . . 40 20

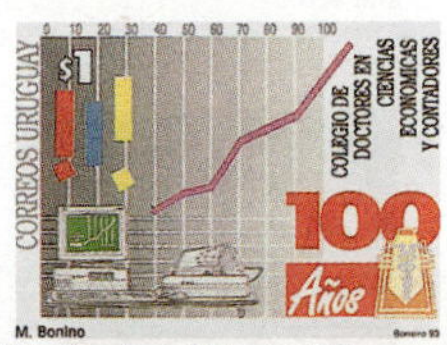

805 Graph and Personal Computer

1993. Centenary of Economic Sciences and Accountancy College.
2106 **805** 1p. multicoloured . . . 40 20

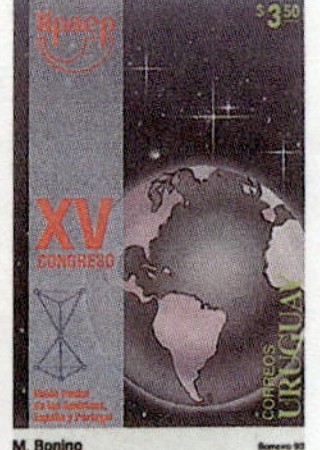

807 Magirus Deutz Fire Engine, 1958 **808** Earth

1993. 50th Anniv of National Fire Service.
2108 **807** 1p. multicoloured . . . 40 20

1993. 15th Congress of Postal Union of the Americas, Spain and Portugal.
2109 **808** 3p.50 multicoloured . . 1·25 60

809 Schooner and Pedro Campbell (first Navy General)

1993. 175th Anniv (1992) of Uruguayan Navy.
2110 **809** 1p. multicoloured . . . 20 10

810 Emblem

1993. 25th Anniv of International University Circles.
2111 **810** 1p. multicoloured . . . 20 10

811 Hupmobile, 1910

1993. 75th Anniv of Uruguay Automobile Club.
2112 **811** 3p.50 multicoloured . . 70 35

813 Bird **814** Armadillo

1993. No value expressed.
2114 **813** (1p.20) blue and azure . . 25 15
2115 (1p.40) emerald and green 30 15
2147 (1p.60) red and pink . . 35 20
2148 (1p.80) brown and pink . . 30 15
2186 (2p.) grey 35 20
2207 (2p.30) violet 35 20
These were sold at the current inland letter rate.

1993.
2116 **814** 1p.20 brown and green . . 25 15

815 Village and Soldier

1993. Uruguayan Battalion of Peace-keeping Force in Cambodia.
2117 **815** 1p. multicoloured . . . 20 10

816 Dish Aerials and Studio

1993. 30th Anniv of National Television Channel 5.
2118 **816** 1p.20 multicoloured . . 25 15

817 "The Tree of Life" (detail, Pablo Serrano)

1993. 60th Anniv of Anda.
2119 **817** 1p.20 multicoloured . . 25 15

818 Arms and Officers

1993. 50th Anniv of Juan Carlos Gomez Folle National Police School.
2120 **818** 1p.20 multicoloured . . 25 15

819 Graphics

1993. 75th Anniv of "Diario El Pais" (newspaper).
2121 **819** 1p.20 multicoloured . . 25 15

820 Broad-nosed Caiman

1993. America. Endangered Animals. Multicoloured.
2122 1p.20 Type **820** 25 15
2123 3p.50 Burrowing owl (vert) . . 3·50 3·50

821 Power Lines supplying Illuminated Building

1993. 14th Latin American Conference on Rural Electrification.
2124 **821** 3p.50 multicoloured . . 70 35

822 Emblem **823** Red-legged Seriema

1993. 150th Anniv of B'nai B'rith (Jewish cultural and social organization).
2125 **822** 3p.70 multicoloured . . 75 40

1993. Natural World.
2126 **823** 20c. brown and pink . . 50 20
2127 – 30c. yellow and violet . . 65 25
2128 – 50c. brown and pink . . 15 15
DESIGNS—VERT: 30c. Saffron-cowled blackbird. HORIZ: 50c. Two-toed anteater.

825 Crucifix, Mother Francisca and Nuns with Sick People **826** Amerindian

1993. Beatification of Mother Francisca Rubatto.
2130 **825** 1p.20 multicoloured . . 25 15

1993. International Year of Indigenous Peoples.
2131 **826** 3p.50 multicoloured . . 70 35

827 Emblem on Map

1993. 75th Anniv of Montevideo Rotary Club.
2132 **827** 3p.50 blue and gold . . 70 35

829 Phoenician Cargo Ship (carving)

1993. 50th Anniv of Independence of Lebanon.
2134 **829** 3p.70 brown, deep brown and green . . . 75 40

830 Haedo

831 Ribbon

1993. Eduardo Victor Haedo.
2135 **830** 1p.20 multicoloured . . 25 15

1993. Anti-AIDS Campaign.
2136 **831** 1p.40 multicoloured . . 30 15

832 Adoration of the Wise Men

833 Adult with Chick and Eggs

1993. Christmas. Multicoloured.
2137 1p.40 Type **832** 30 15
2138 4p. Adoration of the Shepherds 80 40

1993. The Greater Rhea. Multicoloured.
2139 20c. Type **833** 25 25
2140 20c. Adults sitting and standing 25 25
2141 50c. Close-up of head . . . 65 40
2142 50c. Adults feeding 65 40

834 Child's view of life (Alejandro Cuende)

835 Emblem

1994. Children's Rights Day.
2143 **834** 1p.40 multicoloured . . 30 15

1994. National Postal Directorate.
2144 **835** 1p.40 blue and yellow . . 30 15

836 Torch Carrier

1994. 5th World Sports Congress, Punta del Este.
2145 **836** 4p. multicoloured . . . 80 40

837 Frigate

1994. 17th Inter-American Naval Conference.
2146 **837** 3p.70 multicoloured . . 75 40

838 Emblem

839 Sheep

1994. 7th Iberian–American Youth Organization Conference.
2149 **838** 3p.90 multicoloured . . 70 35

1994. 4th International Merino Sheep Conference.
2150 **839** 4p.30 multicoloured . . 75 40

840 Anniversary Emblem

844 Dove flying from Ballot Box

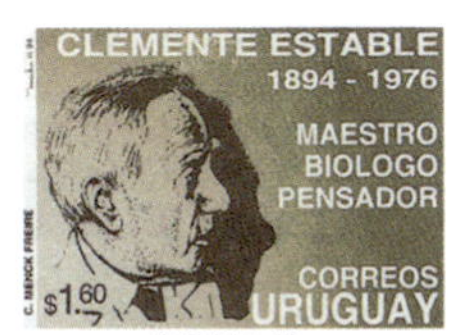
843 Estable

1994. 75th Anniv of I.L.O.
2151 **840** 4p.30 multicoloured . . 75 40

1994. Birth Centenary of Clemente Estable (biologist).
2154 **843** 1p.60 green and black 30 15

1994. 75th Anniv of Electoral Court.
2155 **844** 1p.60 multicoloured . . 30 15

845 Hand pulling Worm from Dog's Mouth

1994. National Commission on Eradication of Tapeworms.
2156 **845** 1p.60 multicoloured . . 30 15

847 First Co-operative Headquarters, Rochdale, England

1994. 150th Anniv of Co-operative Movement.
2158 **847** 4p.30 multicoloured . . 75 40

848 National Flags on Plugs

1994. 30th Anniv of Commission for Regional Integration of Electricity.
2159 **848** 1p.60 multicoloured . . 30 15

849 Astronaut standing on Moon

1994. 25th Anniv of First Manned Moon Landing.
2160 **849** 3p. multicoloured . . . 55 30

850 Family

1994. International Year of the Family.
2161 **850** 4p.80 multicoloured . . 85 45

851 Fr. Pierre (founder)

852 Pillar-box

1994. 45th Anniv of Emmaus Movement (social welfare organization).
2162 **851** 4p.80 multicoloured . . 85 45

1994. 150th Anniv of Neighbourhood Pillar Boxes.
2163 **852** 50c. yellow and green . . 10 10
2164 1p. yellow and brown . . 15 10
2165 1p.80 yellow and blue . . 30 15
2166 2p.60 yellow and brown 40 20
2168 7p.50 yellow and violet 1·10 55

853 "The Man of Lugano"

1994. 50th Death Anniv of Goffredo Sommavilla (painter).
2169 **853** 4p.80 multicoloured . . 85 45

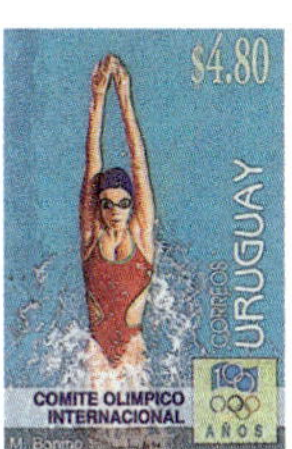
854 Swimmer

856 Saravia

855 Fernandez and Pupils with National Flag

1994. Centenary of International Olympic Committee.
2170 **854** 4p.80 multicoloured . . 85 45

1994. 125th Anniv of Elbio Fernandez School.
2171 **855** 1p.80 multicoloured . . 30 15

1994. 90th Death Anniv of Gen. Aparicio Saravia.
2172 **856** 1p.80 blue, turquoise and deep blue 30 15

857 Statuette

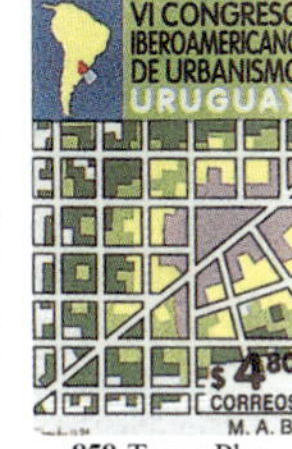
858 Town Plan

1994. 65th Anniv of General Association of Uruguayan Writers.
2173 **857** 1p.80 multicoloured . . 30 15

1994. 6th Latin American Town Planning Congress.
2174 **858** 4p.80 multicoloured . . 85 45

860 Mail Coach

1994. America. Postal Transport. Multicoloured.
2176 1p.80 Type **860** 30 15
2177 4p.80 "Eolo" (paddle-steamer) 85 45

861 Plan

1994. 1st International Seminar on Provision of Roads in Uruguay, Punte del Este.
2178 **861** 2p. multicoloured . . . 35 20

863 Computer Terminal and Reporter

1994. 50th Anniv of Uruguay Press Association.
2180 **863** 2p. multicoloured . . . 35 20

864 Statuette

1994. 50th Anniv of Uruguay Marketing Association.
2181 **864** 2p. multicoloured . . . 35 20

866 Dove over Latin America

1994. 25th Anniv of Latin American Movement "Long Live the People".
2183 **866** 4p.30 multicoloured . . 75 40

867 Draw Balls

1994. 55th Anniv of Lottery.
2184 **867** 2p. multicoloured . . . 35 20

868 Footballers

869 Tree

1994. 85th Anniv of Young Men's Christian Association.
2185 **868** 2p. multicoloured . . . 35 20

1994. Christmas. Multicoloured.
2187 2p. Type **869** 35 20
2188 5p.50 Star over village . . . 1·00 50

870 Emblem and Venue

1994. 4th Assembly of Latin American and Caribbean Organization of Higher Fiscal Entities, Montevideo.
2189 **870** 5p.50 multicoloured . . 1·00 50

871 Cross and Crescent on Globe

1994. 75th Anniv of International Federation of Red Cross and Red Crescent Societies.
2190 **871** 5p. multicoloured . . . 90 45

872 Chuy Post Office

1995.
2191 **872** 20c. green 10 10
2192 10p. brown . . . . . . 1·50 75
2195 10p. mauve and black . . 1·10 55

873 CANT 18 Flying Boat

1995. 70th Anniv of Naval Aviation.
2198 **873** 2p. multicoloured . . . 30 15

874 Swimming Park

1995. 20th Anniv of World Tourism Organization. Multicoloured.
2199 5p. Type **874** 75 40
2200 5p. Deer and greater rhea 75 40
2201 5p. Ranch 75 40
2202 5p. Beach resort 75 40

875 Lifeboat

1995. 17th World Lifeguards' Conference.
2203 **875** 5p. multicoloured . . . 75 40

876 Globe and Emblem forming "90"

1995. 90th Anniv of Rotary International.
2204 **876** 5p. ultramarine, blue and gold 75 40

877 Anniversary Emblem and Airplane

1995. 50th Anniv of International Civil Aviation Organization.
2205 **877** 5p. ultramarine, orange and blue 75 40

878 Mascagni and Set from "Cavalleria Rusticana" (opera)

1995. 50th Death Anniv of Piero Mascagni (composer).
2206 **878** 5p. multicoloured . . . 75 40

879 Cimarron

1995.
2208 **879** 2p.30 multicoloured . . 35 20

881 Paysandu Players

882 Orange incorporating Globe

1995. America Cup Football Championship, Uruguay. Multicoloured.
2210 2p.30 Type **881** 35 20
2211 2p.30 Rivera players 35 20
2212 2p.30 Ball in net 35 20
2213 2p.30 Montevideo players 35 20
2214 2p.30 Maldonado players 35 20
Nos. 2210/14 were issued together, se-tenant, forming a composite design of a match.

1995. 50th Anniv of F.A.O.
2215 **882** 5p.50 multicoloured . . 80 40

883 U.N. Soldier and Detail of World Map

1995. Participation in United Nations Peace-keeping Forces.
2216 **883** 2p.30 multicoloured . . 35 20

884 Italian National Colours on Map of Italy

1995. Visit of President Scalfaro of Italy.
2217 **884** 5p.50 multicoloured . . 80 40

885 People walking Hand in Hand towards Gateway

887 Postal Symbol

1995. Latin American Integration Day.
2218 **885** 5p. multicoloured . . . 75 40

1995. No Value Expressed.
2220 **887** (2p.60) yellow & green 40 20
2221 (2p.90) yellow and blue 40 20
2222 (3p.20) pink and red . . 45 25
2223 (3p.50) brown & purple 50 25

888 Carlos Gardel (entertainer)

1995.
2226 **888** 5p.50 multicoloured . . 80 40

889 "Notocactus roseinflorus"

890 Varela

1995. Flowers. Multicoloured.
2227 3p. Type **889** 45 25
2228 3p. "Verbena chamaedryfolia" 45 25
2229 3p. "Bauhinia candicans" 45 25
2230 3p. "Tillandsia aeranthos" 45 25
2231 3p. "Eichhornia crassipes" 45 25

1995. 150th Birth Anniv of Jose Verela (educationalist).
2232 **890** 2p.60 multicoloured . . 40 20

891 Monument

892 "Dicksonia sellowiana"

1995. Holocaust Monument, Pueblo Judio.
2233 **891** 6p. multicoloured . . . 90 45

1995. America. Environmental Protection. Multicoloured.
2234 3p. Type **892** 45 25
2235 6p. Maned wolf (horiz) . . 90 45

894 Anniversary Emblem over Globe

1995. 50th Anniv of U.N.O.
2237 **894** 6p. multicoloured . . . 90 45

895 Beyer Peacock, 1876

1995. Steam Railway Locomotives. Multicoloured.
2238 3p. Type **895** 45 25
2239 3p. Criollo, 1895 . . . . . 45 25
2240 3p. Beyer Peacock, 1910 . . 45 25

896 Brigantine (privateer of Artigas)

1995. 178th Anniv of Naval Service. Multicoloured.
2241 3p. Type **896** 45 25
2242 3p. "Montevideo" (training frigate) 45 25
2243 3p. "Pte. Rivera" (tanker) 45 25

897 Crib

900 Rosa Luna (dancer)

898 Lumiere Brothers and Film Reel

1995. Christmas. Multicoloured.
2244 2p.90 Type **897** 45 25
2245 6p.50 Beam of light and rose window 95 50

1995. Centenary of Motion Pictures.
2246 **898** 6p. violet, deep mauve and mauve 90 45

1996. Carnival. Multicoloured.
2248 2p.90 Type **900** 45 25
2249 2p.90 Santiago Luz (clarinettist) 45 25
2250 2p.90 Pepino (clown) . . . 45 25

901 Cantegril Country Club

1996. Golf. Multicoloured.
2251 2p.90 Type **901** 45 25
2252 2p.90 Cerro Golf Club . . . 45 25
2253 2p.90 Fay Crocker and trophy 45 25
2254 2p.90 Lago Golf Club . . . 45 25
2255 2p.90 Uruguay Golf Club 45 25

902 Solis Theatre

1996. Montevideo, Latin American Cultural Capital.
2256 **902** 2p.90 multicoloured . . 45 25

904 Zitarrosa

1996. 60th Birth Anniv of Alfredo Zitarrosa (musician).
2258 **904** 3p. multicoloured . . . 45 25

906 Skeletons

1996. Archaeological Congress.
2260 **906** 3p.20 multicoloured . . 45 25

907 "Glyptodon claripes"

1996. Prehistoric Animals. Multicoloured.
2261 3p.20 Type **907** 45 25
2262 3p.20 "Macrauchenia patachonica" 45 25
2263 3p.20 "Toxodon platensis" 45 25
2264 3p.20 "Glossotherium robostum" 45 25
2265 3p.20 "Titanosaurus" . . . 45 25

908 People-Houses

1996. Population and Housing Censuses.
2266 **908** 3p.20 multicoloured . . 45 25

909 Dion-Buton Double-deck Bus, 1912

1996. Old Vehicles. Multicoloured.
2267 3p.20 Type **909** 45 25
2268 3p.20 Ford Model "A" patrol car, 1928 . . . . . 45 25
2269 3p.20 Raleigh bicycle, 1940 45 25
2270 3p.20 Magirus fire-engine, 1926 . . . . 45 25
2271 3p.20 Hotchkiss ambulance, 1917 . . . . 45 25

911 Children and Globe holding Hands (Soraya Campanella)

1996. "Care for Our Planet: Everyone's Mission".
2273 **911** 3p.20 multicoloured . . 45 25

912 New Postal Administration Emblem

914 "Nuestra Senora de la Encina" (caravel), 1726

1996. Postal Emblems.
2273a **912** 5p. yellow and blue . . 60 30
2274 7p. yellow and blue . . 1·00 50

1996. Sailing Ships. Multicoloured.
2276 3p.20 Type **914** 45 25
2277 3p.20 "San Francisco" (ship of the line), 1729 . . . . 45 25
2278 3p.20 Etienne Moreau's fleet, 1720 . . . . 45 25
2279 3p.20 "Atrevida" (corvette), 1789–94 . . . . 45 25
2280 3p.20 "Nuestra Senora de la Luz" (brig), 1752 . . . . 45 25

915 "Flores Landscape" (Carmelo de Arzadun)

1996.
2281 **915** 3p.50 multicoloured . . 50 25

916 Old Jewish Quarter

1996. 80th Anniv of Jewish Community in Uruguay.
2282 **916** 7p.50 red, yellow and purple . . . . 1·10 55

917 Dr. Victor Bertullo (veterinary researcher)

1996. Scientists. Multicoloured.
2283 3p.50 Type **917** 50 25
2284 3p.50 Tomas Beno Hirschfeld (chemical engineer) (horiz) 50 25
2285 3p.50 Enrique Legrand (astronomer and physicist) 50 25
2286 3p.50 Dr. Miguel C. Rubino (veterinary researcher) (horiz) 50 25

919 Aristotle (philosopher)

1996. Scientists. Multicoloured.
2288 7p.50 Type **919** . . . . . . 1·10 55
2289 7p.50 Sir Isaac Newton (mathematician) . . . . . 1·10 55
2290 7p.50 Albert Einstein (physicist) . . . . 1·10 55

920 500 Peso Note

1996. Centenary of Republica Oriental Bank. Mult.
2291 3p.50 Type **920** 50 25
2292 3p.50 Ten peso note 50 25

921 Narbona Chapel

1996. National Heritage Day. Multicoloured.
2293 3p.50 Type **921** 50 25
2294 3p.50 Map of Gorriti Island showing sites of Spanish fortifications 50 25

922 "125" and Emblem

1996. 125th Anniv of Uruguay Rural Association.
2295 **922** 3p.50 multicoloured . . 50 25

924 Angel Rodriguez (South American boxing champion, 1917)

1996. Sports Personalities. Multicoloured.
2297 3p.50 Type **924** 50 25
2298 3p.50 Leandro Noli (winner of first Uruguayan cycling race, 1939) 50 25
2299 3p.50 Eduardo G. Risso (Olympic rowing medallist, 1948) 50 25
2300 3p.50 Estrella Puente (South American javelin champion, 1949) 50 25
2301 3p.50 Oscar Moglia (Olympic basketball medallist, 1956) 50 25

925 Gaucho

1996. America. Traditional Costumes. Multicoloured.
2302 3p.50 Type **925** 50 25
2303 3p.50 Countrywoman . . . 50 25

927 Satellite

1996. 3rd Space Conference of the Americas.
2305 **927** 3p.50 multicoloured . . 50 25

928 "Football Match" (Julio Suarez)

1996. Centenary of Comics. Museum of Humour and Anecdotes, Minas.
2306 **928** 4p. multicoloured . . . 60 30

929 Institute Building

1996. Centenary of Hygiene Institute.
2307 **929** 4p. multicoloured . . . 60 30

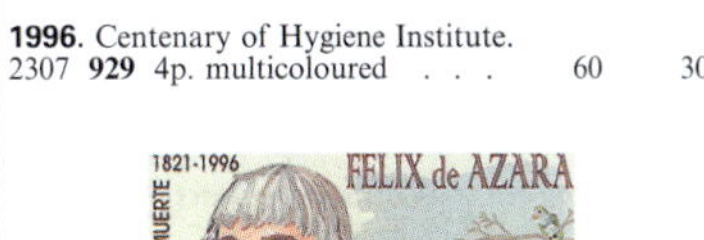

930 De Azara

1996. 175th Death Anniv of Felix de Azara (naturalist).
2308 **930** 4p. multicoloured . . . 60 30

931 Angels blowing Trumpets over Globe

1996. Centenary of Seventh Day Adventist Church in Uruguay.
2309 **931** 3p.50 multicoloured . . 50 25

932 Hands fingering Frets and Lyre (National Folklore Festival, Durazno)

1997. Festivals. Multicoloured. Self-adhesive and imperf (2315) or ordinary (others) gum.
2310 4p. Type **932** 50 25
2311 4p. Man smoking cigar (Festival of Gaucho Traditions, Tacuarembo) (vert) 50 25
2312 5p. Stage (Beer Week, Paysandu) 60 30
2313 5p. Ruben Lena and bridge over river (Olimar River Festival, Treinta y Tres) (vert) 60 30
2314 5p. Guitar and horseman (Minas y Abril Festival, Lavelleja) 60 30
2315 5p. Man mounted on blindfolded horse tied to post (Criolla Parque Roosevelt, Canelones) . . 60 30

933 Naked Mushroom ("Tricholoma nudum")

1997. Fungi. Multicoloured.
2316 4p. Type **933** 50 25
2317 4p. Yellow stainer ("Agaricus xanthodermus") 50 25
2318 4p. "Russula sardonia" . . 50 25
2319 4p. Girl hugging dog and "Microsporum canis" . . 50 25
2320 4p. "Polyporus versicolor" 50 25

934 Black-finned Pearlfish

1997. Fishes. Multicoloured. Self-adhesive. Imperf.
2321 4p. Type **934** 45 25
2322 4p. Uruguayan pearlfish ("Cynolebia viarius") . . 45 25

935 Buceo

1997. Yachting Harbours. Multicoloured. Self-adhesive. Imperf.
2323 4p. Type **935** 50 25
2324 4p. Colonia 50 25
2325 4p. Punta del Este 50 25
2326 4p. Santiago Vazquez . . . 50 25

936 Artigas and Lancer

1997. Bicentenary of Artigas's Lancers (Presidential escort).
2327 **936** 4p. multicoloured . . . 50 25

937 Cadet

1997. 50th Anniv of General Artigas Military Academy.
2328 **937** 4p. multicoloured . . . 50 25

938 Ambulance

1997. 18th Anniv of United Coronary Mobile (first mobile medical emergency unit in the world). Self-adhesive. Imperf.
2329 **938** 5p. multicoloured . . . 60 30

939 Toy holding Box   940 Anchorena, 1920

1997. 50th Anniv (1996) of U.N.I.C.E.F. Self-adhesive. Imperf.
2330 **939** 5p. multicoloured . . . 60 30

1997. Lighthouses. Mult. Self-adhesive. Imperf.
2331 5p. Type **940** 60 30
2332 5p. Farallon, 1870 . . . . . 60 30
2333 5p. Jose Ignacio, 1877 . . . 60 30
2334 5p. Santa Maria, 1874 . . . 60 30
2335 5p. Vigia, 18th-century . . . 60 30

941 "Devincenzia gallinali"

1997. Prehistoric Animals. Multicoloured. Self-adhesive. Imperf.
2336 5p. Type **941** 60 30
2337 5p. "Smilodon populator" . . 60 30
2338 5p. "Mesosaurus tenuidens" . 60 30
2339 5p. "Doedicurus clavicaudatus" 60 30
2340 5p. "Artigasia magna" . . . 60 30

942 Melo Cathedral

1997. Dioceses. Multicoloured.
2341 5p. Type **942** 60 30
2342 5p. Monsignor Mariano Soler (first archbishop of Archdiocese of Montevideo) 60 30
2343 5p. Monsignor Jacinto Vera (first bishop of Archdiocese of Montevideo) 60 30
2344 5p. Salto Cathedral 60 30

943 Boy admiring Stamps in Album

1997. Youth Philately. Multicoloured.
2345 1p. Type **943** 10 10
2346 1p. Winking boy with tweezers and magnifying glass 10 10
2347 2p. Boy thinking "MMMM... FILATELIA?" 25 15
2348 2p. Boy thinking of stamps 25 15
2349 2p. Boy rejecting friend's offer of football game . . 25 15

944 Black Skimmers

1997. "Pacific 97" International Stamp Exhibition, San Francisco, U.S.A.
2350 **944** 10p. multicoloured . . . 1·25 65

945 Theatre

1997. 85th Anniv of Teatro Maccio, San Jose.
2351 **945** 5p. black, red and stone 60 30

946 Toy Steam Train

1997. 70th Anniv of Inter-American Institute for the Child.
2352 **946** 5p. multicoloured . . . 60 30

947 Fola and Boy beside Bed (Geoffrey Foladori)

1997. Comic Strip Characters. Multicoloured.
2353 5p. Type **947** 60 30
2354 5p. Peloduro running for goal (Julio Suarez) . . . 60 30

948 Sun, Birds and Waves

1997. 90th Anniv of Punta del Este.
2355 **948** 5p. multicoloured . . . 60 30

949 Street

1997. World Heritage Site. Colonia del Sacramento.
2356 **949** 5p. multicoloured . . . 60 30

950 Baldwin Steam Locomotive, 1889

1997. Centenary of General Artigas Central Station, Montevideo. Multicoloured.
2357 4p.+1p. Type **950** 60 30
2358 4p.+1p. Hudswell Clarke steam locomotive, 1895 60 30
2359 4p.+1p. Station facade and Luis Andreoni 60 30
2360 4p.+1p. Hawthorn Leslie steam locomotive, 1914 60 30
2361 4p.+1p. General Electric diesel shunting locomotive, 1954 . . . . 60 30

951 Wailing Wall (Jerusalem) and Theodor Herzl (founder)

1997. Centenary of Zionist Congress, Basel.
2362 **951** 5p. multicoloured . . . 60 30

952 Woman giving Letter to Postman   953 Postal Symbol

1997. Collection at Sender's Address Service. Self-adhesive. Imperf.
2363 **952** 15p. multicoloured . . 1·75 90
2363a 20p. multicoloured . . 2·25 1·10
2364 – 25p. green, yell & blk 1·00 1·50
2364a – 32p. green, yell & blk 3·50 1·75
2364b – 80p. green, yell & blk 9·00 4·50
DESIGNS: Nos. 2364/64b Black-chested buzzard eagle (*Geranoaetus melanoleucus*).

1997. No Value Expressed.
2365 **953** (4p.) yellow and brown 50 25
2367 (–) blue 60 30
2368 (–) blue and violet . . . 60 30
2369 (–) green and grey . . . 60 30

954 "Creole Willow" (Dante Picarelli)   955 Clock Tower

1997. Centenary of Discovery of Acetylsalycylic Acid (aspirin) by Dr. Felix Hoffman.
2371 **954** 6p. multicoloured . . . 75 35

1997. 1st National Administration of Posts.
2372 **955** 6p. blue and black . . . 75 35

956 Arms and Map

1997. Department of Salto.
2373 **956** 6p. multicoloured . . . 75 35

957 Felix Mendelssohn-Bartholdy and Score

1997. Composers' Death Anniversaries. Multicoloured.
2374 6p. Type **957** (150th anniv) 75 35
2375 6p. Johannes Brahms and score (centenary) 75 35

958 Antler and Lucas Kraglievich (palaeontologist)

1997. 160th Anniv of National Natural History Museum, Montevideo. Multicoloured.
2376 6p. Type **958** 75 35
2377 6p. Plant and Jose Arechavaleta (botanist) 75 35
2378 6p. Left-eyed flounder and Garibaldi Devincenzi (zoologist) 75 35
2379 6p. Flint axe head and Antonio Tadei (archaeologist) 75 35

959 Members' Flags and Southern Cross   960 Von Stephan (after Anton Weber)

1997. Mercosur (South American Common Market).
2380 **959** 11p. mult (6th anniv) . . 1·40 70

1997. Death Centenary of Heinrich von Stephan (founder of Universal Postal Union).
2382 **960** 11p. multicoloured . . . 1·40 70

962 Postwoman

1997. America. Postal Delivery. Multicoloured.
2384 6p. Type **962** 75 35
2385 11p. Woman receiving letters from postman . . . 1·40 70

963 Base and Gentoo Penguin

1997. Artigas Scientific Base, Antarctica.
2386 **963** 6p. multicoloured . . . 75 35

964 River Scene

1997. 70th Death Anniv (1998) of Domingo Laporte (artist).
2387 **964** 6p. multicoloured . . . 75 35

965 Building

1997. 80th Anniv of Casa de Galicia.
2388 **965** 6p. multicoloured . . . 75 35

966 Arme 2 Biplane "Montevideo"

1997. 3rd International Aeronautical and Space History Congress.
2389 **966** 6p. multicoloured . . . 75 35

967 Map, Painting Materials and Legislative Palace Tower

971 Three Kings

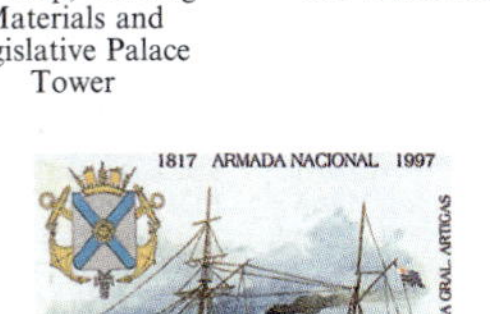

969 "General Artigas" (gunboat)

1997. 1st Interparliamentary Mercosur Paintings Biennale, Montevideo.
2390 **967** 11p. multicoloured . . . 1·40 70

1997. 180th Anniv of Navy.
2392 **969** 6p. multicoloured . . . 75 35

1997. Christmas. Multicoloured.
2394 6p. Type **971** 75 35
2395 11p. Madonna and Child . . 1·40 70

972 Adesio Lambardo and Bronze Medal (Olympic Games, Helsinki, 1952)

1997. Sportsmen. Multicoloured.
2396 6p. Type **972** 75 35
2397 6p. Guillermo Douglas (single sculls) and bronze medal (Olympic Games, Rome, 1932) 75 35
2398 6p. Obdulio Varela (footballer) and World Cup Trophy (Uruguay, 1950 World Cup champion) 75 35
2399 6p. Atilio Francois (cyclist) and silver medal (World Cycling Championships, Paris, 1947) 75 35
2400 6p. Juan Lopez Testa (South American 100 metres champion, Buenos Aires, 1947) 75 35

973 Silhouette and Personal Computer

1997. "Mevifil '97" First International Exhibition of Philatelic Audio-Visual and Computer Systems.
2401 **973** 11p. multicoloured . . . 1·40 70

974 Land Rover

1997. "INDEPEX 97" International Stamp Exhibition, New Delhi. Transport Anniversaries. Multicoloured.
2402 6p. Type **974** (50th anniv) 75 35
2403 6p. Henry Ford (50th death anniv) and motor car . . 75 35
2404 6p. Robert Bosch (centenary of electric motor) 75 35
2405 6p. Rudolf Diesel (centenary of diesel engine) 75 35

975 Academy Flag and Officer

1997. 90th Anniv of Naval Academy.
2406 **975** 6p. multicoloured . . . 75 35

976 Courthouse

1997. 90th Anniv of Uruguay Supreme Court.
2407 **976** 6p. multicoloured . . . 75 35

977 Postal Transport and Stone Relief

1997. 170th Anniv of Uruguay Post Office.
2408 **977** 6p. multicoloured . . . 75 35

978 Houses and Dr. Gallinal (founder)

1997. 30th Anniv of Movement for the Eradication of Insanitary Rural Housing.
2409 **978** 6p. multicoloured . . . 75 35

979 Preparing Materials

1997. Construction. Multicoloured.
2410 6p. Type **979** 75 35
2411 6p. Planning 75 35
2412 6p. Construction in progress 75 35
Nos. 2410/12 were issued together, se-tenant, forming a composite design.

981 Princess Diana with African Boy

982 Constructivist Painting

1998. Death Commemoration of Diana, Princess of Wales. Multicoloured.
2414 2p.+1p. Type **981** 30 15
2415 2p.+1p. Wearing protective mask 30 15

1998. Birth Centenary (1997) of Hector Ragni (artist).
2417 **982** 6p. multicoloured . . . 65 35

983 Naval Station, Montevideo

1998. 220th Anniv (1996) of Establishment of First Spanish Naval Station in America.
2418 **983** 6p. multicoloured . . . 65 35

984 Cartoon by Oscar Abmn

1998. Cartoonists. Multicoloured.
2419 6p. Type **984** 65 35
2420 6p. Cartoon by Emilio Cortinas 65 35

985 Ferreira

1998. 10th Death Anniv of Wilson Ferreira Aldunate (politician).
2421 **985** 6p. multicoloured . . . 65 35

986 Butia Palm

1998. Trees. Multicoloured.
2422 6p. Type **986** 65 35
2423 6p. Butia palms by stream 65 35
2424 6p. Ombu grove 65 35
2425 6p. Ombu ("Phytolacca dioica"), leaf and fruit . . 65 35

987 "Testudinites sellowi"

1998. Prehistoric Animals. Fossilised remains found in Uruguay. Multicoloured.
2426 6p. Type **987** 65 35
2427 6p. "Proborhyaena gigantea" 65 35
2428 6p. "Propachyrucos schiaffinos" 65 35
2429 6p. "Stegomastodon platensis" 65 35

988 "Sabbath" (Nelson Romero)

1998. 50th Anniv of State of Israel.
2430 **988** 12p. multicoloured . . . 1·25 70

989 Map of Americas and Sun

1998. 50th Anniv of Organization of American States.
2431 **989** 12p. blue, yellow & silver 1·25 70

990 Athlete

1998. 61st World Congress of Sports Journalism.
2432 **990** 6p. multicoloured . . . 65 35

991 Farmhouses

1998. 50th Anniv of Land Settlement Institute.
2433 **991** 6p. multicoloured . . . 65 35

992 Common Caracara

1998. Birds. Multicoloured.
2434 6p. Type **992** 65 35
2435 6p. Black-necked swan ("Cygnus melancoryphus") 65 35
2436 6p. Roseate spoonbill ("Platalea ajaja") 65 35
2437 6p. Buff-necked ibis ("Theristicus caudatus") 65 35

995 Demonstration outside Parliament, 1983

1998. Labour Day.
2440 **995** 6p. brown and black . . 65 35

996 Electric Tramcar, 1906

1998. 50th Anniv of Circle for Studies on Public Transport. Trams of Montevideo. Multicoloured.
2441 6p. Type **996** 65 35
2442 6p. German Transatlantica tramcar, 1907 . . . . . . 65 35
2443 6p. German Transatlantica tramcar, 1908 . . . . . . 65 35
2444 6p. Transatlantica double-deck tramcar, 1916 . . . 65 35

997 Pampas Cat

1998. Big Cats. Multicoloured.
2445 6p. Type **997** 65 35
2446 6p. Ocelot ("Felis pardalis") 65 35
2447 6p. Tree-ocelot ("Felis wiedii") 65 35
2448 6p. Jaguar ("Panthera onca") 65 35

998 "Sirius" (schooner)

1998. Ships. Multicoloured.
2449 6p. Type **998** 65 35
2450 6p. "18 de Julio" (sail/steam gunboat) 65 35
2451 6p. "Maldonado" (transport paddle-steamer) 65 35
2452 6p. "Instituto de Pesca No. 1" (fishery research vessel) 65 35

999 Chapel, Orphans Lime-quarry, Colonia

1998. Mercosur. Jesuit Missions.
2453 **999** 12p. multicoloured . . . 1·25 70

1000 Monument (Juan Ferrari)

1998. 125th Anniv of Monument to the Peace of 6 April 1872.
2454 **1000** 6p. multicoloured . . . 65 35

1001 Headquarters and Obus 155 mm. M114 A-2 Gun

1998. Centenary of Fifth Artillery Batallion.
2455 **1001** 6p. multicoloured . . . 65 35

1002 Imperial Moth

1998. Moths. Multicoloured.
2456 6p. Type **1002** 65 35
2457 6p. *Protoparce lucetius* . . . 65 35

1003 Artigas Monument

1004 Lomba and Porcupine

1998. Centenary of First Artigas Monument, San José.
2458 **1003** 6p. multicoloured . . . 65 35

1998. 80th Birth Anniv of Dr. Mauricio Lopez Lomba (doctor and philanthropist).
2459 **1004** 6p. multicoloured . . . 65 35

1005 Conservatory Emblem

1006 Jose Fernandez Vergara (founder)

1998. Centenary of Falleri-Balzo Music Conservatory, Montevideo.
2460 **1005** 6p. multicoloured . . . 65 35

1998. 95th Anniv of Pueblo Vergara (town).
2461 **1006** 6p. multicoloured . . . 65 35

1008 Institution Building

1009 *La Princesa* (frigate) and Emblem

1998. 145th Anniv of Spanish Association of Primary Mutual Assistance (medical organization).
2463 **1008** 6p. multicoloured . . . 65 35

1998. "Espamer'98" Iberian–Latin American Stamp Exhibition, Buenos Aires. 230th Anniv of First Montevideo–La Coruna Maritime Mail Service.
2464 **1009** 12p. multicoloured . . 1·25 65

1010 Students with Banners

1998. 15th Anniv of School and University Students' Demonstration, Montevideo.
2465 **1010** 6p. brown and black . . 65 35

1011 Junkers J52

1998. "IBEROAMERICANA'98" Iberian–American Stamp Exhibition, Maia, Portugal. Aircraft. Mult.
2466 6p. Type **1011** 65 35
2467 6p. SPAD VII 65 35
2468 6p. Ansaldo SVA-10 . . . . 65 35
2469 6p. Neybar 65 35

1012 Allende

1998. 25th Death Anniv of Salvador Allende (Chilean President, 1970–73).
2470 **1012** 12p. multicoloured . . 1·25 65

1013 Fabregat (teacher and writer)

1998. 50th Anniv of Enrique Rodriguez Fabregat's Participation in United Nations Conciliation Commission.
2471 **1013** 6p. multicoloured . . . 65 35

1014 Microphone, Emblem and Station Headquarters, Montevideo and Emblem

1998. 70th Anniv of Radio Carve.
2472 **1014** 6p. multicoloured . . . 65 35

1015 Julia Guarino (architect)

1998. America. Famous Women. Multicoloured.
2473 6p. Type **1015** 65 35
2474 12p. Paulina Luisi (doctor) 1·25 65

1016 Universal Postal Union Emblem and Stars

1998. World Post Day. "ILSAPEX '98" International Stamp Exhibition, Johannesburg, South Africa.
2475 **1016** 12p. multicoloured . . 1·25 65

1017 Emblem and Equipment

1998. 50th Anniv of Association of Pharmacies.
2476 **1017** 6p. multicoloured . . . 65 35

1018 Globe and Postal Services

1998. Small Packets Service. Self-adhesive.
2477 **1018** 25p. multicoloured . . 2·75 1·40

1019 Lancia Fire Engine, 1930

1998. "Italia 98" International Stamp Exhibition, Milan, Italy. Motor Vehicles. Multicoloured.
2478 6p. Type **1019** 65 35
2479 6p. Maserati "San Remo", 1946 . . . . 65 35
2480 6p. Alfa Romeo trolleybus, 1954 . . . . 65 35
2481 6p. Fiat "500" Topolino, 1936 . . . . 65 35

1020 Hector Maria Artola (musician) and Score

1021 "Play in order to help" (Melissa Migliozzi)

1998. Personalities. Multicoloured.
2482 6p. Type **1020** 65 35
2483 6p. Serafin J. Garcia (writer) 65 35
2484 6p. Nerses Ounanian (sculptor) (horiz) 65 35

1998. "Juvenalia'98" Youth Exhibition, Montevideo. Winning Entry in Children's Stamp Design Competition.
2485 **1021** 6p. multicoloured . . . 65 35

1023 Emblem and Facade of First Premises

1998. Centenary of Chamber of Industries.
2487 **1023** 6p. multicoloured . . . 65 35

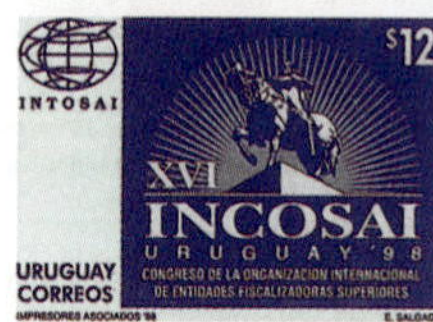

1024 Emblem and Artigas Monument, Montevideo

1998. 16th Triennial Congress of Expenditure Controller Boards.
2488 **1024** 12p. silver and blue . . 1·25 65

1025 Pink *Oxalis pudica*

1998. Flowers. Multicoloured. Self-adhesive.
2489 1p. Type **1025** 10 10
2490 4p. White *Oxalis pudica* . . 45 25
2491 6p. *Eugenia uniflora* 65 35
2492 7p. *Eugenia uniflora* 75 40
2493 9p. *Eugenia uniflora* . . . . 1·00 50
2494 10p. *Aechmea recurvata* . . 1·10 55
2495 14p. *Acca sellowiana* . . . 1·40 70
2498 50p. *Acca sellowiana* . . . . 5·50 3·50

1026 "St. Peter's Tears" (detail, Murillo)

1998. Christmas. Multicoloured.
2500 6p. Type **1026** 65 35
2501 12p. "The Virgin's descent to reward San Ildefonso's writings" (detail, El Greco) . . . . 1·25 65

1027 Grand Hotel, Paso del Molino

1998. 250th Anniv of Founding of Paso del Molino, Montevideo.
2502 **1027** 6p. multicoloured . . . 65 35

1028 Alberto Candeau reading Proclamation

1998. 15th Anniv of 27 November Democracy Demonstrations.
2503 **1028** 6p. brown and black . . 65 35

1029 Statuette

1998. Morosoli Cultural Awards.
2504 **1029** 6p. multicoloured . . . 65 35

1030 Children

1998. 50th Anniv of Universal Declaration of Human Rights.
2505 **1030** 6p. black, blue and red 65 35

1031 Stylized Athlete and Emblem

1998. 75th Anniv of Uruguayan Olympic Committee.
2506 **1031** 6p. multicoloured . . . 65 35

1032 Juan Lopez (football manager)

1998. Sports Personalities. Multicoloured.
2507 6p. Type **1032** 65 35
2508 6p. Hector Scarone (footballer) 65 35
2509 6p. Leandro Gomez Harley (basketball player) 65 35
2510 6p. Liberto Corney (boxer) 65 35

1033 Mother with Baby and Dr. Roberto Caldeyro Barcia

1998. Research Doctors. Multicoloured.
2511 6p. Type **1033** (gynaecologist) 65 35
2512 6p. Dr. Jose Verocay and Verocay neurinomes (anatomist, 70th death anniv) 65 35
2513 6p. Dr. Jose L. Duomarco and patient (cardiologist) 65 35

1034 Zola

1999. Centenary of Publication of "I Accuse" (Emile Zola's open letter regarding the Dreyfus case) in *L'Aurore* (newspaper).
2514 **1034** 14p. multicoloured . . 1·40 70

1035 Olive-backed Warbler and Beach

1999. 50th Anniv of Las Canas Resort.
2515 **1035** 7p. multicoloured . . . 75 40

1036 Map showing Borders

1999. 25th Anniv of Treaty of the River Plate (agreement on maritime borders between Uruguay and Argentine Republic).
2516 **1036** 7p. multicoloured . . . 75 40

1037 Luis Ernesto Aroztegui (artist) and "Self-Portrait" (tapestry)

1999. Anniversaries. Multicoloured.
2517 7p. Type **1037** (fifth death anniv) 75 40
2518 7p. Juan Jose Morosoli (writer, birth centenary) and detail of manuscript of "A Definition of Poetry" 75 40
2519 7p. Joaquin Torres Garcia (painter, 50th death anniv) and detail of "Barco Constructivo, America" 75 40

1038 Fawn-breasted Tanager (*Pipraeidea melanonota*) and *Psidium cattleianum* (shrub)

1999. Flora and Fauna. Multicoloured.
2520 7p. Type **1038** 75 40
2521 7p. *Tabebuia ipe* (tree) and Glittering-bellied emerald (*Chlorostilbon aureoventris*) 75 40
2522 7p. Chestnut-backed tanager (*Tangara preciosa*) and *Duranta repens* (shrub) . . 75 40
2523 7p. *Citharexylum montevidense* (tree) and many-coloured rush tyrant (*Tachuris rubigastra*) . . . 75 40

1039 Break de Chasse

1999. Carriages. Multicoloured.
2524 7p. Type **1039** 75 40
2525 7p. Mylord 75 40
2526 7p. Coupe Trois Quarts . . 75 40
2527 7p. Break de Champ 75 40

1040 B. and C. Cespedes, M. Nebel and Parque Central (first ground)

1999. Centenary of Nacional Football Club. Mult.
2528 7p. Type **1040** 75 40
2529 7p. H. Castro, P. Cea, A. Ciocca and club flag 75 40
2530 7p. R. Porta, A. Garcia, S. Gambetta and present ground 75 40

1041 Spacecraft orbiting Earth (Stefani Andrea Furtado)

1999. Year 2000. "Stampin' the Future". Showing second prize winning entries in "Year 2000" children's stamp design competition. Mult.
2531 7p. Type **1041** 75 40
2532 7p. "2000" (with monkey and people in zeros) (Pilar Trujillo) 75 40
2533 7p. Road, lights and houses (Lucia Lavie) 75 40
2534 7p. Futuristic housing and park (Cecilia Chopitea) 75 40

1042 Chebataroff

1999. 90th Birth Anniv of Jorge Chebataroff (teacher).
2535 **1042** 7p. multicoloured . . . 75 40

1043 "The Battle of Estero Bellaco" (Diogenes Hequet)

1999. Military Anniversaries. Multicoloured.
2536 7p. Type **1043** (60th anniv of No. 1 Infantry Brigade) 75 40
2537 7p. "Battle of Monte Caseros" (Carlos Penuti and Alejandro Bernhein) (160th anniv of No. 2 Infantry Battalion) . . . 75 40
2538 7p. "The Battle of Boqueron" (Diogenes Hequet) (170th anniv of No. 1 Infantry Battalion) 75 40

1044 St. Augustine Church

1046 Festival Poster

1999. 150th Anniv of Villa de la Restauracion.
2539 **1044** 7p. multicoloured . . . 75 40

1999. 1st Film Critics' Festival.
2541 **1046** 7p. multicoloured . . . 75 40

1047 Arab

1999. "Philexfrance 99" International Stamp Exhibition, Paris. Horses. Multicoloured.
2542 7p. Type **1047** 75 40
2543 7p. American quarter horse 75 40
2544 7p. Thoroughbred 75 40
2545 7p. Shetland pony 75 40

1048 Emblem and Title Page of *Marcha*

1999. 60th Anniv of *Marcha* (weekly publication).
2546 **1048** 7p. multicoloured . . . 75 40

1049 Trapeze Bike and Emblem

1999. Inauguration of Permanent Space Science Visitor Centre.
2547 **1049** 7p. multicoloured . . . 75 40

1050 Artigas Base

1999. 15th Anniv of Artigas Antarctic Scientific Base.
2548 **1050** 7p. multicoloured . . . 75 40

1051 University Facade

1999. 150th Anniv of University of the Republic (first Uruguayan university).
2549 **1051** 7p. yellow and black . . 75 40

1052 Emblem

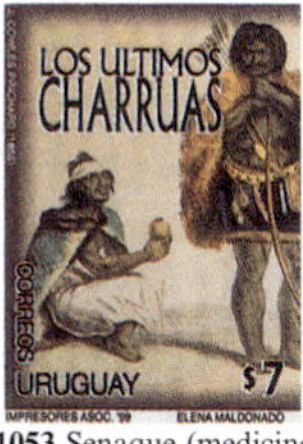

1053 Senaque (medicine man) and Chief Vaimaca-Peru (lancer) (left-hand detail)

1999. 50th Anniv of Regional Office of Science and Technology for Latin America and the Caribbean, Montevideo.
2550 **1052** 7p. multicoloured . . . 75 40

1999. "The Last Charruas" (painting) by Delaunois. Multicoloured.
2551 7p. Type **1053** 75 40
2552 7p. Warrior and wife (right-hand detail) 75 40
Nos. 2551/2 were issued together, se-tenant, forming a composite design of the complete painting.

1055 Emblem

1057 Cocker Spaniel

1056 Piper J-3 Float Plane

1999. 50th Anniv of El Galpon Theatre.
2554 **1055** 7p. multicoloured . . . 75 40

1999. "China 1999" International Stamp Exhibition, Peking. Airplanes. Multicoloured.
2555 7p. Type **1056** 75 40
2556 7p. Short S.25 Sunderland flying boat 75 40

1999. Dogs. Multicoloured.
2557 7p. Type **1057** 75 40
2558 7p. German shepherd . . . 75 40
2559 7p. Dalmatian 75 40
2560 7p. Basset hound 75 40

1058 Mining Bee on *Oxalis* sp.

1999. Insects and Flowers. Multicoloured.
2561 7p. Type **1058** 75 40
2562 7p. *Apanteles* sp. and *Epidendrum paniculosum* 75 40
2563 7p. *Metabolosia univita* and *Baccaris trimera* 75 40
2564 7p. Cantarido and flower . . 75 40

1059 Orlando Aldama (poet and writer)

1060 Open Book

1999. Personalities. Multicoloured.
2565 7p. Type **1059** 75 40
2566 7p. Julio Martinez Oyanguren (guitarist) . . 75 40

1999. Mercosur. The Book. National Heritage Day.
2567 **1060** 7p. multicoloured . . . 75 40

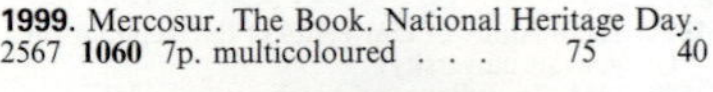

1061 Olympic Poster and Gold Medal

1999. 75th Anniv of Victory of Uruguay Football Team in Olympic Games, Paris, France. Mult.
2568 7p. Type **1061** 75 40
2569 7p. Winning team 75 40
Nos. 2568/9 were issued together, se-tenant, forming a composite design.

1062 Emblem

1999. International Year of the Elderly (1st issue).
2570 **1062** 7p. multicoloured . . . 75 40
See also No. 2576.

1063 "Exuberant Philatelic Gathering" (Mariano Bartasan)

1999. Stamp Day.
2571 **1063** 7p. multicoloured . . . 75 40

1064 Projects and Emblem

1999. 40th Anniv of Inter-American Development Bank.
2572 **1064** 7p. multicoloured . . . 75 40

1065 Weapons in Dustbin

1999. America. A New Millennium without Arms. Multicoloured.
2573 7p. Type **1065** 75 40
2574 14p. Satellites and Earth . . 1·40 70

1066 Cattle pulling Caravan

1999. 50th Anniv of El Ceibo (society for the protection of traditional customs).
2575 **1066** 7p. multicoloured . . . 75 40

1067 Children and Elderly Couple

1999. International Year of the Elderly (2nd issue).
2576 **1067** 7p. multicoloured . . . 75 40

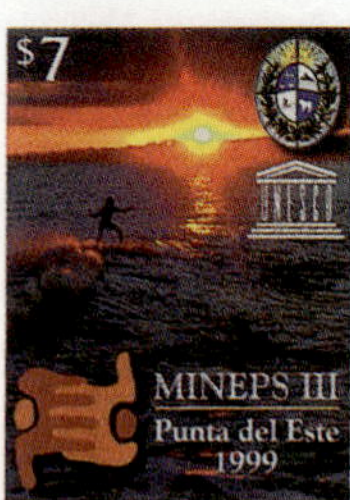

1068 Sunset and Emblem

1999. 3rd International Sports Ministers' and Officials' Conference, Punta del Este.
2577 **1068** 7p. multicoloured . . . 75 40

1070 Emblem

1999. 60th Anniv of Uruguayan Institute of Technical Standards.
2579 **1070** 7p. multicoloured . . . 75 40

1071 Batalla

1072 Front Cover of *Mundo Uruguayo* (magazine), 29 April 1929

1999. 1st Death Anniv of Hugo Batalla (lawyer).
2580 **1071** 7p. multicoloured . . . 75 40

1999. Art and Design in the 1920s.
2581 **1072** 7p. multicoloured . . . 75 40

1073 "1999" and Palacio Salvo, Parliament House, Centenario Stadium's Homage Tower, Engineering Faculty and the University Hospital

1999. Millennium. Multicoloured.
2582 3p.30 Type **1073** 35 20
2583 3p.50 "2000" and Hotel Casino Conrad, airport, Radison Victoria Plaza Hotel, World Trade Centre and Communications Tower 40 20

1074 Cowboy and Indian fighting

1999. 75th Birth Anniv of Celmar Poume (cartoonist).
2584 **1074** 7p. multicoloured . . . 75 40

1075 Christmas Tree and Decorations

1999. Christmas. Multicoloured.
2585 9p. Type **1075** . . . . . 1·00 50
2586 18p. Carol singers (vert) . . 2·00 1·00

1076 "Bearded Drinker" (Nelson Romero)

1999. 20th Anniv of Juanico Wine Cellar. Winning Designs in "Art and Wine" Competition. Mult.
2587 9p. Type **1076** . . . . . 1·00 50
2588 9p. "Carport of the Old Wine Cellar" (Nelson Ramos) . . . . 1·00 50

1077 Council Offices

1999. Inauguration of Maldonado Department Council Building.
2589 **1077** 9p. multicoloured . . . 1·00 50

1078 Stylized Sun (Carlos Paez Vilaro)

2000. Contemporary Art.
2590 **1078** 9p. multicoloured . . . 1·00 50

1080 *Cattleya corcovado*

1081 Punta del Este Lighthouse

2000. Orchids. Multicoloured.
2592 4p. Type **1080** 45 25
2593 4p. *Cattleya* sp. hybrid . . . 45 25
2594 5p. *Laelia purpurata* 55 30
2595 5p. *Laelia tenebrosa* 55 30

2000. Lighthouses. Multicoloured.
2596 4p. Type **1081** 45 25
2597 4p. Cabo Polonio 45 25
2598 5p. Flores Island 55 30
2599 5p. Punta Brava 55 30

1082 Quijano

2000. Birth Centenary of Carlos Quijano (journalist).
2600 **1082** 9p. multicoloured . . . 1·00 50

1083 Charlie Chaplin (leading actor)

2000. "LUBRAPEX 2000" Brazilian–Portuguese Stamp Exhibition, San Salvador de Bahia, Brazil. 75th Anniv of *The Gold Rush* (silent film).
2601 **1083** 18p. multicoloured . . 1·50 90

1084 Chapel

2000. 250th Anniv of El Cordon, Montevideo.
2602 **1084** 9p. multicoloured . . . 75 45

1085 Mural (right-hand detail)

1086 Garcia

2000. Indigenous Flora Mural, Luis Koster Stadium, Mercedes City. Multicoloured.
2603 4p. Type **1085** 35 25
2604 5p. Mural (left-hand detail) 40 25
Nos. 2603/4 were issued together, se-tenant, forming a composite design of a portion of the mural.

2000. 144th Birth Anniv of Francisco Garcia y Santos (Director General of Posts and Telegraphs, 1901–17).
2605 **1086** 9p. multicoloured . . . 75 45

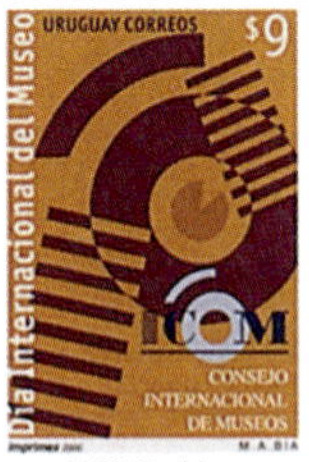

1087 Emblem
1088 Emblem

2000. 125th Anniv of Association of Uruguayan Notaries.
2606 **1087** 9p. multicoloured . . . 75 45

2000. International Museums Day.
2607 **1088** 9p. multicoloured . . . 75 45

1089 Skyscrapers (Maria Pia Pereyra)

2000. "Stampin' the Future". Winning Entries in Children's International Painting Competition. Multicoloured.
2608 4p. Type **1089** 35 25
2609 4p. "2000", fish and national colours (Virginia Regueiro) 35 25
2610 5p. People building globe (Helena Perez Acevedo) 40 25
2611 5p. Letters between postman and computer (Blanca Esther Lima) 40 25

1090 Emblem

2000. 90th Anniv of Club Soriano (cultural and sports association).
2612 **1090** 9p. multicoloured . . . 75 45

1091 Antonio Rupenian (founder)
1092 Woman reading

2000. 65th Anniv of Radio Armenia (Armenian community radio service).
2613 **1091** 18p. multicoloured . . 1·50 90

2000. Centenary of The 1900 Generation (Uruguayan writers).
2614 **1092** 9p. multicoloured . . . 75 45

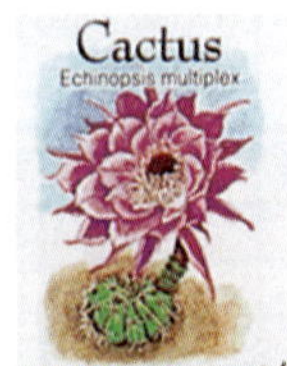

1093 *Echinopsis multiplex*

2000. Cacti. Multicoloured.
2615 4p. Type **1093** 35 25
2616 5p. Thorn ball (*Notocactus ottonis*) 40 25

1094 Team (Olympic Champion, Amsterdam, 1928)

2000. Centenary of Uruguay Football Association. Multicoloured.
2617 4p. Type **1094** 35 25
2618 4p. Stadium (first World Cup Football Champion, Uruguay, 1930) 35 25
2619 5p. Team (Olympic Champion, Paris, 1924) 40 25
2620 5p. Player scoring goal (World Cup Football Champion, Brazil, 1950) 40 25

1095 Georges Bizet (composer) and Scene from *Carmen*

2000. Opera Anniversaries. Multicoloured.
2621 9p. Type **1095** (125th anniv of first performance) . . . 75 45
2622 9p. Giacomo Puccini (composer) and scene from *Tosca* (centenary of first performance) 75 45

1096 Emblem

2000. 20th Anniv of Latin American Association of Integration.
2623 **1096** 18p. multicoloured . . 1·50 90

1097 Vought Sikorsky OS2U Kingfisher (seaplane)

2000. 75th Anniv of Uruguay Naval Aviation.
2624 **1097** 9p. multicoloured . . . 75 45

1098 Fingerprints and Emblem

2000. 120th Anniv of O.R.T. (educational organization).
2625 **1098** 9p. multicoloured . . . 75 45

1099 De La Robla

2000. Luis de la Robla (first Postmaster General in Uruguay) Commemoration.
2626 **1099** 9p. multicoloured . . . 75 45

1100 Rodriguez and Racing Car

2000. 1st Death Anniv of Gonzalo Rodriguez (racing driver). Multicoloured.
2627 9p. Type **1100** 75 45
2628 9p. Racing car and Rodriguez with trophy . . 75 45

1101 Map and Artigas

2000. 150th Death Anniv of Jose Artigas.
2629 **1101** 9p. multicoloured . . . 75 45

1102 Common Miner (*Geositta cunicularia*)

2000. "Espana 2000" World Stamp Exhibition, Madrid. Birds. Multicoloured.
2630 4p. Type **1102** 35 25
2631 4p. Freckle-breasted thornbird (*Phacellodomus striaticollis*) 35 25
2632 5p. Long-tailed reed finch (*Donacospiza albifrons*) . . 40 25
2633 5p. Golden-winged cacique (*Cacicus chrysopterus*) . . 40 25

1103 T. Makiguchi, J. Toda and Emblem

2000. 25th Anniv of Soka Gakkai International (Buddhist organization).
2634 **1103** 18p. multicoloured . . 1·50 90

1104 Noughts and Crosses
1105 Emblem

2000. America. A.I.D.S. Awareness. Multicoloured.
2635 9p. Type **1104** 75 45
2636 18p. A.I.D.S. ribbon and needle . . . . 1·50 90

2000. Mercosur. Cultural Heritage Day.
2637 **1105** 18p. multicoloured . . 1·50 90

1106 "Dragon"

2000. 105th Birth Anniv of Luis Mazzey (artist).
2638 **1106** 9p. multicoloured . . . 75 45

1107 Firemen on Roof

2000. Firemen. Multicoloured.
2639 9p. Type **1107** 75 45
2640 9p. Firemen attending motor vehicle fire (horiz) 75 45

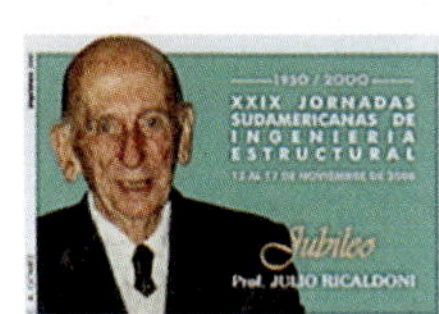

1108 Prof. Julio Ricaldoni (engineer)

2000. 50th Anniv of and 29th South American Conference on Structural Engineering, Punta Del Este.
2641 **1108** 9p. multicoloured . . . 75 45

1109 *Capitan Miranda*

2000. 70th Anniv *Capitan Miranda* (cadet ship).
2642 **1109** 9p. multicoloured . . . 75 45

1110 Charles V and Map

2000. 500th Birth Anniv of Charles V, Holy Roman Emperor.
2643 **1110** 22p. multicoloured . . 2·00 1·25

1111 Fireworks

2000. Christmas. Multicoloured.
2644 11p. Type **1111** 90 55
2645 22p. Holy Family (crib figures) . . . . 2·00 1·25

1112 Emblem
1114 Little Monkey Frog (*Phyllomedusa iheringii*)

1113 Emblem

2000. 125th Anniv of Sarandi Del Yi, Montevideo.
2646 **1112** 11p. multicoloured . . 90 55

2001. Forest Fire Prevention Campaign.
2647 **1113** 11p. multicoloured . . 90 55

2001. Amphibians and Reptiles. Multicoloured.
2648 11p. Type **1114** 90 55
2649 11p. Black spine-necked swamp turtle (*Acanthochelys spixii*) . . 90 55
2650 11p. Hilaire's side-necked turtle (*Phrynops hilarii*) . . 90 55
2651 11p. Striped snouted treefrog (*Scinax squalirostris*) 90 55

1115 Clubhouse, River and Emblem

2001. Centenary of Paysandu Rowing Club.
2652 **1115** 11p. multicoloured . . 90 55

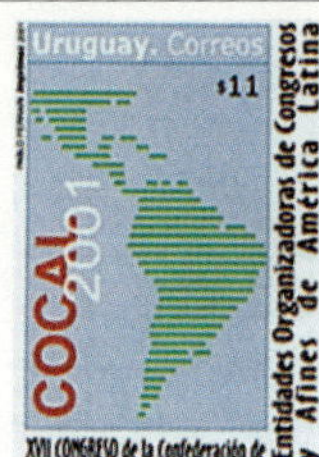

1116 Map of South America and Emblem
1117 Building Facade

2001. 18th Congress of Latin American Confederation of Organizers of Congresses and Similar Events (COCAL) and 17th Congress of International Convention and Congress Association, Montevideo.
2653 **1116** 11p. multicoloured . . 90 55

2001. Bicentenary of Belen.
2654 **1117** 11p. multicoloured . . 90 55

1118 Crow's Gorge

2001. Natural Sights. Multicoloured. Self-adhesive gum.
2655 2p. Waterfall, Salto del Penitente 20 10
2658 11p. Type **1118** 90 55
2661 20p. Palace Cave (vert) . . 1·60 1·00

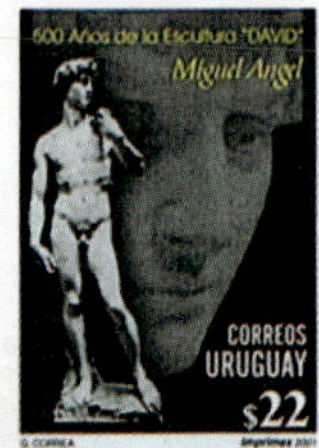

1119 "David"

2001. 500th Anniv of "David" (sculpture, Michelangelo).
2665 **1119** 22p. black, yellow and red . . . . 2·00 1·25

1120 Musicians and Emblem

2001. 50th Anniv of Uruguayan Society of Performers (S.U.D.E.I.).
2666 **1120** 11p. multicoloured . . 90 55

1121 Figure and Emblem
1122 Emblem

2001. 75th Anniv of Casal Catala (Catalan cultural organization).
2667 **1121** 11p. multicoloured . . 90 55

2001. 85th Anniv of Engineering School, Montevideo.
2668 **1122** 11p. blue 90 55

1123 Talice

2001. 2nd Death Anniv of Rudolfo Talice (biologist).
2669 **1123** 11p. multicoloured . . 1·10 70

1124 Anniversary Emblem

2001. 50th Anniv of Lion's Club, Montevideo.
2670 **1124** 11p. multicoloured . . 1·10 70

1125 Early Telephone and Alexander Graham Bell

2001. 125th Anniv of the Telephone.
2671 **1125** 22p. multicoloured . . 2·25 1·40

1126 Urtutu Pit Viper (*Bothrops alternatus*)

2001. Snakes. Multicoloured.
2672 11p. *Philodyras olfersii* . . . 1·10 70
2673 11p. Type **1126** . . . . . . 1·10 70

1127 "Two Ways" (detail, oil painting)

2001. Death Centenary of Juan Manuel Blanes (artist).
2674 **1127** 11p. multicoloured . . 1·10 70

1128 Dr. Morquio
1129 "*Rheingold*"

2001. Centenary of Appointment of Dr. Luis Morquio as Professor of Paediatrics at Uruguay University.
2675 **1128** 11p. multicoloured . . 1·10 70

2001. 125th Anniv of First Performance of Richard Wagner's *Ring of the Nibelungs*. Scenes from the operas. Multicoloured.
2676 11p. Type **1129** . . . . . . 1·10 70
2677 11p. *Valkyrie* . . . . 1·10 70
2678 11p. *Siegfried* . . . . 1·10 70
2679 11p. *Decline of the Gods* and Wagner . . . . 1·10 70

1130 Emblem
1131 Edison

2001. 50th Anniv of International Organization for Migration.
2680 **1130** 22p. blue and black . . 2·25 1·40

2001. 75th Death Anniv of Thomas Alva Edison (inventor).
2681 **1131** 22p. multicoloured . . 2·25 1·40

1132 Container Ship

2001. Centenary of Montevideo Port.
2682 **1132** 11p. multicoloured . . 1·10 70

1133 New Hampshire

2001. Domestic Chickens. Designs showing pairs of each breed. Multicoloured.
2683 11p. Type **1133** . . . . . . 1·10 70
2684 11p. Buff Orpingtons . . . 1·10 70
2685 11p. Araucanas . . . . . . 1·10 70
2686 11p. Light brown leghorns 1·10 70

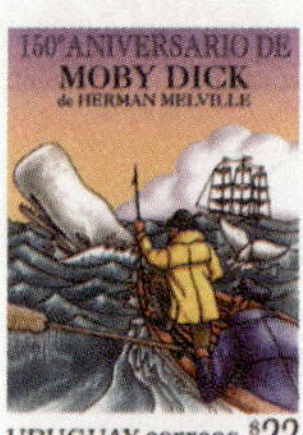

1134 Moby Dick and Whalers

2001. 150th Anniv of Publication of *Moby Dick* (novel by Herman Melville).
2687 **1134** 22p. multicoloured . . 2·25 1·40

1135 Flags, Globe and Gonzalez Pecotche

2001. Birth Centenary of Carlos Bernado Gonzalez Pecotche (founder of Logosophy self-development).
2688 **1135** 11p. multicoloured . . 1·10 70

1136 Concorde

2001. 25th Anniv of First Flight of Concorde.
2689 **1136** 22p. multicoloured . . 2·25 1·40

1137 "Louis Philippe"
1139 Bicentenary Emblem

1138 Bee-keepers

2001. Roses. Multicoloured.
2690 11p. Type **1137** . . . . . . 1·10 70
2691 11p. "Souvenir de Mme Leonie Viennot" . . . . 1·10 70
2692 11p. "Kronenbourg" . . . 1·10 70
2693 11p. "Lady Hillingdon" . . 1·10 70

2001. Bee-keeping. Multicoloured.
2694 12p. Type **1138** . . . . . . 1·25 75
2695 12p. Honey bee on flower 1·25 75
Nos. 2694/5 were issued together, se-tenant, forming a composite design.

2001. Bicentenary of Dolores (village), Soriano Department.
2696 **1139** 12p. multicoloured . . 1·25 75

1140 Girl and Flowers

2001. 80th Anniv of Uruguay–Japan Diplomatic Relations.
2697 **1140** 24p. multicoloured . . 2·40 1·40

1141 Stylized Sun with Face

2001. 75th Anniv of Uruguay Philatelic Club. Multicoloured.
2698 12p. Type **1141** . . . . . . 1·25 75
2699 12p. Square sun . . . . . . 1·25 75

1142 Basilica of the Blessed Sacrament, Colonia Family, Sauce
1144 Altarpiece, Temple of the Sacred

1143 "Experience" (Carlos Amoretti)

2001. America. World Heritage. Multicoloured.
2700 12p. Type **1142** . . . . . . 1·25 75
2701 24p. San Benito Chapel, Colonia . . . . 2·40 1·40

2001. "50 Years in Art" Exhibition by Carlos Amoretti.
2702 **1143** 12p. multicoloured . . 1·25 75

2001. 150th Anniv of Sauce, Canelones.
2703 **1144** 12p. multicoloured . . 1·25 75

1145 "Life and Health" (Mariana Tarigo)

2001. Anti-drugs Campaign. Winning Entry in Stamp Design Competition.
2704 **1145** 12p. multicoloured . . 1·25 75

1146 Children encircling Globe
1147 Family flying Kite

2001. United Nations Year of Dialogue among Civilizations.
2705 **1146** 24p. multicoloured 2·40 1·40

2001. Honorary Anti-Cancer Campaign Committee.
2706 **1147** 12p. multicoloured 1·25 75

1148 Newspapers on Conveyor-belt

1150 Blood Droplet Figure

1149 Emblem, Basket and Ball

2001. 20th Anniv of *Ultimas Noticias* (newspaper).
2707 **1148** 12p. multicoloured 1·25 75

2001. 50th Anniv of Sauce Basketball Club.
2708 **1149** 12p. multicoloured 1·25 75

2001. Voluntary Blood Donation Day.
2709 **1149** 12p. multicoloured 1·25 75

1151 San Martin Portrait overlaid with Grid Pattern

2001. 70th Death Anniv of Juan Zorrilla de San Martin (writer).
2710 **1151** 12p. multicoloured 1·25 75

1152 *Oyarvide* (survey ship)

2001.
2711 **1152** 12p. multicoloured 1·25 75

1153 Mr. and Mrs. King

2001. Visit to Uruguay of Mr. Richard King (president of Rotary Club International).
2712 **1153** 24p. multicoloured 2·40 1·40

1154 Emblems

2001. 110th Anniv of Penarol Athletics Club.
2713 **1154** 12p. multicoloured 1·25 75

1155 Sosa

1156 Nasazzi

2001. 75th Birth Anniv of Julio Sosa (singer).
2714 **1155** 12p. black and violet 1·25 75

2001. Birth Cent of Jose Nasazzi (footballer).
2715 **1156** 12p. multicoloured 1·25 75

1157 "Adoration of the Shepherds" (Jose Ribera)

1158 Bell Tower

2001. Christmas. Multicoloured.
2716 12p. Type **1157** 1·25 75
2717 24p. "Adoration of the Shepherds" (Anton Raphael Mengs) 2·40 1·25

2001. Bicentenary of San Carlos Church.
2718 **1158** 12p. multicoloured 1·25 75

1159 "Cosmic Monument" (Joaquin Torres Garcia)

2001. 90th Anniv of National Museum of Visual Arts.
2719 **1159** 12p. multicoloured 1·25 75

1160 Building Facade

2001. 90th Anniv of State Insurance Bank.
2720 **1160** 12p. multicoloured 1·25 75

1161 *Guettarda uruguensis*

2001. Mercosur.
2721 **1161** 24p. multicoloured 2·40 1·40

EXPRESS MAIL STAMPS

1921. Overprinted **MENSAJERIAS.**
E389 **120** 2c. orange 50 20

E 126 Caduceus

E 153 Caduceus

1923.
E415 **E 126** 2c. red 30 10
E416 2c. blue 30 10

1928.
E591 **E 153** 2c. black on green 15 10
E635a 2c. green 15 10
E636 2c. blue 15 10
E637 2c. pink 15 10
E638 2c. brown 10 10

1957. Surch **$ 0.05.**
E1065 **E 153** 5c. on 2c. brown 15 10

E 859 Motor Scooter

E 913

1994. International Service.
E2170 **E 859** 1p. orange and blue 20 15

1996.
E2275 **E 913** 8p. yellow and blue 1·25 65

LATE FEE STAMPS

L 175

1936.
L774 **L 175** 3c. green 10 10
L775 5c. violet 15 10
L776 6c. green 15 10
L777 7c. brown 20 10
L778 8c. red 40 25
L779 12c. blue 60 50

NEWSPAPER STAMPS

1922. Optd **PRENSA** (= Printed Matter) or surch also.
N519 **128** 3c. olive (imperf) 40 25
N447 **118** 3c. on 2c. black and lake (perf) 40 35
N403 **120** 3c. on 4c. yellow (perf) 20 30
N448 **118** 6c. on 4c. blue and orange (perf) 40 35
N449 9c. on 5c. brown and blue (perf) 40 35
N520 **128** 9c. on 10c. green (imperf) 45 35
N521 15c. mauve (imperf) 60 40

OFFICIAL STAMPS

1880. Optd **OFICIAL.** Perf.
O51 **9** 15c. yellow 2·00 2·00

1880. Optd **OFICIAL.** Roul.
O48 **10** 1c. brown 1·10 1·10
O49 **11** 5c. green 45 45
O61 **15** 7c. blue (perf) 1·50 1·50
O50 **10** 10c. red 70 70
O52 20c. bistre 95 95
O53 50c. black 6·25 6·25
O55 1p. blue 6·25 6·25

1883. Optd **OFICIAL.**
O64 **16** 1c. green 2·00 2·00
O65 – 2c. red (No. 63) 3·75 3·00

1883. Optd **OFICIAL.**
O70 **18** 1c. green 11·50 11·50
O71 2c. red 3·70 3·75
O72 **20** 5c. blue 1·10 85
O73 **21** 10c. brown 2·75 1·40

1884. Optd **FRANCO** in frame.
O74 **18** 1c. green 13·50 11·50

1884. Optd **OFICIAL.**
O80 **10** 1c. on 10c. (No. 76) 80 80
O81 – 2c. red (No. 77) 2·25 2·25
O82 **26** 5c. blue 95 70

1884. Optd **OFICIAL.** Roul.
O 91a **28** 1c. grey 3·75 2·00
O 91 1c. green 75 45
O 92 **29** 2c. red 45 30
O 93a **28** 5c. blue 1·25 1·40
O 94 5c. lilac 1·50 1·25
O 95 **31** 7c. brown 1·10 65
O110 7c. orange 1·10 75
O 96 **32** 10c. brown 60 35
O111 **36** 10c. violet 5·75 3·00
O 97 **33** 20c. mauve 1·10 65
O112 20c. brown 5·75 2·25
O 98 **34** 25c. lilac 1·10 75
O113 25c. red 5·75 2·25

1890. Optd **OFICIAL.** Perf.
O124 **38** 1c. green 40 20
O125 **39** 2c. red 40 20
O126 **40** 5c. blue 75 80
O127 **41** 7c. brown 60 60
O128 **42** 10c. green 60 50
O129 **43** 20c. orange 60 50
O130 **44** 25c. brown 60 50
O131 **45** 50c. blue 2·75 2·75
O132 **46** 1p. violet 3·00 2·75

1891. Optd **OFICIAL.**
O134 **28** 5c. lilac (No. 133) 75 75

1895. Optd **OFICIAL.**
O164 **38** 1c. blue 85 85
O165 **39** 2c. brown 1·10 1·10
O166 **40** 5c. red 1·50 1·50
O167 **45** 50c. purple 3·00 3·00

1895. Optd **OFICIAL.**
O168 **56** 1c. bistre 20 20
O169 **57** 2c. blue 20 20
O170 **58** 5c. red 5·50 2·25
O171 **59** 7c. green 40 40
O172 **60** 10c. brown 40 40
O173 **61** 20c. black and green 2·25 60
O174 **62** 25c. black and brown 60 60
O175 **63** 50c. black and blue 55 55
O176 **64** 1p. black and brown 2·75 2·75

1897. Nos. 180/2 optd **OFICIAL.**
O194 **67** 1c. black and red 60 60
O195 **68** 5c. black and blue 70 60
O196 – 10c. black and lake 95 75

1897. Optd **OFICIAL.**
O201 **56** 1c. blue 35 30
O202 **57** 2c. purple 60 55
O203 **58** 5c. green 6·25 2·50
O204 **72** 10c. red 2·00 1·10
O205 **61** 20c. black and mauve 7·00 2·00
O206 **62** 25c. blue and red 2·25 1·10
O207 **63** 50c. brown and green 3·00 1·10
O208 **64** 1p. blue and brown 4·50 3·00

1899. Optd **OFICIAL.**
O226 **39** 2c. orange 50 25
O227 **58** 5c. blue 5·50 2·25
O228 **72** 10c. purple 95 95
O243 **43** 20c. blue 3·00 2·25

1901. Optd **OFICIAL.**
O238 **78** 1c. green 20 25
O239 **79** 2c. red 25 25
O240 **80** 5c. blue 25 30
O241 **81** 7c. brown 30 30
O242 **82** 10c. lilac 45 35
O245 **46** 1p. green 3·75 3·00

1904. Optd **OFICIAL.**
O272 **86** 1c. green 20 15
O262 **87** 2c. orange 20 20
O263 **88** 5c. blue 20 20
O275 **89** 10c. lilac 20 15
O276 **90** 20c. green 1·10 70
O277 **91** 25c. bistre 75 35

1907. Optd **OFICIAL.**
O273 **96** 5c. blue 20 15
O274 7c. brown 20 15
O278 50c. red 45 40

1910. Optd **OFICIAL 1910.**
O288 **79** 2c. red 3·75 2·25
O289 **80** 5c. blue 2·25 2·00
O290 **82** 10c. lilac 1·10 70
O291 **43** 20c. green 1·10 70
O292 **44** 25c. brown 2·00 1·40
O293 **96** 50c. red 2·50 1·40

O 110

1911.
O307 **O 110** 2c. brown 25 25
O308 5c. blue 25 20
O309 8c. slate 25 20
O310 20c. brown 40 30
O311 23c. red 60 40
O312 50c. orange 75 45
O313 1p. red 2·00 70

1915. Optd **Oficial.**
O340 **107** 2c. pink 40 45
O341 5c. blue 40 45
O342 8c. blue 40 45
O343 20c. brown 85 35
O344 **108** 23c. blue 8·00 4·00
O345 50c. orange 13·00 4·00
O346 1p. red 11·50 4·00

1919. Optd **Oficial.**
O365 **115** 2c. grey and red 60 30
O366 5c. grey and blue 70 25
O367 8c. brown and blue 70 25
O368 20c. grey and brown 1·40 45
O369 23c. brown and green 1·40 45
O370 50c. blue and brown 2·00 95
O371 1p. blue and red 5·00 1·50

1924. Optd **OFICIAL** in frame. (a) Perf.
O439 **128** 2c. mauve 75 30
O440 5c. blue 75 30
O593 8c. red 1·75 45
O594 10c. green 2·50 45
O441 12c. blue 45 30
O442 20c. brown 70 45
O443 36c. green 1·75 1·40
O444 50c. orange 3·75 2·75
O445 1p. red 6·50 5·00
O446 2p. green 12·00 9·25

(b) Imperf.

O499	128	2c. mauve	70	10
O500		5c. blue	70	20
O501		8c. red	70	25
O502		12c. blue	1·10	25
O503		20c. brown	1·75	45
O504		36c. pink	3·75	70

PARCEL POST STAMPS

P 123 P 144

1922. (a) Inscr "EXTERIOR".

P391	P 123	5c. green on buff	20	10
P516		5c. black on yellow	30	10
P392		10c. green on blue	35	10
P517		10c. black on blue	40	10
P393		20c. green on rose	1·10	50
P518		20c. black on pink	85	15
P394		30c. green on green	1·10	20
P395		50c. green on blue	2·00	30
P396		1p. green on orange	2·75	70

(b) Inscr "INTERIOR".

P397	P 123	5c. green on buff	25	10
P512		5c. black on yellow	30	10
P398		10c. green on blue	25	10
P513		10c. black on blue	35	10
P399		20c. green on pink	50	25
P514		20c. black on pink	45	15
P400		30c. green on green	85	25
P515		30c. black on green	85	25
P401		50c. green on blue	1·10	30
P402		1p. green on orange	3·00	60

1927.

P522	P 144	1c. blue	10	10
P606		1c. violet	10	10
P523		2c. green	10	10
P524		4c. violet	15	10
P609a		5c. red	15	10
P526		10c. brown	30	10
P527		20c. orange	40	20

P 152 P 155 P 177 Sea and Rail Transport

1928.

P587	P 152	5c. black on yellow	10	10
P588		10c. black on blue	15	10
P589		20c. black on red	35	10
P590		30c. black on green	55	10

1929. Agricultural Parcels.

P610	P 155	10c. orange	30	20
P611		15c. blue	30	20
P612		20c. brown	45	30
P613		25c. red	50	35
P614		50c. grey	95	45
P615		75c. violet	3·75	3·75
P616		1p. olive	2·75	1·40

1938.

P 971	P 177	5c. orange	10	35
P 801		10c. red	65	40
P 972		10c. purple	1·00	65
P1066		10c. green	30	40
P 973		20c. red	65	55
P1067		20c. blue	55	40
P 974		30c. blue	85	45
P1068		30c. purple	35	40
P1069		50c. green	50	50
P 805		1p. red	4·00	2·75
P 975		1p. blue	3·00	2·50
P1070		1p. green	1·40	1·50

P 188 P 204 University

1943.

P876	P 188	1c. red	10	10
P877		2c. green	10	10

1944. Optd ANO 1943.

P882	P 155	10c. orange	20	10
P883		15c. blue	20	20
P884		20c. brown	30	20
P885		25c. red	50	30
P886		50c. grey	70	50
P887		75c. violet	1·40	95
P888		1p. olive	1·75	1·40

1945.

P 909	A	1c. green	10	10
P 999	P 204	1c. red	10	10
P 910		2c. violet	10	10
P1000	A	2c. blue	10	10
P1047	B	5c. grey	35	10
P1045		5c. brown	10	10
P1001	A	10c. turqoise	10	10
P1002		10c. olive	10	10
P1048	C	20c. yellow	10	10
P1049		20c. brown	15	10
P1046	D	1p. blue	4·50	4·50
P1290		1p. brown	10	10

DESIGNS—HORIZ: A, Bank. VERT: B, Customs House; C. Solis Theatre; D. Montevideo Railway Station.

P 211 Customs House P 212 Mail Coach (Guillermo Rodriguez)

1946.

P934	P 211	5c. blue and brown	15	10

1946.

P935	P 212	5p. brown and red	7·00	2·25

1946. Armorial type as T 187 obliterated by arrow-head device. (a) Optd **IMPUESTO** and **ENCOMIENDAS**.

P936		1c. mauve	10	10
P937		2c. brown	10	10
P938		5c. blue	10	10

(b) Optd **ENCOMIENDAS** only.

P939		1p. blue	75	20
P940		5p. red	2·50	95

1957. No. P1047 surch **$ 0.30**.

P1064		30c. on 5c. grey	20	10

P 263 National Printing Works

1960.

P1127	P 263	30c. green	10	10

1965. Surch with caduceus and **$ 5.00 ENCOMIENDAS**.

P1268	217	5p. on 84c. orange	30	15

1966. No. 1092 surch with caduceus and **ENCOMIENDAS 1.00 PESO**.

P1289	254	1p. on 38c. black	10	10

P 355 Sud Aviation Caravelle and Motor-coach

1969.

P1397	P 355	10p. black, red & grn	15	10
P1398	–	20p. yellow, blk & bl	30	20

DESIGN: 20p. Side views of Sud Aviation Caravelle and motor-coach.

1971. No. 1121 surch **Encomiendas $ 0.60**.

P1448	261	60c. on 1p.+10c. violet and orange	45	30

1971. No. 1380 surch **IMPUESTOS A ENCOMIENDAS $0.60** and diesel locomotive.

P1472		60c. on 6p. black and green	30	25

1972. Nos. 1401/2 surch **$1 IMPUESTO A ENCOMIENDAS** and caduceus.

P1507	358	1p. on 6p. black, red and blue	40	40
P1508	–	1p. on 6p. black, red and blue	40	40

P 460 Parcels and Arrows

1974.

P1555	P 460	75p. multicoloured	15	10

P 461 Mail-van

1974. Old-time Mail Transport.

P1556	P 461	100p. multicoloured	30	20
P1557	–	150p. multicoloured	1·60	1·90
P1558	–	300p. black, bl & orge	75	50
P1559	–	500p. multicoloured	1·25	70

DESIGNS: 150p. Steam locomotive; 300p. Paddle-steamer; 500p. Monoplane.

POSTAGE DUE STAMPS

D 84

1902.

D795	D 84	1c. green	10	10
D405		2c. red	25	15
D796		2c. brown	10	10
D491		3c. brown	35	25
D797		3c. red	10	10
D798		4c. violet	10	10
D799		5c. blue	10	10
D746		5c. red	35	20
D494		6c. brown	40	30
D800		8c. red	15	10
D249		10c. blue	45	35
D409a		10c. green	30	15
D250		20c. orange	85	45

1904. Surch **PROVISORIO UN cent'mo.**

D267	D 84	1c. on 10c. blue	45	45

UZBEKISTAN Pt. 10

Formerly a constituent republic of the Soviet Union, Uzbekistan became independent in 1991.

1992. 100 kopeks = 1 rouble.
1994. (June) Sum (temporary coupon currency).
1994. (Sept) 100 tyin = 1 sum.

1 Princess Nadira (from portrait by Sh. Khasanov) 2 "Melitaea acreina" (butterfly)

1992. Birth Bicentenary of Princess Nadira (poetess).

1	1	20k. multicoloured	10	10

1992. Nature Protection.

2	2	1r. multicoloured	15	10

3 National Flag and Kukeldash Mosque, Tashkent

1992. 1st Anniv of Independence.

3	3	1r. multicoloured	10	10

4 Kutlug-Murad-inak Mosque, Khiva

1992. Uzbek Architecture.

4	4	50k. multicoloured	10	10

5 Mosque, Registan Square, Samarkand

1992. Award of Aga Khan Prize for Architecture to Samarkand.

5	5	10r. multicoloured	15	10

6 Copper Water Pot, Kokand, and Sculptured Relief

1992. Uzbek Handicrafts.

6	6	50k. multicoloured	10	10

7 Plate-tailed Gecko (8)

1993. Animals. Multicoloured.

7	1r. Type **7**	10	10
8	2r. Cobra	10	10
9	2r. Muskrat (vert)	10	10
10	3r. Osprey (vert)	20	20
11	5r. Penduline tit (vert)	25	25
12	10r. Forest dormouse (vert)	20	10
13	15r. Desert monitor	30	15

1993. Stamps of Russia surch as T **8**.

15	2r. on 1k. brown (No. 5940)	30	10
16	8r. on 4k. red (No. 4672)	40	20
17	15r. on 2k. mauve (No. 4670)	1·50	1·00
18	15r. on 2k. brown (No. 6073)	1·50	1·00
19	15r. on 3k. green (No. 5941)	1·50	1·00
20	15r. on 4k. red (No. 4672)	1·50	1·00
21	15r. on 4k. blue (No. 6075)	1·50	1·00
22	15r. on 5k. red (No. 6076)	1·50	1·00
23	15r. on 6k. blue (No. 4673)	1·50	1·00
24	15r. on 7k. blue (No. 6077)	1·50	1·00
25	15r. on 10k. brown (No. 6078)	1·50	1·00
26	15r. on 15k. blue (No. 6081)	1·50	1·00
27	20r. on 4k. red (No. 4672)	80	40
28	30r. on 3k. red (No. 4671)	35	20
29	100r. on 1k. green (No. 4533)	60	30
30	500r. on 1k. green (No. 4533)	1·40	80

9 Arms and Flag 10 "Colchicum kesselringii"

1993.

31	9	8r. multicoloured	10	10
32		15r. multicoloured	15	10
33		50r. mult (19 × 27 mm)	40	20
34		100r. multicoloured	80	40

1993. Flowers. Multicoloured.

35	20r. Type **10**	15	10
36	20r. "Dianthus uzbekistanicus"	15	10
37	25r. "Crocus alatavicus"	20	10
38	25r. "Salvia bucharica"	20	10
39	30r. "Tulipa kaufmanniana"	25	15
40	30r. "Tulipa greigii"	25	15

12 Arms 13 Bakhouddin Nakshband Mosque, Bukhara

1994.

43	12	75s. red	10	10

See also Nos. 58/60 and 103/7. For a similar design inscr "O'ZBEKISTON" see Nos. 160/5.

1994. 675th Birth Anniv of Sheikh Bakhouddin Nakshband.

44	13	100s. multicoloured	15	10

14 Statue of Timur, Tashkent
15 Ulugh Beg Mosque, Samarkand

1994.
45 **14** 20t. multicoloured 10 10

1994. 600th Birth Anniv of Ulugh Beg (central Asian ruler).
46 30t. Type **15** 15 10
47 35t. Ulugh Beg Mosque, Bukhara 20 10
48 40t. Astronomical equipment 25 15
49 45t. Statue, Tashkent 30 15

ЎЗБЕКИСТОН 200 сўм (16)
ЎЗБЕКИСТОН 2·00 (17)

1995. Stamps of Russia surch. (a) With T **16** in coupon currency.
51 200s. on 2k. brown (No. 6073) 2·10 1·00
52 200s. on 2k. brown (imperf) (No. 6073) 75 35
53 200s. on 4k. blue (No. 6075) 75 35
54 200s. on 5k. blue (No. 5061) 75 35
55 200s. on 15k. blue (No. 6081) 75 35

(b) With T 17 in permanent currency.
56 2s. on 1k. green (No. 4533) . . 75 75
57 2s. on 3k. turquoise (No. 5941) 35 35

1995. As T **12** but value expressed as "1.00" etc.
(a) Size 14 × 22 mm.
58 1s. green 10 10

(b) Size 22 × 33 mm.
59 3s. red 25 15
60 6s. blue 35 20

19 Markhor

1995. Endangered Species. The Markhor. Mult.
62 6s. Type **19** 35 20
63 10s. Three markhors on rocks 60 30
64 10s. Head 60 30
65 15s. Lying down 90 45

20 "The Fool"
22 Gur Amir Mausoleum, Samarkand

21 Player and Emblem

1995. Folk Tales. Multicoloured.
66 6s. Type **20** 40 40
67 10s. "The Golden Melon" . . 65 35
68 10s. Man and white stork on nest ("Are you Stupid?") . . 65 35
69 10s. Woman and monster bird ("Thousand Plaits") 35 35
70 15s. "Story of the Parrot" . . 95 50

1995. 2nd President's Cup Tennis Championships.
71 **21** 10s. multicoloured 65 35

1995. Architecture of the Silk Road (1st series). Multicoloured.
72 6s. Type **22** 30 15
73 10s. Mausoleum, Shakhrisabz 50 30
74 10s. Mosque, Bukhara 50 30
75 15s. Kaltaminor Minaret, Khiva 75 45
See also Nos. 155/8.

24 "Karanasa abramovi"

1995. Butterflies and Moths. Multicoloured.
78 6s. Type **24** 40 20
79 10s. "Colias romanovi" . . . 70 35
80 10s. "Parnassius delphius" . . 70 35
81 10s. "Chasara staudingeri" . . 70 35
82 10s. "Colias wiskotti" 70 35
83 10s. "Neohipparchia fatua" . . 70 35
84 15s. "Parnassius tianschanicus" . . . . . . 1·10 55

25 Lisunov Li-2 Airliner

1995. Aircraft. Multicoloured.
86 6s. Type **25** 40 20
87 10s. Kamov Ka-22 helicopter 70 35
88 10s. Antonov An-8 transport 70 35
89 10s. Antonov An-12 transport 70 35
90 10s. Antonov An-22 Anteus jet transport 70 35
91 10s. Ilyushin Il-76 jet transport 70 35
92 15s. Ilyushin Il-114 . . . . . 1·10 55

26 "Madjnun and Laila"
27 Bactrian Camel

1995. 540th Birth Anniv of Kemal ad-Din Behsad (Persian miniaturist).
94 **26** 15s. multicoloured . . . . . 1·00 1·00

1995. Tashkent Zoo. Multicoloured.
95 6s. Type **27** 40 20
96 10s. Brown bear 70 35
97 10s. Cinereous vulture . . . 70 35
98 10s. Rhesus macaque 70 35
99 10s. Dalmatian pelican . . . 70 35
100 10s. Zebra 70 35
101 15s. African elephant . . . . 1·10 55

1995. As T **12**. Value expressed as "2 SUM" etc.
(a) Size 14 × 22½ mm.
103 **12** 2s. green 15 10
104 6s. green 25 15

(b) Size 20 × 32 mm.
105 **12** 3s. mauve 20 10
106 6s. mauve 40 20
107 15s. blue . . . . 1·00 90

28 Argali

1996. Mammals. Multicoloured.
108 10s. Type **28** 55 25
109 15s. Argali ("Ovis ammon cycloceros") 85 30
110 15s. Argali ("Ovis ammon severtzovi") 85 30
111 15s. Argali ("Ovis ammon karelini") 85 30
112 15s. Red deer ("Cervus elaphus") 85 30
113 15s. Siberian ibex ("Capra sibirica") 85 30
114 20s. Saiga ("Saiga tatarica") 1·10 35

30 Football

1996. Olympic Games, Atlanta, U.S.A. Mult.
117 6s. Type **30** 25 10
118 10s. Show jumping 40 10
119 15s. Boxing 70 25
120 20s. Cycling 85 30

33 Trophy
34 Zhuzhaev

1996. 3rd President's Cup Tennis Championships.
124 **33** 12s. green and grey 65 25

1996. Birth Centenary of Faizulla Zhuzhaev (politician).
125 **34** 15s. black and green . . . 70 25

35 Fitrat
36 Spacecraft

1996. 110th Birth Anniv of Abdurauf Fitrat (writer).
126 **35** 15s. black and brown . . . 70 25

1997. Fantasy Spacecraft. Multicoloured.
127 9s. Type **36** 40 15
128 15s. Spacecraft landing on planet 70 25
129 15s. Spacecraft with external "wings" and "probes" . . 70 25
130 15s. Spacecraft and sun's rays (horiz) 70 25
131 15s. Spacecraft passing sun (horiz) 70 25
132 15s. Spacecraft passing Saturn's rings (horiz) . . . 70 25
133 25s. Two cosmonauts in spacecraft . . . . 1·10 35

37 Bird of Paradise

1997. Folk Tales. Multicoloured.
135 15s. Type **37** 70 25
136 15s. Jinn 70 25
137 20s. Queen looking in mirror 90 30
138 20s. Man riding on monkey 90 30
139 25s. Eagle and deer . . . . . 1·10 30
140 25s. Monster and horse . . . 1·10 30
141 30s. Two men kneeling before throne . . . . 1·40 45

38 Leopard
39 Cho'lpon

1997. The Leopard. Multicoloured.
143 9s. Type **38** 50 20
144 15s. Leopard yawning . . . 80 30
145 15s. Leopard stretching . . . 80 30
146 25s. Leopard on prowl . . . 1·25 45

1997. Birth Centenary of Abdulhamid Sulaymon Cho'lpon.
148 **39** 6s. black and mauve . . . 15 10

40 Trophy

1997. 4th President's Cup Tennis Championships. Each green and blue.
149 6s. Type **40** 30 15
150 6s. Woman player 30 15
151 6s. Camel and ball 30 15

41 Tico

1997. Uz-Daewoo Automobile Works. Mult.
152 9s. Type **41** 60 20
153 12s. Damas 80 30
154 15s. Nexia . . . . 1·00 35

42 Ismail Samani Mausoleum, Bukhara
43 Astronomical Instruments

1997. Architecture of the Silk Road (2nd series). Multicoloured.
155 15s. Type **42** 70 25
156 15s. Citadel, Bukhara (horiz) 70 25
157 15s. Minaret, Khiva 70 25
158 15s. Gateway, Khiva (horiz) 70 25

1998. As T **12** (value expressed as "2-00" etc.) but inscr "O'ZBEKISTON".
160 2s. green 10 10
161 3s. pink 10 10
162 6s. green 20 10
163 12s. green 40 15
164 15s. pink 50 25
165 45s. blue . . . . 1·60 50
For 6s. with face value inscr "6 SO'M" see No. 181.

1998. Ahmad al-Farg'ony (astronomer).
166 **43** 15s. ultramarine, green and blue 50 20

44 Students honouring Imam al-Buchari (miniature)
45 Festival Emblem

1998. Mohammed Ibn Ismail al-Buchari, 810–870 (scholar).
167 **44** 15s. multicoloured 50 20

1998. "Sharq Teronalari" International Music Festival, Samarkand.
168 **45** 15s. multicoloured 50 20

46 Player
47 Berdaq (statue), Nukus

1998. 5th President's Cup International Tennis Championship.
169 **46** 15s. brown, blue and black 40 15

1998. 170th Birth Anniv of Berdaq (poet).
170 **47** 15s. brown and blue . . . 40 15

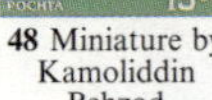

48 Miniature by Kamoliddin Behzod

50 Steam Locomotive (1897–1917)

49 Mother and Baby

1998.
171 **48** 15s. green and red 40 15

1998. Alpomish (folktale). Multicoloured.
172 8s. Type **49** 20 10
173 10s. Rainbow and mountains 25 10
174 15s. Men sitting around fire 35 10
175 15s. Old man and soldier . . 35 10
176 18s. Horsemen 40 15
177 18s. Archers 40 15
178 20s. Blacksmith 45 15
179 20s. Man wrestling lion . . . 45 15
180 25s. Man and woman 55 20
Nos. 172/80 were issued together, se-tenant, forming a composite design.

1999. As No. 162 but value expressed as "6 SO'M".
181 **12** 6s. green 15 10

1999. Locomotives. Multicoloured.
182 18s. Type **50** 20 10
183 18s. Steam locomotive (1931–1935) 20 10
184 28s. Steam locomotive . . . 30 10
185 36s. Steam locomotive . . . 35 15
186 56s. Steam locomotive . . . 60 20
187 56s. VL-22 electric locomotive 60 20
188 69s. TEP-60 electric passenger locomotive 80 30

51 Horse

52 Woman

1999. Horses. Multicoloured.
189 18s. Type **51** 15 10
190 28s. White horse (horiz) . . . 25 10
191 36s. Man on horseback (horiz) 30 10
192 69s. Jockey on racehorse (horiz) 70 25

1999. Badal Qorachi (folktale). Multicoloured.
194 18s. Type **52** 15 10
195 18s. Two horsemen 15 10
196 28s. Horseman 25 10
197 36s. Moon behind demon . . 30 10
198 56s. Man fighting demon . . 55 20
199 56s. Witch with cat 55 20
200 69s. Man and woman 70 25

53 Steppenrunner

1999. Reptiles. Multicoloured.
202 18s. Type **53** 15 10
203 18s. Orsinis' viper ("Vipera ursinii") 15 10
204 28s. Toad-headed agama . . 25 10
205 36s. Halys viper 30 10
206 56s. Steppe agama ("Trapelus sanguinolentus") (vert) . . 55 20
207 56s. Schneider's skink ("Eumeces schneideri") . . 55 20
208 69s. Levantine viper 70 25

54 Emblem and City

55 Ogahiy (poet)

1999. 125th Anniv of Universal Postal Union.
210 **54** 45s. black and green . . . 60 20

1999. Ogahiy Commemoration.
211 **55** 30s. red and green 40 15

VANUATU Pt. 1

The New Hebrides became the Republic of Vanuatu on 30 July 1980.

1980. 100 centimes = 1 franc (Vanuatu).
1981. Vatus.

99 Island of Erromango and Kauri Pine

1980. As Nos. 242/54 of New Hebrides but inscr "VANUATU" and without royal and republican cyphers. (a) Inscr in English.
287E 5f. Type **99** 15 25
288E 10f. Territory map and copra making 15 25
289E 15f. Espiritu Santo and cattle 20 30
290E 20f. Efate and Vila P.O. . . 20 40
291E 25f. Malakula and headdresses 25 40
292E 30f. Aoba, Maewo and pigs' tusks 35 55
293E 35f. Pentecost and land diver 40 60
294E 40f. Tanna and John Frum cross 40 70
295E 50f. Shepherd Is. and outrigger canoe 45 80
296E 70f. Banks Is. and custom dancers . . . . 50 1·75
297E 100f. Ambrym and idols . . 50 80
298E 200f. Aneityum and baskets 60 1·40
299E 500f. Torres Is. and archer fisherman . . . . . . 75 3·00

(b) Inscr in French.
287F 5f. Type **99** 35 15
288F 10f. Territory map and copra making 40 15
289F 15f. Espiritu Santo and cattle 45 25
290F 20f. Efate and Vila P.O. . . 50 30
291F 25f. Malakula and headdresses 55 40
292F 30f. Aoba, Maewo and pigs' tusks 55 55
293F 35f. Pentecost and land diver 60 60
294F 40f. Tanna and John Frum cross 75 60
295F 50f. Shepherd Is. and outrigger canoe 80 80
296F 70f. Banks Is. and custom dancers . . . . 1·00 1·50
297F 100f. Ambrym and idols . . 1·25 1·10
298F 200f. Aneityum and baskets 1·50 1·75
299F 500f. Torres Is. and archer fisherman . . . . . . 2·25 3·50

100 Rotary International

1980. 75th Anniv of Rotary International. Multicoloured. (a) Inscr in English.
300E 10f. Type **100** 10 10
301E 40f. Rotary emblem (vert) 30 30

(b) Inscr in French.
300F 10f. Type **100** 15 15
301F 40f. Rotary emblem (vert) 45 45

101 Kiwanis Emblem and Globe

102 "The Virgin and Child enthroned with Saints and Angels" (Umkreis Michael Pacher)

1980. Kiwanis International (service club), New Zealand District Convention, Port Vila. (a) Inscr in English.
302E **101** 10f. gold, blue and brown 10 20
303E – 40f. green and blue . . . 30 80

(b) Inscr in French.
302F **101** 10f. gold, blue and brown 40 65
303F – 40f. green and blue . . . 85 1·10
DESIGN: 40f. Kiwanis and Convention emblems.

1980. Christmas. Details from Paintings. Mult.
304 10f. Type **102** 10 10
305 15f. "The Virgin and Child with Saints, Angels and Donors" (Hans Memling) 10 10
306 30f. "The Rest on the Flight to Egypt" (Adriaen van der Werff) 20 20

103 Blue-faced Parrot Finch

104 Tribesman with Portrait of Prince Philip

1981. Birds (1st series). Multicoloured.
307 10f. Type **103** 35 25
308 20f. Emerald dove 40 45
309 30f. Golden whistler 45 80
310 40f. Silver-shouldered fruit dove . . . . 50 1·00
See also Nos. 327/30.

1981. 60th Birthday of Prince Philip, Duke of Edinburgh. Multicoloured.
311 15v. Type **104** 10 15
312 25v. Prince Philip in casual dress 15 20
313 35v. Queen and Prince Philip with Princess Anne and Master Peter Phillips . . . 15 25
314 45v. Prince Philip in ceremonial dress 20 35

105 Prince Charles with his Dog, Harvey

106 National Flag and Map of Vanuatu

1981. Royal Wedding. Multicoloured.
315 15v. Wedding bouquet from Vanuatu 10 10
316 45v. Type **105** 20 15
317 75v. Prince Charles and Lady Diana Spencer 35 45

1981. 1st Anniv of Independence.
318 **106** 15v. multicoloured . . . 15 15
319 – 25v. multicoloured . . . 15 15
320 – 45v. yellow and brown . . 20 20
321 – 75v. multicoloured . . . 35 70
DESIGNS—HORIZ: 25v. Vanuatu emblem; 45v. Vanuatu national anthem. VERT: 75v. Vanuatu coat of arms.

107 Three Shepherds

1981. Christmas. Children's Paintings. Mult.
322 15v. Type **107** 10 10
323 25v. Vanuatu girl with lamb (vert) 15 15
324 35v. Angel as butterfly . . . 15 20
325 45v. Boy carrying torch and gifts (vert) 25 30
MS326 133 × 94 mm. Nos. 322/5 80 1·25

108 New Caledonian Myiagra Flycatchers

109 "Flickingeria comata"

1982. Birds (2nd series). Multicoloured.
327 15v. Type **108** 30 20
328 20v. Rainbow lorys 40 30
329 25v. Buff-bellied flycatchers 45 35
330 45v. Collared grey fantails . . 50 65

1982. Orchids. Multicoloured.
331 1v. Type **109** 10 50
332 2v. "Calanthe triplicata" . . 10 50
333 10v. "Dendrobium sladei" . . 15 30
334 15v. "Dendrobium mohlianum" 20 20
335 20v. "Dendrobium macrophyllum" 25 30
336 25v. "Dendrobium purpureum" 30 35
337 30v. "Robiquetia mimus" . . 35 40
338 35v. "Dendrobium mooreanum" (horiz) . . . 50 50
339 45v. "Spathoglottis plicata" (horiz) 55 70
340 50v. "Dendrobium seemannii" (horiz) 60 80
341 75v. "Dendrobium conanthum" (horiz) . . . 95 1·50
342 100v. "Dendrobium macranthum" . . . . . . 1·25 1·50
343 200v. "Coelogyne lamellata" 1·50 2·75
344 500v. "Bulbophyllum longioscapum" . . . . . . 2·50 6·50

110 Scouts round Campfire

1982. 75th Anniv of Boy Scout Movement. Multicoloured.
345 15v. Type **110** 35 20
346 20v. First aid 40 25
347 25v. Constructing tower . . . 40 40
348 45v. Constructing raft . . . 60 70
349 57v. Scout saluting . . . . . 80 1·25

111 Baby Jesus

1982. Christmas. Nativity Scenes. Mult.
350 15v. Type **111** 30 35
351 25v. Mary and Joseph . . . 50 45
352 35v. Shepherds (vert) . . . . 60 1·00
353 45v. Kings bearing gifts (vert) 65 1·40
MS354 132 × 92 mm. As Nos. 350/3 but without yellow borders . . 1·50 2·25

112 "Euploea sylvester"

1983. Butterflies. Multicoloured.
355 15v. Type **112** 65 65
356 15v. "Hypolimnas octocula" . 65 65
357 20v. "Papilio canopus" . . . 80 80
358 20v. "Polyura sacco" 80 80
359 25v. "Luthrodes cleotas" . . 80 80
360 25v. "Danaus pumila" . . . 80 80

113 President Afi George Sokomanu

1983. Commonwealth Day. Multicoloured.
361 15v. Type **113** 15 10
362 20v. Fisherman and liner "Oriana" 20 15
363 25v. Herdsman and cattle . . 25 15
364 75v. World map showing position of Vanuatu with Commonwealth and Vanuatu flags 50 70

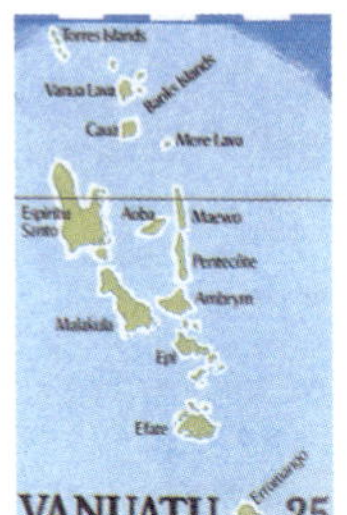

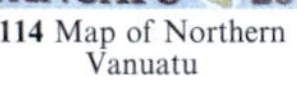

114 Map of Northern Vanuatu
115 Montgolfier Balloon of De Rozier and D'Arlandes, 1783

1983. Economic Zone. Sheet 120 × 120 mm, containing T **114** and similar vert designs. Multicoloured.
MS365 25v. × 6 Yellow-finned tuna; Type **114**; Map of Matthew Island; Map of Hunter Island; Cornet grouper; Skipjack tuna 2·75 2·75

1983. Bicentenary of Manned Flight. Mult.
366 15v. Type **115** 15 15
367 20v. J. A. C. Charles hydrogen balloon (first use of hydrogen, 1783) 25 25
368 25v. Blanchard and Jeffries crossing English Channel, 1785 . . . . 30 30
369 35v. Giffard's steam-powered dirigible airship, 1852 (horiz) 40 40
370 40v. "La France" (airship of Renard and Krebs), 1884 (horiz) 45 45
371 45v. "Graf Zeppelin" (first aerial circumnavigation, 1929) (horiz) 55 55

116 Mail at Bauerfield Airport

1983. World Communications Year. Mult.
372 15v. Type **116** 20 25
373 20v. Switchboard operator 30 35
374 25v. Telex operator 35 40
375 45v. Satellite earth station . . 65 70
MS376 138 × 95 mm. Nos. 372/5 2·00 2·75

117 "Cymatoderma elegans var. lamellatum"
118 Port Vila

1984. Fungi. Multicoloured.
377 15v. Type **117** 60 45
378 25v. "Lignosus rhinocerus" 75 85
379 35v. "Stereum ostrea" (horiz) 1·00 1·25
380 45v. "Ganoderma boninense" 1·25 1·90

1984. 250th Anniv of "Lloyd's List" (newspaper). Multicoloured.
381 15v. Type **118** 20 25
382 20v. "Induna" (container ship) 30 35
383 25v. Air Vanuatu Boeing 737 aircraft 35 40
384 45v. "Brahman Express" (container ship) 65 70

1984. Universal Postal Union Congress, Hamburg. As No. 371 but inscr "UPU CONGRESS HAMBURG" and U.P.U. logo.
385 45v. multicoloured 80 80

119 Charolais

1984. Cattle. Multicoloured.
386 15v. Type **119** 20 25
387 25v. Charolais-afrikander . . 30 40
388 45v. Friesian 50 70
389 75v. Charolais-brahman . . . 90 1·25

120 "Makambo"

1984. "Ausipex" International Stamp Exn, Melbourne. Inter-island Freighters. Multicoloured.
390 25v. Type **120** 60 50
391 45v. "Rockton" 80 90
392 100v. "Waroonga" . . . . . 1·25 3·50
MS393 140 × 70 mm. Nos. 390/2 4·00 5·50

121 Father Christmas in Children's Ward

1984. Christmas. Multicoloured.
394 25v. Type **121** 45 40
395 45v. Nativity play 80 70
396 75v. Father Christmas distributing presents . . . 1·40 1·25

1985. No. 331 surch.
397 5v. on 1v. Type **109** 65 50

123 Ambrym Island Ceremonial Dance
124 Peregrine Falcon diving

1985. Traditional Costumes. Multicoloured.
398 20v. Type **123** 35 35
399 25v. Pentecost Island marriage ceremony 40 40
400 45v. Women's grade ceremony, South West Malakula 75 70
401 75v. Ceremonial dance, South West Malakula . . . . . 1·10 1·25

1985. Birth Bicentenary of John J. Audubon (ornithologist). Peregrine Falcon. Mult.
402 20v. Type **124** 60 35
403 35v. Peregrine falcon in flight 75 50
404 45v. Peregrine falcon perched on branch 90 80
405 100v. "Peregrine Falcon" (John J. Audubon) . . . . 1·60 1·75

125 The Queen Mother with the Queen on her 80th Birthday

1985. Life and Times of Queen Elizabeth the Queen Mother. Multicoloured.
406 5v. Duke and Duchess of York on wedding day, 1923 . . . . 30 70
407 20v. Type **125** 70 45
408 35v. At Ancona, Italy 90 70
409 55v. With Prince Henry at his christening (from photo by Lord Snowdon) . . . . . . 1·10 95

126 "Mala" (patrol boat)

1985. 5th Anniv of Independence and "Expo '85" World Fair, Japan. Multicoloured.
411 35v. Type **126** 45 50
412 45v. Japanese fishing fleet . . 55 70
413 55v. Vanuatu Mobile Force Band 60 85
414 100v. Prime Minister Fr. Walter H. Lini . . . . . . 65 1·75
MS415 116 × 102 mm. Nos. 411/14 2·50 4·25

127 "Youth Activities" (Alain Lagaliu)

1985. Int Youth Year. Children's Paintings. Mult.
416 20v. Type **127** 55 35
417 30v. "Village" (Peter Obed) 65 45
418 50v. "Beach and 'PEACE' Slogan" (Mary Estelle) . . 1·10 75
419 100v. "Youth Activities" (different) (Abel Merani) 1·75 1·50

128 Map of Vanuatu with National and U.N. Flags

1985. 4th Anniv of United Nations Membership.
420 **128** 45v. multicoloured . . . 1·25 70

129 Elizabeth's Nudibranch
130 Scuba Diving

1985. Marine Life (1st series). Sea Slugs. Multicoloured.
421 20v. Type **129** 30 35
422 35v. Tessellated nudibranch (horiz) 45 50
423 55v. "Chromodoris kuniei" (horiz) 75 80
424 100v. "Notodoris minor" . . 1·40 1·50
See also Nos. 442/5 and 519/22.

1986. Tourism. Multicoloured.
425 30v. Type **130** 60 40
426 35v. Yasur volcano, Tanna 75 45
427 55v. Land diving, Pentecost Island 75 70
428 100v. Windsurfing . . . . . 90 1·50

1986. 60th Birthday of Queen Elizabeth II. As T **145a** of St. Helena. Multicoloured.
429 20v. With Prince Charles and Princess Anne, 1951 . . . 15 30
430 35v. Prince William's Christening, 1982 . . . . 20 45
431 45v. In New Hebrides, 1974 25 60
432 55v. On board Royal Yacht "Britannia", Mexico, 1974 30 70
433 100v. At Crown Agents Head Office, London, 1983 . . . 40 1·25

131 Liner S.S. "President Coolidge" leaving San Francisco

1986. "Ameripex '86" International Stamp Exhibition, Chicago. Sinking of S.S. "President Coolidge". Multicoloured.
434 45v. Type **131** . . . . 1·10 60
435 55v. S.S. "President Coolidge" as troopship, 1942 . . . . 1·10 70
436 135v. Map of Espiritu Santo showing site of sinking, 1942 . . . . 2·25 1·75
MS437 80 × 105 mm. Nos. 434/6 4·25 3·00

132 Halley's Comet and Vanuatu Statue

1986. Appearance of Halley's Comet. Mult.
438 30v. Type **132** 90 50
439 45v. Family watching Comet 1·25 1·00
440 55v. Comet passing Earth . . 1·40 1·25
441 100v. Edmond Halley . . . . 2·00 3·25

133 Daisy Coral

1986. Marine Life (2nd series). Corals. Mult.
442 20v. Type **133** 65 40
443 45v. Organ pipe coral . . . . 1·00 75
444 55v. Sea fan . . . . 1·25 1·10
445 135v. Soft coral . . . . . . 2·50 3·50

134 Children of Different Races

1986. Christmas. Int Peace Year. Mult.
446 30v. Type **134** . . . . 1·00 50
447 45v. Church and boy praying 1·40 85
448 55v. U.N. discussion and Headquarters Building, New York . . . . 1·60 1·40
449 135v. People of different races at work . . . . . . 3·00 5·00

135 Datsun "240Z" (1969)

1987. Motor Vehicles. Multicoloured.
450 20v. Type **135** 30 30
451 45v. Ford "Model A" (1927) 60 60
452 55v. Unic lorry (1924–5) . . 70 70
453 135v. Citroen "DS19" (1975) 1·60 2·25

1987. Hurricane Relief Fund. No. 332, already surch, and Nos. 429/33 all surch **Hurricane Relief Fund** and premium.
454 20v.+10v. on 2v. "Calanthe triplicata" . . . . 55 1·00
455 20v.+10v. Princess Elizabeth with Prince Charles and Princess Anne, 1951 . . . 55 1·00
456 35v.+15v. Prince William's Christening, 1982 . . . . 80 1·40
457 45v.+20v. Queen in New Hebrides, 1974 . . . . . . 1·00 1·75
458 55v.+25v. Queen on board Royal Yacht "Britannia", Mexico, 1974 . . . . . . 1·75 2·00
459 100v.+50v. Queen at Crown Agents Head Office, London, 1983 . . . . . . 1·90 3·50
The surcharge on No. 454 also includes the word "Surcharge".

137 Young Coconut Plants

1987. 25th Anniv of I.R.H.O. Coconut Research Station. Multicoloured.
460 35v. Type **137** 40 45
461 45v. Coconut flower and fronds 50 60
462 100v. Coconuts . . . . . . 85 1·40
463 135v. Research station . . . 1·10 2·00
The inscriptions on Nos. 462/3 are in French.

138 Spotted Hawkfish

1987. Fishes. Multicoloured.

464	1v. Type **138**	10	10
465	5v. Moorish idol	15	10
466	10v. Black-saddled pufferfish	15	10
467	15v. Dusky anemonefish	20	20
468	20v. Striped surgeonfish	30	25
469	30v. Six-barred wrasse	40	35
470	35v. Yellow-striped anthias ("Purple queenfish")	45	40
471	40v. Squirrelfish	50	45
472	45v. Clown triggerfish	60	55
473	50v. Dragon wrasse	65	65
474	55v. Regal angelfish	70	70
475	65v. Lionfish	80	80
476	100v. Freckled hawkfish	1·25	1·40
477	300v. Undulate triggerfish	3·00	4·00
478	500v. Saddled butterflyfish	4·00	6·00

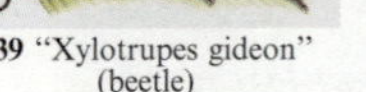
139 "Xylotrupes gideon" (beetle)

140 "Away in a Manger"

1987. Insects. Multicoloured.

479	45v. Type **139**	55	60
480	55v. "Phyllodes imperialis" (moth)	65	70
481	65v. "Cyphogastra sp." (beetle)	75	85
482	100v. "Othreis fullonia" (moth)	1·10	1·75

1987. Christmas. Christmas Carols. Mult.

483	20v. Type **140**	60	30
484	45v. "Once in Royal David's City"	95	65
485	55v. "While Shepherds watched their Flocks"	1·10	90
486	65v. "We Three Kings of Orient Are"	1·25	1·00

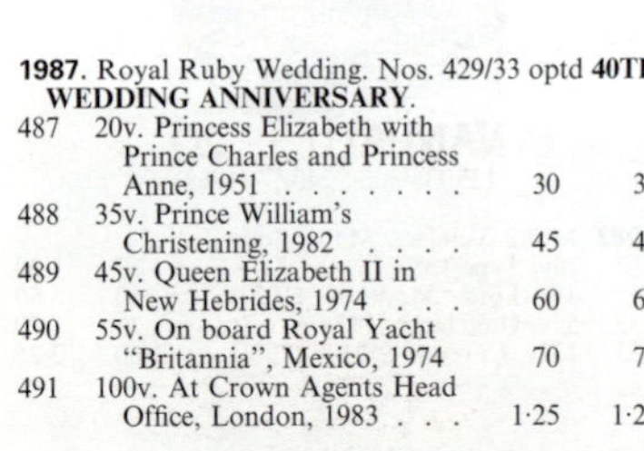

1987. Royal Ruby Wedding. Nos. 429/33 optd **40TH WEDDING ANNIVERSARY**.

487	20v. Princess Elizabeth with Prince Charles and Princess Anne, 1951	30	30
488	35v. Prince William's Christening, 1982	45	45
489	45v. Queen Elizabeth II in New Hebrides, 1974	60	60
490	55v. On board Royal Yacht "Britannia", Mexico, 1974	70	70
491	100v. At Crown Agents Head Office, London, 1983	1·25	1·25

141 Dugong Cow and Calf

1988. Endangered Species. Dugong. Multicoloured.

492	5v. Type **141**	90	35
493	10v. Dugong underwater	1·40	35
494	20v. Two dugongs surfacing to breathe	1·90	1·00
495	45v. Four dugongs swimming	3·25	2·50

142 "Tambo"

1988. Bicentenary of Australian Settlement. Freighters. Multicoloured.

496	20v. Type **142**	20	25
497	45v. "Induna"	50	55
498	55v. "Morinda"	60	65
499	65v. "Marsina"	70	75

143 Captain James Cook

144 Boxer in training

1988. "Sydpex '88" National Stamp Exhibition, Sydney.

500 **143**	45v. black and red	75	75

1988. "Expo '88" World Fair, Brisbane. Sheet 100 × 80 mm, containing designs as Nos. 427/8, but with addition of Australian Bicentenary symbol and imprint date. Multicoloured.

MS501	55v. Land diving, Pentecost Island; 100v. Windsurfing	3·00	3·25

1988. Olympic Games, Seoul. Multicoloured.

502	20v. Type **144**	20	25
503	45v. Athletics	50	55
504	55v. Signing Olympic agreement	60	65
505	65v. Soccer	70	75
MS506	54 × 66 mm. 150v. Tennis	3·00	2·40

1988. 300th Anniv of Lloyd's of London. As T **152a** of St. Helena. Multicoloured.

507	20v. Interior of new Lloyd's Building, 1988	30	25
508	55v. "Shirrabank" (freighter) (horiz)	1·25	65
509	65v. "Adela" (ferry) (horiz)	1·40	75
510	145v. "General Slocum" (excursion paddle-steamer) on fire, New York, 1904	2·25	2·50

145 Agricultural Crops

1988. F.A.O. Multicoloured.

511	45v. Type **145**	40	55
512	55v. Fisherman with catch (vert)	45	65
513	65v. Livestock on smallholding (vert)	50	75
514	120v. Market women with produce	60	1·40

146 Virgin and Child ("Silent Night")

1988. Christmas. Carols. Multicoloured.

515	20v. Type **146**	25	25
516	45v. Angels ("Angels from the Realms of Glory")	45	55
517	65v. Shepherd boy with lamb ("O Come all ye Faithful")	55	75
518	155v. Baby ("In that Poor Stable how Charming Jesus Lies")	1·50	1·90

147 "Periclimenes brevicarpalis"

1989. Marine Life (3rd series). Shrimps. Mult.

519	20v. Type **147**	50	25
520	45v. "Lysmata grabhami"	80	55
521	65v. "Rhynchocinetes sp."	95	75
522	150v. "Stenopus hispidus"	2·25	2·50

148 Consolidated Catalina Flying Boat

1989. Economic and Social Commission for Asia and the Pacific. Aircraft.

523 **148**	20v. black and blue	85	30
524 –	45v. black and green	1·25	65
525 –	55v. black and yellow	1·50	80
526 –	200v. black and red	4·25	3·00

DESIGNS: 45v. Douglas DC-3; 55v. Embraer EMB-110 Bandeirante; 200v. Boeing 737-300.

149 Porte de Versailles Hall No. 1

1989. "Philexfrance '89" International Stamp Exhibition, Paris. Multicoloured.

527	100v. Type **149**	2·25	1·50
528	100v. Eiffel Tower	2·25	1·50
MS529	115 × 101 mm. 100v. black, grey and scarlet (Revolt of French troops, Nancy, 1790 (42 × 28 mm))	1·40	1·50

Nos. 527/8 were printed together, se-tenant, forming a composite design.

1989. 20th Anniv of First Manned Landing on Moon. As T **50a** of St. Kitts. Multicoloured.

530	45v. Command module seen from lunar module	1·50	80
531	55v. Crew of "Apollo 17" (30 × 30 mm)	1·50	90
532	65v. "Apollo 17" emblem (30 × 30 mm)	1·60	1·00
533	120v. Launch of "Apollo 17"	2·75	3·50
MS534	99 × 82 mm. 100v. Recovery of "Apollo 11"	1·75	1·75

1989. "Melbourne Stampshow '89". No. 332 surch **100** and Stampshow emblem.

535	100v. on 2v. "Calanthe triplicata"	3·50	4·25

151 New Hebrides 1978 "Concorde" 30f. (French inscr) Stamp

1989. "World Stamp Expo '89" International Stamp Exhibition, Washington. Multicoloured.

536	65v. Type **151**	3·25	2·50
MS537	105 × 100 mm. 65v. New Hebrides 1978 Concorde 10f. (English inscr) stamp; 100v. White House, Washington	7·50	7·50

152 "Alocasia macrorrhiza"

153 Kava (national plant)

1990. Flora. Multicoloured.

538	45v. Type **152**	60	55
539	55v. "Acacia spirorbis"	70	70
540	65v. "Metrosideros collina"	80	80
541	145v. "Hoya australis"	1·75	2·50

1990. "Stamp World London 90" International Stamp Exhibition. Multicoloured.

542	45v. Type **153**	80	55
543	65v. Luganville Post Office	1·00	95
544	100v. Embraer EMB-110 Bandeirante mail plane and sailing packet	1·90	2·00
545	200v. Penny Black and Vanuatu 1980 10f. definitive	3·00	3·75
MS546	110 × 70 mm. 150v. New Hebrides 1974 New Post Office t%ete-b%eche pair with first day postmark	6·50	6·50

154 National Council of Women Logo

1990. 10th Anniv of Independence.

547 **154**	25v. black and blue	50	40
548 –	50v. multicoloured	75	80
549 –	55v. purple, black and buff	80	80
550 –	65v. multicoloured	1·25	90
551 –	80v. multicoloured	1·25	1·40
MS552	109 × 82 mm. 150v. multicoloured	5·00	6·50

DESIGNS: 50v. President Frederick Kalomuana Timakata; 55v. Preamble to the Constitution; 65v. Vanuaaku Pati party flag; 80v. Reserve Bank of Vanuatu; 150v. Prime Minister Fr. Walter Lini taking oath.

No. **MS**552 also commemorates the South Pacific Forum, Port Vila, 1990.

155 General De Gaulle at Bayeux, 1944

1990. Birth Centenary of General Charles de Gaulle (French statesman). Multicoloured.

553	20v. Type **155**	3·25	4·25
554	25v. Generals De Lattre de Tassigny, De Gaulle, Devers and Patch in Alsace, 1945	3·25	4·25
555	30v. De Gaulle as President of the French Republic	90	1·00
556	45v. De Gaulle at Biggin Hill, 1942	95	1·10
557	55v. Roosevelt, De Gaulle and Churchill, Casablanca, 1943	1·00	1·10
558	65v. General De Gaulle and Liberation of Paris, 1944	1·10	1·25

156 Angel facing Right

157 "Parthenos sylvia"

1990. Christmas. Multicoloured.

559	25v. Type **156**	45	65
560	50v. Shepherds	70	1·00
561	65v. Nativity	80	1·10
562	70v. Three Kings	85	1·25
563	80v. Angel facing left	85	1·40

Nos. 559/63 were printed together, se-tenant, forming a composite design.

1991. Butterflies. Multicoloured.

564	25v. Type **157**	55	30
565	55v. "Euploea leucostictus"	95	60
566	80v. "Lampides boeticus"	1·40	1·25
567	150v. "Danaus plexippus"	2·25	3·25

158 Dance Troupe from South-west Malakula

160 White-collared Kingfisher

1991. 2nd National Art Festival, Luganville. Multicoloured.

568	25v. Type **158**	35	30
569	65v. Women weavers and baskets	85	85
570	80v. Woodcarver and carved animals, masks, dish and ceremonial figures	1·10	1·25
571	150v. Musicians playing bamboo flute, youtatau and pan pipes	1·90	2·50

1991. Nos. 332/4 and 337 surch.

572	20v. on 2v. "Calanthe triplicata"	50	50
573	60v. on 10v. "Dendrobium sladei"	1·25	1·60
574	70v. on 15v. "Dendrobium mohlianum"	1·40	1·75
575	80v. on 30v. "Robiquetia mimus"	1·40	1·75

See also No. 622.

1991. 65th Birthday of Queen Elizabeth II and 70th Birthday of Prince Philip. As T **165a** of St. Helena. Multicoloured.

576	65v. Queen Elizabeth II	1·00	1·25
577	70v. Prince Philip	1·00	1·25

1991. "Phila Nippon '91" International Stamp Exhibition, Tokyo. Birds. Multicoloured.

578	50v. Type **160**	65	70
579	55v. Palm lorikeet ("Green Palm Lorikeet")	70	75
580	80v. Scarlet robin	95	1·10
581	100v. Pacific swallow	1·10	1·75
MS582	75 × 56 mm. 150v. Reef heron	2·25	3·00

161 Group of Islanders

1991. World AIDS Day. Multicoloured.
583 25v. Type **161** 55 30
584 65v. Caring for AIDS victim 1·00 85
585 80v. AIDS shark . . . . . . 1·25 1·50
586 150v. Children's playground 2·25 3·00

1992. 40th Anniv of Queen Elizabeth II's Accession. As T **168a** of St. Helena. Mult.
587 20v. Reserve Bank of Vanuatu Building, Port Vila 30 30
588 25v. Port Vila 40 30
589 60v. Mural, Parliament House 85 75
590 65v. Three portraits of Queen Elizabeth 90 80
591 70v. Queen Elizabeth II . . . 95 1·50

162 Grumman F4F Wildcat

1992. 50th Anniv of Outbreak of the Pacific War (1st issue). Multicoloured.
592 50v. Type **162** . . . . . . 2·25 1·25
593 55v. Douglas SBD-3 Dauntless . . . . 2·25 1·25
594 65v. Consolidated PBY-5A Catalina . . . . 2·50 1·50
595 80v. U.S.S. "Hornet" (aircraft carrier) . . . . . 3·25 3·25
MS596 94 × 62 mm. 200v. Vought-Sikorsky OS-2-3 Kingfisher over Port Vila . . . . 8·50 8·50
See also Nos. 623/7.

163 Meteorological Station, Port Vila

165 Breast-feeding

164 Vanuatu National Football Team

1992. 10th Anniv of Vanuatu's Membership of World Meteorological Organization. Mult.
597 25v. Type **163** 40 30
598 60v. Satellite picture of tropical cyclone 80 80
599 80v. Weather chart of Pacific showing cyclone . . . . . 1·00 1·25
600 105v. Radio Vanuatu broadcasting cyclone warning . . . . 1·25 1·75

1992. Vanuatu's Participation in Melanesian Football Cup and Olympic Games, Barcelona. Multicoloured.
601 20v. Type **164** 65 40
602 65v. Melanesian Cup Final, 1990 . . . . 1·50 1·25
603 70v. Baptiste Firiam (800 m) 1·75 1·50
604 80v. Mary Estelle Kapalu (400, 400 hurdles, and 800 m) . . . . 1·90 2·00

1992. World Food Day. Each brown and green.
605 20v. Type **165** 30 25
606 70v. Central Hospital, Port Vila 95 90
607 80v. Children eating . . . . 1·10 1·00
608 150v. Nutritious food . . . . 1·75 2·50

166 Leatherback Turtle

167 "Hibiscus rosa-sinensis" "Agnes Goult"

1992. Turtles. Multicoloured.
609 55v. Type **166** . . . . 1·25 1·10
610 65v. Loggerhead turtle laying eggs . . . . 1·40 1·25
611 70v. Hawksbill turtle swimming . . . . 1·60 1·40
612 80v. Green turtle under water 2·25 2·00
MS613 81 × 96 mm. 200v. Green turtle hatching on beach . . . 3·75 4·00

1993. Hibiscus Flowers (1st series). Multicoloured.
614 25v. Type **167** 30 30
615 55v. "Hibiscus tiliaceus" . . 70 70
616 80v. "Hibiscus rosa-sinensis linnaeus" . . . . 95 1·00
617 150v. "Hibiscus rosa-sinensis" "Rose of China" . . . . . 1·60 2·50
See also Nos. 682/5 and 736/9.

1993. 14th World Orchid Conference, Glasgow. Nos. 339 and 341/3 surch **WORLD ORCHID CONFERENCE 1993** and value.
618 40v. on 45v. "Spathoglottis plicata" (horiz) 50 50
619 55v. on 75v. "Dendrobium conanthum" (horiz) . . . 70 75
620 65v. on 100v. "Dendrobium macranthum" 75 80
621 150v. on 200v. "Coelogyne lamellata" . . . . 1·60 4·25

1993. No. 338 surch **20**.
622 20v. on 35v. "Dendrobium mooreanum" . . . . . . 4·75 70

1993. 50th Anniv of Outbreak of the Pacific War (2nd issue). As T **162**. Multicoloured.
623 20v. Grumman F6F Hellcat 1·25 80
624 55v. Lockheed P-38F Lightning . . . . 2·25 1·75
625 65v. Grumman TBF Avenger 2·25 1·75
626 80v. U.S.S. "Essex" (aircraft carrier) . . . . 2·50 3·00
MS627 82 × 58 mm. 200v. Douglas C-47 Skytrain . . . . 7·50 7·50

170 Port Vila and Iririki Island

1993. Local Scenery. Multicoloured.
628 5v. Type **170** 20 30
629 10v. Yachts and Iririki Island 30 30
630 15v. Court House, Port Vila 40 40
631 20v. Two girls, Pentecost Island 40 40
632 25v. Women dancers, Tanna Island 45 30
633 30v. Market, Port Vila . . . 50 35
634 45v. Man in canoe, Erakor Island (vert) 60 45
635 50v. Coconut trees, Champagne Beach 60 50
636 55v. Coconut trees, North Efate Islands 70 55
637 60v. Underwater shoal of fishes, Banks Group . . . 75 60
638 70v. Sea fan, Tongoa Island (vert) . . . . 1·00 90
639 75v. Santo Island . . . . . 1·00 95
640 80v. Sunset, Port Vila harbour (vert) . . . . . . 1·25 1·00
641 100v. Mele Waterfall (vert) 1·75 1·25
642 300v. Yasur Volcano, Tanna Island (vert) . . . . 3·50 5·00
643 500v. Aerial view of Erakor Island . . . . 5·00 7·50
For miniature sheet containing Nos. 629, 636/7 and 639 see **MS**673.

171 Commercial Trochus

1993. Shells (1st series). Multicoloured.
644 55v. Type **171** . . . . 1·10 85
645 65v. Camp pitar venus . . . 1·25 95
646 80v. Tapestry turban . . . . 1·60 1·75
647 150v. Trapezium horse conch 2·75 3·75
See also Nos. 665/8 and 692/5.

172 "St. Joseph the Carpenter" (detail) (De la Tour)

1993. Christmas. Bicentenary of the Louvre, Paris. Religious Paintings by Georges de la Tour. Multicoloured.
648 25v. Type **172** 45 30
649 55v. "Holy Child" (detail) . . 80 65
650 80v. "Adoration of the Shepherds" (detail) . . . . 1·00 1·00
651 150v. "Adoration of the Shepherds" (different detail) . . . . 1·75 2·50

1993. South Pacific Mini Games, Port Vila. Nos. 602, 604, 631 and 633 surch **SOUTH PACIFIC MINI GAMES PORT VILA DECEMBER 1993** and value.
652 15v. on 20v. Two girls, Pentecost Island 30 30
653 25v. on 30v. Market, Port Vila 45 40
654 55v. on 65v. Melanesian Cup Final, 1990 . . . . . . 85 75
655 70v. on 80v. Mary Estelle Kapalu (400, 400 hurdles and 800 m) . . . . 95 1·50

174 Charity Horse Race and Kiwanis Emblem

175 Silhouetted Family

1994. "Hong Kong '94" International Stamp Exhibition. Charitable Organizations. Mult.
656 25v. Type **174** 50 30
657 60v. Twin Otter airplane and Lions Club emblem (horiz) 80 75
658 75v. Mosquito and Rotary International emblem . . . 90 1·00
659 150v. Blood donor service ambulance and Red Cross emblem (horiz) . . . . . . 1·60 2·50
MS660 126 × 96 mm. 200v. Charity emblems (horiz) . . . . 2·00 3·00

1994. International Year of the Family.
661 **175** 25v. brown and violet . . 35 30
662 60v. green and red . . 70 75
663 90v. brown and green . . 1·00 1·10
664 150v. violet and brown . . 1·60 2·25

1994. Shells (2nd series). As T **171**. Multicoloured.
665 60v. Eyed cowrie . . . . . . 2·00 1·00
666 70v. Marble cone . . . . . 2·00 1·25
667 85v. Chiragra spider conch 2·25 2·25
668 155v. Adusta murex . . . . 3·50 5·00

176 Traditional Sculpture and Hut

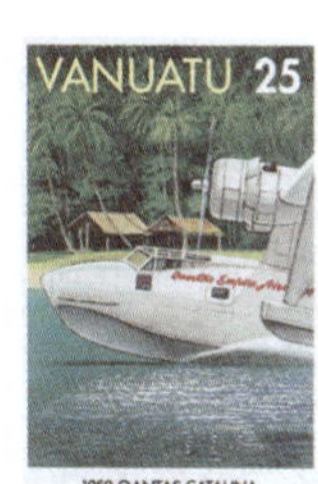

178 Consolidated PBY-5 Catalina Flying Boat

177 Pink Anemonefish

1994. Tourism. Multicoloured.
669 25v. Type **176** 70 80
670 75v. Outrigger canoe and inflatable dinghy . . . . . 1·40 1·50
671 90v. Yachts, airliner and parrot . . . . 1·75 1·90
672 200v. Helicopter and local woman with fruit . . . . 2·75 3·00
Nos. 669/72 were printed together, se-tenant, forming a composite design.

1994. "Philakorea '94" International Stamp Exhibition. Sheet 130 × 68 mm, containing Nos. 629, 636/7 and 639. Multicoloured.
MS673 10v. Yachts and Iririki Island; 55v. Coconut trees, North Efate Islands; 60v. Underwater shoal of fishes, Banks Group; 75v. Santo Island . . . . 3·25 4·00

1994. Anemonefish. Multicoloured.
674 55v. Type **177** . . . . 2·25 80
675 70v. Yellow-tailed anemonefish . . . . 2·50 1·25
676 80v. Fire anemonefish . . . 2·75 2·00
677 140v. Orange-finned anemonefish . . . . 4·75 6·50
MS678 80 × 60 mm. No. 677 . . 3·75 4·50
No. **MS**678 shows the "Philakorea '94" International stamp Exhibition logo on the sheet margin.

1994. 50th Anniv of I.C.A.O. Multicoloured.
679 25v. Type **178** 65 45
680 60v. Douglas DC-3 . . . . . 1·10 90
681 75v. De Havilland D.H.A.3 Drover . . . . 1·25 1·40
682 90v. Boeing 737 on runway 1·50 2·00

179 "Hibiscus rosa-sinensis" "The Path"

1995. Hibiscus Flowers (2nd issue). Multicoloured.
683 25v. Type **179** 60 45
684 60v. "Hibiscus rosa-sinensis" "Old Frankie" . . . . . . 1·10 1·00
685 90v. "Hibiscus sinensis" "Fijian White" . . . . . . 1·60 1·75
686 200v. "Hibiscus rosa-sinensis" "Surfrider" . . . . 3·25 4·50

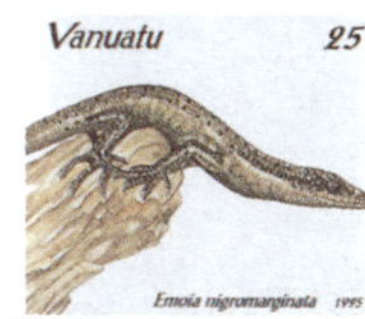

180 "Emoia nigromarginata"

1995. Lizards. Multicoloured.
687 25v. Type **180** 75 45
688 55v. "Nactus multicarinatus" 1·40 1·00
689 70v. "Lepidodactylus" . . . 1·50 1·50
690 80v. "Emoia caeruleocauda" 1·60 1·60
691 140v. "Emoia sanfordi" . . . 2·50 3·75

1995. Shells (3rd series). As T **171**. Multicoloured.
692 25v. "Epitonium scalare" . . 60 50
693 55v. "Strombus latissimus" 1·25 1·25
694 90v. "Conus bullatus" . . . 1·75 1·75
695 200v. "Pterynotus pinnatus" 3·50 4·50

181 "Tanna Girls" (A. Toni)

1995. 15th Anniv of Independence. Multicoloured.
696 25v. Type **181** 45 40
697 55v. "Black Coral Dancers" (sculpture, E. Watt) (vert) 90 90
698 75v. Erromango tapestry by Juliet Peta (vert) . . . . 1·25 1·25
699 90v. "Parade Day" (H. Di-Donna) . . . . 1·40 1·75
700 140v. "Banks Dancers" (J. John) . . . . 2·00 3·00
MS701 100 × 75 mm. No. 699 . . 3·50 5·00
No. **MS**701 also includes the "Singapore '95" International Stamp Exhibition logo on the sheet margin.

182 Children with Doves and Flags

183 Rambaramp (effigy), Malakula

1995. 50th Anniv of United Nations.
702 **182** 60v. multicoloured . . . 1·25 1·00

1995. 50th Anniv of End of Second World War in the Pacific. As T **162** showing aircraft. Mult.

703 60v. Curtiss SB2C Helldiver . . . 2·50 1·50
704 70v. Supermarine Spitfire Mk VIII . . . . 2·50 1·60
705 75v. Chance Vought F4U-1A Corsair . . . . 2·50 1·75
706 80v. Lockheed PV-1 Ventura . . 2·50 1·75
MS707 94 × 68 mm. 140v. Japanese delegation at signing of Unconditional Surrender, Tokyo Bay . . . . 4·00 4·50

No. **MS**707 also includes the "Singapore '95" International Stamp Exhibition logo on the sheet margin.

1995. Vanuatu Culture (1st series). Opening of New National Museum. Artefacts. Multicoloured.

708 25v. Type **183** 35 30
709 60v. Pot from Wusi, Espiritu Santo 75 75
710 75v. Slit gong from Mele, Efate . . . . 90 1·10
711 90v. Tapa cloth, Erromango . . 1·25 1·75

See also Nos. 772/6.

184 Boy throwing Cast Net

1996. Fishing. Multicoloured.

712 55v. Type **184** 85 65
713 75v. Fishing canoes . . . . . 1·10 90
714 80v. "Etelis" (fishing boat) and deep water fish (vert) . . 1·25 1·10
715 140v. Game fisherman catching sailfish (vert) . . . 2·50 3·50

185 "Pteropus anetianus"

1996. Endangered Species. Flying Foxes. Mult.

716 25v. Type **185** 40 55
717 25v. "Notopteris macdonaldi" upside down eating fruit (horiz) 40 55
718 25v. "Pteropus anetianus" hanging on branch 40 55
719 25v. "Notopteris macdonaldi" on branch (horiz) 40 55

1996. "CHINA '96" 9th Asian International Stamp Exhibition, Peking.

MS720 75 × 85 mm. No. 711 . . . 1·75 2·00
MS721 75 × 85 mm. 90v. "Pteropus tonganus" (flying fox); 140v. "Pteropus tonganus" (different) 5·00 5·50

186 Immunization Programme

1996. 50th Anniv of U.N.I.C.E.F. Multicoloured.

722 55v. Type **186** . . . . 1·25 1·00
723 60v. Breast-feeding programme . . . . 1·25 1·00

187 Airliner and Radio Waves

1996. Centenary of Radio. Multicoloured.

724 60v. Type **187** . . . . 90 1·25
725 75v. Radio Vanuatu broadcaster . . . . 1·10 1·40
726 80v. Guglielmo Marconi . . 1·25 1·50
727 90v. Cruise liner and radio waves . . . . 1·40 1·60

Nos. 724/7 were issued together, se-tenant, forming a composite aerial view of Port Vila.

188 Marie Kapalu, Tawai Keiruan, Baptiste Firiam and Tava Kalo

1996. Centenary of Modern Olympics Games. Multicoloured.

728 25v. Type **188** 35 30
729 70v. Athletes training 95 95
730 75v. Athletes from 1950s . . 1·00 1·00
731 200v. Athletes in 1896 . . . 2·75 4·00

189 Children in Front of Presbyterian Church and Roman Catholic Cathedral

1996. Christmas. Religious Buildings. Mult.

732 25v. Type **189** 45 30
733 60v. Children and Church of Christ 90 80
734 75v. Children and Seventh Day Adventist and Apostolic churches . . . . 95 1·00
735 90v. Children and Anglican church . . . . 1·25 1·60

190 "Hibiscus rosa-sinensis" "Lady Cilento"

1996. Hibiscus Flowers (3rd issue). Multicoloured.

736 25v. Type **190** 40 30
737 60v. "Hibiscus rosa-sinensis" "Kinchen's Yellow" . . . 90 70
738 90v. "Hibiscus rosa-sinensis" "D. J. O'Brien" . . . . . 1·25 1·25
739 200v. "Hibiscus rosa-sinensis" "Cuban Variety" . . . . . 3·00 4·25

For miniature sheet containing Nos. 736 and 739 see No. **MS**745.

191 Coral Garden

1997. Diving. Multicoloured.

740 70v. Type **191** 90 80
741 75v. Carving on the "President Coolidge" . . . 95 85
742 90v. "Boris" (Giant grouper) 1·25 1·25
743 140v. Wreck of the "President Coolidge" . . . 2·25 3·75
MS744 124 × 75 mm. Nos. 740/3 6·50 7·00

For further miniature sheet containing Nos. 741 and 743 see No. **MS**750.

1997. "HONG KONG '97" International Stamp Exhibition. Sheet 100 × 85 mm, containing Nos. 736 and 739. Multicoloured.

MS745 25v. Type **190**; 200v. "Hibiscus rosasinensis" "Cuban Variety" . . . . 4·50 5·00

192 View from Cockpit

1997. 10th Anniv of Air Vanuatu. Multicoloured.

746 25v. Type **192** 55 40
747 60v. Boeing 737-400 airliner being serviced, Bauerfield International Airport, Port Vila (81 × 31 mm) . . . . 1·00 75
748 90v. Air stewardess serving drinks . . . . 1·50 1·40
749 200v. Passengers disembarking . . . . . . 2·50 4·00

1997. "Pacific '97" International Philatelic Exhibition, San Francisco. Sheet 100 × 86 mm, containing Nos. 741 and 743. Multicoloured.

MS750 75v. Carving on the "President Coolidge"; 140v. Wreck of the "President Coolidge" 3·75 4·50

193 Sharp-tailed Sandpiper

1997. Birds (1st series). Coastal Birds. Mult.

751 25v. Type **193** 45 40
752 55v. Greater crested tern ("Crested Tern") 80 70
753 60v. Little pied cormorant . . 85 75
754 75v. Brown booby . . . . . 1·00 1·00
755 80v. Reef heron (vert) . . . 1·10 1·25
756 90v. Red-tailed tropic bird (vert) . . . . 1·25 1·50

See also Nos. 804/7 and 848/52.

194 Thomas Edison and Light Bulb

1997. 150th Birth Anniv of Thomas Edison (inventor). Multicoloured.

757 60v. Type **194** . . . . 1·25 1·50
758 70v. Hydro-electric dam, Espiritu Santo . . . . . . 1·25 1·50
759 200v. Port Vila at dusk (80 × 29 mm) . . . . . . 2·40 3·00

195 Yellow-faced Angelfish

1997. Angelfish. Multicoloured.

760 25v. Type **195** 40 30
761 55v. Flame angelfish 85 70
762 60v. Lemonpeel angelfish . . 90 80
763 70v. Emperor angelfish . . . 1·10 1·00
764 140v. Multi-barred angelfish 2·25 3·00

1998. No. 638 surch **5**.

765 5v. on 70v. Sea fan, Tongoa Island (vert) . . . . 1·50 1·50

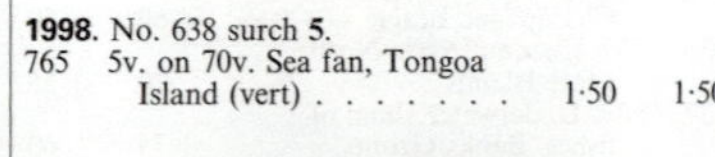

197 Fale, Espiritu Santo

1998. Local Architecture. Multicoloured.

766 30v. Type **197** 35 35
767 65v. National Cultural Centre 80 80
768 80v. University of South Pacific 95 95
769 200v. Chiefs' Nakamal . . . 1·90 2·75

1998. Diana, Princess of Wales Commemoration. As T **62a** of Tokelau. Multicoloured.

770 95v. Wearing black jacket, 1997 . . . . 1·00 1·10
MS771 145 × 70 mm. 75v. Wearing green jacket, 1987; 85v. Wearing cream jacket and hat, 1991; 95v. No. 769; 145v. Wearing red dress, 1992 (sold at 400v. + 50v. charity premium) . . . . 3·75 5·00

198 Nalawan Headdresses from South West Bay, Malakula

1998. Vanuatu Culture (2nd series). Masks. Mult.

772 30v. Type **198** 50 35
773 65v. Rom mask from North Ambrym 75 65
774 75v. Tamate mask from Gaua Island 85 85
775 85v. Banglulu headdress from Uripiv Island, north-east Malakula . . . . 95 1·00
776 95v. Chubwan masks from Vao Island, Malakula, and from Pentecost . . . . . . 1·10 1·40

199 "Danaus plexippus"

1998. Butterflies. Self-adhesive. Multicoloured.

777 30v. Type **199** 40 35
778 60v. "Hypolimnas bolina" . . 65 60
779 65v. "Eurema hecabe" . . . 70 65
780 75v. "Nymphalidae" sp. . . . 85 75
781 95v. "Precis villida" . . . . 1·00 1·25
782 205v. "Tirumala hamata" . . . 1·90 2·75
MS783 105 × 79 mm. No. 782 . . 2·25 2·75

No. **MS**783 also commemorates "SINGPEX '98" International Stamp Exhibition, Singapore.

200 Yasur, Tanna

1998. Volcanoes in Vanuatu. Multicoloured.

784 30v. Type **200** 45 40
785 60v. Marum and Benbow, Ambrym 65 60
786 75v. Mount Garet, Gaua . . 85 85
787 80v. Lopevi 90 90
788 145v. Lake Manaro Voui, Ambae . . . . 1·40 2·25

1998. Nos. 631, 634, 636/42 surch.

789 1v. on 100v. Mele Waterfall (vert) . . . . 70 1·00
790 2v. on 45v. Man in canoe, Erakor Island (vert) . . . 1·75 2·25
791 2v. on 55v. Coconut trees, North Efate Islands . . . 70 1·00
792 3v. on 60v. Underwater shoal of fishes, Banks Group . . . . 70 1·00
793 3v. on 75v. Santo Island . . 2·25 2·25
794 4v. on 45v. Man in canoe, Erakor Island (vert) . . . 1·75 2·25
795 5v. on 70v. Sea fan, Tongoa Island (vert) . . . . . . 7·50 7·50
796a 34v. on 20v. Two girls, Pentecost Island . . . . 1·75 2·00
796b 67v. on 300v. Yasur Volcano, Tanna Island (vert) . . . . 2·25 2·50
797 73v. on 80v. Sunset, Port Vila harbour (vert) . . . 1·75 2·00

Nos. 789/97 were produced as a result of the addition of VAT at 13% to postal rates from 14 September 1998.

204 De Quiros and "San Pedro y Paulo"

1999. Early Explorers. Multicoloured.

798 34v. Type **204** 70 50
799 73v. De Bougainville and "La Boudeuse" . . . . 1·00 1·00

800 84v. Cook and H.M.S. "Resolution" . . . . . . 1·25 1·25
801 90v. La Perouse and "L'Astrolabe" . . . . . . 1·40 1·40
802 96v. Dumont d'Urville and "L'Astrolabe" . . . . . . 1·60 2·00

No. 802 is inscribed "1788" in error.

1999. "Australia '99" World Stamp Exhibition, Melbourne. Multicoloured.
MS803 95 × 82 mm. Nos. 800/2 2·50 2·75

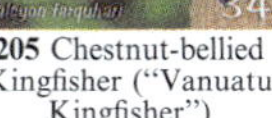

205 Chestnut-bellied Kingfisher ("Vanuatu Kingfisher") 206 Banks Islands Dancers

1999. Birds (2nd series). Bush and Lowland Birds. Multicoloured.
804 34v. Type **205** 70 50
805 67v. Golden-bronze cuckoo ("Shining Cuckoo") . . . 1·00 90
806 73v. Peregrine falcon . . . . 1·10 1·10
807 107v. Rainbow lorikeet . . . 1·60 2·25
MS808 111 × 95 mm. No. 807 (sold at 214v.) . . . . 2·75 3·25

No. **MS**808 has the frame, series inscription and artist's signature shown in gold die-stamping on sheet margins.

1999. "PhilexFrance '99" International Stamp Exhibition, Paris. Multicoloured.
MS809 105 × 82 mm. Nos. 799 and 801/2 . . . . 3·50 4·00

1999. Vanuatu Dances. Multicoloured.
810 1v. Type **206** 10 30
811 2v. Small Nambas, Lamap-Malakula 10 30
812 3v. Small Nambas, Malakula 10 30
813 5v. Smol Bag Theatre 10 30
814 35v. Snake Dance, Banks Island (horiz) 35 40
815 100v. Toka Dance, Tanna (horiz) . . . . 95 1·00
816 107v. South West Bay, Malakula . . . . 1·50 1·50
817 200v. Big Nambas, Malakula 2·50 2·75
818 300v. Rom Dance, Ambrym (horiz) . . . . 2·75 3·00
819 500v. Pentecost Island . . . 6·50 7·00
820 1000v. Brasive Dance, Futuna (horiz) . . . . . . 9·50 9·75

1999. "China '99" International Stamp Exhibition, Beijing. Sheet as No. MS808, but 100 × 80 mm, without gold die-stamped features, with "China '99" logo added to the margin in carmine.
MS822 107v. No. 807 . . . . . 1·25 1·50

207 "Pterois antennata"

1999. Lionfish. Multicoloured.
823 34v. Type **207** 60 40
824 84v. Head of "Pterois antennata" . . . . 1·25 1·10
825 90v. "Pterois volitans" . . . 1·40 1·40
826 96v. Head of "Pterois volitans" . . . . 1·50 2·00

208 Clown Triggerfish

1999. New Millennium. Sheet 165 × 75 mm, containing T **208** and similar multicoloured designs.
MS827 165 × 75 mm. 34v. Type **208**; 68v. Young girl and Pentecost Island land diver (vert); 84v. Statue and pig's tusk (vert); 90c. Vanuatu kingfisher; 96v. Tanna islander blowing Triton shell and Yasur volcano . . . . 4·00 5·00

2000. "The Stamp Show 2000" International Stamp Exhibition, London. Queen Elizabeth the Queen Mother's 100th Birthday. Sheet 105 × 70 mm, containing vert designs as T **274** of Tonga. Multicoloured.
MS828 100v. Queen Elizabeth the Queen Mother holding bouquet; 107v. Lady Elizabeth Bowes-Lyon as young girl . . . . 2·75 3·00

209 Launch of "Intelsat" Satellite

2000. "EXPO 2000" World Stamp Exhibition, Anaheim, U.S.A. Satellite Communications. Multicoloured. Self-adhesive.
829 10v. Type **209** 30 30
830 34v. Port Villa Ground Station 60 40
831 100v. "Intelsat" satellite in orbit over Vanuatu . . . . 1·40 1·40
832 225v. Tam Tam drum and Intelsat satellite . . . . . 2·50 3·50
MS833 122 × 97 mm. Nos. 830 and 832 . . . . 2·75 3·25

210 Abstract Painting (Sero Kuautonga)

2000. 20th Anniv of Independence. Local Art. Mult.
834 34v. Type **210** 60 40
835 67v. Tapa cloth art (Moses Pita) 90 70
836 73v. Tapestry (Juliet Pita) . . 1·00 85
837 84v. Carving (Emmanuel Watt) . . . . 1·00 1·25
838 90v. "Tree of Peace" (watercolour) (Joseph John) . . . . 1·25 1·40

211 Running

2000. Olympic Games, Sydney. Each including the Olympic Torch. Multicoloured.
839 56v. Type **211** 75 75
840 67v. Weightlifting 85 85
841 90v. High-jumping . . . . . 1·10 1·10
842 96v. Boxing . . . . 1·25 1·50

212 Common Dolphin

2000. Dolphins. Multicoloured.
843 34v. Type **212** 60 45
844 73v. Spotted dolphin 90 85
845 84v. Spinner dolphin . . . . 1·00 1·00
846 107v. Bottlenose dolphin . . 1·25 1·60
MS847 Circular, 100 mm diameter. Nos. 845/6 . . . . 2·25 2·75

No. **MS**847 includes the "HONG KONG 2001" Stamp Exhibition logo on the sheet margin.

213 Cardinal Honeyeater 214 Vanilla

2001. Birds (3rd series). Highland Birds. Mult.
848 35v. Type **213** 60 45
849 60v. Yellow-fronted white-eye ("Vanuatu White-eye") . . 80 65
850 90v. Mountain starling ("Santo Mountain Starling") . . . . 1·10 1·10
851 100v. Red-headed parrotf inch ("Royal Parrot finch") 1·25 1·40
852 110v. White-billed honeyeater ("Vanuatu Mountain Honeyeater") . . . . . . 1·25 1·50

In addition to being available in separate sheets Nos. 848/52 were also printed together, se-tenant, with the backgrounds forming a composite design.

2001. Food Exports. Multicoloured.
853 35v. Type **214** 50 40
854 75v. Cacao 85 80
855 90v. Coffee . . . . 1·10 1·10
856 110v. Copra . . . . 1·25 1·50

215 Sperm Whales

2001. Whales. Joint Issue with New Caledonia. Multicoloured.
857 60v. Type **215** 75 75
858 80v. Humpback whales (vert) 90 90
859 90v. Blue whales . . . . . 1·10 1·10
MS860 220 × 90 mm. Nos. 857/9 2·75 3·00

No. **MS**860 is in the shape of a pair of Humpback whales.

216 Lyre-shaped Sand Drawing

2001. Sand Drawings. Multicoloured.
861 60v. Type **216** 65 60
862 90v. Interwoven scroll design 1·10 1·00
863 110v. Drawing of turtle . . . 1·25 1·40
864 135v. Drawing of fish . . . . 1·40 1·75

217 Vanuatan, Yasur Volcano and Pentecost Island Land Diver

2002. U.N. Year of Eco Tourism. Multicoloured.
865 35v. Type **217** 35 40
866 60v. Making kava and dancers 55 60
867 75v. Siri Falls and birds (vert) 70 75
868 110v. Tourist kayaks and scuba diving (vert) . . . . 1·00 1·25
869 135v. Tourist village . . . . 1·25 1·40
MS870 170 × 76 mm. Nos. 865/9 3·75 4·25

218 Horse pulling Plough

2002. Local Horses. Multicoloured.
871 35v. Type **218** 35 40
872 60v. Cattle round-up 55 60
873 75v. Horse racing 70 75
874 80v. Pony trekking on beach 75 80
875 200v. Wild horse from Tanna 1·90 2·00

219 Children's Football

2002. Vanuatu Football Federation. Multicoloured.
877 35v. Type **219** 35 40
878 80v. Under 17's football . . 75 80
879 110v. Women's football . . . 1·00 1·10
880 135v. International football 1·25 1·40

220 Young Girl holding Breadfruit Plant

2002. Year of Reforestation. Multicoloured. Self-adhesive.
881 35v. Type **220** 35 40
882 60v. Man and boy planting seedling (*Endospermum medullosum*) 55 60
883 90v. Man hollowing out canoe 80 85
884 110v. Woman and boy eating fruit . . . . 1·10 1·25

2002. "Philakorea 2002" International Stamp Exhibition, Seoul. Multicoloured.
MS885 115 × 90 mm. No. 875 . . 1·90 2·00

221 Adult Dugong with Calf

2002. Dugong. Multicoloured.
886 35v. Type **221** 35 40
887 75v. Adult and calf swimming 70 75
888 80v. Adult Dugong 75 80
889 135v. Dugong feeding . . . . 1·25 1·40
MS890 133 × 112 mm. Nos. 888/9 2·00 2·10

222 *Dendrobium gouldii*

2002. Orchids. Multicoloured.
891 35v. Type **222** 35 40
892 60v. *Dendrobium polysema* . . 55 60
893 90v. *Dendrobium spectabile* 80 85
894 110v. *Flickingeria comata* . . 1·00 1·25

223 Limousin Cattle

2003. "Year Blong Buluk". Beef Production in Vanuatu. Multicoloured.
895 35v. Type **223** 35 40
896 80v. Charolais cattle 75 80
897 110v. Simmental cattle . . . 1·00 1·25
898 135v. Red Brahman cattle . . 1·25 1·40

224 Land Diver on Platform

2003. Pentecost Island Land Diving. Multicoloured.

No.	Type	Description	Mint	Used
899		35v. Type **224**	35	40
900		80v. Islander making dive	70	75
901		110v. Diving tower and dancers	1·00	1·10
902		200v. Land diver jumping from tower (33 × 89 mm)	1·90	2·00
MS903		90 × 110 mm. No. 902	1·90	2·00

VATHY Pt. 6

A town on the island of Samos, where there was a French Post Office which closed in 1914.

25 centimes = 1 piastre.

1893. Stamps of France optd **Vathy** or surch also.

No.	Type	Description	Mint	Used
82	**10**	5c. green	4·50	9·00
84		10c. black and lilac	10·00	16·00
86		15c. blue	7·50	6·25
87		1pi. on 25c. black on pink	5·75	7·50
88		2pi. on 50c. pink	22·00	27·00
89		4pi. on 1f. green	24·00	10·50
90		8pi. on 2f. brown on blue	65·00	65·00
91		20pi. on 5f. mauve	90·00	80·00

VATICAN CITY Pt. 8

A small area in Rome under the independent sovereignty of the Pope since 1929.

1929. 100 centesimi = 1 lira.
2002. 100 cents = 1 euro.

1 Papal Tiara and St. Peter's Keys — 2 Pope Pius XI — 4

1929.

No.	Type	Description	Mint	Used
1	**1**	5c. brown on pink	20	25
2		10c. green on green	30	35
3		20c. violet on lilac	75	55
4		25c. blue on blue	90	55
5		30c. black on yellow	1·10	70
6		50c. black on orange	1·60	70
7		75c. red on grey	2·20	1·30
8	**2**	80c. red	1·60	40
9		1l.25 blue	2·50	95
10		2l. brown	5·00	1·90
11		2l.50 red	4·25	2·75
12		5l. green	5·00	9·75
13		10l. black	11·00	14·50

1931. Surch **C. 25** and bars.

No.	Type	Description	Mint	Used
14	**1**	25c. on 30c. black on yellow	2·75	1·20

1933. "Holy Year" (1933–1934).

No.	Type	Description	Mint	Used
15	**4**	25c.+10c. green	6·75	4·75
16		75c.+15c. red	14·00	15·00
17		80c.+20c. brown	36·00	22·00
18		1l.25+25c. blue	10·50	16·00

The 80c. and 1l.25 have inscriptions and frame differently arranged.

6 Arms of Pope Pius XI

9 Pope Pius XI

1933.

No.	Type	Description	Mint	Used
19	**6**	5c. red	10	10
20	–	10c. black and brown	10	10
21	–	12½c. black and green	10	10
22	–	20c. black and orange	10	10
23	–	25c. black and green	10	10
24	–	30c. brown and black	10	10
25	–	50c. brown and purple	10	10
26	–	75c. brown and red	10	10
27	–	80c. brown and pink	10	10
28	**9**	1l. black and violet	4·25	2·75
29		1l.25 black and blue	15·00	5·50
30		2l. black and brown	36·00	22·00
31		2l.75 black and purple	44·00	45·00
32	–	5l. green and brown	20	30
33	–	10l. green and blue	20	35
34	–	20l. green and black	35	45

DESIGNS—As Type **6**: 10c. to 25c. Wing of Vatican Palace; 30c. to 80c. Vatican Gardens and Dome of St. Peter's. As Type **9**: 5l. to 20l. St. Peter's Basilica.

1934. Surch.

No.	Type	Description	Mint	Used
35	**2**	40c. on 80c. red	3·75	2·20
36		1l.30 on 1l.25 blue	65·00	46·00
37		2l.05 on 2l. brown	£150	16·00
38		2l.55 on 2l.50 red	95·00	£180
39		3l.05 on 5l. green	£300	£250
40		3l.70 on 10l. black	£300	£475

13 Tribonian presenting Pandects to Justinian

15 Doves and Bell

1935. International Juridical Congress, Rome. Frescoes by Raphael.

No.	Type	Description	Mint	Used
41	**13**	5c. orange	1·80	1·40
42		10c. violet	1·80	1·40
43		25c. green	6·25	4·75
44	–	75c. red	42·00	21·00
45	–	80c. brown	30·00	18·00
46	–	1l.25 blue	34·00	10·50

DESIGN: 75c. to 1l.25, Pope Julius II (wrongly inscribed as representing Pope Gregory IX).

1936. Catholic Press Exhibition, Rome.

No.	Type	Description	Mint	Used
47	**15**	5c. green	1·10	1·00
48	–	10c. black	1·10	1·00
49	–	25c. green	26·00	6·25
50	**15**	50c. purple	1·00	1·00
51	–	75c. red	26·00	24·00
52	–	80c. brown	1·40	2·10
53	–	1l.25 blue	1·25	2·10
54	–	5l. brown	1·25	5·75

DESIGNS: 10, 75c. Church and Bible; 25, 80c. St. John Bosco; 1l.25, 5l. St. Francis of Sales.

16 Statue of St. Peter

17 Ascension of Elijah

1938. Air.

No.	Type	Description	Mint	Used
55	**16**	25c. brown	10	10
56	–	50c. green	10	10
57	**17**	75c. red	20	30
58	–	80c. blue	20	45
59	**16**	1l. violet	35	55
60	–	2l. blue	75	90
61	**17**	5l. black	1·80	2·00
62	–	10l. purple	1·80	2·00

DESIGNS: 50c., 2l. Dove with olive branch and St. Peter's Square; 80c., 10l. Transportation of the Holy House.

18 Crypt of Basilica of St. Cecilia

20 Coronation

1938. International Christian Archaeological Congress. Inscr "CONGRESSVS INTERNAT. ARCHAEOLOGIAE CHRIST".

No.	Type	Description	Mint	Used
63	**18**	5c. brown	20	25
64		10c. red	20	25
65		25c. green	30	30
66	–	75c. red	7·25	6·25
67	–	80c. violet	22·00	19·00
68	–	1l.25 blue	29·00	24·00

DESIGN: 75, 80c. and 1l.25, Basilica of Saints Nereus and Achilles in the Catacombs of Domitilla.

1939. Death of Pope Pius XI. Optd **SEDE VACANTE MCMXXXIX**.

No.	Type	Description	Mint	Used
69	**1**	5c. brown on pink	31·00	7·25
70		10c. green on green	35	25
71		20c. violet on lilac	35	25
72		25c. blue on blue	3·75	3·50
73		30c. black on yellow	75	20
74		50c. black on orange	75	25
75		75c. red on grey	75	25

1939. Coronation of Pope Pius XII.

No.	Type	Description	Mint	Used
76	**20**	25c. green	1·30	35
77		75c. red	30	50
78		80c. violet	3·75	2·75
79		1l.25 blue	30	50

21 Arms of Pope Pius XII

22 Pope Pius XII

1940. 1st Anniv of Coronation of Pope Pius XII.

No.	Type	Description	Mint	Used
80	**21**	5c. red	10	10
99		5c. grey	10	10
100		30c. brown	10	10
101		50c. green	10	10
81	**22**	1l. black and violet	20	10
102	–	1l. black and brown	15	10
82	–	1l.25 black and blue	20	10
103	–	1l.50 black and red	15	10
83	**22**	2l. black and brown	75	1·10
104	–	2l.50 black and blue	15	15
84	–	2l.75 black and purple	1·30	2·20
105	**22**	5l. black and lilac	20	25
106		20l. black and green	35	40

DESIGN: 1l. (No. 102), 1l.25, 1l.50, 2l.50, and 2l.75, as Type **22** but with portrait of Pope facing left.

23

24 Consecration of Archbishop Pacelli

1942. Prisoners of War Relief Fund (1st series). Inscr "MCMXLII".

No.	Type	Description	Mint	Used
85	**23**	25c. green	10	20
86		80c. brown	10	20
87		1l.25 blue	10	20

See also Nos. 92/4 and 107/9.

1943. Pope's Episcopal Silver Jubilee.

No.	Type	Description	Mint	Used
88	**24**	25c. turquoise and green	10	10
89		80c. chocolate and brown	10	20
90		1l.25 blue and ultramarine	10	20
91		5l. blue and black	15	35

1944. Prisoners of War Relief Fund (2nd series). Inscr "MCMXLIII".

No.	Type	Description	Mint	Used
92	**23**	25c. green	10	10
93		80c. brown	10	10
94		1l.25 blue	10	15

25 Raphael

27 St. Ignatius of Loyola

1944. 4th Centenary of Pontifical Academy of the Virtuosi of the Pantheon.

No.	Type	Description	Mint	Used
95	**25**	25c. olive and green	20	20
96	–	80c. violet and lilac	30	35
97	–	1l.25 blue and violet	30	30
98	–	10l. bistre and yellow	55	1·80

PORTRAITS: 80c. Antonio da Sangallo (architect); 1l.25, Carlo Maratti (painter) (after Francesco Maratta); 10l. Antonio Canova (sculptor, self-portrait).

1945. Prisoners of War Relief Fund (3rd series). Inscr "MCMXLIV".

No.	Type	Description	Mint	Used
107	**23**	1l. green	10	15
108		3l. red	10	15
109		5l. blue	10	15

1946. Surch in figures between bars.

No.	Type	Description	Mint	Used
110	**21**	20c. on 5c. grey	10	10
111		25c. on 30c. brown	10	10
112		1l. on 50c. green	10	10
113	–	1l.50 on 1l. black and brown (No. 102)	10	10
114	–	3l. on 1l.50 black and red (No. 103)	30	10
115	–	5l. on 2l.50 black and blue (No. 104)	45	25
116	**22**	10l. on 5l. black and lilac	1·60	65
117		30l. on 20l. black and green	4·25	2·20

1946. 400th Anniv of Inauguration of Council of Trent.

No.	Type	Description	Mint	Used
118	–	5c. brown and bistre	25	25
119	–	25c. brown and violet	25	25
120	–	50c. sepia and brown	25	25
121	**27**	75c. brown and black	25	25
122	–	1l. brown and purple	25	25
123	–	1l.50 brown and red	25	25
124	–	2l. brown and green	25	25
125	–	2l.50 brown and blue	25	25
126	–	3l. brown and red	25	25
127	–	4l. brown and bistre	25	25
128	–	5l. brown and blue	25	25
129	–	10l. brown and red	25	25

DESIGNS: 5c. Trent Cathedral; 25c. St. Angela Merici; 50c. St. Anthony Maria Zaccaria; 1l. St. Cajetan of Thiene; 1l.50, St. John Fisher, Bishop of Rochester; 2l. Cristoforo Madrussi, Bishop of Trent; 2l.50, Reginald Pole, Archbishop of Canterbury; 3l. Marcello Cervini; 4l. Giovanni Maria Del Monte; 5l. Emperor Charles V; 10l. Pope Paul III Farnese.

28 Dove with Olive Branch over St. Peter's Forecourt — 29 Barn Swallows circling Spire of St. Peter's Basilica

1947. Air.

No.	Type	Description	Mint	Used
130	**28**	1l. red	10	10
131	–	4l. brown	10	10
132	**28**	5l. blue	10	10
133	**29**	15l. violet	1·30	1·10
134	–	25l. green	4·50	2·40
135	**29**	50l. black	6·50	4·25
136		100l. orange	31·00	8·00

DESIGN—As Type **28**: 4l., 25l. Transportation of the Holy House.

30 "Raphael accompanying Tobias" (after Botticelli)

1948. Air.

No.	Type	Description	Mint	Used
137	**30**	250l. black	36·00	7·25
138		500l. blue	£550	£350

31 St. Agnes's Basilica

32 Pope Pius XII

1949.

No.	Type	Description	Mint	Used
139	**31**	1l. brown	10	10
140	–	3l. violet	10	10
141	–	5l. orange	10	10
142	–	8l. green	15	15
143	–	13l. green	3·25	3·25
144	–	16l. grey	30	30
145	–	25l. red	6·50	85
146	–	35l. mauve	36·00	16·00
147	–	40l. blue	30	20
148	**32**	100l. black	4·00	4·00

DESIGNS (Basilicas)—VERT: 3l. St. Clement; 5l. St. Praxedes; 8l. St. Mary in Cosmedin. HORIZ: 13l. Holy Cross; 16l. St. Sebastian; 25l. St. Laurence's; 35l. St. Paul's; 40l. Sta. Maria Maggiore.

33 Angels over Globe

1949. Air. 75th Anniv of U.P.U.

No.	Type	Description	Mint	Used
149	**33**	300l. blue	27·00	11·00
150		1000l. green	£130	90·00

34 "I Will Give You the Keys of the Kingdom" **35** Guards Marching

1949. "Holy Year".
151 **34** 5l. brown and light brown . . . 10 10
152 – 6l. brown and black . . . 10 10
153 – 8l. green and blue 90 50
154 – 10l. blue and green 30 10
155 **34** 20l. brown and green . . . 1·50 35
156 – 25l. blue and brown . . . 75 35
157 – 30l. purple and green . . . 1·80 1·10
158 – 60l. red and brown . . . . 1·20 1·10
DESIGNS: 6, 25l. Four Basilicas; 8, 30l. Pope Boniface VIII; 10, 60l. Pope Pius XII opening the Holy Door.

1950. Centenary of Papal Guard.
159 **35** 25l. brown . . . . 5·75 4·00
160 35l. green . . . . 3·25 4·00
161 55l. brown . . . . 1·80 4·00

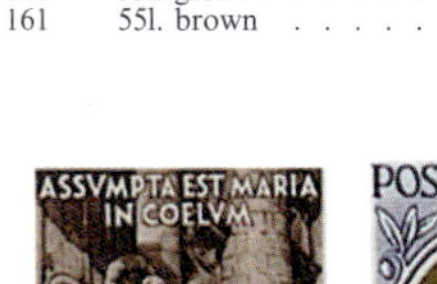

36 Pope Proclaiming Dogma **37** Pope Pius X

1951. Proclamation of Dogma of the Assumption.
162 **36** 25l. purple . . . . 10·00 90
163 – 55l. blue . . . . 4·25 13·50
DESIGN: 55l. Angels over St. Peter's.

1951. Beatification of Pope Pius X.
164 **37** 6l. gold and violet 10 15
165 10l. gold and green 15 15
166 – 60l. gold and blue . . . . 7·25 7·25
167 – 115l. gold and brown . . . 22·00 22·00
DESIGN: 60, 115l. Pope looking left.

38 Final Session of Council (fresco)

1951. 1500th Anniv of Council of Chalcedon.
168 **38** 5l. grey 35 35
169 – 25l. red . . . . 3·00 2·40
170 **38** 35l. red . . . . 5·75 4·50
171 – 60l. blue . . . . 18·00 14·50
172 **38** 100l. brown . . . . 55·00 36·00
DESIGN: 25, 60l. "Pope Leo I meeting Attila" (Raphael).

39 Gratian **41** Mail Coach and First Stamp

1951. Air. 800th Anniv of Decree of Gratian.
173 **39** 300l. purple £300 £200
174 500l. blue . . . . 36·00 18·00

1952. No. 143 surch **L. 12** and bars.
175 12l. on 13l. green . . . . . 1·60 95

1952. Centenary of First Papal States' Stamp.
176 **41** 50l. black & blue on cream 4·25 4·25

42 St. Maria Goretti **43** St. Peter and Inscription

1953. 50th Anniv of Martyrdom of St. Maria Goretti.
177 **42** 15l. violet and brown . . . 4·25 2·50
178 25l. brown and red . . . . 3·00 2·20

1953. St. Peter's Basilica. Medallions in black.
179 **43** 3l. red 10 10
180 – 5l. grey 10 10
181 – 10l. green 10 10
182 – 12l. brown 10 10
183 – 20l. violet 20 10
184 – 25l. brown 10 10
185 – 35l. red 10 10
186 – 45l. brown 20 20
187 – 60l. blue 10 10
188 – 65l. red 30 20
189 – 100l. purple 10 10
DESIGNS: 5l. Pius XII and Roman sepulchre; 10l. St. Peter's tomb; 12l. St. Sylvester I and Constantine's basilica (previous building); 20l. Julius II and Bramante's design; 25l. Paul III and apse; 35l. Sixtus V and cupola; 45l. Paul V and facade; 60l. Urban VIII and baldaquin; 65l. Alexander VII and colonnade; 100l. Pius VI and sacristy.

44 Dome of St. Peter's **45** St. Clare of Assisi (after Giotto)

1953. Air.
190 **44** 500l. brown & deep brown . . . . 24·00 8·25
190a 500l. green and turquoise 7·25 3·75
191 1000l. blue and deep blue 65·00 15·00
191a 1000l. red and lake . . . 75 75

1953. 700th Death Anniv of St. Clare (founder of Poor Clares Order).
192 **45** 25l. dp brown, brown & bl 1·80 1·80
193 35l. brown, lt brown & red 18·00 16·00

46 "St. Bernard" (after Lippi) **47** Lombard's Episcopal Seal

1953. 800th Death Anniv of St. Bernard of Clairvaux.
194 **46** 20l. purple and green . . . 75 75
195 60l. green and blue . . . 7·25 6·50

1953. 800th Anniv of "Libri Sententiarum" (theological treatise by Peter Lombard, Bishop of Paris).
196 **47** 100l. yellow, blue and red 44·00 33·00

48 Pope Pius XI and Vatican City

1954. 25th Anniv of Lateran Treaty.
197 **48** 25l. red, brown and blue 1·10 90
198 60l. blue, grey and brown 3·25 3·00

49 Pope Pius XII

1954. Marian Year and Centenary of Dogma of the Immaculate Conception.
199 – 3l. violet 10 10
200 **49** 4l. red 10 10
201 – 6l. red 10 10
202 **49** 12l. green . . . . 1·10 90
203 – 20l. brown 90 90
204 **49** 35l. blue . . . . 1·80 1·60
DESIGN: 3, 6, 20l. Pope Pius IX facing right with different inscr and dates "1854–1954".

50 St. Pius X

1954. Canonization of Pope Pius X.
205 **50** 10l. yellow, red and brown 20 20
206 25l. yellow, red and violet 2·75 2·00
207 35l. yellow, red and black 4·25 3·75

51 Basilica of St. Francis of Assisi

1954. Bicentenary of Elevaion of Basilica of St. Francis of Assisi to Papal Chapel.
208 **51** 20l. black and cream . . . 1·80 1·10
209 35l. brown and cream . . . 1·50 1·80

52 "St. Augustine" (after Botticelli)

1954. 1600th Birth Anniv of St. Augustine.
210 **52** 35l. green 90 75
211 50l. brown . . . . 1·60 1·50

53 Madonna of Ostra Brama, Vilna

1954. Termination of Marian Year.
212 **53** 20l. multicoloured . . . . 1·30 90
213 35l. multicoloured . . . . 9·75 8·25
214 60l. multicoloured . . . . 16·00 14·50

54 St. Boniface and Fulda Cathedral **55** "Pope Sixtus II and St. Lawrence" (fresco, Niccolina Chapel)

1955. 1200th Anniv of Martyrdom of St. Boniface.
215 **54** 10l. green 10 10
216 35l. violet 55 45
217 60l. green 85 75

1955. 500th Death Anniv of Fra Giovanni da Fiesole, "Fra Angelico" (painter).
218 **55** 50l. red and blue . . . . . 4·25 2·75
219 100l. blue and flesh . . . . 3·00 2·75

56 Pope Nicholas V **57** St. Bartholomew

1955. 5th Death Centenary of Pope Nicholas V.
220 **56** 20l. brown and blue . . . 30 20
221 35l. brown and pink . . . 35 30
222 60l. brown and green . . . 65 65

1955. 900th Death Anniv of St. Bartholomew the Young.
223 **57** 10l. black and brown . . . 10 10
224 25l. black and red 45 35
225 100l. black and green . . . 2·20 1·70

58 "Annunciation" (Melozzo da Forli) **59** Corporal of the Guard

1956. Air.
226 **58** 5l. black 10 10
227 A 10l. green 10 10
228 B 15l. orange 30 30
229 **58** 25l. red 10 10
230 A 35l. red . . . . 3·00 3·00
231 B 50l. brown 10 10
232 **58** 60l. blue 55 55
233 A 100l. brown 10 10
234 B 300l. violet 65 65
PAINTINGS: A, "Annunciation" (P. Cavallini); B, "Annunciation" (Leonardo da Vinci).

1956. 450th Anniv of Swiss Guard.
235 – 4l. red 15 10
236 **59** 6l. orange 15 10
237 – 10l. blue 15 10
238 – 35l. brown 55 55
239 **59** 50l. violet 75 75
240 – 60l. green 85 85
DESIGNS: 4, 35l. Captain Roust; 10, 60l. Two drummers.

60 St. Rita **61** St. Ignatius presenting Jesuit Constitution to Pope Paul III

1956. 5th Death Centenary of St. Rita at Cascia.
241 **60** 10l. grey 10 10
242 25l. brown 55 55
243 35l. blue 40 40

1956. 4th Death Centenary of St. Ignatius of Loyola.
244 **61** 35l. brown 55 55
245 60l. grey 90 90

62 St. John of Capistrano **63** Madonna and Child

1956. 5th Death Centenary of St. John of Capistrano.
246 **62** 25l. green and black . . . 2·00 2·00
247 35l. brown and purple . . 75 75

1956. "Black Madonna" of Czestochowa Commemoration.
248 **63** 35l. black and blue 35 35
249 60l. blue and green 45 45
250 100l. purple and brown . . 65 60

64 St. Domenico Savio **65** Cardinal D. Capranica (founder) and Capranica College

1957. Death Centenary of St. Domenico Savio.
251 **64** 4l. brown 10 10
252 – 6l. red 10 10
253 **64** 25l. green 20 20
254 – 60l. blue . . . . 1·20 85
DESIGN: 6, 60l. St. Domenico Savio and St. John Bosco.

1957. 5th Centenary of Capranica College.
255 **65** 5l. red 10 10
256 – 10l. brown 10 10
257 **65** 35l. grey 10 10
258 – 100l. blue 65 65
DESIGNS: 10, 100l. Pope Pius XII and plaque.

66 Pontifical Academy of Science

1957. 20th Anniv of the Pontifical Academy of Science.
259 **66** 35l. green and blue 55 45
260 60l. blue and brown . . . 55 55

67 Mariazell Basilica

1957. 8th Centenary of Mariazell Basilica.
261 **67** 5l. green 10 10
262 – 15l. black 10 10
263 **67** 60l. blue 85 85
264 – 100l. violet . . . . 1·00 1·00
DESIGN: 15, 100l. Statue of the Virgin of Mariazell within Sanctuary.

68 Apparition of the Virgin Mary

1958. Centenary of Apparition of the Virgin Mary at Lourdes.
265 **68** 5l. blue 10 10
266 – 10l. green 10 10
267 – 15l. brown 10 10
268 **68** 25l. red 10 10
269 – 35l. brown 10 10
270 – 100l. violet 10 10
DESIGNS: 10, 35l. Invalid at Lourdes; 15, 100l. St. Bernadette.

69 "Civitas Dei" ("City of God" at Exhibition)

70 Pope Clement XIII (from sculpture by A. Canova)

1958. Brussels International Exhibition.
271 – 35l. purple 30 30
272 **69** 60l. red 65 65
273 100l. violet . . . . 1·60 1·50
274 – 300l. blue . . . . 1·10 1·30
DESIGN: 35, 300l. Pope Pius XII.

1958. Birth Bicentenary of Antonio Canova (sculptor).
275 **70** 5l. brown 10 10
276 – 10l. red 10 10
277 – 35l. green 30 20
278 – 100l. blue 90 90
SCULPTURES: 10l. Pope Clement XIV; 35l. Pope Pius VI; 100l. Pope Pius VII.

71 St. Peter's Keys

1958. "Vacant See".
279 **71** 15l. brown on yellow . . . 1·40 75
280 25l. brown 10 10
281 60l. brown on lilac 10 10

72 Pope John XXIII

1959. Coronation of Pope John XXIII. Inscr "IV-XI MCMLVIII".
282 **72** 25l. multicoloured 10 10
283 – 35l. multicoloured 10 10
284 **72** 60l. multicoloured 10 10
285 – 100l. multicoloured 10 10
DESIGN: 35, 100l. Arms of Pope John XXIII.

73 St. Lawrence

74 Pope Pius XI

1959. 1700th Death Annivs (15 to 100l. in 1958) of Martyrs under Valerian.
286 **73** 15l. brown, yellow and red 10 10
287 – 25l. brown, yellow and lilac 10 10
288 – 50l. multicoloured 10 15
289 – 60l. brown, yellow & green 10 15
290 – 100l. brown, yellow & pur 10 15
291 – 300l. sepia and brown . . 35 35
PORTRAITS: 25l. Pope Sixtus II; 50l. St. Agapitus; 60l. St. Filisissimus; 100l. St. Cyprian; 300l. St. Fructuosus.

1959. 30th Anniv of Lateran Treaty.
292 **74** 30l. brown 10 10
293 100l. blue 20 20

75 Radio Mast

76 Obelisk and St. John Lateran Basilica

1959. 2nd Anniv of St. Maria di Galeria Radio Station Vatican City.
294 **75** 25l. pink, yellow and black 10 10
295 60l. yellow, red and blue 15 25

1959. Air. Roman Obelisks.
296 **76** 5l. violet 10 10
297 – 10l. green 10 10
298 – 15l. brown 10 10
299 – 25l. green 10 10
300 – 35l. blue 10 10
301 **76** 50l. green 10 10
302 – 60l. red 10 10
303 – 100l. blue 15 10
304 – 200l. brown 20 15
305 – 500l. brown 35 35
DESIGNS: 10, 60l. Obelisk and Church of Sta. Maria Maggiore; 15, 100l. Vatican Obelisk and Apostolic Palace; 25, 200l. Obelisk and Churches of St. Mary in Montesanto and St. Mary of the Miracles, Piazza del Popolo; 35, 500l. Sallustian Obelisk and Trinita dei Monti Church.

77 St. Casimir, Vilna Palace and Cathedral

1959. 500th Birth Anniv of St. Casimir (patron saint of Lithuania).
306 **77** 50l. brown 10 10
307 100l. green 20 20

78 "Christ Adored by the Magi" (after Raphael)

1959. Christmas.
308 **78** 15l. black 10 10
309 25l. red 10 10
310 60l. blue 20 25

79 "St. Antoninus" (after Dupre)

80 Transept of St. John Lateran Basilica

1960. 500th Death Anniv of St. Antoninus of Florence.
311 **79** 15l. blue 10 10
312 – 25l. green 10 10
313 **79** 60l. brown 30 25
314 – 110l. purple 45 45
DESIGN: 25, 110l. "St. Antoninus preaching sermon" (after Portigiani).

1960. Roman Diocesan Synod.
315 **80** 15l. brown 10 10
316 60l. black 15 20

81 "The Flight into Egypt" (after Beato Angelico)

82 Cardinal Sarto (Pius X) leaving Venice for Conclave in Rome

1960. World Refugee Year.
317 **81** 5l. green 10 10
318 – 10l. brown 10 10
319 – 25l. red 20 15
320 **81** 60l. violet 30 30
321 – 100l. blue . . . . 1·10 95
322 – 300l. green . . . . 1·00 85
DESIGNS: 10, 100l. "St. Peter giving Alms" (Masaccio); 25, 300l. "Madonna of Mercy" (Piero della Francesca).

1960. 1st Anniv of Transfer of Relics of Pope Pius X from Rome to Venice.
323 **82** 15l. brown 20 25
324 – 35l. red 75 65
325 – 60l. green . . . . 1·40 1·20
DESIGNS: 35l. Pope John XXIII kneeling before relics of Pope Pius X; 60l. Relics in procession across St. Mark's Square, Venice.

83 "Feeding the Hungry"

1960. "Corporal Works of Mercy". Della Robbia paintings. Centres in brown.
326 **83** 5l. brown 10 10
327 – 10l. green 10 10
328 – 15l. black 10 10
329 – 20l. red 10 10
330 – 30l. violet 10 10
331 – 35l. brown 10 10
332 – 40l. orange 10 10
333 – 70l. stone 10 10
DESIGNS: 10l. "Giving drinks to the thirsty"; 15l. "Clothing the naked"; 20l. "Sheltering the homeless"; 30l. "Visiting the sick"; 35l. "Visiting the imprisoned"; 40l. "Burying the dead"; 70l. Pope John XXIII between "Faith" and "Charity".

84 "The Nativity" after Gerard Honthorst (Gherardo delle Notte)

1960. Christmas.
334 **84** 10l. black and green . . . 10 10
335 15l. deep brown and brown 10 10
336 70l. blue and turqoise . . . 10 15

85 St. Vincent de Paul

1960. Death Tercentenaries of St. Vincent de Paul and St. Louise de Marillac.
337 **85** 40l. violet 20 15
338 – 70l. black 20 20
339 – 100l. brown 40 35
DESIGNS: 70l. St. Louise de Marillac; 100l. St. Vincent giving child to care of St. Louise.

86 St. Meinrad

87 "Pope Leo I meeting Attila" (Algardi)

1961. 11th Death Centenary of St. Meinrad.
340 **86** 30l. black 35 35
341 – 40l. lilac 75 65
342 – 100l. brown . . . . 1·50 1·30
DESIGNS—VERT: 40l. The "Black Madonna", Einsiedeln Abbey. HORIZ: 100l. Einsiedeln Abbey, Switzerland.

1961. 15th Death Centenary of Pope Leo I.
343 **87** 15l. red 10 15
344 70l. green 55 50
345 300l. brown . . . . 1·50 1·20

88 Route of St. Paul's Journey to Rome

1961. 1900th Anniv of St. Paul's Arrival in Rome.
346 **88** 10l. green 10 10
347 – 15l. black and brown . . . 10 10
348 – 20l. black and red 20 10
349 **88** 30l. blue 30 25
350 – 75l. black and brown . . . 35 30
351 – 200l. black and blue . . . 1·30 1·00
DESIGNS: 15, 75l. St. Paul's arrival in Rome (after sculpture by Maraini); 20, 200l. Basilica of St. Paul-outside-the-Walls, Rome.

89 "L'Osservatore Romano", 1861 and 1961

1961. Centenary of "L'Osservatore Romano" (Vatican newspaper).
352 **89** 40l. black and brown . . . 20 25
353 – 70l. black and blue 55 50
354 – 250l. black and yellow . . 1·70 1·30
DESIGNS: 70l. "L'Osservatore Romano" offices; 250l. Printing machine.

90 St. Patrick (ancient sculpture)

1961. 15th Death Centenary of St. Patrick.
355 **90** 10l. green and buff 10 10
356 – 15l. brown and blue . . . 10 10
357 **90** 40l. green and yellow . . . 10 10
358 – 150l. brown and blue . . . 40 35
DESIGN: 15, 150l. St. Patrick's Sanctuary, Lough Derg.

91 Arms of Roncalli Family
92 "The Nativity"

1961. Pope John XXIII's 80th Birthday.

359 **91** 10l. brown and black . . . 10 10
360 – 25l. green and brown . . . 10 10
361 – 30l. violet and blue . . . 10 10
362 – 40l. blue and violet . . . 10 10
363 – 70l. brown and grey . . . 10 15
364 – 115l. black and brown . . 20 25

DESIGNS: 25l. Church of St. Mary, Sotto il Monte; 30l. Church of St. Mary, Monte Santo; 40l. Church of Saints Ambrose and Charles, Rome; 70l. St. Peter's Chair, Vatican Basilica; 115l. Pope John XXIII.

1961. Christmas. Centres multicoloured.

365 **92** 15l. green 10 10
366 40l. black 10 10
367 70l. purple 15 20

POPVLI OMNES CONTRA FEBRES PALVSTRES
SIXTVS V
L.15
POSTE VATICANE

93 "Annunciation" (after F. Valle)
94 "Land Reclamation" Medal of 1588

1962. Air.

368 **93** 1000l. brown . . . . . . 1·10 95
369 1500l. blue . . . . 1·60 1·50

1962. Malaria Eradication.

370 **94** 15l. violet 10 10
371 – 40l. red 10 10
372 **94** 70l. brown 10 10
373 – 300l. green 30 30

DESIGN: 40, 300l. Map of Pontine Marshes reclamation project (at time of Pope Pius VI).

95 "The Good Shepherd" (statue, Lateran Museum)
96 St. Catherine (after Il Sodoma (Bazzi))

1962. Religious Vocations.

374 **95** 10l. black and violet . . . 10 10
375 – 15l. brown and blue . . . 10 10
376 **95** 70l. black and green . . . 20 20
377 – 115l. brown and red . . . 1·30 1·10
378 **95** 200l. black and brown . . . 1·30 1·10

DESIGN: 15, 115l. Wheatfield ready for harvest.

1962. 5th Centenary of St. Catherine of Siena's Canonization.

379 **96** 15l. brown 10 10
380 60l. violet 20 25
381 100l. blue 30 30

97 Paulina M. Jaricot
99 "Faith" (after Raphael)

98 St. Peter and St. Paul (from graffito on child's tomb)

1962. Death Centenary of Paulina M. Jaricot (founder of Society for the Propagation of the Faith). Multicoloured centres.

382 **97** 10l. lilac 10 10
383 50l. green 20 20
384 150l. grey 25 30

1962. 6th International Christian Archaeology Congress, Ravenna.

385 **98** 20l. brown and violet . . . 10 10
386 – 40l. green and brown . . . 10 10
387 **98** 70l. brown and turquoise 10 10
388 – 100l. green and red 10 10

DESIGN: 40, 100l. "The Passion" (from bas relief on tomb in Domitilla cemetery, near Rome).

1962. Ecumenical Council.

389 **99** 5l. brown and blue 10 10
390 – 10l. brown and green . . . 10 10
391 – 15l. brown and red 10 10
392 – 25l. grey and red 10 10
393 – 30l. black and mauve . . . 10 10
394 – 40l. brown and red 10 10
395 – 60l. brown and green . . . 10 10
396 – 115l. red 10 10

DESIGNS—Divine Virtues: 10l. "Hope"; 15l. "Charity" (both after Raphael); 25l. Arms of Pope John XXIII and symbols of Evangelists (frontispiece of "Humanae Salutis" by Arrigo Bravi); 30l. Central Nave, St. Peter's (council venue); 40l. Pope John XXIII; 60l. "St. Peter" (bronze in Vatican Basilica); 115l. The Holy Ghost in form of dove.

100 "The Nativity"

1962. Christmas. Centres multicoloured.

397 **100** 10l. grey 10 10
398 15l. drab 10 10
399 90l. green 10 10

101 "Miracle of the Loaves and Fishes" (after Murillo)
102 Pope John XXIII

1963. Freedom from Hunger.

400 **101** 15l. sepia and brown . . 10 10
401 – 40l. green and red 10 10
402 **101** 100l. brown and blue . . 10 10
403 – 200l. green and turquoise 20 15

DESIGN: 40, 200l. "Miracle of the Fishes" (after Raphael).

1963. Award of Balzan Peace Prize to Pope John XXIII.

404 **102** 15l. brown 10 10
405 160l. black 15 20

103 St. Peter's Keys
104 Pope Paul VI

1963. "Vacant See".

406 **103** 10l. brown 10 10
407 40l. brown on yellow . . 10 10
408 100l. brown on violet . . 10 10

1963. Coronation of Pope Paul VI.

409 **104** 15l. black 10 10
410 – 40l. red 10 10
411 **104** 115l. brown 15 15
412 – 200l. grey 15 20

DESIGN: 40, 200l. Arms of Pope Paul VI.

105 "The Nativity" (African terracotta statuette)
106 St. Cyril

1963. Christmas.

413 **105** 10l. brown and light brown 10 10
414 40l. brown and blue . . . 10 10
415 100l. brown and green . . 10 10

1963. 1100th Anniv of Conversion of Slavs by Saints Cyril and Methodius.

416 **106** 30l. purple 10 10
417 – 70l. brown 10 10
418 – 150l. purple 10 15

DESIGNS: 70l. Map of Moravia; 150l. St. Methodius.

107 Pope Paul VI
108 St. Peter, Pharaoh's Tomb, Wadi-es-Sebua

1964. Pope Paul's Visit to the Holy Land.

419 **107** 15l. black 10 10
420 – 25l. red 10 10
421 – 70l. sepia 10 10
422 – 160l. blue 10 10

DESIGNS: 25l. Church of the Nativity, Bethlehem; 70l. Church of the Holy Sepulchre, Jerusalem; 160l. Well of the Virgin Mary, Nazareth.

1964. Nubian Monuments Preservation.

423 **108** 10l. brown and blue . . . 10 10
424 – 20l. multicoloured 10 10
425 **108** 70l. brown and light brown 10 10
426 – 200l. multicoloured . . . 10 10

DESIGN: 20, 200l. Philae Temple.

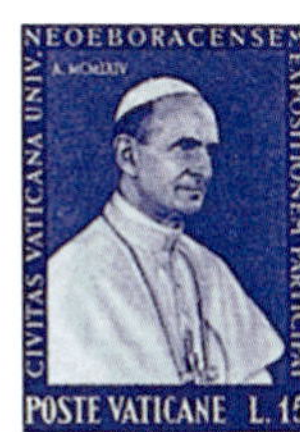

109 Pope Paul VI
110 Michelangelo

1964. Vatican City's Participation in New York World's Fair.

427 **109** 15l. blue 10 10
428 – 50l. brown 10 10
429 **109** 100l. blue 10 10
430 – 250l. brown 10 15

DESIGNS: 50l. Michelangelo's "Pieta"; 250l. Detail of Madonna's head from "Pieta".

1964. 400th Death Anniv of Michelangelo. Paintings in the Sistine Chapel.

431 **110** 10l. black 10 10
432 – 25l. purple 10 10
433 – 30l. green 10 10
434 – 40l. violet 10 10
435 – 150l. green 10 10

PAINTINGS: 25l. Prophet Isaiah; 30l. Delphic Sibyl; 40l. Prophet Jeremiah; 150l. Prophet Joel.

111 "The Good Samaritan" (after Emilio Greco)

1964. Red Cross Centenary (1963). Cross in red.

436 **111** 10l. brown 10 10
437 30l. blue 10 10
438 300l. brown 20 20

112 "Christmas Scene" (after Kimiko Koseki)
114 Pope Paul at prayer

113 Cues's Birthplace

1964. Christmas.

439 **112** 10l. multicoloured 10 10
440 15l. multicoloured 10 10
441 135l. multicoloured . . . 10 10

1964. 500th Death Anniv of Nicholas Cues (Cardinal Cusanus).

442 **113** 40l. green 10 10
443 – 200l. red 10 15

DESIGN: 200l. Cardinal Cusanus's sepulchre, St. Peter's (relief by A. Bregno).

1964. Pope Paul's Visit to India.

444 **114** 15l. purple 10 10
445 – 25l. green 10 10
446 – 60l. brown 10 10
447 – 200l. purple 10 15

DESIGN—HORIZ: 25l. Public altar, "The Oval", Bombay; 60l. "Gateway to India", Bombay. VERT: 200l. Pope Paul walking across map of India.

115 Sts. Mbaga Tuzinde, Carolus Lwanga and Kizito
116 Dante (after Raphael)

1965. Ugandan Martyrs.

448 – 15l. turquoise 10 10
449 **115** 20l. brown 10 10
450 – 30l. blue 10 10
451 – 75l. black 10 10
452 – 100l. red 10 10
453 – 160l. violet 10 10

DESIGNS: 15l. St. Joseph Mukasa and six other martyrs; 30l. Sts. Matthias Mulumba, Noe Mawagalli and Lucas Banabakintu; 75l. Sts. Gonzaga Gonza, Athanasius Bazzekuketta, Pontianus Ngondwe and Bruno Serunkuma; 100l. Sts. Anatolius Kiriggwajjo, Andreas Kaggwa and Adulphus Mukasa; 160l. Sts. Mukasa Kiriwananvu and Gyavira.

1965. 700th Anniv of Dante's Birth.

454 **116** 10l. brown and light brown 10 10
455 – 40l. brown and red . . . 10 10
456 – 70l. brown and green . . 10 10
457 – 200l. brown and blue . . 10 15

DESIGNS—After drawings by Botticelli: 40l. "Inferno"; 70l. "Purgatory"; 200l. "Paradise".

117 St. Benedict (after Perugino)
118 Pope Paul

1965. Declaration of St. Benedict as Patron Saint of Europe.

458 **117** 40l. brown 10 10
459 – 300l. green 20 20

DESIGN: 300l. Montecassino Abbey.

1965. Pope Paul's Visit to the U.N., New York.

460 **118** 20l. brown 10 10
461 – 30l. blue 10 10
462 – 150l. green 10 10
463 **118** 300l. purple 20 20

DESIGN: 30, 150l. U.N.O. Headquarters, New York.

119 "The Nativity" (Peruvian setting)
120 Pope Paul

1965. Christmas.
464 **119** 20l. red 10 10
465 40l. brown 10 10
466 200l. green 10 15

1966.
467 **120** 5l. brown 10 10
468 – 10l. violet 10 10
469 – 15l. brown 10 10
470 – 20l. green 10 10
471 – 30l. brown 10 10
472 – 40l. turquoise 10 10
473 – 55l. blue 10 10
474 – 75l. purple 10 10
475 – 90l. mauve 10 10
476 – 130l. green 10 10
DESIGNS (SCULPTURES): 10l. "Music"; 15l. "Science"; 20l. "Painting"; 30l. "Sculpture"; 40l. "Building"; 55l. "Carpentry"; 75l. "Agriculture"; 90l. "Metallurgy"; 130l. "Learning".

121 Queen Dabrowka and King Mieszko I

1966. Poland's Christian Millennium.
477 **121** 15l. black 10 10
478 – 25l. violet 10 10
479 – 40l. red 10 10
480 – 50l. red 10 10
481 – 150l. grey 10 10
482 – 220l. brown 10 15
DESIGNS: 25l. St. Adalbert (Wojciech) and Wroclaw and Gniezno Cathedrals; 40l. St. Stanislas, Skalka Cathedral and Wawel Royal Palace, Cracow; 50l. Queen Jadwiga (Hedwig); Ostra Brama Gate with Mater Misericordiae, Wilno, and Jagellon University Library, Cracow; 150l. "Black Madonna", Jasna Gora Monastery (Czestochowa) and St. John's Cathedral, Warsaw; 220l. Pope Paul VI greeting Poles.

122 Pope John XXIII and St. Peter's, Rome

1966. 4th Anniv of Opening of Ecumenical Council.
483 **122** 10l. black and red 10 10
484 – 15l. green and brown . . 10 10
485 – 55l. mauve and brown . . 10 10
486 – 90l. black and green . . . 10 10
487 – 100l. yellow and green . . 10 10
488 – 130l. sepia and brown . . 10 10
DESIGNS: 15l. Book of Prayer, St. Peter's; 55l. Mass; 90l. Pope Paul with Patriarch Athenagoras; 100l. Episcopal ring; 130l. Pope Paul at closing ceremony (12.10.65).

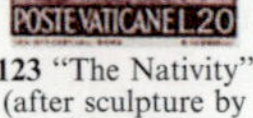

123 "The Nativity" (after sculpture by Scorzelli)
124 Jetliner over St. Peter's

1966. Christmas.
489 **123** 20l. purple 10 10
490 55l. green 10 10
491 225l. brown 10 15

1967. Air.
492 **124** 20l. violet 10 10
493 – 40l. lilac and pink 10 10
494 – 90l. blue and grey 10 10
495 **124** 100l. black and red 10 10
496 – 200l. lilac and grey . . . 10 15
497 – 500l. brown & light brown 35 30
DESIGNS: 40, 200l. Radio mast and St. Gabriel's statue; 90, 500l. Aerial view of St. Peter's.

125 St. Peter
126 "The Three Shepherd Children" (sculpture)

1967. 1900th Anniv of Martyrdom of Saints Peter and Paul. Multicoloured.
498 15l. Type **125** 10 10
499 20l. St. Paul 10 10
500 55l. The two Saints 10 10
501 90l. Bernini's baldachin, St. Peter's 10 10
502 220l. Arnolfo di Cambio's tabernacle, St. Paul's Basilica 15 15

1967. 50th Anniv of Fatima Apparitions. Multicoloured.
503 30l. Type **126** 10 10
504 50l. Basilica of Fatima . . . 10 10
505 200l. Pope Paul VI praying before Virgin's statue at Fatima 20 20

127 Congress Emblem
128 "The Nativity" (Byzantine carving)

1967. 3rd World Apostolic Laity Congress, Rome.
506 **127** 40l. red 15 15
507 130l. blue 15 15

1967. Christmas.
508 **128** 25l. multicoloured 10 10
509 55l. multicoloured 10 10
510 180l. multicoloured . . . 10 15

129 "Angel Gabriel" (detail from "The Annunciation" by Fra Angelico)
130 Pope Paul VI

1968. Air.
511 **129** 1000l. red on cream . . . 85 65
512 1500l. black on cream . . 1·20 1·00

1968. Pope Paul's Visit to Colombia.
513 **130** 25l. brown and black . . 10 10
514 – 55l. brown, grey and black 10 10
515 – 220l. brown, blue & black 10 15
DESIGNS: 55l. Monstrance (Raphael's "Disputa"); 220l. Map of South America.

131 "The Holy Child of Prague"
132 "The Resurrection" (Fra Angelico)

1968. Christmas.
516 **131** 20l. purple and red . . . 10 10
517 50l. violet and lilac . . . 10 10
518 250l. blue and light blue 20 20

1969. Easter.
519 **132** 20l. red and buff . . . 10 10
520 90l. green and buff . . . 10 10
521 180l. blue and buff . . . 10 10

133 Colonnade
134 Pope with Young Africans

1969. Europa.
522 **133** 50l. brown and grey . . . 10 10
523 90l. brown and red . . . 15 15
524 130l. brown and green . . 15 20

1969. Pope Paul's Visit to Uganda.
525 **134** 25l. brown and ochre . . 10 10
526 – 55l. brown and red . . . 10 10
527 – 250l. multicoloured . . . 10 15
DESIGNS: 55l. Pope with African bishops; 250l. Map of Africa and olive branch.

135 Pope Pius IX
136 "Expo 70" Emblem

1969. Centenary of St. Peter's Circle Society.
528 **135** 30l. brown 10 10
529 – 50l. grey 10 10
530 – 220l. purple 10 15
DESIGNS: 50l. Monogram of Society; 220l. Pope Paul VI.

1970. "Expo 70" World's Fair, Osaka. Mult.
531 25l. Type **136** 10 10
532 40l. Osaka Castle 10 10
533 55l. "Madonna and Child" (Domoto) 10 10
534 90l. Vatican pavilion 10 10
535 110l. Mt. Fuji 10 10

137 Commemorative Medal of Pius IX

1970. Centenary of 1st Vatican Council.
536 **137** 20l. brown and orange . . 10 10
537 – 50l. multicoloured 10 10
538 – 180l. purple and red . . . 10 15
DESIGNS: 50l. Arms of Pius IX; 180l. Council souvenir medal.

138 "Christ" (Simone Martini)

1970. 50th Anniv of Pope Paul's Ordination as Priest. Multicoloured.
539 15l. Type **138** 10 10
540 25l. "Christ" (R. v. d. Weyden) 10 10
541 50l. "Christ" (Durer) 10 10
542 90l. "Christ" (El Greco) . . . 10 10
543 180l. Pope Paul VI 10 10

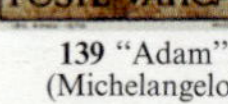

139 "Adam" (Michelangelo)
140 Pope Paul VI

1970. 25th Anniv of United Nations.
544 20l. Type **139** 10 10
545 90l. "Eve" (Michelangelo) . . 10 10
546 220l. Olive branch 10 15

1970. Pope Paul's Visit to Asia and Oceania. Multicoloured.
547 25l. Type **140** 10 10
548 55l. "Holy Child of Cebu" (Philippines) 10 10
549 100l. "Madonna and Child", Darwin Cathedral (G. Hamori) 10 10
550 130l. Manila Cathedral . . . 10 10
551 220l. Sydney Cathedral . . . 10 15

141 "Angel with Lectern"
142 "Madonna and Child" (F. Gnissi)

1971. Racial Equality Year. Multicoloured.
552 20l. Type **141** 10 10
553 40l. "Christ Crucified, and Doves" 10 10
554 50l. Type **141** 10 10
555 130l. As 40l. 10 10

1971. Easter. Religious Paintings. Multicoloured.
556 25l. Type **142** 10 10
557 40l. "Madonna and Child" ("Sassetta", S. di Giovanni) 10 10
558 55l. "Madonna and Child" (C. Crivelli) 10 10
559 90l. "Madonna and Child" (C. Maratta) 10 10
560 180l. "The Holy Family" (G. Ceracchini) 10 15

143 "St. Dominic Guzman" (Sienese School)

1971. 800th Birth Anniv of St. Dominic Guzman (founder of Preaching Friars Order). Mult.
561 25l. Type **143** 10 10
562 55l. Portrait by Fra Angelico 10 10
563 90l. Portrait by Titian . . . 10 10
564 180l. Portrait by El Greco . . 10 15

144 "St. Matthew"

1971. Air.
565 **144** 200l. black and green . . 20 20
566 – 300l. black and brown . . 30 25
567 – 500l. black and pink . . . 55 45
568 – 1000l. black and mauve . . 65 55
DESIGNS—"The Four Evangelists" (ceiling frescoes by Fra Angelico in the Niccolina Chapel, Vatican City): 300l. "St. Mark"; 500l. "St. Luke"; 1000l. "St. John".

145 "St. Stephen" (from chasuble, Szekesfehervar Church, Hungary)
146 Bramante's Design for Cupola, St. Peter's

1971. Millennium of St. Stephen, King of Hungary.
569 **145** 50l. multicoloured 10 10
570 – 180l. black and yellow . . 10 15
DESIGN: 180l. "Madonna, Patroness of Hungary", (sculpture, circa 1511).

1972. Bramante Celebrations.
571 **146** 25l. black and yellow . . 10 10
572 – 90l. black and yellow . . 10 10
573 – 130l. black and yellow . . 15 15

DESIGNS: 90l. Donato Bramante (architect) from medal; 130l. Spiral staircase, Innocent VIII's Belvedere, Vatican.

147 "St. Mark at Sea" (mosaic)

1972. U.N.E.S.C.O. "Save Venice" Campaign. Multicoloured.
574 25l. Type **147** 20 20
575 50l. Venice (top left-hand section) 15 20
576 50l. Venice (top right-hand section) 15 20
577 50l. Venice (bottom left-hand section) 15 20
578 50l. Venice (bottom right-hand section) 15 20
579 180l. St. Mark's Basilica 90 70
Nos. 575/8 are smaller 39 × 28 mm and were issued together, se-tenant, forming a composite design of a 1581 fresco showing a panoramic map of Venice.

148 Gospel of St. Mark (from codex "Biblia dell'Aracoeli")

1972. International Book Year. Illuminated Manuscripts. Multicoloured.
581 30l. Type **148** 10 10
582 50l. Gospel of St. Luke ("Biblia dell'Aracoeli") 10 10
583 90l. 2nd Epistle of St. John (Bologna codex) 10 10
584 100l. Revelation of St. John (Bologna codex) 10 10
585 130l. Epistle of St. Paul to the Romans (Italian codex) 15 15

149 Luigi Orione (founder of "Caritas")

1972. Birth Centenaries. Multicoloured.
586 50l. Type **149** 10 10
587 180l. Lorenzo Perosi (composer) 10 15

150 Cardinal Bassarione (Roselli fresco, Sistine Chapel)
151 Congress Emblem

1972. 500th Death Anniv of Cardinal Bassarione.
588 – 40l. green 10 10
589 **150** 90l. red 10 10
590 – 130l. black 15 15
DESIGNS: 40l. "Reading of Bull of Union" (relief); 130l. Arms of Cardinal Bassarione.

1973. Int Eucharistic Congress. Melbourne. Mult.
591 25l. Type **151** 10 10
592 75l. Michelangelo's "Pieta" 10 10
593 300l. Melbourne Cathedral 20 20

152 St. Theresa's Birthplace
153 Torun (birthplace)

1973. Birth Centenary of St. Theresa of Lisieux.
594 **152** 25l. black and red 10 10
595 – 55l. black and yellow 10 10
596 – 220l. black and blue 20 15
DESIGNS: 55l. St. Theresa; 220l. Basilica of Lisieux.

1973. 500th Birth Anniv of Copernicus.
597 **153** 20l. green 10 10
598 – 50l. brown 10 10
599 **153** 100l. purple 15 15
600 – 130l. blue 15 20
DESIGN: 50, 130l. Copernicus.

154 "St. Wenceslas"

1973. Millenary of Prague Diocese. Mult.
601 20l. Type **154** 10 10
602 90l. Arms of Prague Diocese 10 10
603 150l. Tower of Prague Cathedral 20 15
604 220l. "St. Adalbert" 20 20

155 Church of St. Hripsime
156 "Angel" (porch of St. Mark's, Venice)

1973. 800th Death Anniv of St. Narsete Shnorali (Armenian patriarch).
605 **155** 25l. brown and ochre 10 10
606 – 90l. black and lilac 10 10
607 – 180l. purple and green 15 20
DESIGNS: 90l. Armenian "khatchkar" (stone stele) inscribed "Victory"; 180l. St. Narsete Shnorali.

1974. Air.
608 **156** 2500l. multicoloured 2·00 1·50

157 "And there was Light"
159 Pupils

158 Noah's Ark and Dove

1974. International Book Year (1973). "The Bible". Biblical Texts. Multicoloured.
609 15l. Type **157** 10 10
610 25l. "Noah entrusts himself to God" (horiz) 10 10
611 50l. "The Annunciation" 10 10
612 90l. "The Nativity" 10 10
613 180l. "The Lord feeds His People" (horiz) 15 20

1974. Centenary of U.P.U. Mosaics. Multicoloured.
614 50l. Type **158** 10 10
615 90l. Sheep in landscape 20 20

1974. 700th Death Anniv of St. Thomas Aquinas (founder of Fra Angelico School). "The School of St. Thomas" (painting, St. Mark's Convent, Florence). Each brown and gold.
616 50l. Type **159** 10 10
617 90l. St. Thomas and pupils (24 × 40 mm) 15 15
618 220l. Pupils (different) 20 15
Nos. 616/18 were issued together, se-tenant, forming a composite design.

160 "Civita" (medieval quarter), Bagnoregio
161 Christus Victor

1974. 700th Death Anniv of St. Bonaventura of Bagnoregio. Wood-carvings. Multicoloured.
619 40l. Type **160** 10 10
620 90l. "Tree of Life" (13th-century motif) 10 10
621 220l. "St. Bonaventura (B. Gozzoli) 15 20

1974. Holy Year (1975). Multicoloured.
622 10l. Type **161** 10 10
623 25l. Christ 10 10
624 30l. Christ (different) 10 10
625 40l. Cross and dove 10 10
626 50l. Christ enthroned 10 10
627 55l. St. Peter 10 10
628 90l. St. Paul 10 10
629 100l. St. Peter 10 10
630 130l. St. Paul 10 10
631 220l. Arms of Pope Paul VI 15 20
632 250l. Pope Paul VI giving blessing 15 20

162 Fountain, St. Peter's Square

1975. European Architectural Heritage Year. Fountains.
633 **162** 20l. black and brown 10 10
634 – 40l. black and lilac 10 10
635 – 50l. black and pink 10 10
636 – 90l. black and green 10 10
637 – 100l. black and green 10 10
638 – 200l. black and blue 20 15
FOUNTAINS: 40l. Piazza St. Martha; 50l. Del Forno; 90l. Belvedere courtyard; 100l. Academy of Sciences; 200l. Galley fountain.

163 "Pentecost" (El Greco)

1975. Pentecost.
639 **163** 300l. orange and red 25 25

164 "Miracle of Loaves and Fishes" (gilt glass)

1975. 9th International Christian Archaeological Congress. 4th-century Art. Multicoloured.
640 30l. Type **164** 20 10
641 150l. Christ (painting) 20 10
642 200l. Raising of Lazarus (gilt glass) 20 20

165 Pope Sixtus IV investing Bartolomeo Sacchi as First Librarian (fresco)

1975. 500th Anniv of Apostolic Library.
643 **165** 70l. red and violet 10 10
644 – 100l. green and light green 10 10
645 – 250l. red and blue 20 20
DESIGNS—VERT: 100l. Pope Sixtus IV (codex). HORIZ: 250l. Pope Sixtus IV visiting library (fresco).

166 Passionists' House, Argentario

1975. Death Bicentenary of St. Paul of the Cross (founder of Passionist religious order). Mult.
646 50l. Type **166** 10 10
647 150l. "St. Paul" (D. della Porta) (26 × 31 mm) 15 15
648 300l. Basilica of Saints John and Paul 20 20

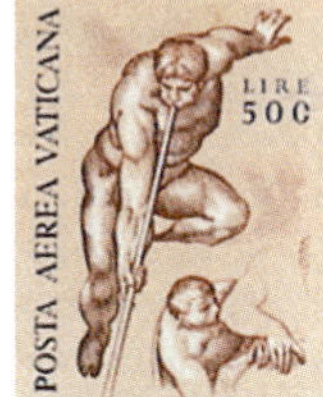

167 Detail from Painting
168 "The Last Judgement" (detail)

1975. International Women's Year. Painting by Fra Angelico. Multicoloured.
649 100l. Type **167** 20 15
650 200l. Detail from painting (different) 20 20

1976. Air.
651 **168** 500l. brown and blue 90 75
652 – 1000l. brown and blue 1·00 75
653 – 2500l. brown and blue 1·40 1·00
DESIGNS: 1000l., 2500l. Different motifs from Michelangelo's "The Last Judgement".

169 "Madonna in Glory with the Child Jesus and Six Saints" (detail)

1976. 400th Death Anniv of Titian. Details from "The Madonna in Glory with the Child Jesus and Six Saints".
654 **169** 100l. red 20 20
655 – 300l. red 25 25

170 Eucharist Ear of Wheat and Globe
171 "Transfiguration" (detail)

1976. 41st Int Eucharist Congress, Philadelphia.
656 **170** 150l. multicoloured 20 15
657 – 200l. gold and blue 20 20
658 – 400l. gold and green 35 30
DESIGNS: 200l. Eucharist within protective hands; 400l. Adoration of the Eucharist.

1976. Details of Raphael's "Transfiguration". Multicoloured.
659 30l. Type **171** ("Moses") 10 10
660 40l. "Christ Transfigured" 10 10
661 50l. "Prophet Elijah" 10 10
662 100l. "Two Apostles" 10 10
663 150l. "The Relatives" 15 10
664 200l. "Landscape" 20 20

172 St. John's Tower and Fountain

1976. Architecture.
665 **172** 50l. brown and lilac 10 10
666 – 100l. sepia and brown 10 10
667 – 120l. black and grey 10 10
668 – 180l. black and grey 20 15

669 – 250l. brown and stone 20 20
670 – 300l. purple 20 20

DESIGNS: 100l. Fountain of the Sacrament; 120l. Fountain at entrance to Gardens; 180l. Cupola of St. Peter's and Sacristy Basilica; 250l. Borgia Tower, Sistine Chapel and Via della Fondamenta; 300l. Apostolic Palace, Courtyard of St. Damasius.

173 "Canticles of Brother Sun" (detail)

1977. 750th Death Anniv of St. Francis of Assisi. Details from "Canticles of Brother Sun" by D. Cambellotti. Multicoloured.

671 50l. Type **173** ("The Lord's Creatures") 10 10
672 70l. "Brother Sun" 10 10
673 100l. "Sister Moon and Stars" 10 10
674 130l. "Sister Water" 10 15
675 170l. "Praise in Infirmities and Tribulations" 15 15
676 200l. "Praise for Bodily Death" 20 15

174 Detail from Fresco
175 "Death of the Virgin"

1977. 600th Anniv of Return of Pope Gregory from Avignon. Fresco by G. Vasari. Multicoloured.

677 170l. Type **174** 20 20
678 350l. Detail from fresco (different) 35 25

1977. Festival of Assumption. Miniatures from Apostolic Library. Multicoloured.

679 200l. Type **175** 20 20
680 400l. "Assumption of Virgin into Heaven" 35 30

176 "God of the Nile"

1977. Classical Sculpture in Vatican Museums (1st series). Statues. Multicoloured.

681 50l. Type **176** 10 10
682 120l. "Pericles" 10 10
683 130l. "Husband and Wife with joined Hands" 15 15
684 150l. "Belvedere Apollo" 15 15
685 170l. "Laocoon" 15 20
686 350l. "Belvedere Torso" 20 25

See also Nos. 687/92.

177 "Creation of the Human Race"

1977. Classical Sculpture in Vatican Museums (2nd series). Paleo-Christian Sarcophagi Carvings. Multicoloured.

687 50l. Type **177** 10 10
688 70l. "Three Youths in the Fiery Furnace" 10 10
689 100l. "Adoration of the Magi" 10 10
690 130l. "Christ raising Lazarus from the Dead" 15 15
691 200l. "The Good Shepherd" 20 20
692 400l. "Resurrection" 30 30

178 "Madonna with the Parrot" (detail)
180 Arms of Pope Pius IX

179 "The Face of Christ"

1977. 400th Birth Anniv of Rubens.
693 **178** 350l. multicoloured 30 30

1978. 80th Birthday of Pope Paul VI. Mult.
694 350l. Type **179** 30 25
695 400l. "Pope Paul VI" (drawing by L. B. Barriviera) 35 30

1978. Death Cent of Pope Pius IX. Multicoloured.
696 130l. Type **180** 10 10
697 170l. Seal of Pius IX 15 15
698 200l. Portrait of Pius IX 20 20

181 Microwave Antenna and Radio Vatican Emblem
182 St. Peter's Keys

1978. Air. 10th World Telecommunications Day.
699 **181** 1000l. multicoloured 85 65
700 2000l. multicoloured 1·70 1·40
701 3000l. multicoloured 2·50 1·90

1978. "Vacant See".
702 **182** 120l. blue and violet 20 15
703 150l. pink and violet 20 15
704 250l. yellow and violet 20 20

183 St. Peter's Keys
184 Pope John Paul I on Throne

1978. "Vacant See".
705 **183** 120l. yellow, blue & black 20 15
706 200l. yellow, red and black 20 15
707 250l. multicoloured 20 20

1978. Pope John Paul I Commem. Mult.
708 70l. Type **184** 10 10
709 120l. The Pope smiling 15 15
710 250l. The Pope in Vatican Gardens 20 20
711 350l. The Pope giving blessing (horiz) 20 20

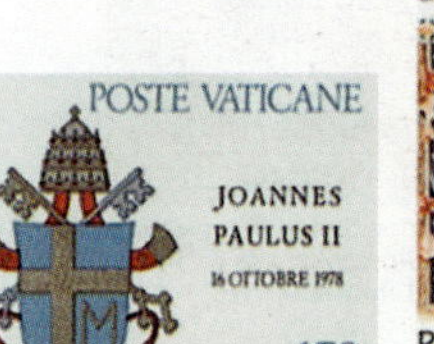

185 Arms of Pope John Paul II
186 The Martyrdom (14th-century Latin codex)

1979. Inauguration of Pontificate of Pope John Paul II. Multicoloured.
712 170l. Type **185** 20 15
713 250l. The Pope giving his blessing 20 20
714 400l. "Christ handing the keys to St. Peter" (relief, A. Buonvicino) 35 30

1979. 900th Death Anniv of St. Stanislaus. Multicoloured.
715 120l. Type **186** 20 15
716 150l. St. Stanislaus appears to the people (14th century Latin codex) 20 15
717 250l. Gold reliquary 20 20
718 500l. Cracow Cathedral 40 35

187 Meteorograph

1979. Death Centenary of Angelo Secchi (astronomer). Multicoloured.
719 180l. Type **187** 20 15
720 220l. Spectroscope 20 20
721 300l. Telescope 25 25

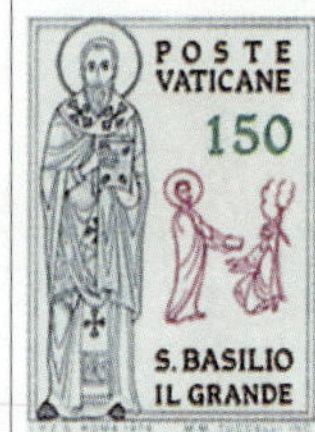

188 St. Basil and Vignette "Handing Monastic Laws to a Hermit"
189 Aerial View of Vatican City

1979. 160th Death Anniv of St. Basil the Great. Multicoloured.
722 150l. Type **188** 20 15
723 520l. St. Basil and vignette "Caring for the Sick" 40 35

1979. 50th Anniv of Vatican City State.
724 **189** 50l. brown, black and pink 10 10
725 – 70l. multicoloured 10 10
726 – 120l. multicoloured 10 10
727 – 150l. multicoloured 10 10
728 – 170l. multicoloured 20 15
729 – 250l. multicoloured 20 20
730 – 450l. multicoloured 35 40

DESIGNS—POPES AND ARMS: 70l. Pius XI; 120l. Pius XII; 150l. John XXIII; 170l. Paul VI; 250l. John Paul I; 450l. John Paul II.

190 Child in Swaddling Clothes (relief, Foundling Hospital, Florence)

1979. International Year of the Child. Sculptures by Della Robbia.
731 **190** 50l. multicoloured 15 15
732 – 120l. multicoloured 20 15
733 – 200l. multicoloured 20 20
734 – 350l. multicoloured 25 30

DESIGNS: 120l. to 350l. Similar sculptures.

191 Abbot Desiderius offering Codices to St. Benedict

1980. 1500th Birth Anniv of St. Benedict of Nursia (founder of Benedictine Order). Multicoloured.
735 80l. Type **191** 10 10
736 100l. St. Benedict composing rules of the Order 10 10
737 150l. Page of St. Benedict's Rules 15 15
738 220l. Death of St. Benedict 20 15
739 450l. Montecassino Abbey (after Paul Bril) 35 35

192 Hands reaching out to Pope and Arms of Santo Domingo

1980. Air. Pope John Paul II's Journeys (1st series). Different coats of arms.
740 **192** 200l. multicoloured 20 15
741 – 300l. multicoloured 30 20
742 – 500l. violet, red and black 45 35
743 – 1000l. multicoloured 90 70
744 – 1500l. multicoloured 1·40 95
745 – 2000l. red, blue and black 1·80 1·50
746 – 3000l. black, red and blue 2·75 2·10

COATS OF ARMS: 300l. Mexico; 500l. Poland; 1000l. Ireland; 1500l. United States; 2000l. United Nations; 3000l. Pope John Paul II, Archbishop Dimitrios and arms of Turkey.

See also Nos. 768/78, 814/25, 862/9, 886/93, 912/16, 940/4, 963/6, 992/6, 1019/22, 1049/51, 1076/80, 1113/14, 1136/41, 1174/9, 1206/11, 1236/40, 1284/8 and 1312/16.

193 Bernini (self-portrait) and Medallion showing Baldacchino, St. Peter's

1980. 300th Death Anniv of Gian Lorenzo Bernini (artist and architect). Multicoloured.
747 80l. Type **193** 10 10
748 170l. Bernini and medallion showing his plan for St. Peter's 20 15
749 250l. Bernini, medallion of bronze chair and group "Doctors of the Church", St. Peter's 20 20
750 350l. Bernini and medallion of Apostolic Palace stairway 30 30

194 St. Albertus on Mission of Peace

1980. 700th Death Anniv of St. Albertus Magnus. Multicoloured.
751 300l. Type **194** 25 25
752 400l. St. Albertus as Bishop 35 30

195 Communion of the Saints

1980. Feast of All Saints. Multicoloured.
753 250l. Type **195** 20 20
754 500l. Christ and saints 40 40

196 Marconi, Pope Pius XI and Radio Emblem

1981. 50th Anniv of Vatican Radio. Mult.
755 100l. Type **196** 10 10
756 150l. Microphone 15 15
757 200l. Antenna of Santa Maria di Galeria Radio Centre and statue of Archangel Gabriel 20 20
758 600l. Pope John Paul II 45 40

197 Virgil and his Writing-desk

1981. Death Bimillenary of Virgil (Roman poet). Multicoloured.
759 350l. Type **197** 35 40
760 600l. As Type **197** but inscr "P. VERGILI MARONIS AENEIDOS LIBRI" . . . 55 55

198 Congress Emblem and Apparition of Virgin to St. Bernadette

1981. 42nd International Eucharistic Congress, Lourdes. Multicoloured.
761 80l. Congress emblem 10 10
762 150l. Type **198** 15 15
763 200l. Emblem and pilgrims going to Lourdes 20 20
764 500l. Emblem and Bishop with faithful venerating Virgin 45 40

199 Jan van Ruusbroec writing Treatise

201 Arms of John Paul II

200 Turin Shroud and I.Y.D.P. Emblem

1981. 600th Death Anniv of Jan van Ruusbroec (Flemish mystic). Multicoloured.
765 200l. Type **199** 20 20
766 300l. Ruusbroec 25 30

1981. International Year of Disabled Persons.
767 **200** 600l. multicoloured . . . 45 45

1981. Pope John Paul II's Journeys (2nd series). Multicoloured.
768 50l. Type **201** 10 10
769 100l. Crucifix and map of Africa 10 10
770 120l. Hands holding crucifix 15 15
771 150l. Pope performing baptism 15 15
772 200l. Pope embracing African bishop 20 20
773 250l. Pope blessing sick man 25 25
774 300l. Notre-Dame Cathedral, Paris 30 25
775 400l. Pope addressing U.N.E.S.C.O., Paris . . . 35 35
776 600l. "Christ of the Andes", Rio de Janeiro 55 50
777 700l. Cologne Cathedral . . 65 60
778 900l. Pope giving blessing . . 85 75

202 Agnes handing Church to Grand Master of the Crosiers of the Red Star

203 "Pueri Cantores" (left panel)

1982. 700th Death Anniv of Blessed Agnes of Prague. Multicoloured.
779 700l. Type **202** 65 55
780 900l. Agnes receiving letter from St. Clare 80 70

1982. 500th Death Anniv of Luca della Robbia (sculptor).
781 **203** 1000l. green and blue . . 90 75
782 – 1000l. multicoloured . . . 90 75
783 – 1000l. green and blue . . 90 75
DESIGNS—As T **203**: No. 783, "Pueri Cantores" (right panel). 44 × 36 mm: No. 782, "Virgin Mary in Prayer".

204 Virgin Mary and St. Joseph clothe St. Theresa

205 Examining Globe

1982. 400th Death Anniv of St. Theresa of Avila.
784 **204** 200l. orange, grey and red 20 15
785 – 600l. grey, orange and blue 55 45
786 – 1000l. grey, orange and mauve 90 75
DESIGNS: 600l. Ecstasy of St. Theresa; 1000l. St. Theresa writing "The Interior Castle".

1982. 400th Anniv of Gregorian Calendar. Details from Pope Gregory XIII's tomb.
787 **205** 200l. green 20 15
788 – 300l. black 30 25
789 – 700l. mauve 65 60
DESIGNS: 300l. Presenting proposals to Pope Gregory XIII; 700l. Kneeling figures.

206 "Nativity" (Veit Stoss)

1982. Christmas.
791 **206** 300l. stone, brown & gold 30 25
792 – 450l. lilac, purple and silver 35 35
DESIGN: 450l. "Nativity with Pope John Paul II" (Enrico Manfrini).

207 Crucifixion

209 "Theology"

1983. Holy Year. Multicoloured.
793 300l. Type **207** 30 25
794 350l. Christ the Redeemer . . 35 25
795 400l. Pope bringing message of redemption to world . . 40 30
796 2000l. Dove of the Holy Spirit passing through Holy Door . . . . 1·80 1·50

1983. 500th Birth Anniv of Raphael (artist).
798 **209** 50l. blue and ultramarine 10 10
799 – 400l. purple and mauve 35 35
800 – 500l. brown and chestnut 50 40
801 – 1200l. green and turquoise 1·10 95
DESIGNS—Allegories on the Segnatura Room ceiling: 400l. "Poetry"; 500l. "Justice"; 1200l. "Philosophy".

210 "Moses explaining the Law to the People" (Luca Signorelli)

1983. Air. World Communications Year. Multicoloured.
804 2000l. Type **210** . . . . . . 1·80 1·30
805 5000l. "St. Paul preaching in Athens" (Raphael) . . . . 4·00 3·25

211 Mendel and Hybrid Experiment

212 St. Casimir and Vilna Cathedral and Castle

1984. Death Centenary of Gregor Johan Mendel (geneticist).
806 **211** 450l. multicoloured . . . 55 50
807 1500l. multicoloured . . . 1·50 1·20

1984. 500th Death Anniv of St. Casimir (patron saint of Lithuania).
808 **212** 550l. multicoloured . . . 55 50
809 1200l. multicoloured . . . 1·30 1·10

213 Pontifical Academy of Sciences

1984. Cultural and Scientific Institutions.
810 **213** 150l. yellow and brown 20 20
811 – 450l. multicoloured . . . 50 40
812 – 550l. yellow and violet . . 60 50
813 – 1500l. yellow and blue . . 1·50 1·20
DESIGNS: 450l. Seals and document from Vatican Secret Archives; 550l. Entrance to Vatican Apostolic Library; 1500l. Vatican Observatory, Castelgandolfo.

214 Pope in Karachi

1984. Pope John Paul II's Journeys (3rd series). Multicoloured.
814 50l. Type **214** 10 10
815 100l. Pope and image of Our Lady of Penafrancia, Philippines 10 10
816 150l. Pope with crucifix (Guam) 15 15
817 250l. Pope and Tokyo Cathedral 35 30
818 300l. Pope at Anchorage, Alaska 20 20
819 400l. Crucifix, crowd and map of Africa 30 25
820 450l. Pope and image of Our Lady of Fatima (Portugal) 35 25
821 550l. Pope, Archbishop of Westminster and Canterbury Cathedral . . . 90 65
822 1000l. Pope and image of Our Lady of Lujan (Argentina) . . . . 1·60 1·10
823 1500l. Pope, Lake Leman and Geneva . . . . 2·40 1·70
824 2500l. Pope and Mount Titano (San Marino) . . . 4·00 2·75
825 4000l. Pope and Santiago de Compostela Cathedral (Spain) . . . . 6·25 4·50

215 Damascus and Sepulchre of Sts. Marcellinus and Peter

1984. 1600th Death Anniv of Pope St. Damasus. Multicoloured.
826 200l. Type **215** 20 20
827 500l. Damasus and epigraph from St. Januarius's tomb 55 55
828 2000l. Damasus and basilica ruins . . . . 1·80 1·70

216 More (after Holbein) and Map

1985. 450th Death Anniv of Saint Thomas More. Multicoloured.
829 250l. Type **216** 30 30
830 400l. St. Thomas More and title page of "Utopia" . . 45 45
831 2000l. St. Thomas More and title page of "Life of Thomas More" by Domenico Regi . . . . . 2·00 1·80

217 St. Methodius holding Religious Paintings

1985. 1100th Death Anniv of Saint Methodius. Multicoloured.
832 500l. Type**217** 55 50
833 600l. Saints Cyril and Methodius with Pope Clement I's body 75 65
834 1700l. Saints Benedict, Cyril and Methodius . . . . . 1·60 1·50

218 Cross on Map of Africa

219 Eagle (from Door, St. Paul's Basilica, Rome)

1985. 43rd International Eucharistic Congress, Nairobi. Multicoloured.
835 100l. Type **218** 20 15
836 400l. Assembly of bishops . . 45 40
837 600l. Chalice 70 50
838 2300l. Family gazing at cross 2·75 2·10

1985. 900th Death Anniv of Pope Gregory VII. Multicoloured.
839 150l. Type **219** 20 20
840 450l. Pope Gregory VII 55 50
841 2500l. Pope Gregory's former sarcophagus (horiz) . . . . 3·00 2·40

220 Mosaic Map of Italy and Symbol of Holy See

1985. Ratification of Modification of 1929 Lateran Concordat.
842 **220** 400l. multicoloured . . . 45 40

221 Carriage

222 "Nation shall not Lift up Sword against Nation. . ."

1985. "Italia '85" Int Stamp Exn, Rome.
843 **221** 450l. red and blue 35 40
844 – 1500l. blue and mauve . . 1·20 1·10
DESIGN: 1500l. Carriage (different).

1986. International Peace Year. Multicoloured.
846 50l. Type **222** 10 10
847 350l. Messenger's feet ("How beautiful ... are the feet ...") 40 35

848 450l. Profiles and olive branch ("Blessed are the peace-makers ...") 60 50
849 650l. Dove and sun ("Glory to God in the highest ...") 75 65
850 2000l. Pope's hand releasing dove over rainbow ("Peace is a value with no frontiers ...") 2·20 1·60

223/228 Vatican City (¼-size illustration)

1986. World Heritage. Vatican City. Mult.
851 **223** 550l. multicoloured 80 70
852 **224** 550l. multicoloured 80 70
853 **225** 550l. multicoloured 80 70
854 **226** 550l. multicoloured 80 70
855 **227** 550l. multicoloured 80 70
856 **228** 550l. multicoloured 80 70
Nos. 851/6 were printed together, se-tenant, forming the composite design illustrated.

229 St. Camillus saving Invalid from Flood (after Pierre Subleyras)

1986. Centenary of Proclamation of St. Camillus de Lellis and St. John of God as Patron Saints of Hospitals and the Sick.
857 **229** 700l. green, violet and red 85 70
858 – 700l. blue, green and red 85 70
859 – 2000l. multicoloured 2·40 2·10
DESIGNS: No. 858, St. John supporting the sick (after Gomez Moreno); 859, Emblems of Ministers of the Sick and Brothers Hospitallers, and Pope John Paul II talking to patient.

230 "The Philosophers"

1986. 50th Anniv of Pontifical Academy of Sciences. Details from fresco "School of Athens" by Raphael. Multicoloured.
860 1500l. Type **230** 1·80 1·50
861 2500l. "The Scientists" 2·75 2·30

231 Pope and Young People (Central America)
232 "St. Augustine reading St. Paul's Epistles" (fresco, Benozzo Gozzoli)

1986. Air. Pope John Paul II's Journeys (4th series). Multicoloured.
862 350l. Type **231** 40 35
863 450l. Pope in prayer, Warsaw Cathedral and Our Lady of Czestochowa (Poland) 55 50
864 700l. Pope kneeling and crowd at Lourdes (France) 85 65
865 1000l. Sanctuary of Mariazell and St. Stephen's Cathedral, Vienna (Austria) 1·20 90
866 1500l. Pope and representatives of nations visited (Alaska, Asia and Pacific Islands) 1·60 1·30
867 2000l. Image of St. Nicholas of Flue, Basilica of Einsiedeln and Pope (Switzerland) 2·20 1·50
868 2500l. Crosses, Notre Dame Cathedral, Quebec, and Pope (Canada) 2·75 1·90
869 5000l. Pope, bishop and young people with cross (Spain, Dominican Republic and Puerto Rico) 5·50 3·75

1987. 1600th Anniv of Conversion and Baptism of St. Augustine. Multicoloured.
870 300l. Type **232** 35 35
871 400l. "Baptism of St. Augustine" (Bartolomeo di Gentile) 45 45
872 500l. "Ecstasy of St. Augustine" (fresco, Benozzo Gozzoli) 55 50
873 2200l. "Dispute of the Sacrament" (detail of fresco, Raphael) 2·30 1·90

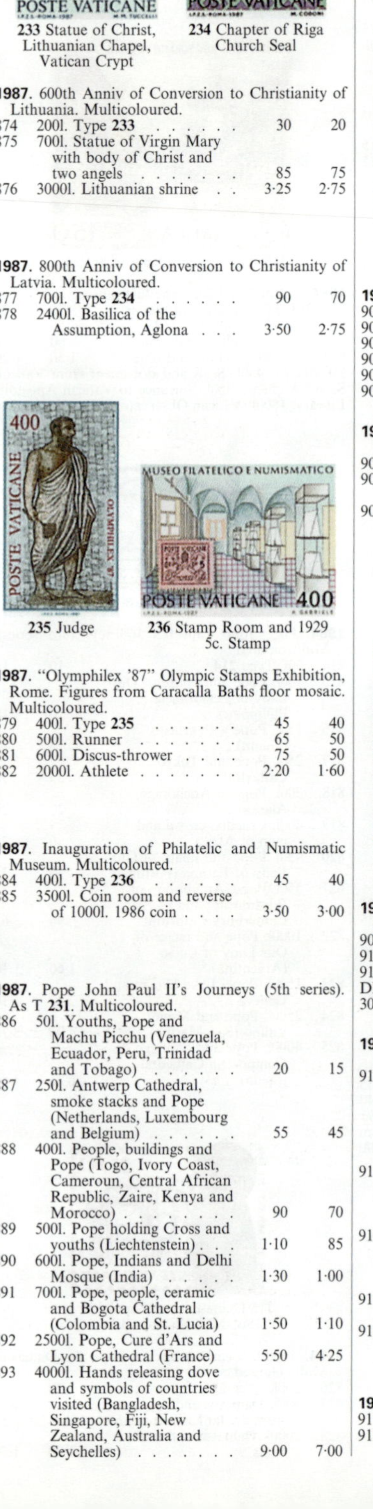

233 Statue of Christ, Lithuanian Chapel, Vatican Crypt
234 Chapter of Riga Church Seal

1987. 600th Anniv of Conversion to Christianity of Lithuania. Multicoloured.
874 200l. Type **233** 30 20
875 700l. Statue of Virgin Mary with body of Christ and two angels 85 75
876 3000l. Lithuanian shrine 3·25 2·75

1987. 800th Anniv of Conversion to Christianity of Latvia. Multicoloured.
877 700l. Type **234** 90 70
878 2400l. Basilica of the Assumption, Aglona 3·50 2·75

235 Judge
236 Stamp Room and 1929 5c. Stamp

1987. "Olymphilex '87" Olympic Stamps Exhibition, Rome. Figures from Caracalla Baths floor mosaic. Multicoloured.
879 400l. Type **235** 45 40
880 500l. Runner 65 50
881 600l. Discus-thrower 75 50
882 2000l. Athlete 2·20 1·60

1987. Inauguration of Philatelic and Numismatic Museum. Multicoloured.
884 400l. Type **236** 45 40
885 3500l. Coin room and reverse of 1000l. 1986 coin 3·50 3·00

1987. Pope John Paul II's Journeys (5th series). As T **231**. Multicoloured.
886 50l. Youths, Pope and Machu Picchu (Venezuela, Ecuador, Peru, Trinidad and Tobago) 20 15
887 250l. Antwerp Cathedral, smoke stacks and Pope (Netherlands, Luxembourg and Belgium) 55 45
888 400l. People, buildings and Pope (Togo, Ivory Coast, Cameroun, Central African Republic, Zaire, Kenya and Morocco) 90 70
889 500l. Pope holding Cross and youths (Liechtenstein) 1·10 85
890 600l. Pope, Indians and Delhi Mosque (India) 1·30 1·00
891 700l. Pope, people, ceramic and Bogota Cathedral (Colombia and St. Lucia) 1·50 1·10
892 2500l. Pope, Cure d'Ars and Lyon Cathedral (France) 5·50 4·25
893 4000l. Hands releasing dove and symbols of countries visited (Bangladesh, Singapore, Fiji, New Zealand, Australia and Seychelles) 9·00 7·00

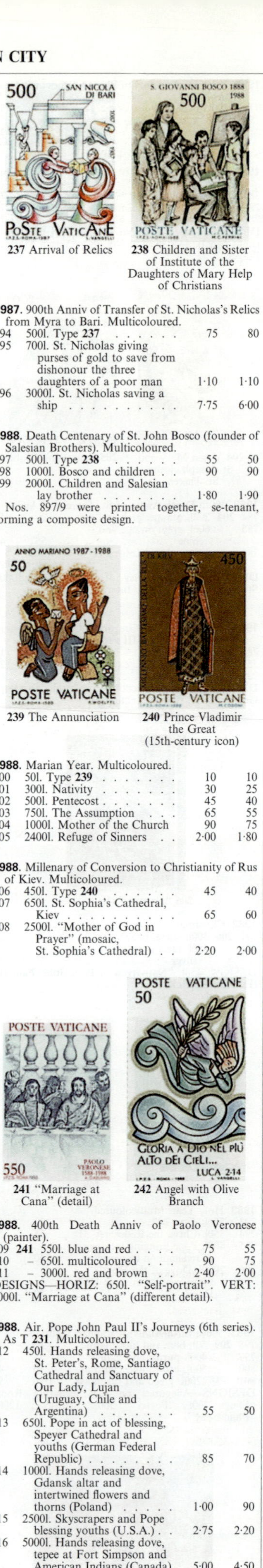

237 Arrival of Relics
238 Children and Sister of Institute of the Daughters of Mary Help of Christians

1987. 900th Anniv of Transfer of St. Nicholas's Relics from Myra to Bari. Multicoloured.
894 500l. Type **237** 75 80
895 700l. St. Nicholas giving purses of gold to save from dishonour the three daughters of a poor man 1·10 1·10
896 3000l. St. Nicholas saving a ship 7·75 6·00

1988. Death Centenary of St. John Bosco (founder of Salesian Brothers). Multicoloured.
897 500l. Type **238** 55 50
898 1000l. Bosco and children 90 90
899 2000l. Children and Salesian lay brother 1·80 1·90
Nos. 897/9 were printed together, se-tenant, forming a composite design.

239 The Annunciation
240 Prince Vladimir the Great (15th-century icon)

1988. Marian Year. Multicoloured.
900 50l. Type **239** 10 10
901 300l. Nativity 30 25
902 500l. Pentecost 45 40
903 750l. The Assumption 65 55
904 1000l. Mother of the Church 90 75
905 2400l. Refuge of Sinners 2·00 1·80

1988. Millenary of Conversion to Christianity of Rus of Kiev. Multicoloured.
906 450l. Type **240** 45 40
907 650l. St. Sophia's Cathedral, Kiev 65 60
908 2500l. "Mother of God in Prayer" (mosaic, St. Sophia's Cathedral) 2·20 2·00

241 "Marriage at Cana" (detail)
242 Angel with Olive Branch

1988. 400th Death Anniv of Paolo Veronese (painter).
909 **241** 550l. blue and red 75 55
910 – 650l. multicoloured 90 75
911 – 3000l. red and brown 2·40 2·00
DESIGNS—HORIZ: 650l. "Self-portrait". VERT: 3000l. "Marriage at Cana" (different detail).

1988. Air. Pope John Paul II's Journeys (6th series). As T **231**. Multicoloured.
912 450l. Hands releasing dove, St. Peter's, Rome, Santiago Cathedral and Sanctuary of Our Lady, Lujan (Uruguay, Chile and Argentina) 55 50
913 650l. Pope in act of blessing, Speyer Cathedral and youths (German Federal Republic) 85 70
914 1000l. Hands releasing dove, Gdansk altar and intertwined flowers and thorns (Poland) 1·00 90
915 2500l. Skyscrapers and Pope blessing youths (U.S.A.) 2·75 2·20
916 5000l. Hands releasing dove, tepee at Fort Simpson and American Indians (Canada) 5·00 4·50

1988. Christmas. Multicoloured.
917 50l. Type **242** 10 10
918 400l. Angel holding olive branch in both hands 35 30
919 500l. Angel with olive branch (flying from right) 55 45
920 550l. Shepherds 60 50
921 850l. Nativity 85 70
922 1500l. Wise Men 1·30 1·10

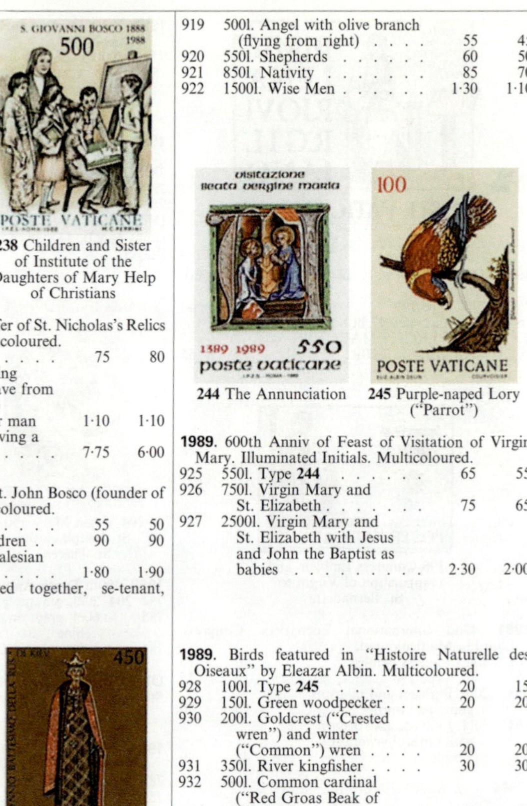

244 The Annunciation
245 Purple-naped Lory ("Parrot")

1989. 600th Anniv of Feast of Visitation of Virgin Mary. Illuminated Initials. Multicoloured.
925 550l. Type **244** 65 55
926 750l. Virgin Mary and St. Elizabeth 75 65
927 2500l. Virgin Mary and St. Elizabeth with Jesus and John the Baptist as babies 2·30 2·00

1989. Birds featured in "Histoire Naturelle des Oiseaux" by Eleazar Albin. Multicoloured.
928 100l. Type **245** 20 15
929 150l. Green woodpecker 20 20
930 200l. Goldcrest ("Crested wren") and winter ("Common") wren 20 20
931 350l. River kingfisher 30 30
932 500l. Common cardinal ("Red Groas Beak of Virginia") 45 45
933 700l. Northern bullfinch ("Bullfinch") 65 60
934 1500l. Northern lapwing ("Lapwing Plover") 1·40 1·30
935 3000l. Green-winged ("French") teal 3·00 2·75

246 Broken Bread (Congress emblem)

1989. 44th International Eucharistic Congress, Seoul.
936 **246** 550l. red and green 55 45
937 – 850l. multicoloured 85 70
938 – 1000l. multicoloured 1·00 85
939 – 2500l. green, pink and violet 2·40 2·00
DESIGNS: 850l. Cross; 1000l. Cross and fishes; 2500l. Small cross on wafer.

247 Pope's Arms, Map of South America and Pope

1989. Pope John Paul II's Journeys (7th series). Multicoloured.
940 50l. Type **247** 20 15
941 550l. Austria 55 50
942 800l. Southern Africa 1·00 75
943 1000l. France 1·20 1·00
944 4000l. Italy 4·25 3·50

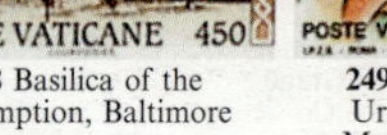

248 Basilica of the Assumption, Baltimore
249 Vision of Ursulines on Mystical Stair

1989. Bicentenary of 1st Catholic Diocese in U.S.A. Each agate and brown.
945 450l. Type **248** 55 50
946 1350l. John Carroll (first Archbishop of Baltimore) 1·60 1·30
947 2400l. Cathedral of Mary Our Queen, Baltimore (after Martin Barry) . . . 2·50 2·10

1990. 450th Death Anniv of St. Angela Merici (founder of Company of St. Ursula). Mult.
948 700l. Type **249** 85 70
949 800l. St. Angela teaching Ursulines . . . . 1·00 85
950 2800l. Ursulines . . . . . . 3·75 2·75

250 Ordination and Arrival in Frisia

251 Abraham

1990. 1300th Anniv of Beginning of St. Willibrord's Missions. Multicoloured.
951 300l. Type **250** 30 30
952 700l. St. Willibrord in Antwerp, creation as bishop by Pope Sergius I and gift of part of Echternach by Abbess of Euren 75 65
953 3000l. Gift of Echternach by King Pepin and St. Willibrord's death . . . 3·00 2·50

1990. 40th Anniv of Caritas Internationalis. Details of mosaic from Basilica of Sta. Maria Maggiore, Rome. Multicoloured.
954 450l. Type **251** 55 50
955 650l. Three visitors 90 70
956 800l. Sarah making bread . . 1·10 95
957 2000l. Visitors seated at Abraham's table . . . . . 2·50 2·20

252 Fishermen on Lake Peking

253 Pope and African Landscape

1990. 300th Anniv of Peking–Nanking Diocese. Details of two enamelled bronze vases given by Peking Apostolic Delegate to Pope Pius IX. Multicoloured.
959 500l. Type **252** 45 45
960 750l. Church of the Immaculate Conception (first Peking church, 1650) 65 60
961 1500l. Lake Peking . . . . . 1·50 1·30
962 2000l. Church of the Redeemer, Peking, 1703 . . 1·80 1·60

1990. Air. Pope John Paul II's Journeys (8th series). Multicoloured.
963 500l. Type **253** 45 45
964 1000l. Northern European landscape (Scandinavia) . . 65 65
965 3000l. Cathedral (Santiago de Compostela, Spain) . . . . 1·50 1·50
966 5000l. Oriental landscape (Korea, Indonesia and Mauritius) . . . . 1·80 1·80

254 Choir of Angels

1990. Christmas. Details of painting by Sebastiano Mainardi. Multicoloured.
967 50l. Type **254** 20 20
968 200l. St. Joseph 20 20
969 650l. Holy Child 75 75
970 750l. Virgin Mary 90 90
971 2500l. "Nativity" (complete picture) (vert) . . . . . 2·75 2·75

255 "Eleazar" (left half)

1991. Restoration of Sistine Chapel. Details of Lunettes of the Ancestors of Christ by Michelangelo. Multicoloured.
972 50l. Type **255** 20 20
973 100l. "Eleazar" (right half) 20 20
974 150l. "Jacob" (left half) . . . 20 20
975 250l. "Jacob" (right half) . . 20 20
976 350l. "Josiah" (left half) . . . 30 30
977 400l. "Josiah" (right half) . . 35 35
978 500l. "Asa" (left half) 45 45
979 650l. "Asa" (right half) . . . 60 60
980 800l. "Zerubbabel" (left half) 75 75
981 1000l. "Zerubbabel" (right half) 90 90
982 2000l. "Azor" (left half) . . . 1·80 1·80
983 3000l. "Azor" (right half) . . 2·75 2·75

256 Title Page and Pope Leo XIII's Arms

1991. Centenary of "Rerum Novarum" (encyclical on workers' rights).
984 **256** 600l. blue and green . . . 55 55
985 – 750l. green and brown . . 75 75
986 – 3500l. purple and black 3·50 3·00
DESIGNS: 750l. Allegory of Church, workers and employers (from Leo XIII's 15th Anniv medal, 1892); 3500l. Profile of Pope Leo XIII (from same medal).

257 Astrograph (astronomical camera)

258 "Apparition of Virgin Mary" (Biagio Puccini)

1991. Centenary of Vatican Observatory. Mult.
987 750l. Type **257** 65 60
988 1000l. Castelgandolfo observatory (horiz) . . . . 1·00 95
989 3000l. Vatican Observatory telescope, Mount Graham, Tucson, U.S.A. . . . . . 3·00 2·50

1991. 600th Anniv of Canonization of St. Bridget (founder of Order of the Holy Saviour). Multicoloured.
990 1500l. Type **258** . . . . . . 1·40 1·20
991 2000l. "Revelation of Christ" (Biagio Puccini) . . . . . 1·90 1·60

259 Cathedral of the Immaculate Conception, Ouagadougou

260 Colonnade of St. Peter's Cathedral, Rome

1991. Pope John Paul II's Journeys (9th series). Multicoloured.
992 200l. Type **259** (Cape Verde, Guinea-Bissau, Mali, Burkina Faso and Chad) 20 20
993 550l. St. Vitus's Cathedral, Prague (Czechoslovakia) 55 55
994 750l. Basilica of Our Lady of Guadaloupe (Mexico and Curacao) 75 75
995 1500l. Ta'Pinu Sanctuary, Gozo (Malta) . . . . . 1·60 1·60
996 3500l. Cathedral of Christ the King, Giteca (Tanzania, Burundi, Rwanda and Ivory Coast) . . . . 4·25 4·25

1991. Synod of Bishops' Special Assembly for Europe. Each black and brown.
997 300l. Type **260** 30 30
998 500l. St. Peter's Cathedral and square 45 45
999 4000l. Apostolic Palace and colonnade . . . . 4·00 4·00
Nos. 997/9 were issued together, se-tenant, forming a composite design.

261 Christopher Columbus

262 "Our Lady of Childbirth"

1992. 500th Anniv of Discovery of America by Columbus. Multicoloured.
1000 500l. Type **261** 45 45
1001 600l. St. Pedro Claver . . . 55 55
1002 850l. "Virgin of the Catholic Kings" 75 70
1003 1000l. Bortolome de las Casas . . . . 1·00 90
1004 2000l. Junipero Serra . . . 2·00 1·80

1992. 500th Death Anniv of Piero della Francesca (painter). Multicoloured.
1006 300l. Type **262** 30 30
1007 750l. "Our Lady of Childbirth" (detail) . . . 75 75
1008 1000l. "The Resurrection" 1·00 1·00
1009 3000l. "The Resurrection" (detail) . . . . 3·00 3·00

263 St. Giuseppe comforting the Sick

264 Maize

1992. 150th Death Anniv of St. Giuseppe Benedetto Cottolengo. Multicoloured.
1010 650l. Type **263** 65 65
1011 850l. St. Giuseppe holding Piccolo Casa della Divina Provvidenza (infirmary), Turin . . . . 1·00 1·00

1992. Plants of the New World. Illustrations from the 18th-century "Phytanthoza Iconographia". Multicoloured.
1012 850l. Type **264** 80 80
1013 850l. Tomatoes ("Solanum pomiferum") 80 75
1014 850l. Cactus ("Opuntia") . . 80 80
1015 850l. Cacao ("Cacaos, Cacavifera") 80 80
1016 850l. Peppers ("Solanum tuberosum") 80 75
1017 850l. Pineapple ("Ananas sagitae") 80 75

265 Our Lady of Guadalupe, Crucifix and Mitres

266 Pope, Dove and Map of Europe

1992. 4th Latin American Episcopal Conference, Santo Domingo.
1018 **265** 700l. gold, emerald and green 85 85

1992. Air. Pope John Paul II's Journeys (10th series). Multicoloured.
1019 500l. Type **266** (Portugal) 45 45
1020 1000l. Map of Europe highlighting Poland . . . 1·00 90
1021 4000l. Our Lady of Czestochowa and map highlighting Poland and Hungary . . . . 3·75 3·25
1022 6000l. Map of South America highlighting Brazil . . . . 6·50 5·00

267 "The Annunciation"

268 "St. Francis healing the Man from Ilerda" (fresco by Giotto in Upper Church, Assisi)

1992. Christmas. Mosaics in Church of Sta.Maria Maggiore, Rome. Multicoloured.
1023 600l. Type **267** 75 75
1024 700l. "Nativity" 85 85
1025 1000l. "Adoration of the Kings" . . . . 1·20 1·20
1026 1500l. "Presentation in the Temple" . . . . 1·60 1·60

1993. "Peace in Europe" Prayer Meeting, Assisi.
1027 **268** 1000l. multicoloured . . 1·40 1·40

269 Dome of St. Peter's Cathedral

270 "The Sacrifice of Isaac"

1993. Architectural Treasures of Rome and the Vatican. Multicoloured.
1028 200l. Type **269** 20 20
1029 300l. St. John Lateran's Basilica 20 20
1030 350l. Basilica of Sta. Maria Maggiore 30 30
1031 500l. St. Paul's Basilica . . 45 45
1032 600l. Apostolic Palace, Vatican 55 55
1033 700l. Apostolic Palace, Lateran 65 65
1034 850l. Papal Palace, Castelgandolfo 75 75
1035 1000l. Chancery Palace . . 90 90
1036 2000l. Palace of Propagation of the Faith . . . . . . 1·60 1·60
1037 3000l. San Calisto Palace . . 2·50 2·50

1993. Ascension Day. Multicoloured.
1038 200l. Type **270** 20 20
1039 750l. Jesus handing New Law to St. Peter 90 90
1040 3000l. Christ watching servant washing Pilate's hands . . . . 3·25 3·25
Nos. 1038/40 were issued together, se-tenant, forming a composite design of the bas-relief "Traditio Legis" from 4th-century sarcophagus.

271 Cross and Grape Vines

273 St. John, Cross, Carp and Moldava River

272 "Crucifixion" (Felice Casorati)

1993. 45th Int Eucharistic Congress, Seville. Mult.
1041 500l. Type **271** 45 45
1042 700l. Cross and hands offering broken bread . . 65 65

1043 1500l. Hands holding chalice 1·40 1·40
1044 2500l. Cross, banner and ears of wheat . . . . . . 2·30 2·30

1993. Europa. Contemporary Art. Multicoloured.
1045 750l. Type **272** 65 75
1046 850l. "Rouen Cathedral" (Maurice Utrillo) 85 85

1993. 600th Death Anniv of St. John of Nepomuk (patron saint of Bohemia). Multicoloured.
1047 1000l. Type **273** 90 90
1048 2000l. Charles Bridge, Prague . . . . 1·80 1·80

274 Pope praying

1993. Pope John Paul II's Journeys (11th series). Multicoloured.
1049 600l. Type **274** (Senegal, Gambia and Guinea) . . 55 55
1050 1000l. Pope with Pastoral Staff (Angola and St. Thomas and Prince Islands) 1·10 1·10
1051 5000l. Pope with hands clasped in prayer (Dominican Republic) . . 5·00 5·00

275 "Madonna of Solothurn" (detail)

1993. 450th Death Anniv of Hans Holbein the Younger (artist). Multicoloured.
1052 700l. Type **275** 75 75
1053 1000l. "Madonna of Solothurn" . . . . 1·10 1·10
1054 1500l. "Self-portrait" . . . 1·60 1·60

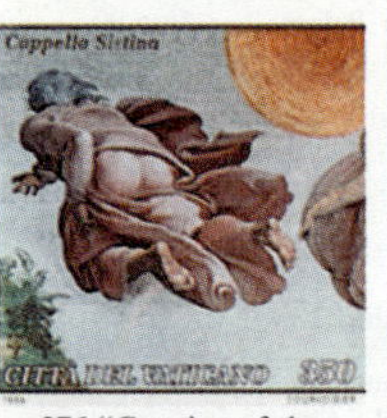

276 "Creation of the Planets" (left detail) **277** Crosier and Dome

1994. Completion of Restoration of Sistine Chapel. Multicoloured.
1055 350l. Type **276** 40 40
1056 350l. God creating planets (right detail) 40 40
1057 500l. Adam (left detail, "The Creation of Adam") . . . 60 60
1058 500l. God (right detail) . . . 60 60
1059 1000l. Adam and Eve taking forbidden fruit (left detail, "The Original Sin") . . . 1·20 1·20
1060 1000l. Angel casting out Adam and Eve from the Garden (right detail) . . . 1·20 1·20
1061 2000l. People climbing from swollen river (left detail, "The Flood") . . . . . . 2·40 2·40
1062 2000l. Floodwaters surrounding temporary shelter (right detail) . . . 2·40 2·40
Stamps of the same value were issued together, se-tenant, each pair forming a composite design.

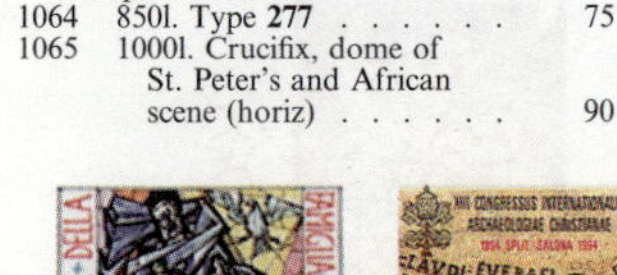

1994. Special Assembly for Africa of Synod of Bishops. Multicoloured.
1064 850l. Type **277** 75 75
1065 1000l. Crucifix, dome of St. Peter's and African scene (horiz) 90 90

278 God creating Man and Woman **280** Bishop Euphrasius and Archdeacon Claudius

279 Timeline of Knowledge from Wheel to Atom

1994. Int Year of the Family. Mult.
1066 400l. Type **278** 35 35
1067 750l. Family 65 65
1068 1000l. Parents teaching son 85 85
1069 2000l. Youth helping elderly couple . . . . 1·80 1·80

1994. Europa. Discoveries. Multicoloured.
1070 750l. Type **279** 75 75
1071 850l. Galileo, solar system and scientific apparatus 90 90

1994. 13th International Congress on Christian Archaeology, Split and Porec, Croatia. Mosaics from Euphrasian Basilica, Porec. Multicoloured.
1072 700l. Type **280** 55 55
1073 1500l. Madonna and Child with two angels . . . . . 1·30 1·30
1074 3000l. Jesus Christ between Apostles St. Peter and St. Paul . . . . 2·75 2·75

281 Route Map, Mongolian Village and Giovanni da Montecorvino

1994. 700th Anniv of Evangelization of China.
1075 **281** 1000l. multicoloured . . 90 90

282 Houses, Mahdi's Mausoleum, Omdurman, and St. Mary's Basilica, Lodonga (Benin, Uganda and Sudan)

1994. Pope John Paul II's Journeys (12th series).
1076 **282** 600l. brown, green & red 55 55
1077 – 700l. violet, brown & grn 65 65
1078 – 1000l. brown, blue & vio 90 90
1079 – 2000l. black, blue and red . . . . 1·80 1·80
1080 – 3000l. blue, violet & brn 2·75 2·75
DESIGNS: 700l. St. Mary's Church, Apollonia, Mosque and statue of Skanderbeg, Tirana (Albania); 1000l. Church of the Saint, Huelva Region, and The Giralda, Real Maestranza and Golden Tower, Seville (Spain); 2000l. Skyscrapers and St. Thomas's Theological Seminary, Denver, "El Castillo" (pyramid), Kulkulkan, Jamaican girl and Mexican boy (Jamaica, Mexico and United States); 3000l. Tallin, "Hymn to Liberty" (monument), Riga, and Tower, Cathedral Square, Vilnius (Lithuania, Latvia and Estonia).

283 Holy Family

1994. Christmas. Details of "Nativity" by Tintoretto. Multicoloured.
1081 700l. Type **283** 75 75
1082 1000l. Upper half of painting (45 × 28 mm) . . 1·30 1·30
1083 1000l. Lower half of painting (45 × 28 mm) . . 1·30 1·30
Nos. 1082/3 were issued together, se-tenant, forming a composite design of the complete painting.

284 Angel with Chalice (Melozzo da Forli) (St. Mark's) **286** Fountain of the Triton (Bernini), Vatican Gardens

285 Hands and Broken Chains

1995. 700th Anniv of Shrine of the Holy House, Loreto. Details from the vaults of sacristies. Multicoloured.
1084 600l. Type **284** 50 50
1085 700l. Angel with lamb (Melozzo) (Sacristy of St. Mark) 55 55
1086 1500l. Angel with lute (Luca Signorelli) (St. John's) . . 1·20 1·20
1087 2500l. Angel (Signorelli) (St. John's) . . . . 2·40 2·40

1995. Europa. Peace and Freedom. Multicoloured.
1089 750l. Type **285** 65 70
1090 850l. Globe, olive wreath, dove and handclasp . . . 85 85

1995. European Nature Conservation Year. Multicoloured.
1091 200l. Type **286** 20 20
1092 300l. Avenue of roses, Castelgandolfo 30 30
1093 400l. Statue of Apollo, Vatican Gardens 35 35
1094 550l. Ruins of Domitian's Villa, Castelgandolfo . . 45 45
1095 750l. Box elder, Vatican Gardens 65 65
1096 1500l. Belvedere Gardens, Castelgandolfo . . . . . 1·40 1·40
1097 2000l. Eagle fountain, Vatican Gardens . . . . 1·80 1·80
1098 3000l. Avenue of cypresses, Castelgandolfo . . . . . 2·50 2·50

287 Guglielmo Marconi and Transmitter

1995. One Hundred Years of Radio. Multicoloured.
1099 850l. Type **287** 90 90
1100 1000l. Archangel Gabriel, Pope John Paul II with microphone and Vatican broadcasting station . . . 1·10 1·10

288 St. Antony of Padua (statue by Donatello) **289** Dove and Hearts

1995. Saints' Anniversaries.
1101 **288** 500l. brown and green 45 45
1102 – 750l. green and violet . . 65 65
1103 – 3000l. blue and purple 2·75 2·75
DESIGNS: 500l. Type **288** (800th birth anniv); 750l. St. John of God (founder of Order of Hospitallers, 500th birth anniv) (sculpture, Filippo Valle); 3000l. St. Philip Neri (founder of Friars of the Oratory, 400th death anniv) (sculpture, Giovanni Battista Maini).

1995. 50th Anniv of U.N.O. Multicoloured.
1104 550l. Type **289** 45 45
1105 750l. Human faces 65 65
1106 850l. Doves 75 75
1107 1250l. Symbolic lymph system . . . . 1·10 1·10
1108 2000l. People gazing at "explosion" of flowers . . 1·80 1·80

290 "The Annunciation" (Johannes of Ienzenstein) **291** Pope, Statue of Virgin Mary and Zagreb Cathedral

1995. Holy Year 2000 (1st issue). Illustrations from illuminated manuscripts in Vatican Apostolic Library. Multicoloured.
1109 400l. Type **290** 35 35
1110 850l. "Nativity" (from King Matthias I Corvinus's breviary) 75 75
1111 1250l. "Flight into Egypt" (from Book of Hours) . . 1·10 1·10
1112 2000l. "Jesus among the Teachers" (Pietro Lombardo) . . . . 2·20 2·20
See also Nos. 1132/5, 1167/70, 1197/1200, 1231/4, 1242/9 and 1265/8.

1995. Pope John Paul II's Journeys (13th series). Multicoloured.
1113 1000l. Type **291** (Croatia) 90 90
1114 2000l. Pope, Genoa Lantern, Orvieto Cathedral and Valley of the Temples, Agrigento (Italy) . . . . 1·80 1·80

292 Marco Polo receiving Golden Book from the Great Khan

1996. 700th Anniv of Marco Polo's Return from China. Multicoloured.
1115 350l. Type **292** 30 30
1116 850l. The Great Khan giving alms to poor, Cambaluc 60 60
1117 1250l. Marco Polo delivering Pope Gregory X's letter to the Great Khan 90 90
1118 2500l. Marco Polo in Persia listening to Nativity story 2·20 2·20

293 Angel with Crosses **294** Gianna Molla (surgeon)

1996. Anniversaries. Multicoloured.
1120 1250l. Type **293** (400th Anniv of Union of Brest-Litovsk) 90 90
1121 2000l. Latin and Byzantine mitres and Tree of Life (350th Anniv of Union of Uzhorod) . . . . 1·60 1·60

1996. Europa. Famous Women.
1122 **294** 750l. blue 65 75
1123 – 850l. brown 75 80
DESIGN: 850l. Edith Stein (Carmelite nun).

295 "Sun and Steel" **297** "Baptism of Jesus"

296 Wawel Cathedral

1996. Cent of Modern Olympic Games. Mult.
1124 1250l. Type **295** . . . . . 1·80 1·80
1125 1250l. "Solar Plexus" . . . 1·80 1·80

1126 1250l. Hand and golden beams . . . . 1·80 1·80
1127 1250l. "Speculum Aevi" (athlete and shadow) . . 1·80 1·80
1128 1250l. Hercules . . . . . . 1·80 1·80

1996. 50th Anniv of Ordination of Karol Wojtyla (Pope John Paul II) at Wawel Cathedral, Crakow, Poland. Multicoloured.
1129 500l. Type **296** 75 75
1130 750l. Pope John Paul II . . 1·10 1·10
1131 1250l. St. John Lateran's Basilica in Rome (seat of Bishop of Eternal City) 1·80 1·80

1996. Holy Year 2000 (2nd issue). Illustrations from 13th-century illuminated New Testament in Vatican Apostolic Library. Multicoloured.
1132 550l. Type **297** 40 40
1133 850l. "Temptation in the Desert" 60 60
1134 1500l. "Cure of a Leper" . . 1·10 1·10
1135 2500l. "Jesus the Teacher" 2·30 2·30

298 Philippines, Papua New Guinea, Australia and Sri Lanka

1996. Pope John Paul II's Journeys (14th series).
1136 **298** 250l. blue and black . . 20 20
1137 – 500l. green and black . . 35 35
1138 – 750l. green and black . . 55 55
1139 – 1000l. brown and black 75 75
1140 – 2000l. grey and black . . 1·80 1·80
1141 – 5000l. pink and black . . 4·25 4·25
DESIGNS: 500l. Czech Republic and Poland; 750l. Belgium; 1000l. Slovakia; 2000l. Cameroun, South Africa and Kenya; 5000l. United States of America and United Nations Headquarters.

299 "Nativity" (Murillo)

1996. Christmas.
1142 **299** 750l. multicoloured . . . 75 65

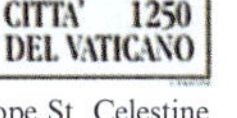

300 Pope St. Celestine V

302 Halberdier

301 Travelling Carriage

1996. Saints' Anniversaries. Multicoloured.
1143 1250l. Type **300** (700th death) 60 60
1144 1250l. St. Alfonso Maria de' Liguori (founder of Redemptorists Order) (300th birth) 70 70

1997. Papal Transport. Multicoloured.
1145 50l. Type **301** 10 10
1146 100l. Graham Paige motor car 10 10
1147 300l. Ceremonial berlin (carriage) 20 20
1148 500l. Citroen Lictoria VI motor car 35 35
1149 750l. Grand ceremonial berlin 55 55
1150 850l. Mercedes Benz motor car 60 60
1151 1000l. Semi-ceremonial berlin 85 85
1152 1250l. Mercedes Benz 300 SEL motor car . . . . . 1·10 1·10
1153 2000l. Travelling carriage (different) . . . . . . 1·60 1·60
1154 4000l. Fiat Campagnola . . 3·75 3·75

1997. Europa. The Swiss Guard. Multicoloured.
1155 750l. Type **302** 55 55
1156 850l. Swordsman 60 60

303 Aristotle describing the Species ("De Historia Animalium" by Aristotle)

1997. "Looking at The Classics" Exhibition. Illustrations from manuscripts of the Classics. Multicoloured.
1157 500l. Type **303** 35 35
1158 750l. Bacchus riding dragon ("Metamorphoses" by Ovid) 65 65
1159 1250l. General reviewing his soldiers ("Iliad" by Homer) . . . . 1·00 1·00
1160 2000l. Horsemen leaving Canne ("Ab Urbe Condita" by Livy) . . . . 1·60 1·60

304 St. Adalbert

305 Eucharist and Arms of Wroclaw

1997. Death Millenary of St. Adalbert (Bishop of Prague).
1162 **304** 850l. lilac . . . . 1·10 1·10

1997. 46th International Eucharistic Congress, Wroclaw, Poland. Multicoloured.
1163 650l. Type **305** 45 45
1164 1000l. Last Supper and Congress emblem 80 80
1165 1250l. Wroclaw Cathedral and the Holy Dove . . . 90 90
1166 2500l. Cross, doves and hands around globe . . . 2·20 2·20

306 Jesus healing Paralysed Man

307 St. Ambrose and Ambrosiana Basilica

1997. Holy Year 2000 (3rd issue). Illustrations from 14th-century illuminated New Testament in Vatican Apostolic Library. Multicoloured.
1167 400l. Type **306** 30 30
1168 800l. Calming the tempest 65 65
1169 1300l. Feeding the five thousand . . . . 1·60 1·60
1170 3600l. Peter acclaiming Christ as the Messiah . . 4·00 4·00

1997. 1600th Death Anniv of St. Ambrose, Bishop of Milan.
1171 **307** 800l. multicoloured . . . 1·10 1·10

308 Pope Paul VI

309 Guatemala Pyramid and Amerindian Boy

1997. Birth Centenary of Pope Paul VI.
1172 **308** 900l. multicoloured . . . 65 65

1997. Pope John Paul II's Journeys (15th series). Multicoloured.
1174 400l. Type **309** (Guatemala, Nicaragua, El Salvador, Venezuela) 30 30
1175 900l. St. Francis de Paul and St. Olive's Cathedral and Mosque (Tunisia) . . 65 65

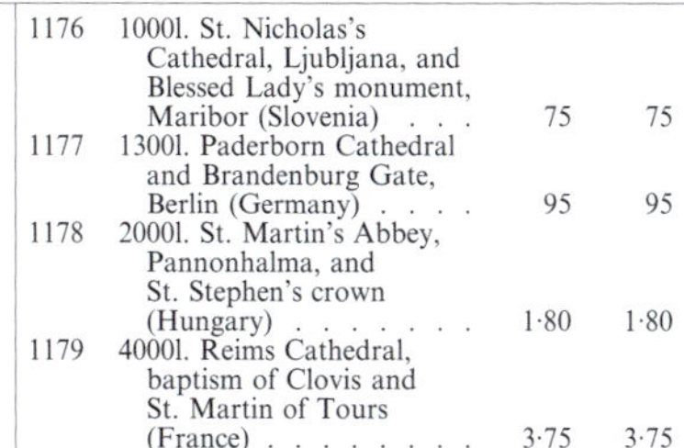

1176 1000l. St. Nicholas's Cathedral, Ljubljana, and Blessed Lady's monument, Maribor (Slovenia) . . . 75 75
1177 1300l. Paderborn Cathedral and Brandenburg Gate, Berlin (Germany) 95 95
1178 2000l. St. Martin's Abbey, Pannonhalma, and St. Stephen's crown (Hungary) . . . . 1·80 1·80
1179 4000l. Reims Cathedral, baptism of Clovis and St. Martin of Tours (France) . . . . 3·75 3·75

310 "Madonna of the Belt" (detail of altarpiece, Gozzoli)

1997. Christmas. 500th Death Anniv of Benozzo Gozzoli (artist).
1180 **310** 800l. multicoloured . . . 3·75 3·75

311 Pope Boniface VIII (1300)

312 St. Peter

1998. Popes and their Holy Years (1st series). Multicoloured.
1181 200l. Type **311** 20 20
1182 400l. Clement VI (1350) . . 30 30
1183 500l. Boniface IX (1390 and 1400) 35 35
1184 700l. Martinus V (1423) . . 50 50
1185 800l. Nicholas V (1450) . . 75 75
1186 900l. Sistus IV (1475) . . . 90 90
1187 1300l. Alexander VI (1500) 1·30 1·30
1188 3000l. Clement VII (1525) 4·00 4·00
See also Nos. 1213/20 and 1255/63.

1998. Europa. National Festival. The Feast of St. Peter and St. Paul. Multicoloured.
1189 800l. Type **312** 65 80
1190 900l. St. Paul 80 85
The designs are details from the Stefaneschi Triptych by Giotto.

313 Angel

315 Turin Shroud

314 Entry into Jerusalem

1998. Musical Angels from "The Ascension" by Melozzo da Forli in the Basilica of the Apostles, Rome. Multicoloured.
1191 450l. Type **313** 35 35
1192 650l. Angel playing lute . . 45 45
1193 800l. Angel playing drum 60 60
1194 1000l. Angel playing viol . . 90 90
1195 1300l. Angel playing violin 1·20 1·20
1196 2000l. Angel with tamborine 2·00 2·00

1998. Holy Year 2000 (4th issue). Illustrations from the illuminated New Testament in Vatican Apostolic Library. Multicoloured.
1197 500l. Type **314** 35 35
1198 800l. Washing of the Apostles' feet 60 60
1199 1500l. The Last Supper . . 1·00 1·00
1200 3000l. The Crucifixion . . . 2·75 2·75

1998. Exhibition of the Holy Shroud, Turin Cathedral.
1201 **315** 900l. white, brown and green 75 75
1202 – 2500l. black, pink and green . . . . 2·20 2·20
DESIGN: 2500l. Turin Cathedral.

316 Pope John Paul II and his Message

1998. "Italia 98" International Stamp Exhibition, Milan (1st issue). Stamp Day.
1203 **316** 800l. multicoloured . . . 1·10 1·10
See also No. 1204.

317 "The Good Shepherd"

1998. "Italia 98" International Stamp Exhibition, Milan (2nd issue). Art Day. Design showing sculpture from sarcophagus.
1204 **317** 900l. multicoloured . . . 75 75

318 Pope and War Refugees

319 "Nativity" (Giulio Clovio)

1998. Pope John Paul II's Journeys (16th series). Multicoloured.
1206 300l. Type **318** (Bosnia and Herzegovina) 20 20
1207 600l. Kneeling in front of statue of Jesus (Czech Republic) 45 45
1208 800l. With girls (Lebanon) 60 60
1209 900l. Welcome by garlanded girls (Poland) 65 65
1210 1300l. With young people (France) 95 95
1211 5000l. With children (Brazil) 3·75 3·75

1998. Christmas.
1212 **319** 800l. multicoloured . . . 65 65

1999. Popes and their Holy Years (2nd series). As T **311**. Multicoloured.
1213 300l. Julius III (1550) . . . 35 35
1214 600l. Gregory XIII (1575) 55 55
1215 800l. Clement VIII (1600) 75 75
1216 900l. Urban VIII (1625) . . 90 90
1217 1000l. Innocent X (1650) . . 1·10 1·10
1218 1300l. Clement X (1675) . . 1·30 1·30
1219 1500l. Innocent XII (1700) 1·60 1·60
1220 2000l. Benedict XIII (1725) 2·50 2·50

320 Rose "John Paul II"

1999. Europa. Parks and Gardens. Multicoloured.
1221 800l. Type **320** 60 60
1222 900l. Water lilies (Fountain of the Frogs, Vatican Gardens) 65 65

321 Father Pio

1999. Beatification of Father Pio da Pietrelcina (Capuchin friar who bore the stigmata).
1223 **321** 800l. multicoloured . . . 60 60

322 Bethlehem

1999. Sacred Places in the Holy Land. Illustrations from "The Holy Land" by I. Messmer. Multicoloured.
1225 200l. Type **322** 20 20
1226 500l. Nazareth 35 35
1227 800l. Lake Tiberius 60 60
1228 900l. Jerusalem 65 65
1229 1300l. Mount Tabor 95 95

323 Deposition from the Cross

1999. Holy Year 2000 (5th issue). Illustrations from illuminated New Testament in Vatican Apostolic Library. Multicoloured.
1231 400l. Type **323** 30 30
1232 700l. The Resurrection . . . 50 50
1233 1300l. Pentecost 95 95
1234 3000l. The Last Judgement 2·20 2·20

324 Refugees

1999. Kosovo Relief Fund.
1235 **324** 3600l. black . . . . . . 2·50 2·50

325 Visit to Cuba 326 Hot Air Balloons, Jigsaw Puzzle of Europe and Magnifying Glass

1999. Pope John Paul II's Journeys (17th series). Multicoloured.
1236 600l. Type **325** 45 45
1237 800l. Stole over hands and staff (Nigeria) 55 55
1238 900l. Dove, cathedral and disabled people (Austria) 75 75
1239 1300l. With crucifix and statue (Croatia) . . . . . 1·10 1·10
1240 2000l. Quirinal Palace, Rome (Italy) . . . . . . 2·00 2·00

1999. 50th Anniv of Council of Europe.
1241 **326** 1200l. multicoloured . . 60 60

327 "The Cherubim at the Doors of Paradise" and "The Banishment from the Garden of Eden"

1999. Holy Year 2000 (6th issue). Opening of Holy Door, St. Peter's Basilica. Door panels. Mult.
1242 200l. Type **327** 20 20
1243 300l. "The Annunciation" and "Angel" 20 20
1244 400l. "Baptism of Christ" and "Straying Sheep" . . 30 30
1245 500l. "The Merciful Father" and "Curing Paralysed Man" 35 35
1246 600l. "The Penitent Woman" and "The Obligation to Forgive" . . 45 45
1247 800l. "Peter's Denial" and "A Thief in Paradise" . . 65 65
1248 1000l. "Jesus appears to Thomas" and "Jesus appears to the Eleven" . . 90 90
1249 1200l. "Jesus appears to Saul" and "Opening of the Holy Door" . . . . . 1·10 1·10

328 St. Joseph (detail)

1999. Christmas. "St. Joseph, the Virgin Mary and the Holy Child" (Giovanni di Petro). Multicoloured.
1251 500l. Type **328** 35 35
1252 800l. Holy Child (detail) . . 55 55
1253 900l. Virgin Mary (detail) 90 90
1254 1200l. Complete painting . . 1·10 1·10

2000. Popes and their Holy Years (3rd series). As T **311**. Multicoloured.
1255 300l. Benedict XIV (1750) 30 30
1256 400l. Pius VI (1775) 35 35
1257 500l. Leo XII (1825) 45 45
1258 600l. Pius IX (1875) 55 55
1259 700l. Leo XIII (1900) . . . 65 65
1260 800l. Pius XI (1925) 75 75
1261 1200l. Pius XII (1950) . . . 1·10 1·10
1262 1500l. Paul VI (1975) . . . 1·30 1·30
1263 2000l. John Paul II (2000) 2·00 2·00

329 St. Peter's Basilica

2000. Holy Year 2000 (7th issue). Multicoloured.
1265 800l. Type **329** 55 55
1266 1000l. St. John Lateran Basilica 75 75
1267 1200l. St. Mary Major Basilica 90 90
1268 2000l. St. Paul-outside-the-Walls Basilica . . . . . 1·50 1·50

330 Embroidered Altar Frontal, Holar Cathedral

2000. Millenary of Christianity in Iceland.
1269 **330** 1500l. multicoloured . . 1·10 1·10

331 "Building Europe" 332 Pope John Paul II

2000. Europa.
1270 **331** 1200l. multicoloured . . 90 90

2000. 80th Birthday of Pope John Paul II.
1271 **332** 800l. lilac 55 55
1272 – 1200l. blue 90 90
1273 – 2000l. green . . . . . 1·50 1·50
DESIGNS: 1200l. Black Madonna of Czestochowa; 2000l. Pastoral Staff.

333 "The Calling of St. Peter and St. Andrew" (Domenico Ghirlandaio)

2000. Restoration of the Sistine Chapel (1st series). Multicoloured.
1274 500l. Type **333** 35 35
1275 1000l. "The Trials of Moses" (Sandro Botticelli) 75 75
1276 1500l. "The Donation of the Keys" (Pietro Perugino) 1·10 1·10
1277 3000l. "The Worship of the Golden Calf" (Cosimo Rosselli) . . . . 2·20 2·20
See also Nos. 1294/7 and 1339/42.

334 Congress Emblem 335 Pope John Paul II and Youths' Faces

2000. 47th International Eucharistic Congress, Rome.
1278 **334** 1200l. multicoloured . . 1·10 1·10

2000. 15th World Youth Day, Rome. Multicoloured.
(a) Ordinary gum.
1279 800l. Type **335** 55 55
1280 1000l. Girl waving flag . . . 65 65
1281 1200l. Youths' cheering . . . 70 90
1282 2000l. Youth waving flag . . 1·20 1·20

(b) Self-adhesive.
1283 1000l. As No. 1280 . . . . 75 75

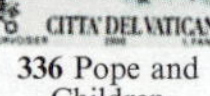

336 Pope and Children

337 Pope John XXIII

2000. Pope John Paul II's Journeys (18th series). Multicoloured.
1284 1000l. Type **336** (Mexico and United States of America) 75 75
1285 1000l. Pope praying, building and children waving (Rumania) 75 75
1286 1000l. Holding Pastoral Staff (Poland) 75 75
1287 1000l. Pope and Bishop Anton Martin Slomsek (Slovenia) 75 75
1288 1000l. Pope, churches and crowd (India and Georgia) 75 75

2000. Beatification of Pope John XXIII.
1289 **337** 1200l. multicoloured . . 90 90

338 Nativity (fresco)

2000. Christmas. Designs showing Fresco by Giotto from St. Francis Basilica. Multicoloured.
1290 800l. Type **338** 55 55
1291 1200l. Baby Jesus (detail) . . 90 90
1292 1500l. Mary (detail) . . . . 1·10 1·10
1293 2000l. Joseph (detail) . . . 1·50 1·50

2001. Restoration of the Sistine Chapel (2nd series). As T **333**. Multicoloured.
1294 800l. "The Baptism of Christ" (Pietro Perugino) 45 45
1295 1200l. "The Passage through the Red Sea" (Biagio d'Antonio) 65 65
1296 1500l. "The Punishment of Core, Datan and Abiron" (Botticelli) 85 85
1297 4000l. "The Sermon on the Mount" (Cosimo Rosselli) 2·20 2·20

339 Freedom of St. Gregory 340 Hands holding Water and Globe

2001. 1700th Anniv of the Adoption of Christianity in Armenia. Multicoloured.
1298 1200l. Type **339** 65 65
1299 1500l. St. Gregory making Agatangel write 85 85
1300 2000l. St. Gregory and King Tirade meet Emperor Constantine and Pope Sylvester I . . . . 1·10 1·10

2001. Europa. Water Resources. Multicoloured.
1301 800l. Type **340** 45 45
1302 1200l. Hand and catching rain water 65 65

341 Verdi and Score of *Nabucco*

2001. Death Centenary of Giuseppe Verdi (composer). Multicoloured.
1303 800l. Type **341** 45 45
1304 1500l. Verdi and character from *Aida* 85 85
1305 2000l. Verdi and scene from *Otello* . . . . 1·10 1·10

342 Children encircling Globe

2001. U.N. Year of Dialogue between Civilizations.
1306 **342** 1500l. multicoloured . . 85 85

343 Couple feeding Poor Man

2001. Cancellation of Foreign Debt of Poor Countries. Showing illustrations from "Works of Corporal Mercy" (15th-century panels by Carlo di Camerino). Multicoloured.
1307 200l. Type **343** 20 20
1308 400l. Giving alms 20 20
1309 800l. Giving clothing . . . 45 45
1310 1000l. Women caring for sick man 55 55
1311 1500l. Man visiting prisoner 85 85

344 Mount Sinai, Monastery of Holy Catherine and Pope

2001. Pope John Paul II's Journeys (19th series). The Holy Land. Multicoloured.
1312 500l. Type **344** 30 30
1313 800l. Pope before Crucifix, Mount Nebo 45 45
1314 1200l. Pope celebrating Mass 65 65
1315 1500l. Pope at prayer Holy Sepulchre 85 85
1316 5000l. Pope praying at Shrine of Fatima . . . . 2·75 2·75

345 "The Annunciation"

2001. Christmas. Designs showing scenes from "Life of Christ" (enamel, Egino G. Weinert). Multicoloured.
1318 800l. Type **345** 45 45
1319 1200l. "The Nativity" . . . 65 65
1320 1500l. "Adoration of the Magi" 85 85

346 Fibula, 675–650 B.C.

2001. Etruscan Museum Exhibits. Multicoloured.
1321 800l. Type **346** 35 35
1322 1200l. 6th-century earrings 55 55
1323 1500l. Embossed Greek stud, 425–400 B.C. 70 70
1324 2000l. 3rd-century Greek head of Medusa 90 90

347 Emblem

2001. 80th Anniv of Guiseppe Toniolo Institute for Higher Studies and the Catholic University of the Sacred Heart.
1325 **347** 1200l. blue and red . . . 65 65

348 Our Lady of Women in Labour (14th-century fresco) **349** Pope Clement XI

2002. Our Lady in the Vatican Basilica. Multicoloured.
1326 8c. Type **348** 15 15
1327 15c. Our Lady with people praying (mosaic) 20 20
1328 23c. Our Lady at the Tomb of Pius XII (15th-century fresco) 30 30
1329 31c. Our Lady of the Fever (13th-century) 45 45
1330 41c. Our Lady of the Slap 60 60
1331 52c. Mary Immaculate (mosaic) 75 75
1332 62c. Our Lady of Christians 90 90
1333 77c. The Virgin of the Deesis . . . . 1·10 1·10
1334 €1.03 L'Addolorata (painting, Lippo Memmi) 1·40 1·40
1335 €1.55 Presentation of Mary at the Temple (mosaic) . . 2·20 2·20

2002. 300th Anniv of Pontifical Ecclesiastical Academy, Rome.
1336 **349** 77c. purple . . . . . . 1·10 1·10
1337 – 77c. green (46 × 33 mm) 1·10 1·10
1338 – 77c. purple . . . . . . 1·10 1·10
DESIGNS: No. 1337 Facade of Piazza della Minerva Institute, Rome; 1338 Pope John Paul II.

2002. Restoration of the Sistine Chapel (3rd series). As T **333**. Multicoloured.
1339 26c. "The Temptation of Christ" (Botticelli) 35 35
1340 41c. "The Last Supper" (Cosimo Rosselli) 60 60
1341 77c. "Moses' Journey into Egypt" (Pietro Perugino) 1·10 1·10
1342 €1.55 "The Last Days of Moses" (Luca Signorelli) 2·20 2·20

350 Regina Viarum (Appian Way) and 1852 Papal States Stamp

2002. Centenary of Pontifical Stamps.
1343 **350** 41c. deep brown, purple and brown 60 60
1344 – 52c. multicoloured . . . 75 75
1345 – €1.03 blue, indigo and green . . . . 1·40 1·40
MS1346 €1.55 brown, buff and purple . . . . 2·30 2·30
DESIGNS: No. 1344, Cassian Way and 1868 80ch. Papal States stamp; 1345, Porta Angelica, Vatican and 1929 Vatican City State 10ch. stamp. 30 × 30 mm (circular)—**MS**1346, Courtyard, Palazzo Madama, Rome.

351 "Christ and the Circus" (Aldo Carpi)

2002. Europa. Circus. Multicoloured.
1347 41c. Type **351** 60 60
1348 62c. Christ with clown (detail of "Christ and the Circus") 90 90

352 Crucifix, St. Dominic Church, Arezzo

2002. 700th Death Anniv of Cenni di Pepo (Cimabue) (artist). Showing the Crucifix and details thereof. Multicoloured.
1349 41c. Type **352** 60 60
1350 62c. Jesus 90 90
1351 77c. Mary . . . . 1·10 1·10
1352 €1.03 John the Baptist . . 1·40 1·40

353 Pope Leo IX and Wall Inscription

2002. Birth Millenary of Pope Leo IX. Multicoloured.
1353 41c. Type **353** 60 60
1354 62c. Arrival in Rome as pilgrim and coronation as Pope 90 90
1355 €1.29 Leo IX in chains . . 1·90 1·90

EXPRESS LETTER STAMPS

E 3

1929.
E14 **E 3** 2l. red . . . . 20·00 14·50
E15 2l.50 blue . . . . 16·00 18·00

E 12 Vatican City

1933.
E 35 **E 12** 2l. brown and red . . . 35 35
E 36 2l.50 brown and blue 35 65
E107 3l.50 blue and red . . 45 55
E108 5l. green and blue . . . 75 1·00

1945. Surch in figures over bars.
E118 **E 12** 6l. on 3l.50 blue & red 5·50 2·75
E119 12l. on 5l. green & blue 5·50 2·75

E 28 Matthew Giberti, Bishop of Verona

1946. 400th Anniv of Council of Trent.
E130 **E 28** 6l. brown and green . . 20 20
E131 – 12l. sepia and brown 20 20
DESIGN: 12l. Cardinal Gaspare Contarini, Bishop of Belluno.

1949. As Nos. 139/48 (Basilicas), but inscr "ESPRESSO".
E149 40l. grey . . . . 14·50 4·50
E150 80l. brown . . . . 50·00 28·00
DESIGNS—HORIZ: 40l. St. Peter's; 80l. St. John's.

1953. Designs as Nos. 179/89, but inscr "ESPRESSO".
E190 50l. brown and turquoise 20 20
E191 85l. brown and orange . . 35 25
DESIGNS: 50l. St. Peter and tomb; 85l. Pius XII and sepulchre.

1960. Designs as Nos. 326/33 (Works of Mercy), but inscr "ESPRESSO". Centres in brown.
E334 75l. red 10 10
E335 100l. blue 10 10
DESIGN: 75, 100l. Arms of Pope John XXIII between "Justice" and "Hope".

1966. Designs as Nos. 467/76, but inscr "ESPRESSO".
E477 – 150l. brown 10 10
E478 **120** 180l. brown 15 15
DESIGN: 150l. Arms of Pope Paul VI.

PARCEL POST STAMPS

1931. Optd **PER PACCHI**.
P15 **1** 5c. brown on pink 20 55
P16 10c. green on green 20 55
P17 20c. violet on lilac . . . . 1·60 2·50
P18 25c. blue on blue . . . . . 7·25 5·75
P19 30c. black on yellow . . . . 8·00 5·75
P20 50c. black on orange . . . 12·50 5·75
P21 75c. red on grey . . . . . 1·50 5·75
P22 **2** 80c. red . . . . 1·10 5·75
P23 1l.25 blue . . . . 1·50 5·75
P24 2l. brown . . . . 1·10 5·75
P25 2l.50 red . . . . 2·00 5·75
P26 5l. green . . . . 2·20 5·75
P27 10l. black . . . . 1·80 5·75

PARCEL POST EXPRESS STAMPS

1931. Optd **PER PACCHI**.
PE15 **E 3** 2l. red . . . . 1·50 5·75
PE16 2l.50 blue . . . . 1·50 5·75

POSTAGE DUE STAMPS

1931. Optd **SEGNATASSE** and cross or surch also.
D15 **1** 5c. brown on pink 20 55
D16 10c. green on green 20 55
D17 20c. violet on lilac . . . . 1·50 1·80
D18 40c. on 30c. black on yell 2·50 4·25
D19 **2** 60c. on 2l. brown . . . . . 33·00 26·00
D20 1l.10 on 2l.50 red . . . . . 6·50 18·00

D 26

D 49 State Arms

1945. Coloured network shown in brackets.
D107 **D 26** 5c. black (yellow) . . 10 10
D108 20c. black (violet) . . 10 10
D109 80c. black (red) . . . 10 10
D110 1l. black (green) . . . 10 10
D111 2l. black (blue) 10 10
D112 5l. black (grey) 15 15

1954. Coloured network shown in brackets.
D199 **D 49** 4l. black (red) 10 10
D200 6l. black (green) . . . 15 15
D201 10l. black (yellow) . . 10 10
D202 20l. black (blue) . . . 30 30
D203 50l. black (brown) . . 10 10
D204 70l. black (brown) . . 10 10

D 130

1968.
D513 **D 130** 10l. black on grey . . 10 10
D514 20l. black on blue . . 10 10
D515 50l. black on pink . . 10 10
D516 60l. black on green 10 10
D517 100l. black on buff 10 10
D518 180l. black on mauve 10 10

VEGLIA Pt. 8

During the period of D'Annunzio's Italian Regency of Carnaro (Fiume), separate issues were made for the island of Veglia (now Krk).

100 centesimi = 1 lira.

1920. Nos. 148 etc of Fiume optd **VEGLIA**.
1B 5c. green . . . . 4·50 5·25
2B 10c. red . . . . 10·50 11·50
3B 20c. bistre . . . . 24·00 18·00
4B 25c. blue . . . . 14·50 18·00
5 50 on 20c. bistre . . . . . 26·00 18·00
6 55 on 5c. green . . . . . . 26·00 18·00

EXPRESS LETTER STAMPS

1920. Nos. E163/4 of Fiume optd **VEGLIA**.
E7 30c. on 20c. bistre . . . . . 95·00 35·00
E8 50 on 5c. green . . . . . . 95·00 35·00

VENDA Pt. 1

The Republic of Venda was established on 13 September 1979, being constructed from tribal areas formerly part of the Republic of South Africa. This independence did not receive international political recognition, but the stamps were accepted as valid on international mail.

Venda was reincorporated into South Africa on 27 April 1994.

100 cents = 1 rand.

1 Flag and Mace

1979. Independence. Multicoloured.
1 4c. Type **1** 25 25
2 15c. Government Buildings, Thohoyandou 30 60
3 20c. Chief Minister P. R. Mphephu 40 70
4 25c. Coat of arms . . . . . 60 1·10

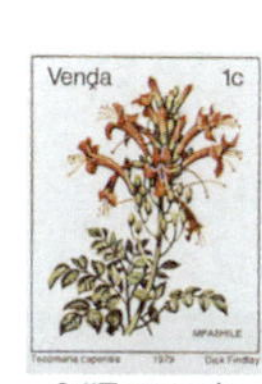

2 "Tecomaria capensis" **3** Man drinking Beer

1979. Flowers. Multicoloured.
5 1c. Type **2** 10 10
6a 2c. "Catophractes alexandri" 20 15
7 3c. "Tricliceras longipedunculatum" . . . 30 10
8 4c. "Dissotis princeps" . . . 30 10
9a 5c. "Gerbera jamesonii" . . 30 10
10 6c. "Hibiscus mastersianus" 15 10
11 7c. "Nymphaea caerulea" . . 20 10
12a 8c. "Crinum lugardiae" . . . 30 15
13 9c. "Xerophyta retinervis" . . 20 15
14a 10c. "Hypoxis angustifolia" 40 15
14b 11c. "Combretum microphyllum" 55 15
14c 12c. "Clivia caulescens" . . . 30 15
15 15c. "Pycnostachys urticifolia" 30 15
16 20c. "Zantedeschia jucunda" 75 15
17a 25c. "Leonotis mollis" . . . 50 40
18 30c. "Littonia modesta" . . 40 30
19 50c. "Protea caffra" 40 40
20 1r. "Adenium multiflorum" 75 85
21 2r. "Strelitzia caudata" . . . 1·25 2·00

1980. Wood Carving. Multicoloured.
22 5c. Type **3** 15 15
23 10c. Frying mealies in gourd 25 25
24 15c. King Nebuchadnezzar (horiz) 40 40
25 20c. Python squeezing woman to death (horiz) 50 60

4 Tea Plants in Nursery

1980. Tea Cultivation. Multicoloured.

26	5c. Type **4**	15	10
27	10c. Tea pluckers	20	20
28	15c. Withering in the factory	35	35
29	20c. Cut, twist, curl unit	40	45

5 Young Banana Plants 6 "Precis tugela"

1980. Banana Cultivation. Multicoloured.

30	5c. Type **5**	15	10
31	10c. Cutting "hands"	25	25
32	15c. Sorting and dividing into clusters	30	30
33	20c. Packing	40	45

1980. Butterflies. Multicoloured.

34	5c. Type **6**	20	15
35	10c. "Charaxes bohemani"	30	40
36	15c. "Catacroptera cloanthe"	40	55
37	20c. "Papilio dardanus"	50	70

7 Collared Sunbird

1981. Sunbirds. Multicoloured.

38	5c. Type **7**	20	15
39	15c. Mariqua sunbird	30	40
40	20c. Southern white-bellied sunbird	35	45
41	25c. Scarlet-chested sunbird	35	55

8 Nwandei Dam

1981. Lakes and Waterfalls. Multicoloured.

42	5c. Type **8**	15	10
43	15c. Mahovhohovho Falls	30	30
44	20c. Phiphidi Falls	35	35
45	25c. Lake Fundudzi	35	40

9 "Cynorkis kassnerana" 10 Mbila

1981. Orchids. Multicoloured.

46	5c. Type **9**	15	10
47	15c. "Eulophia fridericii"	30	35
48	20c. "Bonatea densiflora"	35	45
49	25c. "Mystacidium braybonae"	35	55
MS50	96 × 120 mm. Nos. 46/9	1·25	1·40

1981. Musical Instruments.

51 **10**	5c. orange and black	10	10
52 –	15c. orange and black	25	25
53 –	20c. brown and black	30	35
54 –	25c. brown and black	30	35

DESIGNS: 15c. Phalaphala; 20c. Tshizambi; 25c. Ngoma.

11 Gathering Sisal

1982. Sisal Cultivation. Multicoloured.

55	5c. Type **11**	10	10
56	10c. Drying	20	20
57	20c. Grading	30	35
58	25c. Baling	30	40

12 Bison Petrograph, Altamira, Spain

1982. History of Writing (1st series). Mult.

59	8c. Type **12**	15	10
60	15c. Petroglyph, Eastern California	30	30
61	20c. Pictograph script (Sumerian tablet)	40	40
62	25c. Bushman burial stone, Humansdorp	45	45

No. 59 is inscr "AHAMIRA" in error.

See also Nos. 75/8, 87/90, 107/10, 139/42, 171/4 and 203/6.

13 "Euphorbia ingens"

1982. Indigenous Trees (1st series). Multicoloured.

63	8c. Type **13**	15	10
64	15c. "Pterocarpus angolensis"	25	30
65	20c. "Ficus ingens"	30	40
66	25c. "Andansonia digitata"	40	55

See also Nos. 79/82, 95/8 and 227/30.

14 "Rana angolensis"

1982. Frogs. Multicoloured.

67	8c. Type **14**	15	10
68	15c. "Chiromantis xerampelina"	25	30
69	20c. "Leptopelis sp"	30	40
70	25c. "Ptychadena anchietae"	40	55

15 European Bee Eater

1983. Migratory Birds (1st series). Multicoloured.

71	8c. Type **15**	25	15
72	20c. Tawny eagle ("Steppe Eagle")	50	65
73	25c. Violet starling ("Plum-coloured Starling")	60	75
74	40c. Abdim's stork ("White-bellied Stork")	90	1·50

See also Nos. 91/4.

1983. History of Writing (2nd series). As T **12**. Multicoloured.

75	10c. Indus Valley script	15	10
76	20c. Sumerian cuneiform	20	25
77	25c. Egyptian hieroglyphics	25	30
78	40c. Chinese handscroll	50	70

1983. Indigenous Trees (2nd series). As T **13**. Multicoloured.

79	10c. "Gardenia spatulifolia"	15	10
80	20c. "Hyphaene natalensis"	25	30
81	25c. "Albizia adianthifolia"	30	40
82	40c. "Sesamothamnus lugardii"	40	60

16 Avocado 17 African Paradise Flycatcher ("Paradise Flycatcher")

1983. Subtropical Fruit. Multicoloured.

83	10c. Type **16**	15	10
84	20c. Mango	25	30
85	25c. Papaya	30	40
86	40c. Litchi	40	60

1983. History of Writing (3rd series). As T **12**. Multicoloured.

87	10c. Evolution of cuneiform sign	15	10
88	20c. Evolution of Chinese character	25	30
89	25c. Development of Cretan hieroglyphics	30	40
90	40c. Development of Egyptian hieroglyphics	40	60

1984. Migratory Birds (2nd series). Multicoloured.

91	11c. White stork	30	20
92	20c. Type **17**	50	50
93	25c. Black kite ("Yellow-billed kite")	60	60
94	30c. Wood sandpiper	70	85

1984. Indigenous Trees (3rd series). As T **13**. Mult.

95	11c. "Afzelia quanzensis"	15	10
96	20c. "Peltophorum africanum"	25	30
97	25c. "Gyrocarpus americanus"	30	40
98	30c. "Acacia sieberana"	40	55

18 Dzata Ruins, Nzhelele Valley 19 White-browed Robin Chat

1984. 5th Anniv of Independence. Multicoloured.

99	11c. Type **18**	15	10
100	25c. Traditional hut	25	30
101	30c. Sub-economical house	30	35
102	45c. Modern home	45	65

1985. Songbirds. Multicoloured.

103	11c. Type **19** (inscr "Heuglin's Robin")	25	20
104	25c. Black-collared barbet	35	40
105	30c. African black-headed oriole ("Black-headed Oriole")	40	50
106	50c. Kurrichane thrush	60	80

1985. History of Writing (4th series). As T **12**. Multicoloured.

107	11c. Southern Arabic characters	15	10
108	25c. Phoenician characters	25	30
109	30c. Aramaic characters	30	40
110	50c. Canaanite characters	50	75

20 Transvaal Red Milkwood 21 "Pellaea dura"

1985. Food from the Veld (1st series). Multicoloured.

111	12c. Type **20**	15	10
112	25c. Buffalo thorn	25	30
113	30c. Wild water melon	30	35
114	50c. Brown ivory	40	60

See also Nos. 163/6.

1985. Ferns. Multicoloured.

115	12c. Type **21**	15	10
116	25c. "Actiniopteris radiata"	25	25
117	30c. "Adiantum hispidulum"	30	35
118	50c. "Polypodium polypodioides"	40	65

22 Three-lined Grass Snake

1986. Reptiles. Multicoloured.

119	1c. Type **22**	10	10
120	2c. Mole snake	10	10
121	3c. Ornate scrub lizard	10	10
122	4c. Puff adder	10	10
123	5c. Three-lined skink	10	10
124	6c. Egyptian cobra	15	10
125	7c. Blue-tailed kopje skink	15	10
126	8c. Spotted bush snake	20	20
127	9c. Yellow-throated plated lizard	20	20
128	10c. Northern lined shovelsnout	20	20
129	14c. Transvaal flat lizard	1·25	20
130	15c. Soutpansberg lizard	30	20
131	16c. Iguana water leguan	60	20
132	18c. Black mamba	75	20
133	20c. Transvaal flat gecko	30	20
133b	21c. Flap-necked chameleon	75	20
134	25c. Longtailed garter snake	40	30
135	30c. Tigroid thick-toed gecko	40	35
136	50c. Cape file snake	40	50
137	1r. Soutpansberg girdled lizard	55	1·00
138	2r. African python	70	2·00

23 Etruscan Dish

1986. History of Writing (5th series). Multicoloured.

139	14c. Type **23**	15	10
140	20c. Greek inscription, A.D. 70	30	30
141	25c. Roman inscription	40	40
142	30c. Cyrllic inscription (Byzantine mosaic)	55	60

24 Planting Pine Seedlings

1986. Forestry. Multicoloured.

143	14c. Type **24**	20	15
144	20c. Mule hauling logs	30	30
145	25c. Off-loading logs at sawmill	40	40
146	30c. Using timber in construction	55	60

25 Maxwell, 1910

1986. FIVA International Veteran Car Rally. Multicoloured.

147	14c. Type **25**	20	15
148	20c. Bentley $4\frac{1}{2}$ litre, 1929	30	30
149	25c. Plymouth Coupe, 1933	40	40
150	30c. Mercedes Benz 220, 1958	55	60

26 Comb Duck

1987. Waterfowl. Multicoloured.

151	14c. Type **26**	1·00	40
152	20c. White-faced whistling duck	1·10	70
153	25c. Spur-winged goose (horiz)	1·25	90
154	30c. Egyptian goose (horiz)	1·40	1·25

27 "Iron Master" 28 Tigerfish

1987. Wood Sculptures by Meshack Matamela Raphalalani. Multicoloured.

155	16c. Type **27**	15	15
156	20c. "Distant Drums"	25	25
157	25c. "Sunrise"	30	30
158	30c. "Obedience"	40	40

1987. Freshwater Fishes. Multicoloured.

159	16c. Type **28**	25	20
160	20c. Barred minnow	35	35
161	25c. Mozambique mouthbrooder	45	45
162	30c. Sharp-toothed catfish	55	60

29 Cross-berry

30 Picking Berries

1987. Food from the Veld (2nd series). Multicoloured.
163 16c. Type **29** 20 15
164 30c. Wild date palm 30 30
165 40c. Tree fuchsia 40 40
166 50c. Wild cucumber 50 55

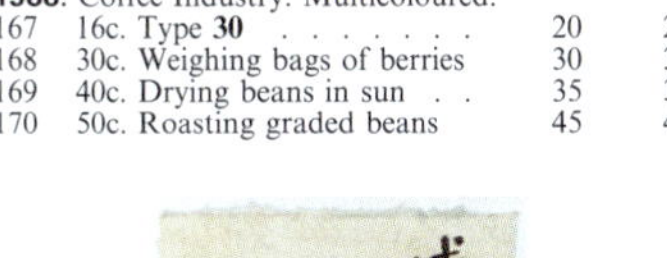

1988. Coffee Industry. Multicoloured.
167 16c. Type **30** 20 20
168 30c. Weighing bags of berries 30 30
169 40c. Drying beans in sun 35 35
170 50c. Roasting graded beans 45 45

31 "Universal Love" in Chinese

1988. History of Writing (6th series).
171 **31** 16c. stone, black and red 20 20
172 – 30c. stone, black and red 25 35
173 – 40c. stone, black and red 35 45
174 – 50c. black and gold 45 60
DESIGNS: 30c. "Picture of a lion on a stone" in Devanagari (Indian script); 40c. "Information" in Russian; 50c. "Peace be upon you" in Thuluth (Arabic script).

32 College

1988. 5th Anniv of Shayandima Nurses' Training College. Multicoloured.
175 16c. Type **32** 20 15
176 30c. Students using microscope 30 35
177 40c. Anatomy class 35 40
178 50c. Clinical training 40 50

33 "Fetching Water"

1988. Watercolours by Kenneth Thabo. Mult.
179 16c. Type **33** 20 15
180 30c. "Grinding Maize" 30 35
181 40c. "Offering Food" 35 40
182 50c. "Kindling the Fire" 40 50

34 Ndongwana (clay bowls)

1989. Traditional Kitchenware. Multicoloured.
183 16c. Type **34** 15 20
184 30c. Ndilo (wooden porridge bowls) 25 30
185 40c. Mufaro (basket with lid) 30 40
186 50c. Muthatha (dish woven from ilala palm) 40 45

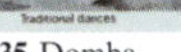
35 Domba

36 Southern Ground Hornbill

1989. Traditional Dances. Multicoloured.
187 18c. Type **35** 15 20
188 30c. Tshinzerere 25 30
189 40c. Malende 30 40
190 50c. Malombo 40 45

1989. Endangered Birds. Multicoloured.
191 18c. Type **36** 70 30
192 30c. Lappet-faced vulture 1·00 70
193 40c. Bateleur 1·25 90
194 50c. Martial eagle 1·50 1·25

37 Pres. Gota F. N. Ravele

38 Lion

1989. 10th Anniv of Independence. Multicoloured.
195 18c. Type **37** 20 20
196 30c. Presidential offices 30 30
197 40c. President's residence 40 40
198 50c. Thohoyandou Sports Stadium 45 45

1990. Nwanedi National Park. Multicoloured.
199 18c. Type **38** 40 25
200 30c. Common zebra 70 55
201 40c. Cheetah 75 65
202 50c. White rhinoceros 1·50 1·25

39 Calligraphy

40 "Aloe globuligemma"

1990. History of Writing (7th series).
203 **39** 21c. black and grey 20 15
204 – 30c. black and brown 40 40
205 – 40c. black and green 50 50
206 – 50c. deep blue, blue & black 60 65
DESIGNS: 30c. Part of score for Beethoven's "Moonlight Sonata"; 40c. Characters from personal computer; 50c. Television picture of message transmitted into outer space from Arecibo 1000 radio telescope.

1990. Aloes. Multicoloured.
207 21c. Type **40** 30 25
208 35c. "Aloe aculeata" 50 50
209 40c. "Aloe lutescens" 60 70
210 50c. "Aloe angelica" 70 90

41 "Pseudacraea boisduvalii"

42 Cape Puff-back Flycatchers

1990. Butterflies. Multicoloured.
211 21c. Type **41** 70 40
212 35c. "Papilio nireus" 1·00 75
213 40c. "Charaxes jasius" 1·10 1·00
214 50c. "Aeropetes tulbaghia" 1·25 1·25

1991. Birds. Paintings by Claude Finch-Davies. Multicoloured.
215 21c. Type **42** 50 40
216 35c. Red-capped robin chat 75 80
217 40c. Collared sunbirds 85 1·00
218 50c. Yellow-streaked greenbul 1·10 1·40

43 Paper made from Pulp

44 Venda Sun Hotel Complex, Thohoyandou

1991. Inventions (1st series). Multicoloured.
219 25c. Type **43** 55 35
220 40c. Magnetic compass 1·00 75
221 50c. Abacus 1·10 1·00
222 60c. Gunpowder 1·75 1·25
See also Nos. 239/42 and 260/3.

1991. Tourism. Multicoloured.
223 25c. Type **44** 55 35
224 40c. Mphephu resort 85 75
225 50c. Sagole Spa 95 95
226 60c. Luphephe-Nwanedi resort 1·00 1·25

1991. Indigenous Trees (4th series). As T **13**. Multicoloured.
227 27c. Fever tree 60 35
228 45c. Transvaal beech 1·00 75
229 65c. Transvaal wild banana 1·10 1·10
230 85c. Sausage tree 1·40 1·50

45 Setting the Web

1992. Clothing Factory. Multicoloured.
231 27c. Type **45** 45 25
232 45c. Knitting 60 55
233 65c. Making up garment 90 1·00
234 85c. Inspection of finished product 1·25 1·50

46 "Apis mellifera"

1992. Bees. Multicoloured.
235 35c. Type **46** 60 40
236 70c. "Anthidium cordiforme" 1·00 90
237 90c. "Megachile frontalis" 1·40 1·25
238 1r.05 "Xylocopa caffia" 1·50 1·40

47 Egyptian Plough

1992. Inventions (2nd series). Multicoloured.
239 35c. Type **47** 60 40
240 70c. Early wheel, Mesopotamia 1·00 90
241 90c. Making bricks, Egypt 1·40 1·25
242 1r.05 Early Egyptian sailing ship 1·50 1·40

48 Nile Crocodile

1992. Crocodile Farming. Multicoloured.
243 35c. Type **48** 65 40
244 70c. Egg laying 1·10 90
245 90c. Eggs hatching 1·40 1·40
246 1r.05 Mother carrying young 1·50 1·60

49 Burmese

1993. Domestic Cats. Multicoloured.
247 45c. Type **49** 90 45
248 65c. Tabby 1·25 1·00
249 85c. Siamese 1·50 1·40
250 1r.05 Persian 1·60 1·75

50 Green-backed Heron

51 Punching-out Sole Lining

1993. Herons. Multicoloured.
251 45c. Type **50** 80 50
252 65c. Black-crowned night heron 1·10 95
253 85c. Purple heron 1·40 1·40
254 1r.05 Black-headed heron 1·60 1·90
MS255 86 × 132 mm. Nos. 251/4 4·50 4·75

1993. Shoe Factory. Multicoloured.
256 45c. Type **51** 30 25
257 65c. Shaping heel 55 60
258 85c. Joining the upper to inner sole 75 85
259 1r.05 Forming sole 90 1·25

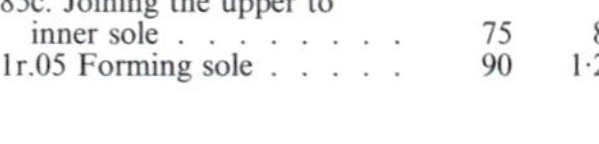

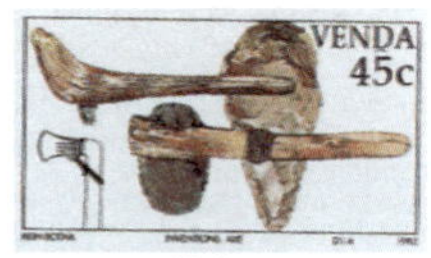
52 Axes

1993. Inventions (3rd series). Multicoloured.
260 45c. Type **52** 30 35
261 65c. Armour 55 65
262 85c. Arches 75 85
263 1r.05 Pont du Gard aqueduct 85 1·25

53 Cocker Spaniel

1994. Dogs. Multicoloured.
264 45c. Type **53** 80 50
265 65c. Maltese 1·10 1·00
266 85c. Scottish terrier 1·40 1·50
267 1r.05 Miniature schnauzer 1·75 2·00

54 Savanna Monkey

1994. Monkeys. Multicoloured.
268 45c. Type **54** 75 55
269 65c. Lesser bushbaby 1·00 1·00
270 85c. Diademed monkey 1·25 1·50
271 1r.05 Thick-tailed bushbaby 1·50 2·00
MS272 119 × 70 mm. Nos. 268/71 4·00 4·50

55 Red-shouldered Glossy Starlings

1994. Starlings. Multicoloured.
273 45c. Type **55** 1·00 65
274 70c. Violet starlings 1·50 1·50
275 95c. African red-winged starlings 1·75 1·90
276 1r.15 Wattled starlings 2·00 2·25

VENEZIA GIULIA AND ISTRIA

Pt. 3

Formerly part of Italy. Stamps issued during Allied occupation, 1945–47. The Peace Treaty of 1947 established the Free Territory of Trieste (q.v.) and gave the rest of the territory to Yugoslavia.

For stamps of Austria overprinted Venezia Giulia see AUSTRIAN TERRITORIES ACQUIRED BY ITALY in Volume 1.

100 centesimi = 1 lira.

A. YUGOSLAV OCCUPATION PROVISIONAL ISSUES

Issue for Trieste.

1945. Stamps of Italian Social Republic 1944, surch **1.V.1945 TRIESTE TRST**, five-pointed star and value.
4 – 20c.+1l. on 5c. brn (No. 106) 15 40
5 **13** +1l. on 25c. green 15 40
6 – +1l. on 30c. brown (No. 110) 15 40
7 – +1l. on 50c. violet (No. 111) 15 40
8 – +1l. on 1l. violet (No. 113) 15 40
9 – +2l. on 1l.25 blue (No. 114) 15 40
2 **12** 2+2l. on 25c. green 15 40
10 – +2l. on 3l. green (No. 115) 15 40
11 – 5+5l. on 1l. violet (No. 113) 15 40
12 – 10+10l. on 30c. brn (No. 110) 1·70 2·75
13 – 20+20l. on 5c. brn (No. 106) 5·00 7·25

Issue for Istria.

In 1945 various stamps of Italy were overprinted "ISTRA" and further surcharged for use in Istria and Pola but they were not issued. However, four of these were further surcharged and issued later.

1945. Stamps of Italy (No. 14) or Italian Social Republic (others) surch **ISTRA** with new value and bars obliterating old surch.

No.	Type	Description	Unused	Used
14	99	4l. on 2l. on 1l. (No. 249) violet	60	80
15	–	6l. on 1,50l. on 75c. (No. 112) red	3·75	5·25
16	–	10l. on 0,10l. on 5c. (No. 106) brown	21·00	16·00
17	103	20l. on 1l. on 50c. (No. 247) violet	4·00	6·00

Issue for Fiume.

1945. Stamps of Italian Social Republic 1944, surch **3-V-1945 FIUME RIJEKA**, five-pointed star over rising sun and new value.

No.	Type	Description	Unused	Used
18	12	2l. on 25c. green	15	40
20	–	4l. on 1l. violet (No. 113)	15	40
21	–	5l. on 10c. brn (No. 107)	15	40
22	–	6l. on 10c. brn (No. 107)	20	40
23	13	10l. on 25c. green	15	40
24	–	16l. on 75c. red (No. 112)	7·00	8·25
25	E 16	20l. on 1l.25c. green	1·90	2·50

B. ALLIED MILITARY GOVERNMENT

1945. Stamps of Italy optd **A.M.G. V.G.** in two lines.

(a) Imperial Series.

No.	Type	Description	Unused	Used
26	–	10c. brown (No. 241)	10	45
27	–	10c. brown (No. 633)	10	50
28	99	20c. red (No. 243)	15	1·60
29		20c. red (No. 640)	15	75
31	–	60c. red (No. 636)	15	85
32	103	60c. green (No. 641)	15	25
33	99	1l. violet (No. 637)	20	15
34	–	2l. red (No. 638)	30	15
35	98	5l. red (No. 645)	70	25
36	–	10l. violet (No. 646)	80	40
37	99	20l. green (No. 257)	1·70	3·25

(b) Stamps of 1945–48.

No.	Type	Description	Unused	Used
38	–	25c. blue (No. 649)	15	55
39	–	2l. brown (No. 656)	55	40
40	–	3l. red (No. 657)	40	30
41	–	4l. red (No. 658)	55	30
42	195	6l. violet (No. 660)	1·30	1·70
43	–	20l. purple (No. 665)	36·00	2·75
44	196	25l. green (No. 666)	4·50	5·75
45		50l. purple (No. 668)	5·00	8·75
46	197	100l. red (No. 669)	19·00	29·00

1945. Air stamps of Italy, optd as above.

No.	Type	Description	Unused	Used
47	110	50c. brown (No. 271)	15	30
48	198	1l. grey (No. 670)	40	3·25
49	–	2l. blue (No. 671)	40	1·40
50	–	5l. green (No. 673)	2·00	1·60
51	198	10l. red (No. 674)	2·00	1·60
52	–	25l. blue (No. 675)	2·50	2·00
53	–	25l. brown (No. 676)	20·00	22·00
54	198	50l. green (No. 677)	4·25	5·50

EXPRESS LETTER STAMPS

1946. Express Letter Stamps of Italy optd **A.M.G. V.G.** in two lines.

No.	Type	Description	Unused	Used
E55	–	10l. blue (No. E680)	3·00	1·90
E56	E 200	30l. violet (No. E683)	7·25	11·50

C. YUGOSLAV MILITARY GOVERNMENT

6 Grapes

7 Roman Amphitheatre, Pula, and Istrian Fishing Vessel

8 Blue-finned Tuna

1945. Inscr "ISTRA SLOVENSKO PRIMORJE – ISTRIA LITTORALE SLOVENO".

No.	Type	Description	Unused	Used
74	6	0.25l. green	25	35
58	–	0.50l. brown	40	40
59	–	1l. red	40	40
76	–	1l. green	50	60
77	–	1.50l. green	25	35
78	–	2l. green	25	35
100	–	3l. red	4·00	3·25
62	7	4l. blue	35	35
79		4l. red	25	35
80	–	5l. black	25	35
101	7	6l. blue	6·00	6·00
81	–	10l. brown	90	1·00
65	8	20l. purple	8·50	10·50
82		20l. blue	3·50	4·25
83	–	30l. mauve	3·50	5·75

DESIGNS—As Type **6**: 0.50l. Donkey and view; 1l. Rebuilding damaged homes; 1.50l. Olive branch; 2, 3l. Duino Castle near Trieste. As Type **7**: 5l. Birthplace of Vladimir Gortan, Piran; 10l. Ploughing. As Type **8**: 30l. Viaduct over River Solkan.

1946. Nos. 82 and 66 surch.

No.	Type	Description	Unused	Used
96	8	1 on 20l. blue	1·40	1·50
97	–	2 on 30l. mauve	1·40	1·50

1947. As Nos. 514 and O540 of Yugoslavia with colours changed, surch **VOJNA UPRAVA JUGOSLAVENSKE ARMIJE** and new value.

No.	Description	Unused	Used
102	1l. on 9d. pink	40	50
103	1.50l. on 0.50d. blue	40	50
104	2l. on 9d. pink	40	50
105	3l. on 0.50d. blue	40	50
106	5l. on 9d. pink	50	60
107	6l. on 0.50d. blue	35	45
108	10l. on 9d. pink	50	60
109	15l. on 0.50d. blue	70	80
110	35l. on 9d. pink	70	80
111	50l. on 0.50d. blue	90	1·00

POSTAGE DUE STAMPS

1945. Stamps of 1945 surch **PORTO** and value in **Lit.**

No.	Type	Description	Unused	Used
D72	8	0.50 on 20l. purple	1·30	1·60
D67	6	1l. on 0.25l. green	10·50	3·50
D73	–	2l. on 30l. mauve	2·50	3·25
D68	–	4l. on 0.50l. brown	1·40	1·30
D69	–	8l. on 0.50l. brown	1·40	1·30
D70	–	10l. on 0.50l. brown	9·25	3·25
D71	–	20l. on 0.50l. brown	10·50	8·00

1946. Stamps of 1945 surch **PORTO** and value expressed in **Lira**.

No.	Type	Description	Unused	Used
D90	6	1l. on 0.25l. green	60	50
D84	–	1l. on 1l. green (No. 76)	40	50
D91	6	2l. on 0.25l. green	95	70
D85	–	2l. on 1l. green (No. 76)	40	60
D92	6	4l. on 0.25l. green	60	50
D86	–	4l. on 1l. green (No. 76)	60	80
D93	8	10l. on 20l. blue	5·00	4·00
D87	–	10l. on 30l. mauve (No. 66)	5·75	4·00
D94	8	20l. on 20l. blue	11·00	9·25
D88	–	20l. on 30l. mauve (No. 66)	11·00	9·25
D95	8	30l. on 20l. blue	11·00	9·25
D89	–	30l. on 30l. mauve (No. 66)	11·00	9·75

1947. No. D528 of Yugoslavia with colour changed and surch **Vojna Uprava Jugoslavenske Armije** and value.

No.	Description	Unused	Used
D112	1l. on 1d. green	95	1·00
D113	2l. on 1d. green	35	40
D114	6l. on 1d. green	35	40
D115	10l. on 1d. green	75	80
D116	30l. on 1d. green	75	80

VENEZUELA Pt. 20

A republic in the N. of S. America, independent since 1811.

1859. 100 centavos = 8 reales = 1 peso.
1879. 100 centesimos = 1 venezolano.
1880. 100 centimos = 1 bolivar.

1 2 3

1859. Imperf.

No.	Type	Description	Unused	Used
7	1	½r. orange	14·00	6·50
8		1r. blue	21·00	12·00
9		2r. red	26·00	13·00

1862. Imperf.

No.	Type	Description	Unused	Used
13	2	¼c. green	20·00	55·00
14		½c. lilac	22·00	£100
15		1c. brown	35·00	£120

1863. Imperf.

No.	Type	Description	Unused	Used
16	3	½c. red	40·00	70·00
17a		1c. grey	45·00	80·00
21		½r. yellow	5·25	2·10
19		1r. blue	15·00	6·50
20		2r. green	23·00	18·00

4

5 Bolivar

1866. Imperf.

No.	Type	Description	Unused	Used
22	4	½c. green	£160	£225
23		1c. green	£160	£180
24		½r. red	6·75	2·00
26		1r. red	32·00	10·00
27a		2r. yellow	£120	60·00

1871. Optd with inscription in very small letters. Imperf.

No.	Type	Description	Unused	Used
58	5	1c. yellow	90	30
59d		2c. yellow	1·25	35
60		3c. yellow	2·25	70
61		4c. yellow	2·40	40
62b		5c. yellow	2·40	40
63b		1r. red	2·00	30
64a		2r. red	3·75	75
65a		3r. red	4·50	75
66a		5r. red	4·25	85
52a		7r. red	5·75	2·00
53a		9r. green	12·50	3·50
54		15r. green	26·00	7·25
68		20r. green	60·00	11·00
56		30r. green	£300	95·00
70		50r. green	£800	£200

1873. Optd with inscription in very small letters. Imperf.

No.	Type	Description	Unused	Used
74a	4	1c. lilac	6·50	13·50
75a		2c. green	32·00	38·00
76a		½r. pink	22·00	3·00
77a		1r. red	29·00	7·75
78a		2r. yellow	95·00	42·00

7 Bolivar

8 Bolivar

1879. New Currency. Optd with inscription in small letters. Imperf.

No.	Type	Description	Unused	Used
83	7	1c. yellow	2·25	15
84		5c. yellow	3·00	30
85		10c. blue	4·25	40
86		30c. blue	5·50	1·00
87		50c. blue	6·50	1·00
88		90c. blue	27·00	5·50
89		1v. red	55·00	12·00
90		3v. red	£100	25·00
91		5v. red	£170	60·00

1880. New Currency. Without opt. Perf.

No.	Type	Description	Unused	Used
92	7	5c. yellow	1·00	15
93		10c. yellow	1·60	15
94		25c. yellow	1·50	20
95		50c. yellow	3·00	25
96		1b. blue	7·75	60
97		2b. blue	12·00	70
98		5b. blue	28·00	1·25
99		10b. red	£140	45·00
100		20b. red	£750	£170
101		25b. red	£3500	£425

1880.

No.	Type	Description	Unused	Used
107	8	5c. blue	9·75	4·00
108		10c. red	15·00	7·50
109		25c. yellow	9·75	4·00
110		50c. brown	55·00	23·00
106		1b. green	85·00	32·00

9 Bolivar

10 Bolivar

1882. Various frames. Perf or roul.

No.	Type	Description	Unused	Used
111	9	5c. green	10	10
112		10c. brown	10	10
113		25c. orange	10	10
114		50c. blue	15	10
115		1b. red	20	10
116		3b. violet	20	10
117		10b. brown	65	50
118		20b. purple	80	55

1882. Various frames. Perf or roul.

No.	Type	Description	Unused	Used
119	10	5c. blue	50	10
120		10c. brown	50	10
121		25c. brown	90	20
122		50c. green	2·00	50
123		1b. violet	3·00	1·25

1892. Surch **RESOLUCION DE 10 DE OCTUBRE DE 1892** and value in circle.

No.	Type	Description	Unused	Used
134	9	25c. on 5c. green	7·00	4·00
138	10	25c. on 5c. blue	29·00	29·00
135	9	25c. on 10c. brown	7·00	4·00
139	10	25c. on 10c. brown	12·50	10·50
136	9	1b. on 25c. orange	8·00	5·00
140	10	1b. on 25c. brown	12·50	10·50
137	9	1b. on 50c. blue	12·00	5·00
141	10	1b. on 50c. green	13·50	12·50

1893. Optd with coat of arms and diagonal shading.

No.	Type	Description	Unused	Used
142	9	5c. green	10	10
150	10	5c. blue	20	10
143	9	10c. brown	10	10
151	10	10c. brown	55	65
144	9	25c. orange	10	10
152	10	25c. brown	35	25
145	9	50c. blue	10	10
153	10	50c. green	50	20
146	9	1b. red	55	20
154	10	1b. violet	1·75	50
147	9	3b. violet	50	35
148		10b. brown	1·90	1·25
149		20b. purple	1·75	1·25

13 Bolivar

14 Bolivar

1893. Schools Tax stamps.

No.	Type	Description	Unused	Used
155	13	5c. grey	10	10
156		10c. green	10	10
157		25c. blue	10	10
158		50c. orange	10	10
159		1b. purple	30	10
160		3b. red	45	20
161		10b. violet	55	60
162		20b. brown	2·25	1·50

See also Nos. 227/35.

1893.

No.	Type	Description	Unused	Used
163	14	5c. brown	90	10
164		10c. blue	3·50	65
165		25c. mauve	16·00	20
166		50c. purple	3·50	20
167		1b. green	3·75	65

15 Landing of Columbus

1893. Columbian Exposition, Chicago, and 400th Anniv of Discovery of America by Columbus.

No.	Type	Description	Unused	Used
168	15	25c. purple	12·00	65

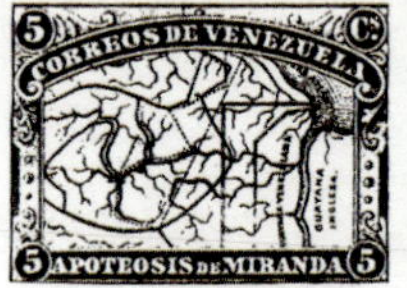

16 Map of Venezuela

18 Bolivar

1896. 80th Death Anniv of Gen. Miranda.

No.	Type	Description	Unused	Used
169	16	5c. green	3·25	2·10
170		10c. blue	3·25	2·10
171		25c. yellow	3·75	4·25
172		50c. red	38·00	18·00
173		1b. mauve	35·00	18·00

1899.

No.	Type	Description	Unused	Used
179	18	5c. green	1·10	15
180		10c. red	1·50	15
181		25c. blue	2·40	50
182		50c. black	2·50	60
183		50c. orange	1·50	30
184		1b. green	24·00	16·00
185		2b. yellow	£300	£170

(21) "R.T.M." = Ramon Tellos Mendoza, Minister of Interior

(23)

1900. Stamps of 1893 optd with T **21**.

No.	Type	Description	Unused	Used
191	13	5c. grey	10	10
192		10c. green	10	10
193		25c. blue	10	10
194		50c. orange	10	10
195		1b. purple	20	10
196		3b. red	30	10
197		10b. violet	65	40
198		20b. brown	4·25	4·25

1900. Stamps of 1899 optd with T **21**.

No.	Type	Description	Unused	Used
199	18	5c. green	80	30
200		10c. red	80	35
201		25c. blue	5·50	60
202		50c. black	2·75	50
203		1b. green	1·25	40
204		2b. yellow	2·25	1·25

1900. Stamps of 1893 optd **1900**. Colours changed.

No.	Type	Description	Unused	Used
206	13	5c. orange	10	10
207		10c. blue	10	10
208		25c. purple	10	10
209		50c. green	60	10
210		1b. black	4·75	55
211		3b. brown	1·25	60
212		10b. red	5·00	1·40
213		20b. violet	10·00	2·75

1900. Stamps of 1899 optd **1900**.

No.	Type	Description	Unused	Used
214	18	5c. green	£200	£200
215		10c. red	£200	£200
216		25c. blue	£275	£120
217		50c. orange	16·00	85
218		1b. black	1·10	60

1900. Stamps of 1899 optd with T **23**.
219 **18** 5c. green . . . . 5·00 50
220 10c. red . . . . 4·50 55
221 25c. blue . . . . 5·00 50

1901. Re-issue of T **13** in new colours.
227 **13** 5c. orange 10 10
228 10c. red 10 10
229 10c. blue 10 10
231 50c. green 15 15
232 1b. black . . . . 4·50 1·10
233 3b. brown 20 10
234 10b. red 35 25
235 20b. violet 80 50

1902. Stamp of 1901 optd **1901**.
236 **13** 1b. black 45 30

1904. No. 231 surch **CORREOS Vale B 0,05 1904**.
310 **13** 5c. on 50c. green 40 55

38 General Sucre  **39** Bolivar

1904.
311 **38** 5c. green 40 15
312 10c. red 25 15
313 15c. violet 45 30
314 25c. blue . . . . 3·25 30
315 50c. red 45 40
316 1b. red 50 40

1904.
317 **39** 5c. green 10 10
318 10c. grey 10 10
319 25c. red 10 10
320 50c. yellow 10 10
321 1b. red . . . . 1·40 25
322 3b. blue 35 15
323 10b. violet 45 25
324 20b. red 75 35

41 President Castro  **42** Liberty

1905. 6th Anniv of General Castro's Revolt.
330 **41** 5c. red . . . . 2·50 2·40
331a 10c. blue . . . . 3·75 3·00
332a 25c. yellow . . . . 1·40 1·25

1910. Independence Centenary.
333 **42** 25c. blue . . . . 9·50 45

43 F. de Miranda  **44**

1911. Portraits as T **43**.
340 **43** 5c. green 25 15
341 10c. red 35 10
342 – 15c. grey (Urdaneta) . . . 3·75 20
343 – 25c. blue (Urdaneta) . . . 2·00 25
344 – 50c. violet (Bolivar) . . . 2·50 25
339 – 1b. orange (Bolivar) . . . 2·50 1·00

1911. Portraits as T **44**.
345 – 5c. blue (Vargas) 10 10
346 – 10c. yellow (Avila) 10 10
347 – 25c. grey (Sanz) 10 10
348 **44** 50c. red (Blanco) 10 10
349 – 1b. green (Bello) 10 10
350 – 2b. brown (Sanabria) . . . 55 35
351 – 3b. violet (Paez) 55 25
352 – 10b. purple (Sucre) . . . . 1·10 50
353 – 20b. blue (Bolivar) . . . . 1·10 70

46 Bolivar  **47** Bolivar

1914.
359 **46** 5c. green . . . . 22·00 25
360 10c. red . . . . 20·00 40
361 25c. blue . . . . 3·75 20

1915. Various Frames.
362a **47** 5c. green . . . . 2·75 25
379 5c. brown 55 10
570 7½c. green . . . . 1·10 35
571 10c. red . . . . 2·50 30
380 10c. green 20 10
381 15c. olive . . . . 1·60 50
382 15c. brown 30 10
383 25c. blue . . . . 1·60 10
384 25c. red 20 10
368 40c. green . . . . 16·00 6·25
385 40c. blue 55 20
369 50c. violet . . . . 4·25 40
386 50c. blue 55 20
371 75c. turquoise . . . . . . 40·00 12·50
387 1b. black 55 25
388 3b. orange . . . . 1·40 75
389 5b. violet . . . . 15·00 7·50
See also Nos. 414/5.

48 Bolivar and Sucre

1924. Centenary of Battle of Ayacucho.
390 **48** 25c. blue . . . . 2·25 35

1926. Fiscal stamps surch **CORREOS VALE 1926** and value.
392 0,05b. on 1b. olive 40 35
393 0,25b. on 5c. brown 40 40
DESIGNS: No. 392, Portrait of Sucre; No. 393, Numeral.

50 General J. V. Gomez and Ciudad Bolivar  **51** Biplane and Venezuela

1928. 25th Anniv of Capture of Ciudad Bolivar and Peace in Venezuela.
394 **50** 10c. green . . . . 1·40 55

1930. Air.
395 **51** 5c. brown 15 10
575 5c. green 30 10
396 10c. yellow 15 10
576 10c. orange 60 15
577 12½c. purple 80 50
397 15c. grey 15 10
578 15c. blue 70 15
398 25c. violet 15 10
579 25c. brown . . . . 1·40 20
399 40c. green 15 10
581 70c. red . . . . 21·00 7·00
400 75c. red 45 15
401 1b. blue 55 15
402 1b.20 green 75 35
403 1b.70 blue 95 40
404 1b.90 green . . . . 1·00 50
405 2b.10 blue . . . . 1·50 40
406 2b.30 red . . . . 1·50 50
407 2b.50 blue . . . . 1·75 50
408 3b.70 green . . . . 1·75 75
409 10b. purple . . . . 3·50 1·50
410 20b. green . . . . 7·50 4·00
See also Nos. 426/49.

52 Simon Bolivar

1930. Death Centenary of Bolivar.
411 **52** 5c. yellow 85 40
412 10c. blue 85 30
413 25c. red 85 30

53

1932. Stamps of 1915 on paper printed with pattern as T **53**.
414 **47** 5c. violet 40 10
415 7½c. green 75 40
416 10c. green 50 10
417 15c. yellow . . . . 1·00 25
418 22½c. red . . . . 2·25 35
419 25c. red 85 10
420 37½c. blue . . . . 3·00 1·25
421 40c. blue . . . . 3·00 30
422 50c. olive . . . . 3·00 40
423 1b. blue . . . . 4·00 45
424 3b. brown . . . . 24·00 10·50
425 5b. brown . . . . 35·00 13·50

1932. Air. Air stamps as 1930 on paper printed with pattern as T **53**.
426 **51** 5c. brown 40 10
427 10c. yellow 40 10
428 15c. grey 40 10
429 25c. blue 55 10
430 40c. green 50 10
431 70c. red 65 10
432 75c. orange 70 25
433 1b. slate 85 10
434 1b.20 green . . . . 1·50 60
435 1b.70 brown . . . . 3·25 40
436 1b.80 blue . . . . 1·90 30
437 1b.90 green . . . . 4·00 2·50
438 1b.95 blue . . . . 4·25 2·10
439 2b. brown . . . . 3·50 1·75
440 2b.10 blue . . . . 6·50 4·25
441 2b.30 red . . . . 3·00 1·60
442 2b.50 blue . . . . 4·50 1·00
443 3b. violet . . . . 4·50 75
444 3b.70 green . . . . 5·00 4·25
445 4b. orange . . . . 4·50 1·00
446 5b. black . . . . 7·00 2·25
447 8b. red . . . . 12·50 3·50
448 10b. violet . . . . 24·00 7·00
449 20b. green . . . . 50·00 19·00

54 Arms of Bolivar

1933. 150th Birth Anniv of Bolivar.
450 **54** 25c. red . . . . 2·25 1·25

1934. Surch **1933** and figures of value and old value blocked out.
451 **47** 7½ on 10c. green (380) . . 55 30
453 22½ on 25c. red (384) . . . 1·40 60
452 22½ on 25c. red (419) . . . 1·25 1·00
454 37½ on 40c. blue (385) . . 1·50 60

1937. Air. Air stamps of 1932 surch **1937 VALE POR** and new value.
455 **51** 5c. on 1b.70 brown . . . . 12·00 6·00
456 10c. on 3b.70 green . . . . 12·00 6·00
457 15c. on 4b. orange . . . . 5·75 3·00
458 25c. on 5b. black . . . . . 5·75 3·00
459 1b. on 8b. red . . . . . . 4·75 3·00
460 2b. on 2b.10 blue . . . . 32·00 22·00

1937. Surch **1937 VALE POR** and value.
461 **47** 25c. on 40c. (No. 421) . . 5·25 80

59 Nurse and Child  **60** Ploughing

61 "Flight"  **64** Caribbean Coast

1937. (a) Postage.
463 **59** 5c. violet 60 25
464 – 10c. green . . . . 1·10 25
465 – 15c. brown . . . . 1·00 35
466 **59** 25c. red . . . . 1·10 40
467 – 50c. green . . . . 6·00 3·25
468 **60** 3b. red . . . . 10·00 6·00
469 **59** 5b. brown . . . . 19·00 12·00
DESIGNS—VERT: 10c. Sailing barges on Orinoco; 15c. Women gathering cocoa-beans. HORIZ: 50c. Rounding up cattle.

(b) Air.
470 **61** 5c. brown 35 35
471 – 10c. orange 20 10
472 – 15c. black 40 35
473 **64** 25c. violet 50 35
474 – 40c. green 95 40
475 **61** 70c. red 95 35
476 – 75c. bistre . . . . 1·90 65
477 **61** 1b. grey . . . . 1·25 45
478 – 1b.20 green . . . . 4·50 1·90
479 **61** 1b.80 blue . . . . 2·50 1·25
480 – 1b.95 blue . . . . 7·50 4·00
481 **64** 2b. brown . . . . 2·75 1·75
482 2b.50 blue . . . . 10·00 6·50
483 – 3b. lilac . . . . 4·75 3·00
484 **64** 3b.70 red . . . . 17·00 8·00
485 – 10b. purple . . . . 17·00 10·00
486 **61** 20b. black . . . . 22·00 14·00
DESIGNS—HORIZ: 10, 40c., 1b.20, 3b. Puerto Cabello; 15, 75c., 1b.95, 10b. Caracas.

65 "Venezuela" welcoming La Guaira  **67** Bolivar

1937. Acquisition of La Guaira Harbour.
487 **65** 25c. blue (postage) . . . . 1·40 55
488 – 70c. green (air) . . . . . . 3·00 80
489 – 1b.80 blue . . . . 5·50 1·50
DESIGN: 70c., 1b.80, Statue of Bolivar and La Guaira Harbour.

1937. Red Cross Fund.
490 **67** 5c. green 75 50

1937. Stamps of 1937 optd **RESELLADO 1937-1938**.
491 **59** 5c. violet (postage) . . . . 3·75 1·60
492 – 10c. green . . . . 1·40 65
493 **59** 25c. red . . . . 1·25 55
494 **60** 3b. red . . . . £140 60·00
495 – 10c. orange (air) . . . . . 1·25 55
496 **64** 25c. violet . . . . 2·00 75
497 – 40c. green . . . . 2·00 1·10
498 **61** 70c. red . . . . 1·60 75
499 1b. grey . . . . 2·50 1·10
500 – 1b.20 green . . . . 32·00 16·00
501 **61** 1b.80 blue . . . . 5·00 85
502 – 1b.95 blue . . . . 7·50 3·75
503 **64** 2b. brown . . . . 60·00 23·00
504 2b.50 blue . . . . 65·00 21·00
505 – 3b. lilac . . . . 32·00 8·50
506 – 10b. purple . . . . 80·00 42·00
507 **61** 20b. black . . . . 90·00 40·00

69 Gathering Coffee Beans  **72** La Guaira

1938. (a) Postage. As T **69**.
508 **69** 5c. green 40 15
509 A 10c. red 40 15
510 B 15c. violet . . . . 1·10 25
544 15c. green 55 30
511 A 25c. blue 40 15
546 37½c. blue . . . . 1·90 55
513 B 40c. sepia . . . . 15·00 4·25
547 40c. black . . . . 12·00 4·25
514 **69** 50c. olive . . . . 18·00 4·50
548 50c. violet . . . . 7·00 55
515 A 1b. brown . . . . 8·25 5·25
516 **69** 3b. orange . . . . 65·00 28·00
517 B 5b. black . . . . 10·00 4·50
750 5b. orange . . . . 35·00 18·00
751 5b. brown . . . . 10·50 4·00
DESIGNS: A, Bolivar; B, G.P.O., Caracas.

(b) Air. As T **72**.
550 **72** 5c. green 20 10
551 C 10c. red 20 10
552 **72** 12½c. violet 35 30
520 D 15c. violet . . . . 2·50 75
553 15c. blue 60 10
521 **72** 25c. blue . . . . 2·50 75
554 25c. brown 25 10
555 D 30c. violet . . . . 1·75 20
522 C 40c. violet . . . . 2·75 1·10
556 40c. brown . . . . 2·00 20
557 **72** 45c. green 95 20
558 C 50c. blue . . . . 1·00 10
523 D 70c. red 60 40
524 **72** 75c. brown . . . . 6·00 1·50
559 75c. green . . . . 1·25 25
560 D 90c. red 90 20
525 C 1b. green . . . . 5·50 1·75
561 1b. violet . . . . 1·10 20
526 D 1b.20 orange . . . . 16·00 5·00
562 1b.20 green . . . . 1·40 60
527 **72** 1b.80 blue . . . . 1·40 60
528 C 1b.90 black . . . . 4·00 2·10
529 D 1b.95 blue . . . . 3·25 1·90
530 **72** 2b. green . . . . 32·00 11·50
563 2b. red . . . . 1·50 75
531 C 2b.50 brown . . . . 32·00 13·00
564 2b.50 orange . . . . 10·50 2·50
565 D 3b. green . . . . 4·00 1·50

No.	Type	Description	Mint	Used
533	**72**	3b.70 black	6·00	3·50
566	D	5b. red	6·75	1·60
771		5b. green	5·50	2·10
534	C	10b. purple	22·00	2·50
773		10b. yellow	7·50	2·75
535	D	20b. orange	70·00	26·00

DESIGNS: C, National Pantheon; D, Oil Wells.

1938. Surch **VALE Bs. 0,40 1938**.

No.	Type	Description	Mint	Used
536	**59**	40c. on 5b. brown	7·50	2·75

1938. Air. Postage stamps surch **1938 VALE** and value in words.

No.	Type	Description	Mint	Used
537	**61**	5c. on 1b.80 blue	70	50
538	**64**	10c. on 2b.50 blue	2·10	60
539		15c. on 2b. brown	1·00	60
540	–	25c. on 40c. green (No. 474)	1·10	70
541	**64**	40c. on 3b.70 red	2·50	1·60

77 Teresa Carreno

78 Allegory of Labour and Statue of Bolivar

1938. Repatriation of Ashes of Teresa Carreno (concert pianist).

No.	Type	Description	Mint	Used
567	**77**	25c. blue	3·25	55

1938. Labour Day.

No.	Type	Description	Mint	Used
568	**78**	25c. blue	3·75	55

80 Monument at Carabobo

81 Monument at Carabobo

82 Gen. J. I. Paz Castillo

1938. Air. Independence Issue.

No.	Type	Description	Mint	Used
583	–	20c. brown	50	35
584	**80**	30c. violet	60	35
585	**81**	45c. blue	85	25
586	–	50c. blue	70	25
587	**81**	70c. red	15·00	8·00
588	**80**	90c. orange	1·25	60
589	**81**	1b.35 black	1·60	75
590	–	1b.40 slate	6·25	1·75
591	**80**	2b.25 green	3·25	1·50

DESIGN: 20, 50c., 1b.40, Airplane over Sucre Monument.

1939. 80th Anniv of Venezuelan Posts.

No.	Type	Description	Mint	Used
592	**82**	10c. red	1·75	55

83 View of Ojeda

84 Dr. Cristobal Mendoza

1939. Founding of Ojeda.

No.	Type	Description	Mint	Used
593	**83**	25c. blue	6·00	40

1939. Centenary of Death of Dr. Mendoza.

No.	Type	Description	Mint	Used
594	**84**	5c. green	25	30
595		10c. red	25	30
596		15c. violet	1·00	40
597		25c. blue	90	30
598		37½c. blue	12·00	5·25
599		50c. olive	12·00	3·75
600		1b. brown	5·75	3·00

85 Diego B. Urbaneja

86 Bolivar and Carabobo Monument

1940. Independence Issue.

No.	Type	Description	Mint	Used
601	**85**	5c. green (postage)	50	15
602		7½c. green	40	25
603		15c. olive	55	25
604		37½c. blue	1·10	40
605		40c. blue	90	30
745		40c. mauve	55	25
746		40c. orange	55	25
606		50c. violet	4·25	1·10
607		1b. brown	2·00	55
748		1b. blue	1·25	25
608		3b. red	6·50	2·25
749		3b. grey	2·10	55
609	**86**	15c. blue (air)	50	15
610		20c. olive	45	10
611		25c. brown	1·90	35
612		40c. brown	1·50	15
613		1b. lilac	3·50	25
614		2b. red	6·50	60

87 Foundation of Greater Colombia

1940. Air. 50th Anniv of Pan-American Union.

No.	Type	Description	Mint	Used
615	**87**	15c. brown	1·00	55

88 Battle of Carabobo

89 "The Crossing of the Andes" (after Salas)

1940. 150th Birth Anniv of Gen. Paez.

No.	Type	Description	Mint	Used
616	**88**	25c. blue	4·00	55

1940. Death Centenary of Gen. Santander.

No.	Type	Description	Mint	Used
617	**89**	25c. blue	4·00	55

90 Monument and Urn

91 Statue of Bolivar at Caracas

1940. 110th Anniv of Death of Simon Bolivar. (a) Postage.

No.	Type	Description	Mint	Used
738	**90**	5c. green	10	10
739		5c. blue	15	10
619	–	10c. pink	30	10
620	–	15c. green	40	15
741	–	15c. red	30	10
621	–	20c. blue	70	10
622	–	25c. blue	40	10
742	–	25c. violet	25	10
623	–	30c. mauve	1·25	25
743	–	30c. black	1·00	35
744	–	30c. purple	50	15
624	–	37½c. blue	2·10	70
625	–	50c. violet	1·50	50
747	–	50c. green	55	25

DESIGNS—VERT: 15c. Bolivar's baptism; 25c. Simon Bolivar on horseback. HORIZ: 10c. Bolivar's bed; 20c. House where Bolivar was born; 30c. Courtyard and Bolivar's baptismal font; 37½c. Courtyard of house where Bolivar was born; 50c. "Rebellion of 1812".

(b) Air.

No.	Type	Description	Mint	Used
626	**91**	5c. green	10	10
752		5c. orange	10	10
627		10c. red	10	10
753		10c. green	10	10
628		12½c. violet	45	35
754		12½c. brown	25	45
629		15c. blue	25	10
755		15c. grey	15	10
630		20c. brown	35	10
756		20c. violet	20	10
631		25c. brown	25	10
757		25c. green	15	10
632		30c. violet	25	10
758		30c. blue	20	10
633		40c. brown	35	10
759		40c. green	35	10
634		45c. green	50	10
760		45c. red	30	15
635		50c. blue	50	10
761		50c. claret	30	15
636		70c. pink	1·40	35
762		70c. red	55	30
637		75c. olive	4·25	1·00
763		75c. orange	3·50	2·00
764		75c. violet	30	15
638		90c. orange	65	35
765		90c. black	45	40
639		1b. mauve	35	10
766		1b. blue	35	20
640		1b.20 green	1·75	60
767		1b.20 brown	65	45
641		1b.35 black	7·00	3·00
642		2b. red	1·40	20
643		3b. black	2·50	65
768		3b. brown	11·50	2·75
769		3b. blue	1·40	35
644		4b. black	2·00	35
645		5b. brown	12·00	5·25

1941. No. 622 surch **HABILITADO 1941 VALE BS. 0.20**.

No.	Type	Description	Mint	Used
646		20c. on 25c. blue	40	15

1941. Optd **HABILITADO 1940**.

No.	Type	Description	Mint	Used
647	**59**	5c. violet	1·50	50
648	–	10c. green (No. 464)	1·25	35

94 Bolivar's Funeral

95 Condor

1941. Centenary of Arrival of Bolivar's Ashes at Caracas and Liberator's Monument Fund.

No.	Type	Description	Mint	Used
649	**94**	20c.+5c. blue (postage)	4·50	35
650	**95**	15c.+10c. brown (air)	1·10	45
651		30c.+5c. violet	1·10	60

96 Symbolical of Industry

97 Caracas Cathedral

100 National and Red Cross Flags

1942. National Industrial Exhibition.

No.	Type	Description	Mint	Used
652	**96**	10c. red	60	25

1943.

No.	Type	Description	Mint	Used
653	**97**	10c. red	40	15
740		10c. orange	10	10

1943. Surch **Habilitado Vale Bs. 0.20**.

No.	Type	Description	Mint	Used
654	**59**	20c. on 25c. red	22·00	19·00
655	**65**	20c. on 25c. blue	55·00	42·00
656	**77**	20c. on 25c. blue	14·50	11·00
657	**78**	20c. on 25c. blue	14·50	11·00

1943. Optd **Resellado 1943**.

No.	Type	Description	Mint	Used
658	**59**	5c. violet	10·50	5·75
659	–	10c. green (No. 464)	5·00	3·50
660	–	50c. green (No. 467)	6·00	2·75
661	**60**	3b. red	32·00	11·50

1943. Air. Optd **Resellado 1943**.

No.	Type	Description	Mint	Used
662	–	10c. orange (No. 471)	1·25	80
663	**64**	25c. violet	1·25	1·00
664	–	40c. green (No. 474)	1·40	1·00
665	**61**	70c. red	1·50	1·00
666	–	70c. green (No. 488)	1·50	1·00
667	–	75c. bistre (No. 476)	1·75	1·10
668	**61**	1b. grey	1·90	1·25
669	–	1b.20 green (No. 478)	2·50	1·40
670	**61**	1b.80 blue	2·25	1·40
671	–	1b.80 blue (No. 489)	3·00	1·50
672	–	1b.95 blue (No. 480)	3·75	2·00
673	**64**	2b. brown	3·75	2·75
674		2b.50 blue	4·00	2·75
675	–	3b. lilac (No. 483)	5·50	3·25
676	**64**	3b.70 red	55·00	45·00
677	–	10b. purple (No. 485)	21·00	14·50
678	**61**	20b. black	35·00	28·00

1944. Air. 80th Anniv of Int Red Cross and 37th Anniv of Adherence of Venezuela.

No.	Type	Description	Mint	Used
680	**100**	5c. green	10	10
681		10c. mauve	15	10
682		20c. blue	15	10
683		30c. blue	35	10
684		40c. brown	50	15
685		45c. green	90	35
686		90c. orange	85	30
687		1b. black	1·25	25

101 Baseball Players

103 Charles Howarth

1944. Air. 7th World Amateur Baseball Championship Games, Caracas. Optd **AEREO**.

No.	Type	Description	Mint	Used
688	**101**	5c. brown	35	25
689		10c. green	40	25
690		20c. blue	50	35
691		30c. red	40	50
692		45c. purple	1·50	45
693		90c. orange	2·40	90
694		1b. grey	2·50	90
695		1b.20 green	8·00	5·25
696		1b.80 yellow	10·50	7·50

1944. Air. No. 590 surch **Habilitado 1944 VALE Bs. 0.30.**

No.	Type	Description	Mint	Used
697		30c. on 1b.40c. slate	35	35

1944. Air. Cent of Rochdale Co-operative Society.

No.	Type	Description	Mint	Used
698	**103**	5c. black	25	15
699		10c. violet	25	15
700		20c. brown	50	30
701		30c. green	60	60
702		1b.20 brown	1·90	1·75
703		1b.80 blue	3·50	2·50
704		3b.70 red	4·75	4·00

104 Antonio Jose de Sucre

105 Antonio Jose de Sucre and Douglas DC-4

1945. 150th Anniv of Birth of Gen. Sucre.

No.	Type	Description	Mint	Used
705	**104**	5c. yellow (postage)	75	35
706		10c. blue	1·25	70
707		20c. red	1·50	70
708	**105**	5c. orange (air)	20	15
709		10c. purple	25	20
710		20c. black	35	25
711		30c. green	55	40
712		40c. olive	55	35
713		45c. brown	70	35
714		90c. brown	1·25	45
715		1b. mauve	90	35
716		1b.20 black	2·50	2·25
717		2b. yellow	3·75	1·50

106 Andres Bello

107 Gen. Rafael Urdaneta

1946. 80th Death Anniv of A. Bello (educationalist).

No.	Type	Description	Mint	Used
718	**106**	20c. blue (postage)	85	35
719		30c. green (air)	70	30

1946. Death Centenary of Gen. R. Urdaneta.

No.	Type	Description	Mint	Used
720	**107**	20c. blue (postage)	85	35
721		30c. green (air)	70	30

108 Allegory of Republic

110 Western Hemisphere and Anti-tuberculosis Inst, Maracaibo

1946. 1st Anniv of Revolution.

No.	Type	Description	Mint	Used
722	**108**	20c. blue (postage)	80	35
723	–	15c. blue (air)	20	30
724	–	20c. bistre	25	30
725	–	30c. violet	30	25
726	–	1b. red	3·00	1·50

Nos. 723/6 are as Type **108**, but vert.

1947. 12th Pan-American Health Conf, Caracas.

No.	Type	Description	Mint	Used
727	**110**	20c. yellow & bl (postage)	50	35
728	–	15c. yellow and blue (air)	35	25
729	–	20c. yellow and brown	35	40
730	–	30c. yellow and violet	35	25
731	–	1b. yellow and red	4·25	2·10

Nos. 728/31 are as Type **110** but vert.

1947. Surch **J. R. G. CORREOS Vale Bs.0.15 1946.**

No.	Type	Description	Mint	Used
732	**85**	15c. on 1b. brown	80	35

1947. Air. Surch **J. R. G. AEREO Vale Bs.**, new value, and **1946**.

No.	Type	Description	Mint	Used
733	**47**	10c. on 22½c. red (No. 418)	20	10
734	–	15c. on 25c. blue (No. 622)	45	15
735	**91**	20c. on 50c. blue	40	25
736	**85**	70c. on 1b. brown	50	35
737	–	20b. on 20b. orange (No. 535)	23·00	12·00

1947. Nos. 743 and 624 surch **CORREOS Vale Bs.**, new value, and **1947**. (a) Postage.

No.	Type	Description	Mint	Used
776		5c. on 30c. black	25	10
777		5c. on 37½c. blue	30	10

(b) Air. No. 621 with **AEREO** instead of **CORREOS**.

No.	Type	Description	Mint	Used
778		5c. on 20c. blue	40	10
779		10c. on 20c. blue	40	10

116 Freighter "Republica de Venezuela" and Ship's Wheel

117 Freighter "Republica de Venezuela" and Ship's Wheel

1948. 1st Anniv of Greater Colombia Merchant Marine. Frame size 37½ × 22½ mm or 22½ × 37½ mm. Inscr "AMERICAN BANK NOTE COMPANY" at foot.

780 **116** 5c. blue (postage) 20 10
781 7½c. red 70 35
782 10c. red 55 10
783 15c. grey 75 15
784 20c. sepia 40 10
785 25c. violet 75 20
786 30c. yellow 5·75 1·90
787 37½c. brown 2·50 1·40
788 40c. olive 3·75 1·75
789 50c. mauve 85 25
790 1b. green 2·50 50

791 **117** 5c. brown (air) 10 10
792 10c. green 10 10
793 15c. buff 15 10
794 20c. purple 20 10
794 25c. grey 25 10
796 30c. olive 35 15
797 45c. blue 60 25
798 50c. black 80 35
799 70c. orange 2·10 35
800 75c. blue 3·75 45
801 90c. red 2·10 1·00
802 1b. violet 2·50 70
803 2b. slate 2·75 1·00
804 3b. green 11·00 3·25
805 4b. blue 5·50 3·25
806 5b. red 21·00 5·50

For stamps as T 116/17 in larger size and inscribed "COURVOISIER S.A." at foot, see Nos. 1012/7.

118 Arms of Venezuela

1948. New Constitution Promulgation.

807 **118** 5c. blue 1·40 55
808 10c. red 1·75 60

120 Santos Michelena

121 Santos Michelena and Silhouette of Douglas DC-3

1949. 110th Anniv of 1st International Postal Convention, Bogota.

810 **120** 5c. blue (postage) 25 15
811 10c. red 50 15
812 20c. sepia 1·50 35
813 1b. green 4·25 1·60

814 **121** 5c. brown (air) 40 15
815 10c. grey 50 15
816 15c. orange 60 15
817 25c. green 1·10 30
818 30c. purple 1·10 30
819 1b. violet 6·25 1·25

122 Columbus, Indian, "Santa Maria" and Map

123 Columbus, Indian, "Santa Maria" and Map

1949. 450th Anniv of Columbus's Discovery of America.

820 **122** 5c. blue (postage) 1·25 15
821 10c. red 5·00 85
822 20c. sepia 7·00 1·25
823 1b. green 14·50 4·50

824 **123** 5c. brown (air) 1·25 10
825 10c. grey 1·40 25
826 15c. orange 2·00 30
827 25c. green 3·75 90
828 30c. mauve 5·00 1·25
829 1b. violet 20·00 3·75

124 Hand, Bird, Airplane and Globe

125 Francisco de Miranda

126 Declaration of Independence

1950. Air. 75th Anniv of U.P.U.

830 **124** 5c. lake 20 10
831 10c. green 10 10
832 15c. brown 20 10
833 25c. grey 50 40
834 30c. olive 65 20
835 50c. black 25 25
836 60c. blue 1·40 60
837 90c. red 1·75 70
838 1b. violet 2·00 60

1950. Birth Bicentenary of Miranda.

839 **125** 5c. blue (postage) 25 10
840 10c. green 30 10
841 20c. brown 95 25
842 1b. red 4·50 1·50

843 **126** 5c. red (air) 35 15
844 10c. brown 35 15
845 15c. violet 30 35
846 30c. blue 90 25
847 1b. green 3·75 1·75

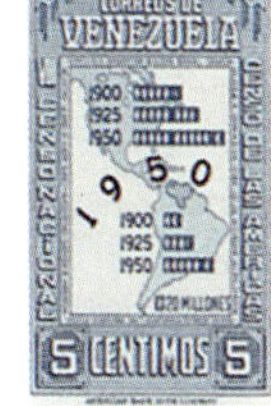

127 Tabebuia (National Tree)

128 Map and Statistics

1950. Air. Protection of Flora. Centres in yellow.

848 **127** 5c. brown 60 20
849 10c. green 50 10
850 15c. mauve 60 15
851 25c. green 4·00 1·60
852 30c. orange 4·50 2·25
853 50c. grey 2·50 60
854 60c. blue 4·00 1·00
855 90c. red 7·50 2·10
856 1b. violet 9·00 2·50

1950. Census of the Americas.

857 **128** 5c. blue (postage) 20 10
858 10c. grey 20 10
859 15c. sepia 30 10
860 25c. green 50 15
861 30c. red 60 25
862 50c. violet 1·00 25
863 1b. brown 2·75 1·10

864 5c. grey (air) 15 10
865 10c. green 10 10
866 15c. olive 30 15
867 25c. black 50 25
868 30c. orange 60 20
869 50c. brown 50 25
870 60c. blue 50 35
871 90c. red 1·50 60
872 1b. violet 2·50 1·75

129 Alonso de Ojeda

131

1950. 450th Anniv of Discovery of Lake Maracaibo.

873 **129** 5c. blue (postage) 25 15
874 10c. red 35 15
875 15c. grey 40 20
876 20c. blue 1·40 40
877 1b. green 5·75 2·10

878 5c. brown (air) 25 10
879 10c. red 35 15
880 15c. sepia 45 20
881 25c. purple 45 40
882 30c. orange 1·25 35
883 1b. green 5·00 1·90

1951. Surch **RESELLADO** and new value.

884 **116** 5c. on 7½c. red 40 15
885 10c. on 37½c. brown 40 15

1951. Telegraph stamps surch as in T **131**.

886 5c. on 5c. brown 15 10
887 10c. on 10c. green 35 10
888 20c. on 1b. black 40 15
889 25c. on 25c. red 55 30
890 30c. on 2b. olive 1·00 55

132 Arms of Caracas and View

133 Statue of Bolivar, New York

1951. Arms issue. Federal District of Caracas.

891 **132** 5c. green (postage) 50 10
892 10c. red 65 10
893 15c. brown 1·50 25
894 20c. blue 2·75 25
895 25c. brown 3·75 55
896 30c. blue 3·25 60
897 35c. violet 32·00 18·00

898 5c. turquoise (air) 65 15
899 7½c. green 2·50 60
900 10c. red 25 25
901 15c. brown 5·50 40
902 20c. blue 4·00 40
903 30c. blue 6·75 85
904 45c. purple 4·00 55
905 60c. green 13·00 1·00
906 90c. red 7·75 4·25

See also Nos. 922/37, 938/53, 954/69, 970/85, 991/1006, 1018/33, 1034/49, 1050/65, 1066/81, 1082/97, 1098/113, 1137/52, 1153/68, 1169/84, 1185/1200, 1201/16, 1217/32, 1258/73, 1274/89, 1290/1305, 1306/21, 1322/37, and 1338/53.

1951. Transfer of Statue of Bolivar to Central Park, New York.

907 **133** 5c. green (postage) 35 10
908 10c. red 35 25
909 20c. blue 60 25
910 30c. grey 70 40
911 40c. green 95 40
912 50c. brown 2·00 45
913 1b. black 6·25 2·50

914 5c. violet (air) 65 15
915 10c. green 25 15
916 20c. grey 25 15
917 25c. olive 40 20
918 30c. red 60 25
919 40c. brown 60 25
920 50c. slate 1·75 45
921 70c. orange 3·00 1·75

134 Arms of Venezuela and Bolivar Statue

138 Isabella the Catholic

1951. Arms issue. National Arms of Venezuela.

922 **134** 5c. green (postage) 25 10
923 10c. red 35 10
924 15c. brown 2·75 35
925 20c. blue 2·75 45
926 25c. brown 4·25 70
927 30c. blue 4·25 70
928 35c. violet 24·00 13·50

929 5c. turquoise (air) 25 10
930 7½c. green 1·00 55
931 10c. red 35 15
932 15c. brown 2·75 55
933 20c. blue 3·75 40
934 30c. blue 6·25 90
935 45c. purple 2·75 35
936 60c. green 13·50 2·25
937 90c. red 8·50 5·00

1951. Arms issue. State of Tachira. As T **132** showing Arms of Tachira and agricultural products.

938 5c. green (postage) 25 10
939 10c. red 30 25
940 15c. brown 60 20
941 20c. blue 1·90 35
942 50c. orange £110 13·00
943 1b. green 1·90 55
944 5b. purple 4·75 2·10

945 5c. turquoise (air) 15 15
946 10c. red 50 10
947 15c. brown 1·00 40
948 30c. blue 13·50 1·25
949 60c. green 10·50 1·25
950 1b.20 lake 10·50 6·25
951 3b. green 2·75 1·10
952 5b. purple 5·75 2·40
953 10b. violet 8·50 4·75

1951. Arms issue. State of Zulia. As T **132** showing Arms of Zulia and Oil Well.

954 5c. green (postage) 25 10
955 10c. red 25 10
956 15c. brown 90 25
957 20c. blue 1·10 35
958 50c. orange 7·00 3·75
959 1b. green 2·50 55
960 5b. purple 5·00 2·50

961 5c. turquoise (air) 55 15
962 10c. red 15 10
963 15c. brown 60 35
964 30c. blue 4·00 1·40
965 60c. green 2·25 35
966 1b.20 lake 9·75 6·00
967 3b. green 2·50 90
968 5b. purple 4·00 2·25
969 10b. violet 7·25 4·50

1951. Arms issue. State of Carabobo. As T **132** showing Arms of Carabobo and agricultural produce.

970 5c. green (postage) 15 10
971 10c. red 15 10
972 15c. brown 20 20
973 20c. blue 55 55
974 25c. brown 60 60
975 30c. blue 1·10 55
976 35c. violet 4·50 2·40

977 5c. turquoise (air) 10 10
978 7½c. green 25 25
979 10c. red 15 10
980 15c. brown 20 20
981 20c. blue 30 30
982 30c. blue 1·60 35
983 45c. purple 70 40
984 60c. green 1·40 45
985 90c. red 4·25 2·00

1951. Air. 500th Birth Anniv of Isabella the Catholic.

986 **138** 5c. green and light green 25 15
987 10c. red and yellow 25 15
988 20c. blue and grey 70 25
989 30c. blue and grey 70 20

1951. Arms issue. State of Anzoategui. As T **132** showing Arms of Anzoategui and globe.

991 5c. green (postage) 15 10
992 10c. red 20 10
993 15c. brown 80 25
994 20c. blue 1·25 30
995 40c. orange 2·75 1·10
996 45c. purple 7·50 3·75
997 3b. blue 3·00 1·25

998 5c. turquoise (air) 50 10
999 10c. red 45 10
1000 15c. brown 50 25
1001 25c. black 70 15
1002 30c. blue 1·50 90
1003 50c. orange 1·50 35
1004 60c. green 2·50 20
1005 1b. violet 3·00 90
1006 2b. violet 5·50 2·10

140 National Stadium

147 Juan de Villegas

1951. Air. 3rd Bolivarian Games, Caracas.

1007 **140** 5c. green 85 50
1008 10c. red 95 50
1009 20c. brown 1·10 60
1010 30c. blue 1·25 70

1951. As Nos. 780/806 but frame size 38 × 23½ mm or 23½ × 38 mm. Inscr "COURVOISIER S.A." at foot.

1012 **116** 5c. green (postage) 85 15
1013 10c. red 1·40 15
1014 15c. slate 4·75 15

1015 **117** 5c. brown (air) 1·10 15
1016 10c. brown 1·75 15
1017 15c. olive 2·40 15

1952. Arms issue. State of Aragua. As T **132** showing Arms of Aragua and Stylized Farm.

1018 5c. green (postage) 20 10
1019 10c. red 15 10
1020 15c. brown 60 10
1021 20c. blue 55 30
1022 25c. brown 1·25 40
1023 30c. blue 1·25 30
1024 35c. violet 7·00 3·75

1025 5c. turquoise (air) 60 15
1026 7½c. green 25 85
1027 10c. red 15 10
1028 15c. brown 1·40 65
1029 20c. blue 75 65
1030 30c. blue 2·40 25
1031 45c. purple 1·90 65
1032 60c. green 3·75 60
1033 90c. red 20·00 9·50

1952. Arms issue. State of Bolivar. As T **132** showing Arms of Bolivar and Iron Foundry.

1034 5c. green (postage) 15 10
1035 10c. red 25 10

No.	Description	Unused	Used
1036	15c. brown	25	20
1037	20c. blue	80	30
1038	40c. orange	3·00	95
1039	45c. purple	7·75	5·00
1040	3b. blue	3·50	2·25
1041	5c. turquoise (air)	4·50	25
1042	10c. red	15	10
1043	15c. brown	55	15
1044	25c. black	50	10
1045	30c. blue	2·50	1·10
1046	50c. red	1·60	35
1047	60c. green	3·50	45
1048	1b. violet	2·50	35
1049	2b. violet	5·50	2·10

1952. Arms issue. State of Lara. As T **132** showing Arms of Lara and Sisal Industry.

No.	Description	Unused	Used
1050	5c. green (postage)	50	10
1051	10c. red	50	10
1052	15c. brown	45	30
1053	20c. blue	90	35
1054	25c. brown	1·10	45
1055	30c. blue	1·75	35
1056	35c. violet	7·50	3·50
1057	5c. turquoise (air)	40	15
1058	7½c. green	25	25
1059	10c. red	15	10
1060	15c. brown	80	20
1061	20c. blue	1·25	30
1062	30c. blue	2·75	35
1063	45c. purple	1·25	30
1064	60c. green	2·75	55
1065	90c. red	17·00	10·50

1952. Arms issue. State of Miranda. As T **132** showing Arms of Miranda and Agricultural Products.

No.	Description	Unused	Used
1066	5c. green (postage)	20	10
1067	10c. red	25	10
1068	15c. brown	35	20
1069	20c. blue	65	30
1070	25c. brown	85	40
1071	30c. blue	1·40	55
1072	35c. violet	8·50	4·75
1073	5c. turquoise (air)	60	10
1074	7½c. green	70	25
1075	10c. red	15	10
1076	15c. brown	60	30
1077	20c. blue	85	40
1078	30c. blue	1·40	35
1079	45c. purple	1·10	30
1080	60c. green	3·00	45
1081	90c. red	15·00	7·75

1952. Arms issue. State of Sucre. As T **132** showing Arms of Sucre, Palms and Seascape

No.	Description	Unused	Used
1082	5c. green (postage)	45	10
1083	10c. red	45	10
1084	15c. brown	75	20
1085	20c. blue	75	15
1086	40c. orange	3·00	55
1087	45c. purple	10·00	5·00
1088	3b. blue	2·40	1·40
1089	5c. turquoise (air)	45	15
1090	10c. red	45	10
1091	15c. brown	50	20
1092	25c. black	9·50	25
1093	30c. blue	3·25	70
1094	50c. red	1·40	35
1095	60c. green	2·00	55
1096	1b. violet	2·50	40
1097	2b. violet	5·50	2·25

1952. Arms issue. State of Trujillo. As T **132** showing Arms of Trujillo and Stylised Coffee Plant.

No.	Description	Unused	Used
1098	5c. green (postage)	15	10
1099	10c. red	25	10
1100	15c. brown	1·10	25
1101	20c. blue	1·10	35
1102	50c. orange	6·75	3·50
1103	1b. green	1·60	45
1104	5b. purple	4·00	2·10
1105	5c. turquoise (air)	7·00	30
1106	10c. red	15	10
1107	15c. brown	1·75	15
1108	30c. blue	8·00	1·25
1109	60c. green	6·00	1·10
1110	1b.20 lake	5·75	3·00
1111	3b. green	2·75	1·10
1112	5b. purple	5·75	2·40
1113	10b. violet	9·50	5·00

1952. 4th Centenary of Barquisimeto.

No.	Description	Unused	Used
1114	**147** 5c. green (postage)	35	10
1115	10c. red	35	10
1116	20c. slate	80	35
1117	40c. orange	3·50	1·75
1118	50c. brown	2·00	90
1119	1b. violet	3·50	1·25
1120	5c. turquoise (air)	55	10
1121	10c. red	15	10
1122	20c. blue	25	10
1123	25c. black	60	25
1124	30c. blue	75	20
1125	40c. orange	4·00	1·50
1126	50c. bronze	1·25	35
1127	1b. purple	5·25	1·90

148 Our Lady of Coromoto

157 G.P.O., Caracas

1952. 300th Anniv of Apparition of Our Lady of Coromoto.

No.	Description	Unused	Used
1128	**148** 1b. red (17×26½ mm)	6·25	1·00
1129	1b. red (26½×41 mm)	4·25	1·00
1130	1b. red (36×65 mm)	2·50	80

1952. National Objective Exn. Telegraph stamps as T **131** surch **Correos Exposicion Objetiva Nacional 1948 - 1952** and new value.

No.	Description	Unused	Used
1131	5c. on 25c. red	35	10
1132	10c. on 1b. black	35	10

1952. Telegraph stamps as T **131** surch **CORREOS HABILITADO 1952** and new value.

No.	Description	Unused	Used
1133	20c. on 25c. red	45	15
1134	30c. on 2b. olive	2·10	1·00
1135	40c. on 1b. black	85	50
1136	50c. on 3b. orange	2·75	1·25

1953. Arms issue. State of Merida. As T **132** showing Arms of Merida and Church.

No.	Description	Unused	Used
1137	5c. green (postage)	15	10
1138	10c. red	15	10
1139	15c. brown	20	25
1140	20c. blue	95	25
1141	50c. orange	4·25	1·40
1142	1b. green	1·10	45
1143	5b. purple	4·25	1·90
1144	5c. turquoise (air)	20	15
1145	10c. red	20	10
1146	15c. brown	60	15
1147	30c. blue	5·25	90
1148	60c. green	2·40	60
1149	1b.20 lake	4·25	2·25
1150	3b. green	2·40	90
1151	5b. purple	5·25	2·25
1152	10b. violet	7·25	4·25

1953. Arms issue. State of Monagas. As T **132** showing Arms of Monagas and Horses.

No.	Description	Unused	Used
1153	5c. green (postage)	15	10
1154	10c. red	20	10
1155	15c. brown	25	25
1156	20c. blue	35	35
1157	40c. orange	2·40	60
1158	45c. purple	7·50	3·50
1159	3b. blue	3·00	1·90
1160	5c. turquoise (air)	20	15
1161	10c. red	15	10
1162	15c. brown	65	20
1163	25c. black	50	15
1164	30c. blue	4·50	1·00
1165	50c. red	1·75	35
1166	60c. green	1·90	35
1167	1b. violet	3·00	70
1168	2b. violet	4·00	2·00

1953. Arms issue. State of Portuguesa. As T **132** showing Arms of Portuguesa and Woodland.

No.	Description	Unused	Used
1169	5c. green (postage)	15	10
1170	10c. red	15	10
1171	15c. brown	20	20
1172	20c. blue	80	20
1173	50c. orange	4·00	2·25
1174	1b. green	1·10	25
1175	5b. purple	4·75	2·40
1176	5c. turquoise (air)	1·40	40
1177	10c. red	60	10
1178	15c. brown	65	25
1179	30c. blue	4·75	1·60
1180	60c. green	3·25	40
1181	1b.20 lake	8·25	4·00
1182	3b. green	2·50	1·10
1183	5b. purple	4·75	2·10
1184	10b. violet	7·25	5·00

1953. Arms issue. Federal Territory of Delta Amacuro. As T **132** showing Arms of Delta Amacuro and map.

No.	Description	Unused	Used
1185	5c. green (postage)	15	10
1186	10c. red	20	10
1187	15c. brown	25	15
1188	20c. blue	40	25
1189	40c. orange	1·90	85
1190	45c. purple	8·50	4·25
1191	3b. blue	2·00	1·25
1192	5c. turquoise (air)	25	10
1193	10c. red	15	10
1194	15c. brown	35	25
1195	25c. black	80	40
1196	30c. blue	3·00	80
1197	50c. red	1·25	40
1198	60c. green	2·25	40
1199	1b. violet	3·00	90
1200	2b. violet	4·50	3·00

1953. Arms issue. State of Falcon. As T **132** showing Arms of Falcon and Stylised Oil Refinery.

No.	Description	Unused	Used
1201	5c. green (postage)	15	10
1202	10c. red	20	10
1203	15c. brown	60	15
1204	20c. blue	60	20
1205	50c. orange	2·75	1·10
1206	1b. green	1·60	65
1207	5b. purple	5·25	2·00
1208	5c. turquoise (air)	65	30
1209	10c. red	15	10
1210	15c. brown	60	25
1211	30c. blue	5·25	1·10
1212	60c. green	3·50	1·10
1213	1b.20 lake	4·75	3·50
1214	3b. green	4·75	2·25
1215	5b. purple	8·00	4·25
1216	10b. violet	8·00	4·75

1953. Arms issue. State of Guarico. As T **132** showing Arms of Guarico and Factory.

No.	Description	Unused	Used
1217	5c. green (postage)	15	10
1218	10c. red	15	10
1219	15c. brown	30	25
1220	20c. blue	60	30
1221	40c. orange	2·50	1·10
1222	45c. purple	6·25	2·50
1223	3b. blue	2·75	1·00
1224	5c. turquoise (air)	25	10
1225	10c. red	60	10
1226	15c. brown	60	20
1227	25c. black	90	25
1228	30c. blue	3·50	1·10
1229	50c. red	1·60	75
1230	60c. green	1·90	80
1231	1b. violet	3·25	80
1232	2b. violet	5·25	2·25

1953. Inscr "EE. UU. DE VENEZUELA".

No.	Description	Unused	Used
1233	**157** 5c. green (postage)	15	10
1234	7½c. green	30	20
1235	10c. red	35	10
1236	15c. black	30	10
1237	20c. blue	40	15
1238	25c. mauve	30	10
1239	30c. blue	2·00	25
1240	35c. mauve	70	25
1241	40c. orange	1·25	35
1242	45c. violet	2·00	55
1243	50c. orange	1·25	35
1244	5c. orange (air)	10	10
1245	7½c. green	20	20
1246	15c. purple	15	10
1247	20c. slate	20	10
1248	25c. sepia	30	10
1249	30c. brown	1·75	85
1250	40c. red	30	15
1251	45c. purple	30	15
1252	50c. red	45	10
1253	60c. red	1·75	1·00
1254	70c. myrtle	90	45
1255	75c. blue	3·75	65
1256	90c. brown	75	35
1257	1b. violet	75	35

See also Nos. 1365/82.

1953. Arms issue. State of Cojedes. As T **132** showing Arms of Cojedes and Cattle.

No.	Description	Unused	Used
1258	5c. green (postage)	15	10
1259	10c. red	25	10
1260	15c. brown	25	10
1261	20c. blue	30	15
1262	25c. brown	1·25	35
1263	30c. blue	1·75	35
1264	35c. violet	2·40	90
1265	5c. turquoise (air)	3·00	45
1266	7½c. green	80	50
1267	10c. red	20	10
1268	15c. brown	35	15
1269	20c. blue	40	20
1270	30c. blue	3·50	40
1271	45c. purple	1·40	35
1272	60c. green	3·00	35
1273	90c. red	4·00	1·50

1954. Arms issue. Federal Territory of Amazonas. As T **132** showing Arms of Amazonas and Orchid.

No.	Description	Unused	Used
1274	5c. green (postage)	40	10
1275	10c. red	40	10
1276	15c. brown	1·25	20
1277	20c. blue	3·50	40
1278	40c. orange	4·25	1·25
1279	45c. purple	6·50	3·00
1280	3b. blue	9·25	3·50
1281	5c. turquoise (air)	1·10	10
1282	10c. red	65	10
1283	15c. brown	1·10	25
1284	25c. black	2·40	25
1285	30c. blue	5·75	35
1286	50c. red	5·00	60
1287	60c. green	5·75	60
1288	1b. violet	22·00	2·50
1289	2b. violet	9·50	3·25

1954. Arms issue. State of Apure. As T **132** showing Arms of Apure, Horse and Bird.

No.	Description	Unused	Used
1290	5c. green (postage)	15	10
1291	10c. red	15	10
1292	15c. brown	25	20
1293	20c. blue	2·25	25
1294	50c. orange	2·50	1·90
1295	1b. green	85	55
1296	5b. purple	5·50	2·50
1297	5c. turquoise (air)	60	15
1298	10c. red	15	10
1299	15c. brown	60	20
1300	30c. blue	2·75	95
1301	60c. green	2·75	35
1302	1b.20 lake	4·25	2·25
1303	3b. green	2·75	95
1304	5b. purple	5·25	2·00
1305	10b. violet	7·50	4·25

1954. Arms issue. State of Barinas. As T **132** showing Arms of Barinas, Cow and Horse.

No.	Description	Unused	Used
1306	5c. green (postage)	15	10
1307	10c. red	15	10
1308	15c. brown	20	20
1309	20c. blue	2·40	35
1310	50c. orange	2·50	1·25
1311	1b. green	80	35
1312	5b. purple	6·00	2·40
1313	5c. turquoise (air)	60	15
1314	10c. red	15	10
1315	15c. brown	95	25
1316	30c. blue	3·25	1·10
1317	60c. green	3·25	40
1318	1b.20 lake	4·75	2·00
1319	3b. green	3·00	1·10
1320	5b. purple	4·75	1·25
1321	10b. violet	7·00	4·00

1954. Arms issue. State of Nueva Esparta. As T **132** showing Arms of Nueva Esparta and Fishes.

No.	Description	Unused	Used
1322	5c. green (postage)	15	10
1323	10c. red	15	10
1324	15c. brown	35	25
1325	20c. blue	65	15
1326	40c. orange	2·75	70
1327	45c. purple	6·50	3·25
1328	3b. blue	3·00	1·75
1329	5c. turquoise (air)	30	15
1330	10c. red	20	10
1331	15c. brown	80	20
1332	25c. black	1·40	35
1333	30c. blue	2·75	40
1334	50c. red	2·75	40
1335	60c. green	2·75	40
1336	1b. violet	3·75	85
1337	2b. violet	5·25	2·25

1954. Arms issue. State of Yaracuy. As T **132** showing Arms of Yaracuy and Tropical Foliage.

No.	Description	Unused	Used
1338	5c. green (postage)	30	10
1339	10c. red	15	10
1340	15c. brown	25	20
1341	20c. blue	35	30
1342	25c. brown	80	40
1343	30c. blue	90	30
1344	35c. violet	2·25	90
1345	5c. turquoise (air)	35	20
1346	7½c. green	7·00	7·00
1347	10c. red	20	10
1348	15c. brown	80	15
1349	20c. blue	1·10	15
1350	30c. blue	2·40	40
1351	45c. purple	1·40	40
1352	60c. green	1·40	40
1353	90c. red	4·25	2·40

164 Simon Rodriguez

165 Bolivar and 1824 Edict

1954. Air. Death Cent of Rodriguez (Bolivar's tutor).

No.	Description	Unused	Used
1354	**164** 5c. turquoise	35	10
1355	10c. red	50	10
1356	20c. blue	35	10
1357	45c. purple	55	35
1358	65c. green	2·40	85

1954. Air. 10th Pan-American Conf, Caracas.

No.	Description	Unused	Used
1359	**165** 15c. black and brown	15	10
1360	25c. brown and grey	45	15
1361	40c. brown and orange	35	15
1362	65c. black and blue	1·25	45
1363	80c. brown and red	1·00	35
1364	1b. violet and mauve	2·00	30

1954. As T **157** but inscr "REPUBLICA DE VENEZUELA".

No.	Description	Unused	Used
1365	5c. green (postage)	15	10
1366	10c. red	15	10
1367	15c. black	30	10
1368	20c. blue	35	10
1369	30c. blue	55	50
1370	35c. mauve	55	20
1371	40c. orange	1·10	30
1372	45c. violet	1·25	40
1373	5c. yellow (air)	15	10
1374	10c. bistre	15	10
1375	15c. purple	20	10
1376	20c. slate	35	10
1377	30c. brown	35	10
1378	40c. red	60	30
1379	45c. purple	60	40
1380	70c. green	2·00	70
1381	75c. blue	1·25	40
1382	90c. brown	55	30

166

167

1955. 400th Anniv of Valencia Del Rey.

No.	Description	Unused	Used
1383	**166** 5c. green (postage)	25	10
1384	20c. blue	50	10
1385	25c. brown	55	10
1386	50c. orange	1·25	35
1387	5c. turquoise (air)	10	10
1388	10c. red	15	10
1389	20c. blue	25	10
1390	25c. black	25	10
1391	40c. violet	35	35
1392	50c. red	35	35
1393	60c. olive	1·00	35

1955. 1st Postal Convention, Caracas.

No.	Description	Unused	Used
1394	**167** 5c. green (postage)	25	10
1395	20c. blue	1·10	10
1396	25c. lake	95	10
1397	50c. orange	1·25	10
1398	5c. yellow (air)	15	10
1399	15c. brown	35	10
1400	25c. black	35	10
1401	40c. red	35	20
1402	50c. orange	35	25
1403	60c. red	1·10	50

168 O'Leary College, Barinas

1956. Air. Public Works.
1404 **168** 5c. yellow 15 10
1405 10c. sepia 15 10
1406 15c. brown 20 10
1407 A 20c. blue 20 10
1408 25c. black 50 10
1409 30c. brown 50 15
1410 B 40c. red 55 20
1411 45c. brown 20 15
1412 50c. orange 60 15
1413 C 60c. olive 60 25
1414 65c. blue . . . . 1·00 35
1415 **168** 70c. green . . . . 1·00 25
1416 C 75c. blue . . . . 1·10 30
1417 A 80c. red . . . . 1·25 35
1418 B 1b. purple 75 20
1419 C 2b. red . . . . 1·50 85
DESIGNS—HORIZ: A, University Hospital, Caracas; B, Caracas–La Guaira Highway; C, Simon Bolivar Centre.

169

170

1956. 1st American Book Festival, Caracas.
1420 **169** 5c. turq & grn (postage) 10 10
1421 10c. purple and red . . . 10 10
1422 20c. blue and ultramarine 25 10
1423 25c. grey and green . . . 35 15
1424 30c. blue and light blue 35 15
1425 40c. sepia and brown . . 50 25
1426 50c. brown and red . . . 55 35
1427 1b. slate and violet . . . 85 40
1428 **170** 5c. brown and orange (air) 10 10
1429 10c. sepia and brown . . 15 10
1430 20c. blue and turquoise 15 10
1431 25c. slate and violet . . 35 10
1432 40c. purple and red . . . 50 15
1433 45c. brown and chocolate 35 15
1434 60c. grey and olive . . . 1·00 35

171 Tamanaco Hotel, Caracas

172 Simon Bolivar

1957. Tamanaco Hotel, Caracas Commem.
1435 **171** 5c. green (postage) . . . 10 10
1436 10c. red 10 10
1437 15c. black 65 10
1438 20c. blue 25 10
1439 25c. purple 25 10
1440 30c. blue 70 35
1441 35c. lilac 25 15
1442 40c. orange 35 25
1443 45c. purple 70 35
1444 50c. yellow 95 25
1445 1b. myrtle . . . . 1·25 35
1446 5c. yellow (air) 10 10
1447 10c. brown 10 10
1448 15c. brown 15 10
1449 20c. slate 55 10
1450 25c. brown 50 10
1451 30c. blue 15 20
1452 40c. red 45 15
1453 45c. brown 50 15
1454 50c. orange 50 20
1455 60c. green 75 25
1456 65c. orange . . . . 2·10 85
1457 70c. black . . . . 1·10 30
1458 75c. turquoise . . . . . . 1·25 35
1459 1b. purple . . . . 1·25 35
1460 2b. black . . . . 2·25 45

1957. 150th Anniv of Oath of Monte Sacro and 125th Anniv of Death of Bolivar.
1461 **172** 5c. green (postage) . . . 10 10
1462 10c. red 15 10
1463 20c. blue 50 15
1464 25c. red 50 15
1465 30c. blue 70 15
1466 40c. orange . . . . 1·00 25
1467 50c. yellow . . . . 1·40 40
1468 5c. orange (air) 15 10
1469 10c. brown 20 10
1470 20c. blue 70 20
1471 25c. purple 75 25
1472 40c. red 70 20
1473 45c. purple 80 35
1474 65c. brown . . . . 1·25 35

173 G.P.O., Caracas

174 Arms of Santiago de Merida

1958.
1475 **173** 5c. green (postage) . . . 10 10
1476 10c. red 10 10
1477 15c. grey 10 10
1478 20c. blue 20 10
1479 25c. yellow 20 10
1480 30c. grey 25 10
1481 35c. purple 30 10
1482 40c. red 50 15
1483 45c. violet . . . . 1·25 70
1484 50c. yellow 45 15
1485 1b. olive 60 50
1486 5c. yellow (air) 10 10
1487 10c. brown 10 10
1488 15c. brown 10 10
1489 20c. blue 10 10
1490 25c. grey 20 10
1491 30c. blue 20 10
1492 35c. olive 30 10
1493 40c. green 30 10
1494 50c. red 30 10
1495 55c. olive 70 20
1496 60c. mauve 15 20
1497 65c. red 20 20
1498 70c. green 80 25
1499 75c. brown . . . . 1·10 20
1500 80c. brown . . . . 1·10 35
1501 85c. red . . . . 1·40 50
1502 90c. violet 30 35
1503 95c. purple . . . . 1·25 50
1504 1b. mauve 35 35
1505 1b.20 brown . . . . . . 5·75 3·50

1958. 400th Anniv of Santiago de Merida de los Caballeros.
1506 **174** 5c. green (postage) . . . 10 10
1507 10c. red 10 10
1508 15c. grey 10 10
1509 20c. blue 20 10
1510 25c. purple 35 10
1511 30c. violet 35 15
1512 35c. violet 65 15
1513 40c. orange 75 35
1514 45c. purple 25 15
1515 50c. yellow 70 35
1516 1b. grey . . . . 1·90 70
1517 5c. ochre (air) 10 10
1518 10c. brown 10 10
1519 15c. brown 15 10
1520 20c. blue 15 10
1521 25c. olive 40 15
1522 30c. blue 35 10
1523 40c. red 75 15
1524 45c. purple 75 20
1525 50c. orange 35 35
1526 60c. olive 75 25
1527 65c. brown . . . . 1·25 35
1528 70c. black 80 50
1529 75c. blue . . . . 1·50 55
1530 80c. violet 90 50
1531 90c. green 90 30
1532 1b. lilac . . . . 1·10 35

175 G.P.O., Caracas

176 Arms of Trujillo and Bolivar Monument

1958.
1533 **175** 5c. green (postage) . . . 35 10
1534 10c. red 50 10
1535 15c. black 40 10
1536 5c. yellow (air) 35 10
1537 10c. brown 50 10
1538 15c. brown 40 10

1958. 400th Anniv of Trujillo.
1539 **176** 5c. green (postage) . . . 10 10
1540 10c. red 10 10
1541 15c. grey 10 10
1542 20c. blue 15 10
1543 25c. mauve 35 10
1544 30c. blue 50 15
1545 35c. lilac 55 25
1546 45c. purple 65 35
1547 50c. yellow 65 25
1548 1b. olive . . . . 1·40 55
1549 5c. buff (air) 10 10
1550 10c. brown 10 10
1551 15c. brown 25 10
1552 20c. blue 30 15
1553 25c. grey 65 20
1554 30c. blue 65 20
1555 40c. green 25 25
1556 50c. orange 55 30
1557 60c. mauve 60 40
1558 65c. red . . . . 1·60 55
1559 1b. violet . . . . 1·10 25

177 Caracas Stadium

178 "Eternal Flame"

1959. 8th Central American and Caribbean Games.
1560 **177** 5c. green (postage) . . . 25 10
1561 10c. mauve 25 10
1562 20c. blue 60 35
1563 30c. blue 80 40
1564 50c. lilac . . . . 1·40 35
1565 **178** 5c. yellow (air) 15 10
1566 10c. brown 35 15
1567 15c. orange 40 20
1568 30c. slate 65 40
1569 50c. green 95 50

179 Venezuelan ½ Real Stamp of 1859, Gen. J. I. Paz Castillo and Postman

180 Alexander von Humboldt

1959. Cent of First Venezuelan Postage Stamps.
1570 **179** 25c. ochre (postage) . . 25 15
1571 – 50c. blue 45 35
1572 – 1b. red . . . . 1·90 70
1573 **179** 25c. ochre (air) 25 15
1574 – 50c. blue 35 35
1575 – 1b. red . . . . 1·50 70
DESIGNS: 50c. (2), 1 real stamp of 1859, Don Jacinto Gutierrez and postman on mule; 1b. (2), 2 reales stamp of 1859, Don Miguel Herrera, steam mail train and Douglas DC-6 airliner.

1960. Death Centenary of Von Humboldt (naturalist).
1576 **180** 5c. olive & grn (postage) 35 10
1577 30c. violet and blue . . . 85 20
1578 40c. brown and orange 1·25 50
1579 5c. brown and bistre (air) 35 10
1580 20c. turquoise and blue 85 20
1581 40c. bronze and olive . . 1·40 50

181 Bolivar Peak, Merida

1960. Tourist issue.
1582 **181** 5c. green and emerald (postage) . . . . . 1·10 85
1583 – 15c. grey and purple . . 3·25 2·25
1584 – 35c. purple and light purple . . . . . . 2·75 1·90
1585 **181** 30c. blue and deep blue (air) . . . . 2·50 1·60
1586 – 50c. brown and orange 2·50 1·60
1587 – 65c. brown and orange 2·50 1·60
DESIGNS: 15, 50c. Caroni Falls, Bolivar; 35, 65c. Cuacharo Caves, Monagas.

182 National Pantheon, Caracas

183 A. Eloy Blanco

1960. Pantheon in olive.
1588 **182** 5c. green (postage) . . . 10 10
1589 20c. blue 50 15
1590 25c. olive 70 20
1591 30c. grey 85 25
1592 40c. brown . . . . 1·50 50
1593 45c. violet . . . . 1·50 50
1594 5c. bistre (air) 10 10
1595 10c. brown 25 10
1596 15c. brown 35 10
1597 20c. blue 75 15
1598 25c. grey . . . . 1·60 35
1599 30c. violet . . . . 1·75 55
1600 40c. green 75 15
1601 45c. violet . . . . 1·10 20
1602 60c. mauve . . . . 1·10 30
1603 65c. red . . . . 1·10 40
1604 70c. grey . . . . 1·25 35
1605 75c. blue . . . . 2·75 60
1606 80c. blue . . . . 2·25 50
1607 1b.20 yellow . . . . . . 2·75 70

1960. 5th Death Anniv of Blanco (poet). Portrait in black.
1608 **183** 5c. green (postage) . . . 15 10
1609 30c. grey 35 15
1610 50c. yellow 60 30
1611 20c. blue (air) 35 15
1612 75c. turquoise . . . . . 1·25 40
1613 90c. violet . . . . 1·40 40

184 1808 Newspaper and Caracas, 1958

185 A. Codazzi

1960. 150th Anniv of "Gazeta de Caracas". Centres in black.
1614 **184** 10c. red (postage) . . . 35 15
1615 20c. blue 45 20
1616 35c. violet . . . . 1·10 70
1617 5c. yellow (air) . . . . . 1·90 65
1618 15c. brown . . . . 1·25 35
1619 65c. orange . . . . 1·50 60

1960. Death Centenary of Codazzi (geographer).
1620 **185** 5c. deep green and light green (postage) . . . 10 10
1621 15c. black and grey . . . 70 15
1622 20c. blue and light blue 65 15
1623 45c. purple and lilac . . 70 30
1624 5c. brown and orange (air) 10 10
1625 10c. sepia and brown . . 15 10
1626 25c. black and grey . . . 60 10
1627 30c. deep blue and blue 70 15
1628 50c. brown and light brown . . . . . . 1·10 30
1629 70c. black and brown . . 2·10 45

186 Declaration of Independence

1960. 150th Anniv of Independence. Centres multicoloured.
1630 **186** 5c. green (postage) . . . 50 10
1631 20c. blue . . . . 1·00 30
1632 30c. blue . . . . 1·00 40
1633 50c. orange (air) 80 30
1634 75c. turquoise . . . . . 1·00 35
1635 90c. violet . . . . 1·25 40

187 Drilling for Oil

188 L. Caceres de Arismendi

1960. Oil Industry.
1636 **187** 5c. myrtle and turquoise (postage) . . . . . . 1·40 70
1637 10c. brown and red . . . 70 25
1638 15c. mauve and purple 85 30
1639 – 30c. indigo and blue (air) 50 20
1640 – 40c. olive and green . . 85 35
1641 – 50c. brown and orange 1·00 40
DESIGN: Nos. 1639/41, Oil refinery.

1960. 94th Death Anniv of Luisa Caceres de Arismendi. Centres multicoloured.
1642 **188** 20c. blue (postage) . . . 1·00 30
1643 25c. yellow 85 30
1644 30c. blue . . . . 1·10 40
1645 5c. bistre (air) 80 30
1646 10c. brown . . . . 1·00 45
1647 60c. red . . . . 1·90 55

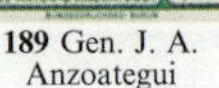

189 Gen. J. A. Anzoategui   **190** Gen. A. J. de Sucre

1960. 140th Death Anniv of Gen. Anzoategui.
1648 **189** 5c. olive & grn (postage) 20 10
1649 15c. purple and brown 65 10
1650 20c. deep blue and blue 70 15
1651 25c. brown and grey (air) 65 20
1652 40c. olive and yellow 65 40
1653 45c. purple and mauve 85 30

1960. 130th Death Anniv of Gen. A. J. de Sucre.
1654 **190** 10c. mult (postage) 35 15
1655 15c. multicoloured 40 20
1656 20c. multicoloured 60 30
1657 25c. multicoloured (air) 60 30
1658 30c. multicoloured 1·10 40
1659 50c. multicoloured 1·60 60

191 Skyscraper   **192** "Population and Farming"

1961. National Census. Skyscraper in orange.
1660 **191** 5c. green 10 10
1661 10c. red 10 10
1662 15c. grey 10 10
1663 20c. blue 15 10
1664 25c. brown 25 15
1665 30c. blue 25 10
1666 35c. purple 35 15
1667 40c. brown 50 25
1668 45c. violet 70 35
1669 50c. yellow 50 20

1961. Air. 9th Population Census and 3rd Farming Census. Animal's head and inscr in black.
1670 **192** 5c. yellow 10 10
1671 10c. brown 10 10
1672 15c. orange 10 10
1673 20c. blue 15 10
1674 25c. grey 20 10
1675 30c. blue 25 10
1676 40c. green 35 15
1677 45c. violet 35 20
1678 50c. orange 40 25
1679 60c. mauve 50 25
1680 65c. red 70 35
1681 70c. grey 1·00 50
1682 75c. turquoise 55 40
1683 80c. violet 85 35
1684 90c. violet 1·25 70

193 R. M. Baralt   **195** Arms of San Cristobal

1961. Death Centenary of R. M. Baralt (writer).
1685 **193** 5c. turq & grn (postage) 10 10
1686 15c. brown and grey 25 10
1687 35c. violet and mauve 65 15
1688 25c. sepia and grey (air) 70 30
1689 30c. violet and blue 80 35
1690 40c. bronze and green 90 35

1961. Air. 4th Centenary of San Cristobal. Arms in red, yellow and blue.
1692 **195** 5c. sepia and orange 10 10
1693 55c. black and green 70 25

196 Yellow-crowned Amazon

1961. Birds. Multicoloured.
1694 30c. Type **196** (postage) 1·25 50
1695 40c. Snowy egret 1·75 50
1696 50c. Scarlet ibis 4·00 1·00
1697 5c. Troupial (air) 2·75 1·50
1698 10c. Guianan cock of the rock 1·25 70
1699 15c. Tropical mockingbird 1·75 80

197 J. J. Aguerrevere (first College President)

1961. Engineering College Centenary.
1700 **197** 25c. blue 15 10

198 Battle Scene

1961. 140th Anniv of Battle of Carabobo. Centres multicoloured.
1702 **198** 5c. green (postage) 10 10
1703 40c. brown 70 30
1704 – 50c. blue (air) 70 15
1705 – 1b.05 orange 1·10 60
1706 – 1b.50 mauve 1·60 60
1707 – 1b.90 violet 1·90 85
1708 – 2b. sepia 2·10 85
1709 – 3b. blue 2·75 1·00
DESIGN: 50c. to 3b. Cavalry charge.

199 Cardinal's Arms   **200** Archbishop Blanco

1962. Air. Elevation to Cardinal of Jose Humberto Quintero.
1710 **199** 5c. mauve 10 10

1962. Air. 4th Anniv of Archbishop Blanco's Pastoral Letter.
1712 **200** 75c. mauve 70 30

201 "Oncidium papilio Lindl"

1962. Orchids. Multicoloured.
1713 5c. Type **201** (postage) 10 10
1714 10c. "Caularthron bilamellatum (Rchb. f.) R.E. Schultes" 15 10
1715 20c. "Stanhopea Wardii Lodd. ex Lindl" 40 10
1716 25c. "Catasetum pileatum Rchb f." 35 10
1717 30c. "Masdevallia tovarensis Rchb f." 40 15
1718 35c. "Epidendrum Stamfordianum Batem" (horiz) 45 25
1719 50c. "Epidendrum atropurpureum Willd" 80 35
1720 3b. "Oncidium falcipetalum Lindl." 4·25 1·60
1721 5c. "Oncidium volvox Rchb f." (air) 10 10
1722 20c. "Cycnoches chlorochilon Kl." 20 10
1723 25c. "Cattleya Gaskelliana Rchb f.var. alba" 55 15
1724 30c. "Epidendrum difforme Jacq." (horiz) 45 15
1725 40c. "Catasetum callosum Lindl" (horiz) 55 20
1726 50c. "Oncidium bicolor Lindl" 65 30
1727 1b. "Brassavola nodosa Lindl" (horiz) 90 25
1728 1b.05 "Epidendrum lividum Lindl" 2·75 1·10
1729 1b.50 "Schomburgkia undulata Lindl" 3·00 1·25
1730 2b. "Oncidium zebrinum Rchb f." 3·50 1·75

202 Signing of Independence

1962. 150th Anniv of Declaration of Independence. Multicoloured centres; frame colours given.
1731 **202** 5c. green (postage) 15 10
1732 20c. blue 35 15
1733 25c. orange 55 30
1734 55c. green (air) 45 20
1735 1b.05 mauve 1·75 60
1736 1b.50 violet 1·50 55

1962. Air. Bicentenary of Upata. Surch **BICENTENARIO DE UPATA 1762 - 1962 RESELLADO AEREO VALOR Bs 2,00**.
1739 **173** 2b. on 1b. olive 1·60 75

204 Putting the Shot

1962. 1st National Games, Caracas, 1961.
1740 **204** 5c. green (postage) 10 10
1741 – 10c. mauve 15 10
1742 – 25c. blue 30 15
1744 – 40c. grey (air) 40 25
1745 – 75c. brown 60 35
1746 – 85c. red 1·75 55
SPORTS: 10c. Football; 25c. Swimming; 40c. Cycling; 75c. Baseball; 85c. Gymnastics.

Each value is arranged in blocks of 4 within the sheet, with the top corners of each stamp converging to the centre of the block.

205 Vermilion Cardinal   **206** Campaign Emblem and Map

1962. Birds. Multicoloured.
1748 5c. Type **205** (postage) 10 10
1749 10c. Great kiskadee 30 10
1750 20c. Glossy-black thrush 60 15
1751 25c. Collared trogons 70 25
1752 30c. Swallow tanager 1·00 30
1753 40c. Long-tailed sylph 1·25 50
1754 3b. Black-necked stilts 8·00 5·50
1755 5c. American kestrel (air) 30 10
1756 20c. Red-billed whistling duck (horiz) 60 10
1757 25c. Amazon kingfisher 70 25
1758 30c. Rufous-vented chachalaca 90 30
1759 50c. Oriole blackbird 1·40 55
1760 55c. Common pauraque 2·75 80
1761 2b.30 Red-crowned woodpecker 8·50 4·25
1762 2b.50 Lined quail dove 8·50 3·75

1962. Malaria Eradication.
1763 **206** 50c. brn & blk (postage) 40 20
1764 – 30c. green and black (air) 35 20
DESIGN: As T **206** but size 26 × 36 mm.

207 Collared Peccary   **208** Fisherman

1963. Venezuelan Wild Life. Multicoloured.
1766 5c. White-tailed deer (postage) 10 10
1767 10c. Type **207** 10 10
1768 35c. Widow monkey 25 10
1769 50c. Giant otter 70 25
1770 1b. Puma 2·50 1·40
1771 3b. Capybara 5·00 2·50
1772 5c. Spectacled bear (vert) (air) 20 10
1773 40c. Paca 85 25
1774 50c. Pale-throated sloth 1·10 35
1775 55c. Giant anteater 1·40 40
1776 1b.50 Brazilian tapir 4·00 1·60
1777 2b. Jaguar 6·25 2·10

1963. Freedom from Hunger.
1778 **208** 25c. bl on pink (postage) 30 15
1779 – 40c. red on green (air) 50 25
1780 – 75c. sepia on yellow 30 40
DESIGNS: 40c. Farmer with lambs; 75c. Harvester.

209 Bocono Cathedral   **211** Flag

210 St. Peter's Basilica, Vatican City

1963. 400th Anniv of Bocono.
1781 **209** 50c. mult on buff (postage) 45 20
1782 – 1b. mult on buff (air) 1·25 40
DESIGNS: 1b. Bocono Arms.

1963. Ecumenical Council, Vatican City.
1783 **210** 35c. brown & bl (postage) 35 15
1784 45c. brown and green 35 20
1785 – 80c. multicoloured (air) 1·10 35
1786 – 90c. multicoloured 1·10 40
DESIGN: 80, 90c. Arms of Vatican City and Venezuela.

1963. National Flag and Arms Centenary. Mult.
1787 30c. Type **211** (postage) 20 15
1788 70c. Venezuela Arms (vert) (air) 85 50

212 Maracaibo Bridge   **213** Arms, Map and Guardsman

1963. Opening of Higher Bridge, Lake Maracaibo.
1789 **212** 30c. brown & bl (postage) 75 10
1790 35c. brown and green 90 20
1791 80c. brown and green 1·60 40
1792 – 90c. ochre, brown and green (air) 1·40 50
1793 – 95c. ochre, brown & blue 1·40 55
1794 – 1b. ochre, brown and blue 95 50
DESIGN—HORIZ: 90c. to 1b. Aerial view of bridge and mainland.

1963. 25th Anniv of National Guard.
1795 **213** 50c. green, red and blue on cream (postage) 40 20
1796 1b. blue and red on cream (air) 1·60 70

214 Dag Hammarskjold and Atlantic Map

1963. 1st Death Anniv (1962) of Dag Hammarskjold (U.N. Secretary-General, 1953–61).
1797 **214** 25c. indigo & bl (postage) 20 15
1798 55c. green and turquoise 75 35
1799 80c. blue and deep blue (air) 75 45
1800 90c. violet and blue . . . 1·00 60

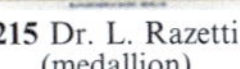

215 Dr. L. Razetti (medallion)
216 Dr. F. A. Risquez (Venezuelan Red Cross President, 1922–23)

1963. Birth Centenary (1962) of Dr. Luis Razetti (founder of University School of Medicine and of Vargas Hospital).
1802 **215** 35c. brown, ochre and blue (postage) 35 20
1803 45c. brown, ochre & mve 50 20
1804 – 95c. blue and mauve (air) 90 60
1805 – 1b.05 sepia and green . . 1·25 70
DESIGN: 95c., 1b.05, Portrait of Dr. Razetti.

1963. Red Cross Centenary. Multicoloured.
1806 15c. Type **216** (postage) . . 15 10
1807 20c. Dr. Carlos J. Bello (President of Venezuelan Red Cross, 1928–31) . . . 20 10
1808 40c. Sir Vincent K. Barrington (first President of Venezuelan Red Cross) (air) 40 35
1809 75c. Nurse and child 70 50
All designs show centenary emblem.

217 Labourer
218 Pedro Gual

1964. Centenary of Venezuelan Ministry of Works and National Industries Exhibition, Caracas. Multicoloured.
1810 5c. Type **217** (postage) . . . 10 10
1811 10c. Petrol industry 20 10
1812 15c. Building construction 25 10
1813 30c. Road and rail transport 80 45
1814 40c. Agricultural machine 60 25
1815 5c. Loading ship (air) . . . 10 10
1816 10c. Tractor and maize . . 10 10
1817 15c. Type **217** 15 10
1818 20c. Petrol industry 20 10
1819 50c. Building construction 60 30

1964. Death Cent (1962) of Pedro Gual (statesman).
1820 **218** 40c. olive (postage) . . . 40 20
1821 50c. brown 45 25
1822 75c. turquoise (air) . . . 60 25
1823 1b. mauve 70 30

219 Dr. C. Arvelo

1964. Death Cent (1962) of Carlos Arvelo (physician).
1824 **219** 1b. black and blue . . . 1·40 40

220 Blast Furnace

1964. Inaug of Orinoco Steel Works. Mult.
1825 20c. Type **220** (postage) . . 25 10
1826 50c. Type **220** 50 20
1827 80c. Cauldron and map (air) 85 35
1828 1b. As 80c. . . . . 1·40 40
The 80c. and 1b. are vert.

221 Arms of Ciudad Bolivar
222 R. Gallegos

1964. Air. Bicentenary of Ciudad Bolivar.
1829 **221** 1b. multicoloured . . . 1·10 70

1964. 80th Birth Anniv of Romulo Gallegos (novelist).
1830 **222** 5c. green and yellow (postage) 10 10
1831 10c. blue and light blue 15 10
1832 15c. purple and mauve 25 15
1833 – 30c. brown & yellow (air) 30 15
1834 – 40c. purple and pink . . 40 20
1835 – 50c. brown and orange 55 30
DESIGN: Nos. 1833/5, Gallegos and book.

223 Angel Falls (Bolivar State)

1964. Tourist Publicity. Inscr "Conozca a Venezuela Primera" ("See Venezuela First"). Multicoloured.
1836 5c. Type **223** 10 10
1837 10c. Tropical landscape (Sucre) 15 10
1838 15c. Rocks, San Juan (Guarico) 20 10
1839 30c. Fishermen casting nets (Anzoategui) 40 15
1840 40c. Mountaineering (Merida) 85 15

224 Eleanor Roosevelt

1964. Air. 15th Anniv (1963) of Declaration of Human Rights.
1841 **224** 1b. orange and violet . . 1·10 40

1965. Various stamps surch **RESELLADO VALOR** and new value. (a) Postage.
1842 5c. on 1b. (No. 1485) . . . 50 10
1843 10c. on 45c. (1668) 15 10
1844 15c. on 55c. (1798) 15 10
1845 20c. on 3b. (1754) 25 20
1846 25c. on 45c. (1623) 20 15
1847 25c. on 3b. (1720) 25 15
1848 25c. on 1b. (1770) 35 15
1849 25c. on 3b. (1771) 20 15
1850 30c. on 1b. (1516) 25 15
1851 40c. on 1b. (1824) 70 20
1852 60c. on 80c. (1791) 85 35

(b) Air.
1853 5c. on 55c. (1495) 10 10
1854 5c. on 70c. (1498) 10 10
1855 5c. on 80c. (1500) 15 10
1856 5c. on 85c. (1501) 10 10
1857 5c. on 90c. (1502) 10 10
1858 5c. on 95c. (1503) 10 10
1859 5c. on 1b. (1796) 50 35
1860 10c. on 3b. (804) 15 10
1861 10c. on 4b. (805) 70 35
1862 10c. on 70c. (1681) 35 15
1863 10c. on 90c. (1684) 25 10
1864 10c. on 1b.05 (1705) . . . 50 25
1865 10c. on 1b.90 (1707) . . . 25 15
1866 10c. on 2b. (1708) 35 15
1867 10c. on 3b. (1709) 35 15
1868 10c. on 80c. (1785) 15 10
1869 10c. on 90c. (1786) 15 10
1870 15c. on 3b. (769) 35 15
1871 15c. on 90c. (1613) 25 10
1872 15c. on 80c. (1799) 25 10
1873 15c. on 90c. (1800) 25 10
1874 15c. on 1b. (1829) 35 15
1875 20c. on 2b. (1460) 40 15
1876 20c. on 55c. (1693) 30 10
1877 20c. on 55c. (1760) 90 30
1878 20c. on 2b.30 (1761) . . . 55 30
1879 20c. on 2b.50 (1762) . . . 90 30
1880 20c. on 70c. (1788) 50 35
1881 25c. on 70c. (1629) 55 30
1882 25c. on 1b.05 (1728) . . . 35 15
1883 25c. on 1b.50 (1729) . . . 35 15
1884 25c. on 2b. (1730) 50 25
1885 25c. on 1b.50 (1776) . . . 50 15
1886 25c. on 2b. (1777) 50 25
1887 25c. on 95c. (1804) 45 25
1888 25c. on 1b.05 (1805) . . . 50 25
1889 30c. on 1b. (1782) 70 35
1890 40c. on 1b.05 (1736) . . . 50 25
1891 50c. on 65c. (1603) 25 15
1892 50c. on 1b.20 (1607) 70 35
1893 50c. on 1b. (1841) 35 15
1894 60c. on 90c. (1792) 70 25
1895 60c. on 95c. (1793) 75 35
1896 75c. on 85c. (1746) 75 40

(c) Revenue stamps additionally optd **CORREOS**.
1897 5c. on 5c. green 10 10
1898 5c. on 20c. brown 10 10
1899 10c. on 10c. bistre 10 10
1900 15c. on 40c. green 10 10
1901 20c. on 3b. blue 35 15
1902 25c. on 5b. blue 70 35
1903 25c. on 5b. blue 35 15
1904 60c. on 3b. blue 60 40

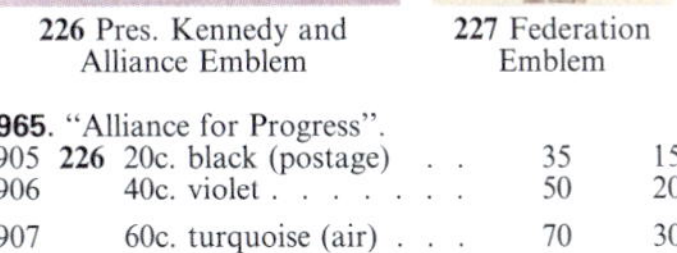
226 Pres. Kennedy and Alliance Emblem
227 Federation Emblem

1965. "Alliance for Progress".
1905 **226** 20c. black (postage) . . 35 15
1906 40c. violet 50 20
1907 60c. turquoise (air) . . . 70 30
1908 80c. brown 85 35

1965. Air. 20th Anniv of Venezuelan Medical Federation.
1909 **227** 65c. red and black . . . 1·00 45

228 Venezuelan Pavilion
229 Andres Bello

1965. Air. New York World's Fair.
1910 **228** 1b. multicoloured . . . 90 35

1965. Air. Death Cent of Andres Bello (poet).
1911 **229** 80c. brown and orange 1·00 60

230 Restrepo's Map, 1827

1965. Guyana Claim. Multicoloured.
1912 5c. Codazzi's map, 1840 (vert) (postage) 10 10
1913 15c. Type **230** 30 10
1914 40c. L. de Surville's map, 1778 . . . . 55 15
1915 25c. Cruz Cano's map, 1775 (air) 40 15
1916 40c. (50c.) Map stamp of 1896 (vert) 55 15
1917 75c. Foreign Relations Ministry map 75 35

231 I.T.U. Emblem, Satellite, and Aerials of 1865 and 1965

1965. Air. I.T.U. Centenary.
1919 **231** 75c. black and green . . 70 30

232 Bolivar and Part of Letter
233 Children on "Magic Carpet" and "Three Kings"

1965. Air. 150th Anniv of Bolivar's Letter from Jamaica.
1920 **232** 75c. black and blue . . . 60 30

1965. Air. Children's (Christmas) Festival.
1921 **233** 70c. blue and yellow . . 1·10 55

234 Father F. Toro

1965. Air. Death Cent of Father Fermin Toro.
1922 **234** 1b. black and orange . . 85 30

235 Sir Winston Churchill

1965. Air. Churchill Commemoration.
1923 **235** 1b. black and lilac . . . 90 40

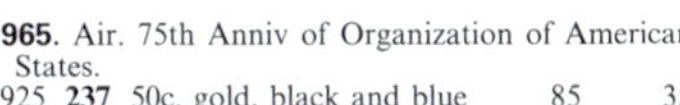

236 I.C.Y. Emblem
237 Emblem and Map

1965. Air. International Co-operation Year.
1924 **236** 85c. violet and gold . . 1·00 40

1965. Air. 75th Anniv of Organization of American States.
1925 **237** 50c. gold, black and blue 85 35

238 "Eurytides protesilaus"
239 Farms of 1936 and 1966

1966. Butterflies. Multicoloured.
1926 20c. Type **238** (postage) . . 40 15
1927 30c. "Morpho peleides" . . 55 20
1928 50c. "Papilio zagreus" . . . 80 30
1929 65c. "Anaea marthesia" (air) 1·00 40
1930 85c. "Anaea clytemnestra" 1·60 55
1931 1b. "Caligo atreus" . . . . 2·10 60

1966. Air. 30th Anniv of Ministry of Agriculture and Husbandry.
1932 **239** 55c. black, green & yellow 85 25

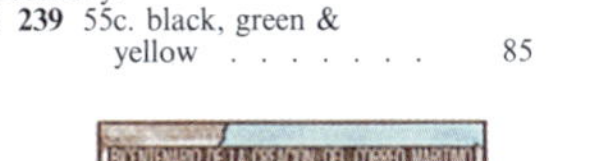

240 19th-century Sailing Packet crossing Atlantic

1966. Bicentenary of Maritime Mail.
1933 **240** 60c. black, blue & brown 2·00 50

241 Sebucan Dance

1966. "Popular Dances". Multicoloured.
1934 5c. Type **241** (postage) . . . 10 10
1935 10c. Candlemas 20 10
1936 15c. Chichamaya 30 10
1937 20c. Carite 40 15
1938 25c. "Round Drum" 60 25
1939 35c. Devil Dance, Feast of Corpus Christi 65 35

1940 40c. Tamunanque (air) . . . 75 35
1941 50c. Parranda de San Pedro 90 40
1942 60c. Las Turas 60 25
1943 70c. Joropo . . . . 1·10 55
1944 80c. Chimbanguele . . . . 1·40 35
1945 90c. "The Shepherds" . . . 1·60 50

242 Title Page

1966. Air. 150th Death Anniv (1964) of Jose Lamas (composer).
1946 **242** 55c. black, bistre & green 60 30
1947 95c. black, bistre & mve 85 40

243 A. Michelena (self-portrait) **244** Lincoln

1966. Birth Centenary (1963) of Arturo Michelena (painter). Multicoloured.
1948 95c. sepia and cream (Type **243**) (postage) . . . 1·25 35
1949 1b. "Pentesilea" (battle scene) . . . . 1·10 35
1950 1b.05 "La Vara Rota" ("The Red Cloak") . . . 1·25 35
1951 95c. "Escena de Circo" ("Circus Scene") (air) . . 1·25 35
1952 1b. "Miranda in La Carraca" . . . . 1·10 35
1953 1b.05 "Carlota Corday" . . 1·25 35
Nos. 1949/53 are horiz.

1966. Air. Death Cent (1965) of Abraham Lincoln.
1954 **244** 1b. black and drab . . . 70 55

245 Construction Worker

1966. 2nd O.E.A. Labour Ministers Conference.
1955 **245** 10c. black and yellow . . 10 10
1956 20c. black and turquoise 20 10
1957 – 30c. violet and blue . . . 15 15
1958 – 35c. olive and yellow . . 25 15
1959 – 50c. purple and pink . . 40 20
1960 – 65c. purple and red . . . 60 30
DESIGNS: 30, 65c. Labour Monument; 35c. Machinist; 50c. Car assembly line.

246 Dr. Hernandez

1966. Air. Birth Centenary (1964) of Dr. Jose Hernandez (physician).
1961 **246** 1b. deep blue and blue 1·25 45

247 Dr. M. Dagnino (founder) and Hospital

1966. Air. Centenary of Chiquinquira Hospital, Maracaibo.
1962 **247** 1b. deep green and green 1·00 40

248 Oscar **249** R. Arevalo Gonzalez

1966. Fishes. Multicoloured.
1963 15c. Type **248** (postage) . . 20 10
1964 25c. Peacock cichlid 40 20
1965 45c. Orinoco piranha . . . 1·25 35
1966 75c. Spotted headstander (vert) (air) . . . . 1·60 70
1967 90c. Sword-tailed characin 1·60 70
1968 1b. Ramirez's dwarf cichlid 1·60 70

1966. Air. Birth Centenary of Rafael Arevalo Gonzalez.
1969 **249** 75c. black and yellow . . 90 35

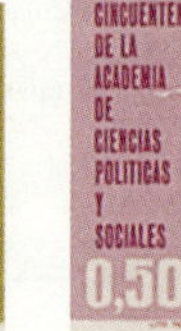

250 Simon Bolivar, 1816 (after anonymous artist) **251** "Justice"

1966. Air. Bolivar Commemoration.
1970 **250** 5c. multicoloured 10 10
1971 10c. multicoloured . . . 10 10
1972 20c. multicoloured . . . 10 10
1973 – 25c. multicoloured . . . 15 10
1974 – 30c. multicoloured . . . 20 10
1975 – 35c. multicoloured . . . 15 10
1976 – 40c. multicoloured . . . 30 15
1977 – 50c. multicoloured . . . 30 15
1978 – 60c. multicoloured . . . 30 15
1979 – 80c. multicoloured . . . 85 30
1980 – 1b.20 multicoloured . . 1·25 60
1981 – 4b. multicoloured . . . 4·00 1·90
BOLIVAR PORTRAITS: 25, 30, 35c. After paintings by Jose Gil de Castro, 1825; 40, 50, 60c. Anonymous artist, 1825; 80c., 1b.20., 4b. Anonymous artist, c. 1829.

1966. Air. 50th Anniv of Political and Social Sciences Academy.
1982 **251** 50c. purple and lilac . . 85 25

252 Nativity **253** Globe and Communications Emblems

1966. Christmas.
1983 **252** 65c. black and violet . . 80 25

1966. 30th Anniv of Venezuelan Communications Ministry.
1984 **253** 45c. multicoloured . . . 65 20

254 Angostura Bridge

1967. Air. Opening of Angostura Bridge, Orinoco River.
1985 **254** 40c. multicoloured . . . 35 20

255 Ruben Dario (poet) **256** University Building and Arms

1967. Birth Centenary of Ruben Dario.
1986 **255** 70c. indigo and blue . . 85 35

1967. 75th Anniv of Zulia University.
1987 **256** 80c. black, red and gold 85 35

257 Venzuelan Pavilion

1967. Air. World Fair, Montreal.
1988 **257** 1b. multicoloured . . . 85 30

258 Cacique Guaicaipuro (statue) **259** Francisco Esteban Gomez

1967. Air. 400th Anniv of Caracas. Multicoloured.
1989 10c. Palace of the Academies (horiz) 10 10
1990 15c. Type **258** 10 10
1991 45c. Capt. F. Fajardo . . . 35 15
1992 50c. St. Teresa's Church . . 35 15
1993 55c. Diego de Losada (founder) 45 20
1994 60c. Constellations over Caracas (horiz) 50 25
1995 65c. Arms of Caracas . . . 55 30
1996 70c. Federal Legislative Building (horiz) 55 25
1997 75c. University City (horiz) 70 30
1998 85c. El Pulpo road junction (horiz) 70 35
1999 90c. Map of Caracas (horiz) 75 35
2000 1b. Plaza Mayor, Caracas c. 1800 (horiz) . . 85 45
2001 2b. Avenida Libertador (horiz) . . . . 2·00 65

1967. Air. 150th Anniv of Battle of Matasiete.
2003 **259** 90c. multicoloured . . . 70 35

260 J. V. Gonzalez **261** Child with Toy Windmill

1967. Air. Death Centenary of Juan Gonzalez (journalist).
2016 **260** 80c. black and yellow . . 80 30

1967. Air. Children's Festival.
2017 **261** 45c. multicoloured . . . 40 20
2018 75c. multicoloured . . . 60 25
2019 90c. multicoloured . . . 70 35

262 "The Madonna of the Rosary" (Lochner) **263** Dr. J. M. Nunez Ponte (educator)

1967. Air. Christmas.
2020 **262** 1b. multicoloured . . . 1·25 40

1968. Air. 3rd Death Anniv of Dr. Jose Manuel Nunez Ponte.
2021 **263** 65c. multicoloured . . . 60 25

264 General Miranda and Printing Press

1968. Air. 150th Death Anniv of General Francisco de Miranda. Multicoloured.
2022 20c. Type **264** 20 10
2023 35c. Portrait and Houses of Parliament, London . . . 35 15
2024 45c. Portrait and Arc de Triomphe, Paris 55 30
2025 70c. Portrait (vert) 90 25
2026 80c. Bust and Venezuelan flags (vert) . . . . 1·10 45

265 Title Page and Printing Press **266** "Spodoptera frugiperda"

1968. 150th Anniv of Newspaper "Correo del Orinoco".
2027 **265** 1b.50 multicoloured . . 1·25 50

1968. Insects. Multicoloured.
2028 20c. Type **266** (postage) . . 50 20
2029 75c. "Anthonomus grandis" 85 30
2030 90c. "Manduca sexta" . . 1·10 40
2031 5c. "Atta sextens" (air) . . 15 10
2032 15c. "Aeneolamia varia" . . 35 15
2033 20c. "Systena sp." 50 20
The 20 (air), 75 and 90c. are horiz.

267 Keys **268** Pistol-shooting

1968. Air. 30th Anniv of Office of Controller-General.
2034 **267** 95c. multicoloured . . . 90 30

1968. Air. Olympic Games, Mexico. Mult.
2035 5c. Type **268** 10 10
2036 15c. Running (horiz) 25 10
2037 30c. Fencing (horiz) 60 20
2038 75c. Boxing (horiz) . . . . 1·10 35
2039 5b. Sailing . . . . 5·25 1·40

269 Guayana Sub-station **270** "The Holy Family" (F. J. de Lerma)

1968. Rural Electrification. Multicoloured.
2040 15c. Type **269** 15 10
2041 45c. Encantado Dam . . . 40 20
2042 50c. Macagua Dam 55 20
2043 80c. Guri Dam . . . . . . 1·10 40
The 45 and 50c. are horiz.

1968. Air. Christmas.
2044 **270** 40c. multicoloured . . . 60 15

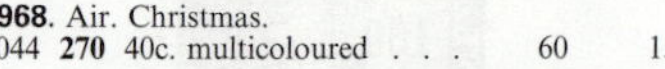

271 House and Savings Bank **272** Children and Star

1968. National Savings System.
2045 **271** 45c. multicoloured . . . 55 20

1968. Air. Children's Festival.
2046 **272** 80c. orange and violet 80 25

273 Planting a Tree

1968. Conservation of Natural Resources. Multicoloured designs each incorporating central motif as in T **273**.
2047 15c. Type **273** (postage) . . 10 10
2048 20c. Plantation 15 10
2049 30c. Waterfall 30 15
2050 45c. Logs 35 15
2051 55c. Cultivated land 70 35
2052 75c. Palambra (fish) 80 25
2053 15c. Marbled wood quails (air) 35 30
2054 20c. Scarlet ibis, jabiru, great blue heron and red-billed whistling duck . . . 35 30
2055 30c. Wood-carving 25 10
2056 90c. Brown trout . . . . . 1·00 35
2057 95c. Mountain highway . . 1·25 55
2058 1b. Red-eyed vireo and shiny-headed cowbird (young) . . . . 1·60 50
The 15c. (both), 20c. (air), 30c. (both) and 55c. are vert, the remainder are horiz.

274 Colorada Beach, Sucre

1969. Tourism. Multicoloured.
2059 15c. Type **274** (postage) . . 15 10
2060 45c. San Francisco de Yare Church, Miranda 50 15
2061 90c. Houses on stilts, Zulia 75 55
2062 15c. Desert landscape, Falcon (air) 20 10
2063 30c. Humboldt Hotel, Caracas 25 15
2064 40c. Mountain cable-car, Merida 45 25

275 Bolivar addressing Congress

1969. 150th Anniv of Angostura Congress.
2066 **275** 45c. multicoloured . . . 65 20

276 Dr. Martin Luther King

278 "On the Balcony" (C. Rojas)

277 "Tabebuia pentaphylla"

1969. 1st Death Anniv of Martin Luther King (American Civil Rights leader).
2067 **276** 1b. multicoloured . . . 80 25

1969. Nature Conservation. Trees. Multicoloured.
2068 50c. Type **277** (postage) . . 50 20
2069 65c. "Erythrina poeppigiana" 70 30
2070 90c. "Platymiscium sp." . . 1·25 50
2071 5c. "Cassia grandis" (air) . . 10 10
2072 20c. "Triplaris caracasana" 25 10
2073 25c. "Samanea saman" . . 35 15

1969. Paintings by Cristobal Rojas. Multicoloured.
2074 25c. Type **278** 20 15
2075 35c. "The Pheasant" 35 20
2076 45c. "The Christening" . . 55 30
2077 50c. "The Empty Place" . . 70 35
2078 60c. "The Tavern" . . . . 1·10 40
2079 1b. "The Arm" (27 × 55 mm) . . . . . . 1·50 70
Nos. 2075/8 are horiz.

279 I.L.O. Emblem

1969. 50th Anniv of I.L.O.
2080 **279** 2b.50 black and brown 2·10 1·10

280 Charter and Arms of Guayana

1969. Industrial Development. Multicoloured.
2081 45c. Type **280** 45 20
2082 1b. SIDOR steel-works . . 90 30

281 Arcade, Casa del Balcon

282 "Alexander von Humboldt" (J. Stieler)

1969. 400th Anniv of Carora. Multicoloured.
2083 20c. Type **281** 15 10
2084 25c. Ruins of La Pastora Church 25 15
2085 55c. Chapel of the Cross . . 90 30
2086 65c. Museum and library building . . . . 1·10 35

1969. Air. Birth Bicent of Alexander von Humboldt (German naturalist).
2087 **282** 50c. multicoloured . . . 50 20

283 A. Alfinger, A. Pacheco and P. Maldonado (founders)

1969. Air. 400th Anniv of Maracaibo. Mult.
2088 20c. Type **283** 20 15
2089 25c. Map of Maracaibo, 1562 . . . . 25 15
2090 40c. City coat-of-arms . . 30 20
2091 70c. University Hospital . . 60 35
2092 75c. Cacique Mara Monument 70 40
2093 1b. Baralt Plaza 80 50
Nos. 2089/92 are vert.

284 "Bolivar's Wedding" (T. Salas)

1969. "Bolivar in Spain".
2094 **284** 10c. multicoloured . . . 10 10
2095 – 15c. black and red . . . 20 10
2096 – 35c. multicoloured . . . 35 15
DESIGNS—VERT: 15c. "Bolivar as a Student" (artist unknown); 35c. Bolivar's statue, Madrid.

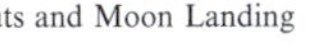
285 Astronauts and Moon Landing

1969. Air. 1st Man on the Moon.
2098 **285** 90c. multicoloured . . . 1·25 45

286 "Virgin of the Rosary" (17th-cent Venetian School)

1969. Air. Christmas. Multicoloured.
2100 75c. Type **286** 85 25
2101 80c. "The Holy Family" (Landaeta School, Caracas, 18th cent) . . . 90 30

287 "Children and Birds"

1969. Children's Day. Multicoloured.
2102 5c. Type **287** 10 10
2103 45c. "Children's Camp" . . 55 30

288 Map of Greater Colombia

1969. 150th Anniv of Greater Colombia Federation.
2104 **288** 45c. multicoloured . . . 50 20

289 San Antonio Church, Clarines

1970. Architecture of the Colonial Era. Mult.
2105 10c. Type **289** 10 10
2106 30c. Church of the Conception, Caroni 25 15
2107 40c. San Miguel Church, Burbusay 50 25
2108 45c. San Antonio Church, Maturin 70 35
2109 75c. San Nicolas Church, Moruy 85 40
2110 1b. Coro Cathedral . . . . 1·25 50

290 Seven Hills of Valera

291 "Simon Bolivar" (M. N. Bate)

1970. 150th Anniv of Valera.
2112 **290** 95c. multicoloured . . . 65 30

1970. Air. Portraits of Bolivar. Stamps in brown on buff; inscriptions in green; colours of country name and value given below.
2113 **291** 15c. brown 15 10
2114 45c. blue 35 15
2115 55c. orange 50 25
2116 – 65c. brown 50 25
2117 – 70c. blue 55 35
2118 – 75c. orange 45 40
2119 – 85c. brown 90 45
2120 – 90c. blue 95 25
2121 – 95c. orange . . . . . . 1·10 25
2122 – 1b. brown . . . . . . 1·10 25
2123 – 1b.50 blue . . . . . . 1·25 55
2124 – 2b. orange . . . . . . 2·75 90
PORTRAITS BY: 65, 70, 75c. F. Roulin; 85, 90, 95c. J. M. Espinoza (1828); 1, 1b.50, 2b. J. M. Espinoza (1830).

292 Gen. A. Guzman Blanco and Dr. M. J. Sanabria

1970. Air. Centenary of Free Compulsory Education in Venezuela.
2125 **292** 75c. black, green & brown 75 30

293 Map of Venezuela

1970. States of Venezuela. Maps and Arms of the various States. Multicoloured.
2126 5c. Federal District (postage) 10 10
2127 15c. Monagas 15 10
2128 20c. Nueva Esparta 20 10
2129 25c. Portuguesa (vert) . . . 25 10
2130 45c. Sucre 35 15
2131 55c. Tachira (vert) 20 20
2132 65c. Trujillo 30 25
2133 75c. Yaracuy 45 35
2134 85c. Zulia (vert) 85 35
2135 90c. Amazonas Federal Territory (vert) . . . . . 1·25 40
2136 1b. Federal Island Dependencies . . . . . . 1·40 45
2137 5c. Type **293** (air) 10 10
2138 15c. Apure 20 10
2139 20c. Aragua 25 10
2140 20c. Anzoategui 25 10
2141 25c. Barinas 25 10
2142 25c. Bolivar 25 10
2143 45c. Carabobo 55 20
2144 55c. Cojedes (vert) 60 25
2145 65c. Falcon 65 25
2146 75c. Guarico 60 30
2147 85c. Lara 95 35
2148 90c. Merida (vert) 95 40
2149 1b. Miranda 95 50
2150 2b. Delta Amacuro Federal Territory . . . . 2·00 80

294 "Monochaetum humboldtianum"

295 "The Battle of Boyaca" (M. Tovar y Tovar)

1970. Flowers of Venezuela. Multicoloured.
2151 20c. Type **294** (postage) . . 30 10
2152 25c. "Symbolanthus vasculosus" 60 15
2153 45c. "Cavendishia splendens" 80 35
2154 1b. "Befaria glauca" . . . . 1·10 50
2155 20c. "Epidendrum secundum (air) 25 10
2156 25c. "Oyedaea verbesinoides" 35 15
2157 45c. "Heliconia villosa" . . 80 35
2158 1b. "Macleania nitida" . . . 1·10 50

1970. 150th Anniv (1969) of Battle of Boyaca.
2159 **295** 30c. multicoloured . . . 35 15

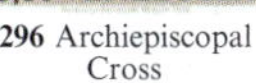

296 Archiepiscopal Cross

297 "Caracciolo Parra Olmedo" (T. Salas)

1970. Religious Art. Multicoloured.
2160 35c. Type **296** 35 15
2161 40c. "Our Lady of the Valley" 45 25
2162 60c. "Our Lady of Belen de San Mateo" 90 35

2163 90c. "The Virgin of Chiquinquira" 1·10 50
2164 1b. "Our Lady of Socorro de Valencia" 1·40 55

1970. Air. 150th Birth Anniv of Caracciola Parra Olmedo (lawyer).
2166 **297** 20c. multicoloured 25 10

298 National Flags and Exhibition Emblem

299 "Guardian Angel" (J. P. Lopez)

1970. "EXFILCA 70" Philatelic Exhibition, Caracas. Multicoloured.
2167 20c. Type **298** 20 10
2168 25c. 1871 1c. stamp and emblem (horiz) 30 15
2169 70c. 1930 2b.50 air stamp and emblem 50 30

1970. Christmas.
2171 **299** 45c. multicoloured 60 15

300 Caudron G-3 Biplane and Dassault Mirage III

1970. 50th Anniv of Venezuelan Air Force.
2172 **300** 5c. multicoloured 20 10

301 People in Question Mark

1971. National Census.
2173 **301** 30c. black, green and red (postage) 60 30
2174 – 70c. multicoloured (air) 95 45
DESIGN: 70c. National flag and "pin-men".

302 Battle Scene

1971. 150th Anniv of Battle of Carabobo.
2175 **302** 2b. multicoloured 1·40 80

303 "Cattleya percivaliana"

304 Adoration of the Child

1971. Air. Venezuelan Orchids. Multicoloured.
2176 20c. Type **303** 25 15
2177 25c. "Cattleya gaskelliana" (horiz) 30 20
2178 75c. "Cattleya mossiae" 85 40
2179 90c. "Cattleya violacea o superba" (horiz) 90 35
2180 1b. "Cattleya lawrenceana" (horiz) 1·10 40

1971. Christmas. Multicoloured.
2181 25c. Type **304** 25 15
2182 25c. Madonna and Child 25 15

305 Dr. Luis D. Beauperthuy

306 Constitution and Government Building

1971. Death Centenary of Luis P. Beauperthuy (scientist).
2183 **305** 1b. multicoloured 70 30

1971. Air. 10th Anniv of 1961 Constitution.
2184 **306** 90c. multicoloured 1·10 35

307 Heart-shaped Globe

308 Arms of Venezuela and National Flags

1972. World Heart Month.
2185 **307** 1b. black, red and blue 85 40

1972. "Venezuela in the Americas". Mult.
2186 3b. Type **308** 2·40 85
2187 4b. Venezuelan flag 2·75 1·40
2188 5b. National anthem 3·25 1·90
2189 10b. "Araguaney" (national tree) 6·75 2·75
2190 15b. Map of the Americas 10·50 3·75

309 Tower Blocks

1972. Central Park Housing Project. Mult.
2191 30c. Type **309** 25 15
2192 30c. View from ground level 25 15
2193 30c. Aerial view 25 15

310 Mahatma Gandhi

1972. Birth Centenary (1969) of Mahatma Gandhi.
2194 **310** 60c. multicoloured 75 35

311 Children making Music

313 Planetary System

312 Head of "Drymarchon corais"

1972. Christmas. Multicoloured.
2195 30c. Type **311** 25 15
2196 30c. Children roller-skating 25 15
Nos. 2195/6 were issued together, se-tenant, forming a composite design.

1972. Snakes. Multicoloured.
2197 10c. Type **312** 10 10
2198 15c. "Spilotes pullatus" 15 10
2199 25c. "Bothrops venezuelensis" 40 15
2200 30c. "Micrurus dumerili carinicaudus" 50 20
2201 60c. "Crotalus vegrandis" 50 35
2202 1b. Boa constrictor 75 50

1973. 500th Birth Anniv of Copernicus (astronomer). Multicoloured.
2203 5c. Type **313** 10 10
2204 10c. Copernicus 20 10
2205 15c. Book "De Revolutionibus Orbium Coelestium" 25 10

314 The Sun

315 Part of Solar System (left-hand)

1973. 10th Anniv of Humboldt Planetarium. Multicoloured. (a) As Type **314**.
2206 5c. Type **314** 10 10
2207 5c. Earth 10 10
2208 20c. Mars 35 10
2209 20c. Saturn 25 10
2210 30c. Asteroids 30 15
2211 40c. Neptune 35 20
2212 50c. Venus 75 35
2213 60c. Jupiter 85 40
2214 75c. Uranus 1·00 50
2215 90c. Pluto 1·25 40
2216 90c. Moon 1·40 70
2217 1b. Mercury 1·60 60

(b) As Type **315**.
2218 10c. Type **315** 30 10
2219 15c. Solar System (centre) 40 10
2220 15c. Solar System (right-hand) 40 10
Nos. 2218/20 form a composite design of the Solar System.

316 O.A.S. Emblem and Map

1973. 25th Anniv of Organization of American States.
2221 **316** 60c. multicoloured 50 20

317 General Paez in Uniform

319 Bishop Ramos de Lora

318 Admiral Padilla, Gen. Montilla and Gen. Manrique

1973. Death Centenary of General Jose A. Paez.
2222 **317** 10c. multicoloured 10 10
2223 – 30c. gold, black and red 25 15
2224 – 50c. black, ultramarine and blue 50 25
2225 – 1b. multicoloured 75 50
2226 – 2b. multicoloured 1·25 75
DESIGNS—VERT: 30c. Paez and horse (old engraving); 50c. Gen. Paez in civilian dress; 1b. Street of the Lancers, Puerto Cabello. HORIZ: 2b. "The Charge at Centauro".

1973. 150th Anniv of Naval Battle of Maracaibo. Multicoloured.
2227 50c. Type **318** 40 20
2228 1b. "Battle of Maracaibo" (M. F. Rincon) 90 40
2229 2b. Plan of opposing fleets 1·40 60

1973. 250th Birth Anniv (1972) of Bishop Ramos de Lora.
2230 **319** 75c. gold and brown 45 20

320 Ship, Jet Airliner and Map

322 General Paez Dam

321 Waterfall and Map

1973. Margarita Island Free Zone.
2231 **320** 5c. multicoloured 15 10

1973. Completion of Golden Highway. Mult.
2232 5c. Type **321** 10 10
2233 10c. Map and scarlet macaw 25 25
2234 20c. Map and Santa Elena Church, Uairen 25 10
2235 50c. Map and ancient mountain sanctuary 65 25
2236 60c. As 50c. 65 25
2237 90c. Map and Santa Teresita church, Cabanayen 85 35
2238 1b. Map and flags of Venezuela and Brazil 90 40

1973. Completion of General Paez Dam, Merida.
2239 **322** 30c. multicoloured 30 10

323 Child on Slide

1973. Children's Festival. Multicoloured.
2240 10c. Type **323** 25 15
2241 10c. Fairy tale animals 25 15
2242 10c. "Paginas Para Imaginar" (children's book) 25 15
2243 10c. Holidaymakers leaving airliner 25 15

324 King on White Horse

326 Vase and Lace ("Handicrafts")

325 Regional Map

1973. Christmas. Multicoloured.

2244	30c. Type **324**	25	10
2245	30c. Two Kings	25	10

1973. Regional Development.

2246 **325**	25c. multicoloured	30	10

1973. Venezuelan Industrial Development Commission. Multicoloured.

2247	15c. Type **326**	15	10
2248	35c. Industrial estate ("Construction")	35	10
2249	45c. Cogwheels and chimney ("Small and medium industries")	50	20

327 Map and Revellers

1974. 10th Anniv of Carupano Carnival.

2250 **327**	5c. multicoloured	10	10

328 Congress Emblem

1974. 9th Venezuelan Engineering Congress, Maracaibo.

2251 **328**	50c. multicoloured	50	15

329 "Law of the Sea" Emblem

1974. 3rd Law of the Sea Conference, Caracas. Multicoloured.

2252	15c. Type **329**	10	10
2253	35c. Great barracuda in seaweed	35	10
2254	75c. Sea-bed scene	70	25
2255	80c. Underwater grotto	75	35

330 Pupil and New School

1974. "Pay Your Taxes" Campaign.

2256	**330**	5c. multicoloured	10	10
2257		10c. multicoloured	10	10
2258		15c. multicoloured	10	10
2259		20c. multicoloured	10	10
2260	A	25c. multicoloured	15	10
2261		30c. multicoloured	40	20
2262		35c. multicoloured	20	10
2263		40c. multicoloured	35	15
2264	B	45c. multicoloured	35	15
2265		50c. multicoloured	35	15
2266		55c. multicoloured	55	30
2267		60c. multicoloured	45	20
2268	C	65c. multicoloured	1·00	50
2269		70c. multicoloured	50	20
2270		75c. multicoloured	50	25
2271		80c. multicoloured	50	25
2272	D	85c. multicoloured	50	25
2273		90c. multicoloured	70	25
2274		95c. multicoloured	1·00	70
2275		1b. multicoloured	70	35

DESIGNS: A, Suburban housing project; B, City centre motorway; C, Sports stadium; D, Surgical team in operating theatre.

331 "Bolivar at Junin" (A. H. Tovar)

1974. 150th Anniv of Battle of Junin.

2276 **331**	2b. multicoloured	1·60	70

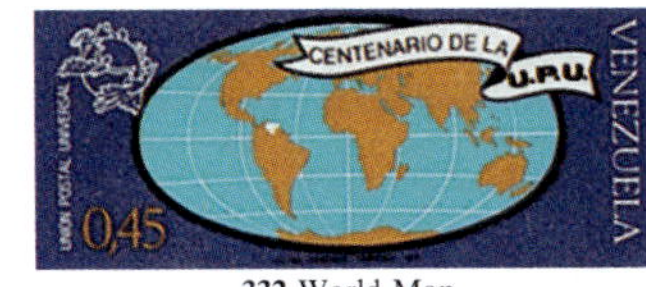

332 World Map

1974. Centenary of U.P.U. Multicoloured.

2277	45c. Type **332**	35	15
2278	50c. Mounted courier, sailing packet, modern liner and jet airliner	40	20

333 Rufino Blanco-Fombona and Books

1974. Birth Centenary of Rufino Blanco-Fombona (writer).

2279	**333**	10c. multicoloured	10	10
2280	–	30c. multicoloured	20	10
2281	–	45c. multicoloured	30	15
2282	–	90c. multicoloured	50	25

DESIGNS: Nos. 2280/2, Portraits of Rufino Blanco-Fombona against a background of books similar to Type **333**.

334 Children on Paper Dart

1974. Children's Festival.

2283 **334**	70c. multicoloured	40	20

335 Marshal Sucre

336 "Shepherd"

1974. 150th Anniv of Battle of Ayacucho. Multicoloured.

2284	30c. Type **335**	20	10
2285	50c. South American flags on globe	30	25
2286	1b. Map showing battle sites	55	35
2287	2b. "Battle of Ayacucho" (43½ × 22 mm)	1·25	70

1974. Christmas. Details from "The Adoration of the Shepherds" (J. B. Mayno). Multicoloured.

2288	30c. Type **336**	25	15
2289	30c. "Holy Family"	25	15

Nos. 2288/9 were issued together se-tenant, forming a composite design.

337 Road Construction, 1905, and El Ciempies Junction, 1972

1974. Centenary of Ministry of Public Works. Multicoloured.

2290	5c. Type **337**	10	10
2291	20c. J. Munoz Tebar (first Minister of Public Works)	25	10
2292	25c. Bridges on Caracas–La Guaira Road, 1912 and 1953	30	10
2293	40c. Views of Caracas, 1874 and 1974	30	15
2294	70c. Tucacas Railway Station, 1911, and projected Caracas underground railway terminal	2·25	55
2295	80c. Anatomical Institute, 1911, and Social Security Hospital, 1969	85	30
2296	85c. Quininari River bridge, 1904, and Orinoco River bridge, 1967	1·00	35
2297	1b. As 20c.	1·40	50

338 Women in Profile

340 The Nativity

339 Emblem and "Tents"

1975. International Women's Year.

2298 **338**	90c. multicoloured	50	30

1975. 14th World Scout Jamboree.

2299	**339**	20c. multicoloured	15	10
2300		80c. multicoloured	55	25

1975. Christmas. Multicoloured.

2301	30c. Type **340**	20	10
2302	30c. "The Shepherds"	20	10

Nos. 2301/2 were issued se-tenant, forming a composite design.

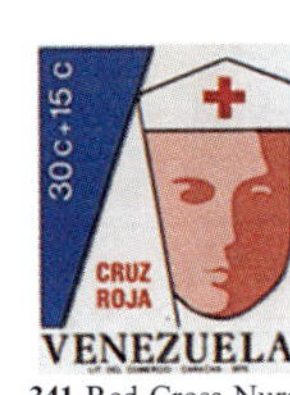

341 Red Cross Nurse

342 Altar

1975. Venezuelan Red Cross.

2303	**341**	30c.+15c. mult	35	20
2304		50c.+25c. mult	50	30

1976. Centenary of National Pantheon.

2305	**342**	30c. grey and blue	15	10
2306	–	1b.05 brown and red	50	25

DESIGN: 1b.05, Pantheon building.

343 Coloured Panels

1976. 150th Anniv of Bolivian Independence (1975).

2307 **343**	60c. multicoloured	25	15

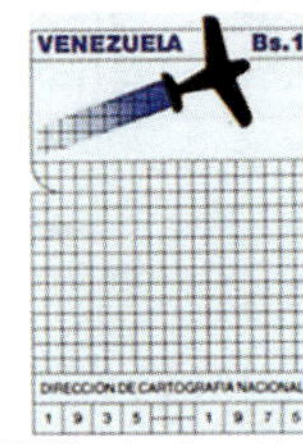

344 "Charting from Aircraft"

1976. 40th Anniv of National Cartographic Institute (1975).

2308 **344**	1b. black and blue	50	20

345 Signature of General Jose Felix Ribas

1976. Birth Bicentenary of General Jose Ribas. Multicoloured.

2309	**345**	40c. green and red	25	10
2310	–	55c. multicoloured	35	15

DESIGN—HORIZ: (40 × 30 mm): 55c. General Jose Felix Ribas.

346 "Musicians of Chacao School" (A. Barrios)

1976. Birth Bicentenary (1975) of Jose Angel Lamas (composer).

2311	**346**	75c. multicoloured	45	25
2312	–	1b.25 red, grey and buff	65	35

DESIGN—40 × 28 mm: 1b.25, Lamas' colophon.

347 "Bolivar" (J. M. Espinoza)

348 Maze symbolizing Opportunity

1976.

2313	**347**	5c. turquoise	10	10
2314		10c. red	10	10
2315		15c. brown	10	10
2316		20c. black	10	10
2317		25c. orange	10	10
2613		25c. red	10	10
2318		30c. blue	10	10
2319		45c. lilac	15	10
2320		50c. orange	20	10
2614		50c. blue	10	10
2321		65c. blue	25	10
2615		75c. mauve	10	10
2322		1b. red	35	15
2616		1b. orange	10	10
2323		2b. grey	70	35
2617		2b. yellow	15	10
2324		3b. blue	1·10	50
2618		3b. green	10	10
2325		4b. orange	1·25	45
2619		4b. brown	15	10
2620		5b. red	15	10
2327		10b. lilac	3·00	1·10
2621		10b. yellow	40	15
2328		15b. blue	4·50	1·60
2622		15b. purple	70	15
2329		20b. red	6·00	2·25
2623		20b. blue	1·10	40
2329a		25b. blue	6·25	2·25
2623a		25b. bistre	1·25	60
2329b		30b. blue	7·00	2·75
2623b		30b. lilac	1·75	75

2329c 50b. purple . . . . . . 12·00 4·50
2623c 50b. red . . . . 2·75 1·25
Nos. 2323/9 are larger, 27 × 33 mm.

1976. 250th Anniv of Central University.
2330 **348** 30c. multicoloured . . . 15 10
2331 – 50c. black, orange & yell 25 15
2332 – 90c. yellow and black . . 50 30
DESIGNS: 50c. University building; 90c. Faculty symbols.

349 C. A. Fernadez de Leoni (founder)
350 "Unity" Emblem

1976. Children's Foundation. Multicoloured.
2333 30c.+15c. Type **349** 25 20
2334 50c.+25c. Children in "home" (31 × 44 mm) . . 45 30

1976. 150th Anniv of Panama Amphictyonic Congress.
2335 **350** 15c. multicoloured . . . 10 10
2336 – 45c. multicoloured . . . 25 10
2337 – 1b.25 multicoloured . . 55 30
DESIGN: 45c., 1b.25, As Type **275**, but with different "Unity" emblems.

351 George Washington

1976. Bicentenary of American Revolution.
2338 **351** 1b. black and brown . . 55 35
2339 – 1b. black and green . . 55 55
2340 – 1b. black and purple . . 55 35
2341 – 1b. black and blue . . 55 35
2342 – 1b. black and brown . . 55 35
DESIGNS: No. 2339, Thomas Jefferson; No. 2340, Abraham Lincoln; No. 2341, Franklin D. Roosevelt; No. 2342, John F. Kennedy.

352 Valve in Oil Pipeline
353 "The Nativity" (B. Rivas)

1976. Oil Nationalization.
2343 **352** 10c. multicoloured . . . 10 10
2344 – 30c. multicoloured . . . 15 10
2345 – 35c. multicoloured . . . 20 10
2346 – 40c. multicoloured . . . 20 10
2347 – 55c. multicoloured . . . 30 15
2348 – 90c. multicoloured . . . 55 25
DESIGNS: 30c. to 90c. Various computer drawings of valves and pipelines.

1976. Christmas.
2349 **353** 30c. multicoloured . . . 25 10

354 Patient
355 Declaration Emblem

1976. Anti-tuberculosis Society Fund.
2350 **354** 10c.+5c. multicoloured 15 15
2351 30c.+10c. multicoloured 20 20

1976. 10th Anniv of Bogota Declaration.
2352 **355** 60c. black and yellow . . 30 15

356 Arms of Barinas

1977. 400th Anniv of Barinas.
2353 **356** 50c. multicoloured . . . 30 15

357 "Christ Crucified"

1977. 400th Anniv (1976) of La Grita.
2354 **357** 30c. multicoloured . . . 15 10

358 Coro Settlement

1977. 450th Anniv of Coro.
2355 **358** 1b. multicoloured . . . 35 15

359 I.P.C.T.T. Emblem and Stylized Dove

1977. 9th Inter-American Postal and Telecommunications Staff Congress, Caracas.
2356 **359** 85c. multicoloured . . . 35 15

360 Cable Links to Domestic Equipment
361 "VENEZUELA" and Value as Rolled Steel

1977. Inauguration of "Columbus" Submarine Cable.
2357 **360** 95c. grey, blue and green 60 15

1977. 1st Anniv of Nationalization and Exploitation of Steel.
2358 **361** 30c. black and yellow . . 15 10
2359 – 50c. black and orange 25 10
2360 – 80c. black and grey . . 35 15
2361 – 1b.05 black and red . . 40 20
2362 – 1b.25 black and yellow 45 20
2363 – 1b.50 black and grey . . 65 25
DESIGNS: 50c. to 1b.50, Similar to Type **361** but each differently arranged.

362 J. P. Duarte
363 "The Holy Family"

1977. Death Cent (1976) of Juan Pablo Duarte.
2364 **362** 75c. black and mauve . . 30 15

1977. Christmas.
2365 **363** 30c. multicoloured . . . 15 10

364 O.P.E.C. Emblem

1977. 50th O.P.E.C. Conference, Caracas.
2366 **364** 1b.05 black and blue . . 50 15

365 Cyclists Racing

1978. World Cycling Championships, San Cristobal, Tachira. Multicoloured.
2367 5c. Type **365** 10 10
2368 1b.25 Cyclist racing 65 20

366 Heads in Profile

1978. Language Day.
2369 **366** 70c. black, grey & mauve 25 15

367 Computer Tape and Satellite
368 "1777–1977"

1978. 10th World Telecommunications Day.
2370 **367** 75c. blue 30 20

1978. Bicentenary of Venezuelan Unification. Multicoloured.
2381 30c. Type **368** 10 10
2382 1b. Computer print of Goya's "Carlos III" . . . 40 15

369 Bolivar in Nurse Hipolita's Arms

1978. Birth Bicent (1983) of Simon Bolivar (1st issue).
2383 **369** 30c. black, brown & grn 15 10
2384 – 1b. black, brown and blue 65 25
DESIGN: 1b. Juan Vicente Bolivar (father).
See also Nos. 2399/40, 2408/9, 2422/3, 2431/2, 2467/8, 2480/1, 2483/4, 2494/5, 2498/9, 2518/19 and 2521/2.

370 "T" ("Trabajadors")
371 Medical Abstract

1978. Workers' Day.
2385 **370** 30c. red and black . . . 10 10
2386 – 30c. blue and black . . . 10 10
2387 – 30c. yellow, blue & black 10 10
2388 – 30c. red, blue and black 10 10
2389 – 30c. red and black . . . 10 10
2390 – 95c. black and red . . . 30 15
2391 – 95c. grey and blue . . . 30 15
2392 – 95c. black and red . . . 30 15
2393 – 95c. blue and black . . . 30 15
2394 – 95c. multicoloured . . . 30 15
DESIGNS: Nos. 2386/94 based on the letter "T", also inscribed "CTV".

1978. Birth Centenary (1977) of Rafael Rangel (physician and scientist).
2395 **371** 50c. brown 40 20

372 Drill Head and Map of Tachira Oilfield

1978. Centenary of Venezuelan Oil Industry. Multicoloured.
2396 30c. Type **372** 15 10
2397 1b.05 Letter "P" as pipeline 50 20

373 Christmas Star

1978. Christmas.
2398 **373** 30c. multicoloured . . . 15 10

1978. Birth Bicentenary (1983) of Simon Bolivar (2nd issue). As T **369**.
2399 30c. black, brown and purple 10 10
2400 1b. black, grey and red . . 30 15
DESIGNS: 30c. Bolivar at 25 (after M. N. Bate); 1b. Simon Rodriguez (Bolivar's tutor).

374 "P T"

1979. Creation of Postal and Telegraph Institute.
2402 **374** 75c. blk & red on cream 25 15

375 Dam holding back Water

1979. 10th Anniv of Guri Dam.
2403 **375** 2b. silver, grey and black 70 30

376 "General San Martin" (E. J. Maury)

1979. Birth Bicentenary of General Jose de San Martin. Multicoloured.
2404 40c. Type **376** 15 10
2405 60c. Portrait by Mercedes San Martin 25 10
2406 70c. San Martin Monument, Guayaquil 30 15
2407 75c. San Martin's signature 35 20

1979. Birth Bicentenary (1983) of Simon Bolivar (3rd series). As T **369**.
2408 30c. black, violet and red . . 10 10
2409 1b. black, orange and red 30 15
DESIGNS: 30c. Alexandre Sabes Petion (President of Haiti); 1b. Bolivar's signature.

377 "Rotary" and Curves
378 Statue of Virgin working Miracles, 1654

1979. 50th Anniv of Rotary Club of Caracas.
2411 **377** 85c. black and gold . . . 25 15

1979. 25th Anniv of Canonization of Virgin of Coromoto.
2412 **378** 55c. black and red . . . 20 10

379 Miranda, London Residence and Arms

1979. Acquisition by Venezuela of Francisco de Miranda's House in London.
2413 **379** 50c. multicoloured . . . 20 10

380 O'Leary and Maps

1979. 125th Death Anniv of Daniel O'Leary (publisher of Bolivar's memoirs).
2414 **380** 30c. multicoloured . . . 10 10

381 Boy with Nest **382** Candle

1979. International Year of the Child.
2415 **381** 70c. black and blue . . . 25 15
2416 – 80c. multicoloured . . . 30 15
DESIGN: 80c. Boys playing in sea.

1979. Christmas.
2417 **382** 30c. multicoloured . . . 10 10

383 Caudron G-3 Biplane

1979. "Exfilve 79" National Stamp Exhibition and 59th Anniv of Air Force. Multicoloured.
2418 75c. Type **383** 35 20
2419 75c. Stearman Kaydett biplane 35 20
2420 75c. Bell Iroquois helicopter 35 20
2421 75c. Dassault Mirage IIIC jet fighter 35 20

1979. Birth Bicentenary (1983) of Simon Bolivar (4th series). As T **369**.
2422 30c. black, red and turquoise 10 10
2423 1b. black, blue and red . . 30 15
DESIGNS: 30c. Bolivar; 1b. Slave.

384 Emblem and World Map

1979. Introduction of New Emblem for Postal and Telegraph Institute.
2425 **384** 75c. multicoloured . . . 25 15

385 Queen Victoria and Hill

1980. Death Centenary of Sir Rowland Hill (1979).
2426 **385** 55c. multicoloured . . . 20 10

386 Augusto Pi Suner

1980. Birth Centenary (1979) of Dr. Augusto Pi Suner (physiologist).
2427 **386** 80c. multicoloured . . . 30 15

387 "Cotyledon hispanica" **388** Lovera (self-portrait)

1980. 250th Birth Anniv of Pedro Loefling (Swedish botanist).
2428 **387** 50c. multicoloured . . . 20 10

1980. Birth Bicentenary (1978) of Juan Lovera (artist).
2429 **388** 60c. blue and red 20 10
2430 75c. violet and orange 25 15

1980. Birth Bicentenary (1983) of Simon Bolivar (5th issue). As T **369**.
2431 30c. black, green and purple 10 10
2432 1b. black, dp brown & brown 30 15

DESIGNS: 30c. Signing document; 1b. Congress House, Angostura.

389 "Self-portrait with Children" (detail) **390** Bernardo O'Higgins

1980. 25th Death Anniv (1979) of Armando Reveron (artist). Multicoloured.
2434 50c. Type **389** 20 10
2435 65c. "Self-portrait" (26 × 41 mm) 35 20

1980. 204th Birth Anniv of Bernardo O'Higgins.
2436 **390** 85c. black, red and blue 50 25

391 Frigate "Mariscal Sucre"

1980. Venezuelan Navy. Multicoloured.
2437 1b.50 Type **391** . . . . . . 1·25 50
2438 1b.50 Submarine "Picua" 1·25 50
2439 1b.50 Naval School . . . . 1·25 50
2440 1b.50 Cadet barque "Simon Bolivar" (33 × 52 mm) . . 1·25 50

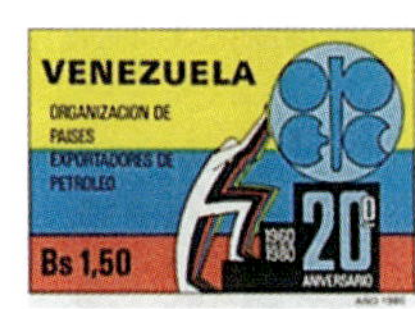

392 Figures supporting O.P.E.C. Emblem

1980. 20th Anniv of Organization of Petroleum Exporting Countries. Multicoloured.
2441 1b.50 Type **392** 50 25
2442 1b.50 O.P.E.C. emblem and globe 50 25

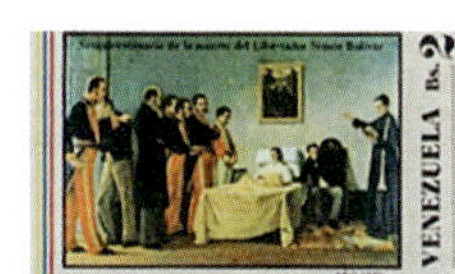

393 "The Death of Bolivar" (Antonio Herrera Toro)

1980. 150th Death Anniv of Simon Bolivar.
2443 **393** 2b. multicoloured . . . 70 30

394 Antonio Jose de Sucre **395** "The Adoration of the Shepherds" (Rubens)

1980. 150th Death Anniv of Marshal Antonio Jose de Sucre.
2444 **394** 2b. multicoloured . . . 70 30

1980. Christmas.
2445 **395** 1b. multicoloured . . . 20 10

396 Helen Keller's Initials in Braille and Print

1981. Birth Centenary (1980) of Helen Keller.
2446 **396** 1b.50 grey, orange & blk 40 15

397 Gateway, San Felipe **398** Jean Baptiste de la Salle (founder)

1981. 250th Anniv of San Felipe.
2447 **397** 3b. blue, grey and red 95 35

1981. 300th Anniv (1980) of Brothers of Christian Schools.
2448 **398** 1b.25 silver, red & black 30 15

399 Municipal Theatre

1981. Centenary of Caracas Municipal Theatre.
2449 **399** 1b.25 pink, black & lilac 30 15

400 U.P.U. Emblem, Map of Venezuela and Envelope

1981. Centenary of Admission to Universal Postal Union.
2450 **400** 2b. multicoloured . . . 75 20

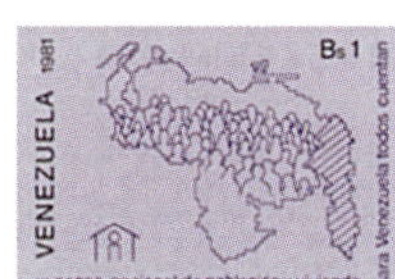

401 People on Map

1981. 11th National Population and Housing Census.
2451 **401** 1b. lilac, violet, and black 30 15

402 Games Emblem **404** Musicians

403 "Penny-farthing" Bicycle

1981. 9th Bolivarian Games, Barquismeto.
2452 **402** 95c. multicoloured . . . 30 15

1981. Transport History (1st series). Mult.
2453 1b. Type **403** 35 20
2454 1b.05 Steam locomotive, 1926 . . . . 1·10 50
2455 1b.25 Buick car, 1937 . . . 40 25
2456 1b.50 Horse-drawn cab . . 50 25
See also Nos. 2490/3 and 2514/7.

1981. Christmas.
2457 **404** 1b. multicoloured . . . 25 10

405 Mt. Autana **407** "Landscape"

406 Calligraphic Script and Arms

1982. 50th Anniv of Venezuelan Natural Sciences Society. Multicoloured.
2458 1b. Type **405** 30 20
2459 1b.50 Sarisarinama 50 20
2460 2b. Guacharo Cave 80 35

1982. 20th Anniv of Constitution.
2461 **406** 1b.85 gold and black . . 70 25

1982. 20th Anniv of Agricultural Reform.
2462 **407** 3b. multicoloured . . . 1·00 40

408 Jules Verne **410** Rose

409 Bars of National Anthem

1982. Jules Verne (writer) Commemoration.
2463 **408** 1b. deep blue and blue 30 15

1982. Centenary of National Anthem (1981).
2464 **409** 1b. multicoloured . . . 30 15

1982. 1300th Anniv of Bulgarian State.
2465 **410** 65c. multicoloured . . . 20 10

411 Flags **412** Cecilio Acosta

1982. 6th National Plan.
2466 **411** 2b. multicoloured . . . 70 15

1982. Birth Bicentenary (1983) of Simon Bolivar (6th issue). As T **369**.
2467 30c. black, brown and orange 10 10
2468 1b. black, brown and green 50 15
DESIGNS: 30c. Col. Rondon; 1b. General Anzoategui.

1982. Death Centenary (1981) of Cecilio Acosta (statesman).
2469 **412** 3b. black, blue and violet 85 25

413 "Fourcroya humboldtiana"

1982. Flora and Fauna. Multicoloured.
2471 1b.05 Type **413** 35 15
2472 2b.55 Turtle ("Podocnemis expansa") . . . . 1·10 30

2473 2b.75 "Oyedaea verbesinoides" . . . . . 1·25 35
2474 3b. Oilbird . . . . 2·25 35

414 Andres Bello and Initials

1982. Birth Bicentenary of Andres Bello (1981).
2475 **414** 1b.05 light blue, blue and black 50 15
2476 2b.55 yellow, violet and black 70 30
2477 2b.75 blue, deep blue and black 80 35
2478 3b. olive, deep olive and black 85 40

415 "Nativity"

416 Bermudez

1982. Christmas.
2479 **415** 1b. multicoloured . . . 20 10

1982. Birth Bicentenary (1983) of Simon Bolivar (7th issue). As T **369**.
2480 30c. black, grey and red . . 10 10
2481 1b. black, grey and red . . 50 15
DESIGNS: 30c. Carabobo Monument; 1b. Gen. Jose Antonio Paez.

1982. Birth Bicentenary (1983) of Simon Bolivar (8th issue). As T **369**.
2483 30c. black, blue and deep blue 10 10
2484 1b. black, violet and red . . 50 15
DESIGNS: 30c. Commemorative plaque to the meeting at Guayaquil; 1b. Bolivar and San Martin (detail of monument).

1982. Birth Bicentenary of General Jose Francisco Bermudez (statesman).
2486 **416** 3b. multicoloured . . . 85 30

417 Briceno

1982. Birth Bicentenary of Antonio Nicolas Briceno (liberation hero).
2487 **417** 3b. multicoloured . . . 85 30

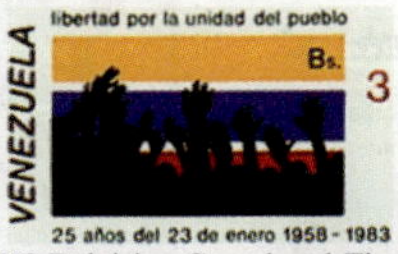

418 Rejoicing Crowd and Flag

1983. 25th Anniv of 1958 Reforms.
2488 **418** 3b. multicoloured . . . 85 30

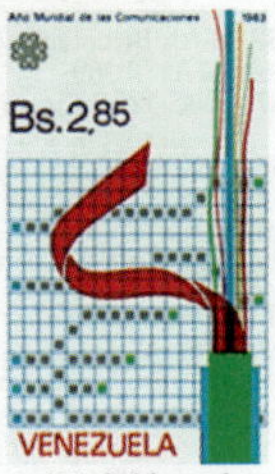

419 Police Badge

420 Cable and Computer Circuitboard

1983. 25th Anniv of Judicial Police Technical Department.
2489 **419** 4b. red and green . . . 1·00 30

1983. Transport History (2nd series). As T **403**. Multicoloured.
2490 75c. Lincoln touring car, 1923 . . . . 20 10
2491 80c. Steam locomotive No. 129, 1889 . . . . . 1·25 75
2492 85c. Willys truck, 1927 . . . 50 10
2493 95c. Cleveland motorcycle, 1920 . . . . 50 10

1983. Birth Bicentenary of Simon Bolivar (9th issue). As T **369**.
2494 30c. black, red and blue . . 10 10
2495 1b. black, gold and blue . . 50 15
DESIGNS: 30c. Gen. Antonio Sucre; 1b. Sword hilt.

1983. World Communications Year.
2497 **420** 2b.85 multicoloured . . 75 30

1983. Birth Bicentenary of Simon Bolivar (10th issue). As T **369**.
2498 30c. multicoloured 10 10
2499 1b. black, yellow and blue 50 15
DESIGNS: 30c. Flags; 1b. "Ascent of Potosi".

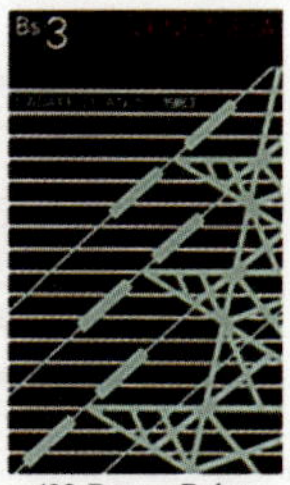

421 Map of the Americas

422 Power Pylon

1983. 9th Pan-American Games, Caracas. Multicoloured.
2501 2b. Type **421** 45 20
2502 2b. Swimming 45 20
2503 2b.70 Cycling 60 30
2504 2b.70 Fencing 60 30
2505 2b.85 Weightlifting 75 40
2506 2b.85 Running 75 40

1983. 25th Anniv of State Electricity Authority.
2508 **422** 3b. blue, silver and red 70 30

423 Nativity

1983. Christmas.
2509 **423** 1b. multicoloured . . . 35 10

424 Erecting a Tent

1983. 75th Anniv (1982) of Scout Movement. Multicoloured.
2510 2b.25 Type **424** 60 15
2511 2b.55 Nature watch 60 15
2512 2b.75 Mountaineering . . . 65 15
2513 3b. Camp at night 65 15

1983. Transport History (3rd series). Caracas Underground Railway. As T **403**. Multicoloured.
2514 55c. black, orange and silver 40 20
2515 75c. black, yellow and silver 60 30
2516 95c. black, green and silver 75 30
2517 2b. black, blue and silver . . 1·75 60
DESIGNS: 55c. Central computer building; 75c. Maintenance bay; 95c. Train on elevated section; 2b. Train at Cano Amarillo station.

1984. Birth Bicentenary of Simon Bolivar (11th issue). As T **369**.
2518 30c. black, red and brown 10 10
2519 1b. black, green and blue . . 35 10
DESIGNS: 30c. Open volume of "Opere de Raimondo Montecuccoli"; 1b. Dr. Jose Maria Vargas (President, 1835–36).

1984. Birth Bicentenary of Simon Bolivar (12th issue). As T **369**.
2521 30c. black, red and lilac . . 10 10
2522 1b. black, green and orange 35 10
DESIGNS: 30c. Pedro Gual (President, 1859 and 1861); 1b. Jose Faustino Sanchez Carrion.

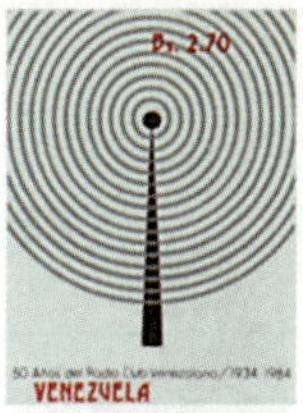

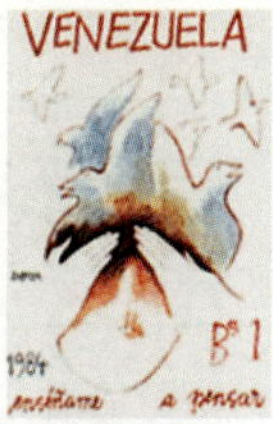

425 Radio Mast and Waves

426 Doves and Hands covering Eyes

1984. 50th Anniv of Venezuela Radio Club.
2524 **425** 2b.70 multicoloured . . 60 15

1984. "Intelligentsia for Peace". Multicoloured.
2525 1b. Type **426** 10 10
2526 2b.70 Profile head 55 15
2527 2b.85 Profile head, flower and hexagonal nut . . . 60 15

427 Romulo Gallegos

1984. Birth Centenary of Romulo Gallegos (writer and President, 1948). Multicoloured.
2528 **427** 1b.70 multicoloured . . 25 15
2529 – 1b.70 multicoloured . . 25 15
2530 – 1b.70 green, grey and black 25 15
2531 – 1b.70 deep green, green and black 25 15
DESIGNS: Nos. 2529/31, Different portraits of Gallegos.

428 Emblem and Digital Eight

1984. 18th Pan-American Union of Engineering Associations Convention.
2532 **428** 2b.55 buff and blue . . . 60 15

429 "Nativity" (Maria Candelaria de Ramirez)

1984. Christmas.
2533 **429** 1b. multicoloured . . . 10 10

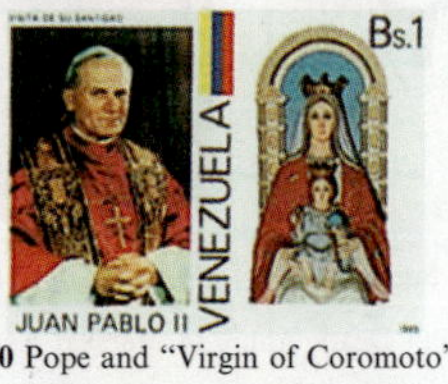

430 Pope and "Virgin of Coromoto"

1985. Visit of Pope John Paul II (1st issue).
2534 **430** 1b. multicoloured . . . 20 10
See also Nos. 2628/33.

431 Cross, Hand holding Candle and Agricultural Scene

1985. Bicentenary of Valle de la Pascua City.
2535 **431** 1b.50 multicoloured . . 45 10

432 St. Vincent de Paul

434 "Divine Shepherdess"

433 Text and "SELA"

1985. Centenary of Venezuelan Society of St. Vincent de Paul.
2536 **432** 1b. brown, yellow and red 15 10

1985. 10th Anniv of Latin American Economic System.
2537 **433** 4b. black and red . . . 70 35

1985. 2000th Birth Anniv of Virgin Mary. Multicoloured.
2538 1b. Type **434** 20 15
2539 1b. "Virgin of Chiquinquira" 20 15
2540 1b. "Virgin of Coromoto" 20 15
2541 1b. "Virgin of the Valley" 20 15
2542 1b. "Virgin of Perpetual Succour" 20 15
2543 1b. "Virgin of Peace" . . . 20 15
2544 1b. "Virgin of the Immaculate Conception" 20 15
2545 1b. "Virgin of Solitude" . . 20 15
2546 1b. "Virgin of Consolation" 20 15
2547 1b. "Virgin of the Snow" 20 15

435 Map and Emblem

1985. 25th Anniv of Organization of Petroleum Exporting Countries.
2548 **435** 6b. black, blue and light blue 95 35

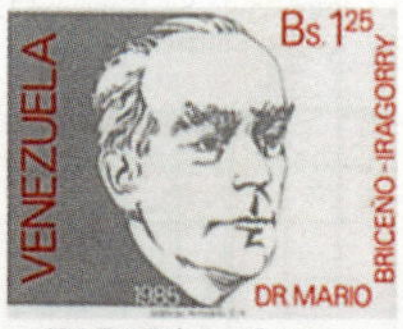

436 Dr Briceno-Iragorry

1985. 27th Death Anniv of Dr. Mario Briceno-Iragorry (politician).
2549 **436** 1b.25 silver and red . . 15 10

437 Museum

1985. 10th Anniv (1983) of Museum of Modern Art, Caracas.
2550 **437** 3b. multicoloured . . . 35 20

438 Emblem and Dove as Hand

1985. 40th Anniv of U.N.O.
2551 **438** 10b. blue and red . . . 1·40 60

439 Rainbow and Emblem

1985. International Youth Year.
2552 **439** 1b.50 multicoloured . . 20 10

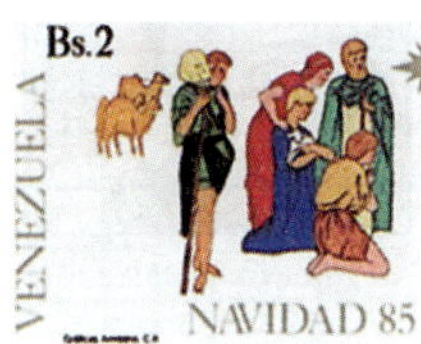

440 Shepherds and Camels

1985. Christmas. Multicoloured.
2553 2b. Type **440** 25 10
2554 2b. Holy Family and the Three Kings 25 10
Nos. 2553/4 were printed together, se-tenant, forming a composite design of the Nativity.

441 Petroleos de Venezuela Emblem

1985. 10th Anniv of National Petrochemical Industry.
2555 **441** 1b. blue and black . . . 15 10
2556 – 1b. multicoloured . . . 15 10
2557 – 2b. multicoloured . . . 25 15
2558 – 2b. multicoloured . . . 25 15
2559 – 3b. multicoloured . . . 35 20
2560 – 3b. multicoloured . . . 1·25 40
2561 – 4b. multicoloured . . . 50 25
2562 – 4b. multicoloured . . . 50 25
2563 – 5b. multicoloured . . . 60 30
2564 – 5b. multicoloured . . . 60 30
DESIGNS: No. 2556, Refinery and Isla S.A. emblem; 2557, Bariven oil terminal; 2558, Pequiven storage tank; 2559, Corpoven drilling site; 2560, Support vessel, oil rig and Maraven emblem; 2561, Meneven refinery; 2562, Intervep scientist; 2563, "Nodding Donkey"; 2564, Lagoven refinery.

442 Five Reales Silver Coin, 1873

443 Drago

1985. Coins with Portrait of Simon Bolivar. Multicoloured.
2565 2b. Type **442** 25 15
2566 2b.70 Five bolivares gold coin, 1886 . . . . . . 30 15
2567 3b. Birth bicentenary gold proof coin, 1983 . . . . 35 20

1985. 125th Birth Anniv (1984) of Dr. Luis Maria Drago (Argentine politician).
2568 **443** 2b.70 black, orge & red 30 15

444 Guayana City

1985. 25th Anniv of Guayana Development Corporation. Multicoloured.
2569 2b. Type **444** 25 15
2570 3b. Orinoco steel mill . . . 35 20
2571 5b. Raul Leoni-Guri dam 60 35

445 Signature

1985. Birth Bicentenary of Dr. Jose Maria Vargas (President, 1835–36). Multicoloured.
2572 3b. Type **445** 30 15
2573 3b. "Vargas" (Martin Tovar y Tovar) (vert) 30 15
2574 3b. Statue at Palace of Academies (vert) 30 15
2575 3b. "Exfilbo '86" National Stamp Exhibition emblem and flags 30 15
2576 3b. Facade of Vargas Hospital, Caracas 30 15
2577 3b. Title page of Vargas's "Manual and Compendium of Surgery" (vert) 30 15
2578 3b. "Vargas" (Alirio Palacios) (vert) 30 15
2579 3b. "Gesneria vargasii" (flower) 30 15
2580 3b. Portraits of Vargas and Bolivar on Sixth Venezuelan Congress of Medical Sciences medal 30 15
2581 3b. "Vargas" (anonymous) (vert) 30 15

446 Francisco Miranda

1986. Bicentenary (1981) of Francisco Miranda's Work for Latin American Liberation.
2583 **446** 1b.05 multicoloured . . 10 10

447 Children painting Wall

1986. Foundation for Educational Buildings and Equipment. Multicoloured.
2584 3b. Type **447** 50 15
2585 5b. Boys at woodwork class 70 15

448 Lorries and Processing Plant

1986. 45th Anniv of Venezuelan Dairy Industry Corporation. Multicoloured.
2586 2b.55 Type **448** 20 15
2587 2b.70 Map and milk containers 50 15
2588 3b.70 Processing plant Machiques, Edo Zulia (horiz) 60 15

449 Emblem

1986. 25th Anniv of VIASA (airline). Mult.
2589 3b. Type **449** 35 20
2590 3b. Douglas DC-8 in flight 35 20
2591 3b. Douglas DC-8 on ground 35 20
2592 3b. Boeing 747 flying out to sea 35 20
2593 3b. Tail fins of Douglas DC-10s 35 20
2594 3b.25 Hemispheres 35 20
2595 3b.25 Douglas DC-10 flying through cloud 35 20
2596 3b.25 Douglas DC-8 and DC-10 on ground 35 20
2597 3b.25 Douglas DC-9 flying over mountains 35 20
2598 3b.25 Manned flight deck 35 20

450 Giant Armadillo

1986. Flora and Fauna. Dated "1983". Mult.
2599 70c. Type **450** 10 10
2600 85c. "Espeletia angustifolia" 10 10
2601 2b.70 Orinoco crocodile . . 45 10
2602 3b. Mountain rose 45 10

451 Romulo Betancourt

452 Library Entrance

1986. 5th Death Anniv of Romulo Betancourt (President, 1959–64). Each black, deep brown and brown.
2603 2b. Type **451** 20 10
2604 2b.70 Betancourt in armchair 20 10
2605 2b.70 Betancourt and inscription 20 10
2606 2b.70 Betancourt wearing sash 20 10
2607 2b.70 Betancourt working 20 10
2608 3b. As No. 2606 . . . . . 25 15
2609 3b. As No. 2607 . . . . . 25 15
2610 3b. As No. 2605 . . . . . 25 15
2611 3b. Type **451** 25 15
2612 3b. As No. 2604 . . . . . 25 15

1986. 40th Anniv of Re-opening of Zulia University. Each grey, black and blue.
2624 2b.70 Type **452** 20 10
2625 2b.70 University building . . 20 10

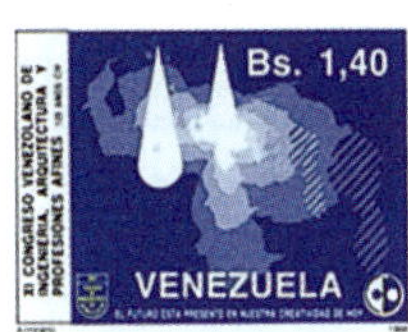

453 Map and Droplets

1986. 11th Venezuelan Engineers, Architects and Affiliated Professions Congress.
2626 **453** 1b.40 blue, black & yell 25 15
2627 1b.55 multicoloured . . 25 15

454 Pope and Andes

1986. Visit of Pope John Paul II (1985) (2nd issue). Multicoloured.
2628 1b. Type **454** 10 10
2629 1b. Pope and Maracaibo bridge 15 10
2630 3b. Pope kissing ground . . 25 15
2631 3b. Pope and "Virgin of Coromoto" 25 15
2632 4b. Pope holding crucifix, Caracas 60 15
2633 5b.25 Pope and waterfall . . 80 20

455 "United Families" (Vianny Hernandez)

1986. 20th Anniv of Childrens' Paintings. Multicoloured.
2634 2b.55 Type **455** 20 10
2635 2b.55 "Love and Peace" (Yuraima L. Jimenez) . . 20 10
2636 2b.55 "Woodland Animals" (Maria Valentina Arias) 20 10
2637 2b.55 "Noah's Ark" (Andreina Acero) 20 10
2638 2b.55 "House on Hillside" (Yenelsa) 20 10
2639 2b.70 "Flowers on Table" (Yenny Jimenez) 20 10
2640 2b.70 "Peace Lover" (Ramon Briceno) 20 10
2641 2b.70 "Children for World Peace" (Blanca Yesenia Hernandez) 20 10
2642 2b.70 "Lighthouse and Cable Railway" (Julio V. Hernandez) 20 10
2643 2b.70 "Flowers of a Thousand Colours" (with butterfly) (Maryolin Rodriguez Ortega) 20 10

456 Three Kings

1986. Christmas. Crib figures modelled by Eliecer Alvarez. Multicoloured.
2644 2b. Type **456** 15 10
2645 2b. Nativity 15 10
Nos. 2644/5 were printed together, se-tenant, forming a composite design.

457 Treating Accident Victim

1986. 17th Anniv of Caracas City Police. Multicoloured.
2646 2b.70 Type **457** 20 10
2647 2b.70 On duty at sporting event 20 10
2648 2b.70 Computer identification bar code . . 20 10
2649 2b.70 Cadets on parade . . 20 10
2650 2b.70 Motor cycle police . . 20 10

458 Prehispanic Musical Instrument

1987. Native Art. Multicoloured.
2651 2b. Type **458** 15 10
2652 2b. Woven fabric 15 10
2653 3b. Prehispanic ceramic bottle 25 15
2654 3b. Basket design 25 15

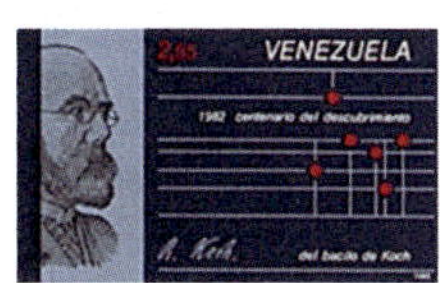

459 Robert Koch (discoverer) and Bacillus Symbol

1987. Centenary (1982) of Discovery of Tubercle Bacillus.
2655 **459** 2b.55 multicoloured . . 20 10

460 "Entry of Jesus into Jerusalem" (Antonio Herrera Toro)

1987. Holy Week. Multicoloured.
2656 2b. Type **460** 15 10
2657 2b. "Christ at the Pillar" (statue, Jose Francisco Rodriguez) 15 10
2658 2b. "Jesus of Nazareth" (wood carving, School of Seville) 15 10
2659 2b. "Descent from the Cross" (Jose Rivadefrecha, El Campeche) 15 10
2660 2b. "Virgin of Solitude" (sculpture) 15 10

2661 2b.25 "The Last Supper" (Arturo Michelena) . . . 15 10
2662 2b.25 "Ecce Homo" (sculpture) 15 10
2663 2b.25 "The Crucifixion" (sculpture, Gregorio de Leon Quintana) 15 10
2664 2b.25 "Holy Sepulchre" (sculpture, Sebastian de Ochoa Montes) 15 10
2665 2b.25 "The Resurrection" (attr. Peter Paul Rubens) 15 10

461 "Bolivar and Bello"(Marisol Escobar)

1987. World Neurochemical Congress. Mult.
2666 3b. Type **461** 25 15
2667 4b.25 Retinal cells 30 15

462 Barquisimeto Hilton Hotel

1987. Tourism Development. Multicoloured.
2668 6b. Type **462** 60 15
2669 6b. Lake Hotel Intercontinental, Maracaibo 60 15
2670 6b. Macuto Sheraton Hotel, Caraballeda 60 15
2671 6b. Melia Caribe Hotel, Caraballeda 60 15
2672 6b. Melia Hotel, Puerto la Cruz 70 20
2673 6b.50 Pool, Barquisimeto Hilton Hotel 60 15
2674 6b.50 Lake Hotel Intercontinental, Maracaibo, at night . . . 60 15
2675 6b.50 Macuto Sheraton Hotel, Caraballeda, and marina 70 20
2676 6b.50 Melia Caribe Hotel, Caraballeda (different) . . . 60 15
2677 6b.50 Melia Hotel, Puerto la Cruz (different) 70 20

463 Amazon Federal Terrritory Map and Ship's Bow

1987. 35th Anniv of National Canals Institute. Multicoloured.
2678 2b. Type **463** 10 10
2679 4b.25 Map of River Orinoco and buoy 25 15

464 Music School, Caracas

1987. Birth Centenary of Vicente Emilio Sojo (composer). Each deep brown and brown.
2680 2b. Type **464** 15 10
2681 4b. Conducting choir . . . 25 15
2682 5b. Score of "Hymn to Bolivar" 30 15
2683 6b. Standing beside blackboard 40 20
2684 7b. Sojo and signature . . . 50 25

465 "Simon Bolivar, Academician" (Roca Rey)

1987. 20th Anniv of Simon Bolivar University. Multicoloured.
2685 2b. Type **465** 10 10
2686 3b. "Solar Delta" (sculpture, Alejandro Otero) 15 10
2687 4b. Rector's residence . . . 20 10
2688 5b. Laser beam 25 15
2689 6b. Owl sculpture 30 15

466 Motor Vehicles

1987. 10th Anniv of Ministry of Transport and Communications. Multicoloured.
2690 2b. Type **466** 10 10
2691 2b. Bulk carrier and crane 40 15
2692 2b. Local electric train . . . 30 15
2693 2b. Envelopes and telegraph key 10 10
2694 2b. Transmission masts and globe 10 10
2695 2b.25 Motorway interchange system 10 10
2696 2b.25 Boeing 737 airliner . . 35 20
2697 2b.25 Mainline diesel train 35 20
2698 2b.25 Dish aerial 10 10
2699 2b.25 Globe and communications satellite 10 10

Nos. 2690/9 were printed together, se-tenant, each horizontal pair forming a composite design.

467 Administration Building, Caracas

1987. 70th Anniv of Venezuelan Navigation Company. Multicoloured.
2700 2b. Type **467** 10 10
2701 2b. Containers being loaded 10 10
2702 3b. Company emblem on ship's funnel 15 10
2703 3b. Ship's engine-room . . . 15 10
2704 4b. "Zulia" (freighter) at sea 75 20
2705 4b. "Guarico" (freighter) off Venezuelan coast 75 20
2706 5b. "Cerro Bolivar" (bulk carrier) 75 20
2707 5b. Ship's bridge 25 15
2708 6b. Map 30 15
2709 6b. Containers being loaded onto Ro-Ro ferry 30 15

468 Air-sea Rescue

1987. 50th Anniv of National Guard. Mult.
2710 2b. Type **468** 50 20
2711 2b. Traffic patrol 10 10
2712 2b. Guard on horseback . . 10 10
2713 2b. Guard with children . . 10 10
2714 2b. Armed guard on industrial site 10 10
2715 4b. As No. 2714 . . . . . 20 10
2716 4b. As No. 2713 . . . . . 20 10
2717 4b. As No. 2712 . . . . . 20 10
2718 4b. As No. 2711 . . . . . 20 10
2719 4b. Type **468** 80 30

469 "Departure from Puerto Palos" (detail, Jacobo Borges)

1987. 500th Anniv (1992) of Discovery of America by Columbus. Multicoloured.
2720 2b. Type **469** 10 10
2721 7b. "Discovery of America" (Tito Salas) 55 15
2722 11b.50 "Fr. de las Casas, Protector of the Indians" (detail, Tito Salas) 85 25
2723 12b. "Trade in Venezuela during the Time of the Conquest" (detail, Tito Salas) . . . . 1·40 70
2724 12b.50 "Rout of Guaicaipuro" (Jacobo Borges) 90 25

470 "Annunciation" (Juan Pedro Lopez)

1987. Christmas. Multicoloured.
2725 2b. Type **470** 10 10
2726 3b. "Nativity" (Jose Francisco Rodriguez) . . 15 10
2727 5b.50 "Adoration of the Kings" (anon) 30 15
2728 6b. "Flight into Egypt" (Juan Pedro Lopez) . . . 30 15

471 Steel Plant Building

1987. 25th Anniv of Steel Production by National SIDOR Mills.
2729 **471** 2b. multicoloured . . . 10 10
2730 – 2b. multicoloured . . . 10 10
2731 – 6b. multicoloured . . . 30 15
2732 – 6b. multicoloured . . . 30 15
2733 – 7b. multicoloured . . . 30 15
2734 – 7b. multicoloured . . . 30 15
2735 – 11b.50 multicoloured . . 75 25
2736 – 11b.50 multicoloured . . 75 25
2737 – 12b. black 80 25
2738 – 12b. multicoloured . . . 80 25

DESIGNS: No. 2730, Rolling strip; 2731, Walkways and towers of plant; 2732, Drawing steel bars; 2733, Walkway, towers and buildings; 2734, Slab mill; 2735, Building and towers; 2736, Steel bar production; 2737, Company emblem; 2738, Anniversary emblem.

Nos. 2729/38 were printed together, se-tenant, Nos. 2729, 2731, 2733 and 2735 forming a composite design of the SIDOR steel plant.

472 Flags

1987. 1st Meeting of Eight Latin-American Presidents of Contadora and Lima Groups, Acapulco.
2739 **472** 6b. multicoloured . . . 30 15

473 Plastics

1987. 10th Anniv of Petro-Chemical Company of Venezuela. Multicoloured.
2740 2b. Type **473** 10 10
2741 6b. Formulae (oil refining) 30 15
2742 7b. Leaves (fertilizers) . . . 30 15
2743 11b.50 Pipes (installations) 1·00 25
2744 12b. Expansion . . . . . . 1·10 25

474 St. John Bosco and People on Map

1987. Birth Centenary of St. John Bosco (founder of Salesian Brothers). Multicoloured.
2745 2b. Type **474** 10 10
2746 3b. National Temple, Caracas 15 10
2747 4b. Vocational training . . . 15 10
2748 5b. Church of Maria Auxiliadora 45 10
2749 6b. Missionary work 50 15

475 Emblem

1988. 29th Governors' Meeting of Inter-American Development Bank.
2750 **475** 11b.50 multicoloured . . 60 30

476 Bank Branch

1988. 30th Anniv of Banco Republica. Mult.
2751 2b. Type **476** 10 10
2752 2b. Pottery (small business finance) 10 10
2753 2b. Factory and security guards (industrial finance) 10 10
2754 2b. Laboratory workers (technology finance) . . . 10 10
2755 2b. Quay-side scene (exports and imports) 10 10
2756 6b. Farm workers (agricultural finance) . . . 35 15
2757 6b. Fishing boat (fisheries finance) 45 15
2758 6b. Milk production (livestock development) 35 15
2759 6b. Building site (construction finance) . . 35 15
2760 6b. Tourist bus (tourism development) 35 15

477 "Mother and Children" and Emblems

1988. Rotary International Anti-polio Campaign Victory Day.
2761 **477** 11b.50 multicoloured . . 90 35

478 Carlos Eduardo Frias (publicist)

1989. 50th Anniv of Publicity Industry. Mult.
2762 4b. Three profiles of Frias 30 15
2763 10b. Type **478** 60 30

479 Smelter

1988. 10th Anniv of Venalum (aluminium company).
2764 **479** 2b. multicoloured . . . 10 10
2765 – 6b. black 30 15
2766 – 7b. multicoloured . . . 55 15
2767 – 11b.50 multicoloured . . 90 35
2768 – 12b. multicoloured . . . 90 35

DESIGNS: 6b. Plan of electrolytic cell; 7b. Aluminium pipes; 11b.50, Loading ship with aluminium for export; 12b. Workers playing football.

480 Red Siskins

1988. Endangered Birds. Multicoloured.
2769 2b. Type **480** 25 15
2770 6b. Scarlet ibis 80 35

2771 11b.50 Harpy eagle . . . . 1·50 55
2772 12b. Greater flamingoes . . 1·75 60
2773 12b.50 Helmeted curassow 2·00 65

481 Bolivar in Dress Uniform, 1828

1988. Army Day. Multicoloured.
2774 2b. Type **481** 10 10
2775 2b. Lieutenant in ceremonial uniform, 1988 . . . . . 10 10
2776 6b. Gen. Jose Antonio Paez in dress uniform, 1821 . . 30 15
2777 6b. Major-General in No. 1 dress, 1988 . . . . 30 15
2778 7b. Major-General, 1820 . . 55 15
2779 7b. Line infantryman, 1820 55 15
2780 11b.50 Brigadier-General, 1820 . . . . 85 30
2781 11b.50 Garrison infantryman, 1820 . . . . 85 30
2782 12b. Artilleryman, 1836 . . 85 30
2783 12b. Light cavalryman, 1820 85 30

482 Urdaneta (after Salas)

1988. Birth Bicentenary of General Rafael Urdaneta. Multicoloured.
2784 2b. Sword and scabbard . . 10 10
2785 4b.75 "Wedding of the General" (Tito Salas) . . 20 10
2786 6b. Type **482** 30 15
2787 7b. "Siege of Valencia" (Tito Salas) 60 15
2788 12b. "Retreat from San Carlos" (Tito Salas) . . . 90 35

483 Marino (after Martin Tovar y Tovar)

1988. Birth Bicentenary of General Santiago Marino.
2789 **483** 4b.75 multicoloured . . 20 10

484 Games Emblem

1988. Olympic Games, Seoul.
2790 **484** 12b. multicoloured . . . 85 30

485 "Virgin of Copacabana" (Bolivia)

1988. Marian Year. Multicoloured.
2791 4b.75 Type **485** 25 15
2792 4b.75 "Virgin of Chiquinquira" (Colombia) 25 15
2793 4b.75 "Virgin of Coromoto" (Venezuela) 25 15
2794 4b.75 "Virgin of the Cloud" (Ecuador) 25 15
2795 4b.75 "Virgin of Antigua" (Panama) 25 15
2796 6b. "Virgin of Evangelisation" (Peru) . . 30 15
2797 6b. "Virgin of Lujan" (Argentina) 30 15
2798 6b. "Virgin of Altagracia" (Dominican Republic) . . 30 15
2799 6b. "Virgin of Aparecida" (Brazil) 30 15
2800 6b. "Virgin of Guadelupe" (Mexico) 30 15

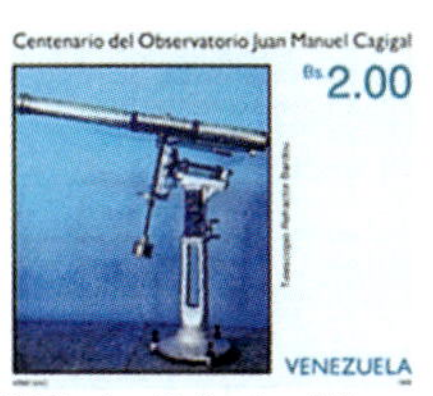

486 Bardou Refracting Telescope

1988. Centenary of Juan Manuel Cagigal Observatory. Multicoloured.
2801 2b. Type **486** 20 10
2802 4b.75 Universal "AUZ-27" theodolite 25 15
2803 6b. Bust of Cagigal 30 15
2804 11b.50 Boulton Cupola and night sky over Caracas in September 85 30
2805 12b. Satellite photographing Hurricane Allen 90 35

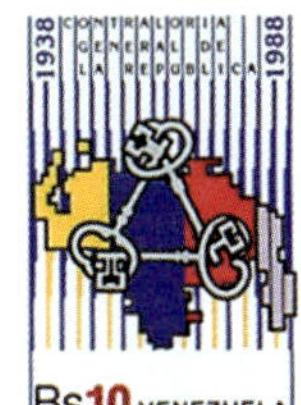

487 Keys **488** Commemorative Medal

1988. 50th Anniv of Controller-General's Office.
2806 **487** 10b. multicoloured . . . 45 25

1988. Cent of National Historical Museum. Mult.
2807 6b. Type **488** 30 15
2808 6b.50 Juan Pablo Rojas Paul (founder) (after Cristobal Rojas) 30 15

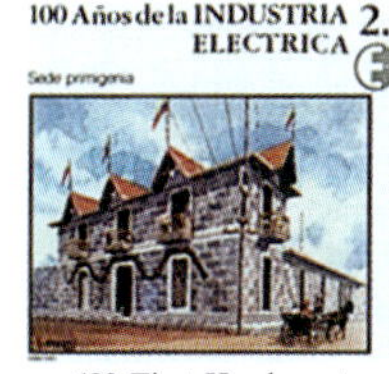

489 First Headquarters

1988. Centenary of Electricity Industry. Mult.
2809 2b. Type **489** 10 10
2810 4b.75 "Electrical Plant, 1888" (Jaime Carrillo) . . 20 15
2811 10b. Plaza Bolivar, 1888 . . 70 25
2812 11b.50 Baralt Theatre, 1888 90 30
2813 12b.50 Ramon Laguna Central Thermo-electricity Station 90 30

490 "Nativity" (Tito Salas, left-hand detail)

1988. Christmas. Multicoloured.
2814 4b. Type **490** 20 10
2815 6b. "Christ Child" (anonymous) 30 15
2816 15b. "Nativity" (Salas, right-hand detail) . . . . 1·00 35
Nos. 2814 and 2816 form a composite design.

491 "Bolivar and Ricardo" (John de Pool)

1989. "The Liberator at Curacao". Multicoloured.
2817 10b. Type **491** 60 15
2818 10b. "The Octagon" (John de Pool) 60 15
2819 11b. "Doctor Mordechay Ricardo" 75 20
Nos. 2817/19 were printed together, se-tenant, Nos. 2817/18 forming a composite design.

492 Cardinal Quintero (Archbishop of Caracas, 1960–80)

1989. 25th Anniv of Convention with Holy See. Multicoloured.
2820 4b. Type **492** 15 10
2821 4b. Dr. Raul Leoni (President, 1964–69) . . . 15 10
2822 12b. Arms of Luciano Storero (Papal Nuncio) 70 20
2823 12b. Arms of Cardinal Lebrun (Archbishop of Caracas) 70 20
2824 16b. Pope Paul VI 90 25

493 "Cacao Harvest" (Tito Salas)

1989. Centenary of Bank of Venezuela. Mult.
2825 4b. Type **493** 15 10
2826 4b. "Teaching Sowing Time of Coffee" (Tito Salas) . . 15 10
2827 4b. Head Office, Caracas . . 15 10
2828 4b. Archive of the Liberator, Caracas 15 10
2829 4b. Tree-planting programme 15 10
2830 4b. Family planting tree . . 15 10
2831 8b. Left-hand side of 50b. banknote 25 15
2832 8b. Right-hand side of 50b. banknote 25 15
2833 8b. Portrait of Bolivar on left-hand side of 500b. banknote 25 15
2834 8b. Right-hand side of 500b. banknote 25 15
Nos. 2825/34 were printed together, se-tenant, Nos. 2831/2 and 2833/4 forming composite designs.

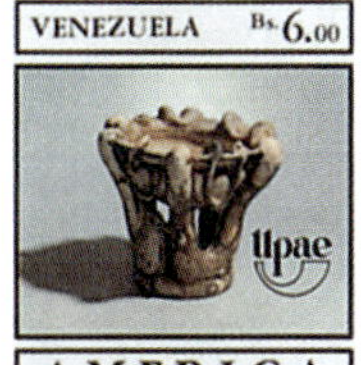

494 Dish

1989. America. Pre-Columbian Artefacts. Mult.
2835 6b. Type **494** 20 10
2836 24b. Figure . . . . 2·00 1·00

495 Shepherds and Sheep

1989. Christmas. Multicoloured.
2837 5b. As Type **495** but inscr at top 10 10
2838 5b. Type **495** 10 10
2839 6b. Angel and shepherds (inscr at top) 15 10
2840 6b. As No. 2839 but inscr at bottom 15 10
2841 6b. Nativity (inscr at top) 15 10
2842 6b. As No. 2841 but inscr at bottom 15 10
2843 12b. Shepherds (inscr at top) 70 15
2844 12b. As No. 2843 but inscr at bottom 70 15
2845 15b. Adoration of the Magi (inscr at top) 85 15
2846 15b. As No. 2845 but inscr at bottom 85 45
Nos. 2837/46 were printed together, each horizontal strip forming a composite design.

496 Araguaney Tree and State Arms

1990. 20th Anniv of Bank of Venezuela Foundation. Multicoloured.
2847 10b. Type **496** 20 10
2848 10b. Silk-cotton tree and Federal District arms . . 20 10
2849 10b. "Myrospermum frutescens" and Anzoategui State arms . . 20 10
2850 10b. "Pithecellobium saman" and Aragua State arms 20 10
2851 10b. West Indian cedar and Barinas State arms . . . 20 10
2852 10b. "Dipteryx punctata" and Bolivar State arms . . 20 10
2853 10b. Pink trumpet tree and Cojedes State arms . . . 20 10
2854 10b. "Prosopis juliflora" and Falcon State arms 20 10
2855 10b. "Copernicia tectorum" and Guarico State arms 20 10
2856 10b. Mountain immortelle and Merida State arms . . 20 10
2857 10b. "Brawnea leucantha" and Miranda State arms 20 10
2858 10b. "Mauritia flexuosa" and Monagas State arms 20 10
2859 10b. Mahogany and Portuguesa State arms . . 20 10
2860 10b. "Platymiscium diadelphum" and Sucre State arms 20 10
2861 10b. "Prumnopitys montana de Laub" and Tachira State arms 20 10
2862 10b. "Roystonea venezuelana" and Yaracuy State arms . . . 20 10
2863 10b. Coconut palm and Zulia State arms 20 10
2864 10b. "Hevea benthamiana" and Amazonas Federal Territory arms 20 10
2865 40b. "Licania pyrofolia" and Apure State arms . . 1·60 85
2866 40b. "Malpighia glabra" and Lara State arms . . . 1·60 85
2867 40b. "Erythrina fusca" and Trujillo State arms . . . 1·60 85
2868 50b. "Sterculia apetala" and Carabobo State arms . . 2·10 1·00
2869 50b. "Lignum vitae" and Nueva Esparta State arms 2·10 1·00
2870 50b. Mangrove and Amacuro Federal Territory arms . . . . . 2·10 1·00

497 Dr. Francisco Ochoa (founder)

1990. Centenary of Zulia University.
2871 **497** 10b. black and blue . . 20 10
2872 – 10b. black and blue . . 20 10
2873 – 15b. multicoloured . . . 60 15
2874 – 15b. multicoloured . . . 60 15
2875 – 20b. multicoloured . . . 85 25
DESIGNS: No. 2872, Dr. Jesus E. Lossada (Rector, 1946–47); 2873, Research into acid soils; 2874, Petroleum research; 2875, Transplant surgery.

498 Santa Capilla, 1943

1990. 50th Anniv of Central Bank. Multicoloured.
2876 10b. Type **498** 20 10
2877 10b. Headquarters, 1967 . . 20 10
2878 10b. Left half of 1940 500b. note 20 10
2879 10b. Right half of 1940 500b. note 20 10
2880 10b. "Sun of Peru" decoration, 1825 . . . . 20 10
2881 10b. Medals 20 10
2882 15b. Peruvian sword, 1825 60 15
2883 15b. Cross, Bucaramanga, 1830 . . . . 60 15

2884 40b. Medallion of George Washington, 1826 . . . . 1·60 85
2885 50b. Gen. O'Leary (enamel portrait) . . . . 2·10 1·00

Nos. 2876/85 were printed together, se-tenant, Nos. 2878/9 forming a composite design.

500 "St. Joseph and the Child" (Juan Pedro Lopez)

1990. Christmas. Multicoloured.
2887 10b. Type **500** 20 10
2888 10b. "Nativity" (Juan Pedro Lopez) 20 10
2889 10b. "Return from Egypt" (Matheo Moreno) 20 10
2890 20b. "Holy Family" (anon) 85 25
2891 20b. "Nativity" (Juan Pedro Lopez) (different) 85 25

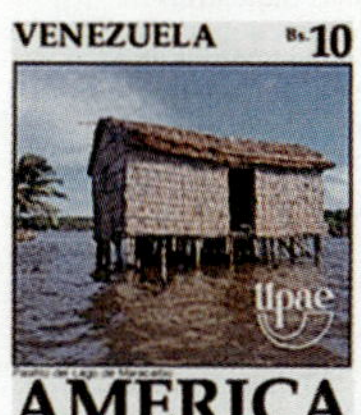

501 Lake House, Maracaibo

1990. America. The Natural World. Mult.
2892 10b. Type **501** 20 10
2893 40b. East Venezuelan shore 1·90 80

502 Globe and "30"

1990. 30th Anniv of O.P.E.C. Multicoloured.
2894 10b. Type **502** 20 10
2895 10b. O.P.E.C. emblem . . . 20 10
2896 20b. Anniversary emblem 85 25
2897 30b. O.P.E.C. emblem and dates . . . . 1·25 60
2898 40b. Members' flags around O.P.E.C. emblem . . . . 1·60 85

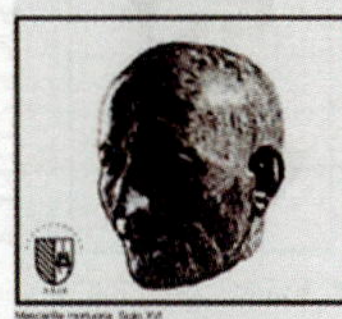

503 Death Mask

1991. 500th Birth Anniv of St. Ignatius de Loyola (founder of Society of Jesus). Multicoloured
2899 12b. Type **503** 25 15
2900 12b. St. Ignatius de Loyola College, Caracas 25 15
2901 40b. Silver statue of Loyola by Francisco de Vergara 1·90 75
2902 50b. "Our Lady of Montserrat" (wooden statue) . . . . 2·40 95

504 Elisa Elvira Zuloaga (painter and engraver)

1991. 50th Anniv of American–Venezuelan Cultural Centre. Designs showing Centre directors.
2903 **504** 12b. green and black . . 25 15
2904 – 12b. violet and black . . 25 15
2905 – 12b. red and black . . 25 15
2906 – 40b. blue and black . . 1·90 80
2907 – 50b. brown and black . . 2·40 80

DESIGNS: No. 2904, Gloria Stolk (writer); 2905, Caroline Lloyd (composer); 2906, Jules Waldman (linguist and journalist); 2907, William Coles (entrepreneur).

505 "Acineta alticola"

1991. Orchids. Multicoloured.
2908 12b. Type **505** 50 15
2909 12b. "Brassavola nodosa" 50 15
2910 12b. "Brachionidium brevicaudatum" 50 15
2911 12b. "Bifrenaria maguirei" 50 15
2912 12b. "Odontoglossum spectatissimum" 50 15
2913 12b. "Catasetum macrocarpum" 50 15
2914 40b. "Mendocella jorisiana" 1·25 65
2915 40b. "Cochleanthes discolor" . . . . 1·25 65
2916 50b. "Maxillaria splendens" 1·50 75
2917 50b. "Pleurothallis dunstervillei" . . . . . . 1·50 75

506 Voters at Ballot Box

1991. 50th Anniv of Democratic Action Party.
2919 **506** 12b. multicoloured . . . 25 15
2920 – 12b. multicoloured . . . 25 15
2921 – 12b. multicoloured . . . 25 15
2922 – 12b. black and blue . . 25 10

DESIGNS: No. 2920, Agrarian reform; 2921, Education; 2922, Nationalization of petroleum industry.

507 Rodrigues Suarez and Terepaima Chieftain

1991. America. Voyages of Discovery. Showing paintings by Pedro Centeno. Multicoloured.
2923 12b. Type **507** 25 15
2924 40b. Paramaconi chieftain and Garcia Gonzalez . . 1·50 80

508 Family in House

1991. 25th Anniv of Children's Foundation. Multicoloured.
2925 12b. Type **508** 45 10
2926 12b. Children's playground 45 10
2927 12b. Fairground 45 10
2928 12b. Mother and daughter 45 10
2929 12b. Boy in hospital 45 10
2930 12b. Children and tree . . . 45 10
2931 40b. Girls at home . . . . 1·40 65
2932 40b. Children in classroom 1·40 65
2933 50b. Children acting in play 1·60 75
2934 50b. Children playing ring-a-ring of roses . . . . . . 1·60 75

509 "Stable" (Barbaro Rivas)

1991. Christmas. Multicoloured.
2935 10b. Type **509** 15 10
2936 12b. "Nativity" (Elsa Morales) 45 10
2937 20b. "Nativity" (model, Glenda Mendoza) 60 15
2938 25b. "Shepherds watching flock (Maritza Marin) . . 85 45
2939 30b. "Nativity" (Antonia Azuaje) . . . . 1·00 55

1991. Nos. 2613/15 surch **RESELLADO** and value.
2940 **347** 5b. on 25c. red 10 10
2941 5b. on 75c. mauve . . . 10 10
2942 10b. on 25c. red 15 10
2943 10b. on 75c. mauve . . . 15 10
2944 12b. on 50c. blue 20 10
2945 12b. on 75c. mauve . . . 20 10
2946 20b. on 50c. blue 65 15
2947 20b. on 75c. mauve . . . 65 35
2948 40b. on 50c. blue . . . . 1·75 65
2949 40b. on 75c. mauve . . . 1·75 65
2950 50b. on 50c. blue . . . . 1·90 85
2951 50b. on 75c. mauve . . . 1·90 85

512 Columbus's Arms

1991. 500th Anniv (1992) of Discovery of America by Columbus.
2953 **512** 12b. multicoloured . . . 45 10
2954 – 12b. black, blue & orange 60 20
2955 – 12b. multicoloured . . . 45 10
2956 – 40b. black, brown & orge . . . . 1·10 35
2957 – 50b. black and orange 1·60 40

DESIGNS: No. 2954, "Santa Maria"; 2955, Juan de la Cosa's map; 2956, Sighting land; 2957, Columbus before King Ferdinand and Queen Isabella the Catholic.

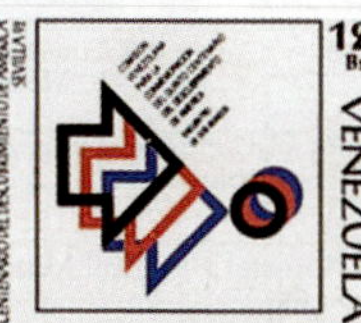

513 Anniversary Emblem

1992. "Expo 92" World's Fair, Seville. 500th Anniv of Discovery of America by Columbus.
2958 **513** 12b. black, red and blue 45 10
2959 – 12b. multicoloured . . . 45 10
2960 – 12b. multicoloured . . . 45 10
2961 – 12b. multicoloured . . . 45 10
2962 – 12b. multicoloured . . . 50 20
2963 – 12b. multicoloured . . . 45 10
2964 – 40b. multicoloured . . . 1·25 60
2965 – 40b. multicoloured . . . 1·25 60
2966 – 50b. multicoloured . . . 1·60 65
2967 – 50b. black and brown . . 1·60 65

DESIGNS: No. 2959, Venezuelan pavilion at "Expo 92"; 2960, Landmarks and map of southern Spain; 2961, Columbus; 2962, "Encounters"; 2963, "0x500 America"; 2964, "Imago-Mundi"; 2965, "The Grand Voyage"; 2966, "Golden Beach"; 2967, Idols.

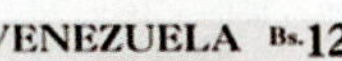

514 Red-footed Tortoise

1992. Tortoises. Multicoloured.
2969 12b. Type **514** 45 10
2970 12b. "Red-footed tortoise ("Geochelone carbonaria") (different) 45 10
2971 12b. South American river turtle ("Podocnemis expansa") (on land) . . . 45 10
2972 12b. South American river turtle (swimming) 45 10

515 Native Hut

1992. Electricity Distribution in the South.
2973 **515** 12b. multicoloured . . . 20 10
2974 – 12b. black and blue . . 20 10
2975 – 12b. multicoloured . . . 20 10
2976 – 40b. multicoloured . . . 90 35
2977 – 50b. multicoloured . . . 1·10 40

DESIGNS: No. 2974, Pylons; 2975, Horses galloping through water; 2976, Engineers working on pylon; 2977, Traditional baskets beside lake.

516 Figure holding Sheaf of Wheat

1992. "Offering to My Race" (Mateo Manaure). Designs showing various "mother" figures. Multicoloured.
2978 12b. Type **516** 20 10
2979 12b. Orange figure 20 10
2980 12b. Yellow figure 20 10
2981 12b. Pink figure 20 10
2982 40b. Brown figure . . . . . 1·00 35
2983 40b. Purple and orange figures . . . . 1·00 35
2984 50b. Three-quarter length figure . . . . 1·25 65
2985 50b. Head and shoulders . . 1·25 65

517 Catechism in Venezuela, 1975

518 "And on the Third Voyage" (Elio Caldera)

1992. Beatification of Josemaria Escriva (founder of Opus Dei).
2986 **517** 18b. multicoloured . . . 50 10
2987 – 18b. multicoloured . . . 50 10
2988 – 18b. multicoloired . . . 50 10
2989 – 18b. black and yellow . . 50 10
2990 – 18b. multicoloured . . . 50 10
2991 – 18b. multicoloured . . . 50 10
2992 – 60b. multicoloured . . . 1·60 65
2993 – 60b. multicoloured . . . 1·60 65
2994 – 75b. multicoloured . . . 1·90 75
2995 – 75b. multicoloured . . . 1·90 75

DESIGNS: No. 2987, Celebrating mass; 2988, Jose Escriva and Dolores Albas (parents); 2989, Text and autograph; 2990, With statuette of Madonna and Child; 2991, Commemorative medal; 2992, With Pope Paul VI, 1964; 2993, Writing at desk; Portrait; 2995, Portrait in St. Peter's Square, 17 May 1992.

1992. America. 500th Anniv of Discovery of America by Columbus. Multicoloured.
2996 18b. Type **518** 45 10
2997 60b. "Descontextura" (Juan Pablo Nascimiento) . . . 1·25 60

519 "Adoration of the Shepherds"

520 Simon Bolivar

1992. Christmas. Paintings by Lucio Rivas. Multicoloured.
2998 18b. Type **519** 45 10
2999 75b. "Adoration of the Magi" . . . . 1·40 75

1993. Portraits and Monuments.
3001 **520** 1b. silver 10 10
3002 2b. blue 10 10
3005 – 5b. red 10 10
3006 – 10b. purple 10 10
3007 – 20b. green 25 15
3008 – 25b. orange 25 15
3009 – 35b. green 35 20
3010 – 40b. blue 40 20
3011 – 50b. orange . . . . . . 1·10 55
3012 – 50b. mauve 50 25
3013 – 100b. brown . . . . . 2·25 1·10
3014 – 100b. blue 95 50
3015 – 200b. orange . . . . . 1·90 95

DESIGNS: 5b. National Pantheon, Caracas; 10b. War of Independence Memorial, Carabobo; 20b. General Jose Antonio de Paez (President, 1830–35, 1837–43 and 1861–63); 25b. Luisa Caceres de Arismendi; 35b. General Ezespiel Zamora (politician); 40b. Cristobal Mendoza (jurist and provincial governor); 50b. (3011) National Library; 50b. (3012) Jose Felix, Ribas (independence fighter); 100b. (3013), 200. Bolivar (different); 100b. (3014) General Manuel Piar.

521 "Cattleya percivaliana"

1993. Orchids. Multicoloured.
3016 20b. Type **521** 25 15
3017 20b. "Anguloa ruckeri" 25 15
3018 20b. "Chondrorhyncha flaveola" 25 15
3019 20b. "Stenia pallida" 25 15
3020 20b. "Zygosepalum lindeniae" 25 15
3021 20b. "Maxillaria triloris" 25 15
3022 80b. "Stanhopea wardii" 1·50 70
3023 80b. "Oncidium papilio" 1·50 70
3024 100b. "Oncidium hastilabium" 1·75 80
3025 100b. "Sobralia cattleya" 1·75 80

522 Woman

524 Smoker and Non-Smoker

523 Locomotive "Tucacas"

1993. 150th Anniv of Tovar Colony, Aragua State. Multicoloured.
3027 24b. Type **522** 30 15
3028 24b. Children 30 15
3029 24b. Catholic church 30 15
3030 24b. St. Martin of Tours (patron saint) 30 15
3031 24b. Vegetables and fruit 30 15
3032 24b. School 30 15
3033 80b. House of Augustin Codazzi (founder) 1·40 70
3034 80b. House of Alexander Benitz 1·40 70
3035 100b. Breidenbach mill 1·60 80
3036 100b. Procession of Jokili (carnival group) 1·60 80

1993. 19th Pan-American Railways Congress. Multicoloured.
3037 24b. Type **523** 60 15
3038 24b. Locomotive "Halcon" heading "El Encanto" on Las Mostazas bridge 60 15
3039 24b. Locomotive "Maracaibo" 60 15
3040 24b. Tender and carriages in Palo Grande station 60 15
3041 24b. Fiat diesel railcar, 1957 60 15
3042 24b. GP-9-L diesel locomotive, 1957 60 15
3043 80b. GP-15-L diesel locomotive, 1982 1·60 80
3044 80b. Underground train, Caracas 1·60 80
3045 100b. Electric multiple unit set (left half) 2·00 1·00
3046 100b. Electric multiple unit set (right half) 2·00 1·00
Nos. 3037/46 were issued together, se-tenant, Nos. 3039/40 and 3043/4 forming composite designs.

1993. World No Smoking Day. Each black, blue and red.
3047 24b. Type **524** 55 15
3048 80b. No smoking sign 1·25 70

525 Yellow-shouldered Amazon

526 Yanomami Boys

1993. America. Endangered Animals. Mult.
3049 24b. Type **525** 50 50
3050 80b. Scarlet macaw 2·25 2·25

1993. Amerindians (1st series). Multicoloured.
3051 1b. Type **526** 10 10
3052 1b. Yanomami woman preparing casabe 10 10
3053 40b. Panare children in Katyayinto ceremony 50 25
3054 40b. Taurepan man paddling canoe 50 25
3055 40b. Piaroa mother holding child 50 25
3056 40b. Panare man playing nose flute 50 25
3057 40b. Taurepan woman weaving 50 25
3058 40b. Masked Piaroa dancers in Warime ceremony 50 25
3059 100b. Hoti man with blowpipe 1·25 65
3060 100b. Hoti woman carrying child and fruit 1·25 65
See also Nos. 3170/9, 3266/75, 3392/3401 and 3568/77.

527 Joseph

1993. Christmas. (a) Each cream, brown and black
3062 24b. Type **527** 30 15
3063 24b. Madonna and Child 30 15
3064 24b. Shepherd girl, wise man and sheep 30 15
3065 80b. Wise man and shepherd girl 1·10 55
3066 100b. Wise man and shepherd girl 1·25 65

(b) Each cream, purple and black
3067 24b. Type **527** 30 15
3068 24b. As No. 3063 30 15
3069 24b. As No. 3064 30 15
3070 80b. As No. 3065 1·10 55
3071 100b. As No. 3066 1·25 65
Nos. 3062/71 were issued together, se-tenant, each horizontal strip forming a composite design of the Nativity.

528 "Chrysocycnis schlimii"

1994. Orchids. Multicoloured.
3072 35b. Type **528** 60 20
3073 35b. "Galeandra minax" 60 20
3074 35b. "Oncidium falcipetalum" 60 20
3075 35b. "Oncidium lanceanum" 60 20
3076 40b. "Sobralia violacea" 65 20
3077 40b. "Sobralia infundibuligera" 65 20
3078 80b. "Mendoncella burkei" 1·10 40
3079 80b. "Phragmipedium caudatum" 1·10 40
3080 100b. "Phragmipedium kaieteurum" 1·40 50
3081 200b. "Stanhopea grandiflora" 2·75 1·25

529 Federation Emblem

1994. 50th Anniv of Federation of Chambers of Industry and Commerce.
3083 – 35b. blue, gold and black 25 15
3084 – 35b. black and brown 25 15
3085 **529** 35b. blue and black 25 15
3086 80b. blue and black 90 30
3087 – 80b. black, brown and blue 90 30
3088 – 80b. blue, gold and black 90 30
DESIGNS: Nos. 3083, 3088, "50" on text; 3084, 3087, Luis Gonzalo Marturet (first Federation President).

530 State Arms

1994. Judicial Service.
3089 **530** 100b. multicoloured 1·10 40

531 "Nativity" (School of Jose Lorenzo de Alvarado)

1994. Christmas. Multicoloured.
3090 35b. Type **531** 25 15
3091 35b. "Nativity" 25 15
3092 35b. "Nativity" (School of Jose Lorenzo de Alvarado) 25 15
3093 35b. Holy Family (inscr "Adoracion de los Pastores") 25 15
3094 35b. "Nativity" (School of Tocuyo) 25 15
3095 80b. As No. 3094 90 30
3096 80b. Type **531** 90 30
3097 80b. As No. 3091 90 30
3098 80b. As No. 3092 90 30
3099 80b. As No. 3093 but inscr "El Nacimiento" 90 30

532 Sucre (anonymous portrait)

1995. Birth Bicentenary of Antonio Jose de Sucre (President of Bolivia, 1825–29). Multicoloured.
3100 25b. Type **532** 20 10
3101 25b. Mariana Carcelen y Larrea, Marquesa de Solanda (Sucre's wife) (after Juan Pinto Ortiz) 20 10
3102 35b. Equestrian statue of Sucre (Turini Verana), Cumana 25 15
3103 35b. Base of statue 25 15
3104 40b. "Battle of Pichincha" (top detail) (Victor Mideros Almeida) 30 15
3105 40b. "Battle of Pichincha" (bottom detail) 30 15
3106 80b. "Battle of Ayacucho" (left detail) (Antonio Herrera Toro) 90 30
3107 80b. "Battle of Ayacucho" (right detail) 90 30
3108 100b. "Capitulation of Ayacucho" (left detail) (Daniel Hernandez) 1·10 40
3109 100b. "Capitulation of Ayacucho" (right detail) 1·10 40
Nos. 3100/9 were issued together, se-tenant, the 35, 40, 80 and 100b. values forming four composite designs.

533 Short S.7 Skyvan Mail Plane

1995. America (1994). Postal Transport. Mult.
3111 35b. Mobile post office 25 15
3112 80b. Type **533** 1·10 55

534 St. John Bosco (founder) and Boy with Salesian

1995. Centenary of Salesian Brothers in Venezuela. Multicoloured.
3113 35b. Type **534** 25 15
3114 35b. Boy sitting in street and Virgin and Child 25 15
3115 35b. Men working machinery 25 15
3116 35b. Youths working on radio 25 15
3117 35b. Boys playing baseball 25 15
3118 35b. Youths playing basketball 25 15
3119 80b. Men planting saplings 90 30
3120 80b. Youth and boxes of produce 90 30
3121 100b. Salesian and Amerindian boys 1·10 40
3122 100b. Amerindian youth 1·10 40

535 Laboratory Technicians

1995. 50th Anniv of Christian Brothers' La Colina School, Caracas. Multicoloured.
3123 35b. As T **535** but country inscr at right 25 15
3124 35b. Young people camping (country inscr at left) 25 15
3125 35b. Youths playing football (country inscr at right) 25 15
3126 35b. Type **535** 25 15
3127 35b. As No. 3124 but country inscr at right 25 15
3128 35b. As No. 3125 but country inscr at left 25 15
3129 80b. School building (country inscr at left) 90 30
3130 80b. As No. 3129 but country inscr at right 90 30
3131 100b. Jean Baptiste de la Salle (founder of Order) (country inscr at right) 1·10 40
3132 100b. As No. 3131 but country inscr at left 1·10 40

536 "Maxillaria guareimensis"

1995. Orchids. Multicoloured.
3133 35b. Type **536** 50 15
3134 35b. "Paphinia lindeniana" 50 15
3135 35b. "Coryanthes biflora" 50 15
3136 35b. "Catasetum pileatum" 50 15
3137 35b. "Mormodes convolutum" 50 15
3138 35b. "Huntleya lucida" 50 15
3139 50b. "Catasetum longifolium" 70 20
3140 50b. "Anguloa clowesii" 70 20
3141 80b. "Maxillaria histrionica" 1·00 55
3142 80b. "Sobralia ruckeri" 1·00 55

537 Anniversary Emblem

1995. 25th Anniv of Andean Pact (international co-operation group).
3144 **537** 80b. multicoloured 60 30

538 People of Different Races

1995. 50th Anniv of U.N.O. Multicoloured.
3145 50b. Type **538** 40 20
3146 50b. U.N. flag 40 20
Nos. 3145/6 were issued together, se-tenant, forming a composite design.

539 Mother Maria

1995. Beatification of Mother Maria de San Jose. Multicoloured.

3147	35b. Type **539**	50	15
3148	35b. Pope John Paul II	50	15
3149	35b. Handing out books to girls	50	15
3150	35b. Embroidering	50	15
3151	35b. Statue of Virgin Mary and altar	50	15
3152	35b. Mother Maria in prayer before altar	50	15
3153	80b. Mother Maria and three nuns in hospital ward	85	30
3154	80b. Nun beside hospital beds	85	30
3155	100b. Nuns with poor children	1·25	65
3156	100b. Nun giving alms to beggar	1·25	65

Nos. 3147/56 were issued together, se-tenant, each horizontal pair forming a composite design.

540 Monagas

1995. Birth Bicentenary of Jose Gregorio Monagas (anti-slavery campaigner and President 1851–55). Multicoloured.

3157	50b. Type **540**	40	20
3158	50b. Freed slaves	40	20

Nos. 3157/8 were issued together, se-tenant, forming a composite design.

541 Chirino

1995. Bicentenary of Jose Chirino's Insurrection. Multicoloured.

3159	50b. Type **541**	40	20
3160	50b. Insurrectionists	40	20

Nos. 3159/60 were issued together, se-tenant, forming a composite design.

542 Red Cross Workers and Child

1995. Centenary of Venezuelan Red Cross. Multicoloured.

3161	35b. Type **542**	25	15
3162	35b. Volunteers carrying injured man on stretcher	25	15
3163	35b. Operating theatre	25	15
3164	80b. Carlos J. Bello Hospital	90	30
3165	100b. Red Cross flag	1·25	65

543 River

1995. America. Environmental Protection. Mult.

(a) With thin frame line over face value.

3166	35b. Type **543**	25	15
3167	80b. Hillside	90	30

(b) Without thin frame line over face value.

3168	35b. Type **543**	25	15
3169	80b. As No. 3167	1·00	30

544 Ye'kuana Chief

1995. Amerindians (2nd series). Multicoloured.

3170	25b. Type **544**	20	10
3171	25b. Ye'kuana woman making manioc cake	20	10
3172	35b. Guahibo musicians	25	15
3173	35b. Guahibo shaman treating boy	25	15
3174	50b. Uruak fisherman	70	30
3175	50b. Uruak woman cooking	40	20
3176	80b. Warao woman making thread	90	30
3177	80b. Warao couple transporting belongings in sailing canoe	90	30
3178	100b. Bari men hunting	1·00	40
3179	100b. Bari man making fire	1·00	40

545 Ricardo Zuloaga (pioneer)

1995. Centenary of Electricity in Caracas. Mult.

3181	35b. Type **545**	25	15
3182	35b. El Encantado Plant	25	15
3183	35b. Caracas sub-station	25	15
3184	35b. Electric tram	25	15
3185	35b. Streetlamps outside Congress building	25	15
3186	35b. Streetlamps, Plaza Bolivar	25	15
3187	80b. Engineer repairing streetlamp	90	30
3188	80b. Avila Cross	90	30
3189	100b. Teresa Carreno Cultural Centre	1·00	40
3190	100b. Ricardo Zuloaga power station	1·00	40

546 The Annunciation

1995. Christmas. Multicoloured.

3191	35b. Type **546**	15	15
3192	35b. Mary and Joseph turned away from the inn	25	15
3193	35b. Archangel Gabriel visits shepherds	25	15
3194	35b. Three wise men bearing gifts	25	15
3195	40b. Family gathering	30	15
3196	40b. Children on rollerskates	30	15
3197	40b. Women and girl preparing food	30	15
3198	40b. Woman and children preparing food	30	15
3199	100b. Mary and Joseph holding Child Jesus	1·10	40
3200	100b. Box of toys	1·10	40

Nos. 3191/3200 were issued together, se-tenant, Nos. 3195/6 and 3197/8 forming composite designs.

547 Arms

1995. 450th Anniv of El Tocuyo. Multicoloured.

3201	35b. Type **547**	25	15
3202	35b. Cutting sugar cane	25	15
3203	35b. Church of Our Lady of the Immaculate Conception	25	15
3204	35b. "Our Lady of the Immaculate Conception" (statue)	25	15
3205	35b. Ruins of Santo Domingo Temple	25	15
3206	35b. Cultural centre	25	15
3207	80b. Natural vegetation	90	30
3208	80b. Cactus	90	30
3209	100b. Sword dance	1·00	40
3210	100b. Man playing guitar	1·00	40

Nos. 3201/10 were issued together, se-tenant, Nos. 3209/10 forming a composite design.

548 Oil Tanker

1995. 20th Anniv of PDVSA National Fossil Fuels Association. Multicoloured.

3211	35b. Type **548**	25	15
3212	35b. Orimulsion storage tanks	25	15
3213	35b. Coal	25	15
3214	35b. Lorry carrying sacks	25	15
3215	35b. Petrol station	25	15
3216	35b. Gas storage cylinders	25	15
3217	80b. Drilling for oil	90	30
3218	80b. Refinery	90	30
3219	100b. Emblems ("Lagoven" at top)	1·00	40
3220	100b. Emblems ("bitor" at top)	1·00	40

549 Pope John Paul II with Children

1996. Papal Visit. Multicoloured.

3221	25b. Type **549**	20	10
3222	25b. Pope with young couple	20	10
3223	40b. Pope with family	30	15
3224	40b. Pope with elderly man	30	15
3225	50b. Pope with mother and son	35	20
3226	50b. Pope with patient	35	20
3227	60b. Pope with prisoner	70	25
3228	60b. Pope with workman	70	25
3229	100b. Pope giving speech to workers	1·00	40
3230	100b. Pope with priest and nuns	1·00	40

550 "Epidendrum fimbriatum"

1996. Orchids. Multicoloured.

3232	60b. Type **550**	45	25
3233	60b. "Myoxanthus reymondii"	45	25
3234	60b. "Catasetum pileatum"	45	25
3235	60b. "Ponthieva maculata"	45	25
3236	60b. "Maxillaria triloris"	45	25
3237	60b. "Scaphosepalum breve"	45	25
3238	60b. "Cleistes rosea"	45	25
3239	60b. "Maxillaria sophronitis"	45	25
3240	60b. "Catasetum discolor"	45	25
3241	60b. "Oncidium ampliatum"	45	25

551 National Olympic Committee Emblem

1996. Olympic Games, Atlanta. Multicoloured.

3243	130b. Type **551**	95	50
3244	130b. Swimming	95	50
3245	130b. Boxing	95	50
3246	130b. Cycling	95	50
3247	130b. Medal winners on podium	95	50

552 Emblem

1996. 25th Anniv of Liberator Simon Bolivar International Airport, Maiquetia, as Autonomous Company. Multicoloured.

3248	80b. Type **552**	60	30
3249	80b. Flight paths into airport	60	30
3250	80b. La Guaira Aerodrome, 1929	60	30
3251	80b. Maiquetia Airport, 1944	60	30
3252	80b. Liberator Simon Bolivar Airport, 1972	60	30
3253	80b. Airport interior by Carlos Cruz Diez	60	30
3254	80b. Control tower and airport police	60	30
3255	80b. Fire tender	60	30
3256	80b. Airplanes at terminal building	60	30
3257	80b. Boeing 747 airliner and terminal buildings	60	30

Nos. 3248/57 were issued together, se-tenant, Nos. 3256/7 forming a composite design.

553 Woman

1996. America. Traditional Costume. Multicoloured.

3258	60b. Type **553**	15	10
3259	130b. Man	35	20

554 As Child in Trujillo, 1913

1996. Birth Centenary (1997) of Dr. Mario Briceno-Iragorry (politician). Designs showing different periods of his life. Multicoloured.

3260	80b. Type **554**	20	10
3261	80b. Student at Merida University, 1919	20	10
3262	80b. Politician making speech, 1944	20	10
3263	80b. Writer, 1947	20	10
3264	80b. Historian of Caracas, 1952	20	10

555 Emblem

1996. 70th Anniv of Rotary International in Caracas.

3265	**555** 50b. multicoloured	15	10

556 Man planting Yucca

1996. Amerindians (3rd series). Multicoloured.

3266	80b. Type **556**	20	10
3267	80b. Child gathering fruits	20	10
3268	80b. Women harvesting reed-mace	20	10
3269	80b. Youth gathering bananas	20	10
3270	80b. Mother carrying child	20	10
3271	100b. Guajiros indians	25	15
3272	100b. Man carrying bundle	25	15
3273	100b. Man fishing with bow and arrow	25	15
3274	100b. Couple grinding maize	25	15
3275	100b. Weaver	25	15

558 Dr. Hernandez as a Boy

1996. 132nd Birth Anniv of Dr. Jose Hernandez (physician). Designs representing different aspects of his life. Multicoloured.

3278 60b. Type **558** 15 10
3279 60b. Student 15 10
3280 60b. Kneeling in prayer and statue of the Madonna . . 15 10
3281 60b. Dining and distributing food to the needy 15 10
3282 60b. Research scientist examining test-tube . . . 15 10
3283 60b. University professor teaching students 15 10
3284 60b. Administering to patient 15 10
3285 60b. Meeting room of Academy of Numbers . . 15 10
3286 60b. Portrait and statue of Hernandez and Vargas hospital 15 10
3287 60b. Dr. Jose Gregorio Hernandez hospital and statue 15 10

559 Child and Nativity figures

1996. Christmas. Multicoloured.

3289 60b. Type **559** 15 10
3290 60b. Guitar players and percussionist 15 10
3291 60b. Crowing cockerel and musicians 15 10
3292 60b. Traditional dancers . . 15 10
3293 60b. Drummers, maracas player and guitarist . . . 15 10
3294 80b. Woman and girl exchanging traditional food 20 10
3295 80b. Family meal 20 10
3296 80b. Child in hammock and gifts 20 10
3297 80b. Couple with child . . . 20 10
3298 80b. Mother kissing baby's foot 20 10

560 As Boy

561 Simon Bolivar (after Jose Maria Espinoza)

1997. Birth Centenary of Andres Eloy Blanco (writer and politician). Multicoloured.

3299 100b. Type **560** 25 10
3300 100b. Councillor for Caracas 25 10
3301 100b. With family 25 10
3302 100b. With two men 25 10
3303 100b. Politician 25 10
3304 100b. President of Constitutional Assembly 25 10
3305 100b. Poet and Juan Bimba (character from poem) . . 25 10
3306 100b. Chancellor of the Republic and Lincoln Memorial 25 10
3307 100b. Eloy Blanco and "Santa Maria" ("Canto a Espana") 25 10
3308 100b. "Pinto" and "Nina" and Don Quixote ("Canto a Espana") 25 10

Nos. 3299/3308 were issued together, se-tenant, Nos. 3307/8 forming a composite design.

1997.

3311 **561** 15b. green 10 10
3312 20b. orange 10 10
3313 40b. brown 10 10
3314 50b. red 15 10
3315 70b. purple 15 10
3316 90b. blue 20 10
3317 200b. blue 45 25
3318 300b. green 70 35
3319 400b. grey 95 50
3320 500b. drab . . . . . . 1·25 65
3321 600b. brown . . . . . . 1·40 70
3322 800b. brown . . . . . . 1·90 95
3323 900b. blue . . . . . . 2·40 1·10
3324 1000b. copper . . . . . 2·75 1·25
3325 2000b. green . . . . . 5·25 2·40

562 "Scuticaria steelei"

1997. Orchids. Multicoloured.

3330 165b. "Phragmipedium lindleyanum" 45 25
3331 165b. "Zygosepalum labiosum" 45 25
3332 165b. "Acacallis cyanea" . . 45 25
3333 165b. "Maxillaria camaridii" 45 25
3334 165b. Type **562** 45 25
3335 165b. "Aspasia variegata" . . 45 25
3336 165b. "Comparettia falcata" 45 25
3337 165b. "Scaphyglottis stellata" 45 25
3338 165b. "Maxillaria rufescens" 45 25
3339 165b. "Vanilla pompona" . . 45 25

563 Espana and Meeting of Conspirators

1997. Bicentenary of Independence Movement of Manuel Gual and Jose Maria Espana. Multicoloured.

3341 165b. Type **563** 40 20
3342 165b. Soldiers escorting Espana to his execution 40 20
3343 165b. Gual, conspirators and soldiers with bayonets 40 20
3344 165b. Gual in exile on Trinidad 40 20
3345 165b. Flag 40 20

Nos. 3341/5 were issued together, se-tenant, each horiz pair forming a composite design.

564 "The People boil"

1997. 30th Anniv of Tlatelolco Treaty (Latin American and Caribbean treaty banning nuclear weapons). Paintings by Alirio Rodriguez from his "Hiroshima" sequence. Multicoloured.

3346 140b. Type **564** 35 20
3347 140b. "An empty Epicentre where Once even a Whisper Sounded" (white and black disc) 35 20
3348 140b. "Darkness like the high Horizon" (red disc on black panel) 35 20
3349 140b. "My God! In the Shell, Emptiness" (red and black "shelves") . . . 35 20
3350 140b. "Devil. Perverse geometry" (yellow atomic model) 35 20
3351 140b. "At the Heart of the Area the Bareness of the Disaster" (four blue discs) 35 20
3352 140b. "Without Thought, only Grief in living Flesh" figure within atomic model) 35 20
3353 140b. "Thus in order to Reveal" (red panel) . . . 35 20
3354 140b. "Calvary of multiple Symbiosis" (drab atomic model) 35 20
3355 140b. "Released Energy which attempts to Silence the Scream" (screaming head with legs) 35 20

Distinguishing parts of the design are given in brackets to aid identification.

565 Rabbit watching Jaguar

1997. Children's Stories (1st series). "Uncle Jaguar and Uncle Rabbit". Multicoloured.

3356 55b. Type **565** 10 10
3357 55b. Rabbit listening to conversation between Jaguar and Anteater . . . 10 10
3358 55b. Jaguar catching Turtle 10 10
3359 55b. Rabbit going to help Turtle 10 10
3360 55b. Rabbit freeing Anteater from net 10 10
3361 55b. Anteater telling Jaguar that his vegetables have been stolen 10 10
3362 55b. Anteater and Rabbit looking at wasps' nest in tree 10 10
3363 55b. Rabbit releasing Turtle from Jaguar's bag and replacing him with wasps' nest 10 10
3364 55b. Jaguar returning from fruitless pursuit 10 10
3365 55b. Jaguar opening bag and being stung by wasps 10 10

A number and the relevant portion of the story is printed on the back of each stamp over the gum.

See also Nos. 3537/46.

566 Dog growling at Postman

1997. America. The Postman. Multicoloured.

3367 110b. Type **566** 25 15
3368 280b. Postman's moped punctured in rain 65 35

567 Signature of Juan Xavier Misares de Solorzano (first owner)

1997. Bicentenary of Quinta de Anauco (historic house). Multicoloured.

3369 110b. Type **567** 25 15
3370 110b. Principal facade . . . 25 15
3371 110b. Entrance passage . . 25 15
3372 110b. Inner courtyard . . . 25 15
3373 110b. Passageway to kitchen 25 15
3374 110b. Kitchen 25 15
3375 110b. Living quarters . . . 25 15
3376 110b. Coach house with fountain 25 15
3377 110b. Cart in stable 25 15
3378 110b. Water trough and stable 25 15

568 Jarwaharlal Nehru (first Prime Minister)

1997. 50th Anniv of Independence of India. Multicoloured.

3379 165b. Type **568** 40 20
3380 165b. Congress building, New Delhi 40 20
3381 165b. Ritual cleansing in River Ganges 40 20
3382 165b. Actress and film cameraman 40 20
3383 165b. "INSAT-1B" meteorological satellite orbiting Earth 40 20
3384 200b. Sardar Patel (politician) and flag . . . 45 25
3385 200b. Mahatma Gandhi . . 45 25
3386 200b. Rabindranath Tagore (poet and philosopher) . . 45 25
3387 200b. Musician playing traditional instrument . . 45 25
3388 200b. Woman at computer 45 25

Nos. 3379/88 were issued together, se-tenant, forming a composite design.

569 Von Stephan (after Anton Weber)

1997. Death Centenary of Heinrich von Stephan (founder of U.P.U.). Multicoloured.

3390 110b. Type **569** 25 15
3391 280b. U.P.U. monument, Berne 65 35

570 Ye'Kuana Basket

1997. Amerindians (4th series). Basketwork. Multicoloured.

3392 140b. Type **570** 35 20
3393 140b. Ye'Kuana basket with handle 35 20
3394 140b. Ye'Kuana lidded jar with bird decoration . . . 35 20
3395 140b. Panare round dish . . 35 20
3396 140b. Pemon baby carrier 35 20
3397 140b. Yanomani basket with strap 35 20
3398 140b. Ye'Kuana lidded jar 35 20
3399 140b. Ye'Kuana dish . . . 35 20
3400 140b. Panare oval dish . . . 35 20
3401 140b. Warao fluted basket 35 20

571 The Annunciation

1997. Christmas. Multicoloured.

3403 110b. Type **571** 25 15
3404 110b. Mary visits St. Isabel 25 15
3405 110b. Mary and Joseph arrive at Bethlehem . . . 25 15
3406 110b. The Nativity 25 15
3407 110b. Angel and shepherds 25 15
3408 110b. Adoration of the Shepherds 25 15
3409 110b. Wise Men following star 25 15
3410 110b. Wise Men offer gifts 25 15
3411 110b. Presentation in the Temple 25 15
3412 110b. Flight into Egypt . . 25 15

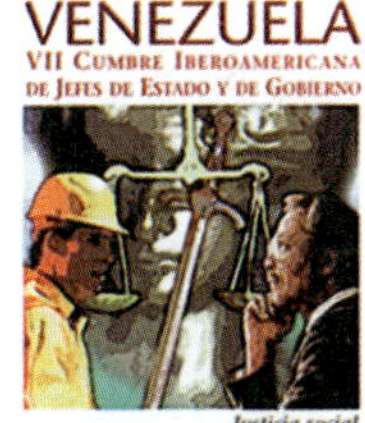

572 Workers and Scales of Justice (social justice)

1997. 7th Summit of Latin American Heads of State, Isla de Margarita. Multicoloured.

3413 165b. Type **572** 40 20
3414 165b. Voting box (open elections) 40 20
3415 165b. Summit emblem . . . 40 20
3416 165b. Broadcaster (true information) 40 20
3417 165b. Constitution and people (human rights) . . 40 20
3418 200b. As No. 3417 . . . . 45 25
3419 200b. As No. 3416 . . . . 45 25
3420 200b. As No. 3415 . . . . 45 25
3421 200b. As No. 3414 . . . . 45 25
3422 200b. As No. 3413 . . . . 45 25

573 Monastery Church, Puerta de Agua

1997. Centenary of Diocese of Zulia. Mult.
3423 110b. Type **573** 25 15
3424 110b. St. Anne's Church 25 15
3425 110b. Reliquary of the Virgin of the Rosary, Chiquinquira 25 15
3426 110b. Basilica of St. John of God, Chiquinquira 25 15
3427 110b. Santo Cristo de Aranza church 25 15
3428 110b. Maracaibo cathedral 25 15
3429 110b. Machiques cathedral 25 15
3430 110b. Arms of Archbishop Ovidio Perez Morales 25 15
3431 110b. Cabimas cathedral 25 15
3432 110b. Cathedral of El Vigia and San Carlos del Zulia 25 15

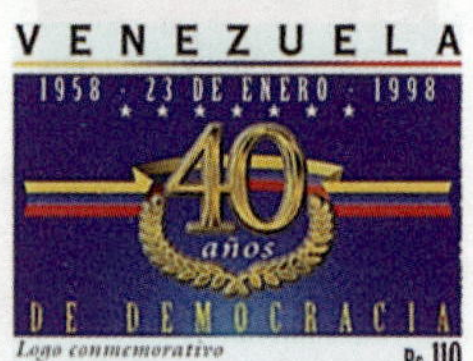

574 Jubilee Emblem

1998. "40 Years of Democracy". Multicoloured.
3433 110b. Type **574** 25 15
3434 110b. People voting 25 15
3435 110b. Child studying globe 25 15
3436 110b. Underground train 25 15
3437 110b. Man making speech (freedom of expression) 25 15
3438 110b. Senate and Constitution 25 15
3439 110b. Orchestra 25 15
3440 110b. Children and Scales of Justice 25 15
3441 110b. Brown bear and El Avila National Park (protection of environment) 25 15
3442 110b. Adult education 25 15

575 Fishermen

577 Helmeted Curassow

576 "Oncidium orthostates"

1998. 500th Anniv of Discovery of Margarita Island. Multicoloured.
3443 100b. Type **575** 25 20
3444 100b. Petronila Mata (freedom fighter) 25 20
3445 100b. Yellow-shouldered amazon 25 20
3446 200b. Angel Rock 45 25
3447 200b. Simon Bolivar 45 25
3448 200b. Pearl diver 45 25
3449 200b. General Santiago Marino 45 25
3450 200b. General Juan Bautista Arismendi 45 25
3451 265b. Christopher Columbus 60 30
3452 265b. "Our Lady the Virgin of the Valley" and church 60 30

Nos. 3443/52 were issued together, se-tenant, Nos. 3446 with 3451 and Nos. 3448/52 forming composite designs.

1998. Orchids. Multicoloured.
3454 185b. Type **576** 40 20
3455 185b. "Epidendrum praetervisum" 40 20
3456 185b. "Odontoglossum schilleranum" 40 20
3457 185b. "Bletia lansbergii" 40 20
3458 185b. "Caularthron bicornutum" 40 20
3459 185b. "Darwiniera bergoldii" 40 20
3460 185b. "Houlletia tigrina" 40 20
3461 185b. "Pleurothallis acuminata" 40 20
3462 185b. "Elleanthus lupulinus" 40 20
3463 185b. "Epidendrum ferrugineum" 40 20

1998. 60th Anniv of Henri Pittier National Park. Multicoloured.
3465 140b. Type **577** 30 15
3466 140b. Swallow tanager ("Tersina virdis") 30 15
3467 150b. Ornate hawk eagle ("Spizaetus ornatus") 30 15
3468 150b. Leaf frog ("Phyllomedusa trinitatis") 30 15
3469 200b. Lilac-tailed parrotlet ("Touit collaris") 45 25
3470 200b. Collared trogon ("Trogon collaris") 45 25
3471 200b. Emperor ("Morpho peleides") 45 25
3472 200b. Longhorn beetle ("Acrocinus longimanus") 45 25
3473 350b. Green jay ("Cyanocorax yncas") 75 40
3474 350b. Hercules beetle ("Dynastes hercules") 75 40

578 Gumersindo Torres Millet (first Comptroller)

1998. 60th Anniv of Office of Comptroller General. Black, red and blue (Nos. 3477, 3479) or multicoloured (others).
3475 140b. Type **578** 30 15
3476 140b. Luis Antonio Pieri Yepez (comptroller, 1958–69) 30 15
3477 140b. Congress building 30 15
3478 140b. Flag 30 15
3479 200b. Banknotes and coins 45 25
3480 200b. Numbers 45 25
3481 350b. Newspapers 75 40
3482 350b. Scales of Justice 75 40
3483 350b. Code of Ethics 75 40
3484 350b. Emblem of Seventh Assembly of Latin American and Caribbean Organization of Higher Fiscal Bodies 75 40

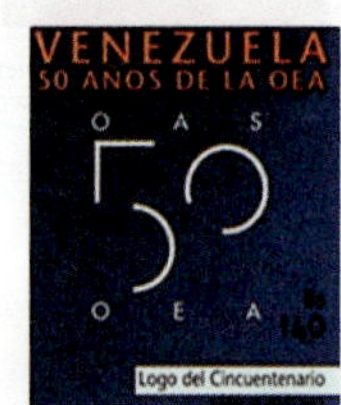

579 Anniversary Emblem

1998. 50th Anniv of Organization of American States. Multicoloured.
3486 140b. Type **579** 25 15
3487 140b. Institutional emblem 25 15
3488 150b. Soldier uncovering landmine 30 15
3489 150b. Official with prisoner (Defence of Human Rights) 30 15
3490 200b. Simon Bolivar 40 20
3491 200b. Scroll commemorating 50th anniv of American Declaration of Human Rights 40 20
3492 200b. Map of the Americas on road sign 40 20
3493 200b. Three rock climbers (anti-drugs co-operation) 40 20
3494 350b. Members' flags including Brazil and U.S.A. forming double helix 70 35
3495 350b. Members' flags including Jamaica and Venezuela forming a double helix 70 35

Nos. 3486/7, 3492/3 and 3494/5 were issued together, se-tenant, forming composite designs.

580 Brown Booby, Turtle and Crab

1998. "Expo '98" World's Fair, Lisbon. Mult.
3496 140b. Type **580** 25 15
3497 140b. Fishermen in boat 25 15
3498 150b. Shells, baby turtle and jellyfish 30 15
3499 150b. Yellow-finned tuna and snapper 30 15
3500 200b. Great barracuda and underwater vegetation (value at top) 40 20
3501 200b. Octopus, fishes and underwater vegetation (value at foot) 40 20
3502 200b. Horse rider 40 20
3503 200b. Cattle in water and common squirrel-monkey 40 20
3504 350b. Great egret and scarlet ibis 70 35
3505 350b. Red howler (monkey), waterfall and plants 70 35

Nos. 3496/3505 were issued together, se-tenant, forming a composite design.

581 Athletics

1998. 18th Central American and Caribbean Games, Maracaibo. Multicoloured.
3506 150b. Type **581** 30 15
3507 150b. Ten-pin bowling 30 15
3508 150b. Cycling 30 15
3509 150b. Gymnastics 30 15
3510 150b. Swimming 30 15
3511 200b. Basketball 40 20
3512 200b. Boxing 40 20
3513 200b. Fencing 40 20
3514 200b. Weightlifting 40 20
3515 200b. Tennis 40 20

582 Anthropomorphic Vessel

1998. 500th Anniv of Discovery of Venezuela. Multicoloured.
3516 140b. Type **582** 25 15
3517 140b. "Catholic Royal Couple" (wood carving, Manuel Cabrera) 25 15
3518 150b. Three women of different races 30 15
3519 150b. Mixed-race people 30 15
3520 200b. Lake houses on stilts 40 20
3521 200b. Modern city 40 20
3522 200b. Juan de la Cosa and 1499 map 40 20
3523 200b. Detail of 1599 map by Jodocus Hondius 40 20
3524 350b. Christopher Columbus 70 35
3525 350b. Alonso de Ojeda 70 35

583 Columbus, Vespucci and Galleon

1998. 500th Anniversaries of Christopher Columbus's Discovery of America and Amerigo Vespucci's Exploration of Venezuela.
3526 **583** 400b. multicoloured 80 40

584 River Casiquiare, Amazon Basin

1998. 20th Anniv of Amazon Co-operation Treaty. Multicoloured.
3527 200b. Type **584** 40 20
3528 200b. River Casiquiare, Amazon Basin (right-hand detail) 40 20
3529 200b. Berries of "Bactris gasipaes" 40 20
3530 200b. "Neblinaria celiae" (plant) 40 20
3531 200b. Cardinal tetra ("Paracheidon axelrodi") 40 20
3532 200b. Yellow-banded poison-arrow frogs ("Dendrobates leucomelas") 40 20
3533 200b. Nocturnal curassows ("Nocthocrax urumatum") 40 20
3534 200b. Bush dogs ("Speothos venaticus") 40 20
3535 200b. Cocuy Stone 40 20
3536 200b. Neblina Ridge 40 20

Nos. 3527/8 were issued together, se-tenant, forming a composite design.

585 Martinez Cockroach cleaning

1998. Children's Stories (2nd series). "Martinez Cockroach and Perez Rat" from "Uncle Jaguar and Uncle Rabbit" by Antonio Arraiz. Mult.
3537 130b. Type **585** 25 15
3538 130b. Doctor Ass writing on pad 25 15
3539 130b. Parakeet in dress 25 15
3540 130b. Photographer and reporter 25 15
3541 130b. Piojo (cat) 25 15
3542 130b. Martinez Cockroach and pig 25 15
3543 130b. Chivo (goat) 25 15
3544 130b. Martinez Cockroach and Perez Rat gazing at moon 25 15
3545 130b. Perez Rat sniffing cauldron in which he later drowned 25 15
3546 130b. Guinea-hen and Misia Rata reviving Martinez Cockroach 25 15

A number and the relevant portion of the story is printed on the back of each stamp over the gum.

586 Ram's-horn Blower

1998. 50th Anniv of State of Israel. Multicoloured.
3548 140b. Type **586** 25 25
3549 140b. Book Museum 25 25
3550 200b. King David 40 20
3551 200b. Knesset building, Jerusalem 40 20
3552 200b. Dr. Theodor Herzl (founder of World Zionist Movement) 40 20
3553 200b. David Ben Gurion (first Israeli Prime Minister) 40 20
3554 350b. Moses holding Ten Commandments 70 35
3555 350b. Man at Wailing Wall 70 35
3556 350b. Menorah 70 35
3557 350b. Torah 70 35

587 Handing Letter over Post Office Counter

1998. 125th Anniv of Universal Postal Union. Multicoloured.
3558 100b. Type **587** 20 10
3559 100b. Checking barcode on envelope 20 10
3560 100b. Computer operators using e-mail 20 10
3561 100b. Woman holding computer disc 20 10
3562 100b. Arrows and binary code, offices and factory 20 10
3563 300b. As Type **587** but design reversed 60 30
3564 300b. As No. 3559 but design reversed 60 30
3565 300b. As No. 3560 but design reversed 60 30
3566 300b. As No. 3561 but design reversed 60 30
3567 300b. As No. 3562 but design reversed 60 30

588 Caruao

1998. Amerindians (5th series). Paintings of Indian Chiefs by Primi Manteiga. Multicoloured.

3568	420b. Type **588**	80	40
3569	420b. Manaure	80	40
3570	420b. Guacamayo	80	40
3571	420b. Tapiaracay	80	40
3572	420b. Mamacuri	80	40
3573	420b. Maniacuare	80	40
3574	420b. Mara	80	40
3575	420b. Chacao	80	40
3576	420b. Tamanaco	80	40
3577	420b. Tiuna	80	40

589 Father Francisco de Cordoba and Juan Garces

1998. 500th Anniv of First Christian Missions to Venezuela. Multicoloured.

3579	100b. Type **589**	20	10
3580	100b. Father Matias Ruiz Blanco	20	10
3581	100b. Father Vicente de Requejada	20	10
3582	100b. Jose Gumilla	20	10
3583	100b. Antonio Gonzalez de Acuna	20	10
3584	300b. Father Pedro de Cordoba	60	30
3585	300b. Father Francisco de Pamplona	60	30
3586	300b. Father Bartolome Diaz	60	30
3587	300b. Felipe Salvador Gilij	60	30
3588	300b. Mariano Marti	60	30

590 Opening Parade

1998. 30th Anniv of First Special Olympics. Mult.

3590	180b. Type **590**	35	20
3591	180b. Two people hugging	35	20
3592	180b. Football	35	20
3593	180b. Medal winner	35	20
3594	180b. Gymnastics	35	20
3595	420b. Swimming	80	40
3596	420b. Athletes and officials walking on track	80	40
3597	420b. Volleyball	80	40
3598	420b. Cheering medal winners	80	40
3599	420b. Baseball	80	40

591 Girl with Sparkler

1998. Christmas. Multicoloured.

3600	180b. Type **591**	35	20
3601	180b. Boy with figurine and paintbrush	35	20
3602	180b. Girl with kite	35	20
3603	180b. Boy with toy windmill	35	20
3604	180b. Girls with tambourine and drum	35	20
3605	420b. Boy in go-cart	80	40
3606	420b. Girl with yo-yo and rag doll	80	40
3607	420b. Boy with bell	80	40
3608	420b. Girl in hat with spinning toy	80	40
3609	420b. Boy on skateboard	80	40

592 Teresa de la Parra (writer)

1998. America. Famous Women. Multicoloured.

3610	180b. Type **592**	35	20
3611	420b. Teresa Carreno (pianist)	80	40

593 Amazonian Umbrellabird

1998. 100 Years of Venezuela–United States Solidarity. Each showing a portrait of William Phelps (ornithologist and entrepreneur). Mult.

3612	200b. Type **593**	40	20
3613	200b. Crimson topaz ("Topaza pella")	40	20
3614	200b. Great antpitta ("Grallaria excelsa")	40	20
3615	200b. Ruby-throated hummingbird ("Chrysolampis mosquitus")	40	20
3616	200b. Yellow-bellied tanager ("Tangara xanthogastra")	40	20
3617	300b. Radio microphone (founder of Broadcasting Caracas)	60	30
3618	300b. Phelps Peak	60	30
3619	300b. Baseball in glove	60	30
3620	300b. Phelps Library, San Antonio de Maturin	60	30
3621	300b. Cash register	60	30

594 Jauregui

597 Angel appearing to Wise Men

595 Worker and Old Lady

1999. Monseigneur Jesus Manuel Jauregui Moreno. Multicoloured.

3622	500b. Type **594**	80	50
3623	500b. Crucifix	80	50
3624	500b. Church of Our Lady of the Angels, La Grita	80	50
3625	500b. Our Lady of the Angels (statue)	80	50
3626	500b. Jauregui in Cardinal's robes	80	50

1999. Centenary of Consecration of Church of the Blessed Sacrament, Caracas. Multicoloured.

3627	250b. Type **595**	40	25
3628	250b. Priest	40	25
3629	250b. Reliquary	40	25
3630	250b. Boy and girl	40	25
3631	250b. Family	40	25
3632	250b. Doctor	40	25
3633	250b. Woman with flower in hair	40	25
3634	250b. Angels beside base of reliquary	40	25
3635	250b. Soldier	40	35
3636	250b. Boy with spear	40	25

1999. Christmas. Multicoloured.

3639	300b. Type **597**	50	30
3640	300b. Wise men on camels	50	30
3641	300b. Wise men presenting gifts	50	30
3642	300b. Flight into Egypt	50	30
3643	300b. Roman soldier chasing Mary and Baby Jesus	50	30
3644	500b. Mary and Joseph	50	30
3645	500b. Mary and Archangel Gabriel	50	30
3646	500b. Women talking	50	30
3647	500b. Joseph with Mary on donkey	50	30
3648	500b. Mary, Baby Jesus and old man	50	30

599 Angel Falls

2000. Organization of Petroleum Exporting Countries Conference, Caracas. Multicoloured.

3650	300b. Type **599**	50	30
3651	300b. View over Forest	50	30
3652	300b. Waterfall	50	30
3653	300b. Aerial view of swamp	50	30
3654	300b. Auyantipuy Peak from Rio Carrao	50	30
3655	400b. Lake Maracaibo	50	30
3656	400b. Humboldt Peak	50	30
3657	400b. Aerial view of swamp	50	30
3658	400b. Rio Morichal swamp	50	30
3659	400b. Auyantepuy Peak	50	30
3660	550b. Emblem of "Riyadh, Cultural Capital of Arab World, 2000", Saudi Arabia	50	30
3661	550b. "Mohammed Racim" (painting, detail), Algeria	50	30
3662	550b. Dubai, United Arab Emirates	50	30
3663	550b. Greater bird of paradise, Indonesia	50	30
3664	550b. Figure from relief depicting Assyrian War, Iraq	50	30
3665	550b. Procession, Tehran, Iran	50	30
3666	550b. National emblem, Kuwait	50	30
3667	550b. "The Great Artificial River" project emblem, Libya	50	30
3668	550b. Bronze mask, Nigeria	50	30
3669	550b. Al-Zubarah Fort, Qatar	50	30

EXPRESS LETTER STAMPS

E 119

E 194

1949.

E809	E **119**	30c. lake	30	25

1961.

E1691	E **194**	30c. orange	50	25

OFFICIAL STAMPS

O 17

1898.

O174	O **17**	5c. black and green	30	50
O175		10c. black and red	85	90
O176		25c. black and blue	1·10	1·25
O177		50c. black and yellow	1·90	1·90
O178		1b. black and mauve	2·10	1·75

1899. Surch **1899** and new value.

O187	O **17**	5c. on 50c. blk & yell	3·75	2·75
O188		5c. on 1b. blk & mve	14·00	13·00
O189		25c. on 50c. blk & yell	14·00	13·00
O190		25c. on 1b. blk & mve	9·50	9·00

1900. Optd **1900** in upper corners.

O222	O **17**	5c. black and green	35	35
O223		10c. black and red	45	45
O224		25c. black and blue	45	45
O225		50c. black and yellow	50	50
O226		1b. black and mauve	55	55

O **40** With Stars

O **45** Without Stars

1904.

O325	O **40**	5c. black and green	25	25
O326		10c. black and red	50	50
O327		25c. black and blue	50	50
O328		50c. black and red	2·40	1·90
O329		1b. black and lake	1·25	90

1912.

O354	O **45**	5c. black and green	15	25
O355		10c. black and red	15	25
O356		25c. black and blue	15	25
O357		50c. black and violet	20	35
O358		1b. black and yellow	40	35

REGISTRATION STAMPS

R **19** Bolivar

1899.

R186	R **19**	25c. brown	2·50	1·60

1899. Optd with T **21**.

R205	R **19**	25c. brown	1·75	1·25

VICTORIA Pt. 1

The south-eastern state of the Australian Commonwealth, whose stamps it now uses.

12 pence = 1 shilling;
20 shillings = 1 pound.

1 Queen Victoria ("half length")

2 Queen on Throne

1850. Imperf.

28	**1**	1d. red to brown	£400	35·00
6		2d. lilac to grey	£1200	£110
17		2d. brown	£550	£110
31a		3d. blue	£375	35·00

1852. Imperf.

38	**2**	2d. brown to lilac	£180	26·00

3

4

1854. Imperf.

25	**3**	1s. blue	£650	22·00

1854. Imperf.

32a	**4**	6d. orange	£180	18·00
35		2s. green on yellow	£1200	£150

7 Queen on Throne

8 Emblems in Corners

1856. Imperf.

40	**7**	1d. green	£140	21·00

1857. Imperf.

41	**8**	1d. green	95·00	14·00
45		2d. lilac	£225	11·00
43		4d. red	£160	7·50

1857. Rouletted.

72	**8**	1d. green	£275	24·00
69		2d. lilac	£120	7·50
48	**1**	3d. blue	—	£190
71c	**8**	4d. red	£120	3·50
53a	**4**	6d. orange	—	35·00
54	**3**	1s. blue	—	90·00
56	**4**	2s. green on yellow	£3500	£350

1858. Rouletted.

73	**7**	6d. blue	£140	14·00

1859. Perf.

98	**8**	1d. green	65·00	4·50
100		2d. grey	£100	5·50
101		2d. lilac	£160	8·00
78	**1**	3d. blue	£750	£110
87		4d. red	£120	7·50
102	**4**	6d. black	£160	40·00
81	**3**	1s. blue	£130	15·00
82	**4**	2s. green on yellow	£275	32·00
129b		2s. blue on green	£150	4·75

9

12

1860. Perf.

90	**9**	3d. blue	£120	7·00
91		3d. purple	£110	25·00
92a		4d. red	80·00	3·50
93		6d. orange	£3250	£225
94		6d. black	£110	5·50

1861.

104a	**12**	1d. green	60·00	5·00

13

14

15

16

17

18

1862.

107	**13**	6d. black	70·00	4·50

1863.

131d	**14**	1d. green	60·00	2·75
132b		2d. lilac	50·00	3·25
118	**15**	3d. lilac	£110	25·00
378		3d. orange	15·00	1·50
135d	**14**	4d. pink	70·00	3·00
136c	**16**	6d. blue	25·00	1·50
380		6d. green	9·00	6·50
112	**14**	8d. orange	£325	55·00
137c		8d. brown on pink	80·00	5·00
119	**16**	10d. grey	£475	£110
123		10d. brown on pink	85·00	5·00
124	**17**	1s. blue on blue	55·00	2·50
139	**18**	5s. blue on yellow	£1700	£300
148		5s. blue and red	£150	13·00
383		5s. red and blue	45·00	38·00

For designs additionally inscribed "POSTAGE" see Nos. 399 etc.

20

1870.

169a	**20**	2d. lilac	50·00	1·00

1871. Surch in figures and words.

174	**14**	½d. on 1d. green	50·00	12·00
171	**16**	9d. on 10d. brown on pink	£300	10·00

22

23

24

25

26

27

1873.

176b	**22**	½d. red	8·50	90
195		½d. red on pink	27·00	17·00
376		½d. green	2·00	1·00
177b	**23**	1d. green	22·00	1·25
196		1d. green on yellow	80·00	14·00
197		1d. green on grey	£110	45·00
179	**24**	2d. mauve	29·00	65
198		2d. mauve on lilac	—	£450
199		2d. mauve on green	£140	17·00
200		2d. mauve on brown	£130	17·00
172a	**25**	9d. brown on pink	60·00	12·00
319		9d. green	24·00	9·00
366		9d. red	15·00	1·75
180	**26**	1s. blue on blue	60·00	3·25
381		1s. yellow	45·00	35·00
190	**27**	2s. blue on green	£120	18·00
382		2s. blue on pink	42·00	20·00

For designs additionally inscribed "POSTAGE" see Nos. 399 etc.

1876. Surch **8d.. 8d.. EIGHTPENCE.**

191	**25**	8d. on 9d. brown on pink	£180	15·00

30

31

1880. Frame differs in 4d.

209b	**30**	1d. green	20·00	1·25
210	**31**	2d. brown	22·00	85
377		2d. mauve	7·00	1·00
213		4d. red	50·00	7·50
379		4d. yellow	25·00	13·00

For designs additionally inscribed "POSTAGE" see Nos. 416 etc.

34

35

36

37

1884. Inscr "STAMP STATUTE". Frames differ.

220	–	1d. green	35·00	27·00
221	**34**	3d. mauve	£500	£250
222	–	4d. pink	£400	£180
223a	–	6d. blue	50·00	17·00
224	–	1s. blue on blue	60·00	20·00
225	**35**	2s. blue on green	90·00	60·00
232	**36**	2s.6d. yellow	£225	£110
227	–	5s. blue on yellow	£225	65·00
228	–	10s. brown on pink	£750	£180
229	–	£1 violet on yellow	£550	£140
230	**37**	£5 black and green	£2750	£650

DESIGNS—As T **34/36**: 1d., 6d., 1s., 5s. to £1, Uncrowned portrait of Queen Victoria in centre; 4d. Obverse and reverse of fourpenny coin.

1884. No. 220 surch **½d HALF.**

234		½d. on 1d. green	50·00	50·00

39

40

44

52

56

58

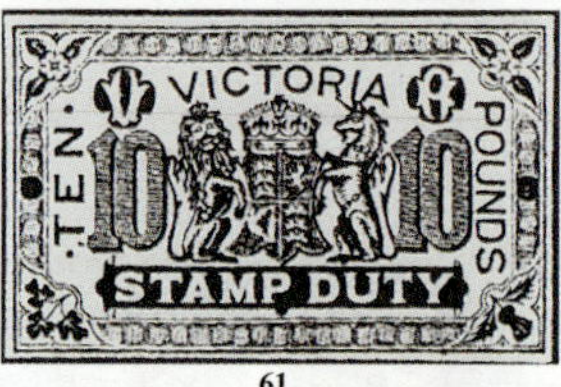

61

1884. Inscr "STAMP DUTY". Frames differ.

253	**39**	1d. green	40·00	17·00
254	**40**	1d. bistre	15·00	3·00
255	–	6d. blue	60·00	9·00
256	–	1s. blue on blue	70·00	5·00
257	–	1s. blue on yellow	85·00	22·00
236	–	1s.6d. red	£160	19·00
258c	**44**	2s. blue on green	£120	25·00
259	–	3s. purple on blue	£300	28·00
345	–	3s. drab	55·00	17·00
371	–	3s. green	£130	21·00
238	–	4s. red to orange	85·00	16·00
260	–	5s. purple on yellow	50·00	5·50
347	–	5s. red	80·00	11·00
348	–	6s. green	85·00	23·00
240	–	10s. brown on pink	£400	75·00
349	–	10s. green	£130	18·00
241	–	15s. mauve	£1000	£170
350	–	15s. brown	£375	48·00
242	–	£1 orange	£400	70·00
243	**52**	£1 5s. pink	£950	£180
275	–	£1 10s. green	£750	80·00
245	–	35s. violet	£3750	
276a	–	£2 blue	£800	80·00
247	**44**	45s. lilac	£1800	£150
248	**56**	£5 red	£1800	£350
249	**58**	£6 blue on pink	—	£550
250		£7 violet on blue	—	£550
251	–	£8 red on yellow	—	£700
252	–	£9 green on green	—	£700
264a	**61**	£10 mauve	£2000	£130

DESIGNS—As T **39/52**: 6d. to 1s.6d., 4s. to £1, £1 10s., £2, Various arms; 35s. "V R STAMP DUTY". As T **56/8**: £8, Crown; £9, Arms.

62

1884.

289	**62**	£25 green	—	£120
352		£50 mauve	—	£150
291		£100 red	—	£250

63

1884.

292a	**63**	2s.6d. yellow	80·00	14·00

64

65

66

67

68

1884. Inscr "STAMP DUTY".

296	**64**	½d. red	7·00	75
297	**65**	1d. green	10·00	9·00
298	**66**	2d. mauve	9·00	30
361	**65**	3d. buff	7·00	1·75
362		3d. green	21·00	9·00
300	**67**	4d. mauve	45·00	3·00
301a	**65**	6d. blue	40·00	2·10
293	**68**	8d. red on pink	24·00	6·00
294	**66**	1s. blue on yellow	70·00	8·50
303	**68**	2s. green on green	28·00	4·75
369		2s. green on white	19·00	7·00

1885. Optd **STAMP DUTY.**

308	**15**	3d. orange	60·00	22·00
309	**31**	4d. red	55·00	29·00
306	**26**	1s. blue on blue	95·00	20·00
307	**27**	2s. blue on green	90·00	18·00

70

71

72

73

74

75

76

77

78

79

80

81

1886. Inscr "STAMP DUTY".

310	**70**	½d. grey	20·00	4·50
330		½d. red	3·50	50
356		½d. green	4·75	40
312	**71**	1d. green	7·00	65
329	**72**	1d. brown on pink	5·50	2·25
332		1d. brown	5·00	10

357a 1d. red . . . . 4·25 10
358 1d. green . . . . 5·00 4·00
333 **81** 1½d. green . . . . 3·00 2·75
355 1½d. red on yellow . . . 3·00 1·75
314d **73** 2d. purple . . . . 3·75 20
315b **74** 2½d. red on yellow . . . 10·00 70
360 2½d. blue . . . . 12·00 1·50
363 **75** 4d. red . . . . 7·00 1·75
317a **76** 5d. brown . . . . 7·00 1·50
365 **77** 6d. blue . . . . 9·00 1·50
341 **78** 1s. red . . . . 14·00 2·00
322 **79** 1s.6d. blue . . . . £130 65·00
323 1s.6d. orange . . . . . . 17·00 6·00
324 **80** £5 blue and purple . . . £1200 90·00
325 £6 yellow and blue . . . £1500 £120
326 £7 red and black £1700 £130
327 £8 mauve and orange . . £1800 £160
328 £9 green and red £2250 £170

For designs additionally inscribed "POSTAGE" see Nos. 416 etc.

83

84

1897. Hospital Charity Fund.
353 **83** 1d. (1s.) blue . . . . . . 18·00 18·00
354 **84** 2½d. (2s.6d.) brown . . . . 85·00 70·00

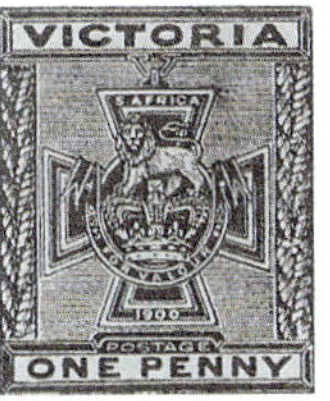
86

87

1900. Empire Patriotic Fund.
374 **86** 1d. (1s.) brown . . . . . 70·00 42·00
375 **87** 2d. (2s.) green £140 £140

93

101

1901. As previous types but inscr "POSTAGE" instead of "STAMP DUTY" or with "POSTAGE" added to design, and new designs.
416 **22** ½d. green . . . . 2·50 30
417a **30** 1d. red . . . . 1·25 10
386a **81** 1½d. purple on yellow . . 2·10 55
418c **31** 2d. mauve . . . . 5·50 75
419 **74** 2½d. blue . . . . 3·00 40
389a **93** 3d. brown . . . . 7·00 55
390 **31** 4d. yellow . . . . 5·50 65
391a **76** 5d. brown . . . . 8·50 40
423 **16** 6d. green . . . . 13·00 80
424d **25** 9d. red . . . . 9·50 1·25
425 **26** 1s. orange . . . . 8·00 2·00
395 **27** 2s. blue on pink . . . . 22·00 2·00
398a **18** 5s. red and blue . . . . 70·00 12·00
399 **101** £1 pink £225 £110
400 – £2 blue £500 £275
DESIGN: £2, as Type **101** but different frame.

1912. Surch **ONE PENNY**.
456 **31** 1d. on 2d. mauve (No. 387) 70 50

POSTAGE DUE STAMPS

D 1

1890.
D 1 **D 1** ½d. blue and red . . . . 4·25 3·00
D 2 1d. blue and red . . . . 5·50 1·40
D 3 2d. blue and red . . . . 9·50 1·75
D 4 4d. blue and red . . . . 12·00 2·00
D 5 5d. blue and red . . . . 11·00 2·00
D 6 6d. blue and red . . . . 13·00 2·75
D 7 10d. blue and red . . . 75·00 42·00
D 8 1s. blue and red . . . . 48·00 6·50
D 9 2s. blue and red . . . . £110 50·00
D10 5s. blue and red . . . . £160 90·00

1895.
D11a **D 1** ½d. red and green . . . 3·50 1·50
D12 1d. red and green . . . 3·75 1·00
D13 2d. red and green . . . 7·00 1·25
D14 4d. red and green . . . 9·50 1·50
D15a 5d. red and green . . . 10·00 6·00
D25 6d. red and green . . . 9·00 3·75
D17 10d. red and green . . . 18·00 10·00
D18 1s. red and green . . . 14·00 3·25
D19 2s. red and green . . . 60·00 20·00
D20 5s. red and green . . . £100 40·00

REGISTRATION STAMP

6

1854. Imperf.
34 **6** 1s. red and blue £950 £130

1857. Roul.
55 **6** 1s. red and blue £3500 £200

TOO LATE STAMP

1855. As T **6** but inscr "TOO LATE". Imperf.
33 6d. lilac and green £800 £160

VICTORIA LAND Pt. 1

Stamps issued in connection with Capt. Scott's Antarctic Expedition.

12 pence = 1 shilling.

1911. Scott Expedition. Stamps of New Zealand optd **VICTORIA LAND.**
A2 **51** ½d. green £550 £650
A3 **53** 1d. red . . . . 45·00 85·00

VIETNAM Pt. 21

A. DEMOCRATIC REPUBLIC

The Democratic Republic was proclaimed by the Viet Minh Nationalists on 2 September 1945 and recognised by France on 6 March 1946 as a free state within the Indo-China Federation. It consisted of Tongking, Annam and Cochin-China.

1945. 100 cents = 1 piastre.
1945. 100 xu = 10 hao = 1 dong.

Stamps of Indo-China overprinted.

VIET-NAM
DAN-CHU CONG-HOA
DOC-LAP
TU-DO HANH-PHUC
BUU-CHINH III
(1)

("DAN-CHU CONG-HOA" = Democratic Republic; "DOC-LAP TU-DO HANH-PHUC = Independence, Freedom, Happiness; "BUU-CHINH" = Postage.)

1945. Independence. Variously optd as T **1** (all with **DOC-LAP TU-DO HANH-PHUC** in opt).
1 **53** 1c. brown 40 40
2 – 2c. mauve (No. 315) 25 25
3 – 3c. brown (Courbet) 25 25
4 – 4c. brown (No. 316) 25 25
5 – 5c. sepia (De Genouilly) . . 35 35
6 – 6c. red (No. 304) 35 35
7 – 6c. red (No. 305) 60 60
8 – 10c. green (No. 307) 60 60
9 – 10c. green (No. 322) 40 40
10 – 20c. red (No. 309) 75 75
11 **64** 40c. blue 35 35
12 – $1 green (No. 311) 75 75

Nos. 3 and 5 were not issued without opt and are as Nos. 304 and 305 of Indo-China respectively.

1945. Variously optd. (a) **VIET-NAM DAN-CHU CONG-HOA.**
13 **69** 10c. purple and yellow . . . 1·50 1·25
14 – 15c. purple (No. 292) . . . 25 25
15 – 30c. brown (No. 294) . . . 40 40
16 **69** 50c. red . . . . 3·75 3·75
17 – $1 green (No. 295) 25 25

(b) **VIET-NAM DAN-CHU CONG-HOA BUU-CHINH.**
18 **53** 3c. brown 40 40
19 – 4c. yellow (No. 317) 40 40
20 **53** 6c. red 40 40
21 10c. green 75 75
22 – 10c. green (No. 320) 70 70
23 – 20c. red (Pavie) 35 35
24 **53** 40c. blue 50 50
25 40c. grey . . . . 1·25 1·25

No. 23 was not issued without opt and is as No. 320 of Indo-China.

VIET-NAM
DAN-CHU
3$00 CONG-HOA
CUU-DOI
(2 "CUU-DOI" = Famine Relief)

1945. Famine Relief. Surch as T **2**.
26 **70** "2$00" on 15c.+60c. purple 5·00 5·00
27 "3$00" on 40c.+$1.10c. blue 5·00 5·00

1945. War Wounded. Surch as T **2** but with **Binh-si Bi-nan** (= Fund for War Wounded).
28 **70** "5$00" on 15c.+60c. purple 7·00 7·00

1945. Surch in new currency and variously optd as before (except Nos. 43/7). (a) **VIET-NAM DAN-CHU CONG-HOA BUU-CHINH.**
29 **64** 30x. on 1c. brown 40 40
30 – 30x. on 15c. purple (Garnier) 35 35
31 **67** 50x. on 1c. brown . . . . . 3·00 3·00
32 – 60x. on 1c. brown (No. 313) 70 70
33 – 1d. on 5c. brown (No. 303) 1·50 1·50
34 – 1d.60x. on 10c. green (No. 319) 40 40
35 **64** 3d. on 15c. purple 75 75
36 **67** 3d. on 15c. purple . . . . . 6·00 6·00
37 – 4d. on 1c. brown (No. 302) 50 50
38 – 5d. on 1c. brown (No. 301) 90 90

(b) **VIET-NAM DAN-CHU CONG-HOA.**
39 – 1d. on 5c. purple (No. 318) 50 50
40 **49** 2d. on 3c. brown . . . . . . 7·50 7·50
41 – 2d. on 10c. green (No. 321) 75 75
42 **49** 4d. on 6c. red . . . . 7·50 7·50

(c) Surch only.
43 **56** 50x. on 1c. brown 60 60
44 2d. on 6c. red . . . . . . 5·00 5·00
45 **48** 5d. on 1c. orange . . . . . 7·50 7·50
46 10d. on 6c. violet . . . . . 8·75 8·75
47 15d. on 25c. blue . . . . . 8·75 8·75

No. 30 was not issued without opt and is as No. 301 of Indo-China.

OVERPRINT. Nos. 48/55 are all optd **VIET-NAM DAN-CHU CONG-HOA** with varying additional words as noted in headings.

1945. National Defence (**Quoc-Phong**).
48 **49** "+5d." on 3c. brown . . . 1·25 1·50
49 "+10d." on 6c. red . . . . 1·25 1·50

1946. People's Livelihood. (**DAN SINH**).
50 **57** "30xu.+3d." on 6c. red . . 65 65
51 **55** "30xu.+3d." on 6c. red . . 65 65

1946. Campaign against Illiteracy (**Chong nan mu chu**).
52 **59** "+4dong" on 6c. red . . . 75 75

1946. New Life Movement (**Doi song moi**).
53 **66** "+4dong" on 6c. red . . . 1·50 1·50

1946. Child Welfare (**Bao-Anh**).
54 – "+2dong" on 6c. red (No. 290) 75 75

1946. War Wounded (**Binh si bi nan**).
55 – "+3dong" on 20c. red (No. 293) . . . . 1·50 1·25

Definitive issues.

3 Ho Chi Minh

1946.
56 **3** 1h. green 40 40
57 3h. red 40 40
58 9h. yellow 40 40

1946. National Defence.
59 **3** 4+6h. blue 75 75
60 6+9h. brown 75 75

The Viet-Minh Government was at war with the French from 19 December 1946 until July 1954, and the stamps issued by the Democratic Republic in this period are listed as North Vietnam Nos. N1/13, NO1/9 and ND1/4.

B. INDEPENDENT STATE

On 14 June 1949, Vietnam, comprising Tongking, Annam and Cochin-China, became an independent state within the French Union under Emperor Bao-Dai. Until the 1951 issue Indo-Chinese stamps continued in use.

By the Geneva Declaration of 21 July 1954, Vietnam was partitioned near the 17th Parallel, and all authority of Bao-Dai's Government north of that line ended. Later issues are therefore those of SOUTH VIETNAM and NORTH VIETNAM.

100 cents = 1 piastre.

4 Bongour Falls, Dalat

1951.
61 **4** 10c. bronze 10 10
62 – 20c. purple 20 10
63 – 30c. blue 25 10
64 – 50c. red 50 20
65 **4** 60c. sepia 25 10
66 – 1p. brown 25 10
67 – 1p.20 brown . . . . 1·90 1·25
68 – 2p. violet 60 20
69 – 3p. blue . . . . 1·90 25
70 **4** 5p. green . . . . 1·40 35
71 – 10p. red . . . . 3·50 65
72 – 15p. brown . . . . 11·50 3·25
73 – 30p. green . . . . 25·00 4·50
DESIGNS—HORIZ: 20c., 2p., 10p. Imperial Palace, Hue; 30c., 15p. Small Lake, Hanoi; 50c., 1p. Temple of Remembrance, Saigon. VERT: 1p.20, 3p., 30p. Emperor Bao Dai.

9

1952. Air.
74 **9** 3p.30 green and lake 45 35
75 4p. yellow and brown 70 25
76 5p.10 pink and blue 60 55
77 – 6p.30 red and yellow (symbolic of airlines) . . . 75 65

10 Empress Nam Phuong

11 Globe and Lightning

1952.
78 **10** 30c. brown, yellow & purple 30 40
79 50c. brown, yellow and blue 60 40
80 1p.50 brown, yellow & olive 1·25 40

1952. 1st Anniv of Admission of Vietnam into I.T.U.
81 **11** 1p. blue . . . . 3·75 1·90

12 Dragon

1952. Air. Day of Wandering Souls.
82 **12** 40c. red . . . . 1·00 65
83 70c. green . . . . 1·00 65
84 80c. blue . . . . 1·00 65
85 90c. brown . . . . 1·00 80
86 – 3p.70 purple . . . . 2·25 90
DESIGN—VERT: 3p.70, Fish dragon.

13 U.P.U. Monument, Berne, and Coastline

1952. 1st Anniv of Admission of Vietnam into U.P.U.
87 **13** 5p. brown . . . . 4·75 1·25

1952. Red Cross. T **10** surch with red cross and **+50c.**
88 **10** 1p.50+50c. brn, yell & bl . . 4·50 4·50

15 Emperor Bao Dai and Gateway

1952. 40th Birthday of Emperor.
89 **15** 1p.50 purple . . . . 2·25 95

16 Sabres and Flag

17 Crown Prince Bao Long

1952. Wounded Soldiers' Relief Fund.
90 **16** 3p.30+1p.70 lake . . . . . 1·60 1·60

1959.
91 **17** 40c. turquoise 50 50
92 70c. lake 60 60
93 80c. sepia 75 75
94 – 90c. green . . . . 1·75 1·75
95 – 20p. red . . . . 3·75 3·75
96 – 50p. violet . . . . 8·00 8·00
97 **17** 100p. blue . . . . 17·00 17·00
PORTRAIT: 90c. to 50p. Crown Prince in uniform.

POSTAGE DUE STAMPS

D **10** Dragon

1952.
D78 D **10** 10c. green and red . . . 20 10
D79 20c. yellow and green 35 10
D80 30c. orange and violet 35 10
D81 40c. pink and green . . 40 15
D82 50c. grey and lake . . 70 25
D83 1p. silver and blue . . . 1·00 35

C. SOUTH VIETNAM

100 cents = 1 piastre.

INDEPENDENT STATE
(Within the French Union)

1 Turtle

1955. 1st Anniv of Govt of Ngo Dinh Diem.
S1 **1** 30c. purple 75 25
S2 50c. green . . . . 2·75 90
S3 1p.50 blue . . . . 1·25 40

2 Phoenix

1955. Air.
S4 **2** 4p. mauve and violet . . . . 1·00 25

3 Refugees

1955. 1st Anniv of Arrival of Refugees from North Vietnam.
S 5 **3** 70c. red 65 40
S 6 80c. purple . . . . 1·50 85
S 7 10p. blue . . . . 2·75 1·60
S 8 20p. brown, orange & violet 5·50 2·25
S 9 35p. sepia, yellow and blue 11·00 8·75
S10 100p. purple, orange & green . . . . 25·00 14·50
No. S9 is inscribed "CHIEN-DICH-HUYNE-DE" in margin at foot.
See also No. S26.

REPUBLIC
(from 26th October, 1955)

4 G.P.O., Saigon
5 Pres. Ngo Dinh Diem

1956. 5th Anniv of Entry of Vietnam into U.P.U.
S11 **4** 60c. green 55 40
S12 90c. violet . . . . 1·75 65
S13 3p. brown . . . . 3·00 90

1956.
S14 **5** 20c. brown 10 10
S15 30c. purple 20 20
S16 50c. red 10 10
S17 1p. violet 30 15
S18 1p.50 violet 50 15
S19 3p. sepia 50 15
S20 4p. blue 70 20
S21 5p. brown 95 20
S22 10p. blue . . . . 1·25 40
S23 20p. black . . . . 3·25 70
S24 35p. green . . . . 8·50 1·60
S25 100p. brown . . . . 18·00 6·25

1956. No. S9 with bottom marginal inscription obliterated by bar.
S26 **3** 35p. sepia, yellow and blue 4·75 3·25

1956. Optd **Cong-thu Buu-dien** (= "Government Postal Building").
S27 **4** 60c. green 85 50
S28 90c. violet . . . . 1·50 50
S29 3p. brown . . . . 2·25 75

7 Bamboo
8 Refugee Children

1956. 1st Anniv of Republic.
S30 **7** 50c. red 30 10
S31 1p.50 purple 65 10
S32 2p. green 85 10
S33 4p. blue . . . . 2·10 20

1956. United Nations "Operation Brotherhood".
S34 **8** 1p. mauve 30 10
S35 2p. turquoise 40 15
S36 6p. violet 75 15
S37 35p. blue . . . . 4·25 1·00

9 Hunters on Elephants
10 Ship's Cargo being offloaded at Saigon

1957. 3rd Anniv of Govt of Ngo Dinh Diem.
S38 **9** 20c. purple and green . . . 30 10
S39 30c. red and bistre 40 10
S40 – 90c. sepia and green . . . 50 20
S41 – 2p. blue and green . . . 85 25
S42 – 3p. brown and violet . . . 1·25 40
DESIGN—VERT: 90c. to 3p. Mountain hut.

1957. 9th Colombo Plan Conference, Saigon.
S43 **10** 20c. purple 15 10
S44 40c. olive 20 15
S45 50c. red 35 15
S46 2p. blue 60 25
S47 3p. green 90 30

11 Torch and Constitution
12 Youth felling Tree

1957. Inauguration of National Assembly.
S48 **11** 50c. salmon, green & black 10 10
S49 80c. purple, blue and black 20 10
S50 1p. red, green and black 25 15
S51 4p. brown, myrtle and black 45 20
S52 5p. olive, turquoise & black 60 30
S53 10p. brown, blue and black 1·00 60

1958. Better Living Standards.
S54 **12** 50c. green 25 20
S55 1p. violet 35 20
S56 2p. blue 45 20
S57 10p. red . . . . 1·10 50

13 Young Girl with Chinese Lantern
14

1958. Children's Festival.
S58 **13** 30c. lemon 20 20
S59 50c. red 20 20
S60 2p. red 20 20
S61 3p. green 50 25
S62 4p. olive 60 25

1958. United Nations Day.
S63 **14** 1p. light brown 25 20
S64 2p. turquoise 35 20
S65 4p. red 40 20
S66 5p. purple 90 40

15 U.N.E.S.C.O. Emblem and Building
16 U.N. Emblem and "Torch of Freedom"

1958. Inauguration of U.N.E.S.C.O. Headquarters Building, Paris.
S67 **15** 50c. blue 20 20
S68 2p. red 25 20
S69 3p. purple 40 20
S70 6p. violet 70 40

1958. 10th Anniv of Declaration of Human Rights.
S71 **16** 50c. blue 30 15
S72 1p. lake 40 20
S73 2p. green 60 20
S74 6p. purple 95 45

17 Phu-Cam Cathedral
18 Saigon Museum

1958.
S75 **17** 10c. slate 20 10
S76 – 30c. green 30 20
S77 **18** 40c. green 15 15
S78 – 50c. green 25 15
S79 – 2p. blue 40 20
S80 – 4p. lilac 40 25
S81 **18** 5p. red 55 25
S82 **17** 6p. brown 65 25
DESIGNS—HORIZ: 30c., 4p. Thien Mu Pagoda; 50c., 2p. Palace of Independence, Saigon.

19 Trung Sisters (national heroines) on Elephants

1959. Trung Sisters Commemoration.
S83 **19** 50c. multicoloured 80 55
S84 2p. multicoloured . . . . 1·25 75
S85 3p. multicoloured . . . . 2·40 1·10
S86 6p. multicoloured . . . . 3·00 1·60

20
21 Diesel Train

1959. Agricultural Reform.
S87 **20** 70c. purple 15 10
S88 2p. green and blue 15 10
S89 3p. olive 30 10
S90 6p. red and deep red . . . 65 40

1959. Re-opening of Trans-Vietnam Railway. Centres in green.
S91 **21** 1p. violet 70 20
S92 2p. grey 95 40
S93 3p. blue . . . . 1·10 30
S94 4p. lake . . . . 2·25 50

22 Tilling the Land
25 Scout climbing Mountain

1959. 4th Anniv of Republic.
S95 **22** 1p. brown, green and blue 30 20
S96 2p. violet, green and orange 30 20
S97 4p. indigo, blue and bistre 75 35
S98 5p. brown, olive and light brown 95 50

1959. 1st National Scout Jamboree, Trang Bom.
S 99 **25** 3p. green 45 20
S100 4p. mauve 60 25
S101 8p. mauve and purple . . 1·40 50
S102 20p. dp turquoise & turq 3·00 1·25

26 "Family Code"

1960. 1st Anniv of Family Code.
S103 **26** 20c. green 15 10
S104 30c. blue 25 15
S105 2p. red and orange . . . 25 15
S106 6p. violet and red 60 30

27 Refugee Family in Flight
28 Henri Dunant

1960. World Refugee Year.
S107 **27** 50c. mauve 35 10
S108 3p. green 30 15
S109 4p. red 70 30
S110 5p. violet 80 40

1960. Red Cross Day. Cross in red.
S111 **28** 1p. blue 45 20
S112 3p. green 55 25
S113 4p. red 85 35
S114 6p. mauve . . . . 1·00 55

29 Co-operative Farm

1960. Establishment of Co-operative Rice Farming.
S115 **29** 50c. blue 20 15
S116 1p. green 20 15
S117 3p. orange 50 25
S118 7p. mauve 90 25

30 X-ray Camera and Patient
31 Flag and Map

1960. National T.B. Relief Campaign Day.
S119 **30** 3p.+50c. green and red 60 60

1960. 5th Anniv of Republic. Flag and map in red and yellow.
S120 **31** 50c. turquoise 15 10
S121 1p. blue 20 10
S122 3p. violet 35 10
S123 7p. green 55 25

32 Woman with Rice

1960. F.A.O. Regional Conference, Saigon.

S124	32	2p. turquoise and green	45	25
S125		4p. ultramarine and blue	65	40

33 Crane carrying Letter

1960. Air.

S126	33	1p. green	50	20
S127		4p. blue and turquoise	75	40
S128		5p. violet and brown	1·25	65
S129		10p. mauve	2·25	1·00

34 Farm Tractor 35 Child and Plant

1961. Agricultural Development and Pres. Diem's 60th Birthday.

S130	34	50c. brown	20	10
S131		70c. mauve	25	10
S132		80c. red	25	20
S133		10p. mauve	80	35

1961. Child Welfare.

S134	35	70c. blue	20	10
S135		80c. blue	20	10
S136		4p. bistre	35	20
S137		7p. green and turquoise	75	40

36 Pres. Ngo Dinh Diem 37 Young People and Torch

1961. 2nd Term of President.

S138	36	50c. blue	25	20
S139		1p. red	40	20
S140		2p. purple	50	20
S141		4p. violet	95	35

1961. Sports and Youth.

S142	37	50c. red	15	10
S143		70c. mauve	25	10
S144		80c. mauve and red	35	20
S145		8p. purple and red	75	35

38 Bridge over Mekong

1961. Inaug of Saigon–Bien Hoa Motor Highway.

S146	38	50c. green	25	15
S147		1p. brown	25	15
S148		2p. blue	35	20
S149		5p. purple	60	25

39 Alexander of Rhodes 40 Vietnamese with Torch

1961. Death Tercent of Alexander of Rhodes.

S150	39	50c. red	20	10
S151		1p. purple	20	10
S152		3p. bistre	30	10
S153		6p. green	70	25

1961. Youth Moral Rearmament.

S154	40	50c. red	15	10
S155		1p. green	20	10
S156		3p. red	35	20
S157		8p. brown and purple	70	25

41 Gateway of Van Mieu Temple, Hanoi 42 Tractor and Cottages

1961. 15th Anniv of U.N.E.S.C.O.

S158	41	1p. green	25	10
S159		2p. red	25	20
S160		5p. olive	50	25

1961. Rural Reform.

S161	42	50c. green	20	10
S162		1p. lake and blue	20	20
S163		2p. brown and green	25	20
S164		10p. turquoise	70	45

43 Attack on Mosquito 44 Postal Cheque Building, Saigon

1962. Malaria Eradication.

S165	43	50c. mauve	25	10
S166		1p. orange	25	15
S167		2p. green	35	20
S168		6p. blue	75	25

1962. Inauguration of Postal Cheques Service.

S169	44	70c. green	25	20
S170		80c. brown	25	20
S171		4p. purple	50	20
S172		7p. red	60	40

45 St. Mary of La Vang 46 Armed Guards and Fortified Village

1962. St. Mary of La Vang Commemoration.

S173	45	50c. red and violet	20	10
S174		1p. blue and brown	25	15
S175		2p. lake and brown	40	15
S176		8p. blue and turquoise	90	35

1962. Strategic Villages.

S177	46	50c. red	20	10
S178		1p. bronze	20	15
S179		1p.50 purple	35	15
S180		7p. blue	60	30

47 Gougah Waterfalls, Dalat 48 Trung Sisters Monument

1963. Pres. Ngo Dinh Diem's 62nd Birthday and Spring Festival.

S181	47	60c. red	20	15
S182		1p. blue	35	15

1963. Women's Day.

S183	48	50c. green	20	10
S184		1p. red	25	15
S185		3p. purple	30	20
S186		8p. blue	60	40

49 Harvester

1963. Freedom from Hunger.

S187	49	50c. red	20	10
S188		1p. red	25	15
S189		3p. purple	35	20
S190		5p. violet	60	35

50 Sword and Fortress 51 Soldier and Emblem

1963. Communal Defence and 9th Anniv of Inaug of Pres. Diem.

S191	50	30c. bistre	20	10
S192		50c. mauve	25	15
S193		3p. green	45	20
S194		8p. red	70	35

1963. Republican Combatants.

S195	51	50c. red	15	10
S196		1p. green	20	15
S197		4p. violet	40	20
S198		5p. orange	65	45

52 Centenary Emblem and Globe 53 Scales of Justice and Book

1963. Red Cross Centenary. Cross in red.

S199	52	50c. blue	25	10
S200		1p. red	35	20
S201		3p. orange	45	20
S202		6p. brown	80	45

1963. 15th Anniv of Declaration of Human Rights.

S203	53	70c. orange	20	10
S204		1p. mauve	25	15
S205		3p. green	35	15
S206		8p. ochre	75	35

54 Danhim Hydro-electric Station

1964. Inauguration of Danhim Hydro-electric Station.

S207	54	40c. red	15	10
S208		1p. brown	25	15
S209		3p. violet	35	20
S210		8p. green	65	35

55 Atomic Reactor

1964. Peaceful Uses of Atomic Energy.

S211	55	80c. olive	20	10
S212		1p.50 brown	25	20
S213		3p. brown	45	20
S214		7p. blue	70	40

56 "Meteorology" 57 "Unification"

1964. World Meteorological Day.

S215	56	50c. ochre	20	10
S216		1p. red	25	20
S217		1p.50 lake	35	20
S218		10p. green	65	40

1964. 10th Anniv of Partition of Vietnam.

S219	57	30c. blue and green	15	15
S220		50c. blue, red and yellow	20	15
S221		1p.50 indigo, blue & orange	25	15

58 Hatien Beach

1964.

S222	58	20c. blue	20	10
S223		3p. green	40	15

59 "Support of the People"

1964. 1st Anniv of Revolution of 1 November 1963.

S224	59	50c. blue and purple	25	10
S225	–	80c. brown and lilac	30	20
S226	–	3p. brown and blue	50	20

DESIGNS—HORIZ: 80c. Soldier breaking chain. VERT: 3p. Allegory of Revolution.

60 Temple and Monument, Botanic Gardens, Saigon

1964. Monuments and Views.

S227	60	50c. brown, green and blue	20	15
S228	–	1p. slate and bistre	25	15
S229	–	1p.50 green and drab	40	20
S230	–	3p. red, green and violet	75	25

DESIGNS: 1p. Tomb of Minh Mang, Hue; 1p.50, Phan Thiet waterfront; 3p. General Le Van Duyet Temple, Gia Dinh.

For 1p. in smaller size, see No. S352.

61 Face of Bronze Drum

1965. Hung Vuong (legendary founder of Vietnam, 2000 B.C.).

S231	61	3p. orange and lake	1·90	65
S232		100p. violet and purple	12·00	6·50

62 Dharmachakra and "Fire of Clemency" 63 I.T.U. Emblem and Symbols

1965. Buddhism.

S233	62	50c. red	20	15
S234	–	1p.50 orange, blue and deep blue	20	15
S235	–	3p. deep brown, sepia and brown	40	20

DESIGNS—HORIZ: 1p.50, Dharmachakra, lotus and globe. VERT: 3p. Dharmachakra and flag.

1965. I.T.U. Centenary.

S236	63	1p. red and bistre	25	20
S237		3p. red, mauve and brown	40	20

64 "World Solidarity" 65 Ixora

1965. International Co-operation Year.
S238 **64** 50c. blue and brown . . . 20 15
S239 1p. sepia and brown . . . 25 15
S240 1p.50 red and grey . . . 35 15

1965. Mid-Autumn Festival.
S241 **65** 70c. red, green & dp green 20 15
S242 – 80c. purple, green & mve 30 20
S243 – 1p. yellow, blue and deep blue 50 25
S244 – 1p.50 green and olive . . 60 25
S245 – 3p. orange and green . . 80 40
FLOWERS—VERT: 80c. Orchid; 1p. Chrysanthemum; 3p. "Ochna harmandii". HORIZ: 1p.50, Nenuphar.

66 Student and University Building

1965. Re-opening of Vietnam University.
S246 **66** 50c. brown 20 15
S247 1p. green 25 20
S248 3p. red 40 20
S249 7p. violet 45 25

67 Young Farmers

1965. 10th Anniv of "4-T" Rural Youth Clubs.
S250 **67** 3p. red and green 50 25
S251 – 4p. violet, blue and purple 50 25
DESIGN: 4p. Young farmer and club banner.

68 Basketball **69** Aerial Mast and Equipment

1965. 3rd S.E. Asia Peninsular Games, Kuala Lumpur (Malaysia).
S252 **68** 50c. bistre, brown and red 35 10
S253 – 1p. red and brown . . . 40 20
S254 – 1p.50 green 55 25
S255 – 10p. lake and purple . . . 1·50 60
DESIGNS: 1p. Throwing the javelin; 1p.50, "Physical Culture" (gymnasts and Olympic Games' symbols); 10p. Pole-vaulting.

1966. 1st Anniv of Saigon Microwave Station.
S256 **69** 3p. sepia, blue and brown 25 15
S257 – 4p. purple, red and green 40 20
DESIGN: 4p. Aerial mast, telephone dial and map.

70 Hook and Hemispheres **71** Help for Refugees

1966. "Free World's Aid to Vietnam".
S258 **70** 3p. red and grey 20 10
S259 4p. violet and brown . . 25 15
S260 6p. blue and green . . . 35 20

1966. Refugee Aid.
S261 **71** 3p. olive, mauve & brown 25 15
S262 7p. violet, brown & mauve 40 20

72 Paper "Soldiers"

1966. Wandering Souls' Festival.
S263 **72** 50c. bistre, brown and red 20 10
S264 – 1p.50 red, green & brown 30 15
S265 – 3p. vermilion, crim & red 50 20
S266 – 5p. brown, ochre and deep brown 65 25
DESIGNS: 1p.50, Obeisance; 3p. Pool of candles; 5p. Votive offering.

73 "Violinist"

1966. Ancient Musical Instruments.
S267 **73** 1p. deep brown, mauve and brown 20 10
S268 – 3p. violet and purple . . 25 15
S269 – 4p. brown and red . . . 40 20
S270 – 7p. deep blue and blue . . 75 30
DESIGNS: 3p. "Harpist"; 4p. Small band; 7p. "Flautists".
For 3p. in smaller size, see No. S302.

74 W.H.O. Building

1966. Inaug of W.H.O. Headquarters, Geneva.
S271 **74** 50c. purple, violet and red 20 10
S272 – 1p.50 black, blue and lake 25 15
S273 – 8p. blue, sepia & turquoise 40 20
DESIGNS—VERT: 1p.50, W.H.O. Building and flag; 8p. U.N. flag and W.H.O. Building.

75 Spade in Hand, and Soldiers

1966. 3rd Anniv of Overthrow of Diem Government.
S274 **75** 80c. brown and bistre . . 20 10
S275 – 1p.50 purple, red & yell 20 15
S276 – 3p. green, brown & chest 25 20
S277 – 4p. lake, black and purple 65 35
DESIGNS—HORIZ: 1p.50, Agricultural workers, soldier and flag. VERT: 3p. Soldier, tractor and labourers; 4p. Soldier and horseman.

76 U.N.E.S.C.O. Emblem and Tree **77** Cashew Apples

1966. 20th Anniv of U.N.E.S.C.O.
S278 **76** 1p. brown and lake . . . 20 10
S279 – 3p. brown, turquoise & blue 25 20
S280 – 7p. blue, turquoise and red 65 30
DESIGNS—VERT: 3p. Globe and laurel sprigs. HORIZ: 7p. Pagoda.

1967. Exotic Fruits.
S281 **77** 50c. red, green and blue 30 10
S282 – 1p.50 orange, green & brown 30 15
S283 – 3p. brown, green & choc 45 20
S284 – 20p. olive, green and lake 1·50 65
FRUITS—HORIZ: 1p.50, Bitter "cucumbers"; 3p. Cinnamon apples; 20p. Areca-nuts.

78 Phan Boi Chau

1967. Vietnamese Patriots.
S285 **78** 1p. purple, brown and red 25 10
S286 – 20p. black, violet & green 90 50
DESIGN: 20p. Phan Chau-Trinh (portrait and making speech).

79 Horse-cab

1967. Life of the People.
S287 – 50c. ultramarine, blue & green 20 10
S288 – 1p. violet, green & myrtle 25 10
S289 **79** 3p. lake and red 30 15
S290 – 8p. violet and red 50 20
DESIGNS: 50c. Itinerant merchant; 1p. Market-place; 8p. Pastoral activities.

80 Pottery-making

1967. Arts and Crafts. Multicoloured.
S291 50c. Type **80** 20 10
S292 1p.50 Wicker basket and vase 25 20
S293 3p. Weavers and potters . . 40 25
S294 35p. Baskets and pottery . . 1·75 90
The 3p. is a horiz design.

81 Wedding Procession

1967. Vietnamese Wedding.
S295 **81** 3p. red, violet and purple 50 25

82 "Culture"

1967. Foundation of Vietnamese Cultural Institute.
S296 **82** 10p. multicoloured . . . 50 25

83 "Freedom and Justice"

1967. Democratic Elections. Multicoloured.
S297 4p. Type **83** 30 20
S298 5p. Vietnamese and hands casting votes 45 25
S299 30p. Two Vietnamese with Constitution and flaming torch . . . . 1·25 65

84 Lions Emblem and Pagoda

1967. 50th Anniv of Lions International.
S300 **84** 3p. multicoloured 75 40

85 Class on Globe

1967. World Literacy Day (8 Sept).
S301 **85** 3p. multicoloured 55 15

1967. Mobile Post Office Inaug. As No. S268 but smaller, size 23 × 17 mm.
S302 3p. violet and purple . . . 12·00 10·00

87 Tractor

1968. Rural Development. Multicoloured.
S303 1p. Type **87** 30 20
S304 9p. Bulldozer 35 20
S305 10p. Workers with wheel-barrow and tractor . . . 50 20
S306 20p. Building construction 1·00 40

88 W.H.O. Emblem

1968. 20th Anniv of W.H.O.
S307 **88** 10p. yellow, black & green 50 25

89 Flags of Allied Nations

1968. Thanks for International Aid. Mult.
S308 1p. Handclasp, flags and soldiers 45 10
S309 1p.50 S.E.A.T.O. emblem and flags 50 20
S310 3p. Handclasp and flags . . 70 25
S311 50p. Type **89** . . . . 3·25 90

92 Farmers, Farm, Factory and Transport **93** Human Rights Emblem

1968. Development of Private Ownership. Mult.
S318 80c. Type **92** 20 10
S319 2p. Motor vehicles and labourers 20 10
S320 10p. Tractor and tri-car . . 40 20
S321 30p. Motor vehicles and labourers . . . . 1·40 60

1968. Human Rights Year. Multicoloured.
S322 10p. Type **93** 40 15
S323 16p. Men of all races acclaiming Human Rights Emblem 55 25

94 Children with U.N.I.C.E.F. "Kite"

1968. U.N.I.C.E.F. Day. Multicoloured.
S324 6p. Type **94** 45 20
S325 16p. Mother and child . . . 70 25

95 Diesel Train, Map and Mechanical Loader

97 Peasant Woman

1968. Re-opening of Trans-Vietnam Railway. Mult.

S326 1p.50 Type **95** 50 20

S327 3p. Type **95** 75 25

S328 9p. Diesel train and permanent-way workers 1·25 45

S329 20p. As No. S328 . . . . . 3·25 1·25

1969. Vietnamese Women.

S331 **97** 50c. violet, ochre and blue 20 10

S332 – 1p. brown and green . . 20 15

S333 – 3p. black, blue and sepia 35 15

S334 – 20p. multicoloured . . . 70 40

DESIGNS—VERT: 1p. Tradeswoman; 20p. "Ladies of fashion". HORIZ: 3p. Nurse.

98 Soldier and Militiaman

1969. "Open-arms" National Unity Campaign. Mult.

S335 2p. Type **98** 30 20

S336 50p. Family welcoming soldier . . . . 1·25 50

99 Vietnamese and Scales of Justice

1969. 1st Anniv of New Constitution. Mult.

S337 1p. Type **99** 25 10

S338 20p. Voters at polling station 50 35

100 Mobile Post Office Van in Street

1969. Vietnamese Mobile Post Offices System. Multicoloured.

S339 1p. Type **100** 25 10

S340 3p. Clerk serving customers 25 15

S341 4p. Child with letter, and mobile post office 35 20

S342 20p. Queue at mobile post office, and postmark . . . 60 40

101 Djarai Woman

1969. 2nd Anniv of Ethnic Minorities Statute. Multicoloured.

S343 1p. Type **101** 45 25

S344 6p. Mnong-gar woman . . 1·00 40

S345 50p. Bahnar man . . . . . 5·00 1·75

102 "Civilians to Soldiers"

1969. General Mobilization.

S346 **102** 1p.50 multicoloured . . 15 10

S347 – 3p. multicoloured . . . 20 10

S348 – 5p. brown, red and yellow 35 20

S349 – 10p. multicoloured . . . 40 25

DESIGNS: 3p. Bayonet practice; 5p. Recruits arriving at depot; 10p. Happy conscripts.

103 I.L.O. Emblem and Globe

104 Imperial Palace, Hue

1969. 50th Anniv of I.L.O.

S350 **103** 6p. black, grey and green 25 10

S351 20p. black, grey and red 65 25

1970. Reconstruction of Hue.

S352 **104** 1p. blue and brown . . 6·50 6·50

105 Asian Golden Weaver and Baya Weaver

1970. Birds of Vietnam. Multicoloured.

S353 2p. Type **105** 80 40

S354 6p. Chestnut mannikin . . . 1·50 80

S355 7p. Great Indian hornbill 2·25 1·40

S356 30p. Eurasian tree sparrow 11·25 3·25

106 Ruined House and Family

1970. Aid for Victims of Communist Tet Offensive. Multicoloured.

S357 10p. Type **106** 40 20

S358 20p. Refugee family, and First Aid 55 30

107 Man, Woman and Priest in Traditional Costume

1970. Vietnamese Traditional Costumes. Mult.

S359 1p. Type **107** 25 10

S360 2p. Seated woman (horiz) 25 10

S361 3p. Three women with carved lion (horiz) . . . 35 20

S362 100p. Man and woman (horiz) . . . . 3·00 1·75

108 Builders and Pagoda

1970. Reconstruction of Hue. Multicoloured.

S363 6p. Type **108** 45 25

S364 20p. Mixing cement 85 40

109 Ploughing Paddyfield

1970. "Land to the Tiller". Agrarian Reform Law.

S365 **109** 6p. black, green & brown 45 25

110 Scaffolding and New Building

1970. Reconstruction after Tet Offensive. Mult.

S366 8p. Type **110** 40 20

S367 16p. Construction workers 55 25

111 A.P.Y. Symbol

1970. Asian Productivity Year.

S368 **111** 10p. multicoloured . . . 50 25

112 Nguyen Dinh Chieu and Poems

113 I.E.Y. Emblem

1970. Nguyen Dinh Chieu (poet) Commem.

S369 **112** 6p. brown, red and violet 25 20

S370 10p. brown, red & green 50 25

1970. International Education Year.

S371 **113** 10p. black, yellow & brown 50 20

114 Senate House

115 Two Dancers

1970. 9th Council Meeting and 6th General Assembly of Asian Interparliamentary Union, Saigon. Multicoloured.

S372 6p. Type **114** 25 20

S373 10p. House of Representatives 50 20

1971. Vietnamese Traditional Dances.

S374 **115** 2p. multicoloured . . . 30 10

S375 – 6p. brown, blue & green 45 20

S376 – 7p. red, blue and brown 65 25

S377 – 10p. multicoloured . . . 80 35

DESIGNS—HORIZ: 6p. Drum dance; 7p. Drum dancers in various positions. VERT: 10p. Flower dance.

116 Paddyfield, Peasants and Agrarian Law

1971. 1st Anniv of "Land to the Tiller" Agrarian Reform Law. Multicoloured.

S378 2p. Type **116** (dated "26.3.1971") 30 20

S378a 2p. Type **116** (dated "26.3.1970") . . . . . .

S379 3p. Tractor and Law . . . 30 20

S380 16p. Peasants ringing Law 45 25

117 Postal Courier

119 Hog-deer

118 Armed Forces on Map of Vietnam

1971. History of Vietnam Postal Service. Mult.

S381 2p. Type **117** 35 20

S382 6p. Mounted courier with banner 75 30

1971. Armed Forces Day.

S383 **118** 3p. multicoloured . . . 35 25

S384 40p. multicoloured . . . 1·60 70

1971. Vietnamese Fauna. Multicoloured.

S385 9p. Type **119** 75 20

S386 30p. Tiger . . . . 1·50 50

120 Rice Harvesters

1971. "The Rice Harvest".

S387 **120** 1p. multicoloured . . . 25 10

S388 – 30p. lilac, black and red 75 25

S389 – 40p. brown, yellow & blue . . . . 1·00 45

DESIGNS: 30p. Threshing and winnowing rice; 40p. Harvesters in paddyfield.

121 New H.Q. Building

1971. New U.P.U. Headquarters Building, Berne.

S390 **121** 20p. multicoloured . . . 80 40

122 Percoid fish

123 "Local Delivery"

1971. Vietnam Fishes. Multicoloured.

S391 2p. Type **122** 50 15

S392 10p. Striped scat (horiz) . . 1·60 30

S393 100p. Freshwater angelfish (horiz) . . . . 11·25 3·75

1971. Development of Rural Post System. Mult.

S394 5p. Type **123** 30 15

S395 10p. Symbolic crane 60 25

S396 20p. Cycle postman delivering letter 70 25

124 Fishermen in Boat, and Modern Trawler

1972. Vietnamese Fishing Industry. Multicoloured.

S397 4p. Type **124** 45 25

S398 7p. Fishermen hauling net 35 25

S399 50p. Trawl net . . . . . . 2·00 1·00

125 Emperor Quang Trung

126 Community Workers

1972. Emperor Quang Trung (victor of Dong Da) Commemoration.

S400 **125** 6p. multicoloured . . . 25 10

S401 20p. multicoloured . . . 65 30

1972. Community Development Projects.

S403 **126** 3p. multicoloured . . . 15 10

S404 8p. multicoloured . . . 25 10

127 Harvesting Rice

1972. Farmers' Day. Multicoloured.
S405 1p. Type **127** 20 10
S406 10p. Sowing rice 30 15

128 Boeing 727 over Dalat

1972. 20th Anniv of Viet-Nam Airlines. Mult.
S407 10p. Type **128** 65 30
S408 10p. Boeing 727 over Ha Tien 65 30
S409 10p. Boeing 727 over Hue 65 30
S410 10p. Boeing 727 over Saigon 65 30
S411 25p. Type **128** 95 65
S412 25p. As No. S408 . . . . . 95 65
S413 25p. As No. S409 . . . . . 95 65
S414 25p. As No. S410 . . . . . 95 65

129 Vietnamese Scholar

130 Sentry

1972. Vietnamese Scholars. Multicoloured.
S415 5p. Type **129** 20 10
S416 20p. Scholar with pupils . . 45 25
S417 50p. Scholar with scroll . . 1·50 50

1972. Civilian Self-defence Force. Multicoloured.
S418 2p. Type **130** 20 10
S419 6p. Young volunteer and badge (horiz) 25 20
S420 20p. Volunteers at rifle practice 50 35

131 Hands supporting Savings Bank

1972. Treasury Bonds Savings Scheme.
S421 **131** 10p. multicoloured . . . 25 10
S422 25p. multicoloured . . . 50 20

132 Three Guards with Horse

133 Wounded Soldier

1972. Traditional Vietnamese Frontier Guards. Mult.
S423 10p. Type **132** 35 20
S424 30p. Pikeman (vert) 65 35
S425 40p. Guards on parade . . . 95 50

1972. Vietnamese War Veterans. Multicoloured.
S426 9p. Type **133** 15 10
S427 16p. Soldier on crutches . . 40 20
S428 100p. Veterans' memorial . . 3·00 1·10

134 Soldiers on Tank, and Memorial

1972. Victory at Binh Long. Mulicoloured.
S429 5p. Type **134** 20 10
S430 10p. Soldiers on map of An Loc (vert) . . . . 1·50 40

135 "Books for Everyone"

136 "200,000th Returnees"

1972. International Book Year. Multicoloured.
S431 2p. Type **135** 15 10
S432 4p. Book Year emblems encircling globe 20 10
S433 5p. Emblem, books and globe 50 20

1973. 200,000th Returnees under "Open Arms" National Unity Campaign.
S434 **136** 10p. multicoloured . . . 50 25

137 Soldiers raising Flag

138 Satellite and Globe

1973. Victory at Quang Tri. Multicoloured.
S435 3p. Type **137** 65 10
S436 10p. Map and defenders . . 95 20

1973. World Meteorological Day.
S437 **138** 1p. multicoloured . . . 60 15

139 Programme Emblem and Farm-workers

1973. Five-Year Agricultural Development Programme. Multicoloured.
S438 2p. Type **139** . . . . 1·50 15
S439 5p. Ploughing in paddy-field . . . . 1·50 15
S439a 10p. As T **149** but dated "26-03-1973" (34 × 54 mm) . . . . . 40·00

140 Emblem and H.Q. Paris

1973. 50th Anniv of International Criminal Police Organization (Interpol). Multicoloured.
S440 1p. Type **140** 10 10
S441 2p. "INTERPOL 1923 1973" 20 15
S442 25p. Emblem and view of headquarters (different) 1·40 25

141 I.T.U. Emblem

142 Lamp in Hand

1973. World Telecommunications Day.
S443 **141** 1p. multicoloured . . . 15 15
S444 – 2p. black and blue . . . 35 15
S445 – 3p. multicoloured . . . 60 15
DESIGNS: 2p. Globe; 3p. I.T.U. emblem in frame.

1973. National Development.
S446 **142** 8p. multicoloured . . . 30 15
S447 – 10p. blue, black & brown 70 15
S448 – 15p. multicoloured . . . 70 15
DESIGNS: 10p. "Agriculture, Industry and Fisheries"; 15p. Workers on power pylon.

143 Water Buffaloes

1973. "Year of the Buffalo". Multicoloured.
S449 5p. Type **143** 50 15
S450 10p. Water buffalo 75 20

144 Flame Emblem and "Races of the World"

1973. 25th Anniv of Declaration of Human Rights. Multicoloured.
S451 15p. Type **144** 45 15
S452 100p. Flame emblem and scales of justice (vert) . . 1·50 30

145 Emblem within "25"

1973. 25th Anniv of W.H.O.
S453 **145** 8p. multicoloured . . . 40 15
S454 – 15p. blue, red and brown 60 15
DESIGN: 15p. W.H.O. emblem and inscription.

146 Sampan crossing River

1974. Vietnamese Sampan Women. Multicoloured.
S455 5p. Type **146** 60 25
S456 10p. Sampan and passengers 95 25

147 Flags and Soldiers of Allies

1974. Allies Day. Multicoloured.
S457 8p. Type **147** 25 15
S458 15p. Soldiers and flags . . . 60 15
S459 15p. Allied Nations Monument 60 15
S460 60p. Raising South Vietnamese flag, and map (vert) . . . . 1·75 30

148 Trung Sisters on Elephant

1974. Trung Sisters' Festival.
S461 **148** 8p. green, yellow & black 30 25
S462 15p. red, yellow and black 45 25
S463 80p. blue, pink and black 95 40

149 Pres. Thieu holding Agrarian Reform Law

1974. Farmers' Day. Multicoloured.
S464 10p. Type **149** 60 15
S465 20p. Farm-workers (32 × 22 mm) 35 15
S466 70p. Girl harvesting rice (22 × 32 mm) 60 35

150 King Hung Vuong

1974. King Hung Vuong (first Vietnamese monarch) Commemoration. Multicoloured.
S467 20p. Type **150** 40 25
S468 100p. Banner inscribed "Hung Vuong, National Founder" . . . . 1·50 60

151 National Library

152 Allied Nations Memorial, Saigon

1974. New National Library Building. Mult.
S469 10p. Type **151** 35 20
S470 15p. Library and Phoenix bas-relief 50 25

1974. Surch.
S470a **142** 10p. on 8p. mult . . .
S470b **145** 10p. on 8p. mult . . .
S470c **120** 25p. on 1p. mult . . .
S470d **140** 25p. on 1p. mult . . .
S470e **138** 25p. on 1p. mult . . .
S470f **141** 25p. on 1p. mult . . .
S470g – 25p. on 7p. red, blue and brown (No. S376) . . . .
S470h **147** 25p. on 8p. mult . . .
S470i – 25p. on 16p. mult (No. S427) . . . .
S470j – 25p. on 16p. mult (No. S380) . . . .

1974. International Aid Day. Multicoloured.
S471 10p. Type **152** 35 10
S472 20p. Flags on crane (horiz) 75 15
S473 60p. Crate on hoist . . . . 2·50 35

153 "Tourist Attractions"

1974. Tourism. Multicoloured.
S474 5p. Type **153** 45 15
S475 10p. Xom Bong Bridge Nhatrang 45 15
S476 15p. Thien Mu Pagoda, Hue (vert) 80 15

154 "Rhynchostylis gigantea"

1974. Orchids. Multicoloured.
S477 10p. Type **154** 20 15
S478 20p. "Cypripedium callosum" (vert) 30 15
S479 200p. "Dendrobium nobile" 3·25 1·00

155 "International Exchange of Mail"

157 Conference Emblem

156 Hien Lam Pavilion, Hue

1974. Centenary of U.P.U. Multicoloured.
S480 20p. Type **155** 50 20
S481 30p. "U.P.U. letter" and Hemispheres 90 20
S482 300p. U.P.U. emblem and Vietnamese girl (vert) . . 3·00 1·25

1975. Historical Sites. Multicoloured.
S483 25p. Type **156** 50 10
S484 30p. Throne Room, Imperial Palace, Hue . . 60 20
S485 60p. Tu Duc's Pavilion, Hue 1·10 25

1975. International Conference on Children and National Development, Saigon. Multicoloured.
S486 20p. Type **157** 35 20
S487 70p. Vietnamese family (32 × 22 mm) . . . . . . 1·25 25

158 Unicorn Dance

1975. Vietnamese New Year Festival. Mult.
S488 20p. Type **158** 40 20
S489 30p. Letting-off fire-crackers (vert) 55 30
S490 100p. New Year greeting custom (vert) . . . . . . 1·25 60

159 Military Mandarin ("San Hau" play)

1975. "Hat Bo" Vietnamese Traditional Theatre. Multicoloured.
S491 25p. Type **159** 50 20
S492 40p. Two characters from "Tam Ha Nam Duong" (vert) 75 35
S493 100p. Heroine "Luu Kim Giai Gia Tho Chau" (vert) . . . . 2·50 1·10

160 Produce for Export and Map

1975. Farmers' Day. Multicoloured.
S494 10p. Type **160** 25 15
S495 50p. Ancient and modern irrigation 75 30

MILITARY FRANK STAMPS

MF 29 Soldier and Barracks

1961. No value indicated. Roul.
SMF115 MF **29** (–) yellow, brown, green and black . . . . . 5·00 5·00
SMF116 (–) yellow, brown and green . . . 6·00 6·00

POSTAGE DUE STAMPS

D 1 Dragon

1955.
SD 1 D **1** 2p. yellow and mauve 40 40
SD 2 3p. turquoise and violet 45 45
SD 3 5p. yellow and violet 75 60
SD 4 10p. red and green . . 95 70
SD14 – 20p. green and red . . 2·50 1·60
SD15 – 30p. yellow and green 3·75 2·50
SD16 – 50p. yellow and brown 8·00 5·75
SD17 – 100p. yellow and violet 12·50 10·00
The 20p. to 100p. are inscribed "BUU-CHINH" instead of "TIMBRE TAXE".

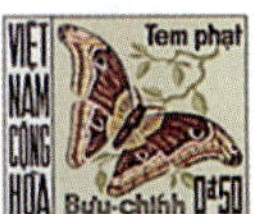

D 90 Butterfly

D 91 Butterflies

1968.
SD312 D **90** 50c. multicoloured 55 50
SD313 1p. multicoloured . . 55 50
SD314 2p. multicoloured . . 1·00 95
SD315 D **91** 3p. multicoloured . . 1·40 1·25
SD316 5p. multicoloured . . 2·50 2·40
SD317 10p. multicoloured 4·00 3·50

1974. Surch.
SD470k D **91** 5p. on 3p. mult . . 5·00
SD470l D **90** 10p. on 50c. mult 5·00
SD470m 40p. on 1p. mult 5·00
SD470n 60p. on 2p. mult 5·00

D. NATIONAL FRONT FOR THE LIBERATION OF SOUTH VIETNAM

The National Front for the Liberation of South Vietnam was formed by the Communists, known as the Vietcong, in December 1960. With the support of troops from North Vietnam the Vietcong gradually gained control of more and more territory within South Vietnam until the surrender of the last South Vietnamese Republican forces in May 1975 enabled them to take control of the entire country. The following stamps were used in those areas controlled by the National Liberation Front.

1963. 100 xu = 1 dong.

The value of the N.L.F. dong fluctuated considerably and was not on parity with the North Vietnamese currency.

1 Vietcong Flag

1963. 3rd Anniv of National Liberation Front.
NLF1 **1** 20x. multicoloured (English inscr) . . . . 3·25 2·75
NLF2 20x. multicoloured (French inscr) . . . . 3·25 2·75
NLF3 20x. multicoloured (Spanish inscr) . . . . 3·25 2·75

2 Attack on Village

1963. 3rd Anniv of Revolutionary Struggle in South Vietnam. Multicoloured.
NLF4 10x. Type **2** . . . . 2·50 1·50
NLF5 10x. Attack on U.S. helicopter . . . . 2·50 1·50

3 Demonstrators with Banner

1964. 4th Anniv of National Liberation Front.
NLF6 10x. Type **3** . . . . 1·00 1·00
NLF7 20x. multicoloured . . . . 1·40 1·40
NLF8 30x. green and blue . . . 3·00 2·25
DESIGNS: 20x. Harvesting rice; 30x. Sinking of U.S.S. "Card" (destroyer).

4 Attack on Bien Hoa Airfield

1965. 5th Anniv of National Liberation Front.
NLF 9 **4** 10x. multicoloured . . . 75 75
NLF10 – 20x. black, grey and red 1·10 1·10
NLF11 – 40x. multicoloured . . . 5·25 5·25
DESIGNS: 20x. Nguyen Van Troi facing firing squad; 40x. Vietcong flags.

5 Vietcong Soldiers on U.S. Tanks

6 "Guerrilla"

1967. 7th Anniv of National Liberation Front. Mult.
NLF12 20x. Type **5** 70 60
NLF13 20x. Vietcong guerrillas (horiz) 70 60
NLF14 30x. Crowd with banners 1·50 1·50

1968. "The Struggle For Freedom". Paintings. Mult.
NLF15 10x. Type **6** 70 70
NLF16 20x. "Jungle Patrol" (horiz) 90 90
NLF17 30x. "Woman Soldier" 1·50 1·50
NLF18 40x. "Towards the Future" (horiz) . . . . 2·25 2·25

7 Casting Votes

1968. 8th Anniv of National Liberation Front. Mult.
NLF19 20x. Type **7** 35 35
NLF20 20x. Bazooka crew and burning airplane . . . 35 35
NLF21 30x. Vietcong flag and crowd (French inscr) 70 70
NLF22 30x. Vietcong flag and crowd (English inscr) 70 70

8 Lenin and Vietcong Flag

1970. Birth Centenary of Lenin.
NLF23 **8** 20x. multicoloured . . . 30 20
NLF24 30x. multicoloured . . . 35 30
NLF25 50x. multicoloured . . . 50 35
NLF26 2d. multicoloured . . . 1·90 1·40

9 Ho Chi Minh watering Kainito Plant

10 Vietcong "Lightning Flash"

1970. 80th Birth Anniv of Ho Chi Minh.
NLF27 **9** 20x. multicoloured . . . 30 20
NLF28 30x. multicoloured . . . 35 30
NLF29 50x. multicoloured . . . 50 35
NLF30 2d. multicoloured . . . 1·60 1·40

1970. 10th Anniv of National Liberation Front.
NLF31 **10** 20x. multicoloured . . 30 20
NLF32 30x. multicoloured . . 35 30
NLF33 50x. multicoloured . . 55 50
NLF34 3d. multicoloured . . . 3·00 2·25

11 Home Guards defending Village

1971. 10th Anniv of People's Liberation Armed Forces. Multicoloured.
NLF35 20x. Type **11** 65 65
NLF36 30x. Surrender of U.S. tank . . . . 1·00 1·00
NLF37 50x. Agricultural workers 1·40 1·40
NLF38 1d. Vietcong ambush . . 2·25 2·25

12 Children in School

13 Harvesting Rice

14 Ho Chi Minh with Vietcong Soldiers

1971. 2nd Anniv of Provisional Government. Life in Liberated Areas. Multicoloured.
NLF39 20x. Type **12** 20 20
NLF40 30x. Women sewing Vietcong flag 35 35
NLF41 40x. Fortifying village . . 1·10 1·10
NLF42 50x. Medical clinic . . . 1·50 1·50
NLF43 1d. Harvesting . . . . . 2·25 2·25

1974. 5th Anniv of Provisional Government. Mult.
NLF44 10d. Type **13** 20 20
NLF45 10d. Demonstrators with banner 20 20
NLF46 10d. Schoolchildren . . . 20 20
NLF47 10d. Women home guards 20 20
NLF48 10d. Vietcong conference delegate 20 20
NLF49 10d. Soldiers and tanks 20 20
NLF50 10d. Type **14** 30 30
NLF51 20d. Type **14** 80 80
For other values as Type **14**, see Nos. NLF57/60.

15 Ho Chi Minh watering Kainito Plant

1975. 85th Birth Anniv of Ho Chi Minh (1st issue).
NLF52 **15** 5d. multicoloured . . 20 20
NLF53 10d. multicoloured . . 25 25
NLF54 30d. mult (mve frame) 1·50 1·50
NLF54a 30d. mult (grn frame) 1·50 1·50

1975. 15th Anniv of National Front for Liberation of South Vietnam. As T **14** but 35½ × 26 mm.
NLF55 **14** 15d. black and green 50 50
NLF56 30d. black and red . . 1·00 1·00
NLF57 60d. black and blue . . 1·50 1·50
NLF58 300d. black and yellow 4·50 4·50

1975. 85th Birth Anniv of Ho Chi Minh (2nd issue). As T **284** of North Vietnam, but inscr "MIEN NAM VIET NAM".
NLF59 30d. multicoloured . . . 60 60
NLF60 60d. multicoloured . . . 1·10 1·10

1976. Various stamps surch in South Vietnamese currency.
NLF61 – 10p. on 1d. multicoloured (No. NLF38) . . . . . .
NLF62 – 20p. on 6x. yellow and red (No. NLF75) . .
NLF63 – 20p. on 20x. multicoloured (No. NLF27) . . . . . .
NLF64 – 20p. on 40x. multicoloured (No. NLF11) . . . . . .
NLF65 **9** 20p. on 2d. multicoloured (No. NLF30) . . . . . .
NLF66 **15** 20p. on 5d. multicoloured (No. NLF52) . . . . . .
NLF67 **14** 20p. on 10d. multicoloured (No. NLF50) . . . . . .
NLF68 **15** 20p. on 10d. multicoloured (No. NLF53) . . . . . .
NLF69 20p. on 30d. multicoloured (No. NLF54) . . . . . .
NLF70 20p. on 30d. mult (No. NLF54a) . . . . .

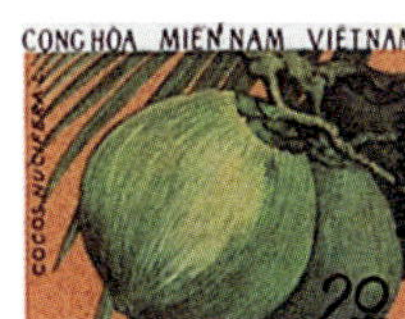

17 "Cocos nucifera"

1976. Fruits. Multicoloured.
NLF71 20d. Type **17** 80 80
NLF72 30d. "Garcinia mangostana" . . . . . 1·25 1·25
NLF73 60d. "Nargifera indica" 2·50 2·50

1976. First Elections to Unified National Assembly. As Nos. N858/60 of North Vietnam, but inscr "MIEN NAM VIET NAM".
NLF74 6x. red and blue (as No. N858) 20 20
NLF75 6x. yellow and red (as No. N859) 20 20
NLF76 12x. red and green (as No. N860) 50 50

18 Flag of Provisional Revolutionary Government

1976. 1st Anniv of Liberation of South Vietnam.
NLF77 **18** 30d. multicoloured . . 60 50

1976. 1st Session of Unified National Assembly. As Nos. N861/2 of North Vietnam, but inscr "MIEN NAM VIET NAM".

NLF78 6x. brown, red and yellow . . 20 20
NLF79 12x. turquoise, red & yell . . 40 40

The unified National Assembly proclaimed the reunification of Vietnam on 2 July 1976 and the united country was then known as the Socialist Republic of Vietnam.

E. NORTH VIETNAM

(Vietnam Democratic Republic)

Issues before April 1954 were made in Tongking and Central Annam, in areas under Viet Minh control. From 21 July 1954 French troops withdrew from north of the 17th Parallel and the Ho Chi Minh Government assumed complete control.

1946. 100 cents = 1 dong.
1959. 100 xu = 1 dong.

GUM. All stamps were issued without gum unless otherwise stated.

I. TONGKING

1946. No. 190 of Indo-China optd **V VIET-NAM N DAN-CHU CONG-HOA BUU CHINH.**

N1 25c. blue . . . . 60·00 60·00

2 Ho Chi Minh

5 Blacksmith

3 Ho Chi Minh and Vietnam Map

1948.

N2a 2 2d. brown . . . . 10·00
N3a 5d. red . . . . 10·00

1951. Imperf or perf.

N4 3 100d. green . . . . 3·00 3·00
N5 100d. brown . . . . 3·00 3·00
N6 200d. red . . . . 3·00 3·00

1953. Production Campaign.

N11 5 100d. violet . . . . 4·25 1·25
N12 500d. brown . . . . 8·00 3·75

7 Malenkov, Ho Chi Minh, Mao Tse-tung and Flags

1954. Friendship Month.

N13 7 100d. red . . . . 18·00 18·00

II. CENTRAL ANNAM

NA 1 Ho Chi Minh

1950. Imperf. (a) Figures of value in white.

NA1 NA 1 1d. violet . . . . . .
NA2 1d. green . . . . . .
NA3 5d. green . . . . . .
NA4 15d. brown . . . . .

(b) Figures coloured.

NA7 NA 1 300d. blue £325 £325
NA8 500d. red £700 £700

1952. Surch in figures. Imperf. (a) Figures in white.

NA5 NA 1 30d. on 5d. green . . £200 £170
NA6 60d. on 1d. violet . . £250 £225
NA8a 90d. on 3d. red . . .

(b) Figures coloured.

NA8b NA 1 5d. on 10d. mauve
NA8c 100d. on 300d. blue

III. GENERAL ISSUES

8 Malenkov, Ho Chi Minh and Mao Tse-tung

1954.

N14 8 50d. brown and red . . . . 18·00 18·00
N15 100d. red and yellow . . . 20·00 20·00

9 Battlefield

1954. Dien Bien Phu Victory. Imperf or perf.

N16a 9 10d. bistre and red . . . 10·00 2·50
N17a 50d. ochre and red . . . 10·00 2·75
N18d 150d. blue and brown . . 10·00 4·50

See also No. NO24.

1954. (a) Handstamped **10 dNH.**

N19 3 10d. on 100d. green . . . . 5·00 5·00
N20 10d. on 100d. brown . . . . 7·00 7·00
N21 20d. on 200d. red . . . . . 5·00 5·00

(b) Handstamped **10d.**

N22 3 10d. on 100d. green . . . . 6·00 6·00
N25 10d. on 100d. brown . . . . 10·00 10·00
N28 20d. on 200d. red . . . . . 10·00 10·00

See also Nos. N46/9.

12 Lake of the Returned Sword, Hanoi

1954. Proclamation of Hanoi as Capital.

N30 12 10d. blue . . . . 3·75 3·75
N31 50d. green . . . . 3·75 3·75
N32 150d. red . . . . 7·50 7·50

13 Distribution of Title Deeds

1955. Land Reform.

N33 13 5d. green . . . . 6·00 6·00
N34 10d. grey . . . . 6·00 6·00
N35 20d. orange . . . . 7·50 7·50
N36 50d. mauve . . . . 18·00 18·00
N37 100d. brown . . . . . . 28·00 28·00

14 Crowd welcoming Steam Train

1956. Hanoi–China Railway Re-opening.

N38 14 100d. blue . . . . 22·00 16·00
N39 200d. turquoise . . . . . 22·00 17·00
N40 300d. violet . . . . . . 40·00 29·00
N41 500d. brown . . . . . . 50·00 36·00

15 Parade, Ba Dinh Square, Hanoi

1956. Return of Govt to Hanoi.

N42 15 1000d. violet . . . . . . 50·00 38·00
N43 1500d. blue . . . . 75·00 55·00
N44 2000d. turquoise . . . . . 75·00 55·00
N45 3000d. turquoise . . . . . 85·00 80·00

1956. Surch **10 d** in frame.

N46 3 10d. on 100d. green . . . . 14·00 14·00
N48 10d. on 100d. brown . . . . 16·00 16·00
N49 20d. on 200d. red . . . . . 12·00 12·00

17 Tran Dang Ninh

1956. 1st Death Anniv of Tran Dang Ninh (patriot).

N50 17 5d. green . . . . 4·00 1·75
N51 10d. red . . . . 4·00 1·75
N52 20d. brown . . . . 5·00 2·40
N53 100d. blue . . . . 5·50 3·00

18 Mac Thi Buoi

1956. 5th Death Anniv of Mac Thi Buoi (guerilla heroine).

N54 18 1000d. red . . . . 12·00 8·00
N55 2000d. brown . . . . . . 19·00 9·25
N56 4000d. green . . . . . . 30·00 23·00
N57 5000d. blue . . . . 50·00 28·00

19 Bai Thuong Dam

1956. Reconstruction of Bai Thuong Dam.

N58 19 100d. violet and brown . . 6·75 6·00
N59 200d. red and black . . . 10·00 6·00
N60a 300d. red and lake . . . 13·50 11·50

1956. Surch **50 DONG.**

N61 2 50d. on 5d. red . . . . . . 50·00 70·00

21 Cotton Mill

1957. 1st Anniv of Opening of Nam Dinh Mill.

N62 21 100d. brown and red . . . . 5·00 5·00
N63 200d. grey and blue . . . 5·75 5·75
N64 300d. light green and green . . . . 7·50 7·50

22 Pres. Ho Chi Minh

23 Arms of Republic

1957. President's 67th Birthday.

N65 22 20d. green . . . . 2·50 1·75
N66 60d. bistre . . . . 2·50 1·75
N67 100d. blue . . . . 3·00 2·75
N68 300d. brown . . . . . . 5·00 4·00

1957. 12th Anniv of Democratic Republic.

N69 23 20d. green . . . . 2·75 2·25
N70 100d. red . . . . 5·75 3·75

24 Congress Emblem

1957. 4th World T.U. Congress, Leipzig.

N71 24 300d. purple . . . . . . 7·50 5·00

See also Nos. NO69/72.

26 Open-air Class

27 Girl Gymnast

1958. Education Campaign.

N75 26 50d. blue . . . . 4·75 3·75
N76 150d. red . . . . 7·00 5·50
N77 1000d. brown . . . . . . 16·00 9·00

1958. Physical Education.

N78 27 150d. brown and blue . . 11·00 9·00
N79 500d. brown and rose . . 18·00 14·00

28

29 Congress Emblem

1958. Labour Day.

N80 28 50d. yellow and red . . . 3·25 2·10
N81 150d. red and yellow . . . 5·00 3·75

1958. 4th International Congress of Democratic Women, Vienna.

N82 29 150d. blue . . . . 7·00 5·75

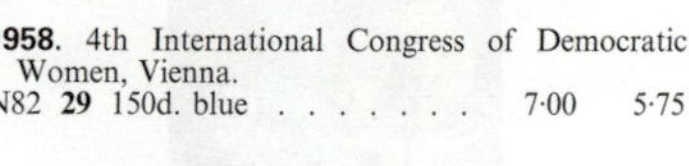

30 Cup, Basket and Lace

31 Hanoi–Saigon Railway Reconstruction

1958. Arts and Crafts Fair, Hanoi.

N83 30 150d. sepia and turquoise . 2·75 1·60
N84 2000d. black and lilac . . 9·00 5·25

1958. Re-unification of Vietnam Propaganda.

N85 31 50d. blue . . . . 2·75 75
N86 150d. brown . . . . 3·25 1·25

32 Revolution in Hanoi

1958. 13th Anniv of Vietnamese Revolution.

N87 32 150d. red . . . . 1·90 1·10
N88 500d. blue . . . . 3·75 1·90

33 Woman Potter

1958. Handicrafts Exhibition.

N89 33 150d. lake and red . . . . 1·90 1·60
N90 1000d. brown and ochre . . 9·00 3·50

34 Vo Thi Sau and Crowd

35 Tran Hung Dao

1958. 13th Anniv of South Vietnam Resistance Movement.

N91 34 50d. green and buff . . . 2·75 1·40
N92 150d. red and orange . . 5·50 1·60

1958. 658th Death Anniv of Tran Hung Dao.

N93 35 150d. grey and blue . . . 1·75 80

36 Hanoi Factories 37 Harvesting Rice

1958. Hanoi Mechanical Engineering Plant.
N94 **36** 150d. sepia . . . . 2·25 95

1958. Mutual Aid Teams.
N95 **37** 150d. lake . . . . 5·25 1·60
N96 500d. brown . . . . . . 6·50 3·25

38 Temple of Jade, Hanoi 39 Furniture-makers

1958.
N 97 **38** 150d. green . . . . . . 3·75 1·75
N 98 – 150d. blue . . . . 2·25 55
N 99 – 350d. brown . . . . . . 3·75 95
N100 **38** 2000d. green . . . . . . 32·00 9·00
DESIGNS—HORIZ: 150d. blue; 350d. Bay of Halong.

1958. Furniture Co-operatives.
N101 **39** 150d. blue . . . . 2·25 60

40 Cam Pha Coal Mines 41 The Trung Sisters

1959.
N102 **40** 150d. blue . . . . 2·00 80

1959. Trung Sisters Commemoration.
N103 **41** 5x. red and yellow . . . 1·10 50
N104 8x. deep brown and brown . . . . 1·75 65

42 Mother and Child

1959. 10th Anniv of World Peace Movement.
N105 **42** 12x. violet . . . . 1·10 55

43 Xuan Quan Dam

1959. Bac Hung Hai Irrigation Project.
N106 **43** 6x. yellow, green & violet 3·25 80
N107 12x. ochre, blue and grey 6·25 1·10

44 Victims in Phu Loi Concentration Camp 45 Radio Mast

1959. The Phu Loi Massacre on 1 December 1958.
N108 **44** 12x. salmon, olive & black . . . . 1·90 45
N109 20x. ochre, grey and black . . . . 4·00 90

1959. Me Tri Radio Station.
N110 **45** 3x. green and orange . . 1·40 35
N111 12x. sepia and blue . . . 2·25 55

46 Hien Luong Railway Bridge

1959. Vietnam Day.
N112 **46** 12x. red and black . . . 1·50 65

47 Rifle-shooting

1959. Sports.
N113 **47** 1x. deep blue and blue 1·60 55
N114 – 6x. olive and red . . . . 2·25 90
N115 – 12x. red and rose . . . . 3·25 1·40
DESIGNS: 6x. Swimming; 12x. Wrestling.

48 Balloons 49 Coconuts

1959. 10th Anniv of Chinese People's Republic.
N116 **48** 12x. red, yellow and green 95 45

1959. Fruits. Multicoloured.
N117 3x. Type **49** . . . . 1·10 45
N118 12x. Bananas . . . . 2·10 85
N119 30x. Pineapple . . . . . . 6·00 1·90

50 Convair CV 340

1959. Air.
N120 **50** 20x. black and blue . . . 10·00 6·25

51 Soldiers

1959. 15th Anniv of N. Vietnam People's Army.
N121 **51** 12x. yellow, brown & blue . . . . 1·50 75

52 Sailing Ship 53 Girl in "E-De" Costume

1959. 30th Anniv of N. Vietnam Workers' Party.
N122 **52** 2x. multicoloured . . . . 1·10 65
N123 12x. multicoloured . . . 2·25 1·25

1960. National Costumes.
N124 **53** 2x. red, blue and purple 80 35
N125 – 10x. blue, orange & green 1·25 45
N126 – 12x. blue and brown . . 1·90 70
N127 – 12x. blue and buff . . . 1·90 70
COSTUMES: No. N125, "Meo"; N126, "Thai"; N127, "Tay".

54 Women of Vietnam

1960. National Census.
N128 **54** 1x. green 40 20
N129 – 12x. brown and red . . . 55 25
DESIGN: 12x. Workers and factories.

55 Emblem and Women 56 Hung Vuong Temple

1960. 50th Anniv of International Women's Day.
N130 **55** 12x. multicoloured . . . 75 35

1960. Hung Vuong Anniversary Day.
N131 **56** 12x. green and buff . . . 6·50 3·75
N132 4d. brown and blue . . . 65·00 28·00

57 Lenin 58 Ballot Box

1960. 90th Birth Anniv of Lenin.
N133 **57** 5x. red and blue 55 30
N134 12x. blue and buff . . . 80 50

1960. 2nd Election of Parliamentary Deputies.
N135 **58** 12x. multicoloured . . . 65 35

59 Red Cross Nurse 60 Pres. Ho Chi Minh

1960. International Red Cross Commemoration.
N136 **59** 8x. blue, red and bistre 65 35
N137 12x. green, red and grey 1·00 50

1960. President Ho Chi Minh's 70th Birthday.
N138 **60** 4x. lilac and green . . . 45 30
N139 12x. purple and rose . . 85 40
N140 – 12x. multicoloured . . . 85 40
DESIGN—24½ × 39 mm: No. N140, Ho Chi Minh and children.

61 "New Constitution"

1960. Opening of 2nd National Assembly.
N141 **61** 12x. sepia and ochre . . 1·50 75

62 Pres. Ho Chi Minh at Microphone

1960. 15th Anniv of Vietnam Democratic Republic.
N142 **62** 4x. multicoloured . . . . 2·50 1·00
N143 12x. multicoloured . . . 3·75 1·10
N144 – 12x. deep blue and blue 3·75 1·10
N145 – 12x. green and yellow . . 3·75 1·10
N146 – 12x. blue and brown . . 3·75 1·10
DESIGNS: No. N144, Ploughing; N145, Electricity Works, Vietri; N146, Classroom.

63 Workers and Flags

1960. 3rd Vietnam Workers' Party Congress.
N147 **63** 1x. multicoloured . . . . 1·75 70
N148 12x. multicoloured . . . 2·25 90

64 Handclasp of Three Races

1960. 15th Anniv of W.F.T.U.
N149 **64** 12x. black and red . . . 5·75 4·00

65 Dragon

1960. 950th Anniv of Hanoi.
N150 **65** 8x. yellow, brown & turquoise . . . . . . 1·75 95
N151 12x. yellow, brown & blue . . . . 3·75 1·40

66 Exhibition Entrance

1960. "Fifteen Years of Republic" Exhibition.
N152 **66** 2x. grey and red 90 60
N153 12x. green and red . . . 1·75 85

67 Badge, Dove and Flag

1960. 15th Anniv of World Federation of Democratic Youth.
N154 **67** 12x. multicoloured . . . 2·50 1·50

68 Emblem of Vietnamese Trade Unions 69 Woman, Globe and Dove

1961. 2nd National Congress of Trade Unions.
N155 **68** 12x. red, blue and yellow 1·75 70

1961. 3rd National Congress of Women.
N156 **69** 6x. green and blue . . . 2·40 50
N157 12x. green and salmon 2·40 75

IMPERF STAMPS. Many issues from here onwards also exist imperf.

70 Sambar 71 Ly Tu Trong (revolutionary)

1961. Vietnamese Fauna.
N158 **70** 12x. buff, black and olive 3·00 1·25
N159 – 20x. multicoloured . . . 4·25 2·50

N160 – 50x. grey, black and green . . . . 7·50 3·75
N161 – 1d. black, grey and green 10·00 5·00
DESIGNS: 20x. Sun bear; 50x. Indian elephant; 1d. Crested gibbon.

1961. 3rd Congress of Vietnam Labour Youth Union.
N162 **71** 2x. olive and blue . . . 90 45
N163 12x. olive and salmon . . 2·10 1·00

72 Bugler and Drummer

73 Disabled Soldier learning to use Crutches

1961. 20th Anniv of Vietnam Youth Pioneers.
N164 **72** 1x. multicoloured . . . . 1·50 75
N165 12x. multicoloured . . . 2·75 1·40

1961. 101st Anniv of Proposal for Int Red Cross.
N166 **73** 6x. multicoloured . . . . 1·90 75
N167 12x. multicoloured . . . 3·50 1·40

74 Nurse weighing Baby

1961. International Children's Day.
N168 **74** 4x. green, black and red 1·25 65
N169 12x. yellow, black and red . . . . 2·75 1·40

75 Major Yuri Gagarin

1961. World's First Manned Space Flight.
N170 **75** 6x. red and violet . . . . 12·50 5·00
N171 12x. red and green . . . 12·50 5·00

76

77 Women

1961. Vietnam Reunification Campaign.
N172 **76** 12x. multicoloured . . . 50 50
N173 2d. multicoloured . . . . 8·50 4·00

1961. Tripling of Hanoi, Hue and Saigon.
N174 **77** 12x. multicoloured . . . 2·50 1·60
N175 3d. brown, myrtle and green . . . . 20·00 11·00

78 Mother and Child

79 Prospecting Team

1961. National Savings Campaign.
N176 **78** 3x. multicoloured 85 40
N177 12x. multicoloured . . . 1·50 85

1961. Geological Research.
N178 **79** 2x. green, blue and purple . . . . 1·50 40
N179 12x. brown, black & turquoise . . . . . . 3·00 85

80 Thien Mu Tower, Hue

81 Workers and Rocket

1961. Ancient Towers.
N180 **80** 6x. brown and chestnut 75 40
N181 – 10x. olive and buff . . . 1·50 55
N182 – 12x. olive and green . . 2·10 65
N183 – 12x. brown and blue . . 2·10 65
TOWERS: No. N181, Pen Brush, Bac Ninh; N182, Binh Son, Vinh Phuc; N183, Cham, Phan Rang.

1961. 22nd Communist Party Congress, Moscow.
N184 **81** 12x. red and black . . . 2·00 1·25

82 Major Titov and Rocket

1961. 2nd Manned Space Flight.
N185 **82** 6x. multicoloured . . . . 2·00 90
N186 12x. multicoloured . . . 3·50 1·75

83 Freighter at Haiphong

1961. Haiphong Port Commemoration.
N187 **83** 5x. grey, green and myrtle . . . . 1·40 60
N188 12x. brown, light brown and sepia . . . . . . 3·25 1·25

84 Cymbalist

85 Congress Emblem

1961. 3rd Writers and Artists Congress. Mult.
N189 12x. Type **84** . . . . 1·25 60
N190 12x. Flautist . . . . 1·25 90
N191 30x. Fan dancer . . . . . 3·50 1·25
N192 50x. Guitarist . . . . . . 5·00 2·40

1961. 5th W.F.T.U. Congress, Moscow.
N193 **85** 12x. mauve and drab . . 60 40

86 Resistance Fighters

1961. 15th Anniv of National Resistance.
N194 **86** 4x. multicoloured 35 20
N195 12x. multicoloured . . . 65 35

87 "Pigs"

1962. New Year.
N196 **87** 6x. multicoloured . . . . 1·00 50
N197 – 12x. multicoloured . . . 2·00 1·00
DESIGN: 12x. "Poultry".

88 Watering Tree

89 Tea Plant

1962. Tree-planting Festival.
N198 **88** 12x. multicoloured . . . 1·60 85
N199 40x. multicoloured . . . 2·50 1·50

1962. Multicoloured.
N200 2x. Type **89** 75 40
N201 6x. Aniseed 75 40
N202 12x. Coffee . . . . 2·75 1·10
N203 12x. Castor-oil . . . . . 2·75 1·10
N204 30x. Lacquer-tree . . . . 5·75 2·50

90 Gong Dance

91 Hibiscus

1962. Folk-dancing. Multicoloured.
N205 12x. Type **90** . . . . 2·00 60
N206 12x. Bamboo dance . . . . 2·00 60
N207 30x. Hat dance . . . . . . 5·00 60
N208 50x. Parasol dance . . . . 10·00 2·00

1962. Flowers. Multicoloured.
N209 12x. Type **91** . . . . 2·00 75
N210 12x. Frangipani . . . . . 2·00 75
N211 20x. Chrysanthemum . . . 3·75 2·10
N212 30x. Lotus . . . . 6·00 2·75
N213 50x. Ipomoea . . . . 9·00 3·50

92 Kim Lien Flats, Hanoi

93 Workers and Rose

1962. 1st Five-Year Plan (1st issue).
N214 **92** 1x. blue, black and grey 40 20
N215 – 3x. multicoloured 70 30
N216 – 8x. violet, black and stone . . . . 1·25 50
DESIGNS: 3x. State agricultural farm; 8x. Institute of Hydraulic and Electro-Dynamic Studies.
See also Nos. N245/8, N251/2, N270/1 and N294/6.

1962. 3rd National "Heroes of Labour" Congress.
N217 **93** 12x. orange, olive and red . . . . 1·75 40

94 Dai Lai Lake

1962.
N218 **94** 12x. turquoise and brown 2·25 85

95 "Plough of Perfection"

1962.
N219 **95** 6x. black and turquoise 1·10 40

96 Titov greeting Children

1962. Visit of Major Titov.
N220 **96** 12x. sepia and blue . . . 85 50
N221 – 20x. sepia and salmon . . 1·75 55
N222 – 30x. sepia and green . . 3·25 1·10
DESIGNS: 20x. Pres. Ho Chi Minh pinning medal on Titov; 30x. Titov in space-suit.

97 Mosquito and Red Cross

1962. Malaria Eradication.
N223 **97** 8x. red, black and blue 1·25 55
N224 12x. red, black and violet 1·50 80
N225 20x. red, black and purple . . . . 2·75 1·10

98 Factory and Soldiers

99 Ban Gioc Falls

1962. 8th Anniv of Geneva Vietnamese Agreements.
N226 **98** 12x. multicoloured . . . 70 35

1962. Vietnamese Scenery.
N227 – 12x. purple and blue . . 1·10 35
N228 **99** 12x. sepia and turquoise 1·10 35
DESIGN—HORIZ: (32½ × 23 mm): No. N227, Ba Be Lake.

99a Weightlifting

1962. Int Military Sports Festival of Socialist States, Prague.
N228a **99a** 12x. multicoloured . . 60·00 95·00

100 Quang Trung

101 Groundnuts

1962. National Heroes.
N229 **100** 3x. yellow, brown & grey 60 25
N230 – 3x. orange, blk & ochre 50 25
N231 **100** 12x. yellow, green & grey 85 35
N232 – 12x. orange, blk & grey 85 35
PORTRAIT: Nos. N230, N232, Nguyen Trai.

1962. Multicoloured.
N233 1x. Type **101** 40 25
N234 4x. Haricot beans 70 30
N235 6x. Sweet potatoes 90 35
N236 12x. Maize . . . . 2·25 80
N237 30x. Manioc . . . . 5·00 2·00

102 Girl feeding Poultry

1962. Farm Stock-breeding.
N238 **102** 2x. red, grey and blue 60 30
N239 – 12x. ochre, turquoise and blue . . . . . . 1·75 40
N240 – 12x. brown, green and deep green . . . . . 1·75 40
N241 – 12x. buff, mauve and sepia . . . . 1·75 40
DESIGNS: No. N239, Woman tending pigs; N240, Herdgirl with oxen; N241, Boy feeding buffalo.

103 Popovich in "Vostok 4"

1962. First "Team" Manned Space Flights.
N242 **103** 12x. multicoloured . . . 1·00 60
N243 – 20x. ochre, blue & black 1·75 60
N244 – 30x. red, blue and black 2·75 1·25
DESIGNS—HORIZ: 20x. Nikolaev in "Vostok 3". VERT: 30x. "Vostoks 3 and 4".

104 Teacher and Students

1962. 1st Five-Year Plan (2nd issue). Higher Education and Land Cultivation.
N245 **104** 12x. black and yellow 1·00 35
N246 – 12x. black, brown & buff . . . . 2·10 90
DESIGN: No. N246, Tree felling.

105 Guerrilla Fighter

106 Hoang Hoa Tham

1963. 1st Five-Year Plan (3rd issue). National Defence.
N247 **105** 5x. green and grey . . . 75 25
N248 12x. brown and buff . . 1·10 40

1963. 50th Death Anniv of Hoang Hoa Tham (freedom fighter).
N249 **106** 6x. myrtle and blue . . 60 40
N250 12x. black and brown 85 50

107 Workers in Field

108 Karl Marx

1963. 1st Five-Year Plan (4th issue). Agricultural and Chemical Manufacture.
N251 **107** 12x. multicoloured . . . 1·00 60
N252 – 12x. red, mauve and black . . . . 1·25 40
DESIGN: No. N252, Lam Thao Fertilizer Factory.

1963. 80th Death Anniv of Karl Marx.
N253 **108** 3x. black and green . . 50 30
N254 12x. black and drab on pink 75 35

109 Castro and Vietnamese Soldiers

111 Nurse tending Child

110 Doves and Labour Emblem

1963. Vietnamese–Cuban Friendship.
N255 **109** 12x. multicoloured . . . 75 45

1963. Labour Day.
N256 **110** 12x. orange, black & bl 75 40

1963. Red Cross Centenary.
N257 **111** 12x. red, black and blue 1·25 55
N258 – 12x. red, grey & turq . . 1·25 55
N259 – 20x. red, grey and yellow . . . . 2·10 75
DESIGNS: No. N258, Child and syringe inscr "BCG". 25 × 42 mm: 20x. Centenary emblem.

112 "Mars 1" Interplanetary Station

1963. Launching of Soviet Rocket "Mars 1". Mult.
N260 6x. Type **112** 60 35
N261 12x. Type **112** 80 45
N262 12x. "Mars 1" in space (vert) 80 45
N263 20x. "Mars 1" in space (vert) . . . . 2·00 80

113 Common Carp

1963. Fishing Industry. Multicoloured.
N264 12x. Type **113** . . . . . . 6·50 1·75
N265 12x. Fishes and trawler . . 6·50 1·75

114 Pres. Ho Chi Minh embracing Prof. Nguyen Van Hien of South Vietnam

1963. Campaign for Reunification of Vietnam.
N266 **114** 12x. black, blue & turq 70 35

115 Globe and "Vostoks 3 and 4"

1963. 1st Anniv of "Team" Manned Space Flights.
N267 **115** 12x. black, brown & yellow 70 35
N268 – 20x. black, blue & green 1·00 60
N269 – 30x. black, violet & blue 1·75 95
DESIGNS: 20x. Nikolaev and "eagle" motif; 30x. Popovich and "phoenix" motif.

116 Viet Tri Insecticide Factory

1963. 1st Five-Year Plan (5th issue).
N270 **116** 3x. buff, brown and blue 30 25
N271 – 12x. pink, brown and bistre 65 40
DESIGN: 12x. Viet Tri chemical factory.

117 Black Carp

1963. Freshwater Fish Culture. Multicoloured.
N272 12x. Type **117** . . . . . . 1·90 75
N273 12x. Common carp ("Cyprinus carpio") . . . 1·90 75
N274 12x. Silver carp ("Hypophthalmichthys molitrix) . . . . 1·90 75
N275 20x. Asiatic snakehead . . 4·50 1·60
N276 30x. Mozambique mouth-brooder . . . . 6·50 3·50

118 Chinese Francolin

119 Broken Chain and Map

1963. Birds. Multicoloured.
N277 12x. Type **118** . . . . . . 3·25 35
N278 12x. Chinese jungle mynah 3·25 35
N279 12x. White-throated kingfisher . . . . 3·25 35
N280 20x. Siamese fireback pheasant (horiz) . . . . 7·25 70
N281 30x. Eastern reef heron . . 11·00 1·10
N282 40x. Slaty-headed parakeet 16·00 1·75

1963. W.F.T.U. Assembly, Hanoi.
N283 **119** 12x. multicoloured . . . 50 40

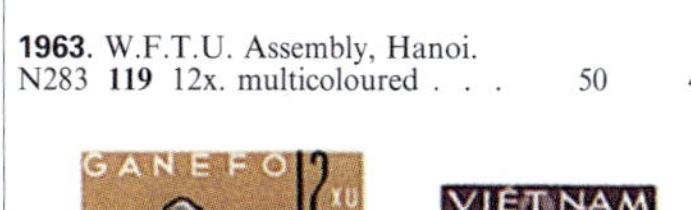

120 Football

121 "Rauwolfia verticillata"

1963. "GANEFO" Athletic Games, Jakarta.
N284 **120** 12x. black, grey & ochre 80 35
N285 – 12x. black, grey & orange 80 35
N286 – 12x. black, grey and blue 80 35
N287 – 30x. black, grey & mag 1·60 75
DESIGNS—VERT: No. N285, Volleyball. HORIZ: No. N286, Swimming; N287, High-jumping.

1963. Medicinal Plants. Multicoloured.
N288 6x. Type **121** 80 35
N289 12x. "Chenopodium ambrosioides" 95 35
N290 12x. "Sophora japonica" 95 65
N291 12x. "Fibraurea tinctoria" 95 65
N292 20x. "Momordica cochinchinensis" . . . . 4·50 1·10

122 "Solidarity"

123 Pylon

1963. 3rd Anniv of South Vietnam National Liberation Front.
N293 **122** 12x. black, brn & ochre 55 35

1964. 1st Five-Year Plan (6th issue).
N294 – 6x. black, red and purple 50 30
N295 – 12x. multicoloured . . . 1·60 50
N296 **123** 12x. black, grey & orange . . . . 1·60 50
DESIGNS—HORIZ: (40 × 22½ mm): 6x. Tapping cast-iron; No. N295, Thai Ngyuen Iron and Steel Works.

124 Sun, Globe and Dragon

1964. International Quiet Sun Years.
N297 **124** 12x. orange, black & green 40 25
N298 50x. drab, black & pur 1·50 85

125 Twin Space Flights

1964. Space Flights of Bykovsky and Tereshkova. Multicoloured.
N299 12x. Type **125** . . . . . . 1·25 35
N300 12x. Bykovsky and "Vostok 5" . . . . 1·25 35
N301 30x. Tereshkova and "Vostok 6" . . . . . . 3·00 1·10

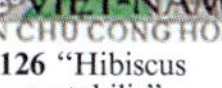
126 "Hibiscus mutabilis"

127 Rural Costume

1964. Flowers. Multicoloured.
N302 12x. Type **126** . . . . . . 1·50 40
N303 12x. "Persica vulgaris" . . 1·50 40
N304 12x. "Saraca dives" . . . . 1·50 40
N305 12x. "Passiflora hispida" 1·50 40
N306 20x. "Michelia champaca" 3·75 1·25
N307 30x. "Camellia amplexicaulis" . . . . . 5·50 1·75

1964. National Costumes. Multicoloured.
N308 6x. Type **127** 50 25
N309 12x. "Ceremonial" . . . . 1·00 35
N310 12x. "Everyday" . . . . . 1·00 35

128 Artillery

130 Spotted Deer

129 Ham Rong Railway Bridge

1964. 10th Anniv of Battle of Dien Bien Phu.
N311 **128** 3x. black and red . . . 40 25
N312 – 6x. black and blue . . . 50 35
N313 – 12x. black and yellow 95 40
N314 – 12x. black and purple 95 40
DESIGNS: 6x. Machine-gun post; No. N313, Bomb-disposal; N314, Dien Bien Phu and tractor.

1964. Inaug of Reconstructed Ham Rong Bridge.
N315 **129** 12x. multicoloured . . . 1·50 50

1964. Wild Animals. Multicoloured.
N316 12x. Type **130** . . . . . . 1·90 60
N317 12x. Malayan tapir (horiz) 1·90 60
N318 12x. Tiger . . . . 1·90 60
N319 20x. Water buffalo (horiz) 3·75 1·25
N320 30x. Sumatran rhinoceros (horiz) . . . . 4·25 1·90
N321 40x. Banteng (horiz) . . . 5·00 2·50

131 Women Fighters, Map, Industrial Scene and Watch-towers

1964. 10th Anniv of Geneva Agreements on Vietnam.
N322 **131** 12x. multicoloured . . . 65 35
N323 – 12x. multicoloured . . . 65 35
DESIGN—VERT: (23 × 45 mm): No. N323, Map of Vietnam, T.U. emblem and flag, inscr ("NHÂN DÂN MIỀN NAM") etc.

132 Nhu Quynh Pumping Station

1964. Irrigation for Agriculture.
N324 **132** 12x. slate and black . . 75 35

133 Populace Greeting Soldiers

1964. 10th Anniv of Liberation of Hanoi. Mult.

N325		6x. Type **133**	35	25
N326		12x. Building construction	70	50

134 Naval Longboat

1964. "National Defence" Games.

N327	**134**	5x. black, grey and blue	90	35
N328	–	12x. black, grey & yellow	1·90	50
N329	–	12x. black, brown & blue	1·90	50
N330	–	12x. multicoloured	1·90	50

DESIGNS—HORIZ: No. N328, Pistol-shooting. VERT: No. N329, Gliding; N330, Parachuting.

135 "Guarcinia mangostana"

1964. Tropical Fruits. Multicoloured.

N331		12x. Type **135**	1·60	45
N332		12x. "Mangifera indica"	1·60	45
N333		12x. "Nephelium litchi"	1·60	45
N334		20x. "Anona squamosa"	2·75	85
N335		50x. "Citrus medica"	7·50	1·90

136 Conference Building

1964. World Solidarity Conf, Hanoi. Mult.

N336		12x. Type **136**	75	35
N337		12x. Soldier greeting workers	75	35
N338		12x. Clenched fist, ships and Boeing B-52 Stratofortress	75	35

137 Soldiers with Standard

1964. 20th Anniv of Vietnamese People's Army. Multicoloured.

N339		12x. Type **137**	1·00	30
N340		12x. Coastguards	1·00	30
N341		12x. Frontier guards (vert)	1·00	30

138 Cuban Revolutionaries
139 Le Hong Phong

140 Party Flag

1965. 6th Anniv of Cuban Republic.

N342	**138**	12x. black, red and blue	75	35
N343	–	12x. multicoloured	75	35

DESIGN: No. N343, Flags of Cuba and North Vietnam.

1965. 35th Anniv of Vietnamese Workers' Party. (a) As T **139**. Portraits and inscr purple-brown; background colours given.

N344	**139**	6x. grey	40	20
N345	–	6x. bistre	40	20
N346	–	6x. drab	40	20
N347	–	6x. brown	40	20
N348	–	6x. lilac	40	20

DESIGNS: No. N345, Tran Phu; N346, Hoang Van Thu; N347, Hgo Gia Tu; N348, Nguyen van Cu (Party leaders).

(b) As T **140**.

N349	**140**	12x. yellow, red and mauve	60	30
N350	–	12x. mauve, yellow and red	60	30

DESIGN: No. N350, Foundryman and guerilla fighter.

141 Women tending Maize
142 Steam Locomotive and Nguyen Van Troi (patriot)

1965. Populating Mountain Settlements.

N351	**141**	2x. multicoloured	25	20
N352		3x. multicoloured	35	25
N353	–	12x. indigo, orange and blue	60	35

DESIGN: 12x. Young girls going to school.

1965. Transport Ministers' Congress, Hanoi.

N354	**142**	12x. blue and red	1·50	50
N355	–	30x. black and green	3·00	1·10

DESIGN: 30x. As Type **142** but position of locomotive, portrait and value transposed.

143 Cosmonauts Komarov, Feoktistov, Yegorov, and "Voskhod I"

1965. Three-manned Space Flight.

N356	**143**	20x. violet, green & blue	1·50	40
N357	–	1d. violet, red & mauve	5·25	1·50

DESIGN: 1d. "Voskhod I" and cosmonauts.

144 Lenin with Red Guards
145 Pres. Ho Chi Minh

1965. Lenin's 95th Birth Anniv.

N358	**144**	8x. purple and buff	50	25
N359		12x. purple and grey	75	30

1965. Pres. Ho Chi Minh's 75th Birthday.

N360	**145**	6x. violet, yellow & green	50	20
N361		12x. violet, yellow & buff	1·00	25

146 Hands clasping Serpent
147 Two Soldiers advancing

1965. 10th Anniv of Afro-Asian Conf, Bandung.

N362	**146**	12x. multicoloured	60	30

1965. Trade Union Conference, Hanoi.

N363	**147**	12x. blue and purple	60	25
N364	–	12x. multicoloured	60	25
N365	–	12x. red, black and green	60	25

DESIGNS—HORIZ: No. N364, Sea battle; N365, "Peoples of the World" on Globe, and soldiers.

148 Yellow-throated Marten

1965. Fauna Protection. Multicoloured.

N366		12x. Type **148**	80	45
N367		12x. Owston's palm civet	1·25	45
N368		12x. Chinese pangolin	1·25	45
N369		12x. Francois' monkey (vert)	1·25	45
N370		20x. Red giant flying squirrel	3·75	1·25
N371		50x. Lesser slow loris (vert)	6·25	2·25

149 Marx and Lenin
150 Nguyen Van Troi (patriot)

1965. Postal Ministers Congress, Peking.

N372	**149**	12x. multicoloured	1·00	35

1965. Nguyen Van Troi Commemoration.

N373	**150**	12x. sepia, brown & green	60	25
N374		50x. sepia, brn & ochre	1·25	70
N375		4d. sepia and red	8·00	3·75

151 "Rhynchocoris humeralis"

1965. Noxious Insects. Multicoloured.

N376		12x. Type **151**	1·00	45
N377		12x. "Tessaratoma papillosa"	1·00	45
N378		12x. "Poecilocoris latus"	1·00	45
N379		12x. "Tosena melanoptera"	1·00	45
N380		20x. "Cicada sp."	3·50	1·60
N381		30x. "Fulgora candelaria"	5·00	2·00

Nos. N379/81 are vert, 20½ × 38 mm.

152 Revolutionaries

1965. 20th Anniv of August Revolution.

N382	**152**	6x. brown, black & blue	30	20
N383		12x. black and red	65	25

153 Prawn

1965. Marine Life. Multicoloured.

N384		12x. Type **153**	2·25	60
N385		12x. Shrimp	2·25	60
N386		12x. Swimming crab	2·25	60
N387		12x. Serrate swimming crab	2·25	60
N388		20x. Spiny lobster	4·25	1·90
N389		50x. Fiddler crab	8·75	3·25

154 Air Battle
155 Foundryman ("Heavy Industries")

1965. "500th U.S. Aircraft Brought Down over North Vietnam".

N390	**154**	12x. green and lilac	5·50	3·75

1965. 20th Anniv of Republic and Completion of 1st Five-Year Plan.

N391	**155**	12x. black and orange	50	20
N392	–	12x. black and green	50	15
N393	–	12x. black and purple	50	15

DESIGNS: No. N392, Irrigation, pylon and power station ("Hydro-electric Power"); N393, Nurse examining child ("Social Medicine").

See also Nos. N417/19.

156 Drummer and Peasants

1965. 35th Anniv of Movement of Nghe An and Ha Tinh Soviet Peasants.

N394	**156**	10x. multicoloured	35	20
N395		12x. multicoloured	65	25

157 Girls and Flags

1965. 16th Anniv of Friendship between China and Vietnam. Multicoloured.

N396		12x. Type **157**	50	25
N397		12x. Vietnamese and Chinese girls with flags (vert)	50	25

158 Tsiolkovsky and "Sputnik 1"

1965. Space Flight of "Voskhod 2".

N398	**158**	12x. blue and purple	90	30
N399	–	12x. ochre and blue	90	30
N400	–	50x. blue and green	2·10	90
N401	–	50x. blue and turquoise	2·10	90

DESIGNS: No. N399, Leonov, Belyaev and "Voskhod 2"; N400, Gagarin; N401, Leonov in space.

159 Red Lacewing

1965. Butterflies. Multicoloured.

N402		12x. Type **159**	2·50	50
N403		12x. Leopard lacewing	2·50	50
N404		12x. Blue triangle	2·50	50
N405		12x. Indian purple emperor	2·50	50
N406		20x. Paris peacock	7·50	1·75
N407		30x. Common rose	10·50	3·00

160 Norman R. Morrison and Demonstrators
161 Birthplace of Nguyen Du (poet)

1965. Homage to Norman R. Morrison (American Quaker who immolated himself).
N408 **160** 12x. black and red . . . 60 30

1965. Nguyen Du Commem. Multicoloured.
N409 12x. Type **161** 50 25
N410 12x. Nguyen Du Museum 50 25
N411 20x. "Kieu" (volume of poems) . . . . 1·00 35
N412 1d. Scene from "Kieu" . . 2·10 1·00

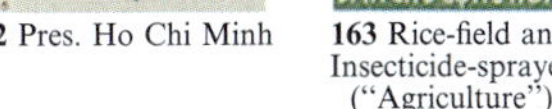

162 Pres. Ho Chi Minh

163 Rice-field and Insecticide-sprayer ("Agriculture")

1965. Engels' 145th Birth Anniv. Multicoloured.
N413 12x. Type **162** 60 25
N414 12x. Marx 60 25
N415 12x. Lenin 60 25
N416 50x. Engels . . . . 1·90 90

1965. Completion of 1st Five-Year Plan (2nd issue).
N417 **163** 12x. orange and green 60 25
N418 – 12x. blue and red . . . 60 25
N419 – 12x. orange and blue . . 60 25
DESIGNS: No. N418, Factory-worker ("Light Industries"); N419, Children at play and students ("Social Education").

164 Soldier and Demonstrators

1965. 5th Anniv of South Vietnam National Liberation Front.
N420 **164** 12x. violet and lilac . . 60 25

165 Casting Votes

1966. 20th Anniv of 1st Vietnamese General Elections.
N421 **165** 12x. black and red . . . 45 20

166 "Dendrobium moschatum"

167 Child on Rocking-horse

1966. Orchids. Multicoloured.
N422 12x. Type **166** . . . . . . 1·25 40
N423 12x. "Vanda teres" . . . . 1·25 40
N424 12x. "Dendrobium crystallinum" . . . . . 1·25 40
N425 12x. "Dendrobium nobile" 1·25 40
N426 20x. "Vandopsis gigantea" 3·00 1·00
N427 30x. "Dendrobium" . . . . 5·75 1·90

1966. New Year.
N428 **167** 12x. multicoloured . . . 50 20

168 "Physignathus cocincinus"

1966. Protection of Nature—Reptiles. Multicoloured.
N429 12x. Type **168** . . . . . . 1·00 40
N430 12x. "Trionyx sinensis" . . 1·00 40
N431 12x. Gecko (inscr "GEKKO GECKO") . . 1·00 40
N432 12x. "Testudo elongata" . . 1·00 40
N433 20x. "Varanus salvator" . . 2·75 1·60
N434 40x. "Eretmochelys imbricata" . . . . 4·50 1·60

169 Wrestling

170 Ly Tu Trong (revolutionary), Badge and Banner

1966. National Games.
N435 **169** 12x. multicoloured . . . 60 30
N436 – 12x. multicoloured . . . 60 30
N437 – 12x. multicoloured . . . 60 30
GAMES: No. N436, Archery (with crossbow); N437, "Fencing".

1966. 35th Anniv of Labour Youth Union.
N438 **170** 12x. multicoloured . . . 45 20

171 Republic Thunderchief in Flames

1966. "1,000th U.S. Aircraft Brought Down over North Vietnam".
N439 **171** 12x. multicoloured . . . 4·25 1·90

172 Worker and Rifle

174 Children and Banners

173 Battle Scene on Con Co Island

1966. Labour Day.
N440 **172** 6x. black, red and salmon 50 25

1966. Defence of Con Co ("Steel Island").
N441 **173** 12x. multicoloured . . . 50 20

1966. 25th Anniv of Vietnam Youth Pioneers.
N442 **174** 12x. black and red . . . 50 25

175 View of Dien An (Yenan)

176 "Luna 9" in Space

1966. 45th Anniv of Chinese Communist Party. Multicoloured.
N443 3x. Type **175** 35 20
N444 12x. Ho Chi Minh and Mao Tse-tung 60 40

1966. "Luna 9" Space Flight. Multicoloured. Inscr "MAT TRANG 9".
N445 12x. Type **176** 50 25
N446 50x. "Luna 9" on Moon 2·00 1·00

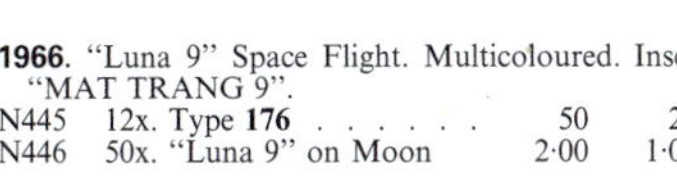

177 Airplane in Flames

1966. "1,500th U.S. Aircraft Brought Down over North Vietnam".
N447 **177** 12x. multicoloured . . . 4·50 2·50
N448 12x. mult (optd **NGAY 14.10.1966**) . . . . . 5·00 3·25

178 Liberation Fighter

1966. Victories of Liberation Army. Inscr "1965–1966".
N449 **178** 1x. purple 25 15
N450 12x. multicoloured . . . 50 25
N451 – 12x. multicoloured . . . 50 25
DESIGN: No. N451, Soldier escorting prisoners-of-war.
See also No. 646.

179 Women from different Regions, and Child

1966. 20th Anniv of Vietnamese Women's Union.
N452 **179** 12x. black and salmon 50 25

180 Moluccan Pittas

1966. Birds. Multicoloured.
N453 12x. Type **180** . . . . . . 1·75 20
N454 12x. Black-naped orioles . . 1·75 20
N455 12x. River kingfisher . . . 3·75 30
N456 12x. Long-tailed broadbill 1·75 20
N457 20x. Hoopoe . . . . 4·25 80
N458 30x. Maroon orioles . . . 7·75 1·00
Nos. N454/5 and N457 are vert.

181 Football

1966. Ganefo Games. Multicoloured.
N459 12x. Type **181** 50 25
N460 12x. Rifle-shooting 50 25
N461 30x. Swimming . . . . . . 1·25 50
N462 30x. Running . . . . 1·25 50

182 Harvesting Rice

1967. Agricultural Production.
N463 **182** 12x. multicoloured . . . 60 25

183 Ho Chi Minh Text and Fighters

1967. Ho Chi Minh's Appeal.
N464 **183** 12x. purple and red . . 30 20
N465 – 12x. purple and red . . 45 20
DESIGN: No. N465, Ho-Chi-Minh text and marchers with banners.
See also Nos. 519/22.

184 Bamboo ("Arundinaria rolleana")

1967. Bamboo. Multicoloured.
N466 12x. Type **184** 75 25
N467 12x. "Arundinaria racemosa" 75 25
N468 12x. "Bambusa bingami" 75 25
N469 12x. "Bambusa arundinaceu" 75 25
N470 30x. "Bambusa nutans" . . 2·00 1·00
N471 50x. "Dendrocalamus patellaris" . . . . 3·75 1·75

185 Dhole

1967. Wild Animals. Multicoloured.
N472 12x. Type **185** . . . . . . 1·00 40
N473 12x. Binturong . . . . . . 1·00 40
N474 12x. Hog-badger . . . . . 1·00 40
N475 20x. Large Indian civet . . 2·00 75
N476 40x. Bear macaque . . . . 3·25 1·25
N477 50x. Clouded leopard . . . 5·00 1·90

186 Captured Pilot

187 Rocket Launching and Agricultural Scene

1967. "2,000th U.S. Aircraft Brought Down over North Vietnam".
N478 **186** 6x. black and red on pink . . . . 1·90 80
N479 12x. black & red on grn 1·90 80

1967. Launching of First Chinese Rocket. Mult.
N480 12x. Type **187** 60 25
N481 30x. Rocket launching, and Gate of Heavenly Peace, Peking . . . . 1·25 50

188 Belted Bearded Grunt

1967. Vietnamese Fishes. Multicoloured.
N482 12x. Type **188** . . . . . . 1·25 25
N483 12x. Japanese mackerel ("Scomberomorus niphonius") . . . . . . 1·25 25
N484 12x. Thread-finned lizardfish ("Saurida filamentosa") . . . . . 1·25 25
N485 20x. Adjutant emperor . . 1·75 55
N486 30x. Black pomfret . . . . 3·50 80
N487 50x. Blood snapper . . . . 5·25 1·00

189 Lenin and Revolutionary Soldiers

1967. 50th Anniv of October Revolution. Mult.
N488 6x. Type **189** 25 15
N489 12x. Lenin and revolutionaries 45 20
N490 12x. Lenin, Marx and Vietnamese soldiers . . . 45 20
N491 20x. Cruiser "Aurora" . . 75 40

190 Air Battle

1967. "2,500th U.S. Aircraft Brought Down over North Vietnam".
N492 **190** 12x. black, red and green . . . . 8·00 1·25
N493 – 12x. black, red and blue 4·25 1·25
DESIGN—VERT: No. N493, Boeing B-52 Stratofortress falling in flames.

191 Atomic Symbol and Gate of Heavenly Peace, Peking

1967. 1st Chinese "H"-Bomb Test. Multicoloured.
N494 12x. Type **191** 75 30
N495 20x. Chinese lantern, atomic symbol & dove (30 × 35 mm) . . . . . . 1·10 45

192 Factory Anti-aircraft Unit

1967. Anti-aircraft Defences. Multicoloured.
N496 12x. Type **192** 50 25
N497 12x. Rifle-fire from trenches 50 25
N498 12x. Seaborne gun-crew . . 70 25
N499 12x. Militiawoman with captured U.S. pilot . . . 50 25
N500 20x. Air battle 95 40
N501 30x. Military anti-aircraft post . . . . 1·75 75

193 Chickens

1968. Domestic Fowl. Multicoloured designs showing cocks and hens.
N502 12x. Type **193** 85 40
N503 12x. Inscr "Ga ri" 85 40
N504 12x. Inscr "Ga trong thien ri" 85 40
N505 12x. Inscr "Ga den chanchi" 85 40
N506 20x. Junglefowl . . . . . 1·90 60
N507 30x. Hen . . . . 2·25 1·00
N508 40x. Hen and chicks . . . 2·75 1·25
N509 50x. Two hens . . . . . 3·25 1·60

194 Gorky

1968. Birth Centenary of Maxim Gorky.
N510 **194** 12x. black and brown 60 30

195 Burning Village

1968. Victories of 1966–67.
N511 **195** 12x. brown and red . . 50 25
N512 – 12x. brown and red . . 50 25
N513 – 12x. brown and red . . 50 25
N514 – 12x. brown and red . . 50 25
N515 – 12x. black and violet . . 50 25
N516 – 12x. black and violet . . 50 25
N517 – 12x. black and violet . . 50 25
N518 – 12x. black and violet . . 50 25
DESIGNS: No. N512, Firing mortars; N513, Attacking tanks with rocket-gun; N514, Sniping; N515, Attacking gun-site; N516, Escorting prisoners; N517, Interrogating refugees; N518, Civilians demonstrating.

197 Ho Chi Minh Text and Fighters 198 Hong boch Rose

1968. Intensification of Production.
N519 **197** 6x. blue on yellow . . . 30 15
N520 12x. blue 40 20
N521 12x. purple 40 20
N522 12x. red 40 20

1968. Roses. Multicoloured.
N523 12x. Type **198** 60 25
N524 12x. Hong canh sap 60 25
N525 12x. Hong leo 60 25
N526 20x. Hong vang . . . . . 1·90 65
N527 30x. Hong nhung . . . . 2·50 80
N528 40x. Hong canh tim . . . . 3·75 1·25

199 Ho Chi Minh and Flag 200 Karl Marx

1968. Ho Chi Minh's New Year Message.
N529 **199** 12x. brown and violet 40 20

1968. 150th Birth Anniv of Karl Marx.
N530 **200** 12x. black and green . . 50 25

201 Anti-aircraft Machine-gun Crew

1968. "3,000th U.S. Aircraft Brought Down over North Vietnam". Multicoloured.
N531 12x. Type **201** . . . . . . 1·50 65
N532 12x. Women manning anti-aircraft gun . . . . . . 1·50 65
N533 40x. Aerial dogfight . . . . 3·50 1·40
N534 40x. Anti-aircraft missile . . 3·50 1·40

202 Rattan-cane Work

1968. Arts and Crafts. Multicoloured.
N535 6x. Type **202** 35 15
N536 12x. Bamboo work 40 25
N537 12x. Pottery 40 25
N538 20x. Ivory carving 80 35
N539 30x. Lacquer work . . . . 1·25 45
N540 40x. Silverware . . . . . 1·60 75

203 Quarter-staff Contest

1968. Traditional Sports. Multicoloured.
N541 12x. Type **203** 50 20
N542 12x. Dagger fighting . . . 50 20
N543 12x. Duel with sabres . . . 50 20
N544 30x. Unarmed combat . . . 1·25 55
N545 40x. Scimitar fighting . . . 2·00 70
N546 50x. Sword and buckler . . 2·25 95

205 Temple, Khue

1968. Vietnamese Architecture. Multicoloured.
N548 12x. Type **205** 50 25
N549 12x. Bell tower, Keo Pagoda 50 25
N550 20x. Bridge, Bonze Pagoda (horiz) 70 30
N551 30x. Mot Cot Pagoda, Hanoi 70 35
N552 40x. Gateway, Ninh Phuc Pagoda (horiz) . . . . . 1·25 55
N553 50x. Tay Phuong Pagoda (horiz) . . . . 1·75 60

206 Vietnamese Militia

1968. Cuban–North Vietnamese Friendship. Mult. With gum.
N554 12x. Type **206** 35 20
N555 12x. Cuban revolutionary (vert) 35 20
N556 20x. "Revolutionary Solidarity" (vert) 80 25

207 "Ploughman with Rifle"

1968. "The War Effort". Paintings. With gum.
N557 **207** 12x. black, blue & yellow 25 15
N558 – 12x. multicoloured . . . 25 15
N559 – 30x. brown, blue and turquoise . . . . . . 1·40 30
N560 – 40x. multicoloured . . . 95 35
DESIGNS—HORIZ: No. N558, "Defending the Mines"; N559, "Repairing Railway Track"; N560, "Crashed Aircraft".

208 Nam Ngai shooting down Aircraft

1969. Lunar New Year. Victories of the National Liberation Front. Multicoloured.
N561 12x. Type **208** 40 20
N562 12x. Tay Nguyen throwing grenade 40 20
N563 12x. Gun crews, Tri Thien 40 20
N564 40x. Insurgents, Tay Ninh 1·00 40
N565 50x. Home Guards . . . . 1·60 80

209 Loading Timber Lorries

1969. North Vietnamese Timber Industry. Mult.
N566 6x. Type **209** 25 15
N567 12x. Log raft on river . . . 35 20
N568 12x. Tug towing "log train" 35 20
N569 12x. Elephant hauling logs 60 20
N570 12x. Insecticide spraying . . 35 20
N571 20x. Buffalo hauling log . . 1·25 40
N572 30x. Logs on overhead cable . . . . 1·90 75

210 "Young Guerrilla" (Co Tan Long Chau)

1969. "South Vietnam—Land and People". Paintings. Multicoloured.
N573 12x. Type **210** 45 30
N574 12x. "Scout on Patrol" (Co Tan Long Chau) 45 30
N575 20x. "Woman Guerrilla" (Le Van Chuong) (vert) 70 45
N576 30x. "Halt at a Relay Station" (Co Tan Long Chau) 70 45
N577 40x. "After a Skirmish" (Co Tan Long Chau) . . 1·50 1·10
N578 50x. "Liberated Hamlet" (Huynh Phuong Dong) 1·90 1·25

211 Woman Soldier, Ben Tre

1969. Victories in Tet Offensive (1968).
N579 **211** 8x. black, green and pink 45 20
N580 12x. black, emer & green 45 20
N581 – 12x. multicoloured . . . 45 20
N582 – 12x. multicoloured . . . 45 20
N583 – 12x. multicoloured . . . 45 20
DESIGNS—VERT: No. N581, Urban guerrilla and attack on U.S. Embassy, Saigon; N582, Two soldiers with flag, Hue; N583, Mortar crew, Khe Sanh.

212 Soldier with Flame-thrower

1969. 15th Anniv of Liberation of Hanoi.
N584 **212** 12x. black and red . . . 1·10 50
N585 – 12x. multicoloured . . . 1·10 50
DESIGN: No. N585, Children with construction toy.

213 Grapefruit 214 Tribunal Emblem and Falling Airplane

1969. Fruits. Multicoloured.
N586 12x. Type **213** 35 15
N587 12x. Pawpaw 35 15
N588 20x. Tangerines 50 20
N589 30x. Oranges 85 35
N590 40x. Lychees . . . . . . 1·40 70
N591 50x. Persimmons . . . . . 1·90 1·00
See also Nos. N617/21 and N633/6.

1969. International War Crimes Tribunal, Stockholm and Roskilde.
N592 **214** 12x. black, red & brown 45 20

215 Ho Chi Minh in 1924

1970. 40th Anniv of Vietnamese Workers' Party. Multicoloured.

N593		12x. Type **215**	40	20
N594		12x. Ho Chi Minh in 1969	40	20
N595		12x. Le Hong Phong	40	20
N596		12x. Tran Phu	40	20
N597		12x. Nguyne Van Cu	40	20

Nos. N595/7 are smaller, size 40 × 24 mm.

216 Playtime in Nursery School

1970. Children's Activities. Multicoloured.

N598		12x. Type **216**	30	20
N599		12x. Playing with toys	30	20
N600		20x. Watering plants	45	25
N601		20x. Pasturing buffalo	45	25
N602		30x. Feeding chickens	60	40
N603		40x. Making music	80	50
N604		50x. Flying model airplane	1·25	75
N605		60x. Going to school	2·10	95

217 Lenin and Red Flag

1970. Birth Centenary of Lenin.

N606	**217**	12x. multicoloured	30	15
N607	–	1d. purple, red & yellow	1·90	50

DESIGN: 1d. Portrait of Lenin.

218 Great Green Turban

1970. Sea-shells. Multicoloured.

N608		12x. Type **218**	1·25	25
N609		12x. Indian volute	1·25	25
N610		20x. Tiger cowrie	1·60	35
N611		1d. Trumpet triton	4·75	1·00

219 Ho Chi Minh in 1930

1970. Ho Chi Minh's 80th Birth Anniv.

N612	**219**	12x. black, brn & flesh	30	15
N613	–	12x. black, blue & green	30	15
N614	–	2d. black, ochre & yell	1·90	1·10

PORTRAITS: No. N613, In 1945 with microphone; N614, In 1969.

220 Vietcong Flag

1970. 1st Anniv of National Liberation Front Provisional Government in South Vietnam.

N616	**220**	12x. multicoloured	40	20

221 Water-melon **222** Power Linesman

1970. Fruits. Multicoloured.

N617		12x. Type **221**	30	20
N618		12x. Pumpkin	30	20
N619		20x. Cucumber	45	25
N620		50x. Courgette	1·00	45
N621		1d. Charantais melon	2·00	85

1970. North Vietnamese Industries.

N622	**222**	12x. blue and red	50	15
N623	–	12x. red, yellow and blue	50	15
N624	–	12x. black, orange & blue	50	25
N625	–	12x. yellow, purple & green	50	25

DESIGNS—VERT: No. N623, Hands winding thread on bobbin ("Textiles"); N624, Stoker and power station ("Electric Power"); N625, Workers and lorry ("More coal for the Fatherland").

223 Peasant Girl with Pigs **225** Chuoi Tieu Bananas

224 Ho Chi Minh proclaiming Republic, 1945

1970. North Vietnamese Agriculture.

N626	**223**	12x. multicoloured	60	25

1970. 25th Anniv of Democratic Republic of Vietnam.

N627	**224**	12x. black, brown & red	25	10
N628	–	12x. deep brown, brown and green	25	10
N629	–	12x. brown, grey and red	25	10
N630	–	12x. deep brown, brown and green	25	10
N631	–	20x. brown, red & bistre	40	15
N632	–	1d. brown, drab and chestnut	1·40	60

DESIGNS: No. N628, Vo Thi Sau facing firing-squad; N629, Nguyen Van Troi and captors; N630, Phan Dinh Giot attacking pill-box; N631, Nguyen Viet Xuan encouraging troops; N632, Nguyen Van Be attacking tank.

1970. Bananas. Multicoloured.

N633		12x. Type **225**	35	20
N634		12x. Chuoi Tay	35	20
N635		50x. Chuoi Ngu	95	35
N636		1d. Chuoi Mat	1·90	75

226 Flags, and Bayonets in Helmet

1970. Indo-Chinese People's Summit Conference.

N637	**226**	12x. multicoloured	35	15

227 Engels and Signature

1970. 150th Birth Anniv of Friedrich Engels.

N638	**227**	12x. black, brown & red	35	15
N639		1d. black, brown & grn	1·10	60

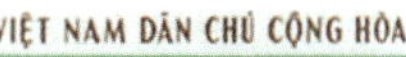

228 "Akistrodon ciatus"

1970. Snakes. Multicoloured.

N640		12x. Type **228**	60	20
N641		20x. "Calliophis macclellandii"	95	40
N642		50x. "Bungarus faciatus"	1·60	55
N643		1d. "Trimeresurus gramineus"	2·50	95

229 Mother and Child with Flag

1970. 10th Anniv of National Front for Liberation of South Vietnam. Multicoloured.

N644		6x. Type **229**	20	15
N645		12x. Vietcong flag and torch (horiz)	25	15

1971. Victories of Liberation Army. As No. N449, but value and colours changed.

N646	**178**	2x. black and orange	30	20

232 Satellite in Earth Orbit

1971. 1st Anniv of Launching of Chinese Satellite.

N649	**232**	12x. multicoloured	50	20
N650		50x. multicoloured	1·10	30

234 Ho Chi Minh Medal

1971. 81st Birth Anniv of Pres. Ho Chi Minh.

N652	**234**	1x. multicoloured	10	10
N653		3x. multicoloured	20	10
N654		10x. multicoloured	25	10
N655		12x. multicoloured	35	20

235 Emperor Quang Trung liberating Hanoi

1971. Bicentenary of Tay Son Rising.

N657	**235**	6x. multicoloured	35	20
N658		12x. multicoloured	50	25

236 Karl Marx and Music of the "Internationale"

1971. Centenary of Paris Commune.

N659	**236**	12x. black, red and pink	50	25

237 Hai Thuong Lan Ong

1971. 250th Birth Anniv of Hai Thuong Lan Ong (physician).

N660	**237**	12x. black, green & brn	25	10
N661		50x. multicoloured	50	25

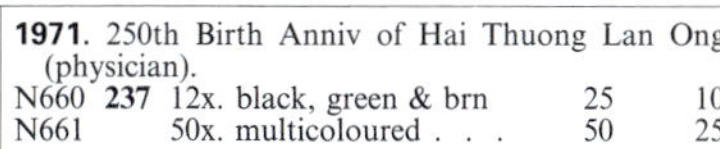

238 "Kapimala"

1971. Folk Sculptures in Tay Phuong Pagoda. Multicoloured.

N662		12x. Type **238**	45	20
N663		12x. "Sangkayasheta"	45	20
N664		12x. "Vasumitri"	45	20
N665		12x. "Dhikaca"	45	20
N666		30x. "Bouddha Nandi"	1·50	35
N667		40x. "Rahulata"	1·60	50
N668		50x. "Sangha Nandi"	1·75	55
N669		1d. "Cakyamuni"	2·10	70

239 Ho Chi Minh, Banner and Young Workers

1971. 40th Anniv of Ho Chi Minh Working Youth Union.

N670	**239**	12x. multicoloured	30	15

240 "Luna 16" on Moon **241** "Luna 17" landing on Moon

1971. Moon Flight of "Luna 16".

N671	–	12x. multicoloured	40	20
N672	–	12x. multicoloured	40	20
N673	**240**	1d. brown, blue & turq	1·75	60

DESIGNS: No. N671, Flight to Moon; N672, Return to Earth. Nos.

N671/2 were issued together horizontally, se-tenant, each pair forming a composite design.

1971. Moon Flight of "Luna 17".

N674	**241**	12x. red, blue and green	40	20
N675	–	12x. pink, green & myrtle	40	20
N676	–	1d. pink, brown & green	1·10	50

DESIGNS—HORIZ: No. N675, "Luna 17" on Moon; N676, "Lunokhod 1" crossing Moon crevasse.

243 "White Tiger"

1971. "The Five Tigers" (folk-art paintings). Mult.

N679		12x. Type **243**	40	25
N680		12x. "Yellow Tiger"	40	25
N681		12x. "Red Tiger"	40	25
N682		40x. "Green Tiger"	1·10	35
N683		50x. "Grey Tiger"	1·50	50
N684		1d. "Five Tigers"	2·50	95

244 Flags and Gate of Heavenly Peace, Peking **245** Mongolian Emblem

1971. 50th Anniv of Chinese Communist Party.
N686 **244** 12x. multicoloured . . . 20 10

1971. 50th Anniv of Mongolian People's Republic.
N687 **245** 12x. multicoloured . . . 30 15

246 Drum Procession

1972. Dong Ho Folk Engravings.
N688 **246** 12x. pink, brown & blk 40 25
N689 – 12x. pink and black . . 40 25
N690 – 12x. multicoloured . . . 40 25
N691 – 12x. multicoloured . . . 40 25
N692 – 40x. multicoloured . . . 1·75 40
N693 – 50x. multicoloured . . . 2·10 75
DESIGNS—HORIZ: No. N689, "Traditional Wrestling"; N692, "Wedding of Mice"; N693, "The Toads' School". VERT: No. N690, "Jealous Attack"; N691, "Gathering Coconuts".

247 Workers

1972. 3rd Vietnamese Trade Unions Congress.
N694 **247** 1x. black and blue . . . 25 10
N695 – 12x. black and orange 35 20
DESIGN: 12x. As Type **247**, but design reversed.

248 Planting Rice

1972. 25th Anniv of National Resistance.
N696 **248** 12x. multicoloured . . . 25 15
N697 – 12x. multicoloured . . . 25 15
N698 – 12x. multicoloured . . . 25 15
N699 – 12x. turq, red & pink 25 15
DESIGNS: No. N697, Munitions worker; N698, Soldier with flame-thrower; N699, Text of Ho Chi Minh's Appeal.

249 Ho Chi Minh's Birthplace

1972. 82nd Birth Anniv of Ho Chi Minh.
N700 **249** 12x. black, drab & ochre 25 15
N701 – 12x. black, green & pink 25 15
DESIGN: No. N701, Ho Chi Minh's house, Hanoi.

250 Captured Pilot and Falling Airplane **251** Georgi Dimitrov

1972. "3,500th U.S. Aircraft Brought Down over North Vietnam".
N702 **250** 12x. green and red . . . 95 60
N703 12x. black and red . . . 95 60
No. N703 has the inscription amended to record the actual date on which the 3,500th aircraft was brought down: 20.4.1972.

1972. 90th Birth Anniv of Georgi Dimitrov (Bulgarian statesman).
N704 **251** 12x. brown and green 25 15
N705 – 12x. black and pink . . 25 15
DESIGN: No. N705, Dimitrov at Leipzig Court, 1933.

252 Falcated Teal **253** Anti-aircraft Gunner

1972. Vietnamese Birds. Multicoloured.
N706 12x. Type **252** 70 20
N707 12x. Red-wattled lapwing 70 20
N708 30x. Cattle egret . . . . . 1·25 25
N709 40x. Water cock . . . . . 1·60 40
N710 50x. Purple swamphen . . 2·50 70
N711 1d. Greater adjutant stork 4·75 1·10

1972. "4,000th U.S. Aircraft Brought Down over North Vietnam".
N712 **253** 12x. black, mauve and pink 65 25
N713 – 12x. green, black and red 65 25
DESIGN: No. N713, Anti-aircraft gunner with shell.

254 Umbrella Dance

1972. Tay Nguyen Folk Dances. Multicoloured.
N714 12x. Type **254** 25 15
N715 12x. Drum dance 25 15
N716 12x. Shield dance 25 15
N717 20x. Horse dance 45 20
N718 30x. Ka-Dong dance . . . 50 20
N719 40x. Grinding-rice dance . . 70 25
N720 50x. Gong dance 90 50
N721 1d. Cham Rong dance . . 1·75 70

255 "Soyuz 11" Spacecraft and "Salyut" Space Laboratory

1972. Space Flight of "Soyuz 11".
N722 **255** 12x. blue and lilac . . . 25 15
N723 – 1d. brown and flesh . . 1·00 45
DESIGN: 1d. "Soyuz 11" astronauts.

256 Dhole

1973. Wild Animals (1st series). Multicoloured.
N724 12x. Type **256** 40 20
N725 30x. Leopard 60 20
N726 50x. Leopard cat . . . . . 1·10 40
N727 1d. European otter . . . . 2·00 50
See also Nos. N736/9.

257 Copernicus and Globe

1973. 500th Birth Anniv of Copernicus (astronomer).
N728 **257** 12x. black, red & brown 30 20
N729 – 12x. black, red & brown 30 20
N730 – 30x. black and brown 65 25
DESIGNS—HORIZ: No. N729, Copernicus and sun. VERT: 30x. Copernicus and facsimile signature.

258 "Drummers"

1973. Engravings from Ngoc Lu Bronze Drums. Each yellow and green.
N731 12x. Type **258** 50 25
N732 12x. "Pounding rice" . . . 50 25
N733 12x. "Folk-dancing" . . . 50 25
N734 12x. "War canoe" . . . 50 25
N735 12x. "Birds and beasts" . . 50 25

259 Lesser Malay Chevrotain **260** Striated Canegrass Warblers

1973. Wild Animals (2nd series). Multicoloured.
N736 12x. Type **259** 35 20
N737 30x. Mainland serow . . . 60 20
N738 50x. Wild boar . . . . . . 1·10 35
N739 1d. Siberian musk deer . . 2·00 50

1973. Birds useful to Agriculture. Multicoloured.
N740 12x. Type **260** 55 25
N741 12x. Red-whiskered bulbuls 55 25
N742 20x. Magpie robin 70 30
N743 40x. White-browed fantails 1·40 40
N744 50x. Great tits . . . . . . 2·40 65
N745 1d. Japanese white-eyes . . 4·50 90

262 "Ready to Learn"

1973. "Three Readies" Youth Movement.
N748 **262** 12x. brown and green 20 10
N749 – 12x. violet and blue . . 20 10
N750 – 12x. green and mauve 20 10
DESIGNS: No. N749, Soldiers on the march ("Ready to Fight"); N750, Road construction ("Ready to Work").

263 Flags of North Vietnam and North Korea

1973. 25th Anniv of People's Republic of Korea.
N751 **263** 12x. multicoloured . . . 25 10

264 Dogfight over Hanoi

1973. Victory over U.S. Air Force.
N752 **264** 12x. multicoloured . . . 25 15
N753 – 12x. multicoloured . . . 25 15
N754 – 12x. multicoloured . . . 25 15
N755 – 1d. black and red . . . 1·25 55
DESIGNS: No. N753, Boeing B-52 Stratofortress exploding over Haiphong; N754, Anti-aircraft gun; N755, Aircraft wreckage in China Sea.

266 Elephant hauling Logs **267** Dahlia

1974. Vietnamese Elephants. Multicoloured.
N758 12x. Type **266** 50 20
N759 12x. War elephant 50 20
N760 40x. Elephant rolling logs 1·25 35
N761 50x. Circus elephant . . . 1·50 45
N762 1d. Elephant carrying war supplies . . . . 3·25 95

1974. Flowers.
N763 **267** 12x. red, lake and green 45 20
N764 – 12x. red, lake and green 45 20
N765 – 12x. yellow, green & blue 45 20
N766 – 12x. multicoloured . . . 75 30
N767 – 12x. multicoloured . . . 75 30
FLOWERS: No. N764, Rose; N765, Chrysanthemum; N766, Bach Mi; N767, Dai Doa.

268 Soldier planting Flag **269** Armed Worker and Peasant

1974. 20th Anniv of Victory at Dien Bien Phu.
N768 12x. Type **268** 20 10
N769 12x. Victory badge 20 10

1974. "Three Responsibilities" Women's Movement.
N770 **269** 12x. blue and pink . . . 25 10
N771 – 12x. blue and pink . . . 25 10
DESIGN: No. N771, Woman operating loom.

270 Cuc Nau Chrysanthemum **271** "Corchorus capsularis"

1974. Vietnamese Chrysanthemums. Mult.
N772 12x. Type **270** 30 20
N773 12x. Cuc Vang 30 20
N774 20x. Cuc Ngoc Khong Tuoc 55 25
N775 30x. Cuc Trang 60 30
N776 40x. Kim Cuc 75 45
N777 50x. Cuc Hong Mi . . . . 1·10 50
N778 60x. Cuc Gam . . . . . . 1·40 55
N779 1d. Cuc Tim . . . . 2·50 1·00

1974. Textile Plants.
N780 **271** 12x. brown, green and olive 50 15
N781 – 12x. brown, grn & pink 50 15
N782 – 30x. brown, green & yellow . . . . 1·00 35
DESIGNS: No. N781, "Cyperus tojet jormis"; N782, "Morus alba".

272 Nike Statue, Warsaw

1974. 30th Anniv of People's Republic of Poland.
N783 **272** 1x. purple, pink and red 25 15
N784 2x. red, pink and red . . 25 15
N785 3x. brown, pink and red 25 15
N786 12x. light red, pink & red 65 25

273 Flags of China and Vietnam

1974. 25th Anniv of People's Republic of China.
N787 **273** 12x. multicoloured . . . 35 15

274 Handclasp with Vietnamese and East German Flags

1974. 25th Anniv of German Democratic Republic.
N788 **274** 12x. multicoloured . . . 35 15

275 Woman Bricklayer
276 Pres. Allende with Chilean Flag

1974. 20th Anniv of Liberation of Hanoi. Mult.
N789 12x. Type **275** 20 10
N790 12x. Soldier with child . . 20 10

1974. 1st Death Annivs of Salvador Allende (President of Chile) and Pablo Neruda (Chilean poet).
N791 **276** 12x. blue and red . . . 20 10
N792 – 12x. blue (Pablo Neruda) 20 10

277 "Rhizostoma"

1974. Marine Life. Multicoloured.
N793 12x. Type **277** 50 15
N794 12x. "Loligo" 50 15
N795 30x. Variously coloured abalone 75 20
N796 40x. Japanese pearl oyster 1·00 25
N797 50x. Common cuttlefish . . 1·60 50
N798 1d. "Palinurus japonicus" 3·25 1·00

278 Flags of Algeria and Vietnam
279 Albanian Emblem

1974. 20th Anniv of Algerian War of Liberation.
N799 **278** 12x. multicoloured . . . 40 15

1974. 30th Anniv of People's Republic of Albania. Multicoloured.
N800 12x. Type **279** 20 10
N801 12x. Girls from Albania and North Vietnam . . . 20 10

280 Signing of Paris Agreement

1975. 2nd Anniv of Paris Agreement on Vietnam.
N802 **280** 12x. black, green & emerald 25 20
N803 – 12x. black, blue and grey 25 20
DESIGN: No. N803, International Conference in session.

281 Tran Phu

1975. 45th Anniv of Vietnamese Workers' Party.
N804 **281** 12x. brown, red and pink 20 10
N805 – 12x. brown, red and pink 20 10
N806 – 12x. brown, red and pink 20 10
N807 – 12x. brown, red and pink 20 10
N808 – 60x. brown, chestnut and pink 75 35
PORTRAITS—HORIZ: No. N805, Nguyen Van Cu; N806, Le Hong Phong; N807, Ngo Gia Tu. VERT: No. N808, Ho Chi Minh in 1924.

282 "Costus speciosus"

1975. Medicinal Plants. Multicoloured.
N809 12x. Type **282** 30 15
N810 12x. "Rosa laevigata" . . . 30 15
N811 12x. "Curcuma zedoaria" . . 30 15
N812 30x. "Erythrina indica" . . 55 20
N813 40x. "Lilium brownii" . . . 70 25
N814 50x. "Hibiscus sagittifolius" 75 35
N815 60x. "Papaver somniferum" 1·10 40
N816 1d. "Belamcanda chinensis" 2·25 70

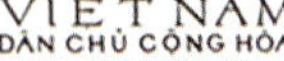

283 "Achras sapota"

1975. Fruits. Multicoloured.
N817 12x. Type **283** 20 10
N818 12x. "Persica vulgaris" . . 20 10
N819 20x. "Eugenia jambos" . . 25 15
N820 30x. "Chrysophyllum cainito" 35 20
N821 40x. "Lucuma mamosa" . . 40 20
N822 50x. "Prunica granitum" . 55 20
N823 60x. "Durio ziberthinus" . 75 35
N824 1d. "Prunus salicina" . . . 1·40 65

284 Ho Chi Minh
285 Ho Chi Minh proclaiming Independence, 1945

1975. 85th Birth Anniv of Ho Chi Minh.
N825 **284** 12x. multicoloured . . . 20 15
N826 60x. multicoloured . . . 45 20

1975. 30th Anniv of Democratic Republic of Vietnam. Multicoloured.
N827 12x. Type **285** 20 10
N828 12x. Democratic Republic emblem 20 10
N829 12x. Democratic Republic flag 20 15

286 "Dermochelys coriacea"
287 Arms of Hungary

1975. Reptiles. Multicoloured.
N831 12x. Type **286** 35 15
N832 12x. "Physignathus cocincinus" 35 15
N833 20x. "Hydrophis brookii" . 50 15
N834 30x. "Platysternum megacephalum" 60 20
N835 40x. "Leiolepis belliana" . . 90 20
N836 50x. "Python molurus" . . 1·00 35
N837 60x. "Naja hannah" . . . 1·25 45
N838 1d. "Draco maculatus" . . 2·50 55

1975. 30th Anniv of Liberation of Hungary.
N839 **287** 12x. multicoloured . . . 35 15

288 "Pathysa antiphates"

1976. Butterflies. Multicoloured.
N840 12x. Type **288** 50 10
N841 12x. "Danaus plexippus" . 50 10
N842 20x. "Gynautocera papilionaria" 65 15
N843 30x. "Maenas salaminia" . 75 20
N844 40x. "Papilio machaon" . . 1·00 20
N845 50x. "Ixias pyrene" . . . . 1·10 30
N846 60x. "Eusemia vetula" . . 1·50 50
N847 1d. "Eriboea sp." . . . . . 2·75 65

289 Hoang Thao Orchid

1976. Lunar New Year.
N848 **289** 6x. yellow, green & blue 60 25
N849 12x. yellow, green & red 95 25

290 Masked Palm Civet

1976. Wild Animals. Multicoloured.
N850 12x. Type **290** 25 10
N851 12x. Belly-banded squirrel 25 10
N852 20x. Rhesus macaque . . . 30 10
N853 30x. Chinese porcupine . . 50 15
N854 40x. Racoon-dog 60 20
N855 50x. Asiatic black bear . . 75 30
N856 60x. Leopard . . . . . . 1·10 45
N857 1d. Malayan flying lemur 1·90 65

291 Voters and Map

1976. 1st Elections Unified National Assembly.
N858 **291** 6x. red and sepia . . . 25 10
N859 – 6x. yellow and red . . . 25 10
N860 **291** 12x. red and blue . . . 75 20
DESIGN:—35 × 24 mm: No. N859, Map and ballot box.
See also Nos. NLF64/6 of National Front for the Liberation of South Vietnam.

292 Map and Text

1976. 1st Session of Unified National Assembly.
N861 **292** 6x. purple, red & yellow 25 10
N862 12x. turquoise, red & yellow 60 20
N863 – 12x. bistre, red & yellow 60 20
DESIGN—VERT (27 × 42 mm): No. N863, Vietnam map and design from Ngoc Lu Drum. No. N862 shows different text from Type **292**.
See also Nos. NLF68/9 of National Front for the Liberation of South Vietnam.

293 "Dendrobium devonianum"

1976. Orchids. Multicoloured.
N864 12x. Type **293** 25 10
N865 12x. "Habenaria rhodocheila" 25 10
N866 20x. "Dendrobium tortile" 40 10
N867 30x. "Doritis pulcherima" . 50 10
N868 40x. "Dendrobium farmeri" 70 15
N869 50x. "Dendrobium aggregatum" 80 25
N870 60x. "Eria pannae" . . . . 1·10 45
N871 1d. "Paphiopedilum concolor" . . . . 1·40 55

FRANK STAMPS

F **29**
F **42** Invalids in Rice-field

1958. No value indicated.
NF82 F **29** (–) red, yellow and green . . . . 10·00 4·50
Issued to war-disabled persons for private correspondence.

1959. No value indicated.
NF105 F **42** (–) brown . . . . . 3·00 90
NF106 (–) olive and blue . . 4·50 1·40
Issued to invalids in agriculture for private correspondence.

F **230** Invalid's Badge

1971. No value indicated.
NF647 F **230** (–) brown and red 60 25
Issued to disabled ex-servicemen for private correspondence.

F **233** Disabled Soldier with Baby
F **261** "Returning Home"

1971. No value indicated.
NF651 F **233** (–) brn, red & yell 45 20

1973.
NF746 F **261** 12x. black and red 30 10
NF747 – 12x. black and blue 30 10
DESIGN—22 × 33 mm: No. NF747, Disabled soldier with drill.
Issued to disabled veterans for private correspondence.

MILITARY FRANK STAMPS

MF **46** Soldier and Steam Train

1959. No value indicated.
NMF112 MF **46** (–) black & green 5·25 1·60

MF **68** Mounted Frontier Guard

MF **118** Military Medal and Invalid's Badge

1961. No value indicated.
NMF154 MF **68** (–) mult . . . . 11·00 5·50

1963.
NMF277 MF **118** 12x. mult . . . 3·50 2·50
For use on disabled soldiers' mail.

MF **133** Soldier and Army Badge

MF **150** Soldier in Action

1964. No value indicated.
NMF325 MF **133** (–) green, black and orge . . 1·90 60

1965. No value indicated.
NMF373 MF **150** (–) black and red . . . . . 1·75 45
NMF374 (–) black & green . . . . 1·75 45

MF **177** Soldiers and Weapons

1966. No value indicated.
NMF447 MF **177** (–) violet & black . . . . 6·50 6·50

MF **189** "Star" Badge of People's Army

MF **204** Soldiers attacking

1967. No value indicated.
NMF488 MF **189** (–) mult 60 30

1968. No value indicated.
NMF519 (–) brown and green . .
No. NMF519 is similar in design to No. NMF447, but shows more modern equipment and is dated "1967".

1968. No value indicated.
NMF547 MF **204** (–) lilac 65 30

1969. Type MF 177, but undated. No value indicated.
NMF579 MF **177** (–) brown & green . . . .

MF **231** Nguyen Van Be attacking Tank

1971. No value indicated.
NMF648 MF **231** (–) blk, red & drab 50 25

MF **242** Nguyen Viet Yuan and Anti-aircraft Gun

1971. No value indicated.
NMF677 MF **242** (–) black, pink and buff . . 40 20
NMF678 (–) brown & green 40 20

MF **265** Soldier with Bayonet advancing

1974. No value indicated.
NMF756 MF **265** (–) black, yellow & blue 25 10
NMF757 – (–) black, red and brown 25 10
NMF758 MF **265** (–) black, flesh and red . . . 50 20
DESIGN: No. NMF757, Soldier with sub-machine gun, and tanks. No. NMF757 is 40 × 24 mm; No. NMF758 31 × 21 mm.

OFFICIAL STAMPS

The values on Official stamps issued 1952 to 1954 are in kilogrammes of rice, the basis of the State's economy.

A. Tongking.

O **6** Rice-harvester

1953. Production and Economy Campaign.
NO17 O **6** 0.600k. red . . . . . . 4·50 1·90
NO18 1.000k. brown . . . . 4·50 3·25
NO19 2.000k. orange . . . . 7·00 3·75
NO20 5.000k. slate . . . . . 9·00 7·00

B. Central Annam.

NAO **3** "Family Left Behind"

1952. Issue for Central Annam. Imperf.
NAO 9 NAO **3** 0.050k. red . . . — £150
NAO10 0.300k. red . . . — £150
NAO11 0.300k. violet . . — £150
NAO12 0.600k. green . . — £150
NAO13 0.600k. blue . . . — £150
NAO14 1000k. green . . . — £250

1954. No. NA5 surch **TEMSU VU 0.k300 THOC**.
NAO15 NA **1** 0.300k. on 30d. on 5d. green £325 £225

1954. Nos. 56/7 of Vietnam Democratic Republic surch in **Kg.** No. NAO17 also optd **LKV** at top and **THOC** below value.
NAO16 **3** 0kg05 on 1h. green . . £170
NAO17 0kg050 on 3h. red . . . £170

1954. Surch **TEMSU VU** and new value. (a) On unsurcharged stamps with coloured (NAO20) or white (others) figures.
NAO20 NA **1** 0,750k. on 10d. mauve . . . . .
NAO21 0,800k. on 1d. violet . . . . .
NAO22 0,900k. on 5d. green . . . . .

(b) On stamps with coloured figures, previously surcharged.
NAO23 NA **1** 0,030k. on 3d. on 35d. purple . . . .
NAO24 0,050k. on 35d. on 300d. blue . . . .
NAO25 0,350k. on 70d. on 100d. grey . . . .

C. General issues.

1954. Dien-Bien-Phu Victory. As T **9** but value in "KILO". Imperf.
NO24 0.600k. ochre and sepia . . 12·50 7·50

1955. Surch **0 k, 100 THOC**.
NO33 **2** 0.100k. on 2d. brown . . £150 £120
NO34 0.100k. on 5d. red £150 £120

1955. Land Reform. As T **13** but inscr "SU VU".
NO38 40d. blue . . . . 10·00 5·00
NO39 80d. red . . . . 15·00 6·25

O **17** Cu Chinh Lan (Tank Destroyer)

1956. Cu Chinh Lan Commemoration.
NO50 O **17** 20d. green & turquoise . . . . . 2·75 2·75
NO51 80d. mauve and red 3·50 3·50
NO52 100d. sepia and drab 4·00 4·00
NO53 500d. blue & light blue . . . . . . 11·50 11·50
NO54 1000d. brown & orge 26·00 26·00
NO55 2000d. purple & green 40·00 40·00
NO56 3000d. lake and lilac 75·00 75·00

1957. 4th World T.U. Conference, Leipzig. As T **24** but inscr "SU VU".
NO69 20d. green . . . . 2·10 1·25
NO70 40d. blue . . . . 2·50 1·25
NO71 80d. lake . . . . 3·75 2·25
NO72 100d. brown . . . . . . 4·00 2·75

O **26** Mot Cot Pagoda, Hanoi

O **30** Lathe

1957.
NO75 O **26** 150d. brown and green . . . . . . 5·50 2·75
NO76 150d. black and yellow . . . . . . 8·50 4·75

1958. Arts and Crafts Fair, Hanoi.
NO83 O **30** 150d. black and pink 1·90 1·40
NO84 200d. blue and orange 2·75 1·90

O **31** Congress Symbol

1958. 1st World Congress of Young Workers, Prague.
NO85 O **31** 150d. red and green 2·25 90

O **34** Soldier, Factory and Crops

1958. Military Service.
NO91 O **34** 50d. blue and purple 1·40 60
NO92 150d. brown and green . . . . . . 2·25 75
NO93 200d. red and yellow 3·00 90

O **40** Footballer and Hanoi Stadium

1958. Opening of New Hanoi Stadium.
NO102 O **40** 10d. lilac and blue 65 30
NO103 20d. olive and salmon . . . . 1·00 50
NO104 80d. brown and ochre . . . . . . 1·75 45
NO105 150d. brown & turq 2·75 85

O **97** Armed Forces on Boat

O **100** Woman with Rice-planter

1962. Military Service.
NO223 O **97** 12x. multicoloured 4·25 1·75

1962. Rural Service.
NO229 O **100** 3x. red 50 20
NO230 6x. turquoise . . . 75 25
NO231 12x. olive 95 35

O **176** Postman delivering Letter

1966. Rural Service.
NO445 O **176** 3x. purple, bistre and lilac 40 25
NO446 – 6x. purple, bistre and turquoise . . 65 25
DESIGN: 6x. As Type O **176** but design reversed.

POSTAGE DUE STAMPS

1952. Handstamped **TT** in diamond frame.
ND33 **3** 100d. green . . . . . . 40·00 40·00
ND34 100d. brown . . . . . . 40·00 40·00
ND35 **5** 100d. violet . . . . . . 50·00 50·00
ND36 **3** 200d. red . . . . 50·00 50·00

D **13** Letter Scales

D **39**

1955.
ND40 D **13** 50d. brown and lemon . . . . . . 11·00 8·75

1958.
ND101 D **39** 10d. red and violet 70 60
ND102 20d. green & orange 1·50 90
ND103 100d. red and slate 3·00 2·40
ND104 300d. red and olive 4·50 3·25

F. SOCIALIST REPUBLIC OF VIETNAM

Following elections in April 1976 a National Assembly representing the whole of Vietnam met in Hanoi on 24 June 1976 and on 2 July proclaimed the reunification of the country as the Socialist Republic of Vietnam, with Hanoi as capital.

100 xu = 1 dong.

18 Red Cross and Vietnam Map on Globe

1976. 30th Anniv of Vietnamese Red Cross.
99 **18** 12x. red, blue and green . . 50 25

20 Emperor Snapper

1976. Marine Fishes. Multicoloured.
102 12x. Type **20** 40 10
103 12x. Black-striped dottyback 40 10
104 20x. Tigerperch 55 10
105 30x. Two-striped anemonefish 80 15
106 40x. Stripe-tailed damselfish 1·00 20
107 50x. Pennant coralfish . . . 1·25 25
108 60x. Large-mouthed anemonefish . . . . 1·50 45
109 1d. Sail-finned snapper . . . 2·50 65

22 Party Flag and Map

1976. 4th Congress of Vietnam Workers' Party (1st issue). Flag in yellow and red, background colours given below.
111 **22** 2x. blue 10 10
112 3x. purple 10 10
113 5x. green 20 10
114 10x. green 25 10
115 12x. green 30 10
116 20x. green 50 20

23 Workers and Flag
24 Ho Chi Minh and Map of Vietnam

1976. 4th Congress of Vietnam Workers' Party (2nd issue).
117 **23** 12x. black, red and yellow 30 10
118 – 12x. red, orange and black 30 10
DESIGN: No. 118, Industry and agriculture.

1976. "Unification of Vietnam".
119 **24** 6x. multicoloured 20 15
120 12x. multicoloured 25 15

25 Soldiers seizing Buon Me Thuot

1976. Liberation of South Vietnam. Mult.
121 2x. Type **25** 20 10
122 3x. Soldiers on Son Tra peninsula, Da Nang . . . 20 10
123 6x. Soldiers attacking Presidential Palace, Saigon 20 10
124 50x. Type **25** 55 20
125 1d. As 3x. 95 45
126 2d. As 6x. . . . . 1·75 90

1976. As Nos. N848/9 but inscr "VIET NAM 1976" at foot and background colours changed.
126a **289** 6x. yellow, green & orange . . . . . . 1·60 50
126b 12x. yellow, light green and green . . . . . 1·60 50

26 "Crocothemis servilia" (Ho)

1977. Dragonflies. Multicoloured.
127 12x. Type **26** 20 10
128 12x. "Ictinogomphus clavatus" (Bao) 20 10
129 20x. "Rhinocypha fenestrella" 30 10
130 30x. "Neurothemis tullia" . . 35 15
131 40x. "Neurobavis chinensis" 50 15
132 50x. "Neurothemis fulvia" . . 75 15
133 60x. "Rhyothemis variegata" 1·00 35
134 1d. "Rhyothemis fuliginosa" 1·75 45

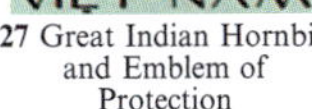

27 Great Indian Hornbill and Emblem of Protection
28 Thang Long Tower and Bronze Drum

1977. Rare Birds. Multicoloured.
135 12x. Type **27** 25 10
136 12x. Tickell's hornbill . . . 25 10
137 20x. Long-crested hornbill . . 60 20
138 30x. Wreathed hornbill . . . 75 25
139 40x. Indian pied hornbill . . 1·00 35
140 50x. Black hornbill . . . . . 1·25 35
141 60x. Great Indian hornbill . . 1·75 50
142 1d. Rufous-necked hornbill 3·25 65

1977. 1st Anniv of National Assembly General Election.
143 **28** 4x. multicoloured 15 10
144 – 5x. multicoloured 15 10
145 – 12x. bistre, black and green 15 10
146 – 50x. multicoloured 40 20
DESIGNS: 5x. Map of Vietnam and drum; 12x. Lotus flower and drum; 50x. Vietnamese flag and drum.

29 "Anoplophora bowringii"

1977. Beetles. Multicoloured.
147 12x. Type **29** 15 10
148 12x. "Anoplophora horsfieldi" 15 10
149 20x. "Aphrodisium griffithi" 25 10
150 30x. Musk beetle 35 15
151 40x. "Calloplophora tonkinea" 50 20
152 50x. "Thysia wallacei" . . . 60 25
153 60x. "Aristobia approximator" . . . . . 1·00 40
154 1d. "Batocera rubus" . . . . 1·60 60

30 "Thevetia peruviana"

1977. Wild Flowers. Multicoloured.
155 12x. Type **30** 20 10
156 12x. "Broussonetia papyrifera" 20 10
157 20x. "Aleurites montana" . . 25 15
158 30x. "Cerbera manghes" . . 35 15
159 40x. "Cassia multijuga" . . . 50 20
160 50x. "Cassia nodosa" 60 20
161 60x. "Hibiscus schizopetalus" 85 35
162 1d. "Lagerstroesnia speciosa" 1·40 55

31 Pink Dahlias (Hoa Dong Tien)
32 Children drawing Map of Vietnam

1977. Cultivated Flowers (1st series). Mult.
163 6x. Type **31** 15 10
164 6x. Orange cactus dahlias (Bong tien kep) 15 10
165 12x. Type **31** 25 10
166 12x. As No. 164 . . . . . . 25 10
See also Nos. 192/5.

1977. Unification of Vietnam.
167 **32** 4x. multicoloured 20 15
168 5x. multicoloured 20 15
169 10x. multicoloured 30 15
170 12x. multicoloured 30 15
171 30x. multicoloured 50 20

33 Goldfish (Dong Nai Hoa)

1977. Veil-tailed Goldfish. Multicoloured.
172 12x. Type **33** 30 10
173 12x. Hoa nhung 30 10
174 20x. Tau xanh 45 15
175 30x. Mat rong 55 20
176 40x. Cam trang 65 25
177 50x. Ngu sac . . . . 1·10 30
178 60x. Dong nai . . . . 1·40 35
179 1d. Thap cam . . . . 2·50 55

34 Ho Chi Minh and Lenin Banner
35 Southern Grackle

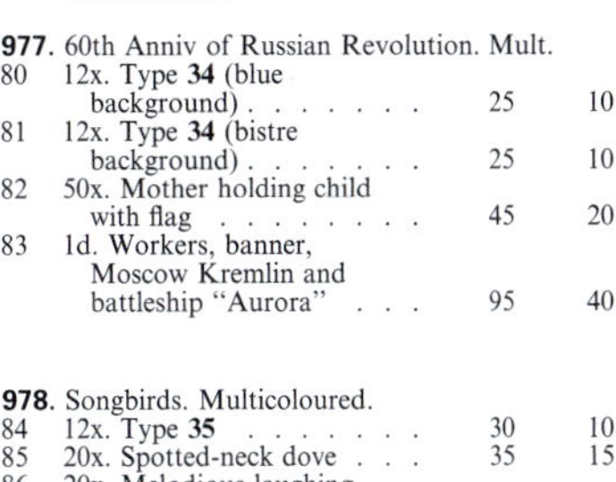

1977. 60th Anniv of Russian Revolution. Mult.
180 12x. Type **34** (blue background) 25 10
181 12x. Type **34** (bistre background) 25 10
182 50x. Mother holding child with flag 45 20
183 1d. Workers, banner, Moscow Kremlin and battleship "Aurora" . . . 95 40

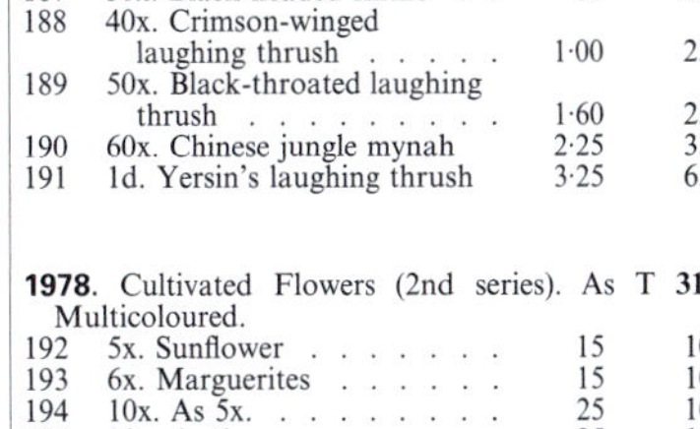

1978. Songbirds. Multicoloured.
184 12x. Type **35** 30 10
185 20x. Spotted-neck dove . . . 35 15
186 20x. Melodious laughing thrush 35 15
187 30x. Black-headed shrike . . 80 20
188 40x. Crimson-winged laughing thrush . . . . . 1·00 25
189 50x. Black-throated laughing thrush . . . . 1·60 25
190 60x. Chinese jungle mynah 2·25 35
191 1d. Yersin's laughing thrush 3·25 65

1978. Cultivated Flowers (2nd series). As T **31**. Multicoloured.
192 5x. Sunflower 15 10
193 6x. Marguerites 15 10
194 10x. As 5x. 25 10
195 12x. As 6x. 25 10

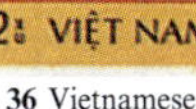

36 Vietnamese Children
37 Throwing the Discus

1978. International Children's Day.
196 **36** 12x. multicoloured 35 20

1978. Athletics. Multicoloured.
197 12x. Type **37** 20 10
198 12x. Long jumping 20 10
199 20x. Hurdling 25 10
200 30x. Throwing the hammer 45 15
201 40x. Putting the shot 55 20
202 50x. Throwing the javelin . . 75 25
203 60x. Sprinting . . . . 1·10 40
204 1d. High jumping . . . . . 1·60 55

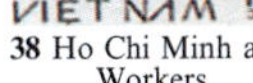

38 Ho Chi Minh and Workers
39 Ho Chi Minh

1978. 4th Vietnamese Trade Union Congress. Multicoloured.
205 10x. Trade Union Emblem 25 10
206 10x. Type **38** 25 10

1978. 88th Birth Anniv of Ho Chi Minh. Mult.
207 10x. Type **39** 35 20
208 12x. Ho Chi Minh Monument (38 × 22 mm) 35 20

40 Young Pioneers' Cultural House, Hanoi

1978. International Children's Day.
209 **40** 10x. black, flesh and red 35 20

41 Sanakavasa

1978. Sculptures from Tay Phuong Pagoda. Mult.
210 12x. Type **41** 20 10
211 12x. Parsva 20 10
212 12x. Punyasas 20 10
213 20x. Kumarata 25 10
214 20x. Nagarjuna 25 10
215 30x. Yayata 30 15
216 40x. Cadiep 45 20
217 50x. Ananda 50 25
218 60x. Buddhamitra 65 30
219 1d. Asvaghosa . . . . 1·10 50

42 Cuban Flag
43 Worker, Peasant, Soldier and Intellectual

1978. 25th Anniv of Cuban Revolution.
220 **42** 6x. red, black and blue . . 25 10
221 12x. red, black and blue . . 30 10

1978. 33rd Anniv of Proclamation of Vietnam Democratic Republic.
222 **43** 6x. red, yellow and mauve 15 10
223 – 6x. turquoise, green & blue 15 10
224 **43** 12x. red, yellow and mauve 25 15
225 – 12x. red and pink 25 15
DESIGN: Nos. 223 and 225, Industrial complex and tractor on field.

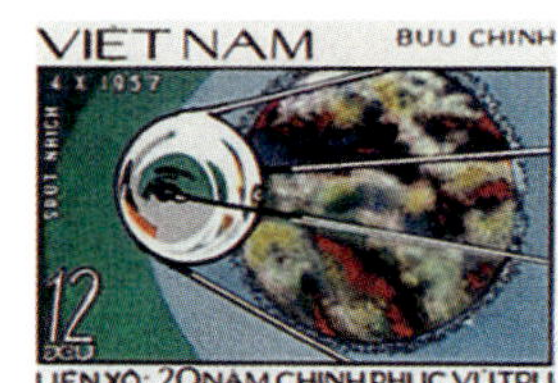

44 "Sputnik"

1978. 20 Years of Russian Space Exploration. Multicoloured.
226 12x. Type **44** 20 10
227 12x. "Venus 1" 20 10
228 30x. Space capsules docking 20 15
229 40x. "Molniya 1" satellite . . 30 20
230 60x. "Soyuz" 50 25
231 2d. A. Gubarev and G. Grechko . . . . 1·75 75

45 Printed Circuit
47 Chrysanthemum "Cuc Tim"

46 Telephone Dial and Letter

1978. World Telecommunications Day.
232 **45** 12x. orange and brown . . 25 10
233 – 12x. brown and orange . . 25 10
DESIGN: No. 233, I.T.U. emblem.

1978. 20th Congress of Socialist Countries' Postal Ministers.
234 **46** 12x. multicoloured 35 10

1978. Chrysanthemums. Multicoloured.
235 12x. Type **47** 20 10
236 12x. "Cuc kim tien" 20 10
237 20x. "Cuc hong" 25 15
238 30x. "Cuc van tho" 35 15
239 40x. "Cuc vang" 35 15
240 50x. "Cuc thuy tim" 55 25
241 60x. "Cuc vang mo" 90 35
242 1d. "Cuc nau do" . . . . . 1·60 50

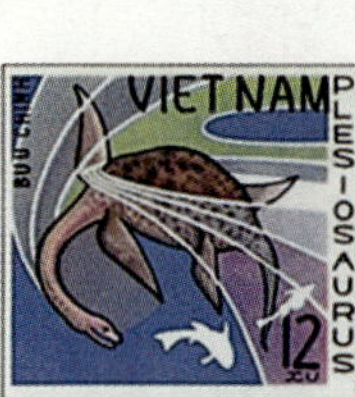

48 Plesiosaurus

49 Cuban and Vietnamese Flags and Militiawomen

1979. Prehistoric Animals. Multicoloured.

243 12x. Type **48** 20 10
244 12x. Brontosaurus 20 10
245 20x. Iguanodon 25 10
246 30x. Tyrannosaurus 30 15
247 40x. Stegosaurus 35 15
248 50x. Mozasaurus 45 20
249 60x. Triceratop 1·10 25
250 1d. Pteranodon 1·60 45

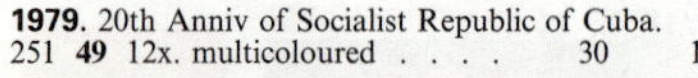

1979. 20th Anniv of Socialist Republic of Cuba.

251 **49** 12x. multicoloured 30 10

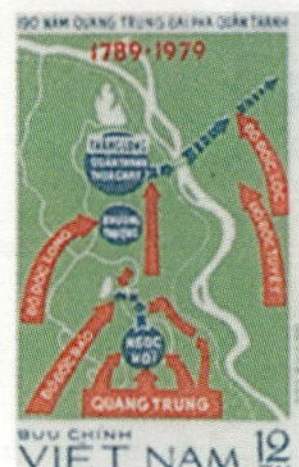

50 Battle Plan

51 Einstein

1979. 190th Anniv of Quang Trung's Victory over the Thanh.

252 **50** 12x. green, red and blue 25 10
253 – 12x. multicoloured 25 10

DESIGN: No. 253, Quang Trung.

1979. Birth Cent of Albert Einstein (physicist).

254 **51** 12x. black, brown and blue 25 10
255 – 60x. multicoloured 80 30

DESIGN: 60x. Equation, sun and planets.

52 Ram

53 Emblem

1979. Domestic Animals. Multicoloured.

256 10x. Type **52** 20 10
257 12x. Ox 20 10
258 20x. Ewe and lamb 35 15
259 30x. White buffalo (vert) 45 15
260 40x. Cow 50 15
261 50x. Goat 60 20
262 60x. Buffalo and calf 1·00 30
263 1d. Young goat (vert) 1·75 55

1979. Five Year Plan.

264 **53** 6x. mauve and light mauve 10 10
265 – 6x. green and buff 10 10
266 – 6x. green and purple 10 10
267 – 6x. orange and green 10 10
268 – 6x. blue and yellow 10 10
269 **53** 12x. red and pink 20 10
270 – 12x. brown and pink 20 10
271 – 12x. green and yellow 20 10
272 – 12x. blue and brown 20 10
273 – 12x. purple and blue 20 10

DESIGNS: Nos. 265, 270, Worker; 266, 271, Peasant and tractor; 267, 272, Soldier; 268, 273, Intellectual.

54 "Philaserdica '79" Emblem

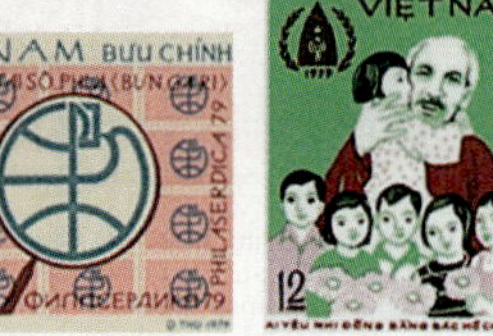

55 Ho Chi Minh and Children

1979. "Philaserdica '79" International Stamp Exhibition, Sofia, Bulgaria.

274 **54** 12x. blue, brown & orange 25 10
275 30x. blue, brown and pink 35 10

1979. International Children's Day. Mult.

276 12x. Type **55** 15 10
277 20x. Nurse, mother and child 30 10
278 50x. Children with painting materials and model glider 45 15
279 1d. Children of different races 95 35

56 Silver Pheasant

58 Cat (Meo Muop)

57 "Dendrobium heterocacpum"

1979. Ornamental Birds. Multicoloured.

280 12x. Siamese fireback pheasant ("Lophura diardi") (horiz) 40 10
281 12x. Temminck's tragopan ("Tragopan temminckii") (horiz) 40 10
282 20x. Common pheasant (horiz) 60 15
283 30x. Edwards's pheasant (horiz) 80 20
284 40x. Type **56** 90 25
285 50x. Germain's peacock-pheasant 1·25 35
286 60x. Great argus pheasant 1·75 40
287 1d. Green peafowl 2·75 60

1979. Orchids. Multicoloured.

288 12x. Type **57** 20 10
289 12x. "Cymbidium hybridum" 20 10
290 20x. "Rhynchostylis gigantea" 25 10
291 30x. "Dendrobium nobile" 30 15
292 40x. "Aerides falcatum" 35 15
293 50x. "Paphiopedilum callosum" 60 25
294 60x. "Vanda teres" 95 25
295 1d. "Dendrobium phalaenopsis" 1·50 45

1979. Cats. Multicoloured.

296 12x. Type **58** 20 10
297 12x. Meo Tam The (horiz) 20 10
298 20x. Meo Khoang 25 10
299 30x. Meo Dom Van (horiz) 35 15
300 40x. Meo Muop Dom 40 15
301 50x. Meo Vang 70 30
302 60x. Meo Xiem (horiz) 1·00 40
303 1d. Meo Van Am (horiz) 1·90 55

60 Citizens greeting Soldiers

1979. 35th Anniv of Vietnam People's Army.

306 **60** 12x. brown and green 30 20
307 – 12x. brown and green 30 20

DESIGN: No. 307, Soldiers in action.

62 Red and Pink Roses

63 "Nelumbium nuciferum"

1980. Roses. Multicoloured.

311 1x. Type **62** 15 10
312 2x. Single pink rose 15 10
313 12x. Type **62** 30 20
314 12x. As No. 312 30 20

1980. Water Flowers. Multicoloured.

315 12x. Type **63** 15 10
316 12x. "Nymphala stellata" 15 10
317 20x. "Ipomola reptans" 20 10
318 30x. "Nymphoides indicum" 30 15
319 40x. "Jussiala repens" 35 15
320 50x. "Eichhornia crassipes" 70 25
321 60x. "Monochoria voginalis" 95 25
322 1d. "Nelumbo nucifera" 1·50 40

64 Peasants with Banner and Implements as Weapons

1980. 50th Anniv of Vietnamese Communist Party. Multicoloured.

323 12x. Type **64** 10 10
324 12x. Ho Chi Minh proclaiming independence 10 10
325 20x. Soldiers with flag at Dien Bien Phu 25 15
326 20x. Map of Vietnam and soldiers and tanks storming Palace (Unification of Vietnam) 25 15
327 2d. Ho Chi Minh, soldier and workers and industrial and agricultural scene 1·60 60

65 Lenin

1980. 110th Birth Anniv of Lenin.

328 **65** 6x. flesh and green 15 10
329 12x. flesh and purple 25 10
330 1d. flesh and blue 80 35

66 Running

67 Ho Chi Minh in 1924

1980. Olympic Games, Moscow. Multicoloured.

331 12x. Type **66** 10 10
332 12x. Hurdles 10 10
333 20x. Basketball 20 15
334 30x. Football 30 15
335 40x. Wrestling 40 15
336 50x. Gymnastics (horiz) 45 20
337 60x. Swimming (horiz) 65 25
338 1d. Sailing (horiz) 95 45

1980. President Ho Chi Minh's 90th Birthday.

339 12x. Type **67** 35 15
340 40x. Ho Chi Minh as President 50 20

68 Children dancing around Globe

69 Soviet and Vietnamese Cosmonauts

1980. International Children's Day.

341 **68** 5x. multicoloured 25 15

1980. Soviet–Vietnamese Space Flight. Mult.

342 12x. Type **69** 10 10
343 12x. Launch of rocket 10 10
344 20x. "Soyuz 37" 20 10
345 40x. "Soyuz–Salyut" space complex 30 15
346 1d. "Soyuz" re-entering Earth's atmosphere 70 25
347 2d. Parachute landing 1·40 65

70 Whale Shark

1980. Fishes. Multicoloured.

349 12x. Type **70** 20 10
350 12x. Tiger shark 20 10
351 20x. Bearded shark 25 10
352 30x. Zebra horn shark 35 15
353 40x. Coachwhip stingray 60 20
354 50x. Wide sawfish 75 25
355 60x. Scalloped hammerhead 1·10 30
356 1d. Tobij-ei eagle ray 1·60 50

71 Ho Chi Minh telephoning

72 Pink Rose (Hong Bach)

1980. Posts and Telecommunications Day. Mult.

357 12x. Ho Chi Minh reading newspaper "Nhan Dan" 20 10
358 12x. Type **71** 25 10
359 50x. Kim Dong, "the heroic postman", carrying magpie robin in cage 2·10 1·40
360 1d. Dish aerial 1·00 35

1980. Flowers.

361 **72** 12x. pink and green 35 15
362 – 12x. red and green 35 15
363 – 12x. mauve and green 35 15

DESIGNS—As Type **72**: No. 362, Red roses (Hong nhung). 15 × 20 mm: No. 363, Camellia.

73 Telephone Switchboard Operator

74 Ho Chi Minh

1980. National Telecommunications Day.

364 12x. Type **73** 20 10
365 12x. Diesel train and railway route map 4·00 60

1980. 35th Anniv of Democratic Republic of Vietnam. Multicoloured.

366 12x. Type **74** 25 10
367 12x. Arms of Vietnam (29 × 40 mm) 25 10
368 40x. Pac Bo cave (29 × 40 mm) 40 15
369 1d. Source of Lenine (40 × 29 mm) 95 40

75 Vietnamese Arms

76 Nguyen Trai

1980. National Emblems.

370 **75** 6x. multicoloured 25 10
371 – 12x. yellow, red and black 25 10
372 – 12x. black, orange & yellow 25 10

DESIGNS—VERT: No. 372, National Anthem. HORIZ: No. 371, National flag.

1980. 600th Birth Anniv of Nguyen Trai (national hero).

373 **76** 12x. yellow and black 20 10
374 – 50x. black and blue 45 20
375 – 1d. black and brown 95 40

DESIGNS—HORIZ: 50x. Three books by Nguyen Trai. VERT: 1d. Ho Chi Minh reading commemorative stele in Con Son Pagoda.

77 Ho Chi Minh with Women

78 "Biguoniaceae venusta"

1980. 50th Anniv of Vietnamese Women's Union.
376 **77** 12x. green, blue and lilac . . 25 10
377 – 12x. blue and lilac 25 10
DESIGN: No. 377, Group of women.

1980. Flowers. Multicoloured.
378 12x. Type **78** 20 10
379 12x. "Ipomoea pulchella" . . 20 10
380 20x. "Petunia hybrida" . . . 30 10
381 30x. "Trapaeolum majus" . . 40 15
382 40x. "Thunbergia grandiflora" 45 15
383 50x. "Anlamanda cathartica" . . 55 20
384 60x. "Campsis radicans" . . 80 25
385 1d. "Bougainvillaea spectabilis" . . . . 1·50 45

79 Blue Discus

1981. Ornamental Fishes. Multicoloured.
386 12x. Type **79** 30 10
387 12x. Siamese fighting fish . . 30 10
388 20x. Platy 45 10
389 30x. Guppy 60 15
390 40x. Tiger barb 65 20
391 50x. Freshwater angelfish . . 90 25
392 60x. Swordtail . . . . 1·25 35
393 1d. Pearl gourami . . . . . 2·25 60

80 Rocket, Flowers and Flag

82 Green Imperial Pigeon

81 Bear Macaque

1981. 26th U.S.S.R. Communist Party Congress. Multicoloured.
394 20x. Type **80** 25 10
395 50x. Young citizens with flag 50 20

1981. Animals of Cue Phuong Forest. Mult.
396 12x. Type **81** 10 10
397 12x. Crested gibbons 10 10
398 20x. Asiatic black bears . . . 20 10
399 30x. Dhole 40 15
400 40x. Wild boar 50 15
401 50x. Sambars 65 25
402 60x. Leopard 75 25
403 1d. Tiger . . . . 1·40 40

1981. Turtle Doves. Multicoloured.
404 12x. Type **82** 35 25
405 12x. Japanese green pigeon (horiz) 35 25
406 20x. Red-collared dove . . . 45 30
407 30x. Bar-tailed cuckoo dove 80 35
408 40x. Mountain imperial pigeon . . . . 1·10 40
409 50x. Pin-tailed green pigeon (horiz) . . . . 1·50 50
410 60x. Emerald dove (horiz) . . 1·75 55
411 1d. Yellow-vented pin-tailed green pigeon (horiz) . . . 2·75 95

83 Yellow-backed Sunbird

85 "Elaeagnus latifolia"

1981. Nectar-sucking Birds. Multicoloured.
412 20x. Type **83** 50 10
413 20x. Ruby-cheeked sunbird 50 10
414 30x. Black-throated sunbird 60 20
415 40x. Mrs. Gould's sunbird . . 1·00 25
416 50x. Macklot's sunbird . . 1·50 30
417 50x. Blue-naped sunbird . . 1·50 30
418 60x. Van Hasselt's sunbird 1·60 35
419 1d. Green-tailed sunbird . . 2·75 60

1981. Fruits. Multicoloured.
422 20x. Type **85** 20 10
423 20x. "Fortunella japonica" 20 10
424 30x. "Nephelium lappaceum" 35 15
425 40x. "Averrhoa bilimbi" . . 40 15
426 50x. "Ziziphus mauritiana" 50 20
427 50x. "Strawberries ("Fragaria vesca") 50 20
428 60x. "Bouea oppositifolia" 60 25
429 1d. "Syzygium aqueum" . . 1·25 40

86 Girl with Rice Sheaf

87 Ho Chi Minh planting Tree

1981. World Food Day.
430 **86** 30x. green 25 15
431 50x. green 30 15
432 – 2d. orange . . . . 1·10 40
DESIGN: 2d. F.A.O. emblem and rice.

1981. Tree Planting Festival.
433 **87** 30x. orange and blue . . . 55 25
434 – 30x. pink and blue 55 25
DESIGN: No. 434, Family planting tree.

88 European Bison

1981. Animals. Multicoloured.
435 30x. Type **88** 25 10
436 30x. Orang-utan 25 10
437 40x. Hippopotamus 40 20
438 40x. Red kangaroo 40 20
439 50x. Giraffe 60 20
440 50x. Javan rhinoceros 60 20
441 60x. Common zebra 65 25
442 1d. Lion . . . . 1·40 45

89 Congress Emblem

1982. 10th World Trade Unions Congress, Havana, Cuba.
443 **89** 50x. multicoloured 30 15
444 5d. multicoloured . . . . 3·25 1·10

90 Ho Chi Minh and Party Flag

1982. 5th Vietnamese Communist Party Congress (1st issue). Multicoloured.
445 30x. Type **90** 50 20
446 30x. Hammer, sickle and rose 50 20
See also Nos. 455/6.

91 "Thyreus decorus" (carpenter bee)

1982. Bees and Wasps. Multicoloured.
447 20x. Type **91** 20 10
448 20x. "Vespa affinis" (wasp) 20 10
449 30x. "Eumenes esuriens" (mason wasp) 30 15
450 40x. "Polistes . . . . . .
451 50x. "Sphex sp." (wasp) . . . 65 25
452 50x. "Chlorion lobatum" (wasp) 65 25
453 60x. "Xylocopa sp." (carpenter bee) 75 35
454 1d. Honey bee . . . . . . 1·25 50

92 Electricity Worker and Pylon

1982. 5th Vietnamese Communist Party Congress (2nd issue).
455 **92** 30x. stone, black and mauve 60 25
456 – 50x. multicoloured 70 25
DESIGN: 50x. Women harvesting rice.

93 Football

1982. Football Training Movement.
457 **93** 30x. multicoloured 35 15
458 – 30x. multicoloured (Two players) 35 15
459 – 40x. multicoloured 40 20
460 – 40x. multicoloured (diag striped background) . . 40 20
461 – 50x. multicoloured (vert striped background) . . 45 20
462 – 50x. multicoloured (horiz striped background) . . 45 20
463 – 60x. multicoloured 65 25
464 – 1d. multicoloured 90 40
DESIGNS: Nos. 458/64, Various football scenes.

94 Militiawoman

1982.
465 **94** 30x. multicoloured 65 25
See also Nos. MF466/7.

95 Arms of Bulgaria

1982. 1300th Anniv of Bulgarian State.
468 **95** 30x. pink and red 40 10
469 50x. stone and red 50 15
470 2d. orange and red . . . . 2·25 75

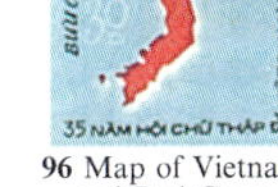

96 Map of Vietnam and Red Cross

97 Georgi Dimitrov

1982. 35th Anniv of Vietnamese Red Cross.
471 **96** 30x. red, blue and black . . 30 15
472 – 1d. red, green and black 1·25 50
DESIGN: 1d. Red Cross.

1982. Birth Centenary of Georgi Dimitrov (Bulgarian statesman).
473 **97** 30x. orange and black . . 35 15
474 3d. brown and black . . . 2·75 95

98 Rejoicing Women

99 Common Kestrel

1982. 5th National Women's Congress. Mult.
475 12x. Type **98** 40 15
476 12x. Congress emblem and three women 40 15

1982. Birds of Prey. Multicoloured.
477 30x. Type **99** 55 15
478 30x. Pied falconet 55 15
479 40x. Black baza 85 20
480 50x. Black kite . . . . 1·10 25
481 50x. Lesser fishing eagle . . . 1·10 25
482 60x. White-rumped pygmy falcon (horiz) . . . . . . 1·40 35
483 1d. Black-shouldered kite (horiz) . . . . 3·00 55
484 1d. Short-toed eagle . . . . 3·00 55

100 Red Dahlia

101 Dribble

1982. Dahlias. Multicoloured.
485 30x. Type **100** 40 15
486 30x. Orange dahlia 40 15
487 40x. Rose dahlia 45 15
488 50x. Red decorative dahlia 60 20
489 50x. Yellow dahlia 60 20
490 60x. Red single dahlia . . . 70 25
491 1d. White dahlia . . . . . . 1·25 50
492 1d. Pink dahlia . . . . . . 1·25 50

1982. World Cup Football Championship, Spain. Multicoloured.
493 50x. Type **101** 50 20
494 50x. Tackle 50 20
495 50x. Passing ball 50 20
496 1d. Heading ball . . . . . . 1·10 40
497 1d. Goalkeeper saving ball 1·10 40
498 2d. Shooting . . . . 1·90 70

102 Cuban Flag

104 Rabindranath Tagore

103 Ho Chi Minh and Children planting Tree

1982. 20th Anniv of Cuban Victory at Giron.
499 **102** 30x. multicoloured . . . 45 15

1982. World Environment Day.
500 **103** 30x. green and black . . . 35 15
501 – 30x. green and black . . . 35 15
DESIGN: No. 501, U.N. environment emblem and plants.

1982. 120th Birth Anniv (1981) of Rabindranath Tagore (Indian poet).
502 **104** 30x. orange, brown and black 45 25

105 "Sycanus falleni" (soldier bug) **106** Lenin and Cruiser "Aurora"

1982. Harmful Insects. Multicoloured.
503 30x. Type **105** 30 10
504 30x. "Catacanthus incarnatus" (shieldbug) . . 30 10
505 40x. "Nezara viridula" (shield-bug) 40 15
506 50x. "Helcomeria spinosa" (squashbug) 70 20
507 50c. "Lohita grandis" (fire bug) 70 20
508 60x. "Chrysocoris stolli" (shieldbug) 75 25
509 1d. "Tiarodes ostentans" (soldier bug) . . . . . . 1·25 50
510 1d. "Pterygamia grayi" (squashbug) . . . . 1·25 50

1982. 65th Anniv of Russian Revolution.
511 **106** 30x. red and black . . . 40 15
512 – 30x. red and black . . . 40 15
DESIGN: No. 512, Russian man and woman, Lenin and space station.

108 Swimming

1982. 9th South East Asian Games, New Delhi.
514 **108** 30x. blue and lilac 40 15
515 – 30x. blue and mauve . . . 40 15
516 – 1d. orange and blue . . . 1·10 40
517 – 2d. green and brown . . . 1·90 65
DESIGNS: 30x. (No. 515) Table tennis; 1d. Wrestling; 2d. Rifle shooting.

109 Gray's Crested Flounder

1982. Fishes. Soles. Multicoloured.
518 30x. Type **109** 50 15
519 30x. Chinese flounder 50 15
520 40x. Queensland halibut ("Psettodes erumei") . . . 75 20
521 40x. Zebra sole ("Zebrias zebra") 75 20
522 50x. Peacock sole ("Pardachirus pavoninus") 1·10 25
523 50x. Spotted tonguesole ("Cynoglossus puncticeps") 1·10 25
524 60x. Oriental sole . . . . . 1·25 30
525 1d. Iijima lefteye flounder . . 1·75 50

110 Foundry and Textile Workers **112** Sampan

111 Lenin on Map

1982. "All for the Socialist Fatherland, All for Happiness of the People".
526 **110** 30x. light blue and blue 30 10
527 – 30x. brown and yellow . . 30 10
528 – 1d. brown and green . . . 1·10 40
529 – 2d. pink and purple . . . 2·00 75
DESIGNS: 30x. Women holding sheaf of wheat and basket of grain; 1d. Soldiers; 2d. Nurse with children holding books.

1982. 60th Anniv of U.S.S.R.
530 **111** 30x. multicolouired . . . 55 20

1983. Boats. Multicoloured.
531 30x. Type **112** 20 10
532 50x. Junk with striped sails 30 10
533 1d. Houseboats 65 25
534 3d. Junk 95 30
535 5d. Sampan with patched sails . . . . 1·40 40
536 10d. Sampan (horiz) . . . . 2·00 95

113 Type 231-300

1983. Steam Railway Locomotives. Multicoloured.
537 30x. Type **113** 25 10
538 50x. Type 230-000 . . . . . 35 10
539 1d. Type 140-601 . . . . . . 50 10
540 2d. Type 241-000 . . . . . . 75 25
541 3d. Type 141-500 . . . . . . 95 35
542 5d. Type 150-000 . . . . . 1·40 60
543 8d. Type 40-300 . . . . . . 2·50 95

114 Montgolfier Balloon, 1783

1983. Bicentenary of Manned Flight. Mult.
544 30x. Type **114** 25 10
545 50x. Charles's hydrogen balloon, 1783 . . . . . . 40 10
546 1d. Parseval Sigsfeld kite-type observation balloon, 1898 65 25
547 2d. Eugene Godard's balloon "L'Aigle", 1864 . . . . . 95 30
548 3d. Blanchard and Jeffries' balloon, 1785 . . . . . 1·10 30
549 5d. Nadar's balloon "Le Geant", 1863 . . . . . . 1·75 40
550 8d. Balloon . . . . 2·75 70

115 Flags and Dove

1983. Laos–Kampuchea–Vietnam Summit Conf.
552 **115** 50x. red, yellow and blue 35 15
553 5d. red, blue and yellow 3·50 1·60

116 Robert Koch

1983. Centenary of Discovery of Tubercle Bacillus.
554 **116** 5d. black, blue and red 3·50 1·60

117 "Teratolepis fasciata"

1983. Reptiles. Multicoloured.
555 30x. Type **117** 20 10
556 30x. Jackson's chameleon . . 20 10
557 50x. Spiny-tailed agamid . . 25 15
558 80x. "Heloderma suspectum" 35 15
559 1d. "Chamaeleo meileri" . . 50 20
560 2d. "Amphibolurus barbatus" 1·00 25
561 5d. "Chlamydosaurus kingi" 2·00 40
562 10d. "Phrynosoma coronatum" . . . . 4·00 90

118 A. Gubarev and V. Remek

1983. Cosmonauts. Multicoloured.
563 30x. Type **118** 20 10
564 50x. P. Klimuk and Miroslaw Hermaszewski 25 10
565 50x. V. Bykovsky and Sigmund Jahn 25 10
566 1d. Nikolai Rukavishnikov and Georgi Ivanov 40 15
567 1d. Bertalan Farkas and V. Kubasov 40 15
568 2d. V. Gorbatko and Pham Tuan 70 25
569 2d. Arnaldo Tamayo Mendez and I. Romanenko 70 25
570 5d. V. Dzhanibekov and Gurragcha . . . . 1·40 40
571 8d. L. Popov and D. Prunariu . . . . 1·75 60

119 "Madonna of the Chair" **121** Burmese King and Rook

1983. 500th Birth Anniv of Raphael (artist). Mult.
573 30x. Type **119** 25 10
574 50x. "Madonna of the Grand Duke" 40 10
575 1d. "Sistine Madonna" . . . 50 15
576 2d. "The Marriage of Mary" . . 90 30
577 3d. "The Beautiful Gardener" 1·25 35
578 5d. "Woman with Veil" . . . 1·75 45
579 8d. "Self-portrait" . . . . . 2·25 65

1983. Chess Pieces. Multicoloured.
582 30x. Type **121** 20 10
583 50x. 18th-century Delhi king (elephant) 25 10
584 1d. Lewis knight and bishop 40 15
585 2d. 8th/9th-century Arabian king (elephant) 80 30
586 3d. 12th-century European knight . . . . 1·25 35
587 5d. 16th-century Russian rook (sailing boat) . . . . 1·75 50
588 8d. European Chinese-puzzle bishop and rook (fool and elephant) . . . . 2·25 75

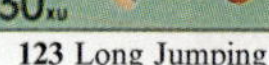

123 Long Jumping **125** Common Grass Yellow

1983. Olympic Games, Los Angeles (1984). Mult.
591 30x. Type **123** 20 10
592 50x. Running 25 10
593 1d. Javelin throwing 40 15
594 2d. High jumping (horiz) . . 70 30
595 3d. Hurdling (horiz) . . . . 1·00 35
596 5d. Putting the shot . . . . 1·40 45
597 8d. Pole vaulting . . . . . . 1·75 65

1983. Butterflies. Multicoloured.
600 30x. Type **125** 30 10
601 30x. Green dragontail ("Leptocircus meges") . . . 30 10
602 40x. "Nyctalemon patroclus" 40 15
603 40x. Tailed jay ("Zetides agamemnon") 40 15
604 50x. Peacock ("Precis almana") 50 20
605 50x. "Papilio chaon" 50 20
606 60x. Tufted jungle king . . . 60 25
607 1d. Leaf butterfly . . . . . 1·00 40

128 Karl Marx

1983. Death Centenary of Karl Marx.
617 **128** 50x. black and red . . . 45 25
618 10d. black and purple . . 5·00 2·75

129 Postman

1983. World Communications Year. Mult.
619 50x. Type **129** 25 10
620 2d. Mail sorting office . . . 75 30
621 8d. Telephonists . . . . . . 2·00 50
622 10d. Wireless operator and dish aerial . . . . 3·00 75

130 Running, Stadium and Sports Pictograms

1983. National Youth Sports Festival.
624 **130** 30x. blue and turquoise 65 25
625 1d. brown and orange . . 1·60 70

131 Oyster Fungus ("Pleurotus ostreatus")

1983. Fungi. Multicoloured.
626 50x. Type **131** 80 10
627 50x. Common ink cap ("Coprinus atramentarius") 60 10
628 50x. Golden mushroom ("Flammulina velutipes") 60 10
629 50x. Chanterelle ("Cantharellus cibarius") 60 10
630 1d. Chinese mushroom . . . 85 15
631 2d. Red-staining mushroom 1·75 30
632 5d. Common morel . . . . . 3·25 70
633 10d. Caesar's mushroom . . 7·25 1·40

132 Child with Fish

1983. World Food Day. Multicoloured.
634 50x. Type **132** 80 10
635 4d. Family . . . . 1·25 45

133 Envelope with I.T.U. Emblem

1983. World Telecommunications Year.
636 **133** 50x.+10x. blue, green & red 95 65
637 – 50x.+10x. red, buff and brown 95 65
DESIGN: No. 637, W.C.Y. emblem and dish aerial.

134 Building Dam

1983. 5th Anniv of U.S.S.R.–Vietnam Co-operation Treaty.
638 – 20x. green and yellow . . 20 10
639 – 50x. chestnut and brown 1·00 50
640 **134** 4d. grey and black . . . 1·90 65
641 20d. pink and brown . . 10·00 3·50
DESIGNS: 20x. Building Cultural Palace; 50x. Building road/rail bridge.

135 Girl with Flowers

1983. 5th Trade Unions Congress.
642 **135** 50x. blue, orange and black 20 10
643 – 2d. black, blue and brown 50 25
644 – 30d. black, blue and pink 7·50 2·25
DESIGNS: 2, 30d. Worker and industrial complex.

136 Grey Herons 137 Conference Emblem and Hands

1983. Birds. Multicoloured.
645 50x. Type **136** 50 15
646 50x. Painted storks ("Ibis leucocephalus") 50 15
647 50x. Black storks ("Ciconia nigra") 50 15
648 50x. Purple herons ("Ardea purpurea") 50 15
649 1d. Common cranes 65 20
650 2d. Black-faced spoonbills . . 1·40 55
651 5d. Black-crowned night herons . . . . 3·00 70
652 10d. Asian open-bill storks 6·25 1·40

1983. World Peace Conference, Prague.
653 – 50x. blue, red and yellow 15 10
654 **137** 3d. green, red and yellow 1·10 45
655 5d. lilac, red and yellow 1·90 75
656 20d. blue, red and yellow 7·50 2·50
DESIGN: 50x. Conference emblem and women.

138 Biathlon

1984. Winter Olympic Games, Sarajevo. Mult.
657 50x. Type **138** 30 10
658 50x. Cross-country skiing . . 30 10
659 1d. Speed skating 45 15
660 2d. Bobsleighing 75 30
661 3d. Ice hockey (horiz) . . . . 1·00 35
662 5d. Ski jumping (horiz) . . . 1·60 45
663 6d. Slalom (horiz) . . . . . 1·90 65

139 Marbled Cat

1984. Protected Animals. Multicoloured.
665 50x. Type **139** 25 10
666 50x. Leopard 25 10
667 50x. Tiger 25 10
668 1d. Common gibbon 50 25
669 1d. Slow loris 50 25
670 2d. Indian elephant . . . . . 1·00 30
671 2d. Gaur . . . . 1·00 30

140 Orchid Tree 141 "Brasse cattleya"

1984. Flowers. Multicoloured.
672 50x. Type **140** 15 10
673 50x. "Caesalpinia pulcherrima" 15 10
674 1d. Golden shower 35 15
675 2d. Flamboyant 70 25
676 3d. "Artabotrys uncinatus" . 1·00 40
677 5d. "Corchorus olitorius" . . 1·75 65
678 8d. "Bauhinia grandiflora" 2·75 1·00

1984. Orchids. Multicoloured.
680 50x. Type **141** 25 10
681 50x. "Cymbidium sp." . . . 25 10
682 1d. "Cattleya dianx" var. "alba" 40 15
683 2d. "Cymbidium sp." (different) 70 30
684 3d. "Cymbidium hybridum" 1·10 35
685 5d. Phoenix-winged orchids 1·75 45
686 8d. Yellow queen orchids . . 2·25 65

1984. Nos. 362 and 373 surch **50xu**.
687 – 50x. on 12x. red and green 60 15
688 **76** 50x. on 12x. yellow and black 60 15

143 Flyingfish

1984. Deep Sea Fishes. Multicoloured.
688a 30x. Type **143** 15 10
688b 30x. Long-horned cowfish 15 10
688c 50x. Porcupinefish 25 10
688d 80x. Copper-banded butterflyfish 40 10
688e 1d. Bearded anglerfish . . . 55 15
688f 2d. Plane-tailed lionfish . . 1·00 30
688g 5d. Oceanic sunfish . . . . 2·50 70
688h 10d. Lionfish . . . . 5·00 1·40

146 Ho Chi Minh discussing Battle Plan

1984. 30th Anniv of Battle of Dien Bien Phu. Multicoloured.
691 50x. Type **146** 25 10
692 50x. Vietnamese soldiers and truck 25 10
693 1d. Students carrying provisions 50 15
694 2d. Pulling field gun up hill 90 30
695 3d. Anti-aircraft gun and crashed airplane . . . . . 1·10 40
696 5d. Fighting against tanks . . 1·60 50
697 8d. Vietnamese soldiers with flag on bunker . . . . . . 2·00 65

148 Three-spotted Gourami

1984. Fishes. Multicoloured.
700 50x. Type **148** 30 10
701 50x. Zebra danio 30 10
702 1d. Paradise fish 55 15
703 2d. Black widow tetra . . . 1·00 30
704 3d. Serpa tetra . . . . 1·75 40
705 5d. Red-tailed black shark . . 2·40 70
706 8d. Siamese fightingfish . . . 3·25 1·10

149 Nguyen Duc Canh

1984. 55th Anniv of Vietnamese Trade Union Movement.
707 **149** 50x. red and black . . . 15 10
708 – 50x. red and black . . . 15 10
709 – 1d. multicoloured 35 15
710 – 2d. multicoloured 70 25
711 – 3d. multicoloured . . . . 1·25 40
712 – 5d. multicoloured . . . . 1·90 90
DESIGNS—VERT: No. 708, Founder's house. HORIZ: No. 709, Workers presenting demands to employer; 710, Ho Chi Minh with workers; 711, Factory; 712, Workers, procession and doves.

150 Hon Dua

1984. Coastal Scenes. Multicoloured.
714 50x. Type **150** 20 10
715 50x. Hang Con Gai 20 10
716 50x. Hang Bo Nau 20 10
717 50x. Nui Yen Ngua 20 10
718 1d. Hon Ga Choi 40 15
719 1d. Hon Coc 40 15
720 2d. Hon Dinh Huong 75 30
721 3d. Hon Su Tu . . . . . . 1·10 35
722 5d. Hon Am . . . . 1·75 50
723 8d. Nui Bai Tho . . . . . . 2·75 80

151 Styracosaurus

1984. Prehistoric Animals. Multicoloured.
724 50x. Type **151** 20 10
725 50x. Diplodocus 20 10
726 1d. Rhamphorhynchus . . . 40 10
727 1d. Corythosaurus 40 10
728 2d. Seymouria 85 25
729 3d. Allosaurus . . . . 1·25 35
730 5d. Dimetrodon . . . . . . 2·10 55
731 8d. Brachiosaurus . . . . . 3·25 85

153 Dove and Flags 155 Students and Cultural and Industrial Motifs

1984. Laos–Kampuchea–Vietnam Co-operation.
733 **153** 50x. red, blue and yellow 25 10
734 10d. red, blue and yellow 3·75 1·25

1984. 5th Anniv of Kampuchea–Vietnam Friendship Treaty. Multicoloured.
736 50x. Type **155** 15 15
737 3d. Type **155** 85 25
738 50d. Kampuchean and Vietnamese dancers . . . . 12·00 2·50

156 Bridge

1984. 30th Anniv of Liberation of Hanoi.
739 **156** 50x. green and yellow . . 55 20
740 – 1d. brown and red . . . 1·00 45
741 – 2d. brown and mauve . . 2·25 75
DESIGNS: 1d. Gateway; 2d. Ho Chi Minh mausoleum.

157 Vis-a-vis 160 "Madonna and Child with St. John"

159 "Lenin" (V. A. Serov)

1984. Motor Cars. Multicoloured.
743 50x. Type **157** 20 10
744 50x. Two-seater 20 10
745 1d. Tonneau 40 15
746 2d. Double phaeton 75 25
747 3d. Landaulet . . . . 1·00 35
748 5d. Torpedo . . . . 1·75 45
749 6d. Town coupe . . . . . . 1·90 65

1984. 60th Death Anniv of Lenin. Multicoloured.
751 50x. Type **159** 20 10
752 1d. Painting by A. Plotnov of Lenin at meeting 40 15
753 3d. Painting by K. V. Filatov of Lenin at factory . . . . 1·25 35
754 5d. Painting by V. A. Serov of Lenin with three comrades . . . . 2·25 65

1984. 450th Death Anniv of Correggio (artist). "Madonna and Child" Paintings. Multicoloured.
755 50x. Type **160** 15 10
756 50x. Bolognini Madonna . . 15 10
757 1d. Campori Madonna . . . 25 15
758 2d. "Virgin adoring the Child" 55 30
759 3d. "Madonna della Cesta" 75 35
760 5d. "Madonna della Scodella" . . . . 1·40 45
761 6d. "Madonna and Child with Angels" . . . . . . 1·90 50

161 "Keep the Peace" (Le Quoc Loc)

1984. U.N.I.C.E.F. Multicoloured.
763 30x. Type **161** 15 10
764 50x. "Sunday" (Nguyen Tien Chung) 20 15
765 1d. "Baby of the Mining Region" (Tran Van Can) 30 15
766 3d. "Little Thuy" (Tran Van Can) (vert) 80 25
767 5d. "Children at Play" (Nguyen Phan Chanh) . . 1·75 65
768 10d. "After Guard Duty" (Nguyen Phan Chanh) (vert) . . . . 3·75 1·10

162 Mounted Frontier Guards 163 Water Buffalo

1984. 25th Anniv of Frontier Forces.
769 **162** 50x. black, blue and brown 20 15
770 30d. black, green & turq 8·00 2·00

1984.
771 **163** 20x. brown 10 10
772 – 30x. red 10 10
773 – 50x. green 30 10
774 – 50x. red 15 10
775 – 50x. mauve 15 10
776 – 50x. brown 15 10
777 – 1d. violet 35 15
778 – 1d. orange 35 15

779 – 1d. blue 35 15
780 – 1d. blue 40 20
781 – 2d. brown 70 25
782 – 2d. orange 70 25
783 – 2d. red 70 25
784 – 5d. mauve 1·75 65
785 – 10d. green 4·25 1·25

DESIGNS: No. 772, Marbled cat; 773, Siamese fighting fish; 774, Cabbage rose; 775, Hibiscus; 776, Lesser panda; 777, "Chrysanthemum sinense"; 778, Tiger; 779, Water lily; 780, Eastern white pelican; 781, Slow loris; 782, Dahlia; 783, Crab-eating macaque; 784, Tokay gecko; 785, Great Indian hornbill.

165 Ho Chi Minh and Troops

1984. 40th Anniv of Vietnamese People's Army. Multicoloured.
787 50x. Type **165** 15 10
788 50x. Oath-taking ceremony 15 10
789 1d. Soldier with flag and Boeing B-52 Stratofortress bomber on fire 35 15
790 2d. Civilians building gun emplacement 70 25
791 5d. Soldiers and tank breaking through gates 1·00 40
792 5d. Soldier instructing civilians 1·75 45
793 8d. Map and soldiers 2·75 1·00

166 Boy on Buffalo

167 "Echinocereus knippelianus"

1985. New Year. Year of the Buffalo.
795 **166** 3d. purple and pink 1·10 40
796 5d. brown and orange 1·75 65

1985. Flowering Cacti. Multicoloured.
797 50x. Type **167** 20 10
798 50x. "Lemaireocereus thurberi" 20 10
799 1d. "Notocactus haselbergii" 40 10
800 2d. "Parodia chrysacanthion" 75 20
801 3d. "Pelecyphora pseudopectinata" 1·10 30
802 5d. "Rebutia frebrighii" 1·90 50
803 8d. "Lobivia aurea" 2·75 70

168 Nguyen Ai Quoc (Ho Chi Minh)

169 Soldiers with Weapons

1985. 55th Anniv of Vietnam Communist Party.
804 **168** 2d. grey and red 75 25

1985. 10th Anniv of Reunification of South Vietnam. Multicoloured.
805 1d. Type **169** 35 10
806 2d. Soldiers and tank 75 25
807 4d. Soldier and oil rig 1·50 50
808 5d. Map, flag and girls 1·75 60

170 Long Chau Lighthouse

172 Soviet Memorial, Berlin-Treptow

171 Ho Chi Minh and Soldiers

1985. 30th Anniv of Liberation of Haiphong.
810 **170** 2d. multicoloured 70 30
811 – 5d. multicoloured 1·75 80

DESIGN—HORIZ: 5d. An Duong bridge.

1985. 95th Birth Anniv of Ho Chi Minh (President). Multicoloured.
813 1d. Type **171** 35 15
814 2d. Ho Chi Minh reading in cave at Viet Bac 70 25
815 4d. Portrait (vert) 1·40 50
816 5d. Ho Chi Minh writing in garden of Presidential Palace 1·75 65

1985. 40th Anniv of Victory in Europe Day. Multi.
818 1d. Type **172** 35 15
819 2d. Soldier and fist breaking swastika 75 25
820 4d. Hand releasing dove and eagle falling 1·50 50
821 5d. Girl releasing doves 1·90 65

173 Globe and People carrying Flags

1985. 12th World Youth and Students' Festival, Moscow. Multicoloured.
823 2d. Type **173** 65 25
824 2d. Workers, pylons and dish aerial 65 25
825 4d. Coastguards and lighthouse 1·40 50
826 5d. Youths and balloons 1·75 65

174 Daimler, 1885

1985. Centenary of Motor Cycle. Multicoloured.
828 1d. Type **174** (wrongly inscr "1895") 30 10
829 1d. Three-wheeled vehicle, France, 1898 30 10
830 2d. Harley Davidson, U.S.A., 1913 60 20
831 2d. Cleveland, U.S.A., 1918 60 20
832 3d. Simplex, U.S.A., 1935 90 30
833 4d. Minarelli, Italy, 1984 1·10 40
834 6d. Honda, Japan, 1984 1·75 1·10

175 King Penguin

1985. "Argentina '85". International Stamp Exhibition, Buenos Aires. Multicoloured.
836 1d. Type **175** 50 20
837 1d. Patagonian cavy 55 10
838 2d. Capybara (horiz) 65 20
839 2d. Leopard (horiz) 65 20
840 3d. Lesser rhea 2·10 45
841 4d. Giant armadillo (horiz) 1·25 45
842 6d. Andean condor (horiz) 6·25 1·00

176 "Holothuria monacaria"

1985. Marine Life. Multicoloured.
844 3d. Type **176** 1·10 30
845 3d. "Stichopus chloronotus" 1·10 30
846 3d. "Luidia maculata" 1·10 30
847 3d. "Nadoa tuberculata" 1·10 30
848 4d. "Astropyga radiata" 1·40 35
849 4d. "Linckia laevigata" 1·40 35
850 4d. "Astropecten scoparius" 1·40 35

177 Flag and Sickle "40"

178 Globe, Transport and People around Postman

1985. 40th Anniv of Socialist Republic. Mult.
851 2d. Type **177** 65 20
852 3d. Doves around globe as heart above handclasp 95 30
853 5d. Banner 1·60 50
854 10d. Ho Chi Minh, flag and laurel branch 3·25 1·00

1985. 40th Anniv of Postal and Telecommunications Service. Multicoloured.
856 2d. Type **178** 45 15
857 2d. Telephonist and telegraph operator 45 15
858 4d. Wartime deliveries and postwoman Nguyen Thi Nghia 90 30
859 5d. Dish aerial 1·10 35

179 Profile of Ho Chi Minh and Policeman

1985. 40th Anniv of People's Police.
860 **179** 10d. red and black 4·50 1·25

180 Gymnasts

1985. 1st National Sports and Gymnastics Games. Multicoloured.
862 5d. Type **180** 1·60 55
863 10d. Badminton player, gymnast, athlete and swimmer 3·25 1·10

181 Locomotive "Beuth", 1843

1985. 150th Anniv of German Railways. Multi.
864 1d. Type **181** 30 10
865 1d. German tank locomotive, 1900 30 10
866 2d. Locomotive "Saxonia", 1836, Saxony 60 20
867 2d. German passenger locomotive 60 20
868 3d. Prussian steam locomotive No. 2024, 1910 90 30
869 4d. Prussian tank locomotive, 1920 1·25 35
870 6d. Bavarian State steam locomotive No. 659, 1890 1·75 55

182 Off-shore Rig, Derrick and Helicopter

1985. 30th Anniv of Geological Service.
872 **182** 1d. blue and purple 65 25
873 – 1d. green and brown 65 25

DESIGN: No. 873, Airplane over coastline.

183 Alfa Romeo, 1922

1985. "Italia'85" International Stamp Exhibition, Rome. Motor Cars. Multicoloured.
874 1d. Type **183** 30 10
875 1d. Bianchi "Berlina", 1932 30 10
876 2d. Isotta Fraschini, 1928 60 20
877 2d. Bugatti, 1930 60 20
878 3d. Itala, 1912 90 30
879 4d. Lancia "Augusta", 1934 1·25 40
880 6d. Fiat, 1927 1·75 60

184 Sei Whale

1985. Marine Mammals. Multicoloured.
882 1d. Type **184** 60 10
883 1d. Blue whale 60 10
884 2d. Killer whale 1·00 20
885 2d. Common dolphin 1·25 20
886 3d. Humpback whale 1·40 30
887 4d. Fin whale 1·60 40
888 6d. Black right whale 2·00 60

185 Goalkeeper attempting to save Ball

1985. World Cup Football Championship, Mexico (1986) (1st issue). Multicoloured.
889 1d. Type **185** 30 10
890 1d. Scoring goal 30 10
891 2d. Goalkeeper diving for ball 60 20
892 2d. Goalkeeper holding ball (vert) 60 20
893 3d. Goalkeeper preparing to catch ball (vert) 90 30
894 4d. Punching ball away (vert) 1·25 40
895 6d. Goalkeeper catching ball (vert) 1·75 60

See also Nos. 920/6.

186 Laotian Girl and Dove

1985. 10th Anniv of Laos People's Democratic Republic. Multicoloured.
897 1d. Type **186** 50 20
898 1d. Laotian girl and arms 50 20

187 Decorated Drum

1985. Traditional Musical Instruments. Mult.
899 1d. Type **187** 40 10
900 1d. Xylophone 40 10
901 2d. Double-ended drum 80 25
902 2d. Flutes 80 25
903 3d. Single-stringed instrument 1·25 35
904 4d. Four-stringed instrument 1·60 45
905 6d. Double-stringed bowed instrument 2·40 70

188 Agriculture

189 Hands, Emblem and Dove

1985. 40th Anniv of Independence.
906 10d. Type **188** 80 20
907 10d. Industry 80 20
908 20d. Health care . . . . . . 1·60 40
909 30d. Education . . . . . . 2·40 60

1986. 40th Anniv of U.N.O.
910 **189** 1d. multicoloured 55 20

190 Ho Chi Minh, Map, Line of Voters and Ballot Box

191 Isaac Newton

1986. 40th Anniv of First Assembly Elections.
911 **190** 50x. mauve and black . . 35 15
912 1d. orange and black . . 65 25

1986. Appearance of Halley's Comet.
913 2d. Type **191** 85 25
914 2d. Edmond Halley 85 25
915 3d. Launch of "Vega" space probe and flags . . . . . 1·25 40
916 5d. Comet and planet . . . . 2·10 65

192 Map of U.S.S.R. and Kremlin Buildings

193 Plan of Battle of Chi Lang

1986. 27th Communist Party Congress, Moscow. Multicoloured.
917 50x. Type **192** 30 15
918 1d. Lenin on flag and transport, industrial and scientific motifs 65 25

1986. 600th Birth Anniv (1985) of Le Loi (founder of Le Dynasty).
919 **193** 1d. multicolourerd 65 25

194 Footballer

1986. World Cup Football Championship, Mexico (2nd issue). Multicoloured.
920 1d. Type **194** 25 10
921 1d. Two players 25 10
922 2d. Player heading ball . . . 50 20
923 3d. Player tackling 75 30
924 3d. Two players chasing ball 75 30
925 5d. Footballer (different) . . 1·25 40
926 5d. Two players (different) 1·25 40

195 Konstantin Tsiolkovski and "Sputnik 1"

1986. 25th Anniv of 1st Man in Space. Mult.
928 1d. Type **195** 25 10
929 1d. Rocket on launch vehicle, Baikanur cosmodrome . . 25 10
930 2d. Yuri Gagarin and "Vostok 1" 50 20
931 3d. Valentina Tereshkova and "Vostok VI" on launch vehicle (vert) 75 30
932 3d. Cosmonaut Leonov and cosmonaut on space walk 70 30
933 5d. "Soyuz"–"Apollo" link and crews . . . . 1·25 40
934 5d. "Salyut"–"Soyuz" link and two cosmonauts . . . 1·25 40

196 Thalmann and Flag

1986. Birth Centenary of Ernst Thalmann (German Communist leader).
936 **196** 2d. red and black . . . . 1·10 25

197 Flag, Hammer and Globe in Sickle

1986. Centenary of May Day.
937 **197** 1d. red and blue 40 10
938 5d. red and brown . . . 2·10 55

198 Hawker Hart

1986. "Expo '86" World's Fair, Vancouver. Historic Aircraft. Multicoloured.
939 1d. Type **198** 25 10
940 1d. Curtiss JN-4 "Jenny" . . 25 10
941 2d. PZL P-23 Karas 55 20
942 3d. Yakovlev Yak-11 . . . . 80 30
943 3d. Fokker Dr-1 triplane . . . 80 30
944 5d. Boeing P12, 1920 . . . . 1·40 55
945 5d. Nieuport-Delage 29C1, 1929 . . . . 1·40 55

199 Ho Chi Minh and People working on Barriers

1986. 40th Anniv of Committee for Protection of Flood Barriers.
946 **199** 1d. pink and brown . . . 50 20

200 Black and White Cat

1986. Cats. Multicoloured.
947 1d. Type **200** 30 10
948 1d. Grey and white cat . . . 30 10
949 2d. White cat 65 20
950 3d. Brown-faced cat 95 30
951 3d. Beige cat 95 30
952 5d. Black-faced cat (vert) . . 1·60 50
953 5d. Beige and cream cat . . . 1·60 50

201 Thai Den House

1986. Traditional Architecture. Multicoloured.
954 1d. Type **201** 35 15
955 1d. Nung house 35 15
956 2d. Thai Trang house 70 25
957 3d. Tay house . . . . 1·00 40
958 3d. H'mong house . . . . . 1·00 40
959 5d. Dao house . . . . 1·75 65
960 5d. Tay Nguyen house (vert) 1·75 65

202 European Bee Eater

203 Plymouth Rock Cock

1986. "Stockholmia 86" International Stamp Exhibition. Birds. Multicoloured.
962 1d. Type **202** 30 15
963 1d. Green magpie 30 15
964 2d. Red-winged shrike babbler 70 25
965 3d. White-crested laughing thrush . . . . 1·00 45
966 3d. Long-tailed broadbill (horiz) . . . . 1·00 45
967 5d. Pied wagtail . . . . . . 2·00 65
968 5d. Azure-winged magpie (horiz) . . . . 2·00 65

1986. Domestic Fowl. Multicoloured.
970 1d. Type **203** 40 15
971 1d. Common turkey 40 15
972 2d. Rhode Island red cock 75 25
973 2d. White Plymouth rock cock 75 25
974 3d. Rhode Island (inscr "Islan") red hen . . . . . 1·10 35
975 3d. White leghorn cock . . . 1·10 35
976 3d. Rhode Island red cock (different) . . . . 1·10 35
977 5d. Barred Plymouth rock cock . . . . 1·90 65

204 Emblem

1986. 11th World Federation of Trades Unions Congress, Berlin.
978 **204** 1d. blue and red 50 15

206 Woman-shaped Sword Handle

1986. Historic Bronzes Excavated at Mt. Do. Mult.
980 1d. Type **206** 35 10
981 1d. Seated figure with man on back 35 10
982 2d. Saddle pommel (horiz) . . 75 25
983 3d. Shoe-shaped hoe (horiz) 1·10 40
984 3d. Bowl (horiz) . . . . . . 1·10 40
985 5d. Vase (horiz) . . . . . . 1·75 60
986 5d. Pot with lid (horiz) . . . 1·75 60

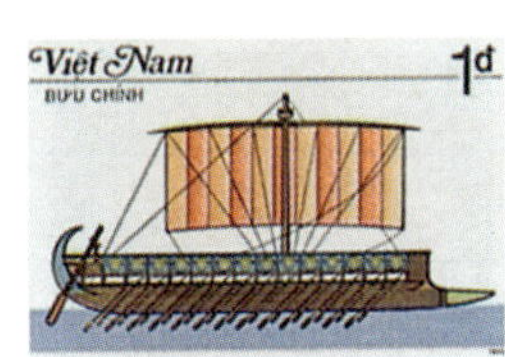

207 Greek Bireme

1986. Sailing Ships. Multicoloured.
988 1d. Type **207** 35 10
989 1d. Viking longship 35 10
990 2d. Medieval kogge (36×46 mm) 75 20
991 3d. Greek cargo galley . . . 1·10 30
992 3d. Phoenician war galley with ram . . . . 1·10 30
993 5d. Ancient Mediterranean cargo ship . . . . 1·75 55
994 5d. Roman trireme . . . . . 1·75 55

208 Hands cupping Red Cross in Flower

1986. 40th Anniv of Vietnamese Red Cross.
995 **208** 3d. mauve and blue . . . 1·10 30

209 "Catopsilia scylla"

1986. Butterflies. Multicoloured.
996 1d. Type **209** 25 10
997 1d. "Euploea midamus" . . 25 10
998 2d. Orange albatross 55 20
999 3d. Common mormon ("Papilio polytes") . . . 80 30
1000 3d. African monarch ("Danaus chrysippus") . . 80 30
1001 5d. Tawny rajah ("Charaxes polyxena") . . . . 1·40 55
1002 5d. Magpie crow ("Euploea diocletiana") . . . . . . 1·40 55

210 Red Flag and Symbols of Industry and Agriculture

1986. 6th Vietnamese Communist Party Congress. Multicoloured.
1003 1d. Type **210** 30 10
1004 2d. Red flag and weapons 65 20
1005 4d. Red flag and Ho Chi Minh . . . . 1·25 40
1006 5d. Red flag and symbols of peace . . . . 1·60 50

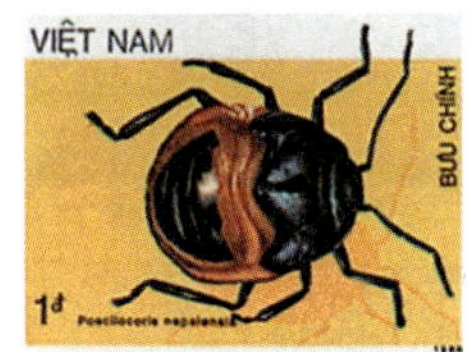

211 "Poecilocoris nepalensis" (shieldbug)

1986. Insects. Multicoloured.
1008 1d. Type **211** 25 10
1009 1d. "Bombus americanorum" (bee) . . 25 10
1010 2d. "Romalea microptera" (grasshopper) 55 20
1011 3d. "Chalcocoris rutilans" (shieldbug) 80 30
1012 3d. "Chrysocoris sellatus" (shieldbug) 80 30
1013 5d. "Crocisa crucifera" (wasp) . . . . 1·40 55
1014 5d. "Paranthrene palmi" (moth) . . . . 1·40 55

212 Dove and Emblem

213 "Ficus glomerata"

1986. International Peace Year.
1016 **212** 1d. green and black . . 40 15
1017 3d. pink and black . . . 1·25 40

1986. Bonsai. Multicoloured.
1018 1d. Type **213** 35 10
1019 1d. "Ficus benjamina" . . . 35 10
1020 2d. "Ulmus tonkinensis" . . 75 25
1021 3d. "Persica vulgaris" . . . 1·10 35
1022 3d. "Strebius asper" . . . . 1·10 35

1023 5d. "Podocarpus macrophyllus" 1·75 60

1024 5d. "Pinus khasya" 1·75 60

214 Basket

1986. Basketry and Wickerwork. Multicoloured.

1026 1d. Type **214** 35 10

1027 1d. Tall basket with lid and handles 35 10

1028 2d. Stool 75 25

1029 3d. Handbag 1·10 35

1030 3d. Dish 1·10 35

1031 5d. Tall basket for carrying on back 1·75 60

1032 5d. Square basket with star-shaped foot 1·75 60

215 Soldiers and Women

216 "Fokienia hodginsii"

1986. 40th Anniv of National Resistance.

1034 **215** 2d. brown and green 80 20

1986. Fruits of Conifers. Multicoloured.

1035 1d. Type **216** 35 10

1036 1d. "Amentotaxus yunnanensis" 35 10

1037 2d. "Pinus kwangtungensis" 70 20

1038 3d. "Cupressus torulosa" 1·10 35

1039 3d. "Taxus chinensis" 1·10 35

1040 5d. "Tsuga yunnanensis" 1·75 55

1041 5d. "Ducampopinus krempfii" 1·75 55

217 Mother and Calf

1986. Elephants.

1043 1d. Type **217** 30 10

1044 1d. Two elephants 30 10

1045 3d. Elephant (vert) 85 30

1046 3d. Elephant feeding 85 30

1047 5d. Working elephant (vert) 1·40 50

1048 5d. Elephants by water (68 × 27 mm) 1·40 50

218 Girl watering Tree

219 My Chan

1987. New Year. Year of the Cat.

1049 **218** 3d. brown and mauve 50 25

1987. "Son Tinh–Thuy Tinh" (folktale). Mult.

1050 3d. Type **219** 1·10 30

1051 3d. Mountain Genius bearing gift and leading horse 1·10 30

1052 3d. Elephants carrying materials for flood barrier 1·10 30

1053 3d. Men working through the night against flood sent by Water Genius 1·10 30

1054 3d. Men felling trees 1·10 30

1055 3d. Pounding rice in preparation for festival after storms 1·10 30

1056 3d. Canoes bringing fruit and grain 1·10 30

1057 3d. Canoe 1·10 30

Nos. 1050/7 were issued together, se-tenant, forming a composite design.

220 "Nymphaea lotus"

222 Temple, Da Nang

221 Crowd attacking Building (August 1945 Revolution)

1987. Water Lilies. Multicoloured.

1058 5d. Type **220** 25 10

1059 10d. "Nymphaea nouchali" 50 15

1060 10d. "Nymphaea pubescens" 50 15

1061 20d. "Nymphaea rubra" 1·00 25

1062 20d. "Nymphaea gigantea" 1·00 25

1063 30d. "Nymphaea laydekeri" 1·60 40

1064 50d. "Nymphaea capensis" 2·50 65

1987. 8th National Assembly. Multicoloured.

1065 10d. Type **221** 60 15

1066 20d. Proclamation of Democratic Republic (September 1945) 1·25 30

1067 30d. Fall of Dien Bien Phu (May 1954) 1·75 45

1068 50d. Tank entering Saigon (April 1975) 3·00 1·75

1987. Cham Culture. Multicoloured.

1069 3d. Type **222** 15 10

1070 10d. Temple, Phu Khanh 50 15

1071 15d. Temple, Da Nang (different) 80 25

1072 20d. Figure of dancer, Nghia Binh 1·00 30

1073 25d. Bust, Da Nang 1·25 40

1074 30d. Woman playing flute (statuette), Nghia Binh 1·60 50

1075 40d. Figure of dancer on capital, Da Nang 2·10 65

223 Hanoi

1987. Tourism. Multicoloured.

1077 5d. Type **223** 25 10

1078 10d. Hai Phong 60 15

1079 15d. Thien Mu Pagoda, Hue 75 25

1080 20d. Da Nang 1·00 25

1081 25d. Nha Trang 1·25 30

1082 30d. Waterfall, Da Lat 1·50 35

1083 40d. Ho Chi Minh City 2·00 50

224 Cactus

226 Man from Bana

225 People on Globe

1987. Cacti.

1085 **224** 5d. multicoloured 15 10

1086 – 10d. multicoloured 30 15

1087 – 15d. multicoloured 50 20

1088 – 20d. multicoloured 65 25

1089 – 25d. multicoloured 80 30

1090 – 30d. multicoloured 1·00 35

1091 – 40d. multicoloured 1·25 40

DESIGNS: 10 to 40d. Various flowering cacti.

1987. Day of Five Billion Inhabitants of Earth.

1093 **225** 5d. mauve and blue 65 20

1987. Costumes. Multicoloured.

1094 5d. Type **226** 25 10

1095 20d. Woman from Bana 1·00 25

1096 20d. Woman from Gia Rai 1·00 25

1097 30d. Man from Gia Rai 1·60 45

1098 30d. Man from Ede 1·60 45

1099 40d. Woman from Ede 2·10 55

227 Silhouettes of Soldiers and Disabled Soldier

228 Rose

1987. 40th Anniv of Association of Disabled Soldiers.

1100 **227** 5d. red and violet 65 20

1987. Roses. Multicoloured.

1101 5d. Type **228** 15 10

1102 10d. Red hybrid tea 35 15

1103 15d. Pink hybrid tea 50 20

1104 20d. Species rose 70 25

1105 25d. Species rose (different) 85 30

1106 30d. Floribunda 1·00 35

1107 40d. "Rosa odorata" 1·40 50

229 Postwoman and Mail Transport

1987. 40th Anniv of Postal Trade Union.

1109 **229** 5d. black and pink 1·40 40

1110 – 30d. black and green 1·25 40

DESIGN: 30d. Linesman, dish aerial and telephonist.

230 Siamese Fighting Fish

1987. Fishes. Multicoloured.

1111 5d. Type **230** 25 10

1112 10d. Red-tailed black shark 60 20

1113 15d. Tiger barb 85 30

1114 20d. Pearl danio 1·10 40

1115 25d. Rosy barb 1·40 55

1116 30d. Rasbora 1·75 65

1117 40d. Silver loach 2·40 85

231 I.Y.S.H. Emblem

1987. International Year of Shelter for the Homeless.

1118 **231** 5d. black and blue 65 25

233 Crested Gibbons

235 Industrial and Agricultural Symbols

234 "Three Musicians"

1987. Monkeys. Multicoloured.

1120 5d. Type **233** 15 10

1121 5d. Variegated langurs 15 10

1122 15d. Crested gibbon (different) 50 20

1123 40d. Variegated langur (different) 1·40 50

1987. Paintings by Picasso. Multicoloured.

1124 3d. Type **234** 10 10

1125 20d. Horse-drawn wagon 70 20

1126 20d. Winged horse on shore 70 20

1127 30d. "Child with Dove" (vert) 1·00 30

1128 30d. "Gertrude Stein" (vert) 1·00 30

1129 40d. "Guernica" (44 × 27 mm) 1·40 40

1987. 70th Anniv of Russian Revolution. Mult.

1131 5d. Type **235** 20 10

1132 20d. Soviet Memorial, Berlin-Treptow, cruiser "Aurora" and Lenin 70 25

1133 30d. "70" and symbols of progress 1·10 35

1134 50d. Ho Chi Minh and scenes of Vietnamese history 1·75 60

236 Consolidated PBY-5 Catalina Flying Boat

1987. "Hafnia 87" International Stamp Exhibition, Copenhagen. Flying Boats. Multicoloured.

1136 5d. Type **236** 15 10

1137 10d. Liore et Olivier LeO 246 35 10

1138 15d. Dornier Do-18 50 15

1139 20d. Short Sunderland 70 20

1140 25d. Flying boat, 1923 85 25

1141 30d. Chetverikov ARK-3 1·00 30

1142 40d. Cant Z.509 1·40 45

237 Epanouis

1987. Corals. Multicoloured.

1144 5d. Type 237 25 10

1145 10d. Acropora 55 15

1146 15d. Rhizopsammia 80 25

1147 20d. Acropora (different) 1·75 35

1148 25d. Alcyone 1·40 40

1149 30d. Corollum 1·60 50

1150 40d. Cristatella 2·10 65

238 Doves as Clasped Hands forming Heart

1987. 5th Anniv of Vietnam–Czechoslovak Friendship Treaty. Each blue, yellow and red.

1151 10d. Type **238** 35 10

1152 50d. Pagoda on One Pillar (Hanoi), flags and buildings of Prague 1·75 50

239 Symbols of Industry and Agriculture

1987. Soviet–Vietnam Friendship Treaty.
1153 **239** 5d. pink, black and orange 15 10
1154 – 50d. pink, brown and orange . . . . . . 1·75 55
DESIGN: 50d. Buildings of Moscow Kremlin and Hanoi.

240 Coloured Circles

1987. Peace.
1155 **240** 10d. multicoloured . . . 90 30

241 Saddle-back Fungus

243 Wrecked Boeing B-52 Stratofortress Bomber and Girl watering Flowers

242 Dove on Open Hands

1987. Fungi. Multicoloured.
1156 5d. Type **241** 25 10
1157 10d. Trumpet agaric 55 15
1158 15d. "Tricholoma terreum" 80 20
1159 20d. Golden russula . . . . 1·10 25
1160 25d. Spindle shank . . . . 1·25 35
1161 30d. "Cortinarius violaceus" 1·60 40
1162 40d. Bronze boletus . . . . 2·25 60

1987. 30th Anniv of Africa–Asia Co-operation Committee.
1163 **242** 10d. blue, black & yellow 40 15
1164 – 30d. black, brown and yellow . . . . 1·25 40
DESIGN—VERT: 30d. Hands and map.

1987. 15th Anniv of U.S. Air Bombardment of Vietnam.
1165 **243** 10d. black and yellow . . 40 15
1166 – 30d. black and orange 1·10 45
DESIGN: 30d. Young Pioneers and weapons.

244 Woman carrying Bales of Cloth

246 Anniversary Emblem and Dove

245 Junk, Man blowing Horn and Map

1987. 6th Party Congress Decisions.
1167 **244** 5d. green and brown . . 20 10
1168 – 20d. orange and brown 80 25
1169 – 30d. violet and blue . . 1·25 45
DESIGNS: 20d. Tractor driver; 30d. Loading crate on freighter.

1988. Paracel and Spratley Islands.
1170 **245** 10d. black, pink and red 45 15
1171 – 100d. light brown, black and brown . . . . . 3·50 1·75
DESIGN: 100d. Maps showing Paracel Islands.

1988. 125th Anniv of International Red Cross.
1172 **246** 10d. red, black and blue 75 25

247 Fleet

1988. 700th Anniv of Battle of Bach Dang River.
1173 **247** 80d. black, red and pink 1·50 45
1174 – 200d. multicoloured . . 3·50 1·10
DESIGN: 200d. Battle scene.

248 Oil Rig

249 Blue and Yellow Macaw

1988. Oil Industry.
1175 **248** 1000d. black, blue and red . . . . 10·50 2·50

1988. Parrots. Multicoloured.
1176 10d. Type **249** 60 20
1177 10d. Slaty-headed parakeet 60 20
1178 20d. Red-winged parrot ("Aprosmictus erythropterus") . . . . . 1·10 40
1179 20d. Green-winged macaw ("Ara chloroptera") . . . 1·10 40
1180 30d. Moustached parakeet ("Psittacula alexandri") 1·75 60
1181 30d. Military macaw ("Ara militaris") . . . . 1·75 60
1182 50d. Vernal hanging parrot 3·00 95

250 Map

251 Child and Syringe

1988. 33rd Council for Mutual Economic Aid Meeting and 10th Anniv of Vietnam's Membership.
1184 **250** 200d. multicoloured . . 1·25 45
1185 – 300d. blue and bistre . 1·90 70
DESIGN: 300d. COMECON headquarters building, Moscow.

1988. Child Vaccination Campaign.
1186 **251** 60d. orange, black & blue 90 40

252 Emblem and Building

1988. 30th Anniv of "Peace and Socialism" (magazine).
1187 **252** 20d. multicoloured . . . 75 30

253 Ton Duc Thang

254 Emblem

1988. Birth Centenary of Pres. Ton Duc Thang.
1188 **253** 150d. multicoloured . . 1·75 75

1988. 6th Trade Unions Congress. Multicoloured.
1189 50d. Type **254** 80 40
1190 100d. "VI" and couple . . . 1·75 75

255 Pointed-scaled Pit Viper

1988. Snakes. Multicoloured.
1191 10d. Type **255** 35 10
1192 10d. Pope's pit viper ("Trimeresurus popeorum") 35 10
1193 20d. Banded krait ("Bungarus fasciatus") . . 1·10 25
1194 20d. Malayan krait ("Bungarus candidus") . . 75 25
1195 30d. Coral snake ("Calliophis maclellandi") 1·10 35
1196 30d. Striped beaked snake ("Ancistridon acutus") . . 1·10 35
1197 50d. King cobra (vert) . . . 1·90 55

256 Family (Trieu Khac Tien)

1988. Children's Drawings. Multicoloured.
1198 10d. Type **256** 35 10
1199 10d. Couple and house (Phuong Ti) 35 10
1200 20d. Fishermen (Lam Hoang Thang) . . . . . 1·10 25
1201 20d. Children flying kite (Nguyen Xuan Anh) . . . 75 25
1202 30d. Couple (Hong Hanh) (vert) . . . . 1·10 35
1203 30d. Animals and girl playing guitar (Quynh May) . . . . 1·10 35
1204 50d. Woman holding dove (Ta Phuong Tra) (vert) . . 1·90 55

257 Tri An

1988. U.S.S.R.–Vietnam Co-operation. Hydro-electric Power Stations.
1206 **257** 2000d. black, orge & red 6·00 4·25
1207 – 3000d. black, bistre and red . . . . 9·00 3·50
DESIGN: 3000d. Hoa Binh.

258 Kamov Ka-26

1988. Helicopters. Multicoloured.
1208 10d. Type **258** 35 10
1209 10d. Boeing-Vertol 234 Commercial Chinook . . 35 10
1210 20d. MBB-Bolkow Bo 105 75 25
1211 20d. Mil Mi-10K 75 25
1212 30d. Kawasaki-Hughes 369HS . . . . 1·10 35
1213 30d. Bell JetRanger . . . . 1·10 35
1214 50d. Mil Mi-8 . . . . . . 1·90 55

259 Gaur

260 Flower and Banners

1988. Mammals. Multicoloured.
1216 10d. Type **259** 30 10
1217 10d. Banteng 30 10
1218 20d. Malayan tapir ("Tapirus indicus") . . . 60 20
1219 20d. Hog deer ("Axis porcinus") 60 20
1220 30d. Mainland serow ("Capricornis sumatraensis") 85 30
1221 30d. Wild boar ("Sus scrofa") 85 30
1222 50d. Water buffalo . . . . 1·50 50

1988. 10th Anniv of U.S.S.R.–Vietnam Friendship.
1224 **260** 50d. multicoloured . . . 55 25

261 Indian Star Tortoise ("Testudo elegans")

262 Skaters

1988. Turtles and Tortoises.
1225 10d. Type **261** 35 10
1226 10d. Three-banded box turtle ("Cuora trifasciata") 35 10
1227 20d. Big-headed turtle ("Platysternon megacephalum") 75 25
1228 20d. Hawksbill turtle ("Eretmochelys imbricata") 75 25
1229 30d. Indian Ocean green turtle ("Chelonia mydas") 1·10 35
1230 30d. Leatherback turtle ("Dermochelys coriacea") 1·10 35
1231 50d. Loggerhead turtle ("Caretta caretta") . . . 1·90 55

1988. Ice Skating. Multicoloured.
1233 **262** 10d. multicoloured . . . 30 10
1234 – 10d. multicoloured . . . 30 10
1235 – 20d. multicoloured . . . 60 20
1236 – 20d. multicoloured (horiz) 60 20
1237 – 30d. multicoloured . . . 85 30
1238 – 30d. multicoloured (horiz) 85 30
1239 – 50d. multicoloured (horiz) . . . . 1·50 50
DESIGNS: Nos. 1234/9, Different skating scenes.

263 Bowden "Spacelander"

1988. Bicycles. Multicoloured.
1241 10d. Type **263** 35 10
1242 10d. Rabasa Derbi with red tyres 35 10
1243 20d. Huffy 70 25
1244 20d. Rabasa Derbi with black tyres 70 25
1245 30d. VMX-PL . . . . . . 1·00 35
1246 30d. Premier . . . . . . 1·00 35
1247 50d. Columbia RX5 . . . . 1·75 55

264 Fidel Castro

265 Cosmonauts on Spacecraft Wing

1988. 30th Anniv of Cuban Revolution. Mult.
1248 100d. Type **264** 40 15
1249 300d. National flags and Cuban and Vietnamese workers . . . . 1·10 45

1988. Cosmonauts Day. Multicoloured.
1250 10d. Type **265** 30 10
1251 10d. Spacecraft moving across surface of planet 30 10
1252 20d. Space rocket heading for planet 60 20
1253 20d. Spacecraft and cosmonauts on planet with Earth in sky . . . 60 20
1254 30d. Spacecraft hovering over surface 85 30
1255 30d. "Soyuz"–"Salyut" complex 85 30
1256 50d. Space "bubble" and rocket . . . . 1·50 50

266 Soldier Cone

1988. Sea Shells. Multicoloured.
1258 10d. Type **266** 35 10
1259 10d. Silver conch ("Strombus lentiginosus") 35 10
1260 20d. Common frog shell ("Bursa rana") 70 25
1261 20d. Tapestry turban ("Turbo petholatus") 70 25
1262 30d. Red-mouth olive ("Oliva erythrostoma") 1·00 35
1263 30d. Chambered nautilus ("Nautilus") 1·00 35
1264 50d. Episcopal mitre 1·75 55
The inscriptions on Nos. 1261 and 1263 have been transposed.

267 Class VL85 Diesel Locomotive, Russia

1988. Railway Locomotives. Multicoloured.
1266 20d. Type **267** 60 20
1267 20d. LRC high speed diesel, Canada 60 20
1268 20d. Monorail train, Japan 60 20
1269 20d. KiHA 80 diesel railcar, Japan 60 20
1270 30d. Class DR 1A diesel-electric, Russia 90 30
1271 30d. Class RC 1 electric, Sweden 90 30
1272 50d. Class TE-136 diesel-electric, Russia 1·50 50

268 Gourd

1988. Fruits. Multicoloured.
1274 10d. Type **268** 35 10
1275 10d. "Momordica charantia" 35 10
1276 20d. Pumpkin ("Cucurbita moschata") 70 25
1277 20d. Eggplant ("Solanum melongena") 70 25
1278 30d. "Benincasa hispida" 1·00 35
1279 30d. Luffa gourd 1·00 35
1280 50d. Tomatoes 1·75 55

269 Soldiers and Field Workers

1989. 10th Anniv of People's Republic of Kampuchea. Multicoloured.
1281 100d. Type **269** 40 15
1282 500d. Crowd greeting soldier and mother with child 1·90 70

270 Junk from Quang Nam

1989. Regional Fishing Junks. Multicoloured.
1283 10d. Type **270** 40 10
1284 10d. Quang Tri 40 10
1285 20d. Thua Thien 80 20
1286 20d. Da Nang 80 20
1287 30d. Quang Tri (different) 1·25 30
1288 30d. Da Nang (different) 1·25 30
1289 50d. Hue 2·10 55

271 Caribbean Buckeye ("Junonia evarete")

1989. "India-89" International Stamp Exhibition, New Delhi (1st issue). Butterflies. Multicoloured.
1290 50d. Type **271** 30 15
1291 50d. "Anaea echemus" 30 15
1292 50d. Great southern white ("Ascia monuste") 30 15
1293 100d. Red-splashed sulphur ("Phoebis avellaneda") 60 25
1294 100d. Jamaican orange ("Eurema proterpia") 60 25
1295 200d. "Papilio palamedes" 1·25 55
1296 300d. Monarch ("Danaus plexippus") 1·90 80
See also Nos. 1298/1301.

272 Flag and Telecommunications

274 Emblems on Banner

273 Festival

1989. "India-89" International Stamp Exhibition, New Delhi (2nd issue).
1298 **272** 100d. multicoloured 65 15
1299 – 100d. multicoloured 40 15
1300 – 300d. multicoloured 1·10 35
1301 – 600d. brown, orge & green 2·25 75
DESIGNS: 100d. (No. 1299), Oil and electricity industries; 300d. Government Secretariat and Asokan capital; 600d. Jawaharlal Nehru (Indian statesman, birth centenary).

1989. Bicentenary of Battle of Dongda.
1302 **273** 100d. violet and green 40 15
1303 – 1000d. mauve and pink 4·00 1·40
DESIGN: 1000d. Battle scene.

1989. Centenary of Interparliamentary Union.
1304 **274** 100d. multicoloured 50 20
1305 – 200d. gold, ultramarine and blue 1·00 40
DESIGN: 200d. "100" on banner.

275 Dachshunds

1989. Dogs. Multicoloured.
1306 50d. Type **275** 30 10
1307 50d. Basset hounds 30 10
1308 50d. Setter (vert) 30 10
1309 100d. Hunting dog (vert) 65 20
1310 100d. Basset hounds (66 × 25 mm) 65 20
1311 200d. Hound (vert) 1·25 40
1312 300d. Basset hound puppy 1·90 65

276 Footballers

277 Jug

1989. World Cup Football Championship, Italy (1st issue). Multicoloured.
1313 50d. Type **276** 30 10
1314 50d. Striker and goalkeeper 30 10
1315 50d. Goalkeeper 30 10
1316 100d. Player No. 5 tackling 65 20
1317 100d. Tackling (vert) 65 20
1318 200d. Player No. 3 (vert) 1·25 40
1319 300d. Players heading ball (vert) 1·90 65
See also Nos. 1382/8 and 1482/9.

1989. Pottery. Multicoloured.
1321 50d. Type **277** 30 10
1322 100d. Bowl with geometric pattern 65 20
1323 100d. Round pot with flower decoration 65 20
1324 200d. Tall pot with animal decoration 1·25 40
1325 300d. Vase 1·90 65

278 Baby Thanh Giong with Mother

1989. Legend of Thanh Giong. Multicoloured.
1326 50d. Type **278** 30 10
1327 100d. Thanh Giong with King's messenger 65 20
1328 100d. Thanh Giong at head of army 65 20
1329 200d. Thanh Giong beating out flames 1·25 40
1330 300d. Thanh Giong riding to heaven 1·90 65

279 "Fuchsia fulgens"

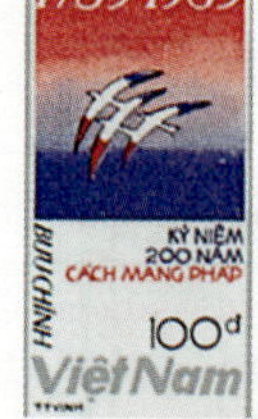

280 Bird carrying Envelope above Dish Aerial

1989. Flowers. Multicoloured.
1331 50d. Type **279** 35 10
1332 50d. Bird-of-paradise flower ("Strelitzia reginae") 35 10
1333 100d. Glory lily ("Gloriosa superba") 70 25
1334 100d. Orange day lily ("Hemerocallis fulva") 70 25
1335 200d. "Paphiopedilum siamense" 1·40 45
1336 300d. "Iris sp." 2·10 70
On Nos. 1332 and 1335 the inscriptions have been transposed.

1989. Communications.
1337 **280** 100d. brown 65 25

281 Birds

283 Man and Ox

282 "Return from Varennes"

1989. Bicentenary of French Revolution and "Philexfrance 89" International Stamp Exhibition, Paris. (a) As T **281**. Multicoloured.
1338 100d. Type **281** 55 20
1339 500d. "Liberty guiding the People" (detail, Eugene Delacroix) 2·75 90

(b) As T **282**.
1340 50d. Type **282** 25 10
1341 50d. "Revolutionary Court" 25 10
1342 50d. "Oath of the Tennis Court" (Jacques-Louis David) (vert) 25 10
1343 100d. "Assassination of Marat" (David) (vert) 55 20
1344 100d. "Storming the Bastille" (vert) 55 20
1345 200d. Two children (Pierre-Paul Prud'hon) (vert) 1·10 35
1346 300d. "Slave Trade" (Jean-Leon Gerome) 1·60 55

1989. Rice Cultivation. Multicoloured.
1348 50d. Type **283** 30 10
1349 100d. Ploughing with ox 65 20
1350 100d. Flooding fields 1·25 20
1351 200d. Fertilizing 1·25 40
1352 300d. Harvesting crop 1·90 65

284 Appaloosa

1989. Horses. Multicoloured.
1353 50d. Type **284** 35 10
1354 50d. Tennessee walking horse 35 10
1355 50d. Tersky 35 10
1356 100d. Kladruber 70 25
1357 100d. Welsh cob 70 25
1358 200d. Pinto 1·40 40
1359 300d. Pony and bridle (68 × 27 mm) 2·10 70

285 Brandenburg Gate, Flag and Emblem

1989. 40th Anniv of German Democratic Republic.
1360 **285** 200d. yellow, black and mauve 65 25

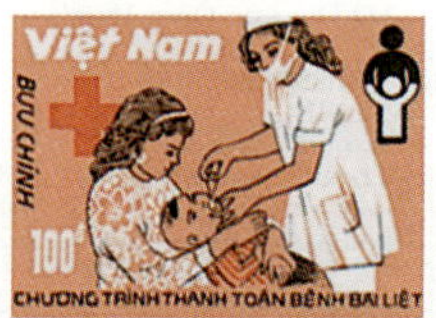

286 Polio Oral Vaccination

1989. Immunization Campaign.
1361 **286** 100d. brown, black & red 30 20
1362 – 100d. pink, black & green 30 20
1363 – 100d. green, black and red 30 20
DESIGNS: No. 1362, Vaccinating pregnant woman; 1363, Health clinic.

287 Horse

1989. Paintings of Horses by Hsu Pei-Hung. Mult.
1364 100d. Type **287** 10 10
1365 200d. Two horses galloping 15 10
1366 300d. Three horses grazing 25 10
1367 500d. Horse galloping (horiz) 45 15
1368 800d. Galloping horse 70 25
1369 1000d. Two horses under tree 85 30
1370 1500d. Galloping horse (different) 1·25 40

288 "Nina", "Pinta" and "Santa Maria" and Mochica Ceramic Figure (⅔-size illustration)

1989. 500th Anniv (1992) of Discovery of America by Columbus (1st issue). Multicoloured.
1372 50d. Type **288** 60 20
1373 100d. Columbus and King Ferdinand the Catholic and Peruvian ceramic bottle 35 10
1374 100d. Columbus's arrival at Rabida and Mexican decorated vessel 35 10

1375 100d. Columbus offering gifts (18th-century engraving) and human-shaped jug 35 10
1376 200d. Early map and Peruvian ceramic 70 25
1377 200d. Portrait and arms of Columbus and Nazca ceramic 70 25
1378 300d. Chart by Toscanelli and Chimu vessel . . . . 1·10 35

See also Nos. 1545/51 and 1664/8.

289 Storming of Presidential Palace, Saigon, and Ho Chi Minh

1990. 60th Anniv of Vietnamese Communist Party. Multicoloured.
1380 100d. Type **289** 10 10
1381 500d. Industry, workers, hammer and sickle and flag 30 10

290 Players

1990. World Cup Football Championship, Italy (2nd issue). Multicoloured.
1382 100d. Type **290** 10 10
1383 200d. Argentina player with possession 10 10
1384 300d. Netherlands and Scotland players 15 10
1385 500d. Soviet Union player tackling 25 10
1386 1000d. Scotland and West Germany player 55 20
1387 2000d. Soviet Union player losing possession . . . . 1·10 35
1388 3000d. Goalkeeper . . . . 1·60 55

291 Hybrids of Mallard and Local Species

1990. Ducks. Multicoloured.
1390 100d. Type **291** 10 15
1391 300d. European mallard . . 20 15
1392 500d. Mallards 40 15
1393 1000d. Red-billed pintails 70 35
1394 2000d. White duck preening 1·25 35
1395 3000d. African yellow-bills 2·10 45

292 Mack Truck and Trailer

1990. Trucks. Multicoloured.
1396 100d. Type **292** 10 10
1397 200d. Volvo "F89" tipper 10 10
1398 300d. Tatra "915 S1" tipper 15 10
1399 500d. Hino "KZ30000" lorry 25 10
1400 1000d. Italia Iveco 55 20
1401 2000d. Leyland-Daf "Super Comet" tipper . . . . . 1·10 35
1402 3000d. Kamaz "53212" lorry . . . . 1·60 55

293 8th/9th-century Viking Longship

1990. Sailing Ships. Multicoloured.
1403 100d. Type **293** 10 10
1404 500d. 15th-century caravel 25 10
1405 1000d. 15th-century carrack (vert) 55 15
1406 1000d. 14th/15th-century carrack 55 15
1407 1000d. 17th-century frigate 55 15
1408 2000d. 16th-century galleons and pinnace (vert) . . . . 1·10 35
1409 3000d. 16th-century galleon 1·60 50

294 Bubble-eyed Goldfish

1990. Goldfish. Multicoloured.
1411 100d. Type **294** 15 10
1412 300d. Calico veil-tailed . . . 25 10
1413 500d. Red-capped 40 15
1414 1000d. Veil-tailed (vert) . . 75 20
1415 2000d. Celestial (vert) . . 1·60 40
1416 3000d. Comet (vert) . . . . 2·40 60

295 Gate of Noble Mankind

1990. Hue Temples. Multicoloured.
1417 100d. Type **295** 35 10
1418 100d. Lotus pool at tomb of Emperor Tu Duc 35 10
1419 200d. Southern Gate 70 25
1420 300d. Thien Pagoda . . . . 1·10 35

296 "Antonia Zarate" (Francisco de Goya)

1990. "Stamp World London 90" International Stamp Exhibition. Multicoloured.
1422 100d. Type **296** 10 10
1423 200d. "Girl with Paper Fan" (Auguste Renoir) 10 10
1424 300d. "Janet Grizel" (John Russell) 15 10
1425 500d. "Love unfasten's Beauty's Girdle" (Joshua Reynolds) 25 10
1426 1000d. "Portrait of a Lady" (George Romney) (wrongly inscr "Omney") 55 20
1427 2000d. "Mme. Ginoux" (Vincent van Gogh) . . . 1·10 35
1428 3000d. "Lady in Green" (Thomas Gainsborough) 1·60 55

297 Henry Giffard's Steam-powered Dirigible Airship

1990. "Helvetia 90" International Stamp Exhibition, Geneva. Airships. Mult. With or without gum.
1430 100d. Type **297** 10 10
1431 200d. Lebaudy-Juillot airship No. 1 "La Jaune" 10 10
1432 300d. "Graf Zeppelin' . . . 15 10
1433 500d. R-101 . . . . 25 15
1434 1000d. "Osoaviakhim" . . . 55 20
1435 2000d. Tissandier Brothers' airship . . . . 1·10 40
1436 3000d. U.S. Navy "N" Class airship . . . . 1·60 60

No. 1431 is wrongly inscr "Lebandy".

298 Silver Tabby and White Cat

1990. Cats. Multicoloured.
1438 100d. Type **298** 10 10
1439 200d. Black cat (vert) . . . 10 10
1440 300d. Black and white cat 15 10
1441 500d. Brown tabby and white (vert) 30 10
1442 1000d. Silver tabby 55 20
1443 2000d. Tortoiseshell and white (vert) . . . . 1·10 35
1444 3000d. Tortoiseshell tabby and white (vert) . . . . . 1·75 60

299 Ho Chi Minh, 1923 **300** King Charles Spaniel

1990. Birth Centenary of Ho Chi Minh. Mult.
1446 100d. Type **299** 10 10
1447 300d. Ho Chi Minh, 1945 15 10
1448 500d. Dove, hand holding rifle, and Ho Chi Minh 25 10
1449 1000d. Ho Chi Minh conducting 50 15
1450 2000d. Ho Chi Minh embracing child . . . . . 1·00 35
1451 3000d. Globe and Ho Chi Minh . . . . 1·50 50

1990. "New Zealand 90" International Stamp Exhibition, Auckland. Dogs. Multicoloured.
1453 100d. Type **300** 10 10
1454 200d. Spaniel 10 10
1455 300d. Saluki 15 10
1456 500d. Dachshund 30 10
1457 1000d. Dalmatian 55 20
1458 2000d. Highland terrier . . 1·10 35
1459 3000d. Boxer . . . . 1·75 60

301 Gorgosaurus

1990. Prehistoric Animals. Multicoloured.
1461 100d. Type **301** 10 10
1462 500d. Ceratosaurus 30 10
1463 1000d. Ankylosaurus . . . 60 20
1464 2000d. Ankylosaurus (different) . . . . 1·25 40
1465 3000d. Edaphosaurus . . . 1·90 65

302 High Jumping

1990. 11th Asian Games, Peking. Multicoloured.
1466 100d. Type **302** 10 10
1467 200d. Basketball 10 10
1468 300d. Table tennis 15 10
1469 500d. Volleyball 25 10
1470 1000d. Gymnastics 55 20
1471 2000d. Tennis . . . . . . 1·10 35
1472 3000d. Judo . . . . 1·60 55

1990. Tourism. Nos. 626/33 optd **DULICH'90** and emblem.
1474 50x. Type **131** 10 10
1475 50x. Common ink cap ("Coprinus atramentarius") 10 10
1476 50x. Golden mushroom ("Flammulina velutipes") 10 10
1477 50x. Chanterelle ("Cantharellus cibarius") 10 10
1478 1d. Chinese mushroom . . . 20 10
1479 2d. Red-staining mushroom 40 15
1480 5d. Common morel . . . . 1·00 35
1481 10d. Caesar's mushroom . . 2·10 70

1990. World Cup Football Championship, Italy (3rd series). Nos. 457/64 optd **ITALIA'90** and ball.
1482 **90** 30x. multicoloured . . . 20 10
1483 – 30x. mult (No. 458) . . . 20 10
1484 – 40x. mult (No. 459) . . . 25 10
1485 – 40x. mult (No. 460) . . . 25 10
1486 – 50x. mult (No. 461) . . . 45 15
1487 – 50x. mult (No. 462) . . . 45 15
1488 – 60x. multicoloured . . . 55 20
1489 – 1d. multicoloured . . . . 1·25 40

305 "Pyotr Yemtsov" (container ship)

1990. Ships. Multicoloured.
1490 100d. Type **305** 10 10
1491 300d. Mexican Lines container ship 15 10
1492 500d. Liner 25 10
1493 1000d. "Ben Nevis" (tanker) 55 20
1494 2000d. Roll-on roll-off ferry 1·10 35
1495 3000d. Sealink train ferry "Nord Pas de Calais" . . 1·75 60

306 Emblem, Globe and Dove

1990. 45th Anniv of Postal Service. Mult.
1496 100d. Type **306** 10 10
1497 1000d. Emblem, dish aerial and globe 55 20

307 Red Flags and Symbols of Construction and Agriculture **308** Thach Sanh collecting Wood

1990. 45th Anniv of Independence. Multicoloured.
1498 100d. Type **307** 10 10
1499 500d. Map, storming of Government Palace (1945), siege of Dien Bien Phu and tank entering Presidential Palace, Saigon (1975) 25 10
1500 1000d. Satellite communications ship, dish aerial and "VI" 65 15
1501 3000d. Hammer and sickle, industrial symbols and couple . . . . 1·50 50

1990. Legend of Thach Sanh. Multicoloured.
1503 100d. Type **308** 10 10
1504 300d. Ly Thong 15 10
1505 500d. Thach Sanh fighting fire-breathing snake . . . 25 10
1506 1000d. Thach Sanh shooting down bird 55 20
1507 2000d. Thach Sanh in prison 1·10 35
1508 3000d. Thach Sanh and wife 1·75 60

1990. World Cup Football Championship Results. Nos. 1382/8 optd **1. GERMANY 2. ARGENTINA 3. ITALY**.
1509 **290** 100d. multicoloured . . 10 10
1510 – 200d. multicoloured . . 10 10
1511 – 300d. multicoloured . . 15 10
1512 – 500d. multicoloured . . 25 10
1513 – 1000d. multicoloured . . 55 20
1514 – 2000d. multicoloured . . 1·10 35
1515 – 3000d. multicoloured . . 1·60 55

1990. Red Cross. Nos. N598/605 optd with red cross and **FOR THE FUTURE GENERATION** in various languages (given in brackets).
1517 12x. multicoloured (Italian) 20 10
1518 12x. multicoloured (Chinese) 20 10
1519 20x. multicoloured (German) 30 10
1520 20x. mult (Vietnamese) . . . 30 10
1521 30x. multicoloured (English) 45 15
1522 40x. multicoloured (Russian) 60 20
1523 50x. multicoloured (French) 75 25
1524 60x. multicoloured (Spanish) 90 30

311 Soldier

1990. 60th Anniv of Vietnamese Women's Union. Multicoloured.
1525 100d. Type **311** 10 10
1526 500d. Women in various occupations 30 10

312 Emblems

1990. 20th Anniv of Asian–Pacific Postal Training Centre, Bangkok.
1527 **312** 150d. multicoloured . . 20 10

313 Hands holding Forest and City

1990. Preservation of Forests. Multicoloured.
1528 200d. Type **313** 10 10
1529 1000d. Forest fire, "S.O.S." and river 55 20

314 Panther Cap **315** Yachting

1991. Poisonous Fungi. Multicoloured.
1530 200d. Type **314** 15 10
1531 300d. Death cap 20 10
1532 1000d. Destroying angel . . 75 20
1533 1500d. Fly agaric . . . . . 1·10 35
1534 2000d. "Russula emetica" 1·50 50
1535 3000d. Satan's mushroom 2·40 75

1991. Olympic Games, Barcelona (1992). Mult.
1536 200d. Type **315** 10 10
1537 300d. Boxing 15 10
1538 400d. Cycling 20 10
1539 1000d. High jumping . . . 45 15
1540 2000d. Show jumping . . . 95 30
1541 3000d. Judo . . . . 1·40 45
1542 3000d. Wrestling (horiz) . . 1·40 45

316 Nguyen Binh Khiem

1991. 500th Birth Anniv of Nguyen Binh Khiem (poet).
1544 **316** 200d. black, brown and ochre 40 25

317 "Marisiliana" **318** Woman in Blue Tunic

1991. 500th Anniv (1992) of Discovery of America by Columbus (2nd issue). Multicoloured.
1545 200d. Type **317** 10 10
1546 400d. "Venitien" 15 10
1547 400d. "Cromster" (vert) . . 15 10
1548 2000d. "Pinta" 75 25
1549 2000d. "Nina" 75 25
1550 3000d. "Howker" (vert) . . 1·10 35
1551 5000d. "Santa Maria" . . . 1·90 65

1991. Golden Heart Charity.
1553 **318** 200d. multicoloured . . 10 10
1554 – 500d. multicoloured . . 10 10
1555 – 1000d. multicoloured . . 45 15
1556 – 5000d. multicoloured . . 2·10 70
DESIGNS: 500d. to 5000d. Traditional women's costumes.

319 Japanese White-naped Crane

1991. Birds. Multicoloured.
1557 200d. Type **319** 15 15
1558 300d. Sarus crane chick (vert) 20 15
1559 400d. Manchurian crane (vert) 25 20
1560 1000d. Sarus cranes (adults) (vert) 70 30
1561 2000d. Black-necked crane (vert) . . . . 1·40 50
1562 3000d. South African crowned cranes (vert) . . 2·10 85
1563 3000d. Great white crane . . 2·10 85

320 Black-finned Reef Shark

1991. Sharks. Multicoloured.
1564 200d. Type **320** 10 10
1565 300d. Grey reef shark . . . 10 10
1566 400d. Leopard shark 20 10
1567 1000d. Great hammerhead 65 20
1568 2000d. White-tipped reef shark . . . . 1·40 35
1569 3000d. Sand tiger . . . . . 2·10 55
1570 3000d. Bull shark . . . . . 2·10 55

321 Lobster

1991. Shellfish. Multicoloured.
1571 200d. Type **321** 10 10
1572 300d. "Alpheus bellulus" . . 10 10
1573 400d. "Periclemenes brevicarpalis" 15 10
1574 1000d. Lobster (different) 40 15
1575 2000d. Lobster (different) 80 25
1576 3000d. Lobster (different) 1·25 40
1577 3000d. "Astacus sp." . . . 1·25 40

322 "Fusee", 1829 **323** Ho Chi Minh, "VII" and Buildings

1991. Early Locomotives. Multicoloured.
1578 400d. Type **322** 15 10
1579 400d. Blenkinsop's rack locomotive (wrongly inscr "Puffing Billy") 15 10
1580 500d. John Stevens rack locomotive, 1825 (horiz) 25 10
1581 1000d. Crampton No 80 locomotive, 1852, France (horiz) 50 15
1582 2000d. "Locomotion", 1825 (horiz) . . . . 1·00 25
1583 3000d. "Saint-Lo", 1843 (horiz) . . . . 1·60 40
1584 3000d. "Coutances", 1855 (horiz) . . . . 1·60 40

1991. 7th Vietnamese Communist Party Congress. Multicoloured.
1586 200d. Type **323** 25 10
1587 300d. Workers 35 10
1588 400d. Mother and children 45 10

324 Pioneers

326 Yellow-banded Poison-arrow Frog

325 Lada

1991. 50th Anniv of Vietnam Youth Pioneers (200d.) and United Nations Convention on Children's Rights (400d.). Multicoloured.
1589 200d. Type **324** 30 10
1590 400d. Child's face and U.N. emblem 65 20

1991. Rally Cars. Multicoloured.
1591 400d. Type **325** 15 10
1592 400d. Nissan 15 10
1593 500d. Ford Sierra RS Cosworth 20 10
1594 1000d. Suzuki 40 15
1595 2000d. Mazda "323" 80 25
1596 3000d. Peugeot . . . . . . 1·25 40
1597 3000d. Lancia . . . . . . 1·25 40

1991. Frogs. Multicoloured.
1599 200d. Type **326** 10 10
1600 400d. Edible frog 15 10
1601 500d. Golden mantella . . . 25 10
1602 1000d. Dyeing poison-arrow frog 40 15
1603 2000d. Tree frog 80 25
1604 3000d. Red-eyed tree frog ("Agalychnis calidryas") 1·25 40
1605 3000d. Golden tree frog ("Hyla aurea") . . . . . 1·25 40

327 Ho Chi Minh and Party Emblem **328** Speed Skating

1991. 60th Anniv (1990) of Vietnamese Communist Party.
1606 **327** 100d. red 10 10

1991. Winter Olympic Games, Albertville (1992) (1st issue). Multicoloured.
1607 200d. Type **328** 10 10
1608 300d. Freestyle skiing . . . 10 10
1609 400d. Four-man bobsleighing (horiz) . . . 15 10
1610 1000d. Biathlon (rifle shooting) (horiz) . . . 40 15
1611 2000d. Skiing (horiz) . . . 80 25
1612 3000d. Cross-country skiing 1·25 40
1613 3000d. Ice skating . . . . . 1·25 40
See also Nos. 1659/63.

329 "Arsinoitherium zitteli"

1991. Prehistoric Animals. Multicoloured.
1615 200d. Type **329** 10 10
1616 500d. "Elephas primigenius" 25 10
1617 1000d. "Baluchitherium" . . 45 15
1618 2000d. "Deinotherium giganteum" 90 30
1619 3000d. "Brontops" . . . . 1·40 45
1620 3000d. "Uintatherium" . . 1·40 45

330 Pawn

1991. Chess. Staunton Pieces.
1621 200d. Type **330** 10 10
1622 300d. Knight 15 10
1623 1000d. Rook 45 15
1624 2000d. Queen 85 30
1625 3000d. Bishop . . . . . . 1·40 40
1626 3000d. King . . . . 1·40 40

331 Atlas Moth

1991. "Phila Nippon '91" International Stamp Exhibition, Tokyo. Moths and Butterflies. Mult.
1628 200d. Type **331** 10 10
1629 400d. Blue morpho 15 10
1630 500d. Birdwing 20 10
1631 1000d. Red admiral 40 15
1632 1000d. "Papilio demetrius" 40 15
1633 3000d. "Papilio weiskei" . . 1·25 40
1634 5000d. Lesser purple emperor . . . . 2·00 65

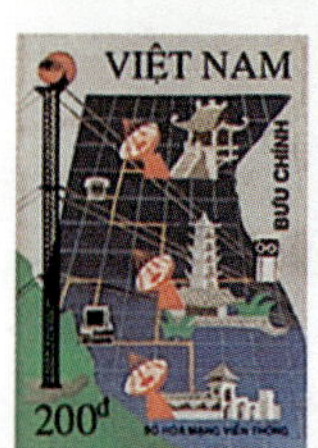
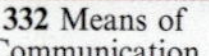

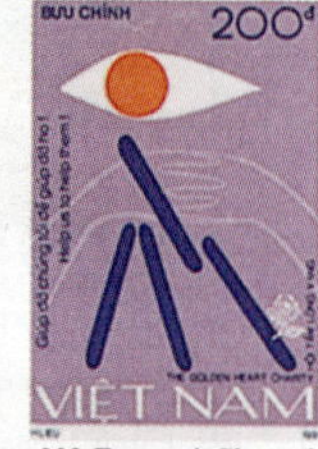

332 Means of Communication **333** Eye and Clasped Hands

1991. 25th Anniv of Posts and Telecommunications Research Institute.
1636 **332** 200d. multicoloured . . 40 20

1991. Golden Heart Charity for Disabled People.
1638 **333** 200d. blue, lilac & orange 10 10
1639 – 3000d. violet, blue and turquoise . . . . . . 1·25 40
DESIGN: 3000d. Tennis player in wheelchair.

334 Gymnastics

1992. Olympic Games, Los Angeles (1984). Mult.
1640 50x. Type **334** 15 10
1641 50x. Football (vert) 15 10
1642 1d. Wrestling 25 10
1643 2d. Volleyball (vert) 50 15
1644 3d. Hurdling 75 25
1645 5d. Basketball (vert) . . . . 1·25 40
1646 8d. Weightlifting . . . . . 2·00 65

1992. "Expo '92" World's Fair, Seville. Nos. 1372/8 optd **SEVILLA'92** and emblem.
1648 **288** 50d. multicoloured . . . 25 10
1649 – 100d. mult (No. 1373) 50 15
1650 – 100d. mult (No. 1374) 50 15
1651 – 100d. mult (No. 1375) 50 15
1652 – 200d. mult (No. 1376) 95 30
1653 – 200d. mult (No. 1377) 95 30
1654 – 300d. multicoloured . . 1·40 45

336 Chu Van An teaching

1992. 700th Death Anniv of Chu Van An.

1656 **336** 200d. multicoloured . . 25 15

337 Atomic Symbol, Communications, Industry and Agriculture

1992. Resolutions of 7th Communist Party Congress. Multicoloured.

1657 200d. Type **337** 10 10

1658 2000d. Hands clasped and map of Asia 55 20

338 Biathlon

1992. Winter Olympic Games, Albertville (2nd issue). Multicoloured.

1659 200d. Type **338** 10 10

1660 2000d. Ice hockey 45 15

1661 4000d. Skiing (slalom) . . . 85 30

1662 5000d. Ice skating . . . . . 1·10 35

1663 6000d. Skiing (downhill) . . 1·25 40

339 Columbus's Fleet

1992. 500th Anniv of Discovery of America by Columbus (3rd issue). Multicoloured.

1664 400d. Type **339** 10 10

1665 3000d. "Santa Maria" . . . 60 20

1666 4000d. Columbus and flag on land 80 25

1667 6000d. Columbus offering gifts to Amerindians . . . 1·25 40

1668 8000d. Ship returning home 1·60 55

340 Tupolev Tu-154M

1992. Aircraft. Multicoloured.

1670 400d. Type **340** 10 10

1671 500d. Concorde 10 10

1672 1000d. Airbus Industrie A-320 . . . . 20 10

1673 3000d. Airbus Industrie A340-300 . . . . 65 20

1674 4000d. De Havilland D.H.C.8 Dash Eight-400 90 30

1675 5000d. Boeing 747-200 . . . 1·10 35

1676 6000d. McDonnell Douglas MD-11CF . . . . 1·25 40

341 Weather System and Forecasting Equipment

342 Archery

1992. International Decade for Natural Disaster Reduction. Multicoloured.

1677 400d. Type **341** 10 10

1678 4000d. Man taking flood depth readings 90 30

1992. Olympic Games, Barcelona (2nd issue). Mult.

1679 400d. Type **342** 10 10

1680 600d. Volleyball 15 10

1681 1000d. Wrestling 20 10

1682 3000d. Fencing 65 20

1683 4000d. Running 90 30

1684 5000d. Weightlifting . . . . 1·10 35

1685 6000d. Hockey . . . . . . 1·25 40

343 Suzuki "500 F"

1992. Racing Motor Cycles. Multicoloured.

1687 400d. Type **343** 10 10

1688 500d. Honda "CBR 600F" 10 10

1689 1000d. Honda "HRC 500F" 20 10

1690 3000d. Kawasaki "250F" (vert) 65 20

1691 4000d. Suzuki "RM 250 F" (vert) 90 30

1692 5000d. Suzuki "500F" . . . 1·10 35

1693 6000d. BMW "1000F" . . . 1·25 40

344 Shuttle Launch

346 Footballer

345 Main Entrance

1992. International Space Year. Multicoloured.

1695 400d. Type **344** 10 10

1696 500d. Launch of space shuttle "Columbia" . . . 10 10

1697 3000d. "Columbia" in space (horiz) 65 20

1698 4000d. Projected shuttle "Hermes" docked at space station (horiz) . . . 85 30

1699 5000d. "Hermes" in space with solar panel (horiz) 1·10 35

1700 6000d. Astronauts repairing Hubble space telescope . . 1·25 40

1992. Centenary of Saigon Post Office.

1701 **345** 200d. multicoloured . . 40 15

1992. European Cup Football Championship. Mult.

1703 200d. Type **346** 10 10

1704 2000d. Goalkeeper 45 15

1705 4000d. Two players with ball on ground 85 30

1706 5000d. Two players with ball in air . . . . 1·10 35

1707 6000d. Three players . . . . 1·25 40

347 "Portrait of a Girl" (Francisco de Zurbaran)

1992. "Expo '92" World's Fair, Seville. Paintings by Spanish Artists. Multicoloured.

1709 400d. Type **347** 10 10

1710 500d. "Woman with a Jug" (Bartolome Esteban Murillo) 10 10

1711 1000d. "Maria Aptrickaia" (Diego Velazquez) 20 10

1712 3000d. "Holy Family with St. Katharine" (Jose de Ribera) 60 20

1713 4000d. "Madonna and Child with Sts. Agnes and Thekla" (El Greco) . . . 80 25

1714 5000d. "Woman with Jug" (Francisco Goya) . . . . 1·00 35

1715 6000d. "The Naked Maja" (Francisco Goya) (horiz) 1·25 40

348 Clean Water sustaining Life and Polluted Water

1992. 20th Anniv of United Nations Conference on Environmental Protection. Multicoloured.

1717 200d. Type **348** 10 10

1718 4000d. Graph comparing current world development and environmentally sound development 95 30

349 Cu Lao Xanh Lighthouse

350 "Citrus maxima"

1992. "Genova '92" International Thematic Stamp Exhibition. Lighthouses. Multicoloured.

1719 200d. Type **349** 10 10

1720 3000d. Can Gio 60 20

1721 5000d. Vung Tau . . . . . 1·00 35

1722 6000d. Long Chau . . . . 1·40 45

1992. Flowers. Multicoloured.

1723 200d. Type **350** 10 10

1724 2000d. "Nerium indicum" 40 15

1725 4000d. "Ixora coccinea" . . 80 25

1726 5000d. "Cananga oborata" 1·00 35

1727 6000d. "Cassia surattensis" 1·25 40

351 Australian Pied Imperial Pigeons

353 Memorials and "45"

352 Guinea Pig

1992. Pigeons and Doves. Multicoloured.

1728 200d. Type **351** 15 15

1729 2000d. Red-plumed pigeon 65 20

1730 4000d. Feral rock pigeon . . 1·40 35

1731 5000d. Top-knot pigeon . . 1·60 45

1732 6000d. Laughing doves (horiz) . . . . 2·00 60

1992. Rodents. Multicoloured.

1733 200d. Type **352** 10 10

1734 500d. Guinea pigs 10 10

1735 3000d. Indian crested porcupine 60 20

1736 4000d. Lesser Egyptian gerbil (vert) 80 25

1737 5000d. Red giant flying squirrel (vert) . . . . . . 1·00 35

1738 6000d. Common rabbit (vert) . . . . 1·25 40

1992. 45th Anniv of Disabled Soldiers' Day.

1739 **353** 200d. multicoloured . . 40 15

354 Stylized Sportsmen

1992. 3rd Phu Dong Games.

1740 **354** 200d. blue, ultramarine and light blue 40 15

355 Siamese Fighting Fish

1992. Siamese Fighting Fishes.

1741 **355** 200d. multicoloured . . 15 10

1742 – 500d. multicoloured . . 15 15

1743 – 3000d. multicoloured . . 95 30

1744 – 4000d. multicoloured . . 1·25 35

1745 – 5000d. multicoloured . . 1·60 50

1746 – 6000d. multicoloured . . 2·00 55

DESIGNS: 500d. to 6000d. Different Siamese fighting fishes.

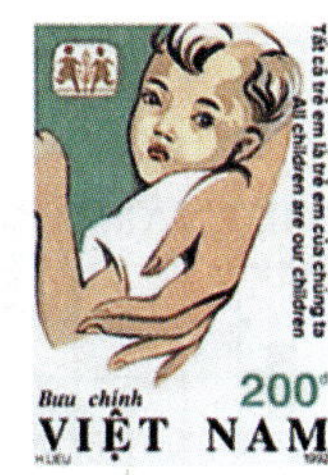

356 Members' Locations on Map

358 Adult protecting Child

357 Trainee Doctors

1992. 40th Anniv of International Planned Parenthood Federation. Multicoloured.

1747 200d. Type **356** 10 10

1748 4000d. Emblem on world map (horiz) 95 30

1992. 90th Anniv of Hanoi Medical School. Mult.

1749 200d. Type **357** 10 10

1750 5000d. Alexandre Yersin (bacteriologist) and school 1·10 35

1992. SOS Children's Villages. Multicoloured.

1751 200d. Type **358** 10 10

1752 5000d. Houses and woman with children . . . . . . 1·10 35

359 Kick Boxing

1993. 17th South-East Asian Games, Singapore.

1753 **359** 200d. multicoloured . . 40 15

360 Giant Bee

1993. Bees. Multicoloured.
1754 200d. Type **360** 10 10
1755 800d. "Apis koschevnikovi" 15 10
1756 1000d. "Apis laboriosa" . . 20 10
1757 2000d. "Apis cerana japonica" 40 15
1758 5000d. "Apis cerana cerana" 1·00 35
1759 10000d. Honey bee (vert) . . 2·00 65

361 Tam-Cam returning from the River
362 Rooster with Family

1993. Legend of Tam-Cam. Multicoloured.
1760 200d. Type **361** 10 10
1761 800d. Apparition of old man by goldfish basin 30 10
1762 1000d. Tam-Cam with unsold rice at the market 20 10
1763 3000d. Tam-Cam trying on slipper for Prince 60 20
1764 4000d. Tam-Cam rising from lotus 80 25
1765 10000d. The royal couple . . 2·00 65

1993. New Year. Year of the Cock. Multicoloured.
1766 200d. Type **362** 10 10
1767 5000d. Rooster with family (different) . . . . 1·10 35

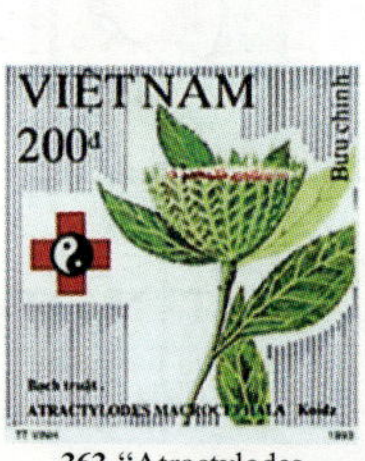

363 "Atractylodes macrocephala"
364 Communications Equipment

1993. Medicinal Plants. Multicoloured.
1768 200d. Type **363** 10 10
1769 1000d. Rangoon creeper ("Quisqualis indica") . . 20 10
1770 1000d. Japanese honeysuckle ("Lonicera japonica") . . 20 10
1771 3000d. "Rehmannia glutinosa" 65 20
1772 12000d. "Gardenia jasminoides" . . . . . . 2·50 85

1993. "Communication in Service of Life". Mult.
1773 200d. Type **364** 10 10
1774 2500d. Fibre-optic cable and map of Hong Kong–Sri Racha submarine cable route 60 20

365 Giant Panda

1993. Mammals. Multicoloured.
1775 200d. Type **365** 10 10
1776 800d. Tiger 15 10
1777 1000d. Indian elephant . . . 20 10
1778 3000d. Indian rhinoceros . . 55 20
1779 4000d. Family of gibbons 75 25
1780 10000d. Clouded leopard . . 1·90 65

366 Players, Statue of Liberty and Emblem

1993. World Cup Football Championship, U.S.A. (1994) (1st issue).
1782 **366** 200d. multicoloured . . 10 10
1783 – 1500d. multicoloured . . 20 10
1784 – 7000d. multicoloured . . 1·10 35
DESIGNS: 1500, 7000d. Different match scenes.
See also Nos. 1865/70.

367 Wheelbarrow

1993. Traditional Transport. Multicoloured.
1785 200d. Type **367** 10 10
1786 800d. Buffalo cart 15 10
1787 1000d. Rickshaw 20 10
1788 2000d. Rickshaw with passenger 40 15
1789 5000d. Rickshaw (different) 1·00 35
1790 10000d. Horse-drawn carriage . . . . 2·00 65

368 Pylon and Lightbulb

1993. 500 kV Electricity Lines.
1791 **368** 300d. black, orange and red 20 10
1792 400d. black, blue and orange 25 10

369 "Sunflowers" (Vincent van Gogh)

1993. "Polska'93" International Stamp Exhibition, Poznan. Paintings. Multicoloured.
1793 200d. Type **369** 10 10
1794 1000d. "Young Woman" (Amedeo Modigliani) . . 20 10
1795 1000d. "Couple in Forest" (Henri Rousseau) 20 10
1796 5000d. "Harlequin with Family" (Pablo Picasso) 90 30
1797 10000d. "Female Model" (Henri Matisse) (horiz) . . 1·75 60

370 "Paphiopedilum hirsutissimum"

1993. Centenary of Da Lat. Orchids. Multicoloured.
1799 400d. Type **370** 10 10
1800 1000d. "Paphiopedilum gratrixianum" 20 10
1801 1000d. "Paphiopedilum malipoense" 20 10
1802 12000d. "Paphiopedilum hennisianum" . . . . . . 2·10 70

371 Wat Phra Sri Rattana Satsadaram, Thailand

1993. Historic Asian Architecture. Multicoloured.
1803 400d. Type **371** 10 10
1804 800d. Prambanan Temple, Indonesia 15 10
1805 1000d. City Hall, Singapore 15 10
1806 2000d. Angkor Vat, Cambodia (horiz) 30 10
1807 2000d. Ubudiah Mosque, Kuala Kangsar, Malaysia (horiz) 30 10
1808 6000d. That Luang, Laos (horiz) 95 30
1809 8000d. Omar Ali Saifuddin Mosque, Brunei (horiz) 1·25 40

372 Industry and Communications

1993. 7th Trade Unions Congress. Multicoloured.
1811 400d. Type **372** 10 10
1812 5000d. Doves, atomic symbol, hammer in hand and flowers 90 30

373 "Scylla serrata"

1993. Salt-water Crabs. Multicoloured.
1813 400d. Type **373** 10 10
1814 800d. "Portunus sanguinolentus" 15 10
1815 1000d. "Charybdis bimaculata" 15 10
1816 2000d. "Paralithodes brevipes" 30 10
1817 5000d. "Portunus pelagicus" 75 25
1818 10000d. "Lithodes turritus" 1·50 50

374 Stamps and Globe

1993. Stamp Day. Multicoloured.
1819 400d. Type **374** 10 10
1820 5000d. Airmail letter 90 30

375 Player
376 Lo Lo Costume

1994. Tennis.
1821 **375** 400d. multicoloured . . 10 10
1822 – 1000d. multicoloured (male player) 15 10
1823 – 1000d. multicoloured (female player) 15 10
1824 – 12000d. multicoloured 2·10 70
DESIGNS: Nos. 1822/4, Different players.

1993. "Bangkok 1993" International Stamp Exhibition.
1825 400d. Type **376** 10 10
1826 800d. Thai costume 15 10
1827 1000d. Dao Do costume . . 15 10
1828 2000d. H'mong costume . . 30 10
1829 5000d. Kho Mu costume . . 70 25
1830 10000d. Kinh costume . . . 1·40 45

377 Dog with Puppies

1994. New Year. Year of the Dog. Multicoloured.
1832 400d. Type **377** 10 10
1833 6000d. Dog . . . . 1·10 35

378 Peach
380 Hoi Lim

379 Anatoly Karpov

1994. Flowers of the Four Seasons. Multicoloured.
1834 400d. Type **378** (spring) . . 15 10
1835 400d. "Chrysanthemum morifolium" (autumn) . . 15 10
1836 400d. "Rosa chinensis" (winter) 15 10
1837 15000d. "Delonix regia" (summer) . . . . 2·10 70

1994. Chess. Multicoloured.
1838 400d. Type **379** 10 10
1839 1000d. Gary Kasparov . . . 15 10
1840 2000d. Robert Fischer . . . 35 10
1841 4000d. Emanuel Lasker . . 70 25
1842 10000d. Jose Raul Capablanca . . . . 1·75 60
No. 1840 is wrongly inscribed "Robers".

1994. "Hong Kong '94" Stamp Exhibition. Traditional Festivals. Multicoloured.
1844 400d. Type **380** 10 10
1845 800d. Cham 15 10
1846 1000d. Tay Nguyen 20 10
1847 12000d. Nam Bo . . . . . 2·10 70

381 Loi Nhuoc
382 Red Gladioli

1994. Operatic Masks. Multicoloured.
1848 400d. Type **381** 10 10
1849 500d. Dao Tax Xuan . . . 10 10
1850 2000d. Ta Ngoc Lan . . . 35 10
1851 3000d. Ly Khac Minh . . . 55 20
1852 4000d. Ta On Dinh 75 25
1853 7000d. Khuong Linh Ta . . 1·25 40

1994. Gladioli. Multicoloured.
1854 400d. Type **382** 10 10
1855 2000d. Salmon gladioli . . . 35 10
1856 5000d. White gladioli . . . 80 25
1857 8000d. Magenta gladioli . . 1·25 40

383 Painting by Utamaro Kitagawa

1994. Paintings by Japanese Artists. Multicoloured.
1858 400d. Type **383** (wrongly inscr "Kigatawa") 10 10
1859 500d. Harunobu Suzuki . . 10 10
1860 1000d. Hokusai Katsushika 15 10
1861 2000d. Hiroshige 35 10
1862 3000d. Hokusai Katsushika (different) 50 15
1863 4000d. Utamaro Kitagawa (different) 65 20
1864 9000d. Choki Eishosai . . . 1·50 50

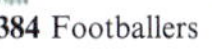
384 Footballers **386** Pioneers reading Newspaper

385 Hauling Piece of Equipment

1994. World Cup Football Championship, U.S.A. (2nd issue). Multicoloured.
1865 400d. Type **384** 10 10
1866 600d. Running with ball . . 10 10
1867 1000d. Heading ball 15 10
1868 2000d. Goalkeeper 35 10
1869 3000d. Two players chasing ball 50 15
1870 11000d. Tackling . . . . . 1·90 65

1994. 40th Anniv of Victory at Dien Bien Phu.
1872 **385** 400d. brown, cinnamon and black 10 10
1873 – 3000d. ultramarine, blue and black 50 15
DESIGN: 3000d. Entertaining the troops.

1994. 40th Anniv of "Young Pioneer" (newspaper).
1874 **386** 400d. red and black . . 30 10

387 Estuarine Crocodile

1994. Reptiles. Multicoloured.
1875 400d. Type **387** 10 10
1876 600d. Mississippi alligator 10 10
1877 2000d. Nile crocodile . . . 35 10
1878 3000d. Chinese alligator . . 50 15
1879 4000d. Paraguay caiman . . 65 20
1880 9000d. Australian crocodile 1·50 50

388 Alexandre Yersin **389** Pierre de Coubertin (founder)

1994. Centenary of Discovery of Plague Bacillus.
1882 **388** 400d. multicoloured . . 30 10

1994. Cent of International Olympic Committee. Multicoloured.
1883 400d. Anniversary and National Committee emblems and sports pictograms 10 10
1884 6000d. Type **389** . . . . . 1·10 35

390 "Cicindela aurulenta"

1994. Beetles. Multicoloured.
1885 400d. Type **390** 10 10
1886 1000d. "Harmonia octomaculata" 15 10
1887 6000d. "Cicindela tennipes" 1·00 35
1888 7000d. "Collyris sp." . . . 1·25 40

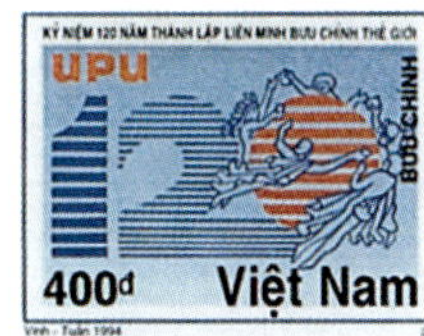

391 Anniversary Emblem

1994. 120th Anniv of U.P.U. Multicoloured.
1889 400d. Type **391** 10 10
1890 5000d. Envelopes forming world map 75 25

392 Curlew **393** "Bambusa blumeana"

1994. "Philakorea 1994" International Stamp Exhibition, Seoul. Sea Birds. Multicoloured.
1892 400d. Type **392** 15 15
1893 600d. Wilson's storm petrel 15 15
1894 1000d. Great frigate bird . . 25 20
1895 2000d. Cape gannet 45 20
1896 3000d. Tufted puffins . . . 85 60
1897 11000d. Band-tailed gulls . . 2·75 1·25

1994. "Singpex '94" Stamp Exhibition, Singapore. Bamboos. Multicoloured.
1899 400d. Type **393** 10 10
1900 1000d. "Phyllostachys aurea" 15 10
1901 2000d. "Bambusa vulgaris" 30 10
1902 4000d. "Tetragonocalamus quadrangularis" 65 20
1903 10000d. "Bambusa venticosa" . . . . 1·60 55

394 Log Bridge with Handrail

1994. Rudimentary Bridges. Multicoloured.
1904 400d. Type **394** 10 10
1905 900d. Interwoven bridge . . 15 10
1906 8000d. Log bridge on stilts 1·10 35

395 Girl in Wheelchair and Boy playing

1994. "For Our Children's Future". Multicoloured.
1907 400d.+100d. Type **395** . . . 10 10
1908 2000d. Children dancing around emblem (vert) . . 40 15

396 Electric Tramcar No. 1

1994. Trams. Multicoloured.
1909 400d. Type **396** 15 10
1910 900d. Paris double-deck battery-powered tram . . 25 10
1911 8000d. Philadelphia U.S. Mail electric tram . . . . 2·10 45

397 Civilians greeting Soldiers

1994. 40th Anniv of Liberation of Hanoi. Mult.
1912 400d. Type **397** 10 10
1913 2000d. Workers and students and symbols of development 35 10

398 Airplane in Air

1994. 50th Anniv of I.C.A.O. Multicoloured.
1914 400d. Type **398** 10 10
1915 3000d. Airplane on ground 50 15

399 Parade

1994. 50th Anniv of Vietnamese People's Army. Multicoloured.
1916 400d. Type **399** 10 10
1917 1000d. Plan of attacks on Saigon 15 10
1918 2000d. Veteran recounting the past to young girl . . 35 10
1919 4000d. Naval anti-aircraft gun crew 70 25

400 Sow with Piglets **401** Osprey ("Pandion haliaetus")

1995. New Year. Year of the Pig. Multicoloured.
1920 400d. Type **400** 10 10
1921 8000d. Pig . . . . 1·00 35

1995. Birds.
1922 **401** 400d. blue 15 15
1923 – 400d. green 15 15
1924 – 400d. purple 15 15
1925 – 400d. orange 15 15
1926 – 5000d. red . . . . . . 1·40 50
DESIGNS—HORIZ: No. 1923, Sociable weaver ("Philetarius socius"); 1924, Sharpbill ("Oxyruncus cristatus"); 1925, Golden plover ("Pluvialis apricaria"). VERT: No. 1926, Red-legged seriema ("Cariama cristata").

402 Girls with Bicycle **403** Statue and Building

1995. Women's Costumes. Multicoloured.
1927 400d. Type **402** 10 10
1928 3000d. Girl with sheaf of flowers 40 15
1929 5000d. Girl with traditional hat 65 20

1995. "Vietstampex '95" Stamp Exhibition. F.I.A.P. Executive Committee Meeting.
1930 **403** 5500d. multicoloured . . 65 20

404 Brown Fish Owl

1995. Owls. Multicoloured.
1931 400d. Type **404** 20 20
1932 1000d. Tawny owl 20 20
1933 2000d. Great grey owl . . . 45 25
1934 5000d. Spotted wood owl 1·00 50
1935 10000d. White-faced scops owl . . . . 2·00 90

405 Grey Angelfish

1995. Fishes. Multicoloured.
1937 400d. Type **405** 10 10
1938 1000d. Rectangle triggerfish 15 10
1939 2000d. Regal angelfish . . . 30 10
1940 4000d. Queen angelfish . . . 55 25
1941 5000d. Queen triggerfish . . 75 30
1942 9000d. Clown triggerfish . . 1·50 50

406 Throwing the Hammer **407** Lenin

1995. Olympic Games, Atlanta (1996) (1st issue). Multicoloured.
1943 400d. Type **406** 10 10
1944 3000d. Cycling 35 10
1945 4000d. Running 45 15
1946 10000d. Pole vaulting . . . 1·25 40
See also Nos. 2063/5.

1995. 125th Birth Anniv of Lenin.
1948 **407** 400d. black and red . . 15 10

408 Adult and Young

1995. The Malayan Tapir. Multicoloured. (a) With World Wildlife Fund emblem.
1949 400d. Type **408** 10 10
1950 1000d. Standing 15 10
1951 2000d. Walking 30 10
1952 4000d. Calling 60 20
Nos. 1949/52 were issued together, se-tenant, forming a composite design.

(b) Without W.W.F. emblem.
1953 4000d. Standing by trees . . 60 20
1954 4000d. Eating 60 20
1955 5000d. Swimming 75 25
1956 6000d. In water 90 30
Nos. 1953/6 were issued together, se-tenant, forming a composite design.

409 Dove and "50"

1995. 50th Anniv of End of Second World War in Europe.
1957 **409** 400d. multicoloured . . 20 10

410 Montgolfier's Hot Air Balloon, 1783 **411** Parachutist

1995. "Finlandia 95" International Stamp Exhibition, Helsinki. Balloons. Multicoloured.
1958 500d. Type **410** 15 10
1959 1000d. Jacques Charles and Marie-Noel Robert's balloon (first untethered flight by manned hydrogen balloon) 20 10
1960 2000d. Jean-Pierre Blanchard's oared balloon 40 15

1961	3000d. Jean-Francois Pilatre de Rozier and Jules Romain's balloon over English Channel, 1785	50	15
1962	4000d. Free balloon	65	20
1963	5000d. Captive balloon over Red Square, Moscow, 1890	75	25
1964	7000d. Auguste Piccard's balloon "F.N.R.S.", 1931	1·25	40

1995. Parachuting. Multicoloured.

1965	400d. Type **411**	10	10
1966	2000d. Two parachutists	40	15
1967	3000d. Landing	50	15
1968	4000d. Gathering in the parachute	65	20

Nos. 1965/8 were issued together, se-tenant, forming a composite design.

412 "Rhododendron fleuryi"

1995. Rhododendrons. Multicoloured.

1969	400d. Type **412**	15	10
1970	1000d. "Rhododendron sulphoreum"	25	10
1971	2000d. "Rhododendron sinofalconeri"	50	15
1972	3000d. "Rhododendron lyi"	65	20
1973	5000d. "Rhododendron ovatum"	90	30
1974	9000d. "Rhododendron tanastylum"	1·60	55

413 Tan and Lang pay Court to Lu's Daughter

1995. "Betel and Areca Nut" (fable). Multicoloured.

1975	400d. Type **413**	15	10
1976	1000d. Girl chooses Tan	25	10
1977	3000d. Lang changes into rock	65	20
1978	10000d. Girl changes into betel pepper plant and Tan into areca nut palm	1·60	55

Nos. 1975/8 were issued together, se-tenant, forming a composite design.

414 Statue of Mother and Child

415 Flags around Emblem

1995. 65th Anniv of Women's Union (400d.) and World Conference on Women, Peking (3000d.). Multicoloured.

1979	400d. Type **414**	15	10
1980	3000d. Globe and women of different races (horiz)	65	20

1995. Admission of Vietnam to Association of South East Asian Nations.

1981	**415** 400d. multicoloured	15	10

416 Ho Chi Minh, Dove and Crowd

1995. Anniversaries. Multicoloured.

1982	400d. Type **416** (65th anniv of Communist Party of Indo-China)	10	10
1983	400d. Ho Chi Minh embracing child (105th birth anniv)	10	10
1984	1000d. Civic building, road bridge, power lines and oil derrick (40th anniv of evacuation of French troops from North Vietnam)	25	10
1985	1000d. Ho Chi Minh saluting and building flying flags (20th anniv of end of Vietnam war)	25	10
1986	2000d. Soldiers and flag (50th anniv of National Liberation Army)	45	15
1987	2000d. Radio mast, dish aerial, motor cycle couriers and mail van (50th anniv of postal and telecommunications services)	45	15

417 Bust of Hill and Penny Black

1995. Birth Bicentenary of Sir Rowland Hill (instigator of postage stamp).

1988	**417** 4000d. multicoloured	75	25

418 Torch Carriers and Sports Pictograms

1995. National Sports Festival.

1989	**418** 400d. blue, red and lilac	25	10

419 "Paphiopedilum druryi"

1995. "Singapore'95" International Stamp Exhibition. Orchids. Multicoloured.

1990	400d. Type **419**	15	10
1991	2000d. "Dendrobium ochraceum"	40	10
1992	3000d. "Vanda sp."	50	15
1993	4000d. "Cattleya sp."	65	20
1994	5000d. "Paphiopedilum hirsutissimum"	90	30
1995	6000d. "Christenosia vietnamica"	1·25	40

420 Palace, Hue

1995. Asian Cityscapes. Multicoloured.

1997	400d. Type **420**	15	10
1998	3000d. Park, Doanh Chau	50	15
1999	4000d. Temple, Macao	65	20
2000	5000d. Kowloon, Hong Kong	90	30
2001	6000d. Pagoda, Dai Loan	1·25	40

421 Dove and Anniversary Emblem

1995. 50th Anniv of U.N.O.

2002	**421** 2000d. multicoloured	40	10

422 Woman with Vase of Flowers (To Ngoc Van)

1995. Paintings. Multicoloured.

2003	400d. Type **422**	15	10
2004	2000d. Woman washing hair (Tran Van Can)	55	15
2005	6000d. Woman and vase of flowers (To Ngoc Van)	85	30
2006	8000d. Two women resting (Tran Van Can)	1·10	35

423 Map and Eclipse

1995. Total Eclipse of the Sun.

2007	**423** 400d. multicoloured	15	10

424 Rats carrying Canopy and on Horseback

1996. New Year. Year of the Rat. Multicoloured.

2008	400d. Type **424**	15	10
2009	8000d. Rats in and carrying sedan chair	1·10	35

425 Apricot

1996. Flowers.

2011	**425** 400d. brown	15	10
2012	– 400d. purple	15	10
2013	– 400d. red	15	10
2014	– 400d. blue	15	10
2015	– 5000d. red	1·10	35

DESIGNS—HORIZ: No. 2012, Chrysanthemums; 2013, Orchid; 2014, Orchids (different). VERT: No. 2015, Asters.

426 Communist Symbols and Ho Chi Minh

1996. 8th Vietnamese Communist Party Congress. Multicoloured.

2016	400d. Type **426**	15	10
2017	3000d. Symbols of communications, industry, Communism and agriculture within outline of dove	35	10

427 Thanh Tru Tai

429 White-throated Kingfisher

428 Tsintaosaurus

1996. Statues in Tay Phuong Pagoda, Thach That. Multicoloured.

2018	400d. Type **427**	10	10
2019	600d. Tich Doc Than	10	10
2020	1000d. Hoang Tuy Cau	15	10
2021	2000d. Bach Tinh Thuy	25	10
2022	3000d. Xich Thanh Hoa	30	10
2023	5000d. Dinh Tru Tai	50	15
2024	6000d. Tu Hien Than	60	20
2025	8000d. Dai Than Luc	75	25

1996. Prehistoric Animals. Multicoloured.

2026	400d. Type **428**	10	10
2027	1000d. Archaeopteryx	15	10
2028	2000d. Psittacosaurus	25	10
2029	3000d. Hypsilophodon	30	10
2030	13000d. Parasaurolophus	1·25	40

1996. Kingfishers. Multicoloured.

2031	400d. Type **429**	10	10
2032	1000d. Belted kingfisher	15	10
2033	2000d. River kingfisher	25	10
2034	4000d. Ruddy kingfisher	45	15
2035	12000d. Lesser pied kingfisher	1·25	40

430 Temple of Literature, Hanoi

431 Dan Ty Ba

1996. Asian Temples. Multicoloured.

2036	400d. Type **430**	10	10
2037	2000d. Wat Mahathtat, Sukhothai, Thailand	25	10
2038	3000d. Lingaraja Temple, Bhubaeshwar, India	30	10
2039	4000d. Kinkakuju Temple, Kyoto, Japan	45	15
2040	10000d. Borobudur Temple, Java, Indonesia	1·10	35

1996. "China '96" Ninth Asian International Stamp Exhibition, Peking. Stringed Musical Instruments. Multicoloured.

2041	400d. Type **431**	10	10
2042	3000d. Dan nhi	30	10
2043	4000d. Dan day	45	15
2044	9000d. Dan tranh	1·00	35

432 Ho Chi Minh

1996. 50th Anniv of Vietnamese Red Cross.

2045	**432** 3000d. multicoloured	35	10

433 Children of Different Races

434 Tiger Beetle

1996. 50th Anniv of U.N.I.C.E.F. Multicoloured.

2046	400d. Type **433**	10	10
2047	7000d. Water droplets containing symbols and globe "plant"	75	25

1996. Beetles. Multicoloured.

2048	400d. Type **434**	10	10
2049	500d. "Calodema wallacei"	10	10
2050	1000d. Blister beetle	20	10
2051	4000d. "Chrysochroa buqueti"	45	15
2052	5000d. "Ophioniea nigrofasciata"	65	20
2053	12000d. Ground beetle	1·25	40

435 Emblem in Hand

1996. 50th Natural Disaster Reduction Day.
2054 **435** 400d. multicoloured . . 15 10

436 Goalkeeper

1996. European Football Championship, England. Multicoloured.
2055 400d. Type **436** 10 10
2056 8000d. Player 85 30
Nos. 2055/6 were issued together, se-tenant, forming a composite design.

437 Airbus Industrie A320

1996. Aircraft. Multicoloured.
2057 400d. Type **437** 10 10
2058 1000d. Antonov An-72 . . . 20 10
2059 2000d. McDonnell Douglas MD-11F 25 10
2060 6000d. RJ-85 . . . . 55 20
2061 10000d. Boeing 747-400F . . 1·10 35

438 Women's Football

1996. Olympic Games, Atlanta, U.S.A. (2nd issue). Multicoloured.
2063 2000d. Type **438** 25 10
2064 4000d. Yachting 45 15
2065 5000d. Hockey 65 20

439 1946 1h. Stamp

1996. Stamp Day. 50th Anniv of First Unoverprinted Vietnamese Stamp.
2066 **439** 400d. multicoloured . . 15 10

440 Orange Peel Fungus **441** Pupils at Main Gate

1996. Fungi. Multicoloured.
2067 400d. Type **440** 10 10
2068 500d. "Morchella conica" 10 10
2069 1000d. "Anthurus archeri" 15 10
2070 4000d. Chicken mushroom 45 15
2071 5000d. "Filoboletus manipularis" 65 20
2072 12000d. "Tremiscus helvelloides" . . . . . . 1·25 40

1996. Centenary of Hue School. Multicoloured.
2073 400d. Type **441** 10 10
2074 3000d. Main building . . . 25 10

442 Woman and Vase of Lotus Flowers

1996. Paintings by Nguyen Sang. Multicoloured.
2075 400d. Type **442** 10 10
2076 8000d. Soldiers at Dien Bien Phu 85 30

443 Variegated Langurs

1996. "Taipeh '96" International Stamp Exhibition, Taiwan. Endangered Animals. Mult.
2077 400d. Type **443** 10 10
2078 2000d. Tigers 15 10
2079 4000d. Javan rhinoceroses 45 15
2080 10000d. South African crowned cranes . . . . . 1·25 40

444 Tree of Children's Heads

1996. Campaign for Use of Iodized Salt.
2081 **444** 400d. multicoloured . . 15 10

445 Armed Combatants, National Flag and Quote from Ho Chi Minh

1996. 50th Anniv of Formation of National Front for the Liberation of South Vietnam.
2082 **445** 400d. multicoloured . . 15 10

446 Rambutan

1997. Fruits.
2083 **446** 400d. red and black . . 15 10
2084 – 400d. brown and black 15 10
2085 – 400d. green and black 15 10
2086 – 400d. violet and black 15 10
2087 – 400d. purple and black 15 10
DESIGNS: No. 2084, Durian; 2085, Avocado; 2086, Mangostela; 2087, Queen-of-the-night.

447 Ox and Calf

1997. New Year. Year of the Ox. Multicoloured.
2088 400d. Type **447** 10 10
2089 8000d. Ox . . . . 1·00 25

448 Flags and Symbols of Development

1997. 8th Vietnamese Communist Party Congress.
2090 **448** 400d. multicoloured . . 10 10

449 Red-capped Goldfish **450** Snake Design

1997. The Goldfish. Multicoloured.
2091 400d. Type **449** 10 10
2092 1000d. Black and red and long-tailed red goldfishes 10 10
2093 5000d. Goldfish with gaping mouth 75 15
2094 7000d. Black and yellow goldfishes . . . . . . 1·00 20
2095 8000d. Red goldfish with black tail and fins . . . . 1·25 25

1997. Ly Dynasty Sculptures. Multicoloured.
2097 400d. Type **450** 10 10
2098 1000d. Terracotta dragon's head 10 10
2099 3000d. Musicians in rectangular panel (horiz) 45 10
2100 5000d. Lion base (horiz) . . 75 15
2101 10000d. Vessel with dragon design (horiz) . . . . . . 1·50 55

451 Pagoda in Lake, Ha Tay

1997. Landscapes. Multicoloured.
2102 400d. Type **451** 10 10
2103 5000d. Bamboo suspension bridge, Lai Chau 75 15
2104 7000d. Mist-wreathed trees behind village, Lao Cai 1·00 20

452 Red Lily **453** Huynh Thuc Khang

1997. The Lily. Multicoloured.
2105 400d. Type **452** 10 10
2106 1000d. White lily 10 10
2107 5000d. Pink and white lily 75 15
2108 10000d. Red and cream lily 1·50 30

1997. 50th Death Anniv of Huynh Thuc Khang.
2109 **453** 400d. multicoloured . . 10 10

454 Tennis

1997. Sports for Disabled People. Multicoloured.
2110 1000d. Type **454** 10 10
2111 6000d. Rifle shooting . . . 80 20

455 Owton's Palm Civet

1997. Cat Ba National Park. Multicoloured.
2112 400d. Type **455** 10 10
2113 3000d. European otter . . . 45 10
2114 4000d. Palla's squirrel . . . 60 10
2115 10000d. Leopard cat . . . . 1·50 55

456 Golden Gate Bridge, San Francisco

1997. "Pacific '97" International Stamp Exhibition, San Francisco. Suspension Bridges. Multicoloured.
2116 400d. Type **456** 10 10
2117 5000d. Raippaluoto Bridge, Finland 75 15
2118 10000d. Seto Great road and rail bridge, Japan . . 1·50 55

457 Women and Girl **458** Umbrella protecting Children

1997. 8th Vietnamese Women's Union Congress.
2119 **457** 400d. multicoloured . . 10 10

1997. Children's Rights. Multicoloured.
2120 400d. Type **458** (United Nations Convention on Rights of the Child) . . . 10 10
2121 5000d. Mother breast-feeding ("Breastmilk is Best") 75 15

459 Chua Lang, Hanoi, Vietnam

1997. Asian Temples. Multicoloured.
2122 400d. Type **459** 10 10
2123 1000d. Persepolis, Iran . . . 10 10
2124 3000d. Statue, Denion, Iraq 45 10
2125 5000d. Kyaiktiyo Pagoda, Myanmar 75 15
2126 10000d. Sleeping Buddha, Polonnaruwa, Sri Lanka 1·50 30

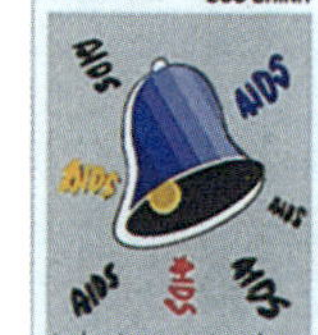

460 San Chay **461** Ringing Bell

1997. Women's Costumes. Multicoloured.
2127 400d. Type **460** 10 10
2128 2000d. Daco 20 10
2129 5000d. Phu La 75 15
2130 10000d. Kho Me . . . . . 1·50 30

1997. Anti-AIDS Campaign.
2131 **461** 400d. multicoloured . . 10 10

462 War Memorial, Cu Chi

1997. 50th Anniv of War Disabled Day.
2132 **462** 400d. multicoloured . . 10 10

463 "Hibiscus rosa-sinensis" 464 Flags of Member Nations

1997. Flowers. Multicoloured.
2133 1000d. Type **463** 10 10
2134 3000d. "Hibiscus schizopetalus" 45 10
2135 5000d. "Hibiscus syriacus" (pink) 75 15
2136 9000d. "Hibiscus syriacus" (yellow) . . . . 1·40 25

1997. 30th Anniv of Association of South East Asian Nations.
2137 **464** 400d. multicoloured . . 10 10

465 Statue and Women using Modern Technology 466 Seahorses

1997. 50th Anniv of Vietnamese Post and Telecommunications Union.
2138 **465** 400d. multicoloured . . 10 10

1997. Seahorses. Multicoloured.
2139 400d. Type **466** 10 10
2140 1000d. Seahorses 10 10
2141 3000d. Common seahorse 45 10
2142 5000d. "Hippocampus kelloggi" 75 15
2143 6000d. "Hippocampus japonicus" 90 20
2144 7000d. Short-snouted seahorse . . . . 1·00 20

467 Globe and Emblem

1997. 7th Francophone Summit, Hanoi.
2145 **467** 5000d. multicoloured . . 1·10 15

468 Table Tennis Player 470 Lamp

469 Elliot's Pheasant

1997. 19th South East Asian Games, Djakarta.
2146 **468** 5000d. multicoloured . . 75 15

1997. Pheasants. Multicoloured.
2147 400d. Type **469** 10 10
2148 3000d. Siamese fireback pheasant 50 10
2149 5000d. Common pheasant 80 15
2150 6000d. Lady Amherst's pheasant . . . . 1·00 20
2151 8000d. Germain's peacock-pheasant . . . . 1·25 25

1998. Wickerwork.
2153 **470** 400d. brown, black and green 10 10
2154 – 400d. black, red and blue 10 10
2155 – 400d. stone, black and blue 10 10
2156 – 400d. lilac, brown and black 10 10
2157 – 2000d. grey, pink and black 20 10
DESIGNS: No. 2154, Dish and bowl; 2155, Swan-shaped basket; 2156, Deer-shaped basket; 2157, Basket with handle.

471 Mother Tiger with Cubs

1998. New Year. Year of the Tiger. Multicoloured.
2158 400d. Type **471** 10 10
2159 8000d. Tiger . . . . 1·10 35

472 Flag, Helmet and Rifle 474 Karl Marx and Friedrich Engels (authors)

473 Ca Na Beach, Ninh Thuan Province

1998. 30th Anniv of Tet Offensive.
2160 **472** 400d. multicoloured . . 10 10

1998. Central Vietnam Landscapes. Multicoloured.
2161 400d. Type **473** 10 10
2162 400d. Phong Nha Cave, Quang Binh Province . . 10 10
2163 10000d. Hoi An Town, Quang Nam Province . . 1·50 50

1998. 150th Anniv of "Communist Manifesto".
2164 **474** 400d. multicoloured . . 10 10

475 "Limonia acidissima"

1998. Bonsai Trees. Multicoloured.
2165 400d. Type **475** 10 10
2166 400d. "Deeringia polysperma" 10 10
2167 400d. "Pinus merkusii" (vert) 10 10
2168 4000d. "Barringtonia acutangula" (vert) 60 20
2169 6000d. India rubber-tree (vert) 80 25
2170 10000d. "Wrightia religiosa" (vert) . . . . 1·50 50

476 Thi Kinh is falsely accused of killing Husband

1998. "Quan Am Thi Kinh" (opera). Multicoloured.
2172 400d. Type **476** 10 10
2173 1000d. Thi Kinh as Buddhist novice and Thi Mau (with fan) 15 10
2174 2000d. Thi Mau and servant with basket on head . . . 30 10
2175 4000d. Me Dop (village chief) and Thi Mau . . . 60 20
2176 6000d. Me Dop, Thi Mau and Thi Kinh 80 25
2177 9000d. Thi Kinh with Thi Mau's baby begging for alms . . . . 1·10 35

477 Pres. Ho Chi Minh and Nha Rong Wharf

1998. 300th Anniv of Ho Chi Minh City (formerly Saigon). Multicoloured.
2178 400d. Type **477** 10 10
2179 5000d. "Uncle Ho with Children" (sculpture, Diep Minh Chau) 75 25

478 Western Honey Buzzard

1998. Birds. Multicoloured.
2181 400d. Type **478** 10 10
2182 400d. Northern goshawk ("Accipter gentilis") . . . 10 10
2183 400d. Ornate hawk eagle ("Spizaetus ornatus") . . 10 10
2184 3000d. Common buzzard . . 50 15
2185 5000d. Pied harrier 85 20
2186 12000d. White-tailed sea eagle . . . . 2·00 60

479 "Paphiopedilum appletonianum"

1998. Orchids. Multicoloured.
2187 400d. Type **479** 10 10
2188 6000d. "Paphiopedilum helenae" 80 25

480 Children going to School (Nguyen Tram)

1998. Vietnamese Children's Fund. Winning Paintings in UNICEF Contest. Multicoloured.
2189 400d. Type **480** 10 10
2190 5000d. Children playing in park (Vu Thi Tuyet) . . . 75 25

481 Players competing for Ball

1998. World Cup Football Championship, France. Multicoloured.
2191 400d. Type **481** 10 10
2192 5000d. Players chasing ball 75 25
2193 7000d. Tackle . . . . . . 1·10 30

482 Dragon, Boi Khe Pagoda

1998. Sculptures from Tran Dynasty. Mult.
2194 400d. Type **482** 10 10
2195 400d. Birds with human heads, Thai Lac Pagoda 10 10
2196 1000d. Dragons' heads, ship's planks and waves (throne back), Thay Pagoda 15 10
2197 8000d. Fairy offering flower, Hang Pagoda . . . . . 1·10 30
2198 9000d. Kneeling figure, Thai Lac Pagoda . . . . . . 1·40 45

483 Wushu

1998. 13th Asian Games, Bangkok.
2199 **483** 2000d. multicoloured . . 30 10

484 Underwater Scene

1998. International Year of the Ocean.
2200 **484** 400d. multicoloured . . 10 10

485 Alexander Graham Bell's Telephone, 1876

1998. Stamp Day. 35th Anniv of Posts and Telecommunications Department.
2201 **485** 400d. multicoloured . . 10 10

486 Ton Duc Thang 488 "Dragonfly and Lotus"

487 "Antheraea helferi"

1998. 110th Birth Anniv of Ton Duc Thang (President 1969–80).
2202 **486** 400d. multicoloured . . 10 10

1998. Moths. Multicoloured.
2203 400d. Type **487** 10 10
2204 400d. Atlas moth ("Attacus atlas") 10 10
2205 4000d. Tailed comet moth (vert) 60 20
2206 10000d. "Argema maenas" (vert) . . . . 1·50 50

1998. 135th Birth Anniv of Qi Baishi (painter). Multicoloured.
2207 400d. Type **488** 10 10
2208 1000d. "Chickens and Chrysanthemum" 10 10
2209 2000d. "Shrimps" 20 10
2210 4000d. "School of Crabs" 40 15
2211 6000d. "Ducks and Lotus" 60 20
2212 9000d. "Shrimps" (different) 90 30

490 King Le Loi on Boat

1998. Legend of Restored Sword Lake, Hanoi. Multicoloured.
2214 400d. Type **490** 10 10
2215 400d. Jade Hill Temple and Huc Sunrise bridge . . . 10 10

491 King Le Thang Tong (statue)

1998. 500th Death Anniv (1997) of King Le Thang Tong.
2216 **491** 400d. multicoloured . . 10 10

492 Emblem and Couple

1998. 8th Trade Unions Congress.
2217 **492** 400d. multicoloured . . 10 10

493 King Quang Trung (statue) and Quy Nhon Port

1998. Centenary of Quy Nhon as Binh Dinh Provincial Capital.
2218 **493** 400d. multicoloured . . 10 10

494 Duong Quang Ham (first Vietnamese headmaster) and School

1998. 90th Anniv of Buoi Chu Van An Secondary School, Hanoi. Multicoloured.
2219 400d. Type **494** 10 10
2220 5000d. Ho Chi Minh and students 50 20

495 Doves around Emblem

1998. 6th Association of South East Asian Nations Summit, Hanoi.
2221 **495** 1000d. multicoloured . . 10 10

496 Industrial Symbols, Revolutionary Memorial, Havana and Cuban Flag forming "40"

1998. 40th Anniv (1999) of Cuban Revolution.
2222 **496** 400d. multicoloured . . 10 10

497 Spring

499 Eagle Kite

1999. Four Seasons Paintings (1st series). Mult.
2223 400d. Type **497** 10 10
2224 1000d. Summer 10 10
2225 3000d. Autumn 30 10
2226 12000d. Winter . . . . . . 1·25 40
See also Nos. 2391/3.

498 Cat going to Tet Flower Market

1999. New Year. Year of the Cat. Multicoloured.
2227 400d. Type **498** 10 10
2228 8000d. Cats fighting 75 25

1999. Kites. Multicoloured.
2230 400d. Type **499** 10 10
2231 5000d. Kite with bamboo flute 50 20
2232 7000d. Peacock 75 25

500 Ha Long Bay Net Boat

1999. "Australia '99" World Stamp Exhibition, Melbourne. Local Craft. Multicoloured.
2233 400d. Type **500** 10 10
2234 400d. Cua Lo bamboo junk 10 10
2235 7000d. Nha Trang bamboo junk 70 25
2236 9000d. Ne Cape junk . . . 90 30

501 *Kaempferia galanga*

1999. Medicinal Herbs. Multicoloured.
2237 400d. Type **501** 10 10
2238 400d. *Tacca chantrieri* Andree (vert) 10 10
2239 400d. *Alpinia galanga* Willd (vert) 10 10
2240 6000d. *Typhonium trilobatum* Schott (vert) 60 20
2241 13000d. *Asarum maximum* Hemsl (vert) . . . . . . 1·25 45

502 Syringe, Fields, City and Family

1999. International Day Against Drugs.
2242 **502** 400d. multicoloured . . 10 10

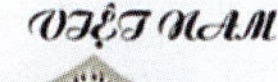

503 Van Trong Mask

1999. Tuong Stage Masks. Multicoloured.
2243 400d. Type **503** 10 10
2244 1000d. Hoang Phi Ho . . . 10 10
2245 2000d. Chau Thuong . . . 20 10
2246 5000d. Tiet Cuong 50 20
2247 6000d. Mao At 60 20
2248 10000d. Tran Long . . . . 1·00 35

504 *Octopus gibertianus*

1999. "iBRA 99" International Stamp Exhibition, Nuremberg, Germany. Octopuses. Multicoloured.
2249 400d. Type **504** 10 10
2250 400d. *Philonexis catenulata* 10 10
2251 4000d. *Paroctopus yendoi* . . 40 10
2252 12000d. Common octopus 1·25 45

505 Cape, Ca Mau Province

1999. Southern Vietnam Landscapes. Mult.
2253 400d. Type **505** 10 10
2254 400d. Father and Son Islet, Kien Giang Province . . 10 10
2255 12000d. Vinh Hung Tower, Bac Lieu Province . . . . 1·25 45

506 Emblem, Map and Satellite

1999. 20th Anniv of Asia-Pacific Telecommunity.
2256 **506** 400d. multicoloured . . 10 10

507 Greater flame-backed Woodpecker

508 Large Hand and Child cowering

1999. Woodpeckers. Multicoloured.
2257 400d. Type **507** 10 10
2258 1000d. Speckled piculet . . 10 10
2259 3000d. Red-collared woodpecker 30 10
2260 13000d. Bay woodpecker . . 1·25 45

1999. Vietnamese Children's Fund.
2261 **508** 400d. lilac, green and black 10 10
2262 – 5000d. blue, grey and black 50 20
DESIGN: 5000d. Young man carrying buildings.

509 Northern Government Office, Hanoi

1999. Architecture. Multicoloured.
2263 400d. Type **509** 10 10
2264 400d. History Museum, Ho Chi Minh City 10 10
2265 12000d. Duc Ba Cathedral (vert) . . . . 1·25 45

510 Da Rang Bridge and Nhan Mountains

1999. Phu Yen Province.
2267 **510** 400d. multicoloured . . 10 10

511 Man fighting Tiger, Chay Communal House, Ha Nam Province

1999. Le Dynasty Sculptures. Multicoloured.
2268 1000d. Type **511** 10 10
2269 1000d. Phoenix, But Thap Pagoda, Bac Ninh Province 10 10
2270 3000d. Playing chess, Ngoc Canh Communal House, Vinh Phuc Province (vert) 30 10
2271 7000d. Oster, Quang Phuc Communal House, Ha Tay Province (vert) . . . 75 25
2272 9000d. Stone dragon, Kinh Thien Temple, Hanoi . . 90 30

512 Globe and Family

1999. Birth of World's Six Billionth Inhabitant.
2273 **512** 400d. multicoloured . . 10 10

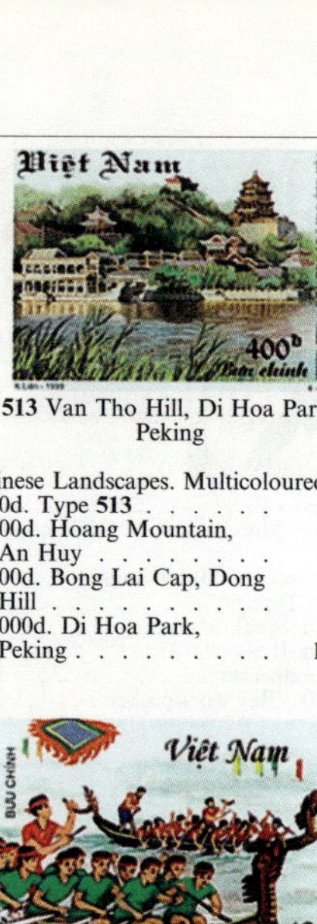

513 Van Tho Hill, Di Hoa Park, Peking

1999. Chinese Landscapes. Multicoloured.

2274	400d. Type **513**	10	10
2275	2000d. Hoang Mountain, An Huy	20	10
2276	3000d. Bong Lai Cap, Dong Hill	30	10
2277	10000d. Di Hoa Park, Peking	1·00	35

514 Racing Boats, North Vietnam

1999. Traditional Boat Racing Festivals. Mult.

2279	400d. Type **514**	10	10
2280	2000d. Three boats, Central Vietnam	20	10
2281	10000d. Two boats, South Vietnam	1·00	35

515 Buffaloes fighting

1999. Buffalo Festival. Multicoloured.

2282	400d. Type **515**	10	10
2283	5000d. Buffalo No. 2 goring fallen animal	50	20

516 Traditional Velvet Dress

518 Van Sieu and The Tower of the Pen Brush, Ba Dinh

517 Ngo Quyen (statue) and Battle of Bach Dang, 938

1999. Women's Costumes. Multicoloured.

2284	400d. Type **516**	10	10
2285	400d. Magenta brocade dress	10	10
2286	12000d. Green dress	1·25	45

1999. 1100th (1998) Birth Anniv of Ngo Quyen (ruler).

2287	**517** 400d. multicoloured	10	10

1999. Birth Bicentenary of Nguyen Van Sieu (scholar).

2288	**518** 400d. multicoloured	10	10

519 Tran Xan Soan

1999. 150th Birth Anniv of Tran Xuan Soan (revolutionary).

2289	**519** 400d. multicoloured	10	10

520 Fisherwoman, Farmer and Woman carrying Child

1999. United Nations Development Programme. Fight Against Poverty. Multicoloured.

2290	400d. Type **520**	10	10
2291	8000d. Buildings and villagers' meeting	80	30

521 Hammer and Sickle above Workers (forming of Vietnamese Communist Party, 1930)

2000. The Twentieth Century. Multicoloured.

2292	400d. Type **521**	10	10
2293	400d. Pres. Ho Chi Minh making Independence speech (formation of Democratic Republic, 1945)	10	10
2294	1000d. Flag, tank and people celebrating (liberation of South Vietnam, 1975)	10	10
2295	1000d. Symbols of agriculture and industry (Communist Party's ten year renovation plan)	10	10
2296	8000d. Symbols of industry and communications (industrialization)	80	30
2297	12000d. Emblems (integration into international community)	1·25	45

522 Dragon

2000. New Year. Year of the Dragon. Mult.

2299	400d. Type **522**	10	10
2300	8000d. Dragon and One Pillar Pagoda, Hanoi	80	30

523 Globe and U.N.E.S.C.O. "City for Peace" Prize (Hanoi, 1999)

2000. International Year of Culture and Peace.

2301	**523** 400d. multicoloured	10	10

524 Pres. Ho Chi Minh (founder)

2000. 70th Anniv of Communist Party. Mult.

2302	400d. Type **524**	10	10
2303	400d. Tran Phu (first General Secretary, 1930–31)	10	10
2304	400d. Le Hong Phong (General Secretary, 1935–36)	10	10
2305	400d. Ha Huy Tap (General Secretary, 1936–38)	10	10
2306	400d. Nguyen Van Cu (General Secretary, 1938–41)	10	10
2307	400d. Truong Chinh (General Secretary, 1941–56 and 1986)	10	10
2308	400d. Le Duan (General Secretary, 1960–86)	10	10
2309	400d. Nguyen Van Linh (General Secretary, 1986–91)	10	10

525 Cocks fighting (Double Cock's Kick)

2000. Cock Fighting. Showing cocks fighting. Multicoloured.

2310	400d. Type **525**	10	10
2311	400d. "Long vu da dao" posture	10	10
2312	7000d. "Song long phuing hoang" posture	70	25
2313	9000d. "Nhan o giap chien" posture	90	30

526 Fringed Palanquin

2000. "Bangkok 2000" International Stamp Exhibition. Processional Litters. Multicoloured.

2314	400d. Type **526**	10	10
2315	7000d. Throne-shaped litter	70	25
2316	8000d. Palanquin with pagoda-style roof	80	30

527 Marriage of Lac Long Quan and Au Co

529 Sao La

2000. Legend of Lac Long Quan and Au Co. Mult.

2318	400d. Type **527**	10	10
2319	400d. Au Co surrounded by sons	10	10
2320	500d. Au Co and children riding elephants	10	10
2321	3000d. Lac Long Quan and sons by the sea	30	10
2322	4000d. Eldest son Hung Vuong	40	15
2323	11000d. Vietnamese ethnic groups	1·40	40

2000. Endangered Species. Sao La. Multicoloured.

2325	400d. Type **529**	10	10
2326	400d. Juvenile in grass	10	10
2327	5000d. Beside lake	50	20
2328	10000d. Head of adult	1·00	35

530 Ho Chi Minh and Birthplace

532 Young Girl waving Flag

531 Buffon Teu

2000. 110th Birth Anniv of President Ho Chi Minh.

2329	**530** 400d. multicoloured	10	10

2000. "World Stamp Expo 2000", Anaheim, California. Water Puppetry. Showing traditional puppets. Multicoloured.

2330	400d. Type **531**	10	10
2331	400d. Fairy and phoenix	10	10

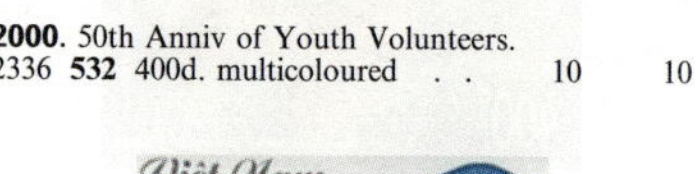

2332	400d. Ploughman	10	10
2333	3000d. Peasant woman	30	10
2334	9000d. Drummer	90	30
2335	11000d. Fisherman	1·10	40

2000. 50th Anniv of Youth Volunteers.

2336	**532** 400d. multicoloured	10	10

533 Swimmers and Emblem

2000. 5th National Youth Sports Festival, Dong Thap.

2337	**533** 400d. multicoloured	10	10

534 Coral Hind

2000. Coral Reef Fishes. Multicoloured.

2338	400d. Type **534**	10	10
2339	400d. Emperor angelfish (*Pomacanthus imperator*)	10	10
2340	400d. Honeycomb grouper (*Epinephelus merra*)	10	10
2341	4000d. Moorish idol (*Zanclus cornutus*) (vert)	40	15
2342	6000d. Saddle butterflyfish (vert)	60	20
2343	12000d. Pennant coralfish (vert)	1·25	45

535 Postal Workers and Means of Communications

2000. 55th Anniv of Vietnam Posts and Telecommunications Service.

2345	**535** 400d. multicoloured	10	10

536 Ho Chi Minh with Policemen

2000. 55th Anniv of National Police Force. Mult.

2346	400d. Type **536**	10	10
2347	2000d. Police personnel (vert)	20	10

537 Statue of Nguyen Tri Phuong, Da Nang

2000. Birth Bicentenary of Nguyen Tri Phuong (provincial Governor).

2348	**537** 400d. multicoloured	10	10

538 Children and Emblem

2000. 10th Anniv of United Nations Convention on Children's Rights. Multicoloured.

2349	400d. Type **538**	10	10
2350	5000d. Children's faces around emblem (vert)	50	20

539 Running

2000. Olympic Games, Sydney. Multicoloured.
2351 400d. Type **539** 10 10
2352 6000d. Shooting 60 20
2353 7000d. Taekwondo (vert) . . 70 25

540 Tran Hung Dao Monument, An Phu

2000. 700th Death Anniv of General Tran Hung Dao.
2354 **540** 400d. multicoloured . . 10 10

541 Silver-eared Mesia

2000. Birds. Multicoloured.
2355 400d. Type **541** 10 10
2356 400d. Eliott's pitta (*Pitta elliotí*) 10 10
2357 400d. Coral-billed scimitar babbler (*Pomatorhinus ferruginosus*) (inscr "Pomatorinus") 10 10
2358 5000d. Greater racquet-tailed drongo (vert) . . . 50 20
2359 7000d. Sultan tit (vert) . . . 70 25
2360 10000d. Spot-necked tree babbler (vert) . . . . . . 1·00 35

542 North Vietnam 1976 12x. Stamp, Magnifying Glass and Emblem

2000. 40th Anniv of Vietnamese Philatelic Association.
2362 **542** 400d. multicoloured . . 10 10

543 Pigs feeding and Agricultural Workers

2000. 70th Anniv of Vietnamese Farmers' Association.
2363 **543** 400d. multicoloured . . 10 10

544 Dien Huu Pagoda and King Ly Thai To

2000. 990th Anniv of Hanoi. Multicoloured.
2364 400d. Type **544** 10 10
2365 3000d. Van Mieu-Quoc Tu Giam (Confucian temple) and university 30 10
2366 10000d. Hanoi city scene . . 1·00 30

545 Harlequin Bat (*Scotomanes ornatus*)

2000. Bats. Multicoloured.
2368 400d. Type **545** 10 10
2369 400d. *Pteropus lylei* 10 10
2370 2000d. *Rhinolophus paradoxolophus* 20 10
2371 6000d. Cave fruit bat (*Eonycteris spelaea*) . . . 60 20
2372 11000d. Short-nosed fruit bat (*Cynopterus sphinx*) 1·10 35

546 "70" and Dove

2000. 70th Anniv of Vietnamese Women's Union.
2373 **546** 400d. multicoloured . . 10 10

547 Workers

2000. 6th National "Heroes of Labour" Congress. Multicoloured.
2374 400d. Type **547** 10 10
2375 3000d. Flower and industrial symbols (vert) 30 10

548 *Oxyspora* sp.

2000. Cornflowers. Multicoloured.
2376 400d. Type **548** 10 10
2377 5000d. *Melastoma villosa* . . 50 15

549 Ho Chi Minh and Crowd

551 Banners and Satellite

550 Hon Khoai Island and Statue

2000. 70th Anniv of Vietnam Fatherland Front.
2378 **549** 400d. multicoloured . . 10 10

2000. 60th Anniv of Hon Khoai Uprising.
2379 **550** 400d. multicoloured . . 10 10

2001. New Millennium.
2380 **551** 400d. multicoloured . . 10 10

552 Snake

2001. New Year. Year of the Snake. Multicoloured.
2381 400d. Type **552** 10 10
2382 8000d. Green snake 70 25

553 Archerfish (*Toxotes macrolepis*)

2001. "HONG KONG 2001" International Stamp Exhibition. Freshwater Fish. Multicoloured.
2383 400d. Type **553** 10 10
2384 800d. Carp (*Cosmochilus harmandi*) (wrongly inscr "Cosmocheilus") 10 10
2385 2000d. Indian short-finned eel (*Anguilla bicolor pacifica*) 20 10
2386 3000d. *Chitala ornata* . . . 25 10
2387 7000d. Indo-Pacific tarpon (*Megalops cyprinoides*) . . 65 20
2388 8000d. Esok (*Probarbus jullieni*) 70 25

554 Alfred Nobel (founder)

555 Spring

2001. Centenary of Nobel Prizes.
2389 **554** 400d. blue, yellow and black 10 10

2001. Four Seasons Paintings (2nd series). Mult.
2390 400d. Type **555** 10 10
2391 800d. Summer 10 10
2392 4000d. Autumn 40 15
2393 10000d. Winter 90 30

556 *Rubus cochinchinensis*

2001. Forest Fruits. Multicoloured.
2394 400d. Type **556** 10 10
2395 400d. *Rhizophora mucronata* 10 10
2396 400d. *Podocarpus neriifolius* 10 10
2397 400d. *Magnolia pumila* . . . 10 10
2398 15000d. *Taxus chinensis* . . 1·40 45

557 Co Tien Mountains, Ha Giang Province

2001. Northern Vietnam Landscapes. Mult.
2399 400d. Type **557** 10 10
2400 400d. Dong Pagoda, Yen Tu, Quang Ninh Province 10 10
2401 10000d. King Dinh Temple, Ninh Binh Province . . . 90 30

558 Medals and Mastheads on "50"

2001. 50th Anniv of *Nhan Dan* (Communist Party newspaper).
2402 **558** 400d. multicoloured . . 10 10

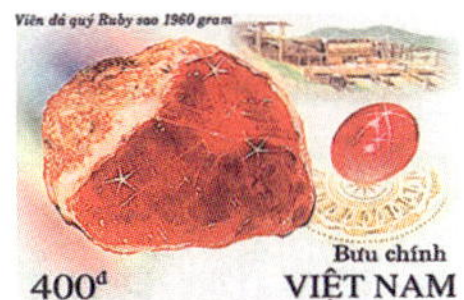

559 Starlight Ruby

2001. Rubies. Design showing named rubies before and after cutting. Multicoloured.
2403 400d. Type **559** 10 10
2404 6000d. Vietnam Star 55 20

560 Youths and Emblem

2001. 70th Anniv of Ho Chi Minh Youth Union.
2405 **560** 400d. multicoloured . . 10 10

561 David's Tree Partridge (*Arborophila davidi*)

2001. Animals in Cat Tien National Park. Mult.
2406 400d. Type **561** 10 10
2407 800d. Jungle queen butterfly (*Stichophthalma uemurai*) 10 10
2408 3000d. Vietnamese Javan rhino (*Rhinoceros sondaicus annamiticus*) . . 25 10
2409 5000d. Siamese crocodile (*Crocodylus siamensis*) . . 45 15

562 Ho Chi Minh, Flag and Map of Vietnam

2001. 9th Vietnamese Communist Party Congress. Multicoloured.
2410 400d. Type **562** 10 10
2411 3000d. Hammer, sickle and Ngoc Lu drum head (vert) 25 10

563 Veiled Stinkhorn (*Phallus indusiatus*)

2001. Fungi. Multicoloured.
2412 400d. Type **563** 10 10
2413 400d. *Aseroe arachnoidea* . . 10 10
2414 400d. *Phallus tenuis* 10 10
2415 2000d. *Phallus impudicus* . . 20 10
2416 5000d. *Phallus rugulosus* . . 45 15
2417 6000d. *Simblum periphragmoides* 55 20
2418 7000d. *Mutinus bambusinus* 65 20

564 Ho Chi Minh, Girl and Flowers

2001. 60th Anniv of Vietnam Youth Pioneers.
2420 **564** 400d. multicoloured . . 10 10

565 Ho Chi Minh, Crowd and Flag

2001. 60th Anniv of Vietnam Independence League.
2421 **565** 400d. multicoloured . . 10 10

566 Cigarette and Flower **567** Children wearing Protective Clothing

2001. World No-Smoking Day.
2422 **566** 800d. multicoloured . . 10 10

2001. United Nations Children's Fund (400d.) and United Nations General Assembly Special Session on Children (5000d.). Multicoloured.
2423 400d. Type **567** 10 10
2424 5000d. Children of different races and emblem 45 15

568 Locomotive D18E

2001. Diesel Locomotives. Multicoloured.
2425 400d. Type **568** 10 10
2426 400d. Locomotive D4H . . 10 10
2427 800d. Locomotive D11H in station 10 10
2428 2000d. Locomotive D5H . . 20 10
2429 6000d. Locomotive D9E . . 55 20
2430 7000d. Locomotive D12E 65 20

569 *Vanda* sp.

2001. Orchids. Multicoloured.
2432 800d. Type **569** 10 10
2433 800d. *Dendrobium lowianum* 10 10
2434 800d. *Phajus wallachii* . . . 10 10
2435 800d. *Habenaria medioflexa* 10 10
2436 800d. *Arundina graminifolia* (vert) 10 10
2437 12000d. *Calanthe clavata* (vert) . . . . 1·10 35

570 Golden Birdwing (*Troides aeacus*)

2001. "PHILA NIPPON '01" International Stamp Exhibition, Tokyo. Butterflies. Multicoloured.
2438 800d. Type **570** 10 10
2439 800d. Peacock (*Inachis io*) 10 10
2440 800d. *Ancyluris formosissima* 10 10
2441 5000d. Red glider (*Cymothoe sangaris*) (wrongly inscr "sanguris") 45 15
2442 7000d. *Taenaris selene* . . . 65 20
2443 10000d. Raja Brooke's birdwing (*Trogonoptera brookiana*) 90 30

571 Footballer

2001. World Cup Football Championship, Japan and South Korea. Multicoloured.
2445 800d. Type **571** 10 10
2446 3000d. Footballer and map including Americas . . . 10 25
Nos. 2445/6 were issued together, se-tenant, forming a composite design.

572 Ho Gao

2001. Traditional Musical Instruments. Mult.
2447 800d. Type **572** 10 10
2448 800d. Kenh (pan-pipes) . . 10 10
2449 800d. Dan Tu (stringed instrument) (vert) 10 10
2450 2000d. Dan T'rung (vert) . . 20 10
2451 6000d. Trong Kinang (drum) (vert) 55 20
2452 9000d. Tinh Tau (stringed instrument) (vert) 80 25

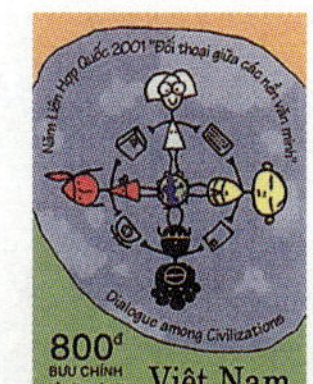

573 Children encircling Globe

2001. United Nations Year of Dialogue among Civilizations.
2453 **573** 800d. multicoloured . . 10 10

574 Tran Huy Lieu and Books

2001. Birth Centenary of Tran Huy Lieu (writer and revolutionary).
2454 **574** 800d. multicoloured . . 10 10

575 Nam Cao and Titles of his Works

2001. 50th Death Anniv of Nam Cao (Tran Huu Tri) (writer).
2455 **575** 800d. multicoloured . . 10 10

576 Leaves around Globe

2001. Environment Protection. Multicoloured.
2456 800d. Type **576** 10 10
2457 3000d. Globe in tree with nesting peace dove . . . 25 10

577 "To He" Horse

2002. New Year. Year of the Horse. Multicoloured.
2458 800d. Type **577** 10 10
2459 8000d. Horse with parasol 70 20
MS2460 76 × 66 mm. 14000d. Flying horse (42 × 31 mm) . . . . . 1·10 1·10

578 Giap Tuong Nam

2002. Tuong (classical opera) Costumes. Costumes. Multicoloured.
2461 1000d. Type **578** 10 10
2462 1000d. Giap Tuong Nu . . 10 10
2463 2000d. Giap Tuong Phan Dien 15 10
2464 3000d. Long Chan 25 10
2465 5000d. Giap Tuong Phien 40 15
2466 9000d. Lung Xiem Quan Giap 75 25

579 Vo Thi Sau

2002. 50th Death Anniv of Vo Thi Sau (resistance fighter).
2467 **579** 1000d. multicoloured . . 10 10

580 Symbols of Industry and Communications **581** *Echinocereus lbatus*

2002. 9th Communist Party Congress Resolutions. Multicoloured.
2468 800d. Type **580** 10 10
2469 3000d. Thang Long Citadel gate, flag and people . . . 25 10

2002. Cacti. Multicoloured.
2470 1000d. Type **581** 10 10
2471 1000d. *Echinocereus delaetii* 10 10
2472 1000d. *Cylindropuntia bigelowii* 10 10
2473 5000d. *Echinocereus triglochidatus* 40 15
2474 10000d. *Epiphyllum truncatum* 85 25

582 Emblem and Woman's Face

2002. 9th National Women's Congress.
2475 **582** 800d. multicoloured . . 10 10

583 Hugo and "Liberty Guiding the People" (painting, Eugene Delacroix)

2002. Birth Bicentenary of Victor Hugo (writer).
2476 **583** 1000d. multicoloured . . 10 10

FRANK STAMPS

F **19** Invalid's Badge F **158** Children and Disabled Teacher

1976. For use by disabled veterans. Dated "27.7.75". No value indicated.
F100 F **19** (–) red and blue . . . 50 25
F101 – (–) green, light green and brown 50 25
DESIGN: No. F101, Disabled veteran in factory.

1984. Disabled and Invalids. No value indicated.
F750 F **158** (–) brown and ochre 50 25

1985. No value indicated. As T **179**.
F861 (–) red and black (Policeman and militia members) 50 25

MILITARY FRANK STAMPS

MF **21** Soldier and Map of Vietnam

1976. No value indicated.
MF110 MF **21** (–) black and red 60 25

MF **59** Pilot

1979. 35th Anniv of Vietnam People's Army. No value indicated.
MF304 MF **59** (–) purple and pink 35 10
MF305 – (–) purple and pink 35 10
DESIGN: No. MF305, Badge of People's Army.

MF **61** Tank Driver and Tanks MF **84** Ho Chi Minh in Naval Uniform

1979. No value indicated.
MF308 MF **61** (–) black and mauve 30 15
MF309 – (–) violet and green 30 15
MF310 – (–) black and red 30 15
DESIGNS: No. MF309, Sailor and ship; MF310, Pilot and jet fighters.

1981. No value indicated.
MF420 MF **84** (–) pink and blue 25 20
MF421 – (–) multicoloured 25 20
DESIGN—13 × 17 mm: No. MF421, Factory militiawoman.

1982. Multicoloured. No value indicated.
MF466 (–) Soldier and militiawoman 25 10
MF467 (–) Type **94** 25 10

MF 107 Disabled Soldier

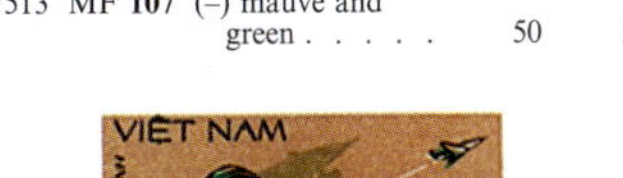

1982. 35th Anniv of Disabled Soldiers' Day. No value indicated.
MF513 MF **107** (–) mauve and green 50 20

MF **120** Militia

1983. No value indicated.
MF581 MF **120** (–) multicoloured 60 25

MF **145** Star and Soldiers on Bunker

MF **152** Coastal Militia

1984. 30th Anniv of Battle of Dien Bien Phu. No value indicated.
MF690 MF **145** (–) yellow, orange & brn 65 20

1984. No value indicated.
MF732 MF **152** (–) brown, orange & yellow . . . 65 25

MF **164** Soldiers and Emblem

MF **205** Soldier and Woman holding Sheaf of Rice

1984. No value indicated.
MF786 MF **164** (–) orange, red and black . . . 50 25

1986.
MF979 MF **205** 1d. brown and black 65 30

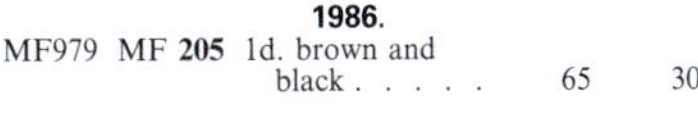

MF **232** Armed Forces Personnel and Flag

1987.
MF1119 MF **232** 5d. red & brown 90 40

WADHWAN Pt. 1

A state of Kathiawar, India. Now uses Indian stamps.

4 pice = 1 anna.

1

1888.
5 **1** ½pice black . . . . 7·50 8·00

WALLIS AND FUTUNA ISLANDS Pt. 6

A group of French islands in the Pacific Ocean north-east of Fiji. Attached to New Caledonia for administrative purposes in 1888. In 1961 they became a French Overseas Territory.

100 centimes = 1 franc.

1920. Stamps of New Caledonia optd **ILES WALLIS et FUTUNA**.
1 **15** 1c. black on green . . . . . 15 2·25
2 2c. brown . . . . 15 2·40
3 4c. blue on orange . . . . 20 2·40
4 5c. green . . . . 65 2·60
18 5c. blue . . . . 50 2·40
5 10c. red . . . . 90 2·60
19 10c. green . . . . 90 2·40
6 15c. lilac . . . . 1·50 3·00
7 **16** 20c. brown . . . . 65 3·25
8 25c. blue on green . . . . . 2·00 3·25
21 25c. red on yellow . . . . . 1·90 3·00
9 30c. brown on orange . . . 2·50 3·50
22 30c. red . . . . 1·50 3·00
24 30c. green . . . . 65 4·00
10 35c. black on yellow . . . . 1·40 3·25
11 40c. red on green . . . . . 1·50 3·25
12 45c. purple . . . . 1·40 3·25
13 50c. red on orange . . . . 2·25 3·00
25 50c. blue . . . . 90 3·25
26 50c. grey . . . . 2·25 3·75
27 65c. blue . . . . 4·25 5·50
14 75c. green . . . . 2·25 4·25
15 **17** 1f. blue on green . . . . . 3·50 5·25
28 1f.10 brown . . . . 1·10 4·50
16 2f. red on blue . . . . . . 6·50 8·00
17 5f. black on orange . . . . 11·00 13·50

1922. As last surch.
29 **15** 0,01 on 15c. lilac . . . . . 50 2·50
30 0,02 on 15c. lilac . . . . . 55 2·50
31 0,04 on 15c. lilac . . . . . 50 2·50
32 0,05 on 15c. lilac . . . . . 75 2·50
33 **17** 25c. on 2f. red on blue . . . 1·50 3·25
34 25c. on 5f. black on orange 1·50 3·25
35 **16** 65 on 40c. red on green . . 2·25 3·25
36 85 on 75c. green . . . . . 2·00 3·25
37 90 on 75c. red . . . . . . 1·10 3·75
38 **17** 1f.25 on 1fr. blue . . . . . 2·50 3·00
39 1f.50 on 1fr. blue on blue 3·75 4·50
40 3f. on 5f. mauve . . . . . 7·00 8·75
41 10f. on 5f. green on mauve 23·00 32·00
42 20f. on 5f. red on yellow . . 32·00 45·00

1930. Stamps of New Caledonia, some with colours changed, optd **ILES WALLIS et FUTUNA**.
43 **22** 1c. blue and purple . . . . 20 2·75
44 2c. green and brown . . . . 15 2·75
45 3c. blue and red . . . . . 35 2·50
46 4c. green and red . . . . . 20 2·75
47 5c. brown and blue . . . . 25 2·50
48 10c. brown and lilac . . . . 40 3·00
49 15c. blue and brown . . . . 45 3·00
50 20c. brown and red . . . . 45 3·00
51 25c. brown and green . . . 2·25 3·25
52 **23** 30c. turquoise and green . . 70 3·25
53 35c. green and deep green 2·00 3·25
54 40c. green and red . . . . 45 3·00
55 45c. red and blue . . . . . 2·50 3·25
56 45c. green and turquoise . . 1·90 3·25
57 50c. brown and mauve . . . 90 3·00
58 55c. red and blue . . . . . 1·75 4·25
59 60c. red and blue . . . . . 75 3·25
60 65c. blue and brown . . . . 2·25 3·50
61 70c. brown and mauve . . . 2·25 3·25
62 75c. drab and blue . . . . 3·00 4·00
63 80c. green and purple . . . 2·50 3·25
64 85c. brown and green . . . 1·75 5·00
65 90c. carmine and red . . . 1·40 4·00
66 90c. red and brown . . . . 2·25 3·25
67 **24** 1f. red and drab . . . . . 4·50 5·00
68 1f. carmine and red . . . . 3·00 3·25
69 1f. green and red . . . . . 90 3·00
70 1f.10 brown and green . . . 30·00 35·00
71 1f.25 green and brown . . . 2·50 4·25
72 1f.25 carmine and red . . . 2·50 3·25
73 1f.40 red and blue . . . . . 2·25 3·25
74 1f.50 blue and ultramarine 2·25 3·25
75 1f.60 brown and green . . . 2·75 3·25
76 1f.75 red and blue . . . . . 14·00 14·00
77 1f.75 blue . . . . 3·25 4·00
78 2f. brown and orange . . . 1·75 3·00
79 2f.25 blue and ultramarine 2·75 3·25
80 2f.50 brown . . . . 2·50 3·25
81 3f. brown and purple . . . 1·60 3·50
82 5f. brown and blue . . . . 2·75 3·50
83 10f. brown & mauve on pink . . . . 1·00 4·50
84 20f. brown and red on yellow . . . . 1·25 5·75

1931. "Colonial Exhibition" key-types.
85 E 40c. green and black . . . . 4·75 7·75
86 F 50c. mauve and black . . . 4·75 7·75
87 G 90c. red and black . . . . 4·50 7·75
88 H 1f.50 blue and black . . . . 5·50 7·75

1939. New York World's Fair. As T **41** of St. Pierre et Miquelon.
89 1f.25 red . . . . 2·25 4·00
90 2f.25 blue . . . . 2·25 4·00

1939. 150th Anniv of French Revolution. As T **42** of St. Pierre et Miquelon.
91 45c.+25c. green and black . . 11·00 19·00
92 70c.+30c. brown and black . . 9·00 19·00
93 90c.+35c. orange and black . . 13·50 19·00
94 1f.25c.+1f. red and black . . 11·00 19·00
95 2f.25c.+2f. blue and black . . 11·00 19·00

1941. Adherence to General de Gaulle. Stamps of 1930 optd **France Libre**.
96 **22** 1c. blue and purple . . . 1·00 3·25
97 2c. green and brown . . . 1·25 3·25
97a 3c. blue and red £100 £100
98 4c. green and orange . . 75 3·25
99 5c. brown and blue . . . 1·25 3·25
100 10c. brown and lilac . . . 65 3·25
101 15c. blue and brown . . . 2·50 3·25
102 20c. brown and red . . . 3·25 4·25
103 25c. brown and green . . 3·25 4·25
104 **23** 30c. green . . . . 2·75 4·25
105 35c. green . . . . 2·00 3·25
106 40c. green and red . . . . 3·00 4·25
107 45c. red and blue . . . . 3·75 4·25
107a 45c. green and turquoise £100 £100
108 50c. brown and mauve . . 1·75 3·25
109 55c. red and blue . . . . 2·00 3·25
109a 60c. red and blue £100 £100
110 65c. blue and brown . . . 1·50 3·75
111 70c. brown and mauve . . 1·90 3·75
112 75c. drab and blue . . . 3·00 4·75
113 80c. green and purple . . 1·75 3·75
114 85c. brown and green . . 2·50 4·75
115 90c. carmine and red . . 2·50 3·75
116 **24** 1f. carmine and red . . . 2·75 4·75
117 1f.25 green and brown . . 2·75 4·75
118 1f.50 blue and deep blue 2·50 3·75
119 1f.75 blue . . . . 1·90 3·75
120 2f. brown and orange . . 2·75 5·00
121 2f.50 brown £150 £150
122 3f. brown and purple . . 2·25 4·25
123 5f. brown and blue . . . 8·00 8·00
124 10f. brown and mauve on pink . . . . 40·00 65·00
125 20f. brown & red on yell 55·00 £100

5 Native Ivory Head

1944. Free French Administration.
126 **5** 5c. brown . . . . 15 2·75
127 10c. blue . . . . 15 2·75
128 25c. green . . . . 15 2·75
129 30c. orange . . . . 15 2·75
130 40c. green . . . . 40 2·75
131 80c. purple . . . . 30 3·00
132 1f. purple . . . . 70 2·75
133 1f.50 red . . . . 80 2·75
134 2f. black . . . . 60 2·75
135 2f.50 blue . . . . 1·40 3·00
136 4f. violet . . . . 75 3·00
137 5f. yellow . . . . 80 3·00
138 10f. brown . . . . 1·60 3·50
139 20f. green . . . . 2·50 4·00

1944. Mutual Aid and Red Cross Funds. As T **49** of St. Pierre et Miquelon.
140 5f.+20f. orange . . . . . . 1·40 3·75

1945. Surch.
141 **5** 50c. on 5c. brown . . . . . 85 3·00
142 60c. on 5c. brown . . . . . 70 3·25
143 70c. on 5c. brown . . . . . 65 3·25
144 1f.20 on 5c. brown . . . . 65 3·00
145 2f.40 on 35c. green . . . . 85 3·00
146 3f. on 25c. green . . . . . 90 3·25
147 4f.50 on 25c. green . . . . 1·50 4·00
148 15f. on 2f.50 blue . . . . . 1·75 4·00

1946. Air. Victory. As T **52** of St. Pierre et Miquelon.
149 8f. violet . . . . 25 3·25

1946. Air. From Chad to the Rhine. As T **53** of St. Pierre et Miquelon.
150 5f. violet . . . . 2·00 3·75
151 10f. green . . . . 2·25 3·75
152 15f. brown . . . . 2·25 3·75
153 20f. blue . . . . 2·25 4·25
154 25f. orange . . . . 1·75 4·50
155 50f. red . . . . 5·75 11·00

1949. Air. 75th Anniv of Universal Postal Union. As T **58** of St. Pierre et Miquelon.
156 10f. multicoloured . . . . . 3·75 12·50

1949. Air. Nos. 325/6 of New Caledonia, with colours changed, optd **WALLIS ET FUTUNA**.
157 **37** 50f. red and yellow . . . . 6·25 12·00
158 – 100f. brown and yellow . . 9·50 18·00

1952. Centenary of Military Medal. As T **60** of St. Pierre et Miquelon.
159 2f. turquoise, yellow and green . . . . 3·50 4·75

1954. Air. 10th Anniv of Liberation. As T **61** of St. Pierre et Miquelon.
160 3f. brown and deep brown 5·75 11·00

7 Making Tapa (cloth)

8 Father Chanel

1955. (a) Postage, as T **7**.
161 – 3f. purple, mauve and lilac 75 3·25
162 **7** 5f. chocolate, brown & grn 3·00 3·50
163 – 7f. brown and turquoise . . 3·50 4·00
164 – 9f. deep purple, purple and blue . . . . 1·25 4·50
165 – 17f. multicoloured . . . . . 4·50 4·75
166 – 19f. green and red . . . . . 5·00 5·25

(b) Air, as T **8**.
167 **8** 14f. blue, green and indigo 1·60 4·25
168 – 21f. green, brown and blue 7·00 6·75
168a – 27f. green, blue and brown 5·75 3·75
169 – 33f. brown, blue & turq . . 12·00 12·50

DESIGNS—HORIZ: 9f. Wallisian and island view; 7f. Preparing kava; 17f. Dancers; 21f. View of Mata-Utu, Queen Amelia and Mgr. Bataillon; 27f. Wharf, Mata-Utu; 33f. Map of Wallis and Futuna Islands and "Stella Matutina" (full-rigged ship). VERT: 19f. Paddle dance.

1958. Tropical Flora. As T **67** of St. Pierre et Miquelon.
170 5f. multicoloured . . . . . . 3·00 5·00
DESIGN—HORIZ: 5f. "Montrouziera".

1958. 10th Anniv of Declaration of Human Rights. As T **66** of St. Pierre et Miquelon.
171 17f. blue and ultramarine . . 2·25 8·75

8a Map of Pacific and Palms

1962. 5th South Pacific Conference, Pago Pago.
172 **8a** 16f. multicoloured . . . . 3·75 4·00

9 Trumpet Triton

10 Throwing the Javelin

1962. Marine Fauna.
173 **9** 25c. brown and green (postage) . . . . 65 2·25
174 – 1f. red and green . . . . . 1·25 2·25
175 – 2f. brown and blue . . . . 1·50 2·75
176 – 4f. brown and blue . . . . 2·00 2·25
177 – 10f. multicoloured . . . . . 5·00 6·25
178 – 20f. brown and blue . . . . 10·00 10·00
179 – 50f. brown, blue & pur (air) 6·75 8·50
180 – 100f. black, green & purple 17·00 20·00

DESIGNS—As T **9**: 1f. Episcopal mitre; 2f. Bull-mouth helmet; 4f. Venus comb murex; 10f. Red-mouth olive; 20f. Tiger cowrie. 26½ × 48 mm: 50f. Ventral harp. 48 × 26½ mm: 100f. Fishing underwater for commercial trochus shells.

1962. Air. 1st Trans-Atlantic TV Satellite Link. As T **71** of St. Pierre et Miquelon.
181 12f. blue, purple and violet 1·60 4·50

1963. Red Cross Centenary. As T **75** of St. Pierre et Miquelon.
182 12f. red, grey and purple . . 3·00 3·25

1963. 15th Anniv of Declaration of Human Rights. As T **76** of St. Pierre et Miquelon.
183 29f. ochre and red . . . . . 7·25 8·00

1964. "PHILATEC 1964" Int Stamp Exn, Paris. As T **77** of St. Pierre et Miquelon.
184 9f. red, green and deep green 2·25 3·50

1964. Air. Olympic Games. Tokyo.
185 **10** 31f. purple, red and green 13·00 18·00

11 Inter-island Ferry "Reine Amelia"

1965.
186 **11** 11f. multicoloured . . . . 7·00 7·25

1965. Air. Centenary of I.T.U. As T **80** of St. Pierre et Miquelon.
187 50f. brown, purple and red 15·00 22·00

1966. Air. Launching of 1st French Satellite. As T **82** of St. Pierre et Miquelon.
188 7f. red, claret and vermilion 4·25 5·00
189 10f. red, claret and vermilion 5·25 6·25

1966. Air. Launching of Satellite "D1". As T **82** of St. Pierre et Miquelon.
190 10f. red, lake and green . . . 2·50 4·50

12 W.H.O. Building

1966. Air. Inauguration of W.H.O. Headquarters, Geneva.
191 **12** 30f. red, yellow and blue 3·50 5·50

13 Art Students

1966. Air. 20th Anniv of U.N.E.S.C.O.
192 **13** 50f. brown, green & orange 4·75 6·25

14 Athlete and Decorative Pattern

1966. Air. South Pacific Games, Noumea.
193 **14** 32f. multicoloured . . . . 4·25 4·50
194 – 38f. green and mauve . . . 6·00 6·25
DESIGN: 38f. Woman with ball, and decorative pattern.

15 Samuel Wallis's Frigate H.M.S. "Dolphin" at Uvea

1967. Air. Bicentenary of Discovery of Wallis Island.
195 **15** 12f. multicoloured . . . . 8·25 6·25

1968. 20th Anniv of W.H.O. As T **90** of St. Pierre et Miquelon.
196 17f. purple, orange and green 4·75 6·25

1968. Human Rights Year. As T **92** of St. Pierre et Miquelon.
197 19f. brown, mauve and purple . . . . 3·25 4·50

1969. Air. 1st Flight of Concorde. As T **94** of St. Pierre et Miquelon.
198 20f. black and purple . . . . 13·50 11·00

16 Gathering Coconuts

1969. Scenes of Everyday Life. Multicoloured.
199 1f. Launching outrigger canoe (35 × 22 mm) (postage) . . 2·50 2·50
200 20f. Type **16** (air) . . . . . 3·25 2·75
201 32f. Horse-riding . . . . . . 5·00 3·25
202 38f. Wood-carving . . . . . 4·50 3·75
203 50f. Fishing . . . . 8·50 6·25
204 100f. Marketing fruit . . . . 12·50 9·75

1969. 50th Anniv of Int Labour Organization. As T **100** of St. Pierre et Miquelon.
205 9f. blue, brown and salmon 3·00 3·75

1970. Inauguration of New U.P.U. Headquarters Building, Berne As T **101** of St. Pierre et Miquelon.
206 21f. brown, blue and purple 4·50 4·50

1971. Surch.
207 12f. on 19f. (No. 166) (postage) . . . . 2·75 2·75
208 21f. on 33f. (No. 169) (air) 5·50 5·00

18 Weightlifting

20 Pacific Island Dwelling

19 Commission Headquarters, Noumea

1971. 4th South Pacific Games, Papeete, Tahiti.
209 **18** 24f. brown, blue and green (postage) . . . . . . 4·75 4·25
210 – 36f. blue, olive and red . . 6·00 5·00
211 – 48f. brown, green and lilac (air) . . . . 6·00 2·25
212 – 54f. red, purple and blue 6·50 6·25
DESIGNS—As T **18**: 36f. Basketball. 47 × 27 mm: 48f. Pole-vaulting; 54f. Archery.

1971. 1st Death Anniv of General Charles de Gaulle. As T **110** of St. Pierre et Miquelon.
213 30f. black and blue . . . . . 8·75 5·00
214 70f. black and blue . . . . . 16·00 10·50

1972. Air. 25th Anniv of South Pacific Commission.
215 **19** 44f. multicoloured . . . . 7·00 5·00

1972. Air. South Pacific Arts Festival, Fiji.
216 **20** 60f. violet, green and red 8·75 6·25

21 Model Pirogue

1972. Sailing Pirogues. Multicoloured.
217 14f. Type **21** (postage) . . . 6·75 4·25
218 16f. Children with model pirogues . . . . 6·50 4·25
219 18f. Racing pirogue . . . . 7·50 6·25
220 200f. Pirogue race (47 × 27 mm) (air) . . . . 13·00 8·00

22 La Perouse and "La Boussole"

1973. Air. Explorers of the Pacific.
221 **22** 22f. brown, grey and red 4·25 3·50
222 – 28f. green, red and blue . . 5·25 4·50
223 – 40f. brown, blue & lt blue 8·50 6·50
224 – 72f. brown, blue and violet 13·00 8·50
DESIGNS: 28f. Samuel Wallis and H.M.S. "Dolphin"; 40f. Dumont d'Urville and "L'Astrolabe"; 72f. Bougainville and "La Boudeuse".

23 General De Gaulle

1973. Air. 3rd Death Anniv of General Charles de Gaulle.
225 **23** 107f. purple and brown . . 15·00 11·00

24 "Plumeria rubra"

1973. Air. Flora of Wallis Islands. Multicoloured.
226 12f. Type **24** . . . . 2·75 2·50
227 17f. "Hibiscus tiliaceus" . . . 2·75 2·50
228 19f. "Phaeomeria magnifica" 3·00 3·75
229 21f. "Hibiscus rosa sinensis" 3·00 3·00
230 23f. "Allamanda cathartica" 3·50 3·50
231 27f. "Barringtonia asiatica" 3·50 4·00
232 39f. Bouquet in vase . . . . 8·75 6·25

25 Rhinoceros Beetle

1974. Insects Multicoloured.
233 15f. Type **25** . . . . 3·00 2·50
234 25f. "Cosmopolites sordidus" (weevil) . . . . 3·50 3·00
235 35f. Tropical fruit-piercer . . 4·50 3·25
236 45f. "Pantala flavescens" (darter) . . . . 7·50 5·00

26 "Flower Hand" holding Letter

1974. Air. Centenary of Universal Postal Union.
237 **26** 51f. purple, brown & green 6·75 5·00

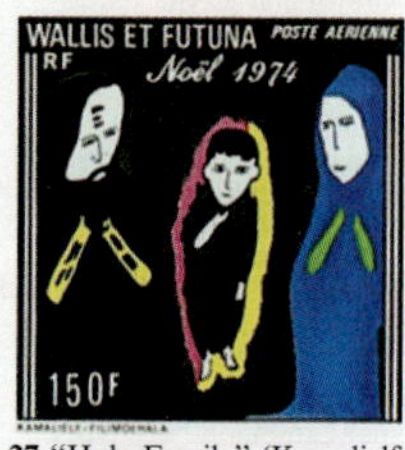
27 "Holy Family" (Kamalielf-Filimoehala)

1974. Air. Christmas.
238 **27** 150f. multicoloured . . . . 11·00 10·00

28 Tapa Pattern

1975. Air. Tapa Mats. Each brown, gold and yellow.
239 3f. Type **28** . . . . 1·90 2·25
240 24f. "Villagers" . . . . . . 2·25 2·75
241 36f. "Fishes" . . . . 4·00 3·50
242 80f. "Fishes and Dancers" . . 8·00 7·25

29 Boeing 707 in Flight

30 Volleyball

1975. Air. 1st Regular Air Service to New Caledonia.
243 **29** 100f. multicoloured . . . . 8·25 7·25

1975. Air. 5th South Pacific Games, Guam. Mult.
244 26f. Type **30** . . . . 2·25 2·50
245 44f. Football . . . . 2·50 3·00
246 56f. Throwing the javelin . . 3·25 4·00
247 105f. Skin diving . . . . . . 6·00 8·00

1976. Pres. Pompidou Commemoration. As T **131** of St. Pierre et Miquelon.
248 50f. grey and blue . . . . . 5·25 4·50

31 Lalolalo Lake, Wallis

1976. Landscapes. Multicoloured.
249 10f. Type **31** (postage) . . . 2·00 2·00
250 29f. Vasavasa, Futuna (air) 3·00 2·75
251 41f. Sigave Bay, Futuna . . . 4·00 3·25
252 68f. Gahi Bay, Wallis . . . . 5·75 4·50

32 Concorde

1976. Air. 1st Commercial Flight of Concorde.
253 **32** 250f. multicoloured . . . . 30·00 20·00

33 Washington and Battle of Yorktown

1976. Bicentenary of American Revolution.
254 **33** 19f. green, blue and red . . 2·50 2·50
255 – 47f. purple, red and blue 11·75 5·75
DESIGN: 47f. Lafayette and Battle of Virginia Capes.

34 Throwing the Hammer

1976. Air. Olympic Games, Montreal.
256 **34** 31f. purple, blue and red 3·25 3·25
257 – 39f. mauve, red and purple 4·75 3·75
DESIGN: 39f. High-diving.

35 Admiral Cone

1976. Sea Shells. Multicoloured.
258 20f. Type **35** . . . . 3·00 3·00
259 23f. Banded cowrie . . . . . 3·00 3·00
260 43f. Tapestry turban . . . . 5·25 4·50
261 61f. Papal mitre . . . . . . 7·75 7·25

36 Father Chanel and Sanctuary Church, Poi

1977. Father Chanel Memorial. Multicoloured.
262 22f. Type **36** . . . . 2·50 2·50
263 32f. Father Chanel and map 3·25 2·75

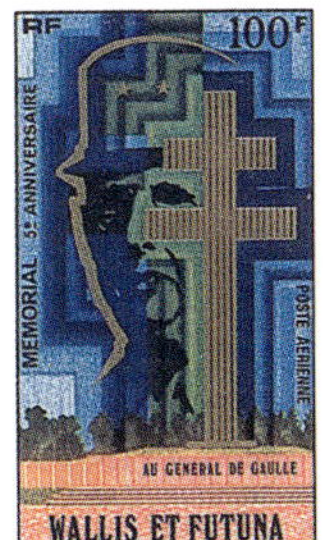

36a De Gaulle Memorial

1977. 5th Anniv of General de Gaulle Memorial.
264 **36a** 100f. multicoloured . . . 8·00 8·00

37 Tanoa (bowl), Lali (mortar trough) and Ipu (coconut shell)

1977. Handicrafts. Multicoloured.
265 12f. Type **37** . . . . 2·25 2·00
266 25f. Wallis and Futuna kumetes (bowls) and tuluma (box) . . . . . . 2·75 2·25
267 33f. Milamila (comb), ike (club) and tutua (model outrigger) . . . . 3·00 2·50
268 45f. Kolo (Futuna clubs) . . 3·25 3·00
269 69f. Kailao (Wallis and Futuna lances) . . . . . . 4·75 3·75

1977. Air. 1st Commercial Flight of Concorde, Paris–New York. Optd **PARIS NEW-YORK 22.11.77 1er VOL COMMERCIAL**.
270 **32** 250f. multicoloured . . . . 20·00 18·00

39 Post Office, Mata-Utu

1977. Building and Monuments. Multicoloured.
271 27f. Type **39** . . . . 2·75 2·50
272 50f. Sia Hospital, Mata-Utu 2·75 3·00
273 57f. Government Buildings, Mata-Utu . . . . 3·00 4·25
274 63f. St Joseph's Church, Sigave . . . . 4·25 4·25
275 120f. Royal Palace, Mata-Utu 5·25 5·50

1977. Bicentenary of Captain Cook's Discovery of Hawaii. Nos. 254/5 optd **JAMES COOK Bicentenaire de la decouverte des Iles Hawaii 1778–1978**.
276 **33** 19f. green, blue and red . . 3·75 3·25
277 – 47f. purple, red and blue 7·25 5·00

41 Clown Triggerfish

1977. Air. Fishes. Multicoloured.
278 26f. Type **41** . . . . 2·50 2·25
279 35f. Barrier Reef anemonefish 2·75 3·50
280 49f. Emperor angelfish . . . 3·50 3·50
281 51f. Moorish idol . . . . . 4·50 3·75

42 Map of Futuna and Alofi

1978. Maps of Wallis and Futuna Islands.
282 **42** 300f. turquoise, blue and ultramarine . . . . . . 19·00 17·00
283 – 500f. brown, blue and ultramarine . . . . . . 25·00 23·00
DESIGN—VERT: 500f. Map of Wallis Island.

43 Father Bataillon and Churches

1978. Air. Arrival of 1st French Missionaries. Mult.
284 60f. Type **43** . . . . 3·00 3·25
285 72f. Monsgr. Pompallier and map . . . . 3·50 3·75

44 I.T.U. Emblem and Antennae

1978. Air. World Telecommunications Day.
286 **44** 66f. multicoloured . . . . 2·75 3·25

45 "Triomphant" (destroyer)

1978. Free French Pacific Naval Force, 1940–44. Multicoloured.
287 150f. Type **45** . . . . 12·00 9·00
288 200f. "Cap des Palmes" and "Chevreuil" (patrol boats) 10·50 11·50
289 280f. "Savorgnan de Brazza" (destroyer) . . . . 14·50 18·00

46 "Solanum seaforthianum"

1978. Tropical Flowers. Multicoloured.
290 16f. Type **46** . . . . 1·90 2·00
291 24f. "Cassia alata" . . . . . 2·00 2·25
292 29f. "Gloriosa superba" . . . 2·50 2·50
293 36f. "Hymenocallis littoralis" 3·00 2·75

47 Reef Heron

1978. Ocean Birds. Multicoloured.
294 17f. Type **47** . . . . 1·40 1·75
295 18f. Red-footed booby . . . 1·40 1·75
296 28f. Brown booby . . . . . 1·75 2·25
297 35f. White tern . . . . . . 2·25 2·50

48 Costumed Carpet-sellers

1978. Costumes and Traditions. Multicoloured.
298 53f. Type **48** . . . . 3·00 2·75
299 55f. "Festival of God" procession . . . . 2·75 3·25
300 59f. Guards of honour . . . 3·25 3·25

49 Nativity Scene

1978. Air. Christmas.
301 **49** 160f. multicoloured . . . . 6·25 6·25

50 Human Rights Emblem

1978. 30th Anniv of Declaration of Human Rights.
302 **50** 44f. multicoloured . . . . 2·75 2·75
303 56f. multicoloured . . . . 2·75 3·25

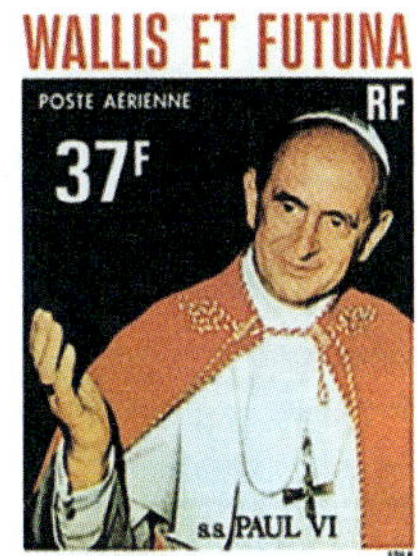

51 Pope Paul VI

1979. Air. Popes. Multicoloured.
304 37f. Type **51** . . . . 2·00 2·75
305 41f. Pope John-Paul I . . . . 2·00 3·00
306 105f. St. Peter's, Rome, and Popes Paul VI and John-Paul I (horiz) . . . . . . 4·75 4·50

52 Britten Norman Islander

1979. Air. Inter-Island Communications (1st series). Multicoloured.
307 46f. Type **52** . . . . 3·00 2·50
308 68f. Freighter "Moana II" . . 1·75 3·00
309 80f. Hihifo Airport . . . . . 4·25 3·25
See also Nos. 349/51.

53 Fishing Boat

1979. Tagging Skipjack Tuna. Multicoloured.
310 10f. Type **53** . . . . 1·60 2·00
311 30f. Weighing skipjack tuna 2·50 2·25
312 34f. Young skipjack tuna . . 2·50 2·50
313 38f. Tagging skipjack tuna 2·25 2·50
314 40f. Angling for skipjack tuna . . . . 2·50 2·75
315 48f. Skipjack tuna . . . . . 3·00 3·25

54 Boy with Model Outrigger Canoe

1979. International Year of the Child. Mult.
317 52f. Type **54** . . . . 2·75 2·75
318 58f. Girl on horseback . . . 3·25 2·75

55 "Bombax ellipticum"

1979. Flowering and Fruiting Trees. Mult.
319 50f. Type **55** . . . . 2·00 2·50
320 64f. "Callophyllum inophyllum" . . . . 2·50 2·75
321 76f. "Pandanus odoratissimus" . . . . . . 3·25 3·50

56 French 1876 5c. Stamp and "Eole" Meteorological Satellite

1979. Air. Death Centenary of Sir Rowland Hill.
322 **56** 5f. multicoloured . . . . . 50 2·00
323 – 70f. multicoloured . . . . 2·50 2·75
324 – 90f. black and red . . . . 2·50 3·25
325 – 100f. brown, yellow & blue 2·75 3·75
DESIGNS—VERT: 70f. Hibiscus and Wallis and Futuna 1920 1f. stamp. HORIZ: 90f. Sir Rowland Hill and Great Britain Penny Black; 100f. "Birds" (Kano School) and Japan 1872 ½s. stamp.

57 Normal and Distorted Landscapes

1979. Anti-alcoholism Campaign.
326 **57** 22f. multicoloured . . . . 1·75 2·50

58 Heads looking at Cross of Lorraine

1979. Air. 39th Anniv of 18 June Appeal by General de Gaulle.
327 **58** 33f. red, blue and grey . . 2·75 2·75

59 "Crinum moorei"

1979. Flowers (1st series). Multicoloured.
328 20f. Type **59** . . . . 1·10 2·00
329 42f. Passion flower . . . . . 2·00 2·50
330 62f. "Canna indica" . . . . 2·25 3·00
See also Nos. 392/4.

60 Map of Islands and French Arms

1979. Air. Presidential Visit.
331 **60** 47f. multicoloured . . . . 3·00 2·75

61 Cook and Death Scene, Hawaii

1979. Air. Death Bicentenary of Captain Cook.
332 **61** 130f. grey, blue and brown 6·50 5·00

62 Swimmers

1979. 6th South Pacific Games, Fiji.
333 **62** 31f. olive, red and green 3·00 2·50
334 – 39f. brown, turquoise & green . . . . 3·50 2·75
DESIGN: 39f. High-jumper.

63 Garlands

1979. Necklaces. Multicoloured.
335 110f. Type **63** . . . . 3·75 3·75
336 140f. Coral necklaces . . . . 5·25 4·50

64 Satellite and Dish Aerial

1979. Air. 3rd World Telecommunications Exhibition, Geneva.
337 **64** 120f. multicoloured . . . . 3·75 4·50

65 Detail of Painting by Mme. Sutita

1979. Works of Local Artists. Multicoloured.
338 27f. Painting by Mme Sutita (detail) (different) . . . . 2·25 2·50
339 65f. Painting by M. A. Pilioko (detail) (vert) . . . 3·00 3·00
340 78f. Type **65** . . . . 3·75 3·50

66 Squilla

1979. South Pacific Fauna. Multicoloured.
341 15f. Type **66** . . . . 1·50 2·00
342 23f. Spanish dancer . . . . . 1·60 2·25
343 25f. Cat's-tongue thorny oyster . . . . 2·00 2·25
344 43f. Sea fan . . . . 2·25 2·25
345 45f. Starfish . . . . 2·00 2·50
346 63f. Fluted giant clam . . . 3·00 3·50

67 "Virgin of the Crescent Moon" (detail, Durer)

1979. Air. Christmas.
347 **67** 180f. black and red . . . . 9·00 7·25
See also No. 554.

68 Concorde, Map and Rotary Emblem

1980. Air. 75th Anniv of Rotary International.
348 **68** 86f. multicoloured . . . . 5·25 4·50

1980. Inter-Island Communications (2nd series). As Nos. 307/9.
349 1f. Type **52** . . . . 90 1·00
350 3f. As No. 308 . . . . 50 1·00
351 5f. As No. 309 . . . . 1·00 1·00

69 Radio Station

71 Rochambeau and Soldiers

1980. 1st Anniv of Radio Station FR3.
352 **69** 47f. multicoloured . . . . 2·75 2·25

70 "Jesus laid in the Tomb" (Maurice Denis)

1980. Easter.
353 **70** 25f. multicoloured . . . . 1·90 1·75

1980. Air. Bicentenary of Rochambeau's Landing at Newport, Rhode Island.
354 **71** 102f. sepia, blue and brown 6·25 5·00

72 Flags and Island

1980. Air. National Day.
355 **72** 71f. multicoloured . . . . 3·00 2·25

73 Mozambique Emperor

1980. Fishes. Multicoloured.
356 23f. Type **73** . . . . 1·40 1·40
357 27f. Crimson jobfish . . . . 1·60 1·60
358 32f. Ruby snapper . . . . . 2·00 2·00
359 51f. Golden hind . . . . . . 2·75 2·50
360 59f. Rusty jobfish . . . . . 4·00 3·75

74 Mermoz and "Arc en Ciel"

1980. Air. 50th Anniv of 1st South Atlantic Airmail Flight.
361 **74** 122f. blue, deep blue & red 6·25 4·50

1980. "Sydpex 80" International Stamp Exhibition, Sydney. No. 315 surch **50F SYDPEX 80 29 Septembre**.
362 50f. on 48f. multicoloured . . 3·50 2·25

76 Fleming and Penicillin Slide

1980. Air. 25th Death Anniv of Alexander Fleming (discoverer of penicillin).
363 **76** 101f. blue, brown and red 4·50 3·25

77 Charles de Gaulle

1980. Air. 10th Death Anniv of Charles de Gaulle (French statesman).
364 **77** 200f. green and brown . . 9·75 7·25

78 "The Virgin, Child and St. Catherine" (Lorenzo Lotto)

1980. Air. Christmas.
365 **78** 150f. multicoloured . . . . 6·00 4·50

79 Alan Shepard and "Freedom 7"

1981. Air. 20th Anniv of First Men in Space. Multicoloured.
366 37f. Type **79** . . . . 1·75 1·75
367 44f. Yuri Gagarin and "Vostok 1" . . . . . . 2·50 2·00

80 Ribbons and I.T.U. and W.H.O. Emblems forming Caduceus and Satellite

1981. World Telecommunications Day.
368 **80** 49f. multicoloured . . . . 2·50 2·00

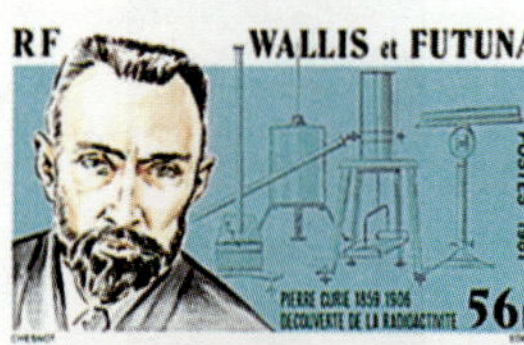

81 Curie and Laboratory Equipment

1981. 75th Death Anniv of Pierre Curie (physicist and discoverer of radium).
369 **81** 56f. multicoloured . . . . 2·50 2·25

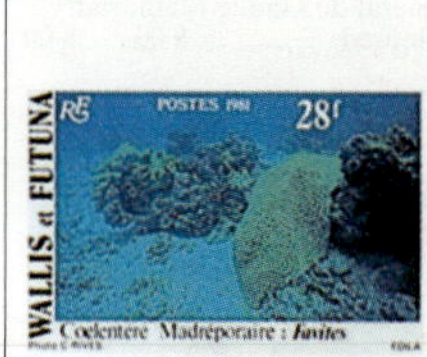

82 Coral

84 Section of Globe

83 Doctor inoculating Child

1981. Undersea Fauna. Multicoloured.
370 28f. Type **82** . . . . 1·25 1·60
371 30f. Blue-green algae . . . . 1·25 1·60
372 31f. "Ceratium vultur" (dinoflagellate) . . . . 1·50 1·75
373 35f. Tomato anemonefish . . 1·50 1·75
374 40f. Textile cone . . . . . . 1·75 2·00
375 55f. Feather-star (echinoderm) . . . . . . 2·00 2·25

1981. 60th Anniv of 1st B.C.G. Anti-tuberculosis Inoculation.
376 **83** 27f. multicoloured . . . . 1·75 1·50

1981. International Year of Disabled Persons.
377 **84** 42f. multicoloured . . . . 2·50 1·90

85 Edison and Phonograph

1981. 50th Death Anniv of Thomas Edison (inventor).
378 **85** 59f. black, blue and red . . 2·75 2·25

1981. No. 341 surch **5F**.
379 5f. on 15f. multicoloured . . 1·10 1·10

87 Battle Scene

1981. Bicentenary of Battle of Virginia Capes.
380 – 66f. purple, blue and slate 2·75 2·25
381 **87** 74f. green, violet and light green . . . . 3·50 2·25
DESIGN: 66f. Admiral Francois de Grasse and battle scene.

88 "Vase of Flowers" (Cezanne)

1981. Air. 75th Death Anniv of Paul Cezanne and Birth Centenary of Pablo Picasso (artists).
382 53f. Type **88** . . . . 2·75 2·25
383 135f. "Harlequin leaning" (Picasso) . . . . 6·25 4·00

89 Football

1981. Air. World Cup Football Championship, Spain (1982).
384 **89** 120f. brown, black & green 4·50 3·75
385 120f. brown, mauve and green . . . . 4·50 3·75

90 Patrol Boat "La Dieppoise"

1981. Surveillance of 200-mile Zone. Mult.
386 60f. Type **90** . . . . 2·00 2·25
387 85f. Frigate "Protet" . . . . 2·75 3·00

91 Crib

1981. Air. Christmas.
388 **91** 180f. multicoloured . . . . 7·00 5·00

92 "Pilioko Aloi" (tapestry)

93 Dr. R. Koch at Microscope

1982. Air.
389 **92** 100f. multicoloured . . . . 4·00 3·25

1982. Centenary of Discovery of Tubercle Bacillus.
390 **93** 45f. multicoloured . . . . 2·25 2·00

94 "Fishing Boats at Collioure"

1982. Air. Death Cent of Georges Braque (painter).
391 **94** 300f. multicoloured . . . . 11·00 8·25

1982. Flowers (2nd series). Multicoloured.
392 1f. As Type **59** . . . . 75 1·00
393 2f. As No. 329 . . . . 1·00 1·00
394 3f. As No. 330 . . . . 1·00 1·00

95 1930 Stamp

1982. "Philexfrance" International Stamp Exhibition, Paris.
395 **95** 140f. violet, blue and red 4·25 3·25

96 "Acanthe phippium"

1982. Orchids. Multicoloured.
396 34f. Type **96** . . . . 1·40 1·60
397 68f. "Acanthe phippium" (different) . . . . 2·50 2·50
398 70f. "Spathoglottis pacifica" 3·00 2·50
399 83f. "Mussaenda raiateensis" 3·75 3·25

97 Lord Baden-Powell

1982. 125th Birth Anniv of Lord Baden-Powell (founder of Boy Scout Movement).
400 **97** 80f. multicoloured . . . . 3·50 2·50

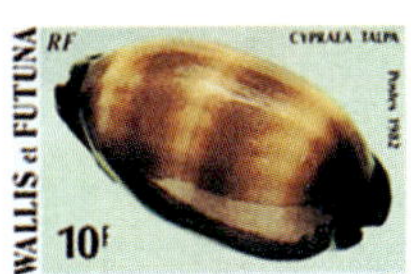

98 Mole Cowrie

1982. Sea Shells (1st series). Multicoloured.
401 10f. Type **98** . . . . 95 1·00
402 15f. Pacific deer cowrie . . . 1·10 1·00
403 25f. Eyed cowrie . . . . . . 1·25 1·25
404 27f. Closely-related carnelian cowrie . . . . 1·40 1·10
405 40f. All-red map cowrie . . . 1·75 1·60
406 50f. Tiger cowrie . . . . . . 2·25 2·00
See also Nos. 428/33, 440/5, 459/64, 481/6 and 510/15.

99 Santos-Dumont, Airship "Ballon No. 14" and Biplane "14 bis"

1982. Air. 50th Death Anniv of Alberto Santos-Dumont (aviation pioneer).
407 **99** 95f. brown, green and blue 4·00 2·75

1982. Air. World Cup Football Championship Result. No. 384 optd **ITALIE VAINQUEUR 1982**.
408 **89** 120f. brown, black and green . . . . 4·50 3·75

101 Beach

1982. Air. Overseas Week.
409 **101** 105f. multicoloured . . . 3·50 3·25

102 Coral

1982. Marine Life. Multicoloured.
410 32f. Type **102** . . . . 1·75 1·40
411 35f. Starfish . . . . 1·90 1·40
412 46f. Spanish dancer . . . . . 2·25 1·90
413 63f. Cat's-tongue thorny oyster . . . . 3·00 2·25

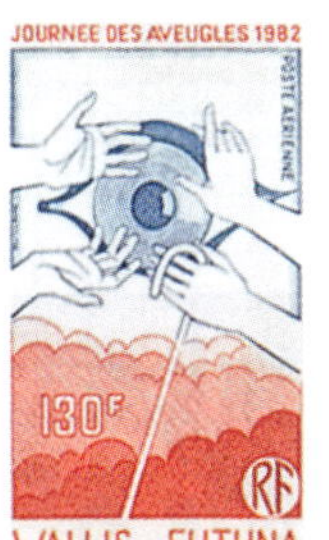

103 Hands reaching towards Eye

1982. Air. Blind Day.
414 **103** 130f. blue, scarlet and red 4·00 3·75

104 St. Theresa of Avila

1982. 400th Death Anniv of St. Theresa of Avila.
415 **104** 31f. brown, green and deep brown . . . . . 1·75 1·60
See also No. 447.

105 "Adoration of the Virgin" (Correggio)

1982. Air. Christmas.
416 **105** 170f. multicoloured . . . 5·75 4·50

106 Wallis Meeting House

1983.
417 **106** 19f. multicoloured . . . . 1·00 1·75

107 Eiffel and Eiffel Tower under Construction

1983. 60th Death Anniv of Gustave Eiffel (engineer).
418 **107** 97f. purple, red and green 3·50 3·00

108 Windsurfing

110 Vincenzo Lunardi's Balloon, 1784

109 Island Scene and U.P.U. Emblem

1983. Air.
419 **108** 270f. multicoloured . . . 9·75 6·00

1983. Air. World U.P.U. Day.
420 **109** 100f. multicoloured . . . 4·00 2·75

1983. Air. Bicentenary of Manned Flight.
421 **110** 205f. multicoloured . . . 7·50 5·00

111 "Cat"

1983. Air. 15th Death Anniv of Foujita (painter).
422 **111** 102f. multicoloured . . . 3·75 2·75

112 Thai Goddess

113 Javelin-thrower

1983. "Bangkok 1983" International Stamp Exn.
423 **112** 92f. red, black and blue 3·00 2·25

1983. Air. Olympic Games, Los Angeles (1984) (1st issue).
424 **113** 250f. brown, green & yellow . . . . 8·00 6·50
See also No. 438.

114 Nobel

1983. Air. 150th Birth Anniv of Alfred Nobel (inventor of dynamite and founder of Nobel Prizes).
425 **114** 150f. red and green . . . 5·25 3·75

115 Satellite, Dish Aerial and W.C.Y. Emblem

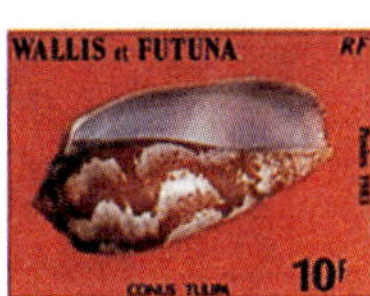

117 Tulip Cone

116 Niepce and Early Photograph

1983. World Communications Year.
426 **115** 20f. multicoloured . . . . 1·10 1·25

1983. Air. Death Centenary of Nicephore Niepce (pioneer of photography).
427 **116** 75f. purple and green . . 3·25 2·25

1983. Sea Shells (2nd series). Multicoloured.
428 10f. Type **117** . . . . . . 65 1·00
429 17f. Captain cone . . . . . 75 1·10
430 21f. Virgin cone . . . . . . 75 1·10
431 39f. Calf cone . . . . 1·10 1·10
432 52f. Marble cone . . . . . . 1·40 1·90
433 65f. Leopard cone . . . . . 2·00 2·25

118 "Triumph of Galatea"

1983. Air. 500th Birth Anniv of Raphael (artist).
434 **118** 167f. multicoloured . . . 5·75 4·50

119 Pandanus Tree

1983. Air.
435 **119** 137f. multicoloured . . . 4·75 3·25

120 "Madonna and Pope Sixtus" (Raphael)

1983. Air. Christmas.
436 **120** 200f. multicoloured . . . 7·00 5·00

121 Frigate "Commandant Bory"

1984. Air.
437 **121** 67f. multicoloured . . . . 2·75 2·25

122 Weightlifting

1984. Air. Olympic Games, Los Angeles (2nd issue).
438 **122** 85f. multicoloured . . . . 3·50 2·75

123 Frangipani

1984. Air.
439 **123** 130f. multicoloured . . . 4·50 3·25

1984. Sea Shells (3rd series). As T **117**. Mult.
440 22f. Silver conch . . . . . . 90 1·25
441 25f. Chiragra spider conch 90 1·25
442 35f. Samar conch . . . . . 1·25 1·40
443 43f. Scorpion conch . . . . 1·75 1·75
444 49f. Diana conch . . . . . . 2·25 2·00
445 76f. Orange spider conch . . 2·75 2·75

124 "Deposition of Christ" (Alele Chapel)

1984. Air. Easter.
446 **124** 190f. multicoloured . . . 6·00 4·50

1984. "Espana 84" International Stamp Exhibition, Madrid. As T **104** but with "Espana 84" emblem.
447 70f. sepia, green and brown 2·50 2·25

125 Diderot and Title Page of Encyclopedia

1984. Death Bicentenary of Denis Diderot (encyclopedist).
448 **125** 100f. brown and blue . . 3·50 2·75

126 Killer Whale

1984. Nature Protection.
449 **126** 90f. multicoloured . . . . 3·75 2·25

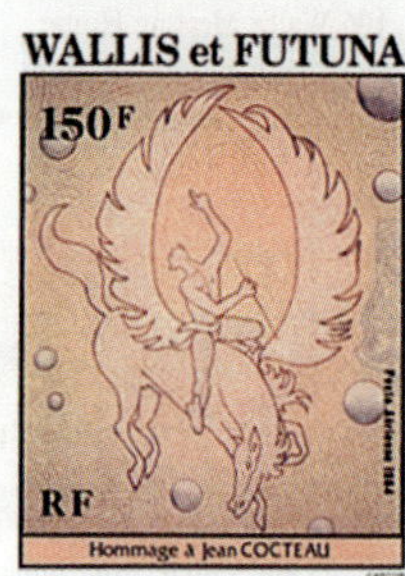

127 Painting

1984. Air. 95th Birth Anniv of Jean Cocteau (artist).
450 **127** 150f. multicoloured . . . 4·75 4·00

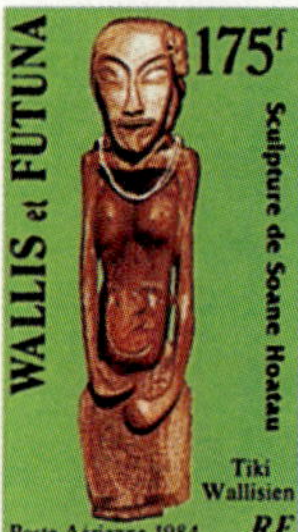

128 Tiki **129** "Alice"

1984. Air. Soane Hoatau Sculpture.
451 **128** 175f. multicoloured . . . 6·00 4·50

1984. Air. Birth Centenary of Amedeo Modigliani (painter).
452 **129** 140f. multicoloured . . . 5·50 3·75

130 "Pilioko Aloi" (tapestry)

1984. Air. "Ausipex 84" International Stamp Exhibition, Melbourne.
453 **130** 180f. multicoloured . . . 6·25 4·00

131 "Local Dances" (Jean Michon)

1984. Air.
454 **131** 110f. multicoloured . . . 4·50 3·25

132 Altar, Mount Lulu Chapel

1984. Air.
455 **132** 52f. multicoloured . . . . 2·25 1·90

133 Islanders wearing Leis

1985. 4th Pacific Arts Festival.
456 **133** 160f. multicoloured . . . 5·25 4·00

134 Common Spider Conch and Virgin and Child

1984. Air. Christmas.
457 **134** 260f. multicoloured . . . 9·00 5·00

135 Lapita Pottery **136** Victor Hugo

1985. Archaeological Expedition, 1983.
458 **135** 53f. multicoloured . . . . 2·25 1·60

1985. Sea Shells (4th series). As T **117**. Mult.
459 2f. Chambered nautilus . . . 35 80
460 3f. Adusta murex 35 80
461 41f. Vibex bonnet . . . . . 1·25 1·40
462 47f. Flag cone . . . . 1·75 1·75
463 56f. True harp . . . . 1·75 1·90
464 71f. Ramose murex . . . . . 2·50 2·25

1985. Death Centenary of Victor Hugo (writer).
465 **136** 89f. deep blue, blue and red . . . . 3·50 2·50

137 "Pilioko Aloi" (tapestry)

1985. Air.
466 **137** 500f. multicoloured . . . 14·50 10·00

138 Flying Fox

1985.
467 **138** 38f. multicoloured . . . . 2·00 1·60

139 Children

1985. International Youth Year.
468 **139** 64f. multicoloured . . . . 2·50 1·90

140 "The Post Office"

1985. Air. 30th Death Anniv of Maurice Utrillo (artist).
469 **140** 200f. multicoloured . . . 6·25 4·00

141 Hands and U.N. Emblem

1985. 40th Anniv of U.N.O.
470 **141** 49f. green, blue and red 2·25 1·75

142 Sailing Canoe

1985. Air.
471 **142** 350f. multicoloured . . . 10·50 6·00

143 Ronsard, Organist and Muse of Poetry

1985. 400th Death Anniv of Pierre de Ronsard (poet).
472 **143** 170f. brown, deep brown and blue . . . . 6·25 4·00

144 Landing Ship "Jacques Cartier"

145 "Portrait of Young Woman" (Patrice Nielly)

1985. Air.
473 **144** 51f. deep blue, blue and turquoise . . . . 1·75 1·75

1985. Air.
474 **145** 245f. multicoloured . . . 7·75 4·00

146 Schweitzer, African Boy and Cathedral Organ

1985. 20th Death Anniv of Dr. Albert Schweitzer (missionary).
475 **146** 50f. black, purple & brown . . . . 2·25 1·75

147 "Virgin and Child" (Jean Michon)

1985. Air. Christmas.
476 **147** 330f. multicoloured . . . 10·50 7·25

148 Bread-fruit

1986. Food and Agriculture Organization.
477 **148** 39f. multicoloured . . . . 1·90 1·60

149 Flamboyant Flower

1986.
478 **149** 38f. multicoloured . . . . 1·75 1·60

150 Comet and "Giotto" Space Probe

1986. Air. Appearance of Halley's Comet.
479 **150** 100f. multicoloured . . . 3·25 2·75

151 Vianney praying

1986. Air. Birth Bicentenary of Cure d'Ars.
480 **151** 200f. light brown, brown and black . . . . . . 6·50 4·50

1986. Sea Shells (5th series). As T **117**. Mult.
481 4f. Giant spider conch . . . 55 1·00
482 5f. Trumpet triton . . . . . 35 1·00
483 10f. Red-mouth olive . . . . 60 1·00
484 18f. Common distorsio . . . 75 1·10
485 25f. Episcopal mitre . . . . 1·10 1·25
486 107f. Distant cone . . . . . 3·00 2·75

152 Players and Boy with Football

1986. World Cup Football Championship, Mexico.
487 **152** 95f. multicoloured . . . . 3·25 2·50

153 Willem Schouten and "Eendracht"

1986. 370th Anniv of Discovery of Horn Islands. Each purple, green and blue.
488 8f. Type **153** . . . . 1·10 1·00
489 9f. Jacob le Maire and "Hoorn" . . . . 1·10 1·00
490 155f. Map of Futuna and Alofi Islands . . . . 5·50 4·50

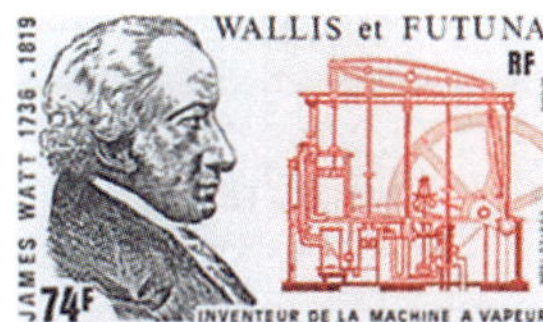

154 Watt and Steam Engine

1986. 250th Birth Anniv of James Watt (inventor).
491 **154** 74f. red and black . . . . 3·25 3·25

155 Queen Amelia

1986. Air. Centenary of Request for Protectorate and 25th Anniv of French Overseas Territory Status. Each purple, red and blue.
492 90f. Type **155** . . . . 3·25 3·25
493 137f. Law of 1961 bestowing Overseas Territory status 4·50 4·50

156 Patrol Boat "La Lorientaise"

1986. Naval Ships.
494 **156** 6f. red, purple and blue 1·00 1·00
495 – 7f. violet, orange and red 1·00 1·00
496 – 120f. turquoise, red & blue . . . . 4·00 3·00
DESIGNS: 7f. Frigate "Commandant Blaison"; 120f. Frigate "Balny".

157 Oleander

1986.
497 **157** 97f. multicoloured . . . . 3·50 2·75

158 U.P.U. Emblem and Dove carrying Envelope

1986. Air. World Post Day.
498 **158** 270f. multicoloured . . . 8·75 6·50

159 New York, Statue and Paris

1986. Air. Centenary of Statue of Liberty.
499 **159** 205f. multicoloured . . . 6·50 4·50

160 "Virgin and Child" (Botticelli)

1986. Christmas.
500 **160** 250f. multicoloured . . . 7·25 5·50

161 "Papilio montrouzieri"

162 Father Chanel and Basilica

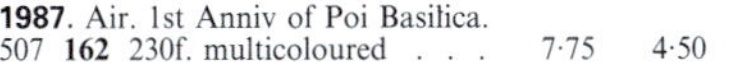

1987. Butterflies. Multicoloured.
501 2f. Type **161** . . . . 95 1·10
502 42f. Caper white . . . . . . 1·60 1·40
503 46f. "Delias ellipsis" . . . . 1·75 1·60
504 50f. "Danaus pumila" . . . . 1·90 1·75
505 52f. "Lutbrodes cleotas" . . 1·90 1·75
506 59f. Meadow argus . . . . . 2·50 2·00

1987. Air. 1st Anniv of Poi Basilica.
507 **162** 230f. multicoloured . . . 7·75 4·50

163 "Telstar", Globe and Pleumeur-Bodou

1987. Air. World Communications Day. 25th Anniv of Launch of "Telstar" Communications Satellite.
508 **163** 200f. blue, black and red 6·25 3·75

164 Wrestlers

1987. World Wrestling Championships, Clermont-Ferrand.
509 **164** 97f. multicoloured . . . . 3·50 2·50

1987. Sea Shells (6th series). As T **117**. Mult.
510 3f. Common hairy triton . . 35 1·00
511 4f. Textile cone . . . . . . 35 1·00
512 28f. Humpback cowrie . . . 95 1·25
513 44f. Giant frog shell . . . . 1·40 1·60
514 48f. Turtle cowrie . . . . . 1·50 1·75
515 78f. Bull-mouth helmet . . . 2·25 2·25

165 Piccard, Stratosphere Balloon "F.N.R.S." and Bathyscaphe

167 Bust of Girl

1987. Air. 25th Death Anniv of Auguste Piccard (physicist).
516 **165** 135f. deep blue, blue and green . . . . 4·50 3·00

1987. "Olymphilex 87" Olympic Stamps Exhibition, Rome. No 509 optd **OLYMPHILEX '87 ROME** and Olympic rings.
517 **164** 97f. multicoloured . . . . 3·50 2·50

1987. 70th Death Anniv of Auguste Rodin (sculptor).
518 **167** 150f. purple . . . . . . 5·00 3·25
See also No. 557.

168 Letters between Globes and Postbird

1987. World Post Day.
519 **168** 116f. blue, deep blue and yellow . . . . 4·00 2·75

169 Pacific Black Duck

1987. Birds. Multicoloured.
520 6f. Type **169** 30 85
521 19f. Pacific golden plover . . 50 95
522 47f. Friendly quail dove . . . 1·40 1·25
523 56f. Ruddy turnstone . . . . 1·60 1·50
524 64f. Buff-banded rail . . . . 1·75 1·50
525 68f. Bar-tailed godwit . . . . 2·25 1·75

170 Mgr. Bataillon, French Frigate and Islands

1987. Air. 150th Anniv of Arrival of First Missionaries.
526 **170** 260f. turquoise, blue and brown . . . . 8·50 5·50

171 Nativity Scene

1987. Air. Christmas.
527 **171** 300f. multicoloured . . . 9·75 6·50

172 Carco and Parisian Scenes

1988. 30th Death Anniv of Francis Carco (writer).
528 **172** 40f. multicoloured . . . . 1·90 1·40

173 Morane Saulnier Type I and Garros

1988. Air. 70th Death Anniv of Roland Garros (aviator).
529 **173** 600f. deep blue, brown and blue . . . . 18·00 12·50

174 La Perouse, "L'Astrolabe" and "La Boussole"

1988. Bicentenary of Disappearance of La Perouse's Expedition.
530 **174** 70f. green, blue and brown . . . . 2·75 2·00

175 "Self-portrait wearing Lace Jabot"

1988. Air. Death Bicentenary of Maurice Quentin de la Tour (painter).
531 **175** 500f. multicoloured . . . 16·00 11·00

176 Arrows and Dish Aerial

1988. Air. World Telecommunications Day.
532 **176** 100f. multicoloured . . . 3·00 2·50

177 Map and Bishop with Crosier

1988. Air. South Pacific Episcopal Conference.
533 **177** 90f. multicoloured . . . . 2·75 2·25

178 Nurse, Child and Anniversary Emblem

1988. 125th Anniv of International Red Cross.
534 **178** 30f. black, green and red 1·25 1·40

179 Throwing the Javelin

1988. Olympic Games, Seoul. Each brown, red and blue.
535 11f. Type **179** . . . . 1·25 1·10
536 20f. Volleyball . . . . 1·25 1·25
537 60f. Windsurfing . . . . . . 2·50 2·25
538 80f. Sailing . . . . 3·00 2·75

180 Envelopes forming Map

1988. World Post Day.
539 **180** 17f. yellow, blue and black . . . . 1·25 1·10

181 Becquerel

1988. Birth Bicent of Antoine Cesar Becquerel (physicist).
540 **181** 18f. black and blue . . . 1·25 1·10

182 Nativity Scene

1988. Air. Christmas.
541 **182** 400f. multicoloured . . . 12·00 8·25

183 "Amiral Charner" (frigate)

1989. International Maritime Organization.
542 **183** 26f. multicoloured . . . . 1·40 1·40

184 Renior and Scene from "The Great Illusion"

1989. 10th Death Anniv of Jean Renoir (film director).
543 **184** 24f. brown, mauve & orange . . . . 1·40 1·40

185 Royal Throne (Aselo Kulimoetoke)
186 Map

1989. Air.
544 **185** 700f. multicoloured . . . 21·00 13·00

1989. Futuna Hydro-electric Power Station.
545 **186** 25f. multicoloured . . . . 1·40 1·25

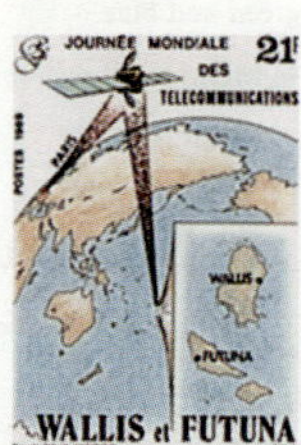

188 Satellite above Earth

1989. International Telecommunications Day.
546 **188** 21f. multicoloured . . . . 1·00 1·25

189 Mural (H. Tailhade)

1989.
547 **189** 22f. multicoloured . . . . 1·40 1·25

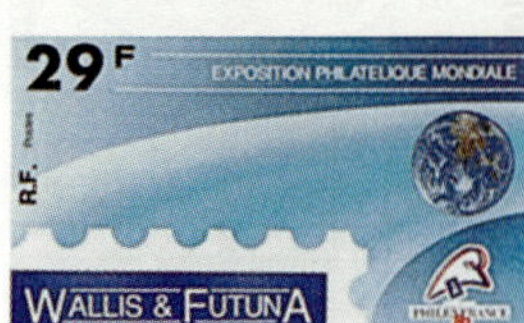

190 Globe and Emblem

1989. "Philexfrance '89" International Stamp Exhibition, Paris (548) and Bicentenary of Declaration of Rights of Man and South Pacific Youth Meeting (549). Multicoloured.
548 29f. Type **190** (postage) . . . 1·40 1·25
549 900f. Sportsmen (air) . . . . 24·00 10·50

191 Cyclists

1989. World Cycling Championships, France.
551 **191** 10f. black, brown & green 1·25 1·00

192 Envelopes around Globe of Flags

1989. World Post Day.
552 **192** 27f. multicoloured . . . . 1·40 1·25

193 Landscape

1989.
553 **193** 23f. multicoloured . . . . 1·75 1·60

1989. Air. Christmas. As No. 347 but date, value and colour changed.
554 **67** 800f. mauve . . . . 23·00 16·00

194 "Star of Bethlehem"

1990.
555 **194** 44f. multicoloured . . . . 1·90 1·60

195 Tortoise Fossil

1990.
556 **195** 48f. multicoloured . . . . 1·75 1·60

1990. 150th Birth Anniv of Auguste Rodin (sculptor). As No. 518 but value and colour changed.
557 **167** 200f. blue . . . . 6·50 4·00

197 Footballers

1990. World Cup Football Championship, Italy.
558 **197** 59f. multicoloured . . . . 2·25 1·90

198 Orchids

1990. Mothers' Day.
559 **198** 78f. multicoloured . . . . 3·00 2·25

199 "Avion III", Airbus Industrie A310 and Clement Ader

1990. Air. Cent of First Heavier-than-Air Flight and 1st Anniv of Wallis–Tahiti Air Link.
560 **199** 56f. brown, mauve and red . . . . 1·75 1·75

200 Red-tailed Tropic Bird

1990. Multicoloured.
561 300f. Type **200** . . . . 7·50 5·50
562 600f. South Pacific islet . . . 20·00 12·50

201 "Moana II" (inter-island freighter)

1990. Ships.
563 **201** 40f. brown, green and blue . . . . 2·00 1·60
564 – 50f. brown, blue and green . . . . 2·25 1·90
DESIGN: 50f. "Moana III" (container ship) at jetty.

202 Traditional Dwellings

1990.
565 **202** 28f. multicoloured . . . . 1·50 1·25

203 Doves and Globe

1990. Stamp Day.
566 **203** 97f. multicoloured . . . . 3·50 2·75

204 Outrigger Canoe

1990.
567 **204** 46f. multicoloured . . . . 2·25 1·75

205 De Gaulle

1990. Air. Birth Centenary of Charles de Gaulle (French statesman).
568 **205** 1000f. multicoloured . . . 26·00 19·00

206 Palm Trees

1990. "Best Wishes".
569 **206** 100f. multicoloured . . . 3·50 2·75

207 Patrol Boat "La Glorieuse"

1991.
570 **207** 52f. blue, green and red 3·00 2·00
See also No. 578.

208 Warrior

1991. Tradition.
571 7f. Breadfruit gatherer . . . 90 1·00
572 54f. Taro planter . . . . . . 2·00 1·60
573 62f. Spear fisherman . . . . 2·25 1·75
574 72f. Type **208** . . . . 2·25 1·75
575 90f. Kailao dancer . . . . . 3·00 1·90

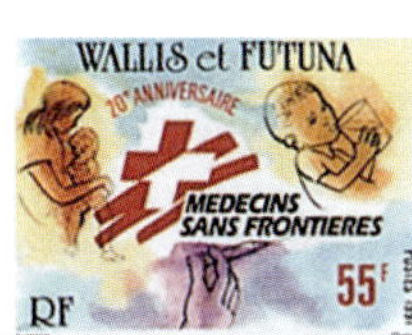

209 Aspects of Health Care

1991. 20th Anniv of Medecins sans Frontieres (medical charity).
577 **209** 55f. multicoloured . . . . 2·25 1·75

1991. Patrol Boat "La Moqueuse". As T **207**.
578 42f. black, blue and red . . . 2·50 1·75

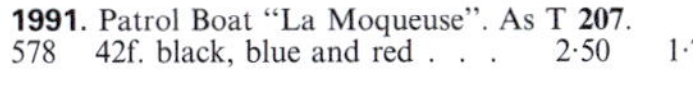

210 Chanel and Reliquary

1991. Air. 150th Death Anniv of Father Chanel (missionary).
579 **210** 235f. multicoloured . . . 7·50 5·00

211 Players through the Ages (½-size illustration)

1991. Air. Centenary of French Open Tennis Championships.
580 **211** 250f. black, orange & green . . . . 8·50 5·00

212 Map and Microlight

1991. Microlight Aircraft Flying in Wallis and Futuna.
581 **212** 85f. multicoloured . . . . 3·25 2·25

213 "Portrait of Jean"

1991. 150th Birth Anniv of Pierre Auguste Renior (painter). Perf or imperf (self-adhesive).
582 **213** 400f. multicoloured . . . 11·50 7·25

214 Map

1991. 30th Anniv of French Overseas Territory Status.
584 **214** 102f. multicoloured . . . 3·00 2·25

215 Islanders in Festive Dress and Angel

1991. Feast of the Assumption.
585 **215** 30f. multicoloured . . . . 1·60 1·25

216 Mozart and Scene from "The Marriage of Figaro"

1991. Air. Death Bicentenary of Wolfgang Amadeus Mozart (composer).
586 **216** 500f. blue, lilac and red 14·00 8·25

217 Imprisoned Figure

1991. 30th Anniv of Amnesty International.
587 **217** 140f. yellow, violet & blue 4·75 2·75

218 House and Generator

1991. 50th Anniv of Central Economic Co-operation Bank.
588 **218** 10f. multicoloured . . . . 1·00 1·00

219 "Allamanda cathartica"

1991. Flowers. Multicoloured.
589 1f. Type **219** . . . . 90 1·00
590 4f. "Hibiscus rosa sinensis" (vert) . . . . 1·00 1·00
591 80f. Water lily . . . . 2·75 2·00

220 Santa Claus on Beach

1991. Christmas.
592 **220** 60f. multicoloured . . . . 2·25 1·60

221 Ski Jumping

1992. Winter Olympic Games, Albertville.
593 **221** 150f. multicoloured . . . 5·00 3·00

222 Map, Plants and Dassault Breguet Mystere Falcon 20

1992. "Escadrille 9S" Maritime Surveillance Service.
594 **222** 48f. multicoloured . . . . 2·00 1·40

223 Canadian 1938 $1 and Wallis and Futuna 1920 2f. Stamps (½-size illustration)

1992. "Canada 92" International Youth Philatelic Exhibition, Montreal.
595 **223** 35f. black, red and violet 1·40 1·25

224 Throwing the Javelin

1992. Olympic Games, Barcelona.
596 **224** 106f. indigo, blue & green 3·00 2·25

225 Spanish 1975 4p. Stamp and Wallis Post Office

1992. "Granada 92" International Stamp Exhibition.
597 **225** 100f. black, blue & purple 2·75 2·00

226 Columbus's Fleet, Pavilion and Seville

1992. "Expo 92" World's Fair, Seville.
598 **226** 200f. green, blue & orange 5·00 4·00

227 Saddle Butterflyfish

1992. Butterfly and Angel Fishes. Multicoloured.
599 21f. Type **227** 1·10 1·10
600 22f. Thread-finned butterflyfish 1·25 1·10
601 23f. Masked bannerfish 1·25 1·10
602 24f. Regal angelfish 1·25 1·10
603 25f. Conspicuous angelfish 1·25 1·10
604 26f. Teardrop butterflyfish 1·25 1·25

228 Columbus and Map

1992. Air. "World Columbian Stamp Expo 92", Chicago.
605 **228** 100f. multicoloured 2·50 1·90
See also No. 612.

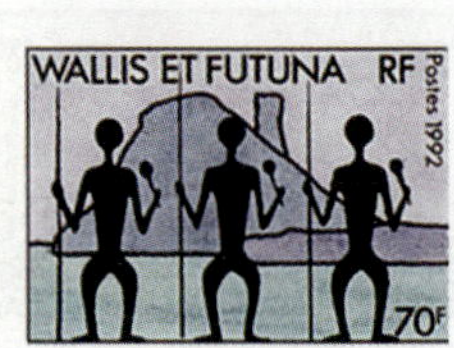

229 Three Spearmen

1992. Wallis Islands. Multicoloured.
606 70f. Type **229** 2·00 1·60
607 70f. Two spearmen and palm trees 2·00 1·60
608 70f. Pirogues 2·00 1·60
609 70f. Two fishermen and palm trees 2·00 1·60
610 70f. Three fishermen and palm trees 2·00 1·60
Nos. 606/10 were issued together, se-tenant, forming a composite design.

1992. Air. "Genova '92" International Thematic Stamp Exhibition. As T **228** but with different Exhibition emblem.
612 800f. multicoloured 16·00 11·00

230 Victorious Marianne

1992. Air. Bicentenary of Year One of First French Republic.
613 **230** 350f. black, blue and red 8·00 5·00

231 "La Garonne" (supply vessel)

1992.
614 **231** 20f. multicoloured 1·25 1·00

232 "L'Idylle d'Ixelles"

1992. 75th Death Anniv of Auguste Rodin (sculptor).
615 **232** 300f. black and mauve 6·75 4·25

233 "Mirabilis jalapa"

1992.
616 **233** 200f. multicoloured 4·00 3·00

234 Dassault Breguet Gardian, Frigate and Native Canoes

1993. French Naval Forces in the Pacific.
617 **234** 130f. multicoloured 3·00 2·50

235 Abstract (J. E. Korda)

1993. School Art.
618 **235** 56f. multicoloured 3·00 2·25
See also Nos. 635/6.

236 Buff-banded Rail

1993. Birds. Multicoloured.
619 50f. Type **236** 1·50 1·40
620 60f. Purple swamphen 1·60 1·50
621 110f. Grey's fruit dove 2·75 2·00

237 Building Facade

1993. Air. Bicentenary of the Louvre, Paris.
622 **237** 315f. ultramarine, red and blue 7·25 4·50

238 Copernicus and Planetary Model

1993. Air. "Polska 93" International Stamp Exhibition, Poznan. 450th Death Anniv of Nicolas Copernicus (astronomer).
623 **238** 600f. red, brown and crimson 13·50 8·75

239 Hibiscus

1993. Mothers' Day. Multicoloured.
624 95f. Type **239** 2·50 1·90
625 120f. Bouquet of stephanotis 2·75 2·25

240 Sail-finned Tang

1993. Fishes. Multicoloured.
626 27f. Spotted rabbitfish 70 1·00
627 35f. Type **240** 1·40 1·25
628 45f. Palette surgeonfish 1·60 1·40
629 53f. Fox-faced rabbitfish 1·90 1·60

241 D'Entrecasteaux and Flagship

1993. Death Bicentenary of Bruni d'Entrecasteaux (explorer).
630 **241** 170f. red, blue and black 4·00 2·75

242 Symbols of Taiwan

1993. "Taipei '93" International Stamp Exhibition.
631 **242** 435f. multicoloured 7·50 6·00

243 Tepa Church, Wallis Island

1993. Churches. Multicoloured.
632 30f. Type **243** 60 50
633 30f. Vilamalia Church, Futuna Island 60 50

244 "La Marseillaise"

1993. Air. Bicentenary of Year Two of First French Republic.
634 **244** 400f. red, blue and black 7·50 5·50

1993. School Art. As T **235**.
635 28f. blue, black and grey 60 40
636 52f. multicoloured 1·00 60
DESIGNS—HORIZ: 28f. Palm trees (T. Tuhimutu). VERT: 52f. People (M. Hakula).

245 Nativity

1993. Christmas.
637 **245** 80f. multicoloured 1·60 1·00

246 "Wallis Landscape" (P. Legris)

1994. Air.
638 **246** 400f. multicoloured 7·00 5·50

247 Landscape and Emblem

1994. Air. "Hong Kong '94" International Stamp Exhibition.
639 **247** 700f. multicoloured 13·00 10·50

248 Emblem

1994. Traditional Crafts Show, Wallis and Futuna.
640 **248** 80f. multicoloured 1·60 1·10

249 Manning the Barricades

1994. 50th Anniv of Liberation of Paris.
641 **249** 110f. black, red and blue 2·40 1·50

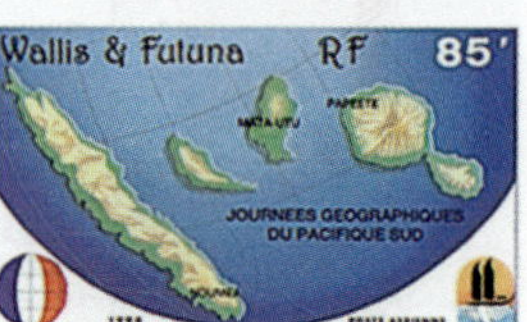

250 Pacific Islands on Globe

1994. Air. South Pacific Geographical Days.
642 **250** 85f. multicoloured 1·60 1·40

251 Earth Station

1994. Satellite Communications.
643 **251** 10f. multicoloured 30 30

252 Goalkeeper saving Ball

1994. World Cup Football Championship, U.S.A.
644 **252** 105f. multicoloured . . . 2·00 1·00

253 Uvean Princesses, 1903

1994.
645 **253** 90f. black, red and blue 1·75 1·25

254 Seaplane

1994. Microlight Aircraft.
646 **254** 5f. multicoloured 10 10

255 Four Suits

1994. Bridge.
647 **255** 40f. multicoloured 80 50

256 Dahlia 257 Trees and Coconuts

1994. Air. 1st European Stamp Salon, Flower Gardens, Paris.
648 **256** 300f. multicoloured . . . 5·50 3·50

1994. The Coconut.
649 **257** 36f. multicoloured 70 50

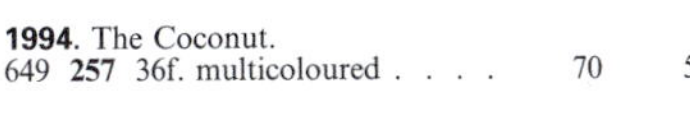

258 Saint-Exupery and Aircraft

1994. Air. 50th Death Anniv of Antoine de Saint-Exupery (author and pilot).
650 **258** 800f. olive, green and blue 14·50 9·50

259 Blue-crowned Lories

1994. Parrots of Futuna.
651 **259** 62f. multicoloured . . . . 1·60 1·10

260 Lodge Emblem and Symbols of Freemasonry

1994. Centenary of Grand Lodge of France.
652 **260** 250f. brown, turquoise and blue . . . . 4·50 3·50

261 Polynesian Baby

1994. Air. Christmas.
653 **261** 150f. multicoloured . . . 3·00 1·90

262 Preparing Traditional Meal (after P. Legris)

1995.
654 **262** 80f. multicoloured . . . . 1·60 90

263 Nukulaelae

1995. Aerial Views of Lagoon Islets. Mult.
655 85f. Type **263** . . . . 1·60 80
656 90f. Nukufetau (vert) . . . . 1·75 90
657 100f. Nukufotu and Nukuloa 1·90 1·50

264 Pasteur

1995. Air. Death Cent of Louis Pasteur (chemist).
658 **264** 350f. multicoloured . . . 6·25 3·50

265 Outrigger Canoes (emblem of district) 266 Emblem

1995. Mua District.
659 **265** 35f. multicoloured 70 40

1995. University of the Pacific Teacher Training Institute.
660 **266** 115f. multicoloured . . . 2·00 1·50

267 Coconuts

1995. Air.
661 **267** 200f. multicoloured . . . 4·00 2·25

268 U.N. Helmet and Blitzed and Rebuilt Cities (½-size illustration)

1995. 50th Anniv of Signing of U.N. Charter.
662 **268** 55f. multicoloured . . . . 1·00 60

269 Young People

1995. Air. 10th Anniv of International Youth Year.
663 **269** 450f. multicoloured . . . 8·25 4·50

270 Javelin Thrower

1995. 10th South Pacific Games, Tahiti.
664 **270** 70f. multicoloured . . . . 1·40 90

271 City Skyline

1995. Air. "Singapore'95" Int Stamp Exn.
665 **271** 500f. multicoloured . . . 8·00 5·50

272 Lumiere Brothers and Film (½-size illustration)

1995. Air. Centenary of Motion Pictures.
666 **272** 600f. multicoloured . . . 9·50 5·50

273 Breadfruit

1995. Shrubs. Multicoloured.
667 20f. Type **273** 50 40
668 60f. Tarot . . . . 1·25 65
669 65f. Kava . . . . 1·40 80
See also Nos. 675/6.

274 De Gaulle

1995. Air. 25th Death Anniv of Charles de Gaulle (French statesman).
670 **274** 315f. black, red and blue 5·50 4·00

275 Human Activities 276 Three Generations

1995. Tapa (bark of paper-mulberry tree) Designs. Multicoloured.
671 25f. Type **275** 50 40
672 26f. Marine life (horiz) . . . 50 40

1995. Island Mothers.
673 **276** 80f. multicoloured . . . . 1·50 90

277 Golf Course

1995. Golfing on Wallis.
674 **277** 95f. multicoloured . . . . 1·75 1·25

1996. Tuberous Plants. As T **273**. Multicoloured.
675 28f. Taro ("Mahoaa") . . . 70 50
676 52f. Yam ("Ufi") . . . . . . 1·00 60

278 Pirogue

1996. Air. World Polynesian Pirogue Championships, Noumea.
677 **278** 240f. multicoloured . . . 4·00 3·00

279 Emblems 280 "Cananga odorata"

1996. Air. Sisia College, Futuna.
678 **279** 235f. multicoloured . . . 4·00 3·00

1996. Flowers. Multicoloured.
679 27f. Type **280** 50 40
680 45f. Hibiscus 80 50

281 Trees reflected in Water

1996. Swamplands.
681 **281** 53f. multicoloured 90 70

282 Chessmen and Board

1996. Chess in Wallis and Futuna.
682 **282** 110f. multicoloured . . . 1·90 1·50

283 Guglielmo Marconi (inventor) and Radio Equipment

1996. Air. Centenary of Radio-telegraphy.
683 **283** 550f. brown, blue and orange . . . . 8·50 6·50

284 Stadium and Sportsmen

1996. Air. Centenary of Modern Olympic Games.
684 **284** 1000f. blue . . . . 17·00 13·00

285 Caladium

1996. Flowers. Multicoloured.
685 30f. Type **285** 60 40
686 48f. Caladium (different) . . 80 50

286 Woman with Stamps in Hair

1996. Air. 50th Autumn Stamp Fair.
687 **286** 175f. multicoloured . . . 3·00 2·25

287 Map and Perroton

1996. Francoise Perroton (first woman missionary to Wallis) Commemoration.
688 **287** 50f. multicoloured 90 70

288 Distressed Woman with Children and Drunken Man

1996. Air. Campaign against Alcohol Abuse.
689 **288** 260f. multicoloured . . . 4·00 3·00

289 Children and Emblem

1996. 50th Anniv of U.N.I.C.E.F.
690 **289** 25f. multicoloured 50 40

290 Emblem

1997. 50th Anniv of South Pacific Commission.
691 **290** 7f. multicoloured 10 10

291 King Lavelua of Uvea (Wallis)

1997. Royal Standards.
692 **291** 56f. red, black and blue 85 40
693 – 60f. multicoloured 90 40
694 – 70f. multicoloured . . . . 1·00 45
DESIGNS: 60f. King Tuiagaifo of Alo (Futuna); 70f. King Tuisigave of Sigave (Futuna).

292 Lapita Pot (1000 B.C.) 293 Kava Brewer

1997. Air. National Centre for Scientific Research.
695 **292** 400f. multicoloured . . . 5·50 4·00

1997.
696 **293** 170f. multicoloured . . . 3·00 2·00

294 Story-telling

1997. Scenes of Island Life. Multicoloured.
697 10f. Type **294** 10 10
698 36f. Hand-weaving mat (vert) 60 50
699 40f. Feasting 70 50

295 Turtle on Beach

1997. The Green Turtle. Multicoloured.
700 62f. Type **295** . . . . 1·00 70
701 80f. Turtle swimming . . . . 1·40 90

296 Airplane approaching Airport

1997. Air. Inauguration of Hihifo Airport.
702 **296** 130f. multicoloured . . . 1·75 1·50

297 Treble Clef, Dancers, Theatre Masks and Fireworks over Papal Palace

1997. 50th Anniv of Avignon Festival.
703 **297** 160f. multicoloured . . . 2·00 1·60

298 Medals and Shot Putter 299 Sunset over Lagoon (after Rebecca Hoatau)

1997. "Handisport" Sporting Event, Berlin.
704 **298** 35f. multicoloured 50 40

1997. Air.
705 **299** 300f. multicoloured . . . 4·00 3·00

300 Club Emblem (½-size illustration)

1997. Uvea Karate Club, Wallis.
706 **300** 24f. multicoloured 40 30

301 Stamps on Globe

1997. Air. 4th Stamp World Cup and 51st Autumn Stamp Show.
707 **301** 350f. multicoloured . . . 4·50 3·50

302 Notre Dame Cathedral, Tanks and Leclerc

1997. Air. 50th Death Anniv of Marshal Leclerc.
709 **302** 800f. multicoloured . . . 10·00 8·00

303 Couple

1997. Anti-AIDS Campaign.
710 **303** 5f. multicoloured 10 10

304 Daudet, Windmill, Foxgloves and Goat

1997. Air. Death Centenary of Alphonse Daudet (writer).
711 **304** 710f. multicoloured . . . 8·50 7·00

305 Nativity

1997. Christmas.
712 **305** 85f. multicoloured . . . . 1·25 90

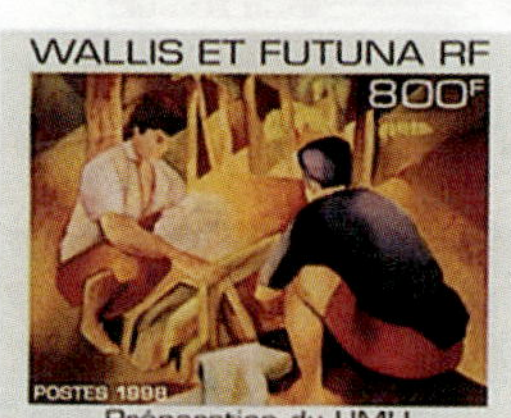

306 "Preparation of Umu" (Christiane Pierret)

1998.
713 **306** 800f. multicoloured . . . 9·75 6·25

307 "Vanda T.M.A."

1998. Orchids. Multicoloured.
714 70f. Type **307** 90 60
715 85f. "Cattleya Bow Bells" (horiz) . . . . 1·25 70
716 90f. "Arachnis" . . . . . . 1·25 70
717 105f. "Cattleya" (horiz) . . . 1·50 85

308 Modern Technology

1998. Telecom 2000.
718 **308** 7f. multicoloured 10 10

309 Alofi Beach

1998. Air.
719 **309** 315f. multicoloured . . . 4·00 3·00

310 Fisherman casting Net

1998. Lagoon Fishing. Multicoloured.
720 50f. Type **310** 60 40
721 52f. Fisherman with catch . . 60 40

311 Footballers

1998. World Cup Football Championship, France.
722 **311** 80f. multicoloured 95 60

312 Darter

1998. Insects. Multicoloured.
723 36f. Type **312** 40 25
724 40f. Cicada 45 30

313 Coral

1998. Corals.
725 **313** 4f. multicoloured 10 10
726 – 5f. multicoloured 10 10
727 – 10f. multicoloured 10 10
728 – 15f. multicoloured 15 10
DESIGNS: 5f. to 15f. Different corals.

314 Cricketer

1998. Air. Cricket.
729 **314** 106f. multicoloured . . . 1·25 75

315 Gauguin and View of Island

1998. Air. 150th Birth Anniv of Paul Gauguin (artist).
730 **315** 700f. multicoloured . . . 8·00 5·00

316 Coral, Sail Canoe and Fishes

1998. 52nd Autumn Stamp Show, Paris.
731 **316** 175f. multicoloured . . . 2·00 1·75

317 "The Garden of Happiness"

1998. Air.
732 **317** 460f. multicoloured . . . 5·25 3·25

318 Jigsaw Pieces

1998. World Anti-AIDS Day.
733 **318** 62f. multicoloured 70 40

319 Polynesian Dancer

321 Precious Wentletrap

320 Carrying Kava

1998. Air.
734 **319** 250f. multicoloured . . . 2·75 1·75

1999. Air.
735 **320** 600f. multicoloured . . . 7·00 4·25

1999. Air. Shells. Multicoloured.
736 95f. Type **321** . . . . 1·10 65
737 100f. Horned helmet . . . . . 1·10 65
738 110f. Trumpet triton (horiz) 1·25 75
739 115f. Common spider conch (horiz) . . . . 1·25 75

322 Rock Formation

1999. Islet of Nuku Taakimoa.
740 **322** 130f. multicoloured . . . 1·50 90

323 "Finemui" (½-size illustration)

1999. Air.
741 **323** 900f. multicoloured . . . 10·50 6·25

325 Little Egrets

1999. Air. Birds of Nuku Fotu. Multicoloured.
743 10f. Type **325** 10 10
744 20f. Audubon's shearwaters 25 15
745 26f. Ascension frigate bird ("Christmas Island Frigate Birds") 30 20
746 54f. Red-tailed tropic bird . . 60 35

326 Emblem and Hibiscus

1999. "Philexfrance 99" International Stamp Exhibition, Paris.
747 **326** 200f. multicoloured . . . 2·00 1·25

327 Senate and Marianne

1999. Bicentenary of French Senate.
748 **327** 125f. blue and red . . . . 1·40 85

328 Assembly Building

1999. Territorial Assembly.
749 **328** 17f. multicoloured 20 10

329 Pandanus Tree

1999.
750 **329** 25f. multicoloured 30 20

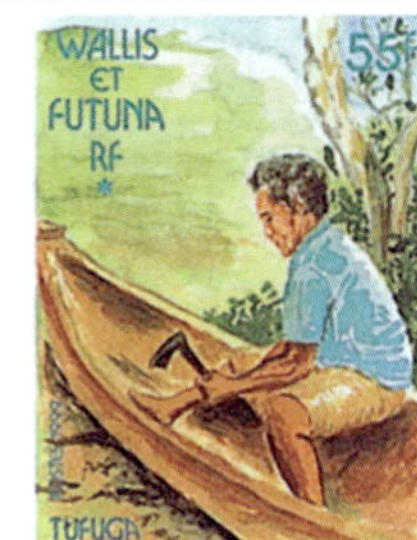

330 Carving Pirogue

1999.
751 **330** 55f. multicoloured 60 35

331 "Wind Song" (modern tourist ship)

1999. Air.
752 **331** 325f. blue, green & ultramarine . . . . . . 3·75 2·25

332 1931 50c. International Colonial Exhibition Stamp

1999. 150th Anniv of First French Postage Stamp.
753 **332** 65f. multicoloured 75 45

333 Sunrise over Lagoon

1999. Air.
754 **333** 500f. multicoloured . . . 5·75 3·50

334 Firework and Globe

2000. New Millennium.
755 **334** 350f. multicoloured . . . 4·00 2·40

335 Mata'Utu Cathedral

2000.
756 **335** 300f. multicoloured . . . 3·50 2·10

336 *La Glorieuse* (patrol boat)

2000.
757 **336** 155f. black, blue and green . . . . 1·75 1·25

337 Makape

2000. 2nd Death Anniv of Sosefo Papilio Makape (President of General Council, 1962–77).
758 **337** 115f. red and blue . . . . 1·25 85

338 Institute Building

2000. French Overseas Monetary Institute.
759 **338** 200f. multicoloured . . . 2·00 1·25

339 Crops

2000.
760 **339** 275f. multicoloured . . . 2·75 1·75

340 Airport and Aircraft

2000. Air. 30th Anniv of Air Transport on Futuna Island.
761 **340** 350f. multicoloured . . . 4·00 2·40

341 Man throwing Spear

2000. Olympic Games, Sydney. Traditional Sports of Wallis and Futuna. Multicoloured.
762 85f. Type **341** . . . . 1·00 60
763 85f. Racing outrigger canoes . . 1·00 60
764 85f. Kayak racing . . . . . 1·00 60
765 85f. Volleyball . . . . 1·00 60

342 Tattooed Profiles

2000. 8th Pacific Arts Festival, Kanaky, New Caledonia.
766 **342** 330f. multicoloured . . . 3·75 2·25

343 Dolphin (fish)

2000. Fishes. Multicoloured.
767 115f. Type **343** . . . . . . 1·25 85
768 115f. Blue-finned trevally (*Caranx melampygus*) (inscr "melanpygus") . . . . . . 1·25 85
769 115f. Yellow-finned tuna (*Thunnus albacares*) . . . . 1·25 85

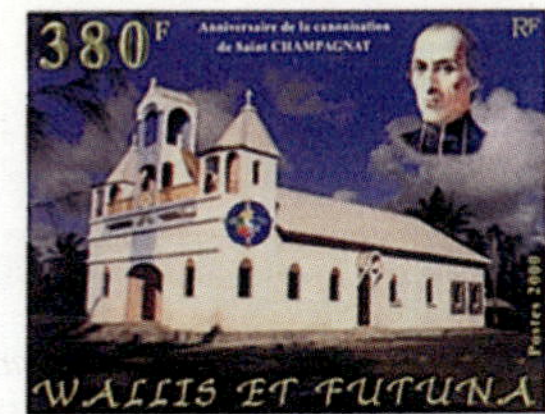

344 Champagnat

2000. Holy Year 2000. First Anniversary of Canonization of Marcellin Champagnat (educationalist and founder of Marist Order).
770 **344** 380f. multicoloured . . . 4·25 2·50

345 Talietumu

2000. Archaeology.
771 **345** 205f. multicoloured . . . 2·00 1·25

346 Mother and Child

2000. Christmas.
772 **346** 225f. multicoloured . . . 2·25 1·40

347 *Jacques Cartier* (landing ship)

2001.
773 **347** 225f. black, blue and green . . . . 2·25 1·40

348 Bottle and Cans

2001. Campaign against Alcoholism.
774 **348** 75f. multicoloured 85 50

349 Design including Shells

2001. Tapas (bark of paper-mulberry tree). Mult.
775 90f. Type **349** . . . . . . 1·10 65
776 90f. Design including leaves, diamonds and triangles . . 1·10 65
777 90f. Scenes of island life . . . 1·10 65
778 90f. Design including overlapping ovals . . . . 1·10 65

350 Mixed Flowers (M. Uhilamoafa)

2001. Children's Flower Paintings. Multicoloured.
779 50f. Type **350** 55 30
780 55f. Stem of flowers 60 35
781 95f. Vase of red and yellow flowers . . . . 1·10 65
782 100f. Pink orchid . . . . . . 1·10 65

351 Man with Arm Raised

2001. 40th Anniv of French Overseas Territory Status.
783 **351** 165f. multicoloured . . . 1·60 1·40

352 Apple Canelle (T. Taika)

2001. Children's Fruit Paintings. Multicoloured.
784 65f. Type **352** 60 50
785 65f. Breadfruit (E. Mougatoga) 60 50
786 65f. Pineapple (E. Hamaivao) 60 50
787 65f. Mango (I. Mougatoga) 60 50

353 Emblem

2001. 1st Anniv of Installation of Delegate of Mediator of the Republic.
788 **353** 800f. multicoloured . . . 7·75 6·25

354 Children encircling Globe

2001. United Nations Year of Dialogue among Civilizations.
789 **354** 390f. multicoloured . . . 3·75 3·00

355 Pacific Pigeon (*Ducula pacifica*)

2001. 55th Autumn Stamp Show. Birds. Mult.
790 150f. Type **355** (inscr "Dacula") . . . . 1·40 1·25
791 150f. Blue-crowned lory (*Vini australis*) . . . . 1·40 1·25
792 150f. Barn owl (*Tyto alba*) 1·40 1·25

356 Grave

2001. Grave of Fakavelikele (first king of Wallis and Futuna).
793 **356** 325f. multicoloured . . . 3·25 2·75

357 Building

2002. Inauguration of Finemui College, Teesi (French college).
794 **357** 115f. multicoloured . . . 1·40 1·10

358 Queen Aloisia

2002. International Women's Day.
795 **358** 800f. brown . . . . . . 9·50 7·50

359 Arms 360 Emblem

2002. Monseigneur Pompallier (first bishop of Western Oceanie).
796 **359** 500f. buff, green and red 6·00 4·75

2002. Fire Service of Uvea Island.
797 **360** 85f. multicoloured . . . . 1·00 80

361 Stylized Footballer

2002. World Cup Football Championship, Japan and South Korea.
798 **361** 65f. multicoloured 40 30

362 Tree, Bird, Turtle and Sea

2002. World Environment Day.
799 **362** 330f. multicoloured . . . 4·00 3·25

363 House with Veranda

2002. Traditional Thatched Houses (fale). Houses. Multicoloured.
800 50f. Type **363** 60 50
801 50f. Without walls (vert) . . 60 50
802 55f. With window shutters . . 65 55
803 55f. Amongst tall trees (vert) 65 55

364 Jacob Lemaire

2002. Discovery of Futuna.
804 125f. Type **364** (joint finder) 1·50 1·25
805 125f. Futuna and Aloti islands . . . . 1·50 1·25
806 125f. William Schouten (joint finder) . . . . 1·50 1·25
MS807 175 × 100 mm (oval) Nos. 804/6 . . . . 4·50 4·50

365 Utua Bay

2002. Landscapes. Multicoloured.
807 95f. Type **365** . . . . 1·10 90
808 100f. Liku Bay . . . . 1·25 1·00
809 105f. Kingfisher and Vele Point . . . . 1·25 1·00
810 135f. Aka Aka Bay . . . . . 1·60 1·25

366 *Enygrus bibroni* (snake)

2002.
811 **366** 75f. multicoloured 90 70

367 Fu Manchu Lion Fish (*Dendrochirus biocellatus*)

2002. 56th Autumn Stamp Show. Fish. Mult.
812 110f. Type **367** . . . . 1·25 1·00
813 110f. Spikefin goby (*Discordipina griessingeri*) 1·25 1·00
814 110f. Spotfin frogfish (*Antennarius nummifer*) (inscr "Antennacius") . . . 1·25 1·00
815 110f. Dragon wrasse (*Novaculichthys taeniourus*) 1·25 1·00

368 Yacht, Sea Cliffs and Beach

2002. Christmas.
816 **368** 140f. multicoloured . . . 1·60 1·25

POSTAGE DUE STAMPS

1920. Postage Due Stamps of New Caledonia optd **ILES WALLIS et FUTUNA**.
D18 **D 18** 5c. blue . . . . 40 3·25
D19 10c. brown on buff . . 40 3·25
D20 15c. green . . . . . . 1·25 3·25
D21 20c. black on yellow . . 80 3·50
D22 30c. red . . . . 50 3·50
D23 50c. blue on cream . . 2·00 4·00
D24 60c. green on blue . . . 1·75 4·25
D25 1f. green on cream . . 2·50 4·75

1927. As Postage Due stamp of New Caledonia, but colour changed, surch.
D43 **D 18** 2f. on 1f. mauve . . . 5·75 17·00
D44 3f. on 1f. brown . . . 7·25 18·00

1930. Postage Due stamps of New Caledonia optd **ILES WALLIS et FUTUNA**.
D85 **D 25** 2c. brown and blue . . 20 2·75
D86 4c. green and red . . 15 3·00
D87 5c. blue and red . . . 20 3·00
D88 10c. blue and purple . . 15 3·00
D89 15c. red and green . . 20 3·00
D90 20c. brown and purple 25 3·00
D91 25c. blue and brown . . 90 3·00
D92 30c. brown and green 1·00 3·50
D93 50c. red and brown . . 1·25 3·00
D94 60c. red and mauve . . 1·75 4·25
D95 1f. green and blue . . 2·00 3·75
D96 2f. brown and red . . 2·00 3·75
D97 3f. brown and mauve 2·00 3·75

1943. Nos. D85/97 optd **FRANCE LIBRE**.
D126 **D 25** 2c. brown and blue . . 11·50 60·00
D127 4c. green and red . . . 11·50 60·00
D128 5c. blue and red . . . 10·50 60·00
D129 10c. blue and purple 10·50 60·00
D130 15c. red and green . . 25·00 60·00
D131 20c. brown and purple 10·50 60·00
D132 25c. blue and brown 10·50 60·00
D133 30c. brown and green 10·50 60·00
D134 50c. red and brown . . 10·00 60·00
D135 60c. red and mauve . . 10·00 60·00
D136 1f. green and blue . . 16·00 65·00
D137 2f. brown and red . . 10·00 65·00
D138 3f. brown and mauve 10·00 65·00

D 10 Moorish Idol

1963. Fishes.
D182 **D 10** 1f. black, yellow & bl 2·00 2·25
D183 – 3f. red, green and blue 2·25 2·75
D184 – 5f. orange, black & bl 3·00 3·25
DESIGNS—HORIZ: 3f. Moon wrasse; 5f. Orange clownfish.

WENDEN Pt. 10

Formerly part of W. Russia but later became part of Latvia. Issued stamps for use within the district until 1903.

100 kopeks = 1 rouble.

2

3

1863. Inscr "Briefmarke des WENDEN-schen Kreises". Imperf.
1 **2** 2k. black and red £200 £250

1863. Inscr "Packenmarke des WENDEN-schen Kreises". Imperf.
2 **3** 4k. black and green £150 £250

6

7

8

1863. Imperf.
6 **6** 2k. green and red . . . . . . 20·00 24·00

1864. As T **6**, but with horse in central oval. Imperf.
5 2k. green and red . . . . . . 60·00 £140

1871. Imperf.
7 **7** 2k. green and red . . . . . . 20·00 25·00

1872. Perf.
8 **8** 2k. red and green . . . . . . 25·00 30·00

9 Arms of Wenden
10 Arms of Wenden

1875.
9 **9** 2k. green and red . . . . . . 6·00 8·50

1878.
10 **10** 2k. green and red . . . . . 6·00 12·00
11 2k. red, brown and green . . 6·00 12·00
13 2k. green, black and red . . 4·00 10·00

11 Castle of Wenden

1901.
14 **11** 2k. brown and green . . . . 5·00 12·00
15 2k. red and green . . . . . 5·00 12·00
16 2k. purple and green . . . . 5·00 12·00

WEST IRIAN Pt. 21

The following stamps superseded Nos. 1/19 of West New Guinea, after the former Dutch territory became part of Indonesia. From 1971 Indonesian stamps have been used.

100 cents or sen = 1 rupiah.

1963. Stamps of Indonesia optd **IRIAN BARAT** or surch also.
1 – 1s. on 70s. red (No. 724) 10 15
2 – 2s. on 90s. green (No. 727) 10 15
3 – 5s. grey (No. 830) 10 15
4 – 6s. on 20s. bistre (No. 833) 10 15
5 – 7s. on 50s. blue (No. 835) 10 15
6 – 10s. brown (No. 831) . . . 20 35
7 – 15s. purple (No. 832) . . . 10 15
8 **134** 25s. green 10 20
9 – 30s. on 75s. red (No. 836) 10 20
10 – 40s. on 1r.15 red (No. 837) 10 20
11 **99** 1r. mauve 20 35
12 2r. green 25 75
13 3r. blue . . . . 1·00 1·25
14 5r. brown . . . . 1·75 2·50

1a Indonesia, from Atjeh to Merauke

1963. Acquisition of West Irian.
21 **1a** 12s. orange, red and black 10 15
22 17s. orange, red and black 10 15
23 – 20s. blue, green and purple 10 15
24 – 50s. blue, green and purple 10 15
25 – 60s. brown, yellow and green 60 90
26 – 75s. brown, yellow and green . . . . 80 1·60
DESIGNS: 20, 50s. Parachutist; 60, 75s. Greater bird of paradise.

2 "Maniltoa gemmipara"

4 Mother and Child Figurine

3 Map of Indonesia

1968. Flora and Fauna.
27 **2** 5s. purple and green 50 75
28 – 15s. violet and green 50 85
29 – 30s. green and orange . . . . 1·00 1·25
30 – 40s. violet and yellow . . . . 1·00 1·25
31 – 50s. black and purple . . . . 2·00 1·75
32 – 75s. black and blue . . . . . 3·25 5·00
33 – 1r. black and brown . . . . 2·25 3·25
34 – 3r. black and green . . . . . 7·00 10·50
35 – 5r. multicoloured . . . . . . 1·50 4·25
36 – 10r. multicoloured . . . . . 2·00 7·25
DESIGNS: 15s. "Dendrobium lancifolium"; 30s. "Gardenia gjellerupii"; 40s. "Maniltoa gemmipara" (blossom); 50s. Common phalanger; 75s. One-wattled cassowary; 1r. Common forest wallaby; 3r. Blue crowned pigeons; 5r. Black-capped lory; 10r. Greater bird of paradise.

1968. West Irian People's Pledge of 9 May 1964.
43 **3** 10s. gold and blue . . . . . 2·25 65
44 25s. gold and red . . . . . 4·00 90

1970. West Irian Woodcarvings. Multicoloured.
45 5s. Type **4** 10 15
46 6s. Carved shield 10 15
47 7s. Man and serpents . . . . 10 1·25
48 10s. Drum . . . . 10 1·25
49 25s. Seated warrior 15 20
50 30s. "Female" drum 20 20
51 50s. Bamboo vessel 45 20
52 75s. Seated man and tree . . . 45 20
53 1r. Decorated shield 50 35
54 2r. Seated figure 60 35
Nos. 45/54 are inscr "I.B." ("Irian Barat").

POSTAGE DUE STAMPS

1963. Postage Due Stamps as Type D **100** of Indonesia optd **IRIAN BARAT**.
D15 1s. slate 10 25
D16 5s. olive 10 25
D17 10s. turquoise 10 25
D18 25s. slate 10 25
D19 40s. orange 10 50
D20 100s. brown . . . . 15 1·25

1968. As Type D **100** of Indonesia, but with coloured network background incorporating "1968", optd **IRIAN BARAT**.
D37 1s. blue and green 10 50
D38 5s. green and pink 10 50
D39 10s. red and grey 10 50
D40 25s. green and yellow . . . 10 50
D41 40s. purple and green . . . 45 1·00
D42 100s. red and olive . . . . . 85 2·00

WEST NEW GUINEA Pt. 4

U.N. Administration of former Netherlands New Guinea from 1 October 1962 to 30 April 1963, when it became known as West Irian and became part of Indonesia.

100 cents = 1 gulden.

1962. "United Nations Temporary Executive Authority". Stamps of Netherlands New Guinea optd **UNTEA**.
1 **5** 1c. yellow and red 50 65
21 – 2c. orange 50 60
3 **5** 5c. yellow and brown 75 65
4 – 7c. purple, bl & brn (No. 60) 80 1·00
5 – 10c. brown and blue (No. 27) 75 60
6 – 12c. pur, bl & grn (No. 61) 1·00 1·25
7 – 15c. brown & yell (No. 28) 1·00 1·25
8 – 17c. pur, bl & blk (No. 62) 1·00 1·00
9 – 20c. brown & green (No. 29) 1·00 1·00
10 **6** 25c. red 85 90
11 30c. blue . . . . 95 1·00
12 40c. orange . . . . 95 1·00
13 45c. green . . . . 2·00 1·90
14 55c. turquoise . . . . 1·50 3·25
34 80c. grey . . . . 10·00 12·00
35 85c. brown . . . . 4·50 5·00
36 1g. purple . . . . 4·50 4·50
37 – 2g. brown (No. 20) . . . . . 11·00 12·50
19 – 5g. green (No. 21) . . . . . 8·50 9·00

For later issues see **WEST IRIAN**.

WEST UKRAINE Pt. 10

Before the 1914/18 War this district, known as E. Galicia was part of Austria. It achieved temporary independence after the war when stamps were issued. In June 1919 it became part of Poland but was transferred to the Ukraine in 1945.

100 heller = 1 krone.

(5)

1919. Stamps of Austria 1916 optd with T **5**.
70 **49** 3h. violet 30
71 5h. green 30
72 6h. orange 30

No.	Type	Description	Price
73		10h. red	30
74		12h. blue	30
75	60	15h. red	30
76		20h. green	30
77		25h. blue	30
78		30h. violet	30
79	51	40h. olive	40
80		50h. green	40
81		60h. blue	40
82		80h. brown	50
83		90h. purple	50
84		1k. red on yellow	55
85	52	2k. blue	65
86		3k. red	90
87		4k. green	5·00
88		10k. violet	6·50

For other issues, which were mainly of a local character, see Part 10 (Russia) of the standard catalogue.

WESTERN AUSTRALIA Pt. 1

The western state of the Australian Commonwealth, whose stamps it now uses.

12 pence = 1 shilling;
20 shillings = 1 pound.

1

2

3

1854. Imperf or roul.

No.	Type	Description	Mint	Used
1	1	1d. black	£800	£180
25		2d. orange	75·00	70·00
3	2	4d. blue	£250	£160
26	1	4d. blue	£250	£1600
28		6d. green	£1200	£400
4c	3	1s. brown	£350	£275

5

7

1857. Imperf or roul.

No.	Type	Description	Mint	Used
15	5	2d. brown on red	£2000	£500
18		6d. bronze	£2250	£600

1861. Perf.

No.	Type	Description	Mint	Used
103	1	1d. red	16·00	2·75
76		1d. yellow	20·00	1·25
39		2d. blue	85·00	32·00
77		2d. yellow	25·00	1·00
104		2d. grey	45·00	1·00
56		4d. red	70·00	4·00
105		4d. brown	75·00	19·00
42		6d. brown	£225	45·00
57		6d. violet	80·00	6·00
61		1s. green	£110	12·00

1871.

No.	Type	Description	Mint	Used
141	7	3d. brown	16·00	1·50

1874. Surch **ONE PENNY**.

No.	Type	Description	Mint	Used
67	1	1d. on 2d. yellow	£275	50·00

1884. Surch in figures.

No.	Type	Description	Mint	Used
90	1	½d. on 1d. yellow	9·00	16·00
91a	7	1d. on 3d. brown	45·00	11·00

12

13

14 15

1885.

No.	Type	Description	Mint	Used
94	12	½d. green	3·25	50
112	13	1d. red	4·75	10
96a	14	2d. grey	23·00	90
113		2d. yellow	14·00	1·75
97a		2½d. blue	9·00	90
98		4d. brown	9·00	90
99		5d. yellow	8·50	3·00
100	15	6d. violet	15·00	1·00
102		1s. green	17·00	3·75

1893. Surch in words.

No.	Type	Description	Mint	Used
110a	7	½d. on 3d. brown	5·50	22·00
107		1d. on 3d. brown	11·00	3·00

23 19

24

21

28

29

30

31

32

1901.

No.	Type	Description	Mint	Used
140	23	2d. yellow	6·50	1·75
114	19	2½d. blue	8·00	50
119	24	4d. brown	12·00	1·75
143	15	5d. olive	14·00	6·00
168	19	6d. violet	11·00	7·00
121	12	8d. green	18·00	2·50
145	24	9d. orange	25·00	4·00
146	19	10d. red	22·00	15·00
116	21	1s. green	27·00	3·50
124b	28	2s. red on yellow	40·00	8·50
125	29	2s.6d. blue on red	40·00	8·00
126	30	5s. green	65·00	22·00
127	31	10s. mauve	£150	65·00
128	32	£1 orange	£275	£150

1906. Surch **ONE PENNY**.

No.	Type	Description	Mint	Used
172	23	1d. on 2d. yellow	80	80

WURTTEMBERG Pt. 7

Formerly an independent kingdom, Wurttemberg became part of the German Empire in 1902.

1851. 60 kreuzer = 1 gulden.
1875. 100 pfennige = 1 mark.

1

2

1851. Imperf.

No.	Type	Description	Mint	Used
1	1	1k. black on buff	£1000	85·00
3		3k. black on yellow	£275	6·00
5		6k. black on green	£1300	30·00
7		9k. black on pink	£4250	32·00
9		18k. black on lilac	£1300	£600

1857. Imperf.

No.	Type	Description	Mint	Used
10	2	1k. brown	£550	65·00
24		3k. orange	£275	6·50
15		6k. green	£550	50·00
17		9k. red	£850	50·00
19		18k. blue	£2500	£1100
85		70k. violet	£1600	£3500

1859. Perf.

No.	Type	Description	Mint	Used
45	2	1k. brown	£300	£275
40		3k. yellow	65·00	25·00
41		6k. green	£250	60·00
42		9k. red	£700	£150
43		9k. purple	£750	£225
44		18k. blue	£1400	£1200

1863. Perf or roul.

No.	Type	Description	Mint	Used
60	2	1k. green	32·00	6·75
63		3k. pink	32·00	2·20
54		6k. blue	£140	48·00
66		7k. blue	£900	£130
57		9k. brown	£250	48·00
59		18k. orange	£1100	£350

3 4

1869. Roul or perf (1k.); perf (others).

No.	Type	Description	Mint	Used
72	3	1k. green	26·00	2·20
74		2k. orange	£170	£120
77		3k. pink	12·50	1·10
78		7k. blue	55·00	£150
80		9k. bistre	75·00	35·00
82		14k. yellow	75·00	£400

1875. New Currency.

No.	Type	Description	Mint	Used
123	4	2pf. grey	1·80	90
89		3pf. green	17·00	1·70
124		3pf. brown	75	55
91		5pf. mauve	7·25	75
127		5pf. green	1·50	55
93		10pf. red	1·10	75
95		20pf. blue	1·10	75
97		25pf. brown	£110	8·75
130		25pf. orange	2·50	1·10
151		30pf. black and orange	3·00	4·00
152		40pf. black and red	3·75	5·00
99		50pf. grey	£650	35·00
101		50pf. green	55·00	5·00
132		50pf. brown	2·50	1·10
102		2m. yellow	£650	£275
103		2m. red on orange	£1800	£150
121		2m. black and orange	7·25	8·50
122		5m. black and blue	40·00	£170

For issues of 1947–49 see Germany (French Zone).

MUNICIPAL SERVICE STAMPS

M 5

1875.

No.	Type	Description	Mint	Used
M147	M 5	2pf. grey	1·40	1·70
M169		2½pf. grey	70	30
M170		3pf. brown	80	30
M104		5pf. mauve	34·00	2·75
M171		5pf. green	80	30
M172		7½pf. orange	70	30
M173		10pf. red	80	30
M261		10pf. orange	45	30
M174		15pf. brown	1·60	30
M262		15pf. violet	45	30
M176		20pf. blue	1·60	30
M263		20pf. green	40	25
M177		25pf. orange	75	25
M178		25pf. black and brown	1·00	25
M179		35pf. brown	2·50	90
M264		40pf. red	40	25
M265		50pf. purple	80	25
M266		60pf. green	1·10	25
M267		1m.25 green	80	25
M268		2m. grey	80	25
M269		3m. brown	80	25

1906. Centenary of Establishment of Kingdom. Optd **1806–1906** under crown.

No.	Type	Description	Mint	Used
M153	M 5	2pf. grey	38·00	10·50
M154		3pf. brown	12·50	10·50
M155		5pf. green	4·00	4·00
M156		10pf. pink	4·00	45·00
M157		25pf. orange	48·00	10·50

1916. Surch **25 Pf.**

No.	Type	Description	Mint	Used
M199	M 5	25pf. on 25pf. orange	3·00	75

M 9

M 14

1916. Jubilee of King Wilhelm II.

No.	Type	Description	Mint	Used
M202	M 9	2½pf. grey	1·80	1·30
M203		7½pf. red	1·80	1·30
M204		10pf. red	1·80	1·30
M205		15pf. bistre	1·80	1·30
M206		20pf. blue	1·80	1·30
M207		25pf. grey	4·00	1·30
M208		50pf. brown	7·50	1·40

1919. Surch **2.**

No.	Type	Description	Mint	Used
M219	M 5	2 on 2½pf. grey	75	75

1919. Optd **Volksstaat Wurttemberg.**

No.	Type	Description	Mint	Used
M222	M 5	2½pf. grey	40	55
M223		3pf. brown	11·00	55
M224		5pf. green	40	55
M225		7½pf. orange	75	55
M226		10pf. pink	40	55
M227		15pf. purple	40	55
M228		20pf. blue	40	55
M229		25pf. black and brown	40	55
M230		35pf. brown	4·50	55
M231		50pf. purple	5·00	55

1920.

No.	Type	Description	Mint	Used
M245	M 14	10pf. purple	2·50	1·50
M246		15pf. brown	2·50	1·50
M247		20pf. blue	2·20	1·50
M248		30pf. green	2·20	1·50
M249		50pf. yellow	2·20	1·50
M250		75pf. bistre	4·50	1·60

1922. Surch in Marks.

No.	Type	Description	Mint	Used
M270	M 5	5m. on 10pf. orange	40	40
M271		10m. on 15pf. violet	40	40
M272		12m. on 40pf. red	40	40
M273		20m. on 10pf. orange	40	40
M274		25m. on 20pf. green	40	40
M275		40m. on 20pf. green	40	40
M276		50m. on 60pf. green	40	40
M277		60m. on 1m.25 green	40	40
M278		100m. on 40pf. red	40	40
M279		200m. on 2m. grey	40	40
M280		300m. on 50pf. purple	40	40
M281		400m. on 3m. brown	55	40
M282		1000m. on 60pf. green	55	45
M283		2000m. on 1m.25 grn	55	45

1923. Surch with new value (T = Tausend (thousand); M = Million; Md = Milliard).

No.	Type	Description	Mint	Used
M284	M 5	5T. on 10pf. orange	55	45
M285		20T. on 40pf. red	55	45
M286		50T. on 15pf. violet	2·50	45
M287		75T. on 2m. grey	5·50	45
M288		100T. on 20pf. green	55	45
M289		250T. on 3m. brown	55	45
M290		1M. on 60pf. green	3·75	45
M291		2M. on 50pf. purple	55	45
M292		5M. on 1m.25 green	95	45
M293		4Md. on 50pf. purple	14·50	45
M294		10Md. on 3m. brown	8·75	45

1923. Surch in figures only, representing gold pfennige.

No.	Type	Description	Mint	Used
M295	M 5	3pf. on 25pf. orange	75	35
M296		5pf. on 25pf. orange	75	35
M297		10pf. on 25pf. orange	75	35
M298		20pf. on 25pf. orange	75	35
M299		50pf. on 25pf. orange	1·70	35

OFFICIAL STAMPS

O 5

O 10 King Wilhelm II

1881.

No.	Type	Description	Mint	Used
O181	O 5	2pf. grey	45	25
O182		2½pf. grey	55	25
O108		3pf. green	21·00	4·00
O183		3pf. brown	45	25
O112		5pf. mauve	5·50	2·20
O184		5pf. green	45	25
O185		7½pf. orange	55	25
O186		10pf. pink	45	25
O187		15pf. brown	55	25
O188		15pf. purple	1·80	65
O189		20pf. blue	45	25
O117		25pf. brown	32·00	6·75
O191		25pf. orange	45	25
O192		25pf. black and brown	90	25
O193		30pf. black and orange	45	25
O194		35pf. brown	2·75	3·00
O195		40pf. black and red	45	25
O119		50pf. green	7·50	9·50
O141		50pf. brown	£225	£1400
O196		50pf. purple	45	25
O120		1m. yellow	70·00	£190
O197		1m. violet	2·20	25
O198		1m. black and grey	4·00	65

1906. Centenary of Establishment of Kingdom. Optd **1806–1906** under crown.

No.	Type	Description	Mint	Used
O158	O 5	2pf. grey	25·00	13·00
O159		3pf. brown	5·00	30
O160		5pf. green	4·50	30
O161		10pf. pink	4·50	30
O162		20pf. blue	4·50	30
O163		25pf. orange	11·00	11·00
O164		30pf. black and orange	11·00	13·00
O165		40pf. black and red	32·00	13·00
O166		50pf. purple	32·00	13·00
O167		1m. violet	65·00	13·00

1916. Surch.

No.	Type	Description	Mint	Used
O200	O 5	25pf. on 25pf. orange	2·50	75
O201		50pf. on 50pf. purple	2·75	90

1916. Jubilee of King Wilhelm II.

No.	Type	Description	Mint	Used
O209	O 10	2½pf. grey	1·70	55
O210		7½pf. red	1·70	55
O211		10pf. red	1·70	55
O212		15pf. bistre	1·70	55
O213		20pf. blue	1·70	55
O214		25pf. grey	3·25	75
O215		30pf. green	3·25	75
O216		40pf. purple	5·00	75
O217		50pf. brown	5·50	75
O218		1m. mauve	5·50	1·00

1919. Surch in figures only.

No.	Type	Description	Mint	Used
O220	O 5	2 on 2½pf. grey	2·75	1·50
O221		75 on 3pf. brown (O183)	2·20	1·10

1919. Optd **Volksstaat Wurttemberg.**

No.	Type	Description	Mint	Used
O232	O 5	2½pf. grey	1·10	40
O233		3pf. brown	15·00	75

O234 5pf. green 75 40
O235 7½pf. orange 85 40
O236 10pf. pink 75 40
O237 15pf. purple 75 40
O238 20pf. blue 85 40
O239 25pf. black and brown 85 40
O240 30pf. black and orange 1·40 40
O241 35pf. brown 1·10 40
O242 40pf. black and red 90 40
O243 50pf. purple 1·50 60
O244 1m. black and green 1·70 75

O 16 Ulm

1920.
O251 – 10pf. purple 1·30 1·00
O252 O 16 15pf. brown 1·30 1·00
O253 – 20pf. blue 1·30 1·00
O254 – 30pf. green 1·30 1·00
O255 – 50pf. yellow 1·30 1·00
O256 O 16 75pf. bistre 1·30 1·00
O257 – 1m. red 1·30 1·00
O258 – 1m.25 violet 1·30 1·00
O259 – 2m.50 blue 3·25 1·00
O260 – 3m. green 4·50 90
VIEWS: 10, 50pf., 2m.50, 3m. Stuttgart; 20pf., 1m. Tubingen; 30pf., 1m.25, Ellwangen.

YEMEN Pt. 19

A Republic in S.W. Arabia, ruled as a kingdom and imamate until 1962. From 1962 stamps were issued concurrently by the Republican Government and the Royalists. The latter are listed after the Republican issues.

In 1990 the Yemen Arab Republic and Yemen People's Democratic Republic united (see YEMEN REPUBLIC (combined)).

1926. 40 bogaches = 1 imadi.
1964. 40 bogaches = 1 rial.
1975. 100 fils = 1 riyal.

KINGDOM

1 (2½b.)

1926. Imperf or perf.
1 1 2½b. black on white 38·00 38·00
2 2½b. black on orange 38·00 38·00
3 5b. black on white 38·00 38·00

2

3

1930.
10 2 ½b. yellow 25 25
11 1b. green 25 15
5 2b. green 65 50
12 2b. brown 40 25
13 3b. lilac 40 25
14 4b. red 75 40
15 5b. grey 90 65
16 3 6b. blue 1·25 90
17 8b. purple 1·50 1·00
18 10b. brown 1·90 1·25
19 20b. green 6·25 4·50
9 1i. blue and brown 18·00 11·50
20 1i. green and purple 16·00 11·00

4 Flags of Saudi Arabia, Yemen and Iraq

7

(6)

8

1939. 2nd Anniv of Arab Alliance.
21 4 4b. blue and red 1·75 75
22 6b. ultramarine and blue 1·00 1·00
23 10b. blue and brown 1·40 1·40
24 14b. blue and green 2·50 2·50
25 20b. blue and green 3·75 3·75
26 1i. blue and purple 7·50 7·50

1939. Surch with T 6.
27 2 4b. on ½b. yellow 7·50 3·25
65 4b. on 1b. green 2·50 1·25
66 4b. on 2b. brown 9·00 3·75
67 4b. on 3b. lilac 2·50 1·25
68 4b. on 5b. grey 2·50 1·25

1940.
28 7 ¼b. blue and orange 25 25
29 1b. red and green 25 25
30 2b. violet and bistre 40 25
31 3b. blue and mauve 40 25
32 4b. green and red 40 25
33 5b. bistre and green 50 25
34 8 6b. orange and blue 65 25
35 8b. blue and purple 65 40
36 10b. green and orange 75 55
37 14b. violet and green 1·00 90
38 18b. black and green 1·90 1·50
39 20b. purple and green 2·50 1·90
40 1i. red, green and purple 6·25 3·75
The 5b. (for which there had originally been no postal use) was released in 1957 to serve as 4b., without surcharge.

9

10

1942.
41 9 1b. green and orange 25 20
42 2b. green and orange 30 20
43 4b. green and orange 40 30
44 6b. green and orange 50 35
45 8b. blue and orange 85 50
46 10b. blue and orange 1·10 65
47 12b. blue and orange 1·40 1·00
48 20b. blue and orange 2·75 1·75
Although inscribed "TAXE A PERCEVOIR" these stamps were only used for ordinary postage purposes as there was no postage due system in Yemen.

1945. Surch with T 6.
49a 7 4b. on ½b. blue and orange 2·50 1·00
50 4b. on 1b. red and green 2·50 1·25
51a 4b. on 2b. violet and bistre 1·75 1·10
52a 4b. on 3b. blue and mauve 2·00 1·25
53 4b. on 5b. bistre and green 2·50 1·25

1949. Inauguration of Yemeni Hospital.
54 10 4b. black and orange 1·25 90
55 6b. pink and green 1·90 1·50
56 10b. blue and green 2·50 2·00
57 14b. olive and green 4·50 3·25

11 Coffee Plant

12 Douglas DC-4 Airliner over Sana'a

1947.
58 11 ½b. brown (postage) 10 10
59 1b. purple 25 20
60 2b. violet 45 40
61 – 4b. red 45 40
62 – 5b. blue 40 40
62a 11 6b. green 75 60
63 12 10b. blue (air) 5·50 5·50
64 20b. green 7·50 7·50
DESIGN—VERT: 4b., 5b. Palace, Sana'a.
The 5b. was put on sale in 1957 to serve as 4b., without surcharge.

1949. Surch as T 6 (size varies).
68a 11 4b. on ½b. brown 2·00 1·40
69a 4b. on 1b. purple 1·90 1·40
70b 4b. on 2b. blue 2·25 70

13 View of Sana'a Parade Ground
15 Palace of the Rock, Wadi Dhahr

14 Flag and View of Sana'a and Hodeida

1951. (a) Postage.
71 13 1b. brown 15 15
72 2b. brown 15 15
73 3b. mauve 25 15
74 – 5b. red and blue 35 15
75 – 6b. red and purple 45 20
76 – 8b. green and blue 45 20
77 – 10b. purple 60 30
78 – 14b. green 90 35
79 – 20b. red 1·75 60
80 – 1i. violet 2·75 1·50
DESIGNS—HORIZ: 5b. Yemeni flag; 10b. Mosque, Sana'a; 14b. Walled city of Sana'a; 20b., 1i. Taiz and citadel. VERT: 6b. Eagle and Yemeni flag; 8b. Coffee plant.

(b) Air. With airplane.
81 6b. blue 1·75 1·40
82 8b. brown 2·50 1·75
83 10b. green 5·00 3·75
84 12b. blue 3·25 2·50
85 16b. purple 3·25 2·50
86 20b. orange 5·00 3·75
87 1i. red 13·00 8·00
DESIGNS—HORIZ: 6b., 8b. Sana'a; 10b. Trees; 16b. Taiz Palace. VERT: 12b. Palace of the Rock, Wadi Dhahr; 20b. Crowd of people; 1i. Land-scape.
The 5b. postage stamp was released in 1956 to serve as 4b. without surcharge and it was again put on sale as 8b. in 1957. The 6b. and 8b. air stamps were released in 1957 to serve as ordinary postage stamps.

1952. 4th Anniv of Accession of King Ahmed. Flag in red. Perf or imperf.
88 14 1i. black and lake (postage) 18·00 18·00
89 1i. blue and brown (air) 15·00 15·00

1952. 4th Anniv of Victory. As T 14 but inscr "COMMEMORATION OF VICTORY". Flag in red. Perf or imperf.
90 30b. green and red (postage) 12·00 12·00
91 30b. blue and green (air) 12·00 12·00

1952. Surch as T 6.
91 13 4b. on 1b. brown 2·00 1·75
92 4b. on 2b. brown 1·25 1·25
93 4b. on 3b. mauve 2·00 1·75

1952. Sky in blue. Perf or imperf.
94 15 12b. green & brn (postage) 6·00 6·00
95 – 20b. brown and red 9·50 9·50
96 15 12b. brown and green (air) 10·00 10·00
97 – 20b. brown and blue 9·00 9·00
DESIGN: 20b. (2), Walls of Ibb.

1953. Surch as T 6.
98 9 4b. on 1b. green and orange 4·50 3·75
99 4b. on 2b. green and orange 4·50 3·75

16

16a Bab al-Yemen Gate, Sana'a

1953.
100 16 4b. orange (postage) 45 20
101 6b. blue 65 40
102 8b. green 90 50
103 10b. red (air) 45 30
104 12b. blue 60 45
105 20b. brown 1·00 65

1956. Unissued official stamps issued for ordinary postal use without surch.
105a 16a 1b. brown 40 25
105b 5b. blue 40 25
105c 10b. blue 70 50
The 1 and 5b. were each sold for use as 4b. and the 10b. as 10b. for inland registered post.

1957. Arab Postal Union. As T **96a** of Syria but inscr "YEMEN" at top and inscriptions in English.
106 4b. brown 1·00 85
107 6b. green 1·25 1·00
108 16b. violet 1·60 1·25

1959. 1st Anniv of Proclamation of United Arab States (U.A.R. and Yemen). As T **139a** of Syria.
109 1b. black and red (postage) 20 20
110 2b. black and green 30 30
111 4b. red and green 40 35
112 6b. black and orange (air) 40 35
113 10b. black and red 70 45
114 16b. red and violet 80 50

1959. Arab Telecommunications Union. As T **138a** of Syria.
115 4b. red 50 50

1959. Inauguration of Automatic Telephone, Sana'a. Optd **AUTOMATIC TELEPHONE INAUGURATION SANAA MARCH 1959** in English and Arabic.
116 3 6b. blue 1·90 1·25
117 8b. red 2·00 2·00
118 10b. brown 2·50 2·50
119 20b. green 5·00 5·00
120 1i. green and red 7·50 7·50

1960. Air. Optd with Douglas DC-4 airliner and **AIR MAIL 1959** in English and Arabic.
121 3 6b. blue 2·00 2·00
122 10b. brown 3·50 3·50

1960. Inaug of Arab League Centre, Cairo. As T **154a** of Syria but with different arms.
123 4b. black and green 30 25

IMPERF STAMPS. From this point many issues also exist imperf. This applies also to Republican and Royalist issues.

1960. World Refugee Year. As T **155a** of Syria.
124 4b. brown 50 50
125 6b. green 75 75

19 Olympic Torch

1960. Olympic Games, Rome.
126 19 2b. red and black 15 15
127 4b. yellow and black 25 25
128 6b. orange and black 45 45
129 8b. green and brown 70 70
130 20b. orange and violet 1·10 90

20 U.N. Emblem

1961. 15th Anniv of U.N.O.
131 20 1b. violet 15 15
132 2b. green 15 15
133 3b. blue 15 15
134 4b. blue 25 25
135 6b. purple 60 60
136 14b. red 1·00 70
137 20b. brown 2·25 1·90

21 Hodeida Port and Freighter

1961. Inauguration of Hodeida Port.
138 21 4b. multicoloured 50 40
139 6b. multicoloured 95 75
140 16b. multicoloured 1·90 1·90

22 Alabaster Death-mask   **23** Imam's Palace, Sana'a

1961. Statues of Marib.
141 1b. black and orange (postage) 15 15
142 2b. black and violet 20 15
143 4b. black and brown 20 15
144 8b. black and mauve 25 15
145 10b. black and yellow 45 30
146 12b. black and blue 60 45
147 20b. black and grey 70 60
148 1i. black and green 1·50 1·10

149 6b. black and green (air) 15 15
150 16b. black and blue 2·50 1·50

DESIGNS: 1b. Type **22**; 2b. Horned head (8th-century B.C. frieze, Temple of the Moon God); 4b. Bronze head of Himyaritic emperor of 1st or 2nd century; 6b. "Throne of Bilqis" (8th-century B.C. limestone columns, Moon God Temple); 8b. Bronze figure of Himyaritic Emperor Dhamar Ali, 2nd or 3rd century; 10b. Alabaster statuette of 2nd or 3rd-century child; 12b. Entrance to Moon God Temple; 16b. Control tower and spillway, Marib dam; 20b. 1st-century alabaster relief of boy with dagger riding legendary monster, Moon God Temple; 1i. 1st-century alabaster relief of woman with grapes, Moon God Temple.

1961. Yemeni Buildings.
151 4b. black, grn & turq (postage) 20 15
152 8b. black, green and mauve 40 30
153 10b. black, green and orange 45 40

154 6b. black, green and blue (air) 25 25
155 16b. black, green and pink 1·75 2·00

DESIGNS—VERT: 4b. Type **23**; 10b. Palace of the Rock, Wadi Dhahr; 16b. Palace of the Rock (different view). HORIZ: 6b. Bab al-Yemen Gate, Sana'a; 8b. Imam's Palace, Sana'a (different view).

24 Hodeida–Sana'a Highway

1961. Inaug of Hodeida–Sana'a Highway.
156 **24** 4b. multicoloured 40 25
157 6b. multicoloured 55 35
158 10b. multicoloured 90 45

25 Nubian Temple

1962. U.N.E.S.C.O. Campaign for Preservation of Nubian Monuments.
159 **25** 4b. brown 65 45
160 6b. green 1·50 1·00

1962. Arab League Week. As T **178** of Syria.
161 4b. green 30 25
162 6b. blue 40 35

26 Nurse weighing Child   **26a** Campaign Emblem

1962. Maternity and Child Centre. Multicoloured.
163 2b. Putting child to bed 25 25
164 4b. Type **26** 30 30
165 6b. Taking child's temperature 35 35
166 10b. Weighing baby 55 45

1962. Malaria Eradication.
167 **26a** 4b. orange and black 25 15
168 – 6b. green and brown 55 40

DESIGN: 6b. As T **26a** but with laurel and inscription around emblem.

1962. 17th Anniv of U.N.O. Nos. 131/7 optd **1945-1962** in English and Arabic with bars over old dates.
169 **20** 1b. violet 45 45
170 2b. green 45 45
171 3b. blue 45 45
172 4b. blue 45 45
173 6b. purple 45 45
174 14b. red 45 45
175 20b. brown 2·25 2·25

REPUBLIC

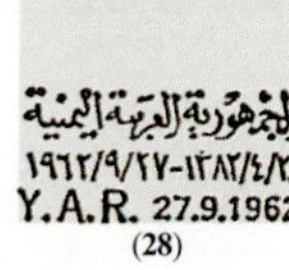

(**28**)

1963. Various issues optd as T **28**. (a) Nos. 141/50.
176 1b. black and orange (postage) 15 15
177 2b. black and violet 15 15
178 4b. black and brown 40 40
179 8b. black and mauve 65 65
180 10b. black and yellow 1·25 1·25
181 12b. black and blue 1·25 1·25
182 20b. black and grey 1·60 1·60
183 1i. black and green 5·00 5·00

184 6b. black and turquoise (air) 70 70
185 16b. black and blue 1·90 1·90

(b) Nos. 151/5.
186 4b. black, grn & turq (postage) 40 40
187 8b. black, green and mauve 1·00 1·00
188 10b. black, green and orange 1·60 1·60

189 6b. black, green and blue (air) 75 75
190 16b. black, green and pink 2·50 2·50

(c) Nos. 163/6.
191 2b. multicoloured 40 40
192 4b. multicoloured 40 40
193 6b. multicoloured 50 50
194 10b. multicoloured 1·90 1·90

29 "Torch of Freedom"

1963. "Proclamation of Republic".
195 – 4b. brown & mauve (postage) 50 50
196 – 6b. red and blue 75 75

197 – 8b. black and purple (air) 95 95
198 **29** 10b. red and violet 1·60 1·60
199 – 16b. red and green 1·90 1·90

DESIGNS—VERT: 4b. Soldier with flag; 6b. Tank and flag; 8b. Bayonet and torch. HORIZ: 16b. Flag and torch.

29a Cow and Emblem

1963. Freedom from Hunger.
200 **29a** 4b. brown and red 65 50
201 – 6b. yellow and violet 75 70

DESIGN: 6b. Corn-cob and ear of wheat.

Y.A.R.
27-9-1962

(**30**)

Y. A. R.
27. 9. 1962

(**31**)

1963. Various issues optd. (a) With T **30**. On Nos. 161/2.
202 4b. green 2·00 2·00
203 6b. blue 4·25 4·25

(b) With T **31**.
207 **2** 5b. grey 95 95
204 **3** 6b. blue 1·25 1·25
208 8b. purple 1·25 1·25
205 10b. brown 1·90 1·90
210 20b. green 2·25 2·25
206 1i. blue and brown 5·50 5·50
211 1i. green and purple 5·50 5·50

(c) As T **31** but with lowest line of inscription at top.
212 **10** 6b. pink and green 1·75 1·75
213 10b. blue and green 3·00 3·00
214 14b. olive and green 5·00 5·00

(d) As T **31** but with lowest line of inscription omitted and bar at top. On Nos. 167/8.
215 4b. orange and black 2·25 2·25
216 6b. green and brown 3·00 3·00

Y. A. R 27. 9. 1962

(**32**)

(e) With T **32**. (i) On Nos. 139/40.
217 **21** 6b. multicoloured 1·25 1·25
218 16b. multicoloured 2·00 2·00

(ii) On Nos. 157/8.
219 **24** 6b. multicoloured 1·25 1·25
220 10b. multicoloured 1·90 1·90

(f) As T **32** but with only one bar over old inscription. (i) Nos. 126/8.
221 **19** 2b. red and black 6·25 6·25
222 4b. yellow and black 6·25 6·25
223 6b. orange and black 6·25 6·25

(ii) Nos. 159/60.
224 **25** 4b. brown 8·25 8·25
225 6b. green 10·50 10·50

(**34**)   **35** Flag and Laurel Sprig

(g) Air. With T **34**.
226 **4** 6b. ultramarine and blue 1·00 1·00
227 10b. blue and brown 1·25 1·25
228 14b. blue and green 1·60 1·60
229 20b. blue and green 2·50 2·50
230 1i. blue and purple 5·00 5·00

1963. 1st Anniv of Revolution.
231 – 2b. red, green and black 40 25
232 – 4b. red, black and green 50 40
233 **35** 6b. red, black and green 1·00 65

DESIGNS—HORIZ: 4b. Flag, torch and broken chain. VERT: 2b. Flag, torch and candle.

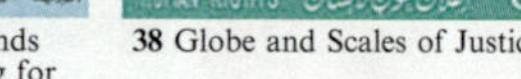

36 Hands reaching for Centenary Emblem   **38** Globe and Scales of Justice

37

1963. Red Cross Centenary. Crescent red; inscription black.
234 **36** ¼b. blue 40 25
235 ⅓b. brown 65 40
236 ½b. grey 65 40
237 – 4b. lilac 90 50
238 – 8b. stone 1·25 1·00
239 – 20b. green 3·25 2·50

DESIGN: 4b. to 20b. Centenary emblem.

1963. Air. "Honouring Astronauts". T **37** and similar designs showing rockets, etc.
240 **37** ¼b. multicoloured 65 65
241 – ⅓b. multicoloured 65 65
242 – ½b. multicoloured 65 65
243 – 4b. multicoloured 1·25 1·25
244 – 20b. multicoloured 6·25 5·00

1963. 15th Anniv of Declaration of Human Rights.
245 – 4b. black, orange and lilac 40 40
246 **38** 6b. black, green & turquoise 50 50

DESIGN: 4b. As Type **38** but differently arranged.

39 Darts   **40** Factory, Bobbins and Cloth

1964. Olympic Games, Tokyo (1st issue).
247 ¼b. green, brown and orange (postage) 10 10
248 ⅓b. brown, blue and violet 10 10
249 ½b. brown, blue and mauve 10 10
250 1b. brown, green and blue 40 25
251 1½b. red, brown and grey 50 25

252 4b. brown, black and blue (air) 50 35
253 20b. blue, deep blue and brown 1·40 1·25
254 1r. red, brown and green 4·50 3·50

DESIGNS—HORIZ: ¼b. Type **39**; ⅓ b. Table tennis; 4b. Horse-racing; 20b. Pole vaulting. VERT: ½b. Running; 1b. Volleyball; 1½b. Football; 1r. Basketball. All designs include the Olympic "Rings" symbol.

See also Nos. 272/80.

1964. Inauguration of Bagel Spinning and Weaving Factory.
255 – 2b. blue & yellow (postage) 25 15
256 – 4b. blue and yellow 40 25
257 **40** 6b. green and brown 65 30

258 – 16b. orange, blue and grey (air) 1·60 1·25

DESIGNS—VERT: 2b. Factory, bobbins and cloth (different); 4b. Loom. HORIZ: 16b. Factory and lengths of cloth.

1964. Air. President Kennedy Memorial Issue. Nos. 240/2 optd **JOHN F. KENNEDY 1917 1963** in English and Arabic and with portrait and laurel.
259 **37** ¼b. multicoloured 85 85
260 – ⅓b. multicoloured 85 85
261 – ½b. multicoloured 85 85

42 Boeing 707 on Runway

1964. Inauguration of Hodeida Airport.
262 **42** 4b. yellow and blue 40 25
263 – 6b. green and blue 45 35
264 – 10b. blue, yellow & dp blue 60 45

DESIGNS: 6b. Control tower and Boeing 707 on runway; 10b. Control tower, Boeing 707 and ship.

43 New York, Boeing 707 and Sana'a

1964. New York World's Fair.
265 **43** ¼b. brn, bl & grn (postage) 20 10
266 – ⅓b. black, red and green 30 10
267 – ½b. green, red and blue 40 20
268 **43** 1b. indigo, blue and green 50 25
269 – 4b. blue, red and green 90 55

270 – 16b. brown, red & blue (air) 1·90 1·25
271 **43** 20b. purple, blue and green 2·50 1·60

DESIGNS: ⅓b., 4b. Flag, Empire State Building, New York, and Mosque, Sana'a; ½b., 16b. Statue of Liberty, New York, liner and Harbour, Hodeida.

44 Globe and Flags   **45** Scout hoisting Flag

1964. Olympic Games, Tokyo (2nd issue). Multicoloured.
272 ¼b. Type **44** (postage) 10 10
273 ⅓b. Olympic Torch 15 10

274 ½b. Discus-thrower 25 15
275 1b. Yemeni flag 25 15
276 1½b. Swimming (horiz) . . . 45 30
277 4b. Swimming (horiz) (air) . . 50 40
278 6b. Olympic Torch 75 55
279 12b. Type **44** . . . . 1·60 1·00
280 20b. Discus-thrower . . . . 3·00 1·75

1964. Yemeni Scouts. Multicoloured.
281 ¼b. Type **45** (postage) 10 10
282 ⅓b. Scout badge and scouts guarding camp 10 10
283 ½b. Bugler 10 10
284 1b. As No. 282 . . . . . . 25 15
285 1½b. Scouts by camp-fire . . 40 20
286 4b. Type **45** (air) 40 20
287 6b. As No. 282 . . . . . . 45 25
288 16b. Bugler . . . . 1·25 75
289 20b. Scouts by camp-fire . . 1·90 1·25

46 Hamadryas Baboons

1964. Animals.
290 **46** ¼b. brown & lilac (postage) 10 10
291 – ⅓b. brown and blue 10 10
292 – ½b. brown and orange . . 20 10
293 – 1b. brown and blue 30 15
294 – 1½b. brown and blue . . . 50 20
295 – 4b. red and green (air) . . 65 30
296 – 12b. brown and buff . . . 1·90 95
297 – 20b. brown and blue . . . 3·75 1·75
ANIMALS: ⅓b. Arab horses; ½, 12b. Bullock; 1, 20b. Lion and lioness; 1½, 4b. Mountain gazelles.

47 Gentian

49 A.P.U. Emblem

48 Boeing 707 and Hawker Siddeley Comet 4 Airliners over Mountains

1964. Flowers. Multicoloured.
298 ¼b. Type **47** (postage) 10 10
299 ⅓b. Lily 10 10
300 ½b. Poinsettia 20 15
301 1b. Rose 30 15
302 1½b. Viburnum 45 20
303 4b. Rose (air) 65 30
304 12b. Poinsettia . . . . 1·90 95
305 20b. Viburnum . . . . 3·75 1·90

1964. Inauguration of Sana'a Int Airport.
306 **48** 1b. brown & blue (postage) 10 10
307 – 2b. brown and blue 15 10
308 – 4b. brown and blue 25 15
309 **48** 8b. brown and blue 60 35
310 – 6b. brown and blue (air) 50 45
DESIGNS: 2b., 4b. Boeing 707 and Vickers Viscount 800 airliners over runway; 6b. Hawker Siddeley Comet 4 airliners in flight and on ground.

1964. 10th Anniv of Arab Postal Union's Permanent Office, Cairo.
311 **49** 4b. black, red and orange (postage) 65 65
312 6b. black, green and turquoise (air) 75 75

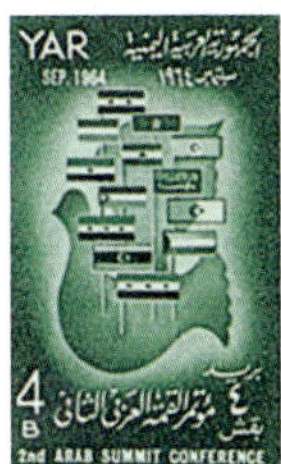

50 Flags and Dove

51 Flaming Torch

1964. 2nd Arab Summit Conference.
313 **50** 4b. green 45 40
314 – 6b. brown 75 60

DESIGN: 6b. Arms within conference emblem and map.

1964. 2nd Anniv of Revolution.
315 **51** 2b. brown and blue 25 15
316 – 4b. green and yellow . . . 35 25
317 – 6b. pink, red and green . . 65 35
DESIGNS: 4b. Yemeni soldier; 6b. Candles on map.

52 Western Reef Heron ("Reef Heron") and Little Egret

52a Dagger on Deir Yassin, Palestine

1965. Birds. Multicoloured.
318 ¼b. Type **52** (postage) 35 15
319 ½b. Arabian chukar (inscr "Arabian red-legged partridge") 75 15
320 b. Desert eagle owl ("Eagle Owl") (vert) 75 15
321 1b. Hammerkop . . . . . . 1·25 25
322 1½b. Yemeni linnets . . . . 1·25 45
323 4b. Hoopoes . . . . 3·50 1·25
324 6b. Violet starlings (air) . . . 2·40 70
325 8b. Waldrapp (inscr "Bald ibis") (vert) . . . . 4·00 1·40
326 12b. Arabian woodpecker (vert) . . . . 7·00 2·75
327 20b. Bateleur (vert) . . . . . 10·00 3·75
328 1r. Yellow-bellied ("Bruce's") green pigeon . . . . 16·00 6·75

1965. Deir Yassin Massacre.
329 **52a** 4b. purple and blue (postage) 65 40
330 6b. red and orange (air) 75 45

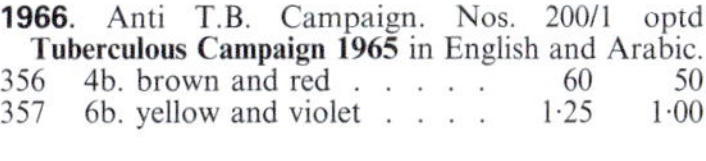

53 I.T.U. Emblem and Symbols

1965. I.T.U. Centenary.
331 – 4b. red and blue 50 40
332 **53** 6b. green and red 75 40
DESIGN—VERT: 4b. As Type **53** but rearranged.

53a Lamp and Burning Library

1965. Burning of Algiers Library.
333 **53a** 4b. green, red and black (postage) 60 35
334 6b. blue, red and deep red (air) 60 35

54 Tractor and Agricultural Produce

1965. 3rd Anniv of Revolution.
335 **54** 4b. blue and yellow 50 40
336 – 6b. blue and yellow 75 50
DESIGN: 6b. Tractor and landscape.

55 I.C.Y. and U.N. Emblems

57 Belyaev and Rocket

56 Pres. Kennedy, Map and Rocket-launching

1965. International Co-operation Year.
337 **55** 4b. green and orange . . . 65 35
338 – 6b. brown and blue 90 50
DESIGN: 6b. U.N. Headquarters and General Assembly Building, New York.

1965. Pres. Kennedy Commem. Designs each include portrait of Pres. Kennedy. Multicoloured.
339 ¼b. Type **56** (postage) 20 10
340 ¼b. Rocket gantries 20 10
341 ¼b. Rocket 20 10
342 ⅓b. Type **56** 20 10
343 ½b. Rocket 20 10
344 4b. Capsule and U.S. flag . . 60 50
345 8b. Capsule in ocean (air) . . 1·25 95
346 12b. Rocket gantries . . . . 2·50 1·60

1965. Space Achievements. Multicoloured.
347 ¼b. Type **57** (postage) 15 10
348 ¼b. Leonov and rocket . . . 15 10
349 ¼b. Scott and capsule 15 10
350 ⅓b. Carpenter and rocket gantry 15 10
351 ½b. Scott and capsule 15 10
352 4b. Leonov and rocket (air) 90 90
353 8b. Type **57** . . . . 1·60 1·60
354 16b. Carpenter and rocket gantry . . . . 2·50 2·50

1966. Anti T.B. Campaign. Nos. 200/1 optd **Tuberculous Campaign 1965** in English and Arabic.
356 4b. brown and red 60 50
357 6b. yellow and violet . . . . 1·25 1·00

59 Torch Signalling

1966. Telecommunications.
359 **59** ¼b. black and red (postage) 15 10
360 – ¼b. black and blue 15 10
361 – ¼b. black and brown . . . 15 10
362 – ⅓b. black and red 15 10
363 – ½b. black and blue 15 10
364 – 4b. black and green (air) 50 40
365 – 6b. black and brown . . . 75 50
366 – 20b. black and blue . . . 3·75 2·75
DESIGNS: No. 360, Morse telegraphy; 361, Early telephone; 362, Wireless telegraphy; 363, Television; 364, Radar; 365, Telex; 366, "Early Bird" Satellite.

1966. Prevention of Cruelty to Animals. Nos. 318/20 optd **Prevention of Cruelty to Animals** in English and Arabic.
368 **52** ¼b. multicoloured 65 35
369 – ½b. multicoloured 90 55
370 – b. multicoloured . . . . . 1·75 85

1966. 3rd Arab Summit Conference Nos. 313/14 optd **3rd. Arab Summit Conference 1965** in English and Arabic.
371 **50** 4b. green 65 65
372 – 6b. brown . . . . 1·25 1·25

62 Pres. Kennedy and Globe

1966. "Builders of World Peace". (a) Postage. Size 39 × 28½ mm.
374 **62** ¼b. brown 20 15
375 – ¼b. green 20 15
376 – ¼b. blue 20 15
377 – ⅓b. brown 20 15
378 – ½b. purple 25 15
379 **62** 4b. purple 50 30

(b) Air. Size 51 × 38 mm.
381 – 6b. brown and green 95 60
382 – 10b. brown and blue . . . . 1·10 95
383 – 12b. brown and mauve . . . 2·10 1·25
PORTRAITS: Nos. 375, 377, Dag Hammarskjold; 376, 378, Nehru; 381, Mohammed Abdul Chalek Hassuna; 382, U. Thant; 383, Pope Paul VI.

YEMEN ARAB REPUBLIC
63 Red Junglefowl

1986. Animals and Insects. Multicoloured. (a) Postage.
385 ¼b. Type **63** 30 25
386 ¼b. Brown hare 25 10
387 ¼b. Pony 25 10
388 ⅓b. Cat 25 10
389 ½b. Sheep and lamb 25 10
390 4b. Dromedary 65 45

(b) Air. Butterflies.
391 6b. Red admiral . . . . . . 3·00 90
392 8b. Swallowtail . . . . . . 3·50 1·10
393 10b. Garden tiger moth . . . 4·00 1·25
394 16b. Mocker swallowtail . . 5·50 1·75

1966. Space Flight of "Luna 9". Nos. 347/54 optd **LUNA IX 3 February 1966** in English and Arabic and spacecraft.
396 **57** ¼b. multicoloured (postage) 20 15
397 – ¼b. multicoloured 20 15
398 – ¼b. multicoloured 20 15
399 – ⅓b. multicoloured 20 15
400 – ½b. multicoloured 20 15
401 – 4b. multicoloured (air) . . 45 30
402 **57** 8b. multicoloured 85 60
403 – 16b. multicoloured . . . . 1·90 1·50

65 Jules Rimet Cup

66 Traffic Signals

1966. World Cup Football Championships, England.
405 **65** ¼b. multicoloured (postage) 20 15
406 – ¼b. multicoloured 20 15
407 – ¼b. multicoloured 20 15
408 – ⅓b. multicoloured 20 15
409 – ½b. multicoloured 20 15
410 – 4b. multicoloured (air) . . 50 45
411 – 5b. multicoloured 75 65
412 – 20b. multicoloured . . . . 1·90 1·60
DESIGNS: No. 406/11, Footballers in play (all different); 412, World Cup emblem.

1966. Traffic Day.
414 **66** 4b. red, emerald and green 95 65
415 6b. red, emerald and green 1·60 95

1966. Space Flight of "Surveyor 1". Nos. 347/51 surch with spacecraft, **SURVEYOR 1 2 June 1966** and new value in English and Arabic.
417 **57** 1b. on ¼b. multicoloured 65 65
418 – 1b. on ¼b. multicoloured 65 65
419 – 1b. on ¼b. multicoloured 65 65
420 – 3b. on ⅓b. multicoloured 1·25 1·25
421 – 4b. on ½b. multicoloured 1·90 1·90

68 Yemeni Flag

1966. 4th Anniv of Revolution.
422 **68** 2b. black, red and green 25 15
423 – 4b. multicoloured 50 25
424 – 6b. multicoloured 80 40
DESIGNS—VERT (25 × 42 mm): 4b. Automatic weapon; 6b. "Agriculture and Industry".

1966. "World Fair, Sana'a, 1965". Nos. 265/71 optd **1965 SANA'A** in English and Arabic.
425 **43** ¼b. brn, bl & grn (postage) 20 15
426 – ⅓b. black, red and green . . 20 15
427 – ½b. green, red and blue . . 20 15
428 **43** 1b. indigo, blue and green 35 25
429 – 4b. blue, red and green . . 50 50
430 – 16b. brown, red & blue (air) . . . . 2·50 2·50
431 **43** 20b. purple, blue and green 3·75 3·25

70 Galen, Helianthus and W.H.O. Building

1966. Inauguration of W.H.O. Headquarters, Geneva. Designs incorporating W.H.O. Building. Mult.

433 ¼b. Type **70** (postage) 30 20
434 ¼b. Hippocrates and ipomoeas 30 20
435 ¼b. Ibn Sina (Avicenna) and peonies 30 30
436 4b. Type **70** (air) 65 30
437 8b. As No. 434 . . . . 1·25 65
438 16b. As No. 435 . . . . 2·50 1·25

71 Spacecraft Launching

1966. Space Flight of "Gemini 6" and "7". Multicoloured.

440 ¼b. Type **71** (postage) 20 15
441 ¼b. Astronauts 20 15
442 ¼b. "Gemini" spacecraft (horiz) 20 15
443 ⅓b. "Gemini 6" and "7" (horiz) 20 15
444 ½b. Recovery operations at sea 20 15
445 2b. As ⅓b. 30 20
446 8b. As ½b. (air) . . . . 1·00 75
447 12b. "Gemini 6" and "7" link (horiz) . . . . 1·50 75

1966. Space Flight of "Gemini 9". Nos. 440/7 optd **GEMINI IX CERNAN - STAFFORD JUNE 3-1966** in English and Arabic.

449 **71** ¼b. multicoloured (postage) 15 15
450 – ¼b. multicoloured 15 15
451 – ¼b. multicoloured 15 15
452 – ⅓b. multicoloured 15 15
453 – ½b. multicoloured 15 15
454 – 2b. multicoloured 40 25
455 – 8b. multicoloured (air) . . 1·40 1·00
456 – 12b. multicoloured . . . . 1·50 1·00

73 Figs

1967. Fruits. Multicoloured.

458 ¼b. Type **73** (postage) 15 10
459 ¼b. Quinces 15 10
460 ¼b. Grapes 15 10
461 ⅓b. Dates 15 10
462 ½b. Apricots 15 15
463 2b. Quinces 50 25
464 4b. Oranges . . . . 1·25 65
465 6b. Bananas (air) . . . . . . 1·25 65
466 8b. Type **73** . . . . 1·50 85
467 10b. Grapes . . . . 2·25 1·00

1967. Arab League Day. As No. 908 of Egypt.

471 4b. brown and violet 50 40
472 6b. brown and violet . . . . 1·00 80
473 8b. brown and violet . . . . 1·40 1·25
474 20b. brown and green . . . . 2·00 1·40
475 40b. black and green . . . . 5·00 4·00

73a Women in Factory

1967. Labour Day.

475a **73a** 2b. blue and violet . . . 40 35
475b 4b. green and red . . . 80 70
475c 6b. purple and green . . 1·25 90
475d 8b. green and blue . . . 1·50 90

74 Ploughing and Sunset

1967.

476 **74** 1b. multicoloured 15 15
477 2b. multicoloured 20 15
478 4b. multicoloured 35 15
479 6b. multicoloured 45 15
480 8b. multicoloured 75 15
481 10b. multicoloured . . . . 1·25 30
482 12b. multicoloured . . . . 1·50 50
483 16b. multicoloured . . . . 1·75 65
484 20b. multicoloured . . . . 2·75 1·10
485 40b. multicoloured . . . . 5·00 2·50

75 Pres. Al-Salal and Soldiers

1968. 6th Anniv of Revolution. Multicoloured.

486 2b. Type **75** 25 25
487 4b. Yemen Arab Republic flag 35 35
488 6b. Pres. Abdullah al-Salal (vert) 75 75

76 Map of Yemen and Dove

1969. 7th Anniv of Revolution. Multicoloured.

490 2b. Type **76** 20 20
491 4b. Government building (horiz) 30 30
492 6b. Yemeni workers (horiz) 75 75

77 "Lenin addressing Crowd"

1970. Air. Birth Centenary of Lenin. Mult.

494 6b. Type **77** . . . . 1·25 95
495 10b. "Lenin with Arab Delegates" . . . . 2·50 1·60

78 Arab League Flag, Arms and Map

1970. 25th Anniv of Arab League.

496 **78** 5b. purple, green and orange 30 30
497 7b. brown, green and yellow 65 65
498 16b. blue, green and olive 1·60 1·60

1971. Various 1968 issues listed in Appendix surch.

499a 40b. on 10b. black, red and green on gold foil (Yemen Red Crescent issue) . . 5·00 5·00
499b 60b. on 15b. multicoloured on gold foil (Olympics—Chariot Racing issue) . . 6·25 6·25
499c 80b. on 10b. multicoloured on gold foil (Int Human Rights and U Thant issue) . . . . 8·75 8·75

79 Yemeni Castle

1971. 8th Anniv (1970) of Revolution. Mult.

500 5b. Type **79** (postage) . . . . 1·25 60
501 7b. Yemeni workers and soldier (air) . . . . 1·50 70
502 16b. Clasped hands, flag and torch . . . . 1·75 90

1971. Air. Proclamation of first Permanent Constitution. No. 502 optd **PROCLAMATION OF THE INSTITUTION 1/11/1390 H. 28/12/1970 C.** in English and Arabic.

504 16b. multicoloured . . . . . 4·00 3·25

81 U.N. Emblems and Globe

1971. 25th Anniv (1970) of U.N.O.

505 **81** 5b. purple, green and olive 50 35
506 7b. indigo, green and blue 75 50

82 View of Sana'a

1972. 9th Anniv (1971) of Revolution.

508 7b. Type **82** 95 95
509 18b. Military parade . . . . 1·90 1·90
510 24b. Mosque, Sana'a . . . . 3·50 3·50

83 A.P.U. Emblem and Flags

1972. 25th Anniv (1971) of Founding of Arab Postal Union at Sofar Conference.

512 **83** 3b. multicoloured 50 50
513 7b. multicoloured 75 75
514 10b. multicoloured . . . . 1·25 1·25

84 Arms and Flags

85 Skeleton and Emblem

1972. 10th Anniv of Revolution.

516 **84** 7b. multicoloured (postage) 75 75
517 10b. multicoloured . . . . 1·10 1·10
518 21b. multicoloured (air) . . 3·00 3·00

1972. 25th Anniv of W.H.O.

519 **85** 2b. multicoloured 50 40
520 21b. multicoloured . . . . 2·00 1·50
521 37b. multicoloured . . . . 3·75 3·00

86 Dome of the Rock, Jerusalem

1973. 2nd Anniv of Burning of Al-Aqsa Mosque, Jerusalem.

522 **86** 7b. multicoloured (postage) 65 50
523 18b. multicoloured . . . . 2·50 2·00
524 24b. multicoloured (air) . . 2·50 1·90

87 Arab Child with Book

1973. 25th Anniv (1971) of U.N.I.C.E.F.

526 **87** 7b. multicoloured (postage) 65 50
527 10b. multicoloured . . . . 1·25 1·00
528 18b. multicoloured (air) . . 1·50 1·25

88 Modern Office Building

1973. Air. 11th Anniv of Revolution.

530 **88** 7b. red and green 40 40
531 – 10b. orange and green . . 55 55
532 – 18b. violet and green . . 1·25 1·25

DESIGNS: 10b. Factory; 18b. Flats.

89 U.P.U. Emblem

90 Yemeni Town and Emblem

1974. Centenary of U.P.U.

533 **89** 10b. red, black and blue 30 30
534 30b. red, black and green 95 95
535 40b. red, black and stone 1·60 1·60

1975. 10th Anniv of F.A.O. World Food Programme.

536 **90** 10b. multicoloured 65 65
537 30b. multicoloured . . . . 1·60 1·60
538 63b. multicoloured . . . . 2·75 2·75

91 Janad Mosque

1975. 12th Anniv (1974) of Revolution. Mult.

539 25f. Type **91** 65 50
540 75f. Althawra Hospital . . . 1·90 1·40

1975. Various stamps surch.

541 **84** 75f. on 7b. mult (postage) 1·25 1·40
542 **86** 75f. on 7b. multicoloured 1·25 95
542b **85** 75f. on 21b. mult . . . . 1·40 1·40
542c **89** 160f. on 40b. red, black and stone . . . . 2·50 2·50
543 **86** 278f. on 7b. mult . . . . 5·00 4·25
544 **87** 75f. on 18b. mult (air) . . 1·25 95
544a **84** 75f. on 21b. mult . . . . 1·50 1·50
545 **88** 90f. on 7b. red and green 1·60 1·25
546 – 120f. on 18b. violet and green (No. 532) . . . . 2·25 1·90

93 Early and Modern Telephones

94 Coffee Beans

1976. Telephone Centenary.

547 **93** 25f. black and purple . . . 40 40
548 75f. black and green . . . 1·25 90
549 160f. black and brown . . 2·10 1·90

1976.

551 **94** 1f. multicoloured 10 15
552 3f. multicoloured 10 15
553 5f. multicoloured 10 10
554 10f. multicoloured 15 10
555 25f. multicoloured 25 25
556 50f. multicoloured 55 55
557 75f. multicoloured . . . . 1·00 75
558 1r. multicoloured . . . . . 1·40 1·00
559 1r.50 multicoloured . . . . 2·50 1·90
560 2r. multicoloured . . . . . 3·75 2·50
561 5r. multicoloured . . . . . 8·75 6·25

Nos. 558/61 are larger, 22 × 30 mm.

95 Industrial Scaffolding

96 Emblem of National Institute of Public Administration

1976. 2nd Anniv of Reformation Movement. Multicoloured.

562 75f. Type **95** . . . . 1·25 1·25
563 135f. Hand holding pick . . 1·90 1·90

1976. 14th Anniv of Revolution. Mult.

565 25f. Type **96** 40 40
566 75f. Yemeni family (Housing and population census) . . 1·25 1·25
567 160f. Shield emblem (Sana'a University) . . . . 2·25 2·25

97 President Ibrahim M. al-Hamdi

1977. 1st Anniv of Assassination of Pres. Ibrahim al-Hamdi.

569 **97** 25f. green and black . . . 30 25
570 75f. brown and black . . . 95 75
571 160f. blue and black . . . 1·90 1·50

98 Sa'ada and Sana'a

1978. 15th Anniv (1977) of Revolution. Mult.

573 25f. Type **98** 35 25
574 75f. Television and transmitter 90 60
575 160f. Type **98** . . . . 1·90 1·50

99 A.P.U. Emblem

100 Dish Aerial

1978. 25th Anniv of Arab Postal Union.

577 **99** 25f. multicoloured 65 50
578 60f. multicoloured . . . . 1·60 1·00

1978. 3rd Anniv of Correction Movement. Multicoloured.

580 25f. Type **100** 35 25
581 75f. Operating a computer . . 90 50

101 View of Sana'a

1979. 30th Anniv (1977) of I.C.A.O.

583 **101** 75f. multicoloured . . . . 1·25 45
584 135f. multicoloured . . . 2·25 1·25

102 Koran on Map of World

1979. The Arabs.

586 **102** 25f. multicoloured 40 25
587 75f. multicoloured . . . . 1·10 75

103 Viewers and Video-screen

104 Dome of the Rock, Jerusalem

1980. World Telecommunications Day (1979). Multicoloured.

589 75f. Type **103** . . . . 1·25 65
590 135f. As No. 589 (horiz) . . 2·10 1·25

1980. Palestinian Welfare.

592 **104** 5f. multicoloured 25 10
593 10f. multicoloured 40 10

105 Girl and Chaffinch

1980. Int Year of the Child (1979). Mult.

594 25f. Type **105** (postage) . . . 1·75 40
595 50f. Girl and great tit . . . . 2·50 90
596 75f. Child and butterfly . . . 1·90 1·00
597 80f. Girl and northern bullfinch (air) . . . . . . 2·75 1·40
598 100f. Child and butterfly . . 2·50 1·10
599 150f. Child and butterfly . . 3·75 1·50

Each stamp shows a different variety of bird or butterfly.

106 Scoring a Goal (Austria v. Spain)

1980. World Cup Football Championship, Argentina (1978). Multicoloured.

601 25f. Type **106** (postage) . . . 45 45
602 30f. Tunisia v. Mexico . . . 50 40
603 35f. Netherlands v. Iran . . . 65 45
604 50f. Brazil v. Sweden 95 65
605 60f. Peru v. Scotland (air) . . 1·25 70
606 75f. Italy v. France . . . . . 1·60 85
607 80f. Argentina v. Hungary . . 1·75 1·00
608 100f. West Germany v. Poland . . . . 2·25 1·40

107 Scout Fishing

1980. World Scout Jamboree. Multicoloured.

610 25f. Type **107** (postage) . . . 65 25
611 35f. Scouts and Concorde Supersonic airliner . . . . 1·10 45
612 40f. Parade and scout on horseback 95 45
613 50f. Scouts with telescope . . 1·25 55
614 60f. Parade and cyclist (air) 1·60 65
615 75f. Poppy and fencer . . . 1·90 90
616 120f. Scouts catching butterflies . . . . 3·00 1·25

108 Match Scene and Flag of Poland

1980. World Cup Football Championship Quarter Finalists. Match Scenes and Flags. Multicoloured.

617 25f. Type **108** (postage) . . . 45 45
618 30f. Peru 50 35
619 35f. Brazil 65 45
620 50f. Austria 95 65
621 60f. Italy (air) . . . . 1·25 65
622 75f. Netherlands . . . . . . 1·50 75
623 80f. West Germany . . . . . 1·75 95
624 100f. Argentina (winners) . . 2·25 1·40

109 Kaaba, Mecca

1980. Pilgrimage to Mecca. Multicoloured.

625 25f. Type **109** 10 10
626 75f. Type **109** 35 25
627 160f. Pilgrims around the Kaaba 75 45

110 Government Buildings, Sana'a

1980. 18th Anniv of Revolution. Multicoloured.

629 25f. Arm and cogwheel encircling flower and factories (vert) 10 10
630 75f. Type **110** 60 50

111 Al-Rawdha Mosque

1980. 1400th Anniv of Hegira. Multicoloured.

632 25f. Type **111** 15 10
633 75f. Al-Aqsa Mosque 45 25
634 100f. Al-Nabawi Mosque . . . 70 35
635 160f. Al-Haram Mosque . . 1·25 60

112 Figure clothed in Palestinian Flag

1980. Int Day of Solidarity with Palestinian People.

637 **112** 25f. multicoloured 15 10
638 75f. multicoloured 60 40

113 Al-Aamiriya Mosque

1981. 9th Arab Archaeological Conf. Mult.

639 75f. Type **113** 60 35
640 125f. Al-Hadi Mosque . . . 70 50

114 Tower and Ramparts

1981. World Tourism Conf, Manila. Mult.

642 25f. Type **114** 15 10
643 75f. Mosque and houses . . 45 25
644 100f. Columns (horiz) 50 30
645 135f. Bridge 60 40
646 160f. View of Sana'a (horiz) 90 50

115 Hill and U.P.U. Emblem

1981. Sir Roland Hill Commemoration. Mult.

648 25f. Type **115** (postage) . . . 90 50
649 30f. U.P.U. and A.P.U. emblems and Y.A.R. 4b. stamp of 1963 . . . . . . 1·00 60
650 50f. Hill, magnifying glass and stamps . . . . 1·50 90
651 75f. Hill and jet airliner circling globe (air) . . . . 2·50 1·50
652 100f. Hill, album and hand holding stamp with tweezers . . . . 3·25 1·90
653 150f. Air letter, jet airliner and Y.A.R. 160f. stamp of 1976 . . . . 5·00 3·00

1981. Nos. 551/5 surch.

654 **94** 125f. on 1f. multicoloured 1·90 1·25
655 150f. on 3f. multicoloured 2·25 1·90
656 325f. on 5f. multicoloured 4·50 3·00
657 350f. on 10f. multicoloured 5·00 3·00
658 375f. on 25f. multicoloured 5·00 3·00

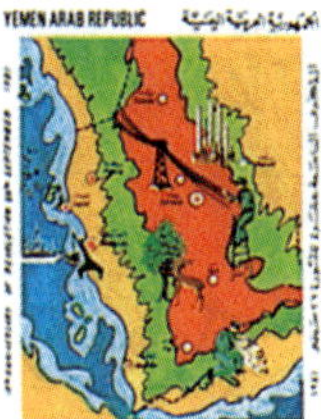

117 Map of Yemen

1982. Air. 19th Anniv (1981) of Revolution. Multicoloured.

659 75f. Type **117** 75 40
660 125f. Yemenis looking towards map within sun . . 1·10 60

661 325f. Sun, fist, dove with flags for wings and industrial scene . . . . . 3·25 2·10
662 400f. Air display . . . . . . 4·25 2·50

118 Al-Hasan ibn Ahmed al-Hamadani

1982. Air. Birth Millenary of Al-Hasan ibn Ahmed al-Hamadani (philosopher).
664 **118** 125f. multicoloured . . . 1·25 65
665 325f. multicoloured . . . 3·25 1·60

119 Common Rabbits

1982. World Food Day. Multicoloured.
667 25f. Type **119** 95 40
668 50f. Cock and hens . . . . . 1·90 90
669 60f. Common turkeys . . . . 3·25 1·40
670 75f. Sheep . . . . 2·75 1·40
671 100f. Cow and calf . . . . . 3·75 1·60
672 125f. Red deer . . . . 4·00 1·90

120 Gymnast

1982. Air. Olympic Games, Moscow (1980). Multicoloured.
674 25f. Type **120** 95 40
675 50f. Pole vault . . . . 1·75 75
676 60f. Throwing the javelin . . 2·25 90
677 75f. Runner . . . . 2·75 1·10
678 100f. Basketball . . . . . . 3·75 1·60
679 125f. Football . . . . 4·00 1·90

121 Otto Lilienthal's Monoplane Glider and Satellite

1982. Air. Progress in Air Transport. Multicoloured.
681 25f. Type **121** . . . . 1·00 40
682 50f. Alberto Santos-Dumonts biplane "14 bis" . . . . . 1·50 55
683 60f. Biplane and satellite . . 1·90 60
684 75f. Early airplane and satellite . . . . 2·25 75
685 100f. De Havilland D.H.60G Gipsy Moth biplane and satellite . . . . 2·50 1·10
686 125f. Fokker F.VIIa/3m airplane and satellite . . . 3·50 1·50

122 Crocuses and Nurse pushing Wheelchair

1982. Air. International Year of Disabled Persons (1981). Multicoloured.
688 25f. Type **122** . . . . 1·00 40
689 50f. Bowl of roses and nurse pushing wheelchair . . . . 1·25 70
690 60f. Bowl of pasque flowers and nurse pushing wheelchair . . . . 1·50 90
691 75f. Mixed flower arrangement and nurse pushing wheelchair . . . . 2·50 1·40
692 100f. Bowl of lilies and nurse pushing wheelchair . . . . 3·25 1·75
693 125f. Bowl of gladioli and nurse pushing wheelchair 4·00 1·90

123 Aerials and Satellite circling Globe

1982. Air. Telecommunications Progress. Mult.
695 25f. Modern radio communications 50 25
696 50f. Type **123** 75 40
697 60f. Radio masts, watch and dish aerials 90 60
698 75f. Dish aerials and landscape . . . . 1·10 75
699 100f. Dish aerials, satellites and morse transmitter . . 1·40 90
700 125f. Aerials, jet airliner and globe . . . . 1·75 1·40

124 Oranges, "TB" and Cross of Lorraine

1982. Air. Centenary of Discovery of Tubercle Bacillus. Multicoloured.
702 25f. Type **124** 55 20
703 50f. Blossom, pears, cross of Lorraine and Robert Koch 85 35
704 60f. Pomegranates, flowers and cross of Lorraine . . . 1·00 50
705 75f. Roses, grapes and bacillus . . . . 1·65 65
706 100f. Cherries, blossom and microscope . . . . 1·60 70
707 125f. Lemons, cross of Lorraine and microscope 2·00 1·00

125 Tackling

1982. Air. World Cup Football Championship, Spain. Multicoloured.
709 25f. Type **125** 45 15
710 50f. Marking the opposition 65 25
711 60f. Players with ball 95 35
712 75f. Scoring a goal . . . . . 1·00 55
713 100f. Dribbling . . . . 1·40 70
714 125f. Intercepting the ball . . 1·60 90

126 Map, Boy with Flag, Tents and Dome of the Rock

1982. Air. Palestinian Children's Day. Multicoloured.
716 75f. Type **126** . . . . 1·50 70
717 125f. As Type **126** but girl with flag . . . . 2·40 1·40
718 325f. As Type **126** but boy and girl . . . . 5·00 2·75

127 Map under Grid and Airplane

1982. Air. 30th Anniv of Arab Postal Union. Multicoloured.
720 75f. Type **127** . . . . 1·00 55
721 125f. Map under grid and ship . . . . 1·50 85
722 325f. Map under grid and emblem . . . . 4·50 1·75

128 Passengers and Airliners

1983. 20th Anniv of Yemen Airways.
724 **128** 75f. multicoloured . . . . 1·10 70
725 125f. multicoloured . . . 2·00 1·10
726 325f. multicoloured . . . 4·50 2·50

129 Man with Donkey and Foal

1983. Traditional Costumes. Multicoloured.
727 50f. Type **129** (postage) . . . 2·10 1·10
728 50f. Woman in embroidered veil carrying jug on head 2·10 1·10
729 50f. Shepherds in country . . 2·10 1·10
730 50f. Man walking through city and shepherds . . . 2·10 1·10
731 75f. Women at well (horiz) (air) . . . . 3·00 1·60
732 75f. Woman sitting by shore (horiz) . . . . 3·00 1·60
733 75f. Man ploughing with camel (horiz) . . . . . . 3·00 1·60
734 75f. Man reading (horiz) . . 3·00 1·60

130 Map of Yemen

1983. 20th Anniv (1982) of Revolution. Mult.
736 100f. Houses, airliner, telephone and dish aerial 1·50 85
737 150f. Literacy campaign emblem . . . . 2·10 1·10
738 325f. Tree and houses . . . . 4·50 2·50
739 400f. Type **130** . . . . 7·00 3·25

131 Emblem, Satellite, Dish Aerial and Telephone on Flag

1983. World Communications Year.
741 **131** 150f. multicoloured . . . 2·40 1·40
742 325f. multicoloured . . . 5·25 3·00

132 Man at Window and Men planting Tree

1984. 21st Anniv (1983) of Revolution. Mult.
744 100f. Type **132** . . . . 1·90 85
745 150f. Fist and bust . . . . . 2·10 1·25
746 325f. Sun, tank and open gates . . . . 4·75 2·40

133 Woman in Bombed Street

134 Profiles and Clasped Hands as Doves

1984. "Israeli Aggression against Lebanon".
748 **133** 150f. multicoloured . . . 2·40 1·25
749 325f. multicoloured . . . 5·50 3·00

1985. International Anti-apartheid Year (1978).
751 **134** 150f. multicoloured . . . 2·00 1·25
752 325f. multicoloured . . . 5·00 2·75

135 Winged Figure and Globe

1985. 40th Anniv of I.C.A.O.
754 **135** 25f. multicoloured 35 15
755 50f. multicoloured 75 25
756 150f. multicoloured . . . 1·75 80
757 325f. multicoloured . . . 4·25 1·75

136 Monument of Unknown Soldier

1985. 22nd Anniv (1984) of Revolution. Mult.
759 50f. Type **136** 85 40
760 150f. Reconstruction of Marem Dam . . . . . . 2·40 1·50
761 325f. Althawrah Sports Stadium . . . . 4·75 2·75

137 Wrestling

1985. Air. Olympic Games, Los Angeles (1984). Multicoloured.
763 20f. Type **137** 30 20
764 30f. Boxing 40 25
765 40f. Running 55 40
766 60f. Hurdling 65 50
767 150f. Pole vaulting . . . . . 1·40 85
768 325f. Throwing the javelin . . 3·25 1·90

138 Emblem and Satellite over Globe

1986. 1st Anniv of "Arabsat" Communications Satellite.
770 **138** 150f. multicoloured . . . 2·50 1·40
771 325f. multicoloured . . . 5·25 2·75

139 Dish Aerial and Cables

1986. 120th Anniv of World Telecommunications.
773 **139** 150f. multicoloured . . . 2·50 1·40
774 325f. multicoloured . . . 5·25 2·75

140 Emblem

1986. 2nd Anniv of General People's Conference.

776	**140**	150f. multicoloured	2·00	1·40
777		325f. multicoloured	4·00	2·75

141 Emblem and Sana'a

142 Emblem and Dove

1986. 15th Islamic Foreign Ministers Conference, Sana'a (1984).

779	**141**	150f. multicoloured	2·00	1·40
780		325f. multicoloured	4·00	2·75

1986. 40th Anniv of U.N.O.

782	**142**	150f. multicoloured	2·00	1·40
783		325f. multicoloured	4·00	2·75

143 Members' Flags, Map and Emblem

1986. 39th Anniv (1984) of Arab League.

785	**143**	150f. multicoloured	2·00	1·40
786		325f. multicoloured	4·00	2·75

144 Anniversary Emblem

1987. 25th Anniv of Revolution.

787	**144**	100f. multicoloured	75	25
788		150f. multicoloured	1·10	60
789		425f. multicoloured	3·25	2·00
790		450f. multicoloured	3·50	2·10

145 Dove, Emblems and Open Hands

1987. International Youth Year (1985).

792	**145**	150f. multicoloured	1·50	75
793		425f. multicoloured	4·50	2·40

146 Burning Oil

1987. 3rd Anniv of Discovery of Oil in Yemen Arab Republic. Multicoloured.

795	150f. Type **146**	1·50	70
796	425f. Oil derrick and refinery	4·50	2·40

147 Numbers and Emblem

1987. General Population and Housing Census (1986).

798	**147**	150f. multicoloured	1·50	75
799		425f. multicoloured	4·50	3·50

148 Footballers and Pique (mascot)

149 Skin Diving

1988. World Cup Football Championship, Mexico (1986). Multicoloured.

801	100f. Type **148**	1·00	50
802	150f. Goalkeeper saving ball	1·50	75
803	425f. Players and Pique (horiz)	4·25	2·10

1988. 17th Scout Conference, Sana'a. Scout Activities. Multicoloured.

805	25f. Type **149**	20	10
806	30f. Table tennis	30	15
807	40f. Tennis	25	20
808	50f. Game with flag	55	25
809	60f. Volleyball	65	35
810	100f. Tug-of-war	1·25	55
811	150f. Basketball	1·75	85
812	425f. Archery	4·75	2·50

150 Old City

1988. Int Campaign for Preservation of Old Sana'a.

814	**150**	25f. multicoloured	30	10
815		50f. multicoloured	50	25
816		100f. multicoloured	1·10	55
817		150f. multicoloured	1·75	85
818		425f. multicoloured	4·50	2·40

151 Horseman

1988. 800th Anniv (1987) of Battle of Hattin.

820	**151**	150f. multicoloured	2·50	1·25
821		425f. multicoloured	7·50	3·75

152 Building, Dish Aerial, Telephone and Emblem

1988. Arab Telecommunications Day (1987).

823	**152**	100f. multicoloured	1·25	60
824		150f. multicoloured	2·00	1·00
825		425f. multicoloured	5·75	2·75

153 Torch and Symbols of Development

1989. 26th Anniv (1988) of Revolution. Mult.

827	300f. Type **153**	1·25	50
828	375f. Type **153**	1·75	70
829	850f. Flag, Koran and symbols of agriculture and industry (vert)	3·75	1·50
830	900f. As No. 829	4·00	1·60

154 Old and New Cities and Crowd

1989. 25th Anniv of 14th October Revolution. Multicoloured.

831	300f. Type **154**	1·25	50
832	375f. Type **154**	1·75	70
833	850f. City street and crowd (vert)	3·75	1·50
834	900f. As No. 833 (vert)	4·00	1·60

155 Sports

1989. Olympic Games, Seoul (1988). Mult.

835	300f. Type **155**	1·50	50
836	375f. Football	1·90	70
837	850f. Football and judo (vert)	4·25	1·50
838	900f. Emblem and torch bearer	4·50	1·60

156 Flag, Couple and Fist

1989. Palestinian "Intifida" Movement. Multicoloured.

840	300f. Type **156**	1·25	50
841	375f. Soldier raising flag (vert)	1·75	70
842	850f. Dome of the Rock, youths and burning tyres	3·75	1·50
843	900f. Crowd of youths (vert)	4·00	1·60

157 Emblem

1990. 1st Anniv of Arab Co-operation Council.

845	**157**	300f. multicoloured	1·25	50
846		375f. multicoloured	1·75	70
847		850f. multicoloured	3·75	1·50
848		900f. multicoloured	4·00	1·60

158 Loading Tanker

1990. 1st Shipment of Oil. Multicoloured.

850	300f. Type **158**	1·25	50
851	375f. Type **158**	1·75	70
852	850f. Pipeline around globe and tanker	3·75	1·50
853	900f. As No. 852	4·00	1·60

159 Emblem

160 Woman feeding Baby

1990. 10th Anniv (1989) of Arab Board for Medical Specializations.

855	**159**	300f. multicoloured	1·00	50
856		375f. multicoloured	1·25	60
857		850f. multicoloured	2·75	1·25
858		900f. multicoloured	3·00	1·50

1990. Immunization Campaign. Multicoloured.

860	300f. Type **160**	1·25	50
861	375f. Type **160**	1·75	70
862	850f. Nurse weighing baby (horiz)	3·75	1·50
863	900f. As No. 862	4·00	1·60

For further issues see **YEMEN REPUBLIC (combined)**.

POSTAGE DUE STAMPS

1964. Designs as Nos. 291, 295/6 (Animals), but inscr "POSTAGE DUE".

D298	4b. brown and green	1·90	65
D299	12b. brown and orange	3·75	1·90
D300	20b. black and violet	7·00	2·50

DESIGNS: 4b. Mountain gazelles; 12b. Bullock; 20b. Arab horses.

1964. Designs as Nos. 303/5, but inscr "POSTAGE DUE". Multicoloured.

D306	4b. Roses	1·60	65
D307	12b. Poinsettia	4·00	1·25
D308	20b. Viburnum	7·00	2·50

1966. Nos. 324/8 optd **POSTAGE DUE** in English and Arabic.

D371	6b. multicoloured	5·25	3·50
D372	8b. multicoloured	5·75	4·50
D373	12b. multicoloured	8·00	7·00
D374	20b. multicoloured	14·00	9·00
D375	1r. multicoloured	27·00	20·00

1966. Designs as Nos. 410/12 (Football), but inscr "POSTAGE DUE".

D414	4b. multicoloured	1·25	95
D415	5b. multicoloured	2·50	1·60
D416	20b. multicoloured	5·75	3·75

1967. Designs as Nos. 465/7, but inscr "POSTAGE DUE" instead of "AIR MAIL". Multicoloured.

D468	–	6b. Bananas	1·90	1·25
D469	**73**	8b. Figs	3·00	1·90
D470	–	10b. Grapes	4·50	2·50

ROYALIST CIVIL WAR ISSUES

Fighting continued between the Royalists and Republicans until 1970. In 1970 Saudi Arabia recognised the Republican government as the rulers of Yemen, and the royalist position crumbled.

1962. Various issues optd. (i) Optd **FREE YEMEN FIGHTS FOR GOD, IMAM, COUNTRY** in English and Arabic.

R1	**19**	2b. red and black	3·00	3·00
R3		4b. yellow and black	3·00	3·00

(ii) Optd **FREE YEMEN FIGHTS FOR GOD, IMAM & COUNTRY** in English and Arabic.

(a) Nos. 156/8.

R5	**24**	4b. multicoloured	3·00	3·00
R6		6b. multicoloured	3·75	3·75
R7		10b. multicoloured	5·75	5·75

(b) Nos. 159/60.

R8	**25**	4b. brown	25·00	25·00
R9		6b. green	25·00	25·00

(c) Nos. 161/2.

R10	4b. green	3·75	3·75
R11	6b. blue	3·75	3·75

(d) Nos. 167/8.

R12	4b. orange and black	3·75	3·75
R13	6b. green and brown	3·75	3·75

(e) Nos. 126/30.

R14	**19**	2b. red and black		
R15		4b. yellow and black		
R16		6b. orange and black		
R17		8b. green and brown		
R18		20b. orange and violet		
		Set of 5	£130	£130

(f) Nos. 169/75.

R19	**20**	1b. violet	95	95
R20		2b. green	95	95
R21		3b. blue	1·25	1·25
R22		4b. blue	1·90	1·90
R23		6b. purple	3·25	3·25
R24		14b. red	5·75	5·75
R25		20b. brown	8·25	8·25

R 6 Five Ears of Wheat

1963. Air. Freedom from Hunger.

R26	R **6**	4b. red, green and stone	75	75
R27		6b. red, green and blue	75	75

(R 7)

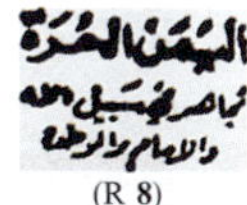
(R 8)

1963. Captured Y.A.R. stamps variously optd. (a) No. 195 optd with Type R 7.

R28	4b. brown and mauve	45·00	50·00

(b) No. 196 optd with Type R 7 plus first line of Arabic inscr repeated at foot.

R29	6b. red and blue	45·00	50·00

(c) No. 196 optd with Types R 7 and R 8.

R30	6b. red and blue	55·00	65·00

1963. Surch in figures with stars over old value, for use on circulars.

R31	R **6**	1b. on 4b. red, green and stone	90	1·00
R32		2b. on 6b. red, green and blue	90	1·00

R 10 Red Cross Field Post

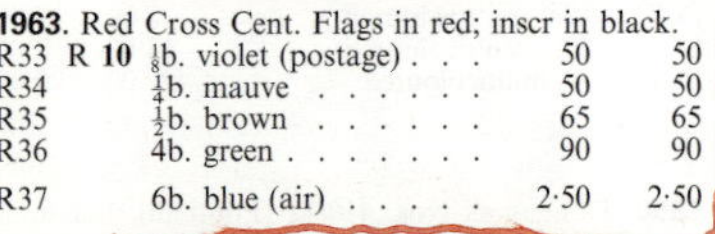

1963. Red Cross Cent. Flags in red; inscr in black.

R33 R 10 ⅛b. violet (postage) 50 50

R34 ¼b. mauve 50 50

R35 ½b. brown 65 65

R36 4b. green 90 90

R37 6b. blue (air) 2·50 2·50

R 11

1963. Consular Fee stamp optd **YEMEN** in English and "POSTAGE 1383" (Moslem Year) in Arabic with bar over old inscr, as in Type R 11.

R38 R 11 10b. black and red 75·00 75·00

R 12 Troops in Action

1964. Air. "The Patriotic War". Flags and emblem in red.

R39 R 12 ⅛b. green 50 55

R40 1b. black 65 70

R41 2b. purple 65 75

R42 4b. green 80 90

R43 6b. blue 1·90 2·10

1964. Air. Surch **AIR MAIL**, red cross, **1963–64 HONOURING BRITISH RED CROSS SURGICAL TEAM** and value and Arabic equivalent.

R44 R 12 10b. on 4b. green 4·25 4·25

R45 18b. on ⅛b. green 6·00 6·00

1964. Air. Surch **AIR MAIL** and value in English and Arabic and airplane motif.

R46 R 10 10b. on ⅛b. violet 3·50 3·50

R47 18b. on ¼b. mauve 5·50 5·50

R48 28b. on ½b. brown 8·50 8·50

1964. Air. Surch **4 REVALUED** in English and Arabic with dotted frameline around stamp.

R49 R 12 4b. on ⅛b. green 9·00 9·00

R50 4b. on 1b. black 9·00 9·00

R51 4b. on 2b. purple 9·00 9·00

R 16 Olympic Flame and "Rings"

1964. Olympic Games, Tokyo.

R52 R 16 2b. blue (postage) 60 60

R53 4b. violet 80 80

R54 6b. brown (air) 1·25 1·25

R 17 Rocket

1964. Astronauts.

R55 R 17 2b. orange, violet and black (postage) 1·90 1·90

R56 4b. brown, blue and black 3·75 3·75

R57 6b. yellow & black (air) 5·00 5·00

R 18 (½-size illustration)

1964. Consular Fee stamps optd across a pair as in Type R 18.

R58 R 18 10b. (5b.+5b.) purple

Owing to a shortage of 10b. postage stamps, 5b. Consular Fee stamps were optd across pairs with **YEMEN** in English and "POSTAGE 1383" (Moslem Year) in Arabic, in frame, together with the Ministry of Communications' Royal Arms seal and a bar over old inscription at foot.

1965. Air. British Yemen Relief Committee. Nos. R 46/8 additionally optd **HONOURING BRITISH YEMEN RELIEF COMMITTEE 1963 1965** in English and Arabic.

R59 R 10 10b. on ⅛b. violet 2·50 2·50

R60 18b. on ¼b. mauve 5·00 5·00

R61 28b. on ½b. brown 7·50 7·50

R 20 Seif-al-Islam Ali

1965. Prince Seif-al-Islam Ali Commemoration.

R62 R 20 4b. grey and red 1·90 1·90

R 21 Kennedy as Young Man

1965. Pres. Kennedy Commemoration.

R63 R 21 ⅛b. black, mauve and gold (postage) 25 25

R64 – ¼b. violet, turq & gold 25 25

R65 – ½b. brown, blue and gold 25 25

R66 – 4b. brown, yell & gold 1·25 1·25

R67 – 6b. black, green and gold (air) 1·75 1·75

DESIGNS (Kennedy): ¼b. As naval officer; ½b. Sailing with Mrs. Kennedy; 4b. In rocking-chair; 6b. Full face portrait.

1965. Churchill Commemoration (1st issue). No. R62, with colours changed, optd **IN MEMORY OF SIR WINSTON CHURCHILL 1874-1965** in English and Arabic.

R68 R 20 4b. blue and red 9·50 9·50

R 23 Satellite and Emblems

1965. I.T.U. Centenary.

R69 R 23 2b. yellow, violet and black (postage) 2·50 2·50

R70 4b. red, blue and black 3·75 3·75

R71 6b. green, violet and black (air) 5·00 5·00

R 24 Hammerkop

1965. Birds. Multicoloured.

R72 ⅛b. Type R 24 (postage) 1·40 1·00

R73 ¼b. Yemeni linnet 1·50 1·00

R74 ½b. Hoopoe 1·75 1·00

R75 4b. Arabian woodpecker 3·50 3·00

R76 6b. Violet starling (air) 9·50 4·00

R 25 Sir Winston Churchill and St. Paul's Cathedral

1965. Churchill Commem (2nd issue). Mult.

R77 ⅛b. Type R 25 20 15

R78 ¼b. Churchill and Houses of Parliament 20 15

R79 ½b. Full-face portrait 20 15

R80 1b. Type R 25 25 35

R81 2b. Churchill and Houses of Parliament 60 50

R82 4b. Full-face portrait 1·25 1·00

R 26 Iman Al-Badr

1965.

R83 R 26 1b. black & bl (postage) 35 35

R83a 1½b. black and green 25 25

R84 – 2b. red and green 1·25 1·25

R85 R 26 4b. black and purple 1·75 1·75

R86 – 6b. red and violet (air) 2·50 2·50

R87 – 18b. red and brown 4·25 4·25

R88 – 24b. red and blue 7·00 7·00

DESIGNS—VERT: 2b., 18b. Royal arms. HORIZ: 6b., 24b. Flag.

1965. Space Flight of "Mariner 4". Nos. R55/7 optd **MARINER 4** in English and Arabic.

R89 R 17 2b. orange, violet and black (postage) 60 60

R90 4b. brown, blue & black 1·75 1·75

R91 6b. yellow & black (air) 2·25 2·25

R 28 I.C.Y. Emblem, King Faisal of Saudi Arabia and Iman Al-Badr

1965. International Co-operation Year.

R92 R 28 2b. blue and brown (postage) 1·25 95

R93 4b. red and green 2·50 1·90

R94 6b. brown and blue (air) 3·75 2·50

1965. Space Flight of "Gemini 5". Nos. R69/71 optd **'GEMINI-V' GORDON COOPER & CHARLES CONRAD AUGUST 21-29, 1965** and space capsule.

R95 R 23 2b. yellow, violet and black (postage) 1·90 1·50

R96 4b. red, blue and black 3·75 3·00

R97 6b. green, violet and black (air) 6·25 6·25

R 30 Black Persian

1965. Cats. Multicoloured.

R 99 ⅛b. Type R 30 40 25

R100 ¼b. Tortoiseshell 40 25

R101 ½b. Sealpoint Siamese 50 30

R102 1b. Silver tabby Persian 75 45

R103 2b. Cream Persian 1·50 95

R104 4b. Red tabby 3·50 1·90

Nos. R102/4 are vert.

R 31 Red Saxifrage

1965. Flowers. Multicoloured.

R106 ⅛b. Verbena (vert) 35 20

R107 ¼b. Dianthus (vert) 35 25

R108 ½b. Dahlia (vert) 65 40

R109 1b. Nasturtium 75 45

R110 2b. Type R 31 1·50 65

R111 4b. Wild rose 2·75 1·25

R 32 Flag and Globe

1965. Pope Paul's Visit to U.N. Organization.

R113 R 32 2b. red, black and green 1·90 1·25

R114 4b. red, black and violet 3·25 2·50

R115 6b. red, black and blue 4·50 3·25

R 33 Moon Landing

1965. Space Achievements. Multicoloured.

(a) Postage. (i) Size as Type R 33.

R117 ⅛b. Type R 33 25 25

R118 ¼b. Astronauts on Moon 30 30

R119 ½b. Pres. Kennedy and Cape Kennedy (vert) 40 40

(ii) Size 48 × 28 mm.

R120 4b. Belyaev and Leonov in space 2·75 2·25

(b) Air. Size 48 × 28 mm.

R121 6b. White and Mcdivitt in space 3·75 2·50

R 34 Football and Gold Medal

1965. Winners of Olympic Games, Tokyo (1964). Each design showing a sport with a gold medal. Multicoloured.

R123 ⅛b. Type R 34 (postage) 20 10

R124 ¼b. Running 20 10

R125 ½b. Throwing the discus 50 25

R126 2b. Judo 1·10 75

R127 4b. Wrestling 2·25 1·25

R128 6b. Horse-jumping (air) 4·50 3·25

R 35 Arms

1966. Air. Size varies. Imperf.

R130 R 35 10b. red on white

R131 10b. violet on white

R132 10b. red on yellow

R133 10b. violet on orange

R134 10b. violet on mauve

These handstamps were also applied directly to envelopes and aerogrammes.

R **36** Nehru

1966. Builders of World Peace (1st series). Portraits in gold and black; inscr in black.

R136	R **36**	⅛b. green	25	15
R137	–	¼b. brown	25	15
R138	–	½b. grey	50	35
R139	–	1b. blue	1·25	65
R140	–	4b. green	2·75	2·50

DESIGNS: ¼b. Dag Hammarskjold; ½b. Pope John XXIII; 1b. Sir Winston Churchill; 4b. Pres. Kennedy.

See also Nos. R146/51.

1966. Nos. R63/5 and R67 surch with new values in English and Arabic.

R142	R **21**	4b. on ⅛b. black, mauve and gold (postage)	35	35
R143	–	8b. on ¼b. violet, turquoise and gold	70	70
R144	–	10b. on ½b. brown, blue and gold	75	75
R145	–	1r. on 6b. black, green and gold (air)	2·50	2·50

1966. Builders of World Peace (2nd series). As Type R **36**. Portraits in black and gold; inscr in black.

R146	⅛b. yellow	10	10
R147	¼b. pink	10	10
R148	½b. mauve	25	25
R149	1b. blue	25	25
R150	1b. green	25	25
R151	4b. green	90	90

PORTRAITS: ⅛b. Pres. Lubke; ¼b. Pres. De Gaulle; ½b. Pope Paul VI; 1b. (R149) Pres. Johnson; 1b. (R150) King Faisal of Saudi Arabia; 4b. U Thant.

1966. Newspaper Stamps. Optd **PERIODICALS** in English and Arabic in frame. (a) Similar to Nos. R26/7, but imperf.

R153	R **6**	4b. red, green and stone	12·00
R154		6b. red, green and blue	12·00

(b) Unissued 1963 Red Cross Centenary issue (Nos. R26/7 surch).

R155	R **6**	1b. on 4b. red, green and stone	16·00
R156		2b. on 6b. red, green and blue	25·00

1966. Air. Olympic Games Preparation, Mexico (1968). Nos. R123/5 in new colours surch **AIR MAIL OLYMPIC GAMES PREPARATION MEXICO 1968** and new value in English and Arabic with aircraft and flag.

R158	R **34**	12b. on ⅛b. mult	5·00	5·00
R159	–	28b. on ¼b. mult	6·00	6·00
R160	–	34b. on ½b. mult	7·50	7·50

R **40** Yemeni Cannon

1966. Shaharah Fortress. Frame and stars in red.

R162	R **40**	½b. bistre (postage)	65	65
R163	–	1b. grey	1·00	1·00
R164	–	1½b. blue	1·25	1·25
R165	–	2b. brown	1·50	1·50
R166	–	4b. green	2·50	2·50
R167	–	6b. violet (air)	4·00	4·00
R168	–	10b. black	5·25	5·25

DESIGNS—VERT: 1b. Bombed Mosque; 2b. Victory Gate; 4b. Yemeni cannon (different); 10b. Bombed houses. HORIZ: 1½b. Shaharah Fortress; 6b. Yemeni cannon (different).

1966. Nos. R33/5 surch **4B REVALUED** in English and Arabic within border of stars. Flags red; inscr in black.

R170	R **10**	4b. on ⅛b. violet	30·00	30·00
R171		4b. on ¼b. mauve	30·00	30·00
R172		4b. on ½b. brown	30·00	30·00

R **42** President Kennedy

1967. 3rd Anniv of Pres. Kennedy's Death and Inauguration of Arlington Grave.

R173	R **42**	12b. multicoloured	1·90	1·90
R174		28b. multicoloured	3·75	3·75
R175		34b. multicoloured	5·50	5·50

1967. England's Victory in World Cup Football Championship (1966). Nos. R123/8 optd **WORLD CHAMPIONSHIP-CUP ENGLAND 1966** in English and Arabic, **ENGLAND WINNER** in English only and World Cup emblem.

R177	R **34**	⅛b. mult (postage)	25	25
R178	–	¼b. multicoloured	25	25
R179	–	½b. multicoloured	25	25
R180	–	2b. multicoloured	2·00	1·90
R181	–	4b. multicoloured	3·50	3·25
R182	–	6b. multicoloured (air)	4·00	2·50

1967. Surch **4B REVALUED** in English and Arabic within border of stars. (a) Nos. R123/5.

R183	R **34**	4b. on ⅛b. mult
R184	–	4b. on ¼b. mult
R185	–	4b. on ½b. mult

(b) Nos. R177/9.

R186	R **34**	4b. on ⅛b. mult
R187	–	4b. on ¼b. mult
R188	–	4b. on ½b. mult

R **44** Bazooka

1967. Freedom Fighters. Designs showing Freedom Fighters with various weapons. Multicoloured.

R189	4b. Type R **44**	90	50
R190	4b. Fighter in fez with rifle	90	50
R191	4b. Bare-headed man with rifle	90	50
R192	4b. Fighters holding bazooka and round	90	50
R193	4b. Anti-aircraft gun	90	50
R194	4b. Heavy machine-gun	90	50
R195	4b. Light machine-gun	90	50
R196	4b. Fighter with bazooka on mount and rifle	90	50

R **45** Rembrandt—Self-portrait

1967. "AMPHILEX" Stamp Exhibition, Amsterdam. Rembrandt Paintings. Multicoloured. (a) Borders in gold.

R198	2b. "An Elderly Man as St. Paul"	10	10
R199	4b. Type R **45**	10	10
R200	6b. "Portrait of Jacob Trip"	15	15
R201	10b. "An Old Man in an Armchair"	25	15
R202	12b. Self-portrait (different)	45	20
R203	20b. "A Woman Bathing"	50	25

(b) Borders in silver.

R205	2b. As No. R198	20	20
R206	4b. Type R **45**	35	35
R207	6b. As No. R200	40	40
R208	10b. As No. R201	60	50
R209	12b. As No. R202	90	55
R210	20b. As No. R203	1·50	65

1967. Pres. Kennedy's 50th Birth Anniv. Nos. R173/5 optd **50th. ann. 29 MAY** in English only.

R212	R **42**	12b. multicoloured	1·60	1·60
R213		28b. multicoloured	3·50	3·50
R214		34b. multicoloured	4·50	4·50

R **47** Triggerfish

1967. Red Sea Fish. Multicoloured.

R216	⅛b. Type R **47** (postage)	1·10	25
R217	¼b. Striped rudderfish	1·10	25
R218	½b. Hooded butterflyfish	1·10	25
R219	1b. Spotted coral grouper	1·40	25
R220	4b. Lionfish	1·60	25
R221	6b. Brown anemonefish	2·25	25
R222	10b. Violet-hued berycid	3·75	25
R224	12b. As No. R222 (air)	1·10	10
R225	14b. Cuckoo wrasse	1·50	10
R226	16b. Japanese bonyhead	2·10	15
R227	18b. As No. R221	2·40	20
R228	24b. As No. R220	2·75	30
R229	34b. As No. R219	3·50	45

Nos. R216/22 are Type R **47**; Nos. R224/9 are larger, size 58 × 42 mm.

R **48** "The Gipsy Girl" (Frans Hals)

1967. Air. Famous Paintings. Multicoloured.

R230	8b. Type R **48**	20	15
R231	10b. "The Zouave" (Van Gogh)	25	15
R232	12b. Self-portrait (Rubens)	25	15
R233	14b. "Boys Eating Melon" (Murilio)	40	20
R234	16b. "The Knight's Dream" (Raphael)	50	20
R235	20b. "St. George and the Dragon" (Ucello) (horiz)	60	25

1967. "For Poison Gas Victims". Surch **FOR POISON GAS VICTIMS** and surcharge in English and Arabic, with skull and crossbones within frame.

R236	R **40**	½b.+1b. (No. R162) (postage)
R237	–	1b.+1b. (R163)
R238	–	1½b.+1b. (R164)
R239	–	2b.+1b. (R84)
R240	–	2b.+1b. (R126)
R241	–	2b.+1b. (R165)
R242	R **20**	4b.+2b. (R62)
R243	–	4b.+2b. (R66)
R244	R **20**	4b.+2b. (R68)
R245	R **26**	4b.+2b. (R85)
R246	R **34**	4b.+2b. (R93)
R247	–	4b.+2b. (R127)
R248	–	4b.+2b. (R166)
R249	–	6b.+3b. (R86) (air)
R250	–	6b.+3b. (R128)
R251	–	6b.+3b. (R167)
R252	R **35**	10b.+5b. (R130)
R253	–	10b.+5b. (R168)
R254	R **32**	12b.+6b. (R158)
R255	–	18b.+9b. (R87)
R256	R **12**	24b.+12b. red and blue (imperf, size 57 × 36 mm)
R257	–	24b.+12b. (R88)
R258	–	28b.+14b. (R159)
R259	–	34b.+17b. (R160)

The amount of surcharge was 50 per cent of the face value of each stamp (except Nos. R236/8 where the surcharge was 1b. each). Some higher values have two handstamps, which, when added together, make up the 50 per cent.

1967. Jordan Relief Fund. Surch **JORDAN RELIEF FUND** and value in English and Arabic with Crown. (a) No. R66 (Kennedy).

R261	–	4b.+2b. brown, yellow and gold	3·00	3·00

(b) Nos. R75/6 (Birds).

R262	–	4b.+2b. mult (postage)	1·00	1·00
R263	–	6b.+3b. mult (air)	1·75	1·75

(c) Nos. R92/4 (I.C.Y.).

R265	R **34**	2b.+1b. blue and brown (postage)	60	60
R266		4b.+2b. red and green	60	60
R267		6b.+3b. brown and blue (air)	60	60

(d) Nos. R102/4 (Cats).

R269	–	1b.+1b. multicoloured	1·00	1·00
R270	–	2b.+1b. multicoloured	1·00	1·00
R271	–	4b.+2b. multicoloured	1·00	1·00

(e) R109/11 (Flowers).

R273	–	1b.+1b. multicoloured	1·00	1·00
R274	R **30**	2b.+1b. multicoloured	1·00	1·00
R275	–	4b.+2b. multicoloured	1·00	1·00

(f) Nos. R136/40 (Builders of World Peace).

R277	R **36**	⅛b.+1b. gold, black and green	30	30
R278	–	¼b.+1b. gold, black and brown	30	30
R279	–	½b.+1b. gold, black and grey	30	30
R280	–	1b.+1b. gold, black and blue	50	50
R281	–	4b.+2b. gold, black and green	1·75	1·75

(g) Nos. R146/51 (Builders of World Peace).

R283	–	⅛b.+1b. gold, black and yellow	30	30
R284	–	¼b.+1b. gold, black and pink	30	30
R285	–	½b.+1b. gold, black and mauve	30	30
R286	–	1b.+1b. gold, black and blue	50	50
R287	–	1b.+1b. gold, black and green	50	50
R288	–	4b.+2b. gold, black and green	75	75

R **51** "The Pharmacy"

1967. Air. Paintings. Multicoloured. (a) Asiatic Paintings.

R290	⅛b. "Mountains and Forests" (Wang Hwei)	10	10
R291	¼b. "Tiger" (Sim Sajoug)	10	10
R292	½b. "Mountain Views" (Tong K'itch'ang)	10	10
R293	b. "Rama Lakshama and Shiva" (Indian 16th century)	10	10
R294	1b. "Ladies" (T. Kiyomitsu)	10	10

(b) Arab Paintings.

R295	1½b. "Bayad plays the Oud and sings"	15	10
R296	2b. Type R **51**	20	10
R297	3b. "Dioscorides and a Student"	20	10
R298	4b. "The Scribe"	25	20
R299	6b. "Abu Zayd asks to be taken over by boat"	50	25

The ⅛, 1½, 2 and 6b. are horiz and the remainder vert.

R **52** Bugler

1967. World Scout Jamboree, Idaho. Mult.

R301	¼b. Type R **52** (postage)	10	10
R302	½b. Campfire	10	10
R303	4b. Type R **52**	25	10
R304	6b. As ½b.	35	15
R305	⅛b. Scout badge and Yemeni flag (air)	10	10
R306	10b. As ⅛b.	35	15
R307	20b. Scout and satellite	70	20

1967. Jordan Refugees Relief Fund. Surch **JORDAN REFUGEES RELIEF FUND** and value in English and Arabic, and Refugee Emblem. (a) Nos. R52/4 (Olympic Games).

No.	Type	Description	Unused	Used
R309	R 16	2b.+2b. bl (postage)	50	50
R310		4b.+4b. violet	70	70
R311		6d.+6d. brown (air)	1·25	1·25
		(b) Nos. R55/7 (Astronauts).		
R313	R 17	2b.+2b. brown, violet and black (postage)	50	50
R314		4b.+4b. brown, blue and black	70	70
R315		6b.+6b. yellow and black (air)	1·25	1·25
		(c) Nos. R63/7 (Kennedy).		
R317	R 21	⅛b.+⅛b. black, mauve and gold (postage)	20	20
R318	–	¼b.+¼b. violet, turquoise and gold	20	20
R319	–	½b.+½b. brown, blue and gold	20	20
R320	–	4b.+4b. brown, yellow and gold	2·00	2·00
R321	–	6b.+6b. black, green and gold (air)	3·00	3·00
		(d) No. R68 (Churchill opt).		
R323	R 20	4b.+4b. blue and red	12·00	12·00
		(e) R69/71 (I.T.U.).		
R324	R 23	2b.+2b. yellow, violet and black (postage)	40	40
R325		4b.+4b. red, blue and black	70	70
R326		6b.+6b. green, violet and black (air)	2·50	2·50
		(f) R77/82 (Churchill).		
R328	R 25	⅛b.+⅛b. multicoloured	10	10
R329	–	¼b.+¼b. multicoloured	10	10
R330	–	⅓b.+⅓b. multicoloured	15	15
R331	R 25	1b.+1b. multicoloured	25	20
R332	–	2b.+2b. multicoloured	40	30
R333	–	4b.+4b. multicoloured	60	40

R 54 Vaquero

1967. Olympic Games, Mexico (1968). Multicoloured.

No.	Description	Unused	Used
R335	⅛b. Type R **54** (postage)	10	10
R336	¼b. Fishermen on Lake Patzcuaro	10	10
R337	⅓b. Football (vert)	10	10
R338	4b. Avenida de la Reforma, Mexico City	10	10
R339	8b. Fine Arts Theatre, Mexico City	30	10
R340	12b. Mayan ruins (air)	40	10
R341	16b. Type R **54**	50	10
R342	20b. As ¼b.	3·00	90

R 55 Battle Scene

1967. Moorish Art in Spain. Multicoloured.

No.	Description	Unused	Used
R344	2b. Moor slaying knight (horiz) (postage)	10	10
R345	4b. Arab kings of Granada (horiz)	15	10
R346	6b. Diagram of chess game (from King Alfonso X's "Book of Chess, Dice and Tablings") (horiz)	50	10
R347	10b. Type R **55**	60	10
R348	12b. Moors with prisoners	80	10
R349	20b. Meeting of Moor and Christian (air)	2·00	10
R350	22b. Bullfight	2·00	10
R351	24b. Lute players	2·75	15

APPENDIX

The following stamps have either been issued in excess of postal needs or have not been available to the public in reasonable quantities at face value. Such stamps may later be given full listing if there is evidence of regular postal use.

REPUBLIC

1967.

5th Anniv of Revolution Nos. 476/81 optd in Arabic 1, 2, 4, 6, 8, 10b.

Paintings by Flemish Masters. Postage ¼, ⅓, ½b.; Air 3, 6b.

Paintings by Florentine Masters. Postage ¼, ⅓, ½b.; Air 3, 6b.

Paintings by Spanish Masters. Postage ¼, ⅓, ½b.; Air 3, 6b.

Winter Olympic Games, Grenoble (1968) (1st issue). Embossed on gold foil. Air 5, 10, 15, 50b.

Winter Olympic Games, Grenoble (1968) (2nd issue). Sports ¼, ⅓, ½, 3, 6b.

Chancellor Adenauer Commemoration (1st issue). Embossed on gold foil. Air 50b.

1968.

Yemen Red Crescent. Embossed on gold foil. Air 5, 10, 15, 50b.

Paintings by Gauguin. Postage ¼, ¼, ⅓, ⅓, ½b.; Air 3, 3, 6, 6b.

Paintings by Van Gogh. Postage ¼, ¼, ⅓, ⅓, ½b.; Air 3, 3, 6, 6b.

Paintings by Rubens. Postage ¼, ¼, ⅓, ⅓, ½b.; Air 3, 3, 6, 6b.

Provisionals. Various 1930/31 values optd "Y.A.R." and date in English and Arabic. ½, 1, 1, 2, 2, 3, 4, 4, 5, 6, 6, 10, 10, 20b., 1, 1i.

Gold Medal Winners. Winter Olympic Games, Grenoble (1st issue). 1967 Winter Olympic Games (1st issue) optd with names of various winners. Air 50b. × 4.

1st Death Anniv of Vladimir Komarov (Russian cosmonaut). Air 5, 10, 15, 50b.

International Human Rights Year and U Thant Commemoration. Embossed on gold foil. Air 5, 10, 15, 50b.

Chancellor Adenauer Commemoration (2nd issue). Air 5, 10, 15b.

Refugee Relief. Adenauer (2nd issue) optd in Arabic only. Air 5, 10, 15, 50b.

Olympic Games, Mexico (1st issue). Chariot-racing. Embossed on gold foil. Air 5, 10, 15, 50b.

Paintings of Horses. Postage ¼, ⅓, ½b.; Air 3, 6b.

Paintings by Raphael. Postage ¼, ⅓, ½b.; Air 3, 6b.

Paintings by Rembrandt. Postage ¼, ⅓, ½b.; Air 3, 6b.

Dr. Martin Luther King Commemoration (1st issue). Human Rights issue optd. Air 50b.

Gold Medal Winners. Winter Olympic Games, Grenoble (2nd issue). Postage ¼, ⅓, ½, 2b.; Air 3, 4b.

Olympic Games, Mexico (2nd issue). Greek and Mexican Folklore. Postage ¼, ⅓, ½, 2b.; Air 3, 4b.

Gold Medal Winners, Olympic Games, Mexico (1st issue). Mexico Olympics (1st issue) optd with names of various winners. Air 50b. × 4.

Gold Medal Winners Olympic Games, Mexico (2nd issue). Postage ¼, ⅓, ½, 2b.; Air 3, 4b.

Dr. Martin Luther King Commemoration (2nd issue). Embossed on gold foil. 16b.

Emblems of Winter Olympic Games. Postage ¼, ⅓, ½, 2b.; Air 3, 4b.

Emblems of Olympic Games. Postage ¼, ⅓, ½, 2b.; Air 3, 4b.

Dag Hammarskjold and Kennedy Brothers Commemoration. ½, 2, 6, 14b.

Dr. Christian Barnard's Heart Transplant Operations. ¼, , 8, 10b.

Dr. Martin Luther King Commemoration (3rd issue). 1, 4, 12, 16b.

John and Robert Kennedy Commemoration. Embossed on gold foil. 10b.

1969.

Paintings from the Louvre, Paris. Postage ¼, ⅓, ½, 2b.; Air 3, 4b.

1st Death Anniv of Yurstet Gagarin (Russian cosmonaut). Optd on 1968 Komarov issue. Air 50b.

Paintings from the Uffizi Gallery, Florence. Postage ¼, ⅓, ½, 2b.; Air 3, 4b.

Paintings from the Prado, Madrid. Postage ¼, ⅓, ½, 2b.; Air 3b, 4b.

Birth Bicentenary of Napoleon (1st issue). Embossed on gold foil. Air 4b.

Space Exploration (1st series). Inscr "DISCOVERIES OF UNIVERSE". Postage ¼, ¼, ⅓, ⅓b.; Air 3, 6, 10b.

Space Exploration (2nd series). Inscr "FLIGHTS TO THE PLANETS". Postage ¼, ¼, ⅓, ⅓ b.; Air 2, 4, 22b.

First Man on the Moon. Embossed on gold foil. Air 10b.

50th Anniv of International Labour Organization. Postage 1, 2, 3, 4b.; Air 6, 8, 10b.

Space Exploration (3rd series). Inscr "MAN IN SPACE". Postage ¼, ¼, ⅓, ⅓b.; Air 3, 6, 10b.

Birth Bicentenary of Napoleon (2nd issue). Postage ¼, ⅓, ½, b.; Air 4, 8, 10b.

Space Exploration (4th series). "Apollo" Moon Flights. Postage ¼, ¼, ⅓, ⅓b.; Air 2, 4, 22b.

Winter Olympic Games, Sapporo (1972) Preparation. Optd on 1967 Grenoble Winter Olympics issue. Air 50b.

Olympic Games, Munich (1972) Preparation. Optd on 1968 Mexico Olympics issue. Air 50b.

Paintings from the National Gallery, Washington. Postage ¼, ⅓, ½, 2b.; Air 3, 4b.

Paintings from the National Gallery, London. Postage ¼, ⅓, ½, 2b.; Air 3, 4b.

French Monarchs and Statesmen. Postage 1, 2, 2¼, 2½b.; Air 3½, 5, 6b.

1970.

Tutankhamun Exhibition, Paris. Postage ¼, ⅓, ½, 2b.; Air 3, 4b.

Siamese Sculptures. Postage ¼, ⅓, ½, 2b.; Air 3, 4b.

"EXPO 70" World Fair, Osaka, Japan (1st issue). Japanese Paintings. Postage ¼, ⅓, ½, 2b.; Air 3, 4b.

EXPO 70" World Fair, Osaka, Japan (2nd issue). Japanese Puppets. Postage ¼, ⅓, ½, 2b.; Air 3, 4b.

World Cup Football Championship, Mexico (1st issue). Views and Maps. Postage 1, 2, 2¼, 2½b.; Air 3½, 5, 6, 7, 8b.

World Cup Football Championship, Mexico (2nd issue). Jules Rimet. Embossed on gold foil. Air 10b.

"United Europe". Postage 1⅓, 1, 2¼, 2½, 5b.; Air 7, 8, 10b.

25th Anniv of Victory in Second World War. Gen. de Gaulle. Embossed on gold foil. Air 6b.

Moon Mission of "Apollo 12". Postage 1, 1¼, 1⅓, 1½b.; Air 4, 4½, 7b.

World Cup Football Championship, Mexico (3rd issue). Teams. Postage ¼, ⅓, ½, b.; Air 4, 4½b.

World Cup Football Championship, Mexico (4th issue). Beckenbauer and Pele. Embossed on gold foil. Air 10b.

World Cup Football Championship, Mexico (5th issue). Footballers and Mexican Antiquities. Postage 1, 1¼, 1⅓, 1½b.; Air 3, 10b.

Interplanetary Space Travel. Postage 1, 2, 2¼, 2½b.; Air 5, 8, 10, 22b.

Inaug of New U.P.U. Headquarters Building, Berne. Postage ⅓, 1¼, 1½, 2b.; Air 3½, 4½, 6b.

"Philympia 70" Stamp Exhibition, London. Postage ¼, ½, 1, 3b.; Air 4b.

8th Anniv of Revolution. Flowers. ¼b. × 5.

Olympic Games, Munich (1972) (1st issue). Buildings. Postage 1, 1, 2½, 3, 3½b.; Air 8, 10b.

Olympic Games, Munich (2nd issue). Statue. Embossed on gold foil. Air 6b.

25th Anniv of United Nations. Human Rights Year issue of 1968 optd. Air 50b.

Winter Olympic Games, Sapporo (1st issue). Buildings and Emblem. Postage 1½, 2½, 4½, 5, 7b.; Air 8, 10b.

Winter Olympic Games, Sapporo (2nd issue). Snow Sculpture. Embossed on gold foil. Air 40b.

General Charles de Gaulle Commemoration. 1970 25th Anniv of Victory issue optd. Air 6b.

German Gold Medal Winners in Olympic Games. Postage ¼, ¼, ⅓, ⅓b. Air 6b.

1971.

Pres. Gamal Nasser of Egypt Commemoration. Postage ¼b. × 4, ½b. × 2; Air 1, 2, 5, 7, 10, 16b.

International Sporting Events. Postage ¼, ⅓, ½, 2b.; Air 3, 4b.

Olympic Games, Munich (3rd issue). Theatre Productions. Postage ½, 1¼, 1, 2¼, 4½b.; Air 5, 6b.

Moon Mission of "Apollo 14" 1969 Moon Landing issue optd. Air 10b.

Olympic Games, Munich (4th issue). Paintings from the Pinakothek. Postage ¼, ⅓, , 1½, 2b.; Air 4, 7b.

Chinese Paintings. Postage ¼, ⅓, ½, 2b.; Air 3, 4b.

Winter Olympic Games, Sapporo (3rd issue). Winter Sports and Japanese Works of Art. Postage ¼, ½, 1, 1⅓, 2b.; Air 3, 4b.

Winter Olympic Games, Sapporo (4th issue). Japanese Skier. Embossed on gold foil. Air 8b.

Launching of Soviet "Salyut" Space Station. Interplanetary issue of 1970 optd. Air 22b.

Olympic Games, Munich (5th issue). Sports and Sculptures. Postage ⅛, 1, 1⅓, 1, 2¼b.; Air 4½, 7, 10b.

Olympic Games, Munich (6th issue). Gold Medals. Embossed on gold foil. Air 8b.

Exploration of Outer Space. Postage ¼, ⅓, ½, b.; Air 3, 3½, 6b.

Birth Bicentenary of Beethoven. Postage ¼ × 4, ½b. × 2; Air 1, 2, 5, 7, 10b.

Indian Paintings. Postage ¼, ⅓, ½, 2b.; Air 3, 4b.

Olympic Games, Munich (7th issue). Sailing Events at Kiel. Postage ¼, ½, 1¼, 2, 3b.; Air 4b.

Winter Olympic Games, Sapporo (5th issue). Sports. Postage ⅓, , 1¼, 1, 2¼b.; Air 3½, 6b.

Winter Olympic Games, Sapporo (6th issue). Slalom Skier. Embossed on gold foil. Air 10b.

Persian Miniatures. Postage ¼, ⅓, ½, 2b.; Air 3, 4b.

Olympic Games, Munich (8th issue). Sports. Postage 1½, 2½, 3½, 5b.; Air 6, 8b.

Olympic Games, Munich (9th issue). Discus-thrower. Embossed on gold foil. Air 10b.

Italian Gold Medal Winners in Olympic Games. Postage ¼b. × 2, ⅓b. × 2; Air 22b.

1972.

French Gold Medal Winners in Olympic Games. Postage 2, 3b.; Air 4, 10b.

Works of Art. Postage 1, 1¼, 1⅓, 1½b.; Air 3, 4½, 7b.

ROYALIST ISSUES

1967.

Visit of Queen of Sheba to Solomon. ⅛, ¼, ½, 4, 6, 20, 24b.

Arab Horses. ⅛, ¼, ½, 4, 10b.

1968.

Winter Olympic Games, Grenoble (1st issue). Nos. R216/29 optd. Postage ⅛, ¼, ½, 1, 4, 6, 10b.; Air 12, 14, 16, 24, 34b.

Butterflies. Air 16, 20, 40b.

Postage Due. Butterflies and Horse. 4, 16, 20b.

Winter Olympic Games, Grenoble (2nd issue). Sports. Postage 1, 2, 3, 4, 6b.; Air 10, 12, 18, 24, 28b.

Gold Medal Winners, Grenoble Winter Olympics. Winter Olympic Games, Grenoble (2nd issue) optd with names of various medal winners. Postage 1, 2, 3, 4, 6b.; Air 10, 12, 18, 24, 28b.

20th Anniv of UNESCO. ½, 1, 1½, 2, 3, 4, 6, 10b.

Mothers' Day. Paintings. Postage 2, 4, 6b.; Air 24, 28, 34b.

Olympic Games, Mexico (1st issue). Sports. Postage 1, 2, 3, 4, 6b.; Air 10, 12, 18, 24, 28b.

UNESCO. "Save Florence" Campaign. Paintings. Postage 2, 4, 6b.; Air 10, 12, 18b.

UNESCO. "Save Venice" Campaign. Paintings. ½, 1, 1½, 24b.; Air 28, 34b.

Olympic Games, Mexico (2nd issue). Athletes and Flags. 4b. × 11.

Winter Olympic Games since 1924. Competitors and Flags. Postage. 1, 2, 3, 4, 6b.; Air 10, 12, 18, 24, 28b.

International Human Rights Year. 2b. × 4, 4b. × 4, 6b. × 4.

Paintings by European and American Artists. Postage 1, 2, 3, 4, 6, 10b.; Air 12, 18, 24, 28b.

Coronation of Shah of Iran. Postage 1, 2, 3, 4b.; Air 24, 28b.

International Philately. Postage 1, 2, 3, 4, 6b.; Air 10, 12, 18, 24, 28b.

World Racial Peace. Postage 4, 6, 18b.; Air 10b.

Children's Day. Paintings. Postage 1, 2, 3, 4b.; Air 6, 10, 12, 18, 24, 28b.

Gold Medal Winners, Mexico Olympic Games (1st issue). Mexico Olympics (1st issue) optd with names of various medal winners. Postage 1, 2, 3, 4, 6b.; Air 10, 12, 18, 24, 28b.

Gold Medal Winners, Mexico Olympics (2nd issue). Athletes and Medals. Air 12, 18, 24, 28, 34b.

Gold Medal Winners, Mexico Olympics (3rd issue). Embossed on gold foil. 28b.

"EFIMEX 68" Stamp Exhibition, Mexico City. Air 12, 18, 24, 28, 34b.

1969.

Motor-racing Drivers. Postage 1, 2, 3, 4, 6b.; Air 10, 12, 18, 24, 28b.

Space Flight of "Apollo 7". 4, 8, 12, 24, 28b.

Space Flight of "Apollo 8" (1st issue). 4, 6, 10, 18, 34b.

Space Flight of "Apollo 8" (2nd issue). Embossed on gold foil. 28b.

5th Anniv of Imam's Meeting with Pope Paul VI at Jerusalem (1st issue). Scenes from Pope's Visit. ⅛, ¼, ¼, 1, 1½, 2, 3, 4, 5, 6b.

5th Anniv of Imam's Meeting with Pope Paul VI at Jerusalem (2nd issue). Paintings of the Life of Christ. Postage 1, 2, 3, 4, 5, 6, 7, 8, 9, 10b.; Air 11, 12, 13, 14, 15, 16, 17, 18, 19, 20, 21, 22, 23, 24, 25, 26, 27, 28, 29, 30b.

5th Anniv of Imam's Meeting with Pope Paul VI at Jerusalem (3rd issue). Abraham's Tomb, Hebron. 4b.

Paintings by Rembrandt (1st series). Postage 1, 2, 4b.; Air 6, 12b., 1i.

Paintings by Rembrandt (2nd series). Embossed on gold foil. 20b.

Paintings by European Artists. Postage ½, 1½, 3, 5b.; Air 10, 18, 24, 28, 34b.

"Apollo" Moon Programme. Postage 1, 2, 3, 4, 5b.; Air 6, 7, 8, 9, 10, 11, 12, 13, 14, 15b.

Moon Flight of "Apollo 10". Postage 2, 4, 6b.; Air 8, 10, 12, 18, 24, 28, 34b.

Olympic Games, Munich (1972). Athletes and Olympic Rings. Postage 1, 2, 4, 5, 6b.; Air 10, 12, 18, 24, 34b.

World Wildlife Conservation. Postage ½b. × 2 1b. × 2, 2b. × 2, 4b. × 2, 6b. × 2; Air 8b. × 2, 10b. × 2, 18b. × 2.

First Man on the Moon (1st issue). Air 6, 10, 12, 18b.

First Man on the Moon (2nd issue). Air 6, 10, 12, 18, 24b.

First Man on the Moon (3rd issue). Embossed on gold foil. 24b. × 2.

First Man on the Moon (4th issue). Embossed on gold foil. 28b.

First Man on the Moon (5th issue). Air 10, 12 18, 24b.

Palestine Holy Places. Postage 4b. × 4, 6b. × 10; Air 12b. × 8.

Famous Men. Postage 4b. × 4, 6b. × 10; Air 12b. × 2.

History of Space Exploration. Air 6b. × 27.

Olympic Sports. Postage 1, 2, 4, 5, 6b.; Air 10, 12, 18, 24, 34b.

World Cup Football Championship, Mexico. Air 12b. × 8.

Christmas. Ikons. Postage ½, 1, 1½, 2, 4, 5, 6b.; Air 10, 12, 18, 24, 28, 34b.

Burning of Al-Aqsa Mosque, Jerusalem. Postage 4b.+2b., 6b.+3b.; Air 10b.+5b.

1970.

Brazil's Victory in World Cup Football Championship, Mexico. 1969 World Cup issue optd. Air 12b. × 3.

Dogs. Postage 2, 4, 6b.; Air 8, 12b.

Paintings of Horses. Postage 2, 4, 6b.; Air 8, 12b.

We close the Appendix with stamps believed to have been issued prior to July 1970, when first Saudi Arabia and the United Kingdom recognised the Republican government in Yemen.

YEMEN PEOPLE'S DEMOCRATIC REPUBLIC Pt. 19

The former People's Republic of Southern Yemen was known by the above title from 30 November 1970.

In 1990 it united with Yemen Arab Republic (see YEMEN REPUBLIC (combined)).

1000 fils = 1 dinar.

22 Temple of Isis, Philae, Egypt

1971. Preservation of Philae Temples Campaign.
65 **22** 5f. multicoloured 10 10
66 35f. multicoloured 50 30
67 65f. multicoloured . . . . . 1·25 80

23 Symbols of Constitution

1971. Introduction of First Constitution.
68 **23** 10f. multicoloured 10 10
69 15f. multicoloured 25 20
70 35f. multicoloured 50 35
71 50f. multicoloured 65 50

24 Heads of Three Races and Flame

1971. Racial Equality Year.
72 **24** 20f. multicoloured 20 20
73 35f. multicoloured 40 40
74 75f. multicoloured 70 70

25 Map, Flag and Products

26 Hand holding Sub-machine Gun, and Map

1971.
75 **25** 5f. multicoloured 10 10
76 10f. multicoloured 10 10
77 15f. multicoloured 15 10
78 20f. multicoloured 15 10
79 25f. multicoloured 20 10
80 35f. multicoloured 25 15
81 40f. multicoloured 35 15
82 50f. multicoloured 50 35
82a 60f. multicoloured . . . . 1·00 40
83 65f. multicoloured 65 45
84 80f. multicoloured 75 60
84a 90f. multicoloured . . . . 1·10 50
84b – 110f. multicoloured . . . . 1·50 65
85 – 125f. multicoloured . . . . 1·25 1·10
86 – 250f. multicoloured . . . . 2·25 1·50
87 – 500f. multicoloured . . . . 4·50 3·00
88 – 1d. multicoloured . . . . 9·75 6·25
DESIGN—42 × 25 mm: Nos. 84b/8, "Dam-al-Khawain" tree, Socotra.

1971. 6th Anniv of Revolutionary Activity in Arabian Gulf Area. Multicoloured.
89 15f. Type **26** 20 15
90 45f. Girl guerrilla and emblem (horiz) 50 40
91 50f. Guerrilla on the march . . 85 55

27 Hands supporting Cogwheel

29 Gamal Nasser

28 Eagle and Flags

1971. 2nd Anniv of "Corrective Move" in Revolutionary Government. Multicoloured.
92 15f. Type **27** 15 10
93 25f. Torch and revolutionary emblems 30 25
94 65f. Salt-works and windmill 75 50

1971. 9th Anniv of 26 September Revolution. Multicoloured.
95 10f. Type **28** 10 10
96 40f. Flag on "United Jemen" 50 40

1971. 1st Death Anniv of Gamal Nasser (Egyptian statesman).
97 **29** 65f. multicoloured 65 50

30 "Children of the World"

31 Domestic Pigeons

1971. 25th Anniv of U.N.I.C.E.F.
98 **30** 15f. black, red and orange 10 10
99 40f. black, purple and blue 30 25
100 50f. black, red and green 50 45

1971. Birds.
101 **31** 5f. black, purple and blue 20 10
102 – 40f. multicoloured 90 30
103 – 65f. black, red and green 2·40 45
104 – 100f. multicoloured . . . . 3·75 75
DESIGNS: 40f. Arabian chukar (inscr "Partridge"); 65f. Helmeted guineafowl and Arabian chukar (inscr "Partridge"); 100f. Black kite (inscr "Glede").

32 Dhow-building

1972. Dhow-building in Aden. Multicoloured.
105 25f. Type **32** 50 25
106 80f. Dhow at sea (vert) . . . 1·50 1·00

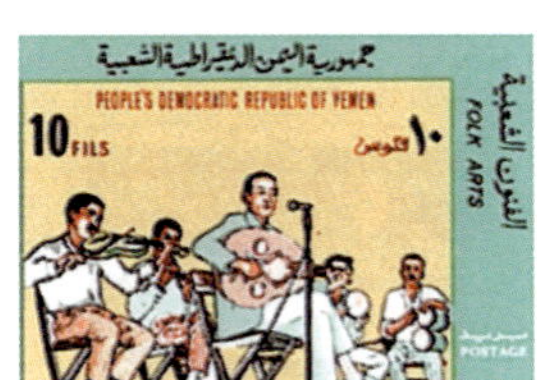

33 Singer with Oud (lute), and Band

1972. Folk Dances. Multicoloured.
107 10f. Type **33** 15 10
108 25f. Yemeni girls dancing . . 40 20
109 40f. Dancing teams 75 40
110 80f. Festival dance . . . . . 1·25 85

34 Palestinian Guerrilla and Barbed-wire

1972. Palestine Day.
111 **34** 5f. multicoloured 15 10
112 20f. multicoloured 40 20
113 65f. multicoloured 90 65

35 Police Colour Party

1972. Police Day. Multicoloured.
114 25f. Type **35** 35 25
115 80f. Girls of People's Militia on parade . . . . 1·60 1·00

36 Start of Cycle Race

1972. Arab Youth Week. Multicoloured.
117 10f. Type **36** 30 10
118 15f. Girls on parade 30 10
119 40f. Guides and scouts 65 40
120 80f. Acrobatic team (vert) . . 1·25 75

37 Turtle

1972. Marine Life. Multicoloured.
121 15f. Type **37** 55 20
122 40f. Sailfish 85 60
123 65f. Narrow-barred Spanish mackerel and John Dory 1·40 90
124 125f. Lobster . . . . 2·25 1·40

38 Book Year Emblem

1972. International Book Year.
125 **38** 40f. multicoloured 50 40
126 65f. multicoloured 75 60

39 Farmworkers and Field

1972. Agriculture Day.
127 **39** 10f. multicoloured 15 10
128 25f. multicoloured 40 25
129 40f. multicoloured 75 50

40 Soldiers advancing

1972. 5th Anniv of Independence. Multicoloured.
130 5f. Type **40** 15 10
131 20f. Soldier and town 40 25
132 65f. Vignettes of Yemeni life (vert) 75 60

41 Population Graph

1973. Population Census.
134 **41** 25f. emerald, red and green 35 20
135 40f. lt blue, mauve and blue 65 35

42 W.H.O. Emblem within "25"

43 Taweela Tanks, Aden

1973. 25th Anniv of W.H.O. Multicoloured.
136 5f. Type **42** 10 10
137 25f. W.H.O. emblem on globe (horiz) 25 20
138 125f. "25" and W.H.O. emblem (horiz) . . . . . . 1·50 1·25

1973. Tourism. Multicoloured.
139 20f. Type **43** 25 15
140 25f. Shibam Town (horiz) . . 40 25
141 40f. Elephant Bay, Aden (horiz) 65 50
142 100f. Al-Mohdar Mosque, Tarim (horiz) . . . . . . 1·25 95

44 Modern Apartments and Slum Clearance

1973. Nationalization of Buildings (1972). Mult.
143 20f. Type **44** 25 15
144 80f. Street scene (vert) . . . 1·00 75

45 Women's Corps on Parade

1973. People's Army. Multicoloured.
145 10f. Type **45** 15 10
146 20f. Soldiers marching . . . 25 15
147 40f. Naval contingent 65 45
148 80f. Column of tanks . . . . 1·50 90

46 Quayside Crane

1973. 10th Anniv of World Food Programme. Multicoloured.
149 20f. Type **46** 25 10
150 80f. Granary workers . . . . 1·00 75

47 "U.P.U. Letter"

1974. Centenary of U.P.U. Multicoloured.
151 5f. Type **47** 10 10
152 20f. "100" formed of people and U.P.U. emblems . . . 25 20

153 40f. U.P.U. emblem and Yemeni flag (vert) 50 35
154 125f. Map of People's Republic (vert) . . . . . . 1·00 80

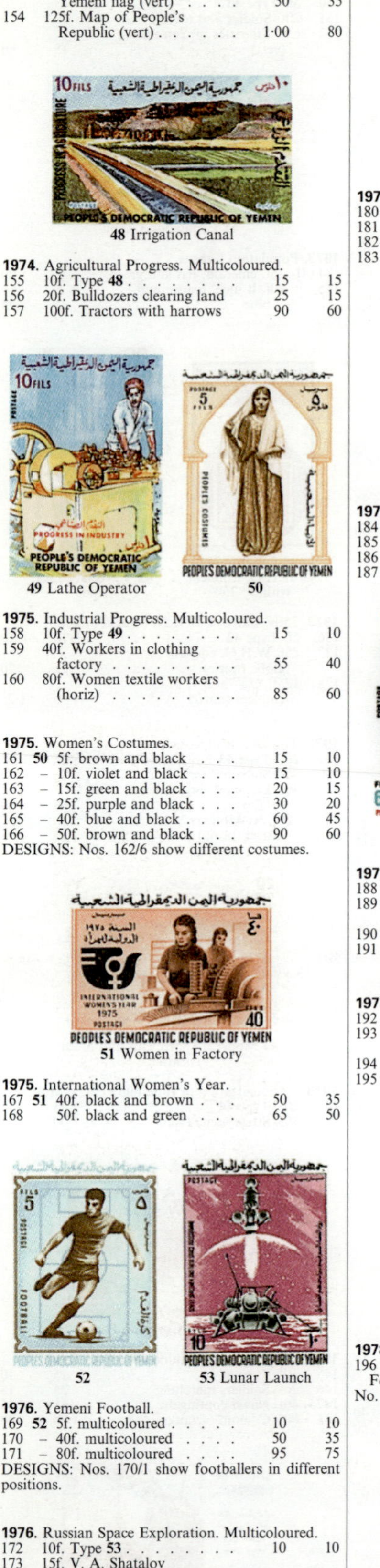

48 Irrigation Canal

1974. Agricultural Progress. Multicoloured.
155 10f. Type **48** 15 15
156 20f. Bulldozers clearing land 25 15
157 100f. Tractors with harrows 90 60

49 Lathe Operator **50**

1975. Industrial Progress. Multicoloured.
158 10f. Type **49** 15 10
159 40f. Workers in clothing factory 55 40
160 80f. Women textile workers (horiz) 85 60

1975. Women's Costumes.
161 **50** 5f. brown and black . . . 15 10
162 – 10f. violet and black . . . 15 10
163 – 15f. green and black . . . 20 15
164 – 25f. purple and black . . . 30 20
165 – 40f. blue and black 60 45
166 – 50f. brown and black . . . 90 60
DESIGNS: Nos. 162/6 show different costumes.

51 Women in Factory

1975. International Women's Year.
167 **51** 40f. black and brown . . . 50 35
168 50f. black and green . . . 65 50

52 **53** Lunar Launch

1976. Yemeni Football.
169 **52** 5f. multicoloured 10 10
170 – 40f. multicoloured 50 35
171 – 80f. multicoloured 95 75
DESIGNS: Nos. 170/1 show footballers in different positions.

1976. Russian Space Exploration. Multicoloured.
172 10f. Type **53** 10 10
173 15f. V. A. Shatalov (cosmonaut) 15 10
174 40f. Luna vehicle (horiz) . . 65 35
175 65f. Valentina Tereshkova and rocket . . . . 1·00 60

54 Members of Presidential Council

1977. 1st Anniv of Unification Congress. Multicoloured.
176 25f. Type **54** 25 15
177 35f. Text of document . . . 35 30
178 65f. Girls of People's Militia 65 45
179 95f. Aerial view of textile factory 95 55

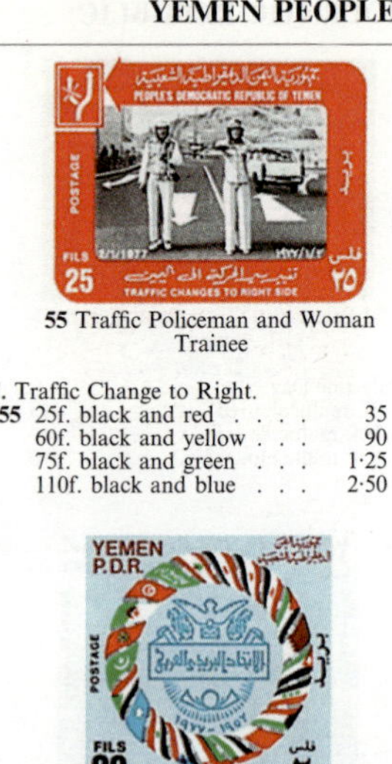

55 Traffic Policeman and Woman Trainee

1977. Traffic Change to Right.
180 **55** 25f. black and red 35 25
181 60f. black and yellow . . . 90 65
182 75f. black and green . . . 1·25 90
183 110f. black and blue . . . 2·50 1·40

56 A.P.U. Emblem within Flags of Member States

1977. 25th Anniv of Arab Postal Union.
184 **56** 20f. multicoloured 25 15
185 60f. multicoloured 60 50
186 70f. multicoloured 75 60
187 90f. multicoloured 90 65

57 Festive Volute **58** Dove of Peace and Flag

1977. Cowries. Multicoloured.
188 60f. Type **57** 60 25
189 90f. Pringle's marginella (horiz) 95 35
190 110f. Clay cone (horiz) . . . 1·25 60
191 180f. Broderip's cowrie (horiz) . . . . 2·25 1·25

1977. 10th Anniv of Independence. Multicoloured.
192 5f. Type **58** 10 10
193 20f. Man with broken manacle 15 10
194 90f. Oil pipeline 50 25
195 110f. "Pillar of Freedom" . . 80 30

59 Dome of the Rock, Jerusalem

1978. Palestinian Welfare.
196 **59** 5f. multicoloured 25 10
For smaller design with value at top right, see No. 264.

60 Almarfaa (drum)

1978. Musical Instruments. Multicoloured.
197 35f. Type **60** 25 10
198 60f. Almizmar (pipes) 60 25
199 90f. Alqnboos (fiddle) . . . . 1·00 35
200 110f. Simsimiya (lyre) . . . . 1·25 50

61 Almotl (armbands)

1978. Silver Ornaments. Multicoloured.
201 10f. Type **61** 10 10
202 15f. Aloodhad (ring) 15 10
203 20f. Al Hizam (necklace) . . 20 10
204 60f. Alhoogaalah (bangle) . . 40 20
205 90f. Al Muk-Hala (perfume flask) 75 40
206 110f. Al Janbiya (dagger) . . 95 50

62 Palm Tree Emblem **63** "V" for Vanguard and Cogwheel

1978. 11th World Youth Festival, Cuba. Mult.
207 5f. Type **62** 10 10
208 60f. Global emblem 40 20
209 90f. Flower emblem 60 30
210 110f. Girl, youth and emblems 85 45

1978. 1st Conference of Vanguard Party.
211 **63** 5f. multicoloured 10 10
212 20f. multicoloured 15 10
213 60f. multicoloured 25 25
214 180f. multicoloured 90 50

64 Calligraphic Emblem, Symbols of Peace and Freedom

1978. 15th Anniv of 14 October Revolution. Mult.
215 10f. Type **64** 10 10
216 35f. Emblems of growth (vert) 20 10
217 60f. Candle and figure "15" (vert) 35 20
218 110f. Revolutionaries and figure "15" (vert) 65 50

65 Map of Yemen, Child with Olive-branch and Dove **66** "Agricultural Progress"

1979. International Year of the Child.
219 **65** 15f. multicoloured 15 10
220 20f. multicoloured 15 10
221 60f. multicoloured 35 15
222 90f. multicoloured 65 40

1979. 10th Anniv of "Corrective Move" in Revolutionary Government. Multicoloured.
223 20f. Type **66** 10 10
224 35f. "Industrial Progress" . . 15 10
225 60f. Students 35 15
226 90f. Woman with star and doves 60 40

67 Sir Rowland Hill and Yemeni Costume Stamp of 1970

1979. Death Cent of Sir Rowland Hill. Mult.
227 90f. Type **67** 20 15
228 110f. Yemeni camel stamp of 1970 . . . . 35 20

68 World Map, Koran and Symbols of Arab Achievements

1979. The Arabs.
230 **68** 60f. multicoloured 45 20

69 Emblem of Yemeni Socialist Party **70** "Cassia adenensis"

1979. 1st Anniv of Yemeni Socialist Party.
231 **69** 60f. multicoloured 45 20

1979. Flowers (1st series). Multicoloured.
232 20f. Type **70** 10 10
233 90f. "Nerium oleander" . . . 50 40
234 110f. "Calligonum comosum" 95 45
235 180f. "Adenium obesum" . . 1·25 65
See also Nos. 265/8.

71 Ayatollah Khomeini and Crowd **73** Woman Basket-making

72 "Dido"

1980. 1st Anniv of Iranian Revolution.
236 **71** 60f. multicoloured 90 75

1980. Screw Steamers. Multicoloured.
237 110f. Type **72** 70 55
238 180f. "Anglia" . . . . 1·10 1·00
239 250f. "India" . . . . 1·60 1·40

1980. "London 1980". Handicrafts. Mult.
240 60f. Type **73** 35 20
241 90f. Making a hubble-bubble pipe 50 25
242 110f. Man at loom 70 40
243 250f. Boy making clay pot . . 1·25 75

74 Skink

1980. Reptiles. Multicoloured.
244 20f. Type **74** 20 10
245 35f. Mole viper 25 15
246 110f. Gecko . . . . 1·00 40
247 180f. Cobra . . . . 1·60 65

75 Misha the Bear (Olympic Mascot) **77** Lenin

76 Farming

1980. Olympic Games, Moscow.
248 **75** 110f. multicoloured 65 30

1980. 10th Anniv of Peasants' Uprising. Multicoloured.
249 50f. Type **76** 30 15
250 90f. Peasants 45 25
251 110f. Corn sickle and fist . . 65 30

1980. 110th Birth Anniv of Lenin.
252 **77** 35f. multicoloured 25 15

78 Douglas DC-3

1981. Democratic Yemen Airlines. Multicoloured.
253 60f. Type **78** 50 35
254 90f. Boeing 707 . . . . . . 95 55
255 250f. De Havilland D.H.C.7 Dash Seven . . . . 2·10 1·25

79 Map, Dish Aerial and Satellite

80 "Conocarpus lancifolius"

1981. Ras Boradli Satellite Station.
256 **79** 60f. multicoloured 60 25

1981. Trees. Multicoloured.
257 90f. Type **80** 60 25
258 180f. "Ficus vasta" . . . . . 1·25 65
259 250f. "Maerua crassifolia" . . 1·90 1·00

81 Council Building, Citizens and Flag

1981. 10th Anniv of Supreme People's Council.
260 **81** 180f. multicoloured . . . . 1·10 50

82 Sand Fox

1981. Wildlife Conservation. Multicoloured.
261 50f. Type **82** 25 20
262 90f. Leopard 70 40
263 250f. Ibex . . . . 1·25 1·00

1981. Palestinian Welfare. As T **59**, but smaller, 25 × 27 mm, and value at top right.
264 5f. multicoloured 25 10

1981. Flowers (2nd series). As T **70**. Mult.
265 50f. "Tephrosia apollinea" 40 25
266 90f. "Citrullus colocynthis" 75 40
267 110f. "Aloe squarrosa" . . . 1·10 40
268 250f. "Lawsonia inermis" . . 2·25 1·25

83 Blind People Basket-weaving and Typing

1982. International Year of Disabled Persons.
269 **83** 50f. multicoloured 15 10
270 100f. multicoloured 35 20
271 150f. multicoloured 50 40

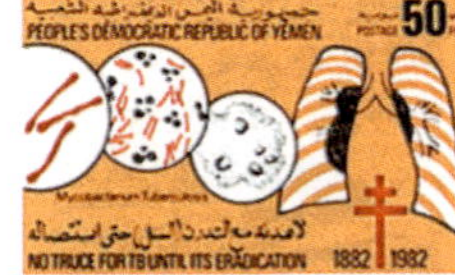

84 Microscope Slides and Lungs

1982. Centenary of Discovery of Tubercle Bacillus.
272 **84** 50f. black, orange and red 65 25

85 A.P.U. Emblem and Map within Heart

1982. 30th Anniv of Arab Postal Union.
273 **85** 100f. red, black and blue 90 40

86 Footballers

1982. World Cup Football Championship, Spain. Multicoloured.
274 50f. Type **86** 40 25
275 100f. Match scene 75 50
276 150f. Players and shield . . . 1·25 75
277 200f. Player and flags . . . . 1·75 1·00

87 Emblems and Flags of Russia and Yemen

1982. 60th Anniv of U.S.S.R.
279 **87** 50f. multicoloured 40 20

1982. World Cup Football Championship Result. Nos. 274/7 optd **WORLD CUP WINNERS 1982 1st ITALY 2nd W-GERMANY 3rd POLAND 4th FRANCE** and player holding trophy.
280 50f. Type **86** 40 25
281 100f. Match scene 75 55
282 150f. Players and shield . . . 1·25 90
283 200f. Player and flags . . . . 1·75 1·10

89 Yasser Arafat

1983. Palestinian Solidarity. Multicoloured.
285 50f. Type **89** 65 40
286 100f. Yasser Arafat and Dome of the Rock . . . . 1·40 55

1983. "Tembal 83" Stamp Exhibition, Basel. No. 248 optd **TEMBAL 83 MAY 21st-29th, 1983** and emblem.
288 **75** 110f. multicoloured . . . . 3·25 1·25

91 Man with Letter, Postal Barge and Postman

1983. World Communications Year.
289 **91** 50f. black and blue 50 35
290 – 100f. black and red . . . . 1·00 45
291 – 150f. black, green and olive 1·60 75
292 – 200f. multicoloured . . . . 1·90 80
DESIGNS: 100f. Postman, stage coach and morse code equipment; 150f. Motor coach and telephones; 200f. Transmitter, airplane, satellite, television, envelope and dish aerial.

92 "The Poor Family"

1983. 10th Death Anniv of Picasso (artist). Multicoloured.
294 50f. Type **92** 60 35
295 100f. "Woman with Crow" 20 20

93 Show Jumping

1983. Olympic Games, Los Angeles (1st issue). Equestrian Events. Multicoloured.
297 25f. Type **93** 65 65
298 50f. Show jumping (different) 1·10 50
299 100f. Horse crossing water (Three-day event) . . . . 1·75 1·00
See also Nos. 316/18.

94 Class P8 Steam Locomotive, 1905, Prussia

1983. Railway Locomotives. Multicoloured.
301 25f. Type **94** 75 25
302 50f. Class 880 steam locomotive, 1915, Italy . . 1·25 55
303 100f. Class Gt2 steam locomotive, 1923, Bavaria 2·10 1·10

95 Liner "Europa"

1983. Ships. Multicoloured.
305 50f. Type **95** . . . . 1·25 60
306 100f. Liner "World Discoverer" . . . . 2·10 1·00

96 "20" and Hand holding Sheaf of Corn

1983. 20th Anniv of Revolution. Multicoloured.
308 50f. Type **96** 65 35
309 100f. Flag, man with gun and "XX" . . . . 1·40 65

97 Pierre Testu-Brissy's Balloon, 1798

1983. Bicentenary of Manned Flight. Mult.
310 50f. Type **97** 50 25
311 100f. Unmanned Montgolfier balloon, 1783 . . . . . . 1·10 50

98 Skiing

1983. Winter Olympic Games, Sarajevo. Multicoloured.
313 50f. Type **98** 65 35
314 100f. Bobsleigh . . . . . . 1·00 50

99 Fencing

1984. Olympic Games, Los Angeles (2nd issue). Multicoloured.
316 25f. Type **99** 25 15
317 50f. Fencing (different) . . . 50 25
318 100f. Fencing (different) . . . 85 50

100 "Soyuz 10"–"Salyut 1" Link-up, 1971

1984. Space. Multicoloured.
320 15f. Type **100** 15 15
321 20f. "Apollo 8" and Moon, 1968 . . . . 20 15
322 50f. "Apollo 11" and first man on Moon, 1969 . . . 50 35
323 100f. "Soyuz"–"Apollo" link-up, 1975 . . . . 85 65

1984. Nos. 83 and 84b surch.
325 **25** 50f. on 65f. multicoloured 65 40
326 – 100f. on 110f. mult . . . . 1·40 65

102 Starry Triggerfish

105 Victory Parade, Red Square

104 Women writing

1984. Fishes. Multicoloured.
327 10f. Type **102** 10 10
328 15f. Golden trevally 15 10
329 20f. Saddled grunt 20 10
330 35f. Diagonal butterflyfish . . 25 15

331 35f. Emperor angelfish . . . 25 15
332 50f. Indian mackerel 50 20
333 100f. Kawakawa 95 30
334 150f. Pennant coralfish . . . 1·50 60
335 200f. Yellow-banded angelfish 2·25 80
336 250f. Plane-tailed lionfish . . 2·75 1·40
337 400f. Long-spined seabream 4·50 2·00
338 500f. Coachwhip stingray . . 5·50 2·40
339 1d. Brown-spotted grouper 12·00 5·75
340 2d. Long-finned drepane . . 25·00 11·50

1984. Olympic Winners, Sarajevo. No. 314 optd **WINNERS B.Lehmann–B. Musiol (DDR).**
341 100f. multicoloured . . . . . 5·00 4·25

1985. National Literacy Campaign. Mult.
343 50f. Type **104** 95 50
344 100f. Pen held in manacled fist . . . . 1·90 75

1985. 40th Anniv of End of Second World War.
345 **105** 100f. multicoloured . . . 1·00 40

106 Flag within Emblem

107 Modern Buildings

1985. 12th World Youth and Students' Festival, Moscow. Multicoloured.
346 50f. Type **106** 95 50
347 100f. Hand holding emblem as placard . . . . 1·90 75

1985. U.N.E.S.C.O. World Heritage Site. Shibam City. Multicoloured.
348 50f. Type **107** 95 60
349 50f. View of city 95 60
350 100f. Screen . . . . 1·90 95
351 100f. Gate (vert) . . . . . . 1·90 95

108 Industrial Symbols

109 Mother feeding Child

1985. 3rd Yemeni Socialist Party General Congress. Multicoloured.
352 25f. Type **108** 50 25
353 50f. Crane loading ship . . . 75 40
354 100f. Combine harvesters . . 1·60 70

1985. U.N.I.C.E.F. Child Survival Campaign. Multicoloured.
355 50f. Type **109** 95 60
356 50f. Immunization 95 60
357 100f. Breastfeeding . . . . . 1·90 95
358 100f. Oral rehydration therapy . . . . 1·90 95

110 Wheat and Al-Mohdar Mosque, Tarim

111 Lenin addressing Crowd in Red Square

1986. World Food Day. 40th Anniv (1985) of F.A.O. Multicoloured.
359 20f. Type **110** 60 20
360 180f. Palm trees . . . . . . 2·50 1·10

1986. 27th Russian Communist Party Congress. Multicoloured.
361 **111** 75f. multicoloured 95 45
362 250f. multicoloured . . . 2·50 1·25

112 Bride in Yashmak

113 Ali Ahmed N. Antar

1986. Brides and Bridegrooms of Yemen. Mult.
363 50f. Type **112** 60 25
364 50f. Bride with striped shawl 60 25
365 50f. Bride with long dressed hair 60 25
366 100f. Bridegroom in modern jacket with knife . . . . 1·25 50
367 100f. Bridegroom in traditional clothes with gun 1·25 50
368 100f. Bride in modern dress 1·25 50

1986. "Party and Homeland Martyrs". Mult.
369 75f. Type **113** 65 35
370 75f. Saleh Musleh Kasim . . 65 35
371 75f. Ali Shayaa Hadi . . . 65 35
372 75f. Abdul Fattah Ismail . . 65 35

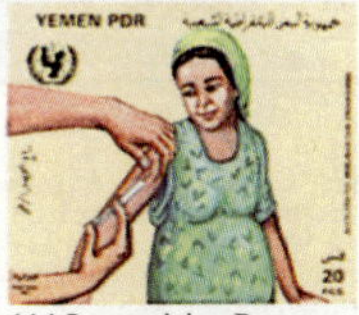

114 Immunizing Pregnant Woman against Tetanus

1987. U.N.I.C.E.F. Immunization Campaign. Multicoloured.
373 20f. Type **114** 25 10
374 75f. Immunizing baby . . . 75 40
375 140f. Nurse giving oral poliomyelitis vaccine to baby . . . . 1·25 65
376 150f. Pregnant woman and children carrying syringes 1·50 75

115 Party Emblem and Worker

116 Lenin and Soldier

1987. Yemeni Socialist Party General Conference.
377 **115** 75f. multicoloured 65 25
378 150f. multicoloured . . . 1·25 65

1987. 70th Anniv of Russian October Revolution.
379 **116** 250f. multicoloured . . . 2·50 1·25

117 Steps to King's Court

1987. Shabwa Remains. Multicoloured.
380 25f. Type **117** 25 10
381 75f. Royal Palace 70 35
382 140f. Winged lion, King's Court (vert) . . . . . . 1·25 65
383 150f. Inscribed bronze plaque (vert) . . . . 1·60 75

118 Students and College Buildings

1987. 20th Anniv of Independence. Mult.
384 25f. Type **118** 25 10
385 75f. Family and housing . . 75 35
386 140f. Workers, oil derrick and power station . . . . 1·40 65
387 150f. Party headquarters and members . . . . 1·40 65

119 Tank and Liberty Monument, Sana'a

1988. 25th Anniv (1987) of 26th September Revolution in Yemen.
388 **119** 75f. multicoloured 65 25

120 Tap, Boy and Rainbow (safe water)

121 Weightlifting

1988. World Health Day. 40th Anniv of W.H.O. Multicoloured.
389 40f. Type **120** 30 20
390 75f. Child with globe as head breaking cigarette (No Smoking day) 60 30
391 140f. Nurse immunizing baby (immunization campaign) 1·25 50
392 250f. Red Crescent worker instructing group (Health for all) . . . . 1·90 90

1988. Olympic Games, Seoul. Multicoloured.
393 40f. Type **121** 35 20
394 75f. Running 65 35
395 140f. Boxing . . . . 1·25 70
396 150f. Football . . . . 1·50 95

122 Crowd and Flag

123 Yellow-bellied Green Pigeon

1988. 25th Anniv of 14 October Revolution.
397 **122** 25f. black and red 10 10
398 – 75f. multicoloured 30 30
399 – 300f. multicoloured . . . 1·00 1·00
DESIGNS—HORIZ: 75f. Radfan mountains and revolutionary. VERT: 300f. Anniversary emblem.

1988. Birds. Multicoloured.
400 40f. Type **123** 40 20
401 50f. Lilac-breasted roller (vert) 60 40
402 75f. Hoopoe (vert) 90 50
403 250f. Houbara bustard . . . 2·50 1·40

124 Incense Burner

125 Shipping entering Old Harbour

1988. Traditional Crafts. Multicoloured.
404 25f. Type **124** 20 20
405 70f. Mashjub (rack used when impregnating dresses with incense) 70 30
406 150f. Cosmetic basket made of palm fibre with cowrie shell decoration . . . . . 1·25 80
407 250f. Woman making palm fibre basket . . . . 2·25 1·25

1988. Centenary of Port of Aden. Mult.
408 75f. Type **125** 95 40
409 300f. Section of new harbour project . . . . 2·75 1·40

126 Old City

1988. International Campaign for Preservation of Old Sana'a. Multicoloured.
410 75f. Type **126** 65 50
411 250f. City (different) . . . . 2·25 1·00

127 Sand Cat Kitten

1989. Endangered Animals. Multicoloured.
412 20f. Type **127** 20 10
413 25f. Adult sand cat 20 10
414 50f. Fennec fox cub 40 20
415 75f. Adult fennec fox 50 25

128 Symbols of War in Star

129 Ismail

1989. 20th Anniv of "Corrective Move" in Revolutionary Government. Multicoloured.
416 25f. Type **128** 20 10
417 35f. Industrial symbols in hook 25 15
418 40f. Agricultural symbols . . 35 15

1989. 50th Birth Anniv of Adbul Fattah Ismail (founder of People's Socialist Party).
419 **129** 75f. multicoloured 50 25
420 150f. multicoloured . . . 1·00 50

130 "Children at Play" (Abeer Anwer)

131 Sana'a and Fighters

1989. 15th Anniv of Ali Anter Pioneer Organization. Multicoloured.
421 10f. Type **130** 10 10
422 25f. Girl pioneer 20 10
423 75f. Pioneers parading at Khormaksar (horiz) . . . 50 40

1989. 22nd Anniv of Siege of Sana'a.
424 **131** 150f. multicoloured . . . 1·25 65

132 Taj Mahal and Nehru

133 Coffee Plant

1989. Birth Centenary of Jawaharal Nehru (Indian statesman).
425 **132** 250f. black and brown . . 1·90 90

1989. Centenary of Interparliamentary Union.
426 **133** 300f. multicoloured . . . 2·50 1·25

134 Seera Rock, Aden, Birds and Arc de Triomphe, Paris

1989. Bicentenary of French Revolution.
427 **134** 250f. multicoloured . . . 2·25 1·25

135 U.S.A. v Belgium (Uruguay, 1930)

1990. World Cup Football Championship, Italy. Matches from previous championships. Mult.

428 5f. Type **135** 10 10
429 10f. Switzerland v Netherlands (Italy, 1934) 10 10
430 20f. Italy v France (France, 1938) 15 10
431 35f. Sweden v Spain (Brazil, 1950) 20 10
432 50f. West Germany v Austria (Switzerland, 1954) 30 15
433 60f. Brazil v England (Sweden, 1958) 40 20
434 500f. U.S.S.R. v Uruguay (Chile, 1962) . . . . . . 2·75 1·00

YEMEN REPUBLIC (combined)

Pt. 19

A draft joint constitution was ratified by the parliaments of Yemen Arab Republic and the Yemen People's Democratic Republic on 21 May 1990 and the unification of the two countries was declared the following day.

The currencies of both the previous republics have legal validity throughout Yemen.

100 fils = 1 rial (North Yemen).
1000 fils = 1 dinar (South Yemen).

1 Scouts supporting Globe

1990. 60th Anniv of Arab Scout Movement. Multicoloured.

1 300f. Type **1** . . . . 1·00 50
2 375f. Type **1** . . . . 1·25 60
3 850f. Oil derrick, scouts with flag, anniversary emblem and tower . . . . 2·75 1·25
4 900f. As No. 3 . . . . 3·00 1·50

Nos. 1/4 are inscribed "YEMEN ARAB REPUBLIC".

2 Pintail 3 City Rooftops

1990. Ducks. Multicoloured.

6 10f. Type **2** 10 15
7 20f. European wigeon 10 15
8 25f. Ruddy shelduck 15 15
9 40f. Gadwall 20 15
10 75f. Common shelduck . . . 35 20
11 150f. Common shoveler pair 75 50
12 600f. Green-winged teal . . . 3·00 2·00

1990. 40th Anniv of U.N. Development Programme.

14 **3** 150f. multicoloured 75 35

4 "Dirphia multicolor"

1990. Moths and Butterflies. Multicoloured.

15 5f. Type **4** 10 10
16 20f. "Automeris io" 10 10
17 25f. Swallowtail 15 10
18 40f. Bhutan glory 20 10
19 55f. Silver king shoemaker . . 25 10
20 75f. Tiger moth 35 15
21 700f. "Attacus edwardsii" (moth) . . . . 3·50 1·40

5 Protembolotherium

1990. Prehistoric Animals. Multicoloured.

23 5f. Type **5** 10 10
24 10f. Diatryma 10 10
25 35f. Mammoth (horiz) 15 10
26 40f. Edaphosaurus (horiz) . . 15 10
27 55f. Dimorphodon (horiz) . . 25 10
28 75f. Phororhacos (horiz) . . . 45 35
29 700f. Ichthyosaurus (wrongly inscr "Ichtyosaurus") . . . 3·75 1·50

6 Abyssinian Kitten 7 "Boletus aestivalis"

1990. Cats. Multicoloured.

31 5f. Type **6** 10 10
32 15f. Blue longhair 10 10
33 35f. Siamese 15 10
34 55f. Burmese 30 15
35 60f. Sealpoint colourpoint . . 30 15
36 150f. Red British shorthair . . 80 30
37 600f. Leopard cat . . . . . . 3·00 1·25

1991. Fungi. Multicoloured.

39 50f. Type **7** 40 15
40 60f. Butter mushroom 50 15
41 80f. Beefsteak morel 55 20
42 100f. Brown birch bolete . . . 80 25
43 130f. Fly agaric . . . . 1·00 35
44 200f. Flaky-stemmed witches' mushroom . . . . 1·60 55
45 300f. Red cap . . . . 2·40 80

8 State Arms 9 Shaking Hands

1991. 1st Anniv of Yemen Republic. Mult.

47 300f. Type **8** 60 25
48 375f. Type **8** 75 30
49 850f. Hand holding flag, map and sun . . . . 1·60 65
50 900f. As No. 49 . . . . 1·75 70

1991. Signing of Unity Agreement (in November 1989) Commemoration. Multicoloured.

52 225f. Type **9** 45 15
53 300f. Hand holding flag over map 60 25
54 375f. As No. 53 . . . . 75 30
55 650f. Type **9** . . . . 1·25 50
56 850f. As No. 53 . . . . 1·60 65

10 Cigarettes and Skull on Globe

1991. World Anti-smoking Day. Multicoloured.

58 225f. Type **10** 45 15
59 300f. Skull smoking and man 60 25
60 375f. As No. 59 . . . . 75 30
61 650f. Type **10** . . . . 1·25 50
62 850f. As No. 59 . . . . 1·60 65

11 Emblem

1991. 45th Anniv of U.N.O.

64 **11** 5r. multicoloured . . . . . 1·00 40
65 8r. multicoloured . . . . . 1·60 65
66 10r. multicoloured . . . . . 2·00 80
67 12r. multicoloured . . . . . 2·40 95

1993. Various stamps surch. (a) Stamps of Yemen Arab Republic. (i) Postage.

69 **94** 5r. on 75f. multicoloured 85 35
70 **144** 8r. on 425f. multicoloured 1·40 55
71 **150** 8r. on 425f. multicoloured 1·40 55
72 – 10r. on 900f. mult (No. 830) . . . . 1·75 70
73 – 10r. on 900f. mult (No. 834) . . . . 1·75 70
74 – 10r. on 900f. mult (No. 838) . . . . 1·75 70
75 – 10r. on 900f. mult (No. 843) . . . . 1·75 70
76 **157** 10r. on 900f. multicoloured 1·75 70
77 – 10r. on 900f. mult (No. 853) . . . . 1·75 70
78 **159** 10r. on 900f. multicoloured 1·75 70
79 – 10r. on 900f. mult (No. 863) . . . . 1·75 70
80 – 12r. on 850f. mult (No. 829) . . . . 2·00 80
81 – 12r. on 850f. mult (No. 833) . . . . 2·00 80
82 – 12r. on 850f. mult (No. 837) . . . . 2·00 80
83 – 12r. on 850f. mult (No. 842) . . . . 2·00 80
84 **157** 12r. on 850f. multicoloured 2·00 80
85 – 12r. on 850f. mult (No. 852) . . . . 2·00 80
86 **159** 12r. on 850f. multicoloured 2·00 80

(ii) Air. Additionally optd **AIR MAIL** (except for No. 87).

87 **118** 3r. on 125f. multicoloured 60 25
88 – 3r. on 125f. mult (No. 672) 60 25
89 – 3r. on 125f. mult (No. 679) 60 25
90 – 3r. on 125f. mult (No. 686) 60 25
91 – 3r. on 125f. mult (No. 700) 60 25
92 – 3r. on 125f. mult (No. 707) 60 25
93 – 5r. on 75f. mult (No. 670) 85 35
94 – 5r. on 75f. mult (No. 677) 85 35
95 – 5r. on 75f. mult (No. 684) 80 35
96 – 5r. on 75f. mult (No. 691) 80 35
97 – 5r. on 75f. mult (No. 698) 80 35
98 – 5r. on 75f. mult (No. 705) 80 35
99 **145** 8r. on 425f. multicoloured 1·40 55
100 – 8r. on 425f. mult (No. 796) . . . . . . 1·40 55
101 **147** 8r. on 425f. multicoloured 1·40 55
102 – 8r. on 425f. mult (No. 803) . . . . . . 1·40 55
103 – 8r. on 425f. mult (No. 812) . . . . . . 1·40 55
104 **151** 8r. on 425f. multicoloured 1·40 55
105 **152** 8r. on 425f. multicoloured 1·40 55
106 – 12r. on 850f. mult (No. 862) . . . . . . 2·00 80

(b) Stamps of Yemen Republic (combined).

107 – 10r. on 900f. mult (No. 4) 1·75 70
108 – 10r. on 900f. mult (No. 50) 1·75 70
109 – 12r. on 850f. mult (No. 3) 2·00 80
110 – 12r. on 850f. mult (No. 49) 2·00 80
111 – 12r. on 850f. mult (No. 56) 2·00 80
112 – 12r. on 850f. mult (No. 62) 2·00 80
113 – 50r. on 150f. mult (No. 11) 12·50 8·25
114 **3** 50r. on 150f. multicoloured 10·50 4·25
115 **10** 50r. on 225f. multicoloured
116 **8** 50r. on 375f. multicoloured 10·50 4·25
117 – 50r. on 375f. mult (No. 54) 10·50 4·25
118 – 50r. on 375f. mult (No. 60) 10·50 4·25
119 **8** 100r. on 300f. mult . . . . 21·00 8·25
120 – 100r. on 300f. mult (No. 53) . . . .
121 – 100r. on 300f. mult (No. 59) . . . .

(c) Stamps of Yemen People's Democratic Republic. (i) In Western and Arabic figures.

122 – 8r. on 110f. mult (No. 84b) . . . . . . 1·50 60
123 – 8r. on 110f. mult (No. 200) . . . . . . 1·50 60
124 – 8r. on 110f. mult (No. 206) . . . . . . 1·50 60
125 – 8r. on 110f. mult (No. 218) . . . . . . 1·50 60
126 – 8r. on 110f. mult (No. 234) . . . . . . 1·50 60
127 **72** 8r. on 110f. multicoloured 1·50 60
128 – 8r. on 110f. mult (No. 246) . . . . . . 1·50 60
129 – 8r. on 110f. mult (No. 267) . . . . . . 1·50 60
130 – 50r. on 500f. mult (No. 434) . . . . . .
131 **133** 100r. on 300f. mult . . . 21·00 8·25
132 – 100r. on 2d. mult (No. 340) . . . . . . 21·00 8·25
133 **25** 200r. on 5f. multicoloured 42·00 17·00
134 **135** 200r. on 5f. multicoloured
135 **127** 200r. on 20f. multicoloured . . . . . 42·00 17·00
136 – 200r. on 20f. mult (No. 430) . . . . . .
137 – 200r. on 75f. mult (No. 423) . . . . . . 42·00 17·00
138 **132** 200r. on 250f. black & brn . . . . 42·00 17·00

(ii) Surch **R.** and Arabic figures.

139 **100** 200r. on 15f. multicoloured . . . . . 42·00 17·00
140 – 200r. on 15f. mult (No. 328) . . . . . . 42·00 17·00
141 – 200r. on 20f. mult (No. 321) . . . . . . 42·00 17·00
142 – 200r. on 20f. mult (No. 329) . . . . . . 42·00 17·00

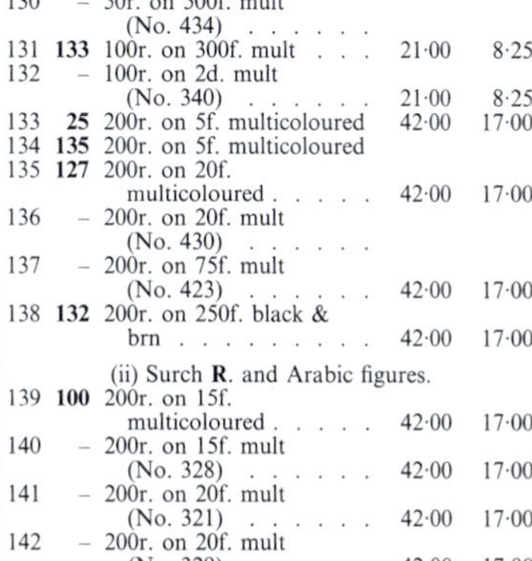

15 Sana'a 16 Player dribbling Ball

1994. 4th Anniv of Yemen Republic.

143 – 3r. multicoloured 55 25
144 – 5r. multicoloured 95 40
145 **15** 8r. multicoloured . . . . . 1·50 60
146 – 20r. multicoloured . . . . 3·75 1·50

DESIGNS: Nos. 143/4, 146, Different views of the principal building in Type **15**.

1994. World Cup Football Championship, U.S.A. Multicoloured.

148 2r. Type **16** 40 15
149 6r. Dribbling (different) . . . 1·10 45
150 10r. Goalkeeper catching ball (horiz) . . . . 1·90 75
151 12r. Player heading ball . . . 2·25 90

17 Arabian Leopard 18 Hand holding Seedling

1995. World Environmental Protection Day. Multicoloured.

153 15r. Type **17** 40 15
154 20r. Caracal lynx 55 25
155 30r. Helmeted guineafowl (horiz) 80 35

1995. 50th Anniv of F.A.O. Multicoloured.

157 10r. Type **18** 25 10
158 25r. Hand holding seeds . . 65 30
159 30r. Hand holding fish . . . 80 35

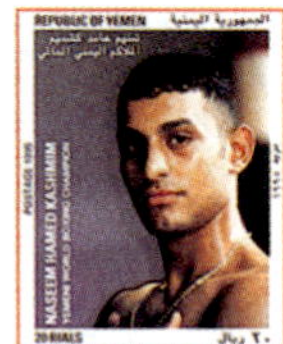

19 Old Sana'a 20 Kashmim

1995. 50th Anniv of U.N.O. Multicoloured.

161 10r. Type **19** 25 10
162 20r. Different viewpoint of scene on 10r 55 25
163 25r. Rampart walk (horiz) . . 65 30

1995. Naseem Hamed Kashmim (boxer). Mult.

165 10r. Kashmim with Lonsdale Belt 25 10
166 20r. Type **20** 55 25
167 25r. Scene from boxing match (horiz) 65 30
168 30r. Kashmim raising arm in triumph 80 35

22 Wrestling 23 Popular Heritage Museum, Seiyoan

1996. Olympic Games, Atlanta, U.S.A. Mult.

171 20r. Type **22** 20 10
172 50r. High jumping (horiz) . . 50 20
173 60r. Running 60 25
174 70r. Gymnastics 65 30
175 100r. Judo 95 40

1996. Heritage Sites. Multicoloured.

177 10r. Type **23** 10 10
178 15r. Rock Palace, Wadi Dhahr (vert) 15 10
179 20r. Old Sana'a city 20 10
180 30r. Al-Mohdhar minaret, Tarim (vert) 30 15
181 40r. As 15r. 40 20
182 50r. As 30r. 50 20
183 60r. As 15r. 60 25
184 70r. As 10r. 65 30
185 100r. As 20r. 95 40
186 150r. As 30r. . . . . 1·40 60
187 200r. As 20r. . . . . 1·90 80
188 250r. As 10r. . . . . 2·40 1·00
189 300r. As 30r. . . . . 3·00 1·25
190 500r. As 15r. . . . . 4·75 1·90

24 Barn Owl

1996. Birds. Multicoloured.

191 20r. Type **24** 20 10
192 50r. Philby's rock partridge 50 20
193 60r. Lammergeier 60 25
194 70r. Arabian chukar 65 30
195 100r. Houbara bustard . . . 95 40

25 "Parodia maasii"

26 Girls reading

1996. Multicoloured. (a) Rare Plants.
197 20r. Type **25** 20 10
198 50r. "Notocatus cristata" . . 50 20
199 60r. "Adenium obesum socotranum" 60 25
200 70r. Dragon's blood tree . . 65 30
201 100r. "Mammillaria erythrosperma" 95 40

(b) Fishes.
203 20r. Moorish idol 20 10
204 50r. Hump-headed wrasse . . 65 30
205 60r. Purple tang 80 40
206 70r. Emperor angelfish . . . 85 50
207 100r. Yellow-faced angelfish 1·40 65

1996. 50th Anniv of U.N.I.C.E.F. Multicoloured.
209 20r. Type **26** 20 10
210 50r. Girls playing 50 20
211 60r. Mother and child . . . 60 25
212 70r. Mother with three children 65 30

27 Players chasing Ball

1998. World Cup Football Championship, France. Multicoloured.
214 10r. Type **27** 10 10
215 15r. Heading ball 15 10
216 35r. Tackle 30 15
217 65r. Tackle (different) 60 25
218 75r. Kicking high ball . . . 65 30

28 Arabian Bustard

1998. Birds. Multicoloured.
220 10r. Type **28** 10 10
221 15r. Egyptian vulture 15 10
222 35r. Abyssinian roller 30 15
223 65r. Violet starling 60 25
224 75r. Dark chanting goshawk 65 30

29 Upraised Hands and Anniversary Emblem

1998. 50th Anniv of Universal Declaration of Human Rights. Multicoloured.
226 15r. Type **29** 15 10
227 35r. Handshakes 30 15
228 100r. Outspread hands reaching to emblem . . . 90 40

30 Dhows and Emblem

2000. 1st General Conference of Yemeni Immigrants, Sana'a. Multicoloured.
230 60r. Type **30** 50 20
231 90r. Wadi Dhahr and emblem 75 30

31 Emblem

32 *Euphorbia abdalkuri*

2000. 10th Anniv of Unification. National Day.
233 **31** 30r. multicoloured 25 15
234 50r. multicoloured 40 20
235 70r. multicoloured 60 25

2000. Plants of Socotra Archipelago. Multicoloured.
237 30r. Type **32** 25 15
238 70r. *Dendrosicyos socotranus* 60 25
239 80r. *Caralluma socotrana* . . 65 30
240 120r. *Dracaena cinnabari* . . 1·00 40

33 Emblem

2000. Olympic Games, Sydney. Showing sports pictograms. Multicoloured.
242 50r. Type **33** 40 20
243 70r. Running 60 25
244 80r. Hurdling 65 30
245 100r. Rifle shooting 85 40

YUGOSLAVIA Pt. 3

The kingdom of the Serbs, Croats and Slovenes, in S.E. Europe, established after the 1914–18 war and comprising Serbia, Montenegro, Bosnia, Herzegovina and parts of pre-war Hungary.

From 1945 it was a Federal Republic comprising six republics. In 1991 four of these republics seceded, from when the Federation consisted of the Republics of Montenegro and Serbia and the two autonomous provinces of Kosovo and Vojvodina.

A. KINGDOM OF THE SERBS, CROATS AND SLOVENES

I. ISSUES FOR BOSNIA AND HERZEGOVINA

100 heller = 1 kruna.

1918. 1910 commem stamps of Bosnia (with date labels) optd **DRZAVA S.H.S. 1918 1918 Bosna i Hercegovina** or the same in Cyrillic characters or surch also.
1 3h. olive (No. 345) . . . . . 60 1·50
2 5h. green 30 45
3 10h. red 25 35
4 20h. sepia 25 35
5 25h. blue 25 35
6 30h. green 25 50
7 40h. orange 25 35
8 45h. red 25 35
9 50h. purple 50 50
10 60h. on 50h. purple 25 40
11 80h. on 6h. brown 25 40
12 90h. on 35h. green 25 40
13 2k. green 40 60
14 3k. on 3h. olive . . . . . . 75 1·75
15 4k. on 1k. lake . . . . . . 2·50 3·50
16 10k. on 2h. violet . . . . . 4·00 4·50

1918. Newspaper Express stamps of Bosnia. 5h. optd as last and **HELERA** and 2h. the same but in Cyrillic.
17 N **35** 2h. red . . . . 4·00 5·00
18 5h. green . . . . 2·00 2·50
These were issued for use as ordinary postage stamps.

1918. Bosnian War Invalids Fund stamps optd **DRAVA S.H.S. Bosna Hercegovina** or the same in Cyrillic characters.
19 **31** 5h. (+2h.) green £150 £160
20 – 10h. (+2h.) red . . . . . . 95·00 £140
21 – 10h. (+2h.) blue . . . . . . 70 4·50
22 **31** 15h. (+2h.) brown . . . . . 1·75 4·00

6a

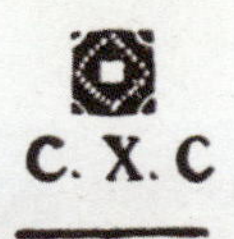

(7)

1918. Newspaper stamps of Bosnia of 1913 (as T **6a**) surch. Imperf.
50 **6a** 2 on 6h. mauve £100 £175
51 2 on 10h. red . . . . . . 50·00 75·00
52 2 on 20h. green . . . . . . 6·00 12·00
23 3 on 2h. blue 20 40
24 5 on 6h. mauve 20 40
Most of these were used for ordinary postage purposes.

1919. Perf.
25 **6a** 2h. blue 20 25
26 6h. mauve . . . . 50 1·00
27 10h. red 25 25
28 20h. green 20 25
The above were issued for use as ordinary postage stamps.

These stamps imperforate were issued as Newspaper stamps for Bosnia q.v.

1919. Types of Bosnia optd with T **7** or similar type with wording **KRALJEVSTVO S.H.S.**, or surch also.
29 **25** 3h. lake 20 75
30 5h. green 20 30
31 10 on 6h. black 20 20
32 **26** 20 on 35h. green 20 20
33 **25** 25h. blue 20 20
34 30h. red 30 45
35 **26** 45h. brown 30 45
36 **33** 45 on 80h. brown 20 20
37 **26** 50h. blue . . . . 45·00 60·00
38 50h. on 72h. blue 20 20
39 60h. purple 20 40
40 **33** 80h. brown 20 40
41 90h. purple 25 40
42 – 2k. green (No. 200) 30 50
43 **26** 3k. red on green 35 75
44 **34** 4k. red on green . . . . . 1·50 2·00
45 **26** 5k. lilac on grey . . . . . 1·50 2·25
46 **34** 10k. violet on grey . . . . 2·50 3·00

1919. War Victims' Fund. Stamps of Bosnia of 1906 surch **KRALJEVSTVO Srba. Hrvata i Slovenaca** or same in Cyrillic characters and new value.
47 – 10x.+10x. on 40h. orange (No. 196) . . . . 1·25 2·25
48 – 20x.+10x. on 20h. sepia (No. 192) . . . . 65 1·50
49 **5** 45x.+15x. on 1k. lake . . . . 4·00 6·00

II. ISSUES FOR CROATIA

100 filir (heller) = 1 kruna (krone).

The provisional issues on Hungarian stamps were sold in Yugoslavia "heller" and "krone" currency, but as this is not expressed on the stamps (except for Nos. 69/73) we have retained the Hungarian descriptions to facilitate reference to the original stamps.

1918. Various issues of Hungary optd **HRVATSKA SHS** and bar or wheel. "Turul" issue of 1900.
53 **7** 6f. olive . . . . 75 1·50
54 50f. lake on blue . . . . . . 1·00 1·75

"Harvesters" and "Parliament" issues of 1916.
55 **18** 2f. brown 30 30
56 3f. red 30 30
57 5f. green 30 30
58 6f. green 30 30
59 10f. red . . . . 6·50 6·50
60 15f. violet (No. 244) . . . . 50·00 70·00
61 15f. violet (No. 251) 30 30
62 20f. brown 30 30
63 25f. blue 30 40
64 35f. brown 30 30
65 40f. green 30 50
66 **19** 50f. purple 30 30
67 75f. blue 30 30
68 80f. green 30 45
69 1k. red 30 30
70 2k. brown 30 30
71 3k. grey and violet 30 45
72 5k. light brown and brown 2·00 2·50
73 10k. mauve and brown . . . 10·00 12·50
The kroner values are overprinted **KRUNA** or **KRUNE** also.

"Charles" and "Zita" issue of 1918.
74 **27** 10f. red 30 40
75 20f. brown 30 40
76 25f. blue 30 65
77 **28** 40f. olive 30 40

1918. Stamps of Hungary optd **HRVATSKA SHS ZF ZA NAROD VIJECE**. War Charity issue of 1916.
78 **20** 10+2f. red 35 45
79 – 15+2f. violet 10 35
80 **22** 40+2f. lake 10 35

Coronation issue of 1916.
81 **23** 10f. mauve . . . . 50·00 70·00
82 – 15f. red . . . . 50·00 70·00

20 "Freedom of Croatia"

1918. Freeing of the Yugoslavs.
83 **20** 10h. red . . . . 2·25 2·75
84 20h. violet . . . . 2·50 3·75
85 25h. blue . . . . 4·25 6·50
86 45h. grey . . . . 40·00 45·00

21 Angel of Peace

22 Sailor with Standard and Falcon

23 Falcon ("Liberty")

1919.
87 **21** 2h. brown 10 35
88 3h. mauve 10 40
89 5h. green 10 10
90 **22** 10h. red 10 10
91 20h. brown 10 10
92 25h. blue 10 10
93 45h. olive 15 15
94 **23** 1k. red 20 20
95 – 3k. purple 65 85
96 – 5k. brown . . . . 1·00 75
DESIGN: 3, 5k. as Type **5** but light background behind falcon.

III. ISSUES FOR SLOVENIA

1919. 100 vinar (heller) = 1 kruna (krone).
1920. 100 paras = 1 dinar.

25 Chainbreaker

26 Chainbreaker

27 "Yugoslavia" with Three Falcons

28 Angel of Peace

29 King Petar I

1919. Perf or rouletted.
97a **25** 3v. violet 15 10
107 5v. green 10 10
108 10v. red 15 10
100 15v. blue 15 10
101 **26** 20v. brown 50 15
102 25v. blue 30 10
103 30v. pink 30 10
111 30v. red 30 15
104a 40v. yellow 35 10
122 **27** 50v. green 25 10
135 60v. violet 60 30
136 **28** 1k. red 45 25
120 2k. blue 50 20
126 **29** 5k. red 50 20
139 10k. blue . . . . 2·75 75
105 15k. green . . . . 7·00 10·00
106 20k. purple . . . . 1·50 2·25

31 Chainbreaker

32 "Yugoslavia" with Three Falcons

34 King Petar I

1920. Perf (2d. to 10d.) or roul.
150 **31** 5p. olive 15 10
151 10p. green 10 10
152 15p. brown 10 10
153 20p. red 35 30
154 25p. brown 35 10
155 **32** 40p. violet 10 15
156 45p. yellow 10 15
157 50p. blue 10 10
158 60p. brown 10 10
159 **34** 1d. brown 10 10
160 – 2d. black 10 10
161 **34** 4d. slate 15 15
162 – 6d. olive 10 50
163 – 10d. brown 30 60
The 2, 6 and 10d. are as Type **34** but larger.

1920. Carinthian Plebiscite. Newspaper stamps of Yugoslavia of 1919 surch **1920 KGCA** and new value. Imperf.
163a N **30** 5p. on 4v. grey 10 25
163b 15p. on 4v. grey . . . 10 25
163c 25p. on 4v. grey . . . 10 50
163d 45p. on 2v. grey . . . 15 1·00
163e 50p. on 2v. grey . . . 10 1·10
163f 2d. on 2v. grey . . . . 1·00 5·00
These stamps were sold at three times face value on aid of the Plebiscite Propaganda Fund.

IV. ISSUES FOR THE WHOLE KINGDOM

100 paras = 1 dinar.

35 King Alexander when Prince

37 Kosovo Maiden, 1389

1921. Inscr "KRALJEVSTVO" at foot.
164 **35** 2p. brown 10 10
165 5p. green 10 10
166 10p. red 10 10
167 15p. purple 10 10
168 20p. black 10 10
169 25p. blue 10 10
170 50p. olive 10 10
171 60p. red 20 10
172 75p. violet 10 10
173 – 1d. orange 15 10
174 – 2d. olive 30 10
175 – 4d. green 50 10
176 – 5d. red . . . . 1·75 10
177 – 10d. brown . . . . 5·00 30
DESIGN: 1d. to 10d. as Type **35**, but portrait of King Petar I.

1921. Disabled Soldiers' Fund.
178 **37** 10+10p. red 10 10
179 – 15+15p. brown 10 10
180 – 25+25p. blue 10 15
DESIGN: 15p. Wounded soldier typifying retreat through Albania, 1915; 25p. Symbol of national unity.

1922. Nos. 178/180 surch.
181 1d. on 10p. red 10 10
183 1d. on 15p. brown 10 10
182 1d. on 25p. blue 10 10
184 3d. on 15p. brown 25 10
186 8d. on 15p. brown . . . . . 1·00 20
187 20d. on 15p. brown . . . . 7·50 65
188 30d. on 15p. brown . . . . 10·00 1·50

1923. As T **35**, but inscr "KRALJEVINA" at foot.
189 **35** 1d. brown 90 10
190 5d. red 35 10
191 8d. purple . . . . 7·00 25
192 20d. green . . . . 18·00 75
193 30d. orange . . . . 50·00 2·25

1924. Nos. 171 and 191 surch.
195 **35** 20p. on 60p. red 25 10
196 5d. on 8d. purple . . . . . 8·50 50

44 King Alexander

46 King Alexander

1924.
197 **44** 20p. black 10 10
198 50p. brown 10 10
199 1d. red 10 10
200 2d. green 30 10
201 3d. blue 30 10
202 5d. brown . . . . 1·25 10
203 – 10d. violet . . . . 10·00 10
204 – 15d. green . . . . 8·00 20
205 – 20d. orange . . . . 8·00 15
206 – 30d. green . . . . 4·00 1·00
The 10d. to 30d. have the head in a square panel.

1925. Surch.
207 **44** 25p. on 3d. blue 10 10
208 50p. on 3d. blue 10 10

1926.
209 **46** 25p. green 10 10
210 50p. brown 10 10
211 1d. red 15 10
212 2d. black 15 10
213 3d. blue 30 10
214 4d. red 50 10
215 5d. violet 75 10
216 8d. brown . . . . 2·75 10
217 10d. green . . . . 1·50 10
218 15d. brown . . . . 10·00 10
219 20d. violet . . . . 12·50 20
220 30d. orange . . . . 90·00 40

1926. Danube Flood Fund. Surch.
221 **46** 25p.+0.25 green 10 10
222 50p.+0.50 brown 10 10
223 1d.+0.50 red 10 10
224 2d.+0.50 black 20 10
225 3d.+0.50 blue 20 10
226 4d.+0.50 red 25 10
227 5d.+0.50 violet 40 10
228 8d.+0.50 brown 85 30
229 10d.+1.00 green . . . . . 1·75 10
230 15d.+1.00 brown . . . . . 5·00 60
231 20d.+1.00 violet . . . . . 7·00 50
232 30d.+1.00 orange . . . . 20·00 2·50

1928. Nos. 223/32 optd **XXXX** over previous surch.
233 **46** 1d. red 15 15
234 2d. black 50 15
235 3d. blue 90 30
236 4d. red . . . . 2·10 40
237 5d. violet . . . . 1·75 15
238 8d. brown . . . . 6·00 70
239 10d. green . . . . 12·00 15
240 15d. brown . . . . 55·00 2·00
241 20d. violet . . . . 30·00 2·00
242 30d. orange . . . . 75·00 8·50

B. KINGDOM OF YUGOSLAVIA

100 paras = 1 dinar.

49 Duvno Cathedral

1929. Millenary of Croatian Kingdom (1925).
243 **49** 50p.+50p. olive 15 15
244 – 1d.+50p. red 50 30
245 – 3d.+1d. blue . . . . . . 1·25 85
DESIGNS—As Type **49**: 3d. King Tomislav. Horiz (34 × 23 mm): Kings Tomislav and Alexander I.

52 Dobropolje

53 Serbian War Memorial, Paris

1931. Serbian War Memorial (Paris) Fund.
246 **52** 50p.+50p. green 10 10
247 **53** 1d.+50p. red 10 10
248 – 3d.+1d. blue 15 15
DESIGN—As Type **52**: 3d. Kajmakcalan.

55 King Alexander

57 Rowing "four" on Lake Bled

1931.
249 **55** 25p. black 10 10
250 50p. green 10 10
262 75p. green 25 10
251 1d. red 15 10
263 1d.50 red 60 10
263b 1d.75 red . . . . 1·10 25
252 3d. blue . . . . 1·00 10
263c 3d.50 blue . . . . 1·50 25
253 4d. orange . . . . 2·50 10
254 5d. violet . . . . 2·50 10
255 10d. olive . . . . 9·00 10
256 15d. brown . . . . 8·50 10
257 20d. purple . . . . 17·00 10
258 30d. red . . . . 9·00 45

1931. Optd **KRALJEVINA JUGOSLAVIJA** and also in Cyrillic characters.
259 **49** 50p.+50p. olive 10 10
260 – 1d.+50p. red 10 10
261 – 3d.+1d. blue 30 50

1932. European Rowing Championship. Inscr ending "EUROPE 1932".
264 – 75p.+25p. green 40 90
265 **57** 1d.+½d. red 40 90
266 – 1½d.+½d. red . . . . . . 75 1·10
267 – 3d.+1d. blue . . . . . . 1·40 2·00
268 – 4d.+1d. blue and orange . . 6·00 13·50
269 – 5d.+1d. lilac and violet . . 6·00 10·00
DESIGNS—HORIZ: 75p. Single sculler on Danube at Smederevo; 1½d. Rowing "eight" on Danube at Belgrade; 3d. Rowing "pair" at Split harbour. VERT: 4d. Rowing "pair" on river and Zagreb Cathedral; 5d. Prince Peter.

1933. 11th International PEN Club Congress, Dubrovnik. As T **55** with additional value and "XI. int. kongres Pen-Klubova u Dubrovniku 1933" inscr below in Roman or Cyrillic characters.
270 **55** 50p.+25p. black . . . . . 3·75 8·50
271 75p.+25p. green . . . . . 3·75 8·50
272 1d.50+50p. red . . . . . 3·75 8·50
273 3d.+1d. blue . . . . . . 3·75 8·50
274 4d.+1d. green . . . . . . 3·75 8·50
275 5d.+1d. yellow . . . . . 3·75 8·50

60 Crown Prince Petar in "Sokol" Uniform

62

1933. "Sokol" Meeting, Ljubjana.
276 **60** 75p.+25p. green 20 25
277 1½d.+½d. red 20 25

1933. Optd **JUGOSLAVIJA** in Roman and Cyrillic characters. (a) Postage.
278 **46** 25p. green 10 10
279 50p. brown 10 10
280 1d. red 30 10
281 2d. black 50 15
282 3d. blue . . . . 1·75 10
283 4d. red . . . . 1·00 10
284 5d. violet . . . . 1·75 10
285 8d. brown . . . . 3·50 1·25
286 10d. olive . . . . 9·00 15
287 15d. brown . . . . 10·00 1·50
288 20d. violet . . . . 19·00 75
289 30d. orange . . . . 16·00 75

(b) Charity stamps. Nos. 221/3.
290 **46** 25p.+0.25 green 40 15
291 50p.+0.50 brown 40 10
292 1d.+0.50 red . . . . 1·25 40

1933. Obligatory Tax. Red Cross.
293 **62** 50p. red and blue 15 20

63 Osprey over R. Bosna

64 Athlete and Falcon (from sculpture by Krsinic)

1934. 20th Anniv of "Sokol" Games, Sarajevo.
294 **63** 75p.+25p. green . . . . . 5·75 5·75
295 1d.50+50p. red . . . . . 8·00 8·00
296 1d.75+25p. brown . . . . 17·00 17·00

1934. 60th Anniv of Croat "Sokol" Games, Zagreb.
297 **64** 75p.+25p. green . . . . . 2·00 2·75
298 1d.50+50p. red . . . . . 2·50 4·50
299 1d.75+25p. brown . . . . 7·50 10·00

65 Dubrovnik

69 Mostar Bridge

1934. Air.
300 **65** 50p. purple 10 15
301 – 1d. green 20 15
302 – 2d. red 35 35
303 – 3d. blue . . . . 1·10 40
304 **69** 10d. orange . . . . 2·50 3·00
DESIGNS: 1d. Lake of Bled; 2d. Waterfall at Jajce; 3d. Oplenac.

1934. King Alexander Mourning issue. With black margins.
305 **55** 25p. black (postage) . . . 10 10
306 50p. green 10 10
307 75p. green 10 10
308 1d. red 10 10
309 1d.50 red 10 10
310 1d.75 red 10 10
311 3d. blue 10 10
312 3d.50 blue 20 10
313 4d. orange 20 10
314 5d. violet 40 10
315 10d. olive . . . . 1·25 10
316 15d. brown . . . . 2·75 20
317 20d. purple . . . . 5·00 20
318 30d. red . . . . 3·50 40
319 – 3d. blue (No. 303) (air) . . 3·75 3·50

70 King Petar II

71 King Alexander

1935.
320 **70** 25p. black 10 10
321 50p. orange 10 10
322 75p. green 15 10
323 1d. brown 15 10
324 1d.50 red 15 10
325 1d.75 red 25 10
325a 2d. red 15 10
326 3d. orange 15 10
327 3d.50 blue 35 10
328 4d. green 90 10
329 4d. blue 30 10
330 10d. violet 75 10
331 15d. brown 90 10
332 20d. blue . . . . 3·50 25
333 30d. pink . . . . 1·75 25

1935. 1st Anniv of King Alexander's Assassination.
334 **71** 75p. green 20 35
335 1d.50 red 20 35
336 1d.75 brown 25 75
337 3d.50 blue . . . . 1·25 2·00
338 7d.50 red . . . . 1·00 1·75

72

73 Queen Marie

1935. Winter Relief Fund.
339 **72** 1d.50+1d. brown . . . . . 1·00 1·00
340 3d.50+1d.50 blue . . . . 1·50 2·50

1936. Child Welfare.
341 **73** 75p.+25p. green 25 35
342 1d.50+50p. red 25 35
343 1d.75+75p. brown . . . . 1·00 1·10
344 3d.50+1d. blue . . . . . . 1·50 2·00

74 Nicola Tesla

1936. 80th Birthday of Dr. Tesla (physicist).
345 **74** 75p. brown and green . . . 15 20
346 1d.75 grey and blue . . . 15 25

75 Prince Paul

76 Dr. Vladan Djordjevic (founder)

1936. Red Cross Fund.
347 **75** 75p.+50p. green 10 25
348 1d.50+50p. red 10 25

1936. Obligatory Tax. Jubilee of Serbian Red Cross.
349 **76** 50p. brown 20 25

77 Princess Tomislav and Andrej

78 Oplenac

1937. Child Welfare. T **77** and similar horiz portrait.
350 – 25p.+25p. brown 15 25
351 – 75p.+75p. orange 30 40
352 **77** 1d.50+1d. orange 35 50
353 2d.+1d. mauve . . . . . . 50 1·00

1937. Little Entente.
354 **78** 3d. green 85 50
355 4d. blue . . . . 85 1·00

80 St. Naum Convent, Lake Ohrid

83 Arms of Yugoslavia, Greece, Rumania and Turkey

1937. Air.
360 **80** 50p. brown 10 10
361 – 1d. green 15 10
362 – 2d. blue 20 15
363 – 2d.50 red 30 15
364 **80** 5d. violet 30 25
365a – 10d. red 55 25
366 – 20d. green 85 85
367 – 30d. blue . . . . 1·10 1·50
DESIGNS—VERT: 1, 10d. Rab (Arbe) Harbour. HORIZ: 2, 20d. Sarajevo; 2d.50, 30d. Laibach (Ljubljana).

1937. Balkan Entente.
368 **83** 3d. green 70 35
369 4d. blue . . . . 1·00 85

84

85

1938. Child Welfare.
370 **84** 50p.+50p. brown 10 15
371 **85** 1d.+1d. green 20 35
372 **84** 1d.50+1d.50 red 45 85
373 **85** 2d.+2d. mauve . . . . . 1·00 1·75

86 Searchlight Display and Parachute Tower

87 Entrance to Demir Kapija Cliff

1938. Int Aeronautical Exhibition, Belgrade, and Yugoslav Air Club Fund.
374 **86** 1d.+50p. green 35 75
375 1d.50+1d. red . . . . . 50 1·00
376 2d.+1d. mauve . . . . . 1·50 2·00
377 3d.+1d. blue . . . . . 2·00 3·50

1938. Railway Employees' Hospital Fund.
378 **87** 1d.+1d. green 40 45
379 – 1d.50+1d.50 red . . . . . 1·10 95
380 – 2d.+2d. mauve . . . . . 2·00 2·10
381 – 3d.+3d. blue . . . . . 2·40 2·40
DESIGNS—HORIZ: 1d.50, Demir Kapija Hospital. VERT: 2d. Runner carrying torch; 3d. King Alexander.

90 Hurdling

1938. 9th Balkan Games.
382 – 50p.+50p. orange . . . . 75 1·00
383 **90** 1d.+1d. green . . . . . 1·50 2·10
384 – 1d.50+1d.50 mauve . . . . 2·00 2·75
385 – 2d.+2d. blue . . . . . 2·75 3·50
DESIGNS—HORIZ: 1d.50, Pole vaulting. VERT: 50p. Breasting the tape; 2d. Putting the shot.

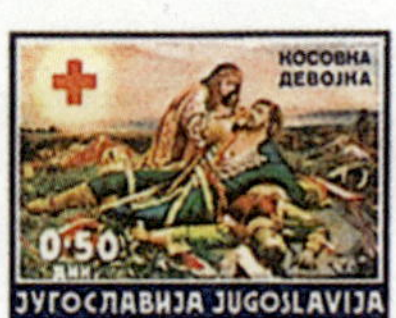

91 Maiden of Kosovo (after P. Jovanovic)

1938. Obligatory Tax. Red Cross.
386 **91** 50p. multicoloured . . . 20 25
386a 50p. red and blue 25 35

1938. Child Welfare. Optd **SALVATE PARVULOS**.
387 **84** 50p.+50p. brown 30 50
388 **85** 1d.+1d. green 30 65
389 **84** 1d.50+1d.50 red . . . . . 60 1·00
390 **85** 2d.+2d. mauve . . . . . 1·25 2·00

93 Mail Carrier

1939. Postal Centenary and Railway Benevolent Association Fund.
391 – 50p.+50p. orange and brown 25 50
392 **93** 1d.+1d. green and black 25 50
393 – 1d.50+1d.50 red . . . . 2·75 1·25
394 – 2d.+2d. purple and violet 1·25 2·50
395 – 4d.+4d. blue and light blue 2·25 4·50
DESIGNS: 50p. Mounted postmen; 1d.50, Steam mail train; 2d. Mail coach; 4d. Lockheed 10 Electra mail plane.

94 Meal-time

95 Milos Obilic

1939. Child Welfare.
396 **94** 1d.+1d. green 40 85
397 – 1d.50+1d.50 red & brown 2·00 3·00
398 – 2d.+2d. mauve & brown 1·25 2·50
399 – 4d.+4d. light blue & blue 1·50 3·50
DESIGNS—HORIZ: 2d. Young carpenter. VERT: 1d.50, Children playing on sands; 4d. Children whispering.

1939. 550th Anniv of Battle of Kosovo.
400 – 1d.+1d. green and olive . . 1·25 1·50
401 **95** 1d.50+1d.50 red and carmine . . . . 1·25 1·50
DESIGN: 1d. Prince Lazar.

96 Motor Cycle and Sidecar

97 Cadet Barquentine "Jadran"

1939. 1st International Motor Races, Belgrade.
402 **96** 50p.+50p. orange and brown 50 75
403 – 1d.+1d. green and black 90 1·25
404 – 1d.50+1d.50 carmine and red . . . . 1·40 2·00
405 – 2d.+2d. blue and indigo . . 2·25 3·00
DESIGNS—HORIZ: 1, 2d. Racing cars. VERT: 1d.50, Motor cycle.

1939. King Petar's Birthday and Adriatic Guard Fund.
406 **97** 50p.+50p. red . . . . . 1·10 1·00
407 – 1d.+50p. green . . . . . 1·25 1·00
408 – 1d.50+1d. red . . . . . 1·60 1·75
409 – 2d.+1d.50 blue . . . . . 2·75 2·25
DESIGNS: 1d. Liner "King Alexander"; 1d.50, Freighter "Triglav"; 2d. Destroyer "Dubrovnik".

98 Unknown Warrior's Tomb, Avala

99 King Petar II

1939. 5th Death Anniv of King Alexander. War Invalids' Fund.
410 **98** 1d.+50p. green . . . . . 85 1·25
411 1d.50+1d. red . . . . . 85 1·25
412 2d.+1d.50 purple . . . . . 1·25 1·75
413 3d.+2d. blue . . . . . 2·00 3·00

1939.
414 **99** 25p. black 10 10
415 50p. orange 10 10
416 1d. green 10 10
417 1d.50 red 10 10
418 2d. pink 10 10
419 3d. brown 15 10
420 4d. blue 15 10
420a 5d. blue 15 15
420b 5d.50 violet 45 10
421 6d. blue 85 10
422 8d. brown 85 10
423 12d. violet . . . . . 1·50 10
424 16d. purple . . . . . 2·00 25
425 20d. blue . . . . . 2·00 25
426 30d. pink . . . . . 4·25 50

100 Postman delivering Letters

101 Arrival of Thorval

1940. Belgrade Postal Employees' Fund. Inscr "ZA DOM P.T.T. ZVAN. I SLUZ".
427 **100** 50p.+50p. orange & brn 50 85
428 – 1d.+1d. green and black 50 85
429 – 1d.50+1d.50 red & brown 90 1·75
430 – 2d.+2d. mauve & purple 6·25 4·00
431 – 4d.+4d. blue and grey . . 3·50 5·00
DESIGNS—VERT: 1d. Postman collecting letters; 4d. Telegraph linesman. HORIZ: 1d.50, Mail-van; 2d. Loading mail train.

1940. Zagreb Postal Employees' Fund. Inscr "ZA DOM P.T.T. CINOV U ZAGREBU".
432 **101** 50p.+50p. orange & brown 30 35
433 – 1d.+1d. green 30 35
434 – 1d.50+1d.50 red 45 50
435 – 2d.+2d. red . . . . . 1·00 1·50
436 – 4d.+4d. blue . . . . . 1·25 1·50
DESIGNS—25½ × 35½ mm: 1d. King Tomislav enthroned; 1d.50, Death of Matija Gubec. 37 × 27 mm: 2d. Radic Brothers. 34 × 25 mm: 4d. Divisional map of Yugoslavia.

102 Winter Games

1940. Child Welfare. Inscr "ZA NASU DECU".
437 **102** 50p.+50p. orange and red 15 35
438 – 1d.+1d. green and olive 15 35
439 **102** 1d.50+1d.50 red and brown 50 75
440 – 2d.+2d. mauve and violet 1·00 1·25
DESIGNS—VERT: 1, 2d. Children at seaside (Summer Games).

103 Arms of Yugoslavia, Greece, Rumania and Turkey

104 Zagreb Cathedral and Junkers Ju 86

1940. Balkan Entente. Inscr "JUGOSLAVIJA" alternately at top in Cyrillic (A) or Roman (B) thoughout the sheet. A.
441A **103** 3d. blue 70 40
442A 4d. blue 70 40

B.
441B **103** 3d. blue 70 40
442B 4d. blue 70 40

1940. Air.
443 **104** 40d. green . . . . . . 1·75 1·75
444 – 50d. blue . . . . 2·00 3·00
DESIGN: 50d. Suspension Bridge at Belgrade and Fokker F.VIIa/3m.

105 Obod, Scene of early Press, 1493

109 Kamenita Gate, Zagreb

107 St. Peter's Cemetery, Ljubljana

1940. 500th Anniv of Invention of Printing Press by Johannes Gutenberg.
445 **105** 5d.50 deep green and green . . . . 1·50 2·75

1940. Anti-T.B. Fund. Nos. 364/7 surch.
446 **80** 50p.+50p. on 5d. violet . . 15 15
447 – 1d.+1d. on 10d. red . . . 20 40
448 – 1d.50+1d.50 on 20d. green 90 1·25
449 – 2d.+2d. on 30d. blue . . . 1·25 2·00

1941. Ljubljana War Veterans' Fund.
450 **107** 50p.+50p. green 20 25
451 – 1d.+1d. red 20 25
452 – 1d.50+1d.50 green . . . 50 85
453 – 2d.+2d. lilac and blue . . 85 1·25
DESIGNS—HORIZ: 2d. War Memorial, Brezje. VERT: 1d. National costumes; 1d.50, Memorial Chapel, Kajmakcalan.

1941. Philatelic Exhibitions. (a) 2nd Croatian Philatelic Exhibition, Zagreb.
454 **109** 1d.50+1d.50 brown . . . 60 1·25
455 – 4d.+3d. black . . . . . 60 1·25

(b) 1st Philatelic Exhibition, Slav Brod.
456 **109** 1d.50+1d.50 black . . . . 9·00 15·00
457 – 4d.+3d. brown . . . . 9·00 15·00
DESIGN: 4d. (2) Old Cathedral, Zagreb.

NOTE. From 1941 until 1945 Yugoslavia ceased to exist as a stamp-issuing entity, except for the following series, Nos 468/81, which were issued by the exiled government for the use of the Yugoslav Merchant Navy working with the Allies.

110 King Petar II

112 V. Vodnik (poet)

1943. 2nd Anniv of Overthrow of Regency and King Petar's Assumption of Power.
468 **110** 2d. blue 10 50
469 3d. grey 10 50
470 5d. red . . . . 15 1·00
471 10d. black . . . . 20 1·50

1943. Red Cross Fund. Surch **CRVENI KRST+12.50**.
472 **110** 2d.+12d.50 blue . . . . . 50 2·50
473 3d.+12d.50 grey . . . . . 50 2·50
474 5d.+12d.50 red . . . . . 50 2·50
475 10d.+12d.50 black . . . . 50 2·50

1943. 25th Anniv of Formation of Yugoslavia.
476 **112** 1d. black and red 10
477 – 2d. black and green . . . 15
478 – 3d. blue and blue 15
479 – 4d. brown and violet . . 40
480 – 5d. brown and purple . . 40
481 – 10d. deep brown and brown . . . . 1·25
DESIGNS: 2d. Petar Njegos (poet); 3d. Ljudevit Gaj (writer); 4d. Vuk Karadzic (poet); 5d. Bishop Josip Strosmajer (politician); 10d. Djordje Petrovic (Karageorge).

C. DEMOCRATIC FEDERATION OF YUGOSLAVIA

I. REGIONAL ISSUES

Bosnia and Herzegovina

Currency: Croatian Kunas.

1945. Mostar Issue. Stamps of Croatia surch **Demokratska Federativna Jugoslavija** and value.

(a) Pictorial Stamps of 1941–43.
R 1 10k. on 25b. red 50 50
R 2 10k. on 50b. green 20 20
R 3 10k. on 2k. red 35 35
R 4 10k. on 3k.50 brown . . . 75 75
R 5 40k. on 1k. green 20 20
R 6 50k. on 4k. blue . . . . . 4·50 4·50
R 7 50k. on 5k. blue . . . . . 18·00 18·00
R 8 50k. on 6k. green . . . . 4·50 4·50
R 9 50k. on 7k. red . . . . . 60·00 60·00
R10 50k. on 8k. brown . . . . 75·00 75·00
R11 50k. on 10k. violet 60 60

(b) Famous Croats issue of 1943.
R12 30k. on 1k. blue 35 35
R13 30k. on 12k.50 purple . . . 20 20

(c) Boskovic issue of 1943.
R14 **28** 30k. on 3k.50 blue . . . . 1·50 1·50
R15 30k. on 12k.50 purple . . 75 75

(d) War Victims Charity Tax stamps of 1944.
R16 **34** 20k. on 1k. green 15 15
R17 **35** 20k. on 2k. red 25 25
R18 20k. on 5k. green 25 25
R19 20k. on 10k. blue 25 25
R20 20k. on 20k. brown . . . 70 70

Croatia

Currency: Kunas.

DEMOKRATSKA FEDERATIVNA

20
KUNA
JUGOSLAVIJA
(R 2)

1945. Split issue. Stamps of Croatia 1941–43 surch as Type **R 2**.
R21 10k. on 25b. red 15 15
R22 10k. on 50b. green 15 15
R23 10k. on 75b. green 15 15
R24 10k. on 1k. green 15 15
R25 20k. on 2k. red 15 15
R26 20k. on 3k. brown 15 15
R27 20k. on 3k.50 brown . . . 15 15
R28 20k. on 4k. blue 15 15
R29 20k. on 5k. blue 30 30
R30 20k. on 6k. green . . . . 9·00 9·00
R31 30k. on 7k. red 15 15
R32 30k. on 8k. brown . . . . 12·00 12·00
R33 30k. on 10k. violet 15 15
R34 30k. on 12k.50 black . . . 15 15
R35 40k. on 20k. brown 15 15
R36 40k. on 30k. brown 20 20
R37 50k. on 50k. green 15 15

1945. Zagreb issue. Stamps of Croatia, 1941–43, surch **DEMOKRATISKA FEDERATIVNA JUGOSLAVIJA**, value and star.
R38 20k. on 5k. blue 25 25
R39 40k. on 1k. green 25 25
R40 60k. on 3k.50 brown . . . 25 25
R41 80k. on 2k. red 25 25
R42 160k. on 50b. green . . . 25 25
R43 200k. on 12k.50 black . . . 25 25
R44 400k. on 25b. red 25 25

Montenegro

Currency: Italian Lire.

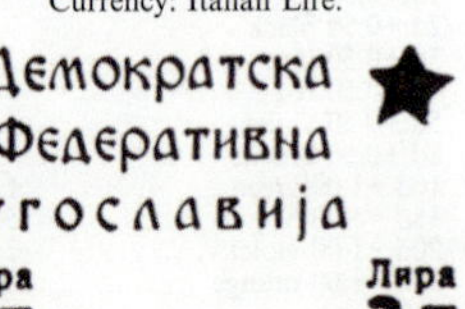

(R 4)

1945. Cetinje issue. Stamps of Italian Occupation surch with Type R **4**. (a) National Poem Issue of 1943.

R50 1l. on 10c. green 75 90
R51 2l. on 25c. green 50 60
R52 3l. on 50c. mauve 50 60
R53 5l. on 11.25 blue 50 60
R54 10l. on 15c. brown . . . . . 90 1·25
R55 15l. on 20c. orange . . . . 90 1·25
R56 20l. on 2l. green . . . . . . 90 1·25

(b) Air stamps of 1943, for use as ordinary postage stamps.

R57 3l. on 50c. brown . . . . . 4·00 4·50
R58 6l. on 1l. blue . . . . 4·00 4·50
R59 10l. on 2l. red . . . . 4·00 4·50
R60 20l. on 5l. green . . . . . . 4·00 4·50

Serbia

Currency: Hungarian Filler.

1944. Senta issue. Various stamps of Hungary optd with a large star, **8.X.1944** and "Yugoslavia" in Cyrillic characters.

R63 1f. grey . . . . 5·50 4·50
R64 2f. red . . . . 5·50 4·50
R65 3f. blue . . . . 5·50 4·50
R66 4f. brown . . . . 5·50 4·50
R67 5f. red . . . . 5·50 4·50
R68 8f. green . . . . 5·50 4·50
R69 10f. brown . . . . 90·00 90·00
R70 24f. brown . . . . 80·00 80·00
R71 24f. purple . . . . 8·00 8·00
R72 30f. red . . . . 90·00 90·00

Slovenia

Currencies: Italian (Ljubljana).
German (Maribor).
Hungarian (Murska Sobota).

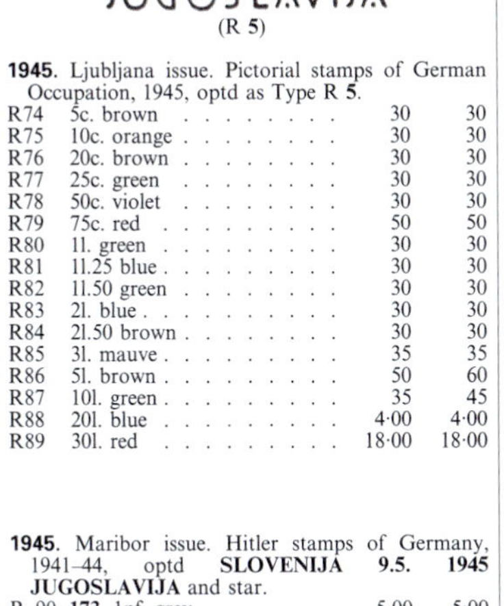

(R 5)

1945. Ljubljana issue. Pictorial stamps of German Occupation, 1945, optd as Type R **5**.

R74 5c. brown 30 30
R75 10c. orange 30 30
R76 20c. brown 30 30
R77 25c. green 30 30
R78 50c. violet 30 30
R79 75c. red 50 50
R80 1l. green 30 30
R81 11.25 blue 30 30
R82 11.50 green 30 30
R83 2l. blue 30 30
R84 21.50 brown 30 30
R85 3l. mauve 35 35
R86 5l. brown 50 60
R87 10l. green 35 45
R88 20l. blue . . . . 4·00 4·00
R89 30l. red . . . . 18·00 18·00

1945. Maribor issue. Hitler stamps of Germany, 1941–44, optd **SLOVENIJA 9.5. 1945 JUGOSLAVIJA** and star.

R 90 **173** 1pf. grey . . . . . . 5·00 5·00
R 91 3pf. brown 50 50
R 92 4pf. grey . . . . 4·00 4·00
R 93 5pf. green . . . . . . 3·00 3·00
R 94 6pf. violet 50 50
R 95 8pf. red 75 75
R 96 10pf. brown (No. 775) 3·00 3·00
R 97 12pf. red (No. 776) . . 35 35
R 98 15pf. brown . . . . . 6·00 6·00
R 99 20pf. blue . . . . . . 3·50 3·50
R100 24pf. brown . . . . . 3·75 3·75
R101 25pf. blue . . . . . . 10·00 10·00
R102 30pf. green 75 75
R103 40pf. mauve 75 75
R104 **225** 42pf. green 60 60
R105 **173** 50pf. green . . . . . 3·00 3·00
R106 60pf. brown 75 75
R107 80pf. blue . . . . . . 1·75 1·75

1945. Murska Sobota issue. Various stamps of Hungary optd as Nos. R90/107.

R108 1f. grey . . . . 6·00 6·00
R109 4f. brown 50 50
R110 5f. red . . . . 6·00 6·00
R111 10f. brown 50 50
R112 18f. black 50 50
R113 20f. brown 50 50
R114 30f. red 50 50
R115 30f. red 50 50
R116 50f. blue . . . . 10·00 10·00
R117 70f. brown . . . . 10·00 10·00
R118 80f. brown . . . . 50·00 50·00
R119 1p. green . . . . 6·00 6·00

II. GENERAL ISSUES

100 paras = 1 dinar.

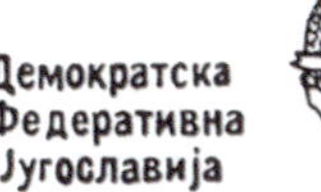

(113)

1944. Monasteries. Stamps of German Occupation of Serbia, 1942, surch as T **113**.

482 – 3d.+2d. pink (No. 64) . . . 10 20
485 – 4d.+21d. blue (No. 65) . . . 10 20
483 – 7d.+3d. green (No. 66) . . . 10 20

114 Marshal Tito

115 Chapel at Prohor Pcinjski

1945.

491 **114** 25p. green 20 15
492 50p. green 20 10
493 1d. red . . . . 3·00 40
494 2d. red 20 10
495 4d. blue 40 10
487 5d. green 10 10
496 6d. violet 50 10
497 9d. brown . . . . 1·00 20
488 10d. red 10 10
498 20d. yellow . . . . . . 4·50 1·40
489 25d. violet 15 15
490 30d. blue 25 15

1945. 1st Anniv of Anti-Fascist Chamber of Deputies, Macedonia.

499 **115** 2d. red 70 25

116 Partisans

1945. Red Cross Fund.

500 **116** 1d.+4d. blue 90 80
501 – 2d.+6d. red 90 80

DESIGN—VERT: 2d.+6d. Child's head.

119 Partisans

120 Marshal Tito

1945. Partisans.

502 **119** 50p. brown 10 10
503 1d. green 15 10
504 – 1d.50 brown 15 10
505 **120** 2d. red 15 10
506 – 2d.50 red 45 10
507 – 3d. brown . . . . 1·25 10
508 – 3d. red 45 10
509 **120** 4d. blue 25 10
510 – 5d. green . . . . 1·25 10
511 – 5d. blue . . . . 1·40 10
512 – 6d. black 45 10
513 – 8d. orange . . . . 1·25 10
514 – 9d. purple 40 10
515 – 12d. blue 80 10
516 **119** 16d. blue 80 10
517 – 20d. red . . . . 1·75 20

DESIGNS—As Type **119**: 1d.50, 12, 20d. Riflemen. VERT: 3, 5d. Town of Jajce inscr "29-XI-1943". HORIZ: 2d.50, 6, 8, 9d. Girl with flag.

122 Russian and Yugoslav Flags

1945. 1st Anniv of Liberation of Belgrade.

518 **122** 2d.+5d. multicoloured . . 70 40

124 "Industry and Agriculture"

126

1945. Meeting of the Constituent Assembly. Inscr in Cyrillic at top and Roman characters at foot (A) or vice-versa (B).

519 **124** 2d. red (A) . . . . . . 3·75 3·75
519b 2d. red (B) . . . . . . 3·75 3·75
520 4d. blue (A) . . . . . . 3·75 3·75
520b 4d. blue (B) . . . . . . 3·75 3·75
521 6d. green (A) . . . . . 3·75 3·75
521b 6d. green (B) . . . . . 3·75 3·75
522 9d. red (A) . . . . . . 3·75 3·75
522b 9d. red (B) . . . . . . 3·75 3·75
523 16d. blue (A) . . . . . 3·75 3·75
523b 16d. blue (B) . . . . . 3·75 3·75
524 20d. brown (A) . . . . 3·75 3·75
524b 20d. brown (B) . . . . 3·75 3·75

D. FEDERAL PEOPLE'S REPUBLIC

100 paras = 1 dinar.

1946. Type of 1945 (Girl with flag), surch.

525 2d.50 on 6d. red 60 10
526 8d. on 9d. orange . . . . . 1·00 10

1946. 1st Anniv of Victory over Fascism. Star in red.

527 **126** 1d.50 yellow 35 40
528 2d.50 red 80 60
529 5d. blue . . . . 1·40 1·25

127 Symbolic of Communications

128 Railway Construction

1946. Postal Congress.

530 **127** 1d.50+1d. green . . . . 4·25 3·50
531 2d.50+1d.50 red . . . 4·25 3·50
532 5d.+2d. blue . . . . . 4·25 3·50
533 8d.+3d.50 brown . . . 4·25 3·50

1946. Volunteer Workers' Railway Reconstruction Fund.

534 **128** 50p.+50p. brown, blue and red . . . . . . 3·50 2·00
535 1d.50+1d. green, blue and red . . . . 3·50 1·75
536 2d.50+2d. lilac, blue and red . . . . 3·50 1·75
537 5d.+3d. grey, blue & red 3·50 2·25

129 Svetozar Markovic

130 Theatre in Sofia

1946. Birth Centenary of S. Markovic (socialist writer).

538 **129** 1d.50 green 75 40
539 2d.50 purple 75 45

1948. Slav Congress.

540 **130** ½d. brown and buff . . . 10 10
541 – 1d. green and light green 15 10
542 – 1½d. red and pink 20 15
543 – 2½d. orange and buff . . 25 15
544 – 5d. blue and light blue . . 1·25 60

DESIGNS—HORIZ: 1d. Charles Bridge and Hradcany, Prague. VERT: 1½d. Sigismund Monument, Warsaw; 2½d. Victory Monument, Belgrade; 5d. Kremlin Tower, Moscow.

131 Roofless Houses

132 Ilyushin Il-4 DB-3 Bomber over Kalimegdan Terrace, Belgrade

1947. Obligatory Tax. Red Cross.

545 **131** 50p. brown 15 10

1947. Air. Inscr in Cyrillic at top and Roman characters at foot (A) or vice versa (B).

546 **132** 50p. green and brown (A) 15 15
546b 50p. green and brown (B) 15 15
547 – 1d. green and red (A) . . 25 20
547b – 1d. green and red (B) . . 25 20
548 **132** 2d. blue and black (A) 40 25
548b 2d. blue and black (B) 40 25
549 – 5d. drab and green (A) 45 30
549b – 5d. drab and green (B) 45 30
550 – 10d. brown and sepia (A) 55 40
550b – 10d. brown and sepia (B) 55 40
551 **132** 20d. green and blue (A) 1·00 65
551b 20d. green and blue (B) 1·00 65

DESIGN: 1, 5, 20d. Ilyushin Il-4 DB-3 over Dubrovnik.

133 "Wreath of Mountains"

134 Petar Njegos (author)

1947. Centenary of Publication of "Wreath of Mountains".

552 **133** 1½d. black and green . . 15 10
553 **134** 2d.50 red and buff . . . 20 15
554 **133** 5d. black and blue . . . 35 20

135 Girl Athlete, Star and Flags

137 Gymnast

1947. Federal Sports Meeting.

555 – 1d.50 brown 15 10
556 **135** 2d.50 red 20 15
557 – 4d. blue 50 40

DESIGNS—VERT: 1d.50, Physical training groups. HORIZ: 4d. Parade of athletes.

1947. Balkan Games.

558 **137** 1d.50+0.50 green 15 10
559 2d.50+0.50 red 30 20
560 4d.+0.50 blue 40 35

138 Star and Map of Julian Province

139 Railway Construction

1947. Annexation of Julian Province to Yugoslavia.

561 **138** 2d.50 red and blue . . . 15 10
562 5d. brown and green . . . 15 10

1947. Juvenile Labour Organizations' Relief Fund.

563 **139** 1d.+0.50 orange 30 15
564 1d.50+1d. green 35 25
565 2d.50+1d.50 red 60 30
566 5d.+2d. blue . . . . . . 1·25 70

140 Music Book and Fiddle

141 Vuk Karadzic (poet)

1947. Centenary of Serbian Literature.

567 **140** 1d.50 green 10 10
568 **141** 2d.50 red 15 15
569 **140** 5d. blue 20 20

142 "B.C.G. Vaccine defeating Tuberculosis"

143 "Illness and Recovery"

144 "Fight against Tuberculosis"

145 Map of Yugoslavia and Symbols of Industry and Agriculture

1948. Anti-T.B. Fund.
570 **142** 1d.50+1d. green and red 10 10
571 **143** 2d.50+2d. green and red 15 15
572 **144** 5d.+3d. blue and red 25 20

1948. International Fair, Zagreb.
573 **145** 1d.50 green, blue and red 10 10
574 2d.50 purple, blue and red 10 10
575 5d. indigo, blue and red 15 10

146 Flag-bearers

147 Djura Danicic

1948. 5th Yugoslav Communist Party Congress, Belgrade.
576 **146** 2d. green and deep green 20 15
577b 3d. purple and red 20 15
578a 10d. ultramarine and blue 45 45

1948. 80th Anniv of Yugoslav Academy.
579 **147** 1d.50+0.50 green 15 15
580 – 2d.50+1d. red 25 15
581 – 4d.+2d. blue 35 30
PORTRAITS: 2d.50, Franjo Racki; 4d. Bishop Josip Strosmajer (inscr "Strossmayer").

148 "Krajina" (former royal yacht) passing under Danube Railway Bridge

1948. Danube Conference.
582 **148** 2d. green 2·40 2·40
583 3d. red 3·50 3·50
584 5d. blue 4·50 4·50
585 10d. brown 8·50 8·50

149 Lovrenz Kosir

150 Kosir and his Birthplace

1948. 80th Death Anniv of Kosir ("idealogical creator of first postage stamp").
586 **149** 3d. purple (postage) 15 10
587 5d. blue 15 15
588 10d. orange 20 10
589 12d. green 35 25
590 **150** 15d. mauve (air) 90 45

151 Putting the Shot

152

153 Arms of Montenegro

1948. Projected Balkan Games.
591 **151** 2d.+1d. green 20 15
592 – 3d.+1d. red 30 20
593 – 5d.+2d. blue 50 40
DESIGNS: 3d. Girl hurdler; 5d. Pole vaulting.

1948. Obligatory Tax. Red Cross.
594 **152** 50p. red and blue 20 15

1948. 5th Anniv of Republic.
595 – 3d. blue (Serbia) 35 25
596 – 3d. red (Croatia) 35 25
597 – 3d. orange (Slovenia) 35 25
598 – 3d. green (Bosnia and Herzegovina) 35 25
599 – 3d. mauve (Macedonia) 35 25
600 **153** 3d. black 35 25
601 – 10d. red (Yugoslavia) 2·00 2·00
No. 601 is larger, 24½ × 34½ mm.

154 F. Preseren

155 Ski-jump, Planica

1949. Death Centenary of Franc Preseren (author).
602 **154** 3d. blue 20 15
603 5d. orange 25 20
604 10d. sepia 1·50 35

1949. Ski Jumping Competition, Planica.
605 **155** 3d. red 50 30
606 – 12d. blue (Ski jumper) 1·25 65

156 Soldiers

158 Globe, Letters and Forms of Transport

1949. 5th Anniv of Liberation of Macedonia.
(a) Postage
607 **156** 3d. red 50 40
608 – 5d. blue 1·25 65
608a – 12d. brown 2·50 2·50
DESIGNS: 5d. Industrial and agricultural workers; 12d. Arms and flags of Yugoslavia and Macedonia.

(b) Air. Optd with Lisunov Li-2 airplane and AVIONSKA POSTA.
609 **156** 3d. red 2·50 2·50
610 – 5d. blue (No. 608) 2·50 2·50
610a – 12d. brown (No. 608a) 2·50 2·50

1949. 75th Anniv of U.P.U.
611 **158** 3d. red 2·75 2·75
612 – 5d. blue 40 40
613 **158** 12d. brown 45 45
DESIGN—HORIZ: 5d. Airplane, train and mail coach.

1949. Surch with bold figures and bars.
614 O **130** 3d. on 8d. brown 50 10
615 3d. on 12d. violet 60 10

160 Nurse and Child

1949. Obligatory Tax. Red Cross.
616 **160** 50p. brown and red 20 15

ФНР ЈУГОСЛАВИЈА
D3
FNR JUGOSLAVIJA
(161)

F N R D10
JUGOSLAVIJA
(162)

1949. Surch with T **161** or **162**.
617 – 3d. on 8d. yellow (No. 513) 65 10
618 – 10d. on 20d. red (No. 517) 85 10

FNR JUGOSLAVIJA
(163)

ФНР

F N R
(164)

F N R JUGOSLAVIJA
(165)

1949. Optd with T **163** on 2d., **164** on 3d. and 5d., or **165** on others.
619 **119** 50p. olive 10 10
620 1d. green 10 10
621 1d. orange 30 10
622 **120** 2d. red 15 10
623 2d. green 30 10
624 – 3d. red (No. 508) 15 10
625 – 3d. pink 30 10
626 – 5d. blue (No. 511) 40 20
627 – 5d. blue 1·10 10
628 – 12d. violet (No. 515) 35 10
629 **119** 16d. blue 1·25 40
630 20d. red 85 15

166 Class 151 Steam Locomotive, 1885

1949. Centenary of National Railways.
631 **166** 2d. green 1·50 35
632 – 3d. red 1·50 35
633 – 5d. blue 5·75 65
633a – 10d. orange 27·00 8·50
DESIGNS: 3d. Class 389 steam locomotive, 1930; 5d. Diesel locomotive, 1937, France; 10d. Electric train on bridge over River Vintgar.

167 Surveying

1950. Completion of Belgrade–Zagreb Road.
634 **167** 2d. green 40 15
635 – 3d. purple 25 15
636 – 5d. blue 1·00 70
DESIGNS: 3d. Map, road and car; 5d.Youth, road and flag.

168 Marshal Tito

169 Child Eating

1950. May Day.
637 **168** 3d. red 2·00 1·00
638 5d. blue 2·00 1·00
639 10d. brown 32·00 18·00
640 12d. black 2·00 2·00

1950. Child Welfare.
641 **169** 3d. red 35 10

170 Launching Model Glider

171 Chessboard and Bishop

1950. 3rd Aeronautical Meeting.
642 **170** 2d. green 80 90
643 – 3d. red 85 90
644 – 5d. violet 2·10 50
645 – 10d. brown 2·25 1·50
646 – 20d. blue 15·00 15·00
DESIGNS—VERT: 3d. Glider in flight; 5d. Parachutists landing; 10d. Woman pilot; 20d. Glider on water.

1950. 9th Chess Olympiad, Dubrovnik.
647 **171** 2d. brown 80 40
648 – 3d. bistre, brown and drab 80 30
649 – 5d. blue, yellow and green 1·50 50
650 – 10d. yellow, purple and blue 2·40 1·25
651 – 20d. yellow and blue 30·00 20·00
DESIGNS—VERT: 3d. Rook and flags; 5d. Globe and chessboard showing 1924 Capablanca v. Lasker game; 10d. Chequered globe, map and players; 20d. Knights and flags.

172 Girl Harvester

173 Steam Locomotive and Map

1950.
652 – 50p. brown 10 10
653 – 1d. green 15 10
705 – 1d. grey 20 10
654 **172** 2d. orange 15 10
706 2d. red 40 10
655 – 3d. red 20 10
656 – 5d. blue 65 10
719 – 5d. orange 4·50 10
657 – 7d. grey 75 10
720 – 8d. blue 4·00 15
658 – 10d. brown 75 10
721 – 10d. green 7·00 10
659 – 12d. brown 3·75 10
723 – 15d. red 19·00 10
660 – 16d. blue 2·25 30
723a – 17d. purple 4·50 10
661 – 20d. olive 2·25 35
710 – 20d. purple 3·50 10
711a **172** 25d. bistre 13·00 10
662 – 30d. brown 5·00 55
712 – 30d. blue 1·90 10
713 – 35d. brown 2·50 10
662a – 50d. violet 45·00 20·00
714 – 50d. green 3·25 10
715 – 75d. violet 3·00 10
716 – 100d. sepia 6·75 15
DESIGNS—VERT: 50, 100d. Metallurgy; 1d. Electrical supply engineer; 3, 35d. Man and woman with wheelbarrow; 5d. Fishing; 7, 8d. Mining; 10d. Apple-picking; 12, 75d. Lumbering; 14, 15, 16d. Picking sunflowers; 17, 20d. Woman and farm animals; 30d. Girl printer; 50d. Dockers unloading cargo.

1950. Zagreb Exhibition.
663 **173** 3d. red 1·60 50

174 Girl in National Costume

175 Galleon

1950. Obligatory Tax. Red Cross
664 **174** 50p. green and red 20 15

1950. Navy Day.
665 **175** 2d. purple 25 15
666 – 3d. brown 25 10
667 – 5d. green 1·75 20
668 – 10d. blue 65 15
669 – 12d. grey 1·60 50
670 – 20d. red 3·75 2·00
DESIGNS: 3d. Partisan patrol boat; 5d. Freighter discharging cargo; 10d. "Zagreb" (freighter) and globe; 12d. Yachts; 20d. Sailor, gun and "Golesnica" (torpedo boat).

176 Patriots of 1941

177 Franc Stane-Rozman

1951. 10th Anniv of Revolt against Pact with Axis.
671 **176** 3d. lake and red 2·25 1·40

1951. 10th Anniv of Partisan Rising in Slovenia.
672 **177** 3d. brown 50 25
673 – 5d. blue (Boy courier) 75 35

178 Children Painting

1951. International Children's Day.
674 **178** 3d. red 70 25

179 "Iron Gates", Danube
181 Zivorad Jovanovic

1951. Air.
675 **179** 1d. orange 15 10
676 – 2d. green 25 10
677 – 3d. red 25 10
677a – 5d. brown 30 10
678 – 6d. blue 4·50 4·00
679 – 10d. brown 50 10
680 – 20d. grey 75 10
681 – 30d. red 2·50 10
682 – 50d. violet 3·75 10
683 – 100d. grey 60·00 5·00
683a – 100d. green 1·40 15
683b – 200d. red 1·75 25
683c – 500d. blue 7·00 1·25

DESIGNS: (all show airplane)—As T **179**: 2, 5d. Plitvice Cascades; 3, 100d. (green) Gozd-Martuljak (mountain village); 6, 200d. Old Bridge, Mostar; 10d. Ohrid; 20d. Kotor Bay; 30d. Dubrovnik; 50d. Bled. 40 × 27 mm: 100d. (grey), 500d. Belgrade.

1951. Air. Zagreb Philatelic Exhibition. No. 678 in new colour optd **ZEFIZ 1951**.
684 6d. green 90 70

1951. 10th Anniv of Serbian Insurrection.
685 **181** 3d. brown 60 40
686 – 5d. blue . . . . 1·25 65
DESIGN—HORIZ: 5d. Armed insurgents.

183 Mt. Kopaonik 184 Sava Kovacevic

1951. Air. International Mountaineering Assn Meeting, Bled. Inscr "UIAA-1951".
687 **183** 3d. mauve . . . . 3·50 3·25
688 – 5d. blue . . . . 3·50 3·25
689 – 20d. green . . . . 90·00 60·00
DESIGNS: 5d. Mt. Triglav, Slovenia; 20d. Mt. Kalnik, Croatia.

1951. 10th Anniv of Montenegrin Insurrection.
690 **184** 3d. red 75 55
691 – 5d. blue . . . . 1·50 85
DESIGN—HORIZ: 5d. Partisan and mountains.

185 Marko Oreskovic (statue) 186 Simo Solaja

1951. 10th Anniv of Croatian Insurrection.
692 **185** 3d. red 75 35
693 – 5d. green . . . . 1·25 65
DESIGN: 5d. "Transport of a Wounded Man" (sculpture, A. Augustincic).

1951. 10th Anniv of Insurrection of Bosnia and Herzegovina.
694 **186** 3d. red 90 40
695 – 5d. blue . . . . 1·25 65
DESIGN—VERT: 5d. Group of insurgents.

187 Parachutists Landing 189 Primoz Trubar (writer)

1951. Air. 1st World Parachute Jumping Championship, Bled.
696 **187** 6d. lake . . . . 5·00 2·00

As No. 682 in new colour optd **I SVETSKO TAKMICENJE PADOBRANACA 1951**.
697 50d. blue . . . . 80·00 45·00

1951. Cultural Anniversaries.
698 **189** 10d. black 40 25
699 – 12d. red 40 25
700 – 20d. lilac . . . . 4·00 3·25
DESIGNS: 12d. Marko Marulic (Croatian writer, 500th birth anniv (1950)); 20d. Tsar Stepan Dusan (600th anniv (1949) of "Tsar Dusan's Book of Laws").

190 National Products 191 Hoisting the Flag

1951. Zagreb International Fair.
701 **190** 3p. yellow, red and blue 1·10 35

1951. Obligatory Tax. Red Cross.
702 **191** 50p. blue and red 20 15

192 Mirce Acev 193 P. P. Njegos

1951. 10th Anniv of Macedonian Insurrection.
703 **192** 3d. mauve 60 50
704 – 5d. violet . . . . 1·25 75
DESIGN—HORIZ: 5d. War Victims' Monument, Skopje.

1951. Death Centenary of Petar Njegos (poet).
724 **193** 15d. purple . . . . 1·50 55

194 Soldier and Badge 195 Marshal Tito

1951. Army Day.
725 **194** 15d. red (postage) 45 10
726 **195** 150d. blue (air) . . . . . 12·50 6·25

196 Marshal Tito 197 Marshal Tito

1952. Marshal Tito's 60th Birthday.
727 **196** 15d. brown . . . . 1·00 1·00
728 **197** 28d. lake . . . . 1·75 1·75
729 – 50d. green . . . . 35·00 25·00
DESIGN—As T **196**: 50d. Statue of Marshal Tito.

198 199 Gymnastics

1952. Children's Week.
730 **198** 15d. red . . . . 7·50 1·25

1952. 15th Olympic Games, Helsinki. Inscr "XV OLIMPIJADA 1952".
731 **199** 5d. brown on buff 60 25
732 – 10d. brown on yellow . . 90 25
733 – 15d. blue on pink 90 30
734 – 28d. brown on flesh . . . 2·50 90
735 – 50d. green on cream . . . 6·50 3·00
736 – 100d. brown on mauve . . 50·00 20·00
DESIGNS: 10d. Running; 15d. Swimming; 28d. Boxing; 50d. Basketball; 100d. Football.

200 "Fishing Boat" (from relief by Krsinic) 200a Belgrade (16th century)

1952. Navy Day. Views. Inscr "1952".
737 – 15d. purple . . . . 1·75 60
738 **200** 28d. brown . . . . 3·25 90
739 – 50d. black . . . . 23·00 19·00
DESIGNS: 15d. Split, Dalmatia; 50d. Sveti Stefan, Montenegro.

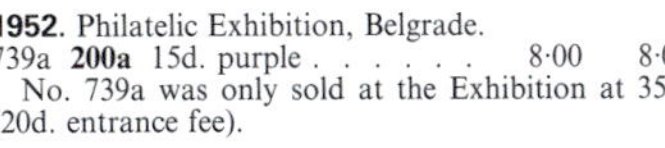
1952. Philatelic Exhibition, Belgrade.
739a **200a** 15d. purple . . . . . . 8·00 8·00
No. 739a was only sold at the Exhibition at 35d. (20d. entrance fee).

201 202 Workers in Procession (from fresco by Slavko Pengov)

1952. Obligatory Tax. Red Cross.
740 **201** 50p. red, grey and black 30 10

1952. 6th Yugoslavia Communist Party Congress.
741 **202** 15d. brown . . . . 1·50 1·10
742 15d. turquoise . . . . . 1·50 1·10
743 15d. brown . . . . 1·50 1·10
744 15d. blue . . . . 1·50 1·10

203 Nikola Tesla 204 Fresco, Sopocani Monastery

1953. 10th Death Anniv of Tesla (inventor).
745 **203** 15d. lake 80 15
746 30d. blue . . . . 4·00 40

1953. United Nations Commemoration.
747 **204** 15d. green . . . . 1·25 35
748 – 30d. blue . . . . 2·10 35
749 – 50d. lake . . . . 17·00 3·00
DESIGNS—VERT: 30d. Fresco, St. Panteleimon Church, Nerezim, Skopje; 50d. Fresco, St. Dimitri Church, Pec.

205

1953. Adriatic Car and Motor Cycle Rally.
750 **205** 15d. mauve and orange 30 15
751 – 30d. deep blue and blue 85 20
752 – 50d. brown and yellow . . 1·75 20
753 – 70d. green and emerald 6·00 1·60
DESIGNS—HORIZ: 30d. Motor cyclist and coastline; 50d. Racing car and flags; 70d. Saloon car descending mountain roadway.

206 Marshal Tito 207

1953. Marshal Tito Commemoration.
754 **206** 50d. violet . . . . 9·00 2·00

1953. 38th Esperanto Congress, Zagreb.
755 **207** 15d. green & black (postage) . . . . 3·25 1·75
756 300d. green and blue (air) £250 £225

208 "Insurrection" (Borko Lazevski) 209

1953. 50th Anniv of Macedonian Insurrection.
757 **208** 15d. purple 80 75
758 – 30d. green . . . . 2·75 2·00
DESIGN: 30d. Nikola Karev (revolutionary).

1953. 10th Anniv of Liberation of Istria and Slovene Coast.
759 **209** 15d. green . . . . 12·50 1·75

210 B. Radicevic 211 Blood-transfusion

1953. Death Centenary of Branko Radicevic (poet).
760 **210** 15d. purple . . . . 6·00 1·25

1953. Obligatory Tax. Red Cross.
761 **211** 2d. red and purple . . . 35 25

212 Jajce 213 European Souslik

1953. 10th Anniv of 1st Republican Legislative Assembly.
762 **212** 15d. green . . . . 1·25 40
763 – 30d. red . . . . 1·50 95
764 – 50d. sepia . . . . 10·00 8·75
DESIGNS: 30d. Assembly Building; 50d. Marshal Tito addressing assembly.

1954. Animals.
765 **213** 2d. grey, buff and green 20 10
766 – 5d. brown, buff and green 35 15
767 – 10d. brown and black . . 60 25
768 – 15d. brown and blue . . . 80 30
769 – 17d. brown and purple . . 1·40 30
770 – 25d. yellow, blue and violet . . . . 2·40 40
771 – 30d. brown and blue . . . 2·40 40
772 – 35d. black and brown . . 6·00 90
773 – 50d. brown and green . . 16·00 1·75
774 – 65d. black and red . . . 22·00 12·00
775 – 70d. brown and green . . 19·00 10·50
776 – 100d. black and blue . . 60·00 30·00
DESIGNS—HORIZ: 5d. Lynx; 10d. Red deer; 15d. Brown bear; 17d. Chamois; 25d. Eastern white pelican. VERT: 30d. Lammergeier; 35d. "Procerus gigas" (ground beetle); 50d. "Callimenius pancici" (cricket); 65d. Black Dalmatian lizard; 70d. Blind cave-dwelling salamander; 100d. Brown trout.

214 Ljubljana (17th century)

1954. Philatelic Exhibition, Ljubljana.
777 **214** 15d. brown, green & black . . . . 13·50 10·00
No. 777 was only sold at the Exhibition at 35d. (20d. entrance fee).

215 Cannon, 1804

1954. 150th Anniv of Serbian Insurrection. Mult.
778 15d. Serbian flag . . . . . . 1·25 40
779 30d. Type **215** . . . . 2·00 75
780 50d. Seal of insurgents' council . . . . 3·75 1·50
781 70d. Karageorge . . . . . . 40·00 12·00

215a 216

1954. Children's Week.
781a **215a** 2d. red 35 60

1954. Obligatory Tax. Red Cross.
782 **216** 2d. red and green 20 10

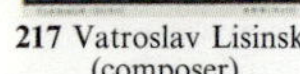

217 Vatroslav Lisinski (composer) **218** "A Midsummer Night's Dream" (Shakespeare)

1954. Cultural Anniversaries.
783 **217** 15d. green 3·00 45
784 – 30d. brown 2·25 1·00
785 – 50d. purple 2·50 1·60
786 – 70d. blue 5·00 3·00
787 – 100d. violet 22·00 18·00
PORTRAITS: 15d. Type **217** (death centenary); 30d. Andrija Kacic-Miosic (writer, 250th birth anniv); 50d. Jury Vega (mathematician, birth bicentenary); 70d. Jovan Jovanovic-Zmaj (poet, 50th death anniv); 100d. Filip Visnjic (poet and musician, 120th death anniv).
See also Nos. 975/80.

1955. Dubrovnik Festival.
788 – 15d. lake 80 35
789 **218** 30d. blue 3·00 1·10
DESIGN—VERT: 15d. Scene from "Robinja" by Hanibal Lucic.

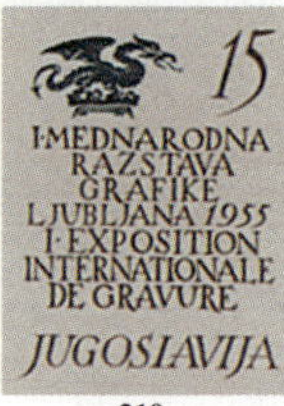

219 **220**

1955. 1st Int Exn of Engraving, Ljubljana.
790 **219** 15d. brown and green on stone 2·50 75

1955. 2nd World Congress of the Deaf and Dumb.
791 **220** 15d. red 1·50 40

221 Hops **222** Laughing Girl

1955. Floral Designs.
792 **221** 5d. green and brown 15 10
793 – 10d. purple, green and buff 15 10
794 – 15d. multicoloured 20 10
795 – 17d. buff, green and lake 30 15
796 – 25d. yellow, green and blue 40 15
797 – 30d. multicoloured 70 45
798 – 50d. red, green and brown 3·75 1·50
799 – 70d. orange, green and brown 5·00 2·50
800 – 100d. multicoloured 25·00 15·00
FLOWERS: 10d. Tobacco; 15d. Opium poppy; 17d. Small-leaved lime; 25d. False chamomile; 30d. Sage; 50d. Dog rose; 70d. Great yellow gentian; 100d. Yellow pheasant's-eye.

1955. Obligatory Tax. Children's Week.
801 **222** 2d. red and cream 25 15

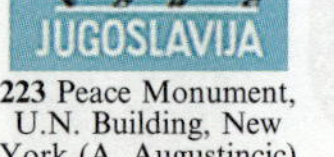

223 Peace Monument, U.N. Building, New York (A. Augustinic) **224** Red Cross Nurse

1955. 10th Anniv of United Nations.
802 **223** 30d. black and blue 1·25 55

1955. Obligatory Tax. Red Cross.
803 **224** 2d. black, grey and red 25 15

225 Woman and Dove **226** St. Donat's Church, Zadar

1955. 10th Anniv of Republic.
804 **225** 15d. violet 40 20

1956. Yugoslav Art.
805 **226** 5d. grey 45 10
806 – 10d. green 45 10
807 – 15d. brown 50 10
808 – 20d. brown 50 15
809 – 25d. sepia 65 15
810 – 30d. purple 65 20
811 – 35d. green 1·25 35
812 – 40d. brown 2·25 45
813 – 50d. brown 5·50 35
814 – 70d. green 12·00 8·25
815 – 100d. purple 32·00 19·00
816 – 200d. blue 55·00 22·00
DESIGNS—VERT: 10d. Bas-relief of Croat King, Diocletian Palace, Split; 15d. Church portal, Studenica, Serbia; 20d. Master Radovan's portal, Trogir Cathedral; 25d. Fresco, Sopocani, Serbia; 30d. Monument, Radimije, Herzegovina; 50d. Detail from Bozidarevic Triptych, Dubrovnik; 70d. Carved figure, Belec Church, Croatia; 100d. Self-portrait of Rikard Jakopic; 200d. Peace Monument by A. Augustinic, New York. HORIZ: 35d. Heads from Cathedral cornice, Sibenik, Dalmatia; 40d. Frieze, Kotor Cathedral, Montenegro.

227 Zagreb through the Centuries **228** Houses ruined by Avalanche

1956. Yugoslav Int Philatelic Exn, Zagreb.
817 **227** 15d. deep brown, brown and black (postage) 30 15
818 30d. blue, red and black (air) 1·50 55

1956. Obligatory Tax. Red Cross.
819 **228** 2d. sepia, brown and red 30 20

229 "Technical Education" **230** Induction Motor

1956. Air. 10th Anniv of Technical Education.
820 **229** 30d. black and red 1·25 90

1956. Birth Centenary of Nikola Tesla (inventor).
821 **230** 10d. olive 15 10
822 – 15d. brown 40 10
823 – 30d. blue 70 15
824 – 50d. purple 2·25 1·00
DESIGNS: 15d. Transformer; 30d. "Telekomanda" (invention); 50d. Portrait of Tesla.

231 Short-snouted Seahorse **232**

1956. Adriatic Sea Creatures.
825 **231** 10d. brown, purple & green 15 10
826 – 15d. black, pink and blue 15 10
827 – 20d. multicoloured 20 10
828 – 25d. multicoloured 35 10
829 – 30d. multicoloured 45 10
830 – 35d. mauve, yellow & blue 90 15
831 – 50d. red, yellow and blue 3·50 85
832 – 70d. multicoloured 5·00 1·40
833 – 100d. multicoloured 16·00 3·75
DESIGNS: 15d. Common paper nautilus; 20d. Rock lobster; 25d. Rainbow wrasse; 30d. Painted comber; 35d. Striped red mullet; 50d. Red scorpionfish; 70d. Cuckoo wrasse; 100d. John Dory.

1956. Obligatory Tax. Children's Week.
834 **232** 2d. green 30 20

233 Running **234**

1956. Olympic Games. Figures, values and country name in ochre.
835 **233** 10d. red 10 10
836 – 15d. blue (Canoeing) 10 10
837 – 20d. blue (Skiing) 20 10
838 – 30d. green (Swimming) 30 10
839 – 35d. sepia (Football) 45 10
840 – 50d. green (Water polo) 1·25 15
841 – 70d. purple (Table tennis) 4·00 1·40
842 – 100d. red (Shooting) 7·00 2·75

1957. Obligatory Tax. Red Cross.
843 **234** 2d. red, black and blue 25 15

235 Common Centaury **236** Factory in Worker's Hand

1957. Flowers. Multicoloured.
844 10d. Type **235** 10 10
845 15d. Deadly nightshade 15 10
846 20d. Saffron crocus 20 10
847 25d. Marsh mallow 20 10
848 30d. Common valerian 25 15
849 35d. Woolly foxglove 30 15
850 50d. Male fern 2·25 40
851 70d. Green-winged orchid 4·00 75
852 100d. Pyrethrum 16·00 7·50

1957. 1st Congress of Workers' Councils, Belgrade.
853 **236** 15d. lake 40 10
854 30d. blue 85 25

237 Gymnastics

1957. 2nd Gymnastics Festival, Zagreb. Vert designs as T **237**.
855 **237** 10d. olive and black 25 10
856 – 15d. brown and black 25 10
857 – 30d. blue and black 65 10
858 – 50d. brown and black 2·00 1·50

239 Musician and Dancers of Slovenia **240** Children

1957. Yugoslav Costumes (1st series).
860 – 10d. multicoloured 15 10
861 – 15d. multicoloured 25 10
862 – 30d. multicoloured 25 10
863 – 50d. green, brown and buff 90 20
864 – 70d. black, brown and buff 1·00 35
865 **239** 100d. multicoloured 5·50 2·50
DESIGNS—HORIZ: 10d. Montenegrin musician, man and woman; 15d. Macedonian dancers; 30d. Croatian shepherdess and shepherd boys. VERT: 50d. Serbian peasants; 70d. Bosnian villagers.
See also Nos. 1020/5.

1957. Obligatory Tax. Children's Week.
866 **240** 2d. slate and red 25 15

241 Revolutionaries **242** Simon Gregorcic (poet)

1957. 40th Anniv of Russian Revolution.
867 **241** 15d. red and ochre 40 20

1957. Cultural Anniversaries.
868 **242** 15d. sepia 30 10
869 – 30d. blue 40 10
870 – 50d. brown 90 10
871 – 70d. violet 8·50 2·25
872 – 100d. green 14·00 13·00
PORTRAITS: 15d. Type **242** (50th death anniv (1956)); 30d. Anton Linhart (dramatist, birth bicentary (1956)); 50d. Oton Kucera (physicist, birth centenary); 70d. Stevan Mokranjac (composer, birth centenary (1956)); 100d. Jovan Popovic (writer, death centenary (1956)).

244 **245** Fresco of Sopocani Monastery

1958. 7th Yugoslav Communist Party Congress.
877 **244** 15d. purple 20 10

1958. Obligatory Tax. Red Cross.
878 **245** 2d. multicoloured 30 20

246 Mallard **247** Pigeon

1958. Yugoslav Game Birds. Birds in natural colours. Background colours given below.
879 **246** 10d. brown 15 15
880 – 15d. mauve 20 15
881 – 20d. blue 40 15
882 – 25d. green 65 15
883 – 30d. turquoise 80 20
884 – 35d. bistre 90 20
885 – 50d. purple 4·25 1·25
886 – 70d. blue 7·75 3·00
887 – 100d. brown 17·00 8·00
DESIGNS—HORIZ: 15d. Western capercaillie; 20d. Common pheasant; 35d. Water rail; 70d. Eurasian woodcock. VERT: 25d. Black coot; 30d. Water rail; 50d. Rock partridge; 100d. Common crane.

1958. Opening of Postal Museum, Belgrade.
888 **247** 15d. black 30 10

248 Battle Flag **249** Pomet (hero of Drzic's comedy "Dundo Maroje") and Ancient Fountain at Dubrovnik

1958. 15th Anniv of Battle of Sutjeska River.
889 **248** 15d. lake 25 15

1958. 450th Birth Anniv of Marin Drzic (writer).
890 **249** 15d. brown and black 25 10

243 Steel Plant, Sisak **250** Children at Play

1958.

891	–	2d. green	10	10
892	–	5d. red	15	10
983	–	5d. orange	30	10
893	–	8d. purple	20	10
984	–	8d. violet	25	10
894	**243**	10d. green	30	10
985		10d. brown	25	10
896	–	15d. red	45	10
986	–	15d. green	35	10
898	–	17d. purple	65	10
899	–	20d. red	50	10
987	–	20d. blue	40	10
987a	–	20d. green	40	10
900	–	25d. grey	50	10
988	–	25d. red	30	10
901	–	30d. blue	25	10
989	–	30d. brown	4·00	10
989a	–	30d. red	70	10
902	–	35d. red	25	10
903	–	40d. red	30	10
904	–	40d. blue	1·40	10
990	–	40d. purple	25	10
905	–	50d. blue	30	10
991	–	50d. blue	70	10
906	–	55d. red	2·00	10
992	–	65d. green	25	10
907	–	70d. red	1·75	10
908	–	80d. red	8·50	10
909	–	100d. green	6·00	10
993	–	100d. green	2·50	10
994	–	150d. red	90	15
910	–	200d. brown	2·50	30
995	–	200d. blue	60	10
996	–	300d. green	2·25	30
911	–	500d. blue	5·00	30
997	–	500d. violet	1·50	10
998	–	1000d. brown	2·25	10
999	–	2000d. purple	5·25	30

DESIGNS—VERT: 2, 100d. (993) Oil derricks, Nafta; 5d. Shipbuilding; 8, 17d. Timber industry, cable railway; 15 (896), 20d. Jablanica Dam; 15 (986), 25d. (900) Ljubljana–Zagreb motor road; 25d. (988) Cable industry; 30d. "Litostroj" turbine factory, Ljubljana; 35, 40d. (990) Coke plant, Lukavac; 50d. (991) Iron foundry, Zenica; 65d. Furnace, Sovojno. HORIZ: 40 (903/4), 150d. Hotel Titograd; 50 (905), 55, 200d. (995) Skopje; 70, 80, 300d. Sarajevo railway station and obelisk; 100 (909), 500d. (997) Bridge, Ljubljana; 200 (910), 1000d. Theatre, Zagreb; 500 (911), 2000d. Parliament House, Belgrade.

See also Nos. 1194/1204.

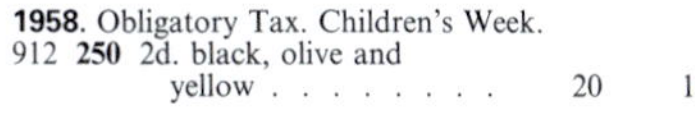

1958. Obligatory Tax. Children's Week.

912	**250**	2d. black, olive and yellow	20	10

251 Ship with Oceanographic Equipment

252 "Human Rights"

1958. International Geophysical Year.

913	**251**	15d. purple (postage)	55	15
914	–	300d. blue (air)	7·50	2·25

DESIGN: 300d. Moon and Earth with orbital tracks of artificial satellites.

1958. 10th Anniv of Declaration of Human Rights.

915	**252**	30d. green	65	45

253 Old City, Dubrovnik

254 Communist Party Emblem and Red Flags

1959. Tourist Publicity (1st series). Views.

916	**253**	10d. yellow and red	10	10
917	–	10d. blue and green	10	10
918	–	15d. violet and blue	10	10
919	–	15d. green and blue	10	10
920	–	20d. green and brown	15	10
921	–	20d. green and blue	15	10
922	–	30d. violet and orange	1·25	10
923	–	30d. green and blue	1·25	10
924	–	70d. black and blue	4·25	1·50

DESIGNS: No. 917, Bled; 918, Postojna grottoes; 919, Ohrid; 920, Plitvice Lakes; 921, Opatija; 922, Split; 923, Sveti Stefan; 924, Belgrade.

See also Nos. 1033/41, 1080/5 and 1165/70.

1959. 40th Anniv of Yugoslav Communist Party.

925	**254**	20d. multicoloured	15	10

255 "Family Assistance"

256 Dubrovnik (15th century)

1959. Obligatory Tax. Red Cross.

926	**255**	2d. blue and red	25	20

1959. Philatelic Exhibition, Dubrovnik ("JUFIZ IV").

927	**256**	20d. myrtle, green and blue	75	65

257 Dutch Lavender

258 Tug-of-War

1959. Medicinal Plants.

928	**257**	10d. violet, green and blue	10	10
929	–	15d. multicoloured	10	10
930	–	20d. multicoloured	10	10
931	**257**	25d. lilac, green and olive	20	10
932	–	30d. green, blue and pink	30	15
933	–	35d. blue, green and brown	60	20
934	–	50d. yellow, green & brn	2·40	50
935	–	70d. multicoloured	3·50	1·00
936	–	100d. grey, green & brown	6·00	2·75

FLOWERS: 15d. Alder blackthorn; 20d. Scopolia; 25d. Monkshood; 30d. Bilberry; 35d. Common juniper; 50d. Cowslip; 70d. Pomegranate; 100d. Thorn-apple.

1959. "Partisan" Physical Culture Festival, Belgrade.

937	**258**	10d. black and ochre	10	10
938	–	15d. blue and sepia	10	10
939	–	20d. violet and brown	10	10
940	–	35d. purple and grey	15	10
941	–	40d. violet and grey	25	10
942	–	55d. green and brown	40	10
943	–	80d. olive and slate	90	50
944	–	100d. violet and ochre	2·75	90

DESIGNS—HORIZ: 15d. High jumping and running; 20d. Gymnastics; 35d. Female exercises with hoops; 40d. Sailors' exercises; 55d. Handball and basketball; 80d. Swimming and diving. VERT: 100d. "Partisan" Association insignia.

259 Fair Emblem

260

1959. Zagreb International Fair.

945	**259**	20d. black and blue	45	15

1959. Obligatory Tax. Children's Week.

946	**260**	2d. slate and yellow	25	15

261 Athletes

262 "Reconstruction" (sculpture by L. Dolinar)

1960. Olympic Games.

947	**261**	15d. yellow, buff and violet	10	10
948	–	20d. drab, lavender & blue	10	10
949	–	30d. blue, stone & ultram	15	10
950	–	35d. grey, brown & purple	15	10
951	–	40d. drab, green and bronze	20	10
952	–	55d. blue, drab and green	35	10
953	–	80d. ochre, grey and red	50	25
954	–	100d. ochre, drab and violet	60	30

DESIGNS: 20d. Swimming; 30d. Skiing; 35d. Graeco-Roman wrestling; 40d. Cycling; 55d. Yachting; 80d. Equestrian; 100d. Fencing.

Nos. 948, 950, 952 and 954 are inscr in Cyrillic characters.

1960. Obligatory Tax. Red Cross.

955	**262**	2d. blue and red	25	15

1960. Yugoslav Forest Mammals. As T **213**. Animals in natural colours. Background colours given.

956	15d. blue (West European hedgehog)	10	10
957	20d. olive (Eurasian red squirrel)	15	10
958	25d. turquoise (Pine marten)	15	10
959	30d. olive (Brown hare)	20	10
960	35d. brown (Red fox)	25	10
961	40d. lake (Eurasian badger)	30	10
962	55d. blue (Wolf)	45	20
963	80d. violet (Roe deer)	70	20
964	100d. red (Wild boar)	1·25	90

263 Lenin

264 Accelerator

1960. 90th Birth Anniv of Lenin.

965	**263**	20d. grey and green	15	10

1960. Nuclear Energy Exhibition, Belgrade.

966	**264**	15d. green	10	10
967	–	20d. red	10	10
968	–	40d. blue	20	15

DESIGNS: 20d. Neutron generator; 40d. Nuclear reactor.

265 Young Girl

266 Serbian National Theatre. Novi Sad (Centenary)

1960. Obligatory Tax. Children's Week.

969	**265**	2d. red	20	15

1960. Anniversaries.

970	**266**	15d. black	10	10
971	–	20d. sepia	10	10
972	–	40d. blue	10	10
973	–	55d. purple	15	10
974	–	80d. green	15	10

DESIGNS: 20d. Detail of "Illyrian Renaissance", V. Bukovac (cent of Croat National Theatre, Zagreb); 40d. Edvard Rusijan and Bleriot XI airplane (50th anniv of 1st flight in Yugoslavia); 55d. Symbolic hand holding fruit (15th anniv of Republic); 80d. Symbol of nuclear energy (15th anniv of U.N.O.).

1960. Portraits as T **217**.

975	15d. green	10	10
976	20d. brown	10	10
977	40d. brown	10	10
978	55d. red	10	10
979	80d. blue	20	10
980	100d. blue	40	15

PORTRAITS: 15d. Ivan Cankar (writer); 20d. Silvije Kranjcevic (poet); 40d. Paja Jovanovic (painter); 55d. Djura Jaksic (writer); 80d. Mihajlo Pupin (physicist); 100d. Rudjer Boskovic (astronomer).

268 "Blood Transfusion"

269 "Atomic Energy"

1961. Obligatory Tax. Red Cross. Perf or imperf.

981	**268**	2d. multicoloured	25	15

1961. Int Nuclear Electronic Conference, Belgrade.

982	**269**	25d. multicoloured	15	10

1961. Medicinal Plants. As T **257**. Multicoloured.

1000	10d. Yellow foxglove	10	10
1001	15d. Marjoram	10	10
1002	20d. Hyssop	15	10
1003	25d. Hawthorn	15	10
1004	40d. Hollyhock	15	10
1005	50d. Soapwort	25	10
1006	60d. Clary	35	15
1007	80d. Blackthorn	70	15
1008	100d. Pot marigold	1·40	60

See also Nos. 1074/9.

271 Stevan Filipovic (statue by V. Bakic)

273 St. Clement (14th-century wood-carving)

272

1961. 20th Anniv of Yugoslav Insurrection. Inscriptions in gold.

1009	**271**	15d. brown and red	10	10
1010	–	20d. yellow and sepia	10	10
1011	–	25d. green and turquoise	10	10
1012	–	60d. violet and blue	15	10
1013	–	100d. indigo and blue	30	20

DESIGNS: 20d. Insurrection Monument, Bosansko Grahovo (relief by S. Stojanovic); 25d. Executed Inhabitants Monument, Kragujevac (by A Grzetic); 60d. Nova Gradiska Victory monument (by A. Augustincic); 100d. Marshal Tito (Revolution Monument, Titovo Uzice, statue by Krsinic).

1961. Non-Aligned Countries Conf, Belgrade.

1014	**272**	25d. sepia (postage)	10	10
1015	–	50d. green	20	10
1016	**272**	250d. purple (air)	75	50
1017	–	500d. blue	2·25	1·25

DESIGN: 50, 500d. National Assembly Building, Belgrade.

1961. 12th International Congress of Byzantine Studies, Ohrid.

1018	**273**	25d. sepia and olive	25	15

274 Bird with Flower in Beak

275 Luka Vukalovic (revolutionary leader)

1961. Obligatory Tax. Children's Week.

1019	**274**	2d. orange and violet	15	10

1961. Yugoslav Costumes (2nd series). As T **239**. Inscr "1941–1961".

1020	15d. multicoloured	15	10
1021	25d. black, red and brown	15	10
1022	30d. sepia, red and brown	25	10
1023	50d. multicoloured	35	10
1024	65d. multicoloured	45	15
1025	100d. multicoloured	1·60	60

DESIGNS—HORIZ: Costumes of: 15d. Serbia; 25d. Montenegro; 30d. Bosnia and Herzegovina; 50d. Macedonia; 65d. Croatia; 100d. Slovenia.

1961. Centenary of Herzegovina Insurrection.

1026	**275**	25d. black	15	10

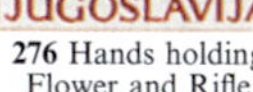

276 Hands holding Flower and Rifle

277 Dimitur and Konstantin Miladinov

1961. 20th Anniv of Yugoslav Partisan Army.

1027	**276**	25d. blue and red	20	10

1961. Centenary of Publication of Macedonian National Songs by Miladinov Brothers.

1028	**277**	25d. purple and buff	20	10

278 "Mother's Play" (after P. Krsinic)

279 Mosquito

1962. 15th Anniv of U.N.I.C.E.F.
1029 **278** 50d. black on drab . . . 15 10

1962. Malaria Eradication.
1030 **279** 50d. black on blue . . . 15 10

280 Goddess Isis (from Temple at Kalabscha) **281** Bandages and Symbols

1962. 15th Anniv of U.N.E.S.C.O. Save Nubian Monuments.
1031 **280** 25d. green on stone . . . 10 10
1032 – 50d. brown on drab . . 20 10
DESIGN: 50d. Rameses II (from temple, Abu Simbel).

1962. Tourist Publicity (2nd series). Views as T **253**. Inscr "1941–1961".
1033 15d. brown and blue 15 10
1034 15d. bistre and turquoise . . 15 10
1035 25d. brown and blue 15 10
1036 25d. blue and light blue . . . 15 10
1037 30d. blue and brown 25 10
1038 30d. blue and purple 40 10
1039 50d. turquoise and bistre . . 1·00 10
1040 50d. blue and bistre . . . . 1·00 10
1041 100d. grey and green . . . . 4·00 70
VIEWS: No. 1033, Portoroz; 1034, Jajce; 1035, Zadar; 1036, Popova Sapka; 1037, Hvar; 1038, Kotor Bay; 1039, Djerdap; 1040, Rab; 1041, Zagreb.

1962. Obligatory Tax. Red Cross.
1042 **281** 5d. red, brown and grey 15 10

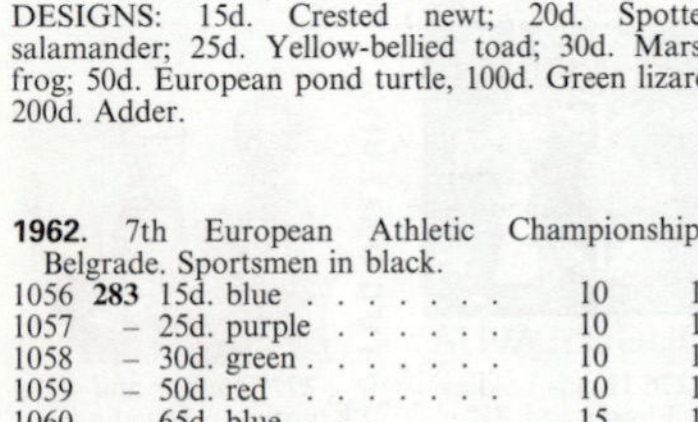

282 Marshal Tito (after sculpture by A. Augustincic) **283** Pole Vaulting

1962. Marshal Tito's 70th Birthday.
1043 **282** 25d. green 10 10
1044 – 50d. brown 20 10
1045 **282** 100d. blue 65 20
1046 – 200d. green and brown 1·50 75
DESIGN: 50, 200d. As Type **282** but profile view of bust.

1962. Amphibians and Reptiles. As T **213**.
1047 15d. brown, red and green 15 10
1048 20d. black, yellow and violet 15 10
1049 25d. multicoloured 15 10
1050 30d. brown, green and blue 15 10
1051 50d. brown, yellow and red 20 10
1052 65d. black, stone and green 25 10
1053 100d. green, brown and black 40 25
1054 150d. red, black and brown 1·00 50
1055 200d. black, drab and red 2·25 1·25
DESIGNS: 15d. Crested newt; 20d. Spotted salamander; 25d. Yellow-bellied toad; 30d. Marsh frog; 50d. European pond turtle, 100d. Green lizard; 200d. Adder.

1962. 7th European Athletic Championships, Belgrade. Sportsmen in black.
1056 **283** 15d. blue 10 10
1057 – 25d. purple 10 10
1058 – 30d. green 10 10
1059 – 50d. red 10 10
1060 – 65d. blue 15 10
1061 – 100d. turquoise 25 10
1062 – 150d. orange 35 20
1063 – 200d. brown 65 40
DESIGNS—HORIZ: 25d. Throwing the discus; 50d. Throwing the javelin; 100d. Start of sprint; 200d. High jumping. VERT: 30d. Running; 65d. Putting the shot; 150d. Hurdling.

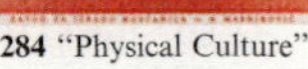

284 "Physical Culture"

285 "Bathing the Newborn Child" (Decani Monastery)

1962. Children's Week.
1064 **284** 25d. black and red . . . 15 10

1962. Yugoslav Art. Multicoloured.
1065 25d. Situla of Vace (detail from bronze vessel) (horiz) 10 10
1066 30d. Golden Mask of Trebiniste (5th-cent burial mask) (horiz) 10 10
1067 50d. The God Kairos (Trogir Monastery) . . . 15 10
1068 65d. Pigeons of Nerezi (detail from series of frescoes, "The Visitation", Nerezi Church, Skopje) 25 20
1069 100d. Type **285** 40 30
1070 150d. Icon of Ohrid (detail from 14th-cent icon, "The Annunciation") (horiz) . . 90 70
See also Nos. 1098/1103.

286 Ear of Wheat and Parched Earth **287** Andrija Mohorovicic (meteorologist)

1963. Freedom from Hunger.
1071 **286** 50d. purple on stone . . 20 10

1963. World Meteorological Day.
1072 **287** 50d. blue on grey . . . 20 10

288 Centenary Emblem **289** Partisans in File

1963. Obligatory Tax. Red Cross Centenary and Red Cross Week.
1073 **288** 5d. red, grey and ochre 20 10

1963. Medicinal Plants.
1074 15d. black, green & lt green 15 10
1075 25d. multicoloured 15 10
1076 30d. multicoloured 15 10
1077 50d. multicoloured 20 10
1078 65d. multicoloured 40 15
1079 100d. drab, green and black 1·40 60
FLOWERS: 15d. Lily of the valley; 25d. Iris; 30d. Bistort; 50d. Henbane; 65d. Perforate St. John's wort; 100d. Caraway.

1963. Tourist Publicity (3rd series). Views as T **253**. Inscr "1963". Multicoloured.
1080 15d. Pula 10 10
1081 25d. Vrnjacka Banja 10 10
1082 30d. Crikvenica 10 10
1083 50d. Korcula 20 10
1084 65d. Durmitor 20 15
1085 100d. Ljubljana . . . . . . 1·50 40

1963. 20th Anniv of Battle of Sutjeska River.
1086 **289** 15d. green and drab . . . 10 10
1087 – 25d. green 10 10
1088 – 50d. violet and brown 20 10
DESIGNS—VERT: 25d. Sutjeska Gorge. HORIZ: 50d. Partisans in battle.
See also No. 1125.

290 Gymnast on "Horse" **291** "Mother"

1963. 5th European Cup Gymnastic Championships.
1089 **290** 25d. green and black . . 10 10
1090 – 50d. blue and black . . 10 10
1091 – 100d. brown and black 40 35
DESIGNS—Gymnast: 50d. on parallel bars; 100d. exercising with rings.

1963. Sculptures by Ivan Mestrovic.
1092 **291** 25d. bistre on brown . . 10 10
1093 – 50d. olive on green . . 15 10
1094 – 65d. green on blue . . . 50 30
1095 – 100d. black on grey . . 65 50
SCULPTURES: 50d. "Reminiscence" (nude female figure); 65d. "Kraljevic Marko" (head); 100d. "Indian on horseback".

292 Children with Toys **293** Soldier and Emblem

1963. Children's Week.
1096 **292** 25d. multicoloured . . . 25 10

1963. 20th Anniv of Yugoslav Democratic Federation.
1097 **293** 25d. red, green and drab 15 10

1963. Yugoslav Art. As T **285**. Inscr "1963". Multicoloured.
1098 25d. "Man", relief on Radimlje tombstone (13th–15th century) . . . 10 10
1099 30d. Detail of relief on door of Split Cathedral (Andrija Buvina) (13th century) (horiz) 10 10
1100 50d. Detail of fresco in Beram Church (15th cent) (horiz) 15 10
1101 65d. Archangel Michael from plaque in Dominican Monastery, Dubrovnik (15th cent) 20 15
1102 100d. Figure of man on Baroque fountain, by Francesco Robba, Ljubljana (18th cent) . . 25 15
1103 150d. Archbishop Eufraise, detail of mosaic in Porec Basilica (6th cent) 70 70

294 Dositej Obradovic (writer) **295** Parachute

1963. Cultural Celebrities.
1104 **294** 25d. black on buff . . . 10 10
1105 – 30d. black on blue . . . 10 10
1106 – 50d. black on cream . . 15 10
1107 – 65d. black on lilac . . . 25 20
1108 – 100d. black on pink . . . 40 35
PORTRAITS: 30d. Vuk Karadzic (language reformer); 50d. Franc Miklosic (philologist); 65d. Ljudevit Gaj (writer); 100d. Petar Njegos (poet).
See also Nos. 1174/9.

1964. Obligatory Tax. Red Cross Week and 20th Anniv of Yugoslav Red Cross.
1109 **295** 5d. red, purple and blue 15 10

296 Peacock **297** Fireman saving Child

1964. Butterflies. Multicoloured.
1110 25d. Type **296** 10 10
1111 30d. Camberwell beauty . . 10 10
1112 40d. Oleander hawk moth 10 10
1113 50d. Apollo 15 10
1114 150d. Viennese emperor moth 45 35
1115 200d. Swallowtail 65 50

1964. Centenary of Voluntary Fire Brigade
1116 **297** 25d. sepia and red . . . 20 10

298 Running

299 "Reconstruction"

1964. Olympic Games, Tokyo.
1117 **298** 25d. yellow, black & grey 10 10
1118 – 30d. violet, black and grey 10 10
1119 – 40d. green, black and grey 10 10
1120 – 50d. multicoloured . . . 10 10
1121 – 150d. multicoloured . . 20 15
1122 – 200d. blue, black and grey 30 25
DESIGNS: 30d. Boxing; 40d. Rowing; 50d. Basketball; 150d. Football; 200d. Water polo.

1964. 1st Anniv of Skopje Earthquake.
1123 **299** 25d. brown 15 10
1124 – 50d. blue 20 10
DESIGN: 50d. "International Aid" (U.N. flag over town).

1964. 20th Anniv of Occupation of Vis Island. As T **289** but inscr "VIS 1944–1964" at foot.
1125 25d. red and grey 15 10

300 Costumes of Kosovo-Metohija (Serbia)

301 Friedrich Engels

1964. Yugoslav Costumes (3rd series). As T **300**. Multicoloured.
1126 25d. Type **300** 10 10
1127 30d. Slovenia 10 10
1128 40d. Bosnia and Herzegovina 10 10
1129 50d. Hrvatska (Croatia) . . 10 10
1130 150d. Macedonia 40 25
1131 200d. Crna Gora (Montenegro) 65 40

1964. Centenary of "First International".
1132 **301** 25d. black on cream . . 10 10
1133 – 50d. black on lilac . . . 15 10
DESIGN: 50d. Karl Marx.

302 Children on Scooter **303** "Victor" (after Ivan Mestrovic)

1964. Children's Week.
1134 **302** 25d. green, black and red 20 10

1964. 20th Anniv of Liberation of Belgrade.
1135 **303** 25d. black and green on pink 15 10

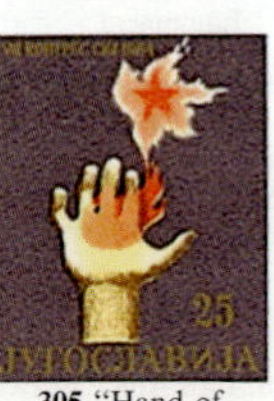

304 Initial of Hilander's Gospel (13th cent) **305** "Hand of Equality"

1964. Yugoslav Art. Inscr "1964". Multicoloured.
1136 25d. Type **304** 10 10
1137 30d. Initial of Miroslav's gospel (12th cent) 10 10
1138 40d. Detail from Cetinje octateuch (15th cent) . . 10 10
1139 50d. Miniature from Trogir's gospel (13th cent) 10 10
1140 150d. Miniature from Hrvoe's missal (15th cent) 20 10
1141 200d. Miniature from Herman Priory, Bistrica (14th cent) (horiz) 40 30

1964. 8th Yugoslav Communist League Congress. Multicoloured.
1142 25d. Type **305** 10 10
1143 50d. Dove and factory ("Peace and Socialism") 10 10
1144 100d. Industrial plant ("Socialism") 20 15

306 Player

307 Children around Red Cross

1965. World Table Tennis Championships, Ljubljana.
1145 **306** 50d. multicoloured . . . 15 10
1146 – 150d. multicoloured . . 25 20
DESIGN: 150d. As Type **306** but design arranged in reverse.

1965. Obligatory Tax. Red Cross Week.
1147 **307** 5d. red and brown . . . 15 10

308 Titograd

309 Young Partisan (after D. Andrejevic-Kun)

1965. 20th Anniv of Liberation. Yugoslav Capitals.
1148 **308** 25d. purple 10 10
1149 – 30d. brown 10 10
1150 – 40d. violet 10 10
1151 – 50d. green 10 10
1152 – 150d. violet 15 30
1153 – 200d. blue 35 55
CAPITALS: 30d. Skopje; 40d. Sarajevo; 50d. Ljubljana; 150d. Zagreb; 200d. Belgrade.

1965. "Twenty Years of Freedom" Pioneer Games.
1154 **309** 25d. black & brown on buff 15 10

310 T.V. Tower, Avala (Belgrade)

311 Yarrow

1965. Centenary of I.T.U.
1155 **310** 50d. blue 15 10

1965. Inauguration of Djerdap Hydro-electric Project. As Nos. 3271/2 of Rumania.
1156 – 25d. (30b.) green and grey 10 10
1157 – 50d. (55b.) red and grey . . 25 10
DESIGN: 25d. Djerdap Gorge; 50d. Djerdap Dam.
Nos. 1156/7 were issued simultaneously in Rumania.

1965. Medicinal Plants. Multicoloured.
1158 25d. Type **311** 10 10
1159 30d. Rosemary 10 10
1160 40d. Elecampane 10 10
1161 50d. Deadly nightshade . . 10 10
1162 150d. Peppermint 15 10
1163 200d. Rusty foxglove . . . 70 40

312 I.C.Y. Emblem

313 Sibenik

1965. International Co-operation Year.
1164 **312** 50d. violet, indigo and blue 15 10

1965. Tourist Publicity (4th series). Multicoloured.
1165 25d. Rogaska Slatina . . . 10 10
1166 30d. Type **313** 10 10
1167 40d. Prespa Lake 10 10
1168 50d. Prizren 10 10
1169 150d. Skadar Lake 25 10
1170 200d. Sarajevo 40 40

314 Cat

316 Marshal Tito

1965. Children's Week.
1171 **314** 30d. lake and yellow . . 35 10

1965. Nos. 984 and 988 surch.
1172 5d. on 8d. violet 40 10
1173 50d. on 25d. red 40 10

1965. Cultural Celebrities. Portraits as T **294**.
1174 30d. red on pink 10 10
1175 50d. slate on blue 10 10
1176 60d. sepia on brown 10 10
1177 85d. indigo on blue 15 10
1178 200d. olive on olive 15 15
1179 500d. mauve on purple . . . 35 30
PORTRAITS: 30d. Branislav Nusic (author and dramatist); 50d. Antun Matos (poet); 60d. Ivan Mazuranic (author); 85d. Fran Levstik (writer); 200d. Josif Pancic (botanist); 500d. Dimitrije Tucovic (politician).

Currency revalued. 100 paras = 1 dinar = 100 old dinars.

1966.
1180 **316** 20p. green 25 10
1181 30p. red 45 10

317 Long Jumping (Balkan Games, Sarajevo)

318 "T", 15th-cent Psalter

1966. Sports Events.
1182 **317** 30p. red 10 10
1183 – 50p. violet 10 10
1184 – 1d. green 10 10
1185 – 3d. brown 20 15
1186 – 5d. blue 45 35
DESIGNS AND EVENTS: 50p. Ice hockey and 3d. Ice hockey sticks and puck (World Ice Hockey Championships, Jesenice, Ljubljana and Zagreb); 1d. Rowing and 5d. Oars (World Rowing Championships, Bled).

1966. Yugoslav Art. Manuscript initials. Mult.
1187 30p. Type **318** 10 10
1188 50p. "V", 14th-cent Divos gospel 10 10
1189 60p. "R", 12th-cent Libri moralium of Gregory I 10 10
1190 85p. "P", 12th-cent Miroslav gospel 10 10
1191 2d. "B", 13th-cent Radomir gospel 20 10
1192 5d. "F", 11th-cent passional 40 30

319 Red Cross Emblem

320 Beam Aerial on Globe

1966. Obligatory Tax. Red Cross Week.
1193 **319** 5p. multicoloured . . . 15 10

1966. As Nos. 983, etc, but values expressed "0.05" etc, colours changed and new values.
1194 5p. orange 10 10
1195 10p. brown 10 10
1196 15p. blue 55 10
1197 20p. green 25 10
1198 30p. red 60 10
1199 40p. purple 25 10
1200 50p. blue 25 10
1201 60p. brown 30 10
1202 65p. green 30 10
1203 85p. purple 35 10
1204 1d. olive 65 10
NEW VALUES: 60p. as No. 988, 85p. as No. 984.

1966. International Amateur Radio Union Regional Conference, Opatija.
1205 **320** 85p. blue 15 10

321 Stag Beetle

322 Serbian 1 para Stamp of 1866

1966. Insects. Multicoloured.
1206 30p. Type **321** 10 10
1207 50p. Rose chafer 10 10
1208 60p. "Meloe violaceus" (oil beetle) 10 10
1209 85p. Seven-spotted ladybird 15 10
1210 2d. Alpine longhorn beetle 25 15
1211 5d. Great diving beetle . . . 55 25

1966. Serbian Stamp Centenary.
1212 **322** 30p. green, lake & brown 10 10
1213 – 50p. lake, bistre and ochre 10 10
1214 – 60p. orange and green 10 10
1215 – 85p. red and blue . . . 15 15
1216 – 2d. blue, deep green & green 45 25
DESIGNS—(Serbian Stamps of 1866): 50p.—2p.; 60p.—10p.; 85p.—20p.; 2d.—40p.

323 Rebels on Shield

324 Josip Strossmayer and Racki (founders)

1966. 25th Anniv of Yugoslav Insurrection.
1218 **323** 20p. brown, gold & green 10 10
1219 30p. mauve, gold & buff 10 10
1220 85p. blue, gold and stone 10 10
1221 2d. violet, gold and blue 15 15

1966. Centenary of Yugoslav Academy, Zagreb.
1222 **324** 30p. black, stone and drab 15 10

325 Old Bridge, Mostar

325a Medieval View of Sibenik

1966. 400th Anniv of Old Bridge, Mostar.
1223 **325** 30p. purple 70 10

1966. 900th Anniv of Sibenik.
1224 **325a** 30p. purple 30 10

326 "The Girl in Pigtails"

327 U.N.E.S.C.O. Emblem

1966. Children's Week.
1225 **326** 30p. multicoloured . . . 50 10

1966. 20th Anniv of U.N.E.S.C.O.
1226 **327** 85p. blue 20 10

328 Stylized Winter Landscape

329 Dinar of Durad I Balsic

1966. Christmas.
1227 **328** 15p. yellow and blue . . 10 10
1228 – 20p. yellow and violet 10 10
1229 – 30p. yellow and green . . 10 10
DESIGNS: 20p. Father Christmas; 30p. Stylized Christmas tree.
See also Nos. 1236/8.

1966. Yugoslav Art. Designs showing different coins.
1230 **329** 30p. multicoloured . . . 10 10
1231 – 50p. multicoloured . . . 10 10
1232 – 60p. multicoloured . . . 10 10
1233 – 85p. multicoloured . . . 10 10
1234 – 2d. multicoloured . . . 20 10
1235 – 5d. multicoloured . . . 50 25
MEDIEVAL COINS (Dinars of): 50p. King Stefan Tomasevic; 60p. Djurad Brankovic; 85p. Ljubljana; 2d. Split; 5d. Emperor Stefan Dusan.

1966. New Year. As Nos. 1227/9 but colours changed.
1236 15p. gold, blue and indigo 15 15
1237 20p. gold, red and pink . . 15 15
1238 30p. gold, myrtle and green 15 15

330 Flower between Red Crosses

331 Arnica

1967. Obligatory Tax. Red Cross Week.
1239 **330** 5p. red, green and blue 15 10

1967. Medicinal Plants. Multicoloured.
1240 30p. Type **331** 10 10
1241 50p. Common flax 10 10
1242 85p. Oleander 10 10
1243 1d.20 Gentian 15 10
1244 3d. Laurel 30 10
1245 5d. African rue 65 40

332 President Tito

333 "Sputnik I" and "Explorer I"

1967. Pres. Tito's 75th Birthday. (a) Size 20 × 27 mm.
1246 **332** 5p. orange 10 10
1247 10p. brown 10 10
1248 15p. violet 10 10
1249 20p. green 10 10
1260 20p. blue . . . . . . 1·50 10
1261 25p. purple 15 10
1250 30p. red 10 10
1263 30p. myrtle 30 10
1251 40p. black 10 10
1252 50p. turquoise 10 10
1266a 50p. red 30 10
1253 60p. lilac 15 10
1268 70p. sepia 40 10
1269 75p. green 50 10
1270 80p. brown . . . . . . 2·25 10
1270a 80p. red 45 10
1254 85p. blue 20 10
1272 90p. brown 35 10
1273 1d. red 25 10
1274 1d.20 blue 75 10
1274a 1d.20 green 70 10
1275 1d.25 blue 55 10
1276 1d.50 green 50 10
(b) Size 20 × 30 mm.
1277 **332** 2d. sepia . . . . . . 1·50 10
1278 2d.50 green . . . . . . 1·50 10
1279 5d. purple . . . . . . 1·25 20
1280 10d. purple . . . . . . 3·00 35
1281 20d. green . . . . . . 2·75 40

1967. World Fair, Montreal. Space Achievements. Multicoloured.
1282 30p. Type **333** 10 10
1283 50p. "Tiros", "Telstar" and "Molyna" 10 10
1284 85p. "Luna 9" and lunar orbiter 10 10
1285 1d.20 "Mariner 4" and "Venus 3" 15 10
1286 3d. "Vostok I" and Gemini-Agena space vehicle . . 40 15
1287 5d. Leonov in space . . . 60 50

334 St. Tripun's Church, Kotor

1967. International Tourist Year.
1288 **334** 30p. green and blue . . 10 10
1289 – 50p. violet and brown 10 10
1290 – 85p. purple and blue . . 10 10
1291 – 1d.20 brown and purple 15 10
1292 – 3d. olive and brown . . 25 10
1293 – 5d. brown and olive . . 50 45
DESIGNS: 50p. Town Hall, Maribor; 85p. Trogir Cathedral; 1d.20, Fortress gate, Nis; 3d. Bridge, Visegrad; 5d. Ancient bath, Skopje.

335 Northern Bobwhite

336 Congress Emblem

1967. International Hunting and Fishing Exhibition and Fair, Novi Sad. Multicoloured.
1294 30p. Type **335** 15 15
1295 50p. Northern pike 15 10
1296 1d.20 Red deer 25 10
1297 5d. Peregrine falcon 65 50

1967. Int Astronautical Federation Congress, Belgrade.
1298 **336** 85p. gold, light blue and blue 15 10

337 Old Theatre Building

338 "Winter Landscape" (A. Becirovic)

1967. Centenary of Slovene National Theatre, Ljubljana.
1299 **337** 30p. brown and green . . 15 10

1967. Children's Week.
1300 **338** 30p. multicoloured . . . 50 10

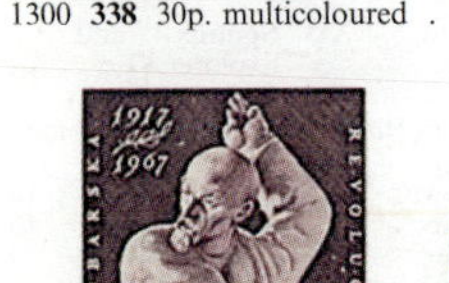

339 "Lenin" (from bust by Ivan Mestrovic)

340 Four-leaved Clover

1967. 50th Anniv of October Revolution.
1301 **339** 30p. violet 10 10
1302 85p. brown 15 10

1967. New Year. Inscr "1968".
1304 **340** 20p. gold, blue and green 10 10
1305 – 30p. gold, violet and yellow 10 10
1306 – 50p. gold, red and lilac 10 10
DESIGNS: 30p. Sweep with ladder; 50p. Horseshoe and flower.
See also Nos. 1347/9.

341 "The Young Sultana" (Vlaho Bukovac)

1967. Yugoslav Paintings. Multicoloured.
1307 85p. "The Watchtower" (Djura Jaksic) (vert) . . . 10 10
1308 1d. Type **341** 15 10
1309 2d. "At Home" (Josip Petkovsek) 20 15
1310 3d. "The Cock-fight" (Paja Jovanovic) 30 25
1311 5d. "Summer" (Ivana Kobilca) (vert) 50 40
See also Nos. 1337/41, 1399/1404, 1438/43, 1495/1500, 1535/40, 1570/5, 1616/19, 1750/5 and 1793/8.

342 Ski Jumping

1968. Winter Olympic Games, Grenoble.
1312 **342** 50p. purple and blue . . 10 10
1313 – 1d. olive and brown . . 10 10
1314 – 2d. lake and black . . 15 10
1315 – 5d. blue and olive . . . 50 40
DESIGNS: 1d. Figure skating (pairs); 2d. Downhill skiing; 5d. Ice hockey.

343 "The Madonna and Child" (St. George's Church, Prizren)

344 Honeycomb on Red Cross

1968. Medieval Icons. Multicoloured.
1316 50p. Type **343** 10 10
1317 1d. "The Annunciation" (Ohrid Museum) 15 10
1318 1d.50 "St. Sava and St. Simeon" (Belgrade Museum) 20 10
1319 2d. "The Descent" (Ohrid Museum) 30 20
1320 3d. "The Crucifixion" (St. Clement's Church, Ohrid) 35 25
1321 5d. "The Madonna and Child" (Gospe od zvonika Church, Split) 75 75

1968. Obligatory Tax. Red Cross Week.
1322 **344** 5p. multicoloured . . . 10 10

345 Northern Bullfinch

346 Running (Women's 800 m)

1968. Song Birds. Multicoloured.
1323 50p. Type **345** 20 20
1324 1d. Eurasian goldfinch . . . 20 20
1325 1d.50 Chaffinch 45 45
1326 2d. Western greenfinch . . . 60 60
1327 3d. Red crossbill . . . . . 1·40 1·40
1328 5d. Hawfinch . . . . 2·00 2·00

1968. Olympic Games, Mexico.
1329 **346** 50p. pur & brn on cream 10 10
1330 – 1d. olive & turq on grn 10 10
1331 – 1d.50 sepia & bl on flesh 10 10
1332 – 2d. green & bis on cream 15 10
1333 – 3d. indigo & violet on blue 15 10
1334 – 5d. purple & green on mauve 35 30
DESIGNS: 1d. Basketball; 1d.50, Gymnastics; 2d. Sculling; 3d. Water polo; 5d. Wrestling.

347 Rebel Cannon

348 "Mother and Children" (fresco in Hrastovlje Church, Slovenia)

1968. 65th Anniv of Ilinden Uprising.
1335 **347** 50p. brown and gold . . 15 10

1968. 25th Anniv of Partisan Occupation of Istria and Slovenian Littoral.
1336 **348** 50p. multicoloured . . . 15 10

349 "Lake of Klansko" (Marko Pernhart)

1968. Yugoslav Paintings. 19th-cent Landscapes. Multicoloured.
1337 1d. Type **349** 10 10
1338 1d.50 "Bavarian Landscape" (Milan Popovic) 15 10
1339 2d. "Gateway, Zadar" (Ferdo Quiquerez) 25 10
1340 3d. "Triglav from Bohinj" (Anton Karinger) 35 20
1341 5d. "Studenica Monastery" (Djordje Krstic) 85 90

350 A. Santic

351 "Promenade" (Marina Cudov)

1968. Birth Centenary of Aleksa Santic (poet).
1342 **350** 50p. blue 10 10

1968. Children's Week.
1343 **351** 50p. multicoloured . . . 20 10

352 Karl Marx (after sculpture by N. Mitric)

353 Aztec Emblem and Olympic Rings

1968. 150th Birth Anniv of Karl Marx.
1344 **352** 50p. red 15 10

1968. Obligatory Tax. Olympic Games Fund.
1345 **353** 10p. multicoloured . . . 10 10

354 Old Theatre and View of Kalemegdan

355 Hassan Brkic

1968. Centenary of Serbian National Theatre, Belgrade.
1346 **354** 50p. brown and green . . 15 10

1968. New Year. Designs as Nos. 1304/6 but colours changed and inscr "1969".
1347 20p. gold, blue and lilac . . 10 10
1348 30p. gold, violet and green 10 10
1349 50p. gold, red and yellow 10 10

1968. Yugoslav National Heroes.
1350 **355** 50p. violet 10 10
1351 – 75p. black 15 10
1352 – 1d.25 brown 15 10
1353 – 2d. blue 20 10
1354 – 2d.50 green 25 15
1355 – 5d. lake 60 60
PORTRAITS: 75p. Ivan Milutinovic; 1d.25, Rade Koncar; 2d. Kuzman Josifovski; 2d.50, Tone Tomsic; 5d. Mosa Pijade.

356 "Family" (sculpture by J. Soldatovic) and Human Rights Emblem

357 I.L.O. Emblem

1968. Human Rights Year.
1357 **356** 1d.25 blue 15 10

1969. 50th Anniv of I.L.O.
1358 **357** 1d.25 black and red . . 15 10

358 Dove on Hammer and Sickle Emblem

359 "St. Nikita" (Manasija Monastery)

1969. 50th Anniv of Yugoslav Communist Party.
1359 **358** 50p. red and black . . . 10 10
1360 – 75p. black and ochre . . 10 10
1361 – 1d.25 black and red . . 15 10
DESIGNS: 75p. "Tito" and star (wall graffiti); 1d.25, Five-pointed crystal formation.

1969. Medieval Frescoes in Yugoslav Monasteries. Multicoloured.
1363 50p. Type **359** 10 10
1364 75p. "Jesus and the Apostles" (Sopocani) . . 10 10
1365 1d.25 "The Crucifixion" (Studenica) 10 10
1366 2d. "Cana Wedding Feast" (Kalenic) 20 10
1367 3d. "Angel guarding Tomb" (Mileseva) 30 10
1368 5d. "Mourning over Christ" (Nerezi) 90 75

360 Roman Memorial and View of Ptuj

1969. 1900th Anniv of Ptuj (Poetovio) (Slovene town).
1369 **360** 50p. brown 10 10

361 Vasil Glavinov

362 Globe between Hands

1969. Birth Centenary of Vasil Glavinov (Macedonian revolutionary).
1370 **361** 50p. purple and brown 10 10

1969. Obligatory Tax. Red Cross Week.
1371 **362** 20p. black, red and deep red 10 10

363 Thin-leafed Peony

365 Games' Emblem

364 "Eber" (V. Ivankovic)

1969. Flowers. Multicoloured.
1372 50p. Type **363** 10 10
1373 75p. Coltsfoot 10 10
1374 1d.25 Primrose 15 10
1375 2d. Hellebore 25 10
1376 2d.50 Sweet violet 30 10
1377 5d. Pasque flower 75 75

1969. Dubrovnik Summer Festival. Sailing Ships. Multicoloured.
1378 50p. Type **364** 15 10
1379 1d.25 "Tare in Storm" (Franasovic) 20 10
1380 1d.50 "Brigantine Sela" (Ivankovic) 30 10
1381 2d.50 "16th-century Dubrovnik Galleon" . . . 35 20
1382 3d.25 "Frigate Madre Mimbelli" (A. Roux) . . 65 25
1383 5d. "Shipwreck" (16th-century icon) . . . 1·50 1·25

1969. 9th World Deaf and Dumb Games, Belgrade.
1384 **365** 1d.25 lilac and red . . . 20 10

366 Bosnian Mountain Horse

1969. 50th Anniv of Veterinary Faculty, Zagreb. Multicoloured.

1385	75p. Type **366**	10	10
1386	1d.25 Lipizzaner horse	15	10
1387	3d.25 Ljutomer trotter	30	10
1388	5d. Yugoslav half-breed	75	65

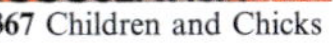
367 Children and Chicks 368 Arms of Belgrade

1969. Children's Week.

1389	**367**	50p. multicoloured	15	10

1969. 25th Anniv of Yugoslav Liberation. Arms of Regional Capitals. Multicoloured.

1390	50p. Type **368**	15	10
1391	50p. Skopje	15	10
1392	50p. Titograd (Podgorica)	15	10
1393	50p. Sarajevo	15	10
1394	50p. Zagreb	15	10
1395	50p. Ljubljana	15	10

369 Dr. Josip Smodlaka 370 Torch, Globe and Olympic Rings

1969. Birth Centenary of Dr. Josip Smodlaka (politician).

1397	**369**	50p. blue	10	10

1969. Obligatory Tax. Olympic Games Fund.

1398	**370**	10p. multicoloured	10	10

371 "Gipsy Girl" (Nikola Martinoski)

1969. Yugoslav Nude Paintings. Multicoloured.

1399	50p. Type **371**	15	10
1400	1d.25 "Girl in Red Armchair" (Sava Sumanovic)	20	10
1401	1d.50 "Girl Brushing Hair" (Marin Tartaglia)	25	10
1402	2d.50 "Olympia" (Miroslav Kraljevic) (horiz)	40	20
1403	3d.25 "The Bather" (Jovan Bijelic)	70	40
1404	5d. "Woman on a Couch" (Matej Sternen) (horiz)	1·50	1·50

372 University Building

1969. 50th Anniv of Ljubljana University.

1405	**372**	50p. green	10	10

373 University Seal 374 Colonnade

1969. 300th Anniv of Zagreb University.

1406	**373**	50p. gold, purple and blue	15	10

1969. Europa.

1407	**374**	1d.25 brown, light brown and green	2·50	2·50
1408		3d.25 blue, grey & purple	7·50	7·50

375 Jovan Cvijic (geographer) 376 "Punishment of Dirka" (4th-cent mosaic)

1970. Famous Yugoslavs.

1409	**375**	50p. purple	10	10
1410	–	1d.25 black	10	10
1411	–	1d.50 purple	15	10
1412	–	2d.50 olive	15	15
1413	–	3d.25 brown	25	15
1414	–	5d. blue	30	40

CELEBRITIES: 1d.25, Dr. Andrija Stampar (hygienist); 1d.50, Joakim Krcovski (author); 2d.50, Marko Miljanov (soldier); 3d.25, Vasa Pelagic (socialist revolutionary); 5d. Oton Zupancic (poet).

1970. Mosaics. Multicoloured.

1415	50p. Type **376**	10	10
1416	1d.25 "Cerberus" (5th-cent) (horiz)	10	10
1417	1d.50 "Angel of Annunciation" (6th-cent)	15	10
1418	2d.50 "Hunters" (4th-cent)	25	10
1419	3d.25 "Bull beside Cherries" (5th-cent) (horiz)	35	15
1420	5d. "Virgin and Child Enthroned" (6th-cent)	90	90

377 Lenin (after sculpture by S. Stojanovic) 378 Trying for Goal

1970. Birth Centenary of Lenin.

1421	**377**	50p. lake	10	10
1422	–	1d.25 blue	15	10

DESIGN: 1d.25, As Type **377**, but showing left side of Lenin's bust.

1970. 6th World Basketball Championships.

1423	**378**	1d.25 red	15	10

379 Red Cross Trefoil

1970. Obligatory Tax. Red Cross Week.

1424	**379**	20p. multicoloured	10	10

380 "Flaming Sun"

1970. Europa.

1425	**380**	1d.25 deep blue, turquoise and blue	15	10
1426		3d.25 brown, vio & pur	35	35

381 Istrian Short-haired Hound 382 Olympic Flag

1970. Yugoslav Dogs. Multicoloured.

1427	50p. Type **381**	10	10
1428	1d.25 Yugoslav tricolour hound	15	10
1429	1d.50 Istrian hard-haired hound	15	10
1430	2d.50 Balkan hound	25	15
1431	3d.25 Dalmatian	40	20
1432	5d. Shara mountain dog	1·25	75

1970. Obligatory Tax. Olympic Games Fund.

1433	**382**	10p. multicoloured	10	10

383 Telegraph Key 384 "Bird in Meadow" (Lidija Dobronjovska)

1970. Centenary of Montenegro Telegraph Service.

1434	**383**	50p. gold, black & brown	10	10

1970. Children's Week.

1435	**384**	50p. multicoloured	15	10

385 "Gymnast" 388 Rusty-leaved Alpenrose

386 "Hand Holding Dove" (Makoto)

1970. 17th World Gymnastics Championships, Ljubljana.

1436	**385**	1d.25 blue and purple	15	10

1970. 25th Anniv of United Nations.

1437	**386**	1d.25 multicoloured	15	10

1970. Yugoslav Paintings. Baroque Period. Designs as T **341** but vert. Multicoloured.

1438	50p. "The Ascension" (Teodor Kracun)	10	10
1439	75p. "Abraham's Sacrifice" (Federiko Benkovic)	10	10
1440	1d.25 "The Holy Family" (Francisek Jelovsek)	15	10
1441	2d.50 "Jacob's Dream" (Hristofor Zefarovic)	20	15
1442	3d.25 "Christ's Baptism" (Serbian village artist)	30	15
1443	5d.75 "Coronation of the Virgin" (Tripo Kokolja)	65	75

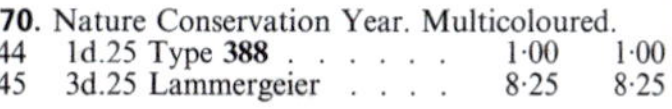

1970. Nature Conservation Year. Multicoloured.

1444	1d.25 Type **388**	1·00	1·00
1445	3d.25 Lammergeier	8·25	8·25

389 Frano Supilo 390 Different Nations' Satellites ("International Co-operation")

1971. Birth Cent of Frano Supilo (politician).

1446	**389**	50p. brown and buff	10	10

1971. Space Exploration. Multicoloured.

1447	50p. Type **390**	10	10
1448	75p. Telecommunications satellite	15	10
1449	1d.25 Unmanned Moon flights	20	10
1450	2d.50 Exploration of Mars and Venus (horiz)	30	15
1451	3d.25 Space-station (horiz)	45	30
1452	5d.75 Astronauts on the Moon (horiz)	1·50	1·25

391 "Proclamation of the Commune" (A. Daudenarde, after A. Lamy)

1971. Centenary of Paris Commune.

1453	**391**	1d.25 brown and orange	15	10

392 Red Cross Ribbon

1971. Obligatory Tax. Red Cross Week.

1454	**392**	20p. multicoloured	10	10

393 Europa Chain

1971. Europa.

1455	**393**	1d.50 multicoloured	15	15
1456		4d. pink, purple & mauve	60	55

394 Congress Emblem (A. Pajvancic)

1971. 20th Anniv of Yugoslav "Self-Managers" Movement.

1457	**394**	50p. red, black and gold	15	10
1458	–	1d.25 red, black and gold	60	60

DESIGN: 1d.25, "Self-Managers" emblem (designed by M. Miodragovic).

395 Common Mallow 396 Olympic "Spiral" and Rings

1971. Flowers. Multicoloured.

1459	50p. Type **395**	10	10
1460	1d.50 Buckthorn	10	10
1461	2d. White water-lily	20	10

1462 2d.50 Common poppy . . . 40 10
1463 4d. Chicory 50 15
1464 6d. Chinese lantern 90 70

1971. Obligatory Tax. Olympic Games Fund.
1465 **396** 10p. black, purple & blue 10 10

397 Krk, Dalmatia

398 "Prince Lazar Hrebeljanovic" (from fresco, Lazarica Church)

1971. Tourism.
1641 – 5p. orange 10 10
1642 – 10p. brown 10 10
1468 – 20p. lilac 15 10
1644 – 25p. red 20 10
1469 **397** 30p. green 55 10
1645 30p. olive 15 10
1646 – 35p. red 15 10
1647 – 40p. olive 15 10
1473 – 50p. red . . . . . . 1·00 15
1474 – 50p. green 20 10
1650 – 60p. purple 15 10
1476 – 75p. green 50 10
1652 – 75p. purple 20 10
1477 – 80p. red . . . . . . 1·10 10
1478 – 1d. red . . . . . . 2·25 30
1656 – 1d. lilac 15 10
1657 – 1d. green 15 10
1479 – 1d.20 green . . . . . . 1·40 30
1480 – 1d.25 blue 65 15
1481 – 1d.50 blue 30 10
1660 – 1d.50 red 20 10
1482 – 2d. turquoise 60 10
1661 – 2d.10 green 25 10
1483 – 2d.50 violet 60 15
1662a – 2d.50 red 20 10
1663 – 2d.50 blue 20 10
1664a – 3d. grey 10 10
1665 – 3d.20 blue 45 10
1666 – 3d.40 green 20 10
1667 – 3d.50 red 20 10
1668a – 4d. red 10 10
1669 – 4d.90 blue 35 10
1670 – 5d. green 15 10
1671 – 5d.60 olive 25 10
1672 – 6d. brown 15 10
1673a – 6d.10 green 20 10
1674 – 8d. grey 30 10
1675a – 8d.80 grey 25 10
1676 – 10d. purple 20 10
1677 – 16d.50 blue 25 10
1678 – 26d. blue 30 10
1679 – 38d. mauve 50 10
1680 – 70d. blue 50 25

DESIGNS: 5p. Krusevo, Macedonia; 10p. Gradacac; 20p., 75p. Bohinj, Slovenia; 25p. Budva; 35p. Omis, Dalmatia; 40p. Pec; 50p. (1473/4), Krusevac, Serbia; 60p. Logarska valley; 75p. (1652), Rijeka; 80p. Piran; 1d. (1478), Bitola, Macedonia; 1d. (1656/7), 16d.50, Ohrid; 1d.20, 4d. Pocitelj; 1d.25, 1d.50 (1481), 8d.80, Herceg Novi; 1d.50 (1660), Bihac; 2d. Novi Sad; 2d.10, 6d.10, Hvar; 2d.50 (1483), Rijeka Crnojevica, Montenegro; 2d.50 (1662a/3), Kragujevac; 3d., 3d.20, Skofja Loka; 3d.40, Vranje; 3d.50, Vrsac; 4d.90, Perast; 5d. Osijek; 5d.60, Travnik; 6d. Kikinda; 8d. Dubrovnik; 10d. Sarajevo; 26d. Korcula; 38d. Maribor; 70d. Zagreb.

1971. 600th Anniv of City of Krusevac.
1487 **398** 50p. multicoloured . . . 10 10

399 "Satyr"

400 "Children in Balloon"

1971. Bronze Archaeological Discoveries. Mult.
1488 50p. Head of Emperor Constantine 10 10
1489 1d.50 "Boy with Fish" (statuette) 10 10
1490 2d. "Hercules" (statuette) 15 10
1491 2d.50 Type **399** 25 10
1492 4d. "Goddess Aphrodite" (head) 35 15
1493 6d. "Citizen of Emona" (statue) 60 60

1971. Children's Week and 25th Anniv of U.N.I.C.E.F.
1494 **400** 50p. multicoloured . . . 30 10

1971. Yugoslav Portraits. As T **371**. Multicoloured.
1495 50p. "Girl in Serbian Dress" (Katarina Ivanovic) . . . 10 10
1496 1d.50 "Ivanisevic the Merchant" (Anastas Bocaric) 10 10
1497 2d. "Anne Kresic" (Vjekoslav Karas) 15 10
1498 2d.50 "Pavla Jagodica" (Konstantin Danil) . . . 20 10
1499 4d. "Louise Pasjakova" (Mihael Stroj) 30 15
1500 6d. "Old Man at Ljubljana" (Matevz Langus) 90 75

402 "Postal Codes"

403 Dame Gruev

1971. Introduction of Postal Codes.
1501 **402** 450p. multicoloured . . 10 10

1971. Birth Cent of Dame Gruev (Macedonian revolutionary).
1502 **403** 50p. blue 15 15

404 Speed Skating

1972. Winter Olympic Games, Sapporo, Japan. Multicoloured.
1503 1d.25 Type **404** 60 45
1504 6d. Skiing . . . . 2·00 1·75

405 First Page of Statute

406 Ski-jump, Planica

1972. 700th Anniv of Dubrovnik Law Statutes.
1505 **405** 1d.25 multicoloured . . 15 10

1972. 1st World Ski-jumping Championships, Planica.
1506 **406** 1d.25 multicoloured . . 20 10

407 Water-polo

408 Red Cross and Hemispheres

1972. Olympic Games, Munich. Multicoloured.
1507 50p. Type **407** 10 10
1508 1d.25 Basketball 10 10
1509 2d.50 Swimming 15 10
1510 3d.25 Boxing 20 10
1511 5d. Running 30 15
1512 6d.50 Sailing 60 55

1972. Obligatory Tax. Red Cross Week.
1513 **408** 20p. multicoloured . . . 15 10

409 "Communications"

410 Wallcreeper

1972. Europa.
1514 **409** 1d.50 multicoloured . . 25 20
1515 5d. multicoloured . . . 90 90

1972. Birds. Multicoloured.
1516 50p. Type **410** 10 10
1517 1d.25 Little bustard 10 10
1518 2d.50 Red-billed chough . . 20 20
1519 3d.25 White spoonbill . . . 45 35
1520 5d. Eagle owl . . . . . . 1·10 45
1521 6d.50 Rock ptarmigan . . . 2·75 1·75

411 President Tito

412 Communications Tower, Olympic Rings and 1972 Games' Emblem

1972. President Tito's 80th Birthday.
1522 **411** 50d. brown and buff . . 15 10
1523 1d.25 blue and grey . . 45 20

1972. Obligatory Tax. Olympic Games Fund.
1525 **412** 10p. multicoloured . . . 10 10

413 Locomotive No. 1 "King of Serbia", 1882

1972. 50th Anniv of International Railway Union. Multicoloured.
1526 1d.50 Type **413** 30 10
1527 5d. Electric locomotive No. 441.013, 1967 . . . . 1·00 40

414 Glider in Flight

415 Pawn

1972. 13th World Gliding Championships, Vrsac.
1528 **414** 2d. black, blue and gold 20 15

1972. 20th Chess Olympiad, Skopje.
1529 **415** 1d.50 brown, vio & pur 30 10
1530 – 6d. black, blue & dp blue 80 75

DESIGN: 6d. Chessboard, king and queen.

416 "Child on Horse" (B. Zlatec)

417 G. Delcev

1972. Children's Week.
1531 **416** 80p. multicoloured . . . 15 10

1972. Birth Cent of Goce Delcev (Macedonian revolutionary).
1532 **417** 80p. black and green . . 15 10

418 Father Martic (sculpture, Ivan Mestrovic)

1972. 150th Birth Anniv of Father Grge Martic (politician).
1533 **418** 80p. black, green and red 10 10

419 National Library

1972. 140th Anniv of and Re-opening of National Library, Belgrade.
1534 **419** 50p. brown 10 10

420 "Fruit Dish and Broken Majolica Vase" (Milos Tenkovic)

1972. Yugoslav Art. Still Life. Multicoloured.
1535 50p. Type **420** 10 10
1536 1d.25 "Mandoline and Book" (Jozef Petkovsec) (vert) 10 10
1537 2d.50 "Basket with Grapes" (Katarina Jovanovic) . . 20 10
1538 3d.25 "Water-melon" (Konstantin Danil) . . . 35 15
1539 5d. "In a Stable" (Nikola Masic) (vert) 45 20
1540 6d.50 "Scrap-books" (Celestin Medovic) . . . 70 65

421 Battle of Stubica

1973. 500th Anniv of Slovenian Peasant Risings and 400th Anniv of Croatian–Slovenian Rebellion. Multicoloured.
1541 2d. Type **421** 20 10
1542 6d. Battle of Krsko 75 60

422 R. Domanovic

1973. Birth Centenary of Radoje Domanovic (Serbian satirist).
1543 **422** 80p. brown and drab . . 25 10

423 Skofja Loka

1973. Millenary of Skofja Loka.
1544 **423** 80p. brown and buff . . 20 10

424 "Novi Sad" (Petar Demetrovic)

1973. Old Engravings of Yugoslav Towns. Each black and gold.
1545 50p. Type **424** 10 10
1546 1d.25 "Zagreb" (Josef Szeman) 10 10
1547 2d.50 "Kotor" (Pierre Montier) 15 10
1548 3d.25 "Belgrade" (Mancini) 15 10
1549 5d. "Split" (Louis Cassas) 30 15
1550 6d.50 "Kranj" (Matthaus Merian) 50 40

425 Table Tennis Bat and Ball

1973. 32nd World Table Tennis Championships, Sarajevo.
1551 **425** 2d. multicoloured . . . 30 10

426 Red Cross Emblem

427 Europa "Posthorn"

1973. Obligatory Tax. Red Cross Week.
1552 **426** 20p. multicoloured . . . 10 10

1973. Europa.
1553 **427** 2d. lilac, green and blue 15 10
1554 5d.50 pink, green & purple . . . . 1·40 1·25

428 Birthwort

429 Globe and Olympic Rings

1973. Medicinal Plants. Multicoloured.
1555 80p. Type **428** 10 10
1556 2d. Globe thistle 20 10
1557 3d. Olive 30 10
1558 4d. "Corydalis cava" . . . 45 15
1559 5d. Mistletoe 65 20
1560 6d. Comfrey . . . . 1·40 1·25

1973. Obligatory Tax. Olympic Games Fund.
1561 **429** 10p. multicoloured . . . 10 10

430 A. Jansa and Bee

431 Aquatic Symbol

1973. Death Bicent of Anton Jansa (apiculturist).
1562 **430** 80p. black 15 10

1973. 1st World Aquatic Championships, Belgrade.
1563 **431** 2d. multicoloured . . . 20 10

432 "Children on Boat" (Ivan Vukovic)

433 Posthorn

1973. Children's Week.
1564 **432** 80p. multicoloured . . . 25 10

1973.
1565 **433** 30p. brown 15 10
1565a 50p. blue 15 10
1566 80p. red 15 10
1566a 1d. green 15 10
1567 1d.20 red 20 10
1567a 1d.50 red 20 10

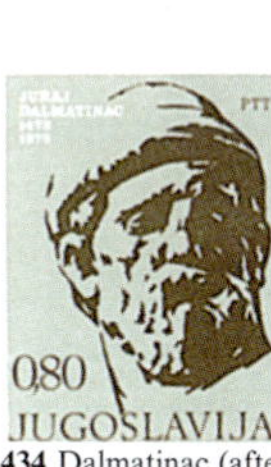
434 Dalmatinac (after sculpture by Ivan Mestrovic)

435 "Self-portrait"

1973. 500th Death Anniv of Juraj Dalmatinac (sculptor and architect).
1568 **434** 80p. green and grey . . 15 10

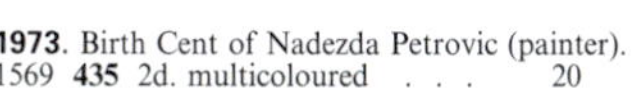

1973. Birth Cent of Nadezda Petrovic (painter).
1569 **435** 2d. multicoloured . . . 20 15

436 "The Plaster Head" (Marko Celebonovic)

1973. Yugoslav Art. Interiors. Multicoloured.
1570 80p. Type **436** 10 10
1571 2d. "St. Duja Church" (Emanuel Vidovic) . . . 10 10
1572 3d. "Slovenian Housewife" (Marino Tartaglia) . . . 10 10
1573 4d. "Dedicated to Karas" (Miljenko Stancic) 15 15
1574 5d. "My Studio" (Milan Konjovic) 25 15
1575 6d. "Tavern in Stara Loka" (France Slana) 40 60

437 Dragojlo Dudic

438 "M" for "Metrication"

1973. National Heroes. (a) Each black.
1576 80p. Type **437** 10 10
1577 80p. Strahil Pindzur 10 10
1578 80p. Boris Kidric 10 10
1579 80p. Radoje Dakic 10 10

(b) Each red.
1580 2d. Josip Mazar-Sosa . . . 15 15
1581 2d. Zarko Zrenjanin 15 15
1582 2d. Emin Duraku 15 15
1583 2d. Ivan Lola Ribar 15 15

1974. Centenary of Introduction of Metric System in Yugoslavia.
1584 **438** 80p. multicoloured . . . 10 10

439 Skater

440 Satjeska Monument

1974. European Figure Skating Championships, Zagreb.
1585 **439** 2d. multicoloured . . . 40 20

1974. Monuments.
1586 – 3d. green 60 10
1587 – 4d.50 brown 90 10
1588 – 5d. violet 90 10
1589 **440** 10d. green . . . . 1·10 20
1590 – 20d. purple . . . . . . 1·40 20
1828 – 50d. blue . . . . 1·50 40

DESIGNS—VERT: 3d. Ljubljana; 4d.50, Kozara; 5d. Belcista. HORIZ: 20d. Podgaric; 50d. Kragujevac.

441 Mailcoach

1974. Centenary of Universal Postal Union.
1592 **441** 80p. black, yellow and buff 10 10
1593 – 2d. black, red and rose 10 10
1594 – 8d. black, blue and pale blue 40 45

DESIGNS: 2d. U.P.U. H.Q. Building; 8d. Boeing 707 jetliner.

442 Montenegrin 25n. Stamp of 1874

443 President Tito

1974. Montenegro Stamp Centenary.
1595 – 80p. bistre, gold and green 15 10
1596 **442** 6d. purple, gold and claret 35 35

DESIGN: 80p. Montenegrin 2n. stamp of 1874.

1974.
1597 **443** 50p. green 10 10
1598 80p. red 15 10
1599 1d.20 green 20 10
1600 2d. blue 25 10

444 Lenin

445 Red Cross Emblems

1974. 50th Death Anniv of Lenin.
1601 **444** 2d. black and silver . . . 15 10

1974. Obligatory Tax. Red Cross Week.
1602 **445** 20p. multicoloured . . . 10 10

446 "Dwarf" (Lepenski settlement, c. 4950 B.C.)

447 Great Tit

1974. Europa. Sculptures. Multicoloured.
1603 2d. Type **446** 15 15
1604 6d. "Widow and Child" (Ivan Mestrovic) . . . . 1·00 1·00

1974. Youth Day. Multicoloured.
1605 80p. Type **447** 85 10
1606 2d. Roses 50 15
1607 6d. Cabbage white (butterfly) . . . . 2·00 1·10

448 Congress Poster

449 Olympic Rings and Stadium

1974. 10th Yugoslav League of Communists' Congress, Belgrade.
1608 **448** 80p. multicoloured . . . 10 10
1609 2d. multicoloured . . . 15 10
1610 6d. multicoloured . . . 35 30

1974. Obligatory Tax. Olympic Games Fund.
1611 **449** 10p. multicoloured . . . 10 10

450 Dish Aerial, Ivanjica

451 World Cup

1974. Inauguration of Satellite Communications Station, Ivanjica.
1612 **450** 80p. blue 20 10
1613 – 6d. lilac 90 60

DESIGN: 6d. "Intelstat 4" in orbit.

1974. World Cup Football Championship, West Germany.
1614 **451** 4d.50 multicoloured . . 70 50

452 Edelweiss and Klek Mountain

1974. Centenary of Croatian Mountaineers' Society.
1615 **452** 2d. multicoloured . . . 15 10

453 "Children's Dance" (Jano Knjazovic)

1974. Paintings. Multicoloured.
1616 80p. Type **453** 10 10
1617 2d. "Crucified Rooster" (Ivan Generalic) (vert) . . 10 10
1618 5d. "Laundresses" (Ivan Lackovic) (vert) 25 15
1619 8d. "Dance" (Janko Brasic) 85 75

454 "Rooster and Flower" (Kaca Milinojsin)

1974. Children's Week and 6th "Joy of Europe" Meeting, Belgrade. Children's Paintings. Mult.
1620 1d.20 Type **454** 10 10
1621 3d.20 "Girl and Boy" (Eva Medrzecka) (vert) 15 10
1622 5d. "Cat and Kitten" (Jelena Anastasijevic) . . 50 25

455 Interior of Library

1974. Bicent of National and University Library.
1623 **455** 1d.20 black 15 10

456 "White Peonies" (Petar Dobrovic)

458 Dove and Map of Europe

457 Title Page of Volume I

1974. Floral Paintings. Multicoloured.
1624 80p. Type **456** 10 10
1625 2d. "Carnations" (Vilko Gecan) 10 10
1626 3d. "Flowers" (Milan Konjovic) 10 10
1627 4d. "White Vase" (Sava Sumanovic) 20 15
1628 5d. "Branching Larkspurs" (Stane Kregar) 35 15
1629 8d. "Roses" (Petar Lubarda) 50 45

1975. 150th Anniv of "Matica Srpska" Annals.
1630 **457** 1d.20 black, olive and green 10 10

1975. 2nd European Security and Co-operation Conference, Belgrade.
1631 **458** 3d.20 multicoloured . . 20 10
1632 8d. multicoloured . . . 90 65

459 Gold-plated Bronze Ear-ring (14th–15th century), Alisici, Bosnia

460 "Svetozar Markovic" (sculpture by S. Bodnarov)

1975. Archaeological Discoveries. Multicoloured.
1633 1d.20 Type **459** 10 10
1634 2d.10 Silver bracelet (19th-century), Kosovo 10 10
1635 3d.20 Gold-plated silver buckle (18th-century), Bitola 15 10
1636 5d. Gold-plated ring (14th-century), Novi Sad 20 10
1637 6d. Silver necklace (17th-century), Kosovo 30 15
1638 8d. Gold-plated bronze bracelet (18th-century), Bitola 50 50

1975. Death Centenary of Svetozar Markovic (writer and statesman).
1639 **460** 1d.20 blue 10 10

461 "Fettered" (sculpture by F. Krsinic)

1975. International Women's Year.
1640 **461** 3d.20 brown and gold 15 15

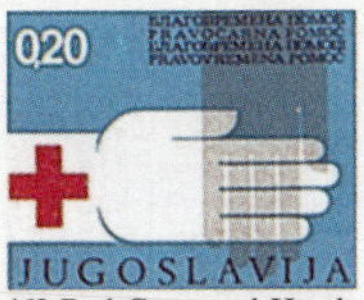

462 Red Cross and Hands

1975. Obligatory Tax. Red Cross Week.
1681 **462** 20p. multicoloured 10 10

463 "Still Life with Eggs" (Mosa Pijade)

1975. Europa. Paintings. Multicoloured.
1682 3d.20 Type **463** 15 15
1683 8d. "The Three Graces" (Ivan Radovic) 60 60

464 "Liberation Monument" (Dzamonja)

465 Garland Flower

1975. 30th Anniv of Liberation.
1684 **464** 3d.20 multicoloured 15 10

1975. National Youth Day. Flowers. Mult.
1685 1d.20 Type **465** 10 10
1686 2d.10 Touch-me-not balsam 10 10
1687 3d.20 Rose-mallow 10 10
1688 5d. Dusty cranesbill 15 10
1689 6d. Crocus 20 15
1690 8d. Rosebay willowherb 50 40

466 Games Emblem

467 Canoeing

1975. Obligatory Tax. Olympic Games Fund.
1691 **466** 10p. multicoloured 10 10

1975. World Canoeing Championships, Macedonia.
1692 **467** 3d.20 multicoloured 20 10

468 "Herzegovinian Insurgents in Ambush"

1975. Cent of Bosnian-Herzegovinian Uprising.
1693 **468** 1d.20 multicoloured 15 10

469 "Skopje Earthquake"

470 Stjepan Mitrov Ljubisa

1975. Obligatory Tax. Solidarity Week.
1694 **469** 30p. black, grey and blue 35 35
See also Nos. 1885 and 1933.

1975. Writers.
1695 **470** 1d.20 black and red 10 10
1696 – 2d.10 black and green 10 10
1697 – 3d.20 black and bistre 10 10
1698 – 5d. black and orange 15 10
1699 – 6d. black and green 15 10
1700 – 8d. black and blue 25 25
PORTRAITS: 2d.10, Ivan Prijatelj; 3d.20, Jakov Ignjatovic; 5d. Dragojla Jarnevic; 6d. Svetozar Corivic; 8d. Ivana Brlic-Mazuranic.

471 "Young Lion" (A. Savic)

1975. Children's Week and 7th "Joy of Europa" Meeting, Belgrade. Children's Paintings. Mult.
1701 3d.20 Type **471** 15 10
1702 6d. "Baby in Pram" 75 40

472 Peace Dove within "EUROPA"

1975. European Security and Co-operation Conference, Helsinki.
1703 **472** 3d.20 multicoloured 10 10
1704 8d. multicoloured 40 25

473 Red Cross and Map within "100"

1975. Centenary of Red Cross. Multicoloured.
1705 1d.20 Type **473** 15 10
1706 8d. Red Cross and people 50 25

474 "Folk Kitchen" (Djordje Andrejevic-Kun)

1975. Republic Day. Paintings. Multicoloured.
1707 1d.20 Type **474** 10 10
1708 2d.10 "On the Doorstep" (Vinko Grdan) 10 10
1709 3d.20 "The Drunken Coach-load" (Marijan Detoni) (horiz) 10 10
1710 5d. "Lunch" (Tone Kralj) (horiz) 15 10
1711 6d. "Waterwheel" (Lazar Licenoski) 25 15
1712 8d. "Justice" (Krsto Hegedusic) 45 40

475 Diocletian's Palace, Split (3rd-century)

1975. European Architectural Heritage Year.
1713 **475** 1d.20 brown 10 10
1714 – 3d.20 black 10 10
1715 – 8d. blue 40 40
DESIGNS—VERT: 3d.20, House in Ohrid (19th century). HORIZ: 8d. Gracanica Monastery, Kosovo (14th century).

476 Ski Jumping

1976. Winter Olympic Games, Innsbruck.
1716 **476** 3d.20 blue 15 10
1717 – 8d. lake 55 50
DESIGN: 8d. Figure skating.

477 Red Flag

1976. Centenary of "Red Flag" Insurrection (workers' demonstration), Kragujevac.
1718 **477** 1d.20 multicoloured 15 10

478 Svetozar Miletic

1976. 150th Birth Anniv of Svetozar Miletic (politician).
1719 **478** 1d.20 green and grey 15 10

479 Bora Stankovic

1976. Birth Cent of Bora Stankovic (writer).
1720 **479** 1d.20 red, brown and yellow 15 10

480 "King Matthias" (sculpture, J. Pogorelec)

1976. Europa. Handicrafts. Multicoloured.
1721 3d.20 Type **480** 10 10
1722 8d. Base of beaker 40 40

481 Ivan Cankar

1976. Birth Centenary of Ivan Cankar (Slovenian writer).
1723 **481** 1d.20 purple, brown and pink 10 10

482 Stylized Figure

1976. Obligatory Tax. Red Cross Week.
1724 **482** 20p. multicoloured 60 60

483 Electric Train crossing Viaduct

485 Vladimir Nazor

484 Emperor Dragonfly

1976. Inauguration of Belgrade–Bar Railway.
1725 **483** 3d.20 brown 35 15
1726 – 8d. blue 90 45
DESIGN: 8d. Electric train crossing bridge.

1976. Youth Day. Freshwater Fauna. Multicoloured.
1727 1d.20 Type **484** 10 10
1728 2d.10 River snail 10 10
1729 3d.20 Rudd 15 10
1730 5d. Common frog 30 10
1731 6d. Ferruginous duck 15 15
1732 8d. Muskrat 60 60

1976. Birth Centenary of Vladimir Nazor (writer).
1733 **485** 1d.20 blue and lilac 15 15

486 "Battle of Vucji Dol" (from "Eagle" journal of 1876)

1976. Centenary of Montenegrin Liberation Wars.
1734 **486** 1d.20 brown, yellow and gold 15 15

487 Jug, Aleksandrovac, Serbia

1976. Ancient Pottery. Multicoloured.
1735 1d.20 Type **487** 10 10
1736 2d.10 Pitcher, Ptuj, Slovenia 10 10
1737 3d.20 Coffee-pot, Visnjica, Sarajevo 15 10
1738 5d. Pitcher, Backi Breg, Vojvodina 15 15
1739 6d. Goblet, Vranestica, Macedonia 20 15
1740 8d. Jug, Prizren, Kosovo 50 35

488 Nikola Tesla Monument and Niagara Falls

1976. 120th Birth Anniv of Nikola Tesla (scientist).
1741 **488** 5d. blue and green 25 10

489 Long Jumping

1976. Olympic Games, Montreal.
1742 **489** 1d.20 purple 10 10
1743 – 3d.20 green 15 10
1744 – 5d. brown 25 10
1745 – 8d. blue 50 35
DESIGNS: 3d.20, Handball; 5d. Shooting; 8d. Rowing.

490 Stadium and Olympic Rings

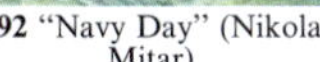
492 "Navy Day" (Nikola Mitar)

491 Globe

1976. Obligatory Tax. Olympic Games Fund.
1746 **490** 10p. blue 10 10

1976. 5th Non-aligned Nations' Summit Conf, Colombo.
1747 **491** 4d.90 multicoloured . . 20 10

1976. Children's Week and 8th "Joy of Europe" Meeting, Belgrade. Children's Paintings. Mult.
1748 4d.90 Type **492** 15 10
1749 8d. "Children's Trains" (Wiggo Gulbrandsen) . . 50 40

493 "Battle of Montenegrins" (Djura Jaksic)

495 Nenadovic (after Uros Knezevic)

1976. Paintings. Historical Events. Mult.
1750 1d.20 Type **493** 10 10
1751 2d.10 "Nikola Subic Zrinjski at Siget" (Oton Ivekovic) 15 10
1752 3d.20 "Herzegovinian Fugitives" (Uros Predic) (horiz) 15 10
1753 5d. "The Razlovic Uprising" (Borko Lazeski) (horiz) 20 15
1754 6d. "Enthronement of the Slovenian Duke, Gosposvetsko Field" (Anton Gojmir Kos) (horiz) 35 20
1755 8d. "Breach of the Solun Front" (Veljko Stanojevic) (horiz) 50 45

1976. No. 1203 surch.
1756 1d. on 85p. purple 15 10

1977. Birth Bicentenary of Prota Mateja Nenadovic (soldier and diplomat).
1757 **495** 4d.90 multicoloured . . 20 25

496 Rajko Zinzifov

497 Phlox

1977. Death Centenary of Rajko Zinzifov (writer).
1758 **496** 1d.50 brown and sepia 10 10

1977. Flowers. Multicoloured.
1759 1d.50 Type **497** 10 10
1760 3d.40 Tiger lily 15 10
1761 4d.90 Bleeding heart 20 10
1762 6d. Zinnia 25 15
1763 8d. French marigold 30 15
1764 10d. Geranium 55 50

498 Institute Building

499 Alojz Kraigher

1977. 150th Anniv of Croatian Music Institute.
1765 **498** 4d.90 brown and black 20 10

1977. Birth Centenary of Alojz Kraigher (author).
1766 **499** 1d.50 brown and black 10 10

500 "Kotor Bay" (Milo Milunovic)

1977. Europa. Landscapes. Multicoloured.
1767 4d.90 Type **500** 15 10
1768 10d. "Zagorje in November" (Ljubo Babic) 40 40

501 Figure and Emblems

1977. Obligatory Tax. Red Cross Week.
1769 **501** 20p. red and brown . . 1·75 70
1770 50p. red and green . . . 50 20
1771 1d. red and blue 25 10

502 "President Tito" (Omer Mujadzic)

503 Alpine Scene

1977. 85th Birthday of President Tito.
1772 **502** 1d.50 brown, olive and gold 10 10
1773 4d.90 brown, pink and gold 20 15
1774 8d. brown, olive and gold 50 45

1977. International Environment Protection Day. Multicoloured.
1775 4d.90 Type **503** 20 10
1776 10d. Plitvice waterfall and red-breasted flycatcher . . 50 50

504 Petar Kocic

1977. Birth Centenary of Petar Kocic (writer).
1777 **504** 1d.50 mauve and green 10 10

505 Dove and Map of Europe

1977. European Security and Co-operation Conf, Belgrade.
1778 **505** 4d.90 multicoloured . . 30 15
1779 10d. multicoloured . . . 1·50 1·50

506 Tree

507 "Bather" (Mrak Franci)

1977. Obligatory Tax. Anti-tuberculosis Week.
1780 **506** 50p. multicoloured . . . 3·00 3·00
1781 1d. multicoloured . . . 40 20

1977. Children's Week and 9th "Joy of Europe" Meeting, Belgrade. Children's Paintings. Mult.
1782 4d.90 Type **507** 15 10
1783 10d. "One Fruit into Pail — the other into Mouth" (Tanja Ilinskaja) 50 40

508 Congress Building, Belgrade

509 Exhibition Emblem

1977. European Security and Co-operation Conf, Belgrade.
1784 **508** 4d.90 grey, blue and gold 25 15
1785 10d. red, rose and gold 1·50 1·50

1977. "Balkanphila 6" Stamp Exhibition, Belgrade.
1786 **509** 4d.90 multicoloured . . 15 10

510 Double Flute

1977. Musical Instruments in Ethnographical Museum, Belgrade.
1787 **510** 1d.50 brown and yellow 10 10
1788 – 3d.40 brown and green 10 10
1789 – 4d.90 yellow and brown 15 10
1790 – 6d. brown and blue . . . 20 15
1791 – 8d. brown and orange 35 20
1792 – 10d. brown and green . . 50 45
DESIGN: 3d.40, Tambura (string instrument; 4d.90, Gusle (string instrument); 6d. Lijerica (string insrtument); 8d. Bagpipe; 10d. Pan's flute.

511 Ivan Vavpotic

1977. Self-portraits. Multicoloured.
1793 1d.50 Type **511** 10 10
1794 3d.40 Mihailo Vukotic . . . 15 10
1795 4d.90 Kosta Hakman . . . 20 10
1796 6d. Miroslav Kraljevic . . . 25 15
1797 8d. Nikola Martinovski . . 35 20
1798 10d. Milena Paviovic-Barili 60 65

512 Globe and Olympic Rings

1977. Obligatory Tax. Olympic Games Fund.
1799 **512** 10p. yellow, turq & bl 10 10

513 "Ceremony of Testaccio" (miniature from Officum Virginis)

514 Pre-stamp Letter (Bavaniste-Kubin)

1978. 400th Death Anniv of Julije Klovic (Croat miniaturist). Multicoloured.
1800 4d.90 Type **513** 15 10
1801 10d. "Portrait of Klovic" (El Greco) 40 30

1978. Post Office Museum Exhibits. Mult.
1802 1d.50 Type **514** 10 10
1803 3d.40 19th-century mail box 10 10
1804 4d.90 Ericsson induction table telephone 15 10
1805 10d. Morse's first electro-magnetic telegraph set . . 30 30

515 Battle of Pirot

1978. Centenary of Serbo-Turkish War.
1806 **515** 1d.50 multicoloured . . 1·10 45

516 S-49A Trainer, 1949

1978. Aeronautical Day.
1807 **516** 1d.50 pink, brown and orange 10 10
1808 – 3d.40 blue, black and slate 15 10
1809 – 4d.90 black and brown 25 10
1810 – 10d. yellow, brown & grn 60 50
DESIGNS: 3d.40, SOKO Gabeb 3 jet trainer; 4d.90, UTVA 75 elementary trainer; 10d. Jurom Orao jet fighter.

517 Golubac

518 Boxing Glove on Glove

1978. Europa. Multicoloured.
1811 4d.90 Type **517** 20 15
1812 10d. St. Naum Monastery 1·00 1·00

1978. 2nd World Amateur Boxing Championship, Belgrade.
1813 **518** 4d.90 brown, blue and deep blue 20 10

519 Symbols of Red Crescent, Red Cross and Red Lion

520 Honey Bee

1978. Obligatory Tax. Red Cross Week. No. 1814 surch.
1814 **519** 20p. on 1d. blue and red 30 10
1815 1d. blue and red 10 10

1978. Bees. Multicoloured.
1816 1d.50 Type **520** 10 10
1817 3d.40 "Halictus scabiosae" (mining bee) 25 10
1818 4d.90 Blue carptenter bee 40 15
1819 10d. Buff-tailed bumble bee 90 70

521 Filip Filipovic and Radovan Dragovic

1978. Birth Centenaries of F. Filipovic and R. Dragovic (socialist movement leaders).
1820 **521** 1d.50 green and red . . 10 10

522 President Tito (poster)
524 Conference Emblem over Belgrade

1978. 11th Communist League Congress. Mult.
1821 2d. Type **522** 10 10
1822 4d.90 Hammer and sickle (poster) 25 10

1978. Various stamps surch.
1829 – 35p. on 10p. brown (No. 1642) 15 10
1830 **332** 60p. on 85p. blue (No. 1271) 15 10
1831 **443** 80p. on 1d.20 green (No. 1599) 15 10
1832 – 2d. on 1d. green (No. 1657) 15 10
1833 – 3d.40 on 2d.10 green (No. 1662) 20 10

1978. Conference of Foreign Ministers of Non-aligned Countries.
1834 **524** 4d.90 blue and light blue 15 10

525 Championship Emblem
526 North Face, Mount Triglav

1978. 14th Kayak and Canoe "Still Water" World Championships, Belgrade.
1835 **525** 4d.90 black, blue and light blue 20 10

1978. Bicent of First Ascent of Mount Triglav.
1836 **526** 2d. multicoloured . . . 15 10

527 Hand holding Flame
528 Black Lake, Durmitor

1978. Obligatory Tax. Anti-tuberculosis Week.
1837 **527** 1d. multicoloured . . . 20 10

1978. Protection of the Environment. Multicoloured.
1838 4d.90 Type **528** 15 10
1839 10d. River Tara 50 40

529 Olympic Rings on Map of World

1978. Obligatory Tax. Olympic Games Fund.
1840 **529** 30p. multicoloured . . . 10 10

530 Star Map

1978. 29th International Astronautical Federation Congress, Dubrovnik.
1841 **530** 4d.90 multicoloured . . 20 10

531 "People in Forest" (Ivana Balen)

1978. Children's Week and 10th "Joy of Europe" Meeting, Belgrade. Multicoloured.
1842 4d.90 Type **531** 20 10
1843 10d. "Family round a Pond" (Vincent Christel) 50 40

532 Seal

1978. Centenary of Kresna Uprising.
1844 **532** 2d. black, brown and gold 15 10

533 Old College Building

1978. Bicentenary of Teachers' Training College, Sombor.
1845 **533** 2d. brown, yellow & gold 15 10

534 Red Cross

1978. Centenary of Croatian Red Cross.
1846 **534** 2d. red, blue and black 15 10

535 Metallic Sculpture "XXII" (Dusan Dzamonja)

1978. Modern Sculpture.
1847 **535** 2d. black, brown & silver 10 10
1848 – 3d.40 blue, grey and silver 15 10
1849 – 4d.90 olive, brown and silver 15 10
1850 – 10d. brown, buff and silver 40 45

DESIGNS—VERT: 3d.40, "Circulation in Space I" (Vojin Bakic); 4d.90, "Tectonic Octopod" (Olga Jevric). HORIZ: 10d. "The Tree of Life" (Drago Trsar).

536 "Crossing the Neretva" (Ismet Mujezinovic)
537 "People from the Seine" (Marijan Detoni)

1978. 35th Anniv of Battle of Neretva.
1851 **536** 2d. multicoloured . . . 15 10

1978. Republic Day. Graphic Art.
1852 **537** 2d. black, stone and gold 10 10
1853 – 3d.40 black, grey and gold 10 10
1854 – 4d.90 black, yellow and gold 15 10
1855 – 6d. black, flesh and gold 20 15
1856 – 10d. black, flesh and gold 35 40

DESIGNS—3d.40, "Labourers" (Maksim Sedej); 4d.90, "Felling of Trees" (Daniel Ozmo); 6d. "At a Meal" (Pivo Karamatijevic); 10d. "They are not afraid, even at a most loathsome crime" (Djordje Andrejevic Kun).

538 Eurasian Red Squirrel
539 Masthead

1978. New Year. Multicoloured.
1857 1d.50 Type **538** 15 10
1858 1d.50 Larch 15 10
1859 2d. Red deer 15 10
1860 2d. Sycamore 15 10
1861 3d.40 Rock partridge (pink background) 85 15
1861a 3d.40 Rock partridge (green background) . . . 85 25
1862 3d.40 Alder (pink background) 25 10
1862a 3d.40 Alder (green background) 40 15
1863 4d.90 Western capercaillie (green background) . . . 95 15
1863a 4d.90 Western capercaillie (yellow background) . . 95 25
1864 4d.90 Oak (green background) 30 10
1864a 4d.90 Oak (yellow background) 55 25

1979. 75th Anniv of "Politika" Newspaper.
1865 **539** 2d. black and gold . . . 15 10

540 Flags
541 Games Mascot

1979. 10th Anniv of Self-Managers' Meeting.
1866 **540** 2d. multicoloured . . . 15 10

1979. Obligatory Tax. Mediterranean Games Fund.
1867 **541** 1d. blue and deep blue 15 10
See also No. 1886.

542 Child
543 Sabre, Mace and Enamluk (box holding Koranic texts)

1979. International Year of the Child.
1868 **542** 4d.90 blue and gold . . 40 30

1979. Ancient Weapons from Ethnographic Museum, Belgrade. Multicoloured.
1869 2d. Type **543** 10 10
1870 3d.40 Pistol and ammunition stick 10 10
1871 4d.90 Carbine and powder-horn 20 10
1872 10d. Rifle and cartridge-pouch 50 45

544 Hammer and Sickle on Star
545 University

1979. 60th Anniv of Yugoslav Communist Party and League for Communist Youth.
1873 **544** 2d. multicoloured . . . 10 10
1874 4d.90 multicoloured . . 15 15

1979. 30th Anniv of Cyril and Methodius University, Skopje.
1875 **545** 2d. brown, buff and pink 10 10

546 "Panorama of Belgrade" (Carl Goebel)

1979. Europa. Multicoloured.
1876 4d.90 Type **546** 15 15
1877 10d. Postilion and view of Ljubljana (after Jan van der Heyden) 40 40

547 Stylized Bird

1979. Obligatory Tax. Red Cross Week.
1878 **547** 1d. turquoise, blue & red 15 10

548 Alpine Sow-thistle
549 Milutin Milankovic (after Paja Jovanovic)

1979. Alpine Flowers. Multicoloured.
1879 2d. Type **548** 10 10
1880 3d.40 "Anemone narcissiflora" 10 10
1881 4d.90 Milk-vetch 25 15
1882 10d. Alpine clover 50 40

1979. Birth Centenary of Milutin Milankovic (scientist).
1883 **549** 4d.90 multicoloured . . 20 10

550 Kosta Abrasevic
551 Rowing Crew

1979. Birth Centenary of Kosta Abrasevic (poet).
1884 **550** 2d. grey, pink and black 10 10

1979. Obligatory Tax. Solidarity Week. As T **469** but inscribed "1.-7.VI".
1885 30p. black, grey and blue . . 45 25
See also Nos. 1933 and 2218/19.

1979. Obligatory Tax. Mediterranean Games Fund. As No. 1867 but colour changed.
1886 **541** 1d. blue and deep blue 10 10

1979. 9th World Rowing Championships. Bled.
1887 **551** 4d.90 multicoloured . . 30 10

552 Games Emblem
553 Girl playing Hopscotch

1979. 8th Mediterranean Games. Multicoloured.
1888 2d. Type **552** 10 10
1889 4d.90 Mascot and emblem 15 10
1890 10d. Map and flags of participating countries . . 30 25

1979. Obligatory Tax. Anti-tuberculosis Week.
1891 **553** 1d. multicoloured . . . 20 15

554 Arms of Zagreb, 1499

1979. 450th Anniv of Zagreb Postal Service.
1892 **554** 2d. grey and red 15 10

555 Lake Palic

1979. Environmental Protection. Multicoloured.
1893 4d.90 Type **555** 15 10
1894 10d. Lake in Prokletije range 45 30

556 Emblems

1979. Meeting of International Bank for Reconstruction and Development and of International Monetary Fund.
1895 **556** 4d.90 multicoloured . . 15 10
1896 10d. multicoloured . . . 40 30

557 Street in Winter (Mirjana Markovic)

1979. 11th "Joy of Europe" Meeting, Belgrade. Children's Paintings. Multicoloured.
1897 4d.90 Type **557** 15 10
1898 10d. House and garden (Jacques An) 50 45

558 Milhailo Pupin **559** Olympic Rings

1979. 125th Birth Anniv of Milhailo Pupin (scientist).
1899 **558** 4d.90 brown, light blue and blue 20 10

1979. Obligatory Tax. Olympic Games Fund.
1900 **559** 30p. red and blue . . . 15 10

560 Marko Cepenkov **561** Pristina University

1979. 150th Anniv of Marko Cepenkov (author and folklorist).
1901 **560** 2d. brown, green and olive 15 10

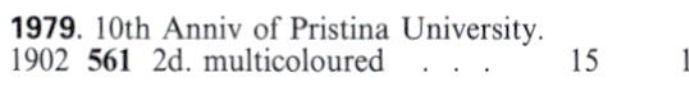
1979. 10th Anniv of Pristina University.
1902 **561** 2d. multicoloured . . . 15 10

562 Lion on Column (Trogir Cathedral) **563** Sarajevo University

1979. Romanesque Sculpture. Multicoloured.
1903 2d. Type **562** 10 10
1904 3d.40 Apostle (detail of choir stall, Split Cathedral) 15 10
1905 4d.90 Window (Church of the Ascension, Decani) . . 20 10
1906 6d. Detail of Buvina door (Split Cathedral) 30 20
1907 10d. Virgin and Child (West door, Church of the Virgin, Studenica) 40 40

1979. 30th Anniv of Sarajevo University.
1908 **563** 2d. black, brown and grey 15 10

564 Djakovic and Hecimovic

1979. 50th Death Anniv of Djuro Djakovic and Nikola Hecimovic (leaders of socialist movement).
1909 **564** 2d. multicoloured . . . 15 10

565 Paddle-steamer "Srbija"

1979. Danube Conference. Multicoloured.
1910 4d.90 Paddle-steamer "Deligrad" 80 50
1911 10d. Type **565** . . . . . . 1·60 1·00

566 Milton Manaki **567** Edvard Kardelj

1980. Birth Centenary of Milton Manaki (first Balkan film maker).
1912 **566** 2d. purple, yellow and brown 15 10

1980. 70th Birth Anniv of Edvard Kardelj (revolutionary).
1913 **567** 2d. multicoloured . . . 15 10

1980. Renaming of Ploce as Kardeljevo. No. 1913 optd **PLOCE-1980-KARDELJEVO**.
1914 **567** 2d. multicoloured . . . 15 10

569 Speed Skating

1980. Winter Olympic Games, Lake Placid. Mult.
1915 4d.90 Type **569** 25 15
1916 10d. Skiing . . . . 1·25 90

570 Belgrade University

1980. 75th Anniv of Belgrade University.
1917 **570** 2d. multicoloured . . . 15 10

571 Fencing

1980. Olympic Games, Moscow. Multicoloured.
1918 2d. Type **571** 10 10
1919 3d.40 Cycling 15 10
1920 4d.90 Hockey 20 10
1921 10d. Archery 40 40

572 President Tito (relief by Antun Augustincic)

1980. Europa. Multicoloured.
1922 4d.90 Type **572** 25 25
1923 13d. Portrait of Tito by Djordje Prudnikov . . . 1·25 1·25

573 Pres. Tito

1980. Death of President Tito. Portraits by Bozidar Jakac.
1924 **573** 2d.50 purple 15 10
1925 – 4d.90 black . . . . . . 85 1·00
DESIGN: 4d.90, Different portrait of President Tito.

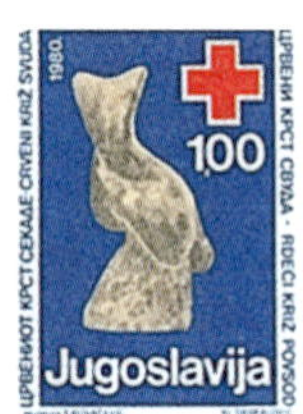

574 Sculpture of S. Kovacevic

1980. Obligatory Tax. Red Cross Week.
1926 **574** 1d. multicoloured . . . 25 15

575 Sava Kovacevic

1980. 75th Birth Anniv of Sava Kovacevic (partisan).
1927 **575** 2d. brown, orange & yell 15 10

576 Estafette and Letter from Youth of Belgrade, 1945

1980. 35th Anniv of Tito's 1st Estafette (youth celebration of Tito's birthday).
1928 **576** 2d. multicoloured . . . 15 10

577 Flying Gurnard **578** Decius Trajan (249–51)

1980. Adriatic Sea Fauna, Multicoloured.
1929 2d. Type **577** 15 10
1930 3d.40 Turtle 25 15
1931 4d.90 Little tern 25 25
1932 10d. Common dolphin . . . 45 40

1980. Obligatory Tax. Solidarity Week. As No. 1885.
1933 **469** 1d. black, grey and blue 50 30

1980. Roman Emperors on Coins. Multicoloured.
1934 2d. Type **578** 10 10
1935 3d.40 Aurelian (270–75) . . 15 10
1936 4d.90 Probus (276–82) . . . 25 10
1937 10d. Diocletian (284–305) 45 40

1980. Nos. 1660 and 1652 surch.
1938 2d.50 on 1d.50 red 20 10
1939 5d. on 75p. purple 50 10
See also Nos. 1992/3.

580 Lipica Horses **581** Tito

1980. 400th Anniv of Lipica Stud Farm.
1940 **580** 2d.50 black 20 10

1980. 30th Anniv of Self-Management Law.
1941 **581** 2d. deep red and red . . 15 10

582 Novi Sad University

1980. 20th Anniv Novi Sad University.
1942 **582** 2d.50 green 15 10

583 Mljet

1980. Protection of the Environment. National Parks. Multicoloured.
1943 4d.90 Type **583** 25 10
1944 13d. Galicica, Ohrid 65 50

584 Pyrrhotine **585** Lake

1980. Crystals. Multicoloured.
1945 2d.50 Type **584** 10 10
1946 3d.40 Dolomite 15 10
1947 4d.90 Sphalerite 25 15
1948 13d. Wulfenite 50 40

1980. Obligatory Tax. Anti-tuberculosis Week.
1949 **585** 1d. multicoloured . . . 15 10

586 Kotor

1980. 21st Session of U.N.E.S.C.O. General Conference, Belgrade.
1950 **586** 4d.90 blue, gold, and deep blue 20 10

587 "Children with Balloons" (Gabrijela Radojevic) **588** Olympic Flag and Globe

1980. 12th "Joy of Europe" Meeting, Belgrade. Children's Drawings. Multicoloured.
1951 4d.90 Type **587** 15 10
1952 13d. "Face" (Renata Pisarcikova) 50 40

1980. Obligatory Tax. Olympic Games Fund.
1953 **588** 50p. multicoloured . . . 15 10

589 Dove and Madrid

1980. European Security and Co-operation Conference, Madrid.
1954 **589** 4d.90 green and deep green 20 15
1955 13d. bistre and brown 40 40

590 Flag of Bosnia and Herzegovina Socialist Republic

1980. Flags of Yugoslav Socialist Republics and of Federal Republic.
1956 **590** 2d.50 multicoloured . . 10 10
1957 – 2d.50 multicoloured . . 10 10
1958 – 2d.50 multicoloured . . 10 10
1959 – 2d.50 multicoloured . . 10 10
1960 – 2d.50 multicoloured . . 10 10
1961 – 2d.50 red, gold and grey 10 10
1962 – 2d.50 multicoloured . . 10 10
1963 – 2d.50 multicoloured . . 10 10
DESIGNS: No. 1957, Montenegro; 1958, Croatia; 1959, Yugoslavia (inscr in Roman alphabet); 1960, Yugoslavia (inscr in Cyrillic alphabet); 1961, Macedonia; 1962, Slovenia; 1963, Serbia.

591 "Complaint" (Milos Vuskovic) **593** Ivan Ribar

592 Sports Complex, Novi Sad

1980. Paintings. Multicoloured.
1964 2d.50 "Woman in a Straw Hat" (Stojan Aralica) (horiz) 10 10
1965 3d.40 "Atelier No. 1" (Gabrijel Stupica) (horiz) 10 10
1966 4d.90 "To the Glory of Sutjeska Fighters" (detail Ismet Mujezinovic) (horiz) 15 10
1967 8d. "Serenity" (Marino Tartaglia) 20 10
1968 13d. Type **591** 40 35

1980. Obligatory Tax. World Table Tennis Championships, Novi Sad.
1969 **592** 1d. green, yellow and blue 15 10

1981. Birth Centenary of Ivan Ribar (politician).
1970 **593** 2d.50 black and red . . 15 10

594 "Cementusa" Hand Bomb

1981. Partisan Arms in Belgrade Military Museum.
1971 **594** 3d.50 black and red . . 10 10
1972 – 5d.60 black and green 15 10
1973 – 8d. black and brown . . 20 10
1974 – 13d. black and purple . . 35 30
DESIGNS: 5d.60, "Partizanka" rifle; 8d. Cannon; 13d. Tank.

595 Virgin of Eleousa Monastery

1981. 900th Anniv of Virgin of Eleousa Monastery, Veljusa, Macedonia.
1975 **595** 3d.50 grey, brown and blue 15 10

596 Table Tennis

1981. "SPENS '81" World Table Tennis Championships, Novi Sad.
1976 **596** 8d. multicoloured . . . 30 15

597 "Lamp" **598** "Herzegovinian Wedding" (detail)

1981. Obligatory Tax. Red Cross Week.
1977 **597** 1d. multicoloured . . . 10 10

1981. Europa. Paintings by Nikola Arsenovic. Multicoloured.
1978 8d. Type **598** 25 10
1979 13d. "Witnesses at a Wedding" 50 30

599 Tucovic and Dimitrije Tucovic Square **600** Tito (after Milivoje Unkovic)

1981. Birth Centenary of Dimitrije Tucovic (socialist leader).
1980 **599** 3d.50 blue and red . . . 15 10

1981. 89th Birth Anniv of Tito.
1981 **600** 3d.50 multicoloured . . 35 20

601 Sunflower **602** Congress Emblem

1981. Cultivated Plants. Multicoloured.
1982 3d.50 Type **601** 10 10
1983 5d.60 Hop 15 10
1984 8d. Corn 25 15
1985 13d. Wheat 50 35

1981. 3rd Congress of Self-managers.
1986 **602** 3d.50 multicoloured . . 15 10

603 Djordje Petrov **604** Star

1981. 60th Death Anniv of Djordje Petrov (politician).
1987 **603** 3d.50 yellow and red . . 15 10

1981. 40th Anniv of Yugoslav Insurrection.
1988 **604** 3d.50 yellow and red . . 15 10
1989 8d. orange and red . . . 25 15

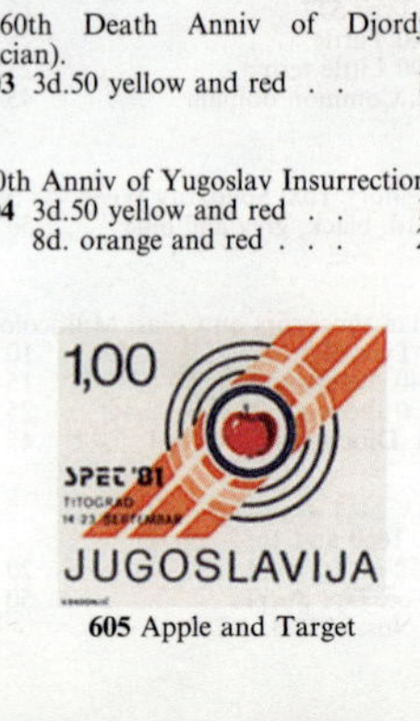
605 Apple and Target

1981. Obligatory Tax. "Spet 81" European Shooting Championships, Titograd.
1991 **605** 1d. blue, red and orange 3·00 3·00

1981. Nos. 1666 and 1669 surch.
1992 3d.50 on 3d.40 green . . . 20 10
1993 5d. on 4d.90 blue 25 10

606 Varazdin (18th-century illustration)

1981. 800th Anniv of Varazdin.
1994 **606** 3d.50 yellow and blue . . 15 10

607 Parliament Building, Belgrade **608** "Flower"

1981. 20th Anniv of 1st Non-aligned Countries Conference, Belgrade.
1995 **607** 8d. blue and red 25 10

1981. Obligatory Tax. Anti-tuberculosis Week.
1996 **608** 1d. red, yellow and blue 15 10

609 Printing Press and Serbian Newspaper

1981. 150th Anniv of First Serbian Printing House.
1997 **609** 3d.50 pink and blue . . 15 10

610 Fran Levstik

1981. 150th Birth Anniv of Fran Levstik (writer).
1998 **610** 3d.50 grey and red . . . 15 10

611 "Village Scene" (Saso Arsovski)

1981. 13th "Joy of Europe" Meeting, Belgrade. Children's Drawings. Multicoloured.
1999 8d. Type **611** 15 10
2000 13d. "Skiers" (Aino Jokinen) 45 40

612 Tug "Karlovac" pushing Barges

1981. 125th Anniv of European Danube Commission. Multicoloured.
2001 8d. Type **612** 55 25
2002 13d. Paddle-steamer towed by steam railway locomotive on Sip Canal 1·50 70

613 Postal Savings Bank Emblem **614** Emblem

1981. 60th Anniv of Postal Savings Bank.
2003 **613** 3d.50 red and yellow . . 15 10

1982. World Intellectual Property Organization Conference.
2004 **614** 8d. red and gold 25 15

615 Forsythia and Rugovo Ravine

1981. Protection of Nature. Multicoloured.
2005 8d. Type **615** 25 10
2006 13d. Lynx and Prokletije . . 60 40

616 August Senoa **617** "Still Life with Fish" (Jovan Bijelic)

1981. Death Centenary of August Senoa (writer).
2007 **616** 3d.50 purple and brown 15 10

1981. Paintings of Animals. Multicoloured.
2008 3d.50 Type **617** 10 10
2009 5d.60 "Raven" (Milo Milunovic) 15 10
2010 8d. "Bird on Blue Background" (Marko Celebonovic) 15 10
2011 10d. "Horses" (Peter Lubarda) 40 15
2012 13d. "Sheep" (Nikola Masic) 40 35

618 Mosa Pijade (politician)

1982. 40th Anniv of Foca Regulations.
2013 **618** 3d.50 blue and mauve 15 10

619 Mastheads **620** Cetinje

1982. 60th Anniv of "Borba" (newspaper).
2014 **619** 3d.50 black and red . . 15 10

1982. 500th Anniv of City of Cetinje.
2015 **620** 3d.50 brown and black 15 10

621 Visin's Ship "Splendido"

1982. Europa. Multicoloured.
2016 8d. Capt. Ivo Visin (first Yugoslav to sail round world) and naval chart . . 25 15
2017 15d. Type **621** 80 25

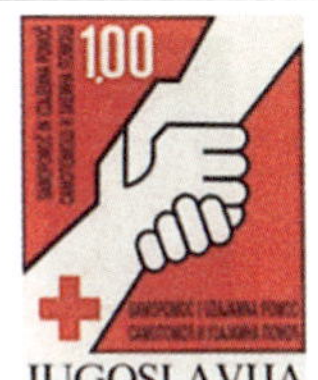

622 Clasped Hands **624** House Sparrow (male)

1982. Obligatory Tax. Red Cross Week.
2018 **622** 1d. black and red . . . 15 10

1982. Multicoloured.
2020 3d.50 Type **624** 30 30
2021 5d.60 House sparrow (female) 35 35
2022 8d. Spanish sparrow (female) 50 50
2023 15d. Eurasian tree sparrow (male) . . . . 1·50 1·50

625 Tito (after Dragan Dosen) **627** Jaksic (self-portrait)

626 Poster (Dobrilo Nikolic)

1982. 90th Birth Anniv of Tito.
2024 **625** 3d.50 multicoloured . . 15 10

1982. 12th Communist League Congress, Belgrade.
2025 **626** 3d.50 brown, orge & red 15 10
2026 8d. light grey, grey and red 25 15

1982. 150th Birth Anniv of Dura Jaksic (writer and painter).
2028 **627** 3d.50 multicoloured . . 15 10

628 Kayaks **629** Ivan Zajc

1982. Sports Championships.
2029 **628** 8d. light blue and blue 25 15
2030 – 8d. light green and green 25 15
2031 – 8d. pink and red 25 15
DESIGNS AND EVENTS: No. 2029, Type **628** (17th World Kayak and Canoe Still Water Championships, Belgrade); 2030, Weightlifting (36th World Weightlifting Championships, Ljubljana); 2031, Gymnastics (6th World Gymnastics Cup, Zagreb).

1982. 150th Birth Anniv of Ivan Zajc (composer).
2032 **629** 4d. orange and brown 15 10

630 Breguet 19 and Potez 25 Biplanes

1982. 40th Anniv of Air Force, Anti-aircraft Defence and Navy.
2033 **630** 4d. black and blue . . . 20 10
2034 – 6d.10 multicoloured . . 30 10
2035 – 8d.80 black and green 50 15
2036 – 15d. multicoloured . . . 90 30
DESIGNS: 6d.10, SOKO G-4 Super Galeb jet trainer; 8d.80, National Liberation Army armed tug; 15d. "Rade Koncar" (missile gunboat).

631 Tara National Park and Pine Cones

1982. Nature Protection. Multicoloured.
2037 8d.80 Type **631** 25 15
2038 15d. Kornati National Park and Mediterranean monk seal 50 40

632 Dr. Robert Koch

1982. Obligatory Tax. Anti-tuberculosis Week.
2039 **632** 1d. orange, black and red 10 10

633 "Traffic" (Tibo Bozo)

1982. 14th "Joy of Europe" Meeting, Belgrade. Children's Drawings. Multicoloured.
2040 8d.80 Type **633** 15 15
2041 15d. "In the Bath" (Heiko Jakel) 40 35

634 Small Onofrio Fountain, Dubrovnik

1982. 16th World Federation of Travel Agents' Associations Congress, Dubrovnik.
2042 **634** 8d.80 multicoloured . . 20 15

635 Herceg Novi (from old engraving)

1982. 600th Anniv of Herceg Novi.
2043 **635** 4d. multicoloured . . . 60 25

636 Bridge, Miljacka

1982. Winter Olympic Games, Sarajevo. Each black, light blue and blue.
2044 4d. Type **636** 30 15
2045 6d.10 Mosque tower and cable cars, Sarajevo . . . 35 25
2046 8d.80 Evangelical Church, Sarajevo 45 30
2047 15d. Old Street, Sarajevo . . 85 70

637 Bihac

1982. 40th Anniv of Avnoj-a (anti-fascist council) Session, Bihac.
2048 **637** 4d. brown and orange 15 10

638 "Prophet on Golden Background" (Joze Ciuha) **639** Predic (self-portrait)

1982. Modern Art. Multicoloured.
2049 4d. Type **638** 10 10
2050 6d.10 "Journey to the West" (Andrej Jemec) 10 10
2051 8d.80 "Black Comb with Red Band" (Riko Debenjak) 15 15
2052 10d. "Manuscript" (Janez Bernik) (horiz) 20 20
2053 15d. "Display Case" (Adriana Maraz) (horiz) 40 35

1982. 125th Birth Anniv of Uros Predic (painter).
2054 **639** 4d. orange and brown 15 10

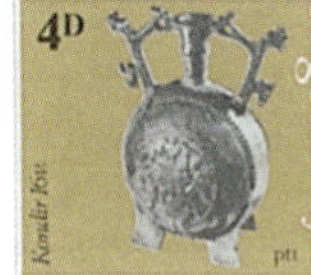

641 Pioneer Badge **644** Lead Pitcher (16th century)

1982. 40th Anniv of Pioneer League.
2056 **641** 4d. brown, silver and red 15 10

1983. Nos. 1663 and 1667 surch.
2057 30p. on 2d.50 blue 25 10
2055a 50p. on 2d.50 blue 10 10
2058 60p. on 2d.50 blue 40 10
2059a 1d. on 3d.50 red 10 10
2060 2d. on 2d.50 red 10 10

1983. Museum Exhibits.
2061 **644** 4d. black, bistre and silver 10 10
2062 – 6d.10 black, brown and silver 15 10
2063 – 8d.80 gold, purple and grey 20 15
2064 – 15d. gold, purple and grey 40 25
DESIGNS: 6d.10, Silver-plated tin jar (18th century); 8d.80, Silver-gilt dish (16th century); 15d. Bronze mortar (15th century).

645 Jalovec Mountain Peak and Edelweiss **646** Ericsson Wall Telephone and War Ministry, Belgrade

1983. 90th Anniv of Slovenian Mountaineering Society.
2065 **645** 4d. blue, light blue and deep blue 15 10

1983. Centenary of Telephone in Serbia.
2066 **646** 3d. brown and blue . . . 15 10

647 I.M.O. Emblem and Freighters

1983. 25th Anniv of International Maritime Organization.
2067 **647** 8d.80 multicoloured . . 35 15

648 Field Mushroom

1983. Edible Mushrooms. Multicoloured.
2068 4d. Type **648** 20 10
2069 6d.10 Common morel . . . 30 10
2070 8d.80 Cep 50 15
2071 15d. Chanterelle . . . . . 1·25 55

649 Series 401 Steam Locomotive **650** Monument, Landovica

1983. 110th Anniv of Rijeka Railway.
2072 **649** 4d. grey and red 30 10
2073 – 23d.70 on 8d.80 grey and red 80 15
DESIGN: 23d.70, Series 442 electric locomotive.
No. 2073 was only issued surcharged.

1983. 40th Death Anniv of Boro Vukmirivic and Ramiz Sadiku (revolutionaries).
2074 **650** 4d. grey and violet . . . 15 10

651 Nobel Prize Medal and Manuscript of "Travnik Chronicle" by Andric

1983. Europa. Multicoloured.
2075 8d.80 Type **651** 20 15
2076 20d. Ivo Andric (author and Nobel Prize winner) and bridge over the Drina . . 50 40

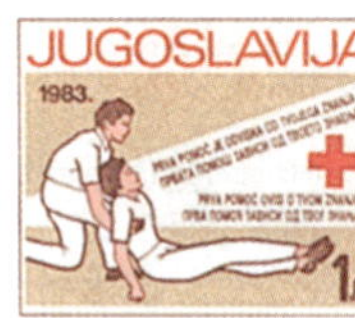

652 First Aid

1983. Obligatory Tax. Red Cross Week.
2077 **652** 1d. deep brown, brown and red 15 10
2078 2d. deep brown, brown and red 15 10

653 Combine Harvester **654** "Assault" (Pivo Karamatijevic)

1983. 50th International Agriculture Fair, Novi Sad.
2079 **653** 4d. green and purple . . 15 10

1983. 40th Anniv of Battle of Sutjeska.
2080 **654** 3d. pink and brown . . 15 10

655 Tito (after Bozidar Jakac) and Parliament Building **656** Delahaye Postbus, 1903

1983. 30th Anniv of Tito's Election to Presidency.
2081 **655** 4d. brown and green . . 10 10

1983. 80th Anniv of Postbus Service in Montenegro.
2082 **656** 4d. black and brown . . 10 10
2083 – 16d.50 black and brown 40 25
DESIGN: 16d.50, Road used by first postbus.

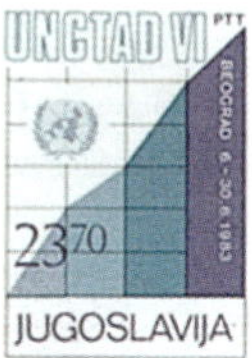

657 Statue by V. Bakic, Valjevo **658** Graph

1983. Monuments.
2084 **657** 100d. orange and blue 2·00 40
2085 – 200d. orange and green 1·90 75
DESIGN—HORIZ: 200d. Triumphal Arch, Titograd.

1983. 6th U.N. Conference for Trade and Development Session, Belgrade.
2086 **658** 23d.70 multicoloured . . 60 30

659 Pazin (after engraving by Valvasor) **660** Skopje

1983. Millenary of Pazin.
2087 **659** 4d. brown and green . . 15 10

1983. 20th Anniv of Skopje Earthquake.
2088 **660** 23d.70 red 40 30

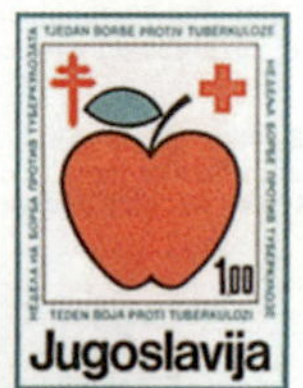
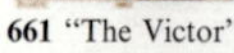

661 "The Victor" **663** Apple

662 Gentian and Kupaonik National Park

1983. Birth Cent of Ivan Mestrovic (sculptor).
2089 **661** 6d. deep brown, brown and blue 15 10

1983. Nature Protection. Multicoloured.
2090 16d.50 Type **662** 40 25
2091 23d.70 Chamois and Sutjeska National Park 50 30

1983. Obligatory Tax. Anti-tuberculosis Week.
2092 **663** 1d. red, black & turquoise 10 10
2093 2d. red, black & turquoise 15 10

664 "Newly Weds" (Vesna Paunkovic) **665** School and Seal

1983. 15th "Joy of Europe" Meeting, Belgrade. Children's Drawings.
2094 **664** 16d.50 yellow, black and red 20 15
2095 – 23d.70 multicoloured . . 40 20
DESIGN: 23d.70, "Andres and his Mother" (Marta Lopez-Ibor).

1983. 150th Anniv of Kragujevac Grammar School.
2096 **665** 5d. brown and blue . . . 15 10

666 Monument by Antun Augustincic **667** Skier and Games Emblem

1983. Centenary of Timocka Buna Uprising.
2097 **666** 5d. blue and purple . . . 15 10

1983. Obligatory Tax. Winter Olympic Games, Sarajevo.
2098 **667** 2d. blue and deep blue 15 10

668 Zmaj and "Neven" Periodical

1983. 150th Birth Anniv of Jovan Jovanovic Zmaj (poet and editor).
2099 **668** 5d. red and green . . . 10 10

669 Ski Jump, Malo Polje, Mt. Igman

1983. Winter Olympic Games, Sarajevo (1st issue).
2100 **669** 4d. black, green & brown 10 10
2101 – 4d. dp blue, blue & brown 10 10
2102 – 16d.50 lilac, deep brown and brown 35 20
2103 – 16d.50 green, blue & brn 35 20
2104 – 23d.70 deep brown, green and brown . . . 45 30
2105 – 23d.70 black, green and brown 45 30
DESIGNS: No. 2101, Womens slalom run, Mt. Jahorina; 2102, Bob-sleigh and luge run, Mt. Trebevis; 2103, Men's alpine downhill ski run, Mt. Bjelasnica; 2104, Olympic Hall (for ice hockey and figure skating), Zetra; 2105, Speed skating rink, Zetra.

670 "The Peasant Wedding" (Brueghel the Younger) **671** Jajce

1983. Paintings. Multicoloured.
2107 4d. Type **670** 10 10
2108 16d.50 "Susanna and the Elders" (Master of "The Prodigal Son") 25 15
2109 16d.50 "The Allegory of Wisdom and Strength" (Paolo Veronese) 25 15
2110 23d.70 "The Virgin Mary from Salamanca" (Robert Campin) 40 30
2111 23d.70 "St. Anne with the Madonna and Jesus" (Albrecht Durer) 40 30

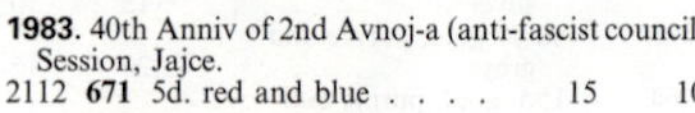

1983. 40th Anniv of 2nd Avnoj-a (anti-fascist council) Session, Jajce.
2112 **671** 5d. red and blue 15 10

672 Drawing by Hasukic Sabina **673** Koco Racin

1983. World Communications Year.
2114 **672** 23d.70 multicoloured . . 40 25

1983. 75th Birth Anniv of Koco Racin (writer).
2115 **673** 5d. blue and brown . . . 15 10

674 First Issue of "Politika"

1984. 80th Anniv of "Politika" (daily newspaper).
2116 **674** 5d. black and red . . . 15 10

675 Veljko Petrovic **677** Marija Bursac

676 Giant Slalom

1984. Birth Centenary of Veljko Petrovic (writer).
2117 **675** 5d. brown, orange and grey 15 10

1984. Winter Olympic Games, Sarajevo (2nd issue). Multicoloured.
2118 4d. Type **676** 10 10
2119 4d. Biathlon 10 10
2120 5d. Slalom 15 10
2121 5d. Bobsleigh 15 10
2122 16d.50 Speed skating . . . 30 20
2123 16d.50 Ice hockey 30 20
2124 23d.70 Ski jumping 50 30
2125 23d.70 Downhill skiing . . 50 30

1984. Women's Day. National Heroines. Each grey, blue and black.
2127 5d. Type **677** 15 10
2128 5d. Jelena Cetkovic 15 10
2129 5d. Nada Dimic 15 10
2130 5d. Elpida Karamandi . . . 15 10
2131 5d. Toncka Cec Olga . . . 15 10
2132 5d. Spasenija Babovic Cana 15 10
2133 5d. Jovanka Radivojevic Kica 15 10
2134 5d. Sonja Marinkovic . . . 15 10

678 Bond and Banknote

1984. 40th Anniv of Slovenian Monetary Institute.
2135 **678** 5d. blue and red 15 10

679 Belgrade Central Station and Steam Mail Train, 1884

1984. Centenary of Serbian Railway.
2136 **679** 5d. brown and deep brown 10 10

680 Jure Franko and Silver Medal **682** Globe as Jigsaw Pieces

681 Bridge

1984. 1st Yugoslav Winter Olympics Medal.
2137 **680** 23d.70 multicoloured . . 45 25

1984. Europa. 25th Anniv of European Post and Telecommunications Conference.
2138 **681** 23d.70 multicoloured . . 35 20
2139 50d. multicoloured . . . 75 40

1984. Obligatory Tax. Red Cross Week.
2140 **682** 1d. multicoloured . . . 10 10
2141 2d. multicoloured . . . 15 10
2142 4d. multicoloured . . . 30 10
2143 5d. multicoloured . . . 35 25

683 Basketball

1984. Olympic Games, Los Angeles. Multicoloured.
2144 5d. Type **683** 15 10
2145 16d.50 Diving 30 20
2146 23d.70 Equestrian 40 30
2147 50d. Running 80 50

684 Tito (after Bozidar Jakac) **685** "Skopje Earthquake"

1984. 40th Anniv of Failure of German Attack on National Liberation Movement's Headquarters at Drvar.
2148 **684** 5d. brown and light brown 15 10

1984. Obligatory Tax. Solidarity Week. Self-adhesive. Imperf.
2149 **685** 1d.50 blue and red . . . 60 35

686 Mt. Biokovo Natural Park and "Centaurea gloriosa"

1984. Nature Protection. Multicoloured.
2150 26d. Type **686** 30 25
2151 40d. Pekel Cave and "Anophthalmus schmidti" (Longhorn beetle) 60 35

687 Great Black-backed Gull

1984. Birds. Multicoloured.
2152 4d. Type **687** 15 10
2153 5d. Black-headed gull . . . 20 10
2154 16d.50 Herring gull 50 20
2155 40d. Common tern . . . . 1·40 50

688 Cradle from Bihac, Bosnia and Herzegovina

1984. Museum Exhibits. Cradles.
2156 **688** 4d. green 10 10
2157 – 5d. purple and red . . . 10 10
2158 – 26d. light brown and brown 35 25
2159 – 40d. ochre and orange 60 40
DESIGNS: Cradles from—5d. Montenegro; 26d. Macedonia; 40d. Rasina, Serbia.

689 Red Cross and Leaves **691** "National Costume" (Erika Sarcevic)

690 Olive Trees, Mirovica

1984. Obligatory Tax. Anti-tuberculosis Week.
2160 **689** 1d. multicoloured . . . 10 10
2161 2d. multicoloured . . . 10 10
2162 2d.50 multicoloured . . 15 10
2163 4d. multicoloured . . . 20 15
2164 5d. multicoloured . . . 25 15

1984.
2165 **690** 5d. multicoloured . . . 15 10

1984. 16th "Joy of Europe" Meeting, Belgrade. Children's Paintings. Multicoloured.
2166 26d. Type **691** 35 20
2167 40d. "Girl pushing bear in buggy" (Eva Gug) . . . 60 40

692 Virovitica (17th-century engraving)

1984. 750th Anniv of Virovitica.
2168 **692** 5d. orange and black . . 15 10

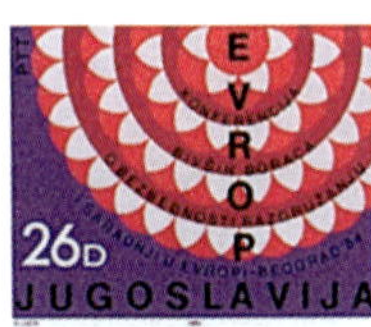

693 Map and Radio Waves **694** "Flower"

1984. 80th Anniv of Radio-Telegraphic Service in Montenegro.
2169 **693** 6d. blue and green . . . 15 10

1984. Veterans' Conference on Security, Disarmament and Co-operation in Europe, Belgrade.
2170 **694** 26d. pink, black and violet . . . . 1·00 1·00
2171 40d. green, black and blue . . . . 1·00 1·00

695 City Arms and "40" **696** Milojevic and Music Score

1984. 40th Anniv of Liberation of Belgrade.
2172 **695** 6d. red, silver and blue 15 10

1984. Birth Centenary of Miloje Milojevic (composer).
2173 **696** 6d. lilac and green . . . 15 10

697 Issues of 1944 and 1984

1984. 40th Anniv of "Nova Makedoniya" (newspaper).
2174 **697** 6d. blue and red 15 10

698 Boxing

1984. Yugoslav Olympic Games Medal Winners. Each blue and red.
2175 26d. Type **698** 30 20
2176 26d. Wrestling 30 20
2177 26d. Canoeing 30 20
2178 26d. Handball 30 20
2179 26d. Football 30 20
2180 26d. Basketball 30 20
2181 26d. Water polo 30 20
2182 26d. Rowing 30 20

699 "Madame Tatichek" (Ferdinand Waldmuller)

1984. Paintings. Multicoloured.
2183 6d. Type **699** 15 10
2184 26d. "The Bathers" (Pierre-Auguste Renoir) 35 20
2185 26d. "At the Window" (Henri Matisse) 35 20
2186 38d. "The Tahitians" (Paul Gauguin) (horiz) 40 25
2187 40d. "The Ballerinas" (Edgar Degas) (horiz) . . 60 40

1984. Nos. 1675a, 1668a and 2088 surch.
2188a 2d. on 8d.80 grey 15 10
2189 6d. on 4d. red 15 10
2190 20d. on 23d.70 red 25 10

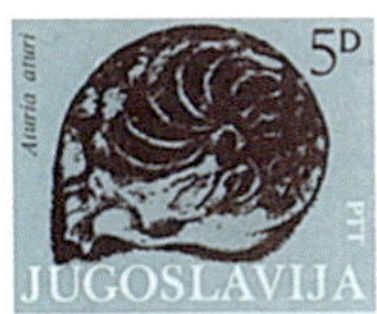

701 "Aturia aturi" (cephalopod)

1985. Museum Exhibits. Fossils.
2191 **701** 5d. purple and blue . . . 10 10
2192 – 6d. brown and light brown 10 10
2193 – 33d. brown and yellow 45 25
2194 – 60d. brown and orange 75 45
DESIGNS: 6d. "Pachyophis woodwardi" (snake); 33d. Hoefer's butterflyfish; 60d. Skull of Neanderthal man.

702 Hopovo Church **703** Three Herons in Flight

1985. 40th Anniv of Organized Protection of Yugoslav Cultural Monuments.
2195 **702** 6d. red, yellow and green 20 10

1985. 50th Anniv of Planica Ski-jump.
2196 **703** 6d. multicoloured . . . 90 30

704 Lammergeier and Douglas DC-10 Jetliner over Mountains **705** Osprey

1985. Air. Multicoloured.
2197 500d. Type **704** . . . . . . 1·75 65
2199 1000d. Red-rumped swallow and airplane at airport . . 2·50 1·25

1985. Nature Protection. Birds. Multicoloured.
2202 42d. Type **705** . . . . . . 1·75 75
2203 60d. Hoopoe . . . . 2·40 1·25

706 Three Herons in Flight

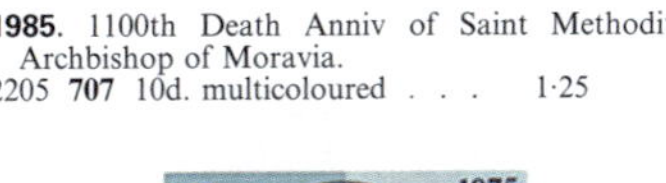
707 "St. Methodius" (detail "Seven Slav Saints", St. Naum's Church Ohrid)

1985. Obligatory Tax. 50th Anniv of Planica Ski-jump.
2204 **706** 2d. blue and green . . . 10 10

1985. 1100th Death Anniv of Saint Methodius, Archbishop of Moravia.
2205 **707** 10d. multicoloured . . . 1·25 60

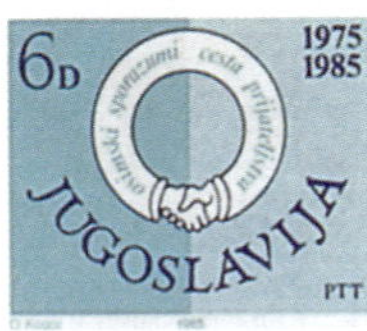

708 Handshake

1985. 10th Anniv of Osimo Agreements between Yugoslavia and Italy.
2206 **708** 6d. blue and deep blue 15 10

709 Flute, Darabukka and Josip Slavenski (composer)

1985. Europa. Multicoloured.
2207 60d. Type **709** 60 60
2208 80d. Score of "Balkanophonia" (Slavenski) 60 60

710 Red Cross and Faces **711** Vujic (after Dimitrije Auramovic)

1985. Obligatory Tax. Red Cross Week.
2209 **710** 1d. violet and red . . . 10 10
2210 2d. violet and red . . . 10 10
2211 3d. violet and red . . . 10 10
2212 4d. violet and red . . . 15 10

1985. 150th Anniv of Joakim Vujic Theatre, Kragujevac.
2213 **711** 10d. multicoloured . . . 15 10

712 Order of Liberty

1985. 40th Anniv of V.E. (Victory in Europe) Day. Multicoloured.
2214 10d. Type **712** 15 10
2215 10d. Order of National Liberation 15 10

713 Franjo Kluz and Rudi Cajavec (pilots) and Potez 25 Biplane **714** Tito (after Bozidar Jakac)

1985. Air Force Day.
2216 **713** 10d. blue, purple & brown 30 10

1985. 93rd Birth Anniv of Tito.
2217 **714** 10d. multicoloured . . . 40 10

715 Red Cross and "Skopje Earthquake" **716** Villa, Map of Islands and Arms

1985. Obligatory Tax. Solidarity Week. (a) As Nos. 1885 and 1933.
2218 2d.50 black, grey and blue 35 25
2219 3d. black, grey and blue . . 40 25

(b) Type **715**.
2220 **715** 3d. blue and red . . . . 1·50 1·25
See also Nos. 2321 5/16, 2460, 2532, 2636 and 2716.

1985. Centenary of Tourism in Cres-Losinj Region.
2221 **716** 10d. multicoloured . . . 15 10

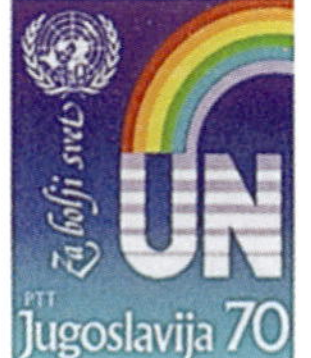

717 U.N. Emblem and Rainbow **718** Regatta Emblem

1985. 40th Anniv of U.N.O.
2222 **717** 70d. multicoloured . . . 50 35

1985. 30th Anniv of International European Danubian Regatta.
2223 **718** 70d. multicoloured . . . 45 35

719 Aerial View of Yacht **720** Model Airplane

1985. Nautical Tourism. Multicoloured.
2225 8d. Type **719** 10 10
2226 10d. Windsurfing 15 10
2227 50d. Yacht in sunset 60 35
2228 70d. Yacht by coastline . . 80 50

1985. World Free Flight Aeromodels Championships, Livno.
2229 **720** 70d. multicoloured . . . 80 35

721 Emblem and Text **722** Boy with Football

1985. Obligatory Tax. 20th European Shooting Championships, Osijek.
2230 **721** 3d. blue 10 10

1985. Obligatory Tax. Anti-tuberculosis Week.
2231 **722** 2d. black, orange and red 10 10
2232 3d. black, orange and red 10 10
2233 4d. black, orange and red 15 10
2234 5d. black, orange and red 20 10

723 "Corallina officinalis" and Seahorses

1985. Marine Flora. Multicoloured.
2235 8d. Type **723** 10 10
2236 10d. "Desmarestia viridis" 10 10
2237 50d. Bladder wrack seaweed 45 25
2238 70d. "Padina pavonia" . . . 1·00 75

724 Federation Emblem

1985. 73rd International Stomatologists Federation Congress, Belgrade.
2239 **724** 70d. multicoloured . . . 45 35

725 Selling Vegetables from Cart (Branka Lukic)

1985. 17th "Joy of Europe" Meeting, Belgrade. Children's Paintings. Multicoloured.
2240 50d. Type **725** 40 20
2241 70d. "Children playing" (Suzanne Straathof) . . . 1·10 1·10

726 Detail of Theatre Facade

1985. 125th Anniv of Croatian National Theatre, Zagreb.
2242 **726** 10d. multicoloured . . . 15 10

727 Miladin Popovic — **728** State Arms

1985. 75th Birth Anniv and 40th Death Anniv of Miladin Popovic (Communist Party worker).
2243 **727** 10d. brown and orange 15 10

1985. 40th Anniv of Federal Republic.
2244 **728** 10d. multicoloured . . . 15 10

729 "Royal Procession" (Iromie Wijewardena)

1985. Paintings. Multicoloured.
2246 8d. Type **729** 10 10
2247 10d. "Return from Hunting" (Mama Cangare) 15 10
2248 50d. "Drum of Coca" (Agnes Ovando Sanz de Franck) 40 20
2249 50d. "The Cock" (Mariano Rodriguez) (vert) 40 20
2250 70d. "Three Women" (Quamrul Hassan) (vert) 90 80

1985. Nos. 1641, 1644, 1646, 1671, 1672 and 1677/9 surch.
2251 1d. on 25p. red 60 10
2252 2d. on 5p. orange 35 10
2253 3d. on 35p. red 15 10
2254 4d. on 5d.60 olive 65 40
2255 8d. on 6d. brown 15 10
2256 20d. on 26d. blue 15 10
2257 50d. on 16d.50 blue 60 15
2258 70d. on 38d. mauve 90 20

731 Zagreb Exhibition Hall

1986.
2259 **731** 100d. violet and yellow 60 30

732 Patrol Car

1986. 40th Anniv of Yugoslav Automobile Association. Multicoloured.
2260 10d. Type **732** 10 10
2261 70d. Red Cross helicopter 1·25 75

733 Wildlife on River Bank — **734** Church of the Virgin

1986. Nature Protection. River Tara. Mult.
2262 100d. Type **733** 40 40
2263 150d. Bridge over river . . . 90 90

1986. 800th Anniv of Studenica Monastery.
2264 **734** 10d. red, green and blue 60 30

735 Postman on Motor Cycle — **736** Player and Ball in Goal

1986. Postal Services.
2265a **735** 20d. purple 15 10
2266a – 30d. brown 20 10
2267 – 40d. red 15 10
2268 – 50d. violet 25 10
2269 – 60d. green 15 10
2270 – 93d. blue 15 10
2271 – 100d. purple 30 10
2272 – 106d. red 15 10
2272a – 106d. brown 15 10
2273 – 120d. green 15 10
2274 – 140d. red 15 10
2275 – 170d. green 15 15
2276 – 200d. blue . . . . . 1·25 30
2277 – 220d. brown 15 15
2278 – 300d. red 20 15
2279 – 500d. blue and orange 40 30
2279a – 500d. blue and yellow 30 20
2280 **735** 800d. blue 15 15
2281 – 1000d. violet and green 40 20
2282 – 2000d. green and orange 25 20
2283 – 5000d. blue and red . . 90 50
2284a – 10000d. violet & orange 30 15
2285a – 20000d. brown and green . . . . . . 1·00 50

DESIGNS—As T **735**. HORIZ: 40d. Forklift truck; 50, 20000d. Electric train; 200d. Freighter. VERT: 30, 10000d. Postman giving letters to man; 60d. Posting letters; 93d. Envelope and leaflet; 106d. (2272), Woman working at computer and woman filling envelopes; 106 (2272a), 140d. Woman working at computer; 120d. Woman with Valentine card; 170, 300d. Flower and post box; 220d. Mail coach and cover; 500d. (both) Postal sorter; 1000d. Woman using public telephone; 2000d. Telephone card, tokens and handset; 5000d. Posthorn, globe and bird with stamp. 20 × 18 mm: 100d. Postman and van.
See also Nos. 2587/98.

1986. World Cup Football Championship, Mexico. Multicoloured.
2286 70d. Type **736** 60 60
2287 150d. Players and ball in goal 60 60

737 St. Clement and Model of Ohrid (fresco, Church of St. Spas)

1986. 1100th Anniv of Arrival of St. Clement of Ohrid in Macedonia.
2288 **737** 10d. multicoloured . . . 1·00 60

1986. No. 1674 surch.
2289 5d. on 8d. grey 10 10

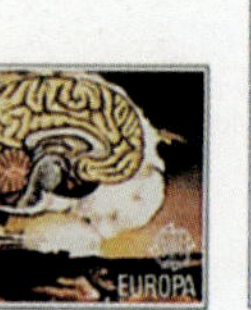

739 Human Brain as Nuclear Cloud — **740** Judo

1986. Europa. Multicoloured.
2290 100d. Type **739** 50 30
2291 200d. Injured deer on road 90 50

1988. European Men's Judo Championships, Belgrade.
2292 **740** 70d. brown, pink and blue 45 30

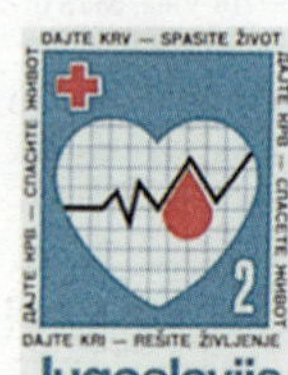
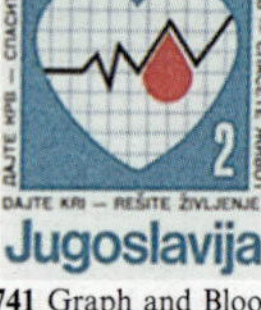

741 Graph and Blood Drop within Heart — **742** Costume of Slovenia

1986. Obligatory Tax. Red Cross Week.
2293 **741** 2d. black, blue and red 10 10
2294 3d. black, blue and red 10 10
2295 4d. black, blue and red 10 10
2296 5d. black, blue and red 15 15
2297 11d. black, blue and red 15 15
2298 20d. black, blue and red 40 30

1986. Yugoslav Costumes. Multicoloured.
2299 50d. Type **742** 30 20
2300 50d. Vojvodina (woman with red apron) 30 20
2301 50d. Croatia (man in embroidered trousers) . . 30 20
2302 50d. Macedonia (woman hand spinning) 30 20
2303 50d. Serbia (woman in bolero) 30 20
2304 50d. Montenegro (man with rifle) 30 20
2305 50d. Kosovo (woman carrying basket) 30 20
2306 50d. Bosnia and Herzegovina (man carrying bag on back) . . 30 20

743 Yachts — **744** Tito (after Safet Zec)

1986. "Flying Dutchman" Class European Sailing Championships, Moscenicka Draga. Mult.
2307 50d. Type **743** 60 15
2308 80d. Yachts (different) . . . 85 25

1986. 94th Birth Anniv of Tito.
2310 **744** 10d. multicoloured . . . 15 10

745 Peacock Moth — **746** "Skopje Earthquake"

1986. Butterflies and Moths. Multicoloured.
2311 10d. Type **745** 10 10
2312 20d. Peacock 15 10
2313 50d. Apollo 40 30
2314 100d. Purple emperor . . . 90 70

1986. Obligatory Tax. Solidarity Week. (a) As No. 2200.
2315 **715** 10d. blue and red . . . 70 50

(b) As Type **715** but inscr "Solidarity Week" in four languages.
2316 10d. blue and red 70 50

(c) Type **746**.
2317 **746** 10d. lilac and red . . . 70 50

747 Bosancica Manuscript

1986. Museum Exhibits. Ancient Manuscripts. Multicoloured.
2319 10d. Type **747** 10 10
2320 20d. Leontije's Gospel . . . 10 10
2321 50d. Astrological writing, Mesopotamia 30 25
2322 100d. Hagada (ritual book), Spain 60 50

748 Congress Poster (Branislav Dobanovacki)

1986. 13th Communist League Conference, Belgrade.
2323 **748** 10d. black and red . . . 10 10
2324 – 20d. black and red . . . 10 10
DESIGN: 20d. Another part of the Congress poster.

749 Trubar and Title Page of "Abecedari"

1986. 400th Death Anniv of Primoz Trubar (founder of Slovenian literary language and religious reformer).
2326 **749** 20d. multicoloured . . . 45 25

750 Emblem — **751** Dancers

1986. 125th Anniv of Serbian National Theatre, Novi Sad.
2327 **750** 40d. multicoloured . . . 20 10

1986. Rugovo Dance.
2328 **751** 40d. multicoloured . . . 20 10

753 Crosses forming Earth and Sky

1986. Obligatory Tax. Anti-tuberculosis Week.
2330 **753** 2d. multicoloured . . . 10 10
2331 5d. multicoloured . . . 10 10
2332 6d. multicoloured . . . 10 10
2333 7d. multicoloured . . . 15 10
2334 8d. multicoloured . . . 15 10
2335 10d. multicoloured . . . 15 10
2336 11d. multicoloured . . . 20 15
2337 14d. multicoloured . . . 20 15
2338 20d. multicoloured . . . 20 15

754 Volleyball — **755** "Bird and Child running on Globe" (Tanja Faletic)

1986. "Universiade '87" University Games, Zagreb. Zagi (games mascot). Multicoloured.
2339 30d. Type **754** 10 10
2340 40d. Canoeing 15 10
2341 100d. Gymnastics 40 30
2342 150d. Fencing 75 50

1986. 18th "Joy of Europe" Meeting, Belgrade. Children's Paintings. Multicoloured.
2343 100d. Type **755** 40 25
2344 150d. "City of the Future" (Johanna Kraus) 60 35

756 Diagram of Rotary Selector and Bled

1986. 50th Anniv of Automatic Telephone Exchange Network.
2345 **756** 40d. multicoloured . . . 15 10

757 Criminal in Stocking Mask

758 Brigade Member addressing Crowd (after Djordje Andrejevic-Kun)

1986. 55th Interpol General Assembly Session, Belgrade.
2346 **757** 150d. multicoloured . . 50 25

1986. 50th Anniv of Formation of International Brigades in Spain.
2347 **758** 40d. brown, gold and orange 15 10

759 Academy

1986. Centenary of Serbian Academy of Arts and Sciences.
2348 **759** 40d. multicoloured . . . 15 10

760 People riding on Doves (Branislav Barnak)

1986. International Peace Year.
2349 **760** 150d. multicoloured . . 65 35

761 "Portrait" (Bernard Buffet)

1986. Paintings in Museum of Contemporary Arts, Skopje. Multicoloured.
2350 30d. "Still Life" (Frantisek Muzika) 10 10
2351 40d. "Disturbance" (detail, Rafael Canogar)(horiz) . . 15 10
2352 100d. Type **761** 40 25
2353 100d. "IOL" (Victor Vasarely) 40 25
2354 150d. "Woman's Head" (Pablo Picasso) 60 35

762 European Otter

1987. Protected Animals. Multicoloured.
2355 30d. Type **762** 10 10
2356 40d. Argali 15 10
2357 100d. Red deer 40 30
2358 150d. Brown bear 75 60

763 Boskovic, Brera Observatory and Solar Eclipse

1987. Death Bicentenary of Ruder Boskovic (astronomer).
2359 **763** 150d. multicoloured . . 50 35

764 Mountains, Woodlands and Animal Feeder

766 Mateja Svet

765 Potez 29-4 Biplane

1987. Nature Protection. Triglav National Park. Multicoloured.
2360 150d. Type **764** 50 50
2361 400d. Mountains, woodland and glacial lake . . . . . 1·60 1·60

1987. 60th Anniv of Civil Aviation in Yugoslavia. Multicoloured.
2362 150d. Type **765** 75 40
2363 400d. Douglas DC-10 jetliner . . . . 1·75 1·00

1987. Yugoslav Medals at World Alpine Skiing Championships, Crans Montana.
2364 **766** 200d. multicoloured . . 60 50

767 Kole Nedelkovski

1987. 75th Birth Anniv of Kole Nedelkovski (poet and revolutionary).
2365 **767** 40d. multicoloured . . . 15 10

768 Gusle and Battle Flags of Vucji Do and Grahovo

1987. 125th Anniv of Liberation Wars of Montenegro.
2366 **768** 40d. multicoloured . . . 15 10

769 "Founding the Party at Cebine, 1937" (Anton Gojmir Kos)

1987. 50th Anniv of Slovenian Communist Party.
2367 **769** 40d. multicoloured . . . 15 10

770 Tito Bridge (Ilija Stojadinovic)

771 Children of Different Races in Flower

1987. Europa. Architecture. Multicoloured.
2368 200d. Type **770** 65 65
2369 400d. Bridges over River Ljubljanica (Joze Plecnik) 1·75 1·00

1987. Obligatory Tax. Red Cross Week.
2370 **771** 2d. multicoloured . . . 25 20
2371 4d. multicoloured . . . 25 20
2372 5d. multicoloured . . . 25 20
2373 6d. multicoloured . . . 25 20
2374 7d. multicoloured . . . 25 20
2375 8d. multicoloured . . . 25 20
2376 10d. multicoloured . . . 25 20
2377 11d. multicoloured . . . 25 20
2378 12d. multicoloured . . . 25 20
2379 14d. multicoloured . . . 25 20
2380 17d. multicoloured . . . 25 20
2381 20d. multicoloured . . . 25 20

772 Almonds

773 Tito (after Mosa Pijade)

1987. Fruit. Multicoloured.
2382 60d. Type **772** 10 10
2383 150d. Pear 20 15
2384 200d. Apple 55 45
2385 400d. Plum . . . . 1·10 90

1987. 95th Birth Anniv of Josip Broz Tito.
2386 **773** 60d. multicoloured . . . 15 10

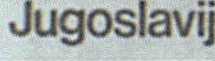

774 "Skopje Earthquake"

776 Mail Coach in Zrenjanin

775 Bust of Karadzic (Petar Ubavkic), Trsic (birthplace) and Vienna

1987. Obligatory Tax. Solidarity Week.
2387 **774** 30d. multicoloured . . . 40 25

1987. Birth Bicentenary of Vuk Stefanovic Karadzic (linguist and historian). Multicoloured.
2388 60d. Type **775** 15 10
2389 200d. Serbian alphabet and Karadzic (portrait by Uros Knezevic) 35 25

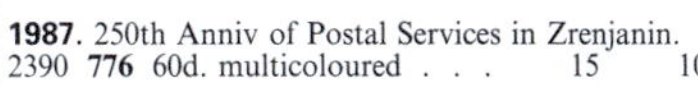

1987. 250th Anniv of Postal Services in Zrenjanin.
2390 **776** 60d. multicoloured . . . 15 10

777 Emblem and Mascot

778 Hurdling

1987. Obligatory Tax. "Universiade '87" University Games, Zagreb.
2391 **777** 20d. blue and green . . 30 20

1987. "Universiade '87" University Games, Zagreb. Multicoloured.
2392 60d. Type **778** 15 10
2393 150d. Basketball 25 20
2394 200d. Gymnastics 30 25
2395 400d. Swimming . . . . . 1·10 85

779 Canadair CL-215 Amphibian spraying Forest Fire

780 Monument, Anindol Park

1987. Fire Fighting. Multicoloured.
2396 60d. Type **779** 25 25
2397 200d. Fire-fighting tug . . . 25 15

1987. 50th Anniv of Croatian Communist Party.
2398 **780** 60d. multicoloured . . . 15 10

781 School and Foundation Document

782 Crosses and Children's Head

1987. 150th Anniv of Sabac High School.
2399 **781** 80d. brown, orange and blue 15 10

1987. Obligatory Tax. Anti-tuberculosis Week.
2400 **782** 2d. multicoloured . . . 10 10
2401 4d. multicoloured . . . 10 10
2402 6d. multicoloured . . . 10 10
2403 8d. multicoloured . . . 10 10
2404 10d. multicoloured . . . 10 10
2405 12d. multicoloured . . . 10 10
2406 14d. multicoloured . . . 10 10
2407 20d. multicoloured . . . 10 10
2408 25d. multicoloured . . . 10 10
2409 40d. multicoloured . . . 10 10

783 Emblem, Map and Flowers

1987. "Balkanphila XI" International Stamp Exhibition, Novi Sad.
2410 **783** 250d. multicoloured . . 30 20

1987. No. 2269 surch **80**.
2412 80d. on 60d. green 10 10

785 "Children playing amongst Trees" (Bedic Aranka)

786 SPRAM Emblem

1987. 19th "Joy of Europe" Meeting. Mult.
2413 250d. Type **785** 45 45
2414 400d. "Child and scarecrow in orchard" (Ingeborg Schaffer) 75 75

1987. Obligatory Tax. Model Airplane Championships, Belgrade.
2415 **786** 20d. blue 10 10

787 Arslanagica Bridge, Trebinje

1987. Bridges. Multicoloured.
2416 80d. Type **787** 10 10
2417 250d. Terzija Bridge, Djakovica 20 15

788 Tug in Canal

1987. 600th Anniv of Titov Vrbas.
2418 **788** 80d. multicoloured . . . 15 10

789 Eclipse, First Telescope and Old Observatory Building

1987. Cent of Astronomocal and Meteorological Observatory, Belgrade.
2419 **789** 80d. multicoloured . . . 15 10

790 "St. Luke the Evangelist" (Raphael)

1987. Paintings in Mimara Museum, Zagreb. Multicoloured.
2420 80d. Type **790** 15 10
2421 200d. "Infanta Maria Theresa" (Diego Velazquez) 25 15
2422 250d. "Nicolaus Rubens" (Peter Paul Rubens) . . . 25 15
2423 400d. "Louise Laure Sennegon" (Camille Corot) 75 60

791 Bull Fighting (Grmec)

1987. Museum Exhibits. Folk Games. Mult.
2424 80d. Type **791** 15 10
2425 200d. Sword used in Ljuvicevo Horse Games 25 15
2426 250d. Crown worn at Moresca Games (Korcula) 25 15
2427 400d. Sinj Iron Ring 75 60

792 Codex and Novi Vinodol

1988. 700th Anniv of Vinodol Law Codex.
2428 **792** 100d. multicoloured . . 15 10

793 Skier

794 Cub

1988. 25th Anniv of Golden Fox Skiing Competition, Maribor.
2429 **793** 350d. multicoloured . . 35 15

1988. Protected Wildlife. The Brown Bear. Mult.
2430 70d. Type **794** 15 10
2431 80d. Bears among branches 15 10
2432 200d. Adult bear 35 15
2433 350d. Adult stalking prey 60 30

795 Skier

797 Basketball

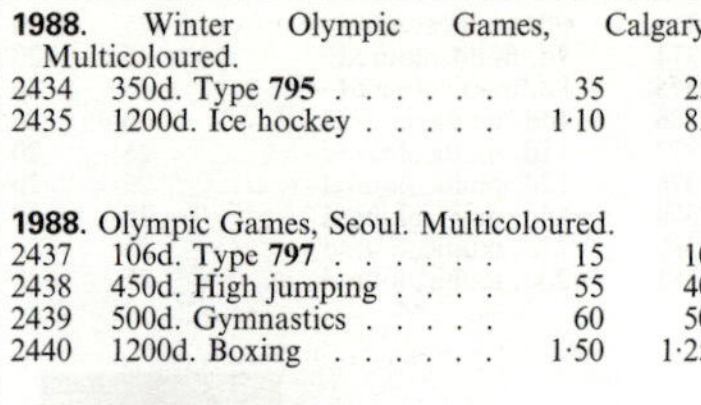

1988. Winter Olympic Games, Calgary. Multicoloured.
2434 350d. Type **795** 35 25
2435 1200d. Ice hockey . . . . . 1·10 85

1988. Olympic Games, Seoul. Multicoloured.
2437 106d. Type **797** 15 10
2438 450d. High jumping 55 40
2439 500d. Gymnastics 60 50
2440 1200d. Boxing . . . . . . 1·50 1·25

798 White Carnations

799 "INTELSAT V-A", Globe and Dish Aerials, Ivanjica

1988. Obligatory Tax. Anti-cancer Campaign. Multicoloured.
2442 4d. Type **798** 10 10
2443 8d. Red flowers 10 10
2444 12d. Red roses 10 10

1988. Europa. Transport and Communications. Multicoloured.
2445 450d. Type **799** 30 20
2446 1200d. Woman using mobile telephone and methods of transport . . . . 1·10 60

800 Anniversary Emblem

801 Great Top Shell

1988. Obligatory Tax. 125th Anniv of Red Cross.
2447 **800** 4d. blue, red and grey 20 15
2448 8d. blue, red and grey 20 15
2449 10d. blue, red and grey 20 15
2450 12d. blue, red and grey 20 15
2451 20d. blue, red and grey 20 15
2452 30d. blue, red and grey 20 15
2453 50d. blue, red and grey 20 15

1988. Molluscs. Multicoloured.
2454 106d. Type **801** 10 10
2455 550d. St. James's scallop . . 55 45
2456 600d. Giant tun 60 50
2457 1000d. "Argonauta cygnus" (wrongly inscr "argo") . . 1·00 85

802 Tito

803 "Skopje Earthquake"

1988. 60th Anniv of Trial of Josip Broz Tito.
2458 **802** 106d. brown and black 10 10

1988. Obligatory Tax. Solidarity Week. (a) Type **803**.
2459 **803** 50d. grey, brown and red 35 20

(b) As No. 2220 but value changed.
2460 **715** 50d. blue and red . . . 35 20

(c) No. 2387 surch **50** and emblem.
2461 **774** 50d. on 30d. mult . . . 35 20

805 First Lyceum Building

806 Krleza

1988. 150th Anniv of Belgrade University.
2462 **805** 106d. multicoloured . . 15 10

1988. Obligatory Tax. Culture Fund. 95th Birth Anniv of Miroslav Krleza (writer).
2463 **806** 30d. brown and orange 15 10

1988. Nos. 2270 and 2272a surch.
2464 120d. on 93d. blue 15 10
2465 140d. on 106d. brown . . . 15 10

808 "Phelypaea boissieri"

809 Globe and Flags

1988. Nature Protection Macedonian Plants. Multicoloured.
2466 600d. Type **808** 45 45
2467 1000d. "Campanula formanekiana" 75 75

1988. Centenary of Esperanto (invented language).
2468 **809** 600d. blue and green . . 50 40

810 Shipping on the Danube

811 Globe as Ball in Basket

1988. 40th Anniv of Danube Conference.
2469 **810** 1000d. multicoloured . . 60 35

1988. 13th European Junior Basketball Championships, Tito Vrbas and Srbobran.
2471 **811** 600d. multicoloured . . 30 25

812 Horse Racing

1988. 125th Anniv of Belgrade Horse Races. Multicoloured.
2472 140d. Type **812** 15 10
2473 600d. Show jumping 35 30
2474 1000d. Trotting race 50 45

813 Douglas DC-10 Jetliner and Globe

1988. Air.
2475 **813** 2000d. multicoloured . . 90 30

814 Museum and Bosnian Bellflower

815 Flame and Hand

1988. Centenary of Bosnia amd Herzegovina Museum, Sarajevo.
2476 **814** 140d. multicoloured . . 10 10

1988. Obligatory Tax. Anti-tuberculosis Week. (a) Type **815**.
2477 **815** 4d. multicoloured . . . 15 15
2478 8d. multicoloured . . . 15 15
2479 12d. multicoloured . . . 15 15
2480 20d. multicoloured . . . 15 15
2481 50d. multicoloured . . . 15 15
2482 70d. multicoloured . . . 15 15

(b) No. 2039 surch **1988 12**.
2483 **632** 12d. on 1d. orange, black and red . . . . 3·25 3·25

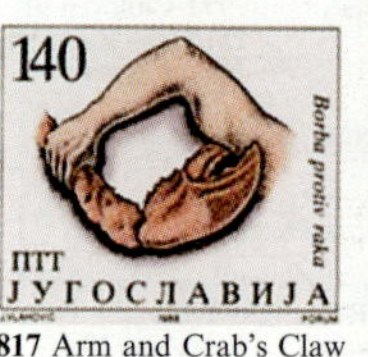

817 Arm and Crab's Claw (anti-cancer)

818 "Daughter of the Artist" (Peter Ranosovic)

1988. Health Campaigns. Multicoloured.
2484 140d. Type **817** 15 10
2485 1000d. Screaming mouth in splash of blood (anti-AIDS) 45 40

1988. 20th "Joy of Europe" Meeting. Mult.
2486 1000d. Type **818** 55 50
2487 1100d. "Girl wuth Straw Hat" (Pierre-Auguste Renoir) 65 60

819 1701 Arms and Present Emblem

1988. 50th Anniv of Slovenian Academy of Arts and Sciences.
2488 **819** 200d. multicoloured . . 15 10

820 Galicnik Wedding

1988. Museum Exhibits. Traditional Crafts and Customs. Multicoloured.
2489 200d. Type **820** 15 10
2490 1000d. Weapons from Bay of Kotor 40 25
2491 1000d. Vojvodina embroidery (horiz) . . . 40 25
2492 1100d. Masks from Ptuj (horiz) 60 40

821 Title Page of "Gorski Vijenac" and Petar II (after J. Boss)

1988. 175th Birth Anniv of Prince-Bishop Petar II of Montenegro. Multicoloured.
2493 200d. Type **821** 15 10
2494 1000d. Njegos Mausoleum, Lovcen and Petar II in bishop's robes (after Josip Tominc) 45 30

822 "Girl with Lyre"

1988. Greek Terracotta Figures from Josip Broz Tito Memorial Centre Collection. Multicoloured.
2495 200d. Type **822** 15 10
2496 1000d. "Girl on a stone" . . 40 25
2497 1000d. "Eros and Psyche" 40 25
2498 1100d. "Girl by Stele" . . . 60 40

823 Krsmanovic House, Belgrade

1988. 70th Anniv of Yugoslavian State.
2499 **823** 200d. multicoloured . . 10 10

1988. Nos. 2273/4 surch.
2500 170d. on 120d. green . . . 15 10
2501 220d. on 140d. red 15 10

825 Pistol shooting

1988. Yugoslavian Medals at Olympic Games. Multicoloured.

2502	500d. Type **825** (2 gold, 1 bronze)	15	10
2503	500d. Handball (bronze)	15	10
2504	500d. Table tennis (silver and bronze)	15	10
2505	500d. Wrestling (silver)	15	10
2506	500d. Rowing (bronze)	15	10
2507	500d. Basketball (2 silver)	15	10
2508	500d. Water polo (gold)	15	10
2509	500d. Boxing (bronze)	15	10

826 Gundulic and Dubrovnik

1989. 400th Birth Anniv of Ivan Gundulic (poet).
2510 **826** 220d. multicoloured . . 10 10

827 Mallards

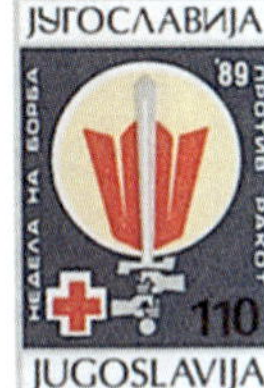
827a Emblem

1989. Wild Ducks. Multicoloured.

2511	300d. Type **827**	20	20
2512	2100d. Green-winged teal	1·10	1·10
2513	2200d. Pintail	1·25	1·25
2514	2200d. Common shoveler	1·25	1·25

1989. Obligatory Tax. Anti-cancer Week. (a) Type **827a**.
2514a **827a** 110d. multicoloured 25 10

(b) Inscr "YUGOSLAVIJA MAKEDONIJA". Surch **1989** and value.
2514b – 110d. on 20d. black, red and gold 25 10

DESIGN: No. 2514b, Sword emblem with blade doubling as Aesculapius rod enclosing crab against background of "flower".

828 Valvasor and Wagensperg Castle

1989. 300th Anniv of Publishing of "The Glory of the Duchy of Kranjska" by Johann Weickhard Valvasor.
2515 **828** 300d. multicoloured . . 15 10

829 "Bulbocodium vernum"

1989. Flowers. Multicoloured.

2516	300d. Type **829**	10	10
2517	2100d. White water-lily	70	35
2518	2200d. "Fritillaria degeniana" (vert)	75	40
2519	3000d. "Orchis simia" (vert)	1·00	60

830 Envelopes and Dish Aerial

1989. Air.

2520 **830**	10000d. blue, mauve and yellow	1·50	90
2521 –	20000d. orange, violet and red	1·40	1·25

DESIGN: 20000d. Europe on globe and satellite.

1989. No. 1657 surch **100**.
2522 100d. on 1d. green 15 10

832 Competitor

1989. 6th World Air Gun Championships, Sarajevo.
2523 **832** 3000d. multicoloured . . 50 40

833 Girl looking through Magic Cube

834 Anniversary Emblem

1989. Europa. Children's Games and Toys. Multicoloured.

2524	3000d. Type **833**	75	60
2525	6000d. Boy playing with marbles and paper boats	1·50	1·10

1989. Obligatory Tax. 125th Anniv (1988) of International Red Cross.

2526 **834**	20d. blue, silver and red	15	15
2527	80d. blue, silver and red	15	15
2528	150d. blue, silver and red	15	15
2529	160d. blue, silver and red	15	15

835 Josip Broz Tito

836 "Skopje Earthquake"

1989. 70th Anniv of Yugoslavian Communist Party.
2530 **835** 300d. multicoloured . . 15 10

1989. Obligatory Tax. Solidarity Week. (a) Perf.
2531 **836** 250d. silver and red . . 60 35

(b) Rouletted.
2532 **715** 400d. blue and red . . . 80 55

837 Pole Vaulting

838 Racers

1989. 15th European Trophy Athletic Clubs Championship, Belgrade.
2533 **837** 4000d. multicoloured . . 40 25

1989. Motor Cycle Grand Prix, Rijeka. Mult.

2534	500d. Type **838**	20	15
2535	4000d. Racers (different)	45	30

839 Ancient Greek Galleys

1989. Sailing Ships. Multicoloured.

2537	1000d. Type **839**	55	25
2538	1000d. Roman warships	55	25
2539	1000d. 13th-century Crusader nefs	55	25
2540	1000d. 16th-century Dubrovnik navas	55	25
2541	1000d. 17th-century French warships	55	25
2542	1000d. 18th-century ships of the line	55	25

840 Flags of Netherlands, Italy, U.S.S.R. and Spain and Ball

1989. 26th European Men's Basketball Championship, Zagreb. Multicoloured.

2544	2000d. Type **840** (Group A)	15	15
2545	2000d. Flags of France, Yugoslavia, Greece and Bulgaria and ball (Group B)	15	15

841 "Battle of Kosovo" (lithograph, Adam Stefanovic)

1989. 600th Anniv of Battle of Kosovo.
2546 **841** 500d. multicoloured . . 15 10

842 Danilovgrad

1989. Centenary of First Reading Room at Danilovgrad.
2547 **842** 500d. multicoloured . . 15 10

1989. No. 2277 surch **700**.
2548 700d. on 220d. brown . . . 15 10

1989. Nos. 2266 and 2275 surch.

2549	400d. on 30d. brown	25	15
2550	700d. on 170d. green	25	15

845 Stone Tablet, Detail of Charter and Mule Train

846 Emblem

1989. 800th Anniv of Kulin Ban Charter (granting free trade to Dubrovnik).
2551 **845** 500d. multicoloured . . 15 10

1989. Obligatory Tax. Construction of Youth House.
2552 **846** 400d. blue and red . . . 15 10

847 Rowers of Bled Lake

848 Houses of Parliament, London

1989. World Rowing Championship, Bled.
2553 **847** 10000d. multicoloured 50 40

1989. Centenary of Interparliamentary Union.

2554	10000d. Type **848**	40	30
2555	10000d. Notre Dame Cathedral, Paris	40	30

849 Belgrade and Cairo

1989. 9th Heads of Non-aligned Countries Conference, Belgrade. Previous Host Cities. Multicoloured.

2556	10000d. Type **849**	50	40
2557	10000d. Lusaka and Algiers	50	40
2558	10000d. Colombo and Havana	50	40
2559	10000d. New Delhi and Harare	50	40

850 Jazinac Lake, Brezovica, and "Paeonia officinalis"

851 Crosses as Basket of Flowers

1989. Nature Protection. Kosovo. Multicoloured.

2561	8000d. Type **850**	40	25
2562	10000d. Mirusa Canyon and "Paeonia corallina"	60	45

1989. Obligatory Tax. Anti-tuberculosis Week.

2563 **851**	20d. red and black	15	10
2564	200d. red and black	15	10
2565	250d. red and black	15	10
2566	400d. red and black	15	10
2567	650d. red and black	15	10

852 "Child with Lamb" (Jovan Popovic)

853 Men Fighting

1989. 21st "Joy of Europe" Meeting. Mult.

2568	10000d. Type **852**	50	30
2569	10000d. "Girl feeding Dog" (Aelbert Cuyp)	50	30

1989. 300th Anniv of Karpos Insurrection.
2570 **853** 1200d. multicoloured . . 15 10

854 Cancelled 100d. Stamp, Quill and Seal

1989. Stamp Day.
2571 **854** 1200d. multicoloured . . 15 10

855 Packsaddle Maker

1989. Museum Exhibits. Traditional Crafts. Multicoloured.

2572	1200d. Type **855**	10	10
2573	14000d. Cooper	45	35
2574	15000d. Wine maker	50	40
2575	30000d. Weaver	95	80

856 Aerospatiale/Aeritalia ATR 42 Airliner, Arrows and Map

856a Emblem

1989. Air.
2576 **856** 50000d. blue and orange 1·60 80

1989. Obligatory Tax. 29th Chess Olympiad, Novi Sad.
2577 **856a** 600d. black and blue 25 10

See also No. 2660.

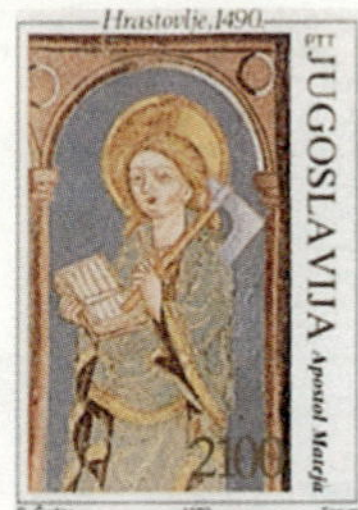
857 "Apostle Matthias"

1989. Frescoes by Iohannes de Kastua from Holy Trinity Church, Hrastovlje, Slovenia. Multicoloured.
2578 2100d. Type **857** 10 10
2579 21000d. "St. Barbara" . . . 45 40
2580 30000d. "Creation of the Universe, the Fourth Day" (horiz) 75 65
2581 50000d. "Creation of the Universe, the Fifth Day" (horiz) . . . . 1·10 1·00

858 Barn Swallow, Envelope and Flower

1989.
2582 **858** 100000d. green & orange 15 15

1989. No. 1680 surch **700**.
2583 700d. on 70d. blue 25 15

860 Colour Spectrum entering Star

1990. 14th Extraordinary Congress of League of Communists of Yugoslavia, Belgrade.
2584 **860** 10000d. multicoloured 30 15
2585 – 50000d. multicoloured 40 35
DESIGN: 50000d. Hammer and sickle on computer screen.

1990. Postal Services. As T **735** but in revised currency.
2587 10p. violet and green . . . 10 10
2588 20p. red and yellow 25 10
2589 30p. green and orange . . . 15 10
2590 40p. green and purple . . . 15 10
2591 50p. green and violet . . . 25 10
2592 60p. mauve and red 25 10
2593 1d. blue and purple 15 15
2594 2d. blue and red 30 15
2595 3d. blue and red 40 25
2596 5d. ultramarine and blue . . 70 40
2597 10d. blue and red . . . . . 4·75 4·75
2598 20d. red and orange 35 25
DESIGNS—VERT: 10p. Man posting letters; 20p. Postal sorter; 30p. Postman giving letters to man; 40p., 20d. Woman telephoning; 50p. Posthorn, globe and bird; 60p. Telephone card, tokens and handset; 3d. Post-box; 5d. Airplane, letters and map; 10d. Barn swallow, flower and envelope. HORIZ: 1d. Electric train; 2d. Freighter.

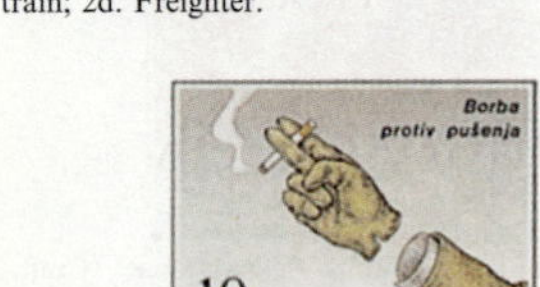
861 Gloved Hand holding Lighted Cigarette

1990. Anti-smoking Campaign.
2605 **861** 10d. multicoloured . . . 1·00 85

862 Northern Pike

862a Pink Flowers

1990. Endangered Fishes. Multicoloured.
2606 1d. Type **862** 25 15
2607 5d. Wels 65 30
2608 10d. Burbot . . . . 1·25 90
2609 15d. Eurasian perch . . . . 1·75 1·40

1990. Obligatory Tax. Anti-cancer Week.
2610 30p. Type **862a** 25 10
2611 30p. Yellow flowers 25 10

863 Zabljak Fortress, Printed Page from 1494 and Arms

1990. 500th Anniv of Enthronement of Djuradj Crnojevic of Montenegro.
2612 **863** 50p. multicoloured . . . 45 35

864 Telegraphist and V.D.U. Screen

1990. 125th Anniv of I.T.U.
2613 **864** 6d.50 multicoloured . . 70 60

865 Footballers

866 Skopje Posts and Telecommunications Centre

1990. World Cup Football Championship, Italy.
2614 – 6d.50 multicoloured . . 1·00 60
2615 **865** 10d. multicoloured . . 1·40 1·00
DESIGN: 6d.50, Footballers (different).

1990. Europa. Post Office Buildings. Mult.
2616 6d.50 Type **866** . . . . . . 1·00 75
2617 10d. Belgrade Telephone Exchange . . . . 1·40 1·10

867 Chicago Water Tower and Carnation

868 Record, Notes and Pen

1990. Centenary of Labour Day.
2618 **867** 6d.50 multicoloured . . 75 50

1990. Eurovision Song Contest, Zagreb. Mult.
2619 6d.50 Type **868** 75 50
2620 10d. Conductor and score of "Te Deum" by Marc-Antoine Charpentier (theme tune of contest) . . 1·40 1·00

869 Cross and Leaves

870 Large Yellow Flowers

1990. Obligatory Tax. (a) Red Cross Week.
2621 **869** 10p. red and green . . . 15 10
2622 20p. red and green . . . 15 10
2623 30p. red and green . . . 15 10

(b) 45th Anniv of Macedonian Red Cross. Flower Paintings by Zivko Popovski. Multicoloured.
2624 20p. Type **870** 15 10
2625 20p. Arrangement of small yellow flowers 15 10
2626 20p. Anniversary emblem 15 10
See also Nos. 2633/4.

871 Server

873 Tito (bronze, Antun Augustincic)

1990. Yugoslav Open Tennis Championship, Umag. Multicoloured.
2627 6d.50 Type **871** 75 60
2628 10d. Receiver . . . . . . 1·50 1·10

1990. No. 2282 surch **0,50**.
2629 **735** 50p. on 800d. blue . . . 20 10

1990. 98th Birth Anniv of Josip Broz Tito.
2630 **873** 50p. multicoloured . . . 25 15

874 "Tartar Post Riders" (Carl Goebel)

1990. 150th Anniv of Public Postal Service in Serbia.
2631 **874** 50p. multicoloured . . . 60 40

875 "Skopje Earthquake"

876 "Skopje Earthquake"

1990. Obligatory Tax. Solidarity Week.
2632 **875** 20p. brown, silver and red 70 35
2633 – 20p. multicoloured . . . 15 10
2634 – 20p. multicoloured . . . 15 10
2635 **876** 20p. blue and red . . . 45 45
2636 **715** 30p. blue and red . . . 40 25
DESIGNS—As T **875**: No. 2633, Mauve flowers; 2634, Red and yellow flowers.
See also No. 2711.

877 Fantail

879 Newspaper Offices, Museum and Mastheads

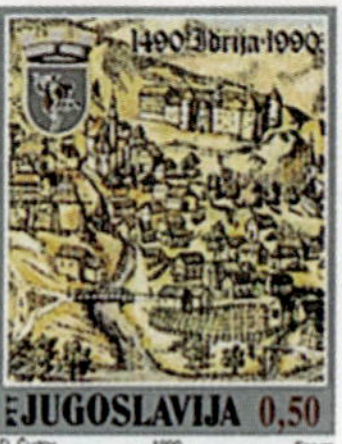
878 Idrija Town

1990. Pigeons. Multicoloured.
2637 50p. Type **877** 15 10
2638 5d. Serbian high flier . . . 75 55
2639 6d.50 Carrier pigeon (vert) 1·25 85
2640 10d. Pouter (vert) . . . . . 1·75 1·25

1990. 500th Anniversaries of Idrija Town (2641) and Mercury Mine (2642). Multicoloured.
2641 50p. Type **878** 15 10
2642 6d.50 Mine 85 50

1990. 50th Anniv of "Vjesnik" (newspaper).
2643 **879** 60p. multicoloured . . . 30 20

1990. Nos. 2588/9 surch.
2644 50p. on 20p. red and yellow 25 15
2645 1d. on 30p. green and orange 20 15

881 Runners leaving Blocks

881a Emblem

1990. European Athletics Championships, Split. Multicoloured.
2646 1d. Type **881** 45 30
2647 6d.50 Runners' feet 80 70

1990. Obligatory Tax. European Athletics Championships, Split.
2649 **881a** 50p. blue and red . . . 25 10

882 Nurse and Sun

883 Flowers in Vase and Birds

1990. Obligatory Tax. Anti-tuberculosis Week.
2650 **882** 20p. yellow, blue and red 15 10
2651 25p. yellow, blue and red 15 10
2652 50p. yellow, blue and red 15 10
2653 **883** 50p. brown, red and grey 15 10

884 "Pec Patriachate" (Dimitrije Cudov)

1990. 300th Anniv of Great Migration of Serbs. Multicoloured.
2654 1d. Type **884** 15 10
2655 6d.50 "Migration of Serbs" (Paja Jovanovic) 85 70

1990. No. 2590 surch **2**.
2656 2d. on 40p. green and purple 45 15

887 "Little Sisters" (Ivana Kobilca)

888 Chess Pieces

1990. 22nd "Joy of Europe" Meeting. Mult.
2658 6d.50 Type **887** 75 60
2659 10d. "Willem III of Orange as a child" (Adriaen Hanneman) (vert) . . . . 1·50 1·10

1990. Obligatory Tax. 29th Chess Olympiad, Novi Sad. As No. 2577 but value in reformed currency.
2660 **856a** 1d. black and blue . . 25 10

1990. 29th Chess Olympiad, Novi Sad. Mult.
2661 1d. Type **888** 15 10
2662 5d. Rook, bishop, knight and chessboard 75 50
2663 6d.50 Knights, queen, king, pawn and chessboard . . 1·00 75
2664 10d. Chess pieces and symbols . . . . 2·00 1·75

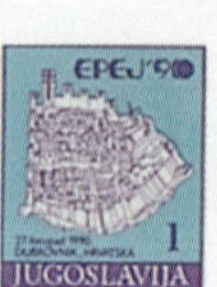
888a Dubrovnik

889 "St. Vlaho and Ragusa" (detail of triptych, Nikola Bozidarevic) and Penny Black

1990. Obligatory Tax. European Judo Championships, Dubrovnik.
2666 **888a** 1d. violet and blue . . 25 10

1990. Stamp Day.
2667 **889** 2d. multicoloured . . . 45 30

890 Vransko Lake

1990. Nature Protection. Multicoloured.

2668	6d.50 Type **890**	65	30
2669	10d. Griffon vulture	1·40	1·40

891 "King Milutin" and Monastery of our Lady, Ljeviska

1990. Monastery Frescoes. Multicoloured.

2670	2d. Type **891**	25	15
2671	5d. "St. Sava" and Mileseva Monastery	75	40
2672	6d.50 "St. Elias" and Moraca Monastery . . .	1·00	70
2673	10d. "Jesus Christ" and Sopocani Monastery . . .	1·40	1·00

892 Milanovic and Kringa (birthplace)

1990. Birth Centenary of Dr. Bozo Milanovic (politician).

2674	**892** 2d. multicoloured . . .	30	20

893 "Arrival of Mary in the Temple"

894 Northern Lapwing

1990. Museum Exhibits. Icon Screens of St. Jovan Bigorski Monastery, Bistra. Multicoloured.

2675	2d. Type **893**	35	35
2676	5d. "Nativity"	75	45
2677	6d. "Flight into Egypt" (horiz)	1·00	60
2678	10d. "Entry into Jerusalem" (horiz)	2·00	90

1991. Protected Birds. Multicoloured.

2679	2d. Type **894**	25	10
2680	5d. Woodchat shrike . . .	60	25
2681	6d.50 Common crane . . .	75	30
2682	10d. Goosander	1·25	50

895 "Crocus kosaninii"

1991. Crocuses. Multicoloured.

2683	2d. Type **895**	20	10
2684	6d. "Crocus scardicus" . . .	60	30
2685	7d.50 "Crocus rujanensis"	75	35
2686	15d. "Crocus adamii" . . .	1·50	75

895a Hands and Flower

895b Emblem

1991. Obligatory Tax. Anti-cancer Week.

2687	**895a** 1d. blue and orange . .	25	10
2688	**895b** 1d.20 multicoloured . .	25	10
2689	– 1d.20 multicoloured . .	25	10
2690	– 1d.20 multicoloured . .	25	10
2691	– 1d.20 multicoloured . .	25	10

DESIGNS: As T **895b**: No 2689, Butterfly; 2690, Sunbathers on rocky beach; 2691, Street in town.

896 Bishop Josip Juraj Strossmayer (founder) (after Vlaho Bukovac)

1991. 125th Anniv of Yugoslav Academy of Arts and Sciences.

2692	**896** 2d. multicoloured . . .	55	20

897 Mozart (after P. Lorenzoni)

898 Edvard Rusijan (Slovenian pioneer) and Bleriot XI

1991. Death Bicentenary of Wolfgang Amadeus Mozart (composer).

2693	**897** 7d.50 multicoloured . .	75	35

1991. Centenary of First Heavier-than-air Flight by Lilienthal. Multicoloured.

2694	7d.50 Type **898**	75	35
2695	15d. Otto Lilienthal and Lilienthal biplane glider	1·50	75

899 Route of Climb and Cesen

1991. 1st Anniv of Tomo Cesen's Ascent of South Face of Lhotse Peak.

2696	**899** 7d.50 multicoloured . .	75	35

900 Satellite and Earth

1991. Europa. Europe in Space. Multicoloured.

2697	7d.50 Type **900**	75	35
2698	15d. Dish aerial reflecting rays from satellite to telephone	1·50	75

901 Figures

902 Red Cross and Rays

1991. Obligatory Tax. Red Cross Week.

2699	**901** 60p. multicoloured . . .	10	10
2700	– 1d.20 multicoloured . .	15	10
2702	– 1d.70 multicoloured . .	15	10
2703	**902** 1d.70 multicoloured . .	15	10
2704	– 1d.70 multicoloured . .	15	10
2705	– 1d.70 multicoloured . .	15	10
2706	– 1d.70 multicoloured . .	15	10
2701	– 2d.50 multicoloured . .	25	10

DESIGNS—29 × 24mm: No. 2702, Similar to T **901** but differently inscribed. As T **902**: No. 2704, Pink flowers; 2705, Children on globe; 2706, Yellow flowers.

903 Miraculous Icon of St. Mary of Trsat (14th century)

904 Danube River Steamer

1991. 700th Anniv of Franciscan Monastery, Rijeka.

2707	**903** 3d.50 multicoloured . .	45	15

1991. Community of Danubian Regions Conference, Belgrade. Multicoloured.

2708	7d.50 Type **904**	75	25
2709	15d. Steamer on river at sunset	1·50	50

905 Woman with Horse

1991. Obligatory Tax. Solidarity Week.

2711	**876** 2d. green and orange . .	55	35
2712	– 2d. brown, red and gold	55	35
2713	**905** 2d. brown, red and gold	15	10
2714	– 2d. brown, red and gold	15	10
2715	– 2d. brown, red and gold	15	10
2716	**715** 2d.20 blue and red . . .	60	40

DESIGNS—As T **905**: No. 2712, "Skopje Earthquake"; 2714, Woman and tree; 2715, Woman holding cockerel.

906 "Karavanke Pass" (17th-century engraving, Johann Valvasor)

1991. Opening of Karavanke Road Tunnel. Multicoloured.

2717	4d.50 Type **906**	30	20
2718	11d. Tunnel entrance . . .	70	40

907 Balls and Baskets

1991. Centenary of Basketball. Multicoloured.

2719	11d. Type **907**	60	35
2720	15d. Aerial view of baskets	80	50

907a Exhibitor carrying Painting

908 Order of the Partisan Star

1991. Obligatory Tax. Cetinje Biennale.

2721	**907a** 2d. red and blue . . .	25	15

1991. 50th Anniversaries of Yugoslav Insurrection and National Army. Multicoloured.

2722	4d.50 Type **908**	30	20
2723	11d. Order for Bravery . . .	70	40

909 Ujevic

910 Score and Gallus

1991. Birth Centenary of Tin Ujevic (writer).

2724	**909** 4d.50 multicoloured . .	40	20

1991. 400th Death Anniv of Jacobus Gallus (composer).

2725	**910** 11d. multicoloured . . .	60	35

911 Savudrija, 1818

1991. Lighthouses of the Adriatic and the Danube. Multicoloured.

2726	10d. Type **911**	75	40
2727	10d. Sveti Ivan na Pucini, 1853	75	40
2728	10d. Porer, 1833	75	40
2729	10d. Stoncica, 1865	75	40
2730	10d. Olipa, 1842	75	40
2731	10d. Glavat, 1884	75	40
2732	10d. Veli Rat, 1849	75	40
2733	10d. Vir, 1881	75	40
2734	10d. Tajerske Sestrice, 1876	75	40
2735	10d. Razanj, 1875	75	40
2736	10d. Derdap, Danube . . .	90	40
2737	10d. Tamis, Danube	75	40

912 "Sremski Karlovci School" (Ljubica Sokic)

1991. Bicent of Sremski Karlovci High School.

2738	**912** 4d.50 multicoloured . .	35	15

913 Girl

914 Inscription

1991. Obligatory Tax. Anti-tuberculosis Week.

2739	**913** 1d.20 blue, red & yellow	15	10
2740	2d.50 blue, red & yellow	20	10
2741	**914** 2d.50 black, yell & mve	20	10
2742	– 2d.50 multicoloured . .	20	10
2743	– 2d.50 multicoloured . .	20	10
2744	– 2d.50 black, yell & mve	20	10

DESIGNS—As T **914**: No. 2742, Doctor and patient; 2743, Children on path; 2744, Girl with birds and flowers.

915 Mayfly

1991. Nature Protection. Multicoloured.

2745	11d. Type **915**	60	35
2746	15d. Pygmy cormorants . .	80	80

916 Town Hall (stained glass)

1991. 600th Anniv of Subotica.

2747	**916** 4d.50 multicoloured . .	35	15

917 Honey Bees and Congress Emblem

918 "Little Dubravka" (Jovan Bijelic)

1991. "Apimondia" 33rd International Bee Keeping Congress, Split.
2748 **917** 11d. multicoloured . . . 70 40

1991. 23rd "Joy of Europe" Meeting. Mult.
2749 5d. Type **918** 30 15
2750 30d. "Little Girl with a Cat" (Mary Cassatt) . . . . . 1·75 1·00

919 Statue of Prince Michael Obrenovic and Serbian 1866 1p. Newspaper Stamp

919a Protecting Refugee

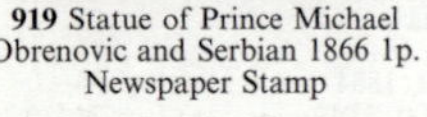

1991. Stamp Day.
2751 **919** 4d.50 multicoloured . . 35 15

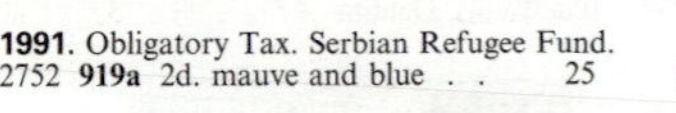

1991. Obligatory Tax. Serbian Refugee Fund.
2752 **919a** 2d. mauve and blue . . 25 15

920 Battle of Vucji. Flag and Medal for Military Valour

1991. Cetinje Museum Exhibits, Montenegrin Flags and Medals. Multicoloured.
2753 20d. Type **920** 25 15
2754 30d. Battle of Grahovo flag and medal 60 45
2755 40d. State flag and Medal for bravery . . . . . . 1·00 75
2756 50d. Court flag and Petrovic dynasty commemorative medal . . . . 1·50 1·00

921 Angel carrying Sun (Andrija Raicevic) (17th century)

923 Delcev

1991. Illustrations from Ancient Manuscripts. Multicoloured.
2757 20d. Type **921** 25 15
2758 30d. "April" (Celnica Gospel) (14th century) . . 60 45
2759 40d. "Annunciation" (Trogir Evangeliarum) (13th century) . . . . 1·00 75
2760 50d. Mary Magdalene in initial V (Miroslav Gospel) (12th century) . . 1·50 1·00

1991. Nos. 2592 and 2587 surch.
2761 5d. on 60p. mauve and red 30 15
2762 10d. on 10p. violet and green 80 40

1992. 120th Birth Anniv of Goce Delcev (Macedonian revolutionary).
2763 **923** 5d. multicoloured . . . 90 75

924 Trophies and Club Emblem

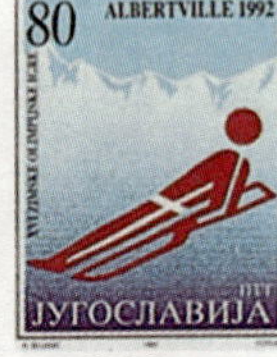

925 Luge

1992. Victories of Red Star Club, Belgrade, in European and World Football Championships.
2764 **924** 17d. multicoloured . . . 2·50 2·00

1992. Winter Olympic Games, Albertville, France. Multicoloured.
2765 80d. Type **925** . . . . . . 1·25 75
2766 100d. Acrobatic skiing . . . 1·75 1·50

926 European Hare

927 "Mary feeding Jesus" (fresco, Pec Patriarchate)

1992. Protected Animals. Multicoloured.
2767 50d. Type **926** 30 20
2768 60d. Siberian flying squirrels 70 50
2769 80d. Forest dormouse . . . 1·50 1·25
2770 100d. Common hamsters . . 2·00 1·75

1992. United Nations Children's Fund Breastfeeding Campaign.
2771 **927** 80d. multicoloured . . . 1·25 1·00

928 Skier

1992. Centenary of Skiing in Montenegro.
2772 **928** 8d. multicoloured . . . 1·75 1·00

929 Fountain, Belgrade

930 "Titanic"

1992.
2773 **929** 50d. violet and lilac . . 45 30
2774 – 100d. deep green and green . . . . 5·00 3·00
DESIGN: 100d. Fisherman Fountain, Kalemegdan Fortress, Belgrade.
See also Nos. 2825/32 and 2889/90.

1992. 80th Anniv of Sinking of Liner "Titanic".
2783 **930** 150d. multicoloured . . 2·50 1·00

931 La Barqueta Bridge and Seville (engraving)

1992. "Expo '92" World's Fair, Seville.
2784 **931** 150d. multicoloured . . 1·50 1·00

932 Christopher Columbus

1992. Europa. 500th Anniv of Discovery of America by Columbus. Multicoloured.
2785 300d. Type **932** . . . . . . 1·75 1·25
2786 500d. Columbus's fleet . . . 2·75 2·00

934 Water Polo

935 Players' Legs

1992. Olympic Games, Barcelona. Multicoloured.
2791 500d. Type **934** 90 70
2792 500d. Shooting 90 70
2793 500d. Tennis 90 70
2794 500d. Handball 90 70

1992. European Football Championship, Sweden. Multicoloured.
2795 1000d. Type **935** . . . . . 1·50 1·25
2796 1000d. Players . . . . 1·50 1·25

936 Red Tabby

1992. Domestic Cats. Multicoloured.
2797 1000d. Type **936** . . . . . 1·10 75
2798 1000d. White Persian . . . 1·10 75
2799 1000d. Blue and white British shorthair . . . . 1·10 75
2800 1000d. Red-point colourpoint longhair . . . 1·10 75

937 Class 162, 1880

1992. Steam Railway Locomotives. Multicoloured.
2801 1000d. Type **937** . . . . . 1·50 1·50
2802 1000d. Class 151, 1885 . . . 1·50 1·50
2803 1000d. Class 73, 1913 . . . 1·50 1·50
2804 1000d. Class 83, 1929 . . . 1·50 1·50
2805 1000d. Class 16 locomotive "Sava", 1936 . . . . . . 1·50 1·50
2806 1000d. Prince Nicholas's steam railcar, 1909 . . . 1·50 1·50

Currency reform.
10 (old) dinars = 1 (new) dinar.

1992. Various stamps surch.
2807 2d. on 30p. green and orange (No. 2589) 40 20
2808 5d. on 20p. red and yellow (No. 2588) 40 20
2809 5d. on 40p. green and purple (No. 2590) 40 20
2810 10d. on 50p. green and violet (No. 2591) 40 20
2811 10d. on 5d. ultramarine and blue (No. 2596) 40 20
2812 20d. on 1d. blue and purple (No. 2593) . . . . 1·00 50
2813 20d. on 5d. blue, green and yellow (as No. 2596) . . . 40 20
2814 50d. on 2d. blue and red (No. 2594) 40 30
2815 100d. on 3d. blue and red (No. 2595) 50 25
No. 2813 was not issued without surcharge.

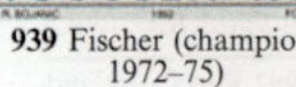

939 Fischer (champion, 1972–75)

941 "Ballerina" (Edgar Degas)

940 Old Telephone and Buildings in Novi Sad, Subotica and Zrenjanin

1992. Unofficial Chess Re-match between Former World Champions Robert Fischer and Boris Spassky. Multicoloured.
2816 500d. Type **939** . . . . . . 1·60 1·25
2817 500d. Spassky (1969–72) . . 1·60 1·25

1992. Centenary of Telephone Service in Vojvodina.
2818 **940** 10d. multicoloured . . . 50 35

1992. 24th "Joy of Europe" Meeting. Paintings. Multicoloured.
2819 500d. Type **941** . . . . . . 1·40 1·00
2820 500d. Youth (V. Knezevic) 1·40 1·00

942 Montenegro 1874 25n. Stamp and Musician

1992. Stamp Day.
2821 **942** 50d. multicoloured . . . 60 40

943 Western Capercaillie, Durmitor Mountains

944 Book and Emblem

1992. Nature Protection. Multicoloured.
2822 500d. Type **943** . . . . . . 2·50 2·00
2823 500d. Eastern white pelican ("Pelecanus onocrotalus"), Skadar Sea . . . . 2·50 2·00

1992. Centenary of Serbian Literary Association.
2824 **944** 100d. multicoloured . . 60 40

1992. As T **929**.
2825 5d. brown and green 30 15
2826 50d. blue and azure 20 10
2827 100d. lilac and pink 20 10
2828 300d. brown and chestnut 40 10
2829 500d. green and flesh . . . 40 10
2830 3000d. orange 20 20
2831 5000d. purple and yellow . . 40 10
2832 500000d. violet and blue . . 50 25
DESIGNS: 5d. 14th-century relief; 50d. As No. 2774; 100d. Type **929**; 300d. Fountain, Kalemegdan Fortress, Belgrade; 500d. Fountain, Sremski Korlovci; 3000d. Fountain, Studenica; 5000d. Fountain, Oplentsu; 500000d. Thermal baths, Vrnjacka Banja.

945 Brvnara Summer Pasture Hut, Zlatibor

946 Sun over Able-bodied and Disabled People

1992. Museum Exhibits. Traditional Houses. Multicoloured.
2833 500d. Type **945** 95 85
2834 500d. House, Morava 95 85
2835 500d. House, Metokhija . . 95 85
2836 500d. Farmhouse, Vojvodina 95 85

1992. Obligatory Tax. Disabled Persons' Week.
2837 **946** 13d. yellow and blue . . 15 10

947 St. Simeon Nemanja with Model of the Church of the Blessed Virgin, Studenica (mosaic, Oplenac)

1992. Mosaics and Icons. Multicoloured.
2838 500d. Type **947** 95 85
2839 500d. Prince Lazarevic with model of Ravanica Monastery (mosaic),Oplenac) 95 85
2840 500d. St. Petka (icon) and St. Petka's Church, Belgrade (horiz) 95 85
2841 500d. St. Vasilii Ostronoski (icon) and Monastery, Montenegro (horiz) . . . 95 85

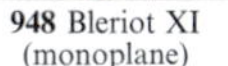

948 Bleriot XI (monoplane) **949** Detail of Fresco, Sirmium

1992. 80th Anniv of Aviation in Yugoslavia.
2842 **948** 500d. multicoloured . . 1·00 1·00

1993. 1700th Anniv of Formation of the Tetrarchy (Diocletian's reform of government of Roman Empire).
2843 **949** 1500d. multicoloured . . 90 75

950 Museum and Medal

1993. Centenary of Cetinje State Museum.
2844 **950** 2500d. multicoloured . . 90 75

1993. Obligatory Tax. Anti-cancer Week. No. 2687 surch **1500 d**.
2844a **895a** 1500d. on 1d. blue and orange 90 75

952 Common Sturgeon **953** Charter and 1868 10p. Coin

1993. Marine Animals. Multicoloured.
2845 10000d. Type **952** 90 75
2846 10000d. Red scorpionfish . . 90 75
2847 10000d. Swordfish 90 75
2848 10000d. Bottle-nosed dolphin 90 75

1993. 125th Anniv of Reintroduction of Serbian Coins (2849) and 120th Anniv of the Dinar (2850). Multicoloured.
2849 10000d. Type **953** . . . . . 1·00 85
2850 10000d. 5d. banknote and 1879 5d. coin . . . . . . 1·00 85

954 Milos Crnjanski (writer) **955** Girl holding Flowers, and Bird (M. Markovski)

1993. Anniversaries. Multicoloured.
2851 40000d. Type **954** (birth centenary) . . . . 1·25 1·00
2852 40000d. Nikola Tesla (physicist, 50th death anniv) . . . . 1·25 1·00
2853 40000d. Mihailo Petrovic (mathematician, 50th death anniv) . . . . . . 1·25 1·00
2854 40000d. Aleksa Santic (poet, 125th birth anniv) . . . . 1·25 1·00

1993. Children for Peace. Multicoloured.
2855 50000d. Type **955** . . . . . 1·50 1·75
2856 50000d. Birds flying above children (J. Rugovac) . . 2·00 1·75

956 Illuminated Letter from Miroslav Gospel **957** "Nude with Mirror" (M. Milunovic)

1993. No value expressed.
2857 **956** A (3000d.) red (18 × 22 mm) 15 10
See also No. 3100.

1993. Europa. Contemporary Art. Multicoloured.
2858 95000d. Type **957** . . . . . 2·00 1·75
2859 95000d. "Composition" (Milena Barili) . . . . . 2·00 1·75

958 **959** Map of Europe and Envelopes

1993. Obligatory Tax. Red Cross Week.
2860 **958** 350d. black and red . . 20 10
2861 1000d. black and red . . 40 15
No. 2860 was for use in Montenegro and No. 2861 for Serbia.

1993.
2862 **959** 50000d. silver and blue 35 15
2863 – 100000d. blue and red 65 30
DESIGN: 100000d. Airplane.

961 Sutorina

1993. Fortresses. Multicoloured.
2865 900000d. Type **961** 75 75
2866 900000d. Kalemegdan, Belgrade 75 75
2867 900000d. Medun 75 75
2868 900000d. Petrovaradin . . . 75 75
2869 900000d. Bar 75 75
2870 900000d. Golubac 75 75

962 Marguerites and Roses

1993. Flower Arrangements. Multicoloured.
2871 1000000d. Type **962** 80 70
2872 1000000d. Roses and gerbera 80 70
2873 1000000d. Roses and lilies 80 70
2874 1000000d. Rose, carnations and stephanotis 80 70

963 Generating Plant, Street Lamp and Town

1993. Centenary of Electrification of Serbia.
2875 **963** 2500000d. mult 60 45

964 Jays

1993. Nature Protection. Fruska Highlands. Mult.
2876 300,000,000d. Type **964** . . 1·75 1·50
2877 300,000,000d. Golden oriole 1·75 1·50

Currency reform.
1000000 (old) dinars = 1 (new) dinar.

1993. Various stamps surch.
2878 10d. on 100000d. blue and red (No. 2863) 30 15
2879 50d. on 5d. brown and green (No. 2825) 30 15
2880 100d. on 5000d. purple and yellow (No. 2831) 30 15
2881 500d. on 50d. blue and azure (No. 2826) 30 15
2882 1000d. on 3000d. orange (No. 2830) 30 15
2883 10000d. on 300d. brown and chestnut (No. 2828) . . . 30 15
2884 50000d. stone, brown and green (No. 2825) 30 15

966 River Freighters

1993. The Danube, "River of Co-operation". Multicoloured.
2885 15000d. Type **966** . . . . . 1·75 1·50
2886 15000d. Passenger ferry . . 1·75 1·50

967 Jagodina Cancellation and Market **968** "Boy with Cat" (Sava Sumanovic)

1993. Stamp Day. 150th Anniv of Jagodina Postal Service.
2888 **967** 12000d. multicoloured 1·00 75

1993. Thermal Baths. As T **929**.
2889 10000d. blue and violet . . 30 15
2890 100000d. brown and red . . 30 15
DESIGNS: 10000d. As No. 2832; 100000d. Bukovicka Banja.

1993. 25th "Joy of Europe" Meeting. Multicoloured.
2891 2000000d. Type **968** . . . . 1·40 1·25
2892 2000000d. "Circus Rider" (Georges Rouault) . . . . 1·40 1·25

969 "Madonna and Child" (from Bogorodica Ljeviska) **970** Summer Pasture Hut, Savardak

1993. Icons. Multicoloured.
2893 400,000,000d. Type **969** . . 1·10 95
2894 400,000,000d. "Christ entering Jerusalem" (from Oplenac) . . . . 1·10 95
2895 400,000,000d. "Birth of Christ" (from Studenica) 1·10 95
2896 400,000,000d. "The Annunciation" (from Mileseva) . . . . 1·10 95

Currency reform.
1,000,000,000 (old) dinars = 1 (new) dinar.

1993. Museum Exhibits. Traditional Buildings. Multicoloured.
2897 50d. Type **970** . . . . . . 1·10 95
2898 50d. "Crmnicka" house, Bar 1·10 95
2899 50d. Watchtower, Chardak (vert) . . . . 1·10 95
2900 50d. Coast house, Primorsten (vert) . . . . 1·10 95

971 Illuminated Page **972** Egyptian Vultures

1994. 500th Anniv of Printing of "Oktoukh" (book). Multicoloured.
2901 1000d. Type **971** 70 60
2902 1000d. Illustration of church and saints 70 60

Currency reform.
13,000,000 (old) dinars = 1 new dinar.

1994. Birds. Multicoloured.
2903 80p. Type **972** . . . . . . 1·60 1·10
2904 80p. Saker falcons ("Falco cherrug") . . . . 1·60 1·10
2905 80p. Long-legged buzzards ("Buteo rufinus") . . . . 1·60 1·10
2906 80p. Lesser kestrels ("Falco naumanni") . . . . . . 1·60 1·10

973 Mimosa **974** Illumination from Miroslav Gospel and Museum

1994. International Mimosa Festival, Herceg Novi.
2907 **973** 80p. multicoloured . . . 1·00 75

1994. 150th Anniv of National Museum (2908) and 125th Anniv of National Theatre (2909), Belgrade. Multicoloured.
2908 80p. Type **974** . . . . . . 1·00 75
2909 80p. Prince Milos Obrenovic and theatre . . . . 1·00 75

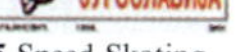

975 Speed Skating **976** Caudron C-61 and Route Map

1994. Winter Olympic Games, Lillehammer, Norway. Multicoloured.
2910 60p. Type **975** . . . . . . 1·00 75
2911 60p. Olympic rings and flame . . . . 1·00 75
2912 60p. Skiing . . . . 1·00 75

1994. Europa. 71st Anniv of First Paris–Belgrade–Bucharest–Istanbul Regular Night Flight. Multicoloured.
2913 60p. Type **976** . . . . . . 1·50 1·10
2914 1d.80 Caudron C-61, Belgrade and route map 2·50 1·75

977 Balloons

1994. Obligatory Tax. Red Cross Week.
2915 **977** 10p. red, black and blue 35 15

978 "The Burning of St. Sava"

1994. 400th Anniv of Burning of St. Sava's Relics.
2916 **978** 60p. multicoloured . . . 1·40 1·00

979 Jubilant Players **980** Basset Hound

1994. World Cup Football Championship, U.S.A. Multicoloured.
2917 60p. Type **979** . . . . . . 1·25 90
2918 1d. Goalkeeper and players on ground . . . . 1·75 1·10

1994. Dogs. Multicoloured.
2919 60p. Type **980** . . . . . . 1·10 80
2920 60p. Maltese terrier . . . . 1·10 80
2921 60p. Welsh terrier . . . . . 1·10 80
2922 1d. Husky . . . . 1·10 80

1994. Nos. 2888/9 surch.
2923 10p. on 100000d. brn & red 30 15
2924 50p. on 10000d. blue & violet 60 30

982 Bell and Globe **983** River Valley

1994. Assembly of Eastern Orthodox Nations.
2925 **982** 60p. multicoloured . . . 95 70

1994. Protection of Environment in Montenegro.
2926 **983** 50p. multicoloured . . . 95 70

984 Moraca **985** St. Arsenius and Sremski

1994. Churches.
2927 **984** 1p. violet and bistre . . 10 10
2928 – 5p. blue and orange . . 10 10
2929 – 10p. green and red . . . 10 10
2930 – 20p. purple and lilac . . 10 10
2931 – 20p. black and red . . 75 10
2932 – 50p. purple and violet 15 10
2933 – 1d. red and blue 35 10
2935 – 5d. violet and blue . . 1·60 75
2936 – 10d. red and orange . . 3·25 2·00
2938 – 20d. turquoise and blue 6·50 3·50
DESIGNS: 5p. Gracanica; 10p. Ostrog Monastery; 20p. (2930/1) Lazarica; 50p. Studenica; 1d. Sopocani; 5d. Ljeviska; 10d. Zica Monastery; 20d. Decani Monastery.

1994. Bicentenary of St. Arsenius Seminary, Sremski Karlovci.
2940 **985** 50p. multicoloured . . . 1·00 75

986 Syringe

1994. Obligatory Tax. Anti-tuberculosis Week.
2941 **986** 10p. black, yellow and red 30 15

987 River Bojana **988** Painting by U. Knezevic

1994. Nature Protection. Multicoloured.
2942 1d. Type **987** . . . . 1·50 1·10
2943 1d.50 Lake Biograd . . . . 2·00 1·50

1994. 26th "Joy of Europe" Meeting.
2944 **988** 1d. multicoloured . . . 1·50 1·10

989 "Revenge" (English galleon) **990** Aerospatiale ATR 42 Mail Plane, Mail Coach and Letter

1994. Ships in Bottles. Multicoloured.
2945 50p. Type **989** 75 75
2946 50p. 17th-century yacht . . 75 75
2947 50p. "Santa Maria" (Columbus's flagship) . . 75 75
2948 50p. 15th-century nau . . . 75 75
2949 50p. "Mayflower" (Pilgrim Fathers' ship) 75 75
2950 50p. 14th-century caravel . . 75 75

1994. Stamp Day.
2951 **990** 50p. multicoloured . . . 1·10 80

991 Tombstone **992** "Madonna and Child" (T. Cesljar)

1994. Museum Exhibits. Illustrated Tombstones. Multicoloured.
2952 50p. Type **991** 85 60
2953 50p. Double stone and railing 85 60
2954 50p. Two stones 85 60
2955 50p. Cemetery 85 60

1994. Paintings. Multicoloured.
2956 60p. Type **992** 90 65
2957 60p. "Adoration of the Three Wise Men" (N. Neshkovic) 90 65
2958 60p. "The Annunciation" (D. Bacevic) 90 65
2959 60p. "St. John baptizing Christ" (T. Kracun) . . . 90 65

993 National Flag

1995. Multicoloured.
2960 1d. Type **993** . . . . . . 1·10 80
2961 1d. National arms . . . . . 1·10 80

994 Wilhelm Steinitz (1886–94)

1995. Chess (1st series). Chessmen or World Champions. Multicoloured.
2962 60p. Type **994** 90 65
2963 60p. Pieces 90 65
2964 60p. Emanuel Lasker (1894–1921) 90 65
2965 60p. Black knight 90 65
2966 60p. Pawns, king and knight 90 65
2967 60p. Jose Raul Capablanca (1921–27) 90 65
2968 60p. Rook, bishop, queen and pawns 90 65
2969 60p. Aleksandr Alekhine (1927–35 and 1937–46) . . 90 65
See also Nos. 2988/95 and 3021/9.

995 Emblem

1995. 50th Anniv of Red Star Sports Club, Belgrade.
2970 **995** 60p. red, blue and gold 1·25 90

996 Fire Salamander **997** Sportsman and Emblem

1995. Amphibians. Multicoloured.
2971 60p. Type **996** 90 65
2972 60p. Alpine newt ("Triturus alpestris") 90 65
2973 60p. Stream frog ("Rana graeca") 90 65
2974 60p. Eastern spadefoot ("Pelobates syriacus balcanicus") 90 65

1995. 75th Anniv of Radnicki Sports Club, Belgrade.
2975 **997** 60p. multicoloured . . . 1·00 75

998 Lammergeier over Mountainside **999** Globes

1995. Europa. Peace and Freedom. Multicoloured.
2976 60p. Type **998** . . . . . . 1·40 1·00
2977 1d.90 Child with tricycle and elderly couple on park bench (horiz) . . . . . . 2·00 1·50

1995. Obligatory Tax. Red Cross Week.
2978 **999** 10p. yellow, blue and red 30 15

1000 Dove with Black Bird in Beak **1001** Station Concourse and Train

1995. 50th Anniv of End of Second World War.
2979 **1000** 60p. multicoloured . . 1·25 90

1995. Opening of Vukov Monument Underground Railway Station, Belgrade.
2980 **1001** 60p. multicoloured . . 1·10 80

1002 Leaves and Flowers

1995. The Whitlow-grass. Multicoloured.
2981 60p. Type **1002** 85 60
2982 60p. Clumps of leaves and flowers 85 60
2983 60p. Plant growing on mountainside 85 60
2984 60p. Plant and tree branch 85 60

1003 Shore Lark, Rtanj

1995. Nature Protection. Multicoloured.
2985 60p. Type **1003** . . . . . . 1·50 1·10
2986 1d.90 Blasius's horseshoe bat, Lazareva Reka Canyon . . . . 2·00 1·50

1004 "Slovakian Village Gathering" (Zuzka Medvedova)

1995.
2987 **1004** 60p. multicoloured . . 1·00 75

1995. Chess (2nd series). Chessmen or World Champions. As T **994**. Multicoloured.
2988 60p. Max Euwe (1935–37) 80 60
2989 60p. Pawn and chessboard and pieces 80 60
2990 60p. Mikhail Botvinnik (1948–57, 1958–60 and 1961–63) 80 60
2991 60p. Queen and chessboard and pieces 80 60
2992 60p. Board and white bishop and knight 80 60
2993 60p. Vasily Smyslov (1957–58) 80 60
2994 60p. Rook, knight, queen and board 80 60
2995 60p. Mikhail Tal (1960–61) 80 60

1005 Wilhelm Rontgen (discoverer of X-rays) **1006** Player on Globe

1995. Obligatory Tax. Anti-tuberculosis Week.
2996 **1005** 10p. red and blue 13 . . 15

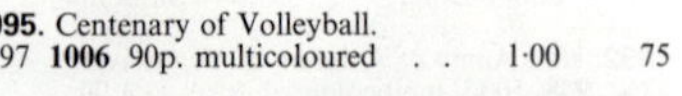

1995. Centenary of Volleyball.
2997 **1006** 90p. multicoloured . . 1·00 75

1007 Church **1008** Coronation of King Petar II

1995. 800th Anniv of St. Luke's Church, Kotor.
2998 **1007** 80p. multicoloured . . 1·00 75

1995. Centenary of Motion Pictures. Each brown and orange.
2999 1d.10 Type **1008** . . . . . 1·00 75
3000 2d.20 Auguste and Louis Lumiere (cine camera pioneers) . . . . 2·00 1·50

1009 Club Emblem **1010** "Flower Seller" (Milos Tenkovic)

1995. 50th Anniv of Partizan Army Sports Club.
3001 **1009** 80p. multicoloured . . 1·00 75

1995. 27th "Joy of Europe" Meeting. Multicoloured.
3002 1d.10 Type **1010** . . . . . 1·00 75
3003 2d.20 "Child at Table" (Pierre Bonnard) . . . . 2·00 1·50

1011 Golden Gate Bridge, San Francisco **1012** Post Office, Seal and Letter

1995. 50th Anniv of U.N.O.
3004 **1011** 1d.10 multicoloured . . 90 65
San Francisco was where the Charter was signed.

1995. Stamp Day.
3005 **1012** 1d.10 multicoloured . . 90 65

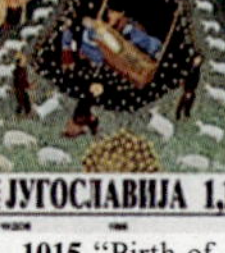

1014 Saric No. 1 **1015** "Birth of Christ" (D. Milojevic)

1995. Museum Exhibits. Aircraft. Multicoloured.
3007 1d.10 Type **1014** 60 45
3008 1d.10 Douglas DC-3 . . . . 60 45

3009 2d.20 Fizir FN biplane . . . 1·10 80
3010 2d.20 Sud Aviation Caravelle jetliner . . . . 1·10 80

1995. Paintings. Multicoloured.
3011 1d.10 Type **1015** 60 45
3012 1d.10 "Flight into Egypt" (Z. Halupova) (horiz) . . 60 45
3013 2d.20 "Sunday" (M. Rasic) 1·10 80
3014 2d.20 "Traditional Christmas Festival" (J. Brasic) (horiz) . . . . 1·10 80

1016 Battle Scene **1017** Painting

1996. 70th Anniv of Battle of Mojkovac.
3015 **1016** 1d.10 multicoloured . . 60 45

1996. Birth Centenary of Save Sumanovic (painter).
3016 **1017** 1d.10 multicoloured . . 60 45

1018 "Pyrgomorphela serbica"

1996. Protected Insects. Multicoloured.
3017 1d.10 Type **1018** 60 45
3018 1d.10 Red wood ant ("Formica rufa") 60 45
3019 2d.20 Searcher ("Calosoma sycophanta") . . . . . . 1·10 80
3020 2d.20 Owl-fly ("Ascalaphus macaronius") . . . . . . 1·10 80

1996. Chess (3rd series). Chessmen and Timepieces or World Champions. As T **994**. Multicoloured.
3021 1d.50 Tigran Vartanovich Petrosyan (1963–69) . . . 55 40
3022 1d.50 Queen, knight and portable sundial 55 40
3023 1d.50 Boris Vasilevich Spassky (1969–72) 55 40
3024 1d.50 Competition clock, chessboard and pieces . . 55 40
3025 1d.50 Garry Kimovich Kasparov (1985–93) . . . 55 40
3026 1d.50 Chessboard, pieces and hourglass 55 40
3027 1d.50 Robert Fischer (1972–75) 55 40
3028 1d.50 Chess pieces, clocks and chessboard 55 40
3029 1d.50 Anatoly Yevgenievich Karpov (1975–85 and 1993–) 55 40

1019 Discus Throwers

1996. Centenary of Modern Olympic Games. Multicoloured.
3030 1d.50 Type **1019** 60 45
3031 2d.50 Ancient Greek and modern athletes . . . . . 1·10 1·10

1020 Athletics

1996. Olympic Games, Atlanta. Multicoloured.
3032 1d.50 Type **1020** 70 50
3033 1d.50 Basketball 70 50
3034 1d.50 Handball 70 50
3035 1d.50 Shooting 70 50
3036 1d.50 Volleyball 70 50
3037 1d.50 Water polo 70 50

1021 Postman, Railway Mail Van and Arms of Royal Serbian Post **1022** Isidora Sekulic

1996. Stamp Day.
3039 **1021** 1d.50 multicoloured . . 65 45

1996. Europa. Famous Women Writers. Mult.
3040 2d.50 Type **1022** . . . . . 1·10 80
3041 5d. Desanka Maksimovic . . 2·25 1·60

1023 Dr. Vladan Djordjevic (founder) **1024** Child and Cross

1996. 120th Anniv of Serbian Red Cross.
3042 **1023** 1d.50 multicoloured . . 50 35

1996. Obligatory Tax. Red Cross Week.
3043 **1024** 15p. blue, brown and red 10 10

1025 Columns, Caryatid and Diagrams of Proportion **1026** White Spoonbill

1996. 150th Anniv of Architecture Education in Serbia.
3044 **1025** 1d.50 light blue, deep blue and blue 50 35

1996. Nature Protection. Multicoloured.
3045 2d.50 Type **1026** 80 60
3046 5d. Glossy ibis . . . . . . 1·60 1·25

1027 Prince Petar I Petrovic (Battle of Martinici)

1996. Battle Bicentenaries. Multicoloured.
3047 1d.50 Type **1027** 50 35
3048 2d.50 "Prince's Guard" (Theodore Valerio) (Battle of Kruse) (vert) 80 60

1028 Waiting for the Off

1996. Ljubicevo Race Meeting. Multicoloured.
3049 1d.50 Type **1028** 50 35
3050 2d.50 Horses racing 80 60

1029 Palm Cockatoo **1030** Landscape on Leaf

1996. 60th Anniv of Belgrade Zoo. Multicoloured.
3051 1d.50 Type **1029** 50 35
3052 1d.50 Common zebra . . . 50 35
3053 2d.50 Maroon-breasted crowned pigeon . . . . . 1·00 75
3054 2d.50 Tiger . . . . 1·00 75

1996. Obligatory Tax. Anti-tuberculosis Week.
3055 **1030** 20p. multicoloured . . 10 10

1031 Fantasy Scene

1996. 28th "Joy of Europe" Meeting. Multicoloured.
3056 1d.50 Type **1031** 50 35
3057 2d.50 Toucan . . . . 1·00 75

1032 Basketball (silver) **1033** Coins, Banknotes and Credit Card

1996. Olympic Games Medal Winners. Mult.
3058 2d.50 Type **1032** 80 60
3059 2d.50 Small-bore rifle shooting (gold) 80 60
3060 2d.50 Air-rifle shooting (bronze) 80 60
3061 2d.50 Volleyball (bronze) . . 80 60

1996. 75th Anniv of Post Office Savings Bank.
3062 **1033** 1d.50 multicoloured . . 45 30

1034 Footballer **1035** Mother and Child (statuette)

1996. Centenary of Football in Serbia.
3063 **1034** 1d.50 multicoloured . . 45 30

1996. Museum Exhibits. Archaeological Finds. Multicoloured.
3064 1d.50 Type **1035** 45 30
3065 1d.50 Tombstone depicting Genius, god of autumn (Komani, nr. Pljevlja) . . 45 30
3066 2d.50 Marble head of woman (from Podgorica) 70 50
3067 2d.50 Statuette of red-headed goddess 70 50

1036 "The Annunciation" (Nikola Neskovic) **1037** Putnik in Dress Uniform

1996. Icons from Serbian Orthodox Church Museum, Belgrade. Multicoloured.
3068 1d.50 Type **1036** 45 30
3069 1d.50 "Madonna and Child" 45 30
3070 2d.50 "Nativity" 70 50
3071 2d.50 "Entry of Christ into Jerusalem" (Stanoje Popovic) 70 50

1997. 150th Birth Anniv of Radomir Putnik (army Commander in Chief).
3072 **1037** 1d.50 multicoloured . . 35 25

1038 Film Frames **1039** Great Spotted Woodpecker

1997. 25th International Film Festival, Belgrade.
3073 **1038** 1d.50 multicoloured . . 35 25

1997. Nature Protection. Woodland Birds. Multicoloured.
3074 1d.50 Type **1039** 35 25
3075 1d.50 Crested tit ("Parus cristatus") 35 25
3076 2d.50 Spotted nutcracker ("Nucifraga caryocatactes") 60 45
3077 2d.50 European robin ("Erithacus rubecula") . . 60 45

1040 Christ and King Dragutin holding Model of Church (fresco) **1041** St. Petar

1997. 700th Anniv of St. Ahilije's Church, Arilje.
3078 **1040** 1d.50 multicoloured . . 35 25

1997. 250th Birth Anniv of Prince-Bishop Petar I of Montenegro (St. Petar of Cetinje).
3079 **1041** 1d.50 multicoloured . . 35 25

1042 Belgrade and Emblem **1043** Ambulance, 1876, and Association Building

1997. 10th Belgrade Marathon.
3080 **1042** 2d.50 multicoloured . . 60 45

1997. 125th Anniv of Serbian Medical Association.
3081 **1043** 2d.50 multicoloured . . 60 45

1044 Loading Air Mail at Night

1997. Stamp Day.
3082 **1044** 2d.50 multicoloured . . 50 30

1045 "1997" and Cross **1046** Belgrade

1997. Obligatory Tax. Red Cross Week.
3083 **1045** 20p. red and blue . . . 10 10

1997. Tennis Championships in Yugoslavia. Design showing player and Town Arms. Multicoloured.
3084 2d.50 Type **1046** 50 30
3085 2d.50 Budva 50 30
3086 2d.50 Novi Sad 50 30

1047 Bas Celik shackled before King

1997. Europa. Myths and Legends. Multicoloured.
3087 2d.50 Type **1047** 50 30
3088 6d. Prince on horseback fighting chained Bas Celik 1·25 75

1048 "Cerambyx cerdo" (longhorn beetle)

1997. Nature Protection. Multicoloured.
3089 2d.50 Type **1048** 50 30
3090 6d. Pedunculate oak 1·25 75

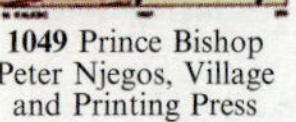

1049 Prince Bishop Peter Njegos, Village and Printing Press **1050** Binicki

1997. 150th Anniv of Publication of "Gorski Vijenc".
3091 **1049** 2d.50 multicoloured 50 30

1997. 125th Birth Anniv of Stanislav Binicki (composer).
3092 **1050** 2d.50 multicoloured 50 30

1051 "Pelargonium grandiflorum" **1053** Dr. Milutin Rankovic

1997. Flowers. Multicoloured.
3093 1d.50 Type **1051** 30 20
3094 1d.50 "Hydrangea x macrophylla" 30 20
3095 2d.50 African violet ("Saintpaulia ionantha") 50 30
3096 2d.50 "Oncidium varicosum" 50 30

1997. Obligatory Tax. Anti-tuberculosis Week.
3098 **1053** 20p. brown, ochre and red 10 10

1054 Society Emblem **1055** Collage (Milan Ugrisic)

1997. Centenary of Serbian Chemical Association.
3099 **1054** 2d.50 multicoloured 30 20

1997. No value expressed. As No. 2857 but 18 × 20 mm.
3100 **956** A red 10 10

1997. 29th "Joy of Europe" Meeting. Multicoloured.
3101 2d.50 Type **1055** 25 15
3102 5d. Collage (Stanislava Antic) 55 35

1056 "May Assembly, Sremski Karlovci, 1848" (Pavle Simic)

1997. 150th Anniv of Matica Srpska Art Gallery.
3103 **1056** 2d.50 multicoloured 25 15

1057 Helmet from Srem (4th century) **1058** "Christ Pantocrator"

1997. Archaeological Finds in Vojvodina Museum. Multicoloured.
3104 1d.50 Type **1057** 15 10
3105 1d.50 Two-headed terracotta figure from Srem 15 10
3106 2d.50 Teracotta figure from Backa 25 15
3107 2d.50 "Madonna and Child" (relief from Srem, 12th century) 25 15

1997. Icons from Chelandari Serbian Monastery, Mount Athos. Multicoloured.
3108 1d.50 Type **1058** 15 10
3109 1d.50 "Madonna and Child" 15 10
3110 2d.50 "Madonna and Child" (different) 25 15
3111 2d.50 "Three-handed Madonna with Child" 25 15

1059 Savina **1060** Ice Skater

1998. Monasteries in Montenegro. Multicoloured.
3112 1d.50 Type **1059** 15 10
3113 2d.50 Donji Brceli 25 15

1998. Winter Olympic Games, Nagano, Japan. Multicoloured.
3114 2d.50 Type **1060** 25 15
3115 6d. Skier 65 40

1061 Mare and Foal

1998. Horses. Multicoloured.
3116 1d.50 Type **1061** 15 10
3117 1d.50 Stallion 15 10
3118 2d.50 Head of grey 25 15
3119 2d.50 Racehorse 25 15

1062 Women and Flowers

1998. International Women's Day.
3120 **1062** 2d.50 multicoloured 25 15

1063 Glider and Emblems

1998. 50th Anniv of Yugoslav Aeronautics Association.
3121 **1063** 2d.50 multicoloured 25 15

1064 "The Adornment of the Bride" (Paja Jovanovic)

1998. Europa. National Festivals. Multicoloured.
3122 6d. Type **1064** 65 40
3123 9d. "The Prince-Bishop celebrates Victory" (Pero Pocek) 1·00 60

1065 Metropolitan Mihailo Jovanovic **1066** Player evading Tackle

1998. Obligatory Tax. Red Cross Week.
3124 **1065** 20p. multicoloured 10 10

1998. World Cup Football Championship, France. Multicoloured.
3125 6d. Type **1066** 65 40
3126 9d. Goalkeeper and players 1·00 60

1068 "Hieracium blecicii" **1069** Djura Jaksic (poet and painter)

1998. Nature Protection. Multicoloured.
3128 6d. Type **1068** 65 40
3129 9d. Oceanic sunfish 1·00 60

1998. Anniversaries. Each brown, black and ochre.
3130 1d.50 Type **1069** (120th death anniv) 15 10
3131 1d.50 Nadezda Petrovic (painter, 125th birth anniv) 15 10
3132 1d.50 Radoje Domanovic (satirist, 125th birth anniv) 15 10
3133 1d.50 Vasilije Mokranjac (composer, 75th birth anniv) 15 10
3134 1d.50 Sreten Stojanovic (sculptor, birth centenary) 15 10
3135 1d.50 Milan Konjovic (painter, birth centenary) 15 10
3136 1d.50 Desanka Maksimovic (writer, birth centenary) 15 10
3137 1d.50 Ivan Tabakovic (painter, birth centenary) 15 10

1071 Pine Marten **1072** Machine-gunners

1998. 50th Anniv of Serbian Nature Protection Institute. Multicoloured.
3139 2d. Type **1071** 20 15
3140 2d. Demoiselle crane ("Anthropoides virgo") 20 15
3141 5d. Lynx ("Lynx lynx") 55 35
3142 5d. Red crossbill ("Loxia curvirostra") 55 35

1998. 80th Anniv of Thessalonica Front.
3143 **1072** 5d. grey and brown 55 35
3144 – 5d. brown and sepia 55 35
DESIGN: No. 3144, Field gun.

1073 "50 Years" on Stamp **1074** "Sea Life" (Bojan Dakic)

1998. Stamp Day. 50th Anniv of Serbian Philatelic Society
3145 **1073** 6d. blue 65 40

1998. 30th "Joy of Europe" Meeting. Multicoloured.
3146 6d. Type **1074** 65 40
3147 9d. "Sea Life" (collage by Ana Rockov) 1·00 60

1075 Steam Locomotive, 1847

1998. Locomotives. Multicoloured.
3148 2d.50 Type **1075** 30 20
3149 2d.50 Steam locomotive, 1900 30 20
3150 2d.50 Steam locomotive, 1920 30 20
3151 2d.50 Steam locomotive, 1930 30 20
3152 2d.50 Diesel locomotive "Kennedy" 30 20
3153 2d.50 High speed train, 1990 30 20

1076 *Pjerino* (brig), 1883

1998. Museum Exhibits. Ship Paintings by Vasilije Ivankovic. Multicoloured.
3154 2d. Type **1076** 20 15
3155 2d. *Vera Cruz* (steamer), 1873 20 15
3156 5d. *Vizin-Florio* (full-rigged ship) 60 40
3157 5d. *Draghetto* (barque), 1865 60 40

1077 Hilandar Monastery

1998. 800th Anniv of Hilandar Monastery. Paintings by Milutin Dedic. Multicoloured.
3158 2d. Type **1077** 20 15
3159 2d. Monastery facade 20 15
3160 5d. Hills behind Monastery buildings 60 40
3161 5d. Aerial view of Monastery 60 40

1078 Flags around Envelope on Map

1998. South-East European Postal Ministers Congress.
3162 **1078** 5d. multicoloured 60 40

1080 Postal Messenger arriving in Belgrade **1081** Visoki Decani Monastery

1998. 75th Anniv of Post and Telecommunications Museum.
3164 **1080** 5d. brown and green 60 40
3165 5d. red and brown 60 40

1999. Serbian Monasteries. Paintings by Milutin Dedic. Multicoloured.
3166 2d. Type **1081** 20 15
3167 5d. Gracanica Monastery 60 40

1082 Woolly Pig

1999. Animals. Multicoloured.
3168 2d. Type **1082** 20 15
3169 2d. Cattle 20 15
3170 6d. Balkan goat 70 45
3171 6d. Hungarian sheep 70 45

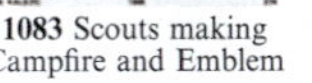

1083 Scouts making Campfire and Emblem

1084 Emblem, Goddess Justitia and Globe

1999. Scouts.
3172 **1083** 6d. multicoloured . . . 70 45

1999. 70th Anniv of Bar Association.
3173 **1084** 6d. brown and buff . . 70 45

1085 Target

1086 Emblem and Player

1999. No value expressed.
3174 **1085** A black 10 10
3175 – A black and red . . . 10 10
DESIGN: No. 3175, Target with heart at centre.

1999. World Table Tennis Championships, Belgrade. Multicoloured.
3176 6d. Type **1086** 70 40
3177 6d. Player facing left 70 40

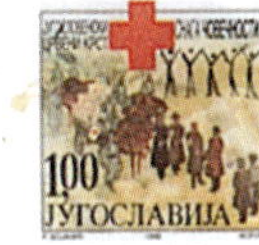

1087 Kopaonik National Park

1088 Red Cross Volunteers

1999. Europa. Parks and Gardens. Multicoloured.
3178 6d. Type **1087** 70 40
3179 15d. Lovcen National Park 1·75 1·10

1999. Obligatory Tax Red Cross Week.
3180 **1088** 1d. multicoloured . . . 15 10

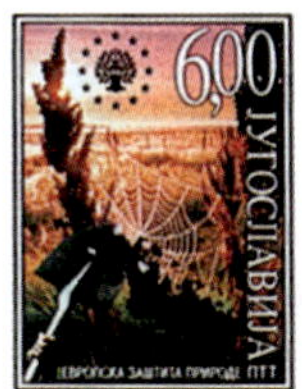

1089 Emblem, Cobweb and Spade

1090 Destroying Angel (*Amanita virosa*)

1999. Nature Protection. Multicoloured.
3181 6d. Type **1089** 70 40
3182 15d. Thumb squeezing water droplet from Earth . . . 1·75 1·10

1999. Fungi. Multicoloured.
3183 6d. Type **1090** 70 40
3184 6d. False blusher (*Amanita pantherina*) 70 40
3185 6d. Clustered woodlover (*Hypholoma fasciculare*) 70 40
3186 6d. *Ramaria pallida* 70 40

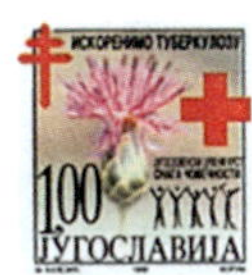

1091 Stjepan Mitrov Ljubisa (author)

1092 Thistle

1999. Personalities. Each brown, yellow and black.
3187 2d. Type **1091** 25 15
3188 2d. Marko Miljanov (author) 25 15
3189 2d. Pero Pocek (painter) . . 25 15
3190 2d. Risto Stijovic (sculptor) 25 15
3191 2d. Milo Milunovic (painter) 25 15
3192 2d. Petar Lubarda (painter) 25 15
3193 2d. Vuko Radovic (painter) 25 15
3194 2d. Mihailo Lalic (author) 25 15

1999. Obligatory Tax. Anti-tuberculosis Week.
3195 **1092** 1d. multicoloured . . . 15 10

1093 World Map and Emblem

1999. 125th Anniv of Universal Postal Union. Multicoloured.
3196 6d. Type **1093** 70 40
3197 12d. Envelopes encircling globe . . . . 1·40 85

1094 Lion (Luka Minic)

1095 Chopin and Music Score

1999. 31st "Joy in Europe" Meeting. Winning Designs in Children's Painting Competition. Multicoloured.
3198 6d. Type **1094** 70 40
3199 15d. Girl with doll (Andreas Kaparis) (vert) . . . . . 1·75 1·10

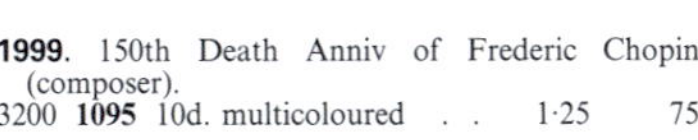

1999. 150th Death Anniv of Frederic Chopin (composer).
3200 **1095** 10d. multicoloured . . 1·25 75

1096 Mastheads

1999. Stamp Day. 50th Anniv of *Philatelist* (magazine).
3201 **1096** 10d. multicoloured . . 1·25 75

1097 Murino Bridge

1999. Bombed Bridges. Multicoloured.
3202 2d. Type **1097** 25 15
3203 2d. Varadinski Most 25 15
3204 2d. Ostruznica 25 15
3205 6d. Bistrica 70 40
3206 6d. Grdelica 70 40
3207 6d. Zezeljev Most 70 40

1098 Fragments of Roman Altars, Sremska Mitrovica and Jupiter (statue), Sabac

1999. Year 2000. Multicoloured.
3208 6d. Type **1098** 70 40
3209 6d. Mosaic depicting Emperor Trajan with army leaders, Sirmium, lamp and lead mirror . . 70 40
3210 6d. Mosaic of Dionysus and painting of Belgrade . . . 70 40
3211 6d. Haghia Sophia, mosaic and bust of Emperor Constantin 70 40
3212 6d. Gold artefacts, pot and lamp 70 40
3213 6d. St. Peter's Church and title page of *Temnic* . . . 70 40

1099 Fireman dousing Flames

1999. Bombed Buildings. Multicoloured.
3215 2d. Type **1099** 25 15
3216 2d. Oil refinery 25 15
3217 2d. Dish aerials 25 15
3218 6d. Hospital 70 40
3219 6d. Radio and television station 70 40
3220 6d. Television tower, Mt. Avala 70 40

1100 Saints

1999. 500th Anniv of Poganovo Monastery Frescoes. Multicoloured.
3221 6d. Type **1100** 70 40
3222 6d. Four saints with long beards 70 40
3223 6d. Four saints, one holding a scroll and one an open book 70 40
3224 6d. Four saints, three holding scrolls and one with a stick 70 40

1101 Couple washing for Gold

1999. Museum Exhibits. Gold Washing on the River Pek. Multicoloured.
3225 6d. Type **1101** 70 40
3226 6d. Man and two youths panning for gold 70 40
3227 6d. Women digging gravel panning for gold 70 40
3228 6d. Man holding spade and pan with two boys . . . 70 40

1102 Krushedol Monastery

2000. Monasteries. Multicoloured.
3229 10d. Type **1102** . . . . . . 1·25 75
3230 10d. Rakovac Monastery . . 1·25 75

1103 Building and Emblem

2000. 50th Anniv of National Archives.
3231 **1103** 10d. lilac and blue . . . 1·25 75

1104 Large Tortoiseshell(*Nymphalis polychloros*)

2000. Butterflies. Multicoloured.
3232 10d. Type **1104** . . . . . . 1·25 75
3233 10d. Southern festoon (*Parnalius polyxena*) . . . 1·25 75
3234 10d. Poplar admiral (*Limenitis populi*) . . . . 1·25 75
3235 10d. Marbled white (*Melanargia galathea*) . . 1·25 75

1105 Grey Partridges (*Perdix perdix*)

2000. Endangered Species. Partridges. Mult.
3236 10d. Type **1105** . . . . . . 1·25 75
3237 10d. Grey partridge (different) . . . . 1·25 75
3238 10d. Rock partridge (*Alectoris graeca*) on nest 1·25 75
3239 10d. Two rock partridges . . 1·25 75

1106 General Staff Building, Belgrade

2000. Bombed Buildings.
3240 **1106** 10d. blue . . . . 1·25 75
3241 – 20d. brown . . . . . . 2·25 1·40
DESIGN: No. 3241, Air Force and Air Defence Command, Zemun.

1108 Tree and World Map

1109 "2000" and View of Bethlehem

2000. Environment Protection. Multicoloured.
3243 30d. Type **1108** . . . . . . 3·50 2·25
3244 30d. Barn swallows in nest 3·50 2·25

2000. Europa. Multicoloured.
3245 30d. Type **1109** . . . . . . 3·50 2·25
3246 30d. "2000" and astronaut on Moon . . . . 3·50 2·25

1110 Players chasing Ball

2000. European Football Championship, Belgium and The Netherlands. Multicoloured.
3247 30d. Type **1110** . . . . . . 3·50 2·25
3248 30d. Players heading ball . . 3·50 2·25

1111 Post Office Building, Post Van, Post Box, Letter, Envelope and Quill

2000. 160th Anniv of Postal Service in Serbia.
3249 **1111** 10d. multicoloured . . 1·25 75

1112 Map of Australia and Kangaroo

2000. Olympic Games, Sydney. Showing map of Australia and animal or bird. Multicoloured.
3250 6d. Type **1112** 25 10
3251 12d. Emu 35 15
3252 24d. Koala . . . . 1·00 60
3253 30d. Cockatoo . . . . . . 1·10 65

1113 Airship LZ-127 "Graf Zeppelin" (1928) and Cover

2000. Stamp Day. Centenary of First Zeppelin Flight.
3254 **1113** 10d. multicoloured . . 30 15

1114 Goats

2000. 32nd "Joy in Europe" Meeting. Winning Designs in Children's Painting Competition. Multicoloured.
3255 30d. Type **1114** . . . . . 1·10 65
3256 40d. Storks (vert) . . . . . 1·40 95

1115 Hand holding Pen

2000. U.N.E.S.C.O. World Teachers' Day.
3257 **1115** 10d. multicoloured . . 30 15

1116 Bee on Flower

2000. 13th Apislavia (Slavonic bee-keeping association) Congress.
3256 **1116** 10d. multicoloured . . 30 15

1117 Water Polo (bronze)

2000. Yugoslav Medals at Olympic Games. Multicoloured.
3259 20d. Type **1117** 50 30
3260 20d. Air pistol (silver) . . . 50 30
MS3261 70 × 83 mm. 30d. Volleyball (gold) (34 × 46 mm) . . . . . 1·10 1·10

1118 Sailing Ships

2000. New Millennium. Multicoloured.
3262 12d. Type **1118** 35 15
3263 12d. Parchment production 35 15
3264 12d. Man and instruments (first accurate maps and optical instruments) . . . 35 15
3265 12d. G. and R. Stephenson's *Rocket* (1829) and *Clermont* (first commercial paddle-steamer) 35 15
3266 12d. Nikola Tesla (Yugoslav scientist), telegraph and telephone 35 15
3267 12d. Futuristic settlement, astronaut and satellite . . 35 15
MS3268 138 × 86 mm. 40d. Horses on river bank, ship in full sail and ice-bound ship (104 × 54 mm) 1·40 1·40

1119 Christ bathing (fresco, Monastery, Pec)
1120 Waistcoat (Jagodina)

2000. No value expressed.
3269 **1119** A multicoloured . . . 10 10

2000. Museum Exhibits. 19th-century Serbian Costumes. Multicoloured.
3270 6d. Type **1120** 25 10
3271 12d. Dress (Metohija) . . . 35 15
3272 24d. Blouse (Pec) . . . . . 1·00 60
3273 30d. Waistcoat (Kupres) . . 1·40 95

1121 Mary and Jesus (icon, Piva Monastery)

2000. Art. Icons and Frescoes of Montenegro. Multicoloured.
3274 6d. Type **1121** 25 10
3275 12d. Nativity (fresco, Holy Cross Church) 35 15
3276 24d. St. Luke painting an icon (fresco, Moraca Monastery) . . . . . . 1·00 60
3277 30d. Mary and Jesus, St. John and St. Stephen (fresco, Mary of the Ascension Church, Moraca) . . . . 1·40 95

1122 Map of Europe and Emblem

2000. Yugoslavia's Resumption of Membership of the Organization for Security and Co-operation in Europe (3278) and the United Nations (3279). Multicoloured.
3278 6d. Type **1122** 25 10
3279 12d. Emblem (vert) 35 15

1123 Vatoped Monastery

2001. Monasteries on Mount Athos. Multicoloured.
3280 10d. Type **1123** 30 15
3281 27d. Esfigmen monastery . . 1·25 75

1124 Association Building

2001. 175th Anniv of "Matice Srpske" (Serbian literary association).
3282 **1124** 15d. multicoloured . . . 40 25

1125 Lions
1126 Vera Mencikova

2001. 50th Anniv of Zoo Palic, Subotica. Endangered Species. Multicoloured.
3283 6d. Type **1125** (*Panthera leo*) (inscr "Felis leo") 25 10
3284 12d. Polar bear and cub (*Ursus maritimus*) 35 15
3285 24d. Japanese macaques (*Macaca fuscata*) . . . . 1·00 65
3286 30d. Humboldt penguins (*Spheniscus humboldti*) . . 1·40 95

2001. Women World Chess Champions. Multicoloured.
3287 10d. Type **1126** 30 15
3288 10d. Lyudmila Vladimirovna Rudenko 30 15
3289 10d. Elizaveta Ivanova Bykova 30 15
3290 10d. Olga Nikelaevna Rubtsova 30 15
3291 10d. Nona Terentievna Gaprindashvili 30 15
3292 10d. Maia Grigorevna Chiburdanidze 30 15
3293 10d. Zsusza Polgar 30 15
3294 10d. Jun Xie 30 15

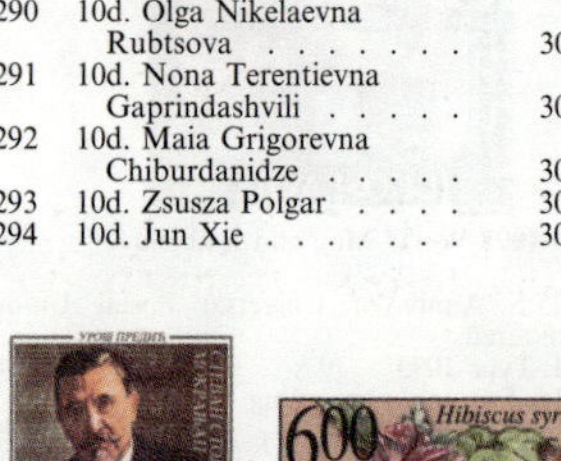

1127 Stevan Stojanovic Mokranjac (portrait, Uros Predic)
1128 Rose-of-Sharon (*Hibiscus syriacus*)

2001. Personalities. Multicoloured.
3295 50d. Type **1127** (composer) 2·10 1·25
3296 100d. Nikola Tesla (inventor) . . . . 4·25 2·50

2001. Flora. Multicoloured.
3297 6d. Type **1128** 25 10
3298 12d. Oleander (*Nerium oleander*) 35 15
3299 24d. Chilean bellflower (*Lapageria rosea*) . . . . 1·00 60
3300 30d. Rowan (*Sorbus aucuparia*) . . . . 1·10 65

1129 River Vratna, Eastern Serbia

2001. Europa. Water Resources. Multicoloured.
3301 30d. Type **1129** . . . . . . 1·10 65
3302 45d. Jerme Gorge, Dimitrovgrad . . . . . . 1·60 95

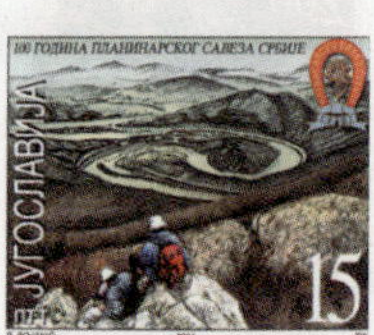

1130 Mountains, Emblem and Climbers

2001. Centenary of Serbian Mountaineering Association.
3303 **1130** 15d. multicoloured . . 40 25

1131 Lake Ludasko and Heron

2001. Nature Protection. Lakes. Multicoloured.
3304 30d. Type **1131** . . . . . . 1·10 65
3305 45d. Lake and stork in flight, Carska Bara Special Nature Reserve 1·60 95

1132 Illuminated Letter

2001. No value expressed.
3306 **1132** E multicoloured 15 10

1133 Players and Ball (½-size illustration)

2001. European Water Polo Champions. Sheet 86 × 67 mm.
MS3307 **1133** 30d. multicoloured 1·10 1·10

1134 Seated Figure

2001. 50th Anniv of Serbian Stamps. "SRBIJAFILA 12" National Stamp Exhibition. Sheet 97 × 85 mm.
MS3308 **1134** 30d. multicoloured 1·10 1·10

1135 Sun and Emblems
1136 Hands holding Bridge

2001. Energy Conservation. Solar Power.
3309 **1135** 15d. multicoloured . . 40 25

2001. Danube Commission. Cleaning the Danube. Multicoloured.
3310 30d. Type **1136** . . . . . . 1·10 65
3311 45d. Hand, clock and ship 1·60 95

EXPRESS LETTER STAMP

CROATIA

1918. Express Letter stamp of Hungary optd **HRVATSKA SHS ZURNO.**
E84 E **18** 2f. olive and red 10 30

NEWSPAPER STAMPS

CROATIA

1918. Newspaper stamp of Hungary optd **HRVATSKA SHS.**
N83 N **9** 2f. orange 10 30

SLOVENIA

N **25**

1919. Imperf.
N97 N **25** 2h. yellow . . . . . . 10 1·00

N 30 Cherub with Newspapers

1919. Imperf.
N150 N 30 2v. grey 10 15
N155 2v. blue 10 10
N151 4v. grey 15 35
N156 4v. blue 10 15
N152 6v. grey 3·00 3·75
N157 6v. blue 4·00 5·00
N153 10v. grey 10 20
N158 10v. blue 10 10
N154 30v. grey 10 35

(N 35)

(N 36)

1920. Surch as Type N 35 (2 to 6p.) or Type N 36 (10p. and 30p.).
N164 N 30 2p. on 2v. grey 30 85
N169 2p. on 2v. blue 10 30
N165 4p. on 2v. grey 30 85
N170 4p. on 2v. blue 10 30
N166 6p. on 2v. grey 40 85
N171 6p. on 2v. blue 10 30
N167 10p. on 2v. grey 45 1·00
N172 10p. on 2v. blue 15 50
N168 30p. on 2v. grey 45 1·00
N173 30p. on 2v. blue 20 70

OBLIGATORY TAX STAMPS

SERBIA

The following obigatory tax stamps were for use in Serbia only. Except for the Children's Week issues they are all inscribed "SRBIJA".

S 1 Child

S 2 Children

1990. Children's Week.
S1 S 1 30p. red 10 10

1991. Children's Week.
S2 S 2 3d. blue 25 10

S 3 Hands and Flower

S 4 Mother and Child

1992. Anti-cancer Week.
S3 S 3 3d. violet and orange 25 10

1993. Anti-cancer Week. No. S3 surch **1500**.
S4 S 3 1500d. on 3d. violet and orange 90 75

1993. Serbian Refugee Fund.
S5 S 4 42d. green and yellow 20 10
S6 75d. blue and light blue 30 15
S7 150d. violet and lilac 40 20

S 5 Hands and Flower

S 6

1994. Anti-cancer Week.
S8 S 5 12p. violet 25 10
See also No. S11.

1994.
S9 S 6 6p. purple 15 10

S 7 Museum

1994. 150th Anniv of National Museum, Belgrade.
S10 S 7 5p. blue 15 10

1995. Anti-cancer Week.
S11 S 5 6p. mauve 15 10

OFFICIAL STAMPS

O 130

1946.
O540 O 130 50p. orange 15 10
O541 1d. green 15 10
O542 1d.50 olive 30 10
O543 2d.50 red 30 10
O544 4d. brown 65 10
O545 5d. blue 85 10
O546 8d. brown 1·25 15
O547 12d. violet 1·60 30

POSTAGE DUE STAMPS

BOSNIA AND HERZEGOVINA

ДРЖАВА С.Х.С.
БОСНА И
ХЕРЦЕГОВИНА

хелера
(D 5)

КРАЉЕВСТВО
СРБА, ХРВАТА
И СЛОВЕНАЦА

ПОРТО

5 х
(D 13)

1918. Postage Due Stamps of Bosnia optd as Type D 5 or **DRZAVA S.H.S. BOSNA I HERCEGOVINA HELERA**.
D19 D 35 2h. red 10 10
D20 4h. red 40 40
D21 5h. red 10 10
D22 6h. red 75 50
D23 10h. red 10 10
D24 15h. red 5·00 6·00
D25 20h. red 10 10
D26 25h. red 50 50
D27 30h. red 50 50
D28 40h. red 25 25
D29 50h. red 1·00 1·00
D30 1k. blue 50 50
D31 3k. blue 40 40

1919. "Eagle" type of Bosnia surch as Type D 13 or **KRALJEVSTVO SRBA, HRVATA I SLOVENACA PORTO** and value.
D50 2 2h. on 35h. blue and black 50 75
D51 5h. on 45h. blue and black 75 1·00
D52 10h. on 10h. red 10 10
D53 15h. on 40h. orange and black 50 60
D54 20h. on 5h. green 10 10
D55 25h. on 20h. pink and black 35 45
D56 30h. on 30h. bistre and black 35 45
D57 1k. on 50h. purple 15 50
D58 3k. on 25h. blue 35 50

КРАЉЕВСТВО
СРБА, ХРВАТА
И СЛОВЕНАЦА
40

40 хелера 40
(D 14)

1919. Postage Due stamps of Bosnia with surch or optd as Type D 14 or **KRALJEVSTVO SRBA, HRVATA SLOVENACA**, and value.
D59 D 4 40h. on 6h. black, red and yellow 10 10
D60 50h. on 8h. black, red and yellow 10 10
D61 200h. black, red & green 6·00 5·00
D62 4k. on 7h. black, red and yellow 40 50

CROATIA

1919. Postage Due stamps of Hungary, with figures in red (except 50f. in black), optd **HRVATSKA SHS**.
D85 D 9 1f. green (No. D190) 25·00 35·00
D86 2f. green 1·25 1·25
D87 10f. green 90 90
D88 12f. green 70·00 90·00
D89 15f. green 65 65
D90 20f. green 65 65
D91 30f. green 1·75 1·75
D92 50f. green (No. D177) 28·00 35·00

SLOVENIA

D 30

1919.
D150 D 30 5v. red 10 10
D151 10v. red 10 10
D152 20v. red 10 10
D153 50v. red 10 10
D154 1k. blue 30 30
D155 5k. blue 60 30
D156 10k. blue 1·10 75

(D 35)

(D 36)

1920. Stamps of 1919 issue surch as Types D 35 or D 36.
D164 25 5p. on 15v. blue 10 10
D165 10p. on 15v. blue 60 60
D166 20p. on 15v. blue 15 10
D167 50p. on 15v. blue 10 10
D168 26 1d. on 30v. pink (or red) 15 15
D169 3d. on 30v. pink (or red) 30 15
D170 8d. on 30v. pink (or red) 85 65

GENERAL ISSUES

D 39 King Alexander I when Prince

D 40

1921.
D182 D 39 10 on 5p. green 15 10
D183 30 on 5p. green 25 10

1921.
D184 D 40 10p. red 10 10
D185 30p. green 15 10
D197 50p. violet 10 10
D198 1d. brown 15 10
D188 2d. blue 25 10
D200 5d. orange 1·50 10
D190 10d. brown 6·00 10
D191 25d. pink 30·00 1·25
D192 50d. green 25·00 1·50
There are two issues in this type, differing in the lettering, etc.

1928. Surcharged **10**.
D233 D 40 10 on 25d. pink 3·00 25
D234 10 on 50d. green 3·00 25

D 56

(D 62)

1931.
D259 D 56 50p. violet 10 10
D260 1d. red 10 10
D261 2d. blue 10 10
D262 5d. orange 10 10
D263 10d. brown 20 15

1933. Optd with Type D 62.
D293a D 40 50p. violet 15 10
D294a 1d. brown 15 10
D295a 2d. blue 30 10
D296b 5d. orange 75 10
D297a 10d. brown 3·50 10

1933. Red Cross. As T 62 but inscr "PORTO" in Latin and Cyrillic characters.
D298 62 50p. red and green 40 10

DEMOCRATIC FEDERATION OF YUGOSLAVIA

(a) REGIONAL ISSUES

CROATIA

1945. Zagreb issue. Croatian Postage Due stamps of 1942 surch **DEMOKRATSKA FEDERATIVNA JUGOSLAVIJA**, value and star.
RD45 D 15 40k. on 50b. brown and blue 25 25
RD46 60k. on 1k. brown and blue 25 25
RD47 80k. on 2k. brown and blue 25 25
RD48 100k. on 5k. brown and blue 25 25
RD49 200k. on 6k. brown and blue 25 25

MONTENEGRO

1945. Cetinje issue. National Poem issue of Italian Occupation surch as Type R 4, with "PORTO" in addition.
RD61 10l. on 5c. violet £225 £250
RD62 20l. on 5l. red on buff 75·00 70·00

SERBIA

1944. Senta issue. No. D684 of Hungary optd with a large star, **8.X.1944** and "Yugoslavia" in Cyrillic characters and surch in addition.
RD73 D 115 10(f.) on 2f. brown 40·00 40·00

(b) GENERAL ISSUES

D 114

D 115

D 126

1944. Postage Due stamps of Serbia optd in Cyrillic characters, as Type D 114.
D487 10d. red 30 50
D488 20d. blue 30 50

1945. (a) Value in black.
D489 D 115 2d. brown 10 10
D490 3d. violet 10 10
D491 5d. green 10 10
D492 7d. brown 10 10
D493 10d. lilac 15 10
D494 20d. blue 20 10
D495 30d. green 35 15
D496 40d. red 40 20

(b) Value in colour.
D497 D 115 1d. green 10 10
D498 1d.50 blue 10 10
D499 2d. red 15 10
D500 3d. brown 30 10
D501 4d. violet 40 20

1946.
D 527 D 126 50p. orange 10 10
D 528 1d. orange 10 10
D 724 1d. brown 40 10
D 529 2d. blue 15 10
D 725 2d. green 40 10
D 530 3d. green 20 10
D 531 5d. violet 20 10
D 726 5d. blue 60 10
D 532 7d. red 75 15
D 533 10d. pink 1·25 25
D 727 10d. red 2·50 10
D 534 20d. lake 1·75 50
D1030 20d. violet 2·50 10
D1031 30d. orange 5·50 20
D1032 50d. blue 27·00 80
D1033 100d. purple 13·00 1·00

1947. Red Cross. As No. 545, but with "PORTO" added. Colour changed.
D546 131 50p. green and red 30 10

1948. Red Cross. As No. 594, but inscr "PORTO".
D595 152 50p. red and green 25 10

1949. Red Cross. As T 160 but inscr "PORTO".
D617 160 50p. purple and red 40 10

ФНР ЈУГОСЛАВИЈА

FNR JUGOSLAVIJA
(D 168)

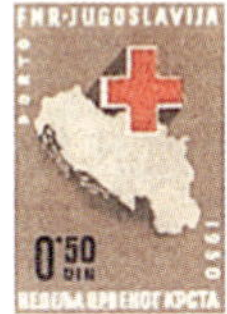

D 175 Map

1950. Optd with Type D 168.
D637 D 115 1d.50 blue 10 10
D638 3d. brown 10 10
D639 4d. violet 20 15

1950. Red Cross.
D665 D 175 50p. brown and red 30 10

1951. Red Cross. Inscr "PORTO".
D703 191 50p. green and red 30 10

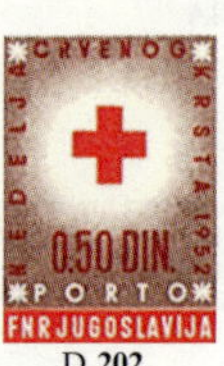

D 202

D 251 Child with Toy

1952. Red Cross.
D741 D **202** 50p. red and grey . . 40 10

1953. Red Cross. Inscr "PORTO".
D762 **211** 2d. red and brown . . . 50 15

1954. Red Cross. Inscr "PORTO".
D783 **216** 2d. red and lilac 45 15

1955. Children's Week. Inscr "PORTO".
D802 **222** 2d. green and light green 40 15

1955. Red Cross. Inscr "PORTO".
D804 **224** 2d. brown, choc & red 40 20

1956. Red Cross. Inscr "PORTO".
D820 **228** 2d. green, turq & red 40 15

1956. Children's Week. Inscr "PORTO".
D835 **232** 2d. chocolate & lt brn 40 15

1957. Red Cross. Inscr "PORTO".
D844 **234** 2d. red, black and grey 40 15

1957. Children's Week. Inscr "PORTO".
D867 **240** 2d. brown and blue . . 40 15

1958. Red Cross. Inscr "PORTO".
D879 **245** 2d. multicoloured . . . 70 25

1958. Children's Week.
D913 D **251** 2d. black and blue 50 15

1959. Red Cross. Inscr "PORTO".
D927 **255** 2d. orange and red . . 30 15

1959. Children's Week. As T **260**. Inscr "PORTO".
D947 2d. purple and yellow . . 35 15
DESIGN: Tree, cockerel and ears of wheat.

1960. Red Cross. Inscr "PORTO".
D956 **262** 2d. purple and red . . . 30 15

1960. Children's Week. As T **265**. Inscr "PORTO".
D970 2d. blue (Young boy) . . . 30 15

1961. Red Cross. Inscr "PORTO". Perf or imperf.
D982 **268** 2d. multicoloured . . . 35 15

1961. Children's Week. Inscr "PORTO".
D1020 **274** 2d. green and sepia . . 30 15

1962. Red Cross. Inscr "PORTO".
D1043 **281** 5d. red, brown and blue 30 15

1963. Red Cross Cent. and Week. Inscr "PORTO".
D1074 **288** 5d. red, purple & orge 35 15

REGISTERED LETTER STAMPS

R 960 Hands holding Envelope

1993. No value expressed.
R2864 R **960** R (11000d.) blue . . 55 15

YUNNANFU Pt. 17

Yunnanfu (formerly Yunnansen), the chief city of the Chinese province of Yunnan, had an Indo-Chinese Post Office from 1900 to 1922.

1901. 100 centimes = 1 franc.
1918. 100 cents = 1 piastre.

Stamps of Indo-China surcharged.

1903. "Tablet" key-type surch with value in Chinese and **YUNNANSEN**.
1 D 1c. black and red on blue . . 7·25 7·75
2 2c. brown and blue on buff 7·00 7·25
3 4c. brown and blue on grey 5·75 7·50
4 5c. green and red . . . . 5·50 6·50
5 10c. red and blue . . . . 5·00 6·50
6 15c. grey and red . . . . 6·50 6·50
7 20c. red and blue on green 6·50 8·25
8 25c. blue and red . . . . 6·00 8·00
9 30c. brown and blue on drab 9·25 8·50
10 40c. red and blue on yellow 70·00 50·00
11 50c. red and blue on pink £275 £275
12 50c. brown and red on blue £160 £160
13 75c. brown and red on orange . . . . 60·00 55·00
14 1f. green and red . . . . 55·00 60·00
15 5f. mauve and blue on lilac £100 £110

1906. Surch **Yunnan-Fou** and value in Chinese.
16 **8** 1c. green . . . . 2·75 3·50
17 2c. purple on yellow . . . . 3·00 4·00
18 4c. mauve on blue . . . . 3·25 3·75
19 5c. green . . . . 3·75 4·00
20 10c. pink . . . . 3·50 4·50
21 15c. brown on blue . . . 8·00 8·75
22 20c. red on green . . . . 4·75 5·25
23 25c. blue . . . . 5·25 5·50
24 30c. brown on cream . . . 5·00 5·25
25 35c. black on yellow . . . 9·00 9·25
26 40c. black on grey . . . . 6·25 6·50
27 50c. brown on cream . . . 7·25 10·50
28 D 75c. brown on orange . . . 50·00 55·00
29 **8** 1f. green . . . . 21·00 30·00
30 2f. brown on yellow . . . 21·00 30·00
31 D 5f. mauve on lilac . . . 70·00 85·00
32 **8** 10f. red on green . . . . 80·00 90·00

1908. Native types surch **YUNNANFOU** and value in Chinese.
33 **10** 1c. black and brown . . . . 1·25 70
34 2c. black and brown . . . . 1·60 1·40
35 4c. black and blue . . . . 1·75 1·75
36 5c. black and green . . . . 1·75 1·60
37 10c. black and red . . . . 2·00 1·00
38 15c. black and violet . . . 4·25 4·00
39 **11** 20c. black and violet . . . 5·00 5·25
40 25c. black and blue . . . . 5·00 5·25
41 30c. black and brown . . . 6·75 7·00
42 35c. black and green . . . 6·50 7·00
43 40c. black and brown . . . 9·00 10·50
44 50c. black and red . . . . 8·00 10·50
45 **12** 75c. black and orange . . . 9·25 10·00
46 1f. black and red . . . . 14·50 15·00
47 2f. black and green . . . . 24·00 30·00
48 5f. black and blue . . . . 55·00 60·00
49 10f. black and violet . . . 95·00 £110

1919. As last, surch in addition with value in figures and words.
50 **10** ⅖c. on 1c. black and brown 1·10 70
51 ⅘c. on 2c. black and brown 1·25 2·00
52 1⅗c. on 4c. black and blue 1·25 3·25
53 2c. on 5c. black and green 1·75 1·40
54 4c. on 10c. black and red 2·50 90
55 6c. on 15c. black and violet 2·00 1·40
56 **11** 8c. on 20c. black and violet 3·00 3·25
57 10c. on 25c. black and blue 3·75 3·75
58 12c. on 30c. black & brown 3·50 3·50
59 14c. on 35c. black and green 4·75 4·75
60 16c. on 40c. black & brown 4·75 4·25
61 20c. on 50c. black and red 3·50 3·25
62 **12** 30c. on 75c. black & orange 4·50 5·25
63 40c. on 1f. black and red . . 5·75 6·00
64 80c. on 2f. black and green 7·75 8·25
65 2p. on 5f. black and blue . . 35·00 42·00
66 4p. on 10f. black and violet 20·00 18·00

ZAIRE Pt. 14

In 1971 the Congo Republic (Kinshasa), formerly Belgian Congo, changed its name to Zaire.

100 sengi = 1 (li)kuta; 100 (ma)kuta = 1 zaire.

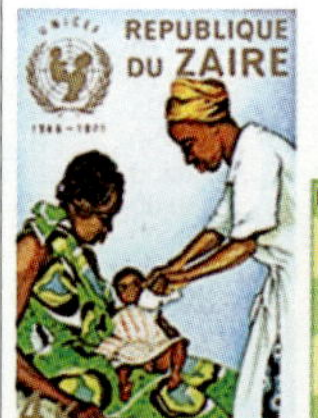

176 Nurse tending Child

177 Pres. Mobutu, Memorial and Emblem

1971. 25th Anniv of U.N.I.C.E.F. Multicoloured.
788 4k. Type **176** 30 20
789 14k. Zaire Republic on map of Africa 85 55
790 17k. Child in African village 1·10 90

1972. 5th Anniv of Revolution.
791 **177** 4k. multicoloured . . . . 3·25 2·75
792 14k. multicoloured . . . . 3·25 2·75
793 22k. multicoloured . . . 4·50 3·25

177a Arms

177b Pres. Mobutu

1972.
794 **177a** 10s. orange and black . . 10 10
795 40s. blue and black . . . 10 10
796 50s. yellow and black . . 10 10
797 **177b** 1k. multicoloured 10 10
798 2k. multicoloured 10 10
799 3k. multicoloured 10 10
800 4k. multicoloured 10 10
801 5k. multicoloured 15 10
802 6k. multicoloured 15 10
803 8k. multicoloured 20 15
804 9k. multicoloured . . . 30 15
805 10k. multicoloured . . . 35 15
806 14k. multicoloured . . . 45 20
807 17k. multicoloured . . . 50 35
808 20k. multicoloured . . . 65 40
809 50k. multicoloured . . . 1·75 85
810 100k. multicoloured . . 3·50 2·00

178 Inga Dam

1973. Inga Dam. Completion of 1st Stage.
811 **178** 0.04z. multicoloured . . . 10 10
812 0.14z. multicoloured . . . 45 35
813 0.18z. multicoloured . . . 80 45

1973. As T **177b**, but face values in Zaires.
814 0.01z. multicoloured 10 10
815 0.02z. multicoloured 10 10
816 0.03z. multicoloured 10 10
817 0.04z. multicoloured 10 10
818 0.10z. multicoloured 45 20
819 0.14z. multicoloured 80 35

179 Africa on World Map

1973. 3rd International Fair, Kinshasa.
820 **179** 0.04z. multicoloured . . . 15 10
821 0.07z. multicoloured . . . 30 15
822 0.18z. multicoloured . . . 80 45

180 Emblem on Hand

1973. 50th Anniv of Criminal Police Organization (Interpol).
823 **180** 0.06z. multicoloured . . . 35 20
824 0.14z. multicoloured . . . 80 35

181 Leopard with Football on Globe

1974. World Cup Football Championship, Munich.
825 **181** 1k. multicoloured 10 10
826 2k. multicoloured 10 10
827 3k. multicoloured 15 10
828 4k. multicoloured 20 10
829 5k. multicoloured 30 10
830 14k. multicoloured . . . 1·40 55

182 Muhamed Ali and George Foreman

185 Waterfall

1974. World Heavyweight Boxing Title Fight, Kinshasa.
831 **182** 1k. multicoloured 10 10
832 4k. multicoloured 15 10
833 6k. multicoloured 20 10
834 14k. multicoloured . . . 55 30
835 20k. multicoloured . . . 90 40

1975. World Heavyweight Boxing Title Fight, Kinshasa. As T **182** optd with amended date **25-9-74**.
836 **182** 0.01z. multicoloured . . . 10 10
837 0.04z. multicoloured . . . 10 10
838 0.06z. multicoloured . . . 20 10
839 0.14z. multicoloured . . . 45 15
840 0.20z. multicoloured . . . 80 30

Nos. 836/40 differ from Type **182** by having the face values expressed as decimals of the zaire. Both dates are in fact incorrect as the fight was held on 30 October 1974.

1975. 12th General Assembly of International Union for Conservation of National Resources, Kinshasa.
858 **185** 1k. multicoloured 15 15
859 2k. multicoloured 15 15
860 3k. multicoloured 30 15
861 4k. multicoloured 45 15
862 5k. multicoloured 60 15

186 Okapis

1975. 50th Anniv of Virunga National Park.
863 **186** 1k. multicoloured 20 20
864 2k. multicoloured 40 20
865 3k. multicoloured 65 20
866 4k. multicoloured 85 20
867 5k. multicoloured . . . . 1·10 20

187 Woman Judge with Barristers

1975. International Women's Year.
868 **187** 1k. multicoloured 10 10
869 2k. multicoloured 10 10
870 4k. multicoloured 20 10
871 14k. multicoloured . . . 65 20

188 Sozacom Building

189 Pende Statuette

1976. 10th Anniv of "New Regime". Mult.
872 1k. Type **188** 10 10
873 2k. Siderna Maluku Industrial Complex (horiz) 10 10
874 3k. Flour mill, Matadi . . . 10 10
875 4k. Women parachutists (horiz) 20 10
876 8k. Pres. Mobutu with Mao Tse-Tung 35 10
877 10k. Soldiers clearing vegetation along the Salongo (horiz) 45 20
878 14k. Pres. Mobutu addressing U.N. General Assembly, 4 October 1973 (horiz) . . 65 30
879 15k. Rejoicing crowd (horiz) 80 20

1977. Masks and Statuettes. Multicoloured.
880 2z. Type **189** 10 10
881 4z. Type **189** 10 10
882 5z. Tshokwe mask 10 10
883 7z. As 5k. 15 10
884 10z. Suku mask 20 10
885 14z. As 10k. 35 15
886 15z. Kongo statuette 40 15
887 18z. As 15k. 45 30
888 20z. Kuba mask 65 35
889 25z. As 20k. 80 45

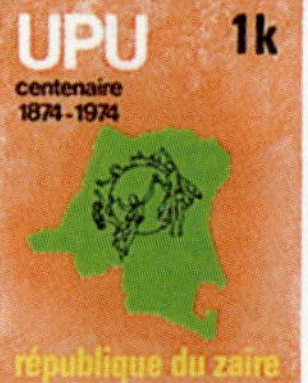

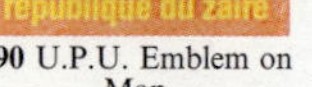

190 U.P.U. Emblem on Map

192 Freshwater Butterflyfish

1977. Centenary of Universal Postal Union.
890 **190** 1k. multicoloured 10 10
891 4k. multicoloured 20 10
892 7k. multicoloured 50 35
893 50k. multicoloured . . . 4·25 2·25

1977. Various stamps of Congo (Kinshasa) and Zaire, surch **REPUBLIQUE DU ZAIRE** or with new value only (No. 904).
894 **158** 1k. on 10s. red and black 10 10
895 **152** 2k. on 9.6k. black on red 10 10
896 **158** 5k. on 30s. green & black 10 10
897 **173** 10k. on 10s. mult . . . 40 10
898 **158** 10k. on 15s. blue & black 15 10
899 – 20k. on 9.6k. mult (No. 673) 40 10
900 **167** 25k. on 10s. mult . . . 75 20

901 **174** 30k. on 12s. mult 75 20
902 **159** 40k. on 9.6k. mult . . . . 1·10 30
903 **168** 48k. on 10s. mult . . . . 1·25 35
904 **158** 100k. on 40s. blue & black . . . . 2·75 60

1978. Fishes. Multicoloured.
905 30s. Type **192** 10 15
906 70s. Striped killifish 10 15
907 5k. Banded ctenopoma . . . 15 15
908 8k. Electric catfish 25 15
909 10k. Jewel cichlid 45 20
910 30k. Isidor's elephantfish . . 70 60
911 40k. Blotched upsidedown catfish . . . . 1·10 65
912 48k. Golden Julie . . . . . 1·40 80
913 100k. Brien's notho . . . . . 3·50 1·75

193 Argentina v. France

194 Mama Mobutu

1978. World Cup Football Championship, Argentina. Multicoloured.
915 1k. Type **193** 10 10
916 3k. Austria v. Brazil 10 10
917 7k. Scotland v. Iran 10 10
918 9k. Netherlands v. Peru . . . 10 10
919 10k. Hungary v. Italy 15 10
920 20k. West Germany v. Mexico 35 20
921 50k. Tunisia v. Poland . . . 85 45
922 100k. Spain v. Sweden . . . 1·90 1·00

1978. 1st Death Anniv of Mama Mobutu Sese Seko (wife of President).
924 **194** 8k. multicoloured 20 10

197 Da Vinci, Lilienthal and Flying Machines

1978. History of Aviation. Multicoloured.
927 30s. Type **197** 15 10
928 70s. Wright Type A and Santos-Dumont's "14 bis" 15 10
929 1k. Farman F 60 Goliath and Bleriot XI 15 10
930 5k. Junkers G.38ce "Deutschland" and "Spirit of St. Louis" 15 10
931 8k. Macchi Castoldi MC-72 seaplane and Sikorsky S-42B flying boat 25 15
932 10k. Boeing 707 and Fokker F.VIIb/3m 45 20
933 50k. "Apollo XI" space capsule and Concorde . . 1·75 55
934 75k. Sikorsky S-61N helicopter and Douglas DC10 . . . . 2·10 90

198 President Mobutu

199 "Phylloporus ampliporus"

1978.
936 **198** 2k. multicoloured . . . 10 10
937 5k. multicoloured . . . 10 10
938 6k. multicoloured . . . 10 10
939 8k. multicoloured . . . 10 10
940 10k. multicoloured . . . 10 10
941 25k. multicoloured . . . 10 10
942 48k. multicoloured . . . 35 15
942a 50k. multicoloured . . . 20 10
943 1z. multicoloured . . . 80 30
943a 2z. multicoloured . . . 65 35
943b 5z. multicoloured . . . 1·50 85

1979. Mushrooms. Multicoloured.
944 30s. Type **199** 10 30
945 5k. "Engleromyces goetzei" 15 30
946 8k. "Scutellinia virungae" . . 30 30
947 10k. "Pycnoporus sanguineus" 35 30
948 30k. "Cantharellus miniatescens" . . . . . . 1·00 75
949 40k. "Lactarius phlebonemus" . . . . . . 1·60 90
950 48k. "Phallus indusiatus" . . 2·50 1·10
951 100k. "Ramaria moelleriana" 4·00 2·40

200 Ntore Dancer

1979. Zaire River Expedition. Multicoloured.
952 1k. Type **200** 10 10
953 3k. Regal sunbird . . . . . 1·50 25
954 4k. African elephant 10 10
955 10k. Diamond, cotton boll and tobacco 10 10
956 14k. Hand holding flaming torch 15 10
957 17k. Lion and water lily . . . 20 15
958 25k. Inzia Falls 30 15
959 50k. Wagenia fisherman . . . 55 35

201 President Mobutu and Flag

1979. 5th Anniv (1970) of 2nd Republic.
961 **201** 3z. gold, red and blue . . 26·00

203 Globe and Drummer

1979. 6th International Fair, Kinshasa.
963 **203** 1k. multicoloured 10 10
964 9k. multicoloured 10 10
965 90k. multicoloured . . . 65 30
966 100k. multicoloured . . . 80 35

204 Boy with Drum

205 Desk standing on Globe

1979. International Year of the Child. Mult.
968 5k. Type **204** 10 10
969 10k. Girl 10 10
970 20k. Boy 20 10
971 50k. Laughing boy 40 20
972 100k. Two children 85 35
973 300k. Mother and child . . . 3·00 1·60

1979. 50th Anniv of International Bureau of Education.
975 **205** 10k. multicoloured . . . 15 10

207 "Puffing Billy", 1813–14, Great Britain

1980. Locomotives. Multicoloured.
977 50s. Type **207** 10 10
978 1k.50 Buddicom No. 33, 1844, France 10 10
979 5k. "Elephant", 1835, Belgium 10 10
980 8k. No. 601, Zaire 10 10
981 50k. No. 171 "Slieve Gullion", 1913, Ireland . . 70 70
982 75k. "Black Elephant", Prussia . . . . 1·00 1·00
983 2z. Type 1-15, Zaire . . . . 2·75 2·75
984 5z. "Golden State Limited" express, U.S.A. . . . . 7·00 7·00

208 Sir Rowland Hill and Congo 5f. Stamp, 1886

1980. Death Cent of Sir Rowland Hill. Mult.
986 2k. Type **208** 10 10
987 4k. Congo 10f. stamp, 1887 10 10
988 10k. Congo 1f. African elephant stamp, 1884 . . . 10 10
989 20k. Belgian Congo overprinted 3f.50 stamp, 1909 . . . . 15 10
990 40k. Belgian Congo 10f. African Elephant stamp, 1925 . . . . 20 10
991 150k. Belgian Congo 1f.50+1f.50 Chimpanzees stamp, 1939 . . . . 85 40
992 200k. Belgian Congo 1f.75 Leopard stamp, 1942 . . . 1·25 60
993 250k. Belgian Congo 2f.50 Railway stamp, 1948 . . . 3·00 2·50

209 Einstein

1980. Birth Cent of Albert Einstein (physicist).
995 **209** 40s. brown, black & mve 10 10
996 2k. brown, black & green 10 10
997 4k. brown, black & yell 10 10
998 15k. brown, black & blue 15 10
999 50k. brown, black and red 35 20
1000 300k. brown, blk & lilac 2·00 1·00

210 Booth Memorial Medical Centre, Flushing, New York

1980. Centenary of Salvation Army in the United States. Multicoloured.
1002 50s. Type **210** 10 10
1003 4k.50 Arrival of Railton in America 10 10
1004 10k. Mobile dispensary, Musina, Zaire 10 10
1005 20k. General Evangeline Booth and salvationist holding child (vert) . . . 10 10
1006 40k. Army band 20 15
1007 75k. Mobile clinic in bush, Zaire 45 20
1008 1z.50 Canteen serving firefighters 90 40
1009 2z. American unit marching with flags (vert) . . . . . 1·40 55

212 Musical Instrument

1980. 75th Anniv of Rotary International. Mult.
1013 50k. Drawing of mother and child (Kamba) 30 15
1014 100k. Type **212** 55 30
1015 500k. Statuette (Liyolo) (vert) . . . . 2·00 1·40

213 Red-tailed butterflyfish

1980. Tropical Fishes Multicoloured.
1017 1k. Type **213** 10 10
1018 5k. Sail-finned tang 10 10
1019 10k. Yellow-faced angelfish 10 10
1020 20k. Blue-ringed angelfish 20 10
1021 50k. Flame angelfish 45 20
1022 150k. Harlequin filefish . . 1·25 55
1023 200k. Black triggerfish . . . 1·75 90
1024 250k. Picasso triggerfish . . 2·25 1·10

214 Belgium 40c. Congo Independence Stamp, 1960 and "Phibelza"

1980. "Phibelza" Belgian–Zaire Stamp Exhibition, Kinshasa. Multicoloured.
1026 1z. Type **214** 40 30
1027 1z. Congo 20f. Independence stamp, 1960 . . . . . . 40 30
1028 2z. Belgium 10f.+5f. Zoo stamp, 1968 . . . . . . 80 20
1029 2z. Congo 40c. Birds stamp, 1963 . . . . 85 40
1030 3z. Belgium 10f.+5f. Brussels stamp, 1971 . . . . . . 1·25 85
1031 3z. Zaire 22k. stamp, 1972 1·25 85
1032 4z. Belgium 25f.+10f. stamp, 1980 . . . . 1·60 1·10
1033 4z. Congo 24f. stamp, 1966 1·60 1·10

Nos. 1026/33 exist in two versions with the exhibition logo either at the right or the left of the design. Prices are the same for either version.

1980. 20th Anniv of Independence. Various stamps optd **20e Anniversaire - Independance - 1960-1980.**
1034 **207** 50s. "Puffing Billy" . . . 25 25
1035 – 1k.50 Buddicom locomotive No. 33 (No. 978) 40 40
1036 – 10k. Boeing 707 and Fokker F.VIIb/3m (No. 932) 50 50
1037 – 50k. "Slieve Gullion" (No. 981) 60 60
1038 – 75k. Sikorsky S-61N helicopter and Douglas DC-10 (No. 934) . . . 70 70
1039 **203** 100k. Globe and drummer 45 25
1040 – 1z. on 5z. on 100k. Two children (No. 972) . . 45 25
1041 – 250k. Rowland Hill and railway stamp of 1948 (No. 993) . . . . . 3·50 3·50
1042 – 5z. on 100k. Two children (No. 972) . . 2·75 1·25

216 Leopold I and 1851 Map of Africa

1980. 150th Anniv of Belgian Independence.
1043 **216** 10k. green and blue . . 10 10
1044 – 75k. brown and blue . . 45 20
1045 – 100k. violet and blue . . 45 20
1046 – 145k. blue and deep blue 1·60 50
1047 – 270k. red and blue . . . 1·60 85

DESIGNS: 75k. Leopold II and Stanley's expedition; 100k. Albert I and colonial troops of 1914–18 war; 145k. Leopold III and African animals; 270k. Baudouin I and visit to Zaire of King Baudouin and Queen Fabiola.

217 Angels appearing to Shepherds

1980. Christmas. Multicoloured.
1048 10k. Type **217** 10 10
1049 75k. Flight into Egypt . . . 35 20
1050 80k. Three Kings 45 20
1051 145k. In the stable 80 45

218 Girl dancing to Cello

1981. Norman Rockwell Paintings. Multicoloured.

1053	10k. Type **218**	10	10
1054	20k. Couple with saluting boy scout	10	10
1055	50k. Sorter reading mail	20	10
1056	80k. Cupid whispering in youth's ear	35	15
1057	100k. Signing Declaration of Independence	50	20
1058	125k. Boy looking through telescope held by sailor	80	25
1059	175k. Boy in armchair playing trumpet	1·10	55
1060	200k. Weakling exercising with dumb bells	1·10	50

219 Pope John-Paul II and Pres. Mobutu

220 Footballers

1981. Papal Visit. Multicoloured.

1061	5k. Pope kneeling at shrine (horiz)	10	10
1062	10k. Pres. Mobutu greeting Pope (horiz)	10	10
1063	50k. Type **219**	20	10
1064	100k. Pope talking to child (horiz)	65	35
1065	500k. Pope leading prayers	2·75	1·25
1066	800k. Pope making speech (horiz)	4·00	2·00

1981. World Cup Football Championship, Spain (1982).

No.	Type	Description		
1067	**220**	2k. multicoloured	10	10
1068	–	10k. multicoloured	10	10
1069	–	25k. multicoloured	10	10
1070	–	90k. multicoloured	35	15
1071	–	2z. multicoloured	65	35
1072	–	3z. multicoloured	1·25	55
1073	–	6z. multicoloured	2·40	1·10
1074	–	8z. multicoloured	3·25	1·60

DESIGN: Nos. 1068/74, Similar football scenes.

221 Archer in Wheelchair

1981. International Year of Disabled People. Multicoloured.

1076	2k. Type **221**	10	10
1077	5k. Ear and sound wave	10	10
1078	10k. One-legged person with crutch	10	10
1079	18k. Glasses, Braille and white cane	10	10
1080	50k. Crippled legs	20	10
1081	150k. Sign language	45	20
1082	500k. Hand and model showing joints	1·60	90
1083	800k. Dove shedding feathers	2·50	1·60

222 Children performing Carols

224 Red Cross Helicopters

1981. Christmas. Multicoloured.

1084	25k. Type **222**	10	10
1085	1z. Boy lighting candle	35	15
1086	1z.50 Boy praying	45	20
1087	3z. Girl with presents	95	45
1088	5z. Children admiring baby	1·75	85

1982. Telecommunications and Health. Mult.

1091	1k. Type **224**	10	10
1092	25k. Doctor and telephone	10	10
1093	90k. Antenna and map	20	15
1094	1z. Patient	35	15
1095	1z.70 Teleprinter	45	20
1096	3z. Nurse and television	90	35
1097	4z.50 Tape recorder	1·60	85
1098	5z. Babies and walkie-talkie	1·75	85

225 U.P.U. Emblem

1982. 20th Anniv (1981) of African Postal Union.

No.	Type	Description		
1099	**225**	1z. green and gold	45	20

226 El Salvador v. Hungary

1982. World Cup Football Championship, Spain. Multicoloured.

1100	2k. Type **226**	10	10
1101	8k. Cameroun v. Peru	10	10
1102	25k. Brazil v. Russia	10	10
1103	50k. Kuwait v. Czechoslovakia	10	10
1104	90k. Yugoslavia v. Northern Ireland	30	15
1105	1z. Austria v. Chile	35	15
1106	1z.45 France v. England	45	15
1107	1z.70 West Germany v. Algeria	55	35
1108	3z. Spain v. Honduras	1·00	50
1109	3z.50 Belgium v. Argentina	1·10	60
1110	5z. Scotland v. New Zealand	1·60	85
1111	6z. Italy v. Poland	2·00	95

228 Hands reaching towards Zaire

1982. Ninth French and African Heads of State Conference, Kinshasa.

No.	Type	Description		
1113	**228**	75k. multicoloured	20	10
1114		90k. multicoloured	30	15
1115		1z. multicoloured	35	15
1116		1z.50 multicoloured	45	20
1117		3z. multicoloured	95	50
1118		5z. multicoloured	1·60	85
1119		8z. multicoloured	2·50	1·10

229 Lions

1982. Virunga National Park. Multicoloured.

1120	1z. Type **229**	40	25
1121	1z.70 African buffalo	65	50
1122	3z.50 African elephant	1·25	90
1123	6z.50 Topi	2·25	1·40
1124	8z. Hippopotamus	3·25	1·90
1125	10z. Savanna monkey	4·50	2·25
1126	10z. Leopard	4·50	2·25

230 Scout Camp

233 Malachite

231 Red-billed Quelea

1982. 75th Anniv of Boy Scout Movement. Multicoloured.

1127	90k. Type **230**	30	15
1128	1z.70 Camp-fire	55	25
1129	3z. Scout	95	45
1130	5z. Scout carrying injured person	1·75	85
1131	8z. Scout signalling with flags	2·75	1·10

1982. Birds. Multicoloured.

1133	25k. Type **231**	10	10
1134	50k. African pygmy kingfisher	15	10
1135	90k. Green turaco	35	15
1136	1z.50 Three-banded plover	45	25
1137	1z.70 Temminck's courser	55	30
1138	2z. Bennett's woodpecker	65	45
1139	3z. Little grebe	80	60
1140	3z.50 Lizard buzzard (vert)	1·00	80
1141	5z. African black crake	2·00	90
1142	8z. White-headed vulture (vert)	3·25	1·75

1983. Minerals. Multicoloured.

1144	2k. Type **233**	10	10
1145	45k. Quartz (horiz)	20	10
1146	75k. Gold (horiz)	35	10
1147	1z. Uranium and pitchblende (horiz)	45	15
1148	1z.50 Bournonite	55	30
1149	3z. Cassiterite (horiz)	1·10	50
1150	6z. Dioptase	2·25	95
1151	8z. Cuprite	3·25	1·40

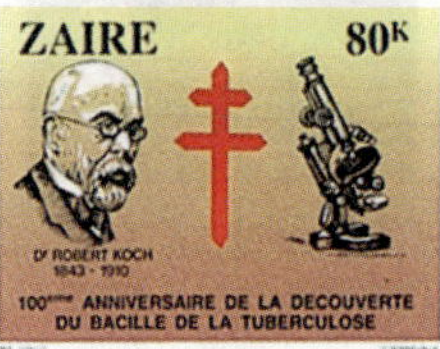

234 Dr. Koch and Microscope

1983. Centenary (1982) of Discovery of Tubercle Bacillus.

No.	Type	Description		
1153	**234**	80k. multicoloured	20	15
1154		1z.20 multicoloured	35	20
1155		3z.60 multicoloured	1·10	55
1156		9z.60 multicoloured	2·75	1·40

235 "Zaire Diplomat" (Lufwa Mawidi)

1983. Kinshasa Monuments. Multicoloured.

1157	50k. Type **235**	15	10
1158	1z. "Echo of Zaire" (Lufwa Mawidi) (horiz)	25	15
1159	1z.50 "Messengers" (Liyolo Limbe Mpuanga)	40	20
1160	3z. "Shield of Revolution" (Liyolo Limbe Mpuanga)	85	20
1161	5z. "Weeping Woman" (Wuma Mbambila) (horiz)	1·40	85
1162	10z. "The Militant" (Liyolo Limbe Mpuanga)	2·50	1·25

236 Satellite over Globe

1983. I.T.U. Delegates' Conference, Nairobi. Multicoloured.

1163	2k. Type **236**	10	10
1164	4k. Dish aerial	10	10
1165	25k. Dish aerial (different)	10	10
1166	1z.20 Satellite and microwave antenna	45	15
1167	2z.05 Satellite	65	30
1168	3z.60 Satellite and microwave antenna (different)	1·10	45
1169	6z. Map of Zaire	1·60	70
1170	8z. Satellite (different)	2·40	1·40

238 Giant Eland

1984. Garamba National Park. Multicoloured.

1172	10k. Type **238**	10	10
1173	15k. Tawny eagles	1·00	30
1174	3z. Servals	25	10
1175	10z. White rhinoceros	90	35
1176	15z. Lions	1·10	55
1177	37z.50 Warthogs	3·00	1·10
1178	40z. Kori bustards	5·75	2·00
1179	40z. South African crowned cranes and game lodge	5·75	2·00

239 Visual Display Unit and Ferry

1984. World Communications Year. Multicoloured.

1180	10k. Type **239**	10	10
1181	15k. Communications satellite	10	10
1182	8z.50 Radio telephone	1·50	75
1183	10z. Satellite and aerial	55	35
1184	15z. Video camera	95	80
1185	37z.50 Satellite and dish antenna	2·75	1·25
1186	80z. Switchboard operator	5·50	2·75

240 "Hypericum revolutum"

241 Basketball

1984. Flowers. Multicoloured.

1187	10k. Type **240**	10	15
1188	15k. "Borreria dibrachiata"	10	15
1189	3z. "Disa erubescens"	15	15
1190	8z.50 "Scaevola plumieri"	40	50
1191	10z. "Clerodendron thompsonii"	60	50
1192	15z. "Thumbergia erecta"	85	95
1193	37z.50 "Impatiens niamniamensis"	2·10	2·25
1194	100z. "Canarina eminii"	6·00	4·75

1984. Olympic Games, Los Angeles. Multicoloured.

1195	2z. Type **241**	15	10
1196	3z. Equestrian	20	10
1197	10z. Running	70	35
1198	15z. Long jump	1·10	55
1199	20z. Football	1·60	80

242 Montgolfier Balloon, 1783

243 Okapi feeding

1984. Bicentenary of Manned Flight. Mult.

1201	10k. Type **242**	10	10
1202	15k. Charles's hydrogen balloon, 1783	10	10
1203	3z. Montgolfier balloon "Le Gustave", 1784	15	10
1204	5z. Santos-Dumont's airship "Ballon No. 3", 1899	30	15
1205	10z. Piccard's stratosphere balloon "F.N.R.S.", 1931	70	40
1206	15z. Airship "Hindenburg"	1·10	60
1207	37z.50 Balloon "Double Eagle II", 1978	2·50	1·40
1208	80z. Hot-air balloons	6·00	3·00

1984. Wildlife Protection. Okapi. Multicoloured.

1209	2z. Type **243**	40	50
1210	3z. Okapi resting	85	50
1211	8z. Okapi and foal	1·75	2·00
1212	10z. Okapi crossing stream	2·40	2·00

1985. 50th Anniv of SABENA Brussels–Kinshasa Air Service. Nos. 927/34 surch **SABENA/1935-1985** and new value.
1214 2z.50 on 30s. multicoloured . . 15 10
1215 5z. on 5k. multicoloured . . 40 20
1216 6z. on 70s. multicoloured . . 45 30
1217 7z.50 on 1k. multicoloured . . 55 35
1218 8z.50 on 1k. multicoloured . . 65 40
1219 10z. on 8k. multicoloured . . 80 45
1220 12z.50 on 75k. multicoloured 90 60
1221 30z. on 50k. multicoloured . . 2·25 1·25

245 Swimming

1985. "Olymphilex '85" Olympic Stamps Exhibition, Lausanne. Multicoloured.
1223 1z. Type **245** 10 10
1224 2z. Football (vert) 15 10
1225 3z. Boxing 20 10
1226 4z. Basketball (vert) 30 15
1227 5z. Show jumping 35 20
1228 10z. Volleyball (vert) 70 45
1229 15z. Running . . . . 1·00 65
1230 30z. Cycling (vert) . . . . . 2·25 1·25

1985. 2nd Papal Visit. Nos. 1061/5 surch **AOUT 1985**.
1231 2z. on 5k. multicoloured . . 15 10
1232 3z. on 10k. multicoloured . . 20 15
1233 5z.50 multicoloured 45 20
1234 10z. on 100k. multicoloured . . 90 50
1235 15z. on 500k. multicoloured . . 1·40 65
1236 40z. on 800k. multicoloured . . 3·00 1·40

247 Great Egrets

1985. Birth Bicentenary of John J. Audubon (ornithologist). Multicoloured.
1238 5z. Type **247** 60 30
1239 10z. Black scoter . . . . . . 1·25 60
1240 15z. Black-crowned night heron . . . . 2·10 95
1241 25z. Surf scoter . . . . . . 4·25 2·00

248 National Flag and "25" on Flag

249 U.N. and Zaire Flags

1985. 25th Anniv of Independence.
1242 **248** 5z. multicoloured 20 10
1243 10z. multicoloured . . . 45 20
1244 15z. multicoloured . . . 65 35
1245 20z. multicoloured . . . 90 40

1985. 40th Anniv of U.N.O. and 25th Anniv of Zaire Membership. Multicoloured.
1247 10z. Type **249** 45 30
1248 50z. U.N. building and emblem . . . . 2·25 1·10

1985. International Youth Year. Nos. 1127/31 optd **1985** and I.Y.Y. emblem and surch also.
1249 3z. on 3z. multicoloured . . 10 10
1250 5z. on 5z. multicoloured . . 20 10
1251 7z. on 90k. multicoloured . . 35 15
1252 10z. on 90k. multicoloured . . 45 15
1253 15z. on 1z.70 multicoloured . . 55 25
1254 20z. on 8z. multicoloured . . 1·10 45
1255 50z. on 90k. multicoloured . . 2·75 1·00

252 "Kokolo" (pusher tug)

1985. 50th Anniv of National Transport Office.
1258 7z. Type **252** 50 20
1259 10z. Early steam locomotive . . 75 40
1260 15z. "Luebo" (pusher tug) . . 75 35
1261 50z. Modern diesel locomotive . . . . 2·25 1·10

253 Pope John Paul II

1985. Beatification of Sister Anuarite Nengapeta. Multicoloured.
1262 10z. Type **253** 45 20
1263 15z. Sister Anuarite 65 35
1264 25z. Pope and Sister Anuarite (horiz) . . . . . 1·10 55

254 Map and 1886 25c. Stamp

1988. Centenary of 1st Congo Free State Stamp.
1266 **254** 25z. blue, grey and deep blue . . . . 1·10 55

255 Congo Free State 1898 10f. stamp

1988. "Cenzapost" Stamp Centenary Exhibition. Multicoloured.
1267 7z. Type **255** 30 10
1268 15z. Belgian Congo 1939 1f.25+1f.25 stamp 55 30
1269 20z. Belgian Congo 1942 50f. stamp (vert) 65 30
1270 25z. Zaire 1982 8k. stamp . . 80 35
1271 40z. Zaire 1984 37z.50 stamp (vert) . . . . . . 1·40 65

256 African Egg Eater

1987. Reptiles. Multicoloured.
1273 2z. Type **256** 15 20
1274 5z. Rainbow lizard 15 20
1275 10z. Royal python 25 20
1276 15z. Cape chameleon . . . 60 30
1277 25z. Green mamba . . . . 1·00 60
1278 50z. Black-necked cobra . . 1·60 1·10

257 "Virgin and Child with Angels" (from Cortone triptych)

1987. Christmas. Paintings by Fr. Angelico. Mult.
1279 50z. Type **257** 65 35
1280 100z. "St. Catherine and St. Peter adoring the Child" . . . . 1·40 65
1281 120z. "Virgin and Child of the Angels and Four Saints" (detail, Fiesole Retable) . . . . 1·60 80
1282 180z. "Virgin and Child and Six Saints" (detail, Annalena Retable) . . . 2·50 1·10

1990. Various stamps surch.
1283 – 20z. on 20k. mult (No. 920) 15 20
1284 **236** 40z. on 2k. mult 30 55
1285 – 40z. on 4k. mult (1164) 30 55
1286 **218** 40z. on 10k. mult . . . 30 55
1287 **231** 40z. on 25k. mult . . . 30 55
1288 – 40z. on 25k. mult (1165) 30 40
1289 – 40z. on 50k. mult (1055) 30 55
1290 – 40z. on 50k. mult (1134) 30 35
1291 **235** 40z. on 50k. mult . . . 30 55
1292 **228** 40z. on 75k. mult . . . 30 55
1293 – 40z. on 80k. mult (1056) 30 40
1294 – 40z. on 90k. mult (1093) 30 55
1295 **228** 40z. on 90k. mult . . . 30 35
1296 – 40z. on 90k. mult (1135) 30 40
1297 **236** 80z. on 2k. mult . . . 55 60
1298 – 80z. on 4k. mult (1164) 60 65
1299 **218** 80z. on 10k. mult . . . 60 65
1300 **231** 80z. on 25k. mult . . . 55 60
1301 – 80z. on 25k. mult (1165) 55 70
1302 – 80z. on 50k. mult (1134) 60 65
1303 **235** 80z. on 50k. mult . . . 55 60
1304 **228** 80z. on 75k. mult . . . 55 60
1305 – 80z. on 80k. mult (1056) 55 45
1306 – 80z. on 90k. mult (1093) 55 60
1307 **228** 80z. on 90k. mult . . . 60 65
1308 – 80z. on 90k. mult (1135) 55 70
1309 **209** 100z. on 40s. brown, black and mauve . . . 70 80
1311 **220** 100z. on 2k. mult . . . 70 80
1312 **221** 100z. on 2k. mult . . . 70 80
1313 **226** 100z. on 2k. mult . . . 70 80
1314 **209** 100z. on 4k. brown, black and yellow . . . 70 65
1315 – 100z. on 5k. mult (930) 70 80
1316 – 100z. on 5k. mult (1061) 70 80
1317 – 100z. on 5k. mult (1077) 70 65
1318 – 100z. on 8k. mult (908) 95 55
1319 – 100z. on 8k. mult (931) 70 65
1320 – 100z. on 8k. mult (946) 70 80
1322 – 100z. on 10k. mult (947) 70 65
1323 – 100z. on 10k. mult (969) 70 80
1324 – 100z. on 10k. mult (1036) 65 70
1325 **217** 100z. on 10k. mult . . . 65 70
1326 – 100z. on 10k. mult (1062) 70 65
1327 – 100z. on 10k. mult (1068) 70 65
1328 **209** 100z. on 15k. brown, black and blue 65 70
1329 – 100z. on 18k. mult (1079) 65 70
1330 – 100z. on 20k. mult (970) 70 65
1331 – 100z. on 20k. mult (1020) 95 80
1332 **177** 100z. on 22k. mult . . . 70 80
1333 – 100z. on 25k. mult (1069) 65 70
1335 – 100z. on 48k. mult (912) 70 65
1336 – 100z. on 48k. mult (950) 65 70
1337 – 100z. on 50k. mult (1013) 70 80
1338 – 100z. on 50k. mult (1080) 85 90
1339 – 100z. on 50k. mult (1103) 65 70
1340 – 100z. on 75k. mult (1038) 70 80
1341 – 100z. on 75k. mult (1049) 70 80
1342 **203** 100z. on 90k. mult . . . 70 80
1343 – 100z. on 80k. mult (1050) 70 70
1344 **234** 100z. on 80k. mult . . . 70 80
1345 – 100z. on 90k. mult (1070) 85 90
1346 – 100z. on 90k. mult (1104) 70 65
1348 **233** 300z. on 2k. mult . . . 2·25 3·00
1349 – 300z. on 8k. mult (980) 3·25 5·50
1350 **216** 300z. on 10k. green & bl 2·25 3·00
1351 – 300z. on 14k. mult (789) 2·25 3·00
1352 **159** 300z. on 17k. mult (807) 2·25 3·00
1353 – 300z. on 20k. mult (989) 2·25 3·00
1354 – 300z. on 45k. mult (1145) . . . . 2·25 2·00
1355 – 300z. on 75k. brown and blue (1044) . . . . 2·25 2·00
1356 – 300z. on 75k. mult (1146) . . . . 2·10 2·50
1357 **198** 500z. on 8k. mult . . . 4·75 5·50
1358 500z. on 10k. mult . . . 3·75 3·50
1359 500z. on 25k. mult . . . 4·00 5·00
1360 500z. on 48k. mult . . . 4·00 3·50

259 "Sida" forming Owl's Face

1990. Anti-AIDS Campaign. Multicoloured.
1361 30z. Type **259** 50 20
1362 40z. Skeleton firing arrow through "SIDA" 60 35
1363 80z. Leopard . . . . 1·10 80

260 Administration Building

1990. 50th Anniv of Regideso (development organization). Multicoloured.
1365 40z. Type **260** 55 35
1366 50z. Modern factory 65 45
1367 75z. Old water treatment plant . . . . 1·00 65
1368 120z. Communal water tap 1·40 80

261 Maps of France and Zaire and Birds

1990. Bicentenary of French Revolution. Mult.
1369 40z. Type **261** 55 35
1370 50z. Article 1 of Declaration of Rights of Man and the Citizen within outline of person 65 45
1371 100z. Crowd . . . . 1·25 65
1372 120z. Globe . . . . 1·40 80

262 Stairs of Venus, Mount Hoyo

1990. Tourist Sites. Multicoloured.
1373 40z. Type **262** 45 20
1374 60z. Scenic road to village 65 35
1375 100z. Lake Kivu . . . . . 1·25 55
1376 120z. Niyara Gongo volcano 1·60 25

1991. Various stamps surch.
1379 – 1000z. on 100k. mult (1064) 25 25
1380 – 1000z. on 1z. mult (1105) 25 25
1381 **214** 1000z. on 1z. mult (1026) 25 25
1383 – 1000z. on 1z. mult (1027) 25 25
1385 – 2000z. on 100k. violet and blue (1045) . . . 50 50
1386 – 2000z. on 1z. mult (1147) 50 50
1387 **228** 2500z. on 1z. mult . . . 65 65
1388 **225** 3000z. on 1z. green and gold 75 75
1389 – 4000z. on 1z. mult (1158) 1·00 1·00
1390 – 5000z. on 1z. mult (1158) 1·25 1·25
1391 **228** 10000z. on 1z. mult . . 2·50 2·50
1392 **225** 15000z. on 1z. green and gold . . . . 3·75 3·75

Nos. 1381 and 1383 exist in two versions with the exhibition logo either at the right or left of the design.

1992. Various stamps surch.
1393 – 50,000z. on 125k. multicoloured (1058) 55 70
1394 – 100,000z. on 1z.20 multicoloured (1166) 55 70
1395 **234** 150,000z. on 1z.20 multicoloured 55 70
1396 – 200,000z. on 145k. blue and indigo (1046) . . 80 70
1397 **234** 250,000z. on 1z.20 multicoloured . . . . 1·10 1·00
1398 – 300,000z. on 1z.20 multicoloured (1166) 1·40 1·40
1399 **234** 500,000z. on 1z.20 multicoloured . . . . 1·90 1·75

1993. Various stamps surch. (a) Nos. 944/51.
1400 **199** 500,000z. on 30s. multicoloured 30 50
1401 – 500,000z. on 5k. multicoloured 30 50
1402 – 750,000z. on 8k. multicoloured 45 50
1403 – 750,000z. on 10k. multicoloured 45 50
1404 – 1,000,000z. on 30k. multicoloured 60 70
1405 – 1,000,000z. on 40k. multicoloured 60 70
1406 – 5,000,000z. on 48k. multicoloured . . . . 3·00 2·75
1407 – 10,000,000z. on 100k. multicoloured . . . . 5·75 5·25

(b) Nos. 1262/4.
1408 **253** 3,000,000z. on 10z. multicoloured . . . . 1·25 1·50
1409 – 5,000,000z. on 15z. multicoloured . . . . 2·50 2·50
1410 – 10,000,000z. on 25z. multicoloured . . . . 5·00 4·75

BOGUS SURCHARGES. Surcharges with commemorative inscriptions on Nos. 1365/8 for the inauguration of a pumping station and on Nos. 1373/6 for the sixth anniversary of the National Tourism Office are bogus.

Currency reform.

1 (new) zaire = 3000000 (old) zaire.

268 Eland and Calf

1993. 50th Anniv of Garamba National Park. Multicoloured.
1412 30k. Type **268** 30 30
1413 50k. African elephants . . . 30 30
1414 1z.50 Giant elands 60 30
1415 3z.50 Two white rhinoceros 90 75
1416 5z. Bongo . . . . 1·75 1·40

1993. Various stamps surch. (a) Nos. 1201/8.
1417 **242** 30k. on 10k. mult . . . 30 35
1418 – 50k. on 15k. mult . . . 65 65
1419 – 1z.50 on 3z. mult . . . . 1·25 1·25
1420 – 2z.50 on 5z. mult . . . . 1·75 1·75
1421 – 3z.50 on 10z. mult . . . . 2·40 2·40
1422 – 5z. on 15z. mult . . . . 3·50 3·50
1423 – 7z.50 on 37z.50 mult . . 4·75 4·75
1424 – 10z. on 80z. mult . . . . 6·75 6·75

(b) Nos. 1043/7.
1425 **216** 30k. on 10k. green and blue 40 15
1426 – 50k. on 75k. brown and blue 60 20
1427 – 1z.50 on 100k. violet and blue . . . . 1·90 60
1428 – 3k.50 on 145k. blue and deep blue . . . . . . 2·75 90
1429 – 5z. on 270k. red and blue . . . . 3·00 1·00

(c) Nos. 1238/41.
1430 **247** 50k. on 5z. mult 60 80
1431 – 1z.50 on 10z. mult . . . 1·90 2·40
1432 – 3z.50 on 15z. mult . . . 2·75 3·50
1433 – 5z. on 25z. mult . . . . 3·00 4·00

1994. Various stamps surch.
1434 – 20z. on 3z. mult (No. 1139) 10 15
1435 – 40z. on 270k. red and blue (No. 1047) . . . 10 15
1436 – 50z. on 3z. mult (No. 1174) 15 15
1437 – 75z. on 3z. mult (No. 1196) 20 15
1438 – 100z. on 2z.05 mult (No. 1167) 35 30
1439 – 150z. on 1z.70 mult (No. 1121) 40 35
1440 – 200z. on 50k. mult (No. 1413) 50 40
1441 – 250z. on 1z.50 mult (No. 1136) 55 60
1442 **234** 300z. on 3z.60 mult . . . 65 65
1443 – 500z. on 3z.60 mult (No. 1168) 90 90

271 Show Jumping

1996. Olympic Games, Atlanta, U.S.A. Mult.
1444 1000z. Type **271** 10 10
1445 12500z. Boxing 65 40
1446 25000z. Table tennis . . . . 1·25 75
1447 35000z. Basketball (vert) . . 1·75 1·10
1448 50000z. Tennis . . . . . . 2·50 1·50

1996. Various stamps. Surch.
1449 – 100z. on 3z.50 mult (No. 1109) 10 15
1450 **234** 500z. on 3z.60 mult . . . 10 15
1451 – 1000z. on 2z.05 mult (No. 1167) 20 20
1452 – 2500z. on 1z.50 multicoloured (No. 1136) 35 35
1453 – 5000z. on 3z.60 multicoloured (No. 1168) 75 75
1454 – 6000z. on 1z.50 multicoloured (No. 1136) 80 80
1455 **234** 15000z. on 3z.60 multicoloured . . . . 1·10 1·10
1456 – 25000z. on 3z.60 multicoloured (No. 1168) . . . . . 1·40 1·50

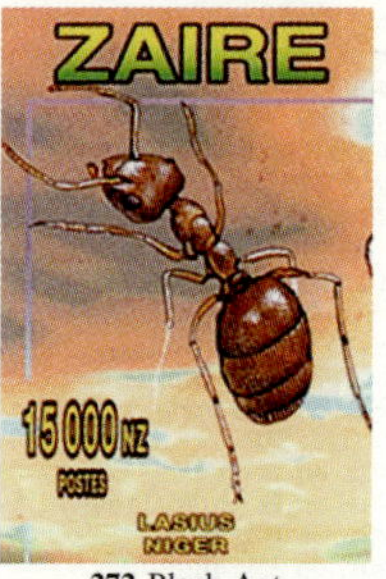

272 Black Ant

1996. Fauna, Flora and Minerals. Multicoloured.
1457 15000z. Type **272** . . . . . 1·25 1·25
1458 15000z. Calopterygides . . . 1·25 1·25
1459 15000z. Green lynx spider (Peucetia) . . . . 1·25 1·25
1460 15000z. Sphecides . . . . . 1·25 1·25
1461 20000z. Scutellosaurus . . . 1·40 1·40
1462 20000z. Compsognathus . . 1·40 1·40
1463 20000z. Dryosaurus . . . . 1·40 1·40
1464 20000z. Velociraptor . . . 1·40 1·40
1465 25000z. Panda eating (face value at left) . . . . . . 2·40 2·40
1466 25000z. Panda eating (face value at right) . . . . . 2·40 2·40
1467 25000z. Sitting . . . . . . 2·40 2·40
1468 25000z. Walking . . . . . 2·40 2·40
1469 25000z. *Eulophia streptopetala* . . . . . . 1·60 1·60
1470 25000z. *Oeceoclades saundersiana* . . . . . 1·60 1·60
1471 25000z. *Eulophia gracilis* . . 1·60 1·60
1472 25000z. *Bulbophyllum falcatum* . . . . 1·60 1·60
1473 35000z. *Termitomyces aurantiacus* . . . . 2·10 2·10
1474 35000z. *Tricholoma lobayensis* . . . . 2·10 2·10
1475 35000z. *Lepiota esculenta* . . 2·10 2·10
1476 35000z. *Phlebopus sudanicus* 2·10 2·10
1477 40000z. Uraninite . . . . . 1·75 1·75
1478 40000z. Malachite . . . . . 1·75 1·75
1479 40000z. Ruby . . . . 1·75 1·75
1480 40000z. Diamond . . . . . 1·75 1·75
1481 50000z. Congo serpent eagle 3·00 3·00
1482 50000z. Crowned eagle ("Aigle Couronne") . . . 3·00 3·00
1483 50000z. Dark chanting goshawk (*Melierax metabates*) . . . . . . 3·00 3·00
1484 50000z. African long-tailed hawk (*Urotriorchis macrourus*) . . . . . . 3·00 3·00
1485 70000z. Red glider (*Cymthoe sangaris*) . . . . 3·50 3·50
1486 70000z. Purple-tip (*Colotis zoe*) . . . . 3·50 3·50
1487 70000z. Physcaeneura leda 3·50 3·50
1488 70000z. Green-veined charaxes (*Charaxes candiope*) . . . . 3·50 3·50
1489 100000z. Diamond . . . . 5·75 5·75
1490 100000z. Dioptase . . . . 5·75 5·75
1491 100000z. Cuprite . . . . . 5·75 5·75
1492 100000z. Chrysocolle . . . 5·75 5·75

Nos. 1457/60 (insects), 1461/4 (dinosaurs), 1465/8 (pandas), 1469/72 (orchids), 1473/6 (fungi), 1477/80, 1489/92 (minerals), 1481/4 (birds) and 1485/8 (butterflies) respectively were issued together, se-tenant, with the backgrounds forming a composite design.

OFFICIAL STAMPS

1975. Optd **SP**.
O841 **172** 10s. orange and black 10 10
O842 40s. blue and black . . 10 10
O843 50s. yellow and black 10 10
O844 **177b** 1k. multicoloured . . . 10 10
O845 2k. multicoloured . . . 10 10
O846 3k. multicoloured . . . 10 10
O847 4k. multicoloured . . . 15 10
O848 5k. multicoloured . . . 20 10
O849 6k. multicoloured . . . 20 10
O850 8k. multicoloured . . . 35 15
O851 9k. multicoloured . . . 35 20
O852 10k. multicoloured . . 45 20
O853 14k. multicoloured . . 55 25
O854 17k. multicoloured . . 80 45
O855 20k. multicoloured . . 1·00 50
O856 50k. multicoloured . . 2·50 1·00
O857 100k. multicoloured . . 6·75 2·75

For later issues see **CONGO DEMOCRATIC REPUBLIC**.

ZAMBEZIA Pt. 9

Formerly administered by the Zambezia Co. This district of Portuguese E. Africa was later known as Quelimane and is now part of Mozambique.

1000 reis = 1 milreis.

1894. "Figures" key-type inscr "ZAMBEZIA".
1 R 5r. orange 15 15
2 10r. mauve 20 20
3 15r. brown 25 25
4 20r. lilac 25 25
12 25r. green 40 30
13 50r. blue 40 30
14 75r. pink 90 90
15 80r. green 75 60
8 100r. brown on buff 70 60
16 150r. red on pink 90 75
17 200r. blue on blue 90 80
18 300r. blue on brown . . . . 1·75 1·50

1898. "King Carlos" key-type inscr "ZAMBEZIA". Name and value in red (500r.) or black (others).
20 S 2½r. grey 20 15
21 5r. red 20 15
22 10r. green 20 15
23 15r. brown 45 40
55 15r. green 65 55
24 20r. lilac 40 35
25 25r. green 40 35
56 25r. red 45 35
26 50r. blue 50 40
57 50r. brown . . . . 1·10 90
58 65r. blue . . . . 2·75 2·25
27 75r. pink . . . . 2·75 2·00
59 75r. purple . . . . 1·25 1·00
28 80r. mauve . . . . 1·75 1·50
29 100r. blue on blue 80 75
60 115r. brown on pink . . . . 3·75 2·75
61 130r. brown on yellow . . . 3·75 2·75
30 150r. brown on yellow . . . 1·75 1·40
31 200r. purple on pink . . . . 1·75 1·40
32 300r. blue on pink . . . . . 2·10 1·50
62 400r. blue on cream . . . . 4·00 3·25
33 500r. black on blue . . . . 3·00 2·50
34 700r. mauve on yellow . . . 3·50 3·00

1902. Surch.
63 S 50r. on 65r. blue . . . . . 2·00 1·25
35 R 65r. on 10r. mauve . . . . 2·10 1·75
36 65r. on 15r. brown . . . . . 2·10 1·75
37 65r. on 20r. lilac . . . . . 2·10 1·75
38 65r. on 300r. blue on brown 2·10 1·75
40 115r. on 5r. orange . . . . 2·10 1·75
41 115r. on 25r. green . . . . 2·10 1·75
42 115r. on 80r. green . . . . 2·10 1·75
46 V 130r. on 2½r. brown . . . . 2·10 1·75
43 R 130r. on 75r. pink . . . . 2·10 1·75
45 130r. on 150r. red on pink 1·75 1·50
47 400r. on 50r. blue 80 70
49 400r. on 100r. brown on buff 80 70
50 400r. on 200r. blue on blue 80 70

1902. 1898 issue optd **PROVISORIO**.
51 S 15r. brown 75 60
52 25r. green 75 60
53 50r. blue 75 60
54 75r. pink . . . . 2·10 1·50

1911. 1898 issue optd **REPUBLICA**.
64 S 2½r. grey 10 10
65 5r. red 10 10
66 10r. green 15 15
67 15r. green 15 15
68 20r. lilac 20 10
69 25r. red 45 20
108 25r. green . . . . 4·00 3·00
70 50r. brown 15 15
71 75r. purple 40 30
72 100r. blue on blue 40 30
73 115r. brown on pink 45 35
74 130r. brown on yellow . . . 45 35
75 200r. purple on pink 45 35
76 400r. blue on cream 75 60
77 500r. black on blue 75 60
78 700r. mauve on yellow . . . 75 60

1914. Provisionals of 1902 optd **REPUBLICA**.
94 S 50r. blue (No. 53) 25 20
95 50r. on 65r. blue . . . . . 1·00 85
81 75r. pink (No. 54) 50 45
96 R 115r. on 5r. orange 25 20
97 115r. on 25r. green 25 20
98 115r. on 80r. green 25 20
99 V 130r. on 2½r. brown 25 20
100 R 130r. on 75r. pink 25 20
102 130r. on 150r. red on pink 25 20
90 400r. on 50r. blue 85 75
92 400r. on 100r. brn on buff 90 75
93 400r. on 200r. blue on blue 90 75

NEWSPAPER STAMP

1893. "Newspaper" key-type inscr "ZAMBEZIA".
N1 V 2½r. brown 20 15

ZAMBIA Pt. 1

Formerly Northern Rhodesia, attained independence on 24 October 1964 and changed its name to Zambia.

1964. 12 pence = 1 shilling;
20 shillings = 1 pound.
1968. 100 ngwee = 1 kwacha.

11 Pres. Kaunda and Victoria Falls

1964. Independence.
91 **11** 3d. sepia, green and blue . . 10 10
92 – 6d. violet and yellow . . . 15 20
93 – 1s.3d. multicoloured 20 25

DESIGNS—HORIZ: 6d. College of Further Education, Lusaka. VERT: 1s.3d. Barotse dancer.

14 Maize – Farmer and Silo

22 Tobacco Worker

1964.
94 **14** ½d. red, black and green . . 10 1·25
95 – 1d. brown, black and blue . 10 10
96 – 2d. red, brown and orange 10 10
97 – 3d. black and red 10 10
98 – 4d. black, brown and orange 15 10
99 – 6d. orange, brown and turquoise 15 10
100 – 9d. red, black and blue . . 15 10
101 – 1s. black, bistre and blue 15 10
102 **22** 1s.3d. multicoloured . . . 20 10
103 – 2s. multicoloured 25 30
104 – 2s.6d. black and yellow . . 60 35
105 – 5s. black, yellow and green 1·00 75
106 – 10s. black and orange . . . 3·50 3·75
107 – £1 multicoloured . . . . . 2·00 5·00

DESIGNS—VERT (as Type **14**): 1d. Health – radiographer; 2d. Chinyau dancer; 3d. Cotton-picking. (As Type **22**): 2s. Tonga basket-making; £1 Makishi dancer. HORIZ (as Type **14**): 4d. Angoni bull. (As Type **22**): 6d. Communications, old and new; 9d. Zambezi sawmills and redwood flower; 1s. Fishing at Mpulungu; 2s.6d. Luangwa Game Reserve; 5s. Education – student; 10s. Copper mining.

28 I.T.U. Emblem and Symbols

1965. Centenary of I.T.U.
108 **28** 6d. violet and gold 15 10
109 2s.6d. grey and gold . . . 85 1·50

29 I.C.Y. Emblem

1965. International Co-operation Year.
110 **29** 3d. turquoise and gold . . 15 10
111 1s.3d. blue and gold . . . 35 45

30 State House, Lusaka

35 University Building

34 W.H.O. Building and U.N. Flag

1965. 1st Anniv of Independence. Mult.
112 3d. Type **30** 10 10
113 6d. Fireworks, Independence Stadium 10 10
114 1s.3d. Clematopsis (vert) . . 15 10
115 2s.6d. "Tithonia diversifolia" (vert) . . . . 30 1·25

1966. Inaug of W.H.O. Headquarters, Geneva.
116 **34** 3d. brown, gold and blue 20 10
117 1s.3d. violet, gold and blue 80 95

1966. Opening of Zambia University.
118 **35** 3d. green and bronze . . . 10 10
119 1s.3d. violet and bronze . . 20 10

36 National Assembly Building

1967. Inaug of National Assembly Building.

120	**36** 3d. black and gold	10	10
121	6d. green and gold	10	10

37 Airport Scene

1967. Opening of Lusaka International Airport.

122	**37** 6d. blue and bronze . . .	15	10
123	2s.6d. brown and bronze	60	1·00

38 Youth Service Badge 43 Lusaka Cathedral

1967. National Development.

124	**38** 4d. black, red and gold . .	10	10
125	– 6d. black, gold and blue	10	10
126	– 9d. black, blue and silver	15	50
127	– 1s. multicoloured	50	10
128	– 1s.6d. multicoloured . . .	70	2·25

DESIGNS—HORIZ: 6d. "Co-operative Farming"; 1s.6d. Road link with Tanzania. VERT: 9d. "Communications"; 1s. Coalfields.

1968. Decimal Currency.

129	**43** 1n. multicoloured	10	10
130	– 2n. multicoloured	10	10
131	– 3n. multicoloured	10	10
132	– 5n. brown and bronze . .	10	10
133	– 8n. multicoloured	15	10
134	– 10n. multicoloured	25	10
135	– 15n. multicoloured	2·75	10
136	– 20n. multicoloured	4·50	10
137	– 25n. multicoloured	25	10
138	– 50n. brown, orange and bronze	30	15
139	– 1k. blue and bronze . . .	4·50	20
140	– 2k. black and bronze . . .	2·25	1·25

DESIGNS—VERT (as Type **43**): 2n. Baobab tree; 5n. National Museum, Livingstone; 8n. Vimbuza dancer; 10n. Tobacco picking. (26 × 32 mm); 20n. South African crowned cranes; 25n. Angoni warrior; 50n. Chokwe dancer. HORIZ (as Type **43**): 3n. Zambia Airways Vickers VC-10 jetliner. (32 × 26 mm): 15n. "Imbrasia zambesina" (moth); 1k. Kafue Railway Bridge; 2k. Eland.

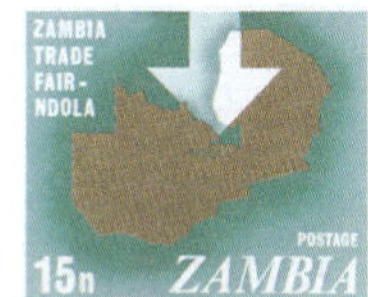

55 Ndola on Outline of Zambia

1968. Trade Fair, Ndola.

141	**55** 15n. green and gold . . .	10	10

56 Human Rights Emblem and Heads

1968. Human Rights Year.

142	**56** 3n. blue, violet and gold	10	10

57 W.H.O. Emblem

1968. 20th Anniv of World Health Organization.

143	**57** 10n. gold and violet . . .	10	10

58 Group of Children

1968. 22nd Anniv of U.N.I.C.E.F.

144	**58** 25n. black, gold and blue	15	70

59 Copper Miner 61 Zambia outlined on Map of Africa

1969. 50th Anniv of Int Labour Organization.

145	**59** 3n. copper and violet . . .	25	10
146	– 25n. yellow, copper & brown	1·00	1·00

DESIGN—HORIZ: 25n. Poling a furnace.

1969. International African Tourist Year. Mult.

147	5n. Type **61**	10	10
148	10n. Waterbuck (horiz) . . .	15	10
149	15n. Kasaba Bay golden perch (horiz)	35	40
150	25n. Carmine bee eater . . .	1·00	1·75

PREVENTIVE MEDICINE

65 Satellite "Nimbus 3" orbiting the Earth 66 Woman collecting Water from Well

1970. World Meteorological Day.

151	**65** 15n. multicoloured	20	50

1970. Preventive Medicine.

152	**66** 3n. multicoloured	15	10
153	– 15n. multicoloured	30	30
154	– 25n. blue, red and sepia . .	65	70

DESIGNS: 15n. Child on scales; 25n. Child being immunized.

67 "Masks" (mural by Gabriel Ellison)

1970. Conference of Non-Aligned Nations.

155	**67** 15n. multicoloured	30	30

68 Ceremonial Axe

1970. Traditional Crafts. Multicoloured.

156	3n. Type **68**	10	10
157	5n. Clay smoking-pipe bowl	10	10
158	15n. Makishi mask	25	30
159	25n. Kuomboka Ceremony	40	1·00
MS160	133 × 83 mm. Nos. 156/9. Imperf	6·00	13·00

SIZES—HORIZ: 5n. as T **68**; 25n. 72 × 19 mm. VERT: 15n. 30 × 47 mm.

69 Dag Hammarskjold and U.N. General Assembly

1971. 10th Death Anniv of Dag Hammarskjold. Multicoloured.

161	4n. Type **69**	10	10
162	10n. Tail of aircraft	15	10
163	15n. Dove of Peace	15	25
164	25n. Memorial tablet	30	1·50

70 Red-breasted Tilapia

1971. Fish. Multicoloured.

165	4n. Type **70**	40	10
166	10n. Long-finned tilapia ("Green-headed bream")	60	40
167	15n. Tigerfish	75	2·50

71 North African Crested Porcupine

1972. Conservation Year (1st issue). Mult.

168	4n. Cheetah (horiz)	20	25
169	10n. Lechwe (horiz)	25	60
170	15n. Type **71**	35	85
171	25n. African elephant	1·40	3·00

Nos. 168/9 are size 58 × 21 mm.

1972. Conservation Year (2nd issue). As T **71**. Multicoloured.

172	4n. Soil conservation	15	20
173	10n. Forestry	15	30
174	15n. Water	20	80
175	25n. Maize	45	1·60

Nos. 174/5 are size 58 × 21 mm.

72 Giraffe and Common Zebra

1972. National Parks. Sheet 114 × 140 mm, containing T **72** and similar vert designs. Multicoloured.

MS176 10n. (× 4) Type **72**; Black rhinoceros; hippopotamus and common panther, lion . . . . 6·50 12·00

Each design includes part of a map showing Zambian National Parks, the four forming a composite design.

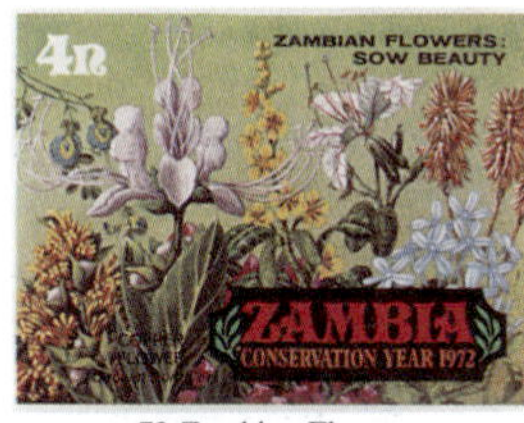

73 Zambian Flowers

1972. Conservation Year (3rd issue). Mult.

177	4n. Type **73**	30	30
178	10n. "Papilio demodocus" (butterfly)	80	80
179	15n. "Apis mellifera" (bees)	85	1·40
180	25n. "Nomadacris septemfasciata" (locusts)	1·25	2·25

74 Mary and Joseph

1972. Christmas. Multicoloured.

181	4n. Type **74**	10	10
182	9n. Mary, Joseph and Jesus	10	10
183	15n. Mary, Jesus and the shepherds	10	10
184	25n. The Three Wise Men . .	20	40

75 Oudenodon and Rubidgea

1973. Zambian Prehistoric Animals. Mult.

185	4n. Type **75**	85	85
186	9n. Broken Hill Man	90	90
187	10n. Zambiasaurus	1·00	1·50
188	15n. "Luangwa drysdalli" . .	1·10	2·00
189	25n. Glossopteris	1·25	3·00

Nos. 186/9 are smaller, 38 × 21 mm.

76 "Dr. Livingstone, I Presume"

1973. Death Cent of Dr. Livingstone. Mult.

190	3n. Type **76**	15	15
191	4n. Scripture lesson	15	15
192	9n. Victoria Falls	30	40
193	10n. Scattering slavers . . .	20	45
194	15n. Healing the sick	30	1·60
195	25n. Burial place of Livingstone's heart	30	2·75

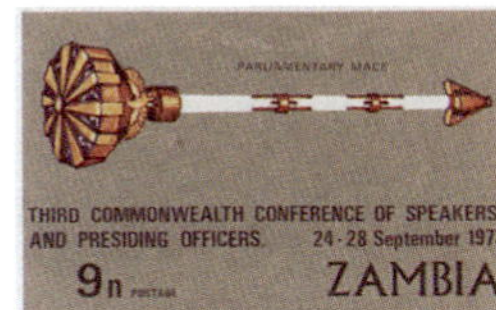

77 Parliamentary Mace

1973. 3rd Commonwealth Conference of Speakers and Presiding Officers, Lusaka.

196	**77** 9n. multicoloured	50	55
197	15n. multicoloured	60	1·10
198	25n. multicoloured	70	1·50

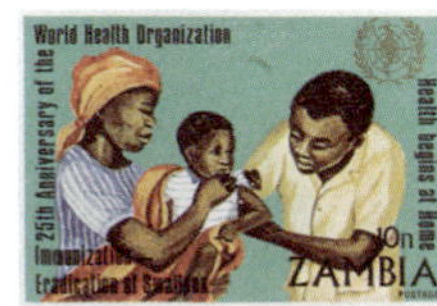

78 Inoculation

1973. 25th Anniv of W.H.O. Multicoloured.

199	4n. Mother washing baby (vert)	40·00	23·00
200	9n. Nurse weighing baby (vert)	45	2·25
201	10n. Type **78**	50	3·00
202	15n. Child eating meal . . .	90	5·00

79 U.N.I.P. Flag 80 President Kaunda at Mulungushi

1974. 1st Anniv of Second Republic. Mult.

203	4n. Type **79**	7·00	7·00
204	9n. Freedom House	30	1·50
205	10n. Army band	30	2·00
206	15n. "Celebrations" (dancers)	50	3·25
207	25n. Presidential chair . . .	75	5·00

1974. 50th Birthday of President Kaunda. Multicoloured.
208 4n. Type **80** 40 40
209 9n. President's former residence 20 20
210 15n. President holding Independence flame 50 1·25

81 Nakambala Sugar Estate

1974. 10th Anniv of Independence. Mult.
211 3n. Type **81** 15 10
212 4n. Local market 15 10
213 9n. Kapiri glass factory 20 10
214 10n. Kafue hydro-electric scheme 25 10
215 15n. Kafue Railway Bridge 50 95
216 25n. Non-aligned Conference, Lusaka, 1970 60 1·25
MS217 141 × 105 mm. 15n. (×4) Academic Education; Teacher Training College; Technical Education; Zambia University 6·00 8·50

82 Mobile Post-van

1974. Centenary of U.P.U. Multicoloured.
218 4n. Type **82** 20 15
219 9n. Hawker Siddeley H.S.748 airplane on tarmac 30 30
220 10n. Chipata Post Office 30 40
221 15n. Modern training centre 45 1·75

83 Dish Aerial

1974. Opening of Mwembeshi Earth Station. Multicoloured.
222 4n. Type **83** 25 20
223 9n. View at dawn 35 30
224 15n. View at dusk 40 70
225 25n. Aerial view 50 1·50

84 Black Rhinoceros and Calf

86 Map of Namibia

85 Independence Monument

1975. Multicoloured.
226 1n. Type **84** 75 1·00
227 2n. Helmeted guineafowl 75 1·00
228 3n. National Dancing Troupe 15 1·00
229 4n. African fish eagle 1·00 10
230 5n. Knife-edge Bridge 1·00 1·00
231 8n. Sitatunga (antelope) 1·00 75
232 9n. African elephant, Kasaba Bay 1·25 70
233 10n. Temminck's ground pangolin 20 10
234 15n. Type **85** 30 10
235 20n. Harvesting groundnuts 85 1·00
236 25n. Tobacco growing 1·25 50
237 50n. Flying Doctor service 3·00 2·00
238 1k. Lady Ross's turaco 4·50 1·75
239 2k. Village scene 3·00 5·50
Nos. 234/9 are as Type **85**.

1975. Namibia Day.
240 **86** 4n. green and yellow 20 20
241 9n. blue and green 25 30
242 15n. orange and yellow 40 75
243 25n. red and orange 50 1·50

87 Erection of Sprinkler Irrigation

1975. Silver Jubilee of International Commission on Irrigation and Drainage. Multicoloured.
244 4n. Type **87** 15 15
245 9n. Sprinkler irrigation 30 40
246 15n. Furrow irrigation 65 1·50

88 Mutondo

1976. World Forestry Day. Multicoloured.
247 3n. Type **88** 20 10
248 4n. Mukunyu 20 10
249 9n. Mukusi 35 25
250 10n. Mopane 35 25
251 15n. Musuku 55 1·40
252 25n. Mukwa 65 2·00

89 Passenger Train

1976. Opening of Tanzania–Zambia Railway. Multicoloured.
253 4n. Type **89** 30 30
254 9n. Copper exports 45 55
255 15n. Machinery imports 70 95
256 25n. Goods train 1·10 1·75
MS257 140 × 106 mm. 10n. Clearing bush; 15n. Laying track; 20n. Railway workers; 25n. Completed track 3·50 4·00

90 Kayowe Dance

1977. 2nd World Black and African Festival of Arts and Culture, Nigeria. Multicoloured.
258 4n. Type **90** 15 10
259 9n. Lilombola dance 15 15
260 15n. Initiation ceremony 30 40
261 25n. Munkhwele dance 55 1·00

91 Grimwood's Longclaw

1977. Birds of Zambia. Multicoloured.
262 4n. Type **91** 40 10
263 9n. Shelley's sunbird 55 60
264 10n. Black-cheeked lovebird 55 60
265 15n. Locust finch 1·25 2·00
266 20n. White-chested tinkerbird 1·40 2·25
267 25n. Chaplin's barbet 1·50 2·75

92 Girls with Building Blocks

1977. Decade for Action to Combat Racism and Racial Discrimination. Multicoloured.
268 4n. Type **92** 15 10
269 9n. Women dancing 20 20
270 15n. Girls with dove 30 1·00

93 Angels and Shepherds

1977. Christmas. Multicoloured.
271 4n. Type **93** 10 10
272 9n. The Holy Family 10 10
273 10n. The Magi 10 15
274 15n. Jesus presented to Simeon 20 1·00

94 African Elephant and Road Check

1978. Anti-poaching Campaign. Multicoloured.
275 8n. Type **94** 45 20
276 18n. Lechwe and canoe patrol 30 65
277 28n. Warthog and Bell 206 JetRanger helicopter 75 1·10
278 32n. Cheetah and game guard patrol 75 1·50

1979. Various stamps surch.
279 – 8n. on 9n. multicoloured (No. 232) 70 10
280 – 10n. on 3n. multicoloured (No. 228) 10 10
281 – 18n. on 25n. mult (No. 236) 15 15
282 **85** 28n. on 15n. mult 20 25

96 Kayowe Dance

1979. Commonwealth Summit Conference, Lusaka. Multicoloured.
283 18n. Type **96** 15 25
284 32n. Kutambala dance 20 40
285 42n. Chitwansombo drummers 20 60
286 58n. Lilombola dance 25 80

97 "Kalulu and the Tug of War"

1979. International Year of the Child. Mult.
287 18n. Type **97** 20 30
288 32n. "Why the Zebra has no Horns" 30 55
289 42n. "How the Tortoise got his Shell" 40 85
290 58n. "Kalulu and the Lion" 50 1·00
MS291 90 × 120 mm. Nos. 287/91 1·50 2·75

98 Children of Different Races holding Anti-Apartheid Emblem

1979. International Anti-Apartheid Year. Mult.
292 18n. Type **98** 15 25
293 32n. Children with toy car 25 40
294 42n. Young children with butterfly 35 70
295 58n. Children with microscope 50 1·00

99 Sir Rowland Hill and 2s. Definitive Stamp of 1964

1979. Death Cent of Sir Rowland Hill. Mult.
296 18n. Type **99** 15 25
297 32n. Sir Rowland Hill and mailman 20 55
298 42n. Sir Rowland Hill and Northern Rhodesia 1963 ½d. definitive stamp 20 70
299 58n. Sir Rowland Hill and mail-carrying oxwaggon 20 1·10
MS300 112 × 89 mm. Nos. 296/9 1·00 2·50

1980. "London 1980" International Stamp Exhibition. Nos. 296/9 optd **LONDON 1980.**
301 **99** 18n. multicoloured 25 40
302 – 32n. multicoloured 30 60
303 – 42n. multicoloured 40 75
304 – 58n. multicoloured 60 90
MS305 112 × 89 mm. Nos. 301/4 2·50 3·75

101 Rotary Anniversary Emblem

1980. 75th Anniv of Rotary International.
306 **101** 8n. multicoloured 10 10
307 32n. multicoloured 30 40
308 42n. multicoloured 35 50
309 58n. multicoloured 45 80
MS310 115 × 89 mm. Nos. 306/9 1·50 2·25

102 Running

1980. Olympic Games, Moscow. Multicoloured.
311 18n. Type **102** 25 25
312 32n. Boxing 40 45
313 42n. Football 50 80
314 58n. Swimming 80 1·25
MS315 142 × 144 mm. Nos. 311/14 2·50 3·25

103 "Euphaedra zaddachi"

1980. Butterflies. Multicoloured.
316 18n. Type **103** 15 15
317 32n. "Aphnaeus questiauxi" 25 40
318 42n. "Abantis zambesiaca" 40 90
319 58n. "Spindasis modesta" 60 1·75
MS320 114 × 86 mm. Nos. 316/19 4·25 4·25

104 Zambia Coat of Arms

105 Nativity and St. Francis of Assisi (stained glass window, Ndola Church)

1980. 26th Commonwealth Parliamentary Association Conference, Lusaka.
321 **104** 18n. multicoloured . . . 15 25
322 32n. multicoloured . . . 25 45
323 42n. multicoloured . . . 30 75
324 58n. multicoloured . . . 40 1·50

1980. 50th Anniv of Catholic Church on the Copperbelt.
325 **105** 8n. multicoloured 10 10
326 28n. multicoloured . . . 30 70
327 32n. multicoloured . . . 30 70
328 42n. multicoloured . . . 45 1·10

106 Musikili

1981. World Forestry Day. Seedpods. Mult.
329 8n. Type **106** 10 10
330 18n. Mupapa 20 45
331 28n. Mulunguti 25 90
332 32n. Mulama . . . . 25 1·40

107 I.T.U. Emblem

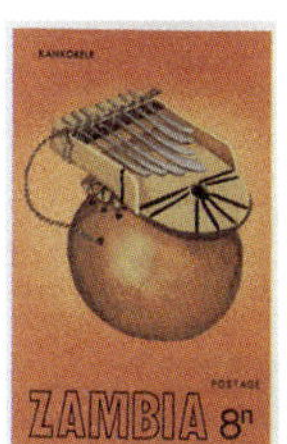

108 Mask Maker

1981. World Telecommunications and Health Day. Multicoloured.
333 8n. Type **107** 20 10
334 18n. W.H.O. emblems . . . 25 35
335 28n. Type **107** 30 70
336 32n. As 18n. 35 85

1981. Native Crafts. Multicoloured.
337 1n. Type **108** 10 10
338 2n. Blacksmith 10 10
339 5n. Pottery making 10 10
340 8n. Straw-basket fishing . . . 10 10
341 10n. Thatching 10 10
342 12n. Mushroom picking . . . 3·00 1·75
343 18n. Millet grinding on stone 30 10
344 28n. Royal Barge paddler . . 75 10
345 30n. Makishi tightrope dancer 50 10
346 35n. Tonga Ila granary and house 55 10
347 42n. Cattle herding . . . . . 55 1·50
348 50n. Traditional healer (38 × 26 mm) 75 10
349 75n. Women carrying water (38 × 26 mm) 55 60
350 1k. Pounding maize (38 × 26 mm) 55 60
351 2k. Pipe smoking, Gwembe Valley belle (38 × 26 mm) 55 60

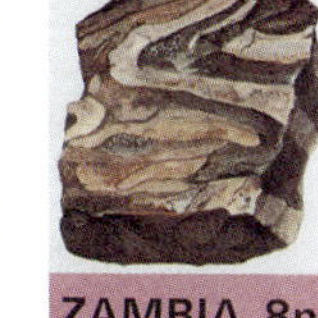

109 Kankobele

110 Banded Ironstone

1981. Traditional Musical Instruments. Mult.
356 8n. Type **109** 20 10
357 18n. Inshingili 25 55
358 28n. Ilimba . . . . 30 1·50
359 32n. Bango . . . . 35 1·75

1982. Minerals (1st series). Multicoloured.
360 8n. Type **110** . . . . 1·00 10
361 18n. Cobaltocalcite . . . . . 2·00 80
362 28n. Amazonite . . . . . . 2·75 2·25
363 32n. Tourmaline . . . . . . 3·00 2·75
364 42n. Uranium ore . . . . . 3·25 4·00
See also Nos. 370/4.

111 Zambian Scouts

1982. 75th Anniv of Boy Scout Movement. Multicoloured.
365 8n. Type **111** 20 10
366 18n. Lord Baden-Powell and Victoria Falls 60 40
367 28n. African buffalo and Zambian scout patrol pennant 60 50
368 1k. African fish eagle and Zambian conservation badge . . . . 1·40 4·50
MS369 105 × 78 mm. Nos. 365/8 2·50 5·00

1982. Minerals (2nd series). As T **110**. Mult.
370 8n. Bornite 95 10
371 18n. Chalcopyrite . . . . . 2·25 90
372 28n. Malachite . . . . 2·75 3·00
373 32n. Azurite . . . . 2·75 3·00
374 42n. Vanadinite . . . . . . 3·25 4·25

112 Drilling Rig, 1926

1983. Early Steam Engines. Multicoloured.
375 8n. Type **112** 45 10
376 18n. Fowler road locomotive, 1900 . . . . 55 70
377 28n. Borsig ploughing engine, 1925 . . . . 1·00 2·25
378 32n. Rhodesian Railways 7th Class steam locomotive, 1900 . . . . 1·25 2·50

113 Cotton Picking

1983. Commonwealth Day. Multicoloured.
379 12n. Type **113** 20 10
380 18n. Mining 40 30
381 28n. Ritual pot and traditional dances 30 50
382 1k. Violet-crested turaco and Victoria Falls . . . . . . 2·75 5·50

114 "Eulophia cucullata"

115 Giraffe

1983. Wild Flowers. Multicoloured.
383 12n. Type **114** 20 10
384 28n. "Kigelia africana" . . . 25 40
385 35n. "Protea gaguedi" . . . 30 80
386 50n. "Leonotis nepetifolia" 50 2·25
MS387 141 × 71 mm. Nos. 383/6 1·00 3·50

1983. Wildlife of Zambia. Multicoloured.
388 12n. Type **115** 70 10
389 28n. Blue wildebeest 75 70
390 35n. Lechwe 80 90
391 1k. Yellow-backed duiker . . 1·25 4·25

116 Tigerfish

1983. Fishes of Zambia. Multicoloured.
392 12n. Type **116** 35 15
393 28n. Silver catfish 50 70
394 35n. Large-spotted squeaker 60 1·75
395 38n. Red-breasted tilapia . . 60 1·75

117 The Annunciation

1983. Christmas. Multicoloured.
396 12n. Type **117** 15 10
397 28n. The Shepherds 30 40
398 35n. Three Kings . . . . . . 40 1·25
399 38n. Flight into Egypt . . . 45 1·75

118 Boeing 737

1984. Air Transport. Multicoloured.
400 12n. Type **118** 25 10
401 28n. De Havilland D.H.C.2 Beaver 45 40
402 35n. Short S-45A Solent 3 flying boat 55 70
403 1k. De Havilland D.H.66 Hercules "City of Basra" 1·00 3·00

119 Receiving Flowers

1984. 60th Birthday of President Kaunda. Mult.
404 12n. Type **119** 20 10
405 28n. Swearing-in ceremony (vert) 25 40
406 60n. Planting cherry tree . . 50 2·25
407 1k. Opening of 5th National Assembly (vert) . . . . . 65 3·25

120 Football

1984. Olympic Games, Los Angeles. Multicoloured.
408 12n. Type **120** 25 10
409 28n. Running 30 50
410 35n. Hurdling 40 80
411 60n. Boxing . . . . 45 1·75

121 Gaboon Viper

1984. Reptiles. Multicoloured.
412 12n. Type **121** 20 10
413 28n. Chameleon 40 50
414 35n. Nile crocodile 50 70
415 1k. Blue-headed agama . . . 1·00 2·75
MS416 120 × 101 mm. Nos. 412/15 2·00 4·00

122 Pres. Kaunda and Mulungushi Rock

1984. 26th Anniv of United National Independence Party and 20th Anniv of Independence (1st issue). Multicoloured.
417 12n. Type **122** 20 10
418 28n. Freedom Statue 30 50
419 1k. Pres. Kaunda and agricultural produce ("Lima Programme") . . . 75 3·00

123 "Amanita flammeola"

1984. Fungi. Multicoloured.
420 12n. Type **123** . . . . 1·10 30
421 28n. "Amanita zambiana" . . 1·25 1·25
422 32n. "Termitomyces letestui" 1·25 2·25
423 75n. "Cantharellus miniatescens" . . . . . . 1·75 4·50

1985. No. 237 surch **K5**.
424 5k. on 50n. Flying Doctor service . . . . 1·75 2·75

125 Chacma Baboon

1985. Zambian Primates. Multicoloured.
425 12n. Type **125** 55 10
426 20n. Diademed monkey . . . 75 40
427 45n. Diademed monkey (different) . . . . 1·25 1·25
428 1k. Savanna monkey . . . . 2·00 4·50

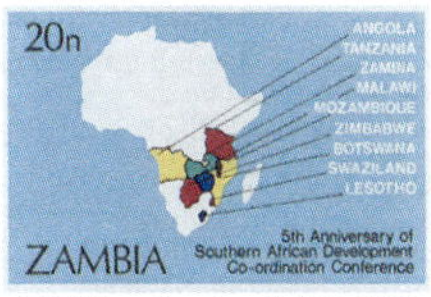

126 Map showing S.A.D.C.C. Member States

1985. 5th Anniv of Southern African Development Co-ordination Conference.
429 **126** 20n. multicoloured . . . 75 15
430 – 45n. black, blue and light blue . . . . 1·75 1·10
431 – 1k. multicoloured . . . . 2·00 3·75
DESIGNS: 45n. Mining; 1k. Flags of member states and Mulungushi Hall.

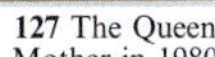

127 The Queen Mother in 1980

130 Boy in Maize Field

129 Postman and Lusaka Post Office, 1958

1985. Life and Times of Queen Elizabeth the Queen Mother.
432 **127** 25n. multicoloured . . . 10 10
433 – 45n. blue and gold . . . 10 15
434 – 55n. blue and gold . . . 15 25
435 – 5k. multicoloured . . . . 1·25 2·75

DESIGNS—VERT: 45n. The Queen Mother at Clarence House, 1963. HORIZ: 55n. With the Queen and Princess Margaret, 1980; 5k. At Prince Henry's Christening, 1984.

1985. Nos. 340 and 342 surch.

436 20n. on 12n. Mushroom picking . . . . 2·75 1·00
437 25n. on 8n. Straw-basket fishing . . . . 1·00 65

1985. 26th Anniv of United National Independence Party (No. 438) and 20th Anniv of Independence (others) (2nd issue). As Nos. 417/19 but larger, 55 × 34 mm. On gold foil.

438 5k. As Type **122** . . . . . 70 2·00
439 5k. Freedom Statue . . . . 70 2·00
440 5k. Pres. Kaunda and agricultural produce ("Lima Programme") . . . 70 2·00

1985. 10th Anniv of Posts and Telecommunication Corporation. Multicoloured.

441 20n. Type **129** 55 10
442 45n. Postman and Livingstone Post Office, 1950 . . . . 85 25
443 55n. Postman and Kalomo Post Office, 1902 . . . . . 1·00 70
444 5k. Africa Trans-Continental Telegraph Line under construction, 1900 . . . . 2·50 6·00

1985. 40th Anniv of United Nations Organization.

445 **130** 20n. multicoloured . . . 25 10
446 – 45n. black, blue and brown 40 20
447 – 1k. multicoloured . . . . 75 2·00
448 – 2k. multicoloured . . . . 1·10 3·00

DESIGNS: 45n. Logo and "40"; 1k. President Kaunda addressing U.N. General Assembly, 1970; 2k. Signing of U.N. Charter, San Francisco, 1945.

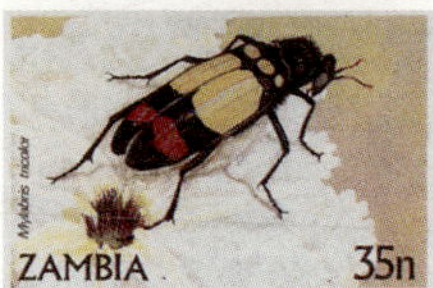

131 "Mylabris tricolor"

1986. Beetles. Multicoloured.

449 35n. Type **131** 15 10
450 1k. "Phasgonocnema melanianthe" 20 20
451 1k.70 "Amaurodes passerinii" 30 50
452 5k. "Ranzania petersiana" . . 85 2·00

1986. 60th Birthday of Queen Elizabeth II. As T **145a** of St. Helena. Multicoloured.

453 35n. Princess Elizabeth at Flower Ball, Savoy Hotel, 1951 . . . . 10 10
454 1k.25 With Prince Andrew, Lusaka Airport, 1979 . . . 15 20
455 1k.70 With President Kaunda 15 25
456 1k.95 In Luxembourg, 1976 15 30
457 5k. At Crown Agents Head Office, London, 1983 . . . 25 85

1986. Royal Wedding. As T **146a** of St. Helena. Multicoloured.

458 1k.70 Prince Andrew and Miss Sarah Ferguson . . . 30 35
459 5k. Prince Andrew in Zambia, 1979 . . . . . . 80 1·40

132 Goalkeeper saving Goal

1986. World Cup Football Championship, Mexico. Multicoloured.

460 35n. Type **132** 85 15
461 1k.25 Player kicking ball . . 2·00 1·40
462 1k.70 Two players competing for ball . . . . 2·25 1·90
463 5k. Player scoring goal . . . 3·25 6·00

133 Sculpture of Edmond Halley by Henry Pegram

1986. Appearance of Halley's Comet.

464 **133** 1k.25 multicoloured . . . 1·00 55
465 – 1k.70 multicoloured . . . 1·25 85
466 – 2k. multicoloured . . . . 1·75 1·75
467 – 5k. blue and black . . . 3·50 6·50

DESIGNS: 1k.70, "Giotto" spacecraft approaching nucleus of Comet; 2k. Studying Halley's Comet in 1682 and 1986; 5k. Part of Halley's chart of southern sky.

134 The Nativity

1986. Christmas. Children's Paintings. Mult.

468 35n. Type **134** 40 10
469 1k.25 Visit of the Three Kings . . . . 1·50 75
470 1k.60 The Holy Family with Shepherd and King . . . . 1·75 1·50
471 5k. Angel and Christmas tree 3·75 7·00

135 Diesel Train in Kasama Cutting

1986. 10th Anniv of Tanzania–Zambia Railway. Multicoloured.

472 35n. Type **135** 25 10
473 1k.25 Passenger train leaving Tunnel No. 21 . . . . . . 35 50
474 1k.70 Train between Tunnels Nos. 6 and 7 . . . . . . 35 70
475 5k. Trains near Mpika Station . . . . 70 3·00

136 President Kaunda and Graduate

1987. 20th Anniv of University of Zambia. Multicoloured.

476 35n. Type **136** 25 10
477 1k.25 University badge (vert) 55 60
478 1k.60 University statue . . . 60 1·00
479 5k. President Kaunda laying foundation stone (vert) . . 2·00 6·50

137 Arms of Kitwe

138 African Chestnut-headed Crake

1987. Arms of Zambian Towns. Mult.

480 35n. Type **137** 10 10
481 1k.25 Ndola 15 10
482 1k.70 Lusaka 20 25
483 20k. Livingstone . . . . . . 3·00 6·00

1987. Birds (1st series). Multicoloured.

484 5n. Cloud-scraping cisticola 10 10
485 10n. White-winged starling 10 10
486a 20n. on 1n. Yellow swamp warbler 20 20
487 25n. Type **138** . . . . . . 2·50 1·00
488 30n. Miombo pied barbet 20 10
489 35n. Black and rufous swallow . . . . 2·50 2·00
490 40n. Wattled crane 20 10
491 50n. Slaty egret 20 10
492 75n. on 2n. Olive-flanked robin chat . . . . 30 1·10
493 1k. Bradfield's hornbill . . . 2·50 40
494 1k.25 Boulton's puff-back flycatcher ("Margaret's Batis") . . . . 2·50 2·75
495 1k.60 Anchieta's sunbird . . 2·50 1·50
496 1k.65 on 30n. Miombo pied barbet . . . . 30 1·25
497 1k.70 Boehm's bee eater . . 2·50 2·75
498 1k.95 Perrin's bush shrike 2·50 2·25
499 2k. Whale-headed stork ("Shoebill") 35 35
500 5k. Taita falcon . . . . . . 3·00 80
501 10k. on 50n. Slaty egret . . 1·10 2·50
502 20k. on 2k. Whale-headed stork . . . . 1·25 3·75

Nos. 491, 493/5 and 497/502 are larger, size 24 × 39 mm.

No. 502 is surcharged "K20". For No. 499 surcharged "K20.00" see No. 594.

See also Nos. 587/95 and 625/38.

139 Look-out Tree, Livingstone

1987. Tourism. Multicoloured.

503 35n. Type **139** 30 15
504 1k.25 Rafting on Zambezi . . 30 25
505 1k.70 Tourists photographing lions, Luangwa Valley . . 1·75 90
506 10k. Eastern white pelicans ("White Pelican") . . . . 7·00 8·50

1987. Various stamps surch. (a) Nos. 432/5.

507 **127** 3k. on 25n. mult 90 90
508 – 6k. on 45n. blue and gold 1·75 1·75
509 – 10k. on 55n. blue and gold . . . . 2·25 2·25
510 – 20k. on 5k. mult . . . . 4·50 5·50

(b) Nos. 453/7.

511 3k. on 35n. Princess Elizabeth at Flower Ball, Savoy Hotel, 1951 . . . . 55 65
512 4k. on 1k.25 With Prince Andrew, Lusaka Airport, 1979 . . . . 65 75
513 6k. on 1k.70 With President Kaunda . . . . 1·00 1·25
514 10k. on 1k.95 In Luxembourg, 1976 . . . . 1·60 2·00
515 20k. on 5k. At Crown Agents Head Office, London, 1983 3·75 4·50

(c) Nos. 460/3.

516 3k. on 35n. Type **132** 90 75
517 6k. on 1k.25 Player kicking ball . . . . 1·75 1·50
518 10k. on 1k.70 Two players competing for ball . . . . 2·25 2·25
519 20k. on 5k. Player scoring goal . . . . 4·25 5·50

(d) Nos. 464/7.

520 **133** 3k. on 1k.25 mult . . . . 1·75 1·00
521 – 6k. on 1k.70 mult . . . . 2·50 2·00
522 – 10k. on 2k. mult . . . . 3·75 4·00
523 – 20k. on 5k. blue and black . . . . 7·00 8·00

141 De Havilland D.H.C.2 Beaver

1987. 20th Anniv of Zambia Airways. Aircraft. Multicoloured.

524 35n. Type **141** 85 10
525 1k.70 Douglas DC-10 . . . . 2·00 70
526 5k. Douglas DC-3 . . . . . 4·25 3·75
527 10k. Boeing 707 . . . . . . 6·50 8·00

142 Friesian/Holstein Cow

1987. 40th Anniv of F.A.O. Multicoloured.

528 35n. Type **142** 10 10
529 1k.25 Simmental bull 20 25
530 1k.70 Sussex bull 20 30
531 20k. Brahman bull . . . . . 1·00 3·00

143 Mpoloto Ne Mikobango

144 Black Lechwe at Waterhole

1987. People of Zambia. Multicoloured.

532 35n. Type **143** 10 10
533 1k.25 Zintaka 20 25
534 1k.70 Mufuluhi 25 30
535 10k. Ntebwe . . . . 75 1·50
536 20k. Kubangwa Aa Mbulunga . . . . 1·25 3·00

1987. Black Lechwe. Multicoloured.

537 50n. Type **144** 65 10
538 2k. Black lechwe resting by pool (horiz) . . . . . . 1·75 40
539 2k.50 Running through water (horiz) . . . . 1·75 80
540 10k. Watching for danger . . 4·50 6·00

MS541 Two sheets, each 105 × 74 mm. (a) 20k. Caracal (predator). (b) 20k. Cheetah (predator) Set of 2 sheets . . . 12·00 11·00

145 Cassava Roots

1988. International Fund for Agricultural Development. Multicoloured.

542 50n. Type **145** 10 10
543 2k.50 Fishing 60 50
544 2k.85 Farmer and cattle . . . 65 55
545 10k. Picking coffee beans . . 1·25 2·00

146 Breast-feeding

147 Asbestos Cement

1988. U.N.I.C.E.F. Child Survival Campaign. Multicoloured.

546 50n. Type **146** 20 10
547 2k. Growth monitoring . . . 50 30
548 2k.85 Immunization 60 70
549 10k. Oral rehydration . . . . 1·25 3·25

1988. Preferential Trade Area Fair. Mult.

550 50n. Type **147** 10 10
551 2k.35 Textiles 20 30
552 2k.50 Tea 20 40
553 10k. Poultry . . . . 75 2·75

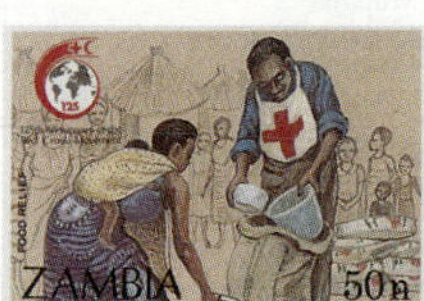

148 Emergency Food Distribution

1988. 125th Anniv of Int Red Cross. Mult.

554 50n. Type **148** 20 10
555 2k.50 Giving first aid 50 60
556 2k.85 Practising bandaging 55 75
557 10k. Henri Dunant (founder) 1·75 3·50

149 Aardvark

1988. Endangered Species of Zambia. Mult.

558 50n. Type **149** 25 10
559 2k. Temminck's ground pangolin 50 40
560 2k.85 Hunting dog 60 75
561 20k. Black rhinoceros and calf . . . . 6·00 7·00

150 Boxing

1988. Olympic Games, Seoul. Multicoloured.

562 50n. Type **150** 15 10
563 2k. Athletics 35 40
564 2k.50 Hurdling 40 70
565 20k. Football . . . . 3·75 6·50

MS566 Two sheets, each 97 × 72 mm. (a) 30k. Tennis. (b) 30k. Karate Set of 2 sheets . . 8·00 11·00

151 Red Toad

1989. Frogs and Toads. Multicoloured.

567 50n. Type **151** 15 10
568 2k.50 Puddle frog 50 50
569 2k.85 Marbled reed frog . . 55 75
570 10k. Young reed frogs . . . 1·60 3·25

152 Common Slit-faced Bat

1989. Bats. Multicoloured.
571 50n. Type **152** 15 10
572 2k.50 Little free-tailed bat 45 55
573 2k.85 Hildebrandt's horseshoe bat 55 75
574 10k. Peters' epauletted fruit bat 1·50 3·25

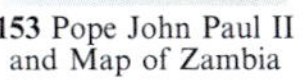

153 Pope John Paul II and Map of Zambia
156 "Parinari curatellifolia"

1989. Visit of Pope John Paul II. Designs each with inset portrait. Multicoloured.
575 50n. Type **153** 75 20
576 6k.85 Peace dove with olive branch 2·75 2·75
577 7k.85 Papal arms 3·00 3·25
578 10k. Victoria Falls 4·50 4·50

1989. Various stamp surch. (a) On Nos. 339, 341/3, 345/6, 349 and 351.
579 1k.20 on 35n. Tonga Ila granary and house 20 15
580 3k.75 on 5n. Pottery making 30 20
581 8k.11 on 10n. Thatching 50 50
582 9k. on 30n. Makishi tightrope dancer 50 50
583 10k. on 75n. Women carrying water (38 × 26 mm) 50 50
584 18k.50 on 2k. Pipe-smoking Gwembe Valley belle (38 × 26 mm) 1·00 1·75
585 19k.50 on 12n. Mushroom picking 3·00 3·00
586 20k.50 on 18n. Millet grinding on stone 1·25 2·00

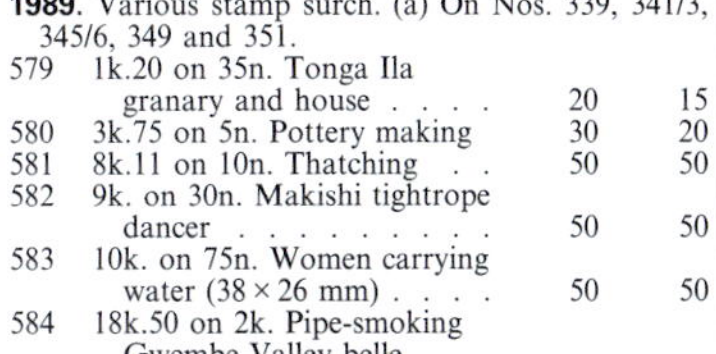

(b) On Nos. 484, 489, 493/5 and 497/500.
587 70n. on 35n. Black and rufous swallow 1·00 15
588 3k. on 5n. Cloud-scraping cisticola 1·00 30
589 8k. on 1k.25 Boulton's puff-back flycatcher 1·25 60
590 9k.90 on 1k.70 Boehm's bee eater 1·25 80
591 10k.40 on 1k.60 Anchieta's sunbird 1·25 90
592 12k.50 on 1k. Bradfield's hornbill 1·25 1·25
593 15k. on 1k.95 Perrin's bush strike 1·25 1·75
594 20k. on 2k. Whale-headed stork 1·75 2·50
595 20k.35 on 5k. Taita falcon 1·75 2·50
No. 594 shows the surcharge as "K20.00". The previously listed 20k. on 2k., No. 499, is surcharged "K20" only.

1989. Edible Fruits. Multicoloured.
596 50n. Type **156** 15 10
597 6k.50 "Uapaca kirkiana" 1·25 1·50
598 6k.85 Wild fig 1·25 1·75
599 10k. Bottle palm 2·25 3·00

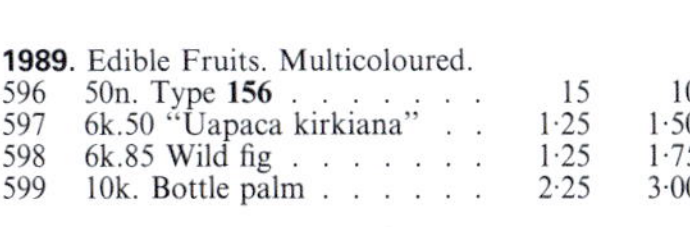

157 "Lamarckiana sp."

1989. Grasshoppers. Multicoloured.
600 70n. Type **157** 20 10
601 10k.40 "Dictyophorus sp." 1·50 1·75
602 12k.50 "Cymatomera sp." 1·75 2·50
603 15k. "Phymateus iris" 2·25 3·50

158 Fireball

160 Footballer and Ball

159 Postvan, Postman on Bicycle and Main Post Office, Lusaka

1989. Christmas. Flowers. Multicoloured.
604 70n. Type **158** 15 10
605 10k.40 Flame lily 1·00 1·25
606 12k.50 Foxglove lily 1·40 1·75
607 20k. Vlei lily 2·40 4·00

1990. "Stamp World London 90" International Stamp Exhibition. Multicoloured.
608 1k.20 Type **159** 10 10
609 19k.50 Zambia 1980 18n. butterflies stamp 2·50 2·50
610 20k.50 Rhodesia and Nyasaland 1962 9d. and Northern Rhodesia 1925 ½d. stamps 2·50 2·50
611 50k. 1840 Penny Black and Maltese Cross cancellation 5·00 6·50

1990. World Cup Football Championship, Italy.
612 **160** 1k.20 multicoloured 10 10
613 – 18k.50 multicoloured 2·00 2·50
614 – 19k.50 multicoloured 2·00 2·50
615 – 20k.50 multicoloured 2·00 2·50
MS616 100 × 73 mm. 50k. multicoloured 8·00 8·50
DESIGNS: 18k.50 to 50k, Different football scenes.

161 Road Tanker

1990. 10th Anniv of Southern African Development Co-ordination Conference. Each showing map of Southern Africa. Multicoloured.
617 1k.20 Type **161** 30 10
618 19k.50 Telecommunications 2·00 2·25
619 20k.50 "Regional Co-operation" 2·00 2·25
620 50k. Transporting coal by cable 7·00 8·00

162 Irrigation

1990. 26th Anniv of Independence. Mult.
621 1k.20 Type **162** 10 10
622 19k.50 Shoe factory 1·10 1·40
623 20k.50 Mwembeshi II satellite earth station 1·25 1·60
624 50k. "Mother and Child" (statue) 2·50 4·25

1990. Birds (2nd series). As T **138**. Mult.
625 10n. Livingstone's flycatcher 50 50
626 15n. Bar-winged weaver 50 50
627 30n. Purple-throated cuckoo shrike 75 50
628 50n. Retz's red-billed helmet shrike 75 50
629 50n. As 10n. 1·40 70
630 1k. As 15n. 1·40 50
631 1k.20 Bronze-naped pigeon ("Western Bronze-naped Pigeon") 1·25 20
632 2k. As 30n. 1·40 70
633 3k. As 50n. 1·40 70
634 5k. As 1k.20 1·50 70
635 15k. Corn crake 50 40
636 20k. Dickinson's kestrel 2·25 1·50
637 20k.50 As 20k. 70 1·00
638 50k. Denham's bustard 50 1·25
Nos. 635/8 are larger, size 23 × 39 mm.

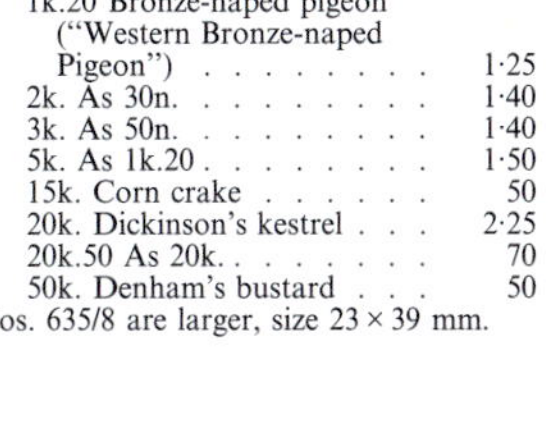

163 The Bird and the Snake

166 Woman cooking

164 Genet

1991. Int Literacy Year. Folklore. Mult.
639 1k.20 Type **163** 30 10
640 18k.50 Kalulu and the Leopard 2·75 3·00
641 19k.50 The Mouse and the Lion 2·75 3·00
642 20k.50 Kalulu and the Hippopotamus 2·75 3·00

1991. Small Carnivores. Multicoloured.
643 1k.20 Type **164** 30 10
644 18k.50 Civet 2·75 3·25
645 19k.50 Serval 2·75 3·25
646 20k.50 African wild cat 2·75 3·25

1991. Nos. 441/4 surch **K2**.
647 2k. on 20n. Type **129** 6·00 4·50
648 2k. on 45n. Postman and Livingstone Post Office, 1950 6·00 4·50
649 2k. on 55n. Postman and Kalomo Post Office, 1902 6·00 4·50
650 2k. on 5k. African Trans-Continental Telegraph Line under construction, 1900 6·00 4·50

1991. Soya Promotion Campaign. Mult.
651 1k. Type **166** 10 10
652 2k. Soya bean and field 10 10
653 5k. Mother feeding child 20 15
654 20k. Healthy and malnourished children 1·25 1·75
655 50k. President Kaunda holding child 2·25 3·25

1991. Various stamps surch **K2**.
656 **130** 2k. on 20n. mult 32·00 5·00
657 **127** 2k. on 25n. mult 80·00 5·00
658 – 2k. on 28n. mult (No. 344) 32·00 5·00
659 – 2k. on 28n. mult (No. 393) 42·00 5·00
660 – 2k. on 28n. mult (No. 401) — 5·00
661 – 2k. on 28n. mult (No. 418) — 5·00
662 – 2k. on 32n. mult (No. 422) 26·00 5·00
663 – 2k. on 35n. mult (No. 453) — 5·00
664 **134** 2k. on 35n. mult 70·00 5·00
665 **137** 2k. on 35n. mult 42·00 5·00
666 – 2k. on 45n. mult (No. 427) 42·00 5·00
667 – 2k. on 45n. black, blue and light blue (No. 430) 55·00 5·00
668 – 2k. on 45n. blue and gold (No. 433) 80·00 5·00
669 – 2k. on 45n. black, blue and brown (No. 446) 42·00 5·00
670 – 2k. on 1k.60 mult (No. 470) 70·00 5·00
671 – 2k. on 1k.70 mult (No. 451) 42·00 5·00
672 – 2k. on 1k.70 mult (No. 482) — 5·00
673 – 2k. on 5k. mult (No. 435) 15·00 5·00
674 – 2k. on 5k. mult (No. 452) 15·00 5·00
675 – 2k. on 6k.50 mult (No. 597) 42·00 5·00
676 – 2k. on 6k.85 mult (No. 576) 55·00 5·00
677 – 2k. on 6k.85 mult (No. 598) 15·00 5·00
678 – 2k. on 7k.85 mult (No. 577) 80·00 5·00

167 Chilubula Church near Kasama

169 "Disa hamatopetala"

168 "Adansonia digitata"

1991. 500th Birth Anniv of St. Ignatius Loyola. Multicoloured.
679 1k. Type **167** 10 10
680 2k. Chikuni Church near Monze 15 15
681 20k. Bishop Joseph du Pont 2·25 2·50
682 50k. Saint Ignatius Loyola 4·00 5·50

1991. Flowering Trees. Multicoloured.
683 1k. Type **168** 20 10
684 2k. "Dichrostachys cinerea" 30 15
685 10k. "Stereospermum kunthianum" 1·75 1·40
686 30k. "Azana garckeana" 3·25 4·25
No. 685 is inscribed "Sterospermum" in error.

1992. 40th Anniv of Queen Elizabeth II's Accession. As T **168a** of St. Helena. Mult.
687 4k. Queen's House 10 10
688 32k. Traditional village 1·00 70
689 35k. Fisherman hauling nets 1·00 90
690 38k. Three portraits of Queen Elizabeth 1·25 1·25
691 50k. Queen Elizabeth II 1·60 2·75

1992. Orchids. Multicoloured.
692 1k. Type **169** 50 15
693 2k. "Eulophia paivaeana" 50 20
694 5k. "Eulophia quartiniana" 85 40
695 20k. "Aerangis verdickii" 3·50 5·00

170 Kasinja Mask

1992. Tribal Masks. Multicoloured.
696 1k. Type **170** 15 10
697 2k. Chizaluke 20 10
698 10k. Mwanapweu 80 65
699 30k. Maliya 2·25 3·50

171 Bushbuck

1992. Antelopes. Multicoloured.
700 4k. Type **171** 10 30
701 40k. Eland 60 50
702 45k. Roan antelope 60 50
703 100k. Sable antelope 1·40 3·25

172 De Havilland D.H.66 Hercules "City of Basra"

174 Hurdling

173 Wise Men with Gifts

1992. 60th Anniv of Airmail Service. Mult.
704 4k. Type **172** 50 40
705 40k. Vickers Super VC-10 2·00 85
706 45k. Short S.45A Solent 3 flying boat "Severn" 2·00 85
707 100k. Douglas DC-10 3·50 5·50

1992. Christmas. Multicoloured.
708 10k. Type **173** 20 10
709 80k. Nativity 1·75 1·90
710 90k. Angelic choir 1·90 2·25
711 100k. Angel and shepherds 1·90 2·50
MS712 209 × 57 mm. Nos. 708/11 9·00 9·50

1992. Olympic Games, Barcelona. Mult.
713 10k. Type **174** 20 10
714 40k. Boxing 60 40
715 80k. Judo 1·25 1·75
716 100k. Cycling 3·25 3·25

175 Nkundalila Falls

1993. Waterfalls. Multicoloured.
717 50k. Type **175** 40 10
718 200k. Chishimba Falls 1·25 1·10
719 250k. Chipoma Falls 1·40 1·40
720 300k. Lumangwe Falls 1·50 1·75

176 Athlete and Cardiograph

1993. Heartbeat Campaign. Multicoloured.
721 (O) Type **176** 75 55
722 (P) Heart and cardiograph 75 55

These stamps were initially sold at 50k. (No. 721) for ordinary post and 80k. (No. 722) for priority mail. These face values were increased to reflect postage rate increases.

177 Bronze Sunbird

178 Tiger Snake

1994. Sunbirds. Multicoloured. (a) Face values as T **177**.
723 20k. Type **177** 30 50
724 50k. Violet-backed sunbird 40 40
725 100k. Scarlet-chested sunbird 55 10
726 150k. Bannerman's sunbird 65 10
727 200k. Oustalet's white-bellied sunbird 65 10
728 250k. Anchieta's sunbird ("Red and blue sunbird") 65 20
729 300k. Olive sunbird 75 40
730 350k. Green-headed sunbird 75 40
731 400k. Red-tufted malachite sunbird 75 50
732 500k. Variable sunbird 75 50
733 800k. Coppery sunbird 1·00 1·25
734 1000k. Southern orange-tufted sunbird ("Orange-tufted Sunbird") 1·10 1·40
735 1500k. Amethyst sunbird ("Black Sunbird") 1·50 2·00
736 2000k. Green-throated sunbird 1·75 2·25
(b) Face values shown as capital letters.
737 (O) Mariqua sunbird ("Marico Sunbird") 1·00 55
738 (P) Eastern double-collared sunbird 1·00 55

Nos. 737/8 were initially sold at 50k. for ordinary post (No. 737) and 80k. for priority mail (No. 738). These rates were increased to 100k. for ordinary post and 150k. for priority mail on 20th June 1994. On 1 March 1995 the difference between the two rates was abolished and both "O" and "P" stamps were sold at 500k. This was reduced to 400k. each on 1 April 1995, but the rate reverted to 500k. on 8 February 1996.

1994. Snakes. Multicoloured.
739 50k. Type **178** 40 10
740 200k. Egyptian cobra 1·25 60
741 300k. African python 1·50 1·25
742 500k. Green mamba 1·90 2·50

179 Women working on Road

1995. 75th Anniv of I.L.O. Multicoloured.
743 100k. Type **179** 50 20
744 450k. Women making cement blocks 1·75 2·00

180 Angel playing Kalimba and Flowers

1995. Christmas (1994). Multicoloured.
745 100k. Type **180** 35 10
746 300k. Angel at prayer and animals 80 60
747 450k. Angel with flute and birds 1·10 1·25
748 500k. Angel with drum and Baobab trees 1·25 1·50

181 Anniversary Emblem, Rainbow and Map

182 David Livingstone (missionary) and Memorial

1995. 50th Anniv of United Nations.
749 **181** 700k. multicoloured 1·75 2·00

1995. Monuments. Multicoloured.
750 100k. Type **182** 25 10
751 300k. Mbereshi Mission 70 60
752 450k. Von Lettow-Vorbeck Monument 1·10 1·40
753 500k. Niamkolo Church 1·25 1·50

183 Saddle-bill Stork

1996. Endangered Species. Birds. Multicoloured.
754 200k. Type **183** 40 20
755 300k. Black-cheeked lovebird 55 35
756 500k. Pair of black-cheeked lovebirds 75 85
757 900k. Saddle-bill stork and chicks 1·00 1·60
MS758 120 × 90 mm. Nos. 754/7 55·00 55·00

1996. Christmas. Nos. 709/10 surch.
759 (O) on 90k. Angelic choir 10 15
760 900k. on 80k. Nativity 20 25

No. 759 was sold at 500k., which was the minimum local postage rate for ordinary post.

185 "Precis octavia sesamus"

187 Verreaux's Eagle Owl

1997. Butterflies and Moths. Multicoloured.
761 300k. Type **185** 10 10
762 500k. "Argema mimosae" 10 15
763 700k. "Imbrasia dione" 15 20
764 900k. "Papilio ophidicephalus cotterell" 20 25
MS765 85 × 120 mm. As Nos. 761/4, but each with face value of 900k. 85 90

1997. Nos. 688/90 surch.
766 (O) on 32k. Traditional village 1·25 55
767 500k. on 35k. Fishermen hauling nets 1·25 70
768 900k. on 38k. Three portraits of Queen Elizabeth 2·50 3·00

No. 766 was sold at 500k. which was the minimum local postage rate for ordinary post.

1997. Owls of Zambia. Multicoloured.
769 300k. Type **187** 10 10
770 500k. Pel's fishing owl 10 15
771 700k. Barn owl 15 20
772 900k. Spotted eagle owl 20 25
MS773 128 × 85 mm. As Nos. 769/72, but each with face value of 900k. 85 90

188 Gandhi as Law Student, London, 1888

190 Traveller and Dog ("Luchele nganga")

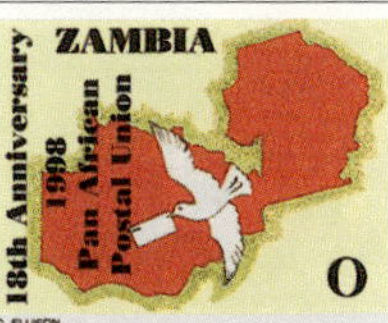

189 Dove and Map of Zambia

1998. 50th Death Anniv of Mahatma Gandhi. Multicoloured.
774 250k. Type **188** 10 10
775 (O) Gandhi at Red Fort, Delhi 10 15
776 500k. Gandhi with Nehru, 1946 (horiz) 10 15
777 900k. Gandhi at prayer 20 25
MS778 70 × 100 mm. 2000k. At Second Round Table Conference, London, 1931 50 55

No. 775 was sold at 500k. which was the minimum local postage rate for ordinary post.

1998. 18th Anniv of Pan African Postal Union.
779 **189** (O) multicoloured 10 15
780 – 500k multicoloured 10 15
781 – 900k. black, red and orange 20 25

DESIGNS: 500k. Lechwe at Kafue Flats; 900k. Dove with "18th" note in beak.

No. 779 was sold at 500k. which was the minimum local postage rate for ordinary post.

1998. Christmas. Traditional Stories. Mult.
782 300k. Type **190** 10 10
783 500k. Man feeding crocodile ("Kasuli") 10 15
MS784 111 × 70 mm. 2000k. Type **190**; 2000k. As 500k. 1·00 1·10

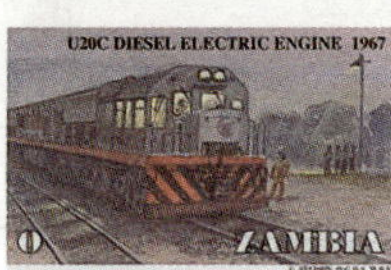

191 "U20C" Diesel-electric Locomotive, 1967

1999. Trains. Multicoloured.
785 (O) Type **191** 10 15
786 800k. Beyer-Garratt Class 15A No. 401 steam locomotive, 1950 20 25
787 800k. Class 7 No. 70 steam locomotive, 1900 20 25
788 900k. Class 20 No. 708 steam locomotive, 1954 20 25
789 900 k. H.P. diesel-electric railcar, 1966 20 25
MS790 112 × 85 mm. 1000k. Class 7 No. 955 steam locomotive, 1892 25 30

1999. No. 743 surch **K500**.
791 500k. on 100k. Type **179** 1·75 1·25

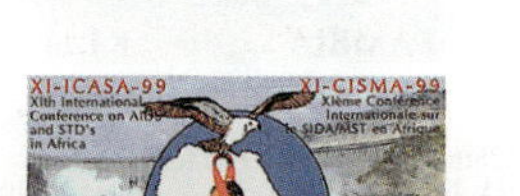

193 Conference Emblem and Dam

1999. 11th International Conference on AIDS and STDs in Africa, Lusaka. Multicoloured.
792 500k. Type **193** 10 15
793 900k. Conference emblem and Victoria Falls 20 25

194 Blacksmith Plover

1999. Water Birds. Multicoloured.
794 50k. Type **194** 10 10
795 100k. Sacred ibis 10 10
796 200k. Purple swamphen ("Purple Gallinule") 10 10
797 250k. Purple heron 10 10
798 300k. Glossy ibis 10 10
799 400k. Marabou stork 10 15
800 450k. African spoonbill 10 15
801 500k. Peters's finfoot ("African Finfoot") 10 15
802 (O) Comb duck ("Knob-billed Duck") 10 15
803 600k. African darter 15 20
804 700k. African skimmer 15 20
805 800k. Spur-winged goose 20 25
806 900k. Hammerkop 20 25
807 1000k. Eastern white pelican 25 30
808 1500k. Black-winged stilt 35 40
809 2000k. Black-crowned night heron 50 55

No. 802 was sold at 500k. which was the minimum local postage rate for ordinary post.

No. 794 is inscribed "Sarkidiomis melamotos" and No. 805 "Plectroterus gambensis", both in error.

2000. No. 750 surch **K700**.
810 700k. on 100k. Type **182** 1·75 1·50

2000. Nos. 774 and 776 surch **K1,200**.
811 1200k. on 250k. Type **188** 1·25 1·25
812 1500k. on 500k. Gandhi with Nehru, 1946 (horiz) 1·50 1·50

No. 775 was re-issued with Nos. 811/12 and sold at 700k.

POSTAGE DUE STAMPS

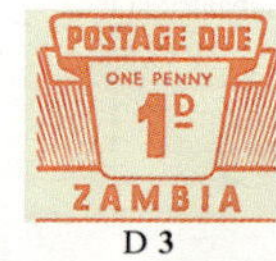

D 3

1964.
D11 **D 3** 1d. orange 30 2·00
D12 2d. blue 35 2·00
D13 3d. lake 45 1·75
D14 4d. blue 45 2·25
D15 6d. purple 45 2·25
D16 1s. green 55 4·25

APPENDIX

The following stamps have either been issued in excess of postal needs, or have not been made available to the public in reasonable quantities at face value.

1984.

Olympic Games, Los Angeles. 90n. × 5, each embossed on gold foil.

1987.

Classic Cars 1k.50 × 25, each embossed on gold foil.

The following issues are reported by the Zambia Postal Services Corporation as being available from Philatelic Counters only.

1997.

Disney's Chinese New Year. 250, 400, 500k. × 7, 600, 750, 1000k.

Endangered Species. 500k. × 6, 1000k. × 6

Trains of the World. 200, 300, 500k. × 7, 900, 1000, 1500k.

Golden Wedding of Queen Elizabeth II and Prince Philip. 500k. × 6.

50th Death Anniv of Paul P. Harris (founder of Rotary International). 1000k.

"Pacific '97" International Stamp Exhibition, San Francisco. Death Centenary of Heinrich von Stephan (founder of the U.P.U.). 1000k. × 3.

Christmas. Religious Paintings. 50k. × 2, 100k. × 2, 500, 1000k.

1998.

Diana, Princess of Wales Commemoration. 500k. × 6, 700k. × 6.

Flowers. 500k. × 13.

Chinese New Year ("Year of the Tiger"). 700k. × 4.

Indian landmarks. 900k. × 3.

Indian art. 700k. × 4.

World Cup Football Championship, France. 450k. × 8, 500k. × 16.

Muhamed Ali. 500k. × 6.

Parrots, Lories and Cockatoos. 500k. × 6, 1000k. × 6.

Mushrooms. 250k. × 2, 450k. × 2, 500k. × 2, 900k. × 14, 1000k. × 2.

Cars. 300k., 500, 900k. × 13, 1000k.

1999.

Lunar New Year ("Year of the Rabbit"). 700k. × 4.

Orchids. 100k. × 2, 500k. × 2, 900k. × 18, 1000k. × 2.

China '99 International Stamp Exhibition, Beijing. Hang Daqian Paintings. 500k. × 10.

"Queen Elizabeth the Queen Mother's Century". 2000k. × 4.

Prehistoric Animals. 50, 100, 500, 900k. × 19, 1000, 1800k.

Fauna and Flora. 50, 100, 500k. × 5, 700k. × 36, 900k., 1000, 1800k.

250th Birth Anniv of Johann von Goethe (German writer). 2000k. × 3.

Royal Wedding. 500k., 900k., 1000k.

"iBra '99" International Stamp Exhibition, Nuremberg. 1000, 3200k.

Cats and Dogs. 50, 100k. × 2, 500k. × 2, 900k. × 2, 1000k. × 25.

Princess Diana Photomosaic. 1000k. × 8.

New Millennium. Events of Second Half of 20th Century. 500k. × 18.

2000.

"The Stamp Show 2000" International Stamp Exhibition, London. Orchids. 1500k. × 22.

Popes of the Millennium. 1500k. × 12.

Birds of the World. 400, 500, 600, 700, 800, 100k. × 10, 1200k. × 9, 1400k. × 9, 1500k. × 25, 2000, 3000k.

ZANZIBAR Pt. 1

A Br. Protectorate consisting of several islands off the coast of Tanganyika, E. Africa. Independent in 1963 and a republic within the Br. Commonwealth in 1964. The "United Republic of Tanganyika and Zanzibar" was proclaimed in July 1964, and the country was later renamed Tanzania. Separate issues for Zanzibar ceased on 1 January 1968 and Tanzania stamps became valid for the whole country.

1895. 16 annas = 1 rupee.
1908. 100 cents = 1 rupee.
1936. 100 cents = 1 shilling.

1895. Stamps of India (Queen Victoria) optd **Zanzibar**.
3 **23** ½a. turquoise 3·50 3·25
4 1a. purple 3·75 3·25
5 1½a. brown 4·25 3·25
6 – 2a. blue 4·50 4·25
8 – 2½a. green 7·00 4·50
10 – 3a. orange 9·50 9·00
12 – 4a. green (No. 96) 10·00 12·00
13 – 6a. brown (No. 80) 17·00 11·00
15 – 8a. mauve 14·00 21·00
16 – 12a. purple on red 15·00 10·00
17 – 1r. grey 70·00 70·00
18 **37** 1r. green and red 14·00 24·00
19 **38** 2r. red and orange 50·00 75·00
20 3r. brown and green 45·00 60·00
21 5r. blue and violet 50·00 75·00

1895. Nos. 4/6 surch 2½.
23 **23** 2½ on 1a. purple £150 £100
22 2½ on 1½a. brown 50·00 38·00
26 – 2½ on 2a. blue 50·00 28·00

1896. Stamps of British East Africa (Queen Victoria) optd **Zanzibar**.
41 **11** ½a. green 29·00 16·00
42 1a. red 25·00 15·00
43 2½a. blue 75·00 42·00
44 4½a. yellow 42·00 48·00
45 5a. brown 48·00 30·00
46 7½a. mauve 35·00 48·00

13 Sultan Seyyid Hamed-bin-Thwain

19 Sultan Seyyid Hamoud-bin-Mahommed bin Said

1896. The Rupee values are larger.
178 **13** ½a. green and red 1·50 35
179 1a. blue and red 2·00 55
159 2a. brown and red 2·75 75
181 2½a. blue and red 2·25 30
182 3a. grey and red 5·50 60
183 4a. green and red 3·25 1·00
184 4½a. orange and red 6·50 80
166 5a. brown and red 3·50 2·50
167 7½a. mauve and red 3·50 2·50
187 8a. olive and red 10·00 2·25
169 – 1r. blue and red 12·00 9·00
171 – 2r. green and red 23·00 9·50
172 – 3r. purple and red 22·00 9·50
173 – 4r. red 17·00 13·00
174 – 5r. brown and red 23·00 13·00

1896. Surch 2½.
175 **13** 2½ on 4a. green and red 55·00 38·00

1899. The Rupee values are larger.
188 **19** ½a. green and red 2·00 60
189 1a. blue and red 4·50 20
190 1a. red 2·00 20
191 2a. brown and red 2·25 50
192 2½a. blue and red 2·25 60
193 3a. grey and red 2·50 2·25
194 4a. green and red 3·25 1·25
195 4½a. orange and red 10·00 3·00
196 4½a. black and red 13·00 12·00
197 5a. brown and red 3·00 1·25
198 7½a. mauve and red 3·25 3·75
199 8a. olive and red 3·25 4·50
200 – 1r. blue and red 18·00 15·00
201 – 2r. green and red 18·00 18·00
202 – 3r. purple and red 30·00 35·00
203 – 4r. red 45·00 50·00
204 – 5r. brown and red 50·00 60·00

1904. Surch in words.
205 **19** 1 on 4½a. orange and red 4·00 4·50
206 1 on 4½a. black and red 4·50 18·00
207 2 on 4a. green and red 14·00 18·00
208 2½ on 7½a. mauve and red 13·00 20·00
209 2½ on 8a. olive and red 15·00 29·00

23 Monogram of Sultan Seyyid Ali bin Hamoud bin Naherud

1904. The Rupee values are larger.
210 **23** ½a. green 1·25 90
211 1a. red 1·25 10
212 2a. brown 1·50 45
213 2½a. blue 2·50 35
214 3a. grey 2·25 2·25
215 4a. green 2·25 1·60
216 4½a. black 3·00 2·50
217 5a. brown 3·25 1·25
218 7½a. mauve 4·00 7·00
219 8a. olive 3·75 2·75
220 – 1r. blue and red 20·00 12·00
221 – 2r. green and red 22·00 35·00
222 – 3r. violet and red 40·00 75·00
223 – 4r. deep red and red 45·00 90·00
224 – 5r. brown and red 48·00 95·00

25

27 Sultan Ali bin Hamoud

26

28 View of Port

1908.
225 **25** 1c. grey 2·25 30
226 3c. green 4·50 10
227 6c. red 8·00 10
228 10c. brown 2·25 2·00
229a 12c. violet 10·00 1·25
230 **26** 15c. blue 9·00 40
231 25c. brown 3·25 1·00
232 50c. green 5·00 4·00
233 75c. black 9·00 12·00
234 **27** 1r. green 24·00 12·00
235 2r. violet 18·00 14·00
236 3r. brown 25·00 48·00
237 4r. red 48·00 75·00
238 5r. blue 40·00 55·00
239 **28** 10r. green and brown £120 £250
240 20r. black and green £250 £450
241 30r. black and brown £300 £600
242 40r. black and orange £425
243 50r. black and mauve £375
244 100r. black and blue £650
245 200r. black and blue £1000

29 Sultan Kalif bin Harub

30 Sailing Canoe

31 Dhow

1913.
246 **29** 1c. grey 40 20
247 3c. green 50 20
278 3c. orange 30 10
279 4c. green 50 60
280 6c. red 30 50
281 6c. purple on blue 35 10
264 8c. purple on yellow 75 3·25
249 10c. brown 1·10 1·75
265 10c. green on yellow 75 30
283 12c. violet 40 30
284 12c. red 40 40
251 15c. blue 1·25 30
286 20c. blue 1·00 30
252 25c. brown 1·00 1·00
288 50c. green 1·25 3·75
254 75c. black 2·00 2·75
290 **30** 1r. green 4·25 3·50
291 2r. violet 3·25 8·00
292 3r. brown 4·25 7·50
293 4r. red 12·00 35·00
259 5r. blue 35·00 35·00
260 **31** 10r. green and brown £100 £170
260b 20r. black and green £150 £325
260c 30r. black and brown £160 £400
260d 40r. black and orange £325 £550
260e 50r. black and purple £300 £550
260f 100r. black and blue £375
260g 200r. brown and black £650

32 Sultan Kalif bin Harub

33 Sultan Kalif bin Harub

1926.
299 **32** 1c. brown 50 10
300 3c. orange 20 15
301 4c. green 20 30
302 6c. violet 20 10
303 8c. grey 1·00 4·50
304 10c. olive 1·00 40
305 12c. red 1·50 10
306 20c. blue 50 30
307 25c. purple on yellow 4·00 2·50
308 50c. red 1·75 35
309 75c. brown 16·00 20·00

1936.
310 **33** 5c. green 10 10
311 10c. black 10 10
312 15c. red 10 1·25
313 20c. orange 10 10
314 25c. purple on yellow 10 10
315 30c. blue 10 10
316 40c. brown 15 10
317 50c. red 30 10
318 **30** 1s. green 50 10
319 2s. violet 75 1·50
320 5s. red 10·00 6·00
321 7s.50c. blue 21·00 24·00
322 **31** 10s. green and brown 22·00 22·00

In Type **33** the letters of the word "CENTS" are without serifs. In Type **32** they have serifs.

36 Sultan Kalif bin Harub

37 "Sham Alam" (Sultan's dhow)

1936. Silver Jubilee of Sultan.
323 **36** 10c. black and olive 1·75 30
324 20c. black and purple 4·00 75
325 30c. black and blue 8·00 35
326 50c. black and red 8·50 3·50

1944. Bicentenary of Al Busaid Dynasty.
327 **37** 10c. blue 75 3·25
328 20c. red 75 3·00
329 50c. green 75 30
330 1s. purple 75 50

1946. Victory. Optd **VICTORY ISSUE 8TH JUNE 1946.**
331 **33** 10c. black 20 40
332 30c. blue 20 40

1948. Silver Wedding. As T **33b/c** of St. Helena.
333 20c. orange 30 1·50
334 10s. brown 17·00 28·00

1949. 75th Anniv of U.P.U. As T **33d/g** of St. Helena.
335 20c. orange 30 2·75
336 30c. blue 1·60 80
337 50c. mauve 1·00 2·50
338 1s. green 1·00 4·00

39 Sultan Kalif bin Harub

40 Seyyid Khalifa Schools, Beit-el-Ras

1952.
339 **39** 5c. black 10 10
340 10c. orange 10 10
341 15c. green 65 2·00
342 20c. red 50 70
343 25c. purple 85 10
344 30c. green 85 10
345 35c. blue 50 3·25
346 40c. brown 50 1·25
347 50c. violet 2·25 10
348 **40** 1s. green and brown 50 10
349 2s. blue and purple 2·00 2·00
350 5s. black and red 2·00 3·25
351 7s.50 black and green 18·00 23·00
352 10s. red and black 9·50 9·50

41 Sultan Kalif bin Harub

42 Cloves

43 "Ummoja Wema" (dhow)

47 Dimbani Mosque

1954. 75th Birthday of Sultan.
353 **41** 15c. green 10 10
354 20c. red 10 10
355 30c. blue 10 10
356 50c. purple 20 10
357 1s.25 red 20 75

1957.
358 **42** 5c. orange and green 10 40
359 10c. green and red 10 10
360 **43** 15c. green and sepia 20 2·50
361 – 20c. blue 10 10
362 – 25c. brown and black 10 1·00
363 **43** 30c. red and black 15 1·00
364 – 35c. slate and green 15 20
365 – 40c. brown and black 15 10
366 – 50c. blue and myrtle 15 20
367 **47** 1s. red and black 20 20
368 **43** 1s.25 slate and red 3·00 20
369 **47** 2s. orange and green 3·50 2·25
370 – 5s. blue 4·75 2·00
371 – 7s.50 green 7·50 4·00
372 – 10s. red 8·00 5·00

DESIGNS—HORIZ (as Type **47**): 20c. Sultan's Barge; 25, 35, 50c. Map of East African coast. VERT (as Type **47**): 40c. Minaret Mosque. (As Type **43**) 5, 7s.50c., 10s. Kibweni Palace.

49 Sultan Seyyid Sir Abdulla bin Khalifa

50 "Protein Foods"

1961. As 1957 issue but with portrait of Sultan Sir Abdulla as in T **49**.
373 5c. orange and green 10 85
374 10c. green and red 10 10
375 15c. green and sepia 75 2·50
376 20c. blue 30 30
377 25c. brown and black 60 50
378 30c. red and black 2·00 1·00
379 35c. slate and green 1·75 3·00
380 40c. brown and black 30 20
381 50c. blue and myrtle 1·00 10
382 1s. red and black 40 1·00
383 1s.25 slate and red 2·50 3·25
384 2s. orange and green 50 3·25
385 5s. blue 3·00 7·50
386 7s.50 green 3·00 15·00
387 10s. red 3·00 9·00
388 20s. sepia (Kibweni Palace) 17·00 28·00

1963. Freedom from Hunger.
389 **50** 1s.30 sepia 1·25 75

51 Zanzibar Clove

58 Axe, Spear and Dagger

1963. Independence. Inscr "UHURU 1963". Multicoloured.
390 30c. Type **51** 10 30
391 50c. "To Prosperity" (Zanzibar doorway) 10 30
392 1s.30 "Religious Tolerance" (mosques and churches) 15 4·00
393 2s.50 "Towards the Light" (Mangapwani Cave) 20 4·75
No. 392 is horiz.

1964. Optd **JAMHURI 1964**. (a) Nos. 373/88.
414 5c. orange and green 10 10
415 10c. green and red 10 10
416 15c. green and sepia 10 10
417 20c. blue 10 10
418 25c. brown and black 10 10
419 30c. red and black 10 10
420 35c. slate and green 10 10
421 40c. brown and black 10 10

422 50c. blue and myrtle 10 10
423 1s. red and black 10 10
424 1s.25 slate and red . . . . 1·50 20
425 2s. orange and green 50 20
426 5s. blue 50 35
407 7s.50 green . . . . 2·00 1·75
408 10s. red . . . . 2·00 1·75
429 20s. sepia . . . . 2·25 7·50

(b) Nos. 390/3.
430 30c. multicoloured 10 10
431 50c. multicoloured 10 10
432 1s.30 multicoloured 10 10
433 2s.50 multicoloured 15 30

The opt is in two lines on Nos. 421, 423, 425/429, 430, 431, 433.

NOTE. For the set inscribed "UNITED REPUBLIC OF TANGANYIKA & ZANZIBAR" see Nos. 124/7 of Tanganyika.

1964. Multicoloured.
434 5c. Type **58** 20 10
435 10c. Bow and arrow breaking chains 30 10
436 15c. Type **58** 30 10
437 20c. As 10c. 50 10
438 25c. Zanzibari with rifle . . . 50 10
439 30c. Zanzibari breaking manacles 30 10
440 40c. As 25c. 50 10
441 50c. As 30c. 30 10
442 1s. Zanzibari, flag and sun . . 30 10
443 1s.30 Hands breaking chains (horiz) 30 70
444 2s. Hand waving flag (horiz) . 30 30
445 5s. Map of Zanzibar and Pemba on flag (horiz) . . . 55 2·00
446 10s. Flag on map . . . . . 3·25 3·50
447 20s. National flag (horiz) . . 3·25 18·00

68 Soldier and Maps

1965. 1st Anniv of Revolution.
448 **68** 20c. light green and green 10 10
449 – 30c. brown and orange . . 10 10
450 **68** 1s.30 blue and deep blue 10 10
451 – 2s.50 violet and red . . . 10 15

DESIGN—VERT: 30c., 2s.50, Building construction.

70 Planting Rice

1965. Agricultural Development.
452 **70** 20c. sepia and blue . . . 10 1·00
453 – 30c. sepia and mauve . . . 10 1·00
454 – 1s.30 sepia and orange . . 20 2·00
455 **70** 2s.50 sepia and green . . 30 3·75

DESIGN: 30 c, 1s.30, Hands holding rice.

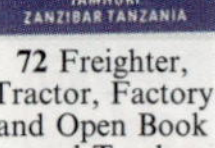

72 Freighter, Tractor, Factory and Open Book and Torch

74 Tree-felling

1966. 2nd Anniv of Revolution. Mult.
456 20c. Type **72** 20 20
457 50c. Soldier 15 20
458 1s.30 Type **72** 15 20
459 2s.50 As 50c. 25 80

1966.
460 **74** 5c. purple and olive . . . 50 80
461 – 10c. purple and green . . . 50 80
462 – 15c. purple and blue . . . 50 80
463 – 20c. blue and orange . . . 30 20
464 – 25c. purple and yellow . . 30 30
465 – 30c. purple and yellow . . 50 20
466 – 40c. brown and red . . . 70 20
467 – 50c. green and yellow . . . 70 20
468 – 1s. purple and blue . . . 70 20
469 – 1s.30 purple and turquoise 70 2·25
470 – 2s. purple and green . . . 70 30
471 – 5s. red and blue . . . . 1·25 4·25
472 – 10s. red and yellow . . . 2·25 16·00
473 **74** 20s. brown and mauve . . 4·25 25·00

DESIGNS—HORIZ: 10c., 1s. Clove cultivation; 15c., 40c. Chair-making; 20c., 5s. Lumumba College; 25c., 1s.30, Agriculture; 30c., 2s. Agricultural workers. VERT: 50c., 10s. Zanzibar street.

81 "Education"

1966. Introduction of Free Education.
474 **81** 50c. black, blue and orange 10 1·00
475 1s.30 black, blue and green 15 1·75
476 2s.50 black, blue and pink 40 4·50

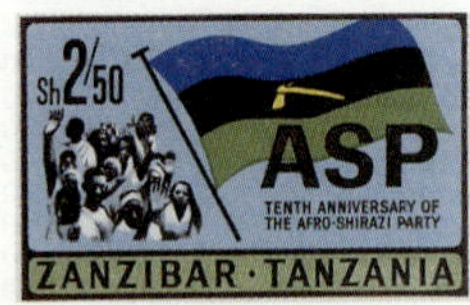

82 A.S.P. Flag

1967. 10th Anniv of Afro-Shirazi Party.
477 **82** 30c. multicoloured . . . . 10 1·00
478 – 50c. multicoloured . . . . 10 1·00
479 – 1s.30 multicoloured . . . 10 2·00
480 **82** 2s.50 multicoloured . . . 30 3·25

DESIGN—VERT: 50c., 1s.30, Vice-President M. A. Karume of Tanzania, flag and crowd.

84 Voluntary Workers

1967. Voluntary Workers Brigade.
481 **84** 1s.30 multicoloured . . . 15 2·25
482 2s.50 multicoloured . . . . 40 5·50

POSTAGE DUE STAMPS

Insufficiently prepaid.
Postage due.
1 cent.

D 1

1930. Roul or roul × imperf.
D 1 D 1 1c. black on orange . . 11·00 95·00
D18 2c. black on orange . . 14·00 28·00
D 3 3c. black on orange . . 5·00 40·00
D19 3c. black on red . . . 3·00 48·00
D21 6c. black on yellow . . 3·00 32·00
D 5 9c. black on orange . . 2·75 21·00
D 6 12c. black on orange . . £9000 £8500
D 7 12c. black on green . . £1400 £600
D22 12c. black on blue . . . 4·00 25·00
D 8 15c. black on orange . . 2·75 23·00
D 9 18c. black on orange . . 4·25 38·00
D11 20c. black on orange . . 4·00 50·00
D12 21c. black on orange . . 3·50 30·00
D13 25c. black on purple . . £2750 £1300
D14 25c. black on orange . . £10000 £10000
D23 25c. black on red . . . 9·00 70·00
D24 25c. black on lilac . . . 13·00 48·00
D15 31c. black on orange . . 9·50 70·00
D16 50c. black on orange . . 21·00 £140
D17 75c. black on orange . . 65·00 £300

D 3

1936.
D25 D 3 5c. violet . . . . . . 3·75 8·50
D26 10c. red . . . . 3·25 2·75
D27 20c. green . . . . . . 2·25 4·25
D28a 30c. brown . . . . . . 35 13·00
D29a 40c. blue . . . . . . 60 28·00
D30a 1s. grey . . . . 1·00 20·00

ZIL ELWANNYEN SESEL Pt. 1

Beginning in June 1980 stamps were issued for use in Zil Elwannyen Sesel (Seychelles Outer Islands), including Aldabra, Coetivy, Farquhar and the Amirante Islands.

100 cents = 1 rupee.

A. Inscr "ZIL ELOIGNE SESEL"

1980. As Nos. 404/19 of Seychelles but inscr "ZIL ELOIGNE SESEL".
1 – 5c. multicoloured 15 75
2 – 10c. multicoloured 15 75
3 – 15c. multicoloured 15 75
4 – 20c. multicoloured 20 75
5 – 25c. multicoloured . . . . 1·00 75
6 **103** 40c. multicoloured 30 75
7 – 50c. multicoloured 30 60
8 – 75c. multicoloured 35 60
9 – 1r. multicoloured . . . . 1·25 1·00
10 – 1r.10 multicoloured . . . . 40 1·00
11 – 1r.25 multicoloured . . . . 1·50 70
12 – 1r.50 multicoloured 45 70
13 – 5r. multicoloured . . . . 70 1·00
14 – 10r. multicoloured . . . . 80 1·50
15 – 15r. multicoloured . . . . 80 3·00
16 – 20r. multicoloured . . . . 80 3·25

2 "Cinq Juin"

1980. Establishment of Travelling Post Office. Multicoloured.
17 1r.50 Type **2** 20 20
18 2r.10 Hand-stamping covers . . 25 25
19 5r. Map of Zil Eloigne Sesel . . 40 40

3 Yellow-finned Tuna

1980. Marine Life. Multicoloured.
20 1r.50 Type **3** 15 20
21 2r.10 Blue marlin 20 35
22 5r. Sperm whale 50 70

1981. Royal Wedding. As T **14a/b** of St. Kitts. Multicoloured.
23 40c. "Royal Escape" 10 10
24 40c. Prince Charles and Lady Diana Spencer 40 55
25 5r. "Victoria and Albert" . . 35 40
31 5r. As No. 24 . . . . 1·00 1·75
27 10r. "Britannia" 60 85
28 10r. As No. 24 . . . . . . 1·50 3·25
MS29 120 × 109 mm. 7r.50 As No. 24 . . . . 1·40 1·75

4 Wright's Skink

1981. Wildlife. (1st series). Multicoloured.
32 1r.40 Type **4** 15 15
33 2r.25 Tree frog 20 20
34 5r. Robber crab 40 40

See also Nos. 45/7.

5 "Cinq Juin" ("Communications")

1982. Island Development. Ships.
35 **5** 1r.75 black and orange . . . 35 30
36 – 2r.10 black and blue . . . 40 45
37 – 5r. black and red 50 60

DESIGNS: 2r.10, "Junon" (fisheries protection); 5r. "Diamond M. Dragon" (drilling ship).

B. Inscr "ZIL ELWAGNE SESEL"

6 "Paulette"

1982. Local Mail Vessels. Multicoloured.
38 40c. Type **6** 45 45
39 1r.75 "Janette" 60 80
40 2r.75 "Lady Esme" 70 95
41 3r.50 "Cinq Juin" . . . . . 70 1·00

7 Birds flying over Island

1982. Aldabra, World Heritage Site. Mult.
42 40c. Type **7** 30 15
43 2r.75 Map of the atoll 45 35
44 7r. Giant tortoises 50 75

8 Red Land Crab

1983. Wildlife (2nd series). Multicoloured.
45 1r.75 Type **8** 35 40
46 2r.75 Black terrapin 45 55
47 7r. Madagascar green gecko . . 90 1·25

9 Map of Poivre Island and Ile du Sud

1983. Island Maps. Multicoloured.
48 40c. Type **9** 20 40
49 1r.50 Ile des Roches 40 55
50 2r.75 Astove Island 50 80
51 7r. Coetivy Island . . . . . 80 1·60
MS52 93 × 129 mm. Nos. 48/51 . . 1·75 3·00

10 Aldabra Warbler

1983. Birds. Multicoloured.
53 5c. Type **10** 40 60
54 10c. Zebra dove ("Barred Ground Dove") . . . . . . 1·00 60
55 15c. Indian nightjar 30 40
56 20c. Madagascar cisticola ("Malagasy Grass Warbler") 30 40
57 25c. Madagascar white-eye . . 60 60
58 40c. Mascarene fody 30 40
59 50c. White-throated rail . . . 4·00 60
60 75c. Black bulbul 40 60
61 2r. Western reef heron ("Dimorphic little egret") . . 2·00 1·25
62 2r.10 Souimanga sunbird . . . 50 1·00
63 2r.50 Madagascar turtle dove . 1·00 65
64 2r.75 Sacred ibis 70 75
65 3r.50 Black coucal (vert) . . . 1·00 1·10
66 7r. Seychelles kestrel (vert) . . 3·00 1·90
67 15r. Comoro blue pigeon (vert) 3·50 5·00
68 20r. Greater flamingo (vert) . . 4·00 5·50

See also Nos. 165 etc. (1985).

11 Windsurfing

1983. Tourism. Multicoloured.
69 50c. Type **11** 10 10
70 2r. Hotel 25 25
71 3r. View of beach 35 35
72 10r. Islands at sunset . . . . 1·00 1·75

1983. Nos. 23/8 surch.
73 30c. on 40c. "Royal Escape" . . 25 25
74 30c. on 40c. Prince Charles and Lady Diana Spencer . . 50 60
75 2r. on 5r. "Victoria and Albert II" 70 70
76 2r. on 5r. As No. 74 . . . . 1·25 1·75
77 3r. on 10r. "Britannia" . . . 85 85
78 3r. on 10r. As No. 74 . . . . 1·60 2·50

12 Map of Aldabra and Commemorative Postmark

1984. Re-opening of Aldabra Post Office. Multicoloured.
79 50c. Type **12** 15 30
80 2r.75 White-throated rail . . . 60 1·10
81 3r. Giant tortoise . . . . . . 60 1·25
82 10r. Red-footed booby . . . . 2·25 3·50

13 Fishing from Launch

1984. Game Fishing. Multicoloured.
83 50c. Type **13** 15 30
84 2r. Hooked fish (vert) 45 75
85 3r. Weighing catch (vert) . . . 60 1·00
86 10r. Fishing from boat (different) . . . . 2·00 3·00

14 Giant Hermit Crab

1984. Crabs. Multicoloured.
87 50c. Type **14** 25 40
88 2r. Fiddler crabs . . . . . . 55 1·10
89 3r. Sand crab . . . . 65 1·50
90 10r. Spotted pebble crab . . . 1·40 4·25

15 Constellation of "Orion"

1984. The Night Sky. Multicoloured.
91 50c. Type **15** 25 15
92 2r. "Cygnus" 50 55
93 3r. "Virgo" 60 80
94 10r. "Scorpio" . . . . 1·40 2·25

C. Inscr "ZIL ELWANNYEN SESEL"

16 "Lenzites elegans" **17** The Queen Mother attending Royal Opera House, Covent Garden

1985. Fungi. Multicoloured.
95 50c. Type **16** 60 85
96 2r. "Xylaria telfairei" . . . . 1·50 2·00
97 3r. "Lentinus sajor-caju" . . . 1·50 2·00
98 10r. "Hexagonia tenuis" . . . 2·75 3·50

1985. As Nos. 53/4, 57 and 61 but inscr "Zil Elwannyen Sesel".
165 5c. Type **10** . . . . 2·00 2·25
166 10c. Zebra dove ("Barred Ground Dove") . . . . . 2·00 2·25
103 25c. Madagascar white eye . . . 1·75 1·50
105 50c. White-throated rail . . . 2·75 1·60
226 2r. Western reef heron ("Diomorphic Little Egret") . . . . 3·50 3·75

1985. Life and Times of Queen Elizabeth the Queen Mother. Multicoloured.
115 1r. The Queen Mother, 1936 (from photo by Dorothy Wilding) 20 25
116 2r. With Princess Anne at Ascot, 1974 . . . . 35 50
117 3r. Type **17** 45 70
118 5r. With Prince Henry at his christening (from photo by Lord Snowdon) . . . . . 60 1·25
MS119 91 × 73 mm. 10r. In a launch, Venice, 1985 . . . . . 1·50 2·75

18 Giant Tortoise

1985. Giant Tortoises of Aldabra (1st series). Multicoloured.
120 50c. Type **18** . . . . 3·00 1·25
121 75c. Giant tortoises at stream 3·25 1·40
122 1r. Giant tortoises on grassland . . . . 3·50 1·60
123 2r. Giant tortoise (side view) 4·50 2·25
MS124 70 × 60 mm. 10r. Two tortoises . . . . 15·00 15·00
For stamps as Nos. 120/3 but without circular inscription around W.W.F. emblem see Nos. 153/6.

19 Phoenician Trading Ship (600 B.C.)

1985. Famous Visitors. Multicoloured.
125 50c. Type **19** 80 80
126 2r. Sir Hugh Scott and H.M.S. "Sealark", 1908 . . 1·50 2·00
127 10r. Vasco da Gama and "Sao Gabriel", 1502 . . . 2·50 4·50

1986. 60th Birthday of Queen Elizabeth II. As T **145a** of St. Helena. Multicoloured.
128 75c. Princess Elizabeth at Chester, 1951 . . . . . . 15 25
129 1r. Queen and Duke of Edinburgh at Falklands Service, St. Paul's Cathedral, 1985 . . . . . 15 25
130 1r.50 At Order of St. Michael and St. George service, St. Paul's Cathedral, 1968 25 40
131 3r.75 In Mexico, 1975 . . . 40 90
132 5r. At Crown Agents Head Office, London, 1983 . . . 45 1·25

1986. Royal Wedding. As T **146a** of St. Helena. Multicoloured.
133 3r. Prince Andrew and Miss Sarah Ferguson on Buckingham Palace balcony 45 75
134 7r. Prince Andrew in naval uniform . . . . 65 1·75

20 "Acropora palifera" and "Tubastraea coccinea" **21** "Hibiscus tiliaceus"

1986. Coral Formations. Multicoloured.
135 2r. Type **20** . . . . 1·75 1·75
136 2r. "Echinopora lamellosa" and "Favia pallida" . . . 1·75 1·75
137 2r. "Sarcophyton sp." and "Porites lutea" . . . . . . 1·75 1·75
138 2r. "Goniopora sp." and "Goniastrea retiformis" . . 1·75 1·75
139 2r. "Tubipora musica" and "Fungia fungites" . . . . 1·75 1·75
Nos. 135/9 were printed together, se-tenant, forming a composite design.

1986. Flora. Multicoloured.
140 50c. Type **21** 35 30
141 2r. "Crinum angustum" . . . 1·60 1·50
142 3r. "Phaius tetragonus" . . . 2·25 2·00
143 10r. "Rothmannia annae" . . 3·75 4·00

22 Teardrop Butterflyfish and Lined Butterflyfish **23** Coconut

1987. Coral Reef Fishes. Multicoloured.
144 2r. Type **22** . . . . 1·10 1·40
145 2r. Knifejaw . . . . 1·10 1·40
146 2r. Narrow-banded batfish . . 1·10 1·40
147 2r. Ringed-sergeant . . . . . 1·10 1·40
148 2r. Lined butterflyfish and Meyer's butterflyfish . . . 1·10 1·40
Nos. 144/8 were printed together, se-tenant, forming a composite design.

1987. Trees. Multicoloured.
149 1r. Type **23** 80 85
150 2r. Mangrove . . . . 1·40 1·75
151 3r. Pandanus palm . . . . . 2·00 2·50
152 5r. Indian almond . . . . . 3·00 3·75

1987. Giant Tortoises of Aldabra (2nd series). Designs as Nos. 120/3 but without circular inscr around W.W.F. emblem. Multicoloured.
153 50c. As Type **18** . . . . . . 2·25 1·75
154 75c. Giant tortoises at pool . 2·75 2·50
155 1r. Giant tortoises on grassland . . . . 3·75 3·50
156 2r. Giant tortoise (side view) 4·75 4·50

1987. Royal Ruby Wedding. Nos. 128/32 optd **40TH WEDDING ANNIVERSARY.**
157 75c. Princess Elizabeth at Chester, 1951 . . . . . . 20 20
158 1r. Queen and Duke of Edinburgh at Falklands Service, St. Paul's Cathedral, 1985 . . . . . 25 25
159 1r.50 At Order of St. Michael and St. George service, St. Paul's Cathedral, 1968 35 40
160 3r.75 In Mexico, 1975 . . . 50 90
161 5r. At Crown Agents Head Office, London, 1983 . . . 60 1·25

24 "Vallee de Mai" (Christine Harter)

1987. Tourism. Multicoloured.
162 3r. Type **24** . . . . 2·50 2·50
163 3r. Ferns . . . . 2·50 2·50
164 3r. Bamboo . . . . 2·50 2·50
Nos. 162/4 were printed together, se-tenant, forming a composite picture.

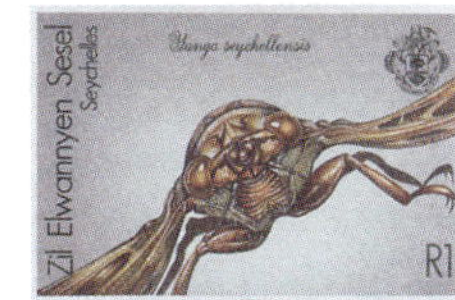

25 "Yanga seychellensis" (beetle)

1988. Insects. Multicoloured.
180 1r. Type **25** . . . . 1·00 1·00
181 2r. "Belenois aldabraensis" (butterfly) . . . . 1·75 1·60
182 3r. "Polyspilota seychelliana" (mantid) . . . . 2·00 2·25
183 5r. "Polposipus herculeanus" (beetle) . . . . 2·50 3·00

26 Olympic Rings

1988. Olympic Games, Seoul. Sheet 99 × 73 mm.
MS184 **26** 10r. multicoloured . . 4·00 2·75

1988. 300th Anniv of Lloyd's of London. As T **152a** of St. Helena. Multicoloured.
185 1r. Modern Lloyd's Building, London 70 65
186 2r. "Retriever" (cable ship) (horiz) . . . . 1·00 1·10
187 3r. "Chantel" (fishing boat) (horiz) . . . . 1·75 1·50
188 5r. Wreck of "Torrey Canyon" (tanker), Cornwall, 1967 . . . . . 2·25 1·75

27 "Father Christmas landing with Presents" (Jean-Claude Boniface)

1988. Christmas. Children's Paintings. Mult.
189 1r. Type **27** 35 40
190 2r. "Church" (Francois Barra) (vert) 60 80
191 3r. "Father Christmas flying on Bird" (Wizy Ernesta) (vert) . . . . 85 1·25
192 5r. "Father Christmas in Sleigh over Island" (Federic Lang) . . . . . . 1·40 2·00

1989. 20th Anniv of First Manned Landing on Moon. As T **50a** of St. Kitts. Multicoloured.
193 1r. Firing Room, Launch Control Centre . . . . . 1·75 1·50
194 2r. Crews of "Apollo–Soyuz" mission (30 × 30 mm) . . . 2·25 2·25
195 3r. "Apollo–Soyuz" emblem (30 × 30 mm) . . . . . . 2·50 2·75
196 5r. "Apollo" and "Soyuz" docking in space . . . . . 3·50 4·25
MS197 82 × 100 mm. 10r. Recovery of "Apollo 11" . . . . 11·00 12·00

28 Dumb Cane

1989. Poisonous Plants (1st series). Mult.
198 1r. Type **28** . . . . 2·25 1·75
199 2r. Star of Bethlehem . . . . 2·75 2·50
200 3r. Indian liquorice . . . . . 3·00 3·00
201 5r. Black nightshade . . . . 4·00 4·50
See also Nos. 214/17.

29 Tec-Tec Broth

1989. Creole Cooking. Multicoloured.
202 1r. Type **29** . . . . 1·50 1·50
203 2r. Pilaff a la Seychelloise . . 2·00 2·25
204 3r. Mullet grilled in banana leaves . . . . 2·25 2·50
205 5r. Daube . . . . 3·25 3·75
MS206 125 × 80 mm. Nos. 202/5 11·00 12·00

30 1980 Marine Life 5r. Stamp

1990. "Stamp World London 90" International Stamp Exhibition. Showing stamps. Mult.
207 1r. Type **30** . . . . 2·25 1·75
208 2r. 1980 5r. definitive . . . . 2·75 2·50
209 3r. 1983 2r.75 definitive . . . 3·00 3·00
210 5r. 1981 Wildlife 5r. . . . . 4·00 4·50
MS211 124 × 84 mm. Nos. 207/10 10·00 12·00

1990. 90th Birthday of Queen Elizabeth the Queen Mother. As T **116a** of St. Helena.
212 2r. multicoloured . . . . . . 2·00 2·25
213 10r. black and brown . . . . 3·75 5·00
DESIGNS—21 × 36 mm: 2r. Duchess of York with baby Princess Elizabeth, 1926. 29 × 37 mm: 10r. King George VI and Queen Elizabeth visiting bombed district, London, 1940.

1990. Poisonous Plants (2nd series). As T **28**. Multicoloured.
214 1r. Ordeal plant . . . . . . 1·75 1·75
215 2r. Thorn apple . . . . . . 2·25 2·50
216 3r. Strychnine tree . . . . . 2·50 2·75
217 5r. Bwa zasmen . . . . . . 3·50 4·00

1991. 65th Birthday of Queen Elizabeth II and 70th Birthday of Prince Philip. As T **165a** of St. Helena. Multicoloured.
234 4r. Queen Elizabeth II . . . 1·75 2·00
235 4r. Prince Philip . . . . . . 1·75 2·00

31 "St. Abbs" (full-rigged ship), 1860

1991. Shipwrecks. Multicoloured.
236 1r.50 Type **31** . . . . . . 2·50 2·00
237 3r. "Norden" (barque), 1862 3·00 2·50

238 3r.50 "Clan Mackay" (freighter), 1894 . . . . . 3·25 2·75
239 10r. "Glenlyon" (freighter), 1905 . . . . 7·00 7·50

1992. 40th Anniv of Queen Elizabeth II's Accession. As T **168a** of St. Helena. Mult.
240 1r. Beach 75 75
241 1r.50 Aerial view of Desroches . . . . 1·10 1·25
242 3r. Tree-covered coastline . . 1·50 1·75
243 3r.50 Three portraits of Queen Elizabeth II . . . . 1·60 1·90
244 5r. Queen Elizabeth II . . . 1·75 2·25

32 "Lomatopyllum aldabrense" (plant)

1992. 10th Anniv of Aldabra as a World Heritage Site. Multicoloured.
245 1r.50 Type **32** . . . . 1·75 1·75
246 3r. White-throated rail . . . 4·50 3·50
247 3r.50 Robber crab . . . . . 2·75 3·50
248 10r. Aldabra drongo . . . . 9·00 10·00

ZIMBABWE Pt. 1

Rhodesia became independent on 18 April 1980 and was renamed Zimbabwe.

100 cents = 1 dollar.

113 Morganite

114 Rotary Anniversary Emblem

1980. As Nos. 555/69 of Rhodesia and new value inscr "ZIMBABWE".
576 1c. Type **113** 10 30
577 3c. Amethyst 15 30
578 4c. Garnet 15 10
579 5c. Citrine 15 10
580 7c. Blue topaz 15 10
581 9c. White rhinoceros 15 10
582 11c. Lion 15 15
583 13c. Warthog 15 15
584 15c. Giraffe 15 20
585 17c. Common zebra 15 20
586 21c. Odzani Falls 15 25
587 25c. Goba Falls 15 30
588 30c. Inyangombi Falls . . . 15 50
588a 40c. Bundi Falls . . . . . 4·00 4·50
589 $1 Bridal Veil Falls . . . . 25 1·50
590 $2 Victoria Falls . . . . . 35 3·00

1980. 75th Anniv of Rotary International.
591 **114** 4c. multicoloured 10 10
592 13c. multicoloured 15 20
593 21c. multicoloured 20 35
594 25c. multicoloured 20 60
MS595 140 × 84 mm. Nos. 591/4 75 1·60

115 Olympic Rings

1980. Olympic Games, Moscow.
596 **115** 17c. multicoloured 30 40

116 Gatooma Post Office, 1912

1980. 75th Anniv of Post Office Savings Bank.
597 **116** 5c. black and brown . . . 10 10
598 – 7c. black and orange . . 10 10
599 – 9c. black and yellow . . . 10 10
600 – 17c. black and white . . . 25 25
MS601 125 × 84 mm. Nos. 597/600 55 1·25
DESIGNS: 7c. Salisbury Post Office, 1912; 9c. Umtali Post Office, 1901; 17c. Bulawayo Post Office, 1895.

117 Stylized Blind Person

118 Msasa

1981. Int Year of Disabled Persons. Mult.
602 5c. Type **117** 10 10
603 7c. Deaf person 10 10
604 11c. Person with one leg . . 15 10
605 17c. Person with one arm . . 20 25

1981. National Tree Day. Multicoloured.
606 5c. Type **118** 10 10
607 7c. Mopane 10 10
608 21c. Flat-crowned acacia . . 20 25
609 30c. Pod mahogany 25 45

119 Painting from Gwamgwadza Cave, Mtoko Area

1982. Rock Paintings. Multicoloured.
610 9c. Type **119** 40 20
611 11c. Epworth Mission, near Harare 50 20
612 17c. Diana's Vow, near Harare 50 30
613 21c. Gwamgwadza Cave, Mtoko Area (different) . . 70 50
614 25c. Mucheka Cave, Msana Communal Land . . . . . 80 1·25
615 30c. Chinzwini Shelter, Chiredzi Area . . . . . . 80 1·50

120 Scout Emblem

1982. 75th Anniv of Boy Scout Movement. Multicoloured.
616 9c. Type **120** 15 10
617 11c. Scouts around campfire . 15 10
618 21c. Scouts map-reading . . 20 35
619 30c. Lord Baden-Powell . . . 25 65

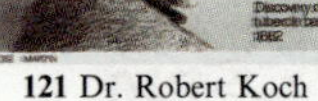

121 Dr. Robert Koch

122 "Wing Woman" (Henry Mudzengerere)

1982. Centenary of Dr. Robert Koch's Discovery of Tubercle Bacillus.
620 **121** 11c. orange, black and grey 40 10
621 – 30c. multicoloured . . . . 60 1·50
DESIGN: 30c. Man looking through microscope.

1983. Commonwealth Day. Sculptures. Mult.
622 9c. Type **122** 10 10
623 11c. "Telling Secrets" (Joseph Ndandarika) (horiz) . . . 10 10
624 30c. "Hornbill Man" (John Takawira) (horiz) 15 15
625 $1 "The Child" (Nicholas Mukomberanwa) . . . . . 40 1·25

123 Traditional Ploughing Team (moving right)

1983. World Ploughing Contest. Mult.
626 21c. Type **123** 15 25
627 21c. Traditional ploughing team (moving left) 15 25
628 30c. Tractor ploughing . . . 20 35
629 30c. Modern plough 20 35
The two designs of each value were issued in horizontal se-tenant pairs, forming composite designs.

124 Postman on Cycle

125 Map of Africa showing Zimbabwe

1983. World Communications Year. Mult.
630 9c. Type **124** 20 10
631 11c. Aircraft controller directing airliner 25 10
632 15c. Switchboard operator . . 25 20
633 17c. Printing works 25 20
634 21c. Road transport (horiz) . . 40 40
635 30c. Rail transport (horiz) . . 60 1·00

1984. Zimbabwe Int Trade Fair, 1984. Mult.
636 9c. Type **125** 10 10
637 11c. Globe 15 10
638 30c. Zimbabwe flag and Trade Fair logo 45 50

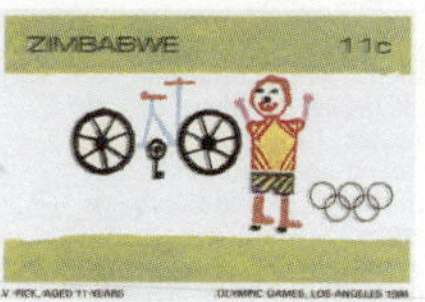

126 Cycling

1984. Olympic Games, Los Angeles. Children's Pictures. Multicoloured.
639 11c. Type **126** 35 15
640 21c. Swimming 35 30
641 30c. Running 50 65
642 40c. Hurdling . . . . 60 1·40

127 Liberation Heroes

1984. Heroes' Day. Multicoloured.
643 9c. Type **127** 20 10
644 11c. Symbolic tower and flame (vert) 20 10
645 17c. Bronze sculpture (vert) . . 30 30
646 30c. Section of bronze mural . 40 70
DESIGNS: 9c. to 30c. Various aspects of Heroes' Acre.

128 African Fish Eagle ("Fish Eagle")

1984. Birds of Prey. Multicoloured.
647 9c. Type **128** 40 20
648 11c. Long-crested eagle . . . 40 20
649 13c. Bateleur 50 30
650 17c. Verreaux's eagle ("Black Eagle") 60 30
651 21c. Martial eagle 70 60
652 30c. African hawk eagle . . . 1·00 1·25

129 9th Class Locomotive No. 86

1985. "Zimbabwe Steam Safaris". Railway Locomotives. Multicoloured.
653 9c. Type **129** 55 20
654 11c. 12th Class locomotive No. 190 . . . . 55 20
655 17c. 15th Class Beyer-Garratt locomotive No. 424 "Isilwane" 75 25
656 30c. 20th Class Garratt locomotive No. 726 "Gwaai" . . . . 1·50 1·50

130 "Intelsat V" Telecommunications Satellite

131 Tobacco

1985. Earth Satellite Station, Mazowe. Mult.
657 26c. Type **130** 75 40
658 57c. Earth Satellite Station, Mazowe (65 × 25 mm) . . 2·00 4·50

1985. National Infrastructure. Multicoloured.
659 1c. Type **131** 10 10
660 3c. Maize 10 10
661 4c. Cotton 15 10
662 5c. Tea 30 10
663 10c. Cattle 30 10
664 11c. Birchenough Bridge . . 75 10
665 12c. Ore stamp mill . . . . 1·25 10
666 13c. Gold pouring . . . . . 2·25 15
667 15c. Dragline coal mining . . 1·75 15
668 17c. Uncut amethyst . . . . 2·25 75
669 18c. Electric locomotive . . . 2·25 2·25
670 20c. Kariba Dam . . . . . 1·50 30
671 23c. Elephants at water hole . 3·50 45
672 25c. Sunset over Zambezi . . 65 30
673 26c. Baobab tree 65 20
674 30c. Ruins of Great Zimbabwe 75 70
675 35c. Traditional dancing . . 60 30
676 45c. Village women crushing maize 75 40
677 57c. Woodcarving 75 70
678 $1 Playing Mbira (musical instrument) . . . . 1·25 90
679 $2 Mule-drawn Scotch cart 2·00 3·00
680 $5 Zimbabwe coat-of-arms 2·25 4·50

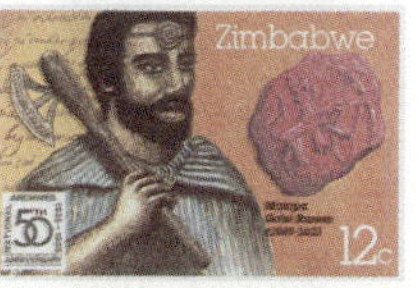

132 Chief Mutapa Gatsi Rusere and 17th-century Seal

1985. 50th Anniv of National Archives. Multicoloured.
681 12c. Type **132** 20 15
682 18c. Chief Lobengula, seal and 1888 Treaty 25 40
683 26c. Exhibition gallery . . . 35 45
684 35c. National Archives building 45 75

133 Computer Operator

1985. U.N. Decade for Women. Mult.
685 10c. Type **133** 30 10
686 17c. Nurse giving injection . . 50 40
687 26c. Woman student . . . . 1·00 2·00

134 Harare Conference Centre

1986. Harare Int Conference Centre. Mult.
688 26c. Type **134** 40 20
689 35c. Interior of conference hall 70 90

135 Grain Storage Silo

1986. 6th Anniv of Southern African Development Co-ordination Conference. Multicoloured.
690 12c. Type **135** 55 20
691 18c. Rhinoceros and hawk at sunset . . . . 2·50 1·50

692 26c. Map showing S.A.D.C.C. member states and Boeing 737 . . . . . 2·50 2·00
693 35c. Map and national flags of S.A.D.C.C. members . . 2·75 2·25

136 "Bunaeopsis jacksoni"

1986. Moths of Zimbabwe. Multicoloured.
694 12c. Type **136** 80 20
695 18c. "Deilephila nerii" . . . 1·25 80
696 26c. "Bunaeopsis zaddachi" . 1·50 1·10
697 35c. "Heniocha apollonia" . 1·75 4·00

137 Victoria Falls

1986. 8th Non-Aligned Summit Conference. Multicoloured.
698 26c. Type **137** . . . . 1·75 30
699 $1 Ruins of Great Zimbabwe (62 × 24 mm) . . . . . . 3·50 5·00

138 Sopwith Motorcycle (1921)

1986. Centenary of Motoring. Multicoloured.
700 10c. Type **138** 50 10
701 12c. Gladiator motor car (1902) 50 20
702 17c. Douglas motorcycle (1920) 65 20
703 26c. Ford "Model A" (1930) 80 30
704 35c. Schacht motor car (1909) 1·00 1·25
705 40c. Benz three-wheeled car (1886) . . . . 1·75 1·75

139 Growth Monitoring

140 African Barred Owlet ("Barred Owl")

1987. Child Survival Campaign. Mult.
706 12c. Type **139** . . . . 1·50 1·75
707 12c. Breast-feeding . . . . . 1·50 1·75
708 12c. Oral rehydration therapy 1·50 1·75
709 12c. Immunization . . . . . 1·50 1·75

1987. Owls (1st series). Multicoloured.
710 12c. Type **140** . . . . 2·50 40
711 18c. Pearl-spotted owlet ("Pearl Spotted Owl") . . 3·00 1·00
712 26c. White-faced scops owl ("White Faced Owl") . . . 3·50 1·00
713 35c. African scops owl ("Scops Owl") . . . . . . 4·75 3·00
See also Nos. 850/3 and 988/91.

141 Brownie, Guide and Ranger saluting ("Commitment")

1987. 75th Anniv of Girl Guides Association of Zimbabwe. Multicoloured.
714 15c. Type **141** 55 15
715 23c. Guides preparing meal over campfire ("Adventure") 75 30
716 35c. Guide teaching villagers to read ("Service") 85 45
717 $1 Handshake and globe ("International Friendship") . . . . 2·00 3·00

142 Common Grey Duiker

144 "Cockerel" (Arthur Azevedo)

143 "Pseudocreobotra wahlberghi" (mantid)

1987. Duikers of Africa Survey. Mult.
718 15c. Type **142** 70 15
719 23c. Zebra duiker 80 25
720 25c. Yellow-backed duiker . . 80 90
721 30c. Blue duiker . . . . . . 95 1·10
722 35c. Jentink's duiker . . . . 95 1·25
723 38c. Red duiker . . . . . . 1·00 1·75

1988. Insects. Multicoloured.
724 15c. Type **143** 70 15
725 23c. "Dicranorrhia derbyana" (beetle) 85 30
726 35c. "Dictyophorus spumans" (grasshopper) . . . . . . 1·10 85
727 45c. "Chalcocoris rutilus" (bug) . . . . 1·40 2·00

1988. 30th Anniv of National Gallery of Zimbabwe. Designs showing painting (38c.) or sculptures (others). Multicoloured.
728 15c. Type **144** 20 10
729 23c. "Man into Hippo" (Bernard Matemera) . . . 30 20
730 30c. "Spirit Python" (Henry Munyaradzi) 35 30
731 35c. "Spirit Bird carrying People" (Thomas Mukarobgwa) (horiz) . . . 35 30
732 38c. "The Song of the Herd Boy" (George Nene) (horiz) 35 40
733 45c. "War Victim" (Joseph Muzondo) (horiz) 40 50

145 "Aloe cameronii var. bondana"

146 White-faced Whistling Duck ("White-faced Duck")

1988. Aloes. Multicoloured.
734 15c. Type **145** 20 10
735 23c. "Orbeopsis caudata" . . 35 20
736 25c. "Euphorbia wildii" . . . 35 35
737 30c. "Euphorbia fortissima" 40 45
738 35c. "Aloe aculeata" 40 55
739 38c. "Huernia zebrina" . . . 45 70

1988. Wild Ducks and Geese of Zimbabwe. Multicoloured.
740 15c. Type **146** 75 20
741 23c. African pygmy goose ("Pygmy Goose") 85 20
742 30c. Hottentot teal 95 85
743 35c. Comb duck ("Knob-billed duck") . . . . . . 1·10 1·00
744 38c. White-backed duck . . . 1·10 1·25
745 45c. Maccoa duck . . . . . 1·60 2·25

147 O'Shaughnessy's Banded Gecko

1989. Geckos. Multicoloured.
746 15c. Type **147** 70 15
747 23c. Tiger rock gecko 85 40
748 35c. Tasman's gecko . . . . 1·25 1·25
749 45c. Bibron's gecko . . . . 1·50 2·00

148 Spotted Leaved Arum-Lily

1989. Wild Flowers (1st series). Multicoloured.
750 15c. Type **148** 45 10
751 23c. Grassland vlei-lily . . . 55 25
752 30c. Manica protea 60 40
753 35c. Flame lily 70 40
754 38c. Poppy hibiscus 75 55
755 45c. Blue sesbania 85 65
See also Nos. 1093/99.

149 Red-breasted Tilapia

1989. Fishes (1st series). Multicoloured.
756 15c. Type **149** 60 15
757 25c. Chessa 80 25
758 30c. Eastern bottlenose . . . 90 70
759 35c. Vundu 90 70
760 38c. Large-mouthed black bass . . . . 1·00 1·00
761 45c. Lesser tigerfish . . . . . 1·40 1·75
See also Nos. 864/9.

150 Black Rhinoceros

1989. Endangered Species. Multicoloured.
762 15c. Type **150** . . . . 1·25 40
763 23c. Cheetah . . . . 1·25 45
764 30c. Wild dog . . . . 1·40 90
765 35c. Pangolin . . . . 1·40 1·25
766 38c. Brown hyena . . . . . 1·50 2·00
767 45c. Roan antelope . . . . . 1·60 2·25

151 Giant Tigerfish

152 Headrest

153 Bicycles

1990. Multicoloured. (a) Wildlife. As T **151**.
768 1c. Type **151** 30 20
769 2c. Helmeted guineafowl . . 75 20
770 3c. Scrub hare 20 20
771 4c. Temminck's ground pangolin 30 20
772 5c. Greater kudu 40 20
773 9c. Black rhinoceros . . . . 1·50 30

(b) Cultural Artifacts. As T **152**.
774 15c. Type **152** 20 20
775 20c. Hand axe and adze . . . 20 20
776 23c. Gourd and water pot . . 20 20
777 25c. Snuff container 20 20
778 26c. Winnowing tray and basket 40 30
779 30c. Grinding stone 30 30

(c) Transport. As T **153**.
780 33c. Type **153** 70 30
781 35c. Buses . . . . 1·50 40
782 38c. Diesel train . . . . . . 1·50 40
783 45c. Mail motorcycle and trailer . . . . 1·25 40
784 $1 Air Zimbabwe Boeing 737 airliner . . . . 1·75 90
785 $2 Lorry . . . . 1·50 1·60

154 Pres. Mugabe and Joshua Nkomo at Signing of Unity Accord, 1987

1990. 10th Anniv of Independence. Mult.
786 15c. Type **154** 40 10
787 23c. Conference Centre, Harare 45 20
788 30c. Children in class 50 40
789 35c. Intelsat aerial, Mazowe Earth Satellite Station . . 60 70
790 38c. National Sports Stadium 60 80
791 45c. Maize field . . . . . . 90 1·40

155 Runhare House, 1986

1990. Cent of the City of Harare. Mult.
792 15c. Type **155** 30 10
793 23c. Market Hall, 1894 . . . 50 20
794 30c. Charter House, 1959 . . 55 35
795 35c. Supreme Court, 1927 . . 60 80
796 38c. Standard Chartered Bank, 1911 . . . . 60 90
797 45c. The Town House, 1933 80 1·40

156 Speaker's Mace

157 Small-spotted Genet

1990. 36th Commonwealth Parliamentary Conference, Harare. Multicoloured.
798 35c. Type **156** 50 25
799 $1 Speaker's chair . . . . . 1·25 2·00

1991. Small Mammals. Multicoloured.
800 15c. Type **157** 80 20
801 23c. Red squirrel 85 30
802 35c. Night-ape . . . . 1·25 1·25
803 45c. Bat-eared fox . . . . . 1·75 2·25

158 Hosho (rattles)

159 Snot-apple

1991. Traditional Musical Instruments. Mult.
804 15c. Type **158** 45 10
805 23c. Mbira (thumb piano) . . 50 15
806 30c. Ngororombe (pan pipes) 55 40
807 35c. Chipendani (mouth bow) 65 70
808 38c. Marimba (xylophone) . . 65 80
809 45c. Ngoma (drum) . . . . 75 1·10

1991. Wild Fruits (1st series). Multicoloured.
810 20c. Type **159** 50 10
811 39c. Marula 50 30
812 51c. Mobola plum 60 80
813 60c. Water berry 70 85
814 65c. Northern dwaba berry 75 85
815 77c. Mahobohobo . . . . . 85 1·10
See also Nos. 1038/43.

160 Bridal Veil Falls

162 "Amanita zambiana"

161 Lion

1991. Commonwealth Heads of Government Meeting, Harare. Multicoloured.
816 20c. Type **160** 65 15
817 39c. Meeting logo 65 35
818 51c. Chinhoyi Caves 90 75
819 60c. Kariba Dam 90 1·00
820 65c. Victoria Falls 1·10 1·25
821 77c. Balancing rocks 1·40 1·50

1992. Wildlife Conservation. Big Cats. Mult.
822 20c. Type **161** 65 15
823 39c. Leopard 95 40
824 60c. Cheetah 1·40 1·75
825 77c. Serval 1·75 2·00

1992. Edible Mushrooms. Multicoloured.
826 20c. Type **162** 50 20
827 39c. "Boletus edulis 70 40
828 51c. "Termitomyces sp." 75 75
829 60c. "Cantharellus densifolius" 90 1·00
830 65c. "Cantharellus longisporus" 1·00 1·25
831 77c. "Cantharellus cibarius" 1·25 1·50

163 Garden Bulbul ("Blackeyed Bulbul") 164 "Charaxes jasius"

1992. Birds. Multicoloured.
832 25c. Type **163** 65 15
833 59c. Fiscal shrike 85 45
834 77c. Forktailed drongo 95 80
835 90c. Cardinal woodpecker 1·00 95
836 98c. Southern yellow-billed hornbill ("Yellowbilled Hornbill") 1·10 95
837 $1.16 Crested francolin 1·25 1·40

1992. Butterflies. Multicoloured.
838 25c. Type **164** 1·00 20
839 59c. "Eronia leda" 1·60 75
840 77c. "Princeps ophidicephalus" 1·75 1·25
841 90c. "Junonia oenone" 2·25 1·75
842 98c. "Danaus chrysippus" 2·50 1·90
843 $1.16 "Junonia octavia" 2·50 2·25

165 Uranium

1993. Minerals. Multicoloured.
844 25c. Type **165** 1·40 20
845 59c. Chrome 2·00 55
846 77c. Copper 2·50 1·00
847 90c. Coal 2·75 1·50
848 98c. Gold 2·75 1·75
849 $1.16 Emerald 3·00 2·25

1993. Owls (2nd series). As T **140**. Mult.
850 25c. African wood owl ("Wood Owl") 2·00 50
851 59c. Pel's fishing owl 3·00 1·10
852 90c. Spotted eagle owl 4·00 4·00
853 $1.16 Verreaux's eagle owl ("Giant Eagle Owl") 4·50 5·50

166 Hadyana (relish pot) 167 "Polystachya dendrobiflora"

1993. Household Pottery. Multicoloured.
854 25c. Type **166** 55 10
855 59c. Chirongo (water jar) 70 30
856 77c. Mbiya (relish bowl) 80 60
857 90c. Pfuko (water jar) 90 85
858 98c. Tsaya (cooking pot) 95 85
859 $1.16 Gate (beer pot) 1·10 1·00

1993. Orchids. Multicoloured.
860 35c. Type **167** 1·00 20
861 $1 "Diaphananthe subsimplex" 2·00 75
862 $1.50 "Ansellia gigantea" 2·50 1·90
863 $1.95 "Vanilla polyepis" 2·75 2·50

1994. Fishes (2nd series). As T **149**. Mult.
864 35c. Manyame labeo ("Hunyani salmon") 50 10
865 $1 Sharp-toothed catfish ("Barbel") 80 30
866 $1.30 Rainbow trout 90 65
867 $1.50 African mottled eel 95 70
868 $1.65 Common carp 1·00 85
869 $1.95 Nembwe ("Robustus bream") 1·10 1·00

168 City Hall, 1940

1994. Centenary of Bulawayo. Multicoloured.
870 35c. Type **168** 15 10
871 80c. Cresta Churchill Hotel, 1974 30 20
872 $1.15 High Court, 1938 40 40
873 $1.75 Douslin House, 1902 50 70
874 $1.95 Goldfields Building, 1895 60 90
875 $2.30 Parkade Centre, 1975 85 1·25

169 Strelitzia 170 The Annunciation

1994. Export Flowers. Multicoloured.
876 35c. Type **169** 35 10
877 80c. Protea 65 25
878 $1.15 Phlox 80 60
879 $1.75 Chrysanthemum 90 1·40
880 $1.95 Ullum 1·10 1·90
881 $2.30 Rose 1·40 2·50

1994. Christmas. Multicoloured.
882 35c. Type **170** 30 10
883 80c. Journey to Bethlehem 55 15
884 $1.15 The Nativity 70 40
885 $1.75 Shepherds 1·00 1·50
886 $1.95 Wise Men 1·10 1·90
887 $2.30 Mary and Jesus 2·50 2·50

171 Harvesting Maize 173 Football

172 Spider-hunting Wasp

1995. Zimbabwe Culture. Multicoloured.
888 1c. Type **171** 10 40
889 2c. Loading sugar cane 10 40
890 3c. Sunflowers 10 40
891 4c. Sorghum 10 40
892 5c. Miners 40 30
893 10c. Drilling for gold 70 30
894 20c. Opencast coal mining, Wankie 80 30
895 30c. Chrome smelting, Kwekwe 85 30
896 40c. Opencast iron extraction, Redcliff 85 20
896a 45c. Underground mining team 1·00 20
897 50c. Gold smelting 75 20
898 70c. Bogie Clock Tower, Gweru 20 20
899 80c. Masvingo Watchtower 20 20
900 $1 Hanging Tree, Harare 20 25
901 $2 Cecil House, Harare 20 40
902 $5 The Toposcope, Harare 35 75
903 $10 Paper House, Kwekwe 60 1·25

1995. Insects. Multicoloured.
904 35c. Type **172** 40 10
905 $1.15 European dragonfly 1·00 45
906 $1.75 Foxy charaxes (butterfly) 1·50 2·00
907 $2.30 Antlion 2·00 2·75

1995. 6th All-Africa Games, Harare. Each showing sport within map of Africa. Multicoloured.
908 35c. Type **173** 30 10
909 80c. Running 40 20
910 $1.15 Boxing 45 30
911 $1.75 Swimming 65 90
912 $1.95 Hockey 2·25 1·75
913 $2.30 Volleyball 1·40 2·25

174 Weighing Baby (Health) 175 Fernandoa Tree

1995. 50th Anniv of United Nations. Multicoloured.
914 35c. Type **174** 15 10
915 $1.15 Women at pump (Environment) 30 35
916 $1.75 Workers on lorry (Food distribution) 50 80
917 $2.30 Teacher and children (Education) 60 1·60

1996. Indigenous Flowering Trees. Multicoloured.
918 45c. Type **175** 25 10
919 $1 Round leaf mukwa 40 20
920 $1.50 Luckybean ree 60 50
921 $2.20 Winter cassia 75 90
922 $2.50 Sausage tree 80 1·25
923 $3 Sweet thorn 90 1·60

176 Mazvikadei Dam

1996. Dams of Zimbabwe. Multicoloured.
924 45c. Type **176** 15 10
925 $1.50 Mutirikwi Dam 45 40
926 $2.20 Ncema Dam 65 90
927 $3 Odzani Dam 75 1·40

177 Matusadonha National Park at Sunset

1996. Scenic Views. Multicoloured.
928 45c. Type **177** 15 10
929 $1.50 Juliasdale rocky outcrop 45 40
930 $2.20 Honde Valley 75 1·00
931 $3 Finger Rocks at Morgenster Mission 85 1·60

178 Carved Frog

1996. Animal Wood Carvings. Multicoloured.
932 45c. Type **178** 15 10
933 $1.50 Tortoise 30 20
934 $1.70 Kudu 35 40
935 $2.20 Chimpanzee 50 80
936 $2.50 Porcupine 55 90
937 $3 Rhinoceros 60 1·10

179 Mashona Cow

1997. Cattle Breeds. Multicoloured.
938 45c. Type **179** 25 10
939 $1.50 Tuli cow 50 25
940 $2.20 Nkoni bull 70 90
941 $3 Brahman bull 1·00 1·50

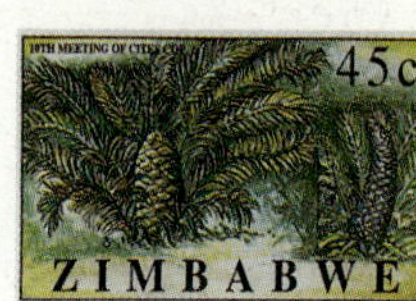

180 Cycad

1997. 10th Meeting of Convention on International Trade in Endangered Species Members, Harare. Multicoloured.
942 45c. Type **180** 10 10
943 $1.50 Peregrine falcon 65 55
944 $1.70 Temminck's ground pangolin 30 60
945 $2.20 Black rhinoceros 80 1·00
946 $2.50 African elephant 80 1·00
947 $3 Python 60 1·25

181 Wood Carving

1997. Rural Life. Multicoloured.
948 65c. Type **181** 15 10
949 $1 Winnowing 15 10
950 $2.40 Dancing 25 35
951 $2.50 Ploughing 25 35
952 $3.10 Stamping cereals 30 50
953 $4.20 Fetching water 45 70

182 Passenger Coach No. 1826

1997. Centenary of Zimbabwe Railways. Mult.
954 65c. Type **182** 20 15
955 $1 Class 12 steam locomotive No. 257 20 15
956 $2.40 Class 16A steam locomotive No. 605 25 35
957 $2.50 Class EL 1 electric locomotive No. 4107 25 35
958 $3.10 Steam locomotive No. 7 "Jack Tar" 30 50
959 $4.20 Class DE 2 diesel-electric locomotive No. 1211 40 70

183 Aardwolf

1998. Lesser Known Animals of Zimbabwe. Multicoloured.
960 65c. Type **183** 20 10
961 $2.40 Large grey mongoose 25 30
962 $3.10 Clawless otter 30 55
963 $4.20 Antbear 35 80

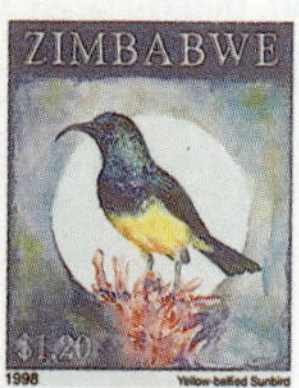

184 Honeybee on Flower 186 Variable Sunbird ("Yellow-bellied Sunbird")

185 Fossil Fish

1998. Bees and Bee-keeping. Multicoloured.
964 $1.20 Type **184** 20 10
965 $4.10 Queen, worker and drone 25 35
966 $4.70 Queen and retinue 25 35
967 $5.60 Rural bee-keeper 30 40

968 $7.40 Commercial bee-keepers 40 70
969 $9.90 Products of the hive 55 90

1998. Fossils. Multicoloured.
970 $1.20 Type **185** 60 10
971 $5.60 Allosaurus footprints 85 60
972 $7.40 Left foot of Massospondylus 95 95
973 $9.90 Fossil wood 1·25 1·60

1998. Birds. Multicoloured.
974 $1.20 Type **186** 35 15
975 $4.10 Lesser blue-eared glossy starling ("Lesser Blue-eared Starling") 50 30
976 $4.70 Grey-headed kingfisher ("Grey-hooded Kingfisher") 50 40
977 $5.60 Miombo grey tit 55 55
978 $7.40 Chirinda apalis 70 80
979 $9.90 Swynnerton's robin 80 1·00

187 Philatelic Counter **188** Serval

1999. 125th Anniv of U.P.U. Multicoloured.
980 $1.20 Type **187** 20 10
981 $5.60 Postman delivering letters 35 25
982 $7.40 19th-century runner, motorcycle and truck 1·00 70
983 $9.90 Harare Central Sorting Office 60 80

1999. Cats. Multicoloured.
984 $1.20 Type **188** 25 10
985 $5.60 Cheetah 55 35
986 $7.40 Caracal 70 80
987 $9.90 Leopard 1·10 1·40

1999. Owls (3rd series). As T **140**. Multicoloured.
988 $1.20 Cape eagle owl 50 25
989 $5.60 Grass owl 85 60
990 $7.40 Barn owl 1·00 1·10
991 $9.90 African marsh owl ("Marsh Owl") 1·10 1·50

189 Canoe Safari

190 Family Reunion

1999. Tourism in Zimbabwe. Multicoloured.
992 $2 Type **189** 15 15
993 $6.70 Rock climbing 40 40
994 $7.70 Flying microlight 45 50
995 $9.10 White water rafting 60 70
996 $12.00 Mountain scenery 70 95
997 $16.00 Game watching 1·00 1·50
No. 997 is inscribed "Game Veiwing" in error.

1999. Christmas. Multicoloured.
998 $2 Type **190** 15 10
999 $6.70 Elephants around Christmas tree 25 25
1000 $7.70 Children and dog with balloons 25 25
1001 $9.10 Flame Lily 30 35
1002 $12 Madonna and Child 45 65
1003 $16 The Nativity 55 85

191 Nyala

192 Basketball

2000. Fauna, Industry and Development. Mult.
1004 1c. Type **191** 10 10
1005 10c. Building development 10 10
1006 30c. Timber yard 10 10
1007 50c. Tobacco auction 10 10
1008 70c. Central Sorting Office, Harare 10 10
1009 80c. Harare New International Airport 10 10
1010 $1 Westgate shopping complex 10 10
1011 $2 Nile Crocodile 10 10
1012 $3 Pungwe river water project 10 10
1013 $4 Zebra 10 15
1014 $5 Mining 10 15
1015 $7 National University of Science and Technology 15 20
1016 $10 Ostrich 25 30
1017 $15 Brown-necked parrot ("Cape Parrot") 35 40
1018 $20 Leather products 50 55
1019 $30 Lilac-breasted roller 75 80
1020 $50 Victoria Falls 1·25 1·40
1021 $100 Mukorsi Dam, Tokwe River 2·50 2·75

2000. Sporting Activities. Multicoloured.
1022 $2 Type **192** 15 10
1023 $6.70 Tennis 40 35
1024 $7.70 Netball 40 45
1025 $9.10 Weightlifting 40 50
1026 $12 Taekwondo 55 65
1027 $16 Diving 65 75

193 Dr. Joshua Nkomo

194 Nurse with Baby and Ministry of Health Logo

2000. 1st Death Anniv of Dr. Joshua Nkomo (nationalist leader). Multicoloured.
1028 $2 Type **193** 15 10
1029 $9.10 Nkomo in traditional costume 40 50
1030 $12 Type **193** 55 65
1031 $16 As $9.10 65 75

2000. Health Promotion Campaign. Multicoloured.
1032 $2 Type **194** 15 10
1033 $6.70 Boy with football and anti-tuberculosis emblem 30 30
1034 $7.70 Couple with baby and "New Start" logo 35 30
1035 $9.10 Health technician on motorcycle and Riders for Health badge 60 50
1036 $12 Ribbon emblem on map and Ministry of Health logo 65 70
1037 $16 Fisherman and Rotary International emblem 70 80

195 Masawu Fruit

2000. Wild Fruits (2nd series). Multicoloured.
1038 $2 Type **195** 15 10
1039 $6.70 Spiny monkey orange 30 30
1040 $7.70 Bird plum 30 35
1041 $9.10 Shakama plum 40 45
1042 $12 Wild medlar 60 65
1043 $16 Wild custard apple 65 75

196 Boeing 737-200

2001. Aircraft. Multicoloured.
1044 $8 Type **196** 30 25
1045 $12 BAe Hawk MK 60 45 40
1046 $14 Hawker Hunter FGA-9 50 50
1047 $16 Cessna/Reims F-337 60 60
1048 $21 Aerospatiale Alouette III helicopter 70 85
1049 $28 Boeing 767-200ER 85 1·10

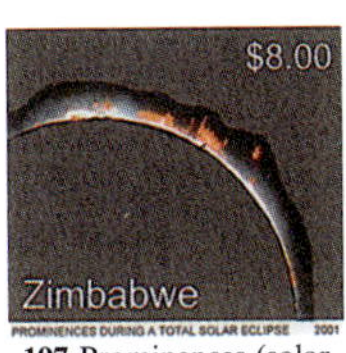

197 Prominences (solar gas outbursts) during Total Solar Eclipse

198 "The Hare who rode Horseback"

2001. Total Solar Eclipse, 21 June 2001. Multicoloured.
1050 $8 Type **197** 30 25
1051 $21 Path of eclipse over Southern Africa 70 80
1052 $28 Phases of total solar eclipse (62 × 22 mm) 85 1·10

2001. African Folk Tales. Multicoloured..
1053 $8 Type **198** 30 25
1054 $12 "The Hippo who lost his Hair" 40 35
1055 $13 "The Lion who was saved by a Mouse" 40 40
1056 $16 "The Bush Fowl who wakes the Sun" 50 50
1057 $21 "The Chameleon who came too Late" 70 80
1058 $28 "The Tortoise who collected Wisdom" 85 1·10
MS1059 126 × 105 mm. Nos. 1053/8 2·75 3·00

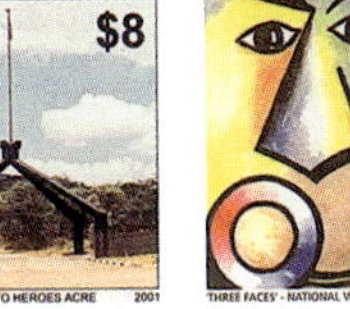

199 Entrance, Heroes Acre Memorial, Harare **200** "Three Faces" (N. Mguni) (national winner)

2001. 21st Anniv of Independence. Heroes Acre Memorial, Harare. Multicoloured.
1060 $8 Type **199** 30 25
1061 $16 Statue of Unknown Soldier 50 45
1062 $21 Obelisk 70 80
1063 $28 Aerial view 85 1·10

2001. U.N. Dialogue Among Civilizations. Mult.
1064 $8 Type **200** 30 25
1065 $21 "Children encircling globe" (Urska Golob) (international winner) 70 75

201 *Charaxes bohemani*(butterfly)

2001. Butterflies (2nd series). Multicoloured.
1066 $12 Type **201** 40 35
1067 $20 *Vanessa cardui* 60 60
1068 $25 *Precis oenone cebrene* 70 75
1069 $30 *Euphaedra neophron* 85 90
1070 $35 *Iolaus silas* (female) 95 1·10
1071 $45 *Acrea aglanice* 1·25 1·50
MS1072 140 × 95 mm. Nos. 1066/71 4·25 4·75

202 Knitting and Crochet Work

2002. Local Crafts. Multicoloured.
1073 $12 Type **202** 30 35
1074 $20 Art and design 50 55
1075 $25 Baskets 65 70
1076 $30 Pottery 75 80
1077 $35 Woodcarving 80 85
1078 $45 Sculpture 1·10 1·25

203 Agate

2002. Gemstones. Multicoloured.
1079 $12 Type **203** 30 35
1080 $25 Aquamarine 65 70
1081 $35 Diamond 80 85
1082 $45 Emerald 1·10 1·25

204 "Two Girls arm-in-arm" (Tazivei Makwavarara)

2002. 5th Anniv of Childline in Zimbabwe. Multicoloured.
1083 $12 Type **204** 30 35
1084 $25 "Girl using telephone" (Ashley Elkington) 60 65
1085 $35 "Teddy bear" (Goldine Hobbs) 75 80
1086 $45 "Hand holding telephone" (Admire Kacheche) 1·10 1·25

205 Sally Mugabe

2002. 10th Death Anniv of Sally Mugabe (wife of President). Multicoloured.
1087 $20 Type **205** 50 55
1088 $50 Mrs. Mugabe in black and white dress 1·25 1·40
1089 $70 Type **205** 1·50 1·60
1090 $90 As $50 2·25 2·40

206 "Mail Runner and Local Post Office" (Agreement Ngwenya)

2002. "Technology Today" School Design Competition Winners. Multicoloured.
1091 $20 Type **206** 50 55
1092 $70 "Mail runner and Airliner" (Kudzai Chikomo) 1·50 1·60

207 *Dissotis princeps*

2002. Wild Flowers (2nd series). Multicoloured.
1093 $20 Type **207** 50 55
1094 $35 *Leonotis nepetifolia* 75 80
1095 $40 *Hibiscus vitifolius* 1·00 1·10
1096 $50 *Boophane disticha* 1·25 1·40
1097 $70 *Pycnostachys urticifolia* 1·50 1·60
1098 $90 *Gloriosa superba* 2·25 2·50
MS1099 120 × 105 mm. Nos. 1093/8 7·25 7·50

POSTAGE DUE STAMPS

D **4** Zimbabwe Bird (soapstone sculpture)

D **5**

1980.
D23 D **4** 1c. green 20 1·00
D24 2c. blue 20 1·00
D25 5c. violet 25 1·00
D26 6c. yellow 30 1·75
D27 10c. red 40 2·25

1985.
D28 D **5** 1c. orange 25 80
D29 2c. mauve 25 80
D30 6c. green 55 1·00
D31 10c. brown 60 1·00
D32 13c. blue 60 1·00

1990. No. D27 surch **25**.
D33 D **4** 25c. on 10c. red 6·00 6·00

D **7**

D **8** Bird Carving

1995.
D34 D **7** 1c. yellow 10 40
D35 2c. orange 10 40
D36 5c. mauve 10 40
D37 10c. blue 10 40
D38 25c. violet 15 40
D39 40c. green 25 50
D40 60c. orange 35 60
D41 $1 brown 45 75

2000.
D42 D **8** 1c. black and green 10 10
D43 10c. black and blue 10 10
D44 50c. black and brown 10 10
D45 $1 black and red 10 10
D46 $2 black and yellow 10 10
D47 $5 black and mauve 10 15
D48 $10 black and red 25 30

ZULULAND Pt. 1

A territory of south-eastern Africa, annexed by Great Britain in 1887, and incorporated in Natal in 1897.

12 pence = 1 shilling;
20 shillings = 1 pound.

1888. Stamps of Gt. Britain (Queen Victoria) optd **ZULULAND**.

1	**71**	½d. red	3·00	2·50
2	**57**	1d. lilac	25·00	3·75
3	**73**	2d. green and red	12·00	24·00
4	**74**	2½d. purple on blue	20·00	20·00
5	**75**	3d. purple on yellow	25·00	22·00
6	**76**	4d. green and brown	42·00	55·00
7	**78**	5d. purple and blue	90·00	£120
8	**79**	6d. purple on red	13·00	17·00
9	**80**	9d. purple and blue	85·00	90·00
10	**82**	1s. green	£110	£130
11	–	5s. red (No. 181)	£500	£600

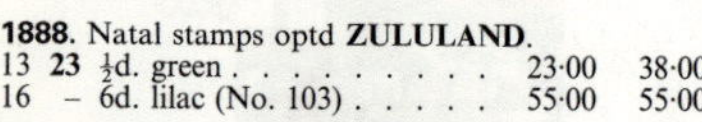

1888. Natal stamps optd **ZULULAND**.

13	**23**	½d. green	23·00	38·00
16	–	6d. lilac (No. 103)	55·00	55·00

3

1894.

20	**3**	½d. mauve and green	3·25	4·25
21		1d. mauve and red	5·00	1·75
22		2½d. mauve and blue	14·00	8·50
23		3d. mauve and brown	8·00	3·00
24		6d. mauve and black	20·00	20·00
25		1s. green	38·00	38·00
26		2s. 6		
27		4s. green and red	£110	£150
28		£1 purple on red	£450	£550
29		£5 purple and black on red	£4500	£1500

INDEX

- Abu Dhabi *see Vol. 1*
- Abyssinia (*Ethiopia*) *see Vol. 2*
- Aden *see Vol. 1*
- Aegean Islands (*Dodecanese Islands*) *see Vol. 1*
- Afghanistan *see Vol. 1*
- Africa (*Portuguese Colonies*) *see Vol. 3*
- Aitutaki *see Vol. 1*
  - New Zealand Dependancy *see Vol. 1*
  - Part Of Cook Islands *see Vol. 1*
- Ajman *see Vol. 1*
- Aland Islands *see Vol. 1*
- Alaouites *see Vol. 1*
- Albania *see Vol. 1*
  - German Occupation *see Vol. 1*
  - Independent State *see Vol. 1*
  - Italian Occupation *see Vol. 1*
  - People's Republic *see Vol. 1*
- Alexandretta *see Vol. 1*
- Alexandria *see Vol. 1*
- Algeria *see Vol. 1*
  - Independent State *see Vol. 1*
- Allenstein *see Vol. 1*
- Alsace And Lorraine *see Vol. 1*
- Alwar *see Vol. 1*
- Andorra *see Vol. 1*
  - Spanish Post Offices *see Vol. 1*
- Angola *see Vol. 1*
- Angora (*Turkey 1922*) 502
- Angra *see Vol. 1*
- Anguilla *see Vol. 1*
- Anjouan *see Vol. 1*
- Ankara (*Angora*) 502
- Annam And Tongking *see Vol. 1*
- Antigua *see Vol. 1*
- Antioquia *see Vol. 1*
- Arad (*French Occupation of Hungary*) *see Vol. 2*
- Arbe *see Vol. 1*
- Argentine Republic *see Vol. 1*
- Armenia *see Vol. 1*
  - Independent Republic *see Vol. 1*
  - Soviet Republic *see Vol. 1*
  - Transcaucasian Federation Issues For Armenia *see Vol. 1*
- Aruba *see Vol. 1*
- Ascension *see Vol. 1*
- Australia *see Vol. 1*
- Australian Antarctic Territory *see Vol. 1*
- Austria *see Vol. 1*
- Austrian Italy (*Lombardy and Venetia*) *see Vol. 3*
- Austrian Levant (*Austro-Hungarian Post Offices in the Turkish Empire*) *see Vol. 1*
- Austrian Territories acquired by Italy (*Austrian Italy*) *see Vol. 3*
- Austrian Territories Acquired By Italy *see Vol. 1*
  - General Issue *see Vol. 1*
  - Venezia Giulia *see Vol. 1*
- Austro-Hungarian Military Post *see Vol. 1*
  - General Issues *see Vol. 1*
  - Issues For Italy *see Vol. 1*
  - Issues For Montenegro *see Vol. 1*
  - Issues For Rumania *see Vol. 1*
  - Issues For Serbia *see Vol. 1*
- Austro-Hungarian Post Offices In The Turkish Empire *see Vol. 1*
  - Lombardy And Venetia Currency *see Vol. 1*
  - Turkish Currency *see Vol. 1*
  - French Currency *see Vol. 1*
- AVIANCA (*Columbia, Private Air Companies*) *see Vol. 1*
- Azerbaijan *see Vol. 1*
- Azores *see Vol. 1*

- Baden *see Vol. 1*
- Baghdad *see Vol. 1*
- Bahamas *see Vol. 1*
- Bahawalpur *see Vol. 1*
- Bahrain *see Vol. 1*
- Bamra *see Vol. 1*
- Banat Bacska (*Rumanian Occupation of Hungary*) *see Vol. 3*
- Bangkok (*British Post Offices in Siam*) *see Vol. 1*
- Bangladesh *see Vol. 1*
- Baranya (*Serbian Occupation of Hungary*) 136
- Barbados *see Vol. 1*
- Barbuda *see Vol. 1*
- Barwani *see Vol. 1*
- Basutoland *see Vol. 1*
- Batum *see Vol. 1*
- Bavaria *see Vol. 1*
- Bechuanaland *see Vol. 1*
  - British Bechuanaland *see Vol. 1*
  - Bechuanaland Protectorate *see Vol. 1*
  - Bechuanaland *see Vol. 1*
- Beirut (*Free French Forces in the Levant*) *see Vol. 2*
- Belarus *see Vol. 1*
- Belgian Congo *see Vol. 1*
  - Independent State Of The Congo *see Vol. 1*
  - Belgian Congo *see Vol. 1*
- Belgian Occupation Of Germany *see Vol. 1*
- Belgium *see Vol. 1*
  - Express Letter Stamps *see Vol. 1*
  - Parcel Post Stamps *see Vol. 1*
  - Railway Parcel Postage Due Stamps *see Vol. 1*
  - Railway Parcel Tax Stamps *see Vol. 1*
- Belize *see Vol. 1*
- Benadir (*Somalia 1903*) 204
- Benin *see Vol. 1*
  - French Colony *see Vol. 1*
  - People's Republic *see Vol. 1*
- Bergedorf *see Vol. 1*
- Bermuda *see Vol. 1*
- Bhopal *see Vol. 1*
- Bhor *see Vol. 1*
- Bhutan *see Vol. 1*
- Biafra *see Vol. 1*
- Bijawar *see Vol. 1*
- Bohemia And Moravia *see Vol. 1*
- Bolivar *see Vol. 1*
- Bolivia *see Vol. 1*
- Bophuthatswana *see Vol. 1*
- Bosnia And Herzegovina *see Vol. 1*
  - Austro-Hungarian Military Post *see Vol. 1*
  - Independent Republic *see Vol. 1*
  - Sarajevo Government *see Vol. 1*
  - Croatian Posts *see Vol. 1*
  - Republika Srpska *see Vol. 1*
- Botswana *see Vol. 1*
- Boyaca *see Vol. 1*
- Brazil *see Vol. 1*
- Bremen *see Vol. 1*
- British Antarctic Territory *see Vol. 1*
- British Central Africa (*Nyasaland Protectorate*) *see Vol. 3*
- British Columbia And Vancouver Island *see Vol. 1*
  - British Columbia *see Vol. 1*
  - Vancouver Island *see Vol. 1*
- British Commonwealth Occupation Of Japan *see Vol. 1*
- British East Africa *see Vol. 1*
- British Forces In Egypt *see Vol. 1*
- British Guiana *see Vol. 1*
- British Honduras *see Vol. 1*
- British Indian Ocean Territory *see Vol. 1*
- British Levant *see Vol. 1*
  - British Post Offices In Turkish Empire *see Vol. 1*
  - British Field Office In Salonica *see Vol. 1*
    - Turkish Currency *see Vol. 1*
    - British Currency *see Vol. 1*
- British New Guinea (*Papua 1901*) *see Vol. 3*
- British Occupation of German East Africa (*Tanganyika 1915*) 388
- British Occupation of Iraq (*Iraq 1918*) *see Vol. 2*
- British Occupation Of Italian Colonies *see Vol. 1*
  - Cyrenaica *see Vol. 1*
  - Eritrea *see Vol. 1*
  - Middle East Forces *see Vol. 1*
  - Somalia *see Vol. 1*
  - Tripolitania *see Vol. 1*
- British Occupation of Mafia Island (*Tanganyika 1915*) 388
- British Post Offices In China *see Vol. 1*
- British Post Offices In Crete *see Vol. 1*
- British P.O.s in Morocco (*Morocco Agencies*) *see Vol. 3*
- British Post Offices In Siam *see Vol. 1*
- British P.O.s in Tangier (*Morocco Agencies*) *see Vol. 3*
- British P.O.s in Turkey (*British Levant*) *see Vol. 1*
- British Postal Agencies In Eastern Arabia *see Vol. 1*
- British Somaliland (*Somaliland Protectorate*) 210
- British South Africa Company (*Rhodesia 1890–1917*) *see Vol. 3*
- British Virgin Islands *see Vol. 1*
- Brunei *see Vol. 1*
  - Japanese Occupation Of Brunei *see Vol. 1*
- Brunswick *see Vol. 1*
- Buenos Aires *see Vol. 1*
- Bulgaria *see Vol. 1*
- Bulgarian Occupation Of Rumania *see Vol. 1*
- Bundi *see Vol. 1*
- Burkina Faso *see Vol. 1*
- Burma *see Vol. 1*
  - Japanese Occupation Of Burma *see Vol. 1*
- Burundi *see Vol. 1*
- Bushire *see Vol. 1*
- Bussahir (Bashahr) *see Vol. 1*

- Caicos Islands *see Vol. 1*
- Calimno (*Dodecanese Islands*) *see Vol. 1*
- Cambodia *see Vol. 1*
- Cameroon *see Vol. 1*
  - Cameroons Expeditionary Force *see Vol. 1*
  - Cameroons Trust Territory *see Vol. 1*
- Cameroun *see Vol. 1*
  - French Administration Of Cameroun *see Vol. 1*
  - German Colony Of Kamerun *see Vol. 1*
  - Independent Republic *see Vol. 1*
- Canada *see Vol. 1*
  - Colony Of Canada *see Vol. 1*
  - Dominion Of Canada *see Vol. 1*
- Canal Zone *see Vol. 1*
- Canton *see Vol. 1*
- Cape Juby *see Vol. 1*
- Cape Of Good Hope *see Vol. 1*
- Cape Verde Islands *see Vol. 1*
- Carinthia (*Austria 1920*) *see Vol. 1*
- Carinthia (*Yugoslavia 1920*) 808
- Caroline Islands *see Vol. 1*
- Carriacou and Petite Martinique (*Grenadines of Grenada*) *see Vol. 2*
- Caso (*Dodecanese Islands*) *see Vol. 1*
- Castelrosso *see Vol. 1*
  - French Occupation *see Vol. 1*
  - Italian Occupation *see Vol. 1*
- Cauca *see Vol. 1*
- Cavalla (Kavalla) *see Vol. 1*
- Cayes Of Belize *see Vol. 1*
- Cayman Islands *see Vol. 1*
- Central African Empire *see Vol. 1*
- Central African Republic *see Vol. 1*
- Central Lithuania *see Vol. 1*
- Ceylon *see Vol. 1*
- Chad *see Vol. 1*
- Chamba *see Vol. 1*
- Channel Islands, General Issues (*Great Britain*) *see Vol. 2*
- Charkhari *see Vol. 1*
- Chile *see Vol. 1*
- China *see Vol. 1*
  - Chinese Empire *see Vol. 1*
  - Chinese Provinces *see Vol. 1*
    - Manchuria *see Vol. 1*
      - Kirin and Heilungkiang *see Vol. 1*
      - North-Eastern Provinces *see Vol. 1*
    - Sinkiang *see Vol. 1*
    - Szechwan *see Vol. 1*
    - Yunnan *see Vol. 1*
  - Communist China *see Vol. 1*
    - East China People's Post *see Vol. 1*
    - North China People's Post *see Vol. 1*
    - Port Arthur and Dairen *see Vol. 1*
    - North-East China People's Post *see Vol. 1*
    - North-West China People's Post *see Vol. 1*
    - South-West China People@s Post *see Vol. 1*
    - Chinese People's Republic *see Vol. 1*
  - China–Taiwan (Formosa) *see Vol. 1*
    - Chinese Province *see Vol. 1*
    - Chinese Nationalist Republic *see Vol. 1*
  - Chinese Republic *see Vol. 1*
- China Expeditionary Force *see Vol. 1*
- Christmas Island *see Vol. 1*
- Cilicia *see Vol. 1*
- Ciskei *see Vol. 1*
- Cochin *see Vol. 1*
- Cochin-China *see Vol. 1*
- Cocos (Keeling) Islands *see Vol. 1*

Colombia *see Vol. 1*
Lansa *see Vol. 1*
AVIANCA Company *see Vol. 1*
Private Air Companies *see Vol. 1*
Comoro Islands *see Vol. 1*
Confederate States (*United States of America*) 603
Confederate States Of America *see Vol. 1*
Congo (Brazzaville) *see Vol. 1*
Congo (Kinshasa) *see Vol. 1*
Congo Democratic Republic (Ex Zaire) *see Vol. 1*
Cook Islands *see Vol. 1*
Cos or Coo (*Dodecanese Islands*) *see Vol. 1*
Costa Rica *see Vol. 1*
Council of Europe (*France*) *see Vol. 2*
Court of International Justice (*Netherlands*) *see Vol. 3*
Crete *see Vol. 1*
Crete, Revolutionary Assembly (*Crete*) *see Vol. 1*
Revolutionary Assembly, 1905 *see Vol. 1*
Crimea (*South Russia*) 227
Croatia *see Vol. 1*
Serbian Posts In Croatia *see Vol. 1*
Sremsko Baranjska Oblast *see Vol. 1*
Croatian Posts (*Bosnia and Herzegovina*) *see Vol. 1*
Cuba *see Vol. 1*
Independent Republic *see Vol. 1*
Spanish Colony *see Vol. 1*
United States Administration *see Vol. 1*
Cundinamarca *see Vol. 1*
Curacao *see Vol. 1*
Cyprus *see Vol. 1*
Turkish Cypriot Posts *see Vol. 1*
Cyrenaica *see Vol. 1*
Czech Republic *see Vol. 1*
Czechoslovak Army In Siberia *see Vol. 1*
Czechoslovakia *see Vol. 1*

Dahomey *see Vol. 1*
Dakar-Abidjan (*French West Africa 1959*) *see Vol. 2*
Danish West Indies *see Vol. 1*
Danzig *see Vol. 1*
Debrecen (*Rumanian Occupation of Hungary*) *see Vol. 3*
Dedeagatz *see Vol. 1*
Denmark *see Vol. 1*
Dhar *see Vol. 1*
Diego-Suarez *see Vol. 1*
Djibouti *see Vol. 1*
Djibouti Republic *see Vol. 1*
Dobruja (*Bulgarian Occupation of Rumania*) *see Vol. 1*
Dodecanese Islands *see Vol. 1*
Greek Military Administration *see Vol. 1*
Italian Occupation *see Vol. 1*
Dominica *see Vol. 1*
Dominican Republic *see Vol. 1*
Don Territory (*South Russia*) 227
Dubai *see Vol. 1*
Dungarpur *see Vol. 1*
Duttia (Datia) *see Vol. 1*

East Africa and Uganda Protectorates (*Kenya, Uganda and Tanganyika*) *see Vol. 3*
East Africa, German (*Tanganyika 1893–1905*) 388
East India (*India 1855–60*) *see Vol. 2*
East Silesia *see Vol. 2*
East Timor, (see United Nations Transitional Administration) 603
Eastern Command Area (*German Commands*) *see Vol. 2*
Eastern Roumelia (South Bulgaria) *see Vol. 2*
South Bulgaria *see Vol. 2*
Eastern Roumelia And South Bulgaria *see Vol. 2*
Ecuador *see Vol. 2*
Egypt *see Vol. 2*
United Arab Republic *see Vol. 2*
Egyptian Expeditionary Forces (*Palestine 1918–22*) *see Vol. 3*
Egyptian Occupation of Palestine (*Gaza*) *see Vol. 2*
Eire (*Ireland*) *see Vol. 2*
El Salvador *see Vol. 2*
Elobey, Annobon And Corisco *see Vol. 2*
Equatorial Guinea *see Vol. 2*
Eritrea *see Vol. 2*
Independent State *see Vol. 2*
Italian Colony *see Vol. 2*
Estonia *see Vol. 2*
Ethiopia *see Vol. 2*
Independence Restored *see Vol. 2*
Independent Empire *see Vol. 2*

Eupen and Malmedy (*Belgian Occupation of Germany*) *see Vol. 1*

Falkland Islands *see Vol. 2*
Falkland Islands Dependencies *see Vol. 2*
General Issues *see Vol. 2*
Graham Land *see Vol. 2*
South Georgia *see Vol. 2*
South Orkneys *see Vol. 2*
South Shetlands *see Vol. 2*
Far Eastern Republic (*Siberia 1920*) 146
Faridkot *see Vol. 2*
Faroe Islands *see Vol. 2*
Federated Malay States *see Vol. 2*
Fernando Poo *see Vol. 2*
Fezzan *see Vol. 2*
Issues For Fezzan And Ghadames *see Vol. 2*
Issues For Fezzan Only *see Vol. 2*
Fiji *see Vol. 2*
Finland *see Vol. 2*
Finnish Occupation Of Aunus *see Vol. 2*
Finnish Occupation Of Eastern Karelia *see Vol. 2*
Fiume *see Vol. 2*
Fiume And Kupa Zone *see Vol. 2*
Fiume, Yugoslav Occupation of (*Venezia Giulia and Istria*) 711
France *see Vol. 2*
Free French Forces In The Levant *see Vol. 2*
French Colonies *see Vol. 2*
French Committee of National Liberation (*French Colonies 1943–45*) *see Vol. 2*
French Congo *see Vol. 2*
French Equatorial Africa *see Vol. 2*
French Guiana *see Vol. 2*
French Guinea *see Vol. 2*
French Indian Settlements *see Vol. 2*
French Levant (*French Post Offices in Turkish Empire*) *see Vol. 2*
French Morocco *see Vol. 2*
French Occupation Of Hungary *see Vol. 2*
French Occupation of Stria (*Syria 1919*) 360
French Polynesia *see Vol. 2*
French Post Offices In China *see Vol. 2*
French Post Offices In Crete *see Vol. 2*
French Post Offices In Ethiopia *see Vol. 2*
French Post Offices in Madagascar (*Madagascar and Dependencies 1889–96*) *see Vol. 3*
French Post Offices In Morocco *see Vol. 2*
French Post Offices In Tangier *see Vol. 2*
French Post Offices In Turkish Empire *see Vol. 2*
French Post Offices In Zanzibar *see Vol. 2*
French Somali Coast *see Vol. 2*
French Southern And Antarctic Territories *see Vol. 2*
French Sudan *see Vol. 2*
French Territory Of The Afars And The Issas *see Vol. 2*
French West Africa *see Vol. 2*
Fujeira *see Vol. 2*
Funchal *see Vol. 2*

Gabon *see Vol. 2*
Galapagos Islands *see Vol. 2*
Gambia *see Vol. 2*
Gaza *see Vol. 2*
Gaza (*Egyptian Occupation of Palestine*) *see Vol. 2*
Egyptian Occupation *see Vol. 2*
United Arab Republic *see Vol. 2*
Gdansk (*Polish Post in Danzig*) *see Vol. 3*
Georgia *see Vol. 2*
German Commands *see Vol. 2*
Eastern Command *see Vol. 2*
Western Command *see Vol. 2*
German Democratic Republic (*East Germany*) *see Vol. 2*
German East Africa (*Tanganyika 1893–1905*) 388
German East Africa (*Tanganyika 1917*) 388
German East Africa *see Vol. 2*
German Federal Republic (*West Germany*) *see Vol. 2*
German Levant (*German P.O.s in The Turkish Empire*) *see Vol. 2*
German Military Command Areas 1916–18 (*German Commands*) *see Vol. 2*
German New Guinea *see Vol. 2*
German Occupation Of Alsace *see Vol. 2*
German Occupation Of Belgium *see Vol. 2*
German Occupation Of Dalmatia *see Vol. 2*
Zara (Zadar) *see Vol. 2*
Gulf Of Kotor *see Vol. 2*

German Occupation Of Estonia *see Vol. 2*
German Occupation Of Latvia *see Vol. 2*
German Occupation Of Lithuania *see Vol. 2*
German Occupation Of Lorraine *see Vol. 2*
German Occupation Of Poland *see Vol. 2*
German Occupation of Poland (*Poland 1915–18*) *see Vol. 3*
German Occupation of Poland (*Poland 1939–45*) *see Vol. 3*
German Occupation Of Rumania *see Vol. 2*
German Occupation Of Russia *see Vol. 2*
German Occupation Of Zante *see Vol. 2*
German Post Offices In China *see Vol. 2*
German Post Offices In Morocco *see Vol. 2*
German Post Offices In The Turkish Empire *see Vol. 2*
German South West Africa *see Vol. 2*
Germany *see Vol. 2*
Germany 1871–1945 *see Vol. 2*
Allied Occupation *see Vol. 2*
Allied Military Post (British and American Zones) *see Vol. 2*
American, British and Russian Zones 1946–48 *see Vol. 2*
British and American Zones 1948–49 *see Vol. 2*
French Zone. *see Vol. 2*
Russian Zone. *see Vol. 2*
German Federal Republic *see Vol. 2*
West Berlin *see Vol. 2*
German Democratic Republic (East Germany) *see Vol. 2*
Ghadames *see Vol. 2*
Ghana *see Vol. 2*
Gibraltar *see Vol. 2*
Gilbert And Ellice Islands *see Vol. 2*
Gilbert Islands *see Vol. 2*
Gold Coast *see Vol. 2*
Graham Island (*Falkland Islands Dependencies*) *see Vol. 2*
Granadine Confederation (*Colombia 1859*) *see Vol. 1*
Great Britain *see Vol. 2*
Regional Issues *see Vol. 2*
Channel Islands *see Vol. 2*
Guernsey *see Vol. 2*
Isle Of Man *see Vol. 2*
Jersey *see Vol. 2*
England *see Vol. 2*
Northern Ireland *see Vol. 2*
Scotland *see Vol. 2*
Wales *see Vol. 2*
Great Comoro *see Vol. 2*
Greater Lebanon (*Lebanon 1924–26*) *see Vol. 3*
Greece *see Vol. 2*
Greek Occupation Of Albania *see Vol. 2*
Greenland *see Vol. 2*
Grenada *see Vol. 2*
Grenadines Of Grenada (Carriacou And Petite Martinique) *see Vol. 2*
Grenadines Of St. Vincent *see Vol. 2*
Griqualand West *see Vol. 2*
Guadeloupe *see Vol. 2*
Guam *see Vol. 2*
Guanacaste *see Vol. 2*
Guatemala *see Vol. 2*
Guernsey *see Vol. 2*
Alderney *see Vol. 2*
Guinea *see Vol. 2*
Guinea-Bissau *see Vol. 2*
Guyana *see Vol. 2*
Gwalior *see Vol. 2*

Hague Court of International Justice (*Netherlands*) *see Vol. 3*
Haiti *see Vol. 2*
Hamburg *see Vol. 2*
Hanover *see Vol. 2*
Hatay *see Vol. 2*
Hawaii *see Vol. 2*
Hejaz (*Saudi Arabia*) 103
Hejaz-Nejd (*Saudi Arabia*) 103
Heligoland *see Vol. 2*
Hoi-Hao (Hoihow) *see Vol. 2*
Holkar (*Indore*) *see Vol. 2*
Holstein (*Schleswig-Holstein*) 118
Honduras *see Vol. 2*
Hong Kong *see Vol. 2*
Japanese Occupation Of Hong Kong *see Vol. 2*
Horta *see Vol. 2*

Hungary *see Vol. 2*
Szeged *see Vol. 2*
Hyderabad *see Vol. 2*

Iceland *see Vol. 2*
Idar *see Vol. 2*
Ifni *see Vol. 2*
India *see Vol. 2*
Dominion Of India *see Vol. 2*
Republic Of India *see Vol. 2*
Indian Custodian Forces In Korea *see Vol. 2*
Indian Expeditionary Forces *see Vol. 2*
Indian Forces In Indo-China *see Vol. 2*
Indian U.N. Force In Congo *see Vol. 2*
Indian U.N. Force In Gaza (Palestine) *see Vol. 2*
Indo-China *see Vol. 2*
Indo-Chinese Post Offices In China *see Vol. 2*
Indonesia *see Vol. 2*
Dutch Administration *see Vol. 2*
Republic *see Vol. 2*
United States Of Indonesia *see Vol. 2*
Indonesian Republic *see Vol. 2*
Indore (Holkar State) *see Vol. 2*
Inhambane *see Vol. 2*
Inini *see Vol. 2*
International Commission in Indo China (*Indian Forces in Indo-China*) *see Vol. 2*
International Education Office (*Switzerland*) 342
International Labour Office (*Switzerland*) 342
International Olympic Committee (*Switzerland*) 342
International Refugees Organization (*Switzerland*) 342
International Telecommunications Union (*Switzerland*) 342
Ionian Islands *see Vol. 2*
Iran *see Vol. 2*
Iraq *see Vol. 2*
Ireland (Republic) *see Vol. 2*
Irian Barat (*West Irian*) 791
Isle Of Man *see Vol. 2*
Israel *see Vol. 2*
Palestinian Authority *see Vol. 2*
Istria, Yugoslav Occupation of (*Venezia Giulia and Istria*) 711
Italian Colonies *see Vol. 2*
Italian East Africa *see Vol. 2*
Italian Occupation Of Cephalonia And Ithaca *see Vol. 2*
Italian Occupation Of Corfu *see Vol. 2*
Italian Occupation Of Corfu And Paxos *see Vol. 2*
Italian Occupation Of Ionian Islands *see Vol. 2*
Italian Post Offices In China *see Vol. 2*
Peking *see Vol. 2*
Tientsin *see Vol. 2*
Italian Post Offices In Crete *see Vol. 2*
General Issue *see Vol. 2*
Offices In Turkish Empire *see Vol. 2*
Albania. *see Vol. 2*
General Offices in Europe and Asia. *see Vol. 2*
Individual Offices In Europe And Asia. *see Vol. 2*
Constantinople. *see Vol. 2*
Durazzo. *see Vol. 2*
Janina. *see Vol. 2*
Jerusalem. *see Vol. 2*
Salonica. *see Vol. 2*
Scutari. *see Vol. 2*
Smyrna. *see Vol. 2*
Valona. *see Vol. 2*
Offices In Africa. *see Vol. 2*
Benghazi. *see Vol. 2*
Tripoli. *see Vol. 2*
Italian Social Republic (*Italy 1944*) *see Vol. 2*
Italian Somaliland (*Somalia 1915–36*) 204
Italy *see Vol. 2*
Italian Social Republic *see Vol. 2*
Ivory Coast *see Vol. 2*
Republic *see Vol. 2*

Jaipur *see Vol. 2*
Jamaica *see Vol. 2*
Jammu And Kashmir *see Vol. 2*
Japan *see Vol. 2*
Japanese Taiwan (Formosa) *see Vol. 2*
Japanese Occupation Of China *see Vol. 2*
Kwangtung *see Vol. 2*
Mengkiang (Inner Mongolia) *see Vol. 2*
North China *see Vol. 2*
Nanking And Shanghai *see Vol. 2*
Japanese Occupation Of Netherlands Indies *see Vol. 2*
Java *see Vol. 2*
Sumatra *see Vol. 2*
Japanese Naval Control Area *see Vol. 2*
Japanese Occupation Of Philippines *see Vol. 2*
Japanese Post Offices In China *see Vol. 2*
Japanese Post Offices In Korea *see Vol. 2*
Japanese Naval Control Area (*Japanese Occupation of Netherlands Indies*) *see Vol. 2*
Jasdan *see Vol. 2*
Java (*Japanese Occupation of Netherlands Indies*) *see Vol. 2*
Jersey *see Vol. 2*
War Occupation Issues *see Vol. 2*
Independent Postal Administration. *see Vol. 2*
Jhalawar *see Vol. 2*
Jind *see Vol. 2*
Johore *see Vol. 2*
Jordan *see Vol. 2*
Jordanian Occupation Of Palestine *see Vol. 2*
Jubaland *see Vol. 2*
Jugoslavia (*Yugoslavia*) 808
Junagadh (*Soruth*) 211

Kamerun (*Cameroun*) *see Vol. 1*
Kampuchea *see Vol. 3*
Karki (*Dodecanese Islands*) *see Vol. 1*
Katanga *see Vol. 3*
Kathiri State Of Seiyun *see Vol. 3*
Kazakhstan *see Vol. 3*
Kedah *see Vol. 3*
Kelantan *see Vol. 3*
Kenya *see Vol. 3*
Kenya and Uganda (*Kenya, Uganda and Tanganyika 1922*) *see Vol. 3*
Kenya, Uganda And Tanganyika (Tanzania) *see Vol. 3*
Khmer Republic *see Vol. 3*
Khor Fakkan *see Vol. 3*
Kiautschou (Kiaochow) *see Vol. 3*
King Edward VII Land *see Vol. 3*
Kionga *see Vol. 3*
Kiribati *see Vol. 3*
Kirin and Heilungkiang (*Chinese Provinces*) *see Vol. 1*
Kishangarh *see Vol. 3*
Klaipeda (*Memel*) *see Vol. 3*
Korce (*Albania 1917*) *see Vol. 1*
Korea *see Vol. 3*
North Korea *see Vol. 3*
Russian Occupation *see Vol. 3*
Korean People's Democratic Republic *see Vol. 3*
North Korean Occupation. *see Vol. 3*
South Korea *see Vol. 3*
United States Military Government *see Vol. 3*
Republic Of Korea *see Vol. 3*
Korean Empire *see Vol. 3*
Kosovo, (see United Nations Interim Administration Mission) 603
Kouang Tcheou (Kwangchow) *see Vol. 3*
Kuban Territory (*South Russia*) 227
Kuwait *see Vol. 3*
Kwangtung (*Japanese Occupation of China*) *see Vol. 2*
Kyrgyzstan *see Vol. 3*

La Aguera *see Vol. 3*
Labuan *see Vol. 3*
Lagos *see Vol. 3*
Laibach (*Slovenia*) 188
LANSA (*Private Air Companies*) *see Vol. 1*
Laos *see Vol. 3*
Las Bela *see Vol. 3*
Latakia *see Vol. 3*
Latvia *see Vol. 3*
League of Nations (*Switzerland*) 342
Lebanon *see Vol. 3*
Leeward Islands *see Vol. 3*
Leros (*Dodecanese Islands*) *see Vol. 1*
Lesotho *see Vol. 3*
Liberia *see Vol. 3*
Libya *see Vol. 3*
Italian Colony *see Vol. 3*
Independent *see Vol. 3*
Liechtenstein *see Vol. 3*
Lipso (*Dodecanese Islands*) *see Vol. 1*
Lithuania *see Vol. 3*
Lombardy And Venetia *see Vol. 3*
Lourenco Marques *see Vol. 3*
Lubeck *see Vol. 3*
Lubiana (*Slovenia*) 188
Luxembourg *see Vol. 3*

Macao *see Vol. 3*
Macedonia *see Vol. 3*
German Occupation *see Vol. 3*
Independent Republic *see Vol. 3*
Madagascar *see Vol. 3*
French Post Offices *see Vol. 3*
French Colony Of Madagascar And Dependencies *see Vol. 3*
Madeira *see Vol. 3*
Mafeking *see Vol. 3*
Mafia Island, British Occupation of (*Tanganyika 1915*) 388
Mahra Sultanate Of Qishn And Socotra *see Vol. 3*
Malacca *see Vol. 3*
Malagasy Republic *see Vol. 3*
Malawi *see Vol. 3*
Malaya (British Military Administration) *see Vol. 3*
Malaya (Japanese Occupation Of) *see Vol. 3*
Johore *see Vol. 3*
Kedah *see Vol. 3*
Kelantan *see Vol. 3*
Penang *see Vol. 3*
Selangor *see Vol. 3*
Singapore *see Vol. 3*
Trengganu *see Vol. 3*
General Issues *see Vol. 3*
Malaya (Thai Occupation) *see Vol. 3*
Malayan Federation *see Vol. 3*
Malayan Postal Union *see Vol. 3*
Malaysia *see Vol. 3*
National Series *see Vol. 3*
Federal Territory Issues *see Vol. 3*
Maldive Islands *see Vol. 3*
Mali *see Vol. 3*
Federation *see Vol. 3*
Republic *see Vol. 3*
Malmedy, Eupen and (*Belgian Occupation of Germany*) *see Vol. 1*
Malta *see Vol. 3*
Manama *see Vol. 3*
Manchukuo *see Vol. 3*
Manchuria (*Chinese Provinces*) *see Vol. 1*
Mariana Islands *see Vol. 3*
Marienwerder *see Vol. 3*
Marshall Island, British Occupation of (*New Guinea 1914*) *see Vol. 3*
Marshall Islands *see Vol. 3*
German Protectorate *see Vol. 3*
Republic *see Vol. 3*
Martinique *see Vol. 3*
Mauritania *see Vol. 3*
Mauritius *see Vol. 3*
Mayotte *see Vol. 3*
Mecklenburg-Schwerin *see Vol. 3*
Mecklenburg-Strelitz *see Vol. 3*
Memel *see Vol. 3*
Lithuanian Occupation *see Vol. 3*
Mengkiang (*Japanese Occupation of China*) *see Vol. 2*
Mexico *see Vol. 3*
Micronesia *see Vol. 3*
Middle Congo *see Vol. 3*
Modena *see Vol. 3*
Moheli *see Vol. 3*
Moldavia (*Rumania 1858*) *see Vol. 3*
Moldova *see Vol. 3*
Monaco *see Vol. 3*
Mongolia *see Vol. 3*
Mong-Tseu (Mengtsz) *see Vol. 3*
Montenegro *see Vol. 3*
German Occupation *see Vol. 3*
Italian Occupation *see Vol. 3*
Montserrat *see Vol. 3*
Morocco *see Vol. 3*
Northern Zone *see Vol. 3*
Southern Zone *see Vol. 3*
Issues For The Whole Of Morocco *see Vol. 3*
Morocco Agencies *see Vol. 3*
Gibraltar Issues Overprinted *see Vol. 3*
British Currency *see Vol. 3*
Spanish Currency *see Vol. 3*
French Currency *see Vol. 3*
Tangier International Zone *see Vol. 3*
Morvi *see Vol. 3*
Mosul *see Vol. 3*
Mozambique *see Vol. 3*

Mozambique Company *see Vol. 3*
Muscat *see Vol. 3*
Muscat And Oman *see Vol. 3*
Myanmar *see Vol. 3*

Nabha *see Vol. 3*
Nagorno-Karabakh *see Vol. 3*
Nakhichevan *see Vol. 3*
Namibia *see Vol. 3*
Nandgaon *see Vol. 3*
Nanking and Shanghai (*Japanese Occupation of China*) *see Vol. 2*
Naples *see Vol. 3*
Natal *see Vol. 3*
Nauru *see Vol. 3*
Nawanagar *see Vol. 3*
Neapolitan Provinces *see Vol. 3*
Negri Sembilan *see Vol. 3*
Nejd (*Saudi Arabia*) 103
Nepal *see Vol. 3*
Netherlands *see Vol. 3*
Netherlands Antilles *see Vol. 3*
Netherlands Indies *see Vol. 3*
Netherlands New Guinea *see Vol. 3*
Nevis *see Vol. 3*
New Brunswick *see Vol. 3*
New Caledonia *see Vol. 3*
New Guinea *see Vol. 3*
New Hebrides *see Vol. 3*
British Administration *see Vol. 3*
French Administration *see Vol. 3*
New Republic *see Vol. 3*
New South Wales *see Vol. 3*
New Zealand *see Vol. 3*
Newfoundland *see Vol. 3*
Nicaragua *see Vol. 3*
Niger *see Vol. 3*
Niger Coast Protectorate *see Vol. 3*
Nigeria *see Vol. 3*
Nisiros (*Dodecanese Islands*) *see Vol. 1*
Niuafo'Ou *see Vol. 3*
Niue *see Vol. 3*
Norfolk Island *see Vol. 3*
North Borneo *see Vol. 3*
Japanese Occupation *see Vol. 3*
North Eastern Provinces (*Chinese Provinces*) *see Vol. 1*
North German Confederation *see Vol. 3*
North Ingermanland *see Vol. 3*
North West Pacific Islands (*New Guinea 1915*) *see Vol. 3*
North West Russia *see Vol. 3*
Northern Ireland (*Great Britain Regional Issues*) *see Vol. 2*
Northern Ireland (*Great Britain*) *see Vol. 2*
Northern Nigeria *see Vol. 3*
Northern Rhodesia *see Vol. 3*
North-Western Army (*North West Russia*) *see Vol. 3*
Norway *see Vol. 3*
Nossi-Be *see Vol. 3*
Nova Scotia *see Vol. 3*
Nyasaland Protectorate *see Vol. 3*
Nyasa-Rhodesian Force (*Tanganyika 1916*) 388
Nyassa Company *see Vol. 3*

Obock *see Vol. 3*
Oceanic Settlements *see Vol. 3*
Oil Rivers Protectorate (*Niger Coast Protectorate 1892–3*) *see Vol. 3*
Oldenburg *see Vol. 3*
Oman (Sultanate) *see Vol. 3*
Orange Free State (Orange River Colony) *see Vol. 3*
Orange River Colony (*Orange Free State 1900–03*) *see Vol. 3*
Orchha *see Vol. 3*
Ostland (*German Occupation of Russia*) *see Vol. 2*
Oubangui-Chari (*Ubangi-Shari*) 554

Pahang *see Vol. 3*
Pakhoi *see Vol. 3*
Pakistan *see Vol. 3*
Palau *see Vol. 3*
Palestine *see Vol. 3*
Panama *see Vol. 3*
Panama Canal Zone (*Canal Zone*) *see Vol. 1*
Papal States *see Vol. 3*
Papua *see Vol. 3*
Papua New Guinea *see Vol. 3*
Paraguay *see Vol. 3*
Parma *see Vol. 3*
Patiala *see Vol. 3*
Patmos (*Dodecanese Islands*) *see Vol. 1*
Pechino (*Italian Post Offices in China*) *see Vol. 2*
Penang *see Vol. 3*
Penrhyn Island *see Vol. 3*
New Zealand Dependency *see Vol. 3*
Part Of Cook Islands *see Vol. 3*
Perak *see Vol. 3*
Perlis *see Vol. 3*
Persia (*Iran 1868–1935*) *see Vol. 2*
Peru *see Vol. 3*
Philippines *see Vol. 3*
Commonwealth Of The Philippines *see Vol. 3*
Independent Republic *see Vol. 3*
Spanish Administration *see Vol. 3*
United States Administration *see Vol. 3*
Piscopi (*Dodecanese Islands*) *see Vol. 1*
Pitcairn Islands *see Vol. 3*
Poland *see Vol. 3*
1939–1945. German Occupation *see Vol. 3*
1944. Independent Republic *see Vol. 3*
Poland, German Occupation of (*Poland 1915–18*) *see Vol. 3*
Polish Levant (*Polish Post Offices in Turkey*) *see Vol. 3*
Polish Post In Danzig *see Vol. 3*
Polish Post Office In Turkey *see Vol. 3*
Ponta Delgada *see Vol. 3*
Poonch *see Vol. 3*
Port Arthur and Dairen (*Communist China*) *see Vol. 1*
Port Lagos *see Vol. 3*
Port Said *see Vol. 3*
Portugal *see Vol. 3*
Portuguese Africa (*Portuguese Colonies*) *see Vol. 3*
Portuguese Colonies *see Vol. 3*
Portuguese Congo *see Vol. 3*
Portuguese Guinea *see Vol. 3*
Portuguese India *see Vol. 3*
Portuguese Timor *see Vol. 3*
Priamur and Maritime Provinces (*Siberia*) 146
Prince Edward Island *see Vol. 3*
Prussia *see Vol. 3*
Puerto Rico *see Vol. 3*
Spanish Occupation *see Vol. 3*
United States Occupation *see Vol. 3*
Puttiala (*Patiala*) *see Vol. 3*

Qatar *see Vol. 3*
Qu'Aiti State In Hadhramaut *see Vol. 3*
Queensland *see Vol. 3*
Quelimane *see Vol. 3*

Rajasthan *see Vol. 3*
Rajnandgaon (*Nandgaon*) *see Vol. 3*
Rajpipla *see Vol. 3*
Rarotonga (*Cook Islands 1919–31*) *see Vol. 1*
Ras Al Khaima *see Vol. 3*
Redonda *see Vol. 3*
Republika Srpska (*Bosnia and Herzegovina*) *see Vol. 1*
Reunion *see Vol. 3*
Rhineland-Palatinate (*Germany, French Zone.*) *see Vol. 2*
Rhodesia *see Vol. 3*
Rhodesia And Nyasaland *see Vol. 3*
Riau-Lingga Archipelago *see Vol. 3*
Rijeka (*Venezia Giulia and Istria*) 711
Rio De Oro *see Vol. 3*
Rio Muni *see Vol. 3*
Rodi or Rhodes (*Dodecanese Islands*) *see Vol. 1*
Romagna *see Vol. 3*
Roman States (*Papal States*) *see Vol. 3*
Romania (*Rumania*) *see Vol. 3*
Ross Dependency *see Vol. 3*
Rouad Island (Arwad) *see Vol. 3*
Ruanda-Urundi *see Vol. 3*
Rumania *see Vol. 3*
Transylvania *see Vol. 3*
Rumanian Occupation Of Hungary *see Vol. 3*
Banat Bacska *see Vol. 3*
Debrecen *see Vol. 3*
Temesvar *see Vol. 3*
Rumanian Post Offices In The Turkish Empire *see Vol. 3*
General Issues *see Vol. 3*
Constantinople *see Vol. 3*
Russia *see Vol. 3*
Russian Federation *see Vol. 3*
Russian Army Issues (*North West Russia*) *see Vol. 3*
Russian Levant (*Russian Post Offices in Turkish Empire*) *see Vol. 3*
Russian Post Offices In China *see Vol. 3*
Russian Post Offices In Crete *see Vol. 3*
Russian Post Offices In Turkish Empire *see Vol. 3*
Rwanda *see Vol. 3*
Ryukyu Islands *see Vol. 3*

Saar 1
French Occupation 1
Return To Germany 3
Sabah 4
Salonica, British Field Office in (*British Levant 1916*) *see Vol. 1*
Samoa 74
German Colony 74
Independent State 75
San Marino 83
Santander 102
Sao Tome e Principe (*St. Thomas and Prince Islands*) 40
Sarajevo Government (*Bosnia and Herzegovina*) *see Vol. 1*
Sarawak 102
Japanese Occupation 103
Sardinia 103
Saseno 103
Saudi Arabia 103
Hejaz 103
Nejdi Occupation Of Hejaz 104
Hejaz And Nejd 104
Saudi Arabia 105
Newspaper Stamps 117
Saurashtra (*Soruth*) 211
Saxony 118
Scarpanto (*Dodecanese Islands*) *see Vol. 1*
Schleswig-Holstein 118
Scinde (*India 1852*) *see Vol. 2*
Scotland (*Great Britain*) *see Vol. 2*
Selangor 118
Senegal 119
Senegambia And Niger 135
Serbia 135
German Occupation 135
Serbian Occupation Of Hungary 136
Seychelles 136
Shahpura 143
Shanghai 143
Sharjah 143
Shihr and Mukalla (*Hadhramaut*) *see Vol. 3*
Siam (*Thailand 1883–1939*) 401
Siberia 146
Far East Republic 146
Priamur And Maritime Provinces 146
Soviet Union Issue For The Far East 146
Sicily 146
Sierra Leone 146
Simi (*Dodecanese Islands*) *see Vol. 1*
Singapore 172
Sinkiang (*Chinese Provinces*) *see Vol. 1*
Sirmoor 182
Slesvig 183
Slovakia 183
Republic Of Slovakia 183
Slovak Republic 184
Slovenia 188
German Occupation, 1943–45 188
Independent State 189
Solomon Islands 195
Somalia 204
Somalia, British Administration of (*Somalia 1950*) *see Vol. 1*
Somalia, British Military Administration of (*Somalia 1948*) *see Vol. 1*
Somalia, Italian (*Somalia 1915–36*) *see Vol. 1*
Italian Trust Territory 205
Republic 205
Somali Democratic Republic 207
Somaliland Protectorate 210
Soruth 211
Junagadh 211
United State Of Saurashtra 211
South Africa 211
South African Republic (*Transvaal 1869–74*) 464
South Arabian Federation 224
South Australia 224
South Bulgaria (*Eastern Roumelia*) *see Vol. 2*
South Georgia 225

South Georgia And The South Sandwich Islands 225
South Kasai 227
South Orkneys (*Falkland Islands Dependencies*) see Vol. 2
South Russia 227
South Shetlands (*Falkland Islands Dependencies*) see Vol. 2
South West Africa 227
Southern Nigeria 231
Southern Rhodesia 231
Southern Yemen 232
Spain 233
Spanish Guinea 272
Spanish Morocco 274
Spanish Administration (*Philippines 1854–96*) see Vol. 3
Spanish Post Offices In Tangier 277
Spanish Sahara 277
Spanish West Africa 280
Sremsko Baranjska Oblast (*Croatia*) see Vol. 1
Sri Lanka 280
Srpska Krajina (*Croatia*) see Vol. 1
St. Christopher 4
St. Christopher, Nevis and Anguilla (*St. Kitts-Nevis*) 17
St. Helena 4
St. Kitts 12
St. Kitts-Nevis 17
St. Lucia 20
St. Pierre Et Miquelon 30
St. Thomas And Prince Island 40
St. Vincent 43
Stampalia (*Dodecanese Islands*) see Vol. 1
Ste. Marie De Madagascar 30
Stellaland 295
Straits Settlements 295
Sudan 296
Sumatra (*Japanese Occupation of Netherlands Indies*) see Vol. 2
Sungei Ujong 301
Surinam 301
Swaziland 315
Sweden 321
Switzerland 342
  International Organizations Situated In Switzerland 358
Syria 360
Szechwan (*Chinese Provinces*) see Vol. 1
Szeged (*Hungary*) see Vol. 2

Tahiti 386
Tajikistan 386
Tanganyika 388
Tangier, British P.O.s in (*Morocco Agencies*) see Vol. 3
Tanzania 388
Tasmania 401
Tchad (*Chad*) see Vol. 1
Tchongking (Chungking) 401
Tete 401
Thailand 401
Thessaly 426
Thrace 426
Thurn And Taxis 426
  Northern District 426
  Southern District 427
Tibet 427
  Chinese Post Offices 427
  Independent State 427
Tientsin (*Italian Post Offices in China*) see Vol. 2
Tierra Del Fuego 427
Tobago 427
Togo 427
Tokelau 445
Tolima 448
Tonga 449
Transcaucasian Federation 462
Transjordan (*Jordan*) see Vol. 2
Transkei 462
Transvaal 464
Transylvania (*Rumania 1919*) see Vol. 3
Travancore 465
Travancore-Cochin 465
Trengganu 465
Trentino (*Austrian Italy*) see Vol. 3
Trieste 466
  Zone A - Allied Military Government 466
  Zone B - Yugoslav Military Government 468
Trinidad 468
Trinidad And Tobago 469
Tripoli (*Italian Levant*) see Vol. 2
Tripolitania 476
Tristan Da Cunha 477
Trucial States 483
Tunisia 483
Turkey 502
Turkish Empire, French P.O.s in (*French Levant*) see Vol. 2
Turkish Empire, Rumanian P.O.s in (*Rumanian Post Offices Abroad*) see Vol. 3
Turkmenistan 531
Turks And Caicos Islands 532
Turks Islands 531
Tuscany 543
Tuva 543
Tuvalu 545

U.N.E.S.C.O (*France*) see Vol. 2
U.S.S.R. (*Russia from 1923*) see Vol. 3
Ubangi-Shari 554
Uganda 554
Ukraine 571
Umm Al Qiwain 577
United Arab Emirates 578
United Nations 584
  New York Headquarters 584
  Geneva Headquarters 594
  Vienna Headquarters. 599
  Transitional Administration in East Timor 603
  Interim Administration Mission in Kosovo 603
United States Of America 603
United States Postal Agency In Shanghai 644
Universal Postal Union (*Switzerland*) 342
Upper Senegal And Niger 645
Upper Silesia 645
Upper Volta 645
Upper Yafa 655
Uruguay 655
Uzbekistan 688

Vanuatu 690
Vathy 696
Vatican City 696
Veglia 709
Venda 709
Venezia Giulia (*Austrian Italy*) see Vol. 3
Venezia Giulia And Istria 711
Venezuela 712
Victoria 735
Victoria Land 737
Vietnam 737
  National Front For The Liberation Of South Vietnam 743
  North Vietnam 744
  South Vietnam 738
  Democratic Republic 737
  Independent State 737
  Socialist Republic Of Vietnam 754

Wadhwan 777
Wales (*Great Britain*) see Vol. 2
Wallis And Futuna Islands 777
Wenden 791
Western Command Area (*German Commands*) see Vol. 2
West Berlin (*Germany*) see Vol. 2
West Irian 791
West New Guinea 791
West Ukraine 791
Western Army (*North West Russia*) see Vol. 3
Western Australia 792
World Health Organization (*Switzerland*) 342
World Intellectual Property Organization (*Switzerland*) 342
World Meteorological Organization (*Switzerland*) 342
Wrangel Russian Government (*South Russia*) 227
Wurttemberg 792

Yemen 793
Yemen People's Democratic Republic 803
Yemen Republic (combined) 807
  Kingdom 793
  Republic 794
  Royalist Civil War Issues 799
Yugoslavia 808
  Kingdom Of The Serbs, Croats And Slovenes 808
  Kingdom Of Yugoslavia 809
  Democratic Federation Of Yugoslavia 810
  Federal People's Republic 811
Yunnan (*Chinese Provinces*) see Vol. 1
Yunnanfu 844
Yunnansen (*Yunnanfu*) 844

Zaire 844
Zambezia 848
Zambia 848
Zanzibar 855
Zara (*Zadar*) see Vol. 2
Zil Elwannyen Sesel 856
Zimbabwe 858
Zululand 862